W9-DDT-614

KS & VANS

S & TRUCKS

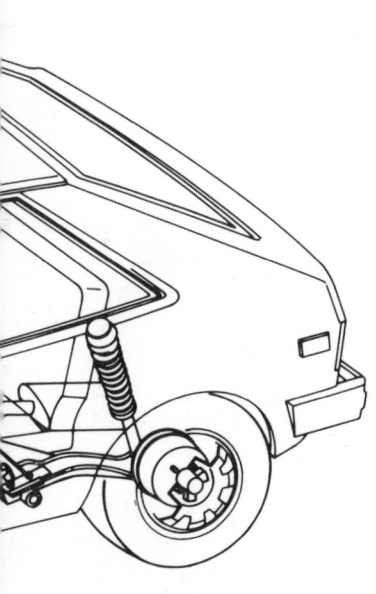

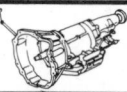

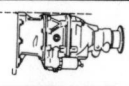

PREFACE

This is the 1983 edition of Mitchell Manuals'
Transmission Service and Repair Manual.
This book, like the many Mitchell publications which have preceded it,
represents our commitment to professionalism
in the automotive service market.

The automotive industry advances every year,
and Mitchell Manuals pledges to advance and improve its products
as we maintain the quality and usefulness of all Mitchell Manuals' publications.

We cordially acknowledge the good will
and mutual goals that exist in the automotive business,
and it is in this spirit that we thank the automotive manufacturers,
distributors, dealers and the entire automotive industry
for their fine cooperation and assistance
which have made this publication possible.

1983 EDITION
TRANSMISSION
SERVICE & REPAIR

DOMESTIC CARS, LIGHT TRUCKS & VANS

IMPORTED CARS & TRUCKS

National Service Data
Manuals For The Automotive Professional

Published By:
MITCHELL MANUALS, INC.
A Cordura Company
P.O. BOX 26260
SAN DIEGO, CA 92126

ISBN 0-8470-1200-X

© 1983 MITCHELL MANUALS, INC. LITHO IN U.S.A.

629.287
Tra

ACKNOWLEDGEMENT

Mitchell Manuals thanks the automotive and equipment manufacturers, distributors, dealers and the entire automotive industry for their fine cooperation and assistance which makes the publication of this manual possible.

MITCHELL MANUALS, INC.

A Cordura Company

PUBLISHER
Barry A. Norton, President

DIRECT MARKETING
Alan Hirschfeld, Vice President

EDITORIAL
Editorial Director
Kenneth A. Young

Managing Editor
Daniel M. Kelley

Ass't. Managing Editor
Michael Roeder

Art Director
Eloise S. Stiverson

Detroit Editor
Lynn D. Meeker

Technical Editors
Daryl F. Visser
Terry L. Blomquist
Thomas L. Landis
Daniel D. Fleming
Philip G. Wallan
Cliff Herrin
Jeffrey C. Wedeking
Thomas J. Kelley
Eddie Santangelo
Patrick T. Rice
David L. Skora

PUBLISHED BY

MITCHELL MANUALS, INC.
9889 Willow Creek Road
P.O. Box 26260
San Diego, California 92126

a subsidiary of
CORDURA PUBLICATIONS, INC.
C.L. Kobrin, President
John Opelt, Senior Vice President of Finance & Administration
Malcolm Ferrier, Senior Vice President of Technology
Robert W. Ladd, Vice President of Manufacturing

For Subscription Information:
CALL TOLL FREE 800 - 854-7030. In California CALL COLLECT 619 - 578-8770. Or WRITE: P.O. Box 26260, San Diego, CA 92126

ISBN 0-8470-1200-X

COPYRIGHT: No part of this publication may be reproduced, stored in a retrieval system or transmitted, in any form or by any means, electronic, mechanical, photocopying, recording or otherwise, without the prior written permission of the publisher. This includes text, figures and tables.

DISCLAIMER OF WARRANTIES: Although the information contained within this volume has been obtained from sources generally believed to be reliable, no warranty (express or implied) can be made as to its accuracy or completeness, nor is any responsibility assumed by the publisher or anyone connected with it for loss or damages suffered through reliance on any information contained in this volume. Specifically, no warranty of merchantability, fitness for a particular purpose or any other warranty is made or to be implied with respect to this volume, and no person has the authority to modify such limitation except in a writing signed by a corporate officer of the publisher. The acceptance of this manual is conditional on the acceptance of this disclaimer. If the buyer does not accept the terms of this disclaimer, return the manual within fifteen (15) days and the publisher will refund any money advanced by the buyer toward the purchase of this manual.

Pub 3-7-84

Tool Applications

ALL MANUFACTURERS

DESCRIPTION

Tool applications used in this manual are noted in the text of all articles where applicable. These tools are usually specific tools that must be used to perform a specific function in Removal, Installation, Overhaul or Testing of a component.

For example; "Using Spline Adapter (J-28513) and Holding Wrench (J-28514), tighten pinion nut until end play is taken up." Although other tools could possibly be substituted, the tool references in text are those that are recommended by the vehicle manufacturer. These tools should be used whenever possible. In cases where a non-specific tool is called for, no tool number will be given.

For example; "Place bearing insert in rod and install guides on rod bolts. Compress piston rings using ring compressor." Since just about any ring compressor that works and does not damage the components can be used, no specific tool number will be called out.

The following descriptions show an example of the reference in text, the maker of the tools recommended by the manufacturer and the tool maker address. Further information on tools and local suppliers of the tools can be obtained from the tool maker. It is also possible, for example, that a Kent-Moore tool may be cross-referenced to another tool maker. In this case it is imperative that the tools be exactly the same in design, or the specific function of the tool may not be able to be performed.

AMERICAN MOTORS/JEEP

Jeep tool applications called out in this manual will appear as follows: "Use bearing remover (J-21473-1) and extension (J-21054-1) to drive out bearing." The "J" in front of the first set of numbers means that it is a Kent-Moore tool. The second set of numbers is the basic tool part number. Part numbers with no additional characters after the basic part number means that the tool listed is a complete tool. The last number means that it is either part of a set (-2,-3 etc.), or a revised tool number (-02,-03, or -B,-C etc,).

TOOL MANUFACTURER

Kent-Moore Tool Division
29784 Little Mack
Roseville, Mich., 48066-2298
Telephone (313) 774-9500
Telex 23-5377

CHRYSLER CORP.

Chrysler Corp. tool applications called out in this manual will appear as follows: "Assemble pinion locating spacer (SP-6030) over body of main tool (SP-5385). Install shaft locating sleeve (L-4507), washer (C-4656) and compression nut (SP-533)."

The prefixes "C," "L" and "SP" mean that the tools are manufactured by Miller Special Tools. The number after the letter prefix is the basic tool part number. Any letters or numbers after the basic part number designate either a revised tool number or that the tool is part of a set.

TOOL MANUFACTURER

Miller Special Tools
Division of Utica Tool Co., Inc.
32615 Park Lane
Garden City, Mich. 48135
Telephone (313) 522-6717

FORD MOTOR CO.

Ford Motor Co. tool applications called out in this manual will appear as follows: "Remove pinion bearing with slide hammer (T50T-100A with attachment T58L-101-A). Remove bearing with puller (T81P-3504-S, T58L-101-A and T81P-3504-T)."

Ford Motor Co. tools are manufactured by Owatonna Tools. The prefix used with Ford tool numbers means that the tools are essential tools. The number after the prefix is the basic tool part number. Any letters or numbers after the basic part number designate either a revised tool number or that the tool is part of a set.

TOOL MANUFACTURER

Owatonna Tool Co. Inc.
Owatonna, Minn. 55060
Telephone (507) 455-2626
Telex 29-0876

GENERAL MOTORS

General Motors tool applications called out in this manual will appear as follows; "Install pivot pin remover (J-21854-1) and remove pins. Using pin punch (J-22635), drive out lever pin."

The "J" in front of the first set of numbers means that it is a Kent-Moore tool. The second set of numbers is the basic tool part number. Part numbers with no additional characters after the basic part number means that the tool listed is a complete tool. The last number means that it is either part of a set (-2,-3 etc.), or a revised tool number (-02,-03, or -B,-C etc,).

TOOL MANUFACTURER

Kent-Moore Tool Division
29784 Little Mack
Roseville, Mich., 48066-2298
Telephone (313) 774-9500
Telex 23-5377

Copy 2

1983 Light Truck Model Identification

In this manual, Light Truck models will be referred to by the manufacturer's model and/or series designation. When a specific model does not have a designated model or series designation, it will be referred to by model name.

NOTE: When General Motors is referred to within this manual (rather than Chevrolet or GMC), the Chevrolet numerical vehicle series designations will be abbreviated for common reference to both Chevrolet and GMC models. The GMC counterpart models will be identified as follows: 10 = 1500 (except S15); 20 = 2500; 30 = 3500.

CHEVROLET

MODEL IDENTIFICATION

Model	Description
C10	[1] 1/2 Ton Conventional Cab 2WD
C20	[1] 3/4 Ton Conventional Cab 2WD
C30	1 Ton Conventional Cab 2WD
K10	[1] 1/2 Ton Conventional Cab 4WD & Blazer
K20	[1] 3/4 Ton Conventional Cab 4WD
K30	1Ton Conventional Cab 4WD
G10	1/2 Ton Van
G20	3/4 Ton Van
G30	[2] 1 Ton Van
P20	3/4 Ton Parcel Delivery Van
P30 (42)	1 Ton Parcel Delivery Van
S10	1/2 Ton Conventional Cab 2WD & Blazer
T10	1/2 Ton Conventional Cab 4WD & Blazer

[1] — Includes Suburban models.
[2] — Includes Front Section and Hi-Cube models.

DODGE

MODEL IDENTIFICATION

Model	Description
AD150	Ramcharger 2WD
AW150	Ramcharger 4WD
B150	1/2 Ton Van
B250	3/4 Ton Van
B350	1 Ton Van
CB350	1 Ton Van (Kary Van)
CB450	1 1/2 Ton Van (Kary Van)
MB250	3/4 Ton Van (Front Section)
MB350	1 Ton Van (Front Section)
MB450	1 1/2 Ton Van (Front Section)
D150	Heavy Duty 1/2 Ton Conventional Cab 2WD
D250	3/4 Ton Conventional Cab 2WD
D350	1 Ton Conventional Cab 2WD
W150	Heavy Duty 1/2 Ton Conventional Cab 4WD
W250	1/2 Ton Conventional Cab 4WD
W350	1Ton Conventional Cab 4WD

FORD

MODEL IDENTIFICATION

Model	Description
Bronco	Family 4WD Wagon
Bronco II	Family 4WD Wagon

FORD (Cont.)

MODEL IDENTIFICATION

Model	Description
E100	1/2 Ton Van
E150	Heavy Duty 1/2 Ton Van
E250	3/4 Ton Van
E350	[1] 1 Ton Van
F100	1/2 Ton Conventional Cab 2WD
F150	Heavy Duty 1/2 Ton Conventional Cab 2WD & 4WD
F250	3/4 Ton Conventional Cab 2WD & 4WD
F350	1 Ton Conventional Cab 2WD & 4WD
Ranger	1/2 Ton Conventional Cab 2WD & 4WD

[1] — Includes Front Section and Parcel Delivery models.

GMC

MODEL IDENTIFICATION

Model	Description
C1500	[1] 1/2 Ton Conventional Cab 2WD
C2500	[1] 3/4 Ton Conventional Cab 2WD
C3500	1 Ton Conventional Cab 2WD
K1500	[1] 1/2 Ton Conventional Cab 4WD & Jimmy
K2500	[1] 3/4 Ton Conventional Cab 4WD
K3500	1 Ton Conventional Cab 4WD
G1500	1/2 Ton Van
G2500	3/4 Ton Van
G3500	[2] 1 Ton Van
P2500	3/4 Ton Parcel Delivery Van
P3500 (42)	1 Ton Parcel Delivery Van
S15	1/2 Ton Conventional Cab 2WD & Jimmy
T15	1/2 Ton Conventional Cab 4WD & Jimmy

[1] — Includes Suburban models.
[2] — Includes Front Sections and Hi-Cube models.

JEEP

MODEL IDENTIFICATION

Model	Description
Cherokee	Cherokee 4WD
CJ5	84" Wheelbase Utility Vehicle 4WD
CJ7	94" Wheelbase Utility Vehicle 4WD
J10	1/2 Ton Conventional Cab 4WD
J20	3/4 Ton Conventional Cab 4WD
Scrambler	104" Wheelbase Utility Vehicle 4WD
Wagoneer	Wagoneer 4WD

PLYMOUTH

MODEL IDENTIFICATION

Model	Description
PB150	1/2 Ton Van
PB250	3/4 Ton Van
PB350	1 Ton Van

1983 DOMESTIC GENERAL INDEX

The first step in using these pages
is to locate the listed components that you require
information on. Go down the list under the specific component heading
to the model or transmission type of the vehicle you are working on. On the
right-hand side of the column is the number of the article you require.

1983 Domestic General Index

Cont.

Cont.

Cont.

SECTION 1

DOMESTIC GENERAL SERVICING

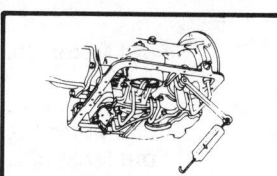

NOTE: **ALSO SEE GENERAL INDEX.**

Transmission Application

AUTOMATIC TRANSMISSIONS

MANUFACTURER & MODEL	TRANSMISSION MODEL
AMERICAN MOTORS Alliance 1.4L All RWD Models — 2.5L Concord & Spirit — 4.2L Eagle — 4.2L	 Renault MB1 (Transaxle) Torque-Command 904 Torque-Command 904 & 998 Torque-Command 998

CHRYSLER CORP.
All RWD Passenger Cars
All RWD Trucks & Vans
Horizon & Omni — 1.6L
Horizon & Omni — 1.7L
Aries, E Class, Horizon, LeBaron, New Yorker (FWD), Omni,
  Rampage, Reliant, Scamp, 400 & 600 — 2.2L
Aries, E Class, Le Baron, New Yorker (FWD), Reliant,
  400 & 600 — 2.6L
	
	Torqueflite A-727, A-904 & A-904LA
	Loadflite A-727, A-904T & A-999
	Torqueflite A-415 (Transaxle)
	Torqueflite A-404 (Transaxle)
	
	Torqueflite A-413 (Transaxle)
	
	Torqueflite A-470 (Transaxle)

FORD MOTOR CO.
Escort, EXP, LN7, Lynx, Tempo & Topaz
Capri, Fairmont, LTD, Marquis,
  Mustang, Thunderbird, Zephyr — 2.3L
Ranger
Bronco II, Ranger
Fairmont, LTD, Marquis, Zephyr — 3.3L
LTD, Marquis — 3.8L
Bronco, E100/350 Van, F100/350 Pickup
Capri, Continental, Cougar, Mustang, Thunderbird — 3.8L
Capri, Crown Victoria, Continental, Cougar, Grand Marquis,
  Econoline, Mark VI, Mustang, Thunderbird, Town Car — 5.0L
F100/150 (2WD)
	
	Ford Motor Co. ATX
	
	Ford Motor Co. C-3
	
	Ford Motor Co. C-5
	Ford Motor Co. C-6
	
	Ford Motor Co. Automatic Overdrive

GENERAL MOTORS BUICK — Century, Skyhawk, Skylark CADILLAC — Cimarron CHEVROLET — Cavalier, Celebrity, Citation OLDSMOBILE — Ciera, Firenza, Omega PONTIAC — Phoenix, 2000, 6000	 Turbo Hydra-Matic 125C Transaxle
CHEVROLET — Chevette 1.6L PONTIAC — T1000 1.6L	 Turbo Hydra-Matic 180C

BUICK — Regal 4.3L Diesel
CHEVROLET/GMC — Caballero, El Camino
  & Malibu 2.8L & 4.3L Diesel
  S10 Pickup & Blazer, S15 Pickup & Jimmy
  Camaro 2.5L, 2.8L & 5.0L, Chevette 1.8L Diesel
OLDSMOBILE — Cutlass 4.3L Diesel
PONTIAC — Firebird 2.5L, 2.8L & 5.0L
	
	Turbo Hydra-Matic 200C

BUICK — Electra & LeSabre 4.1L, 5.0L & 5.7L Diesel
  Regal 3.8L (VIN 8), 4.1L & 5.7L Diesel
CADILLAC — All Models With 4.1L & 5.7L Diesel
CHEVROLET — Caballero, El Camino & Malibu
  2.8L, 3.8L (VIN 9), 4.3L Diesel & 5.0L
  Caprice, Impala & Monte Carlo 5.0L & 5.7L Diesel
OLDSMOBILE — Cutlass 4.3L Diesel, 5.0L & 5.7L Diesel
  88 5.0L & 5.7L Diesel
  98 4.1L, 5.0L & 5.7L Diesel
PONTIAC — Bonneville & Grand Prix 4.1L,
  5.0L & 5.7L Diesel
	
	Turbo Hydra-Matic 200-4R

AUTOMATIC TRANSMISSIONS (Cont.)

MANUFACTURER & MODEL	TRANSMISSION MODEL

GENERAL MOTORS (Cont.)
BUICK — Electra & LeSabre 3.8L (VIN A) & 5.0L
  Regal 3.8L (VIN A), 4.1L & 5.0L
CHEVROLET — Caballero, El Camino & Malibu 3.8L (VIN A & 9),
  & 5.7L Diesel
  Caprice, Impala & Monte Carlo 3.8L (VIN A & 9),
  5.0L & 5.7L Diesel
OLDSMOBILE — Cutlass 3.8L (VIN A) & 5.0L
  88 3.8L (VIN A), 5.0L, 98 5.0L
PONTIAC — Bonneville & Grand Prix 3.8L (VIN A) & 5.0L
	Turbo Hydra-Matic 250C

BUICK — Riviera 3.8L, 4.1L, 5.0L & 5.7L Diesel CADILLAC — Eldorado & Seville 4.1L, 5.0L & 5.7L Diesel OLDSMOBILE — Toronado 4.1L, 5.0L & 5.7L Diesel	Turbo Hydra-Matic 325-4L

BUICK — Electra & LeSabre 3.8L (VIN A), 4.1L & 5.7L Diesel
  Regal 3.8L (VIN A), 4.1L, 5.0L & 5.7L Diesel
CADILLAC — DeVille & Fleetwood 4.1L & 5.7L Diesel
CHEVROLET/GMC — Caballero, El Camino & Malibu 3.8L (VIN A),
  5.0L & 5.7L Diesel
  Caprice, Impala & Monte Carlo 3.8L (VIN A),
  5.0L & 5.7L Diesel
  C10 2WD Pickup & Suburban
OLDSMOBILE — Cutlass 3.8L (VIN A), 5.0L
  & 5.7L Diesel
  88 3.8L (VIN A), 5.0L & 5.7L Diesel
  98 4.1L, 5.0L & 5.7L Diesel
PONTIAC — Bonneville & Grand Prix 3.8L (VIN A),
  4.1L & 5.7L Diesel
	Turbo Hydra-Matic 350C

CADILLAC — All With 6.0L
CHEVROLET/GM — C20 2WD Pickup & Suburban,
  C30 2WD Pickup, G30 Van
  K20 4WD Pickup & Suburban, K30 4WD Pickup
  P30 Parcel Delivery Van
	Turbo Hydra-Matic 400

CHEVROLET/GM — Camaro 5.0L
  C10/20 2WD Pickup & Suburban, G20/30 Van
  S10 Pickup & Blazer, S15 Pickup & Jimmy
  K10 4WD Blazer, Pickup & Suburban,
  K20 4WD Pickup & Suburban
PONTIAC — Firebird 2.5L, 2.8L & 5.0L
	Turbo Hydra-Matic 700-R4

JEEP
All Except CJ-7 & Scrambler
  With 6-Cyl. Engine & 2.73 Axle Ratio
  All Others
CJ-7 & Scrambler
	Torque-Command 999
	Torque-Command 727
	Torque-Command 999

Automatic Transmissions
OIL PAN GASKET IDENTIFICATION

Fig. 1: AMC/Renault (Alliance) MB1

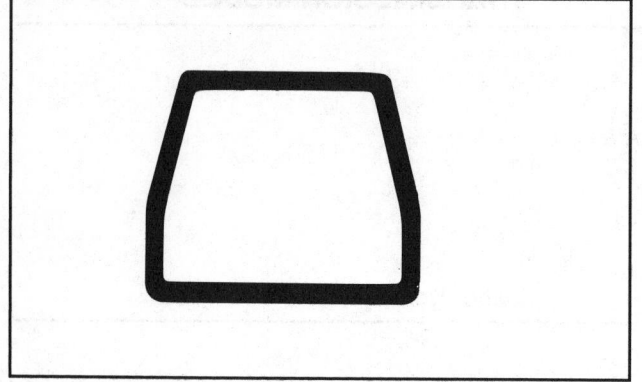

Fig. 2: AMC 904 and 998, Chrysler Corp. A-904, A-904LA and A-904T

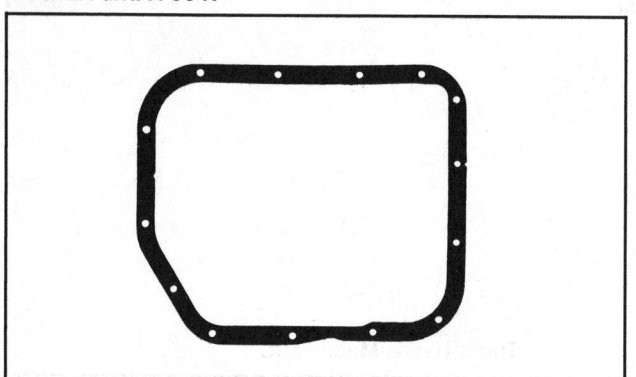

Fig. 3: Chrysler Corp. A-404, A-413 and A-470

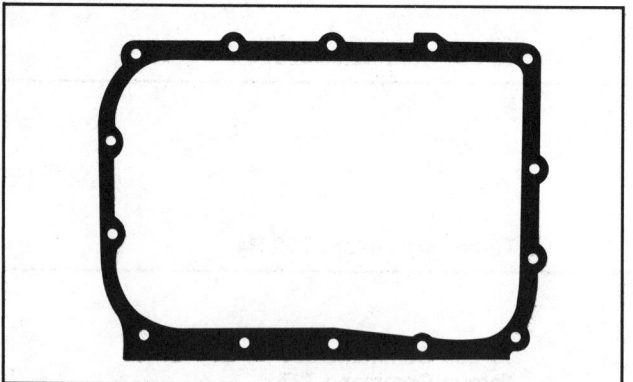

Fig. 4: Chrysler Corp. A-727 and A-999, Jeep 727 and 999

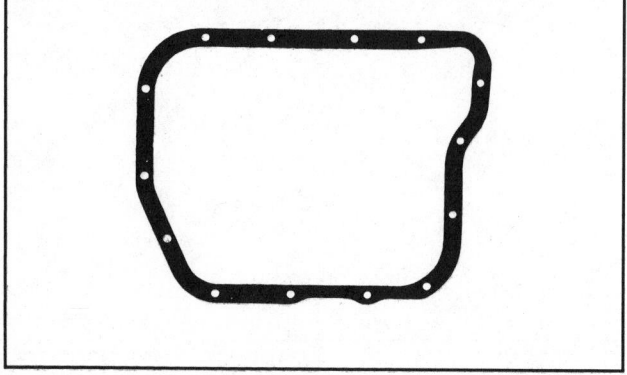

Fig. 5: Ford Motor Co. AOT

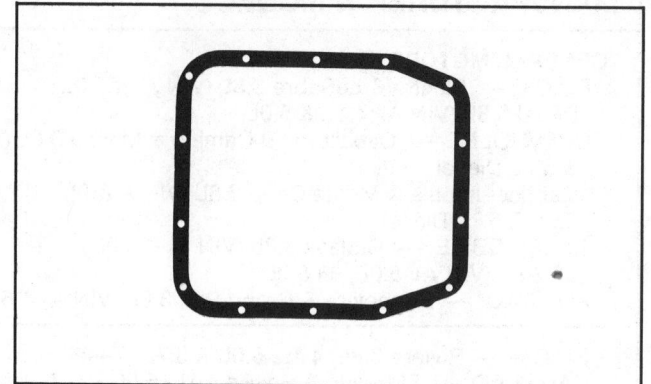

Fig. 6: Ford Motor Co. ATX

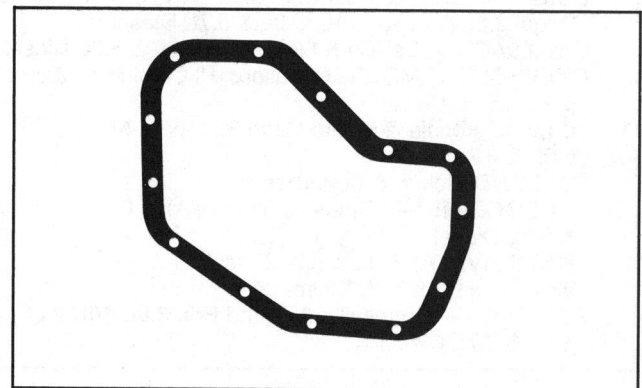

Fig. 7: Ford Motor Co. C-3

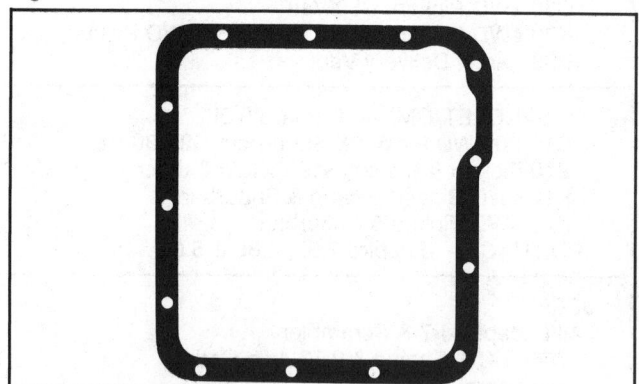

Fig. 8: Ford Motor Co. C-5

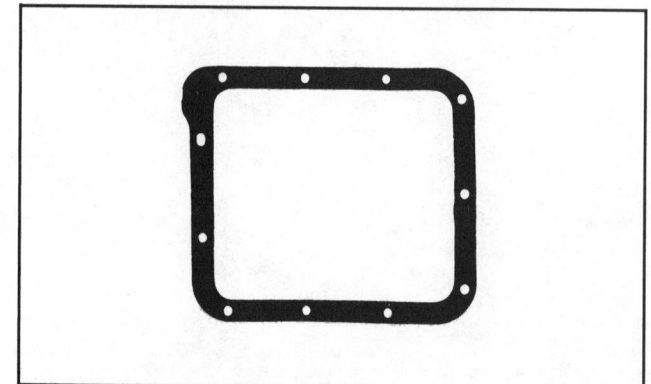

Fig. 9: Ford Motor Co. C-6

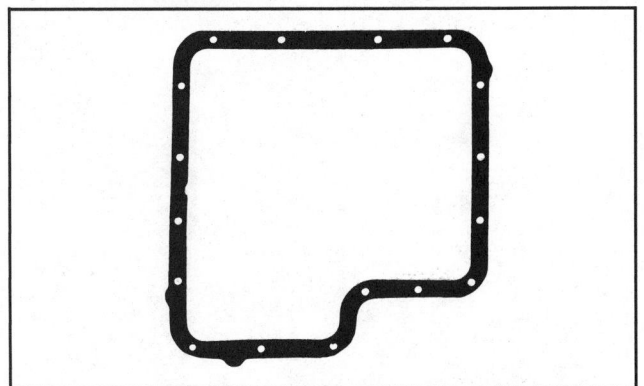

Fig. 13: General Motors THM 200-4R

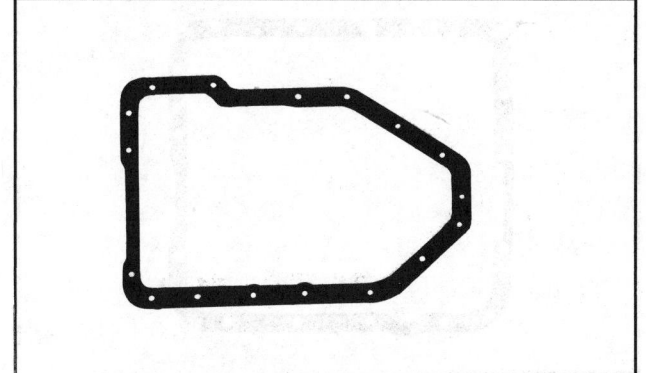

Fig. 10: General Motors THM 125C

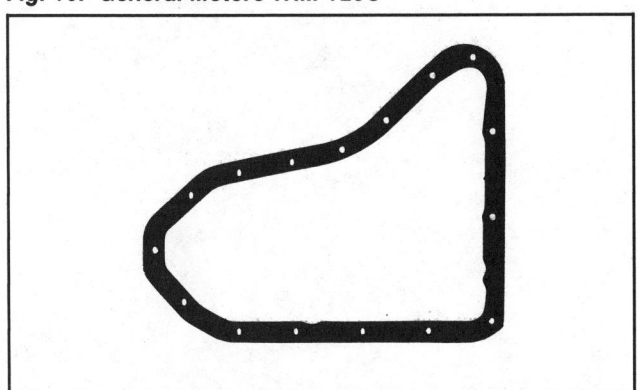

Fig. 14: General Motors THM 250C and 350C

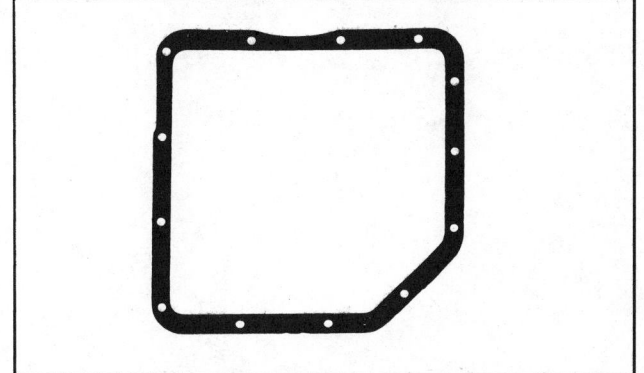

Fig. 11: General Motors THM 180C

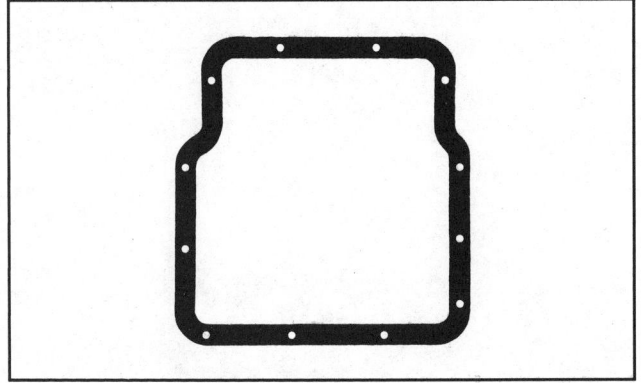

Fig. 15: General Motors THM 325-4L

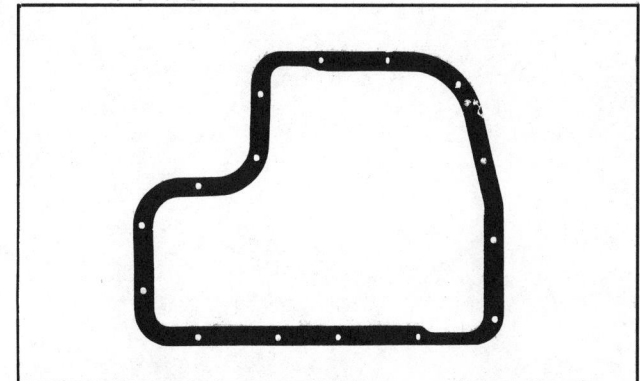

Fig. 12: General Motors THM 200C

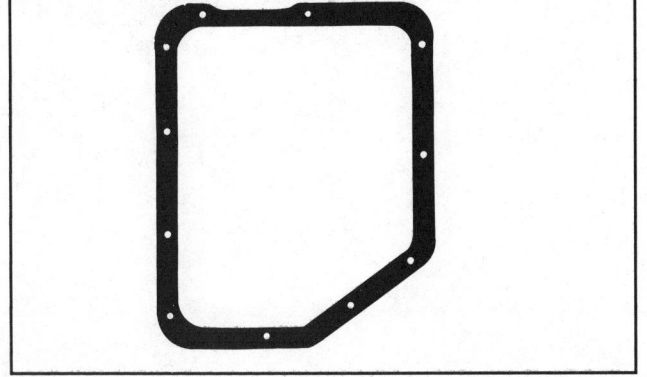

Fig. 16: General Motors THM 400

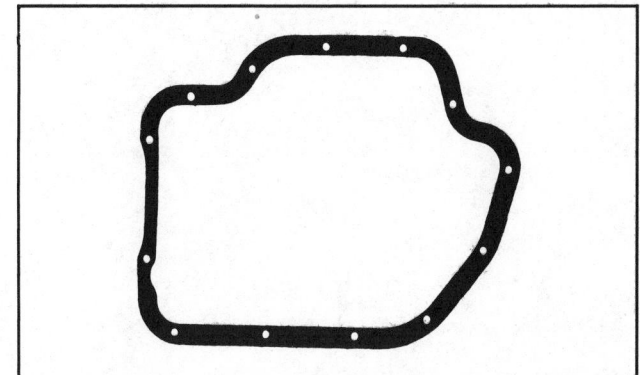

Automatic Transmissions

OIL PAN GASKET IDENTIFICATION (Cont.)

Fig. 17: General Motors THM 700-R4

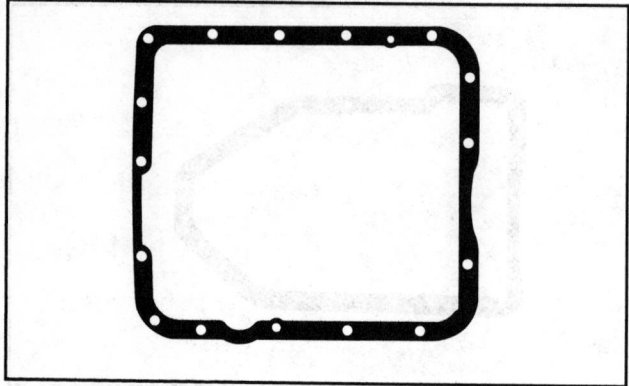

AMERICAN MOTORS/JEEP

LUBRICATION

SERVICE INTERVALS

Check fluid level and condition of fluid at each engine oil change. Under normal, light duty operating conditions, change fluid, replace filter and adjust bands at intervals as indicated in *Transmission Service Intervals* chart. On Alliance models, band adjustment is not required.

TRANSMISSION SERVICE INTERVALS

	Service Interval	
Application	Months	Miles
AMC		
Alliance	24	30,000
Eagle	28	27,500
Concord & Spirit	1	1
All Jeep Models		
Light Duty	28	27,500
Heavy Duty	12	12,500

1 — Regular service is not required. If operated under heavy duty conditions (such as trailer towing), service every 25 months or 30,000 miles.

CHECKING FLUID LEVEL

1) Park vehicle on a level surface and apply parking brake. With engine idling at normal operating temperature, move transmission selector lever through all gears, ending in "N" ("P" on Alliance). Check fluid level.

2) Fluid level should be between "FULL" and "ADD ONE PINT" mark on dipstick ("ADD" mark on Alliance). Add fluid as needed. DO NOT overfill.

NOTE: **Alliance models require only 1/2 pint (.25L) of fluid to raise the level from the "ADD" mark to the "FULL" mark on the dipstick.**

RECOMMENDED FLUID

Use only Dexron or Dexron II type automatic transmission fluid.

CAPACITY

Transmission and converter capacities listed in the *Transmission Refill Capacities* table are approximate. Fluid level should always be determined by reading on dipstick, rather than amount of fluid added.

Torque converters used on AMC models are welded assemblies which are not serviceable. Replacement of the converter is recommended if it becomes contaminated. The converter used in Jeep models may be drained and refilled during regular transmission service.

DRAINING & REFILLING

Alliance

1) Remove drain plug on bottom of transaxle oil pan and drain fluid. Remove transaxle mount bolt and raise transaxle assembly to gain clearance for oil pan removal.

2) Remove oil pan bolts and remove pan. Remove oil filter and seal. Install new oil filter and seal. Clean oil pan and install with new gasket. Lower transaxle, install transaxle mount bolt and tighten.

3) Pour 4 quarts (3.8L) of fluid into transaxle. Start engine and allow to idle for a few minutes. Vehicle

TRANSMISSION REFILL CAPACITIES

Application	Capacity Pints (Liters)
AMC	
Alliance	7.4 (3.5)
Concord, Eagle & Spirit	
With 904 Transmission	
4-Cyl. Models	14.2 (6.7)
6-Cyl. Models	17.1 (8.1)
With 998 Transmission	17.1 (8.1)
Jeep (All Models)	
Including Converter	17.0 (8.0)
Without Converter	8.5 (4.0)

should be on a level surface with engine at curb idle. With parking brake applied, move shift selector through all positions, ending in "P".

4) Add fluid as needed to bring level to the "ADD" mark on dipstick. Recheck fluid level after transaxle has reached normal operating temperature.

All Other Models

1) Loosen oil pan bolts, tap pan to break it loose and allow fluid to drain. Remove pan. Install new filter on bottom of valve body and tighten retaining screws. Install new "O" ring on fluid pickup pipe (if needed). Clean oil pan and install with new gasket.

2) Pour 6 quarts (5.7L) of transmission fluid through filler tube (5 quarts on Jeep models). Start engine and allow to run at curb idle for a few minutes. With vehicle on level surface, engine idling and parking brake applied, move shift selector lever through all gear ranges, ending in neutral. Add fluid up to "ADD ONE PINT" mark on dipstick.

3) Recheck fluid level when transmission reaches normal operating temperature. Fluid should be between "ADD ONE PINT" and "FULL" marks on dipstick. Transmission must NOT be overfilled. Seat dipstick fully to seal out water and dirt.

ADJUSTMENT

KICKDOWN (FRONT) BAND

All Except Alliance

1) Locate kickdown band adjusting screw on left side of case, near throttle lever shaft. Loosen adjusting screw lock nut and back off approximately 5 turns. Make sure adjusting screw turns freely in case.

Fig. 1: Kickdown Band Adjusting Screw Location

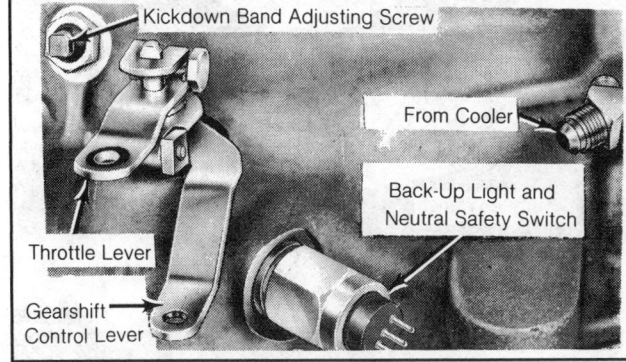

Tighten screw to 72 INCH lbs. (8 N.m), back off specified number of turns and tighten lock nut.

Automatic Transmission Servicing

AMERICAN MOTORS/JEEP (Cont.)

2) Using adapter tool (J-24063) and 5/16" square socket, tighten screw to 36 INCH lbs. (4 N.m). If adapter is not used, tighten screw to 72 INCH lbs. (8 N.m). Back off screw number of turns indicated in *Kickdown (Front) Band Adjustment* table. Hold adjusting screw in position and tighten lock nut to 35 ft. lbs. (48 N.m).

KICKDOWN (FRONT) BAND ADJUSTMENT

Application	[1] Back Off Screw
AMC	
4-Cyl. Models	2 1/2 Turns
6-Cyl. Models	
Concord & Spirit	2 Turns
Eagle	3 Turns
Jeep	
All Models	2 1/2 Turns

[1] — Tighten screw to 72 INCH lbs. (8 N.m) and back off indicated number of turns.

LOW-REVERSE (REAR) BAND

All Except Alliance

1) Raise vehicle, drain transmission fluid and remove oil pan. Locate adjusting screw on rear servo lever. Loosen adjusting screw lock nut and back off about 5 turns.

2) Tighten screw to correct torque and back off indicated number of turns. *See Low-Reverse (Rear) Band Adjustment table.* Hold adjusting screw in position and tighten lock nut to 35 ft. lbs. (48 N.m). Install oil pan and fill transmission with fluid.

LOW-REVERSE (REAR) BAND ADJUSTMENT

Application	Tighten Screw to INCH Lbs. (N.m)	Back Off Screw
AMC		
4-Cyl. Models	41 (4.6)	7 Turns
6-Cyl. Models	72 (7.9)	4 Turns
Jeep		
Model 727	41 (4.6)	2 Turns
Model 999	41 (4.6)	4 Turns

Fig. 2: Adjusting Low-Reverse Band

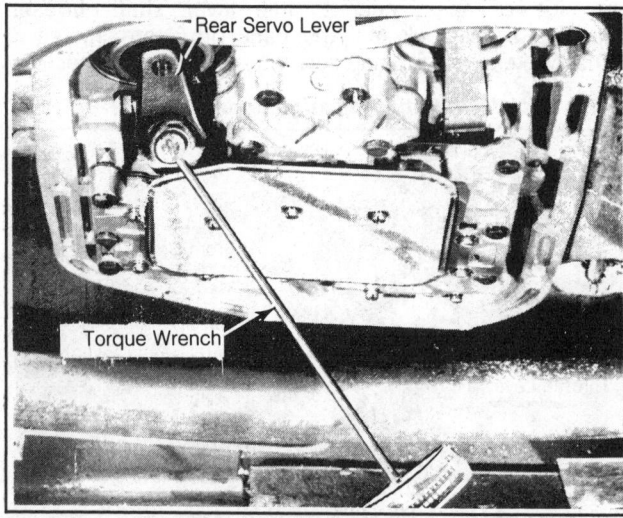

Band should be adjusted whenever oil pan is removed.

TRANSMISSION THROTTLE CABLE

AMC 4-Cylinder Models (Except Alliance)

1) Remove air cleaner, remove spark plug wire separator from throttle cable bracket and set aside. Remove strut rod bushing heat shield. Hold throttle control lever rearward against its stop.

2) Block choke plate open and set carburetor linkage completely off fast idle cam. On models without air conditioning, turn ignition "ON" to energize throttle stop solenoid.

3) Unlock throttle control cable by lifting "T" shaped adjuster clamp with small screwdriver. Move cable outer sheath forward to remove any cable load on throttle cable bellcrank.

4) Adjust cable by moving cable and sheath rearward until there is no lash between cable and throttle linkage. Lock cable by pressing "T" shaped clamp downward until clamp snaps into place. Install and reconnect any parts removed and/or disconnected.

Fig. 3: Throttle Cable Adjustment

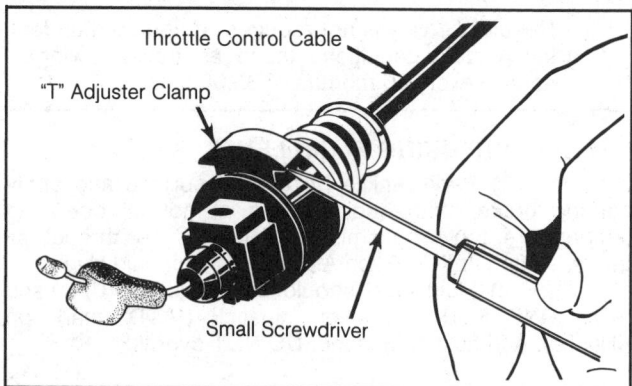

AMC 4-cylinder models, except Alliance.

TRANSMISSION THROTTLE LINKAGE

AMC 6-Cylinder Models

1) Disconnect throttle control rod spring and use spring to hold transmission throttle valve control lever

Fig. 4: Throttle Linkage Adjustment

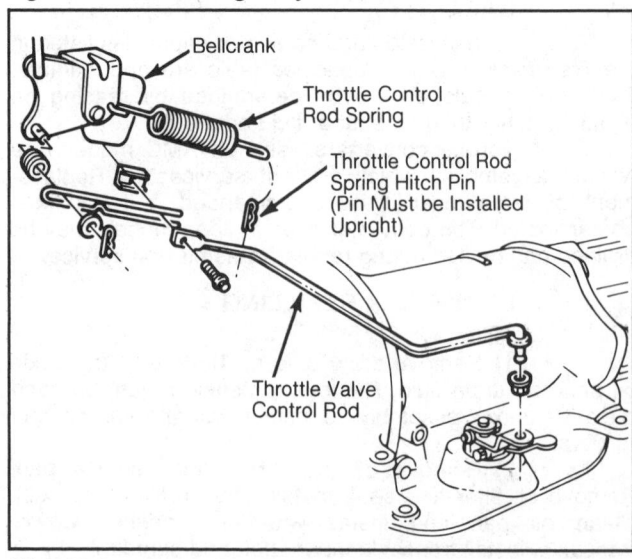

All AMC 6-cylinder models and all Jeep 6-cylinder models with 727 transmission.

AMERICAN MOTORS/JEEP (Cont.)

forward against stop. Block choke plate open and release fast idle cam.

2) On carburetors equipped with throttle operated solenoid valve, energize solenoid by turning key to "ON" position. Open throttle halfway to allow solenoid to lock. Return throttle to idle position.

3) On all models, loosen both retaining bolts on throttle control adjusting link. DO NOT remove spring clip and nylon washer. Hold transmission throttle lever forward against stop. Push on end of link to eliminate lash.

4) Pull clamp rearward so bolt in rod bottoms in rear of slot in rod. Tighten clamp to adjusting link.

5) Pull control rod rearward so bolt in rod bottoms in front of slot in rod. Tighten rearward retaining bolt. Install throttle control rod spring on control rod.

Jeep 6-Cyl. Models with 727 Transmission

1) Disconnect throttle control rod spring. Use spring to hold transmission throttle control lever forward, against stop. Block choke open and release fast idle cam.

2) On carburetors equipped wih throttle operated solenoid valve, turn key to "ON" position to energize solenoid. Open throttle halfway to allow solenoid to lock. Return throttle to idle position.

3) Loosen retaining bolt on throttle control adjusting link. DO NOT remove spring clip or nylon washer. Pull on end of link to eliminate lash. Tighten link retaining bolt. Reconnect throttle control rod spring.

Jeep 6-Cyl. Models with 999 Transmission

1) Disconnect throttle control rod spring. Use spring to hold adjusting link in forward position, against nylon washer. Block choke open and release fast idle cam.

2) Raise vehicle. Loosen both retaining bolts on adjusting link clamp. DO NOT remove spring clip or nylon washer.

3) Use a spare spring to hold transmission throttle lever against forward stop.

4) Push adjusting link to eliminate lash and pull clamp to rear so that bolt in rod bottoms in rear of slot in rod. Tighten forward clamp retaining bolt.

Fig. 5: Throttle Linkage Adjustment

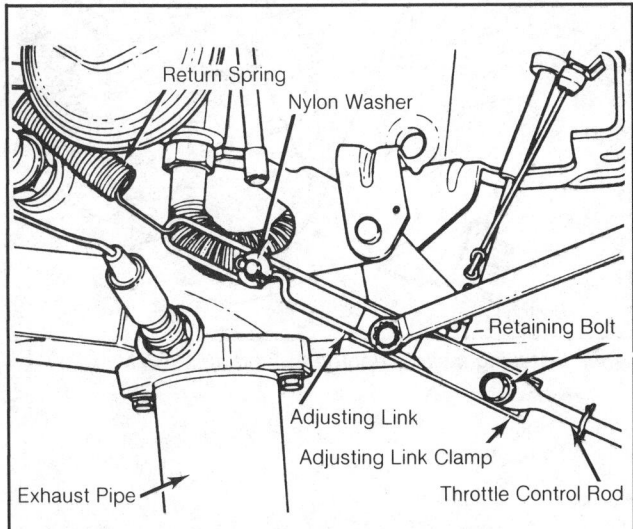

Jeep 6-cylinder models with 999 transmission.

5) Pull throttle control rod to the rear so that bolt in rod bottoms in front of slot and tighten rear retaining bolt. Remove spare spring. Lower vehicle and reconnect throttle control rod spring.

Jeep V8 Models

1) Disconnect throttle control rod spring. Use spring to hold transmission throttle valve control lever against forward stop. Block choke open and release fast idle cam.

Fig. 6: Throttle Linkage Adjustment

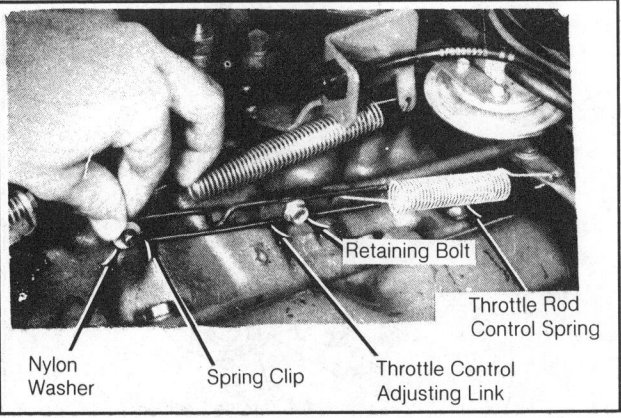

All Jeep models equipped with V8 engines.

2) On carburetors equipped wih throttle operated solenoid valve, turn key to "ON" position to energize solenoid. Open throttle halfway to allow solenoid to lock. Return throttle to idle position.

3) Loosen retaining bolt on throttle control rod adjusting link. Remove spring clip and slide nylon washer to rear of link. Push on end of link to eliminate lash and tighten retaining bolt. Install nylon washer and spring clip. Reconnect throttle control rod spring.

THROTTLE POSITION POTENTIOMETER

AMC Alliance

1) On models with Bendix TBI, remove air filter assembly. On all models, turn ignition key to "ON" position. Insert negative lead of a digital volt-ohmmeter into terminal "C" of potentiometer. See Fig. 7.

2) DO NOT disconnect the connector. Insert voltmeter lead in back of connector and push in to make contact with terminal. Insert positive lead of voltmeter into terminal "B" of throttle position sensor.

3) Move throttle plate to wide open throttle position by hand. Be sure throttle contacts stop. Note exact voltmeter reading. It should be about 4.3 volts. This is input voltage.

4) Remove positive lead from terminal "B" and insert in terminal "A" of throttle position sensor. Open throttle plate to wide open throttle position. Note exact voltmeter reading. This is output voltage.

5) Adjust potentiometer so that output voltage is 3.5-4.5% of input voltage. Adjust potentiometer by loosening bottom potentiometer retaining screw "C" and pivoting potentiometer on adjustment slot for rough adjustment.

6) Loosen top retaining screw "D" and pivot potentiometer for fine adjustment.

AMERICAN MOTORS/JEEP (Cont.)

Fig. 7: View of Throttle Position Potentiometer Showing Testing and Adjustment Locations

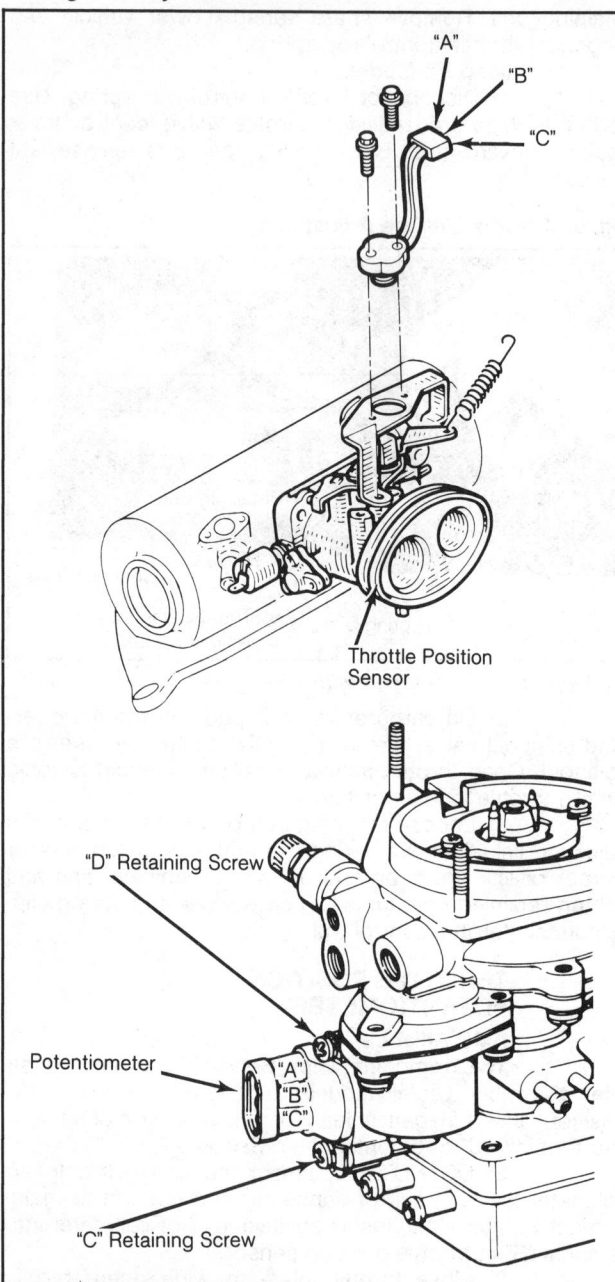

Throttle Position Sensor

"D" Retaining Screw

Potentiometer

"A"
"B"
"C"

"C" Retaining Screw

Testing and adjusting procedures are the same for the Bendix TBI and Bosch AFC system.

SHIFT LINKAGE

Alliance

1) Place gear selector in "P" position. Raise and support vehicle. Loosen adjustment yoke nuts and slide yoke and cable forward to remove slack in cable.

2) Tighten yoke nuts and lower vehicle. Be sure that all 6 gear selector lever positions are functional and that vehicle starts in "P" position.

All Other Models

1) Loosen shift rod trunnion jam nuts at transmission lever. Remove shift rod-to-bellcrank lock pin. Disengage trunnion and shift rod. Place selector lever in "P" position and lock steering column. Move transmission shift lever to full rear (park) position.

2) Adjust shift rod trunnion to obtain free pin fit in bellcrank arm. Tighten jam nuts. On vehicles with shift lever on column, make sure linkage lash is eliminated by pulling down on shift rod and pushing up on outer bellcrank when tightening jam nuts.

3) Check steering column lock for ease of operation. Check that engine starts in "N" or "P", only. If starter engages in any drive gear, or does not work in "N" or "P", check for proper shift linkage adjustment or faulty neutral safety switch.

NEUTRAL SAFETY SWITCH

AMC Alliance

The neutral safety switch used on Alliance models is not adjustable. It is incorporated in a multifunction switch, located on the transaxle.

All Other Models

1) Switch combines functions of neutral safety switch and back-up light switch. With transmission linkage properly adjusted, switch should allow starter operation in "P" and "N" only.

2) To test switch, remove wire connector and test for continuity between center pin of switch and case. Continuity should only exist when transmission is in "P" or "N".

3) Check for continuity between 2 outer pins. Continuity should exist with transmission in "R" only. There should be no continuity between either outer pin and transmission case. If any of these conditions are not met, the switch should be replaced.

4) To replace, unscrew switch from case (some fluid will drain). Move selector lever to "P" and "N" positions and check that switch operating fingers are centered in switch opening. Install switch and new seal in case. Check fluid level and add as needed.

Fig. 8: Back-Up Light/Neutral Safety Switch Location

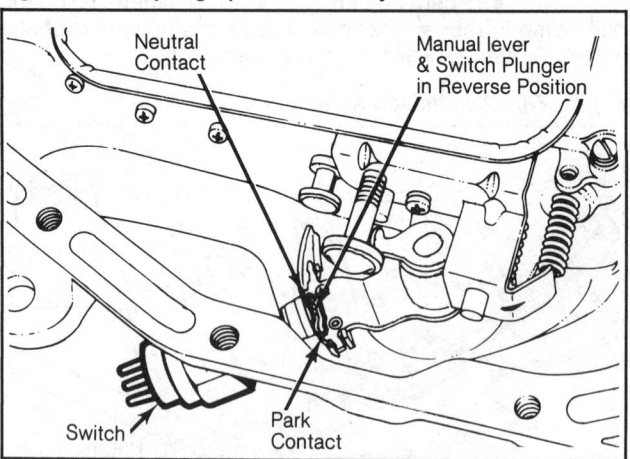

Neutral Contact

Manual lever & Switch Plunger in Reverse Position

Switch

Park Contact

When installing switch, tighten to 24 ft. lbs. (33 N.m).

CHRYSLER CORP.

LUBRICATION

SERVICE INTERVALS

Check fluid level at each engine oil change. When operated under normal conditions, passenger car transmissions do not require periodic service. However, under heavy duty conditions, transmission should be drained, refilled and bands adjusted every 15,000 miles.

Trucks and Vans used in normal, light duty service require transmission servicing (fluid drained and refilled, bands adjusted) every 37,500 miles. Under normal heavy duty conditions, service transmission every 24,000 miles. Vehicles subjected to severe heavy duty conditions should have transmission serviced every 12,000 miles.

CHECKING FLUID LEVEL
All Models

1) Check fluid level with vehicle parked on level surface, engine idling at normal operating temperature and parking brake applied. Move selector lever through all gear ranges, ending in "P" (FWD models) or "N" (RWD models).

2) Fluid level should be between "FULL" and "ADD" marks on dipstick. Check condition of fluid for contamination or burned smell. Seat dipstick carefully to seal out water and dirt. NEVER overfill transmission.

RECOMMENDED FLUID

Use only Dexron II type automatic transmission fluid when topping off or refilling transmission.

CAPACITY

When filling transmission, use capacities listed in table as a guideline, only. Correct fluid level should always be determined by marks on dipstick, rather than by amount of fluid added. Capacities listed include torque converter.

TRANSMISSION REFILL CAPACITIES

Application	Capacity Pints (Liters)
A-404 & A-415	14.5 (6.8)
A-413 & A-470	15.0 (7.1)
A-727	
Lock-Up	16.7 (7.9)
Non Lock-Up	17.1 (8.1)
A-904 Series	
Lock-Up & All Trucks	17.1 (8.1)
Non Lock-Up	17.6 (8.3)
A-999	17.1 (8.1)

DRAINING & REFILLING
All Models

1) Loosen oil pan bolts. Tap lightly at one corner to break loose and allow fluid to drain. Remove pan. Install new filter on bottom of valve body and tighten retaining screws. Clean oil pan. Ensure that magnet (if used) is over boss in right front corner of pan. Install pan with new gasket.

2) Pour 4 quarts (3.7L) of transmission fluid through filler tube. Start engine and allow to run at idle for at least 2 minutes. With engine at curb idle trand parking brake applied, move shift selector lever through all

ranges, ending in "P" (FWD vehicles) or "N" (RWD vehicles). Add fluid up to "ADD" mark on dipstick. Do not overfill.

3) Reseat dipstick fully to seal out water and dirt. Recheck fluid level when transmission reaches normal operating temperature.

ADJUSTMENT

KICKDOWN (FRONT) BAND
All Models

1) Locate kickdown band adjusting screw at left side of transmission case, near throttle lever shaft. Loosen adjusting screw lock nut and back off 5 turns. Make sure adjusting screw turns freely in case.

2) Using special wrench (C-3380-A) with adapter (C-3705), tighten adjusting screw to 48 INCH lbs. (5 N.m). If adapter is not used, tighten adjusting screw to 72 INCH lbs. (8 N.m), which is the true torque.

3) Back off adjusting screw specified number of turns, as given in *Kickdown (Front) Band Adjustment* table. Hold adjusting screw in position and tighten lock nut to 35 ft. lbs. (47 N.m).

KICKDOWN BAND ADJUSTMENT

Application	Back Off Screw
A-404 & A-415	3 Turns
A-413 & A-470	2 3/4 Turns
All Others	2 1/2 Turns

Fig. 1: Adjusting Kickdown Band

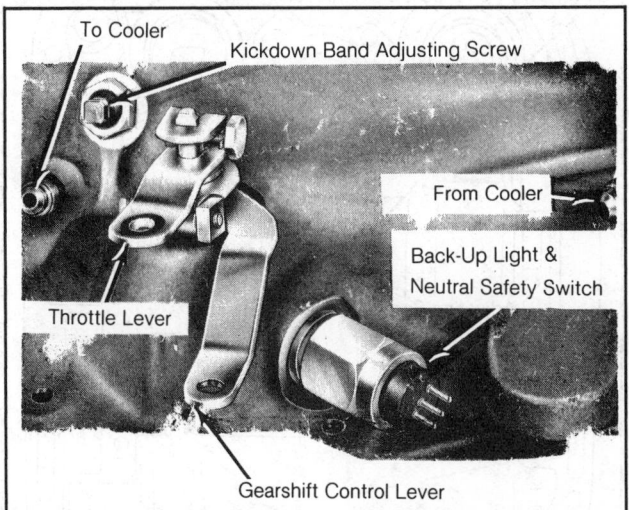

With band properly adjusted, tighten lock nut to 35 ft. lbs. (47 N.m).

LOW-REVERSE (REAR) BAND
Rear Wheel Drive Models

1) Drain transmission and remove oil pan. Locate low-reverse band adjusting screw on rear servo lever. On passenger cars with A-904 transmission and 6-cylinder engine, remove band adjusting screw lock nut and tighten Allen screw at servo end of lever to 41 INCH lbs. (4.6 N.m).

2) On all other models, loosen adjusting screw lock nut and back off about 5 turns. Make sure that screw

Automatic Transmission Servicing

CHRYSLER CORP. (Cont.)

turns freely in lever. Using special wrench (C3380-A), tighten adjusting screw to 72 INCH lbs. (8 N.m).

3) On all models, back off adjusting screw specified number of turns as given in *Low-Reverse (Rear) Band Adjustment* table. Hold adjusting screw in position and tighten lock nut to 30 ft. lbs. (41 N.m). Clean oil pan, install new gasket with pan and fill transmission with fluid.

Front Wheel Drive Models

1) Drain transaxle fluid and remove oil pan. Apply 30 psi (2.1 kg/cm²) air pressure to low-reverse servo and measure gap between band ends. If less than .080" (2.0 mm), band is excessively worn and should be replaced.

2) To adjust band on A-413 and A-470 models, loosen lock nut approximately 5 turns and tighten adjusting screw to 41 INCH lbs. (4.6 N.m). Back off adjusting screw specified number of turns as given in table, hold screw in position and tighten lock nut.

NOTE: Low-reverse band on model A-404 transaxle is not adjustable.

LOW-REVERSE BAND ADJUSTMENT

Application	Back Off Screw
A-413 & A-470	3 1/2 Turns
A-904 (6-Cyl.)	7 Turns
A-904LA, A-904T & A-999	4 Turns
A-727	2 Turns

Fig. 2: Low-Reverse (Rear) Band Adjustment Location

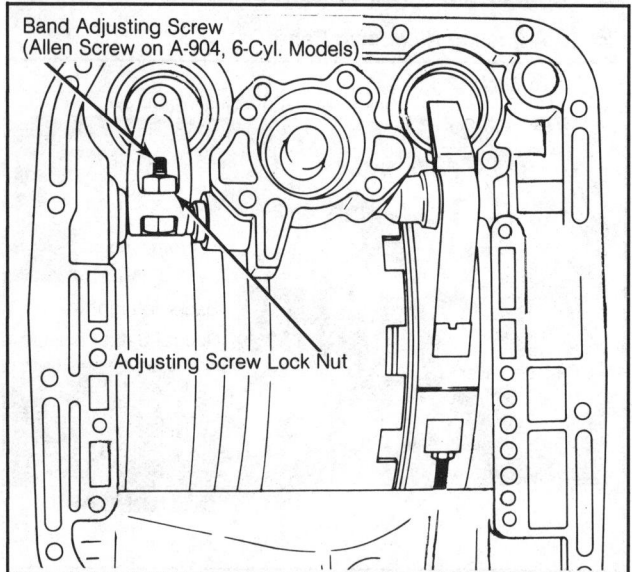

Adjust band and tighten lock nut to 30 ft. lbs. (41 N.m).

TRANSMISSION THROTTLE ROD

Rear Wheel Drive Models

1) With engine at normal operating temperature and carburetor off fast idle cam, check and adjust idle speed as needed. Turn off engine and disconnect choke at carburetor or block choke valve in full open position. Open throttle slightly to release fast idle cam and return throttle to curb idle position.

2) Raise vehicle on hoist. Loosen swivel lock screw. Be sure swivel is free to slide along flat end of

throttle rod so that preload spring action is not restricted. If necessary, disassemble and clean parts to assure free action.

Fig. 3: Throttle Rod Adjustment Diagram

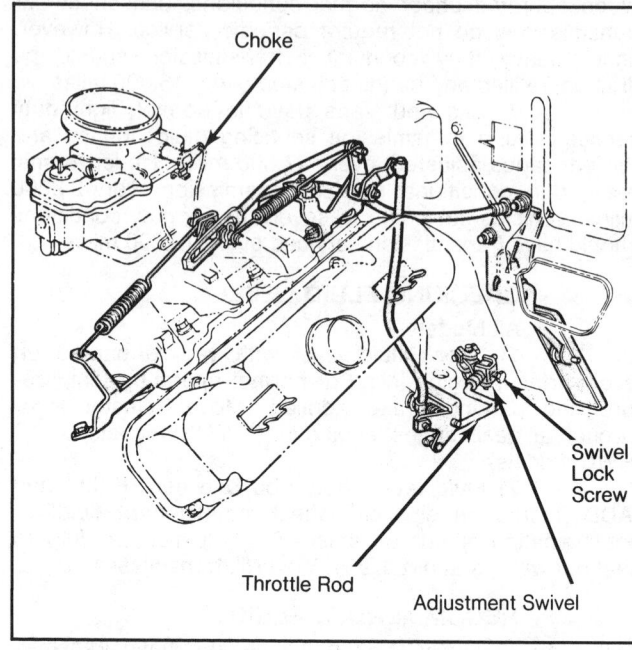

Linkage for vehicles equipped with 6-cylinder engine.

3) Hold transmission lever firmly forward against internal stop and tighten swivel lock screw. Adjustment is complete. Linkage backlash is automatically removed by preload spring.

4) Lower vehicle and reconnect choke. To test linkage, move throttle rod rearward and slowly release it to confirm full forward return.

Fig. 4: Throttle Rod Adjustment

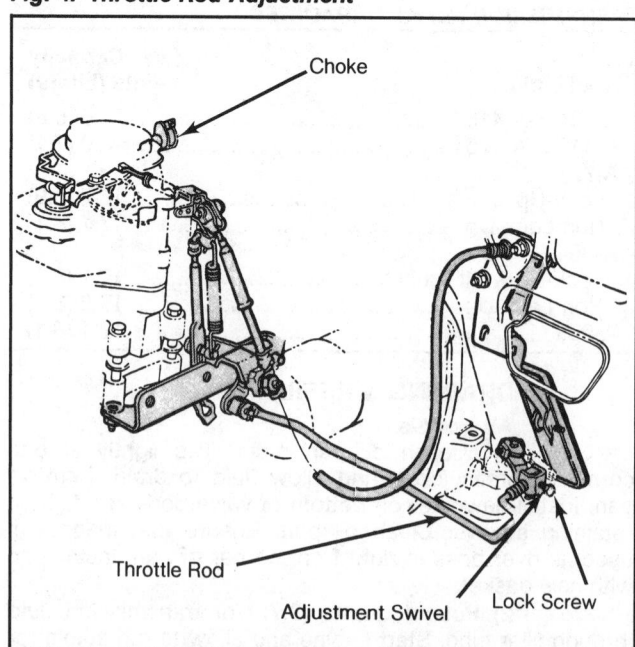

Linkage for vehicles equipped with V8 engines.

Front Wheel Drive Models

1) Make sure carburetor is not on fast idle cam (disconnect choke if necessary). Loosen adjustment bracket lock screw. Make sure bracket slides freely along full length of adjustment.

2) Hold transmission lever firmly rearward against its internal stop and tighten lock screw. This completes adjustment. Cable backlash is automatically removed.

3) To check linkage freedom of operation, move transmission lever forward and slowly release, making sure it returns to full rear position.

Fig. 5: Throttle Cable Adjustment

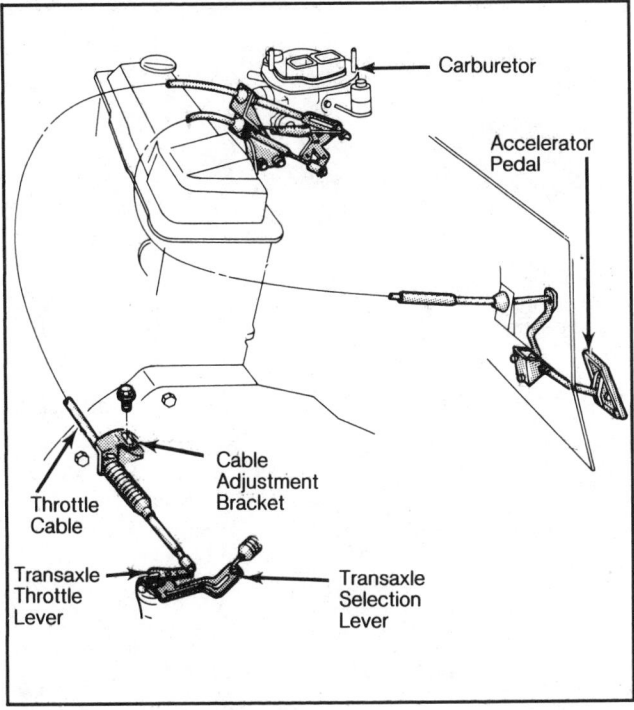

All front wheel drive models.

SHIFT LINKAGE

Column Shift (RWD Models Except Imperial)

1) With column shift lever in "P" position, loosen adjustable swivel lock screw and ensure that swivel is free to move on shift rod. Disassemble and clean components if required.

2) Move shift lever on transmission to full rear detent (park) position and tighten swivel lock screw. When linkage is properly adjusted, detent positions for neutral and drive will be within limits of shift lever gate stops and engine will start in "P" or "N", only.

Column Shift (Imperial)

1) With shift indicator in "P" position, loosen 2 screws attaching shift indicator (PRND21) to steering column. Holding indicator switch in position on column, apply downward pressure on switch and tighten attaching screws.

2) Check each gear position to ensure that proper shift character is illuminated and that no double characters are indicated.

Fig. 6: Column Shift Linkage Adjustment

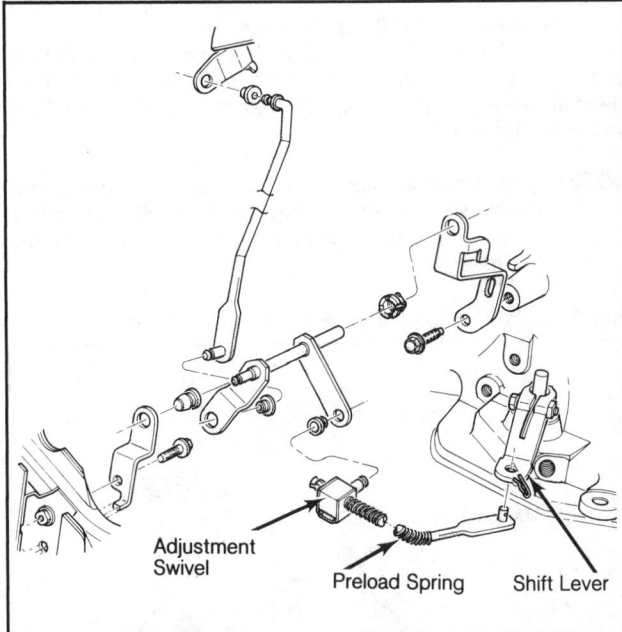

Passenger car linkage shown. Trucks and Vans are similar.

Floor Shift (RWD Models)

1) Loosen adjustable rod swivel lock screw, place selector in "P" and move shift lever on transmission all the way to rear detent (park) position.

2) Adjust swivel so no load is placed on linkage in either direction, then tighten swivel lock screw. Check adjustment so shift effort is free, detents are solid, and all gate stops are positive.

Fig. 7: Floor Shift Linkage Adjustment on RWD Models

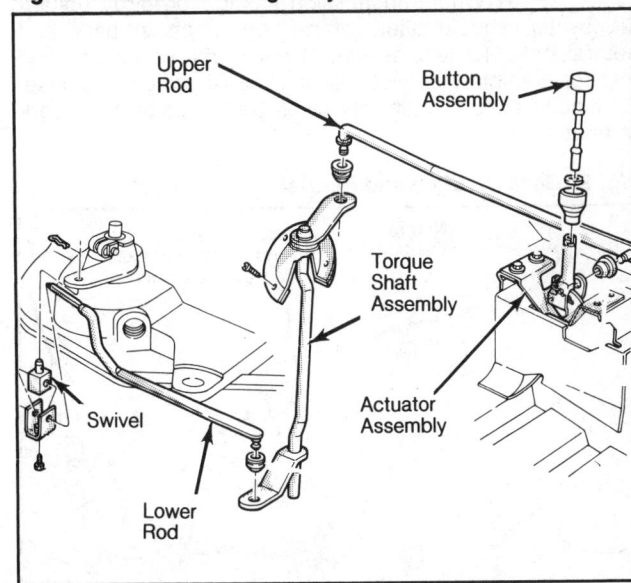

Swivel is located near transmission housing.

3) Detent position should be close enough to gate stops in "N" and "D" so shift selector lever will not remain out of detent position when placed against gate

CHRYSLER CORP. (Cont.)

and released. Starter should operate in "N" or "P" positions, only.

Floor Shift (FWD Models)

Place shift selector in "P" position. Loosen lock bolt on cable adjusting bracket on transaxle. Move shift lever on transaxle all the way to rear detent (park) position and hold. Tighten lock bolt.

NOTE: If linkage cable is disconnected from transmission lever for any reason, always use a new plastic grommet when reassembling linkage.

Fig. 8: Shift Linkage Adjustment on FWD Models

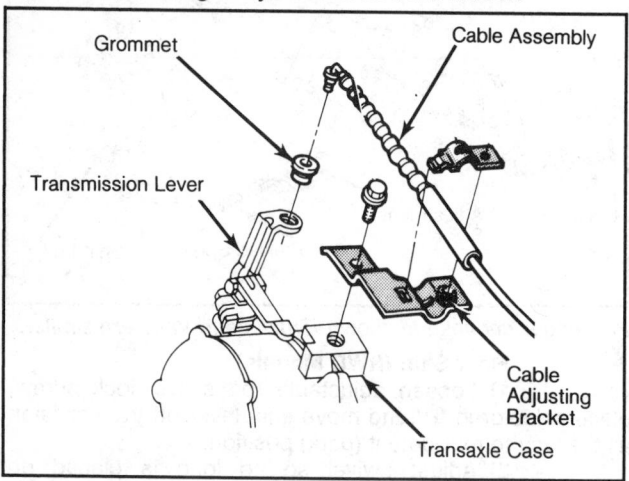

Adjusting bracket is located on transaxle case.

NEUTRAL SAFETY SWITCH

All Models

1) With transmission linkage properly adjusted, switch should allow starter operation in park and neutral only. To test switch, remove wire connector and test for continuity between center pin of switch and case. Continuity should exist only when transmission is in park or neutral.

Fig. 9: Back-Up Light and Neutral Safety Switch

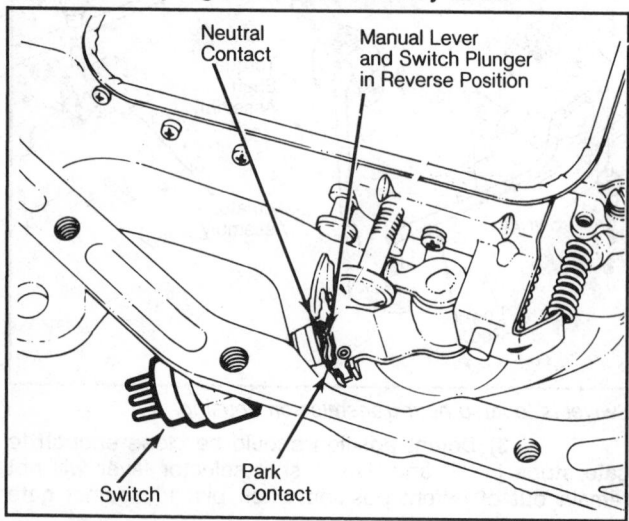

When installing new switch, tighten to 24 ft. lbs. (33 N.m).

2) Check for continuity between 2 outer pins. Continuity should exist with transmission in reverse, only. There should be no continuity between either outside pin and the transmission case.

NOTE: Be sure gearshift linkage is properly adjusted before replacing a switch which tests bad.

3) To replace, remove switch from case and allow fluid to drain. Move selector lever to park and neutral positions and check that switch operating fingers are centered in switch opening. Install new switch and seal. Retest switch for continuity and add transmission fluid.

FORD MOTOR CO.

LUBRICATION

SERVICE INTERVALS

Vehicles used in normal service do not require regularly scheduled maintenance. Fluid level should be checked whenever underhood maintenance is performed, or if leakage is detected. Clutch bands (except AOT and ATX) should be adjusted when quality of shifts deteriorates or otherwise indicates improper band adjustment.

On vehicles used for fleet service or those operated under severe conditions (such as police, taxi or towing), regular transmission fluid changes are required. On 100 series Trucks and Vans with 4.9L engine, change fluid every 20,000 miles. On all other models, drain and refill transmission every 22 months or 22,500 miles.

If vehicle is used for off-highway operation, check fluid level every 1000 miles. If operated in water, check fluid level and condition daily. Drain and refill if necessary.

CHECKING FLUID LEVEL

1) Check fluid level with vehicle parked on level surface, engine and transmission at normal operating temperatures and engine idling. Apply parking brake and move transmission selector lever through all ranges, ending in "P".

2) Fluid level should check between "ADD" and "FULL" (or "DON'T ADD") marks on dipstick (or in crosshatched area). Add fluid through filler tube as needed. DO NOT overfill. When check is complete, seat dipstick fully to seal out water and dirt.

RECOMMENDED FLUID

On C-5 transmissions, use fluid which meets Ford Motor Co. specification ESP-M2C166-H or type H fluid (or equivalent). On all other models, Ford Motor Co. specification ESP-M2C138-CJ, Dexron II, Series D or equivalent must be used.

CAPACITY

Fluid capacities listed are approximate. Always determine correct fluid level by mark on dipstick rather than by amount of fluid added.

TRANSMISSION REFILL CAPACITIES

Application	[1] Capacity Quarts (Liters)
C-3 Transmission	8.0 (7.6)
C-5 Transmission	
All Except Bronco II & Ranger	11.0 (10.4)
2WD Ranger	7.5 (7.1)
Bronco II & 4WD Ranger	7.9 (7.5)
C-6 Transmission	
2WD Models	11.8 (11.2)
4WD Models	13.5 (12.8)
AOT Transmission	12.0 (11.4)
ATX Transaxle	
All Except Tempo/Topaz	10.0 (9.4)
Tempo/Topaz	8.3 (7.9)

[1] — Includes oil cooler (if equipped).

DRAINING & REFILLING

1) On C-3 and C-5 models, disconnect fluid filler tube from oil pan to drain fluid, then remove pan. On all other models, loosen oil pan bolts and tap pan to break gasket seal. Allow fluid to drain, then remove oil pan bolts and oil pan.

2) On ATX, C-3 and C-5 models, remove and clean filter screen. Reinstall filter screen using a new gasket. On all other models, discard used filter and gasket. Install new filter and gasket. On all models, clean pan and install with new gasket. On C-3 and C-5 models, install filler tube.

3) On all models, add 3 quarts transmission fluid through filler tube. Check fluid level as described. When filling a dry transmission and converter, refer to *Transmission Refill Capacities* chart.

4) Recheck fluid level when transmission is at normal operating temperature. Do not overfill.

ADJUSTMENT

INTERMEDIATE (FRONT) BAND

1) On C-3 transmissions, remove downshift rod from transmission downshift lever. On all models, clean dirt from band adjusting screw area. Remove and discard band adjusting screw lock nut. Install new lock nut.

2) Tighten adjusting screw to 120 INCH lbs. (14 N.m). Then back off screw exact number of turns as indicated in *Intermediate (Front) Band Adjustment* table. Hold adjusting screw in position and tighten new lock nut to 40 ft. lbs. (56 N.m).

3) On C-3 models, re-install downshift rod on transmission downshift lever.

INTERMEDIATE (FRONT) BAND ADJUSTMENT

Application	Back Off Screw
C-3	2 Turns
C-5	4 1/4 Turns
C-6	1 1/2 Turns

Fig. 1: Adjusting Intermediate Band (C-3 & C-5)

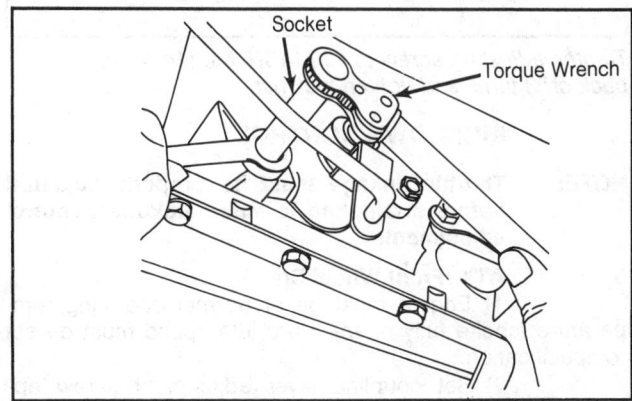

Tighten adjusting screw to 120 INCH lbs. (14 N.m). Back off 2 turns on C-3, 4 1/4 turns on C-5, and tighten lock nut.

Automatic Transmission Servicing
FORD MOTOR CO. (Cont.)

Fig. 2: Adjusting Intermediate Band (C-6)

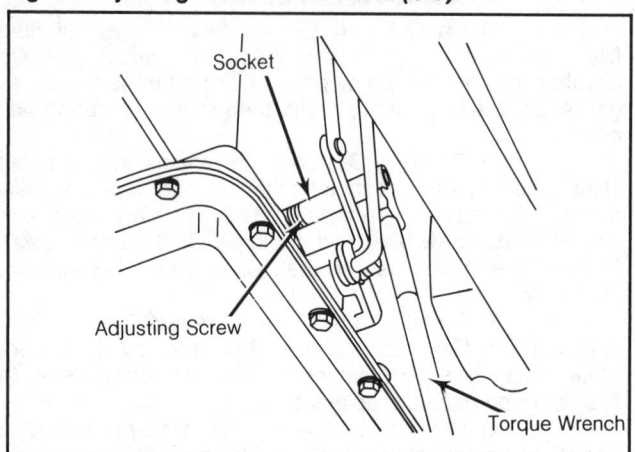

Tighten adjusting screw to 120 INCH lbs. (14 N.m), back off 1 1/2 turns and tighten lock nut.

LOW-REVERSE (REAR) BAND
C-5 Only

1) Clean all dirt from band adjusting screw area, then remove and discard band adjusting screw lock nut. Install new lock nut on adjusting screw.

2) Tighten screw to 120 INCH lbs. (14 N.m), then back off 3 full turns. Hold screw in position and tighten lock nut to 40 ft. lbs. (54 N.m).

Fig. 3: Adjusting Low-Reverse Band (C-5)

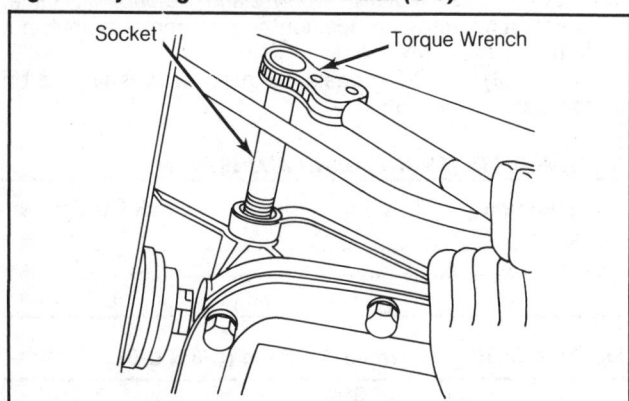

Tighten adjusting screw to 120 INCH lbs. (14 N.m), back off 3 turns and tighten lock nut.

KICKDOWN CONTROL

NOTE: Throttle linkage must be properly adjusted before attempting to make kickdown control adjustment.

ATX (Front Wheel Drive)

1) Engine must be at normal operating temperature (choke fully open). Curb idle speed must be set to specification.

2) Set coupling lever adjustment screw approximately mid-range. TV linkage shaft assembly must be fully seated upward into the coupling lever.

CAUTION: The following step requires working very close to the EGR system. Allow EGR system to cool before proceeding.

Fig. 4: Kickdown Linkage Adjustment on ATX Transaxle

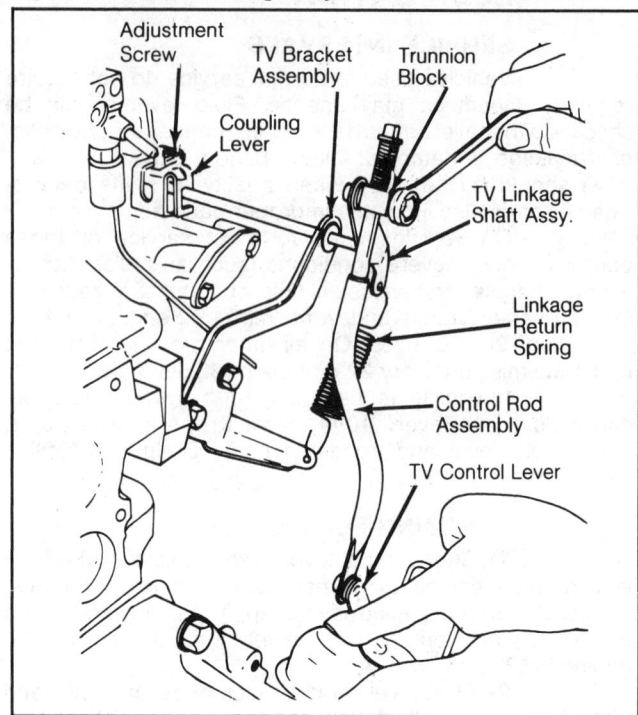

Hold TV control lever in full up position while making linkage adjustment.

3) Loosen bolt on sliding trunnion block at least 1 full turn and ensure that block can slide freely on rod.

4) Rotate transaxle TV control lever upward using a force of about 1 lb. to ensure that it is against internal idle stop. Hold this pressure and tighten trunnion block bolt. *See Fig. 4.*

Automatic Overdrive Transmission (AOT)

1) Check and adjust engine idle speed as needed. Release fast idle cam on carburetor so that throttle lever is at idle stop. Place shift lever in "N" position and set parking brake.

2) With engine off, back off adjusting screw completely, then turn screw back in to obtain .005" (.13 mm) clearance between end of screw and throttle lever. Open and close throttle several times to eliminate friction and recheck clearance.

3) Turn adjusting screw in 3 full turns (4 on Trucks and Vans). If screw travel is limited, 1 turn is permitted (2 on Trucks and Vans), however, the higher limit is preferred. If adjustment results in idle speed change of more than 50 RPM, throttle valve control rod length at transmission must be adjusted.

AOT Throttle Valve (TV) Control Rod

1) Check and adjust engine curb idle speed as needed. With engine off, release fast idle cam so that throttle lever is against idle stop.

2) Place shift lever in neutral and apply parking brake. Set linkage lever adjustment screw at its approximate mid-range.

3) Raise vehicle on hoist. Loosen nut on sliding stud of TV control assembly. Push lower end of control rod to be sure linkage lever at carburetor is against throttle lever. Release force on rod.

4) Push TV control lever on transmission up against internal stop with firm force (about 5 lbs.). Tighten

FORD MOTOR CO. (Cont.)

nut on stud. Manually operate gearshift and throttle linkage to check for smooth operation and ensure that no binding or interference takes place.

C-3 & C-5 — Passenger Cars

1) Hold carburetor at wide open throttle position. Place kickdown rod downward against "through detent" stop.

2) Turn kickdown screw to obtain .010-.080" (.25-2.0 mm) clearance between screw and throttle arm.

3) Tighten adjusting screw lock nut (if equipped) and return carburetor and kickdown rod to normal position.

Fig. 5: C-3 and C-5 Transmission Kickdown Linkage Adjustment on 2.3L Engine

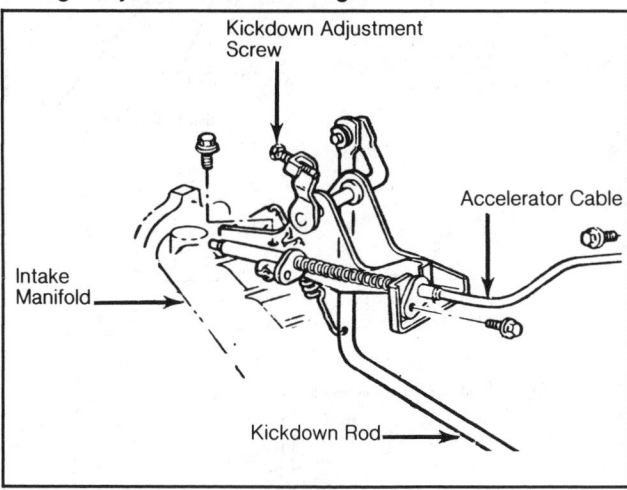

Fig. 6: C-3 and C-5 Transmission Kickdown Linkage Adjustment on 3.3L Engine

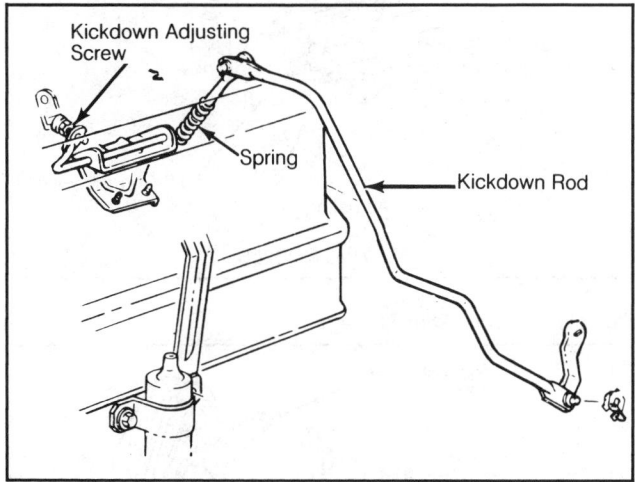

C-5 & C-6 — Trucks & Vans

With throttle pedal held to floor, check for full throttle linkage travel. When carburetor is at full throttle and throttle linkage is at full throttle stop, there should be a slight amount of movement left in downshift linkage. Make sure downshift lever return spring is connected and downshift lever returns to closed position.

Fig. 7: C-3 and C-5 Transmission Kickdown Linkage Adjustment on 4.2L & 5.0L Engines

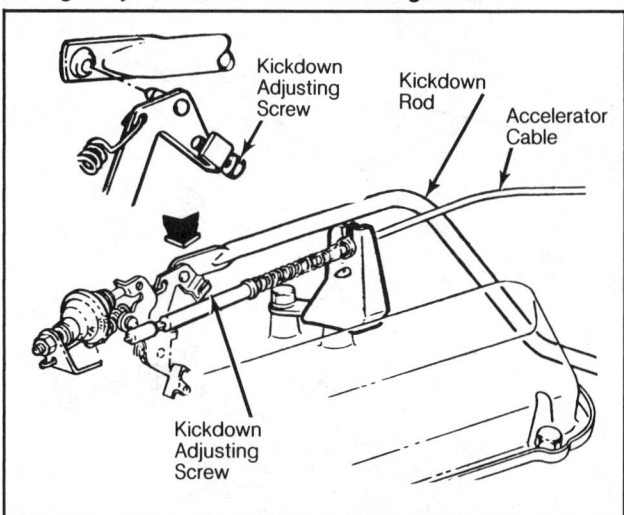

SHIFT LINKAGE

Floor Shift (All Except Bronco II & Ranger)

1) Move selector lever rearward against stop in "D" position. Loosen manual lever-to-control cable (or rod) retaining nut.

2) Move transmission manual lever to drive position (3rd detent from rear of transmission on 4.2L models, 2nd detent from rear on others).

3) Hold selector against rear of "D" position and tighten retaining nut. Check for normal operation in all selected positions.

Floor Shift (Bronco II & Ranger)

1) With engine off and parking brake applied, place shift lever in "D". Loosen nut on slotted shift rod at transmission. Move shift lever at transmission all the way to the rear, then forward 3 steps. This places lever in "D" position.

2) Apply light forward pressure on shift control lever (at transmission) and tighten nut at slotted lever to 144-216 INCH lbs. (16-24 N.m). Move lever through all positions making sure transmission is at full detent in each position.

Column Shift (Ford, Mercury, Town Car & Mark VI)

1) Place selector in "D" or overdrive position and apply downward force on end of selector lever to keep lever against "D" stop during adjustment.

2) Loosen shift rod adjusting bolt and push rod downward to lowest position, then pull up 2 detents. Tighten bolt and check operation in all selector detent positions.

Column Shift (All Others)

1) Place selector lever in "D" position against "D" stop and apply downward force on end of selector lever to keep lever against stop during adjustment.

2) Loosen retaining nut at slotted end of lower rod and place manual lever into drive position (2nd detent from full counterclockwise position).

3) Tighten nut and check transmission operation in all selector lever detent positions.

FORD MOTOR CO. (Cont.)

Fig. 8: *Floor Shift Linkage — Except Bronco II & Ranger*

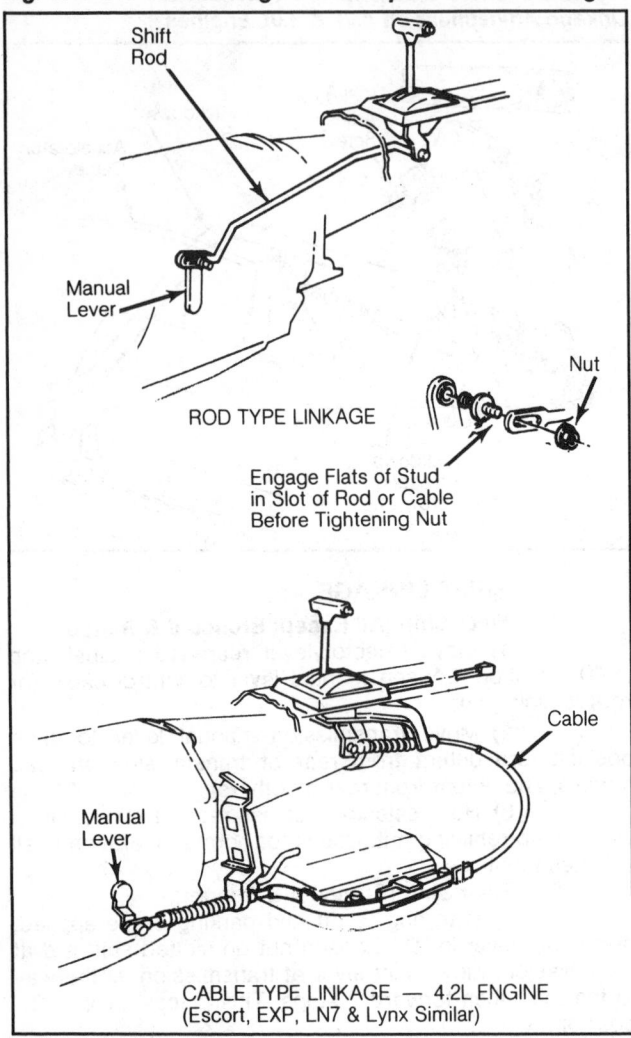

ROD TYPE LINKAGE

Engage Flats of Stud
in Slot of Rod or Cable
Before Tightening Nut

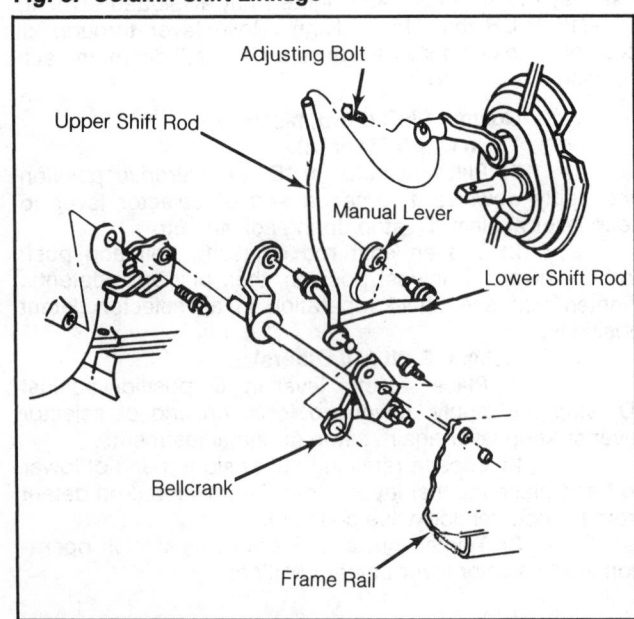

CABLE TYPE LINKAGE — 4.2L ENGINE
(Escort, EXP, LN7 & Lynx Similar)

Fig. 9: *Column Shift Linkage*

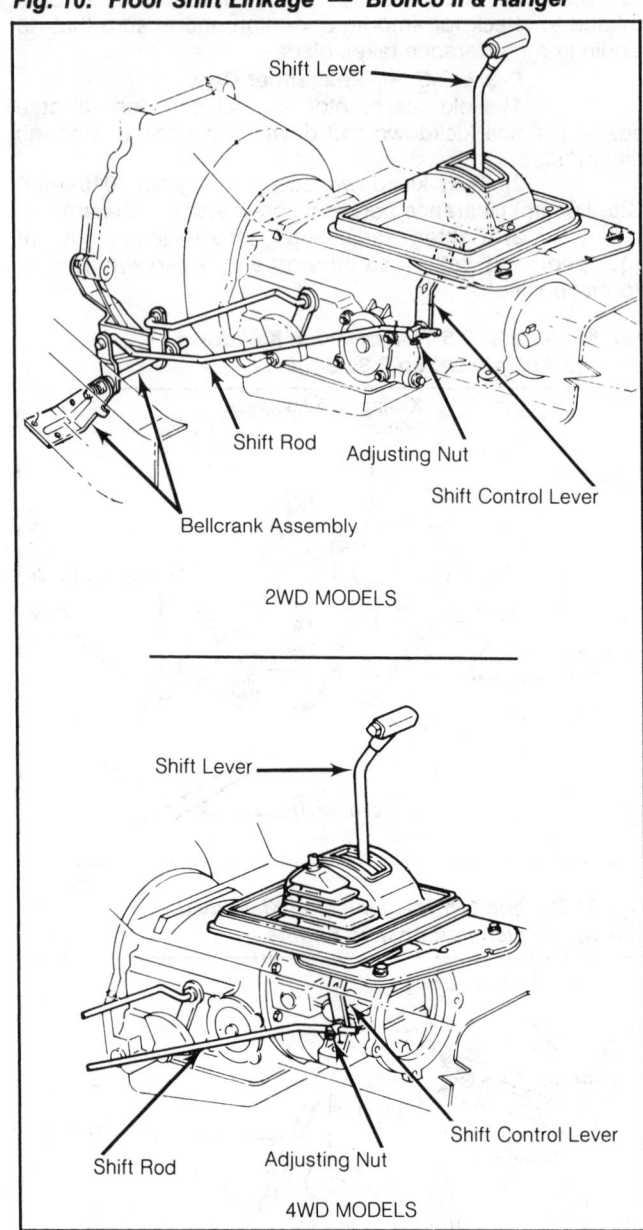

Fig. 10: *Floor Shift Linkage — Bronco II & Ranger*

2WD MODELS

4WD MODELS

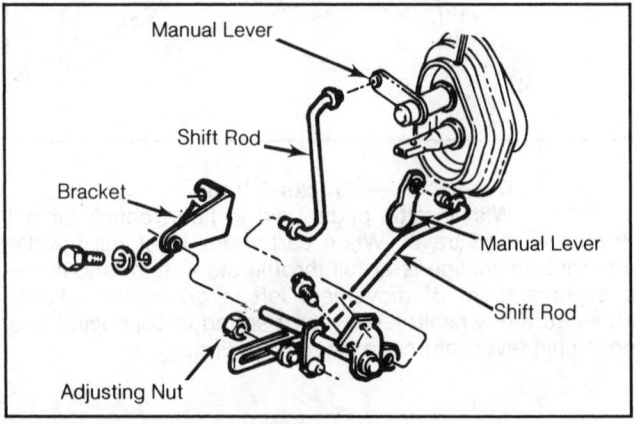

Ford, Mercury, Town Car and Mark VI with AOT.

Fig. 11: *Column Shift Linkage*

Cougar, Fairmont and Zephyr
with C-3 and C-5 transmission.

FORD MOTOR CO. (Cont.)

Fig. 12: Column Shift Linkge

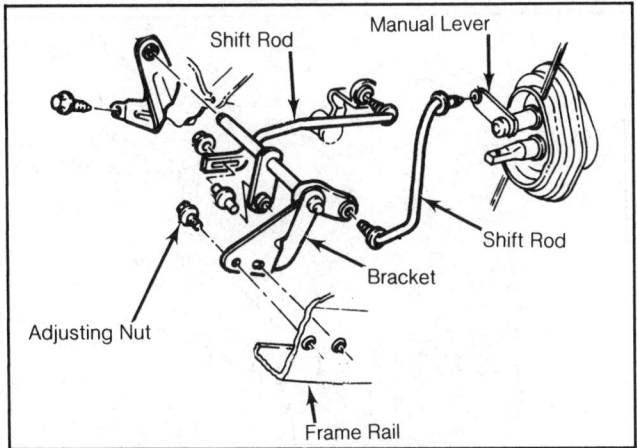

Continental, Cougar & Thunderbird with AOT.

Fig. 13: Column Shift Linkage

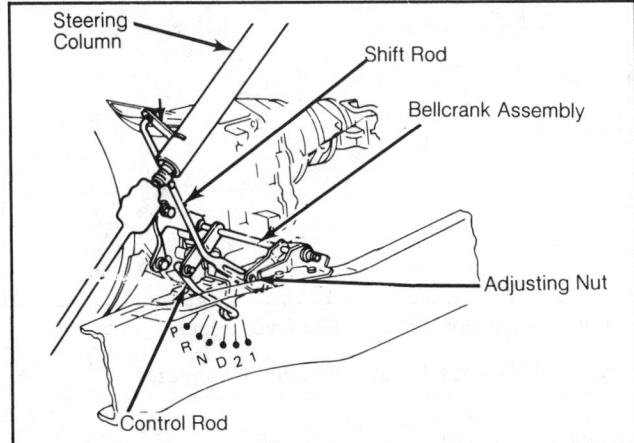

All "F" series vehicles.

Fig. 14: Column Shift Linkage

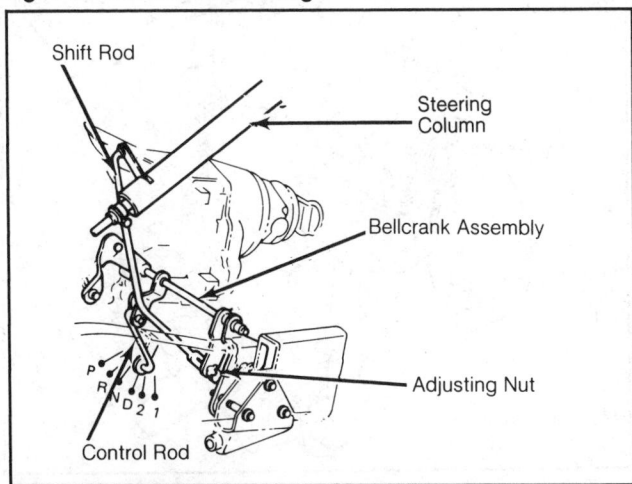

All "E" series vehicles.

Grommet Removal & Installation

1) Shift linkage systems use an oil impregnated plastic grommet to connect various rods trand levers. A new grommet must be installed each time any rod is disconnected from this type of connector.

Fig. 15: Column Shift Linkage

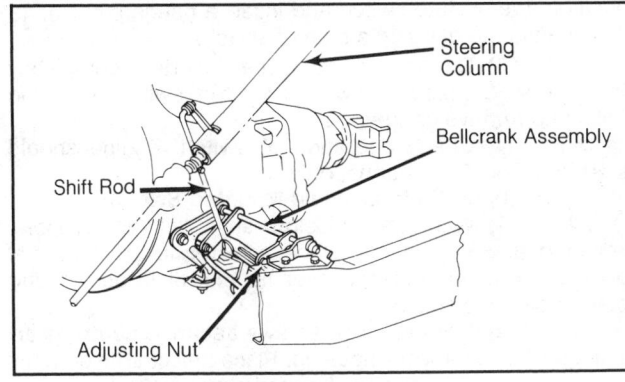

All Trucks and Vans with AOT.

2) Removal tool (Ford T67P-7341-A) is required to install grommet into shift lever and to install shift linkage rod into grommet.

3) Remove grommet as follows: Place lower jaw of tool between shift lever and shift rod. Position stop pin against end of shift rod and force rod out of grommet. Remove grommet by cutting off the large shoulder with a sharp knife.

4) Before installing new grommet, adjust stop pin to 1/2" (12.7 mm) and coat outside of grommet with light grease. Place grommet on stop pin and force into lever hole.

5) Turn grommet several times to be sure it is properly seated. Squeeze rod into bushing until stop washer seats against grommet.

NEUTRAL SAFETY SWITCH

Column Shift

Vehicles equipped with an automatic transmission and a column shift do not use a neutral safety switch. The ignition switch mechanism in the steering column is designed so that ignition switch may be turned to start position only when selector lever is in "N" or "P" position. The switch is blocked from start position in all other selector lever positions.

Floor Shift (Transmission Mounted Switch)

1) With transmission shift linkage properly adjusted, loosen the 2 switch attaching bolts.

Fig. 16: Transmission Mounted Neutral Safety Switch

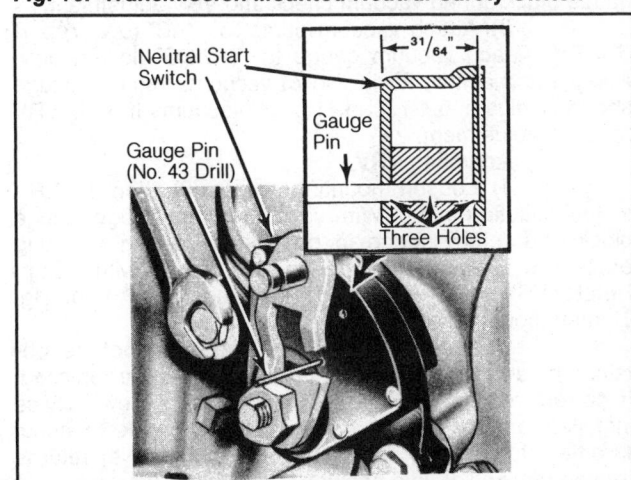

FORD MOTOR CO. (Cont.)

2) Place transmission manual lever in neutral position, then rotate switch and insert a gauge pin (No. 43 drill shank) into gauge pin hole of switch.

3) Gauge pin must be inserted completely through all 3 holes of switch. Tighten switch attaching bolts and remove gauge pin.

4) Check operation of switch. Engine should start in "N" or "P" positions, only.

Floor Shift (Console Mounted Switch)

1) With transmission shift linkage properly adjusted and engine off, place selector lever in neutral position. Remove selector lever handle, dial housing and pointer back-up shield.

2) Loosen the 2 screws securing neutral start switch to selector lever housing. Place selector lever in "P" position and hold it against forward stop.

3) Move neutral switch rearward to end of its travel. Hold switch in rearward position and tighten 2 attaching screws. Check operation of switch. Engine should start in "N" or "P" only.

Floor Shift (C-3 Transmissions Only)

1) Switch is threaded into transmission at left side. If replacement is required, remove wires from switch and use a thin-walled socket to remove switch.

2) DO NOT use an open end wrench due to danger of crushing switch. Install new switch with same socket, connect wires and check switch operation.

VACUUM REGULATOR VALVE

All trucks and vans equipped with the 6.9L V8 diesel engine and automatic transmission include a vacuum pump. Mounted on the left side of the fuel injection pump, it provides a vacuum signal to the transmission to control shift points. Signal strength is determined by a vacuum regulator valve (VRV).

Checking VRV Operation

1) Disconnect vacuum connector from VRV. Remove throttle cable from injection pump throttle lever located on right side of pump. Disconnect throttle return spring.

2) Attach 1 end of return spring over throttle lever ball stud. Install other end of spring over throttle cable support bracket. Insert gauge block (T83T-7B200-AH) between pump boss and wide-open throttle stop screw. See Fig. 17. Spring will hold throttle lever against gauge block during vacuum check and VRV adjustment.

3) Attach vacuum pump to "VAC" (upper) port of VRV. Attach vacuum gauge to "TRANS" (lower) port. Apply and maintain 20 in. Hg of vacuum. Vacuum gauge should indicate 6.4-7.4 in. Hg of vacuum. If not, VRV requires adjustment.

Adjusting VRV

1) Loosen mounting screws (2) attaching VRV to fuel injection pump. With vacuum pump, gauge, gauge block and return spring in position as during checking procedure, maintain 20 in. Hg of vacuum with pump. Rotate VRV until vacuum gauge reads 6.4-7.4 in. Hg. Tighten mounting screws.

2) If correct vacuum reading cannot be obtained by adjusting VRV, it is faulty and must be replaced. If correct reading can be obtained, or after new VRV is installed and adjusted, remove gauge block, connect throttle return spring and ensure that pump lever returns to, and remains at, idle position.

Fig. 17: Checking VRV Adjustment

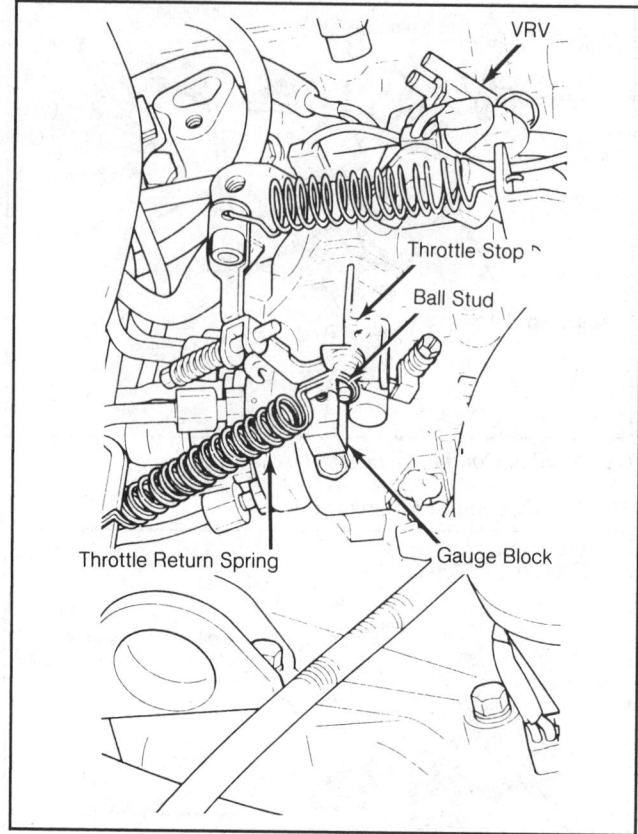

Return spring must hold throttle lever against gauge block.

Fig. 18: VRV Location and Vacuum Connector

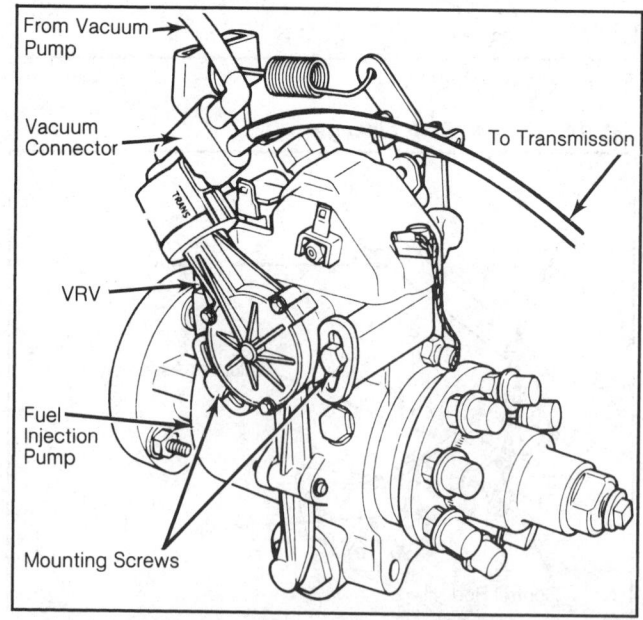

Loosen mounting screws to allow for VRV adjustment.

3) Apply 20 in. Hg of vacuum with vacuum pump and check gauge reading. If vacuum gauge reads less than 13 in. Hg, replace VRV. Remove vacuum pump and gauge and re-connect vacuum connector to VRV. Connect throttle cable.

GENERAL MOTORS
BUICK

LUBRICATION

SERVICE INTERVALS

Check fluid level every 12 months or 7500 miles, whichever comes first. Transmission fluid and filter should be changed every 100,000 miles. On THM 250C transmissions, intermediate (front) band requires adjustment every 60,000 miles, or as required.

NOTE: For heavy duty operation, transmission should be serviced (change fluid and filter or service the screen), at 15,000 mile intervals.

CHECKING FLUID LEVEL

CAUTION: Do not overfill. One pint of fluid will raise level from "ADD 1 PT." to "FULL HOT" mark on dipstick with a hot transmission.

All Models (Exc. THM 125C)

1) With vehicle on level surface, apply parking brake and let engine run at curb idle. Move selector lever through all ranges, ending in "PARK".

2) Remove dipstick and wipe clean, reinstall, then remove again and check fluid level mark on dipstick. Fluid level should check between "ADD 1 PT." and "FULL HOT" marks on dipstick.

THM 125C

1) Place vehicle on level surface. Apply parking brake and start engine. Move selector lever through all ranges, ending in "PARK".

2) Remove dipstick and wipe dipstick clean, reinstall, then remove and check fluid level on dipstick. Fluid level should check between the "ADD" and "FULL" marks on dipstick.

CAUTION: If vehicle has been operated for an extended period of time at high speed, or in city traffic in hot weather, or if vehicle has been pulling a trailer, an accurate fluid level cannot be determined until fluid has cooled down (approximately 30 minutes after vehicle has been parked).

RECOMMENDED FLUID

Use only Dexron II or equivalent automatic transmission fluid.

CAPACITY

NOTE: Quantities listed are approximate. Correct fluid level should be determined by mark on dipstick rather than by amount added.

TRANSMISSION REFILL CAPACITIES PTS. (L)

Application	Refill	Total Capacity
THM 125C	8 (3.8)	12 (5.7)
THM 200C	7 (3.3)	19 (9.0)
THM 200-4R	7 (3.3)	22 (10.4)
THM 250C	8 (3.8)	21 (9.9)
THM 325-4L	10 (4.7)	24 (11.4)
THM 350C	6 (2.8)	20 (9.4)

DRAINING & REFILLING
All Models

1) With vehicle raised and drain pan placed under transmission, remove front and side transmission oil pan bolts. Loosen rear pan bolts approximately 4 turns each.

2) Carefully pry pan loose with screwdriver, allowing fluid to drain. Remove remaining bolts and oil pan with gasket. Remove screen/filter-to-valve body bolts and remove screen/filter with gasket.

3) Thoroughly clean pan and screen with solvent and dry with compressed air. Paper type filters should be replaced. Install new gasket or "O" rings, lubricated with clean oil, into screen/filter assembly.

4) Install screen/filter assembly to transmission. Use new pan gasket and install pan. Add proper amount of fluid to transmission through filler tube.

5) Start engine with shift selector lever in "PARK" position and with parking brake set. Check fluid level and add as required. See checking fluid level in this section.

CAUTION: DO NOT overfill.

ADJUSTMENT

INTERMEDIATE BAND (FRONT) TURBO HYDRA-MATIC 250C

1) Position selector lever in "NEUTRAL" position. Loosen lock nut on right side of transmission 1/2 turn, hold in this position.

2) Tighten adjusting screw to 30 INCH lbs. (3.4 N.m). Back off screw 3 complete turns. Hold adjusting screw in this position and tighten lock nut.

THROTTLE VALVE (TV) CABLE
Gasoline Models

1) Depress metal lock tab on adjuster and hold it in depressed position. Move slider back through fitting, away from carburetor lever, until slider stops at fitting.

2) Release lock tab and open carburetor lever to full throttle stop to automatically adjust slider to correct setting. Release carburetor lever.

Diesel Models (Exc. Century)

1) Remove cruise control rod (if equipped). Disconnect detent cable terminal from throttle assembly. Loosen lock nut on pump rod and shorten several turns. Rotate lever assembly to full throttle position and hold.

2) Lengthen pump rod until injection pump lever contacts full throttle stop. Release lever and tighten pump rod lock nut.

3) Remove pump rod from lever assembly. Reconnect detent cable terminal to throttle assembly. Depress and hold metal tab on cable upper end. Move slider through fitting in direction away from lever assembly until slider stops against fitting.

4) Release tab and rotate lever assembly to full throttle stop. Release lever. Reconnect pump rod. If equipped with cruise control, reconnect rod and adjust servo rod to minimum slack, then install clip in first free hole closest to bellcrank, but within servo bail.

Automatic Transmission Servicing

GENERAL MOTORS
BUICK (Cont.)

Diesel Models (Century)

1) Remove pump rod from lever assembly and depress metal lock tab. Hold tab and move slider through fitting away from lever assembly until slider stops against fitting.

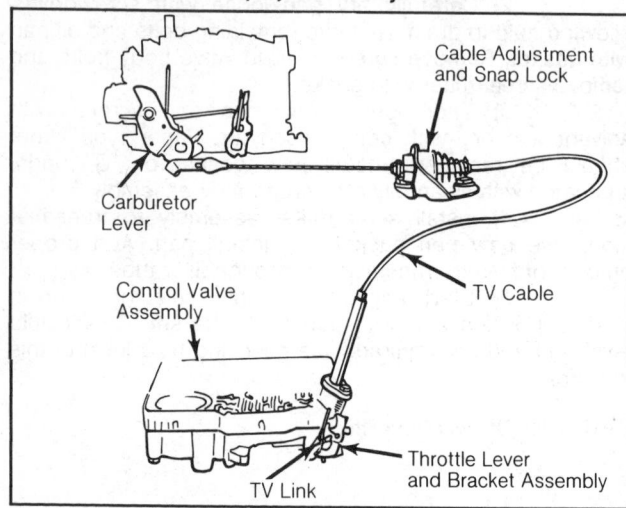

Fig. 1: Throttle Valve (TV) Cable Adjustment

2) Release lock tab and rotate lever assembly to full throttle position to automatically adjust slider to correct setting. Release the lever and reconnect pump rod to lever assembly.

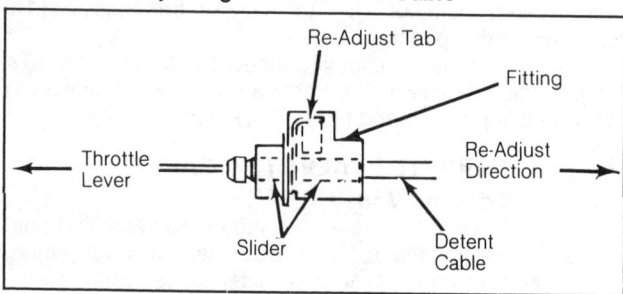

Fig. 2: Self-Adjusting Throttle Valve Cable

Press tab to move slider in correct direction.

SHIFT LINKAGE

NOTE: **Manual linkage must be adjusted so that engine will not start in positions except "PARK" and "NEUTRAL." With selector lever in "PARK" position, parking pawl should engage within rear/reaction internal gear lugs or output ring gear lugs, preventing vehicle from moving.**

Rod Type Linkage

1) Place steering column shift lever in "N" position. Loosen swivel clamp lock screw and set transmission lever in neutral detent.

2) Hold swivel clamp against equalizer lever. Tighten clamp screw without tension on equalizer lever or selector rod.

Fig. 3: Rod Type Column Shift Linkage

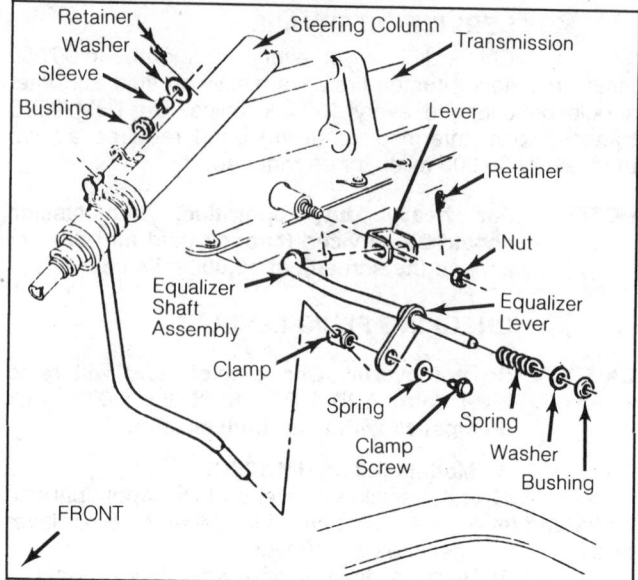

Tighten clamp screw without tension on equalizer lever or selector rod.

Cable Type Linkage (Exc. Riviera)

1) Position shift selector lever in "N" position and transaxle lever in neutral detent. Loosely assemble pin and nut through transaxle lever with transaxle cable assembled to pin.

Fig. 4: Cable Type Adjustment — Front Wheel Drive

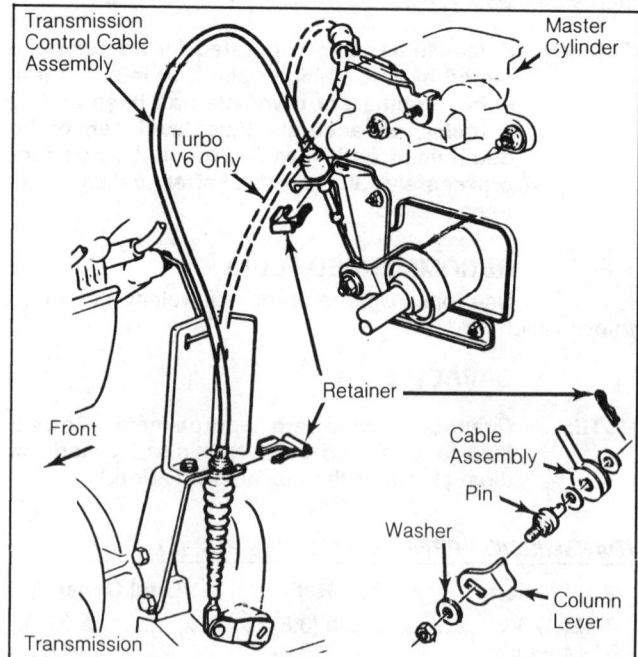

Ensure pin is free to move in slot.

GENERAL MOTORS
BUICK (Cont.)

2) Assemble steering column shift lever pin and transaxle control cable bracket. Tighten nut (lever must be held out of "PARK" when tightening nut).

Cable Type Linkage (Riviera)

1) Position shift selector lever in "N" position. Loosen nut on pin at attachment point of cable to steering column.

2) Move transaxle lever to neutral position and ensure that pin is free to move in slot. Tighten pin without applying tension on cable or lever.

NEUTRAL SAFETY SWITCH

Column Shift Models

Column shift models use a mechanical interference-type neutral start system. A wedge-shaped finger, attached to the ignition switch actuator rod, blocks movement of switch to "Start" position in all shift positions except "PARK" or "NEUTRAL."

Floor Shift (Century & Skylark)

1) Place control shifter assembly in Neutral gate notch. Loosen switch attaching screws. Rotate switch on shifter to align adjustment hole with carrier tang hole.

2) Insert a 3/32 gauge pin into the hole to a depth of .60" (15 mm). Tighten switch attaching screws. Remove gauge pin.

TRANSMISSION VACUUM REGULATOR VALVE

The vacuum regulator valve (VRV) used on diesel equipped Buicks is not adjustable.

CADILLAC

LUBRICATION

SERVICE INTERVALS

Check fluid level at every oil change. Transmission fluid should be changed and filter replaced every 100,000 miles under normal operating conditions.

Under continuous extreme operating conditions (trailer towing, heavy city traffic with ambient temperature over 90°F, police, taxi or delivery service), fluid and filter should be changed every 15,000 miles.

CHECKING FLUID LEVEL

CAUTION: Do not overfill. One pint of fluid will raise level from "ADD 1 PT." to "FULL HOT" mark on dipstick with a hot transmission.

1) With engine at curb idle, move selector lever through all ranges, ending in "PARK".

2) Remove dipstick and wipe dipstick clean, reinstall, then remove again and inspect level.

3) Fluid level should check close to the "ADD 1 PT." mark (either above or below) on dipstick.

CAUTION: If vehicle has been operated for an extended period of time at high speed, in city traffic or in hot weather, or if vehicle has been pulling a trailer, an accurate fluid level cannot be determined. Allow transmission to cool for about 30 minutes, with engine off, before checking fluid level.

RECOMMENDED FLUID

Use only Dexron II or equivalent automatic transmission fluid.

CAPACITY

NOTE: Quantities listed are approximate. Correct fluid level should be determined by mark on dipstick rather than by amount added.

TRANSMISSION REFILL CAPACITIES PTS. (L)

Application	Refill	Total Capacity
THM 125C	8 (3.8)	12 (5.7)
THM 200-4R	7 (3.3)	22 (10.4)
THM 325-4L	10 (4.7)	24 (11.4)
THM 350C	6 (2.8)	20 (9.4)
THM 400	6 (2.8)	20 (9.4)

DRAINING & REFILLING

1) With vehicle raised and drain pan placed under transmission, remove front and side transmission oil pan bolts. Loosen rear pan bolts approximately 4 turns each.

2) Pry pan loose carefully with screwdriver, allowing fluid to drain. Remove remaining bolts and oil pan with gasket attached. Remove screen/filter-to-valve body bolts and remove screen filter with gasket.

3) Thoroughly clean pan with solvent and dry with compressed air. Install new gasket or "O" rings lubricated with clean oil into new screen/filter assembly and install screen/filter assembly to transmission.

4) Use new pan gasket and install pan. Add proper amount of fluid to transmission through filler tube and start engine in "PARK" position with parking brake set.

5) With engine idling, move selector lever through all positions, ending in "PARK". Check fluid level and add as required.

NOTE: DO NOT overfill. See Checking Fluid Level in this section.

GENERAL MOTORS
CADILLAC (Cont.)

ADJUSTMENT

DETENT (DOWNSHIFT) SWITCH
DeVille & Fleetwood
with THM 400 Transmission

1) Remove air cleaner and check that carburetor is correctly adjusted and that throttle linkage is at low speed idle setting.

2) Loosen switch mounting screws and insert a (.094") size drill into calibrating hole below lower wire terminal.

3) Adjust position of switch so that lever just touches carburetor adapter plate arm. With this adjustment, downshift switch should make contact above 60° throttle.

Fig. 1: THM 400 Downshift Switch Adjustment

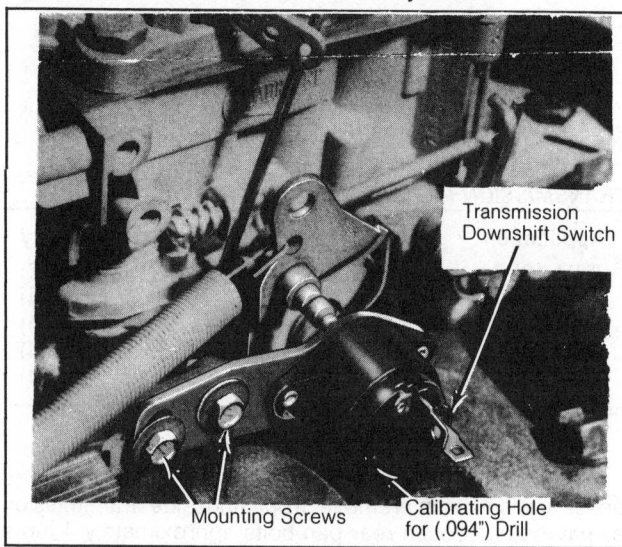

Mounting Screws   Calibrating Hole for (.094") Drill

Transmission Downshift Switch

Downshift switch should make contact above 60° throttle.

4) With switch positioned, tighten mounting screws and remove drill from calibrating hole.

THROTTLE VALVE CABLE

This system not only controls downshift, but also controls line pressure, shift points, shift feel, part throttle downshifts and detent downshifts.

Diesel Models

1) Remove cruise control rod (if equipped). Disconnect detent cable terminal from throttle assembly. Loosen lock nut on pump rod and shorten several turns.

2) Rotate lever assembly to full throttle position and hold. Lengthen pump rod until injection pump lever contacts full throttle stop. Release lever and tighten pump rod lock nut.

3) Remove pump rod from lever assembly. Reconnect detent cable terminal to throttle assembly. Depress and hold metal tab on cable upper end.

4) Move slider through fitting in direction away from lever assembly until slider stops against fitting. Release tab and rotate lever assembly to full throttle stop. Release lever. Reconnect pump rod.

5) If equipped with cruise control, reconnect rod and adjust servo rod to minimum slack, then install clip in first free hole closest to bellcrank, but within servo bail.

Self-Adjusting Type TV Cable (Gasoline)

1) Depress lock tab and move slider back through fitting away from throttle body or pump lever until slider stops against fitting.

2) Release lock tab and open throttle to full throttle stop position to automatically adjust TV cable. Release throttle.

Fig. 2: Self-Adjusting Throttle Valve Cable

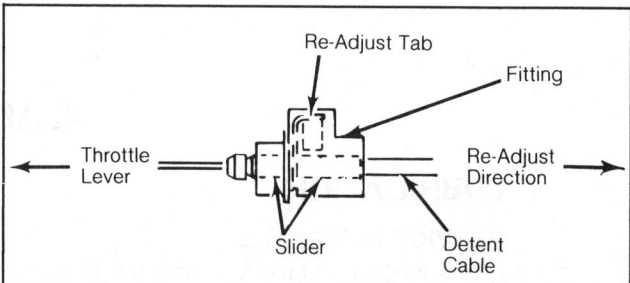

Re-Adjust Tab

Fitting

Throttle Lever

Re-Adjust Direction

Slider

Detent Cable

Press tab to move slider in correct direction.

SHIFT LINKAGE

1) Linkage should be adjusted so that engine cannot be started in any position except "PARK" or "NEUTRAL."

2) With selector lever in "PARK", parking pawl should engage rear/reaction internal gear lugs or output ring gear lugs. Pointer on indicator quadrant should line up properly with range indicators in all ranges.

NEUTRAL SAFETY SWITCH

Column Shift Models

Column shift models use a mechanical interference type neutral start system. A wedge-shaped finger, attached to the ignition switch actuator rod, blocks movement of switch to "Start" position in all shift positions except "NEUTRAL" or "PARK."

TRANSMISSION VACUUM REGULATOR VALVE

A vacuum regulator valve (VRV) is used on vehicles equipped with diesel engines, only. *Refer to Chevrolet & GMC Servicing section for applicable adjustment procedures.*

GENERAL MOTORS
CHEVROLET & GMC

LUBRICATION

SERVICE INTERVALS

Check transmission fluid level in Truck and Van models at each engine oil change. Check passenger car fluid level every 7500 miles or 12 months. Change transmission fluid and filter at 100,000 mile intervals on vehicles in normal use.

On all models, if vehicle is used in severe service conditions (commercial use, trailor pulling, constant stop and go city traffic), change fluid and filter every 15,000 miles. Adjust intermediate (front) band of THM 250C transmission every 60,000 miles, or as required.

CHECKING FLUID LEVEL

NOTE: **One pint of fluid will raise level from "ADD 1 PT." ("ADD") mark to "FULL" mark on dipstick in a hot transmission. Do not overfill.**

Bring engine and transmission to normal operating temperature. With vehicle parked on a level surface and engine at idle, move selector lever through all positions, ending in "P". Remove dipstick, wipe clean and check fluid level. Fluid level should be between "ADD 1 PINT" ("ADD") and "FULL" marks on dipstick.

If vehicle has been operated for an extended period of time at high speed, in city traffic, or pulling a trailer, an accurate fluid level cannot be immediately determined. Transmission must cool for about 30 minutes after vehicle is parked, before fluid level is checked.

RECOMMENDED FLUID

Use only DEXRON or DEXRON-II automatic transmission fluid, or equivalent.

CAPACITY

The transmission refill capacities given below are approximations, only. Correct fluid level should always be determined by marks on dipstick, rather than by amount of fluid added. DO NOT overfill transmission.

TRANSMISSION REFILL CAPACITIES

Application	Capacity in Pints (Liters)	
	Drain & Refill	Overhaul
THM 125C	8.0 (3.8)	12.0 (5.7)
THM 180C	6.0 (2.8)	10.0 (4.8)
THM 200C		
Chevette	7.0 (3.3)	10.0 (4.8)
All Others	7.0 (3.3)	19.0 (9.0)
THM 200-4R	7.0 (3.3)	22.0 (10.4)
THM 250C	8.0 (3.8)	21.0 (10.0)
THM 350C	6.0 (2.8)	20.0 (9.5)
THM 400	7.0 (3.8)	22.0 (10.4)
THM 700-R4	10.0 (4.8)	23.0 (10.9)

DRAINING & REFILLING

1) Loosen transmission oil pan bolts. Pry pan loose with a large screwdriver and allow fluid to drain. Remove oil pan, gasket and filter or filter screen.

2) Replace paper element filter (if used). Clean filter screen and pan with solvent and blow dry with compressed air. Install oil pan with new gasket. Add fluid to proper mark on dipstick.

ADJUSTMENT

FRONT BAND
THM 250C

1) With shift lever in "N" position, loosen lock nut on right side of transmission 1/2 turn and hold in this position.

2) Tighten adjusting screw to 30 INCH lbs. (3.4 N.m). Back off screw 3 full turns. Hold adjusting screw in position and tighten lock nut.

DETENT (DOWNSHIFT) OR THROTTLE VALVE (TV) CABLE
Diesel Engines — Exc. Celebrity & Chevette

1) Remove cruise control rod (if equipped). Disconnect detent cable terminal from throttle assembly. Loosen lock nut on pump rod and back off several turns. Rotate throttle lever assembly (at valve body) to full open position and hold.

2) Lengthen pump rod until injection pump lever contacts full throttle stop. Release throttle lever and tighten pump rod lock nut.

Fig. 1: Detent/TV Cable Adjustment Components

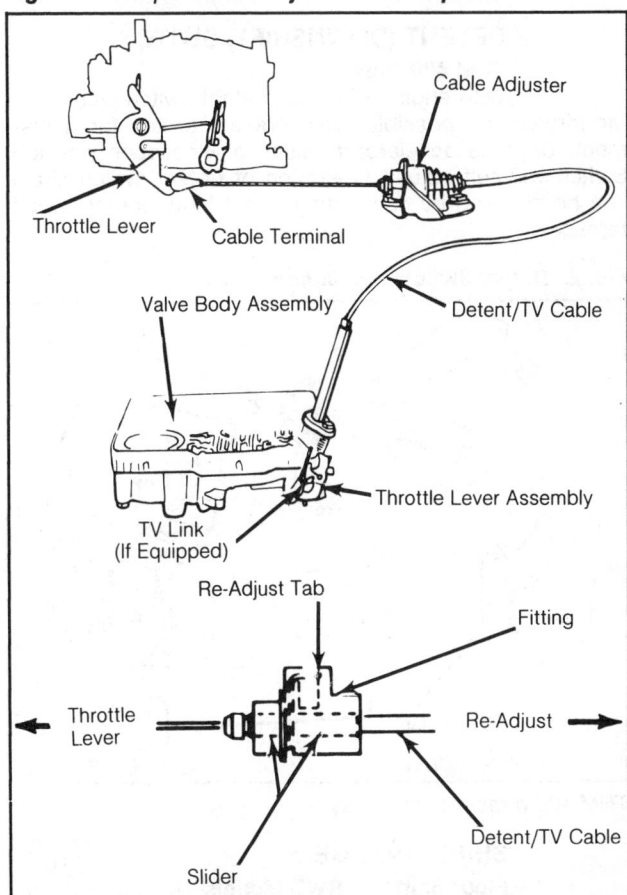

TV cable is used on 200C and 700-R4 transmissions, only. All other models use detent cable.

3) Remove pump rod from lever assembly. Reconnect detent cable terminal to throttle assembly. Depress and hold metal adjusting tab on cable adjuster. Move slider through fitting, away from throttle lever, until slider stops against fitting. Release tab.

Automatic Transmission Servicing
GENERAL MOTORS
CHEVROLET & GMC (Cont.)

4) Rotate lever assembly to full throttle position and release. Reconnect pump rod. If equipped with cruise control, reconnect rod and adjust servo throttle rod to minimum slack with engine off. Install clip in free hole nearest to bellcrank and within servo bail.

Diesel Engines — Celebrity & Chevette
1) Remove pump rod from lever assembly and depress metal lock tab. Hold tab and move slider through fitting away from lever assembly until slider stops against fitting.

2) Release lock tab and rotate lever assembly to full throttle position. Slider is automatically adjusted to correct setting. Release lever and reconnect pump rod to lever assembly.

Gasoline Engines
1) Depress metal lock tab on adjuster and hold. Move slider back through fitting away from carburetor lever until slider stops at fitting.

2) Release lock tab and, on all except 4-cylinder Camaro, open carburetor lever to full throttle stop. This automatically adjusts slider to correct setting.

3) On 4-cylinder Camaro models, rotate idler lever to maximum travel stop position. The cable will automatically adjust. Release throttle idler lever.

DETENT (DOWNSHIFT) SWITCH
THM 400 Only
With engine off, push detent switch plunger as far forward as possible. This presets switch for adjustment. Depress accelerator pedal to wide open position. Switch will self adjust. Operation of detent switch circuit can be checked by connecting a test lamp across switch terminals.

Fig. 2: Detent Switch Installation

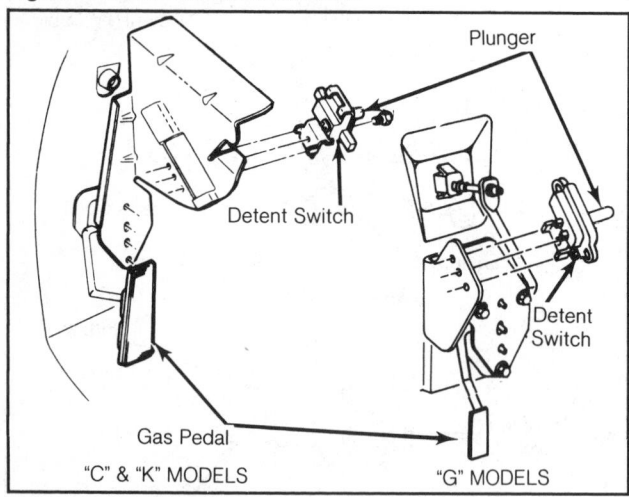

THM 400 transmissions, only.

SHIFT LINKAGE
Floor Shift — RWD Models
1) Disconnect shifter link from shifter assembly and place shifter assembly in neutral notch of detent plate.

2) Place transmission lever in neutral position by moving clockwise to maximum detent position, then

back (counterclockwise) 2 detents. Adjust link until hole and pin line up. Install shim and retainer.

Fig. 3: Floor Shift Linkage — RWD Models

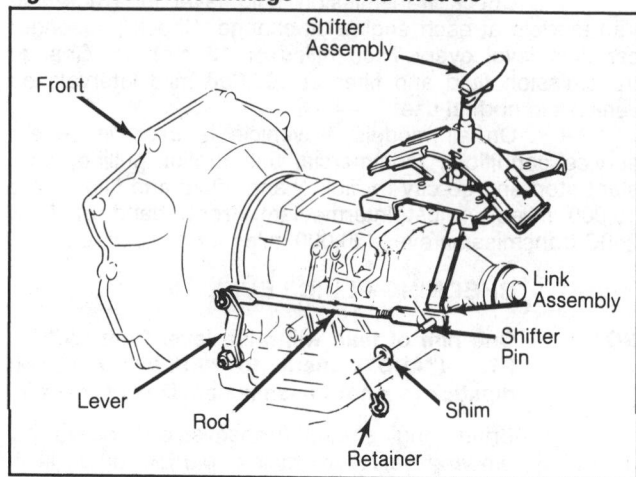

Chevette shown, others similar.

Floor Shift — FWD Models
1) Place shift lever in "N" position. Place transaxle lever in neutral notch. Loosely assemble nut to pin through transaxle lever with transaxle cable assembled to pin.

2) Assemble steering column shift lever pin and transaxle control cable bracket. Tighten nut. Lever must be held out of park when tightening nut.

Fig. 4: Floor Shift Linkage — FWD Models

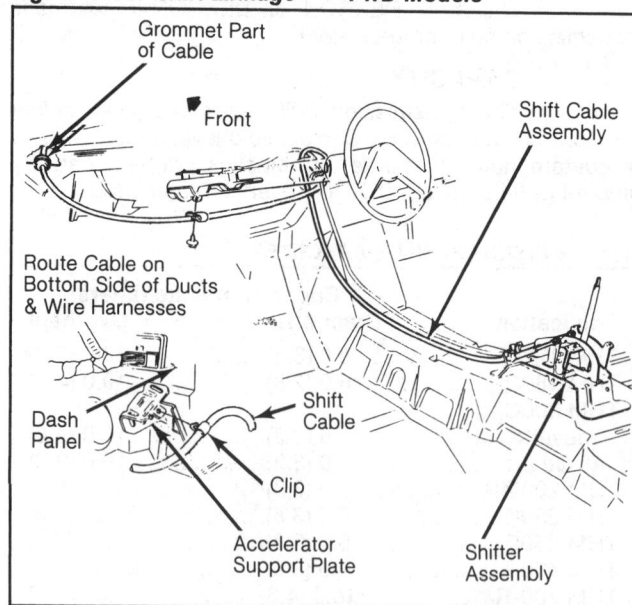

Column Shift — All Passenger Cars
1) Position steering column shift lever in neutral gate notch. Loosen swivel clamp lock screw and place transmission lever in neutral.

2) Hold swivel clamp against equalizer lever and tighten clamp screw without applying tension on either equalizer lever or selector rod.

GENERAL MOTORS
CHEVROLET & GMC (Cont.)

Fig. 5: Passenger Car Column Shift Linkage

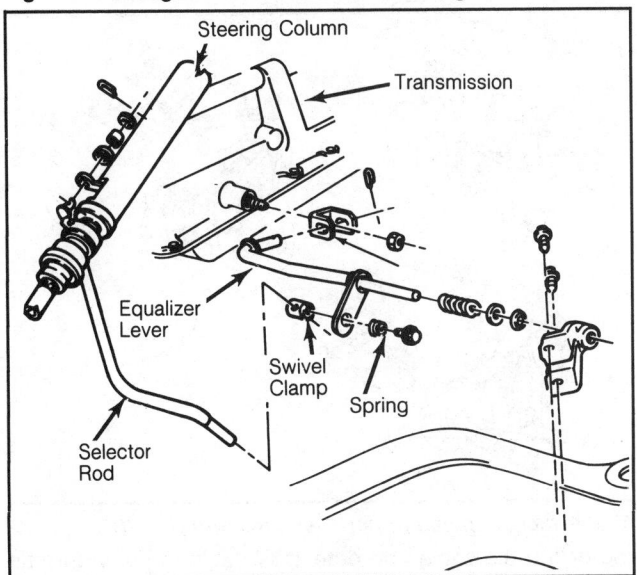

Ensure there is no tension on either equalizer lever or selector rod during final adjustment.

"C", "K" & "G" Model Trucks & Vans

1) Make sure shift tube and lever assembly are free in steering column. Disconnect shift lever rod from swivel at lower column lever. Move transmission lever clockwise to stop, then counterclockwise 2 detents. This is neutral position. Place selector lever in neutral. Locate position using mechanical stops, NOT indicator pointer.

Fig. 6: Shift Linkage Components

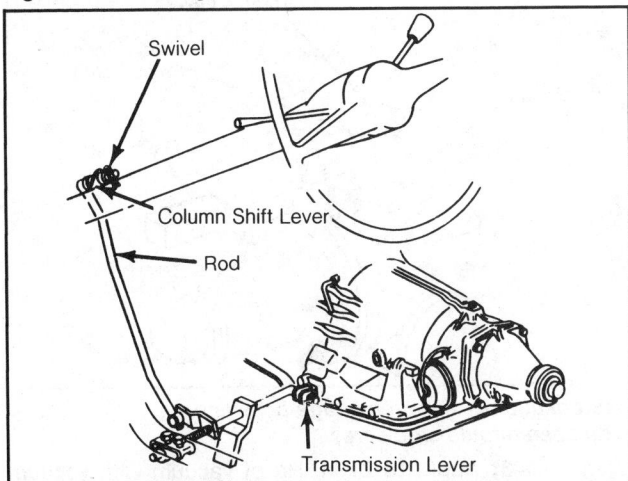

"C" and "K" models, only.

2) Slide swivel and clamp onto shift lever rod. Install grommets, washers and nut (as needed) but do not tighten nut. Hold lower column lever against neutral stop on park side. Tighten swivel nut to 20 ft. lbs. (27 N.m).

"S" Model Trucks

1) Make sure shift tube and lever are free in steering column. To adjust linkage, remove screw and spring washer from swivel. Turn transmission lever clockwise to stop, then counterclockwise 2 detents. This is neutral position.

Fig. 7: Shift Linkage Components

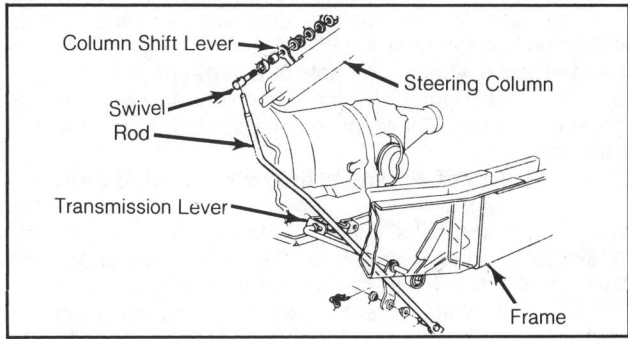

"G" models, only.

2) Place selector lever in neutral. Locate proper position using mechanical stops, NOT indicator pointer. Hold swivel against shift lever, install spring washer and screw and tighten finger tight. Avoid applying force in either direction (along shift rod or lever) while tightening screw to 20 ft. lbs. (27 N.m).

Fig. 8: Shift Linkage Components

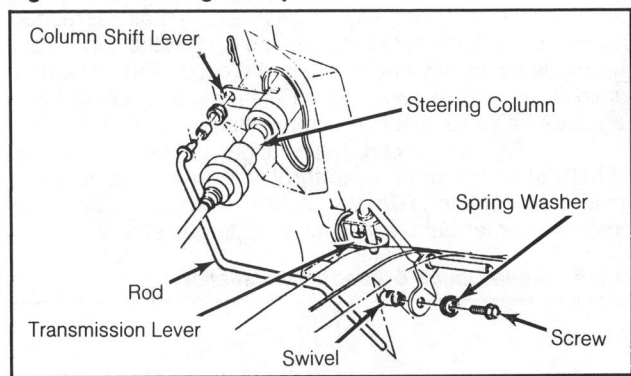

"S" models, only.

NEUTRAL SAFETY SWITCH

Column Shift Models — Passenger Cars

Column shift models use a mechanical interference type neutral start system. A wedge-shaped finger, attached to the ignition switch actuator rod, blocks movement of switch to "Start" position in all shifter positions except "P" or "N".

Floor Shift — Camaro, Celebrity & Citation

1) Place shifter assembly in "N" gate notch. Loosen switch attaching screws. Rotate switch on shifter to align adjustment hole with carrier tang hole.

2) Insert a .05" (1.2 mm) gauge pin into the hole to a depth of .60" (15.2 mm). Tighten switch attaching screws. Remove gauge pin.

Floor Shift — Chevette

1) Remove floor console cover and loosen switch attaching screws. Align hole in contact carrier with hole in back of switch and insert .09" (2.3 mm) gauge pin.

2) Make sure that shift lever is in "N" position and that shift lever pin is in slot of switch.

3) Tighten switch attaching screws and remove pin. Check switch operation. Starter should only engage with shifter in "P" and "N" positions.

Automatic Transmission Servicing
GENERAL MOTORS
CHEVROLET & GMC (Cont.)

Trucks & Vans With Column Mounted Switch

1) Place gearshift selector lever in neutral position and loosen switch attaching screws. Rotate switch on column until a .095" (2.5 mm) gauge pin can be inserted into switch gauge hole to a depth of .4" (10 mm).

2) Tighten switch attaching screws and remove gauge pin. Check for engine starting in neutral and park only.

Trucks & Vans With Trans. Mounted Switch

1) Raise and support vehicle and loosen switch mounting bolts. Align hole in switch lever with hole in switch assembly. Insert a .095" (2.5 mm) gauge pin through switch holes to hold switch in neutral position.

2) With selector lever on transmission in neutral detent position, tighten switch mounting bolts and remove gauge pin. Lower vehicle and check operation of switch.

TRANSMISSION VACUUM REGULATOR VALVE

NOTE: This adjustment procedure applies to vehicles with diesel engines, only.

4.3L V6 & 5.7L V8

1) Remove air crossover. Install screened covers on intake manifold. Remove throttle rod from throttle lever on V8 engines; throttle cable and detent/TV cable from throttle lever on V6 engines. Loosen vacuum regulator valve-to-injection pump bolts.

2) Install carburetor angle gauge adapter (J-26701-15) on injection pump throttle lever and place angle gauge on adaptor. Rotate throttle lever to wide open position. Center bubble in level with gauge set at 0°.

Fig. 9: Angle Gauge & Adapter Installation

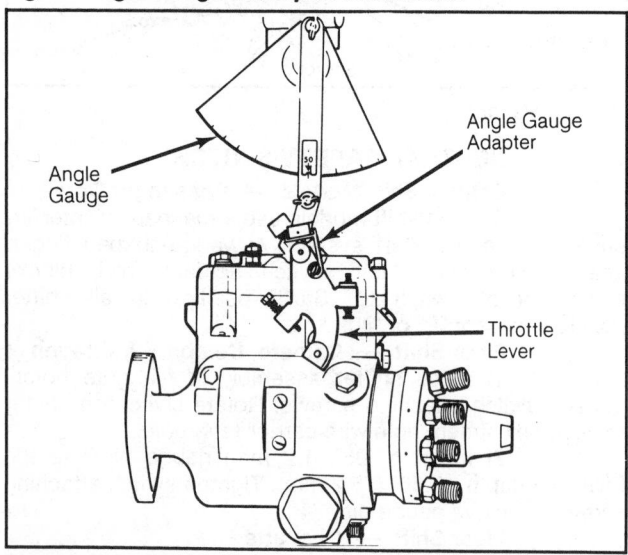

File tool as needed to fit on thicker V6 throttle lever.

3) Set gauge to 58° (V8) or 49° (V6) and rotate throttle lever until bubble is centered. Attach vacuum pump to regulator port "A" and a vacuum gauge to port "B". Apply 18-24 in. Hg of vacuum at port "A".

4) Rotate vacuum valve clockwise until vacuum gauge reads 10.6 in. Hg and tighten valve mounting bolts. Remove vacuum source and gauge. Install throttle

Fig. 10: Vacuum Regulator Valve Port Locations

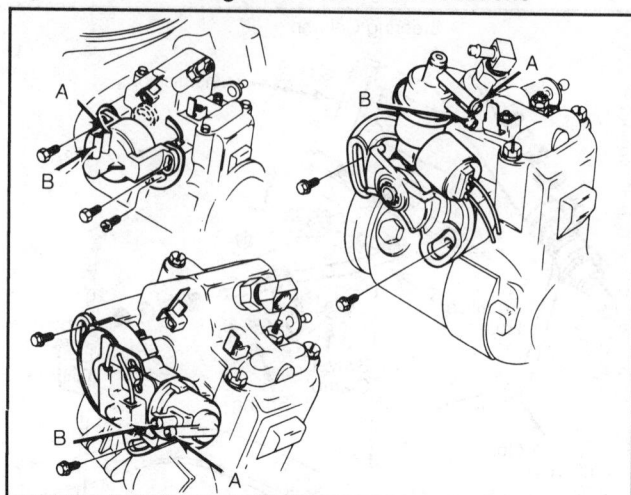

Attach vacuum pump to port "A", gauge to port "B".

rod or throttle cable and detent/TV cable to pump throttle lever. Remove screened covers and install air crossover.

6.2L V8

1) Loosen vacuum regulator valve-to-injection pump bolts enough to allow for regulator valve rotation. Attach vacuum pump to bottom vacuum port of valve; vacuum gauge to top port.

2) Insert measuring gauge bar (.646" thick) between gauge boss on injection pump and wide open stop screw on throttle lever. *See Fig. 11.* Rotate throttle shaft against bar.

Fig. 11: Adjusting Vacuum Regulator Valve

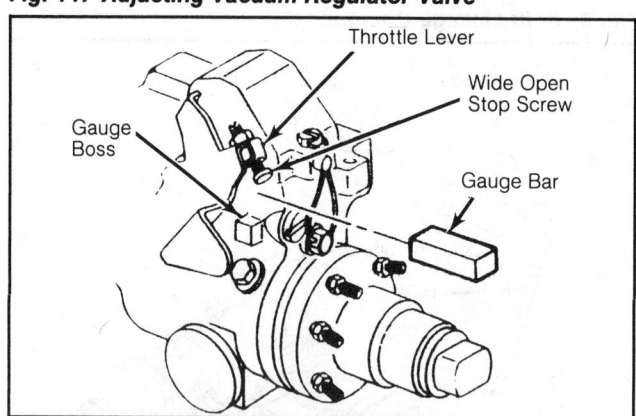

Insert gauge bar between gauge boss and wide open throttle stop screw.

3) Apply 18-21 in. Hg of vacuum with vacuum pump. Slowly rotate vacuum regulator valve body clockwise (facing valve) until vacuum gauge reads 7-9 in. Hg. Hold valve body in this position and tighten mounting screws.

NOTE: Valve MUST be set while rotating in a clockwise direction.

4) Check adjustment by allowing throttle shaft to return to idle position, then rotate shaft back against gauge bar. If vacuum gauge reading is not 7-9 in. Hg, readjust valve.

GENERAL MOTORS
OLDSMOBILE

LUBRICATION

SERVICE INTERVALS

Check fluid level every 12 months or 7500 miles, whichever comes first. Transmission fluid and filter should be changed every 100,000 miles. On THM 250C transmissions, intermediate (front) band requires adjustment every 60,000 miles, or as required.

NOTE: For heavy duty operation, transmission should be serviced every 15,000 miles.

CHECKING FLUID LEVEL

CAUTION: Do not overfill, One pint of fluid will raise level from "ADD 1 PT." to "FULL HOT" mark on dipstick with a hot transmission.

All Models (Exc. THM 125C)

1) Place vehicle on level surface. Apply parking brake and start engine. Move selector through all gear ranges, ending in "PARK".

2) Remove dipstick and wipe clean. Reinstall stick and check fluid level. Fluid should check between "ADD 1 PT." and "FULL HOT" marks on dipstick.

THM 125C

1) Place vehicle on level surface. Apply parking brake and start engine. Move selector through all ranges, ending in "PARK".

2) Remove dipstick and wipe dipstick clean, reinstall, then remove and check fluid level. Fluid level should check between the "ADD" and "FULL" marks on dipstick.

CAUTION: If vehicle has been operated for an extended period of time at high speed, in city traffic in hot weather, or if vehicle has been pulling a trailer, an accurate fluid level cannot be determined until fluid has cooled down (approximately 30 minutes after vehicle has been parked).

RECOMMENDED FLUID

Use only Dexron II or equivalent automatic transmission fluid.

CAPACITY

NOTE: Quantities listed below are approximate, and correct fluid level should be determined by mark on dipstick, rather than by amount added.

TRANSMISSION REFILL CAPACITIES PTS. (L)

Application	Refill	Total Capacity
THM 125C	8 (3.8)	12 (5.7)
THM 200C	7 (3.3)	19 (9.0)
THM 200-4R	7 (3.3)	22 (10.4)
THM 250C	8 (3.8)	21 (9.9)
THM 325-4L	10 (4.7)	24 (11.4)
THM 350C	6 (2.8)	20 (9.5)

DRAINING & REFILLING
All Models

1) With vehicle raised and drain pan placed under transmission, remove front and side transmission oil pan bolts. Loosen rear pan bolts approximately 4 turns each.

2) Pry pan loose carefully with screwdriver, allowing fluid to drain. Remove remaining bolts and oil pan with gasket. Remove screen/filter-to-valve body bolts and remove screen/filter with gasket.

3) Thoroughly clean pan and screen with solvent and dry with compressed air. Paper type filters should be replaced. Install new gasket or "O" rings lubricated with clean oil into screen/filter assembly and install screen/filter assembly to transmission. Use new pan gasket and install pan.

4) Add proper amount of fluid to transmission through filler tube and start engine with selector in "PARK" position with parking brake set. Check fluid level and add as required. See checking fluid level in this section.

CAUTION: DO NOT overfill.

ADJUSTMENT

INTERMEDIATE (FRONT) BAND
THM 250C

1) Position selector lever in "NEUTRAL" position. Loosen lock nut on right side of transmission 1/2 turn and hold in this position.

2) Tighten adjusting screw to 30 INCH lbs. (3.4 N.m). Back off screw 3 complete turns. Hold adjusting screw in this position and tighten lock nut.

THROTTLE VALVE CABLE
Gasoline Models

1) Depress metal lock tab on adjuster and hold. Move slider back through fitting away from carburetor lever until slide stops at fitting.

2) Release lock tab and open carburetor lever to full throttle stop to automatically adjust slider to correct setting. Release carburetor lever.

Diesel Models (Exc. Ciera)

1) Remove cruise control rod (if equipped). Disconnect detent cable terminal from throttle assembly. Loosen lock nut on pump rod and shorten several turns. Rotate lever assembly to full throttle position and hold.

2) Lengthen pump rod until injection pump lever contacts full throttle stop. Release lever and tighten pump rod lock nut.

3) Remove pump rod from lever assembly. Reconnect detent cable terminal to throttle assembly. Depress and hold metal tab on cable upper end. Move slider through fitting in direction away from lever assembly until slider stops against fitting.

4) Release tab and rotate lever assembly to full throttle stop. Release lever. Reconnect pump rod. If equipped with cruise control, reconnect rod and adjust servo rod to minimum slack, then install clip in first free hole closest to bellcrank, but within servo bail.

GENERAL MOTORS
OLDSMOBILE (Cont.)

Fig. 1: Throttle Valve Cable and Linkage

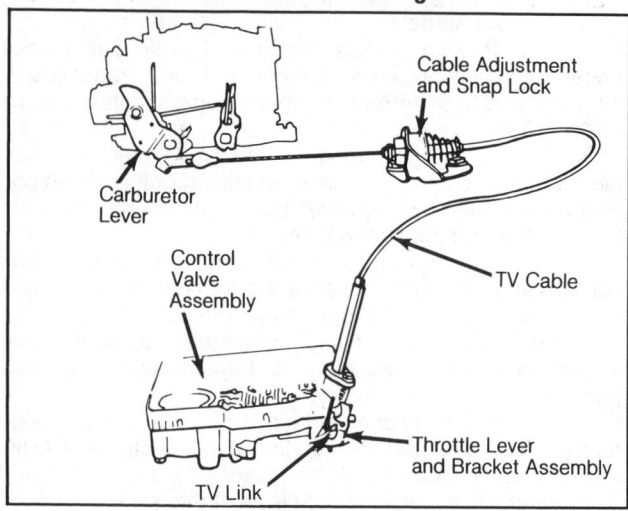

Diesel Models (Ciera)

1) Remove pump rod from lever assembly and depress metal lock tab. Hold tab and move slider through fitting away from lever assembly until slider stops against fitting.

2) Release lock tab and rotate lever assembly to full throttle position to automatically adjust slider to correct setting. Release lever and reconnect pump rod to lever assembly.

Fig. 2: Self-Adjusting Throttle Valve Cable

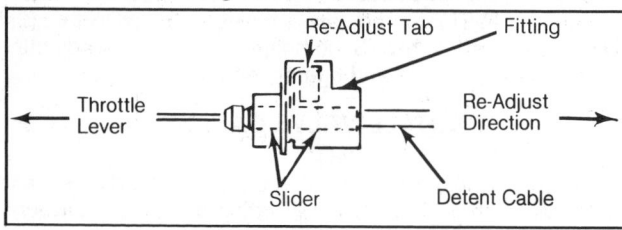

Press tab to move slider in correct direction.

SHIFT LINKAGE

NOTE: **Manual linkage must be adjusted so that engine will not start in any position except "PARK" and "NEUTRAL." With selector lever in "PARK" position, parking pawl should engage within rear/reaction internal gear lugs or output ring gear lugs and prevent vehicle from moving.**

Column Shift (Rear Wheel Drive)

1) Position steering column shift lever in "N" position. Loosen swivel clamp lock screw and set transmission lever in neutral detent.

2) Hold swivel clamp against equalizer lever and tighten clamp screw without tension on equalizer lever or selector rod.

Column Shift (Front Wheel Drive)

1) Position column shift lever in "N" gate notch. Loosen nut on pin attaching cable to column lever.

2) Ensure that pin is free in column lever. Set transmission lever in neutral detent. Tighten nut and check operation in all selector positions.

Fig. 3: Column Shift Linkage (Rear Wheel Drive)

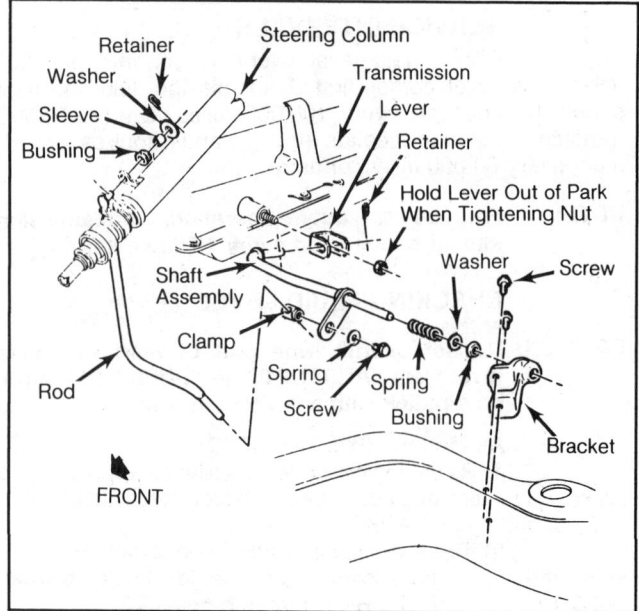

Ensure steering column shift lever is in Neutral gate notch.

Floor Shift (Rear Wheel Drive)

1) With console shift lever in "PARK" position. Loosen nut attaching pin to transmission lever.

2) Ensure that pin is free to slide to lever and position lever in Park detent. Tighten nut on lever pin.

Floor Shift (Front Wheel Drive)

1) Position shift lever in "NEUTRAL" position. Place transaxle lever in Neutral notch. Loosely assemble nut to pin through transaxle lever with transaxle cable assembled to pin.

2) Assemble steering column shift lever pin and transaxle control cable bracket. Tighten nut. Lever must be held out of "PARK" when tightening nut.

NEUTRAL SAFETY SWITCH
Column Shift Models

Column shift models use a mechanical interference type neutral start system. A wedge-shaped finger, attached to the ignition switch actuator rod, blocks movement of switch to "Start" position in all shift positions except "PARK" or "NEUTRAL."

Floor Shift (Front Wheel Drive)

1) Position selector lever in "NEUTRAL". Loosen switch attaching screws (on shifter). Rotate switch to align adjustment hole with carrier tang hole.

2) Insert a 3/64" gauge pin to a depth of .60" (15 mm) in the hole. Tighten switch attaching screws. Remove gauge pin.

TRANSMISSION VACUUM REGULATOR VALVE

The vacuum regulator valve (VRV) used on diesel equipped Oldsmobiles is not adjustable.

GENERAL MOTORS
PONTIAC

LUBRICATION

SERVICE INTERVALS

Check fluid level every 12 months or 7500 miles, whichever comes first. Transmission fluid and filter should be changed every 100,000 miles. On THM 250C transmissions, intermediate band (front) requires adjustment every 60,000 miles, or as required.

NOTE: For severe service (heavy duty) operation, transmission should be serviced at 15,000 mile intervals.

CHECKING FLUID LEVEL

CAUTION: Do not overfill. One pint of fluid will raise level from "ADD 1 PT." to "FULL HOT" mark on dipstick with a hot transmission.

All Models (Exc. THM 125C)

1) With vehicle on level surface, apply parking brake and let engine run at curb idle. Move selector lever through all ranges, ending in "PARK".

2) Remove dipstick and wipe dipstick clean, reinstall, then remove again and inspect level. Fluid level should check between "ADD 1 PT." and "FULL HOT" marks on dipstick.

THM 125C

1) Place vehicle on level surface. Apply parking brake and start engine. Move selector lever through all ranges, ending in "PARK".

2) Remove dipstick and wipe dipstick clean, reinstall, then remove and check fluid level. Fluid level should check between the "ADD" and "FULL" marks on dipstick.

CAUTION: If vehicle has been operated for an extended period of time at high speed, in city traffic in hot weather, or if vehicle has been pulling a trailer, an accurate fluid level cannot be determined until fluid has cooled down (approximately 30 minutes after vehicle has been parked).

RECOMMENDED FLUID

Use only Dexron II (or equivalent) automatic transmission fluid.

FLUID CAPACITY

NOTE: Quantities listed are approximate, and correct fluid level should be determined by mark on dipstick, rather than by amount added.

TRANSMISSION REFILL CAPACITIES PTS. (L)

Application	Refill	Total Capacity
THM125C	8 (3.8)	12 (5.7)
THM 180C	6 (2.8)	10 (4.7)
THM 200C	7 (3.3)	19 (9.0)
THM 250C	8 (3.8)	21 (9.9)
THM 350C	6 (2.8)	20 (9.4)

DRAINING & REFILLING
All Models

1) With vehicle raised and drain pan placed under transmission, remove front and side transmission oil pan bolts. Loosen rear pan bolts approximately 4 turns each.

2) Pry pan loose carefully with screwdriver, allowing fluid to drain. Remove remaining bolts and oil pan with gasket. Remove screen/filter-to-valve body bolts and remove screen/filter with gasket.

3) Thoroughly clean pan and screen with solvent and dry with compressed air. Paper type filters should be replaced. Install new gasket or "O" rings lubricated with clean oil into screen/filter assembly and install screen/filter assembly to transmission. Use new pan gasket and install pan.

4) Add proper amount of fluid to transmission through filler tube and start engine in "PARK" position with parking brake set. Check fluid level and add as required. See checking fluid level in this section.

CAUTION: DO NOT overfill.

ADJUSTMENT

INTERMEDIATE BAND (FRONT)
THM 250C

1) Position selector lever in "N" position. Loosen lock nut on right side of transmission 1/2 turn and hold in this position.

2) Tighten adjusting screw to 30 INCH lbs. (3.4 N.m). Back off screw 3 complete turns. Hold adjusting screw in position and tighten lock nut.

THROTTLE VALVE CABLE
Gasoline Models

1) Depress metal lock tab on adjuster and hold. Move slider back through fitting away from carburetor lever until slider stops at fitting.

2) Release lock tab and on all models except 4-cylinder Firebird, open carburetor lever to full throttle stop to automatically adjust slider to correct setting.

3) On 4-cylinder Firebird models, rotate idler lever to maximum travel stop position. The cable will automatically adjust itself. Release throttle idler lever.

Diesel Models (Exc. T1000 & 6000)

1) Remove cruise control rod (if equipped). Disconnect detent cable terminal from throttle assembly. Loosen lock nut on pump rod and shorten several turns. Rotate lever assembly to full throttle position and hold.

2) Lengthen pump rod until injection pump lever contacts full throttle stop. Release lever and tighten pump rod lock nut.

3) Remove pump rod from lever assembly. Reconnect detent cable terminal to throttle assembly. Depress and hold metal tab on cable upper end. Move slider through fitting in direction away from lever assembly until slider stops against fitting.

4) Release tab and rotate lever assembly to full throttle stop. Release lever. Reconnect pump rod. If equipped with cruise control, reconnect rod and adjust servo rod to minimum slack, then install clip in first free hole closest to bellcrank, but within servo bail.

GENERAL MOTORS
PONTIAC (Cont.)

Diesel Models (T1000 & 6000)

1) Remove pump rod from lever assembly and depress metal lock tab. Hold tab and move slider through fitting away from lever assembly until slider stops against fitting.

2) Release lock tab and rotate lever assembly to full throttle position to automatically adjust slider to correct setting. Release lever and reconnect pump rod to lever assembly.

Fig. 1: Throttle Valve Cable Adjustment

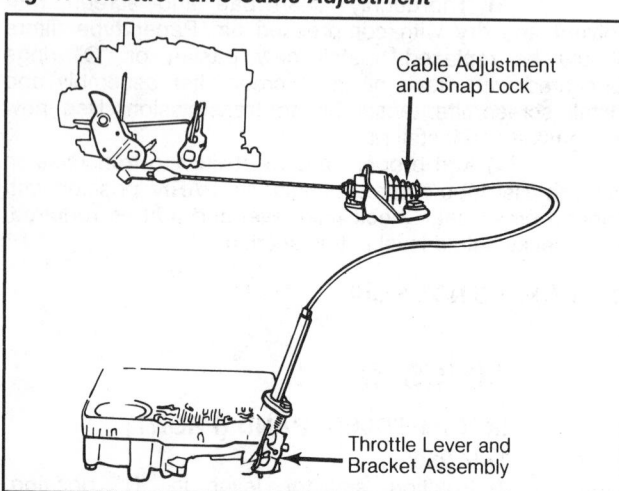

Cable Adjustment and Snap Lock

Throttle Lever and Bracket Assembly

Press tab to move slider in correct direction.

SHIFT LINKAGE

1) Linkage should be adjusted so that engine cannot be started in any position except "PARK" or "NEUTRAL."

2) With selector lever in "PARK", parking pawl should engage rear/reaction internal gear lugs or output ring gear lugs.

3) Pointer on indicator quadrant should line up properly with range indicators in all ranges.

Column Shift (Rod Type)

1) Position steering column shift lever in "NEUTRAL" gate notch. Loosen swivel clamp screw and place transmission lever in Neutral. Hold swivel clamp against lever and tighten clamp screw without tension on either lever or selector rod.

Fig. 2: Rod Type Column Shift Linkage

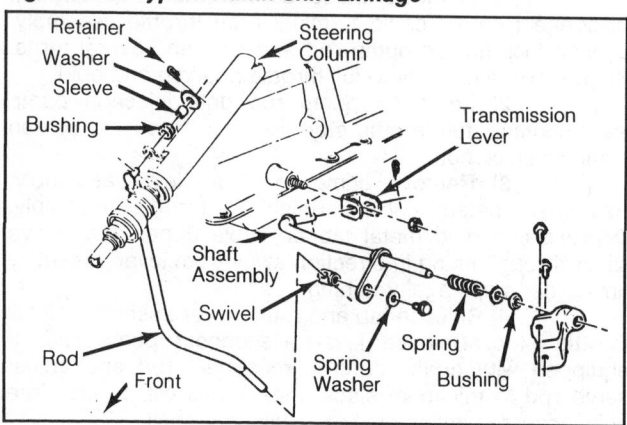

Retainer
Washer
Sleeve
Bushing
Steering Column
Transmission Lever
Shaft Assembly
Swivel
Rod
Front
Spring Washer
Spring
Bushing

2) To position shift indicator, ensure that shift lever is in "NEUTRAL" gate notch and guide clip on steering column shift bowl so that pointer is at Neutral. Indicator cable must rest on shift bowl, NOT on steering column jacket.

Floor Shift (Rear Wheel Drive Exc. T1000)

Place console shift lever in "PARK" position. Loosen nut attaching pin to transmission lever. Ensure that pin is free to slide in lever and position lever in Park detent. Tighten nut on lever pin.

Floor Shift (Front Wheel Drive)

1) Position shift lever in "NEUTRAL" position. Place transaxle lever in Neutral notch. Loosely assemble nut to pin through transaxle lever with transaxle cable assembled to pin.

2) Assemble steering column shift lever pin and transaxle control cable bracket. Tighten nut. Lever MUST BE held out of "PARK" when tightening nut.

Floor Shift (T1000)

1) Disconnect shifter link from shifter assembly. Place shifter assembly in Neutral notch of detent plate.

2) Place transmission lever in Neutral position by moving clockwise to maximum detent position, then back (counterclockwise) 2 detents to Neutral. Adjust link until hole and pin line up, then install shim and retainer.

Fig. 3: Cable Type Shift Linkage

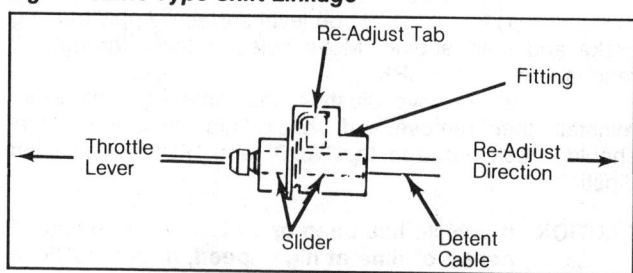

Re-Adjust Tab
Fitting
Throttle Lever
Re-Adjust Direction
Slider
Detent Cable

NEUTRAL SAFETY SWITCH
Column Shift Models

A mechanical interference neutral start system is used. A wedge shaped finger added to the ignition switch actuator rod will block movement of the ignition switch to Start position in all shift lever positions except "PARK" or "NEUTRAL." Back-up light switch will remain in same location but will have fewer electrical connections.

Console Shift Models

1) With linkage properly adjusted, place console shifter lever in "NEUTRAL" position. Loosen switch retaining screws and insert a .090" (2.2 mm) diameter gauge pin into outer "service" hole in switch.

2) Rotate switch until gauge pin goes into alignment hole in inner plastic slide. Tighten switch in position, remove guide pin and check for starting in "NEUTRAL" or "PARK" positions only.

TRANSMISSION VACUUM REGULATOR VALVE

A vacuum regulator valve (VRV) is used on vehicles equipped with diesel engines, only. *Refer to Chevrolet & GMC Servicing section for applicable adjustment procedures.*

AMERICAN MOTORS

REMOVAL & INSTALLATION

TORQUE-COMMAND

NOTE: **Transmission and converter must be removed as an assembly to prevent damage to drive plate, pump bushing, and oil seal.**

Removal

1) Disconnect fan shroud (if equipped). Disconnect transmission filler tube at upper bracket. Place transmission in Neutral. Raise vehicle on a hoist.

NOTE: **Hood must remain open during transmission removal to prevent damage to hood and air cleaner when rear crossmember is removed.**

2) Remove converter housing inspection cover. On 6-cylinder Concord and Spirit models, remove screw attaching exhaust pipe clamp to exhaust pipe support bracket and slide clamp off bracket.

3) On all models, remove transmission filler tube. Remove starter and stiffening braces (Eagle). Mark propeller shaft(s) and yoke(s) for installation reference, then remove propeller shaft(s) and skid plate (Eagle).

NOTE: **On 6-cylinder Eagle, disconnect exhaust pipe from manifold and move it aside to provide working clearance.**

4) On all models, remove speedometer adapter and cable assembly. Plug adapter bore in case. Disconnect gearshift and throttle linkage. If equipped with column shift, remove linkage, and bellcrank bracket-to-converter housing bolt. Disconnect neutral safety switch wires.

5) Mark converter drive plate and converter for installation reference. Remove converter-to-drive plate attaching bolts.

NOTE: **Use a ratchet and socket on crankshaft front pulley bolt to rotate crankshaft and drive plate for access to converter attaching bolts.**

6) Support transmission (and transfer case on Eagle) with a transmission jack. Retain transmission on jack with safety chain. Lower transmission slightly and disconnect oil cooler lines at transmission.

7) On 4-cylinder models, remove bolt attaching rear support cushion to rear support cushion bracket (attached to extension housing). Remove rear crossmember attaching nuts, then remove crossmember and support cushion as an assembly. Support front of engine with a safety stand. Remove catalytic converter support bracket-to-transmission bolts (if equipped).

8) On 6-cylinder models, remove rear support cushion-to-transmission attaching bolts. Remove crossmember.

9) On all models, remove engine-to-transmission attaching bolts. Move transmission (and transfer case on Eagle) and converter rearward to clear crankshaft. Hold converter in place and lower transmission assembly until converter housing clears engine, then lower assembly from vehicle.

Installation

CAUTION: **If transmission was removed to correct a malfunction that generated sludge or heavy accumulations of metal or friction material**

particles, the oil cooler and cooler lines must be thoroughly flushed and torque converter replaced.

1) If torque converter was removed, insert pump alignment tool into pump. Engage pump rotor, rotate tool until drilled hole is vertical, then remove tool. Rotate converter until pump drive slots are vertical and carefully install converter into pump.

2) Using a transmission jack, raise assembly and align converter with drive plate (aligning marks made during removal). Move transmission forward, carefully aligning bell housing pilot holes with dowels in engine.

3) Install 2 lower bell housing attaching bolts and pull housing up snug. Install remaining bolts, then tighten all bell housing bolts. To complete installation, reverse removal procedures.

MB 1 TRANSAXLE

NOTE: **Engine and transaxle must be removed as an assembly.**

Removal

1) Disconnect negative battery cable. Drain the transaxle oil, and engine oil. Drain cooling system from bottom of the radiator and from cylinder block.

2) Remove air cleaner assembly. Remove radiator. Disconnect wire harness connectors attached to engine assembly. Disconnect vacuum hoses that would interfere with engine removal. Disconnect the ground cable from transaxle.

3) Disconnect accelerator cable. Remove exhaust pipe clamp from exhaust manifold. Remove heater hoses, and set aside. Disconnect power brake booster vacuum hose.

4) Remove the 2 selector lever bracket retaining bolts and spacers, and remove gear shift selector lever assembly. Disconnect automatic transaxle cooler hoses.

5) Remove the front wheels. Using an extractor tool, remove the tie rod end ball joints. Remove brake calipers and suspend from vehicle body using a piece of wire.

6) Remove the drive shaft on the left side by removing the 3 bolts attaching the boot plate, and remove shock absorber bottom mounting bolts. Tilt the stub axle assembly to release the drive shaft. Use care to avoid damaging the boot at the wheel end.

7) Remove the drive shaft on the right side by removing the rollpins holding the drive shaft to the sunwheel. Remove the shock absorber bottom mounting bolts and withdraw the drive shaft. Do not damage the boot at the wheel end.

8) Using a engine hoist, support engine/transaxle assembly. Remove the front and rear engine and transaxle mounting nuts, then carefully lift engine/transaxle assembly from vehicle.

Installation

To install reverse removal procedure, and note the following: Fill the engine and transaxle oil sumps to the correct fluid level. *See Automatic Transmission Servicing in this Section.* Fill and purge cooling system. Use new bolts when installing exhaust pipe clamp.

Automatic Transmission Removal

CHRYSLER CORP. — PASSENGER CARS

REMOVAL & INSTALLATION

TORQUEFLITE
Removal

1) Disconnect negative battery cable. Remove engine-to-transmission struts (if equipped). Remove cooler lines at transmission. Remove cooler line bracket and converter access cover. Loosen oil pan bolts, tap pan to break it loose allowing fluid to drain. Reinstall pan.

NOTE: **Some models require that exhaust system be dropped for clearance.**

2) Mark converter and drive plate for installation reference. Using a socket wrench on crankshaft vibration damper bolt, rotate engine clockwise to position converter attaching bolts for removal, then remove bolts. Mark propeller shaft and yoke for installation reference, then remove propeller shaft.

3) Disconnect electrical leads. Disconnect gearshift rod, torque shaft assembly, and throttle rod lever from left side of transmission. Remove linkage at bellcrank (if so equipped) from transmission.

4) Remove oil filler tube and speedometer cable. Support rear of engine with safety stand. Raise transmission slightly to relieve load on supports. Remove bolts securing transmission mount to crossmember and crossmember to frame, then remove crossmember.

NOTE: **All models except Diplomat and LeBaron have a torsion bar anchor crossmember, which remains in place, requiring a careful downward tilt of front of transmission as it is being removed.**

5) Remove converter housing-to-engine attaching bolts, then carefully work transmission and converter assembly rearward off engine block dowels, and disengage converter hub from end of crankshaft.

NOTE: **Attach a small "C" clamp to edge of converter housing to hold torque converter in place during transmission removal.**

6) Lower transmission and remove from under vehicle. To remove converter assembly, remove "C" clamp from edge of converter housing, and carefully slide assembly out of transmission.

Installation

CAUTION: If transmission was removed to correct a malfunction that generated sludge or heavy accumulations of metal or friction material particles, the oil cooler and and cooler lines must be thoroughly flushed and torque converter replaced.

1) To install, reverse removal procedures and note the following: To install the converter, rotate pump rotors with pump tool (C-3756 for A-904 series; C-3881 for A-727) until 2 small holes in handle are vertical.

2) Carefully slide converter over input shaft and reaction shaft. Make sure converter hub slots are also vertical and fully engage pump inner rotor lugs. Test for full engagement by placing a straightedge on face of case. Surface of converter front cover lug should be at least 1/2" to rear of straightedge when converter is pushed all the way into transmission.

3) Attach a small "C" clamp to converter housing to hold converter in place during transmission installation. Inspect converter drive plate for distortion or cracks and replace if necessary. Coat converter hub hole in crankshaft with multi-purpose grease.

NOTE: **When drive plate replacement is necessary, make sure both transmission dowel pins are in engine block and that they are protruding far enough to hold transmission in alignment.**

4) Place transmission and converter assembly on a transmission jack and position under vehicle for installation. Raise or tilt as necessary to align transmission to engine. Rotate converter so mark on converter (made during removal) will align with mark on drive plate.

5) Offset holes in drive plate are located next to 1/8" hole in inner circle of plate. A stamped "O" identifies offset hole in converter.

6) Carefully work transmission assembly forward over engine block dowels with converter hub entering crankshaft opening. After transmission is in position on engine, install and tighten all bolts. Adjust shift and throttle linkage, then refill transmission with DEXRON II automatic transmission fluid.

7) To complete installation, reverse removal procedures. On models equipped with engine-to-transmission struts, tighten bolts holding strut to transmission before strut-to-engine bolts.

A404, A413 & A470 TORQUEFLITE TRANSAXLE
Removal

NOTE: **Transaxle and torque converter must be removed as an assembly, otherwise, the converter drive plate, pump housing, or oil seal may be damaged.**

1) Disconnect negative battery cable. Disconnect throttle and shift linkage from transaxle. Disconnect upper transaxle cooler line at transaxle fitting.

2) Using a support fixture, support engine. Remove upper bell housing attaching bolts. Raise and support vehicle and remove both front wheels.

3) Remove splash shield from left fender. Drain transaxle fluid, then remove differential cover. Disconnect speedometer cable and pinion assembly from transaxle. Remove sway bar. Remove drive axle shafts as previously described.

4) Mark torque converter and drive plate for reassembly reference, then remove converter-to-drive plate bolts. Use access hole in right splash shield to rotate crankshaft for access to converter-to-drive plate bolts.

5) Disconnect lower cooler line and neutral safety switch wire from transaxle. Remove engine mount bracket from front crossmember, then remove front mount insulator through bolt and remaining bell housing attaching bolts.

6) Support transaxle with a transmission jack. Remove left engine mount. Pry transaxle away from engine, then lower assembly from vehicle.

NOTE: **For removal clearance, it may be necessary to pry transaxle away from engine between extension housing and engine block.**

CHRYSLER CORP. — PASSENGER CARS (Cont.)

Installation

1) To install, reverse removal procedures, and note the following:

2) Prior to transaxle installation, place a straightedge across face of bell housing and measure distance from straight edge to torque converter face to ensure converter is fully seated. Distance should be 7/8" from bell housing face to converter mounting bolt flat.

3) If a new or rebuilt transaxle is being installed, do not remove differential cover.

4) Push axle shafts (with retaining rings installed) into differential. A slight force may be required to insert shafts into differential side gears.

5) Adjust throttle and shift linkage as necessary. Fill transmission and differential sumps to correct level when installation is completed. *See Automatic Transmission Servicing in this section.*

FORD MOTOR CO. — PASSENGER CARS

REMOVAL & INSTALLATION

AUTOMATIC OVERDRIVE & C-3

Removal

1) Raise and support vehicle. Place drain pan under transmission oil pan, then loosen pan bolts and allow transmission fluid to drain. Remove converter drain plug access cover and adapter plate bolts from lower end of converter housing.

2) Remove the 4 converter-to-flywheel attaching nuts. Using a wrench on crankshaft pulley bolt, turn engine to gain access to converter attaching nuts.

CAUTION: **On belt driven overhead camshaft engines, NEVER turn engine backwards.**

3) Place a drain pan under converter, then remove converter drain plug and allow fluid in converter to drain. After all fluid has drained, reinstall drain plug and tighten.

4) Remove propeller shaft and install a seal remover tool in extension housing to prevent fluid leakage. Disconnect speedometer cable from extension housing. Disconnect shift rod and downshift rod from transmission levers.

5) Remove starter attaching bolts and place starter out of the way. Disconnect neutral safety switch wires from switch and vacuum line from transmission vacuum unit. Position jack under transmission and raise it slightly.

6) Remove crossmember attaching bolts from engine rear support and frame side support, then remove crossmember. Remove inlet pipe steady rest from inlet pipe and rear engine support, then disconnect muffler inlet pipe at exhaust manifold and secure it out of way.

7) Lower transmission jack and allow transmission to hang. Place jack under front of engine and raise engine to gain access to the 2 upper converter housing-to-engine attaching bolts.

8) Disconnect oil cooler lines at transmission and plug all openings to prevent entry of dirt. Remove lower converter housing-to-engine attaching bolts.

9) Remove transmission filler tube. Secure transmission to jack with a safety chain. Remove the 2 upper converter housing-to-engine attaching bolts. Move transmission to the rear and down to remove it from vehicle.

Installation

1) If not previously done, tighten torque converter drain plug. Position converter to transmission making sure the converter hub is fully engaged in pump gear.

2) With converter correctly installed, place transmission on a jack and secure with safety chain. Rotate converter so that drive studs and drain plug are in alignment with holes in flywheel.

3) With transmission mounted on jack, move converter and transmission assembly forward into position being careful not to damage flywheel and converter pilot. Install the 2 upper converter housing-to-engine attaching bolts and tighten.

CAUTION: **Do not allow transmission to get into a nosed down position as this will cause converter to move forward and disengage from pump gear. Converter must rest squarely against flywheel.**

4) To complete installation, reverse removal procedure and note the following: Fill transmission with fluid to proper level. *See Automatic Transmission Servicing in this section.* Adjust manual and downshift linkage as required.

C-5

Removal

1) Raise and support vehicle. Place drain pan under transmission oil pan, then loosen pan bolts and allow transmission fluid to drain. Remove converter drain plug access cover and adapter plate bolts from lower end of converter housing.

2) Remove the propeller shaft. Disconnect muffler and pipe assembly securing it to a convenient underbody bracket. Remove nuts attaching exhaust pipe(s) to exhaust manifold(s).

3) Pull back on catalytic converter to release converter hangers from mounting bracket. Remove speedometer cable from transmission housing and separate neutral start switch harness connector.

4) Disconnect kick down rod at transmission lever and shift linkage at bellcrank. On vehicles with floor mounted shift levers, remove shift cable routing, bracket attaching bolts and disconnect cable at transmission lever.

5) Remove converter dust shield. Using a wrench, turn crankshaft and drive plate and remove converter-to-drive plate attaching nuts. Remove starter and loosen nuts attaching rear support to crossmember.

6) Position a transmission jack under transmission. Secure transmission to jack with a safety chain. Remove bolts attaching crossmember-to-body brackets. Lower transmission enough to allow access to cooler line fittings and disconnect lines.

7) Remove transmission-to-engine attaching bolts, pull transmission back to disengage converter studs from drive plate, and lower transmission out of vehicle.

Automatic Transmission Removal

FORD MOTOR CO. — PASSENGER CARS (Cont.)

Installation

To install reverse removal procedure, and note the following: Adjust manual and downshift linkage. Fill transmission with fluid to proper level. *See Automatic Transmission Servicing in this section.*

CAUTION: The converter must rest squarely against flywheel. This indicates that converter pilot is not binding in engine crankshaft.

ATX TRANSAXLE

Removal

1) Disconnect negative battery cable. Remove bolts attaching managed air valve-to-valve body cover. Disconnect wiring from neutral safety switch. Disconnect throttle valve linkage and manual lever cable at respective levers.

2) Remove the 2 upper transaxle-to-engine attaching bolts. Raise and support vehicle. Remove control arm-to-steering knuckle attaching bolt and nut (at ball joint). Repeat this step on remaining side. Using a pry bar, separate control arms from steering knuckles.

CAUTION: Use care not to damage ball joint boot with pry bar when separating control arms from steering knuckles. Pry bar must not contact lower arm.

3) Remove bolts attaching stablizer bar brackets to frame. Remove stabilizer bar-to-control arm attaching nut and washer, then pull bar out of control arms.

4) Remove bolts attaching brake hose routing clips to suspension strut brackets. Disconnect steering gear tie rods from steering knuckles. Pry drive axle shaft out of right side of transaxle and position shaft on transaxle housing.

5) Using a driver, inserted through right side differential side gear, drive left side axle shaft from differential side gear. Pull axle shaft from transaxle and support out of way. Install plugs into differential seals to prevent fluid leakage.

6) Remove starter support bracket and disconnect starter cable. Remove starter. Remove transaxle support bracket. Remove dust cover from torque converter housing, then remove converter attaching nuts.

7) Remove nuts attaching left front insulator to body bracket, then remove bracket-to-body bolts, and remove bracket. Remove left rear insulator bracket attaching nut.

8) Disconnect transaxle cooler lines at transaxle. Remove bolts attaching manual lever bracket to transaxle case. Position transmission jack under transaxle and remove the 4 remaining transaxle-to-engine attaching bolts.

9) Insert a screwdriver between flywheel and torque converter, and carefully move transaxle and converter away from engine. When converter studs are clear of flywheel, lower transaxle slightly (2-3"). Disconnect speedometer cable and lower transaxle from vehicle.

NOTE: If transaxle contacts body before converter studs clear flywheel, remove left front insulator.

Installation

1) To install, reverse removal procedure, and note the following: Prior to installing drive axle shaft, replace snap ring on CV joint stub shaft.

2) To install axle shaft, carefully align splines on shaft with differential splines, then push CV joint until snap ring is felt to seat in groove in side gear.

3) Attach lower ball joint to steering knuckle, taking care not to damage or cut ball joint boot. Install new service pinch bolt, and install new nut.

4) Fill transaxle with fluid to proper level. *See Automatic Transmission Servicing in this Section.*

GENERAL MOTORS — PASSENGER CARS

REMOVAL & INSTALLATION

TURBO HYDRA-MATIC 180C, 200C, 200-4R, 250C, 350C, 400 & 700-R4

NOTE: Not all steps apply to all models.

Removal

1) Disconnect negative battery cable. Remove air cleaner assembly, and transmission dipstick. Disconnect the detent cable at carburetor linkage.

2) On models equipped with air conditioning, remove heater core cover screws from heater assembly, then disconnect wire connector and with hoses attached place heater core cover out of the way.

3) Raise vehicle on a hoist. Mark propeller shaft, for reassembly in same position, then remove propeller shaft. Disconnect speedometer cable, and electrical lead-to-case connector. Disconnect transmission cooler lines, and shift control linkage. Remove tunnel strap (if equipped).

4) Remove nuts holding the catalytic converter bracket to support assembly (if equipped). Support transmission with a jack. Remove rear transmission mount bolt(s). Remove support-to-frame bolts, and slide support rearward and remove.

5) Disconnect exhaust pipe at rear of converter and at exhaust manifold, then remove exhaust pipe, converter and converter bracket as an assembly. Remove torque converter inspection cover to gain access to drive plate. Mark flywheel and torque converter to maintain original position.

6) Remove torque converter-to-drive plate attaching bolts. Lower transmission until jack is barely supporting it and remove transmission-to-engine mounting bolts.

NOTE: Some models use shims at transmission mount which control drive line angles. Whenever removing the transmission on these models, be sure to install the same number of shims, and in the same direction, as were removed.

7) Raise transmission to normal position, then support engine with a jack and slide transmission rearward from engine and lower it away from vehicle.

NOTE: Use a torque converter holding tool when removing transmission or keep rear of transmission lower than front to prevent converter from falling out.

GENERAL MOTORS — PASSENGER CARS (Cont.)

Installation

1) To install, reverse removal procedure, and note the following:

2) Before installing drive plate-to-converter bolts, make sure that converter pilot hub is installed in crankshaft, and that welded brackets on converter are flush with drive plate and the converter rotates freely in this position.

3) To ensure proper converter alignment, move converter forward to contact attaching surface of drive plate. Align mark on drive plate with mark on converter, made during removal procedure.

4) Install converter-to-drive plate attaching bolts, and tighten. After installation of transmission, remove vehicle from hoist and check linkage adjustment and fluid level and correct as needed. *See Automatic Transmission Servicing in this section.*

TURBO HYDRA-MATIC 125C (TRANSAXLE)

Removal

NOTE: Not all steps apply to all models.

1) Remove battery ground cable at transaxle. Disconnect speedometer cable, shift linkages and T.V. control cable. Remove any hoses or wires attached to or supported by transaxle. Remove any exhaust system components, guards and shields that may interfere with transaxle removal.

2) Disconnect transaxle cooler lines. Raise and support rear of engine only enough to relieve pressure from motor mounts. If beam type of engine support is used, it should be located in center of cowl and left side of radiator support on 4-cylinder models. On 6-cylinder models, beam should be located across strut towers.

3) Remove vibration absorber (if equipped). Remove transaxle strut brackets. Remove 4 upper transaxle-to-engine bolts and 1 engine-to-transaxle bolt nearest cowl. Loosen the transaxle-to-engine bolt nearest the starter, but do not remove it at this time.

4) On "J" body models, remove transaxle mount bolts. Remove transaxle mount bracket bolts and nuts. Raise and support vehicle and remove left front wheel. Remove left end of stabilizer bar and left lower ball joint. Remove left suspension support assembly.

5) On "X" body models, remove steering gear shaft-to-intermediate shaft bolts. Raise and support vehicle, and remove left front wheel. Remove and support steering gear. Remove left lower ball joint at steering knuckle. Remove left end of stabilizer bar.

6) Remove both stabilizer bar reinforcements and bushings. Using a 1/2" drill bit, drill out spot weld between rear bolt holes of left side stabilizer bar mounting. Position a jack under transaxle. Remove engine and transaxle mount bolts. Remove sidemember-to-crossmember bolts. Remove bolts from left sidemember body mounts. Remove left sidemember and front crossmember assembly (gentle prying may be necessary).

7) On all models, disconnect both driveshafts from transaxle. Remove left driveshaft and support it away from transaxle (right driveshaft will slide out as transaxle is removed from vehicle). Remove flex plate and starter shields.

8) Attach transaxle securely to jack and remove last transaxle-to-engine bolt. Remove transaxle by sliding it toward left side of vehicle, guiding right driveshaft out of transaxle and carefully lowering jack.

Installation

Reverse removal procedure and note the following: As transaxle is being reinstalled, guide right driveshaft into transaxle. Adjust T.V. and shift cables. Refill transaxle to proper level with fluid. *See Automatic Transmission Servicing in this section.*

TURBO HYDRA-MATIC 325-4L (TRANSAXLE)

Removal

1) Disconnect negative battery cable (both negative cables on Diesel models). Disconnect speedometer cable from transaxle. Disconnect T.V. cable from carburetor or throttle body and remove bracket, then position cable out of way.

2) Support engine with a holding fixture (engine hoist). On Riviera models with turbocharged V-6 engine, remove air intake assembly from top of carburetor and remove exhaust heated air intake at exhaust manifold.

3) Remove upper transaxle-to-engine attaching bolts and upper final drive-to-transaxle attaching bolts. Remove transaxle filler tube. On Cadillac models with Digital Fuel Injection, remove fuel line clip. Place transaxle shift linkage in "LOW" position.

4) Raise and support vehicle. Disconnect shift linkage from transaxle. On models with V-8 engine, remove nuts and bolts holding left side exhaust pipe to "Y" pipe and slide flanges apart for clearance needed to remove transaxle.

5) Disconnect oil cooler lines from transaxle and plug lines. Disconnect electrical leads from starter, then remove starter and note position of shims for installation. Remove flywheel inspection cover.

6) Remove converter-to-flywheel attaching bolts. Remove left and right side transaxle mount bolts. Support transaxle with a jack. Remove remaining final drive-to-transaxle bolts and transaxle-to-engine bolts. Remove left and right side transaxle mounts.

7) Loosen final drive-to-engine support bracket. Lower transaxle slightly and move rearward to disengage splines from final drive unit. Carefully lower transaxle from vehicle.

NOTE: Install a torque converter holding tool on transaxle to prevent converter from falling during transaxle removal.

Installation

1) Reverse removal procedure and note the following: To assist in the engagement of final drive to transmission splines, ensure all mounting faces are in alignment with each other.

2) After splines are engaged, loosely install 2 final drive-to-transaxle lower attaching bolts. After final drive and transaxle are mated, align transaxle bell housing with engine and install remaining attaching bolts.

3) Before installing converter-to-flywheel bolts, make sure that the weld nuts on converter are flush with flywheel and the converter rotates freely by hand in this position. Hand start all 3 bolts and then tighten. This will ensure proper converter alignment.

4) Adjust shift linkage and T.V. cable as necessary. Fill transaxle to proper level with fluid. *See Automatic Transmission Servicing in this section.*

Automatic Transmission Removal

CHRYSLER CORP. — TRUCKS & VANS

TRANSFER CASE

MODEL NP-205

Removal

1) Raise vehicle, remove plug and drain transfer case. Replace plug. Disconnect speedometer cable. Remove skid plate, crossmember and strut rods as needed. Disconnect propeller shafts and wire out of way. Do not allow propeller shafts to hang free, as damage to universal joints may result.

2) Disconnect shift lever rod from shift rail link. Support transfer case and remove transfer case-to-transmission adapter bolts. Move transfer case to rear until input shaft clears adapter. Lower transfer case from vehicle.

Installation

Reverse removal procedures to install transfer case. Ensure that all attaching bolts are tight. Fill transfer case with lubricant.

MODEL NP-208

Removal

1) Raise vehicle, remove plug and drain transfer case. Mark front and rear output shaft yokes and propeller shafts for reassembly reference. Disconnect speedometer cable and indicator switch wires. Disconnect shift lever link from operating lever.

2) Support transfer case with transmission jack and remove crossmember. Disconnect front and rear propeller shafts at yokes and wire to frame.

3) If necessary, disconnect parking brake cable guide from pivot on right frame rail. Remove bolts attaching exhaust pipe support bracket to transfer case. Remove transfer case-to-transmission bolts. Move assembly to the rear until clear of output shaft. Lower transfer case from vehicle.

4) Remove all gasket material from rear of transmission adapter housing.

Installation

Install new transmission-to-transfer case gasket with sealer on both sides. Align transfer case with transmission. Rotate transfer case output shaft until transmission output shaft engages transfer case input shaft. Move transfer case until case seats flush against transmission. Install transfer case attaching bolts. Reverse removal procedures to complete installation.

TRANSMISSION

ALL MODELS

NOTE: **Transmission and converter must be removed and installed as an assembly to prevent damage to converter drive plate, front pump bushing, and oil seal. DO NOT allow weight of transmission to rest on plate during removal or installation.**

Removal

1) Remove transfer case from 4WD vehicles. Disconnect negative battery cable. Disconnect lower exhaust system as needed for removal clearance. Remove engine-to-transmission struts (if equipped). Disconnect cooler lines at transmission. Remove starter, cooler line bracket and converter access cover.

2) Loosen oil pan bolts, tap pan to break loose and allow fluid to drain. Reinstall pan. Rotate crankshaft clockwise with socket on vibration damper bolt to gain access to converter-to-drive plate bolts. Remove bolts. Mark propeller shaft for reassembly reference and remove from vehicle.

NOTE: **Crankshaft flange bolt circle, inner and outer circle of holes in drive plate and tapped holes in converter all have 1 hole offset so parts can only be installed in original position.**

3) Disconnect wiring connector from back-up light/neutral safety switch. Disconnect gearshift rod and torque shaft assembly from transmission. Disconnect transmission throttle rod from lever. Remove linkage bellcrank assembly, if equipped. Remove oil filler tube. Disconnect speedometer cable.

4) Install an engine support fixture under rear of engine. Raise transmission with service jack to relieve load on suports. Remove bolts securing crossmember to transmission and frame, then remove crossmember. Remove all converter housing-to-engine attaching bolts.

5) Carefully work transmission and converter assembly rearward off engine block dowel pins, disengaging converter hub from end of crankshaft. Attach a small "C" clamp on edge of converter housing to hold converter in place while transmission is being removed. Lower transmission and remove from vehicle.

Installation

1) Before installing converter, rotate front pump rotors with alignment tool (C3881) until 2 small holes in tool handle are vertical. Slide torque converter over input and reaction shafts, making sure converter hub slots are vertical, and fully engage pump inner rotor lugs.

2) Test for full engagement by placing a straightedge across face of transmission case. Surface of converter front cover lug should be at least 1/2" to rear of straightedge when converter is fully engaged. Attach a small "C" clamp to edge of converter housing to hold converter in place while installing transmission.

3) Inspect converter drive plate for distortion or cracks and replace if necessary. Install drive plate and tighten bolts to 55 ft. lbs. (75 N.m).

NOTE: **When drive plate replacement has been necessary, make sure both transmission dowel pins are in engine block and are protruding far enough to hold transmission in alignment.**

4) Coat converter hub hole in crankshaft with multi-purpose grease. Place transmission assembly on jack and position under vehicle. Make sure marks on converter and drive plate (made during removal) are aligned. Carefully work transmission assembly into position over dowels. Install all converter housing-to-engine retaining bolts. Tighten bolts to 30 ft. lbs. (41 N.m).

5) Reverse removal procedures to complete installation. Adjust shift and throttle linkages and fill transmission with fluid. On 4WD models, install transfer case.

CHRYSLER CORP. — TRUCKS & VANS (Cont.)

TIGHTENING SPECIFICATIONS

Application	Ft. Lbs. (N.m)
Converter Housing-to-Engine	30 (41)
Cooler Line Fitting	15 (20)
Drain & Fill Plugs	
NP-205 Transfer Case	130 (41)
NP-208 Transfer Case	18 (24)
Oil Pan Bolts	13 (18)
Torque Converter-to-Drive Plate Bolts	22 (30)
Transfer Case-to-Transmission	40 (54)

FORD MOTOR CO. — TRUCKS & VANS

TRANSFER CASE

NP-208 (BRONCO, F-150 & F-250)
Removal
1) Raise and support vehicle. Remove drain plug and drain fluid from transfer case. Replace plug. Disconnect 4WD indicator switch connector at transfer case. Disconnect speedometer driven gear from transfer case rear bearing retainer.

2) Remove transmission shift lever-to-transfer case retaining nut. Remove skid plate from frame. Support transfer case with transmission jack. Disconnect front and rear propeller shafts from transfer case output shaft yokes and wire out of way. Do not allow shafts to hang free as damage to universal joints may result.

3) Remove transfer case-to-transmission adapter bolts. Remove gasket between transfer case and adapter and lower transfer case out of vehicle.

Installation
To install transfer case, reverse removal procedures. Fill case with 7 pints (3.3 liters) of Dexron II type automatic transmission fluid.

BORG-WARNER 1345 (F-250 & F-350)
Removal
1) Raise vehicle. Remove drain plug and drain fluid from transfer case. Replace plug. Disconnect 4WD indicator switch connector at transfer case. If equipped, remove skid plate.

2) Disconnect front and rear propeller shafts from transfer case output shaft yokes, and wire out of way. Do not allow shafts to hang free as damage to universal joints may result.

3) Disconnect speedometer driven gear from rear bearing retainer. Remove retaining clips and shift rod from transfer case control and transfer case shift levers. Disconnect vent hose from case.

4) Remove heat shield. Support transfer case with transmission jack, remove transfer case-to-transmission adapter bolts and slide transfer case off of transmission output shaft (towards rear). Lower transfer case out of vehicle and remove gasket from between transfer case and adapter.

Installation
Reverse removal procedures to install transfer case. Fill case with 6.5 pints (3.1 liters) of Dexron II type automatic transmission fluid.

BORG-WARNER 13-50 (BRONCO II & RANGER)
Removal
1) Raise vehicle. Remove skid plate (if equipped). Remove drain plug and drain fluid from case. Replace plug. Disconnect 4WD indicator switch connector at transfer case. Disconnect front propeller shaft from front axle. Loosen front shaft boot clamp and slide out propeller shaft and boot as an assembly.

2) Disconnect rear propeller shaft from transfer case. Disconnect speedometer driven gear from transfer case rear cover. Disconnect vent hose from control lever.

3) Loosen or remove large and small bolts (1 each) retaining shifter to extension housing. Pull on control lever until bushing slides off transfer case shift lever pin. Unscrew shift lever from control lever, as needed.

4) Remove heat shield from transfer case. Support transfer case with jack and remove transfer case-to-transmission extension housing bolts (5). Slide transfer case to the rear and off of transmission output shaft. Lower case from vehicle. Remove gasket from between transfer case and extension housing.

Installation
Reverse removal procedures to install transfer case, noting the following:
1) When installing shift lever assembly, tighten large bolt first, then small bolt.

2) When installing vent assembly, White marking on hose should be positioned in notch in shifter with upper end of hose 2 inches above top of shifter, inside of shift lever boot.

3) Before installing front propeller shaft into transfer case, lubricate female splines of transfer case input shaft with multi-purpose grease.

4) Fill transfer case to bottom of fill plug hole with Dexron-II automatic transmission fluid.

TRANSMISSION

C-3 (BRONCO II & RANGER)
Removal
1) Disconnect battery negative cable. Raise vehicle. Loosen transmission pan bolts, tap edge of pan to break seal and allow fluid to drain. Replace pan after fluid

Automatic Transmission Removal
FORD MOTOR CO. — TRUCKS & VANS (Cont.)

has drained. Remove converter drain plug access cover. Remove adapter plate bolts from lower end of converter housing.

2) Remove flywheel-to-converter attaching nuts and converter drain plug. Allow fluid to drain from converter, then reinstall and tighten drain plug. Mark propeller shaft for reassembly. Disconnect shaft at rear axle and slide out of transmission.

3) Remove speedometer cable from extension housing. Disconnect shift rod at manual lever and downshift rod at downshift lever. Remove starter-to-converter housing bolts and position starter out of way. DO NOT allow starter to hang by cables.

4) Disconnect neutral start switch connector from switch. Remove vacuum line from vacuum modulator. Raise slightly and support transmission with transmission jack. Remove rear mount-to-crossmember bolts.

5) Remove crossmember-to-frame side support bolts and remove crossmember insulator, support and damper. Lower jack under transmission and allow transmission to hang. Position a second jack at front of engine and raise enough to gain access to 2 top converter housing-to-engine bolts. DO NOT remove bolts at this time.

6) Disconnect transmission cooler lines and plug connections. Remove lower converter housing-to-engine bolts. Remove transmission filler tube. Raise transmission jack up to transmission and secure transmission to jack with safety chain.

7) Remove 2 top converter housing-to-engine bolts. Move transmission rearward and down to remove from vehicle.

Installation
Reverse removal procedures to install, noting the following: Ensure full converter engagement in transmission before installing transmission. During installation, keep transmission in a "nose-up" position at all times to prevent disengagement of the torque converter and pump gear.

C-5 (BRONCO II, RANGER & F-100)
Removal
1) Disconnect battery negative cable. On 4WD vehicles, remove filler tube bracket bolt from valve cover bracket. On all models, raise and support vehicle. Drain transmission fluid and replace pan. Remove converter drain plug access cover. On 2WD models, remove adapter plate bolts from lower end of converter housing.

2) On all models, remove flywheel-to-converter attaching nuts and converter drain plug. Allow fluid to drain from converter, then reinstall and tighten drain plug. On 2WD models, mark propeller shaft for reassembly. Disconnect shaft at rear axle and slide out of transmission.

3) On all models, disconnect battery cable from starter motor and remove starter. Disconnect neutral start switch wires at connector. Remove rear mount-to-crossmember nuts and 2 crossmember-to-frame bolts. Remove right and left gussets. On 4WD vehicles, remove rear insulator-to-extension housing bolts (2).

4) On all models, disconnect throttle valve (TV) linkage rod from transmission TV lever. Disconnect manual rod from manual lever at transmission. On 4WD models, disconnect downshift and manual linkage rods from levers on transmission. Remove vacuum hose from diaphragm unit. Remove vacuum line from retaining clip.

5) On all models, remove bellcrank housing-to-converter housing bolts (2). Remove transfer case (4WD models). Raise transmission enough to allow removal of crossmember. Remove rear mount from crossmember, then remove crossmember.

6) Lower transmission as needed to disconnect oil cooler lines. Disconnect cooler lines. Disconnect speedometer cable from extension housing. On 2WD models, remove transmission filler tube-to-engine bolt and lift filler tube out of transmission.

7) On all models, secure transmission to jack with safety chain. Remove converter housing-to-engine bolts. Carefully remove transmission and converter assembly from vehicle.

Installation
To install transmission, reverse removal procedures, noting the following:

1) Ensure that converter is fully engaged with pump gear before installation.

2) When installing filler tube, install a new "O" ring on bottom of tube.

3) On 2WD models, when installing damper assembly over engine rear support studs, make sure that the painted surface of the damper is facing forward when installed in vehicle.

4) Before installing rear propeller shaft, apply a small amount of multi-purpose grease to splines of yoke.

C-6 (ALL "E" MODELS)
Removal
1) Working inside vehicle, remove engine compartment cover and disconnnect electrical leads at plug connector. Remove flex hose from air cleaner heat tube (V8 models only), then remove upper converter housing-to-engine attaching bolts. Remove fluid filler tube-to-engine bolt.

2) Raise vehicle, drain transmission pan and remove converter drain plug access cover. Remove converter-to-flywheel attaching nuts and converter drain plug. Drain fluid and replace drain plug.

3) Disconnect propeller shaft. Remove filler tube. Disconnect starter cable and remove starter. Position an engine support bar to side rail and oil pan flanges. Disconnect oil cooler lines and vacuum lines from transmission.

4) Remove speedometer driven gear from extension housing and manual and downshift linkage rods from transmission control levers. Support transmission with transmission jack and secure with safety chain.

5) Remove bolts and nuts securing rear mount to crossmember and bolts retaining crossmember to side rails. Remove 2 support inserts, raise transmission with jack and remove crossmember. Remove remaining converter housing-to-engine bolts and lower assembly out of vehicle.

Installation
Reverse removal procedures to install, noting the following: Be sure that converter is fully engaged with pump gear during installation. Always use a new "O" ring on the end of the fluid filler tube. When installation is complete, fill transmission with Dexron II type automatic transmission fluid.

FORD MOTOR CO. — TRUCKS & VANS (Cont.)

C-6 (BRONCO & "F" MODELS)
Removal

1) Disconnect negative cable from battery. Remove 2 upper converter housing-to-engine bolts. Raise vehicle, drain transmission pan and remove converter drain plug access cover.

2) Remove converter-to-flywheel attaching nuts and converter drain plug. Allow fluid to drain, then reinstall and tighten converter drain plug. On 2WD models, disconnect propeller shaft at rear axle and slide shaft out of transmission.

3) On all models, disconnect speedometer cable from extension housing. Disconnect downshift and manual linkage rods from levers at transmission. Disconnect oil cooler lines from transmission.

4) Remove vacuum line from vacuum unit. Remove vacuum line retaining clip. Disconnect starter cable from starter and remove starter. On 4WD models, remove transfer case.

5) On all models, remove 2 rear crossmember-to-frame attaching bolts. Remove 2 rear support-to-extension housing attaching bolts and 6 bolts securing second crossmember to frame side rails.

6) Raise transmission with a transmission jack and remove both crossmembers. Secure transmission to the jack with safety chain. Remove remaining converter housing-to-engine attaching bolts. Move transmission away from engine, lower the jack and remove converter and transmission assembly from vehicle.

Installation

Reverse removal procedure to install, noting the following: Make sure that torque converter is fully engaged in transmission before and during installation. When installing fluid filler tube, always use a new "O" ring on end of tube. When installation is complete, fill transmission with Dexron II type automatic transmission fluid.

AUTOMATIC OVERDRIVE ("F" MODELS)
Removal

1) Disconnect negative battery cable. Raise vehicle and drain transmission fluid. Remove converter drain plug access cover. Remove converter-to-flywheel attaching nuts and torque converter drain plug. Drain converter, then reinstall and tighten converter drain plug.

2) Disconnect propeller shaft from rear axle and remove shaft from transmission. Disconnect starter cable and remove starter. Disconnect neutral start switch wires at connector.

3) Remove rear mount-to-crossmember bolts and crossmember-to-frame bolts. Remove bolts securing engine rear support to extension housing. Disconnect TV linkage rod and manual rod from transmission levers.

4) Remove bellcrank bracket-to-converter housing bolts (2). Raise transmission with jack and remove crossmember. Lower transmission enough to remove oil cooler lines.

5) Disconnect speedometer cable from extension housing. Remove bolt securing filler tube to engine and remove filler tube. Secure transmission to jack with safety chain. Remove converter housing-to-engine bolts. Move transmission to rear and down to remove from vehicle.

Installation

Reverse removal procedures to install transmission, noting the following: Ensure that converter is fully seated in transmission before and during installation procedure. Install new "O" ring on end of fluid filler tube before installing tube. When installation is complete, fill transmission with Dexron II type automatic transmission fluid.

TIGHTENING SPECIFICATIONS

Application	Ft. Lbs. (N.m)
Converter Housing-to-Engine	
C-3	28-38 (38-51)
C-5	
Bronco II, Ranger & All 3.8L V6	28-38 (38-51)
All Others	40-50 (55-67)
C-6	
Gas Engines	40-50 (55-67)
Diesel Engines	50-65 (67-87)
AOT	40-50 (55-67)
Converter-to-Flywheel	
C-3	27-49 (37-66)
All Others	20-30 (28-40)
Starter Mounting Bolts	
Bronco II & Ranger	15-20 (20-27)
All Other Models	
Gas Engine	40-50 (56-70)
Diesel Engine	50-65 (70-91)
Control Lever-to-Transfer Case (Bronco II & Ranger)	
Large Bolt	70-90 (95-112)
Small Bolt	31-42 (42-57)

GENERAL MOTORS — TRUCKS & VANS

TRANSFER CASE

"S" SERIES
Removal

1) With transfer case shift lever in "4 Hi" position, disconnect negative battery cable. Raise vehicle and remove skid plate. Drain transfer case. Mark front and rear output shaft yokes and propeller shafts for reassembly reference and remove shafts.

2) Disconnect speedometer cable and vacuum harness from transfer case. Remove shift lever from case. Remove catalytic converter hanger bolts at converter.

Raise transmission and transfer case assembly with jack and remove transmission mount bolts. Remove mount.

3) Lower complete assembly. Support transfer case alone and remove transmission-to-transfer case bolts. Remove shift lever bracket from transfer case adapter in order to reach upper left attaching bolt.

4) Separate transfer case from transmission adapter and remove from vehicle.

Installation

Reverse removal procedures to install. Always use a new gasket between the transfer case and adapter.

GENERAL MOTORS — TRUCKS & VANS (Cont.)

TRANSMISSIONS

ALL EXCEPT "S" & "K" SERIES

Removal

1) Disconnect negative battery cable. Remove air cleaner and disconnect TV or detent cable at carburetor. Remove dipstick and filler tube support bracket bolt. Raise and support vehicle. Mark propeller shaft for reassembly reference and remove from vehicle.

2) Disconnect speedometer cable and shift linkage and all electrical leads from transmission. Remove transmission support brackets (if present) and flywheel inspection cover.

3) Mark flex plate and torque converter for reassembly in same position and remove torque converter-to-flex plate bolts. Disconnect catalytic converter support bracket (if equipped).

4) Remove transmission rear mount bolts. Support transmission with jack and raise slightly. Remove transmission support-to-frame bolts and insulators. Remove support.

5) Lower transmission enough to remove oil cooler lines and TV or detent cable from transmission. Disconnect lines and cable. Support engine with jack and remove transmission-to-engine bolts.

6) Disconnect transmission assembly from engine. Install torque converter retaining tool (J-21366) and remove transmission from vehicle.

Installation

To install, reverse removal procedure and note the following: Before installing flex plate-to-converter bolts, make certain that the weld nuts on converter are flush with the flex plate and the converter rotates freely by hand in this position. Install converter-to-flex plate bolts (3) and tighten finger tight before tightening to proper specification.

"K" SERIES

Removal

1) Disconnect negative battery cable. Remove air cleaner and disconnect TV or detent cable at carburetor. Remove transfer case shift lever knob and boot. Raise and support vehicle.

2) Mark propeller shafts for reassembly reference and remove from vehicle. Disconnect speedometer cable, shift linkage and all electrical leads from transmission and transfer case. Disconnect transfer case shift linkage.

3) Remove transmission support strut rods and flywheel inspection cover. Mark flex plate and converter for reassembly reference. Remove torque converter-to-flex plate retaining bolts.

4) Disconnect transmission oil cooler lines from transmission. Support transmission and transfer case assembly with a jack and remove transfer case-to-frame bracket bolts. Remove mount bolts and crossmember.

5) Remove transmission/transfer case assembly mounting bolts and remove assembly from vehicle. Separate transmission from transfer case.

Installation

Reverse removal procedures to install, noting the following: Before installing flex plate-to-converter bolts, make certain that the weld nuts on converter are flush with the flex plate and the converter rotates freely by hand in this position. Then, hand start all 3 bolts and tighten finger tight before tightening to specifications.

"S" SERIES

NOTE: If vehicle is a 4WD model, refer to Transfer Case removal procedures and remove case.

Removal

1) Disconnect negative battery cable. Remove air cleaner and disconnect TV cable at carburetor. On models with 1.9L 4-cylinder engine, remove upper starter retaining nut. On all models, raise and support vehicle.

2) Mark propeller shaft for reassembly reference and remove shaft. Disconnect speedometer cable, shift linkage and all electrical leads from transmission. Remove brake line to crossmember clips and remove crossmember (4WD only).

3) Remove transmission support brace bolts and converter cover (if equipped). Remove exhaust crossover pipe and converter attaching bolts. Remove crossover and converter as an assembly.

4) Remove flywheel inspection plate and mark flex plate and torque converter for reassembly reference. Remove torque converter-to-flex plate bolts. Disconnect catalytic converter support bracket.

5) Place a jack under transmission and raise slightly. Remove transmission support-to-mount bolt and support-to-frame bolts and insulators. Remove left body mounting bolts and loosen radiator support mount bolt.

6) Raise cab on left side as needed to remove upper transmission-to-engine bolts. Support cab with wood block between body and frame. Slide transmission support towards rear and lower transmission enough to remove oil cooler lines and TV cable. Disconnect lines and cable.

7) Support engine with jack and remove remaining transmission-to-engine bolts. Slide transmission away from engine and install torque converter retaining tool (J-21366) to prevent converter damage as transmission is removed from vehicle. Remove transmission.

Installation

Reverse removal procedures to install, noting the following: Before installing flex plate-to-converter bolts, make certain that the weld nuts on converter are flush with the flex plate and the converter rotates freely by hand in this position. Then, hand start all 3 bolts and tighten finger tight before tightening to specifications.

TIGHTENING SPECIFICATIONS

Application	Ft. Lbs. (N.m)
Transmission-to-Engine	
"S" Series	
1.9L 4-Cylinder	25 (35)
2.8L V6	55 (75)
All Others	35 (50)
Converter-to-Flex Plate	
"S" Series	35 (50)
All Others	35 (45)
Transmission-to-Mount	
"S" Series	35 (50)
All Others	35 (48)
Transfer Case-to-Adapter	
"S" Series	20-25 (27-34)
All Others	25 (35)
Transmission-to-Adapter	25 (35)

JEEP

REMOVAL

ALL MODELS

1) Disconnect fan shroud and transmission fill tube upper bracket. Raise vehicle. Remove converter inspection cover and fill tube. Remove starter.

2) Mark propeller shafts for reassembly. Disconnect shafts at transfer case and wire to frame rails. Do not allow shafts to hang free as damage to universal joints may result. On V8 models, disconnect exhaust pipes from exhaust manifolds. Drain transfer case lubricant on Cherokee, Wagoneer and Truck models. Disconnect speedometer cable from transmission.

3) Disconnect all shift and throttle linkages and wiring from transmission and transfer case. Mark converter drive plate and converter for reassembly and remove torque converter-to-drive plate bolts. Rotate crankshaft to gain access to bolts.

4) Suport transmission/transfer case assembly with jack and secure with chain. Remove bolts and rear crossmember. Lower transmission enough to disconnect cooler lines at transmission. Remove transmission-to-engine retaining bolts and slowly slide transmission assembly away from engine.

5) Hold converter in position while lowering transmission assembly from vehicle. Separate transmission from transfer case.

INSTALLATION

ALL MODELS

Reverse removal procedures to install, noting the following: Do not tighten exhaust pipe attaching bolts until crossmember has been installed and transmission jack has been removed. Make sure all index marks made at removal are aligned. Tighten all bolts to specification and fill transmission and transfer case with fluid.

TIGHTENING SPECIFICATIONS

Application	Ft. Lbs. (N.m)
Cooler Line Nuts	25 (34)
Torque Converter-to-Drive Plate	22 (30)
Transfer Case-to-Transmission	40 (54)
Transmission-to-Engine	30 (41)

Automatic Transmissions

AMERICAN MOTORS, CHRYSLER & JEEP TROUBLE SHOOTING

Every diagnosis of automatic transmission problems should begin with a check of the transmission fluid and linkage. Most of the following conditions can be caused by one or more of the following factors: (1) Incorrect fluid level, (2) Contaminated fluid, (3) Improperly adjusted linkage, or (4) Damaged or worn linkage.

CONDITION & POSSIBLE CAUSE	CONDITION & POSSIBLE CAUSE
Harsh Engagement From Neutral to "D" or "R" • Engine idle speed too high. • Valve body malfunction or leakage. • Hydraulic pressures too high. • Worn or faulty rear clutch. • Faulty lock-up clutch (except A-404). • Rear band out of adjustment. • Sticking or faulty accumulator. **Delayed Engagement From Neutral to "D" or "R"** • Hydraulic pressures too low. • Valve body malfunction or leakage. • Low-reverse servo, band or linkage malfunction. • Oil filter clogged. • Faulty oil pump. • Worn or broken input shaft seal rings. • Engine idle speed too low. • Worn or faulty front or rear clutch. • Worn or broken reaction shaft support seal rings. • Sticking or faulty accumulator. **Runaway Upshifts** • Hydraulic pressures too low. • Valve body malfunction or leakage. • Oil filter clogged. • Worn or broken reaction shaft support seal rings. • Kickdown servo, band or linkage malfunction. • Worn or faulty front clutch. **No Upshifts** • Hydraulic pressures too low. • Valve body malfunction or leakage. • Governor support seal rings worn or broken. • Worn or broken reaction shaft support seal rings. • Governor malfunction. • Kickdown servo, band or linkage malfunction. • Worn or faulty front clutch. • Front band out of adjustment.	**3-2 Kickdown Runaway** • Hydraulic pressures too low. • Valve body malfunction or leakage. • Kickdown band out of adjustment. • Reaction shaft support seal rings worn or broken. • Kickdown servo, band or linkage malfunction. • Worn or faulty front clutch. **No Kickdown or Normal Downshift** • Valve body malfunction or leakage. • Governor malfunction. • Kickdown servo, band or linkage malfunction. • Front band out of adjustment. • Incorrect hydraulic pressures. **Delay or Erratic Shifts (Shifts Harsh at Times)** • Hydraulic pressures too low. • Valve body malfunction or leakage. • Oil filter clogged. • Faulty oil pump. • Worn or broken reaction shaft support seal rings. • Worn or broken governor support seal rings. • Governor malfunction. • Kickdown servo, band or linkage malfunction. • Worn or faulty front clutch. • Faulty lock-up clutch. **Slips in Forward Drive Positions** • Hydraulic pressures too low. • Valve body malfunction or leakage. • Oil filter clogged. • Faulty oil pump. • Worn or broken input shaft seal rings. • Overrunning clutch not holding. • Worn or faulty rear clutch. • Overrunning clutch worn, seized or broken. • Worn or faulty accumulator. • Faulty front or rear servo or linkage.

AMERICAN MOTORS, CHRYSLER & JEEP TROUBLE SHOOTING (Cont.)

CONDITION & POSSIBLE CAUSE	CONDITION & POSSIBLE CAUSE

Slips in Reverse Only

- Hydraulic pressures too low.
- Low-Reverse band out of adjustment.
- Valve body malfunction or leakage.
- Low-Reverse servo, band or linkage malfunction.
- Faulty oil pump.
- Reaction shaft support seal rings worn or broken.
- Worn or faulty front clutch.

Slips or No Drive in Any Position

- Hydraulic pressures too low.
- Valve body malfunction or leakage.
- Clogged oil filter.
- Faulty oil pump.
- Input shaft seal rings worn or broken.
- Planetary gear set broken or seized.

No Drive in Forward Drive Positions

- Hydraulic pressures too low.
- Valve body malfunction or leakage.
- Input shaft seal rings worn or broken.
- Overrunning clutch not holding.
- Worn or faulty rear clutch.
- Planetary gear set worn or broken.
- Overrunning clutch worn, broken or seized.

No Drive in Reverse

- Hydraulic pressures too low.
- Low-Reverse band out of adjustment.
- Valve body malfunction or leakage.
- Low-Reverse servo, band or linkage malfunction.
- Reaction shaft support seal rings worn or broken.
- Worn or faulty front clutch.
- Worn or faulty rear clutch.
- Planetary gear set broken or seized.

Drives in Neutral (Creeps)

- Valve body malfunction or leakage.
- Insufficient clutch plate clearance.
- Worn or faulty rear clutch.
- Rear clutch dragging.

Drags or Locks Up

- Stuck lock-up valve.
- Low-reverse band out of adjustment.
- Faulty oil pump.
- Kickdown band too tight.
- Planetary gear set broken or seized.
- Overrunning clutch broken, worn or seized.
- Worn park lock components.
- Valve body malfunction or leakage.
- Faulty front servo or linkage.
- Sticking or faulty accumulator.

TRANSMISSION NOISY

Growling, Grating or Scraping Noise

- Worn park lock components.
- Worn or damaged output shaft bearing, bushing, or seal.
- Clogged oil filter.
- Broken or loose converter drive plate.
- Worn or faulty oil pump.
- Worn or faulty front clutch.
- Seized or broken planetary gear set.
- Worn or broken overrunning clutch.
- Faulty torque converter.
- Low-Reverse band out of adjustment.
- Kickdown band out of adjustment.
- Drive shaft(s) bushing(s) damaged (A-404 only).

Buzzing Noise

- Worn or faulty governor.
- Worn or damaged output shaft bearing, bushing, or seal.
- Valve body malfunction or leakage.
- Worn or faulty oil pump.
- Faulty torque converter.
- Overrunning clutch inner race damaged.

Hard to Fill, Oil Blows Out Filler Tube

- Clogged oil filter.
- High fluid level.
- Transmission case vent plugged.
- Oil cooler or lines plugged or leaking.
- Worn or faulty oil pump.

Automatic Transmissions

AMERICAN MOTORS, CHRYSLER & JEEP TROUBLE SHOOTING (Cont.)

CONDITION & POSSIBLE CAUSE	CONDITION & POSSIBLE CAUSE

Transmission Overheats

- Stuck switch valve.
- Engine idle speed too high.
- Hydraulic pressures too low.
- Faulty oil pump.
- Kickdown band too tight.
- Faulty oil cooler or cooling system.
- Insufficient clutch plate clearance.
- Oil filter clogged.

Starter Will Not Operate in Neutral or Park

- Neutral Safety Switch faulty.
- Manual valve lever assembly faulty.
- Valve body malfunctioning or leaking.

Sluggish Acceleration, Excessive Throttle Needed to Maintain Speed

- Poor engine performance.
- Faulty torque converter.
- Incorrect hydraulic pressures.
- Worn or faulty rear clutch.

LOCK-UP CONVERTER DIAGNOSIS

No Lock-Up

- Faulty oil pump.
- Sticking governor valve.
- Valve body malfunction.
- Stuck switch valve.
- Stuck lock-up valve.
- Stuck fail-safe valve.
- Faulty torque converter.
- Failed locking clutch.
- Leaking turbine hub seal.
- Faulty input shaft or seal ring.

Will Not Unlock

- Sticking governor valve.
- Valve body malfunction.
- Stuck switch valve.
- Stuck lock-up valve.
- Stuck fail-safe valve.

Stays Locked Up To Too Low A Speed In Direct

- Sticking governor valve.
- Valve body malfunction.
- Stuck switch valve.
- Stuck lock-up valve.
- Stuck fail-safe valve.

Locks Up or Drags in Low or Second

- Faulty oil pump.
- Valve body malfunction.
- Stuck switch valve.
- Stuck fail-safe valve.

Stalls or Is Sluggish In Reverse

- Faulty oil pump.
- Plugged cooler, lines or fittings.
- Valve body malfunction.
- Stuck switch valve.
- Faulty input shaft or seal ring.

Loud Clatter During Lock-Up Engagement (Cold)

- Faulty torque converter.
- Failed locking clutch.
- Leaking turbine hub seal.

Shudder After Lock-Up Engagement

- Faulty oil pump.
- Plugged cooler, lines or fittings.
- Valve body malfunction.
- Faulty torque converter.
- Failed locking clutch.
- Align exhaust system.
- Engine out of tune.
- Throttle linkage out of adjustment.

Vibration After Lock-Up Engagement

- Faulty torque converter.
- Align exhaust system.
- Engine out of tune.
- Throttle linkage out of adjustment.

Vibration When "Reved" In Neutral

- Drive plate and/or mounting loose.
- Torque converter out of balance.

Overheating; Blowing Oil Out Dipstick or Pump Seal

- Plugged cooler, lines or fittings.
- Stuck switch valve.

FORD MOTOR CO. TROUBLESHOOTING

Every diagnosis of automatic transmission problems should begin with a check of the transmission fluid and linkage. Most of the following conditions can be caused by one or more of the following factors: (1) Incorrect fluid level, (2) Contaminated fluid, (3) Improperly adjusted linkage, or (4) Damaged or worn linkage.

CONDITION & POSSIBLE CAUSE	CONDITION & POSSIBLE CAUSE
Slow Initial Engagement • Improper clutch or band application. • Incorrect hydraulic pressures. • Damaged 2-3 accumulator valve (A.O.T.). **Rough Initial Engagement** • Engine idle speed too high. • Automatic choke on (warm temperature). • Looseness in propeller shaft, "U" joints or engine mounts. • Incorrect clutch or band application. • Incorrect hydraulic pressures. • Sticking or dirty valve body. • Damaged 2-3 accumulator valve (A.O.T.). **Slipping, Shudders or Chatters Upon Forward Engagement** • Throttle valve misadjusted (A.O.T.) • Incorrect hydraulic pressures. • Dirty or sticking valve body. • Valve body bolts loose. • Forward clutch piston check ball not seating. • Forward clutch piston seal cut or worn. • Forward clutch feed hole blocked. • Low one-way clutch damaged. **No Drive in Any Gear** • Improper clutch or band application. • Internal leakage. • Valve body loose. • Damaged or worn clutches. • Sticking or dirty valve body. • Output shaft broken. • Turbine input shaft broken. **No Drive Forward (Reverse OK)** • Improper clutch or band application. • Incorrect hydraulic pressures. • Damaged or worn forward clutch. • Damaged or worn governor. • Valve body loose. • Dirty or sticking valve body. • Damaged 2-3 accumulator valve (A.O.T.).	**No Drive, Slips or Chatters in Reverse (Forward OK)** • Looseness in propeller shaft, half shafts (A.T.X.), "U" joints or engine mounts. • Reverse band out of adjustment. • Damaged or worn reverse clutch. • Incorrect hydraulic pressures. • Damaged or worn reverse clutch or servo. • Valve body loose. • Sticking or dirty valve body. **No Drive, Slips or Chatter in First Gear in "D" (All Other Gears OK); First Gear in "OD" or 3 (A.O.T. Only)** • Damaged or worn one-way clutch. • Damaged or worn band (A.T.X.). **No Drive, Slips or Chatters in Second Gear** • Intermediate friction clutch or one way clutch (A.O.T. only). • Intermediate band out of adjustment (except A.O.T.). • Improper clutch or band application. • Incorrect hydraulic pressures. • Damaged or worn servo and/or leakage. • Dirty or sticking valve body. • Polished or glazed intermediate band or drum. **Starts Up in 2nd or 3rd** • Improper clutch or band application. • Incorrect hydraulic pressures. • Damaged or worn governor. • Sticking governor. • Loose valve body. • Dirty or sticking valve body. • Cross leaks between valve body and case mating surface. **Incorrect Shift Points** • Improper vacuum hose routing or leaks (except A.O.T.). • Improper operation of EGR system (except A.O.T.). • Improper speedometer gear installation. • Improper clutch or band application. • Incorrect hydraulic pressures. • Damaged or worn governor. • Dirty or sticking valve body.

Automatic Transmissions

FORD MOTOR CO. TROUBLESHOOTING (Cont.)

CONDITION & POSSIBLE CAUSE	CONDITION & POSSIBLE CAUSE

No Upshift at Any Speed in "D"
(3 or "OD" with A.O.T.)

- Vacuum leak to diaphragm assembly.
- Improper clutch or band application.
- Incorrect hydraulic pressures.
- Damaged or worn governor.
- Dirty or sticking valve body.

Shifts 1-3 in "D"
("OD" Range for A.O.T.)

- Intermediate band out of adjustment.
- Defective intermediate friction clutch or one way clutch.
- Damaged intermediate servo and/or internal leakage.
- Polished or glazed intermediate band or drum.
- Improper clutch or band application.
- Incorrect hydraulic pressures.
- Dirty or sticking valve body.

Engine Overspeeds on 2-3 Shift

- Throttle linkage out of adjustment (A.O.T. only).
- Improper clutch or band application.
- Incorrect hydraulic pressures.
- Damaged or worn high clutch.
- Damaged or worn intermediate servo.
- Dirty or sticking valve body.

No 1-2 Upshifts

- Throttle linkage misadjusted (A.O.T.)
- Kickdown linkage misadjusted (Exc. A.O.T.)
- Intermediate friction clutch low pressure (A.O.T.)
- Governor valve sticking.
- Valve body bolts loose.
- Valve body dirty or sticking.
- Intermediate clutch/band and or servo burnt.

Mushy 1-2 Shift

- Improper engine performance.
- Intermediate band out of adjustment (except A.O.T.).
- Improper clutch or band application.
- Incorrect hydraulic pressures.
- Worn or damaged high clutch.
- Worn or damaged intermediate servo or band.
- Polished or glazed band or drum.
- Dirty or sticking valve body.
- Damaged intermediate clutch (A.O.T.)
- Governor valve sticking.

Rough 1-2 Shift

- Incorrect engine idle speed or performance.
- Intermediate band out of adjustment (except A.O.T.).
- Improper clutch or band application.
- Incorrect hydraulic pressures.
- Worn or damaged intermediate servo.
- Dirty or sticking valve body.
- Governor valve sticking.
- Engine vacuum leak (A.O.T.)

No 2-3 Upshifts

- Incorrect hydraulic pressures.
- Valve body bolts loose.
- Valve body dirty or sticking.
- Converter damper hub weld broken.
- Direct clutch assembly burned or worn (A.O.T.)

Rough 2-3 Shift

- Incorrect engine performance.
- Improper clutch or band application.
- Incorrect hydraulic pressures.
- Damaged or worn intermediate servo release and high clutch piston check ball.
- Dirty or sticking valve body.
- Engine vacuum leak.
- Damaged 2-3 accumulator or accumulator piston seals (A.O.T.)

Rough 3-1 Shift (3-2 Shift for A.T.X.) at Closed Throttle in "D"

- Incorrect engine idle speed or performance.
- Improper clutch or band application.
- Incorrect hydraulic pressures.
- Improper governor operation.
- Dirty or sticking valve body.

Mushy 3-4 or Rough 3-4 Shift (A.O.T. Only)

- Incorrect engine performance.
- Improper band application.
- Damaged or glazed reverse clutch drum.
- Polished or glazed band.
- Dirty or sticking valve body.

Rough or Mushy 4-2 or 3-1 Shift (A.O.T. Only)

- Incorrect engine performance.
- Improper throttle or manual linkage adjustment.
- Improper application of intermediate friction and one-way clutch.
- Dirty or sticking valve body.

FORD MOTOR CO. TROUBLESHOOTING (Cont.)

CONDITION & POSSIBLE CAUSE	CONDITION & POSSIBLE CAUSE
Rough or Mushy 4-3 Shift (A.O.T. Only) • Incorrect engine performance. • Improper throttle linkage adjustment. • Improper overdrive servo release. • Dirty or sticking valve body or governor. **No Forced Downshift** • Improper clutch or band application. • Incorrect hydraulic pressures. • Damaged internal kickdown linkage. • Dirty or sticking valve body. • Dirty or sticking governor. **Runaway Engine on 3-2 Downshift** • Intermediate band out of adjustment. • Improper clutch or band application. • Incorrect hydraulic pressures. • Damaged or worn intermediate servo or seals. • Polished or glazed band or drum. • Dirty or sticking valve body. **No Engine Braking in Manual First Gear** • Band or clutch out of adjustment. • Incorrect hydraulic pressures. • Damaged or worn reverse servo. • Polished or glazed band or drum. **No Engine Braking in Manual Second Gear (No Manual Second Gear on A.O.T.)** • Intermediate band out of adjustment. • Improper clutch or band application. • Incorrect hydraulic pressures. • Intermediate servo leaking. • Polished or glazed band or drum.	**Transmission Overheats** • Incorrect engine idle speed or performance. • Improper clutch or band application. • Incorrect hydraulic pressures. • Restriction in cooler or lines. • Seized converter one-way clutch. • Dirty or sticking valve body. **Transmission Fluid Leaks** • Leakage at gaskets and seals. • Vacuum diaphragm unit leaking. **TRANSMISSION NOISY** **Valve Resonance** • Improper clutch or band application. • Incorrect hydraulic pressures. • Cooler line grounding. • Dirty or sticking valve body. • Internal leakage. • Oil pump cavitation. **Other Than Valve Resonance** • Faulty torque converter. • Faulty oil pump. • Faulty speedometer driven gear. • Worn or damaged extension housing bushing or seal. • Faulty propeller shaft. • Faulty planetary gear set. • Faulty one-way clutch. • Loose converter-to-flywheel mounting bolts.

GENERAL MOTORS CONVERTER CLUTCH TROUBLE SHOOTING

Every diagnosis of automatic transmission or torque converter clutch problems should begin with a check of the transmission fluid and linkage. Road test vehicle to verify complaint. Most of the following conditions can be caused by one or more of the following factors: (1) Incorrect fluid level, (2) Contaminated fluid, (3) Improperly adjusted linkage, or (4) Worn or damaged linkage.

CONDITION & POSSIBLE CAUSE	CONDITION & POSSIBLE CAUSE
NOTE — *Engine and vacuum systems must be in perfect operating order when diagnosing Converter Clutch problems.*	**Converter Clutch Applied at All Times in 3rd Gear** • Governor pressure switch shorted to ground. • Ground wire from solenoid shorted to case.

Automatic Transmissions

GENERAL MOTORS CONVERTER CLUTCH TROUBLE SHOOTING (Cont.)

CONDITION & POSSIBLE CAUSE	CONDITION & POSSIBLE CAUSE
Converter Clutch Does Not Apply Or Applies Erratically Or at Wrong Speed During Road Test • Disconnect electrical connector at transmission case. Test female connector for 12 volts (2000 RPM in Neutral). If 12 volts shown, problem is internal; if less than 12 volts, problem is external. • Blown fuse. • Brake switch defective. • Low vacuum switch defective. • Intermittent or continuous open in harness. • Open in internal transmission circuitry. • Throttle position switch defective or out of adjustment **Converter Clutch Applied in All Ranges. Engine Stalls When Transmission Is Put in Gear** • Converter clutch valve stuck in "Apply" position.	**Converter Clutch Applies Erratically With a Shudder, Jerking, Jumping Or Rocking Sensation** • Vacuum hose leak. • Vacuum switch malfunction. • Release oil exhaust orifice at pump blocked or restricted. • Turbine shaft "O" ring damaged. • Converter malfunction. • Clutch pressure plate warped. • "O" ring damaged at solenoid. • Solenoid bolts loose. • Governor pressure switch malfunction. **Converter Clutch Applies At a Very Low or High 3rd Speed Gear** • Governor switch malfunction. • Governor switch shorted to ground. • High hydraulic line pressure. • Converter clutch valve sticking or binding. • Solenoid inoperative or shorted to case.

GENERAL MOTORS THM 125C TROUBLE SHOOTING

Every diagnosis of automatic transmission problems should begin with a check of the transmission fluid and linkage. Most of the following conditions can be caused by one or more of the following factors: (1) Incorrect fluid level, (2) Contaminated fluid, (3) Improperly adjusted linkage, or (4) Damaged or worn linkage.

CONDITION & POSSIBLE CAUSE	CONDITION & POSSIBLE CAUSE
No Drive in Drive Range • Low hydraulic pressure. • Clogged suction screen. • Screen "O" ring seal cut or missing. • Pressure regulator valve stuck. • Pump rotor splines damaged by shaft. • Porosity in intake bore. • Case cover manual valve disconnected. • Case cover gaskets mispositioned. • Forward clutch does not apply due to damage. • Forward clutch oil seal rings missing or damaged. • Forward clutch housing check ball stuck or missing. • Wrong number of clutch plates. • Clutch feed orifice plugged in input shaft. • Roller clutch springs missing. • Roller clutch rollers galled or missing. • Drive oil passage in driven sprocket support blocked. • Control valve body pipe leaking or missing. • Sleeve turned in driven sprocket support.	**High or Low Oil Pressures** • Throttle valve cable improperly adjusted or broken. • Throttle lever assembly damaged or mispositioned. • Throttle valve or plunger binding. • Shift T.V. valve binding. • Line boost valve binding. • Line boost valve bore plug installed incorrectly. • Throttle valve boost valve binding or orifices plugged. • Reverse boost valve binding or orifices plugged. • Pressure regulator valve and spring binding. • Pressure relief valve ball missing or spring damaged. • Manual valve unhooked. • Pump slide stuck or seal damaged or missing. • Missing, damaged, wrong or improperly installed gaskets or seals. • Control valve and pump assembly bolts loose. • Internal pump or case cover leaks.

GENERAL MOTORS THM 125C TROUBLE SHOOTING (Cont.)

CONDITION & POSSIBLE CAUSE	CONDITION & POSSIBLE CAUSE

No Drive Forward or Reverse — Any Range

- Manual linkage not moving manual valve.
- Input shaft to forward clutch drum broken loose.
- Reaction carrier broken.
- Worn pump seals.
- Pressure regulator valve sticking.
- Converter-to-flex plate bolts missing.
- Chain assembly broken.
- Oil pump shaft broken.

No Upshifts, Delayed Upshifts or Full Throttle Upshifts

- Governor cover worn, thrust washer missing, seal worn or cut, spring not seated, weights binding, ball missing or driven gear stripped.
- Intermediate servo has wrong apply pin, seals cut or damaged, leaking, piston damaged or porous case.
- Improper valve body-to-case spacer height, governor feed orifices blocked.
- Intermediate band burned or worn.
- Porous case, undrilled holes or missing plugs.
- Case or case cover 2nd oil passage leaking.
- Control valve assembly gaskets or spacer plate leaking, damaged or incorrectly installed.

First Speed Only (No 1-2 Upshift)

- Governor damaged or feed passages restricted.
- 1-2 shift valve or 1-2 throttle valve stuck in downshift position.
- Porosity in case channels or 2nd speed feed holes.
- Excessive leakage between case bore and intermediate band apply pin.
- Broken or missing band.
- Intermediate servo oil seal ring missing or damaged.
- Porosity in intermediate servo cover or piston.
- Wrong intermediate apply pin.

First and Second Speed Only (No 2-3 Shift)

- Direct clutch feed orifice in spacer plate plugged.
- Defective pump and control valve assembly.
- 2-3 shift valve or 2-3 throttle valve stuck in downshift position.
- Defective case or case cover (porosity, 3rd oil cup plug missing, direct clutch accumulator check valve missing or servo bleed orifice cup missing).
- Driven sprocket support oil seals damaged; feed passages blocked.
- Defective direct clutch (damaged or missing parts).
- Intermediate servo oil seal ring damaged or missing.
- Governor assembly shaft seal damaged or missing.
- Governor cover worn, thrust washer missing, weights binding, ball missing, driven gear stripped or loose.
- Number 6 check ball missing or mislocated, case-to-governor shaft sleeve damaged or missing, oil seal rings on driven sprocket support missing or damaged.
- Case center gasket leaking, cover bolts loose.

1-2 Shift at Full Throttle Only

- Throttle valve cable binding, unhooked or broken.
- Throttle lever assembly binding or mispositioned.
- Throttle valve and plunger binding.
- Pump and control valve gasket or spacer plate leaking.

No Drive or Slips in Reverse

- Throttle valve cable binding or improperly adjusted.
- Throttle valve or shift throttle valve binding.
- Reverse boost valve binding or bushing orifices blocked.
- Low and reverse clutch piston or plates damaged or missing.
- Defective case or case cover.
- Direct clutch defective (damaged, missing or plugged parts)
- Line pressure low.
- Forward clutch will not release; plates severely burned.
- Seal ring off piston.
- Exhaust check ball sticking.
- "O" ring or washer on lo and reverse pipe damaged or missing.

Third Speed Only

- 2-3 shift valve stuck in upshift position.
- Governor oil pipe or feed passages plugged.

Drive in Neutral

- Manual linkage misadjusted.
- Forward clutch does not release.
- Case cross leakage to forward clutch passages.

Slips on 1-2 Shift

- Second speed feed orifice partially blocked.
- Spacer plate gaskets damaged or mispositioned.
- Accumulator valve defective.
- Accumulator piston damaged or leaking.
- Incorrect intermediate band apply pin or leakage.
- Damaged intermediate servo assembly.
- Throttle valve cable improperly adjusted.
- Throttle or shift T.V. valves binding.
- Intermediate band worn or burned.
- Porosity in case passages.

Rough 1-2 Shift

- Throttle valve cable improperly adjusted.
- Throttle or shift T.V. valves binding.
- 1-2 accumulator valve binding.
- Defective 1-2 accumulator.
- Damaged intermediate servo assembly.
- Servo seals cut, damaged or missing; piston damaged, porous case.
- Wrong servo apply pin.
- Incorrect or improperly installed spacer plate and/or gaskets.

Automatic Transmissions
GENERAL MOTORS THM 125C TROUBLE SHOOTING

CONDITION & POSSIBLE CAUSE	CONDITION & POSSIBLE CAUSE
Slips on 2-3 Shift • Throttle valve cable improperly adjusted. • Throttle valve binding. • Direct clutch orifice partially blocked in spacer plate. • Spacer plate gaskets damaged or improperly positioned. • Intermediate servo assembly defective. • Direct clutch defective. • Accumulator exhaust check valve not seating in case. • Check ball number 5 not seating. **Rough 2-3 Shift** • Throttle valve cable improperly adjusted. • Throttle valve and shift T.V. valve binding. • Direct clutch accumulator exhaust hole blocked. • Direct clutch exhaust valve check valve number 1 missing, mislocated or leaking. **No Engine Braking (Intermediate Range Second Gear)** • Intermediate servo assembly damaged. • Intermediate band broken or burned. **Misses First at Times Second Speed Start** • Governor springs distorted or out of place. • Governor weights binding. • 1-2 shift valve or 1-2 throttle valve stuck in up-shifted position. **Shifts 3-1 at High Speeds For Passing Gear** • Intermediate servo sticking. • Direct clutch orifice no. 2 check ball restricted. • 1-2 accumulator piston missing or seal leaking. **Slips or Chatters in First** • Hydraulic pressure incorrect. • Restricted feed to forward clutch. • Burned forward clutch. • Rough surface on driven sprocket support. • Incorrect case cover gaskets.	**Shifts 1-3, Misses 2nd** • Intermediate servo sticking, leaking or damaged. • Accumulator exhaust check valve sticking. • 1-2 valve sticking in control valve pump. • Governor feed to 1-2 valve blocked. • Intermediate band apply feed orifice blocked. • Wrong spacer plate. • Intermediate servo apply passage blocked. • Intermediate band improperly installed. • Intermediate band burned or broken. **No Full Throttle Downshift 3-2** • Throttle valve cable misadjusted or binding. • Accelerator linkage not opening carburetor. • Control valve pump assembly binding. • Spacer plate holes plugged. • Gaskets improperly installed. **No Engine Braking (Low Range Second Gear)** • Low-reverse clutch assembly defective. • Lo-reverse pipe or piston seals leaking. • Lo relief valve assembly damaged. **Transmission Noisy** • Pump noisy due to plugged strainer or damaged parts. • Drive link assembly rubbing on case. • Pump or driven sprocket needle bearing installed wrong. • Converter damaged, loose bolts or cracked flex plate. • Transmission cooler lines grounded. • Motor mounts loose. • Drive link assembly worn or damaged. • Speedometer driven seal worn. • Speedometer adapter too long. • Final drive or differential gear set damaged. • Input gear set damaged. • Reaction gear set damaged. • Planetary gear set roller thrust bearings damaged.

GENERAL MOTORS THM 180C TROUBLE SHOOTING

Every diagnosis of automatic transmission problems should begin with a check of the transmission fluid and linkage. Most of the following conditions can be caused by one or more of the following factors: (1) Incorrect fluid level, (2) Contaminated fluid, (3) Improperly adjusted linkage, or (4) Damaged or worn linkage.

CONDITION & POSSIBLE CAUSE	CONDITION & POSSIBLE CAUSE
No Drive After Shifting from "P" to "D", "L2" or "L1" (Inadequate Acceleration) • Parking pawl does not disengage.	**Drives Only in 1st Gear of "D" and "L2" Range (Transmission Blocks in 2nd Gear and Reverse)** • "L1" and "R" control valve stuck in "L1" or "R".

GENERAL MOTORS THM 180C TROUBLE SHOOTING (Cont.)

CONDITION & POSSIBLE CAUSE	CONDITION & POSSIBLE CAUSE

No Drive in Any Drive Range

- Clogged suction screen.
- Manual valve disconnected.
- Broken input shaft.
- Pressure regulator valve stuck open.
- Faulty oil pump.

No Drive in Any Range for a Time
(Only After Repeated Selector Lever Shifting)

- Manual valve position does not coincide with valve body channels.
- Selector lever shaft retaining pin dropped out.
- Connecting rod to manual valve shifting.
- Selector lever shaft nut loose.

Drive Only After
Increase in Engine RPM

- Band servo piston jamming.
- Faulty oil pump.
- Oil screen missing.
- Sealing ball in valve body dropped out.

Heavy Jerking When Starting

- Low hydraulic pressure.
- Wrong modulator valve installed.
- Pressure regulator valve stuck.
- Sealing ball in valve body dropped out.

No Drive in "D" or "L2"
("L1" and "R" are OK)

- Input sprag installed backwards.
- Input sprag failure.

No Drive in "D", "L1" & "L2"
(Reverse OK)

- Worn band.
- Band servo piston jamming.
- Excessive leakage in band servo.
- Parking pawl not disengaging.

No Drive in Reverse
(Other Ranges OK)

- Reverse clutch failure.

Drives in Neutral

- Planetary gear set broken.
- Band out of adjustment.

No 1-2 Upshift in "D" or "L2"
(Transmission Remains in 1st Gear)

- Governor valve stuck.
- 1-2 shift valve stuck.
- Oil pump hub seal rings leaking.
- Leak in governor pressure circuit.
- Governor screen clogged.

No 2-3 Upshift in "D"
(Transmission Remains in 2nd Gear)

- 2-3 shift valve stuck.
- Leak in governor pressure circuit.

Upshifts in "D" and "L2" at Part Throttle Only
(No Detent Upshift)

- Detent pressure regulator valve stuck.
- Detent cable broken or out of adjustment.

No Forced Downshift

- Detent cable broken or out of adjustment.
- Detent pressure regulator valve stuck.

Upshifts in "D" and "L2" at Full Throttle Only

- Defective vacuum modulator.
- Leak in modulator vacuum line.
- Engine vacuum leak.
- Detent valve or cable stuck.

After Full Throttle Upshift, Transmission Shifts to Lower Gear When Foot Eases Off Accelerator Pedal

- Detent valve stuck open.
- Detent cable stuck.
- Modulator vacuum interrupted.

At Higher Speed, Transmission Shifts to Lower Gear

- Selector lever shaft retaining pin in transmission dropped out.
- Loose selector lever linkage to manual valve connection.
- Pressure loss at governor.

Slipping 1-2 Shift (Engine Flares)

- Low hydraulic pressures.
- Sealing ball in valve body dropped out.
- Second clutch piston seals leaking.
- Second clutch piston check ball stuck open.
- Second clutch piston cracked or broken.
- Worn second clutch plates.
- Oil pump hub seal rings leaking.

Automatic Transmissions

GENERAL MOTORS THM 180C TROUBLE SHOOTING (Cont.)

Every diagnosis of automatic transmission problems should begin with a check of the transmission fluid and linkage. Most of the following conditions can be caused by one or more of the following factors: (1) Incorrect fluid level, (2) Contaminated fluid, (3) Improperly adjusted linkage, or (4) Damaged or worn linkage.

CONDITION & POSSIBLE CAUSE	CONDITION & POSSIBLE CAUSE
No Drive in Drive Range • Plugged oil screen. • Oil pump malfunction. • Forward clutch malfunction. • Roller clutch malfunction. **1-2 Shift at Full Throttle Only** • Throttle valve cable disconnected or broken. • Throttle valve exhaust ball lifter or No. 5 ball binding or out of position. • Throttle valve or plunger binding. • Valve body gasket damaged. • Case porosity. **First Speed Only (No 1-2 Shift)** • Governor malfunction. • Governor oil feed orifice plugged. • 1-2 shift valve or 1-2 throttle valve stuck. • Porosity in case channels. • Undrilled second speed feed holes. • Intermediate servo, band or linkage malfunction. • Wrong intermediate band apply pin installed. **First & Second Speeds Only (No 2-3 Shift)** • 2-3 shift valve or 2-3 throttle valve stuck. • Valve body gasket leaking. • Case porosity. • Oil pump malfunction. • Direct clutch malfunction. • Intermediate servo malfunction. **Drives in Neutral** • Forward clutch not releasing. • Cross leakage in oil pump passages. • Cross leakage in forward clutch passages. **No Drive or Slips in Reverse** • Throttle valve cable binding or out of adjustment. • Valve body malfunction. • Throttle, shift T.V., and reverse boost valves binding. • Reverse clutch malfunction. • Direct clutch malfunction. • Intermediate servo seal rings damaged. • Pump cover seal rings damaged.	**Slipping 1-2 Shift** • Spacer plate or gasket damaged. • 1-2 accumulator valve malfunction. • Intermediate band apply pin worn. • Wrong intermediate band apply pin installed. • Intermediate servo worn or damaged. • Throttle valve cable out of adjustment. • Throttle valve binding • Shift T.V. valve binding. • Intermediate band worn or burned. • Case porosity in 2nd clutch passage. **Rough 1-2 Shift** • Throttle valve cable out of adjustment or binding. • Throttle valve or plunger binding. • Shift T.V. valve binding. • 1-2 accumulator valve binding. • Worn or damaged intermediate servo. • 1-2 accumulator malfunction. **Slipping 2-3 Shift** • Throttle valve cable out of adjustment. • Throttle valve binding. • Spacer plate or gaskets damaged. • Intermediate servo malfunction. • Direct clutch malfunction. **Rough 2-3 Shift** • Throttle valve cable damaged. • Throttle valve or plunger binding. • Shift T.V. valve binding. • Intermediate servo malfunction. • Direct clutch malfunction. **No Engine Braking in "L2"** • Intermediate boost valve binding. • Intermediate-Reverse check ball missing. • Shift T.V. check ball missing. • Intermediate servo-to-cover seal rings damaged. • Intermediate band broken or burned. **Will Not Hold in Park** • Manual linkage out of adjustment. • Internal linkage damaged. • Detent lever and pin assy. worn or damaged. • Detent roller and spring assy. worn or damaged.

GENERAL MOTORS THM 200C TROUBLE SHOOTING

CONDITION & POSSIBLE CAUSE	CONDITION & POSSIBLE CAUSE

Slipping 2-3 Shift (Engine Flares)

- Low hydraulic pressures.
- Band out of adjustment.
- Third clutch piston seals leaking.
- Third clutch piston check ball stuck open.
- Third clutch piston defective.
- Input shaft bushing worn.
- Sealing ball in valve body dropped out.

Abrupt 1-2 Shift

- High hydraulic pressures.
- 1-2 accumulator valve stuck.
- Broken second clutch cushion spring.
- Second gear ball valve missing.

Abrupt 2-3 Shift

- High hydraulic pressures.
- Band out of adjustment.

Abrupt 3-2 Detent Downshift at High Speed

- High speed downshift valve stuck open.
- Band out of adjustment.

Abrupt 3-2 Coast Downshift

- Low speed coast downshift timing valve stuck open.

At Low Vehicle Speeds, No Part Throttle 3-2 Downshift

- 3-2 downshift control valve stuck.

Flare on High Speed Forced Downshift

- Low oil pressure.
- Band adjustment loose.

Flare on Low Speed Forced Downshift

- Low oil pressure.
- Band adjustment loose.
- High speed downshift timing valve stuck closed.
- Sprag race does not grip on 3-1 downshifting.

No Engine Braking in "L1"

- Selector lever linkage improperly adjusted.
- Manual low control valve stuck.

No Engine Braking in "L2"

- Selector lever linkage out of adjustment.

Difficult Disengagement of Selector Lever from "P" Position

- Parking pawl actuating rod guide bushing missing.
- Manual selector lever stuck.

No Park

- Selector lever linkage out of adjustment.
- Worn parking lock actuator spring.
- Defective parking pawl.
- Defective governor hub.

Excessive Iron Dust in Oil Pan

- Oil pump worn.
- Governor hub worn.
- Second clutch hub worn.

Excessive Aluminum Dust in Oil Pan

- Thrust face in case worn.
- Rear bore of case worn.
- Stator thrust washer worn (check converter end clearance).

TRANSMISSION NOISE

In All Drive Ranges

- Excessive backlash between sun gear and planetary gears.
- Planetary carrier lock plate loose.
- Worn thrust bearings.
- Worn bearing bushings.
- Excessive transmission end play.
- Parking pawl spring touching governor hub.
- Converter balancing weights loose.
- Converter housing bolts loose and touching converter.

Short Vibrating, Hissing Noise Shortly Before 1-2 Upshift

- Reverse clutch dampening cushion wearing into case.

Screeching Noise When Starting

- Defective torque converter.

Automatic Transmissions

GENERAL MOTORS THM 200C TROUBLE SHOOTING (Cont.)

CONDITION & POSSIBLE CAUSE	CONDITION & POSSIBLE CAUSE
Incorrect Shift Points • Throttle valve cable out of adjustment. • Throttle valve or plunger binding. • Shift T.V. valve binding. • T.V. shift ball missing or out of position. • 1-2 or 2-3 throttle valves binding. • Valve body gasket damaged. • Pressure regulator valve binding. • T.V. exhaust check ball and lifter mispositioned, unhooked, or missing. • Throttle lever and bracket damaged. • Governor shaft or cover seal rings damaged. • Case porosity.	**No Part Throttle Downshift** • Throttle plunger bushing passages not open. • 2-3 throttle valve bushing passages not open. • Valve body gasket damaged. • Spacer plate hole plugged or undrilled. • Throttle valve cable out of adjustment. • Shift T.V. valve binding. • Throttle valve binding. **No Engine Braking in "L1" Range First Gear** • Low overrun clutch valve binding. • Low-Reverse clutch malfunction.

GENERAL MOTORS THM 200-4R TROUBLE SHOOTING

Every diagnosis of automatic transmission problems should begin with a check of the transmission fluid and linkage. Most of the following conditions can be caused by one or more of the following factors: (1) Incorrect fluid level, (2) Contaminated fluid, (3) Improperly adjusted linkage, or (4) Damaged or worn linkage.

CONDITION & POSSIBLE CAUSE	CONDITION & POSSIBLE CAUSE
No Drive in Drive Range • Low oil pressure due to plugged or restricted filter, defective seals or gasket, defective pump, porosity in oil intake bore. • Springs missing or rollers galled or missing in roller clutch. • Forward clutch does not apply due to cracked piston, missing or damaged seals, leak in feed circuits, pump gasket mispositioned or damaged. • Clutch housing ball check stuck or missing, cup plug leaking or missing in clutch apply passage. • Lo and reverse roller clutch springs and rollers damaged or missing. **High or Low Oil Pressure** • Misadjusted, binding, disconnected, broken or wrong TV cable link. • Damaged or leaking TV assembly. • Pressure regulator or reverse boost valve binding. • Manual valve mispositioned or unhooked. • Pressure relief ball and/or spring missing or damaged. • Pump slide stuck or orifice plugged. • TV or line bias valve binding. • Incorrect orifices in control valve spacer plate or case.	**1-2 Shift at Full Throttle Only** • Throttle lever and bracket binding or unhooked. • No. 5 ball stuck, lifter mispositioned, binding or unhooked. • Throttle valve and plunger binding. • Control valve body or gaskets leaking, damaged or incorrectly installed. • Porous case. **First Speed Only — No 1-2 Shift** • Governor driven gear stripped, weights binding, shaft seal defective, inner cover "O" ring seal missing or leaking. • Governor ball or balls missing from assembly. • Oil feed orifice in spacer plate plugged. • Control valve stuck in downshift position, spacer plate or gaskets improperly installed. • Porous case. • Broken or missing band, anchor pin missing or unhooked. • Intermediate servo assembly malfunction. • 1-2 accumulator housing bolts loose, face damaged, plate missing or damaged.

GENERAL MOTORS THM 200-4R TROUBLE SHOOTING

CONDITION & POSSIBLE CAUSE	CONDITION & POSSIBLE CAUSE

First and Second Speeds Only — No 2-3 Shift

- Control or shift valve stuck in downshift position.
- Valve body gaskets leaking, damaged or improperly installed.
- Reverse/3rd check ball not seating, damaged or missing.
- Porous case.
- Direct clutch feed passage in center support plugged or steel seal rings damaged.
- Direct clutch components damaged or mislocated.
- Intermediate servo oil passages blocked or components broken or missing.

No Drive or Slips in Reverse

- Binding throttle valve, limit valve, line bias valve or reverse boost valve.
- Reverse/3rd or Lo/Reverse check ball missing or seat in spacer plate damaged.
- Reverse clutch components damaged or missing.
- Center support porous, passages blocked or attaching bolts loose or missing.
- Direct clutch housing or components missing or damaged, clutch plates burned.
- Orifice in Lo/Reverse clutch spacer plate plugged.

Drives in Neutral

- Forward clutch not releasing, exhaust check ball sticking or plates burned together.
- Cross leakage to clutch passage.

Slipping 1-2 Shift

- Spacer plate and gaskets damaged or improperly installed.
- Accumulator valve sticking, weak or missing spring.
- 1-2 accumulator piston leaking or binding in bore.
- Wrong or defective intermediate band apply pin, pin feed hole blocked.
- Intermediate servo assembly defective or leaking.
- Throttle, limit or line bias valves sticking.
- Intermediate band worn or burned.
- Case porosity in 2nd clutch passage.

Rough 1-2 Shift

- Throttle, limit, or line bias valves binding.
- Wrong intermediate servo apply pin, bleed cup plug missing or servo piston seal damaged.
- 1-2 accumulator piston stuck, oil ring damaged, broken or missing spring, bore damaged.
- 1-2 shift ball No. 8 missing or sticking.

Rough 2-3 Shift

- Exhaust hole plugged between intermediate servo piston seals.
- 3-2 exhaust check ball No. 4 or 3rd accumulator check ball No. 2 missing or mispositioned.

Slipping 2-3 Shift

- Spacer plate and/or gasket damaged or mispositioned.
- Direct clutch orifice in spacer plate blocked.
- Intermediate servo piston or bore damaged, oil seal ring damaged or missing, bleed cup plug missing.
- Case porous in servo bore area.
- Direct clutch components damaged, support bolts loose, porosity in feed channels of case.
- Center support chanels cross feeding, leaking or restricted, oil seal rings damaged.

Slipping 3-4 Shift

- Control valve assembly and spacer plate or gaskets damaged or improperly installed.
- Accumulator valve spring weak or missing, valve sticking.
- 3-4 accumulator oil ring or bore damaged, piston stuck.
- Center support porous or attaching bolts loose.
- 4th clutch piston or seals damaged, plates burned.
- Porosity of case, 1-2 accumulator housing bolts loose.

Rough 3-4 Shift

- TV plunger or valve binding.
- 3-4 accumulator piston stuck or 4th clutch piston binding.

No Part Throttle Downshifts

- Throttle valve or limit valve binding, body gaskets mispositioned or damaged.
- Spacer plate hole or bushing passages plugged.
- Check valve No. 3 missing or out of position.

Low or High Shift Points

- TV cable or limit valve binding.
- Modulator upshift or downshift valve binding.
- Valve body gaskets mispositioned, leaking or damaged.
- 1-2, 2-3 or 3-4 throttle valves, plunger or pressure regulator valve binding.
- TV exhaust ball (No. 5) and lifter mispositioned, unhooked or missing.
- Throttle lever and bracket assembly out of position, binding, unhooked or loose at mounting bolt.
- Governor cover gasket or shaft-to-seal ring broken or missing.
- Porous case.

Automatic Transmissions

GENERAL MOTORS THM 200-4R TROUBLE SHOOTING (Cont.)

CONDITION & POSSIBLE CAUSE	CONDITION & POSSIBLE CAUSE
First, Second and Third Speed Only — No 3-4 Shift • 3-4 Shift valve or throttle valve stuck, orifice in spacer plate plugged. • Center support oil passages blocked, support bolts loose or missing. • 4th clutch assembly damaged, improper or burned clutch plates, overrun clutch plates binding. • 3-4 accumulator bore damaged, cup plug missing, or case porous. **No Engine Braking in Manual Lo-1st Gear** • D-3 orifice in control valve spacer plate plugged. • D-2 oil pipe leaking or out of position. • Lo-overrun clutch valve binding. • Check balls No. 3, 9 or 10 missing or out of position. • Valve body and/or gaskets damaged or out of position. • Overrun clutch orifice plugged in spacer plate. • D-3 oil passages blocked. • Overrun clutches burned or snap ring out of groove. • Missing or damaged overrun clutch piston seals. • Case porosity. • Cup plug or rubber seal missing or damaged between lo/reverse clutch housing and case. • Clutch housing snap ring out of case.	**No Engine Braking in Manual 2nd-2nd Gear or Manual 3rd-3rd Gear** • Valve body, spacer plate and/or gaskets damaged, leaking or improperly installed. • D-2 oil pipe leaking or out of position. • D-3 orifice in spacer plate plugged. • Check ball No. 3 mispositioned or missing. • Case porous. • Intermediate servo cover-to-case oil seal ring missing or damaged. • Intermediate band off anchor pin, broken or burned. • D-3 oil passages blocked in turbine shaft or overrun clutch hub. • Overrun clutches burned or backing plate snap ring out of groove. **Will Not Hold in Park** • External or internal linkage out of adjustment. • Pawl binding in case or broken. • Parking bracket loose or damaged, actuator rod, spring or plunger damaged. • Manual shaft-to-case pin missing or damaged. • Inside detent lever and pin nut loose or lever hole worn. • Manual detent lever and spring assembly mounting bolt loose or pin/roller damaged or mispositioned.

GENERAL MOTORS THM 250C TROUBLE SHOOTING

Every diagnosis of automatic transmission problems should begin with a check of the transmission fluid and linkage. Most of the following conditions can be caused by one or more of the following factors: (1) Incorrect fluid level, (2) Contaminated fluid, (3) Improperly adjusted linkage, or (4) Damaged or worn linkage.

CONDITION & POSSIBLE CAUSE	CONDITION & POSSIBLE CAUSE
No Drive in Drive Range • Low hydraulic pressure. • Forward clutch malfunction. • Broken spring or damaged cage on Low/Reverse roller clutch assembly. **Low Line Pressure** • Vacuum modulator malfunction. • Strainer assembly restricted or damaged gasket. • Oil pump faulty. • Valve body malfunction. • Internal leakage at forward or direct clutch. • Check ball missing from case passages.	**High Line Pressure** • Vacuum leak or improper engine vacuum. • Modulator valve stuck or water in modulator. • Detent valve or cable stuck in detent position. • Valve body malfunction. **1-2 Shift at Full Throttle Only** • Detent valve sticking or misadjusted. • Vacuum line or fitting leaking. • Control valve malfunction. • Porosity of case assembly.

GENERAL MOTORS THM 250C TROUBLE SHOOTING (Cont.)

CONDITION & POSSIBLE CAUSE	CONDITION & POSSIBLE CAUSE
No 1-2 Shift (First Speed Only) • Detent downshift cable binding. • Governor assembly defective. • Control valve malfunction. • Intermediate band improperly adjusted. • Intermediate band servo damaged. • Porosity between case channels. • Governor feed channel in case blocked. **No 2-3 Shift (First and Second Speed Only)** • Control valve malfunction or gasket leak. • Direct clutch pump hub, piston seals or plates damaged. **Drive in Neutral** • Manual or internal linkage misadjusted or disconnected. • Oil Pump leakage into forward clutch apply passage. • Incorrect forward clutch plate or burned clutches. **Slips in Reverse (No Motion)** • Low hydraulic pressure. • Control valve malfunction. • Intermediate servo piston or pin stuck applying band. • Low and reverse clutch piston outer seal damaged. • Direct clutch outer seal damaged or plates burned. • Forward clutch not releasing. **Slips in All Ranges or Slips on Start** • Low hydraulic pressure. • Forward clutch plates burned. • Forward clutch pump cover oil seal rings broken or worn. • Case cross leaks or porosity. **Slipping 1-2 Shift** • Low hydraulic pressure. • 1-2 accumulator oil ring or case bore damaged. • Pump-to-case gasket damaged or mispositioned. • Intermediate band burned or piston seals damaged. • Case porosity between channels. • Improper intermediate band adjustment. **Rough 1-2 Shift** • High hydraulic pressure. • 1-2 accumulator malfunction. • Incorrect number and location of case check balls. • Porosity between case channels. • Improperly adjusted intermediate band or broken servo spring.	**Slipping 2-3 Shift** • Low hydraulic pressure. • Direct clutch plates burned or piston seals leaking. • Improper number of direct clutch plates or improper type. • Case porosity. **Rough 2-3 Shift** • High hydraulic pressures. • 2-3 accumulator malfunction. **No First Speed (Starts in Second Speed)** • Intermediate band adjustment too tight. • 1-2 Shift valve stuck in upshifted position. **No Engine Braking in "L1"** • Low hydraulic pressure. • Intermediate servo oil rings leaking or piston stuck. • Intermediate band broken, burned, not engaged on servo pin or misadjusted. **No Engine Braking in "L2"** • Low hydraulic pressure. • Manual low control valve stuck. • Low and reverse clutch piston inner seal damaged. **No Part Throttle Downshift** • Vacuum modulator, modulator or pressure regulator valves malfunctioning. • Detent valve or linkage stuck or broken. • 2-3 shift valve stuck. **No Detent (Wide Open Throttle) Downshift** • Detent cable or retainer improperly adjusted. • Valve body malfunction. **High or Low Shift Points** • Vacuum lines or vacuum modulator leaking. • Governor valve sticking or feed holes restricted. • Detent valve stuck open. • Control valve malfunction. • Case porosity. **Won't Hold in Park Position** • Manual or internal linkage misadjusted. • Parking pawl broken or inoperative. • Parking lock bracket loose or incorrectly installed.

GENERAL MOTORS THM 250C TROUBLE SHOOTING (Cont.)

CONDITION & POSSIBLE CAUSE	CONDITION & POSSIBLE CAUSE
1-2 Shift at Full Throttle Only • Detent valve sticking. • Vacuum leak. • Case porosity. • Control valve assembly malfunction. **Transmission Noisy In "P",** **"N" and All Driving Ranges** • Check transmission after eliminating water pump, generator and power steering as noise source by removing individual belts. • Pump cavitation due to restricted strainer, damaged body or gasket, porosity. • Pump gears damaged or improperly assembled. • Converter or flex plate damaged or mounting bolts loose.	**Transmission Noisy During Acceleration** • Transmission grounded to underbody. • Motor mounts loose or broken. **Transmission Noisy in First,** **Second and Reverse Gear** • Planetary gears or thrust bearings damaged. • Planetary input and output ring gear damaged. **Transmission Squeal at Low Vehicle Speed** • Speedometer driven gear shaft seal needs lubrication. • Speedometer driven gear shaft seal needs replacement.

GENERAL MOTORS THM 325-4L TROUBLE SHOOTING

Every diagnosis of automatic transmission problems should begin with a check of the transmission fluid and linkage. Most of the following conditions can be caused by one or more of the following factors: (1) Incorrect fluid level, (2) Contaminated fluid, (3) Improperly adjusted linkage, or (4) Damaged or worn linkage.

CONDITION & POSSIBLE CAUSE	CONDITION & POSSIBLE CAUSE
No Upshifts • T.V. cable out of adjustment or broken. • Governor cover worn or seals missing or damaged. • Intermediate servo malfunction. • Sticking valves in valve body. • Valve body spacer plate gaskets leaking or incorrectly installed. • Intermediate band anchor pin missing. • Governor feed orifice to 1-2 and 2-3 valves in spacer plate plugged or not drilled. • Intermediate band worn or burned. • Porosity in case channels. • Porosity, undrilled holes, or missing cup plugs in case cover. **Harsh or Delayed 1-2 Shift** • T.V. cable out of adjustment. • Intermediate servo malfunction. • T.V. plunger, shift T.V. valve or 1-2 accumulator valve binding in valve body. • 1-2 accumulator malfunction. • Valve body spacer plate or gaskets out of position, or incorrect gaskets or plate installed.	**Hunts 1-2-1 at Low Speed,** **Feels Like Locking Up or** **Binding Accompanied by a Thumping Noise** • Governor springs distorted, or weights binding. **Soft Shift, Early Shift or** **Slipping 1-2 Shift With End Bump** • Incorrect T.V. cable, cable binding or disconnected. • Intermediate servo malfunction. • T.V. plunger, shift T.V. valve or 1-2 accumulator valve binding in valve body. • 1-2 accumulator malfunction. • Incorrect spacer plate and gaskets, or gaskets installed wrong. • Porosity in case in 2nd or servo apply passage and/or 1-2 accumulator passage. • Intermediate band burned. **No Drive In "D" or "L2"** **("L1" and "R" OK)** • Low roller clutch not holding.

GENERAL MOTORS THM 325-4L TROUBLE SHOOTING (Cont.)

CONDITION & POSSIBLE CAUSE	CONDITION & POSSIBLE CAUSE

Soft Shift, Early Shift or Slipping 2-3 Shift With End Bump

- Intermediate servo malfunction.
- Orifice plug missing from case in servo bore area.
- Incorrect servo assembly.
- Direct clutch feed orifice in spacer plate restricted.
- Incorrect spacer plate or gaskets, or gasket leaking, damaged, or incorrectly installed.
- Porosity in direct clutch case passage.
- Driven sprocket support gasket or oil seal rings leaking, damaged or out of position.
- Driven sprocket support passages interconnected.
- Direct clutch malfunction.

Harsh 2-3 Shift

- T.V. cable out of adjustment.
- Servo exhaust hole plugged or undrilled.
- Incorrect servo assembly.
- Direct clutch exhaust check ball #4 missing, out of position or leaking.

No 2-3 Shift or Delayed 2-3 Shift

- T.V. cable out of adjustment, binding, disconnected, or wrong cable installed.
- Governor malfunction.
- Intermediate servo malfunction.
- Intermediate servo orifice bleed cup plug missing.
- Porosity in case in servo bore area.
- Valves sticking in valve body.
- Spacer plate or gaskets leaking, damaged, or incorrectly installed.
- #6 check ball in case missing or out of position.
- Driven sprocket support oil seal rings missing or damaged.
- #7 check ball missing from case cover.
- Direct clutch malfunction.

Intermittent Loss of Drive When Cornering or After Quick Stop

- Oil screen pulled out from crimp causing leak between screen intake pipe and case.

No Drive In Reverse (All Others Ranges OK)

- Forward clutch not releasing or clutch plates burned.
- Low overrun clutch valve in valve body stuck.
- Case-to-Low reverse clutch housing cup plug missing or leaking.
- Low-reverse clutch malfunction.

No Drive In Any Range

- Internal mechanical damage.
- Converter-to-drive plate bolts missing.
- Burned clutch plates.
- Manual linkage damaged.
- Turbine hub in converter broken loose.
- Input shaft-to-forward clutch drum broken loose.
- Rear carrier broken at low roller clutch cam.

No Drive In "D" (All Other Ranges OK)

- Forward clutch feed orifice in input shaft restricted.
- Inner area of forward clutch piston bottoming out in housing and restricting oil flow to piston.

No Drive in Forward Ranges (Reverse Ties Up)

- Sleeve turned in driven sprocket support.
- T.V. cable out of adjustment.

No Drive In Forward Ranges (Reverse OK)

- Manual linkage damaged.
- Exhaust passages in case blocked with flash.
- Drive oil passage in driven sprocket support or sprocket-to-case gasket restricted.
- Drive oil passage leak in case or case cover.
- Sleeve in driven sprocket support loose or out of position.
- Forward clutch plates burned.

Second Speed Start (Missing First At Times)

- Engine idle speed too high.
- Governor malfunction.
- Valve body 1-2 shift valve or 1-2 throttle valve sticking in upshift position.

Slips — Chatters In First

- T.V. cable out of adjustment, or wrong cable installed.
- Restricted feed to forward clutch.
- Burned forward clutch plates.

Ties Up or Binds in Low Range, Third and Reverse (Has Second Speed Start in "D" and "L2")

- Oil screen bolt installed in wrong hole (will lock up direct clutch housing).

Automatic Transmissions

GENERAL MOTORS THM 325-4L TROUBLE SHOOTING (Cont.)

CONDITION & POSSIBLE CAUSE	CONDITION & POSSIBLE CAUSE

Shifts 1-3 (Missing 2nd)

- Intermediate servo malfunction.
- Valve body gaskets installed incorrectly.
- Valve body 1-2 valve sticking.
- Valve body 1-2 accumulator piston missing; seals leaking.
- Blocked governor feed to 1-2 valve or intermediate band apply feed orifice in spacer plate.
- Intermediate servo apply passage (2nd oil) in case blocked.
- Intermediate band malfunction.

Shifts 3-1 At High Speeds
For Passing Gear (Detent Downshifts)

- Governor malfunction.
- Intermediate servo malfunction.
- Spacer plate orifice controlled by #2 check ball restricted.
- 1-2 accumulator piston missing; seal leaking.
- Shift T.V. valve stuck.

No Full Throttle (Detent) Downshift 3-2

- T.V. cable out of adjustment, binding or wrong cable or link installed.
- Accelerator pedal and/or linkage will not open carburetor to wide open throttle.
- Valve body throttle valve or shift T.V. valve sticking.
- Wrong spacer plate or valve body gaskets installed.

No Overrun Braking In "L2"
(1-2 Upshift OK)

- Intermediate boost valve sticking.
- #1 or #3 check ball missing.

No Overrun Braking In "L1"
(Reverse OK)

- Manual linkage out of adjustment.
- Low overrun clutch valve in valve body sticking or spring missing.

Won't Hold In Park

- Internal or external linkage misadjusted.
- Park pawl binding in case or broken.
- Actuator rod or plunger damaged.
- Inside detent lever worn, damaged or nut loose.
- Manual detent roller and spring assembly bolt loose.
- Manual detent pin or roller damaged, missing or out of position.

TRANSMISSION NOISE

In All Ranges

- Pump cavitation caused by: Plugged or restricted screen; damaged screen "O" ring seal; porosity in case intake area; water in oil; porosity or voids at transmission intake port.
- Oil pump gears damaged, driving gear installed backwards, or crescent interference.
- Converter-to-drive plate bolts loose.
- Converter damaged.
- Drive plate broken or cracked.

In First, Second and/or Reverse

- Planetary gear set worn or damaged.

During Acceleration
(In Any Gear)

- Transmission or oil cooler lines grounded to underbody.
- Motor mount loose or broken.
- Drive link assembly worn or damaged (may sound like popcorn popping).

Squeal at Low Vehicle Speed
(Especially When Hot)

- Speedometer driven gear shaft seal worn or damaged.

GENERAL MOTORS THM 350C TROUBLE SHOOTING

Every diagnosis of automatic transmission problems should begin with a check of the transmission fluid and linkage. Most of the following conditions can be caused by one or more of the following factors: (1) Incorrect fluid level, (2) Contaminated fluid, (3) Improperly adjusted linkage, or (4) Damaged or worn linkage.

GENERAL MOTORS THM 350C TROUBLE SHOOTING (Cont.)

CONDITION & POSSIBLE CAUSE	CONDITION & POSSIBLE CAUSE

No Drive in Drive Range

- Low hydraulic pressures.
- Manual valve disconnected from linkage.
- Forward clutch malfunction.
- Damaged low and reverse roller clutch.
- Damaged shifter shaft.

1-2 Shift at Full Throttle Only

- Detent valve sticking or out of adjustment.
- Vacuum line or fitting leaking.
- Valve body gasket damaged.
- Detent valve train stuck.
- 1-2 shift valve stuck.
- Case porosity.

No 1-2 Shift (Makes 1-3 Shift and 3-1 Shift, But Has All Shifts Manually)

- Intermediate roller clutch not locking.

First Speed Only (No 1-2 Shift)

- Detent downshift cable binding.
- Governor malfunction.
- 1-2 shift valve train stuck closed.
- Valve body governor feed channels blocked.
- Valve body gaskets damaged.
- Case porosity.
- Intermediate clutch malfunction.
- Intermediate piston seals damaged.

First and Second Speed Only (No 2-3 Shift)

- 2-3 shift valve train stuck.
- Valve body gaskets damaged or incorrectly installed.
- Direct clutch pump hub oil seal rings broken.
- Direct clutch piston seals missing.
- Direct clutch piston check ball stuck.

Slips in All Ranges

- Vacuum modulator valve sticking.
- Oil filter plugged or leaking.
- Pressure regulator valve stuck.
- Pump-to-case gasket damaged.
- Case cross leaks or porosity.

Drives in Neutral

- Manual linkage out of adjustment.
- Forward clutch not releasing.

No Drive or Slips in Reverse

- Incorrect hydraulic pressures.
- Valve body gaskets leaking.
- 2-3 valve train stuck in upshift position.
- 1-2 valve train stuck in upshift position.
- Intermediate servo piston or pin stuck.
- Low-Reverse clutch malfunction.
- Direct clutch malfunction.
- Forward clutch not releasing.

Slipping 1-2 Shift

- Vacuum modulator malfunction.
- Modulator valve sticking.
- Oil pump pressure regulator valve faulty.
- 2-3 accumulator oil ring damaged.
- 1-2 accumulator oil ring or bore damaged.
- Pump-to-case gasket mispositioned.
- Case porosity between channels.
- Intermediate clutch piston seals damaged.
- Intermediate clutch plates burned.

Rough 1-2 Shift

- Vacuum modulator fittings loose or line plugged.
- Modulator valve stuck.
- Valve body regulator or boost valve stuck.
- Pump-to-case gasket damaged.
- Case porosity between channels.
- 1-2 accumulator malfunction.

Slipping 2-3 Shift

- Low hydraulic pressures.
- Case porosity.
- Direct clutch malfunction.

Rough 2-3 Shift

- High hydraulic pressures.
- 2-3 accumulator malfunction.
- Vacuum leak.

Automatic Transmissions

GENERAL MOTORS THM 350C TROUBLE SHOOTING (Cont.)

CONDITION & POSSIBLE CAUSE	CONDITION & POSSIBLE CAUSE

No Engine Braking in "L2"

- Intermediate servo malfunction.
- 2-3 accumulator malfunction.
- Intermediate overrun band broken or burned.
- Pressure regulator and/or boost valve stuck.

No Engine Braking in "L1"

- Manual low control valve stuck.
- Pressure regulator and/or boost valve stuck.
- Low-Reverse clutch malfunction.

No Part Throttle Downshift

- Incorrect hydraulic pressures.
- Detent valve or linkage stuck or damaged.
- 2-3 shift valve stuck.

No Detent Downshift

- 2-3 shift valve stuck.
- Detent valve or linkage stuck or damaged.

Incorrect Shift Points

- Faulty vacuum modulator.
- Governor malfunction.
- Detent valve or linkage stuck open.
- 2-3 valve train sticking.
- 1-2 shift valve train sticking.
- Case porosity.
- Vacuum leak.

Will Not Hold in Park

- Manual linkage out of adjustment.
- Worn or damaged internal linkage.
- Parking pawl broken or inoperative.

Locks Up in Manual Low
(Usually Hot Only)

- Direct clutch malfunction.
- Converter pressure leaking into direct clutch thru stator shaft.
- Low and reverse clutch piston center seal damaged.

Locks Up in Reverse
(Usually Hot Only)

- Wrong forward clutch piston or drum installed.
- Direct clutch feeding forward clutch thru stator shaft (check stator shaft index).

Second Gear Start or
Slips in Second Gear Only

- Intermediate clutch — Wrong number or clutch plates installed or wrong piston installed.

Slow Reverse (Hot Only)

- Leaking valve body support plate.
- Bent "S" hook or mislocated "S" hook holes.
- Detent roller spring hole mislocated.

Locks in Reverse from
Park to Reverse Only

- Parking pawl staying in due to a burr on leading edge.

Cold Morning Reverse No
Drive Until Engine Warms Up

- Pressure regulator bore or sleeve too tight.

Shifts Cold But Not Warm

- Governor nylon gear pin too short.

No Drive But Has Manual Low

- Low-Reverse roller clutch installed backwards.

Harsh 1-2 Shift

- 1-2 accumulator piston or spring damaged.
- Accumulator feed hole in valve body plate damaged.

Transmission Noisy in All Ranges

- Pump cavitation or damage.
- Converter-to-drive plate bolts loose.
- Converter damaged.
- Flex-plate damaged.

Transmission Squeal at Low Vehicle Speed

- Speedometer driven gear shaft seal needs lubrication.
- Speedometer driven gear damaged.
- 1-2 shift valve or 1-2 throttle valve stuck.
- Case porosity in channels or undrilled 2nd speed feed holes.
- Intermediate band anchor pin missing or disconnected.
- Broken or missing intermediate band.
- Intermediate servo assembly malfunction.

GENERAL MOTORS THM 350C TROUBLE SHOOTING (Cont.)

CONDITION & POSSIBLE CAUSE	CONDITION & POSSIBLE CAUSE
Transmission Noisy in First, Second and/or Reverse • Planetary gears or thrust bearings damaged. • Input or output ring gear damaged. • Converter damaged.	**Transmission Noisy During Acceleration** • Transmission or cooler lines grounded to underbody. • Engine mounts loose or broken. • Flex-plate or converter damaged. • Converter mounting bolts loose.

GENERAL MOTORS THM 400 TROUBLE SHOOTING

Every diagnosis of automatic transmission problems should begin with a check of the transmission fluid and linkage. Most of the following conditions can be caused by one or more of the following factors: (1) Incorrect fluid level, (2) Contaminated fluid, (3) Improperly adjusted linkage, or (4) Damaged or worn linkage.

CONDITION & POSSIBLE CAUSE	CONDITION & POSSIBLE CAUSE
No Drive in Drive Range • Manual linkage out of adjustment. • Low hydraulic pressures. • Manual valve disconnected from lever. • Forward clutch malfunction. • Pump assembly feed passage blocked. • Lo roller clutch damaged or improperly installed.	**Rough 1-2 Shift** • Engine improperly tuned. • Incorrect hydraulic pressure. • Control valve 1-2 accumulator stuck. • Rear accumulator stuck or leaking. • Rear accumulator feed restricted. • Incorrect number of check balls installed. • Intermediate clutch burned or damaged. • Improper number of clutch plates.
No 1-2 Upshift or Delayed Upshift • Short in detent switch or wiring. • Defective governor control valve or feed system. • Vacuum leaks. • Modulator valve stuck. • Leaking modulator diaphragm. • Solenoid malfunctioning. • Detent system defective. • Blocked orifice in spacer plate.	**Drives in Neutral** • Outside manual linkage out of adjustment. • Inside linkage disconnected or pin broken. • Internal leak in pump assembly. • Damaged or incorrect clutch plate usage.
Soft or Slipping 1-2 Shift • Engine improperly tuned. • Improper engine vacuum due to restrictions, carburetion or leaks. • Modulator assembly defective. • Pump and/or pressure regulator defective. • Internal seals, gaskets or circuits leaking. • Filter blocked or restricted. • Control valve improperly torqued. • Intermediate clutch plates of wrong type. • Improper number and/or type release springs and installed position. • Porous case.	**Rough 2-3 Shift** • Faulty vacuum modulator. • Modulator valve stuck. • Pump pressure regulator or boost valve stuck. • Front servo accumulator spring damaged or missing. • Front servo accumulator piston stuck. • Extra waved steel plate installed in direct clutch. • Control valve assembly drilled passage blocked.

Automatic Transmissions

GENERAL MOTORS THM 400 TROUBLE SHOOTING (Cont.)

CONDITION & POSSIBLE CAUSE	CONDITION & POSSIBLE CAUSE

Slipping 2-3 Shift

- Incorrect hydraulic pressure.
- Direct clutch leaking.
- Leaky passages or stuck valves in control valve assembly.
- Spacer plate damaged in control valve.
- Blocked direct clutch feed orifice.
- Servo pin leakage.
- Broken or missing front servo spring.
- Improper number of direct clutch plates.
- Damaged or missing piston seals.
- Broken or undersize oil rings.
- Case-to-center support leakage.

Will Not Hold or Will Not Release from Park

- Misadjusted linkage.
- Parking pawl broken or chamfer missing.

No Engine Braking in "L1"

- Low-Reverse check ball missing.
- Rear servo oil seal ring, bore or piston damaged.
- Rear band apply pin too short or improperly installed.
- Rear band damaged.

No Reverse or Slips in Reverse

- Manual linkage out of adjustment.
- Incorrect hydraulic pressures.
- Spacer plate gaskets damaged.
- Low-Reverse check ball missing from case.
- 2-3 valve train stuck open.
- Rear servo piston seal damaged.
- Rear band apply pin too short.
- Reverse or low band burned.
- Reverse or low band broken.
- Direct clutch malfunction.
- Forward clutch not releasing.

First & Second Speeds Only (No 2-3 Shift)

- 2-3 shift valve stuck.
- Spacer plate gaskets damaged.
- Direct clutch malfunction.
- Improper vacuum.

No Detent Downshift

- 3-2 valve stuck, spring missing or broken.
- Detent switch faulty.
- Detent solenoid faulty.
- Detent valve train sticking.

Transmission Noisy in Park, Neutral and All Driving Ranges

- Wrong or restricted filter.
- Intake pipe "O" ring damaged.
- Case porosity.
- Pump gears damaged or malfunctioning.
- Pressure regulator orifice cup plug damaged.
- Seal rings damaged or worn.
- Loose converter-to-flywheel bolts.

Transmission Noisy in 1st, 2nd and Reverse

- Planetary gear set or thrust bearings damaged or worn.

Transmission Noisy During Acceleration

- Transmission cooler lines grounded to body.
- Motor mounts loose.

Transmission Squeak at Low Speeds

- Speedometer shaft seal damaged.
- Extension housing oil seal damaged.

No Engine Braking in "L2"

- Front servo or accumulator oil rings or bore damaged.
- Front servo piston stuck.
- Front band damaged.
- Front band not engaged on anchor pin and/or servo pin.

GENERAL MOTORS THM 700-R4 TROUBLE SHOOTING

Every diagnosis of automatic transmission problems should begin with a check of the transmission and linkage. Most of the following conditions can be caused by one or more of the following factors: (1) Incorrect fluid level, (2) Contaminated fluid, (3) Improperly adjusted linkage, or (4) Damaged or worn linkage.

CONDITION & POSSIBLE CAUSE	CONDITION & POSSIBLE CAUSE

Oil Pressure Too High or Low

- Pressure regulator valve binding, damaged or dirty.
- T.V. and reverse boost plugs and bushings dirty, sticking, damaged or incorrectly installed.
- Pressure relief ball not seated.
- Excess pump rotor clearance.
- Manual valve not engaged or damaged.
- T.V. exhaust valve binding or damaged.
- Valve body valve or plunger sticking.
- T.V. limit valve sticking.
- Throttle link not engaged or hung-up.
- Filter restricted or missing "O" ring.

High or Low Shift Points

- T.V. cable binding or not set.
- Valve body valve or plunger binding.
- T.V. modulator up or down valve sticking.
- Gaskets and spacer plates missing or damaged.
- T.V. limit valve sticking.
- Pressure regulator valve sticking.
- Pump slide sticking.

First Speed Only, No Upshift

- Sticking governor valve.
- Governor driven gear damaged or missing pin.
- Nicks or burrs on output shaft.
- Governor assembly has burrs on sleeve or case.
- 1-2 shift valve sticking.
- Valve body spacer plate or gaskets wrong.
- Case porosity.
- Governor screen restricted or damaged.
- 2-4 servo missing piston seals or apply pin damaged.
- 2-4 band assembly burned, anchor pin not engaged or apply end broken.

Slips in First Gear

- Forward clutch plates burned.
- Forward clutch piston porosity, cut seals, damaged housing, internal leaks or check ball damaged.
- Valve body accumulator valve sticking.
- Damaged valve body lands or passages.
- Valve body gaskets spacer plate damaged.
- Binding internal T.V. linkage.
- 1-2 accumulator porous piston or bore, damaged seals, leaking or broken accumulator spring.

1-2 Full Throttle Shifts Only

- T.V. cable not connected.
- Interconnected passages in case, pump or valve body.
- Throttle valve or plunger hanging up or sticking.
- Throttle link has burrs or not connected.

Slipping or Rough 1-2 Shift

- Throttle valve or bushing sticking.
- Sticking 1-2 shift valve train.
- Gaskets or spacer plate mispositioned.
- Line bias valve sticking.
- Accumulator valve sticking.
- T.V. limit valve sticking.
- Incorrect 2-4 servo apply pin.
- Damaged 2-4 servo seals or rings.
- Damaged 2-4 servo bores or porous piston.
- Restricted 2-4 servo oil passages.
- Damaged 2nd accumulator piston seal.
- Missing accumulator spring.
- Burned 2-4 band.

Slipping or Rough 2-3 Shift

- Sticking 2-3 shift valve train.
- Accumulator valve sticking.
- Throttle valve sticking.
- Gaskets or spacer plate mispositioned.
- T.V. limit valve sticking.
- 3-4 clutch burned plates.
- Excessive 3-4 clutch plate travel.
- Cut or damaged 3-4 clutch piston seals.
- 3-4 piston porosity or exhaust ball open.
- Restricted apply passages.
- Check ball no. 7 damaged.

Slipping or Rough 3-4 Shift

- Missing 3-4 accumulator spring.
- Accumulator piston porous.
- Restricted 3-4 accumulator feed passage.
- Broken 3-4 accumulator seal ring.
- Case porosity.
- Incorrect servo band apply pin.
- Damaged or missing servo piston seals.
- Damaged piston servo bores.
- 3-4 clutch burned.
- 2-4 band burned.
- Valve body 2-3 shift valve train sticking.
- Valve body accumulator valve sticking.
- Valve body spacer plates or gaskets missing.
- Throttle valve sticking.
- T.V. limit valve sticking.

CONDITION & POSSIBLE CAUSE	CONDITION & POSSIBLE CAUSE

No Reserve or Slips in Reverse

- Forward clutch will not release.
- Pump reverse boost plug sticking.
- Valve body gaskets or spacer plate wrong.
- Lo/reverse clutch piston seals damaged.
- Blocked or missing lo/reverse apply passage.
- Burned lo/reverse clutch plates.
- Lo/reverse clutch cover plate loose.
- Burned reverse input clutch plates.
- Damaged reverse input clutch piston seals.
- Reverse input clutch apply passages blocked.
- Reverse input clutch housing exhaust ball and capsule damaged.

No Overrun Braking Manual 1, 2 & 3

- Burned overrun clutch plates.
- Damaged overrun clutch piston seals.
- Piston exhaust ball sticking or missing.
- Case porosity.
- Valve body gaskets or spacer plate wrong.
- 4-3 sequence valve sticking.
- Check balls 3, 9 or 10 mispositioned.
- Blocked or missing turbine shaft oil feed passage.
- Damaged turbine shaft teflon oil rings.
- Turbine shaft plug missing.

No Part Throttle Downshifts

- T.V. modulator downshift valve binding.
- Throttle valve binding.
- Throttle valve bushing/feed hole restricted.
- Check ball no. 3 mispositioned.

Drives In Neutral

- Forward clutch burned or not releasing.
- Interconnected passages in case.
- Manual linkage or manual valve improperly set.

Second Speed Start

- Governor assembly.
- T.V. cable.

No Park or Will Not Hold in Park

- Actuator rod assembly bent or damaged.
- Actuator rod spring binding or improper crimp.
- Parking lock pawl return spring damaged or assembled improperly.
- Actuator rod not attached to inside detent lever.
- Parking brake bracket damaged or bolts not tight.
- Inside detent lever not torqued.
- Detent roller improperly installed or damaged.
- Parking lock pawl binding or damaged.
- Parking lock pawl interfering with lo/reverse piston.

MANUAL TRANSMISSIONS

MANUFACTURER & MODEL	TRANSMISSION MODEL
AMERICAN MOTORS Alliance All RWD Models	Renault JB0 & JB1 Transaxles Borg-Warner T4 4-Speed & T5 5-Speed
CHRYSLER CORP. All FWD Models 2WD Pickups, 4WD Pickups, 4WD Ramcharger Ram Van, Voyager Wagon, 1/2 Ton 2WD Pickup	A-412 & A-460 4-Speed & A-465 5-Speed New Process 435 4-Speed New Process A833 4-Speed Overdrive
FORD MOTOR CO. Escort, EXP, LN7, Lynx, Tempo & Topaz E100/350 Van & F100/350 Pickup Bronco II & Ranger Bronco & F150/350 Pickup Bronco & F150/350 Pickup (2WD & 4WD) Bronco, Capri, F100/250 Pickup (2WD), F150 Pickup (4WD) & Mustang Capri, Fairmont, Futura, LTD, Marquis, Mustang & Zephyr E100/350 Van F250/350 Pickup with 6.9L Diesel or 7.5L Gas Engines Bronco II & Ranger Capri & Mustang Capri, Cougar, Mustang & Thunderbird	Ford MTX 4 or 5-Speed Transaxle Ford 3.03 3-Speed Ford 4-Speed New Process 435 4-Speed Warner T18 4-Speed SROD 4-Speed 83 ET 4-Speed Ford RUG 4-Speed Overdrive Warner T19B 4-Speed Ford 5-Speed Overdrive 5-Speed Overdrive Borg-Warner T5 5-Speed
GENERAL MOTORS BUICK — Century, Skyhawk, Skylark CHEVROLET — Cavalier, Celebrity, Citation OLDSMOBILE — Cutlass Ciera, Firenza, Omega PONTIAC — Phoenix, 2000, 6000	GM 4 & 5-Speed Transaxle
CHEVROLET/GMC — C10 Pickup, G10/30 Van	GM 76 MM 3-Speed
CHEVROLET — S10 Pickup & Blazer, S15 Pickup & Jimmy	Isuzu 77.5 MM 4-Speed
CHEVROLET — Chevette Diesel PONTIAC — T1000 Diesel	Isuzu 69.5 MM 5-Speed
CHEVROLET — Chevette Gasoline PONTIAC — T1000 Gasoline	GM 70 MM 4-Speed
CHEVROLET — Camaro PONTIAC — Firebird	GM 76 MM 4-Speed
CHEVROLET/GMC — S10 Pickup & Blazer, S15 Pickup & Jimmy	GM 77 MM 4-Speed
CHEVROLET — Camaro, Chevette, S10 Pickup & Blazer, S15 Pickup & Jimmy PONTIAC — Firebird, T1000	Borg-Warner T5 5-Speed

CHEVROLET/GMC
  C10/30 Pickup & Suburban, G10/30 Van,
  K10/30 4WD Blazer, Pickup & Suburban
	New Process 833 4-Speed Overdrive

CHEVROLET/GMC
  K10 4WD Blazer, Pickup & Suburban,
  K20 4WD Pickup & Suburban, K30 4WD Pickup
	GM 117 MM 4-Speed

JEEP CJ5, CJ7, Scrambler Cherokee, CJ5, CJ7, J10 Pickup, Scrambler J20 Pickup Cherokee, CJ5, CJ7, J10 Pickup, Scrambler	Borg-Warner T4 4-Speed Borg-Warner T5 5-Speed Borg-Warner T18A 4-Speed Borg-Warner T176 4-Speed

Manual Transmission Servicing

AMERICAN MOTORS/JEEP

LUBRICATION

SERVICE INTERVALS

Under normal driving conditions, check fluid level every 5000 miles. Jeep models operated under severe driving conditions should have fluid level checked every 3000 miles.

AMC vehicles do not require periodic draining and refilling of transmission. Fluid should be changed every 27,500 miles on all Jeep models.

CHECKING FLUID LEVEL

Check lubricant level at filler plug hole on side of transmission. Lubricant should be level with bottom of hole. Add as needed.

RECOMMENDED FLUID

Borg-Warner T4 & T5 Transmissions
Use Jeep Automatic Transmission Fluid or equivalent, labeled Dexron II.
All Other Models
On all Jeeps, use only SAE 85W-90 multipurpose gear lubricant of API GL-5 quality. On AMC models, use SAE 80W or SAE 90W gear lube.

NOTE: **DO NOT use gear lubricants containing lead, chlorine or sulphur compounds in T-176 or T18 transmissions, or in any AMC models.**

CAPACITY

Capacities given in chart are approximate. Correct fluid level should be determined by level at filler plug hole.

TRANSMISSION REFILL CAPACITIES

Application	Capacity Pints (Liters)
AMC	
4-Speed	
Borg-Warner T4	4.3 (2.0)
JB 0 Transaxle	6.7 (3.2)
5-Speed	
Borg-Warner T5	4.8 (2.3)
JB 1 Transaxle	7.2 (3.4)
Jeep	
4-Speed	
Borg-Warner T4	3.5 (1.7)
T-18A	6.5 (3.1)
T-176	3.5 (1.7)
5-Speed	
Borg-Warner T5	4.0 (1.9)

ADJUSTMENT

SHIFT LINKAGE

All models use transmission shift linkage which does not require external adjustment.

CHRYSLER CORP.

LUBRICATION

SERVICE INTERVALS

NOTE: **Trucks and Vans are identified by 2 different emissions control standard classifications: Light Duty refers to vehicles up to 8500 lbs. GVW; Heavy Duty refers to vehicles over 8500 lbs. GVW.**

Passenger Cars
Check fluid level every 6 months. Draining and refilling are not required, except during transmission overhaul.

Trucks & Vans
1) Check fluid level whenever vehicle is serviced. On vehicles used in normal service with heavy duty emissions, transmission should be drained and refilled every 36,000 miles.

2) On vehicles with light duty emissions, transmission should be drained and refilled every 37,500 miles. On vehicles used under severe conditions, drain and refill transmission every 18,000 miles.

Shift Linkage for Overdrive 4-Speed
1) On all Trucks and Vans with New Process A-833 transmission, gearshift control mechanism should be lubricated every 22,500 miles or every 2 years. Lubricate more frequently if shift effort or noise is apparent.

2) Gearshift linkage has grease fitting located on left side of mechanism. Use multipurpose grease and high pressure grease gun to lubricate linkage. Lubricate mechanism until grease is visible on operating levers.

NOTE: **Vehicle must be in reverse gear position with engine OFF, when lubricating gearshift control mechanism.**

CHECKING FLUID LEVEL

Check lubricant level at filler plug hole at top of transmission. Lubricant should be level with bottom of hole. Add lubricant as needed to bring to correct level.

RECOMMENDED FLUID

A412 Transaxle
Use SAE 80W or SAE 90W multipurpose gear lubricant of API GL-5 quality.
A460 & A465 Transaxles
Use Dexron II automatic transmission fluid.
New Process 435 4-Speed
Either multipurpose gear lubricants meeting API specification GL-5 or engine oils labeled for API Service "SF" may be used.

If multipurpose gear lubricant is used and the minimum anticipated atmospheric temperature is:
• Above 90°F (32°C), use SAE 140.
• As low as -10°F (-23°C), use SAE 90.
• Below -10°F (-23°C), use SAE 80.

If engine oil is used, and the minimum anticipated atmospheric temperature is:

CHRYSLER CORP. (Cont.)

- Above 32°F (0°C), use SAE 50.
- Below 32°F (0°C), use SAE 30.

New Process A-833 4-Speed Overdrive

Use Dexron II automatic transmission fluid. If gear rattle is apparent during idle or acceleration, multipurpose gear lubricant SAE 90, SAE 75W, 75W-80, SAE 80W-90 or SAE 85W-90 may be used.

CAPACITY

TRANSMISSION REFILL CAPACITIES

Application	Pints (Liters)
Passenger Cars	
A412 4-Speed	3.0 (1.4)
A460 4-Speed	4.0 (1.8)
A465 5-Speed	4.6 (2.1)
Trucks & Vans	
NP 435	7.0 (3.3)
NP A833 Overdrive	7.0 (3.3)

ADJUSTMENT

SHIFT LINKAGE

NOTE: New Process 435 transmission uses internal shift linkage which is not adjustable.

New Process A833 4-Speed Overdrive

1) Install floor shift lever aligning tool to hold levers in neutral crossover position. See Fig. 1. Remove all rods from transmission shift levers and place levers in neutral detent positions.

2) Rotate shift rods until they are centered in transmission lever mounting holes, starting with 1st-2nd shift rod. Replace all washers and clips. Remove aligning tool and test shifting action.

Fig. 1: 4-Speed Overdrive Shift Linkage Adjustment

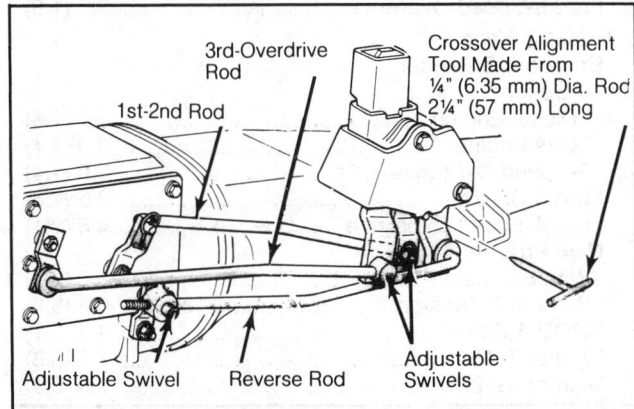

Rotate shift rods until they are exactly centered in transmission lever mounting holes.

A412 Transaxle

1) Place gearshift in neutral at 3-4 position. Loosen clamp nut on shift tube. Align tab on slider with hole on blocker bracket. Place a 3/4" spacer between slider and blocker bracket. See Fig. 2.

2) Apply slight upward pressure on shift tube clamp, and tighten clamp nut. Remove spacer. Road test vehicle to ensure transaxle shifts smoothly.

Fig. 2: A412 Transaxle Shift Linkage Adjustment Points

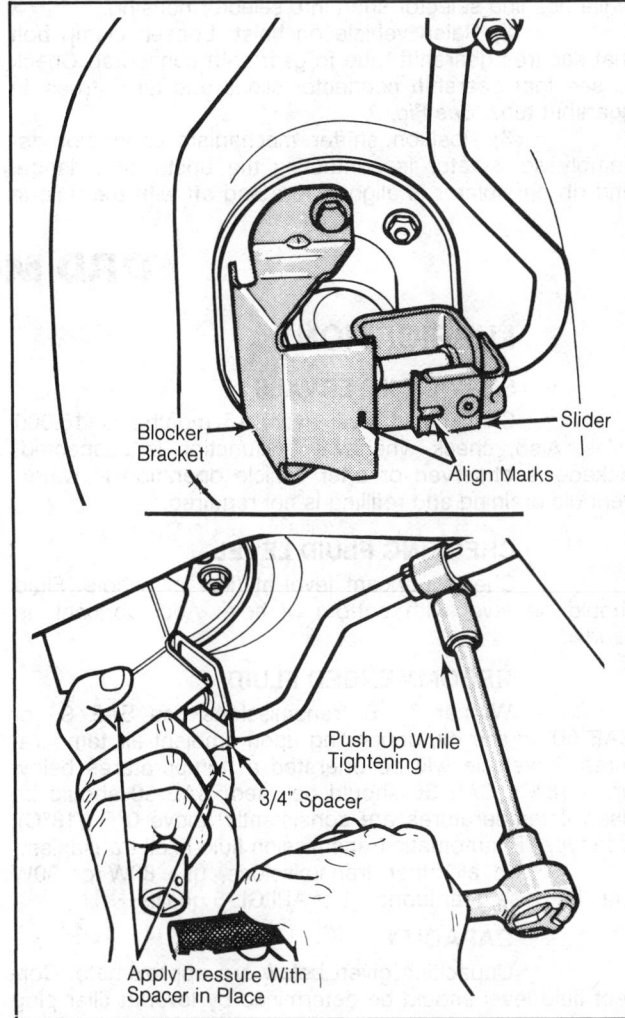

Gearshift must be in Neutral when making this adjustment.

A460 & A465 Transaxles

1) Working over left front fender, remove lock pin from transaxle selector shaft housing. Reverse lock

Fig. 3: A460 & A465 Shift Linkage Adjustment

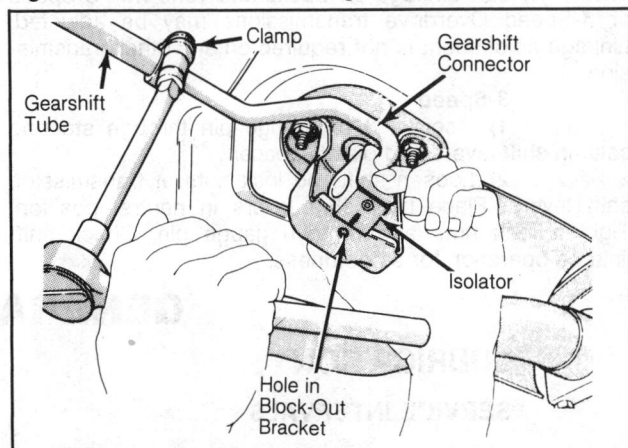

No significant force should be exerted on linkage during this operation.

Manual Transmission Servicing

CHRYSLER CORP. (Cont.)

pin (long end down) and insert into same threaded hole while pushing selector shaft into selector housing.

2) Raise vehicle on hoist. Loosen clamp bolt that secures gearshift tube to gear shift connector. Check to see that gearshift connector slides and turns freely in gearshift tube. *See Fig. 3.*

3) Position shifter mechanism connector assembly so isolator is contacting the upstanding flange, and rib on isolator is aligned fore and aft with the hole in the block-out bracket. Hold in this position while tightening clamp bolt on gearshift tube to 170 INCH lbs. (19.2 N.m). No significant force should be exerted on linkage during this operation.

4) Lower vehicle. Remove lock pin from selector shaft housing and reinstall lock pin upside down in selector shaft housing. Tighten lock pin. Check for shift into 1st and reverse. Check for block-out into reverse.

FORD MOTOR CO.

LUBRICATION

SERVICE INTERVALS

Check fluid level every 15 months or 15,000 miles. Also, check whenever malfunction is suspected, leakage is observed or after vehicle operation in water. Periodic draining and refilling is not required.

CHECKING FLUID LEVEL

Check lubricant level at filler plug hole. Fluid should be level with bottom of hole. Add lubricant as needed.

RECOMMENDED FLUID

Warner T19B transmissions use SAE 30 or SAE 50 engine oil, depending upon ambient air temperatures. If vehicle will be operated at temperatures below 0°F (-18°C), SAE 30 should be used. SAE 50 should be used if temperatures are consistently above 0°F (-18°C). Use type "F" automatic transmission fluid in all transaxles.

In all other transmissions, use 80W or 90W multipurpose gear lubricant of API GL-5 quality.

CAPACITY

Capacities given below are approximate. Correct fluid level should be determined by level at filler plug hole, rather than by amount added.

ADJUSTMENT

SHIFT LINKAGE

Shift linkage adjustment is not required on any passenger car. Linkage on trucks and vans with 3-Speed or 4-Speed Overdrive transmissions may be adjusted. Linkage adjustment is not required on any other transmission.

3-Speed

1) Insert a 3/16" gauge pin through steering column shift levers and plastic spacer.

2) Loosen shift rod lock nuts at transmission shift levers. Place both shift levers in neutral position. Tighten lock nuts and remove gauge pin. Check shift linkage operation for smoothness.

4-Speed Overdrive

1) Disconnect all 3 shift rods and insert a 1/4" diameter pin in alignment hole in shifter assembly. Align 1-2 (rear) and 3-4 (front) shift levers in neutral position. Turn Reverse (middle) lever counterclockwise to neutral position.

2) Rotate transmission output shaft to be sure all levers are in neutral. Then turn reverse lever fully clockwise to reverse position. This causes the interlock system to align 1-2 and 3-4 rails in precise neutral positions. Install 1-2 and 3-4 shift rods on shift levers and tighten lock nuts.

3) Rotate reverse lever back to neutral position. Install reverse shift rod and lock nut. Remove alignment pin and check for proper linkage operation.

TRANSMISSION REFILL CAPACITIES

Application	Capacity Pints (Liters)
Passenger Cars	
4-Speed Transaxle	5.0 (2.5)
5-Speed Transaxle	6.1 (2.9)
SROD 4-Speed	4.5 (2.1)
83ET 4-Speed	2.8 (1.3)
Borg-Warner T5 5-Speed	5.0 (2.5)
Ford 5-Speed Overdrive	3.7 (1.8)
Trucks & Vans	
Bronco II & Ranger	
4-Speed	
Diesel Engine	3.2 (1.5)
Gas Engine	3.0 (1.4)
5-Speed Overdrive	3.0 (1.4)
Ford 3-Speed	3.5 (1.6)
Ford 4-Speed Overdrive	4.5 (2.1)
New Process 435	
With Extension	7.0 (3.3)
Without Extension	6.5 (3.0)
SROD 4-Speed	4.5 (2.1)
Warner T-18	7.0 (3.3)
Warner T-19B	7.0 (3.3)

GENERAL MOTORS

LUBRICATION

SERVICE INTERVALS

NOTE: Trucks and Vans are identified by 2 different emissions control standard classifications: Light Duty and Heavy Duty. Light Duty refers to vehicles up to 8500 lbs. GVW; Heavy Duty refers to vehicles over 8500 lbs. GVW.

Check fluid level every 12 months or 7500 miles (6000 miles on heavy duty vehicles). Periodic draining and refilling of transmission is not required, with the following exceptions:

• On vehicles equipped with 5-speed manual transaxle, drain and refill at 30,000 mile intervals.

• On all "S" model vehicles with 4-speed transmission, change transmission fluid after the first 7500 miles and at 35,000 mile intervals thereafter.

GENERAL MOTORS (Cont.)

CHECKING FLUID LEVEL

Check lubricant level at transmission filler plug hole. Lubricant should be level with bottom of hole. Add as needed.

NOTE: On FWD vehicles, check fluid level when transaxle is cold. If hot, fluid may flow from filler hole when plug is removed, possibly resulting in burned hands or incorrect level readings.

RECOMMENDED FLUID

All "S" series trucks, 4-speed manual transaxles and the New Process 833 4-Speed Overdrive transmission use Dexron II automatic transmission fluid.

Isuzu 69.5 MM 5-speed transmission and all 5-speed transaxles use 5W-30 engine oil rated SF or equivalent.

All other transmissions use 80W or 80W-90 GL-5 multipurpose gear lubricant or equivalent.

CAPACITY

The capacities listed in the following chart are approximations only. Correct fluid level should be determined by level at filler plug hole, rather than by amount added.

76 MM 4-Speed

1) Raise and support vehicle. Loosen lock nuts at swivel on shift rods. Place transmission shift levers in neutral. Place shift control lever in neutral. *See Fig. 1.*

2) Align control assembly levers and insert gauge pin into levers and assembly to hold levers in neutral position.

3) Tighten lock nuts at shift rod swivels and remove gauge pin. Check transmission shift operation. Readjust as necessary.

Fig. 1: 76 MM 4-Speed Floor Mounted Shift Linkage

TRANSMISSION REFILL CAPACITIES

Application	Capacity Pints (Liters)
Passenger Cars	
4-Speed	
Transaxle	[1] 6.0 (2.8)
70 MM	3.4 (1.6)
76 MM	3.5 (1.7)
5-Speed	
Transaxle	[1] 6.0 (2.8)
Isuzu 69.5 MM	3.3 (1.6)
Borg-Warner T5	[2]
Trucks & Vans	
76 MM 3-Speed	3.0 (1.4)
117 MM 4-Speed	8.0 (3.7)
New Process 833 4-Speed Overdrive	4.5 (2.1)
All "S" Models	[2]

[1] — Includes differential.
[2] — Add fluid to bottom of filler plug hole.

ADJUSTMENT

SHIFT LINKAGE — PASSENGER CARS

NOTE: The 70 MM 4-Speed, Borg-Warner T5 5-Speed and Isuzu 69.5 MM 5-Speed transmissions all use integral shift linkage which is not adjustable.

4-Speed Transaxle

1) Place transaxle into 1st gear before making adjustments. Remove shifter boot and retainer. Install 2 pins (No. 22 drill bits or 5/32" pins) into alignment holes in shifter control assembly. This will secure assembly in 1st gear position. *See Fig. 2.*

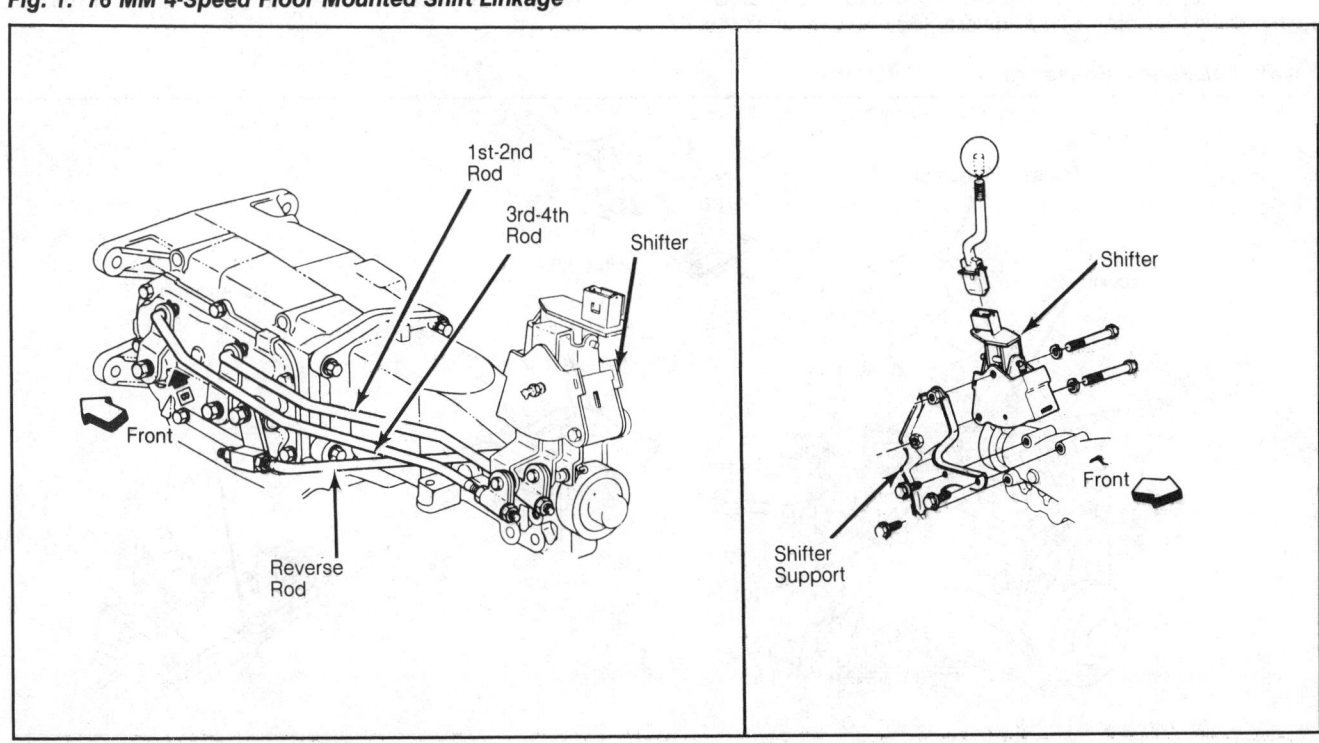

Shift rods should pass freely through swivels.

Manual Transmission Servicing

GENERAL MOTORS (Cont.)

Fig. 2: Adjusting 4-Speed Transaxle Shift Cables

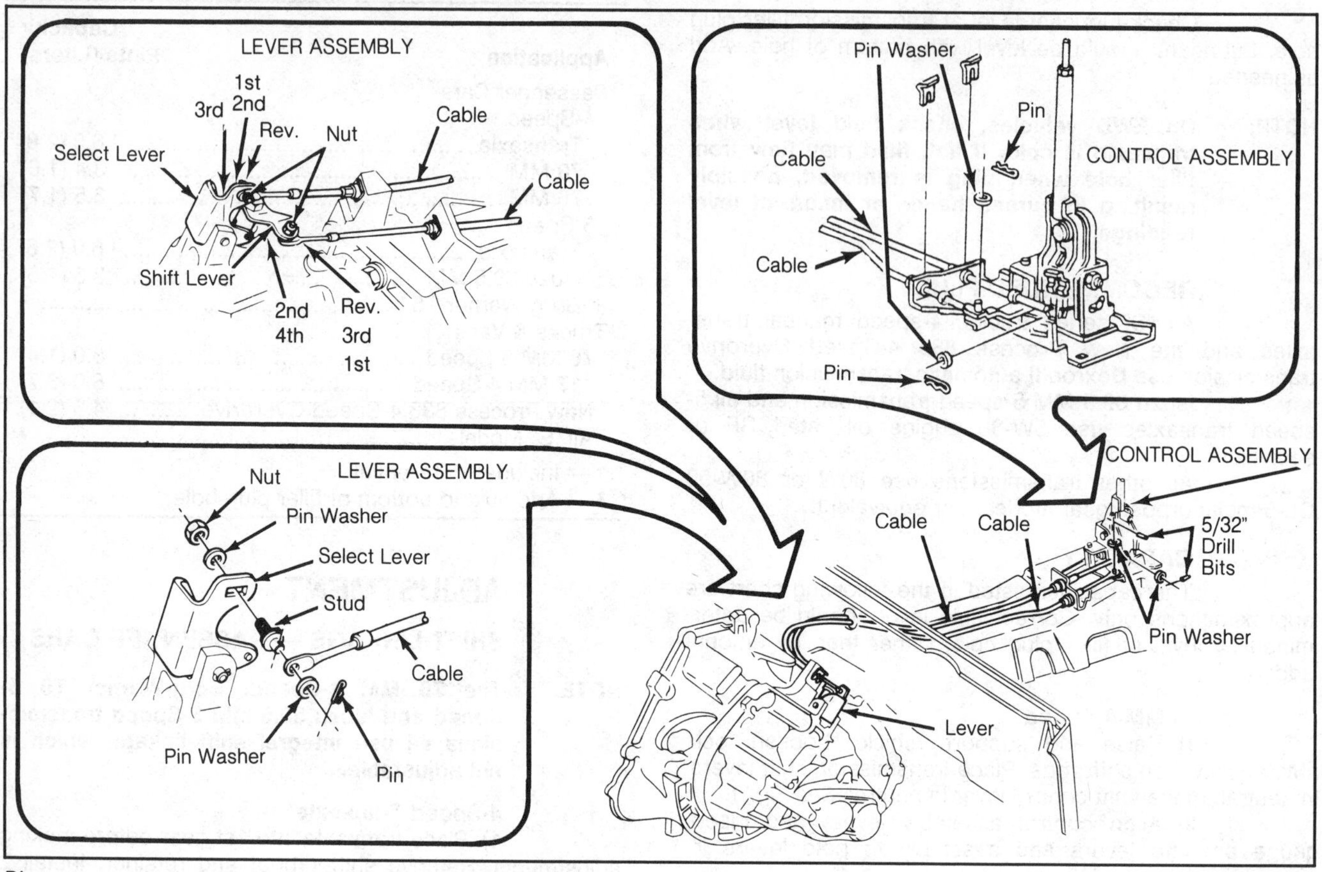

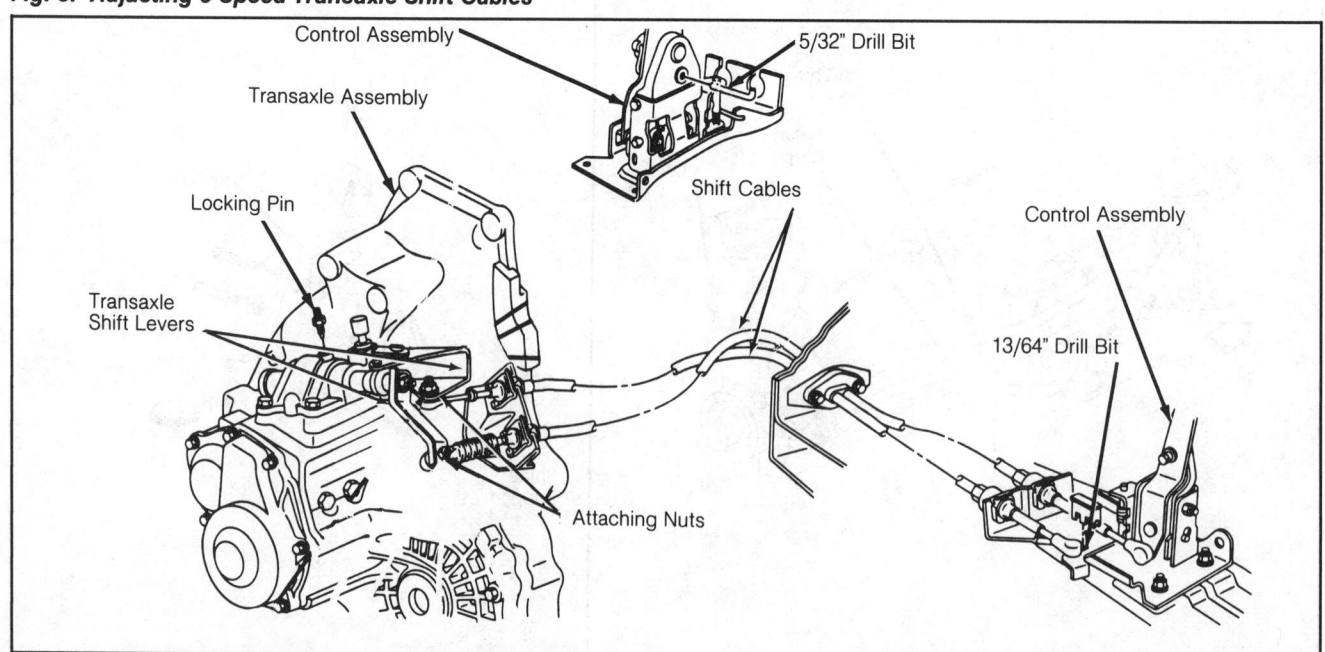

Place transaxle in 1st gear before making adjustment.

2) Attach 2 shift cables to control assembly, using studs with pin retainers. Be sure cables are properly routed and operate freely.

3) Manually place transaxle into 1st gear by pushing rail selector shaft inward (down) until inhibitor spring resistance is first felt. Rotate shift lever fully clockwise.

4) Install stud of cable (1) into slotted area in shift lever (2). Install stud of cable (3) into slotted hole of

Fig. 3: Adjusting 5-Speed Transaxle Shift Cables

Adjustment is performed with transaxle in 3rd gear range.

GENERAL MOTORS (Cont.)

select lever (4) to remove lash. *See Fig. 2.* Tighten nuts on studs.

    5) Remove 2 drill bits or pins from control assembly and road test vehicle. Particularly check for a good neutral gate feel during shifting. Adjust cable position as necessary after road testing.

5-Speed Transaxle

    1) Disconnect negative battery cable and place shift lever in 3rd gear position. Remove locking pin at transaxle and reinstall tapered end down, locking transaxle in 3rd gear. *See Fig. 3.* Loosen shift cable attaching nuts at transaxle shift levers.

    2) Working from inside vehicle, remove console trim plate, slide shifter boot up shifter and remove console. Install a 5/32" drill bit (No. 22) in alignment hole in shifter assembly. Align slot in shift lever with slot in shifter plate and install 13/64" drill.

    3) Tighten attaching nuts loosened in step **1)**. Remove both drill bits. Remove locking pin at transaxle and reinstall, tapered end up. Install console, shifter boot and trim plate. Reconnect negative battery cable.

    4) Road test vehicle to ensure proper linkage adjustment as indicated by a good neutral gate feel during normal shifting. Some "fine-tuning" of adjustment may be necessary.

SHIFT LINKAGE — TRUCKS & VANS

All With Shifter on Column

    1) Place gear selector lever in reverse position. Turn transmission shift lever fully clockwise to forward stop. Turn ignition switch to "LOCK" position. Attach primary shift rod to column shift lever with retainer. *See Fig. 4.*

    2) Slide swivel onto end of shift rod and insert swivel into transmission shift lever. Loosely assemble with bolt and washer. Turn column shift lever down as far as possible and tighten bolt.

Fig. 4: Adjusting Shift Linkage

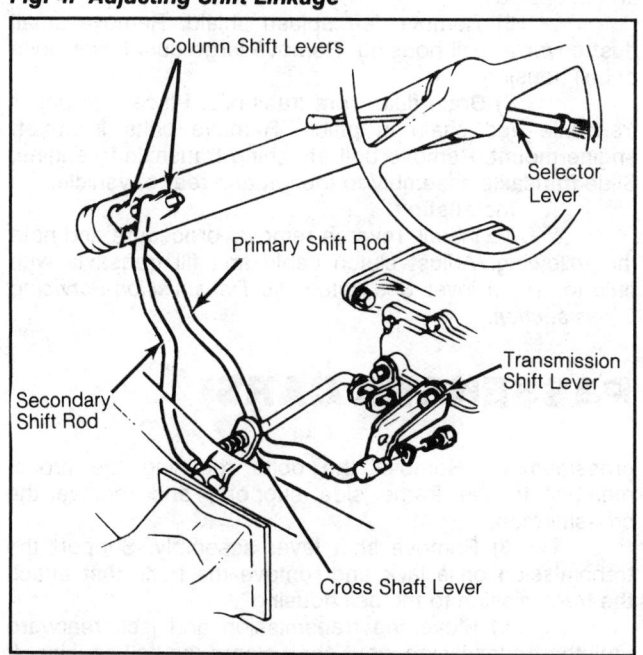

3-Speed with column mounted shifter.

    3) Turn ignition switch to "UNLOCK" position and move gear selector lever to neutral. Turn transmission shift lever and cross shaft lever clockwise to full forward positions, then back 1 detent to neutral.

    4) Align gauge holes in column shift levers (3) and insert 1/4" gauge pin through holes. Repeat adjustment procedure with secondary shift rod. Remove gauge pin and check for proper linkage operation. Ignition switch should turn to "LOCK" position with shifter in reverse position only.

All With Floor-Mounted Shifter

    1) Disconnect all shift rods from transmission shift levers. With shift selector lever in neutral position, insert a 1/4" diameter pin through alignment holes in shifter assembly.

    2) Align all shift levers at transmission in neutral position. Rotate transmission output shaft to be sure all levers are in neutral. Loosen lock nuts on shift rod ends and align rod ends with shift lever holes. Install shift rods in levers, tighten lock nuts and install lock pins.

    3) Remove alignment pin and check for proper linkage operation.

Manual Transmission Removal

AMERICAN MOTORS

REMOVAL & INSTALLATION

CONCORD & SPIRIT
Removal

1) Shift transmission into neutral. Remove console (if equipped). Remove gearshift lever, bezel and boot from floor pan. Raise vehicle and support. Remove speedometer cable. Disconnect drive shaft and mark for installation reference.

2) Disconnect exhaust (if necessary). Disconnect back-up light switch wire and support engine. Remove starter and inspection cover. Remove bolts attaching catalytic converter bracket-to-transmission rear support bracket.

3) Place a stand under front of engine. Remove rear crossmember. Remove transmission retaining bolts and remove transmission.

EAGLE
Removal

1) Shift transmission into neutral. Remove console (if equipped). Remove gearshift lever, bezel and boot from floor pan. Slide boot upward on lever to remove bolts attaching gearshift lever to lever mounting cover.

2) Remove gearshift lever. Raise vehicle and support on jack stands. Remove skid pan and mark position of speedometer adapter for installation reference. Remove speedometer retainer, adapter and cable. Plug adapter hole to prevent oil spillage.

3) Disconnect drive shafts and mark for installation reference. Disconnect exhaust (if necessary).

Disconnect back-up light switch wire. Place a jack stand under engine. Support transmission and transfer case with a transmission jack.

4) Remove rear crossmember. Remove catalytic converter bracket from transfer case. Remove bolts attaching transmission to clutch housing. Remove transmission and transfer case as an assembly.

ALLIANCE
Removal

1) Raise vehicle and support on jack stands. Remove wheel assemblies and disconnect drive axle shafts. Disconnect gearshift lever linkage and engine-to-transaxle rod. Remove clutch shield and all mounting pad nuts.

2) Remove air filter. Disconnect back-up light switch wire connector and remove sensor. Disconnect clutch cable, speedometer cable and ground wire. Remove radiator and lay it on engine without disconnecting hoses.

3) Raise engine slightly to free rear mounts. Remove starter motor. Remove transaxle retaining bolts, separate transaxle from engine and lift it free of chassis. On models with JB 1 transaxle, slide 5th gear casing between side members.

Installation (All Models)

To install, reverse removal procedure and note the following: Fill Transmission/Transaxle with fluid to proper level. *See Automatic Transmission Servicing in this section.*

CHRYSLER CORP. — PASSENGER CARS

REMOVAL & INSTALLATION

ALL MODELS
Removal

1) On all models, disconnect negative battery cable. Disconnect shift linkage rods. On Horizon, Omni, Rampage and Scamp disconnect starter wire and ground wire. Disconnect back-up light switch wire. Remove starter.

2) Disconnect clutch cable. Remove bolt securing speedometer adapter to transaxle. Carefully work adapter and pinion out of transaxle.

3) On all models, support engine with engine support fixture. On Horizon, Omni, Rampage and Scamp loosen left wheel hub nut with vehicle on floor.

4) On all models, raise and support vehicle. Remove wheel assemblies. Disconnect right drive axle shaft and tie out of the way. Remove left drive axle shaft and set aside.

5) Remove left splash shield. Remove small dust cover at bell housing. Remove large dust cover bolts at bell housing.

6) Drain fluid from transaxle. Place jack under transaxle and chain in place. Remove bolts from left engine mount. Remove bolt attaching transaxle-to-engine. Slide transaxle assembly to the left and rear of vehicle.

Installation

To install, reverse removal procedure and note the following: Adjust clutch cable and fill transaxle with fluid to proper level. *See Automatic Transmission Servicing in this section.*

FORD MOTOR CO. — PASSENGER CARS

REMOVAL & INSTALLATION

REAR WHEEL DRIVE MODELS
Removal

1) Raise vehicle on hoist. Disconnect starter cable and remove starter motor. Disconnect speedometer cable from the extension housing. Mark drive shaft for installation in same position. Remove drive shaft.

2) Support the engine with a jack. Raise the rear of engine high enough to remove the weight from the

crossmember. Remove the bolts retaining the crossmember to the frame side supports and remove the crossmember.

3) Remove shift lever assembly. Support the transmission on a jack and remove the bolts that attach the transmission to the bell housing.

4) Move the transmission and jack rearward until the transmission input shaft clears the bell housing. If necessary, lower the engine enough to obtain clearance for transmission removal.

FORD MOTOR CO. — PASSENGER CARS (Cont.)

Installation

Reverse removal procedure and note the following: Fill the transmission with fluid to proper level. *See Automatic Transmission Servicing in this section.*

ESCORT EXP, LN7 & LYNX
Removal

1) Remove 2 transaxle-to-engine top mounting bolts. Disconnect clutch cable from clutch release lever. Raise vehicle on hoist. Remove bolt attaching brake hose routing clip to suspension strut bracket at wheels.

2) Remove ball joint stud nut and pry lower control arm away from steering knuckle. Using a pry bar, pry inboard CV joint assembly from transaxle. Remove inner CV joint from transaxle by grasping steering knuckle and swinging knuckle shaft outward from transaxle.

3) Wire halfshaft assembly in near level position. Remove front stabilizer bar. Disconnect speedometer cable from transaxle. Disconnect back-up light switch. Remove engine roll restrictor bracket and remove starter motor.

4) Remove stiffener brace attaching bolts from lower portion of clutch housing. Remove shift mechanism stabilizer bar-to-transaxle attaching bolt. Remove transmission control selector switch and bracket. Remove shift mechanism from shift shaft.

5) Position a transmission jack under transaxle. Loosen nut on rear mount stud. Remove attaching bolt from bottom of rear mount and loosen 2 bolts at top of mount. Remove 3 bolts from front mount-to-transaxle case.

6) Lower jack until transaxle clears rear mount. Support engine with screw type stand. Remove 4 remaining engine-to-transaxle bolts. Remove transaxle from engine and lower from vehicle.

Installation

To install, reverse removal procedure, and note the following: Fill transaxle with fluid to proper level. *See Automatic Transmission Servicing in this section.*

GENERAL MOTORS — PASSENGER CARS

REMOVAL & INSTALLATION

FRONT WHEEL DRIVE MODELS

NOTE: Not all steps apply to all models.

Removal

1) Disconnect battery ground cable. On "J" models, install engine holding fixture so one end is supported on cowl tray over wiper motor and other end rests on radiator support.

2) Attach fixture hook to engine lift ring and raise engine enough to take pressure off motor mounts. Remove heater hose clamp at transaxle mount bracket.

3) On all models, disconnect electrical lead from horn and remove horn. On "A" and "X" models, remove air cleaner assembly. Disconnect clutch cable. If equipped with V6 engine, disconnect fuel lines and clamps at clutch cable bracket.

4) Remove clutch cable bracket from transaxle. If equipped with V6 engine, remove exhaust crossover pipe. On all models, remove retaining clips and washers from transaxle shift linkage at transaxle.

5) Remove clips securing shift cables to mounting bosses on transaxle case. Disconnect speedometer cable at transaxle. On "A" and "X" models, remove 5 top engine-to-transaxle bolts.

6) On "J" models, disconnect ground cables at transaxle mounting stud. Remove air management valve attaching bolts to gain clearance for removal of right upper transaxle-to-engine bolt.

7) Remove 4 upper transaxle-to-engine mounting bolts. Raise vehicle and remove left wheel assembly. Remove left inner splash shield. Remove axle strut and bracket. Remove clutch housing cover bolts.

8) Disconnect speedometer cable at transaxle. Disconnect stabilizer bar at left suspension support and control arm. Disconnect ball joint from steering knuckle. Remove left suspension support attaching bolts and remove support and control as an assembly.

9) On "A" and "X" models, install engine support fixture. Raise vehicle and drain fluid from transaxle. On all models, install drive axle shaft boot seal protectors. Remove left front wheel assembly.

10) Remove left side cradle and crossmember assembly. Disengage right and left hand inboard drive axle shaft joints from transaxle. Remove left hand drive axle shaft from transaxle and support.

11) Right hand drive axle shaft can be removed as transaxle is being removed. Remove flywheel and starter motor shield bolts. Securely attach transaxle case to jack for removal.

12) Remove the last transaxle-to-engine bolt. Remove transaxle by sliding to driver's side, away from engine. Carefully lower jack, and move transaxle away from vehicle.

Installation

Place transmission in gear, raise assembly into position, and move forward, turning output shaft to engage input shaft with clutch splines. To complete installation, reverse removal procedure, and fill transmission with fluid to proper level. *See Automatic Transmission Servicing in this section.*

ALL OTHERS
Removal

1) On Chevette and T1000, remove floor console and/or boot retainer. Raise shift boot to gain access to lock nut on shift lever. Loosen lock nut and unscrew upper portion of shift lever. Remove foam insulator, shifter-to-extension bolts, and remove shifter assembly.

2) On Camaro and Firebird, remove shift lever boot attaching screws and slide boot up shift lever. Remove shift lever from transmission.

3) On all models, disconnect battery ground cable and release parking brake. Raise and support vehicle. Drain transmission lubricant. On Camaro and Firebird, remove rear axle torque arm. On all models, remove drive shaft assembly and mark for reassembly reference.

4) Disconnect clutch return spring and clutch release fork. Disconnect electrical connections at transmission. Remove crossmember-to-transmission bolts.

Manual Transmission Removal

GENERAL MOTORS — PASSENGER CARS (Cont.)

Remove exhaust manifold nuts. Remove catalytic converter-to-tailpipe nuts and bolts.

5) Remove converter assembly from vehicle. Raise transmission with a floorjack to take pressure off crossmember. Remove crossmember from vehicle. Remove clutch dust cover.

6) Remove transmission attaching bolts. Slide transmission rearward and remove from under vehicle.

Installation

Place transmission in gear, raise assembly into position, and move forward, turning output shaft to engage input shaft with clutch splines. To complete installation, reverse removal procedure, and fill transmission with fluid to proper level. *See Automatic Transmission Servicing in this section.*

CHRYSLER CORP. — TRUCKS & VANS

TRANSFER CASE

MODEL NP-205

Removal

1) Raise vehicle, remove plug and drain transfer case. Replace plug. Disconnect speedometer cable. Remove skid plate, crossmember and strut rods as needed. Disconnect propeller shafts and wire out of way. Do not allow propeller shafts to hang free, as damage to universal joints may result.

2) Disconnect shift lever rod from shift rail link. Support transfer case and remove transfer case-to-transmission adapter bolts. Move transfer case to rear until input shaft clears adapter. Lower transfer case from vehicle.

Installation

Reverse removal procedures to install transfer case. Ensure that all attaching bolts are tight. Fill transfer case with lubricant.

MODEL NP-208

Removal

1) Raise vehicle, remove plug and drain transfer case. Mark front and rear output shaft yokes and propeller shafts for reassembly reference. Disconnect speedometer cable and indicator switch wires. Disconnect shift lever link from operating lever.

2) Support transfer case with transmission jack and remove crossmember. Disconnect front and rear propeller shafts at yokes and wire to frame.

3) If necessary, disconnect parking brake cable guide from pivot on right frame rail. Remove bolts attaching exhaust pipe support bracket to transfer case. Remove transfer case-to-transmission bolts. Move assembly to the rear until clear of output shaft. Lower transfer case from vehicle.

4) Remove all gasket material from rear of transmission adapter housing.

Installation

Install new transmission-to-transfer case gasket with sealer on both sides. Align transfer case with transmission. Rotate transfer case output shaft until transmission output shaft engages transfer case input shaft. Move transfer case until case seats flush against transmission. Install transfer case attaching bolts. Reverse removal procedures to complete installation.

TRANSMISSION

ALL MODELS

Removal

1) Disconnect negative battery cable. Remove retaining screws from floor pan and slide boot up and off shift lever.

2) On models equipped with New Process 435 transmission, remove shift lever retainer by pressing down, rotating retainer clockwise and releasing.

3) On models equipped with Overdrive 4-Speed transmission, remove shift lever by inserting a .010" (.25 mm) feeler gauge between floor shift assembly and shift lever, and disengaging internal spring clip.

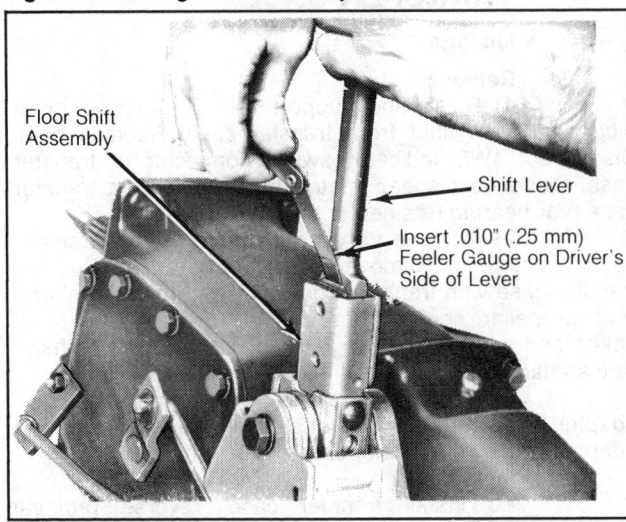

Fig. 1: Removing Overdrive 4-Speed Shift Lever

Floor Shift Assembly

Shift Lever

Insert .010" (.25 mm) Feeler Gauge on Driver's Side of Lever

Insert feeler gauge to remove spring clip.

4) Remove bolts and washers securing shift lever to mounting plate on extension housing and remove.

5) On all models, drain fluid from transmission. On 4WD models, remove transfer case. On all vehicles, remove propeller shaft from transmission at rear universal joint. Disconnect speedometer cable and back-up light switch. Install engine support fixture (C-3487-A).

6) On models equipped with New Process 435 transmission, place adapters (DD-1279) firmly over frame rails. On all models, make sure support ends of engine fixture tool are up against underside of oil pan flange.

7) Raise engine slightly with support fixture. On models with Overdrive 4-Speed transmission, disconnect extension housing from removable center crossmember.

8) On all models, support transmission with a jack and remove crossmember. Remove transmission-to-clutch housing bolts. Slide transmission rearward until drive pinion shaft clears clutch disc, then lower and remove transmission.

Installation

Reverse removal procedures to install, noting the following: apply a small amount of high-temperature grease to the pilot shaft bushing in the flywheel and on pinion bearing retainer release bearing sleeve area before installing transmission. As transmission is installed, engage pinion shaft with clutch disc by slowly turning shaft to engage teeth. DO NOT allow transmission to hang free once clutch disc has been engaged.

TIGHTENING SPECIFICATIONS

Application	Ft. Lbs. (N.m)
Transfer Case-to-Transmission	40 (54)
Transmission Case-to-Clutch Housing	
Overdrive 4-Speed	50 (68)
NP-435	105 (142)
Crossmember-to-Frame	30 (41)
Ext. Housing-to-Rear Mount Bolt	50 (68)

Manual Transmission Removal

FORD MOTOR CO. — TRUCKS & VANS

TRANSFER CASE

NP-208
Removal

1) Raise and support vehicle. Remove drain plug and drain fluid from transfer case. Replace plug. Disconnect 4WD indicator switch connector at transfer case. Disconnect speedometer driven gear from transfer case rear bearing retainer.

2) Remove transmission shift lever-to-transfer case retaining nut. Remove skid plate from frame. Support transfer case with transmission jack. Disconnect front and rear propeller shafts from transfer case output shaft yokes and wire out of way. Do not allow shafts to hang free as damage to universal joints may result.

3) Remove transfer case-to-transmission adapter bolts. Remove gasket between transfer case and adapter and lower transfer case out of vehicle.

Installation

To install transfer case, reverse removal procedures. Fill case with 7 pints (3.3 liters) of Dexron II type automatic transmission fluid.

BORG-WARNER 1345
Removal

1) Raise vehicle. Remove drain plug and drain fluid from transfer case. Replace plug. Disconnect 4WD indicator switch connector at transfer case. If equipped, remove skid plate.

2) Disconnect front and rear propeller shafts from transfer case output shaft yokes and wire out of way. Do not allow shafts to hang free as damage to universal joints may result.

3) Disconnect speedometer driven gear from rear bearing retainer. Remove retaining clips and shift rod from transfer case control and transfer case shift levers. Disconnect vent hose from case.

4) Remove heat shield. Support transfer case with transmission jack, remove transfer case-to-transmission adapter bolts and slide transfer case off of transmission output shaft. Lower transfer case out of vehicle and remove gasket from between transfer case and adapter.

Installation

Reverse removal procedures to install transfer case. Fill case with 6.5 pints (3.1 liters) of Dexron II type automatic transmission fluid.

BORG-WARNER 1350
Removal

1) Raise vehicle. Remove skid plate (if equipped). Remove drain plug and drain fluid from case. Replace plug. Disconnect 4WD indicator switch connector at transfer case. Disconnect front propeller shaft from front axle. Loosen front shaft boot clamp and slide out propeller shaft and boot as an assembly.

2) Disconnect rear propeller shaft from transfer case. Disconnect speedometer driven gear from transfer case rear cover. Disconnect vent hose from control lever.

3) Loosen or remove large and small bolts (1 each) retaining shifter to extension housing. Pull on control lever until bushing slides off transfer case shift lever pin. Unscrew shift lever from control lever, as needed.

4) Remove heat shield from transfer case. Support transfer case with jack and remove transfer case-

to-transmission extension housing bolts (5). Slide transfer case to the rear and off of transmission output shaft. Lower case from vehicle. Remove gasket from between transfer case and extension housing.

Installation

Reverse removal procedures to install transfer case, noting the following:

1) When installing shift lever assembly, tighten large bolt first, then small bolt.

2) When installing vent assembly, White marking on hose should be positioned in notch in shifter with upper end of hose 2 inches above top of shifter, inside of shift lever boot.

3) Before installing front propeller shaft into transfer case, lubricate female splines of transfer case input shaft with multipurpose grease.

4) Fill transfer case to bottom of fill plug hole with Dexron II automatic transmission fluid.

TRANSMISSION

BRONCO II & RANGER
Removal

1) Place shift lever in neutral position. Remove boot retainer screws and bolts attaching retainer cover to gearshift lever retainer. Disconnect clutch master cylinder push rod from clutch pedal.

2) Pull gearshift lever assembly, shim and bushing straight up and away from lever retainer. Disconnect negative cable from battery. Raise and support vehicle.

3) Disconnect propeller shaft at rear axle and remove shaft. Remove clutch housing dust shield and slave cylinder. Wire to one side. Disconnect speedometer cable, starter motor cable and backup light wiring.

4) Place jack and wood block under engine oil pan to support engine. On 4WD vehicles, remove transfer case. On all models, remove starter. Place transmission jack under transmission.

5) Remove bolts, lockwashers and flat washers attaching transmission to engine rear plate. Remove transmission mount-to-crossmember bolts. Remove nuts attaching crossmember to frame. Remove crossmember.

6) Lower jack under engine. Work transmission to the rear until input shaft clears clutch housing. Remove transmission.

Installation

Reverse removal procedures to install.

3-SPEED ("E" MODELS)
Removal

1) Raise and support vehicle. Remove lower extension housing-to-transmission bolt to drain lubricant. Disconnect propeller shaft from flange at transmission and wire out of way. Do not allow shaft to hang free as damage to universal joint may result.

2) Disconnect speedometer cable and shift control rods from transmission shift levers. Place jack under transmission and secure transmission to jack with safety chain.

3) Raise transmission slightly and remove 4 bolts retaining transmission extension housing to insulator and retainer assembly. Remove transmission-to-clutch housing bolts. Install engine support bar on frame, under engine, and lower transmission out of vehicle.

FORD MOTOR CO. — TRUCKS & VANS (Cont.)

Installation

Reverse removal procedures to install. Fill transmission with lubricant. Adjust clutch and shift linkages.

3-SPEED ("F" MODELS)

Removal

1) Raise vehicle and support on safety stands. Support engine with jack and wood block under oil pan. To drain fluid from transmission, remove lower extension housing-to-transmission bolt.

2) Place jack under transmission and secure transmission to jack with safety chain. Disconnect shift linkage at transmission. Disconnect speedometer cable and back-up switch wires.

3) Disconnect propeller shaft and wire out of way. Do not allow shaft to hang free as damage to universal joint may result. Raise transmission and remove rear support, insulator and retainer.

4) Remove transmission-to-clutch housing attaching bolts. Move transmission rearward until input shaft clears clutch housing. Lower transmission out of vehicle. Do not depress clutch pedal at any time while transmission is out of vehicle.

Installation

Reverse removal procedures to install, noting the following: Apply a thin film of multi-purpose grease to the release bearing inner hub surfaces, release lever fulcrum and fork, and the transmission front bearing retainer. With installation complete, fill transmission with lubricant. Adjust clutch and shift linkage.

4-SPEED OVERDRIVE

Removal

1) Raise and support vehicle. Mark propeller shaft position for reassembly reference. Disconnect propeller shaft from rear axle and slide shaft out of transmission. Disconnect speedometer cable and shift rods. Remove bolts connecting shift control to transmission case.

2) Remove rear transmission support-to-crossmember bolts. Support engine with transmission jack and raise transmission enough to take weight off number 3 crossmember. Remove bolts holding crossmember to frame side supports. Remove crossmember.

3) Place jack under rear of engine and raise high enough to remove weight from forward crossmember. Remove crossmember. With transmission supported by and secured to transmission jack, remove clutch housing-to-transmission bolts.

4) Move transmission to the rear until input shaft clears clutch housing and remove transmission. Do not depress clutch pedal while transmission is out of vehicle.

Installation

Reverse removal procedures to install.

S.R.O.D. 4-SPEED

1) Raise vehicle and support on safety stands. Drain transmission and transfer case (if equipped). On 4WD vehicles, remove retaining clips and shift rod from transfer case control lever and transfer case shift lever. Disconnect vent hose from transfer case.

2) On all models, mark propeller shaft position for reassembly reference. Disconnect propeller shaft from rear "U" joint flange. Remove propeller shaft. Disconnect

speedometer cable and backup light switch. Remove screws holding shift lever to turret and remove shift lever.

3) Support engine with transmission jack, and remove extension housing-to-engine support bolts. Raise engine enough to remove weight from crossmember. Remove bolts securing crossmember to frame side supports. Remove crossmember.

4) On 4WD vehicles, remove transfer case. On all models, support transmission with jack and remove transmission-to-flywheel housing bolts. Move transmission rearward, until input shaft clears flywheel housing. Remove transmission. Do not depress clutch pedal at any time while transmission is out of vehicle.

Installation

Reverse removal procedures to install.

NP 435

Removal

1) Remove floor mat. Remove shift lever, shift ball and boot as an assembly. On 4WD models, remove transfer case shift lever, shift ball and boot as an assembly. Remove floor pan transmission cover or weather pad on F150-350 models. Remove seat if necessary.

2) To remove gearshift lever and knob, first remove inner cap with puller (T73T-7220-A or equivalent). Remove seat and spring. Remove gearshift lever. Disconnect back-up light.

3) Raise vehicle. Disconnect speedometer cable and rear propeller shaft. Wire shaft out of way. On 4WD models, drain transfer case, remove front propeller shaft from case and wire out of way.

4) Remove cotter pin holding shift link and remove link. Remove bolts holding bracket to transfer case. Position transmission jack under transfer case.

5) Remove transfer case-to-transmission bolts and remove transfer case. On all models, place transmission jack under transmission and lift slightly. Remove transmission-to-insulator, insulator-to-crossmember and crossmember-to-frame bolts. Remove insulator and crossmember.

6) Remove transmission-to-clutch housing bolts and lower transmission out of vehicle.

Installation

Reverse removal procedures to install.

WARNER T-18 (2WD MODELS)

Removal

1) Working from inside vehicle, remove floor mat and body floor pan cover. Remove gearshift lever, shift ball and boot as an assembly. Remove weather pad. Raise and support vehicle. Disconnect speedometer cable.

2) Disconnect back-up light switch from rear of gear shift housing cover. Disconnect propeller shaft from transmission and wire out of way. Do not allow shaft to hang free as damage to universal joint may result. Disconnect clutch linkage.

3) Remove skid plate (if equipped) and heat shield. Support transmission with jack. Remove crossmember gusset-to-frame bolts and gusset-to-crossmember bolts. Remove transmission-to-insulator bolts. Raise transmission and remove insulator-to-crossmember bolts. Remove insulator

4) Remove right gusset, crossmember-to-frame bolts and crossmember. Remove transmission-to-

Manual Transmission Removal

FORD MOTOR CO. — TRUCKS & VANS (Cont.)

clutch housing bolts. Move transmission away from clutch housing until input shaft clears housing. Lower transmission out of vehicle.

Installation
Reverse removal procedures to install, noting the following: When installing shift lever, shift ball and boot assembly, lubricate the spherical ball seat with multi-purpose grease.

WARNER T-18 (4WD MODELS)
Removal
1) Working from inside vehicle, remove floor mat and access cover to floor pan. Place shift lever in reverse position and remove cover, insulator and dust cover. Remove transfer case shift lever, shift ball and boot as an assembly.

2) Remove transmission shift lever, shift ball and boot as an assembly. Raise vehicle. Remove drain plug and allow transmission to drain. Replace plug. Disconnect front and rear propeller shafts from transfer case and wire out of way. Do not allow shafts to hang free as damage to universal joint may result.

3) Remove shift link retainer ring and remove shift link from transfer case. Disconnect speedometer cable. Place transmission jack under transfer case. Remove transfer case-to-transmission bolts and lower transfer case out of vehicle.

4) Remove rear support bracket-to-transmission bolts (8), position transmission jack under transmission and remove rear support bracket and brace. Remove transmission-to-clutch housing bolts (4) and remove transmission.

Installation
Reverse removal procedures to install.

WARNER T19B (2WD MODELS)
Removal
1) Working from inside vehicle, remove floor mat and body floor pan cover. Remove gearshift lever, shift ball and boot as an assembly. Remove weather pad.

2) Raise vehicle. Place transmission jack under transmission and disconnect speedometer cable. Disconnect back-up light switch from rear of gear shift housing cover. Disconnect propeller shaft and clutch linkage. Wire out of way.

3) Remove transmission rear insulator and lower retainer. Remove skid plate (if equipped) and heat shield. Remove upper gusset bolts and gusset-to-crossmember bolts. Remove left side gusset.

4) Remove transmission-to-support plate bolts, raise transmission slightly and remove support plate-to-crossmember bolts. Remove support plate and right gusset. Remove crossmember-to-frame bolts and remove crossmember.

5) Remove transmission-to-clutch housing bolts. Move transmission to the rear until input shaft clears housing and remove transmission.

Installation
Reverse removal procedures to install transmission, noting the following: When installing the shift lever, shift ball and boot assembly, lubricate spherical ball seat with multipurpose grease.

WARNER T19B (4WD MODELS)
Removal
1) Working from inside vehicle, remove floor mat and access cover to floor pan (shift lever in reverse when removing cover). Remove insulator and dust cover. Remove transfer case shift lever, shift ball and boot as an assembly.

2) Remove transmission shift lever, shift ball and boot as an assembly. Raise vehicle. Drain transmission and replace drain plug. Disconnect front and rear driveshafts from transfer case and wire out of way.

3) Remove shift link retainer ring and remove link from transfer case. Disconnect speedometer cable. Place transmission jack under transfer case and remove transfer case-to-transmission bolts (6). Lower transfer case out of vehicle.

4) Remove rear support bracket-to-transmission bolts (8). Place transmission jack under transmission and remove rear support bracket and brace. Remove transmission-to-clutch housing bolts (4) and remove transmission.

Installation
Reverse removal procedures to install.

TIGHTENING SPECIFICATIONS

Application	Ft. Lbs. (N.m)
Transmission-to-Clutch Housing	
Bronco II & Ranger	30-40 (42-56)
All Others	
3-Speed	42-50 (59-70)
4-Speed	35-50 (49-70)
Transfer Case-to-Transmission	
NP-208	20-25 (28-35)
Borg-Warner 1345	25-43 (35-60)
Borg-Warner 13-50	25-35 (35-49)
Insulator-to-Crossmember	
3-Speed	50-70 (70-98)
4-Speed Overdrive	50-70 (70-98)
Bronco II & Ranger	71-94 (98-132)
All Others	
2WD	50-70 (70-98)
4WD	35-45 (49-63)
Insulator-to-Transmission	
3-Speed ("E" Models)	50-70 (70-98)
4-Speed Overdrive	50-70 (70-98)
SROD 4-Speed (2WD)	40-60 (56-84)
T19B 4-Speed	45-60 (63-84)
All Others	60-80 (84-112)

GENERAL MOTORS — TRUCKS & VANS

TRANSFER CASE

"S" SERIES
Removal

1) Disconnect negative battery cable. Place transfer case in "4 Hi" position. Raise vehicle and remove skid plate. Drain transfer case. Mark front and rear output shaft yokes and propeller shafts for reassembly reference and remove shafts.

2) Disconnect speedometer cable and vacuum harness from transfer case. Remove shift lever from case. Remove catalytic converter hanger bolts at converter. Raise transmission and transfer case assembly with jack and remove transmission mount bolts. Remove mount.

3) Lower complete assembly, support transfer case only and remove transmission-to-transfer case attaching bolts. Separate transfer case from extension housing and remove from vehicle.

Installation

Reverse removal procedures to install. Always use a new gasket between the transfer case and the extension housing.

TRANSMISSION

ALL EXCEPT "S" & "K" SERIES
Removal

1) On models with 117 MM 4-speed, remove attaching screws from shift lever boot retainer. Slide boot assembly up shift lever and remove lever. To remove shift lever, push down on collar and turn counter-clockwise.

2) On all models, raise and support vehicle under frame. Drain fluid from transmission. Disconnect speedometer cable at transmission. Remove shift controls from transmission (if not already removed). Remove parking brake lever, controls, and back-up switch wire as needed.

3) Disconnect propeller shaft at transmission and position support under transmission assembly. Disconnect exhaust pipes from exhaust manifolds as needed. Remove frame crossmember and flywheel inspection plate.

4) On 117 MM 4-speed, remove top 2 transmission-to-clutch housing bolts and install guide pins. On all models, remove all transmission-to-clutch housing attaching bolts, slide transmission rearward until input shaft is clear of clutch hub and remove assembly from vehicle. Remove guide pins if used.

NOTE: Support clutch release bearing and support assembly when removing transmission main drive gear from flywheel housing. This will prevent release bearing from falling out of flywheel housing.

Installation

Apply a light coating of high temperature grease to main drive gear bearing retainer and splined portion of transmission main drive gear shaft. Reverse removal procedures to complete installation.

ALL "K" SERIES
Removal

1) On models with 117 MM 4-speed, remove attaching screws from shift lever boot retainer. Slide boot assembly up shift lever and remove lever. To remove shift lever, push down on collar and turn counter-clockwise.

2) On all models, raise and support vehicle under frame. Drain fluid from transmission and transfer case. Disconnect speedometer cable. Disconnect front and rear propeller shafts at transfer case and wire out of way. Disconnect transfer case shift lever.

3) Position support under transfer case. Remove transfer case-to-adapter bolts and remove transfer case. Disconnect shift control rods from shifter levers if not already removed. Separate exhaust pipes from exhaust manifolds as needed.

4) Support rear part of engine and remove 2 adapter bolts. Remove crossmember. Remove 2 top transmission-to-clutch housing cap screws. Insert 2 guide pins (J-1126 on 117 MM, J-2216 all others) in holes. Remove 2 lower transmission-to-clutch housing cap screws.

5) Slide transmission and adapter assembly rearward until clutch gear is free of splines in clutch disc. Guide pins will support transmission and prevent damage to clutch disc. Remove transmission and adapter as an assembly. Remove adapter from transmission.

Installation

Apply a light coating of high temperature grease to main drive gear bearing retainer and splined portion of transmission main drive gear shaft. Reverse removal procedures to complete installation.

ALL "S" SERIES

NOTE: If vehicle is a 4WD model, refer to Transfer Case removal procedures and remove case.

Removal

1) Disconnect negative battery cable. On 77.5 MM 4-speed, remove upper starter motor nut. On all models, remove shift lever boot screws and slide boot up shift lever. Shift transmission into neutral and remove shift lever bolts at transmission. Remove shift lever.

2) Disconnect electrical connector and clip at transmission, if present. Raise vehicle and remove propeller shaft. Disconnect exhaust pipe at manifold, if needed.

3) Disconnect speedometer cable, electrical connector and clutch cable at transmission. Support transmission on jack and remove mount attaching bolts. Remove catalytic converter hanger. Remove crossmember attaching bolts and crossmember. Remove flywheel inspection cover.

4) On 77.5 MM 4-speed, remove lower starter motor attaching bolt. Remove body mounting bolts on left side of body and loosen radiator support bolt. Raise cab on left side as needed to remove upper bell housing attaching bolts. Support cab with wood block between frame and cab.

5) Remove transmission-to-engine bolts on all models. Remove transmission.

Installation

Reverse removal procedures to install transmission, noting the following: On 77 MM 4-speed, coat main drive gear bearing retainer and splined portion of transmission main drive gear with high temperature grease before installation.

Manual Transmission Removal

GENERAL MOTORS — TRUCKS & VANS (Cont.)

TIGHTENING SPECIFICATIONS

Application	Ft. Lbs. (N.m)
Transmission-to-Clutch Housing	
"S" Series	
1.9L 4-Cylinder	25 (35)
2.8L V6	55 (75)
All Others	75 (102)
Crossmember-to-Frame	
"S" Series	25 (35)
All Others	55-65 (75-88)
Crossmember-to-Mount	
"S" Series	25 (35)
All Others	40-45 (54-61)
Mount-to-Transmission Bolt	35 (50)
Radiator Support Mounting Bolt	45-60 (60-84)
Cab Mounting Bolts	45-60 (60-84)
Transfer Case-to-Extension Housing	
"S" Series	19-29 (26-40)
All Others	26-40 (36-56)
Adapter-to-Transmission	
"S" Series	20-25 (28-35)
All Others	26-40 (36-56)

JEEP

ALL MODELS

1) Remove screws attaching shift lever boot to floorpan. Slide boot over lever. On models with T4 or T5 transmission, remove shift lever and lever housing from transmission.

2) On models equipped with T-18A transmission, unthread shift lever cap and remove cap, gasket, spring seat, spring and shift lever as an assembly. Remove shift lever locating pins from housing.

3) On models with T-176 transmission, press and turn shift lever retainer counterclockwise to release lever. Remove lever, boot, spring and seat as an assembly.

4) On all models, raise vehicle and support with safety stands. Disconnect rear propeller shaft from transfer case and wire out of way. Do not allow shaft to hang free, as damage to universal joint may result.

5) On Cherokee, Wagoneer and Truck models, disconnect front parking brake cable at equalizer. Remove rear cable clip from crossmember. On all models, place a jack under clutch housing to support engine. Remove rear crossmember from frame.

6) Disconnect speedometer cable, back-up light switch wire and 4WD indicator switch wire. Disconnect transfer case vent hose. Disconnect front propeller shaft and wire out of way.

7) On "CJ" and Scrambler models, remove transfer case shift lever by removing shifter shaft retaining nut. Remove cotter pins retaining shift control link pins in

shift rods and remove pins. Remove shifter shaft and disengage shift lever from shift control links. Move lever out of the way.

NOTE: **On some models, shifter shaft must be unthreaded from shift lever in order to be removed. On other models, shaft can be removed by sliding it out of lever.**

8) On Cherokee, Wagoneer and Truck models, remove cotter pin and washers connecting link to shift lever. Separate link from lever. On all models, support transmission and transfer case with jack.

9) Remove bolts securing transmission to clutch housing and remove transmission and transfer case. Separate transfer case and transmission.

Installation

Reverse removal procedures to install transmission. Adjust clutch and shift linkage.

TIGHTENING SPECIFICATIONS

Application	Ft. Lbs. (N.m)
Transmission-to-Clutch Housing	55 (75)
Transmission Cover Bolts	55-65 (75-88)
Housing-to-Transmission Case	40-45 (54-61)
Crossmember Attaching Bolts	34-40 (47-54)
Filler Plug	13-15 (18-20)

GENERAL MANUAL TRANSMISSION/TRANSAXLE TROUBLE SHOOTING

It is essential that thorough trouble shooting and diagnostic procedures be followed prior to disassembly of any transmissions/transaxle components for repair. Shift difficulties are frequently caused by conditions outside the transmission/transaxle such as linkage, cable, alignment of assemblies or clutch problems.

Drive train noises may come from many sources, such as tires, road surfaces, wheel bearings, drive axles, engine or exhaust system, etc. Adjustment or replacement of transmission/transaxle parts will not correct these problems. Gear "roll-over" noise is inherent in most constant mesh transmissions and will disappear when clutch is disengaged or transmission is in gear. Clutch release bearing noise will disappear when clutch release mechanism is moved enough to slide release bearing away from contact with pressure plate. DO NOT attempt transmission/transaxle repairs to correct gear roll-over or clutch release bearing noise.

If noise persists, drive vehicle on a smooth asphalt road to reduce tire and body noises. With vehicle fully warmed up, note speed and in which gear noise appears, whether noise occurs on pull, coast, or steady drive conditions. Refer to following conditions and possible causes and take appropriate corrective action.

CONDITION & POSSIBLE CAUSE	CONDITION & POSSIBLE CAUSE
Noisy in Forward Gears • Improper type or quantity of lubicant. • Contaminated lubricant. • Road or tire noise. • Drive axle/shaft noise telescoped to transmission. • Vehicle body or chassis components grounding on transmission. • Exhaust system grounding on chassis. • Transmission or clutch housing bolts loose. • Clutch housing misaligned with crankshaft. • Worn bearings or gears. • Brake noise telescoped through drive train. • Loose or worn engine mounts. • Speedometer gear/teeth worn. **Gear Clash when Shifting Forward Gears** • Engine idle speed too high. • Clutch out of adjustment. • Shift linkage damaged or out of adjustment. • Pilot bushing or bearing damaged. • Gears or synchros damaged. • Insufficient or improper lubricant. **Transmission Shifts Hard** • Clutch out of adjustment. • Incorrect or insufficient lubricant. • Clutch disc warped or deformed. • Shift lever or rail binding or deformed. • Sliding gears or synchro rings binding. • Pilot bearing binding. • Housing and/or shafts out of alignment. • Shift linkage binding or in need of lubricant. **Will Not Shift into One Gear — Shifts into All Others** • Shift linkage out of adjustment. • Shift linkage damaged or worn. • Back-up switch ball frozen or damaged. • Damaged or worn synchro sleeves or hubs. • Internal gearshift mechanism worn, damaged or improperly adjusted.	**Locked in One Gear — Cannot be Shifted Out** • Shift linkage damaged or out of adjustment. • Gearshift internal mechanism worn, broken or misadjusted. • Broken gear teeth on clutch shaft, countershaft gear or reverse idler gear. • Shift fork loose on shift rail. **Transmission Jumps Out of Gear** • Shift linkage damaged or out of adjustment. • Engine mounts loose or broken. • Engine, transmission, or shift lever bolts loose. • Clutch shaft or roller bearings worn. • Clutch housing misaligned with crankshaft. • Pilot bushing or bearing worn. • Gear teeth worn or tapered. • Internal shift mechanism worn, damaged or misadjusted. • Shift lever seal binding. **Shift Linkage Binds, Sticks or Rattles** • Shift rods or cables out of adjustment. • Steering column shift tube out of alignment. • Console shift assembly damaged or worn. • Engine and/or transmission mounts worn or broken. • Shift lever pivot balls worn or loose. • Control assembly body weld bolts missing or loose. • Shift linkage bushings worn, broken or missing. **Transmission Leaks** • Incorrect lubricant. • Transmission/transaxle overfilled. • Shift lever seal. • Propeller shaft yoke worn. • Extension housing oil seal. • Components other than transmission leaking.

General Servicing

DRIVE AXLE GEAR TOOTH PATTERNS

INSPECTION

Wipe lubricant from internal parts. Rotate gears and inspect for wear or damage. Mount a dial indicator to housing and check backlash at several points around ring gear. Backlash must be within specifications at all points. If no defects are found, check gear tooth contact patterns.

GEAR TOOTH CONTACT PATTERN

NOTE: Drive pattern should be well centered on ring gear teeth. Coast pattern should be centered but may be slightly toward toe of ring gear teeth.

1) Paint ring gear teeth with gear marking compound. Apply some form of load to differential case to resist rotation. Rotate pinion gear until ring gear has made 1 full revolution.

2) Turn pinion gear in opposite direction to complete 1 full revolution of ring gear. Examine ring gear teeth for contact pattern. Correct as necessary by moving appropriate shims.

ADJUSTMENTS

GEAR BACKLASH & PINION SHIM CHANGES

NOTE: Change in tooth pattern is directly related to change in shim and/or backlash adjustment.

1) With no change in backlash, moving pinion further from ring gear moves drive pattern toward heel and top of tooth, and moves coast pattern toward toe and top of tooth.

2) With no change in backlash, moving pinion closer to ring gear moves drive pattern toward toe and bottom of tooth, and moves coast pattern toward heel and bottom of tooth.

3) With no change in pinion shim thickness, an increase in backlash moves ring gear further from pinion. Drive pattern moves toward heel and top of tooth, and coast pattern moves toward heel and top of tooth.

4) With no change in pinion shim thickness, a decrease in backlash moves ring gear closer to pinion gear. Drive pattern moves toward toe and bottom of tooth, and coast pattern moves toward toe and bottom of tooth.

Fig. 1: Drive Axle Gear Tooth Patterns Showing Necessary Corrections

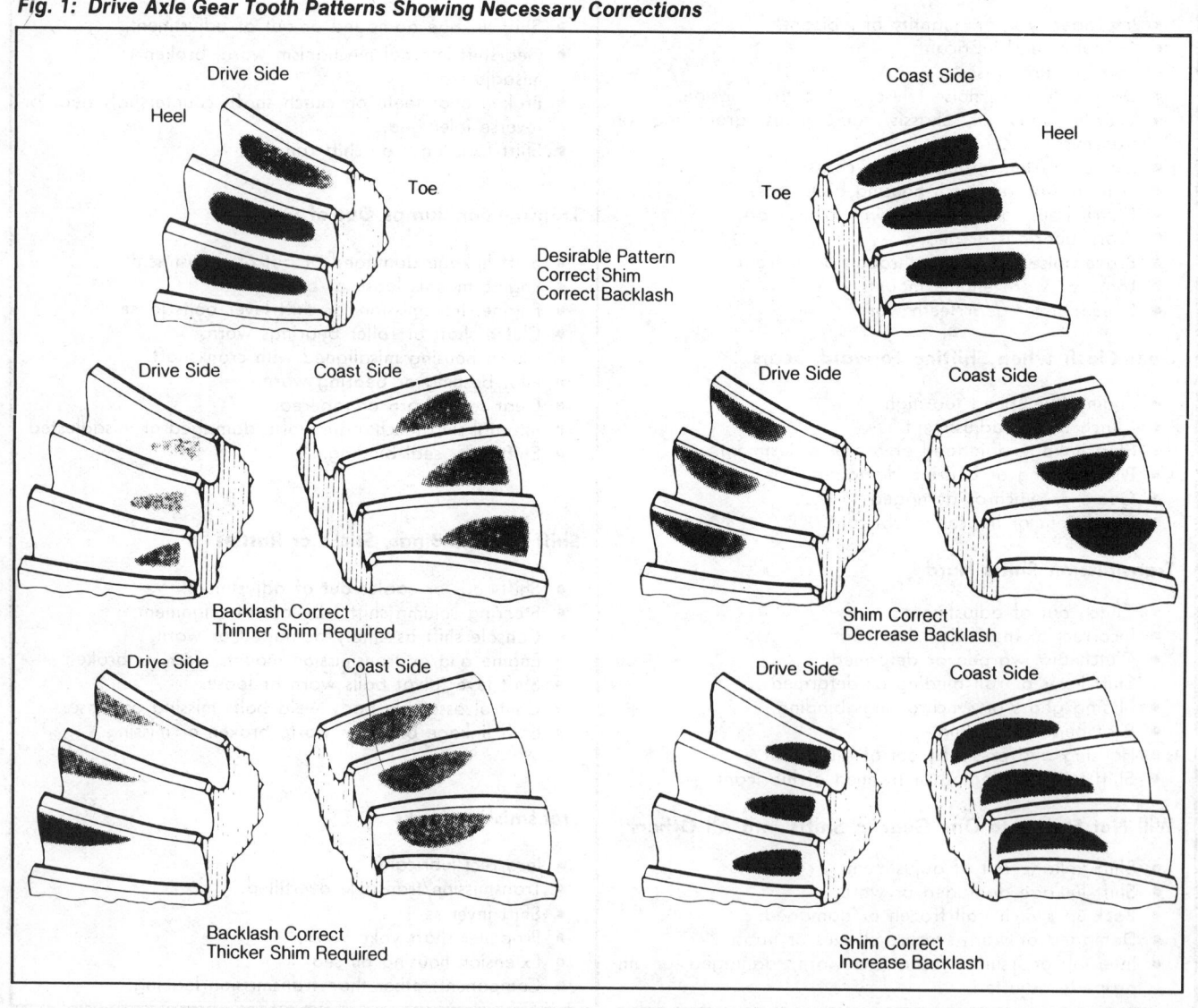

SECTION 2

DOMESTIC AUTOMATIC TRANSMISSIONS

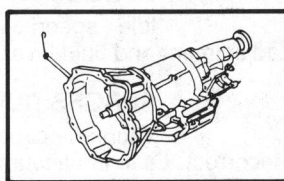

NOTE: ALSO SEE GENERAL INDEX.

AMC/RENAULT ALLIANCE MB1

APPLICATION

All Alliance models with automatic transaxle use the Renault model MB1.

IDENTIFICATION

Transmission identification number is stamped on metal tag attached to transaxle case under a rear case-to-intermediate case attaching bolt. Model is identified by "TYPE MB1" stamped on tag.

Fig. 1: Transaxle Identification Tag

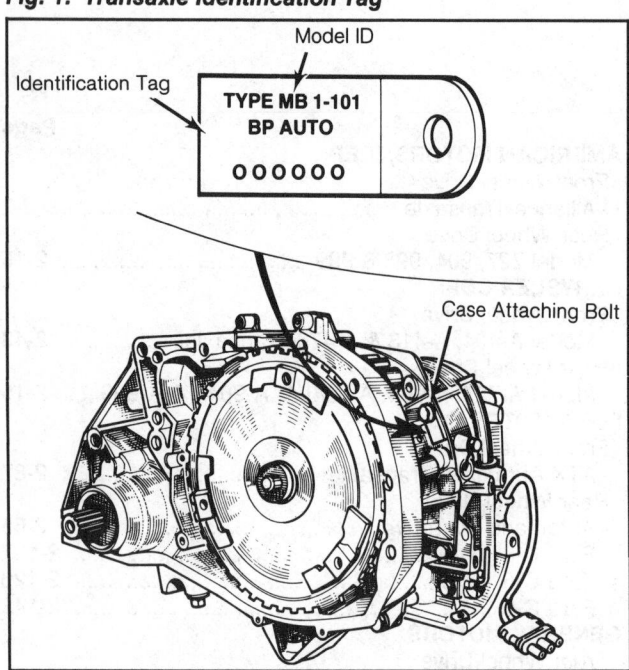

Always replace tag when reassembling transaxle case.

DESCRIPTION

The Renault MB1 automatic transaxle is a 3-speed unit consisting basically of the torque converter, differential assembly and transmission. The differential assembly consists primarily of the differential case and 2 planetary gears. Step down gears are used to change direction of the drive centerline.

The transmission assembly consists of 2 planetary gear sets, a clutch assembly (containing 2 clutches), 2 brakes, a one-way clutch and the transmission control systems. Control systems are of 3 types: mechanical, hydraulic and electrical.

LUBRICATION & ADJUSTMENT

See the appropriate article in AUTOMATIC TRANSMISSION SERVICING Section.

TROUBLE SHOOTING

After each vehicle condition, several possible causes of that condition are listed. Refer to *Component Testing* when specific components are called out.

ENGINE IDLES ROUGH OR STALLS

Idle speed incorrect. Check ignition timing and spark plug condition. Check throttle cable adjustment. Check vacuum capsule and line for leak in vacuum circuit.

VEHICLE CREEPS IN "N"

Shift lever out of adjustment. E1-E2 clutch defective or damaged.

EXCESSIVE CREEPING IN "D"

Idle speed incorrect. Check throttle cable adjustment. Torque converter damaged.

SLIPS WHEN STARTING IN "D" OR "R"

Incorrect fluid level. Vacuum capsule adjustment (oil pressure) incorrect. Faulty or defective valve body. Torque converter damaged.

SLIPS WHEN STARTING IN "D", ONLY

Defective E1-E2 clutch. Defective or damaged one-way clutch.

SLIPS DURING SHIFTS

Vacuum capsule adjustment (oil pressure) incorrect. Faulty or defective valve body. Oil pump screen clogged. Faulty E1-E2 clutch assembly or F2 brake.

SURGES WHEN MOVING OFF

Idle speed incorrect. Check throttle cable adjustment and fluid level.

SURGES DURING SHIFTS

Vacuum capsule adjustment (oil pressure) incorrect. Leak in vacuum circuit. Faulty or defective valve body.

SHIFT SPEEDS INCORRECT

Check throttle cable and throttle position sensor adjustment. Faulty wiring or loose ground connections. Kickdown switch or control computer faulty. Defective vehicle speed sensor.

NO MOVEMENT

In "D" Only

Shift lever out of adjustment. Incorrect fluid level. Faulty or defective valve body. Defective oil pump or pump screen clogged. Oil pump shaft or turbine shaft damaged. Final drive damaged. Converter drive plate or torque converter damaged. Faulty E1-E2 clutch assembly.

In "D" or "1"

Faulty or defective valve body. Faulty E1-E2 clutch assembly. Defective or damaged one-way clutch.

In "R" or 3rd Gear

Faulty or defective valve body. Faulty E1-E2 clutch assembly.

NO REVERSE

Faulty multi-function switch. Faulty or defective valve body or F1 brake.

NO 1ST GEAR IN "D"

Faulty wiring or loose ground connections. Solenoid valves damaged. Defective or damaged one-way clutch.

AMC/RENAULT ALLIANCE MB1 (Cont.)

NO 2ND GEAR IN "D"

Faulty wiring or loose ground connections. Faulty or defective valve body or F2 brake.

NO 3RD GEAR IN "D"

Faulty wiring or loose ground connections. Control computer faulty. Solenoid valves damaged. Faulty multi-function switch. Faulty or defective valve body.

NO 1ST GEAR HOLD

Shift lever out of adjustment. Faulty wiring or loose ground connections. Control computer faulty. Faulty multi-function switch or valve body.

NO 2ND GEAR HOLD

Shift lever out of adjustment. Faulty wiring or loose ground connections. Control computer faulty. Faulty multi-function switch.

REMAINS IN 1ST IN "D"

Faulty wiring or loose ground connections. Control computer faulty. Solenoid valves damaged. Vehicle speed sensor defective. Faulty or defective valve body.

REMAINS IN 3RD GEAR

Check fuses. Check for damaged wiring or loose ground connections. Control computer faulty. Defective oil pump. Faulty or defective valve body.

SKIPS SOME GEARS, SHIFT LEVER ABNORMAL

Shift lever or selector control out of adjustment. Faulty manual valve control.

IMPROPER OPERATION IN "P"

Shift lever out of adjustment. Faulty manual valve control.

STARTER NOT WORKING

Shift lever or selector control incorrectly adjusted. Faulty wiring or loose ground connections. Control computer faulty. Faulty multi-function switch.

NO BACKUP LIGHTS

Shift lever or selector control incorrectly adjusted. Faulty wiring or loose ground connections. Control computer faulty. Faulty multi-function switch.

TESTING

TESTING EQUIPMENT

No special equipment is needed for road testing. Diagnosis of the electrical control system of the MB1 transaxle is possible with a volt-ohmmeter. However, the use of Renault test box B. Vi. 958 will both reduce time required for diagnosis and give more accurate test results.

Procedures given here are for testing with standard shop equipment (volt-ohmmeter).

ROAD TEST

1) Before road testing, make sure that fluid level and condition and control linkage (cable) adjustments have been checked and corrected as needed. During test, transaxle should upshift and downshift at approximately the speeds shown in *Shift Speed Specifications* chart.

2) All shifts may vary somewhat due to production tolerances or tire size. What is important is the quality of the shifts. All shifts should be smooth, responsive and with no slippage or engine speed runaway.

SHIFT SPEED SPECIFICATIONS

Application	Shift Speed (MPH)
Closed Throttle	
1-2 Upshift	16
2-3 Upshift	28
3-2 Downshift	16
2-1 Downshift	9
Full Throttle [1]	
1-2 Upshift	37
2-3 Upshift	62
3-2 Downshift	40
2-1 Downshift	25
Kickdown [1]	
1-2 Upshift	43
2-3 Upshift	68
3-2 Downshift	59
2-1 Downshift	34

[1] — Full throttle test is with kickdown switch disconnected. Connect switch for kickdown test.

3) Slippage or engine speed runaway in any gear usually indicates clutch or brake problems. The slipping unit in a particular gear can usually be identified

TRANSAXLE COMPONENT APPLICATION CHART (ELEMENTS IN USE)

Selector Lever Position	E1 Clutch	E2 Clutch	F1 Brake	F2 Brake	One-Way Clutch	Solenoid Valve 1	Solenoid Valve 2
D — DRIVE							
First	X				X		X
Second	X			X		X	X
Third	X	X					
2 — SECOND HOLD	X			X		X	X
1 — FIRST HOLD	X		X				X
R — REVERSE		X	X				X
NEUTRAL OR PARK							X

Automatic Transmissions

AMC/RENAULT ALLIANCE MB1 (Cont.)

by noting transaxle operation in other selector positions and comparing which internal units are applied in those positions. *See Transaxle Component Application Chart.*

4) This process of elimination can be used to detect any unit which slips, and to confirm proper operation of good units; however, the actual cause of the malfuncion usually cannot be easily determined. Practically any condition can be caused by electrical control system malfunction. Therefore, unless an obvious condition exists, do not disassemble transaxle until electronic diagnosis of transaxle controls has been made.

GEAR SHIFT PHASING TEST

NOTE: Shift cable must be properly adjusted before performing test.

1) Drive vehicle with gear selector lever in "1" position. Increase speed to about 35 MPH. Transaxle should remain in low range. If transaxle shifts to 2nd gear, replace multifunction switch.

2) Move selector lever to "2" position and maintain sustained speed of 35 MPH. Transaxle should shift automatically from low range to 2nd gear. If not, multifunction switch should be replaced.

3) With gear selector lever still in "2" position, increase vehicle speed to 50 MPH. Transaxle should remain in 2nd gear. If shift to 3rd occurs, replace

multifunction switch. If all tests are satisfactory, shift operation is correct.

4) In any test, if multifunction switch is replaced and problem remains, check control module electrical connections. If connections are good, replace control module.

ELECTRONIC CONTROL COMPONENT TESTING

6-Way Connector

1) With connector unplugged from control module and ignition off, check resistance between pin "B" and ground. If resistance is not 1-7 ohms, check backup light bulbs and wiring circuit. Repair as needed.

2) Connect voltmeter between terminal "A" and ground. With ignition off, voltage should be 10-14 volts. If not, check backup light fuse and accessory plate wiring. Repair as needed.

3) Turn ignition switch on and check resistance from terminal "E" to ground. If resistance is not zero, check chassis ground circuit and repair as needed.

4) Connect voltmeter between terminal "F" and ground with ignition switch on. Voltage reading should be 10-14 volts. If not, check power supply circuit to control module. Repair wiring as needed.

5) Connect voltmeter between terminal "C" and ground. Check voltage reading while operating

Fig. 2: Electronic Control Module With Electrical Components & Connectors

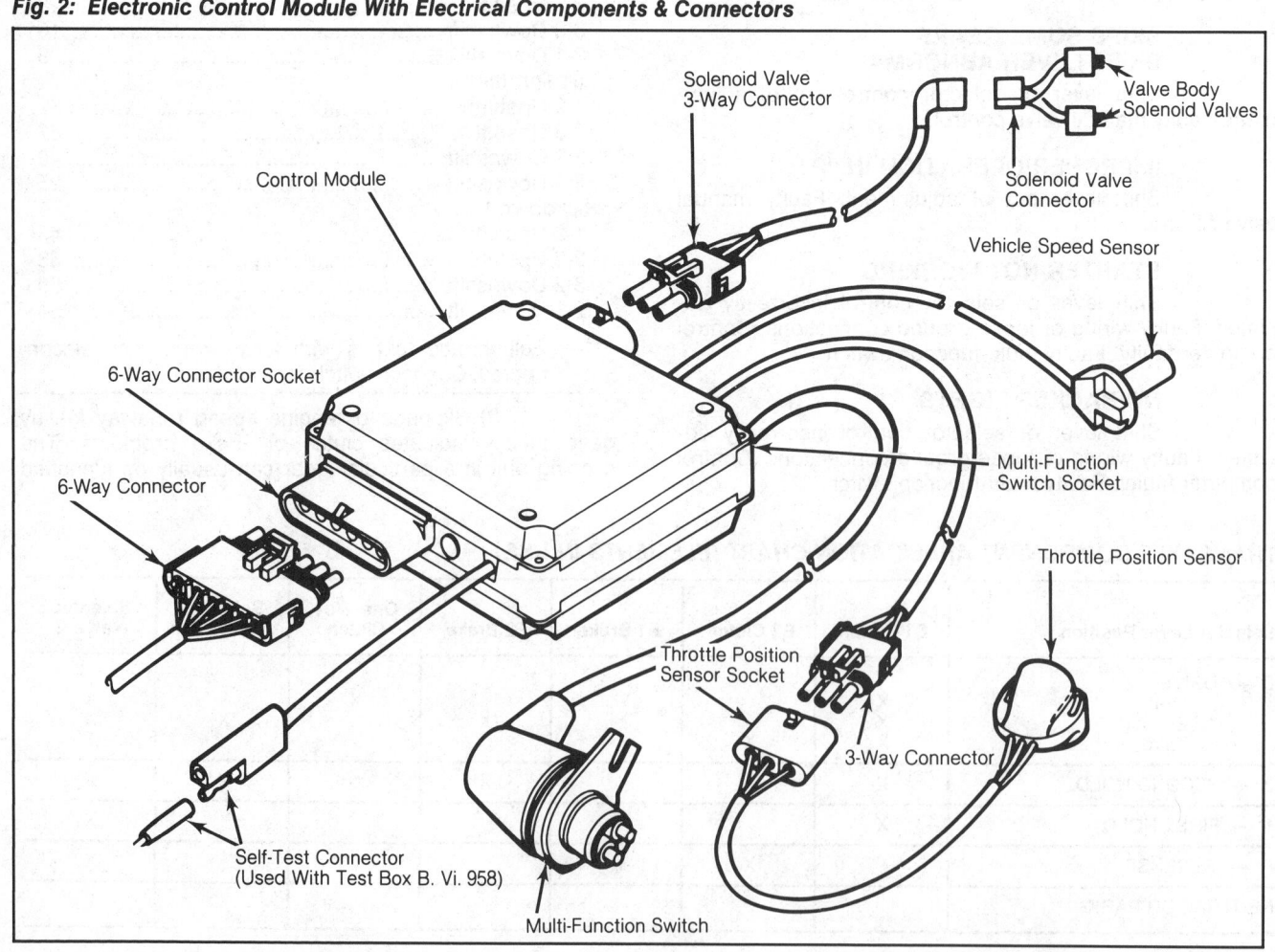

AMC/RENAULT ALLIANCE MB1 (Cont.)

starter. If reading is not 10-14 volts, check starter, starter relay and wiring circuit. Repair or replace as needed.

Fig. 3: 6-Way Connector Terminal Identification

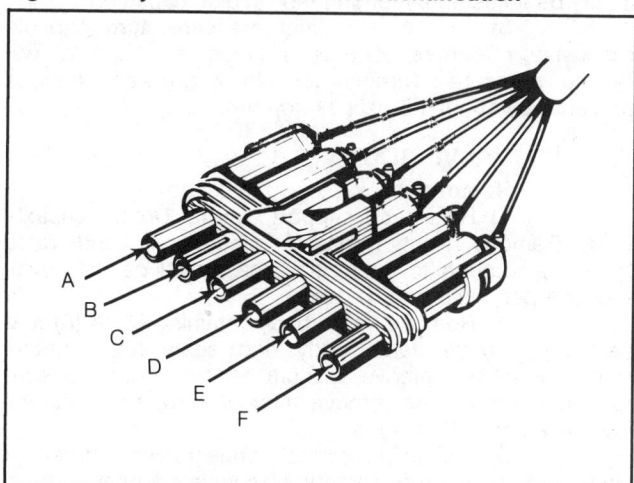

Fig. 4: 3-Way Connector Terminal Identification

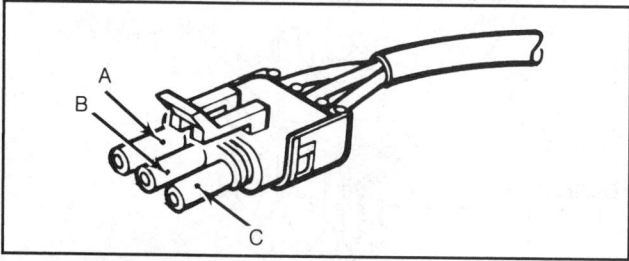

Terminal identification is the same for both 3 terminal connectors.

3-Way Connector

With ignition switch on, connect voltmeter between terminal "B" (center terminal) and ground. Reading should be 3.8-4.8 volts. If not, perform 6-way connector test. If 6-way connector check reveals no problems, control module is defective and should be replaced.

Solenoid Valves & Harness

1) Disconnect solenoid valve connector at control module. Check resistance between terminals "A" and "C" of connector. *See Fig. 4.* Reading on ohmmeter should be 20-40 ohms. If resistance is zero, closely inspect wiring harness from connector to solenoid valves and repair or replace as needed. If harness is OK, replace solenoid valves.

2) If resistance value in step 1) is between 40 and 80 ohms, connection is loose or dirty. Inspect and repair.

3) Check resistance between terminals "B" and "C". If resistance value is not 20-40 ohms, inspect wiring and replace if damaged. If wiring harness is OK, replace solenoid valves.

4) Connect ohmmeter between terminal "C" and ground. Resistance value should be infinite. If not, solenoid valves are shorted to ground. Check wiring harness for short and repair or replace as needed. If harness is OK, replace solenoid valves.

Solenoid Valves

1) Disconnect wiring harness connector at solenoid valves. Check resistance value between termi-

nals "A" and "C" of solenoid connector. Check value between terminals "B" and "C". Resistance value should be 20-40 ohms in both cases.

2) If either reading is zero, replace the solenoid valves. If resistance value obtained is greater than 40 ohms, but less than 80 ohms, check wiring and connections to solenoid valves. Clean or repair as needed.

3) If resistance between either set of terminals is infinite, replace solenoid valves. Finally, check resistance from terminal "C" to ground. Reading should be infinite. If it is not, there is a short between solenoid valve windings and ground. Replace valves.

Fig. 5: Solenoid Valve Connector Terminal Identification

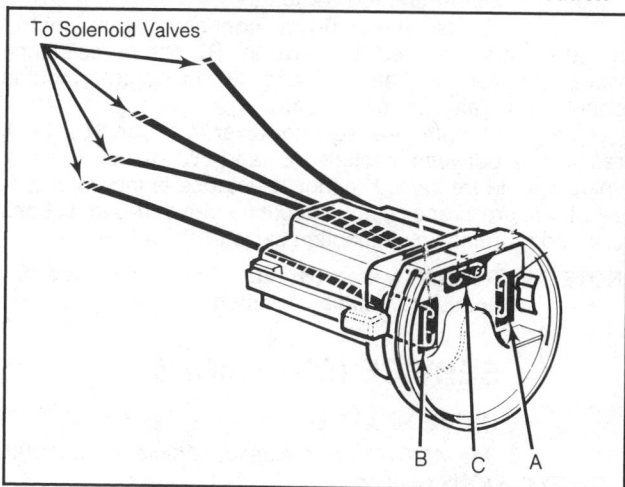

Throttle Position Sensor

1) Unplug throttle position sensor connector. With throttle closed, check resistance between connector sockets "C" and "B". Value should be 3000-5000 ohms. Check resistance between sockets "A" and "B". Value should be 1500-2500 ohms.

2) If either reading in step 1) is incorrect, sensor is either faulty or incorrectly adjusted.

3) With ohmmeter connected between terminals "A" and "B", slowly open throttle from closed to full open position. Resistance value should change with respect to throttle valve position, but should never go to infinity.

Fig. 6: Throttle Position Sensor Socket Identification

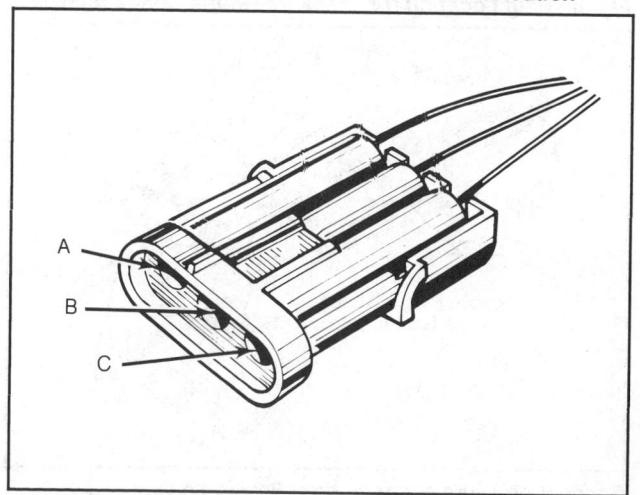

AMC/RENAULT ALLIANCE MB1 (Cont.)

Fig. 7: Multi-Function Switch Socket Identification

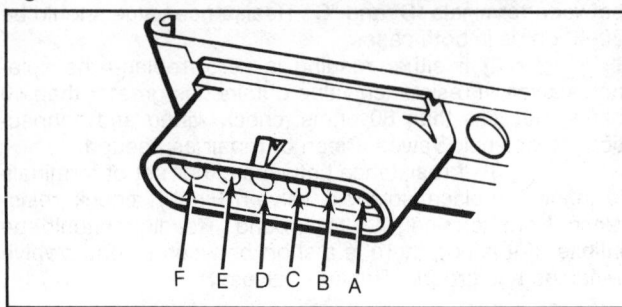

Multi-Function Switch

1) Disconnect 6-way connector from control module. With gear selector lever in "R", check resistance value between sockets "A" and "B" in control module connection. Value should be zero.

2) With gear selector lever in "P" or "N", check resistance between sockets "E" and "C". As in step **1)**, value should be zero. If either resistance is incorrect (not zero), ensure proper electrical connections. If connections are good, replace multifunction switch.

NOTE: Renault tester (B. Vi. 958) is required for complete testing of switch.

SERVICE (IN-VEHICLE)

DRIVE SHAFTS

See *AMC/Renault Alliance* article in *MANUAL TRANSMISSIONS* Section.

VACUUM CAPSULE
Removal

Drain about 2 quarts of fluid from transaxle. Remove vacuum hose from capsule. Remove retaining bolt and retainer. Remove capsule.

Installation

Reverse removal procedure to install capsule. Add fluid to proper level.

Oil Pressure Check & Adjustment

1) Remove lower plug on side of transaxle case. *See Fig. 8.* Install pressure gauge (B. Vi. 466-04) at port and position gauge so that it may be seen from inside vehicle.

Fig. 8: Plug Location for Pressure Gauge Connection

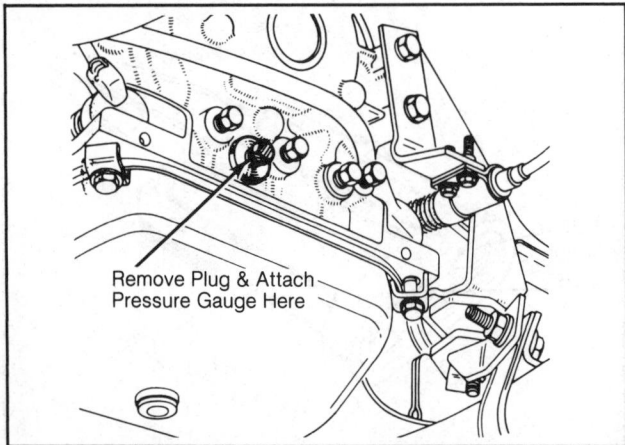

Connect pressure gauge at port. Position gauge so that it may be seen from inside vehicle.

2) Test drive vehicle and note pressure on gauge just before full-throttle 2-3 upshift. Pressure reading should be 75 psi (5.3 kg/cm²). If fluid pressure is incorrect it may be adjusted by turning the vacuum capsule.

3) To increase fluid pressure, turn capsule clockwise. Counterclockwise rotation of capsule will reduce pressure. Turning capsule 2 notches changes pressure by about 1.5 psi (.11 kg/cm²).

VALVE BODY
Removal

1) Raise and support vehicle. Drain transaxle fluid. Remove front transaxle mount bolt and raise transaxle enough to gain clearance for oil pan removal. Remove pan, filter and "O" ring.

2) Remove valve body retaining bolts (8) and carefully remove valve body and seals (2). Remove regulator valve. Remove vacuum capsule from pressure regulator valve, then remove manual valve from manual lever assembly. *See Fig. 9.*

3) Locate electrical connector in corner of case, remove retaining clip and disconnect connector.

Fig. 9: Removing Valve Body From Transaxle Case

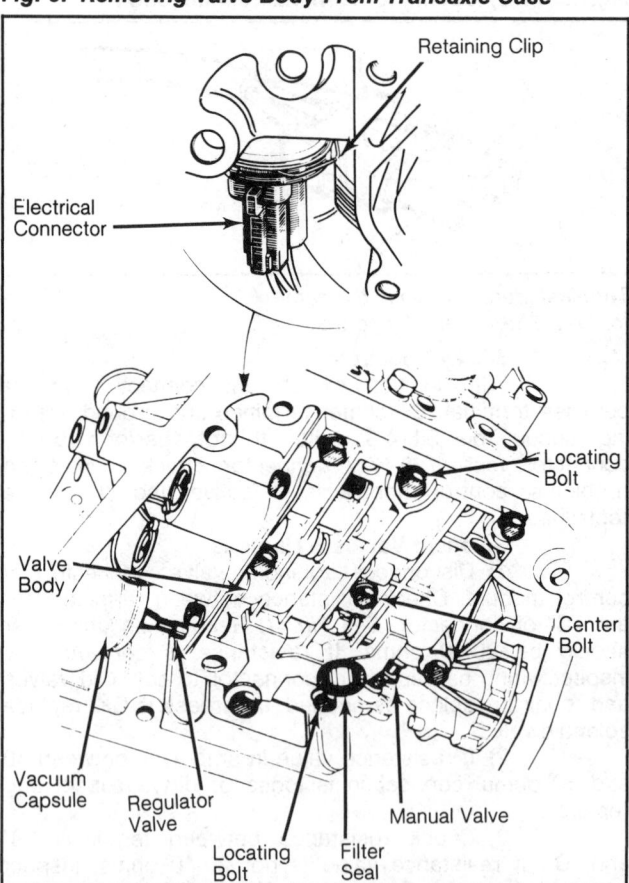

Use center bolt to support valve body during installation. Tighten locating bolts first. Then tighten remaining bolts.

Installation

1) Assemble electrical connector and install in case. Retain with clip. Place valve body and seals in position and install center valve body bolt finger tight.

2) Install manual valve and connect to manual lever. Install vacuum capsule and position it against regulator valve. Install remaining valve body bolts finger tight.

AMC/RENAULT ALLIANCE MB1 (Cont.)

3) Tighten 2 locating bolts. *See Fig. 9*. Tighten remaining bolts, center bolt first. Install oil filter and seal. Install oil pan. Lower transaxle and install transaxle mount bolt. Lower vehicle and fill transaxle with fluid.

THROTTLE POSITION SWITCH

Throttle position information is supplied to the computer by the throttle position sensor. This information is used, in part, to determine optimum gear selection under any given set of operating conditions. Proper sensor adjustment is essential to smooth transaxle operation.

Removal

On models equipped with throttle body fuel injection, remove air cleaner assembly. On all models, disconnect electrical connector from throttle position sensor. Remove attaching screws (2) and remove sensor.

Installation

Reverse removal procedure to install sensor. Whenever sensor is removed, or if a new sensor is installed, it must be adjusted.

**Fig. 10: Throttle Position Sensor —
Location and Adjustment**

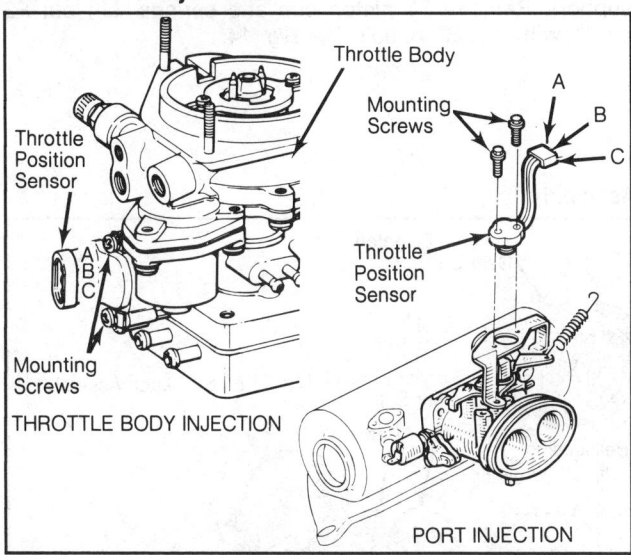

Loosen lower mounting screw to make coarse sensor adjustment, upper screw for fine adjustment.

Adjustment

1) With engine off, turn ignition switch to "ON" position. With electrical connector attached, insert negative probe of digital volt-ohmmeter through back of connector at terminal "C", until probe contacts terminal. Insert positive lead of meter into terminal "B".

2) Hold throttle at wide open position, ensuring that throttle contacts stop. Note exact voltage reading on meter. Reading should be about 4.3 volts. This is input voltage.

3) Remove positive probe from terminal "B" and insert in terminal "A" of connector. With throttle still held in wide open position, check voltage reading. This is output voltage.

4) Output voltage should be within .5% of 4% of input voltage. For example, if input voltage is 5.0 volts, output voltage should be within .03 (.5% of 5) of .20 volts (4% of 5), or .17-.23 volts.

5) If voltage relationship is incorrect, loosen bottom mounting screw and pivot sensor to make coarse adjustment. Tighten screw. Loosen upper mounting screw and pivot sensor to make fine adjustment.

SPEEDOMETER PINION OIL SEAL

Removal

NOTE: Special tool (B. Vi. 905) should be used to remove seal. It includes an extractor, nut, 2 spacers and an inserting tool.

1) Disconnect speedometer cable at transaxle. With nut and thin spacer installed on extractor, screw extractor into case until it contacts seal.

2) Turn extractor in an additional 3 turns to engage seal. Tighten nut while holding extractor in position. As nut is tightened, seal will be pulled from case.

Fig. 11: Replacing Speedometer Pinion Oil Seal

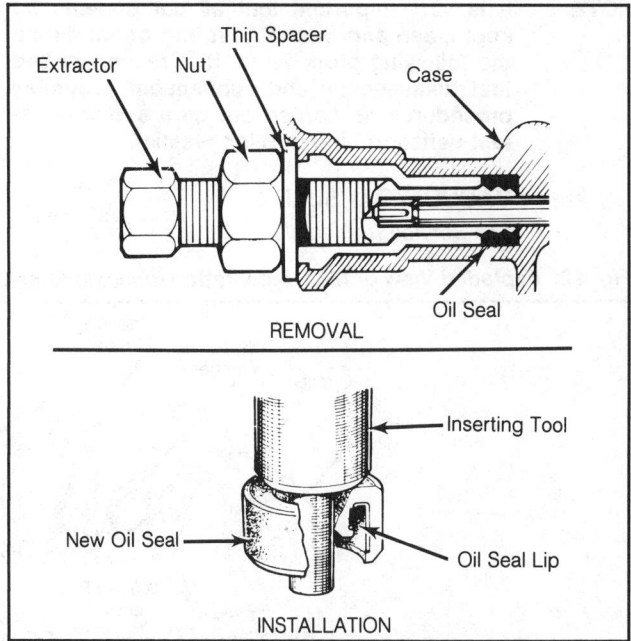

Place seal on inserting tool as shown and push into case.

Installation

To install new seal, install seal on inserting tool, lip first. Lubricate seal with transmission fluid and push into case.

TRANSAXLE REMOVAL & INSTALLATION

See the appropriate article in Automatic Transmission Removal section.

TORQUE CONVERTER

REMOVAL

With transaxle removed from vehicle, pull torque converter straight out of converter housing. Pry oil seal off of stator support.

AMC/RENAULT ALLIANCE MB1 (Cont.)

INSPECTION

Check general condition of converter components (center boss on flywheel side, seal bearing surface, bushings on 3 mounting points, timing target, etc.). If converter is damaged in any way, it must be replaced. If oil is contaminated by burned brake or clutch linings (black oil and/or burned smell), replace the converter. Inspect stator support in converter housing for nicks or scratches.

INSTALLATION

Install new oil seal on stator support with tool (B. Vi. 962). Lubricate face of seal with transmission fluid. Install converter so that White paint mark on converter is aligned with sharp corners on flex plate. Install retaining lug (B. Vi. 465) to hold converter in place. When transaxle is bolted to engine, remove retaining lug.

TRANSAXLE DISASSEMBLY

NOTE: **It is very important that all components be kept clean and free of dust, dirt or lint during the following procedures. It is recommended that disassembly and subsequent assembly procedures be carried out on a shock resistant bench (rubber or thick plastic).**

VACUUM CAPSULE

See Service (In Vehicle).

VALVE BODY

See Service (In Vehicle).

REAR CASE

1) Remove torque converter from transaxle assembly. With transaxle on work bench, remove case attaching bolts and separate cases. Remove "O" ring from locator bolt. *See Fig. 25.*

2) When separating cases, leave end play adjusting shim in position on output shaft. Lift park wheel and nylon washer from rear case. Remove park latch linkage and safety clip.

3) Remove large circlip. Lift out one-way clutch and reverse planetary gear set. Remove F1 plates and discs. To remove F1 piston, apply compressed air to valve body passage indicated in *Fig. 13.* Note position of springs on piston for reassembly reference and remove springs.

4) Lift out washer, E2 bellhousing, washer, forward planatery gear set, bearing and E1-E2 clutch assembly.

5) Remove circlip and lift out F1 piston carrier, F2 plates and discs, thrust bearing and turbine shaft support. Remove F2 piston cup and springs. Lift out F2 piston with tool B. Vi. 952. *See Fig. 14.*

Fig. 12: Exploded View of MB1 Automatic Transaxle Rear Case Assembly

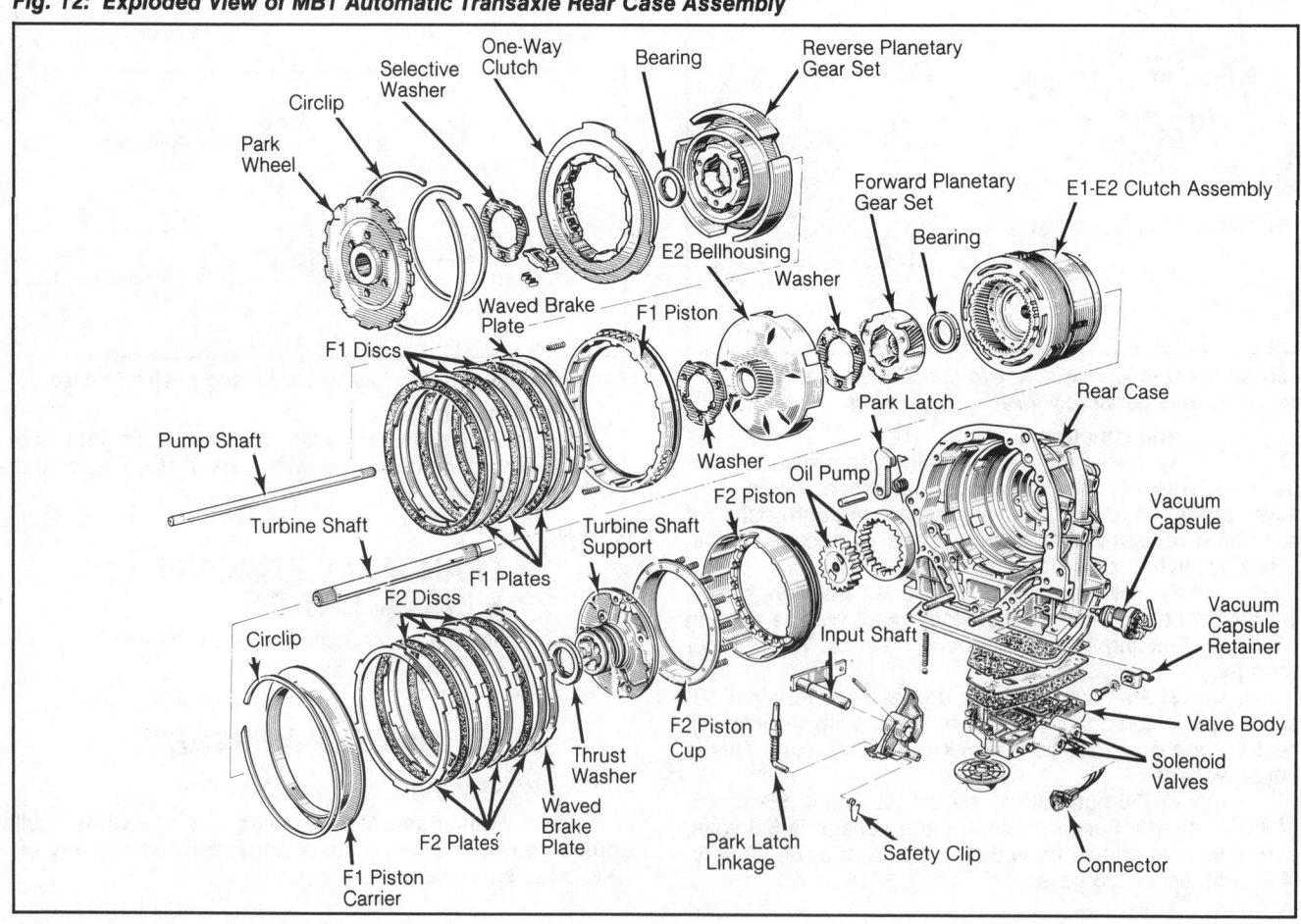

AMC/RENAULT ALLIANCE MB1 (Cont.)

Fig. 13: Removing F1 Piston

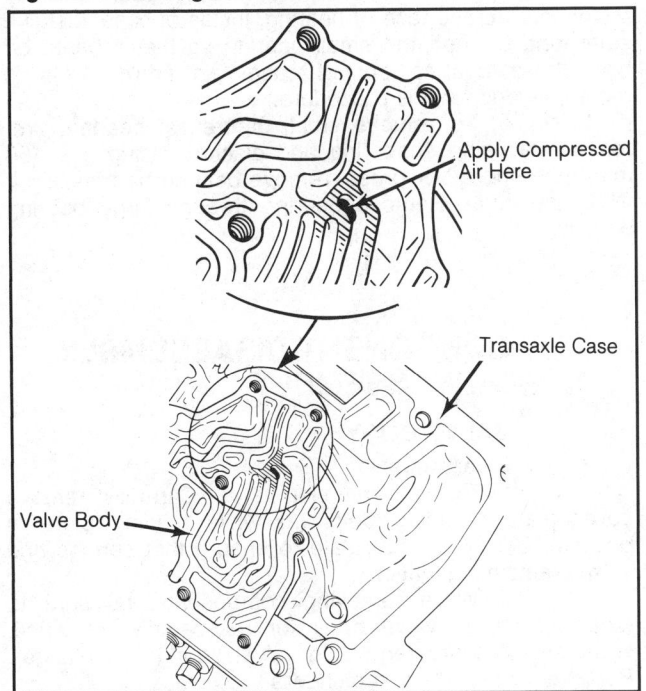

To remove piston, apply compressed air at valve body passage indicated.

Fig. 14: Removing F2 Piston

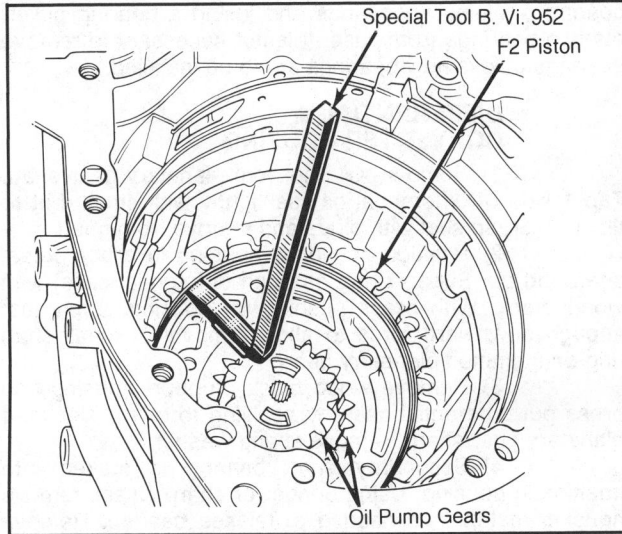

Lift out piston with tool (B. Vi. 952).

INTERMEDIATE CASE

1) If not already separated, remove remaining attaching bolts and separate intermediate case from differential and converter housing. Remove secondary shaft and output shaft snap rings. Remove output shaft assembly, secondary shaft and step down driven gear.

Fig. 15: Exploded View of Intermediate Case, Differential & Converter Housing Assemblies

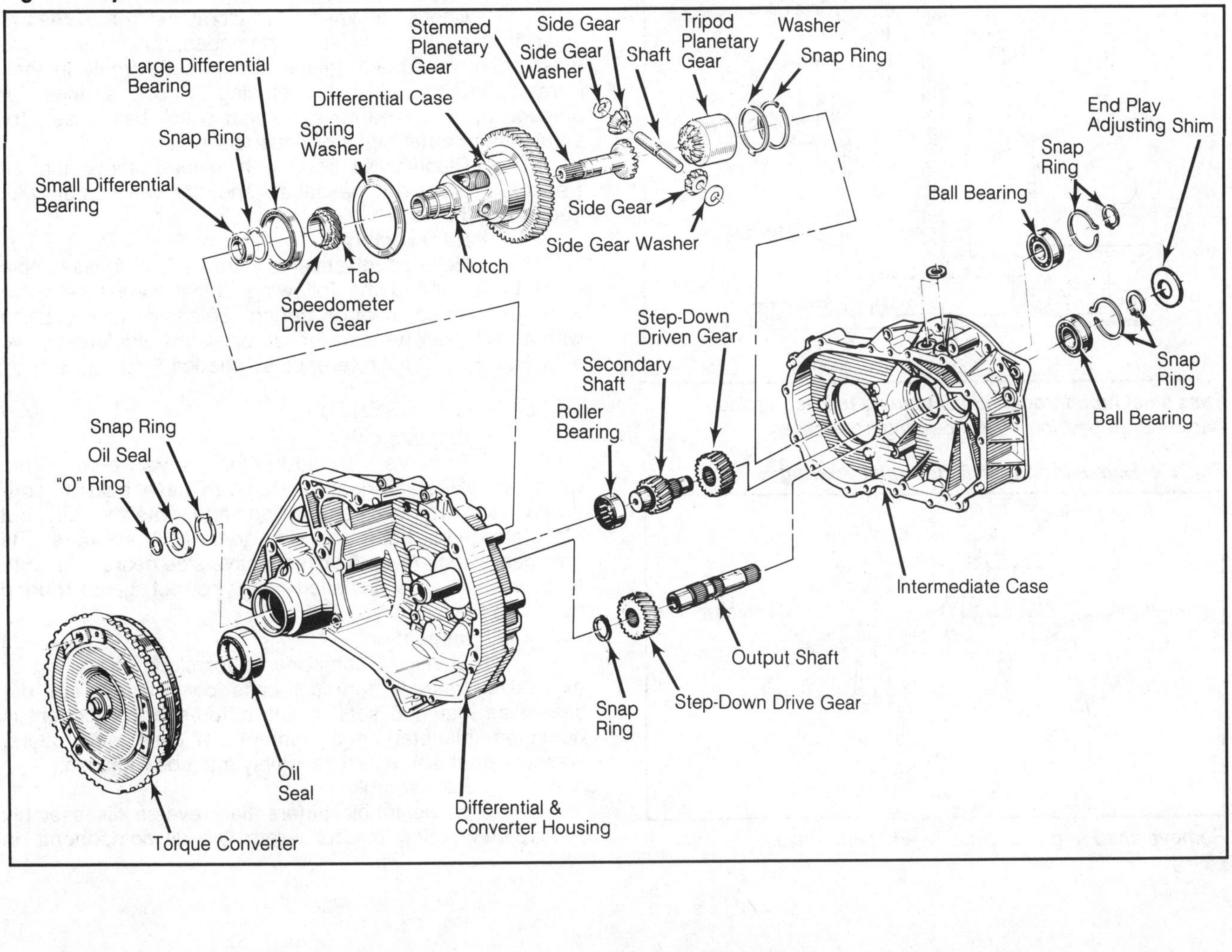

2) If bearings are to be replaced, remove bearing retaining snap rings and, using a bearing puller, remove bearings from case. It is not necessary to remove bearings unless new bearings are to be installed.

DIFFERENTIAL & CONVERTER HOUSING

1) Remove "O" ring from planetary gear shaft. Tap 1 side of differential oil seal lightly with small drift to tilt seal. Grasp seal with pliers and remove from shaft.

2) Position converter housing in arbor press, shaft end up. Support ring gear (on differential case) with wood block. With press pushing on housing, apply just enough downward force to allow removal of small snap ring on stemmed planetary gear.

3) Remove wood block. Support housing and press out differential case by applying force on stemmed planetary gear shaft. Remove spring washer.

4) Secondary shaft bearing is staked into position in housing. Using grinder or sharp chisel, remove housing material as needed to release bearing. Remove bearing.

NOTE: Do not remove secondary shaft bearing and differential bearings unless new bearings are to be installed.

Fig. 16: Removing Large Differential Bearing

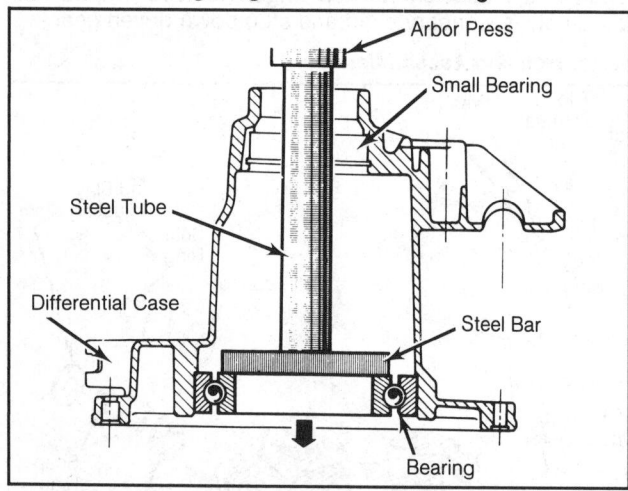

Pass steel tube through small bearing to bear against bar on large bearing. Press bearing from case.

Fig. 17: Removing Small Differential Bearing

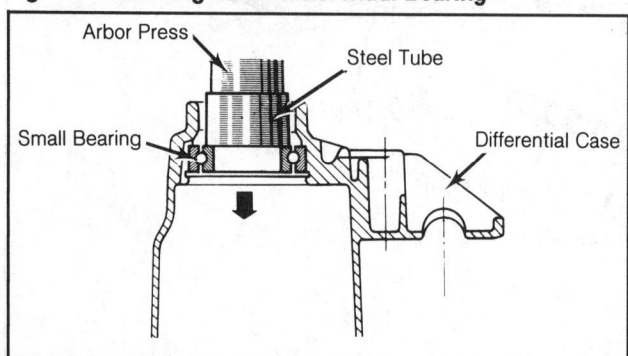

Remove snap ring and press bearing into case.

5) To remove large differential bearing, place a steel bar across face of bearing, inside of case. Install a steel tube through the small bearing so that it bears on bar. Press bearing out of case. An arbor press is recommended for this procedure.

6) To remove small differential bearing, first remove retaining snap ring and discard. Using a 2" (50 mm) tube and arbor press, remove bearing by pressing it INTO the case. Remove bearing through large bearing opening.

COMPONENT DISASSEMBLY & REASSEMBLY

VALVE BODY

Disassembly

1) Remove manual valve. Carefully remove cover plate retaining bolts (2) while holding plate in position. Slowly release plate to ensure that springs and valves remain in position.

2) While removing components, be sure to note position in valve body for reassembly reference. Withdraw pressure regulating valve, spring and plunger. Remove pilot valves and plungers.

3) Remove sequence valves and spring. Remove pressure limiting valve seal. Remove pressure limiting valve, spring and check ball.

Inspection

Check all valves for scratches or excessive wear. If any valve or valves is damaged, entire valve body must be replaced. All valves should slide freely in their bores without sticking or binding. Check springs for damage or collapsed coils. Inspect check ball closely for scratches or other signs of unusual wear.

Clean valve body with mineral spirits and lint free rags. Blow out passages and dry valve body with compressed air.

Reassembly

Reverse disassembly procedure to assemble valve body, noting the following: Install sequence valve with larger head towards spring. Solenoid valve marked with arrow must be installed on pressure regulating valve side. Use *Fig. 18* for reference as needed.

DIFFERENTIAL

Disassembly

Remove speedometer drive gear from stemmed planetary gear shaft. With case held in soft-jawed vice, remove snap ring and washer. Lift out planetary gears, shaft and side gears (with washers). Tie side gear washers to their respective side gears to ensure that washers are installed with correct gears during transaxle reassembly.

Inspection

Check all components for signs of scoring or excessive wear. Differential case components are designed as matched sets. If any differential component is damaged (planetary gear, differential case, side gears, washers or shaft), entire assembly must be replaced.

Reassembly

To assemble differential, reverse disassembly procedures noting the following: Dip all components in

AMC/RENAULT ALLIANCE MB1 (Cont.)

Fig. 18: Exploded View of Renault Model MB1 Valve Body Assembly

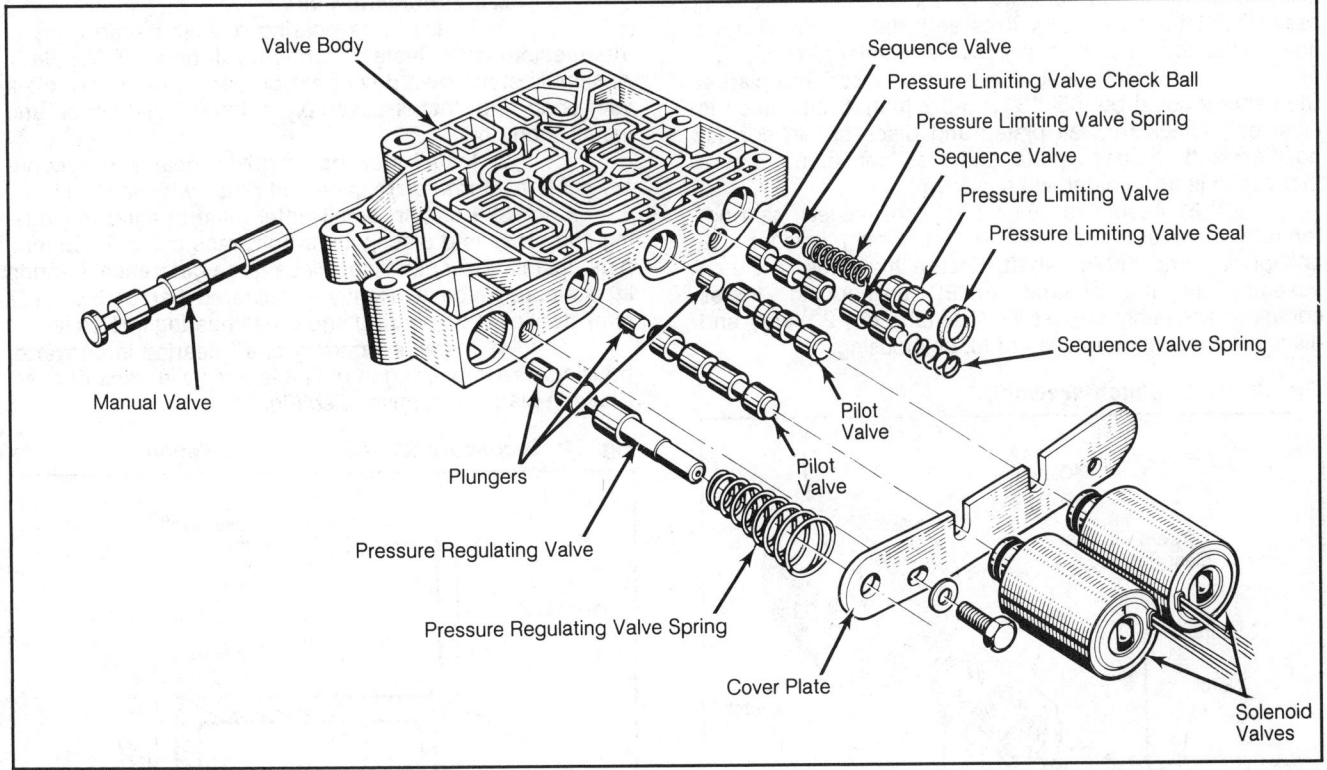

automatic transmission fluid before assembly. Be sure that tab on speedometer drive gear is aligned with notch in differential case when parts are assembled.

TRANSAXLE INSPECTION, REASSEMBLY & ADJUSTMENT

INSPECTION

1) Clean case and housings thoroughly with solvent and lint free rags. DO NOT use solvents containing trichloroethylene as it may damage seals. Dry components with compressed air. Direct air stream into all holes, oil feed passages and lubrication channels.

2) Check condition of F1 and F2 brake plates and discs. Any plates which show signs of overheating (discoloration) should be replaced. Check for damage to plate surfaces, excessive runout or taper. Replace as needed.

3) Inspect discs for excessive wear and burned or torn linings. In most cases, if either or both brakes show signs of having been severely overheated, E1-E2 clutch assembly as well as all F1 and F2 plates and discs should be replaced.

4) Check sealing ring lands on turbine shaft support. If excessively worn, or if bottom of lands is not square, support should be replaced. Ensure that seal ring ends are square and hooked together properly.

5) Inspect all snap ring and circlip grooves. Worn or damaged grooves will prevent proper seating of retainers. Therefore, any component with worn grooves should be replaced. Check condition of machined surfaces and sleeves on all components. Replace as needed.

6) Check condition of teeth on all geared components. Ensure that forward and reverse planetary gear sets rotate freely on shafts.

7) Inspect secondary shaft bearing seat area in converter housing. Remove any burrs or scratches with emery cloth. Wipe bore clean with dry cloth and blow out with compressed air.

REASSEMBLY

Rear Case

1) Install oil pump gears in case. Ensure that gears rotate freely. Replace seals on F2 piston and install piston and piston cup in case. Make sure that piston springs are seated correctly in piston.

2) Install guide pins (B. Vi. 952) in case and install turbine shaft support, using pins to guide support into position. See Fig. 19. Remove pins, install retaining bolts and tighten alternately and evenly. Install thrust bearing. Install F2 brake steel clips.

Fig. 19: Installing Turbine Shaft Support in Rear Case

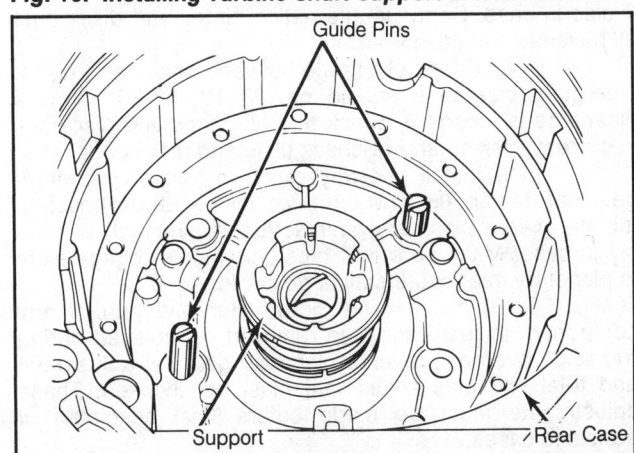

Install guide pins in case to align support.

Automatic Transmissions

AMC/RENAULT ALLIANCE MB1 (Cont.)

3) Install waved brake plate. Dip F2 plates and discs in transmission fluid. Install 1 disc, then 1 plate in case. Continue alternating discs and plates until all have been installed. Install F1 piston carrier and large circlip.

4) Check clearance between discs and plates. Clearance should be .05-.13" (1.3-3.2 mm). If clearance is incorrect, check that all plates and discs are in correct position and re-check plate and disc condition. Ensure that circlip is fully seated in its groove.

5) Assemble E1-E2 clutch, roller bearing, forward planetary gear set, .06" (1.5 mm) washer, E2 bellhousing and turbine shaft. Ensure that tabs of clutch assembly fit into notches of E2 bellhousing. Install complete assembly in case so that tabs of F2 plates and discs are located in notches of E2 bellhousing.

Fig. 20: E1-E2 Clutch Assembly

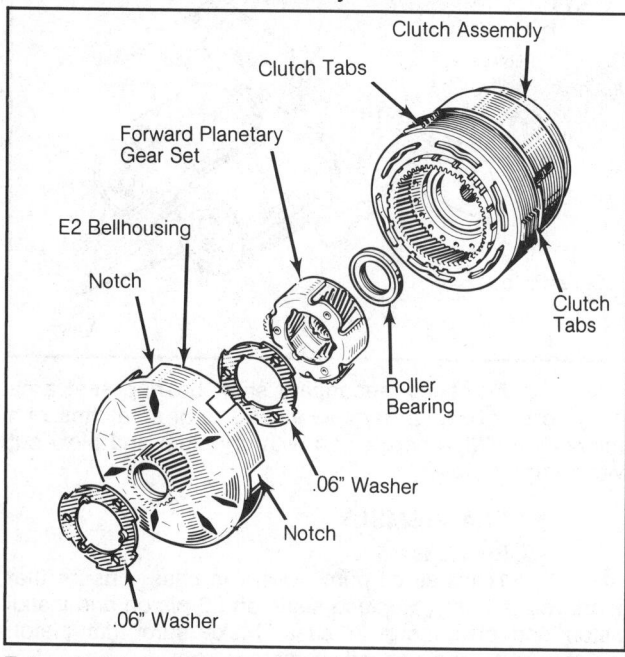

Tabs of clutch must align with slots in bellhousing.

6) Measure distance from face of F1 piston carrier to outside face of E1-E2 clutch assembly. Total distance should be 1.56-1.62" (39.9-41.3 mm). If not, check that all components are correctly installed.

7) Install F1 piston on piston carrier. Dip F1 plates and discs in transmission fluid. Install 1 plate, then 1 disc in case. Continue alternating plates and discs until all have been installed.

8) Check clearance between plates and discs. Operating clearance should be .03-.10" (.8-2.7 mm). If clearance is incorrect, check that all plates and discs are in correct position and re-check plate and disc condition.

9) Install one-way clutch in reverse planetary gear set. Install .06" (1.5 mm) washer on E2 bellhousing. Install reverse planetary gear set/one-way clutch assembly in case. Make sure that tabs on washer engage slots in planetary gear set. Install large circlip.

10) Install valve body, filter and pan. If any component in rear case was removed or replaced during transaxle overhaul, reverse planetary gear set adjustment and total end play adjustment must be checked. These adjustments must be made before final assembly of transaxle cases.

Differential/Converter Housing & Intermediate Case

1) Install large bearing retaining snap rings in intermediate case. Install bearings with driver (B. Vi. 947). Assemble step down drive gear on output shaft and retain with snap ring. Install assembly in intermediate case and install snap ring.

2) Install step down driven gear and secondary shaft in intermediate case and retain with snap ring.

3) Position small differential bearing in housing and press into place with arbor press and 2.5" (65 mm) pipe. Install new snap ring. Place large differential bearing in position. Place a slightly shouldered bar or 5.0" (127 mm) steel pipe on bearing and press bearing into case.

4) Install secondary shaft bearing in converter housing. Press bearing in until it is flush with face of case. Stake in place with chisel. *See Fig. 21.*

Fig. 21: Secondary Shaft Bearing Installation

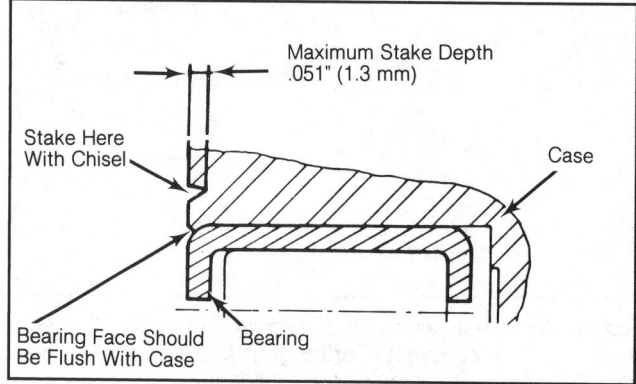

Stake bearing in place with sharp chisel. Do not exceed maximum stake depth as shown.

5) Using tool (B. Vi. 962), install new converter oil seal over stator shaft support. Tap new seal onto shaft until outer face of tool is flush with end of support.

6) Install spring washer on base of differential case with outside edge of washer against gear. Install differential in housing.

7) Support differential case with wood block. Install part C of tool (B. Vi. 946) on planetary gear stem and install snap ring on part C. *See Fig. 22.* Position part D

Fig. 22: Installing Snap Ring in Differential Case

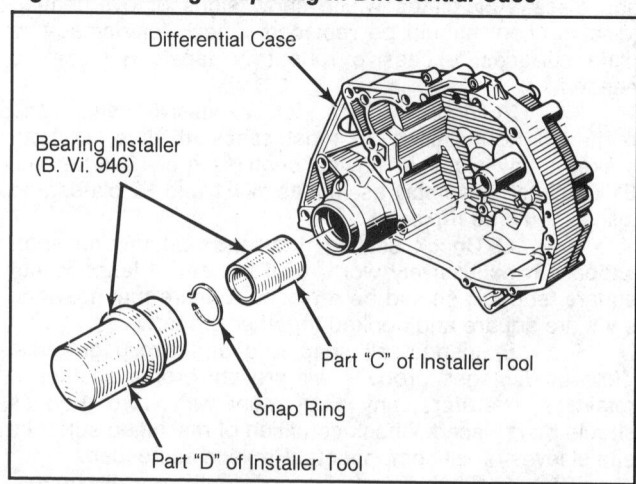

Assemble tools as shown and press snap ring into position.

AMC/RENAULT ALLIANCE MB1 (Cont.)

of tool (B. Vi. 946) on part C and press snap ring into groove. Install oil seal on planetary gear shaft.

NOTE: **Manufacturer recommends use of arbor press when installing snap ring.**

Fig. 23: Case Attaching Bolt Identification

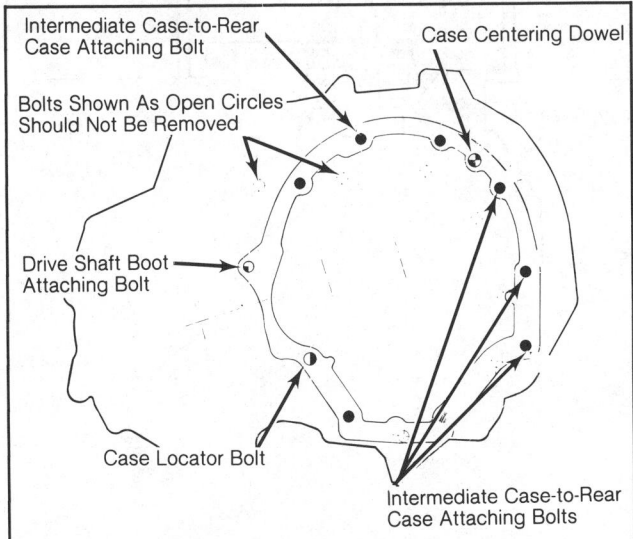

Always install new "O" ring on locator bolt when re-assembling cases.

8) Carefully align intermediate case with differential/converter housing, ensuring that secondary shaft and output shaft assemblies are correctly located in both cases. Install and tighten case attaching bolts.

9) Perform total end play adjustment procedure if needed. When assembling rear case to intermediate case assembly, use new "O" ring on locator bolt, and gasket sealing compound (AMC/Jeep/Renault Part No. 8993539) between cases. Install and tighten case attaching bolts.

ADJUSTMENT
Reverse Planetary Gear Set Adjustment

1) To adjust reverse planetary gear set, assemble tool (B. Vi. 715) to rear case as shown in *Fig. 24*. Measure dimensions "A" and "B" and record. Dimension "A" is between inside face of tool and top of roller bearing. Dimension "B" is from inside face of tool to planetary gear set. Measure dimension "C" on park wheel and record.

2) Using these measurements, thickness of required selective washer can be determined. First, subtract dimension "B" from "A" to determine value "X". Then add this value to dimension "C" to obtain "T". Thrust washer required to obtain correct gear set adjustment is determined by subtracting average operating clearance, a constant equal to .016" (.4 mm), from "T". An example is given in *Fig. 24*.

3) Selective washers are available in thicknesses of .059" (1.5 mm), .079" (2.0 mm), .102" (2.6 mm) and .126" (3.2 mm). Since the value obtained will probably not be exactly the same as an available washer, use the size which is closest to the ideal value.

Fig. 24: Measuring Reverse Planetary Gear Set Adjustment

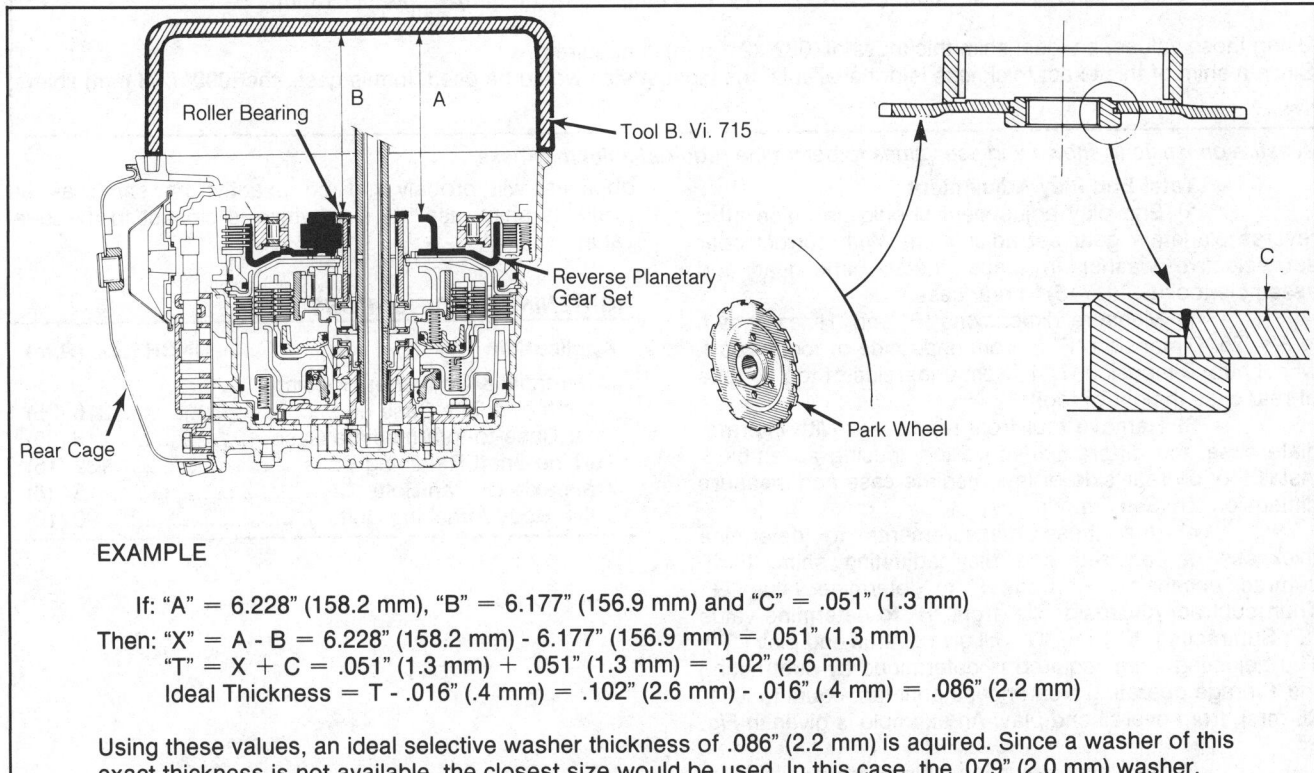

EXAMPLE

If: "A" = 6.228" (158.2 mm), "B" = 6.177" (156.9 mm) and "C" = .051" (1.3 mm)

Then: "X" = A - B = 6.228" (158.2 mm) - 6.177" (156.9 mm) = .051" (1.3 mm)
"T" = X + C = .051" (1.3 mm) + .051" (1.3 mm) = .102" (2.6 mm)
Ideal Thickness = T - .016" (.4 mm) = .102" (2.6 mm) - .016" (.4 mm) = .086" (2.2 mm)

Using these values, an ideal selective washer thickness of .086" (2.2 mm) is aquired. Since a washer of this exact thickness is not available, the closest size would be used. In this case, the .079" (2.0 mm) washer.

Measure dimensions shown and use values to determine required selective washer thickness.

Fig. 25: *Measurements Required for Total End Play Adjustment*

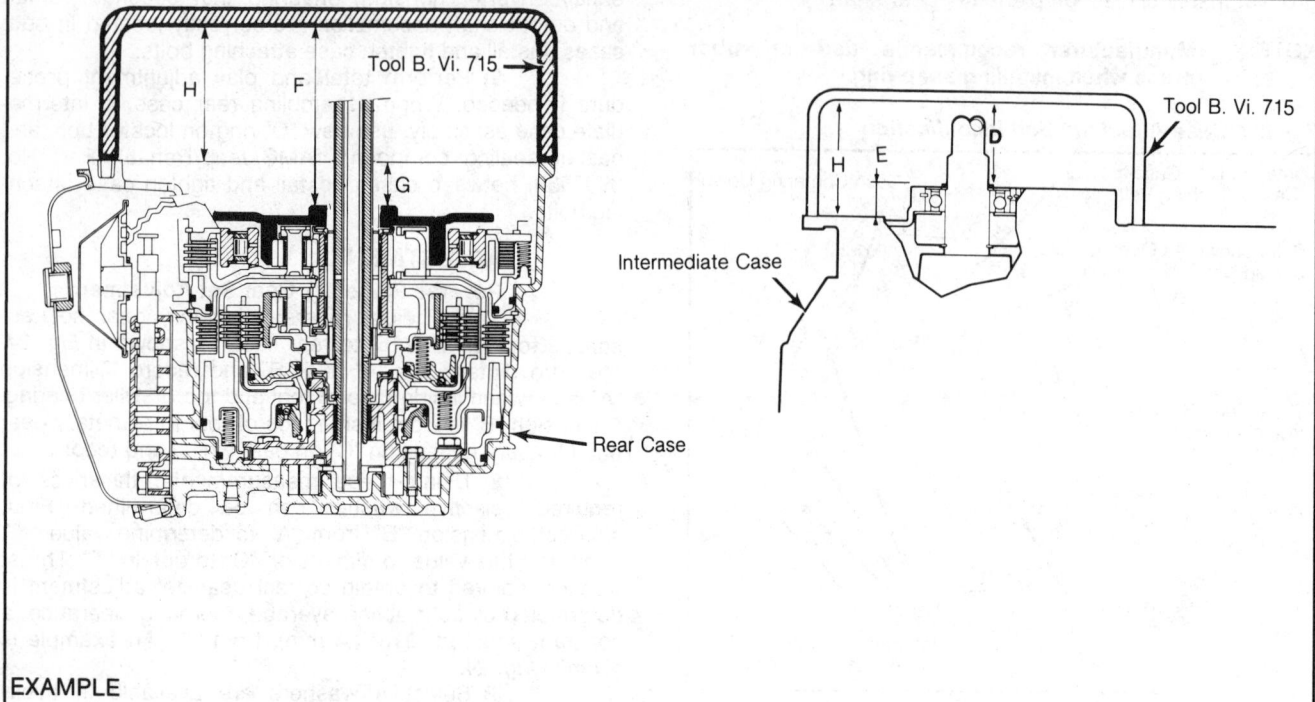

EXAMPLE

If: "H" = 4.724" (120 mm), "F" = 5.720" (145.3 mm) and "D" = 3.843" (97.6)

Then: "G" = F - H = 5.720" (145.3 mm) - 4.724" (120 mm) = .996" (25.3 mm)

"E" = H - D = 4.724" (120 mm) - 3.843" (97.6) = .882" (22.4 mm)

"T" = G - E = .996" (25.3 mm) - .882" (22.4 mm) = .114" (2.9 mm)

Ideal Shim Thickness = T - .032" (.8 mm) = .114" (2.9 mm) - .032" (.8 mm) = .082" (2.1 mm)

Using these values, an ideal shim thickness of .082" (2.1 mm) is acquired.

Since a shim of this exact thickness is not available, the closest size would be used. In this case, the .090" (2.3 mm) shim.

Measure dimensions shown and use values to determine required shim thickness.

Total End Play Adjustment

1) End play adjustment should be made after reverse planetary gear set adjustment. With correct gear set selective washer in place, install park gear and assemble tool (B. Vi. 715) to rear case.

2) Measure dimensions "F" and "H" as shown in *Fig. 25*. Dimension "F" is from underside of tool to park wheel hub. Dimension "H" is from underside of tool to face of rear case (height of tool).

3) Remove tool from rear case. With intermediate case and differential/converter housing assembled, install tool on rear side of intermediate case and measure dimension "D". *See Fig. 25.*

4) Use these measurements to determine thickness of required end play adjusting shim. First, subtract dimension "H" from "F" to determine value "G". Then subtract dimension "D" from "H" to determine value "E". Subtracting "E" from "G" will give overall end play ("T"). The adjusting shim required is determined by subtracting the average operating clearance, a constant equal to .031" (.8 mm), from overall end play. An example is given in *Fig. 25*.

5) End play adjusting shims are available in thicknesses of .010" (.25 mm), .028" (.70 mm), .043" (1.1 mm), .067" (1.7 mm) and .090" (2.3 mm). Since the value obtained will probaly not be exactly the same as an available shim, use the size which is closest to the ideal value.

TIGHTENING SPECIFICATIONS

Application	INCH Lbs. (N.m)
Differential & Converter Housing-to-Intermediate Case	216 (25)
Rear Case-to-Intermediate Case	216 (25)
Turbine Shaft Retaining Bolts	132 (15)
Transaxle Oil Pan Bolts	54 (6)
Valve Body Attaching Bolts	90 (10)

AMERICAN MOTORS, CHRYSLER & JEEP
727, 904, 998 & 999

APPLICATIONS

CHRYSLER CORP.

Chrysler Corp. passenger cars use either the A-727, A-904 or A-904LA Torqueflite transmission. All models with 5.2L V8 engine use a lock-up type torque converter. Dodge and Plymouth Trucks and Vans use the Loadflite A-727, A-904T or A-999 transmission. Those with the A-904T and A-999 transmissions use a lock-up converter, while A-727 equipped models may use the lock-up type or a conventional converter, depending on GVWR and application.

AMC/JEEP

AMC vehicles use either the 904 or 998 automatic transmission, while Jeep's use either the 727 or 999. A lock-up torque converter may be used with any of these transmissions. *See AMC & Jeep Transmission Application chart.*

AMC & JEEP TRANSMISSION APPLICATIONS

Application	Model No.	Lock-Up Converter
AMC		
4-Cylinder	904	No
6-Cylinder		
Concord		
Fleet Use Only	998	No
All Others	904	Yes
Eagle	998	Yes
Jeep		
CJ-7/Scrambler	999	Yes
All Others	[1] 727	Yes

[1] — With 6-Cylinder engine and 2.73 axle ratio: 999 with Lock-Up Converter.

NOTE: **All future references to transmission will be by number only (i.e. 727, 904, 999). Unless otherwise specified, model reference will include all models of that series. For example, reference to 904 includes A-904, A-904LA and A-904T as well as 904.**

IDENTIFICATION

The transmission identification number is stamped on a pad on the left side of the transmission case oil pan flange. The identification number is decoded as shown in *Fig. 1.*

Fig. 1: Transmission Identification Number

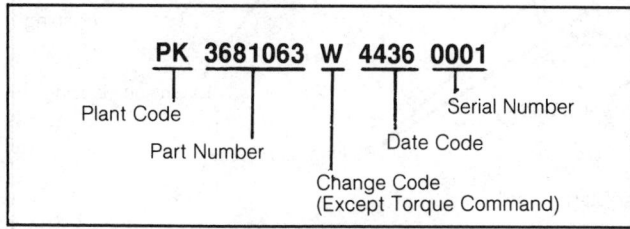

CAUTION

CAUTION: **Transmission operation requirements are different for each vehicle and engine combination, and some internal parts will be different to provide for this. Therefore, when replacing parts, refer to the seven digit part number for positive transmission identification.**

DESCRIPTION

Transmission is a 3-speed unit combining a torque converter and a compound planetary gear system. Transmission case and converter housing are an integral aluminum casting. Transmission consists of 2 multiple-disc clutches, 2 bands and servos, an overrunning clutch, 2 planetary gear sets and a hydraulic control system. This hydraulic system consists of an oil pump and a valve body, which contains all control valves except governor valve.

Torque converters are of 2 types: Conventional torque converter and lock-up torque converter. The lock-up converter has an internal mechanism for locking the turbine and impeller in direct drive (above a minimum preset vehicle speed). In the conventional converter, there is always some slippage between the turbine and impeller in direct drive. By locking these components, slippage is eliminated resulting in improved fuel economy and lower fluid operating temperatures.

The lock-up system consists of a lock-up mechanism within the converter, a lock-up module attached to the valve body, and a switch valve in the valve body. The switch valve is actually the converter control valve, which has been modified for lock-up system use.

NOTE: **Conventional converters are not interchangeable with the lock-up converter.**

LUBRICATION & ADJUSTMENT

See Automatic Transmission Servicing.

TESTING

ROAD TEST

1) Before road testing, be certain that fluid level and control linkage adjustments have been checked and corrected as needed. During testing, transmission should upshift and downshift automatically at approximately the speeds shown in *Automatic Shift Speeds and Governor Pressures* charts.

2) Exact speeds will vary somewhat from one vehicle to the next due to production tolerances, rear axle ratio and tire size. Of greater importance than shift speed is the quality of the shifts. All shifts should be smooth, responsive, and with no slipping or engine speed flare-up.

NOTE: **Information in shift speed chart is from Chrysler. AMC/Jeep specifications were not available.**

Automatic Transmissions
AMERICAN MOTORS, CHRYSLER & JEEP
727, 904, 998 & 999 (Cont.)

Fig. 2: Cross-Sectional View of Chrysler Corp. Model 727 Automatic Transmission

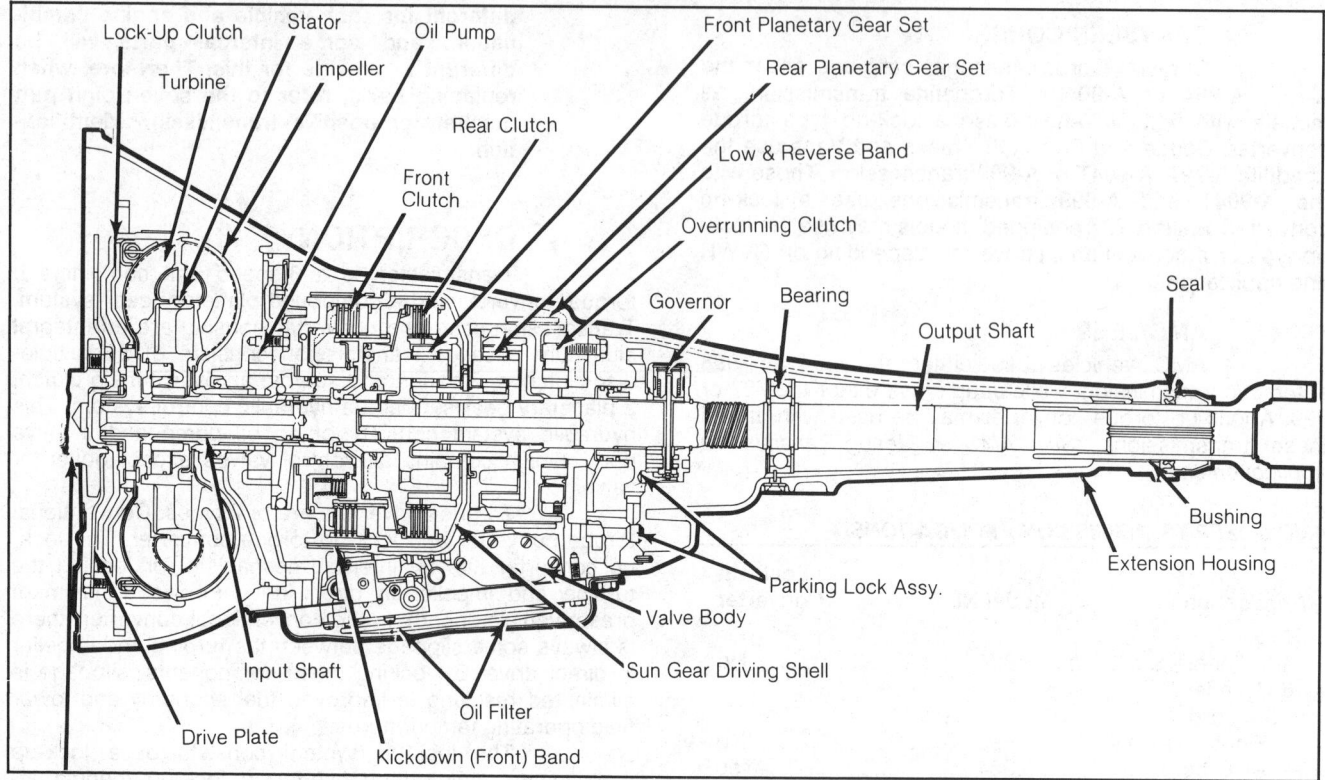

Fig. 3: Cross-Sectional View of Chrysler Corp. Model 904/999 and AMC/Jeep Model 904 Automatic Transmission

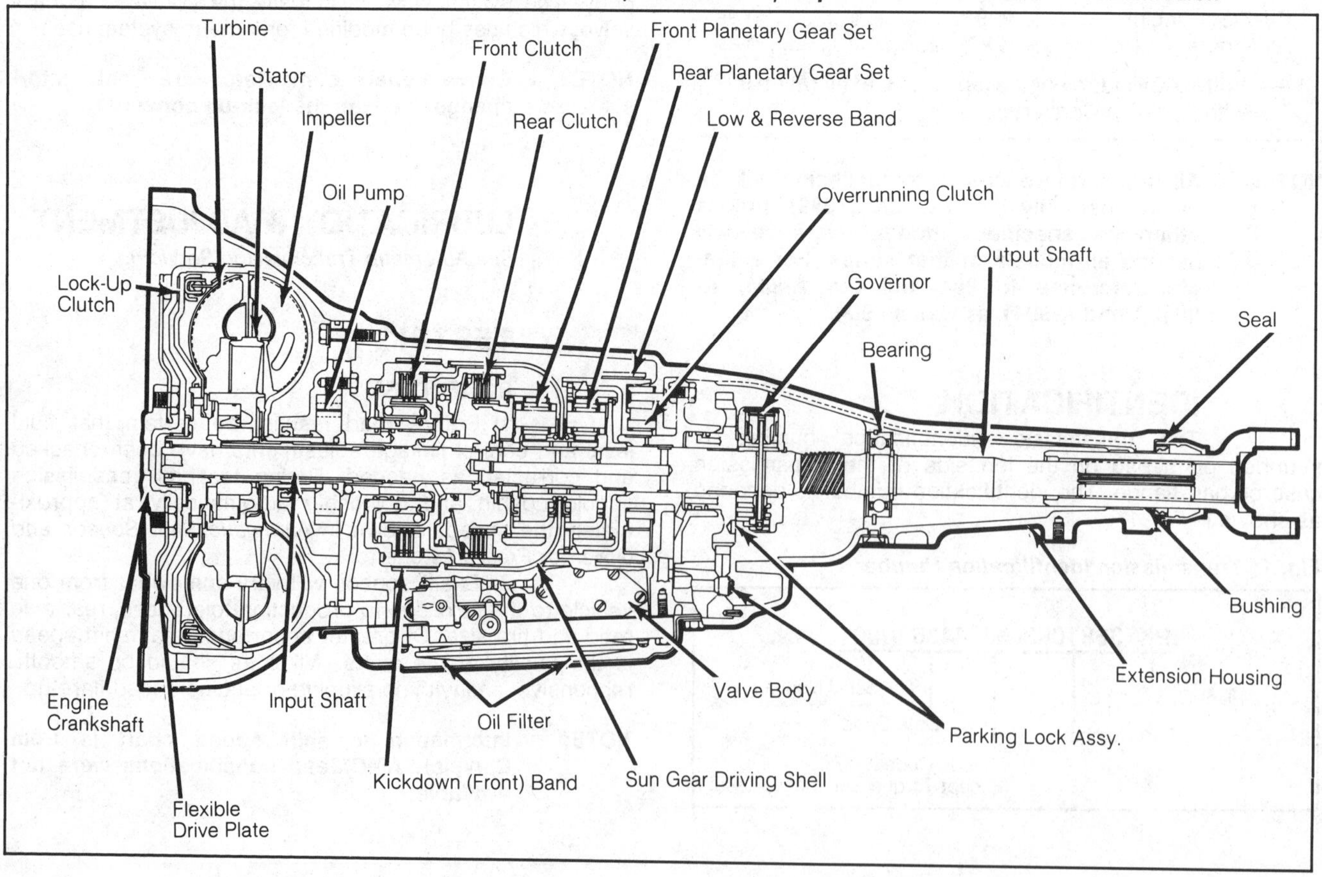

AMERICAN MOTORS, CHRYSLER & JEEP
727, 904, 998 & 999 (Cont.)

Fig. 4: Cross-Sectional View of AMC/Jeep Model 727 Automatic Transmission

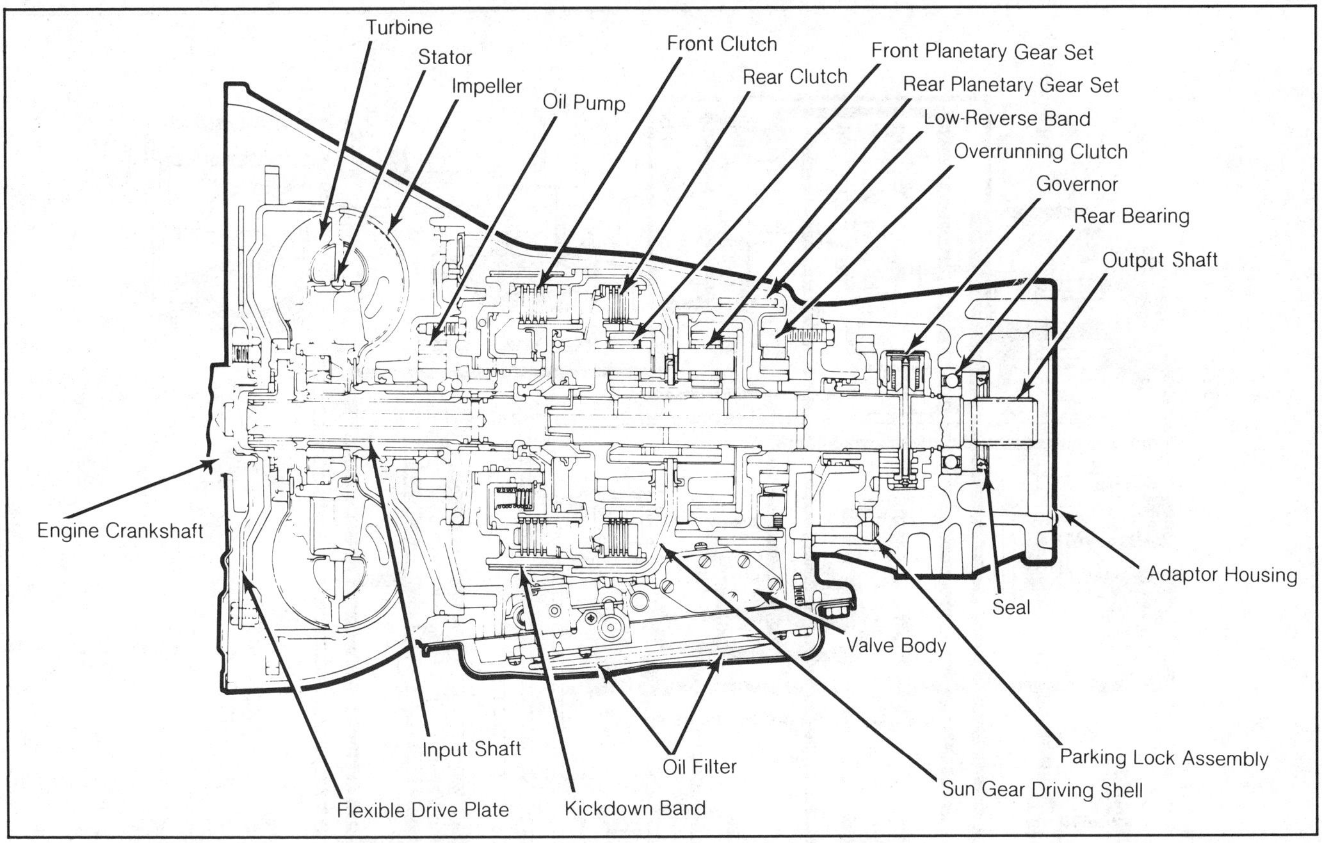

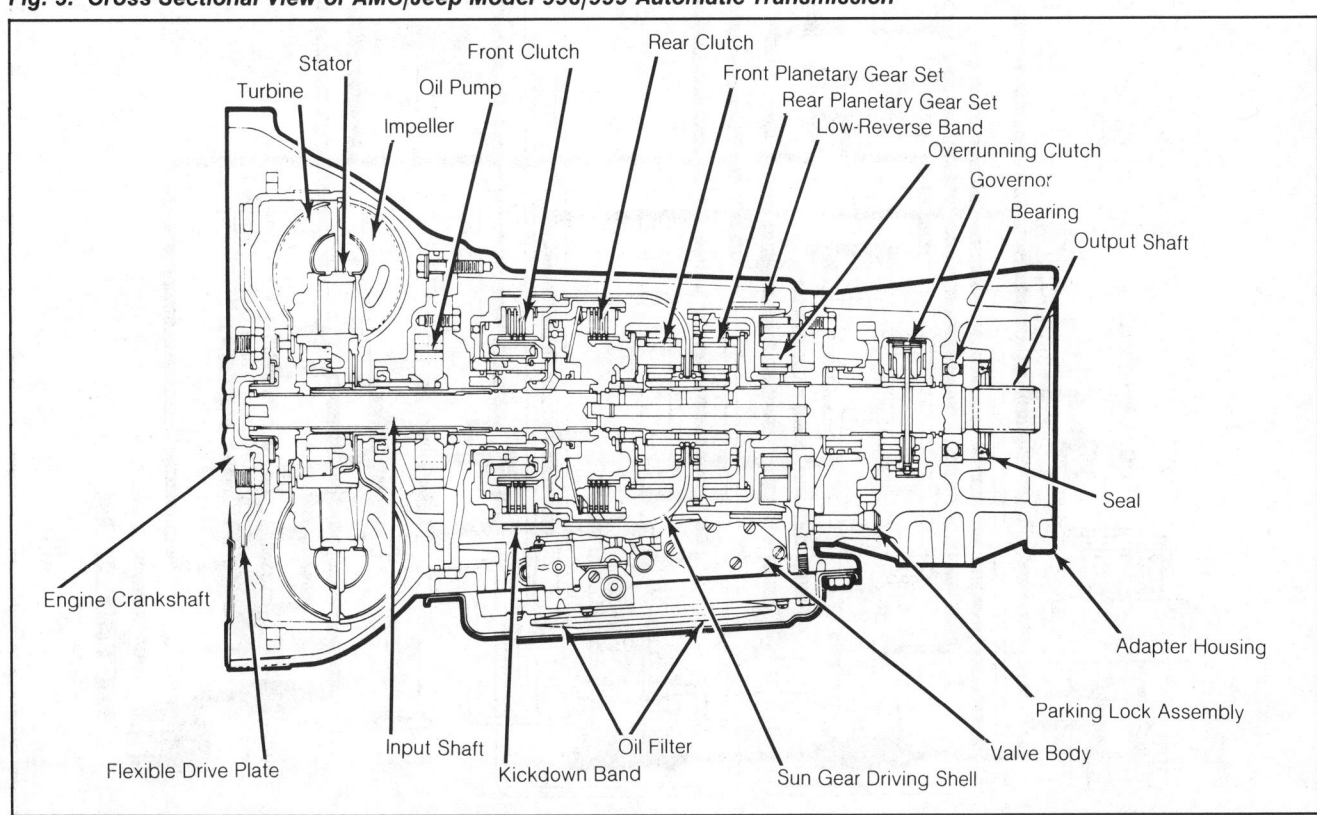

Fig. 5: Cross-Sectional View of AMC/Jeep Model 998/999 Automatic Transmission

Automatic Transmissions
AMERICAN MOTORS, CHRYSLER & JEEP
727, 904, 998 & 999 (Cont.)

Fig. 6: Chrysler Corp. & AMC/Jeep Automatic Transmission Hydraulic Circuits Diagram

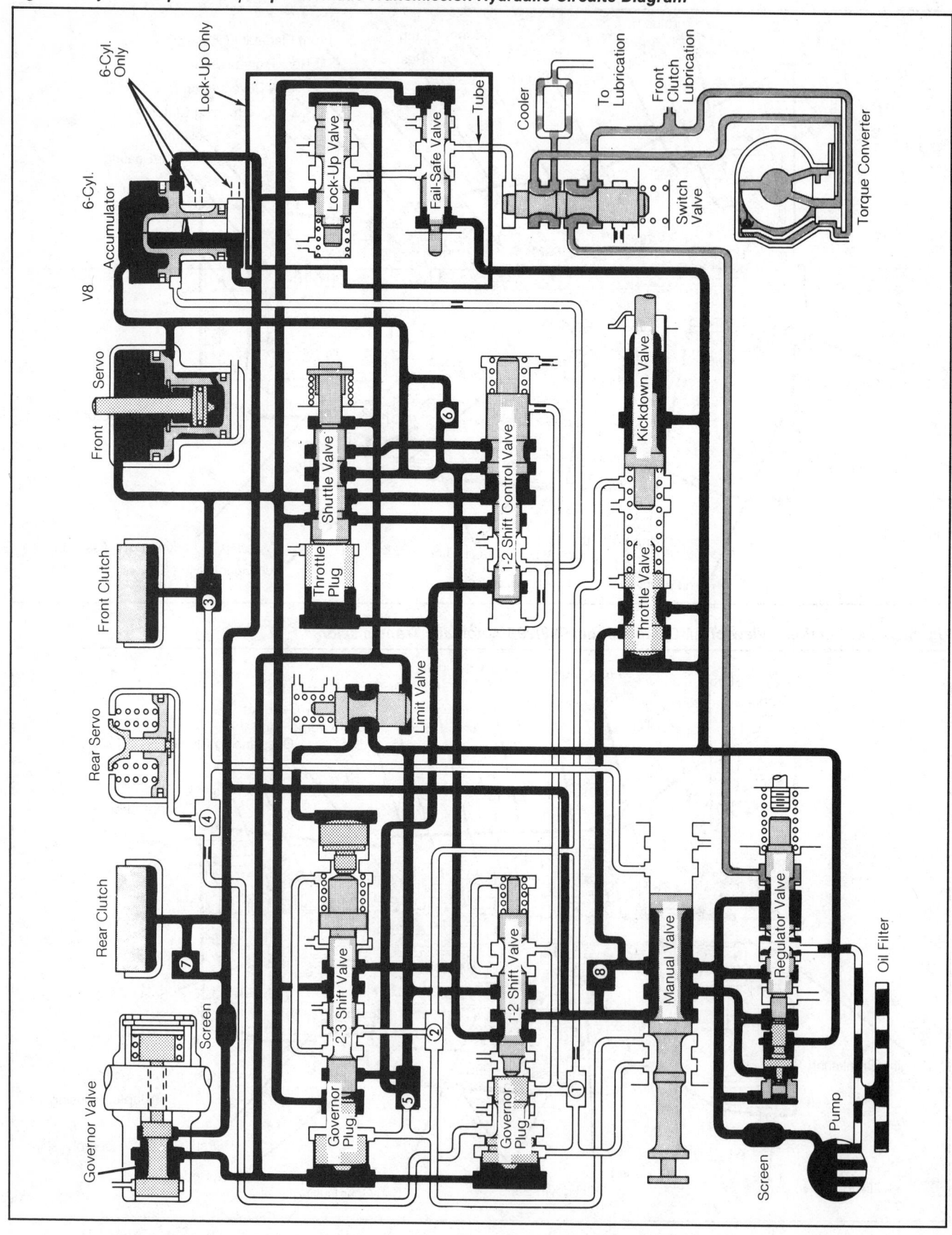

Automatic Transmissions
AMERICAN MOTORS, CHRYSLER & JEEP
727, 904, 998 & 999 (Cont.)

2-19

AUTOMATIC SHIFT SPEEDS & GOVERNOR PRESSURES — *PASSENGER CARS*

Engine	3.7L	5.2L 2-Bbl	5.2L EFI
Axle Ratio - Tire Size	2.94 - P195/75R15	2.26 - P195/75R15	2.24 - P205/75R15
Throttle Closed			
1-2 Upshift	9-11	12-15	12-15
2-3 Upshift	12-15	16-20	16-20
Closed Throttle Lock-Up	.....	37-49	38-50
3-1 Downshift	9-11	11-14	12-15
Throttle Wide Open			
1-2 Upshift	29-42	38-54	38-56
2-3 Upshift	57-70	74-91	76-93
Kickdown Range			
3-2 Downshift	52-65	68-85	70-87
3-1 Downshift	27-30	35-40	36-47
Governor Pressure [1]			
15 psi	17-20	23-25	23-26
50 psi	39-45	51-59	53-60
75 psi	60-66	78-85	81-88

[1] — Governor pressure should be from zero to 1.5 psi at stand-still or downshift may not occur.

AUTOMATIC SHIFT SPEEDS & GOVERNOR PRESSURES — *TRUCKS & VANS*

Engine	3.7L		5.2L & 5.9L			
Model	150	250	150	150	250	300/450
Axle Ratio	3.21	3.54	2.71	2.94	4.10	4.56
Tire Size	P195/75R15	8.00 X 16.5-D	P195/75R15	P195/75R15	8.00 X 16.5-D	8.00 X 16.5-E
Throttle Closed						
1-2 Upshift	8-11	8-11	9-12	9-11	7-9	6-8
2-3 Upshift	11-14	11-14	13-17	12-15	9-12	8-11
3-1 Downshift	8-11	8-11	9-12	9-11	7-9	6-8
Throttle Wide Open						
1-2 Upshift	30-40	30-40	36-48	33-44	26-35	23-31
2-3 Upshift	55-60	55-60	65-77	60-71	47-56	42-50
Kickdown Range						
3-2 Downshift	51-61	51-61	60-72	55-67	44-53	39-47
3-1 Downshift	24-33	24-33	29-39	26-36	21-29	19-26
Governor Pressure [1]						
15 psi	16-18	16-18	19-21	17-19	14-15	12-14
50 psi	39-45	39-45	46-53	43-49	34-39	30-35
75 psi	59-62	59-62	67-74	62-68	48-54	43-48

[1] — Governor pressure should be from zero to 1.5 psi at stand-still or downshift may not occur.

3) Slipping or flare-up in any gear usually indicates clutch, band or overrunning clutch problems. The slipping clutch or band in a particular gear can usually be identified by noting transmission operation in other selector positions and comparing which internal units are applied in those positions.

4) For example, if transmission slips in high gear with selector lever in "D", either the front or rear clutch is slipping. By selecting another gear which does not use one of those units, the unit which is slipping can be identified. *See Clutch and Band Application Chart.* If transmission slips in reverse, the front clutch is slipping. If transmission does not slip in reverse, the rear clutch is slipping.

5) Although this process of elimination can be used to detect any unit which slips and to confirm proper operation of good units, the actual cause of the malfunction usually cannot be determined. Practically any condition can be caused by leaking hydraulic circuits or sticking valves. Therefore, unless an obvious condition exists, transmission should never be disassembled until hydraulic and air pressure tests have been performed.

6) An engine tachometer can be used to determine if the lock-up clutch in the converter is functioning. An instantaneous rise in engine speed of more than 150 RPM at 40 MPH when the throttle is opened just short of kickdown, indicates that the lock-up clutch is slipping more than normal. Slippage less than 150 RPM is normal.

Automatic Transmissions
AMERICAN MOTORS, CHRYSLER & JEEP
727, 904, 998 & 999 (Cont.)

CLUTCH AND BAND APPLICATION CHART (ELEMENTS IN USE)

Selector Lever Position	Front Clutch	Rear Clutch	Over-running Clutch	Converter Lock-up Clutch	Front (Kickdown) Band	Rear (Low-reverse) Band
D — DRIVE						
First		X	X			
Second		X			X	
Third	X	X		X		
2 — SECOND						
First		X	X			
Second		X			X	
1 — LOW (First)					X	X
R — REVERSE	X					X

NEUTRAL OR PARK — All clutches and bands released and/or ineffective.

HYDRAULIC PRESSURE TESTS

1) Before making pressure tests, be certain that fluid level, condition and control linkage adjustments have been checked and corrected as necessary.

2) Transmission fluid must be at normal operating temperature during all tests. Connect tachometer to engine, raise vehicle on hoist to allow rear wheels to turn freely and position tachometer so it can be read from under vehicle.

3) Disconnect throttle rod and shift rod from transmission levers so they can be controlled from under vehicle.

Pressure Test (Selector in "1")

1) Attach 0-100 psi gauges to line and rear servo ports. Operate engine at 1000 RPM for test. Move selector lever on transmission all the way forward ("1" position).

2) Read pressures on both gauges as throttle lever on transmission is moved from full forward position to full rearward position. Line pressure should read 54-60

psi (3.8-4.2 kg/cm²) with throttle lever forward. As lever is moved rearward, pressure should gradually increase to 90-96 psi (6.3-6.7 kg/cm²).

3) Rear servo pressure should read the same as line pressure within 3 psi (.2 kg/cm²). This tests pump output, pressure regulation and condition of rear clutch and rear servo hydraulic circuits.

Pressure Test (Selector in "2")

1) Install a "T" fitting at rear cooler line fitting. Attach 0-100 psi gauges to "T" connection and line pressure port. Operate engine at 1000 RPM for test. Move selector lever on transmission 1 detent rearward from full forward position ("2" position).

2) Read pressures on both gauges as throttle lever on transmission is moved from full forward position to full rearward position. Line pressure should read 54-60 psi (3.8-4.2 kg/cm²) with throttle lever forward. As lever is moved rearward, pressure should gradually increase to 90-96 psi (6.3-6.7 kg/cm²).

3) Lubrication pressure should be 5-15 psi (.35-1.05 kg/cm²) with lever forward, and 10-30 psi (.7-2.1 kg/cm²) with lever rearward. This tests pump output, pressure regulation, and conditon of rear clutch and lubrication hydraulic circuits.

Pressure Test (Selector in "D")

1) Attach 0-100 psi gauges to line and front servo release ports. Operate engine at 1600 RPM for test. Move selector lever on transmission 2 detents rearward from full forward position ("D" position).

2) Read pressures on both guages as throttle lever on transmission is moved from full forward position to full rearward position. Line pressure should read 54-60 psi (3.8-4.2 kg/cm²) with throttle lever forward, and should gradually increase as lever is moved rearward.

3) Front servo release is pressurized only in direct drive and should be the same as line pressure, within 3 psi (.2 kg/cm²), up to downshift point.

4) This tests pump output, pressure regulation, and condition of front and rear clutch hydraulic circuits.

Pressure Test (Selector in Reverse)

1) Attach 0-300 psi gauge to rear servo apply port. Operate engine at 1600 RPM for test. Move selector lever on transmission 4 detents rearward from full forward position ("R" position).

Fig. 7: Transmission Case Right Side Pressure Test Ports

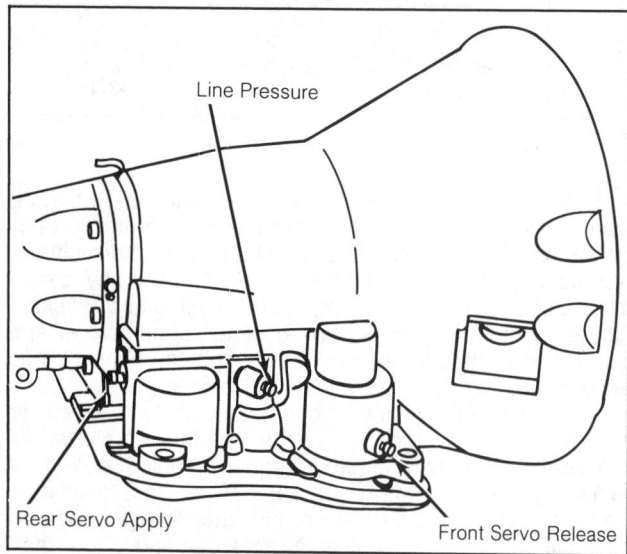

Line Pressure

Rear Servo Apply

Front Servo Release

Fluid level, condition and control linkage adjustments must be correct before performing hydraulic tests.

Fig. 8: Rear View of Transmission Pressure Test Ports

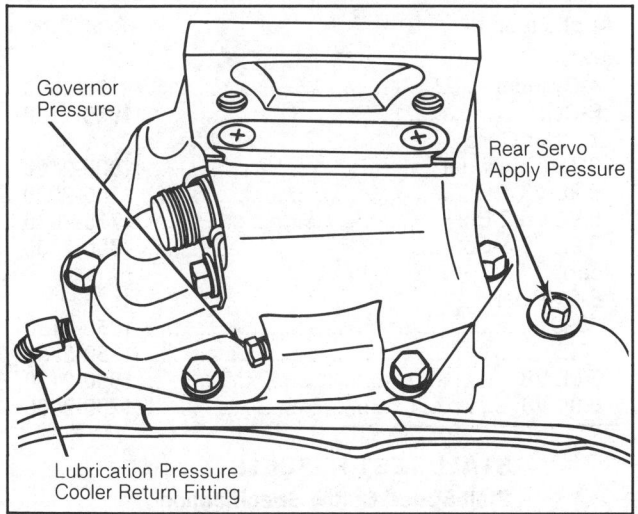

A 300 psi gauge MUST be used when checking pressure at rear servo apply port with shift lever in "R".

2) Rear servo pressure should read 145-175 psi (10.2-12.3 kg/cm²) with throttle lever forward and should gradually increase, as lever is moved rearward, to 230-280 psi (16.2-19.7 kg/cm²).

3) This tests pump output, pressure regulation and condition of front clutch and rear servo hydraulic circuits.

4) Move selector lever on transmission to "D" position and check that rear servo pressure drops to zero. This tests for leakage into rear servo due to case porosity, which can cause reverse band to burn out.

Governor Pressure

1) Connect a 0-100 psi gauge to governor pressure port. Operate transmission in 3rd gear and read pressures. Compare readings with those shown in *Automatic Shift Speeds and Governor Pressure Charts*.

NOTE: **This test should only be performed if transmission shifts at wrong vehicle speeds when the throttle rod is correctly adjusted.**

2) If governor pressures are incorrect at given speeds, governor valve and/or weights are sticking. Governor pressure should return to 0-1.5 psi (0-.11 kg/cm²) when vehicle is stopped.

NOTE: **High governor pressure at stand-still (above 2 psi) will prevent transmission from downshifting.**

Throttle Pressure

No gauge port is provided for testing throttle pressure. Incorrect throttle pressure should only be suspected if part throttle upshift speeds are delayed, or occur too early in relation to vehicle speeds. Engine runaway on either upshifts or downshifts can also be an indicator of incorrect (low) throttle pressure.

Pressure Test Diagnosis

1) If line pressure is normal (minimum to maximum) in any one test, the pump and pressure regulator are working properly.

2) If line pressure is normal in "R" but low in all forward gears ("D", "2" and "1"), rear clutch circuit leakage is indicated (servo, clutch seals, governor support seal rings).

3) Normal line pressure in "1" and "2" with low pressure in "D" and "R" indicates leakage in the front clutch area (servo, clutch seals, retainer bore, pump seal rings).

4) Normal line pressure in "2" with low pressure in "R" and "1" indicates leakage in the rear servo circuit.

5) Low line pressure in all positions indicates a defective pump, a clogged filter or a stuck pressure regulator valve.

6) If front servo pressure is high in "2", leakage in the servo is indicated (broken servo ring, cracked servo piston).

7) Low lubrication pressure at all throttle lever positions indicates a clogged oil cooler or lines, leaking seal rings, plugged output shaft, or worn bushings in the pump and/or clutch retainer.

HYDRAULIC PRESSURE ADJUSTMENTS

NOTE: **Throttle rod should always be checked and adjusted as needed, before checking and/or adjusting throttle pressure.**

Throttle Pressure

1) Throttle pressures cannot be tested accurately; therefore, adjustment should be measured if a malfunction is evident.

2) Remove valve body assembly from transmission. Loosen throttle lever stop screw lock nut and back off screw approximately 5 turns.

3) Insert gauge pin of gauging tool (C-3763 Chrysler Corp. or J-24031 Jeep) between throttle lever cam and kickdown valve. Push in on tool and compress kickdown valve against spring so valve is completely bottomed inside valve body.

4) As force is being exerted to compress spring, turn throttle lever stop screw with Allen wrench. Adjustment is correct when head of screw touches throttle lever tang, with throttle lever cam touching tool and throttle valve bottomed.

Fig. 9: Adjusting Throttle Pressure

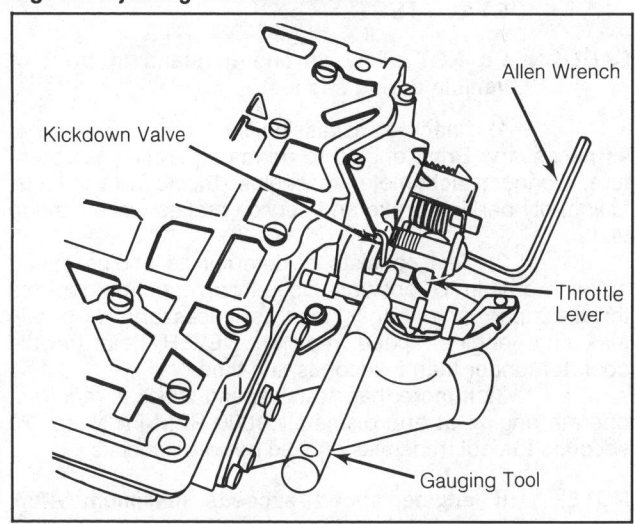

Gauge tool must be used to obtain proper adjustment.

2-22

Automatic Transmissions
AMERICAN MOTORS, CHRYSLER & JEEP
727, 904, 998 & 999 (Cont.)

CAUTION: Be sure adjustment is made with spring fully compressed and valve bottomed in valve body.

Line Pressure

1) An incorrect throttle pressure setting will cause incorrect line pressure readings even though line pressure adjustment is correct. Always inspect and correct throttle pressure adjustment before adjusting line pressure.

2) Turn Allen screw in end of pressure regulator spring bracket so measurement between valve body and inner edge of adjusting nut is 1 5/16" (33.34 mm). Due to manufacturing tolerances, adjustment can be varied to obtain specified line pressure.

Fig. 10: Measuring Line Pressure Adjustment

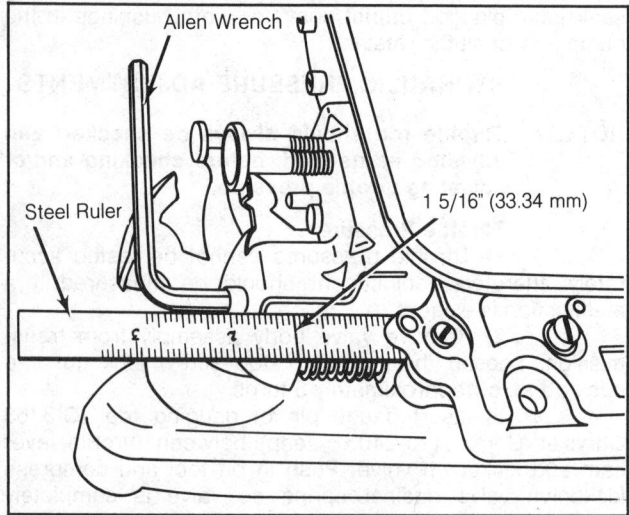

Allen Wrench

Steel Ruler

1 5/16" (33.34 mm)

Exact adjustment may be varied slightly to obtain correct pressure reading.

3) One complete turn of adjusting screw changes closed throttle line pressure approximately 1.7 psi (.12 kg/cm²). Turning adjusting screw counterclockwise increases pressure; clockwise decreases pressure.

STALL TEST

CAUTION: Do NOT allow anyone to stand in front of vehicle during this test.

1) Check transmission fluid level and correct as necessary. Bring engine to normal operating temperature. Connect tachometer to engine. Block front wheels, fully apply parking brake and service brakes while making test.

2) Test consists of determining engine speed at full throttle in "D" position. Open throttle, but do not hold throttle open any longer than is necessary to obtain maximum engine speed reading. NEVER hold throttle open for longer than 5 seconds at a time.

3) If more than 1 stall speed check is required, operate engine at approximately 1000 RPM in "N" for 20 seconds to cool transmission fluid between checks.

NOTE: If engine speed exceeds maximum RPM, immediately release throttle as transmission clutch slippage is indicated.

Stall Speed Specifications

Application	Stall RPM
AMC	
4-Cylinder	2750-3000
6-Cyl.	1850-2150
Chrysler Corp.	
3.7L 6-Cylinder	1800-2100
5.2L V8	1700-2000
5.9L V8 2-Bbl	1775-2075
5.9L V8 4-Bbl	1700-2000
Jeep	
6-Cylinder	
999	1850-2150
727	1950-2250
5.0L V8	1850-2150
6.0L V8	1700-2000

STALL TEST RESULTS
Stall Speed Below Specification

1) Low stall speeds with a properly tuned engine indicate torque converter stator clutch problems. A road test will be necsssary to identify the exact problem.

2) If stall speeds are 250-350 RPM below specifications and vehicle operates properly at highway speeds, but has poor through-gear acceleration, stator overrunning clutch is slipping.

3) If stall speed and acceleration are normal, but abnormally high throttle opening is required to maintain highway speeds, stator clutch has seized (non lock-up converters only). Both of these defects require replacement of torque converter.

Stall Speed Above Specification

If stall speed exceeds maximum limits shown by more than 200 RPM, transmission clutch slippage is indicated. Make hydraulic pressure and air pressure checks to determine cause of slippage.

Noise During Stall Test

1) A whining or siren-like noise due to fluid flow is normal during stall test with some converters. However, loud metallic noises from loose parts or interference within the assembly indicates a defective converter.

2) To be sure noise originates in converter, raise vehicle on a hoist and operate at light throttle in "D" and "N" while listening under transmission bell housing.

AIR PRESSURE TESTS

A "No Drive" condition can exist even with correct fluid pressure because of inoperative clutches and/or bands. The cause can be located by applying compressed air to appropriate case passages after valve body has been removed. If clutches and servos operate correctly, a no upshift and/or erratic shift condition indicates a malfunction in valve body.

NOTE: Compressed air must be free of any dirt or moisture. Use air pressure of 30-100 psi (2.1-7.0 kg/cm²) for tests.

Front Clutch

Direct air pressure into front clutch apply passage. Operation of clutch is indicated by a dull thud which may be heard or felt. Hold air pressure for a few seconds to check system for excessive air leaks.

Automatic Transmissions
AMERICAN MOTORS, CHRYSLER & JEEP
727, 904, 998 & 999 (Cont.)

2-23

Fig. 11: Air Pressure Test Points in Bottom of Transmission Case

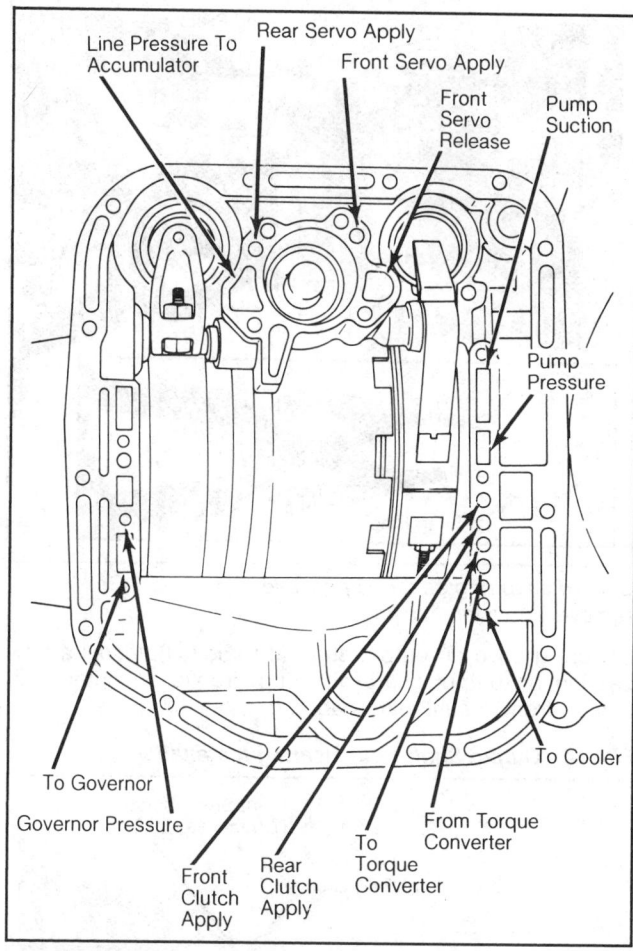

connected, carefully work adapter and pinion out of extension housing.

Fig. 12: Exploded View of Speedometer Drive Assembly

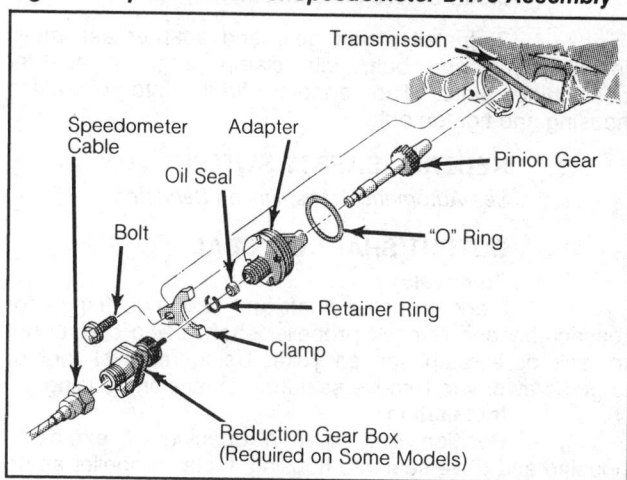

Chrysler Torqueflite shown, other models similar.

Seal Replacement

If transmission fluid is found inside cable housing, replace seal in adapter. Start seal and retainer ring in adapter. Push into adapter using seal installer tool (C-4004) until tool bottoms.

Fig. 13: Installing Speedometer Cable Adapter Oil Seal

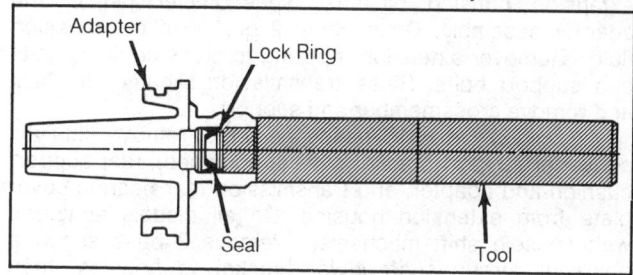

Installation

1) Note number of gear teeth and install speedometer pinion gear into adapter. Rotate pinion gear and adapter assembly so that number on adapter, corresponding with number of teeth on gear, is in the 6 o'clock position.

Fig. 14: Speedometer Pinion and Adapter Installation

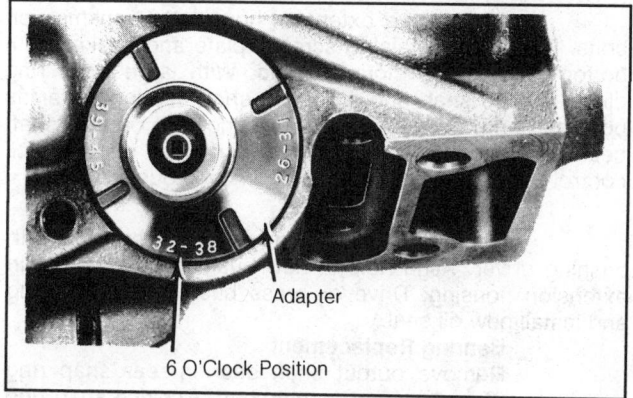

Adapter and mounting surface must be clean.

Use only filtered, compressed air to check system.

Rear Clutch

1) Direct air pressure into rear clutch apply passage. Operation of clutch is indicated by a dull thud which may be heard or felt.

2) If clutch operation is not detected, place finger tips on clutch housing and again apply air pressure. Movement of piston can be felt as air is applied. Also check for excessive air leaks.

Front (Kickdown) Servo

Direct air pressure into front servo apply passage. Operation of servo is indicated by a tightening of front band. Spring tension on servo piston should release band.

Rear (Low-Reverse) Servo

Direct air pressure into rear servo apply passage. Operation of servo is indicated by a tightening of rear band. Spring tension of servo piston should release band.

SERVICE (IN VEHICLE)

SPEEDOMETER PINION

Removal

Remove bolt and clamp securing speedometer pinion adapter in extension housing. With cable housing

2-24

Automatic Transmissions
AMERICAN MOTORS, CHRYSLER & JEEP
727, 904, 998 & 999 (Cont.)

NOTE: To avoid misalignment and possible damage to speedometer pinion gear, make sure adapter flange and its mating surfaces are clean before installation.

2) Install pinion gear and adapter assembly. Install clamp and bolt, with clamp tangs in adapter positioning slots. Tap adapter firmly into extension housing and tighten bolt.

NEUTRAL SAFETY SWITCH
See Automatic Transmission Servicing.

OUTPUT SHAFT OIL SEAL
Removal
Mark propeller shaft and rear axle flange for reassembly and remove propeller shaft, being careful not to nick or scratch splined yoke. Using removal tool or large screwdriver, remove seal from extension housing.
Installation
Position new seal in opening of extension housing and drive seal into housing. Install propeller shaft, aligning marks made during disassembly.

EXTENSION HOUSING, BEARING & BUSHING
Removal
1) On AMC Eagle, remove transfer case. On all models, disconnect propeller shaft at rear axle, and slide shaft assembly out of extension housing. Remove extension housing oil seal, speedometer pinion and adapter assembly. Drain about 2 quarts of transmission fluid. Remove extension housing-to-crossmember bolts and support bolts. Raise transmission slightly with jack and remove crossmember and support.

2) On AMC passenger cars, remove catalytic converter support bracket bolts (if equipped), rear support cushion and adapter, and transmission rear bearing cover plate from extension housing. On all models equipped with console shift mechanism, remove 2 bolts securing gearshift torque shaft lower bracket to housing, then swing bracket out of the way for extension housing removal.

NOTE: When removing or installing extension housing, gearshift lever must be in "1" (Low) position, placing parking lock control rod rearward so it can be disengaged or engaged with parking lock sprag.

3) Remove extension housing-to-transmission bolts. Remove 2 retaining screws, plate and gasket from bottom of housing mounting pad. With large snap ring pliers, spread snap ring on output shaft bearing as far as possible and tap extension housing off output shaft bearing. Pull housing rearward to disengage parking lock control rod knob from sprag and remove housing.
Bushing Replacement
Remove bushing from extension housing with bushing driver. Align hole in new bushing with oil slot in extension housing. Drive or press bushing into housing and install new oil seal.
Bearing Replacement
Remove output shaft bearing rear snap ring and remove bearing from output shaft. Replace snap ring

Fig. 15: Extension Housing Removal

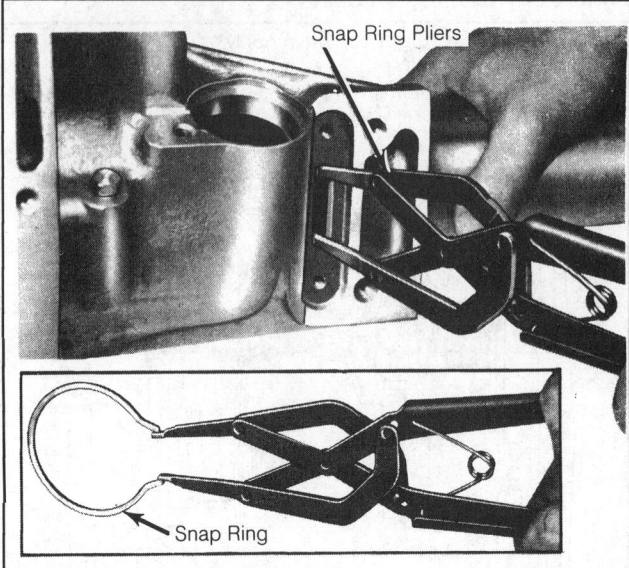

Spread snap ring as far as possible and remove extension housing.

in front groove on output shaft (if removed). Install a new bearing on output shaft with ring groove on outer race toward front. Install rear snap ring.

Fig. 16: Output Shaft Rear Bearing Installation

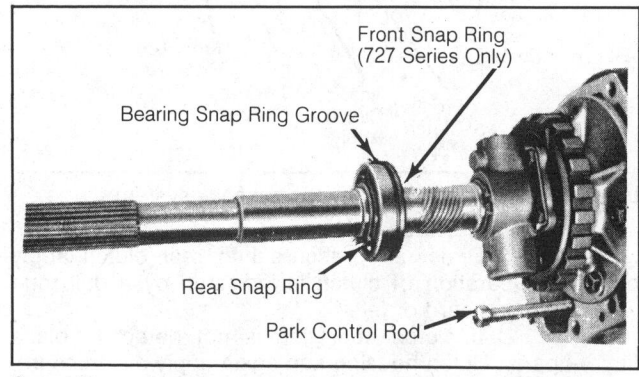

Snap ring groove on outer race must face toward front.

Installation
1) Install a new gasket on transmission case. Position output shaft bearing retaining snap ring in extension housing. Slide extension housing on output shaft, guiding parking lock control rod knob past parking sprag. While spreading large snap ring in housing, carefully tap housing into place and release snap ring.

NOTE: Ensure that snap ring is fully seated in bearing outer race ring groove.

2) Install and tighten extension housing-to-transmission case bolts. Install gasket, plate, and screws on bottom of extension housing mounting pad. Install center crossmember and rear mount assembly. Lower transmission. Install and tighten extension housing-to-support bolts.

3) On vehicles with console shift, align gearshift torque shaft lower bracket with extension housing,

Automatic Transmissions
AMERICAN MOTORS, CHRYSLER & JEEP
727, 904, 998 & 999 (Cont.)

2-25

then install and tighten retaining bolts. On AMC vehicles, install transmission rear bearing cover plate, rear support cushion and adapter, and catalytic converter support bracket bolts (if equipped).

4) On all models, install speedometer pinion and adapter. Install transfer case on AMC Eagle. Install propeller shaft and fill transmission to correct fluid level.

ADAPTER HOUSING BEARING & SEAL
Removal
Remove seal from adapter housing using screwdriver or punch. Remove snap rings and remove bearing from adapter housing.

Installation
Install new bearing in housing and install snap rings. Install new seal in housing. Seal should be seated flush with edge of seal bore.

GOVERNOR & PARKING GEAR
Removal

NOTE: To remove governor and parking gear from Eagle models, transfer case must first be removed.

1) Remove adapter or extension housing and output shaft bearing. Carefully pry snap ring from small side of governor valve shaft. Slide valve and shaft assembly out of governor body. Remove large snap ring from weight end of governor body and lift out governor weight assembly.

Fig. 17: Governor, Support and Parking Gear Assembly

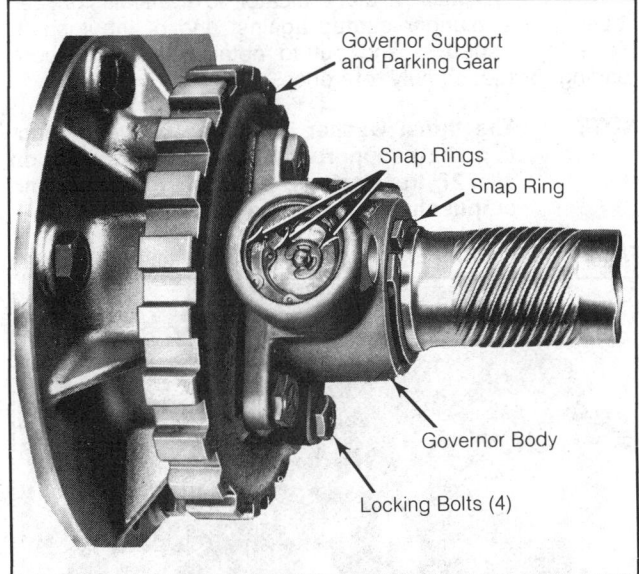

2) Remove snap ring from inside governor weight. Remove inner weight and spring from outer weight. Remove snap ring from behind governor body. Slide body and support assembly off output shaft. Remove bolts and separate governor body from support and parking gear.

Inspection
Inspect all parts for wear or damage. Check spring for distortion. Weights and valves should fall freely in bores when clean and dry. Remove any roughness with crocus cloth.

Installation
1) Assemble governor body to support and tighten bolts finger tight, making sure oil passage in governor body aligns with passage in support. Position support and governor assembly on output shaft. Align assembly so valve shaft hole in body mates with hole in output shaft.

2) Slide assembly into place, install snap ring behind governor body and tighten body-to-support bolts. Assemble governor weights and spring. Secure with snap ring inside large governor weight.

3) Place assembly in governor body and install snap ring. Place governor valve on valve shaft, insert assembly into body and through governor weights, and install valve shaft retaining snap ring.

4) Inspect valve and weight assembly for free movement. Install output shaft bearing and extension housing or adapter housing.

Fig. 18: Exploded View of Governor Assembly

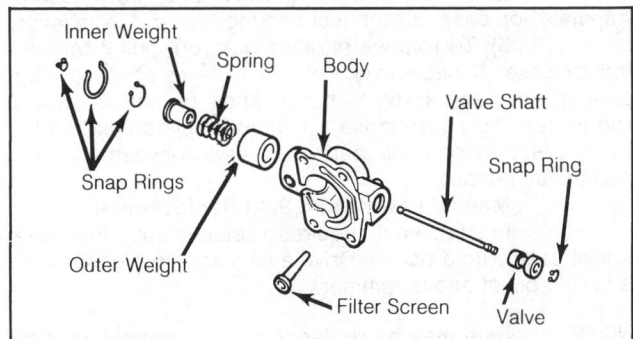

PARKING LOCK
Removal
With extension or adapter housing removed, slide shaft out of housing to remove parking sprag and spring. Remove snap ring and slide reaction plug and pin assembly out of housing.

Inspection
Check sprag shaft for scores and free movement in housing and sprag. Check springs for loss of tension or distortion. Check square lug on sprag and lugs on governor support (park gear) for broken edges. Check knob on end of control rod for nicks, burrs, and free turning.

Fig. 19: Parking Lock Component Installation

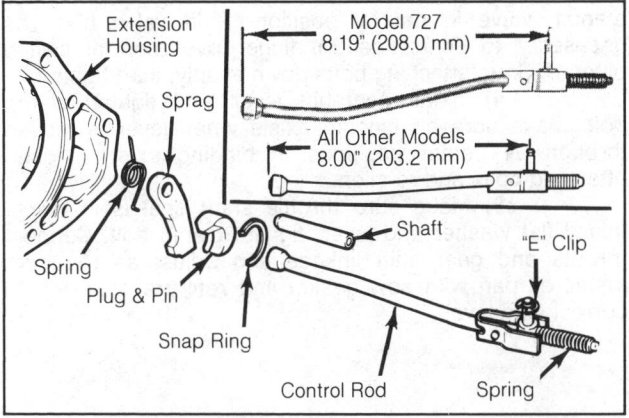

Adjust control rod to length as shown.

2-26

Automatic Transmissions
AMERICAN MOTORS, CHRYSLER & JEEP
727, 904, 998 & 999 (Cont.)

Installation

Install reaction plug and pin assembly in housing and secure with snap ring. Position sprag and spring in housing and insert shaft, making sure square lug on sprag is toward parking gear and spring is positioned so it moves sprag away from gear. Control rod length should be adjusted to 8.19" (208.0 mm) on 727 transmissions and 8.00" (203.2 mm) on all others. Install extension or adapter housing.

VALVE BODY ASSEMBLY & ACCUMULATOR PISTON

Removal

1) Loosen oil pan bolts, tap pan to break loose and allow fluid to drain. Remove oil pan. Loosen clamp bolts and remove transmission levers. Remove "E" clip securing parking lock rod to valve body manual lever.

2) Remove neutral safety switch. While holding valve body in position, remove valve body-to-transmission case bolts. While lowering valve body down out of transmission case, disconnect parking lock rod from lever.

3) To remove parking lock rod, pull it forward out of case. If necessary, rotate propeller shaft to align parking gear and sprag to permit knob on end of control rod to pass sprag. Remove accumulator piston and spring from case. Inspect all parts for wear or damage and replace as needed.

Manual Lever Shaft Seal Replacement

If shaft seal requires replacement, drive seal out of case with a punch. Drive a new seal into case using a 5/16" socket and a hammer.

NOTE: Seal may be replaced without removing valve body from case by using a small screwdriver to pry seal out of case. Take care not to damage shaft or seal bore in case.

Installation

1) Insert parking lock rod through opening in rear of case with knob positioned against plug and sprag. Move front end of rod toward center of transmission while exerting rearward pressure to force it past sprag. If necessary, rotate propeller shaft.

2) Install accumulator piston in transmission case and accumulator spring on valve body. Place valve body manual lever in LOW position. Lift valve body into its approximate position. Connect parking lock rod to manual lever and secure with "E" clip. Position valve body in case and install retaining bolts finger tight.

3) With neutral safety switch installed, place manual valve in neutral position. Shift valve body as necessary to center neutral finger over neutral switch plunger. Snug attaching bolts down evenly, then tighten.

4) Install gearshift lever and tighten clamp bolt. Make sure no binding exists when lever is moved through all detent positions. If binding exists, loosen attaching bolts and re-align.

5) Make sure throttle shaft seal is in place. Install flat washer and lever, tighten clamp bolt. Connect throttle and gear shift linkage and adjust as required. Install oil pan with new gasket and refill transmission to correct fluid level.

TRANSMISSION REMOVAL & INSTALLATION

See *Transmission Removal & Installation* in *Automatic Transmission Servicing*.

TORQUE CONVERTER

1) The torque converter is a welded assembly and is not serviceable. Therefore, if a malfunction occurs or if the converter becomes contaminated with foreign material, it must be replaced. It cannot be flushed or repaired.

2) The input shaft and valve body used with a lock-up converter are significantly different from those used in transmissions utilizing a non lock-up converter. As a result, the 2 types of converters are NEVER interchangeable, and no attempt to do so should be made.

3) If the starter ring gear on a lock-up type torque converter requires replacement, the complete converter must be replaced. Welding a new ring gear onto a lock-up converter will damage the friction material used in the converter.

TRANSMISSION DISASSEMBLY

INPUT SHAFT END PLAY

1) Measuring end play before disassembly will usually indicate when a change in thrust washer is required to properly adjust end play during reassembly (except when major parts are replaced).

2) Attach a dial indicator to transmission bell housing with plunger seated against end of input shaft. Move input shaft in and out to obtain reading. Record reading for reassembly reference.

NOTE: The thrust washer is located between reaction shaft support and front clutch retainer on all 727 transmissions; between the input and output shafts on all other models.

Fig. 20: Measuring Input Shaft End Play

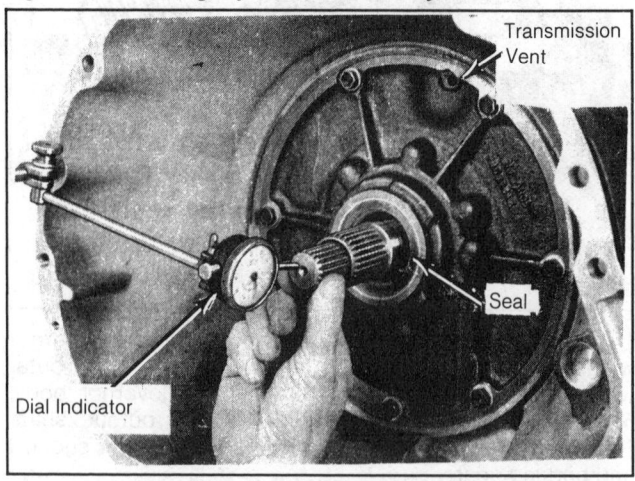

Measure end play before disassembly.

AMERICAN MOTORS, CHRYSLER & JEEP
727, 904, 998 & 999 (Cont.)

TRANSMISSION END PLAY SPECIFICATIONS

Application	End Play Inches (mm)
Model 727	.034-.084 (.86-2.13)
All Others	.022-.091 (.56-2.31)

VALVE BODY & ACCUMULATOR PISTON
See SERVICE (IN VEHICLE).

EXTENSION/ADAPTER HOUSING
See SERVICE (IN VEHICLE).

GOVERNOR
See SERVICE (IN VEHICLE).

OIL PUMP & REACTION SHAFT SUPPORT
1) Tighten front band adjusting screw until band is tight on front clutch retainer, preventing retainer from coming out with pump and damaging clutches.

2) Remove oil pump housing retaining bolts. Install 2 slide hammers in threaded holes in pump housing flange. Operating both hammers evenly, withdraw pump and reaction shaft support assembly from case.

FRONT BAND & CLUTCH
Loosen front band adjuster, remove band strut (and 727 anchor) and slide band out of case. Slide front clutch out of case.

INPUT SHAFT & REAR CLUTCH
Grasp input shaft by hand. Slide input shaft and rear clutch assembly out of case.

CAUTION: Do not lose thrust washer located between rear end of input shaft and forward end of output shaft.

PLANETARY GEAR ASSEMBLIES, SUN GEAR & DRIVING SHELL
While supporting output shaft and driving shell, carefully slide assembly forward and out through case.

CAUTION: Do not damage machined surfaces on output shaft during removal.

REAR BAND & LOW-REVERSE DRUM
AMC/Jeep
Remove low-reverse drum. Loosen rear band adjusting screw and thread a 1/4" bolt into actuating lever pivot pin and remove pin from case. Remove lever, linkage and rear band from case.
Chrysler
Remove drum, loosen rear band adjuster and remove band strut and link. Remove band from case. On A-904LA models with double-wrap band, loosen band adjusting screw, then remove band and low-reverse drum.

OVERRUNNING CLUTCH
Note relative positions of overrunning clutch rollers and springs before disassembly for reassembly reference. Carefully slide out clutch hub, then remove rollers and springs.

FRONT (KICKDOWN) SERVO
Compress kickdown servo and remove snap ring. Remove rod guide, springs, and piston rod from case. Take care not to damage piston rod or guide. Remove piston from transmission case.

REAR (LOW-REVERSE) SERVO
Compress low-reverse servo piston spring and remove snap ring. Remove spring retainer, spring, servo piston and plug assembly from case. Tag spring for reassembly reference.

COMPONENT DISASSEMBLY & REASSEMBLY

VALVE BODY DISASSEMBLY

NOTE: Tag all valves and springs for reassembly reference as they are removed.

Filter, Transfer Plate & Pressure Regulators
1) Place valve body assembly on stand, remove filter retaining screws and filter. Remove top and bottom screws from spring retainer/adjustment screw bracket. Holding spring retainer firmly against spring pressure, remove last screw from side of valve body.

Fig. 21: Valve Body Assembly Prepared for Disassembly

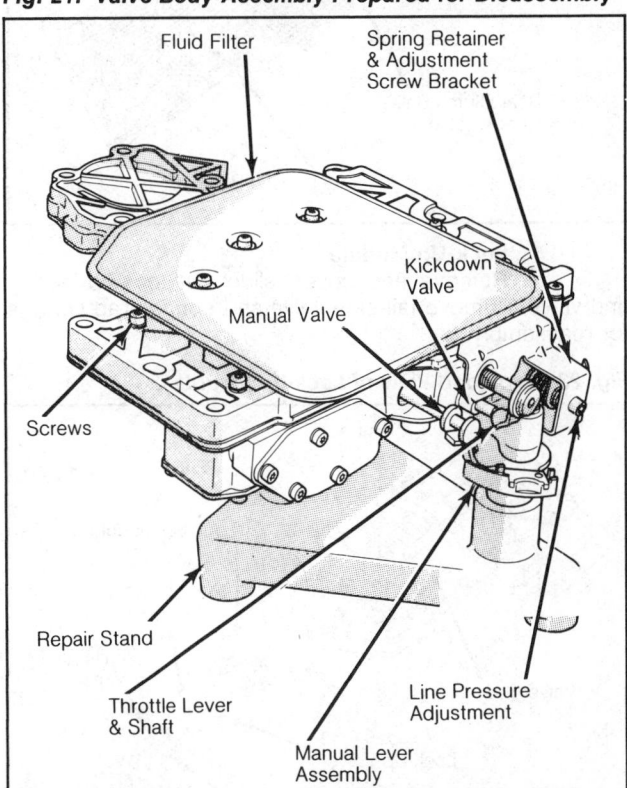

Support valve body in stand during disassembly procedure.

2) Remove spring retainer with line and throttle pressure adjusting screws (do not disturb settings). Remove line pressure and switch valve regulator springs.

Automatic Transmissions
AMERICAN MOTORS, CHRYSLER & JEEP
727, 904, 998 & 999 (Cont.)

3) Slide switch valve and line pressure valve from bores. Remove screws from lock-up module (stiffener plate on non lock-up valve body) and carefully remove tube and lock-up module (or stiffener plate). Disassemble lock-up module, tagging springs for reassembly reference.

4) Remove transfer plate retaining screws and lift off transfer plate and separator plate assembly. Remove screws from stiffener and separator plate and separate parts for cleaning. Remove rear clutch check ball and line pressure regulator screen from separator plate. Remove all check balls from valve body.

Fig. 22: *Transfer and Separator Plate*

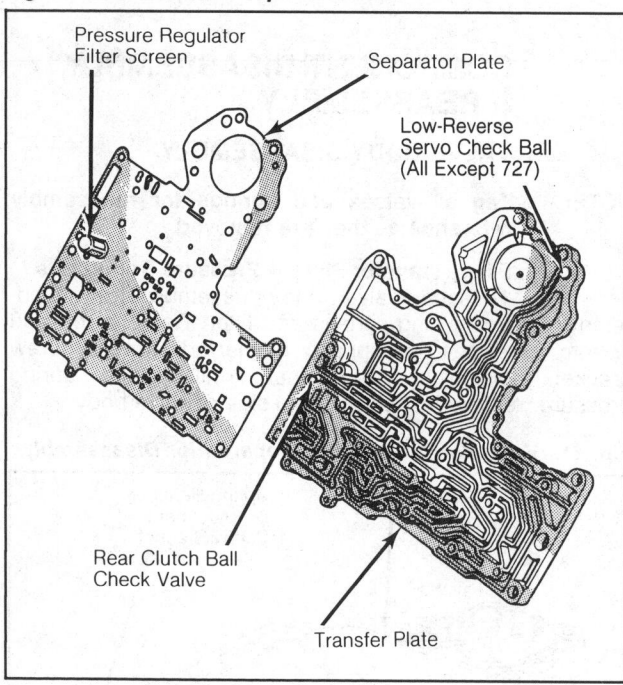

Lock-Up Module
Remove end cover, slide out lock-up spring and valve. Remove fail-safe valve and spring. Tag springs for reassembly.

Fig. 23: *Exploded View of Lock-Up Module*

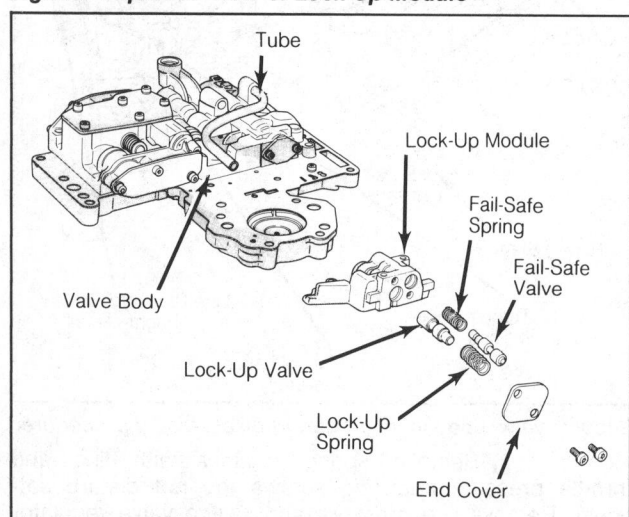

Shuttle Valve & Governor Plugs
1) Turn valve body over and remove shuttle valve cover plate. Remove governor plug end plate and slide out shuttle valve throttle plug and spring, 1-2 shift valve governor plug, and 2-3 shift valve governor plug. *See Fig. 26.*

2) Remove shuttle valve "E" clip and slide shuttle valve from bore. Also remove secondary spring and guides retained by "E" clip. Remove "E" clip and park control rod from manual lever.

Pressure Regulators & Manual Control
1) Remove "E" clip and washer from throttle lever shaft. Remove any burrs from shaft. While holding manual lever detent ball and spring in bore, slide manual lever off throttle shaft. *See Fig. 25.*

2) Remove detent ball and spring. Slide manual lever from bore, and remove kickdown detent, kickdown valve, throttle valve spring and throttle valve.

Shift Valves & Regulator Valve
Pressure Sensing Plugs
1) Remove line pressure regulator valve end plate. *See Fig. 24.* Slide out regulator valve sleeve, line pressure plug, throttle pressure plug and spring.

2) Remove end plate. On models with downshift valve housing, remove housing assembly. Remove throttle plug, slide out retainer and remove spring and limit valve from housing. On all models, remove shift valves and springs (3) from valve body.

VALVE BODY INSPECTION
1) Wash all parts in solvent and dry with compressed air. Inspect all parts for nicks, burrs, scratches or distortion. Small nicks and burrs can be removed with crocus cloth. Use extreme care not to round off any machined sharp edges. These edges are necessary to prevent foreign matter from lodging between any valve and its bore, causing valve to stick or drag.

2) Make sure all passages are clean and free of obstructions and all metering holes in steel plate and valve body are open. Insert a 1/32" diameter drill through orifice into 1-2 shift control bore to make sure it is open. Inspect all springs for distortion and/or collapsed coils.

3) Inspect manual and throttle valve operating levers and shafts. If bent, worn or loose on shaft, assembly should be replaced. DO NOT attempt to straighten bent levers.

4) When bores, valves and plugs are clean and dry, valves and plugs should fall freely into bores.

VALVE BODY REASSEMBLY
Shift Valves & Regulator Valve
Pressure Sensing Plugs
1) Slide shift valves and springs into proper valve body bores. On models with downshift housing assembly, insert limit valve and spring into housing and slide spring retainer into groove. Install throttle plug in housing bore. Position assembly against shift valve springs.

2) On all models, install end plate and tighten retaining screws. Install throttle pressure spring, plug, sleeve and regulator valve plug. Install end plate and tighten retaining screws.

Automatic Transmissions
AMERICAN MOTORS, CHRYSLER & JEEP
727, 904, 998 & 999 (Cont.)

2-29

Fig. 24: Exploded View of Shift Valves and Pressure Regulator Valve Plugs

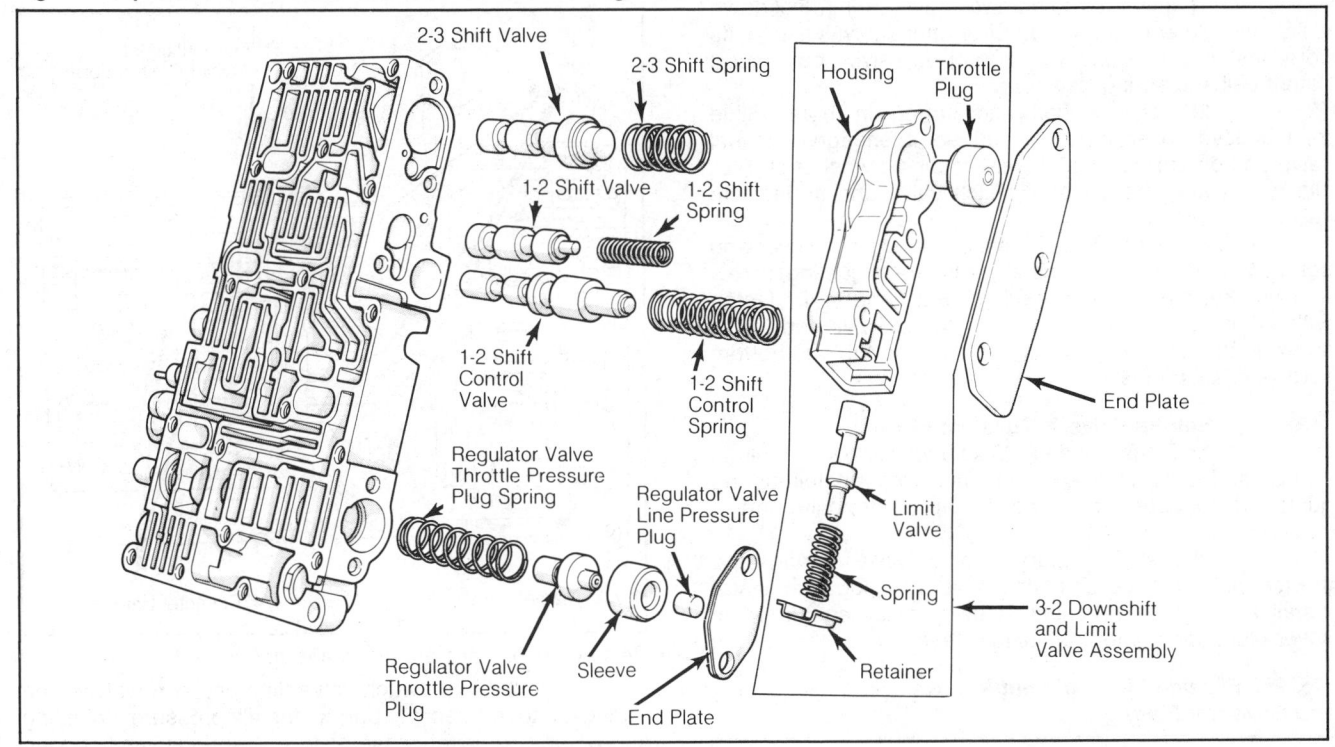

Fig. 25: Exploded View of Pressure Regulators and Manual Controls

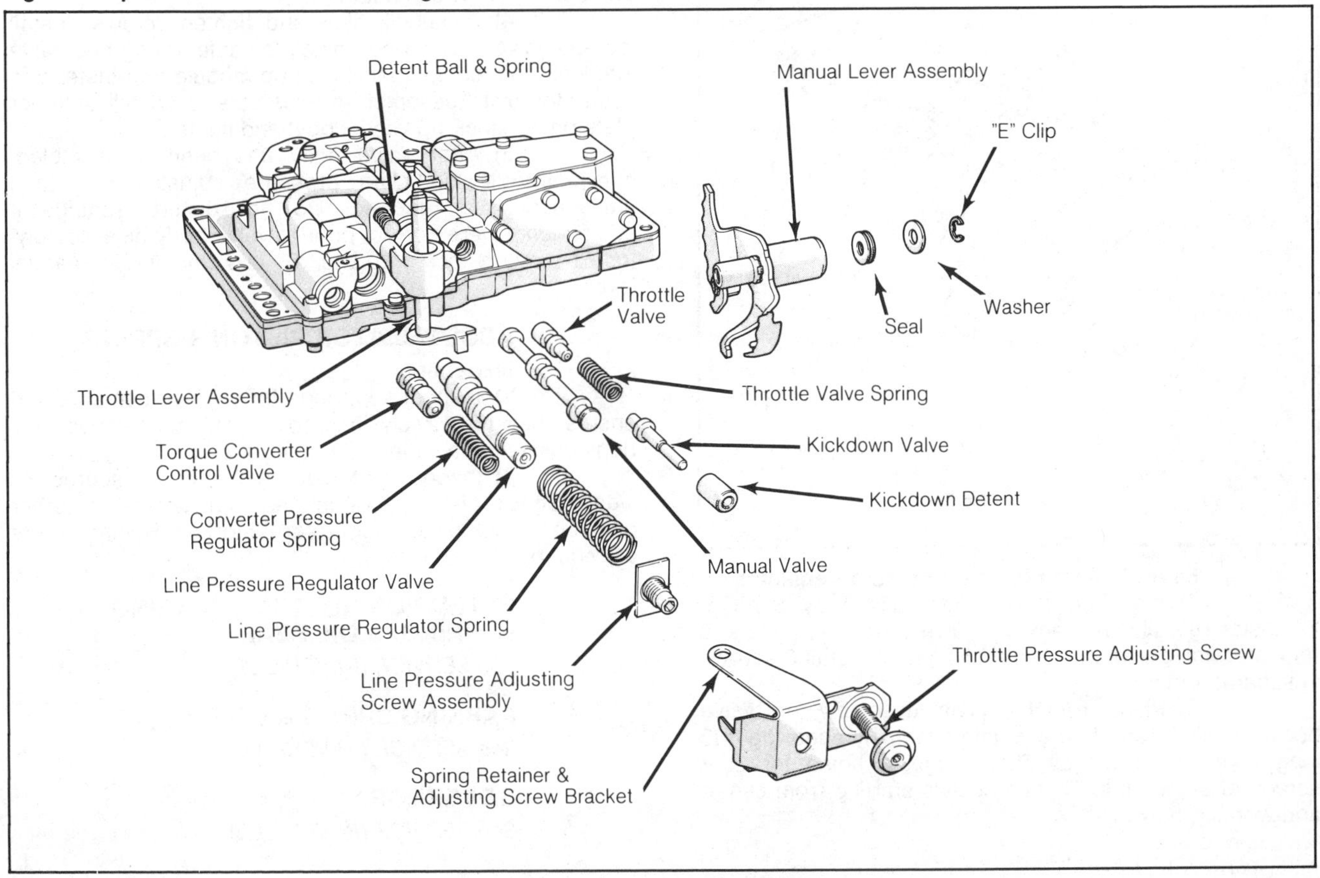

2-30

Automatic Transmissions
AMERICAN MOTORS, CHRYSLER & JEEP
727, 904, 998 & 999 (Cont.)

Pressure Regulators & Manual Control

1) Install throttle valve, valve spring, kickdown valve and detent into bore. Slide manual valve into its bore. Install throttle lever and shaft on valve body. Insert detent ball and spring into bore.

2) Depress ball and spring in bore. Slide manual lever over throttle shaft so it engages manual valve and detent ball. Install seal, retaining washer and "E" clip on throttle shaft. Insert switch valve and spring into valve body.

3) Insert line pressure regulator valve and spring into valve body. Install pressure adjusting screw and bracket assembly on springs and temporarily fasten with single screw which goes into side of valve body. This screw is to be tightened first, after starting top and bottom screws in a later step.

Shuttle Valve & Governor Plugs

1) Place 1-2 and 2-3 shift valve governor plugs in bores. Install shuttle valve into bore. Install spring guides, secondary spring and "E" clip on opposite end of valve.

2) Install primary shuttle valve spring and throttle plug into bore. Install governor plug end plate. Install and tighten retaining screws. Install shuttle valve cover plate and tighten retaining screws.

Fig. 26: Exploded View of Shuttle Valve and Governor Plugs

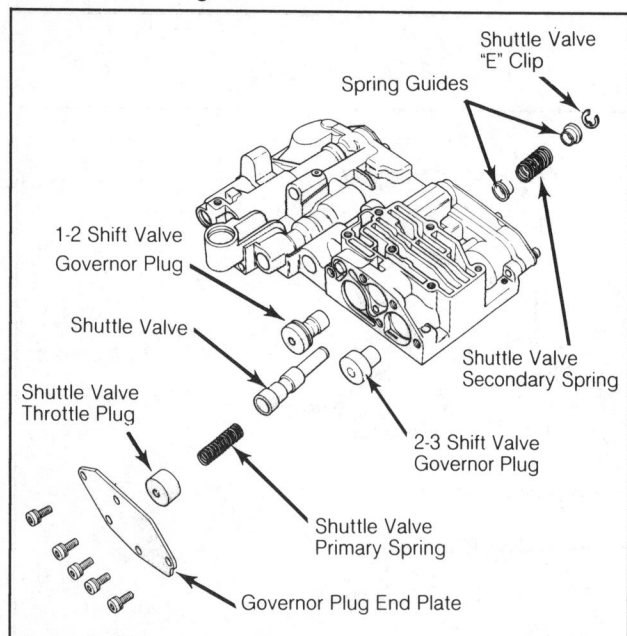

Filter, Transfer Plate & Pressure Regulator

1) Install check balls into valve body. See Fig. 27. Install rear clutch check ball valve in transfer plate and regulator valve screen in separator plate. Install 3 screws in separator plate.

2) Place transfer plate assembly on valve body. Install 17 short screws into assembly finger tight (3 long screws are for oil filter), aligning holes for filter screen at same time. Tighten screws starting from center and working outward.

Fig. 27: Location of Check Balls in Valve Body

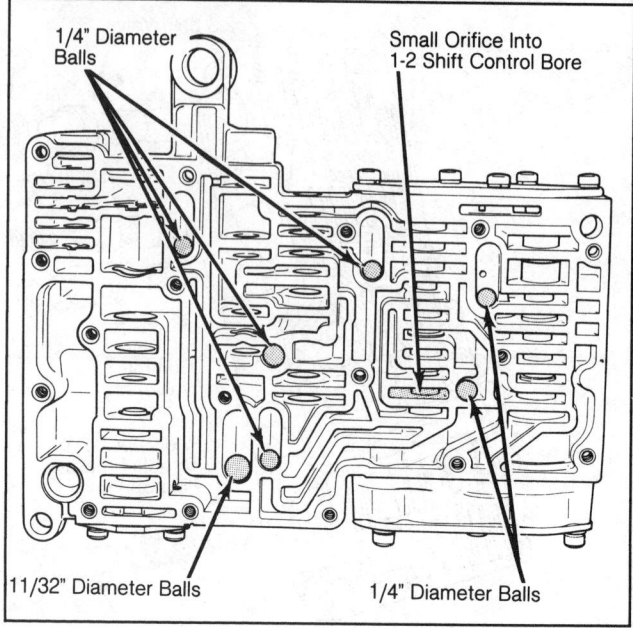

Be sure check balls are clean and not scored.

3) Slide switch valve, line pressure valves and springs into respective bores. Install pressure adjusting screw and bracket assembly on springs and fasten temporarily single screw which goes into side of valve body. This screw will be tightened first, after starting top and bottom screws in a later step.

4) Install oil filter and tighten screws. Install lock-up valve and spring. Install fail-safe spring and valve into lock-up module. Install lock-up module to transfer and separator plate assembly with 3 screws (install stiffener plate on non lock-up valve body) and tighten.

5) After valve body has been reassembled, check throttle and line pressure adjustments. Make adjustments as required. Do not disturb settings if adjustments were correct prior to valve body disassembly. Install parking lock rod and "E" clip retainer to manual lever.

ACCUMULATOR PISTON & SPRING
Inspection

1) Inspect seal rings for wear or damage, and ensure they turn freely in grooves. Do not remove seal rings unless replacement is required.

2) Inspect piston for nicks, burrs, scores, or wear. Check piston bore in case for scores or other damage. Check piston spring for distortion. Replace parts as required.

EXTENSION HOUSING, BEARING, BUSHING, & OIL SEAL

See SERVICE (IN VEHICLE).

PARKING SPRAG & LEVER

See SERVICE (IN VEHICLE).

GOVERNOR

See SERVICE (IN VEHICLE).

Fig. 28: Exploded View of Model 727 Oil Pump and Reaction Shaft Support

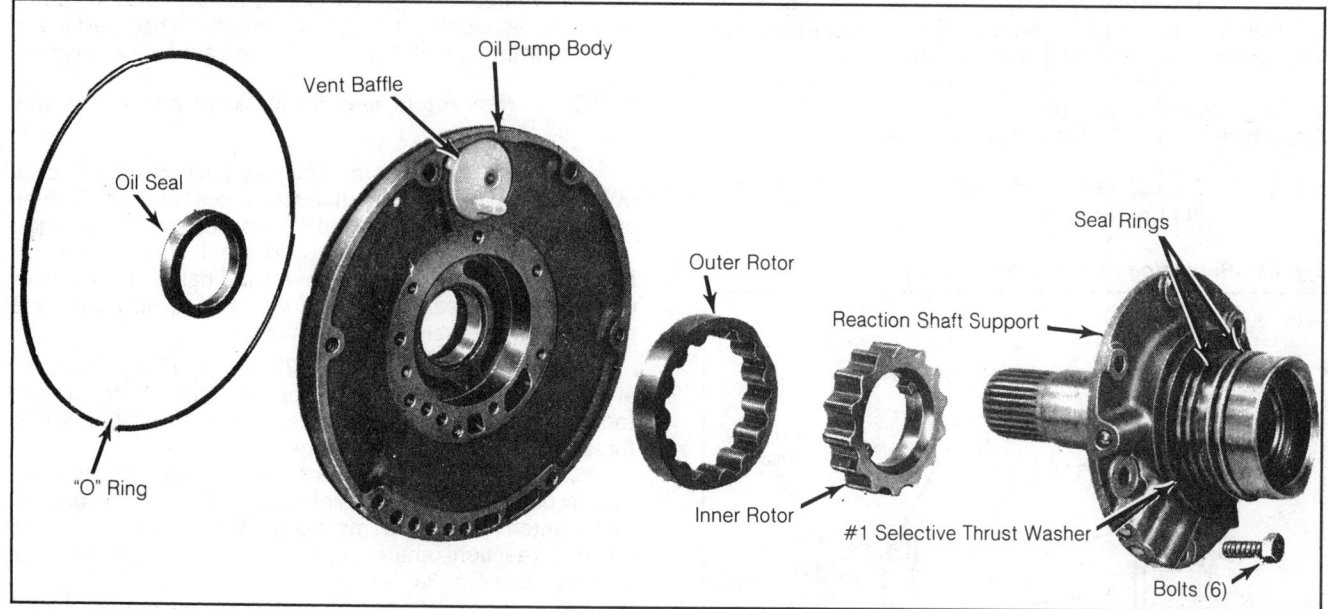

OIL PUMP/REACTION SHAFT SUPPORT

Disassembly

Remove bolts from rear side of reaction shaft support and lift support off pump. Remove rubber seal ring from pump body flange. Drive out oil seal with a blunt punch. Mark top of pump rotors with chalk to ensure proper installation during reassembly.

Fig. 29: Exploded View of Oil Pump and Reaction Shaft Support — All Except 727

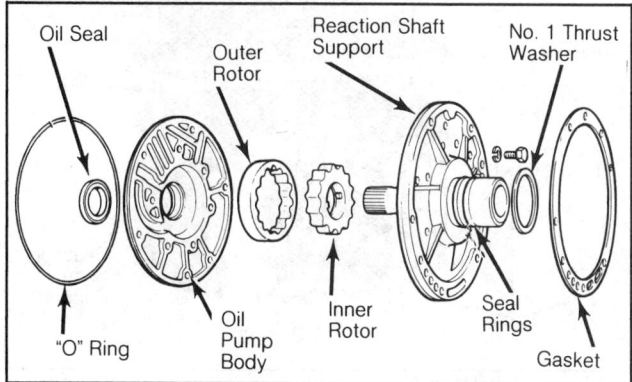

Inspection

1) Inspect interlocking seal rings on support for wear or damage. Make sure rings turn freely in grooves. Do not remove rings unless replacement is required. Inspect pump body and support bushings for wear or scores.

2) Check machined surfaces of pump body and support for nicks or burrs. Check pump rotors for scoring or pitting. With rotors cleaned and installed in pump body, place a straightedge across face of rotors and pump body. Using a feeler gauge, measure clearance between straightedge and rotor faces. Clearance should be .001-.003" (.03-.06 mm).

3) Measure rotor tip clearance between inner and outer rotor teeth. Clearance should be .005-.010" (.13-.25 mm). Clearance between outer rotor and oil pump body bore should be .004-.008" (.10-.20 mm).

NOTE: **On all models except 727, remove seal rings so that front clutch retainer-to-reaction shaft thrust washer can be removed. If washer thickness is not .061-.063" (1.55-1.60 mm), it should be replaced.**

Pump Bushing Replacement

1) Place pump housing (rotor cavity down) on a clean smooth surface. Drive bushing straight down and out of bore, being careful not to cock tool in bore.

2) With hub end of pump housing down, drive new bushing into place in pump cavity. Stake bushing in place using a blunt punch or other tool.

3) Using a narrow bladed knife, remove high points or burrs around staked area. Do not use a file or any tool that would remove more metal than necessary.

Fig. 30: Installing New Oil Pump Bushing

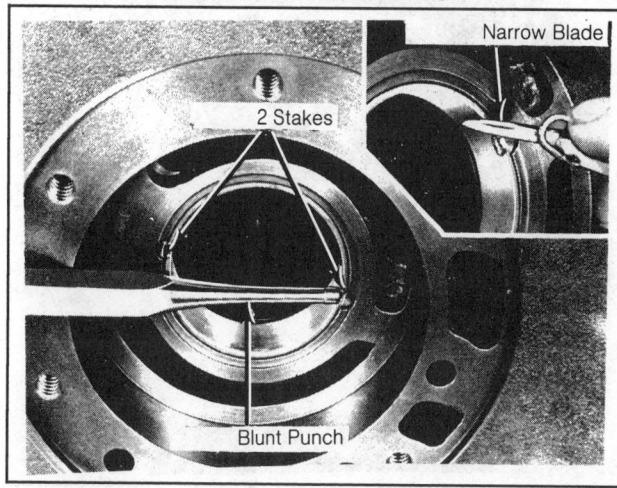

Stake bushing in place with blunt punch.

2-32

Automatic Transmissions
AMERICAN MOTORS, CHRYSLER & JEEP
727, 904, 998 & 999 (Cont.)

Reaction Shaft Bushing Replacement

1) Thread a bushing remover tool into bushing. Remove bushing from reaction shaft. Support reaction shaft upright on a clean smooth surface.

2) Using brushing installer tool, drive new bushing (chamfer end up) into place in reaction shaft. Stake bushing in 2 places to hold in place.

NOTE: **Do not clamp any part of reaction shaft or support in a vice.**

Fig. 31: Replacing Reaction Shaft Bushing

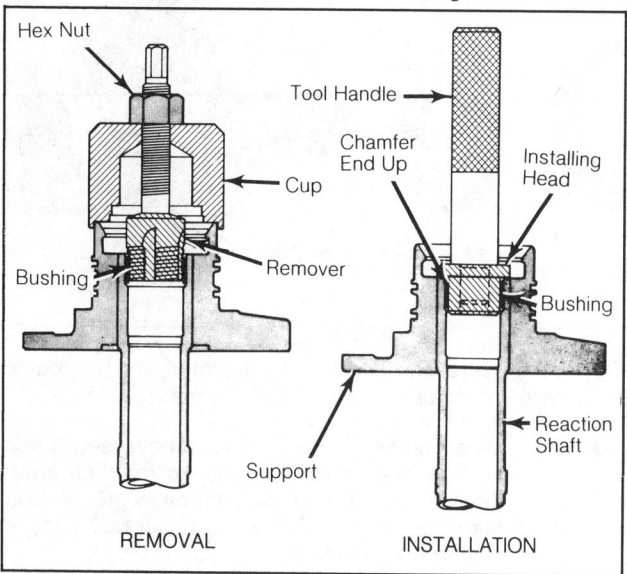

Drive in new bushing with chamfer end up

Reassembly

AMC/Jeep — 1) Install rotors in pump housing with marks made at disassembly facing up. Align and loosely assemble reaction shaft support to pump housing. Do not tighten bolts at this time.

Fig. 32: Aligning AMC Oil Pump

Place pump assembly in transmission case BACKWARDS to properly align pump and reaction shaft.

2) Thread 2 slide hammer bolts (from back to front) into threaded reaction shaft support holes, until bolt ends are recessed 1/16" below front machined surface of pump housing. Install 1 pilot stud into case pump opening.

NOTE: **New rotors may be installed with either face up.**

3) Insert pump assembly backwards into case opening, tapping pump as needed to seat in case. Tighten screws attaching reaction shaft support to pump housing.

4) Remove pump and reaction shaft support assembly from case and remove slide hammer bolts from pump. Using a seal installer tool, drive a new seal into pump housing (seal lip facing inward).

Chrysler (Exc. 727) — 1) Place reaction shaft support in a clamping tool with hub of support and tool on a smooth flat surface. Install 2 pilot studs in threaded holes in support flange.

2) Assemble rotors in center of support. Lower pump body over pilot studs. Using an alignment tool, center rotors in pump body. With pump body firmly against reaction shaft support, tighten clamping tool securely. *See Fig. 33.*

3) Invert pump and tool assembly. Install support-to-pump bolts and tighten bolts evenly. Remove clamping tool, pilot studs and aligning tool. Drive a new pump oil seal into housing with lip of seal facing in.

Fig. 33: Assembling Oil Pump & Reaction Shaft Support

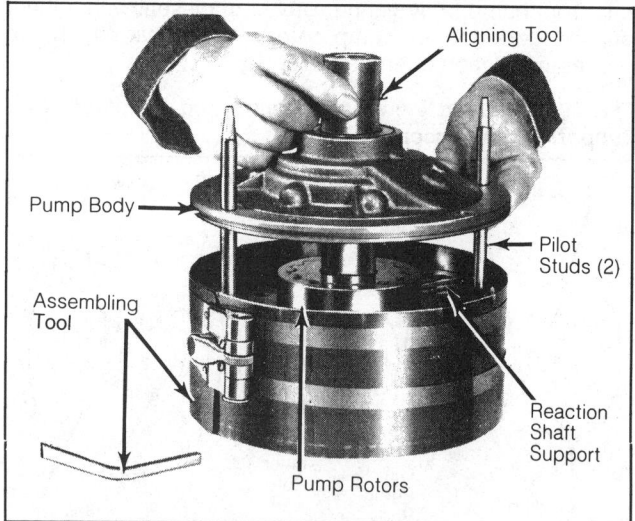

All Chrysler Corp. models, except 727.

Chrysler 727 — 1) Install pump rotors and "O" ring in pump housing. Install reaction shaft support and retaining bolts.

2) Place new seal in opening of pump housing with lip of seal facing inward and press into place with driver.

FRONT CLUTCH

Disassembly

1) Remove large waved snap ring securing pressure plate in clutch piston retainer (snap ring in 5 disc clutch may not be waved). Lift out pressure plate and clutch plates. Compress spring retainer and spring(s), remove snap ring and release tool until retainer is free of hub.

Fig. 34: Exploded View of Front Clutch Assembly

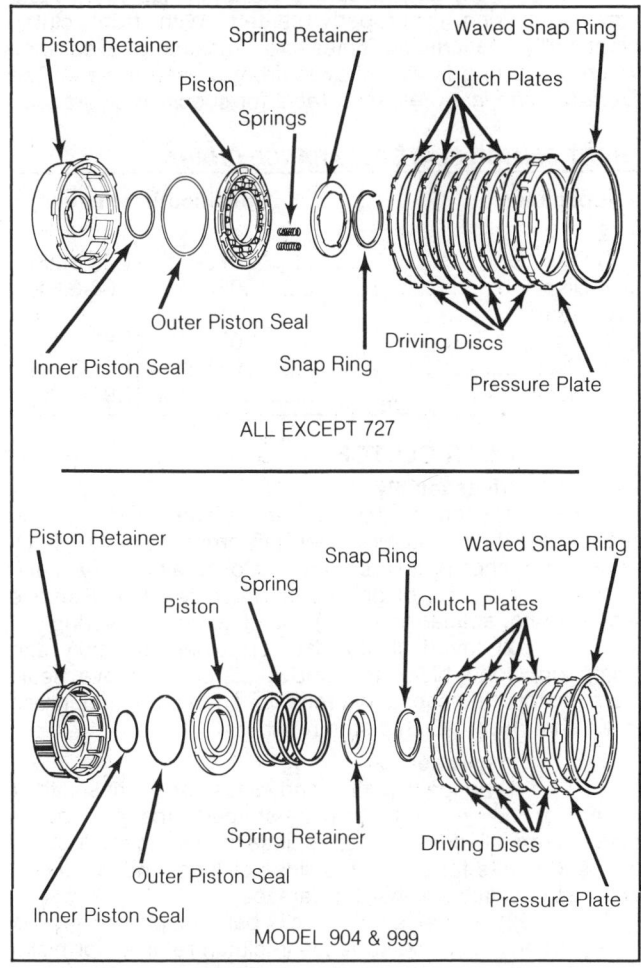

ALL EXCEPT 727

MODEL 904 & 999

2) Remove tool, retainer and spring(s), noting location and number of springs (727 only) for reassembly. Remove clutch piston and remove seals from piston and hub.

Inspection

1) Inspect plates and discs for flatness; they must not be warped or cone-shaped. Inspect facing material on all driving discs. Replace discs as needed.

2) Inspect discs and plates for wear on splines or lugs. Check clutch retainer for damaged lug grooves or band contacting surface. Make sure check ball in clutch retainer moves freely.

3) Check neoprene seals for wear, hardness or deterioration. Inspect piston spring(s), retainer and snap ring for distortion.

Front Clutch Retainer Bushing Replacement

1) Lay clutch retainer (open end down) on a clean smooth surface. Drive bushing straight down and out of bore, taking care not to cock tool in bore.

2) To install, lay clutch retainer (open end up) on a clean smooth surface. Drive bushing into place in clutch retainer bore with bushing installer tool.

Reassembly

1) Lubricate and install inner seal on hub of clutch retainer. Make sure lip of seal faces down and is properly seated in groove. Install outer seal on clutch piston, with lip of seal toward bottom of clutch retainer.

2) Lubricate seals to ease installation. Install and carefully seat piston in bottom of retainer. Install return spring on piston hub. On 727 transmissions, install the same number of springs as were removed. See *Fig. 35* for spring location.

3) Position spring retainer and snap ring over hub. Compress and install snap ring in hub groove. Remove compressor tool. Lubricate all clutch plates. Install 1 steel plate followed by 1 faced disc until all clutch plates are installed. *See Front Clutch Plate Chart.*

Fig. 35: Model 727 Front Clutch Spring Installation

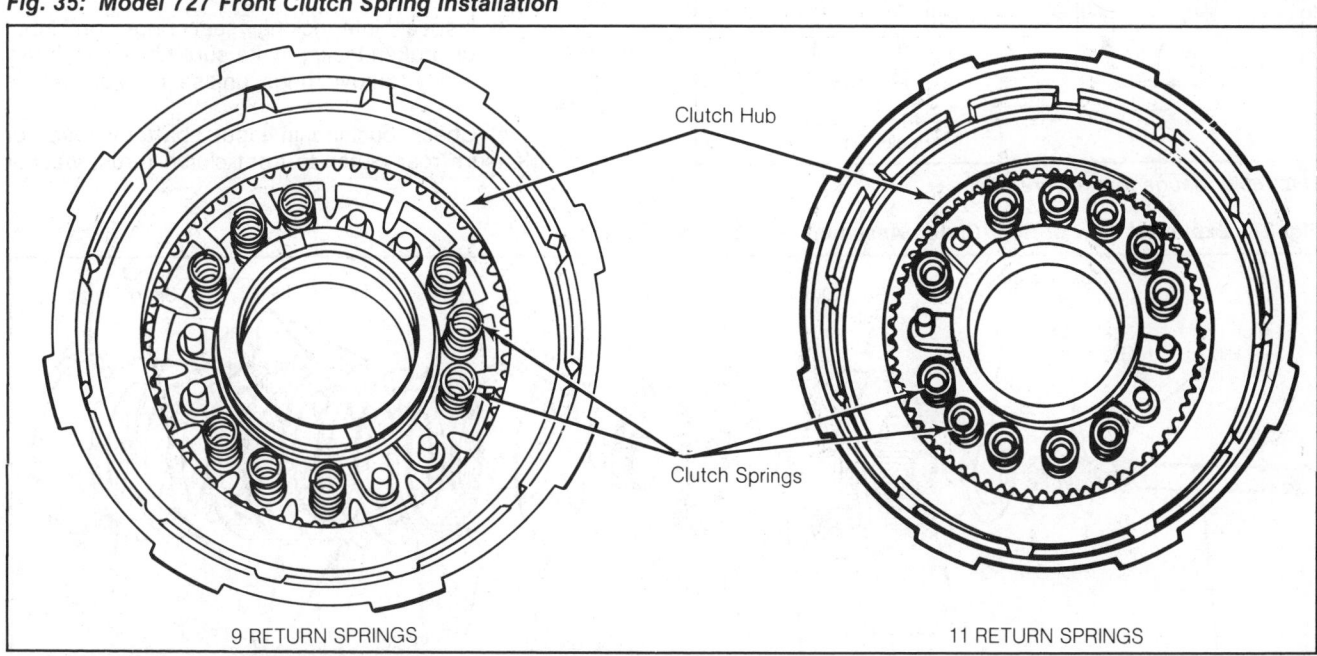

9 RETURN SPRINGS   11 RETURN SPRINGS

Springs must be installed in position as shown.

Automatic Transmissions
AMERICAN MOTORS, CHRYSLER & JEEP
727, 904, 998 & 999 (Cont.)

FRONT CLUTCH PLATE CHART

Application	Steel Plates	Composition Plates
AMC		
4-Cylinder	3	3
6-Cylinder	4	4
Chrysler Corp.		
Model A-904LA	5	5
Model A-999	5	5
All Other Models	4	4
Jeep		
Model 727	4	4
Model 999	5	5

Fig. 36: Measuring Front Clutch Plate Clearance

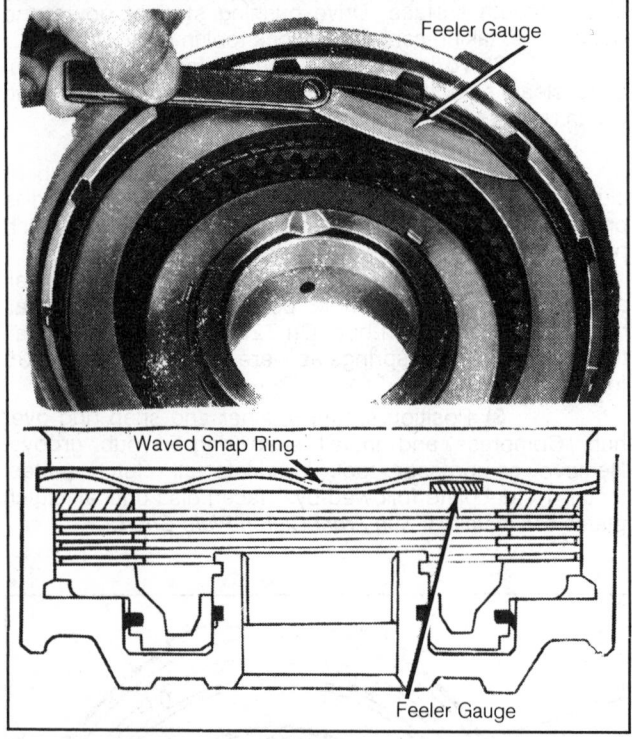

Use feeler gauge to measure gap.

4) Install pressure plate and snap ring. Make sure snap ring is properly seated. With front clutch completely assembled, measure maximum clearance where snap ring is waved away from pressure plate. See *Front Clutch Plate Clearance Table* for specified clearance.

FRONT CLUTCH PLATE CLEARANCE CHART

Application	Specification In. (mm)
727	
3 Disc.	.070-.129 (1.78-3.28)
4 Disc.	.082-.151 (2.08-3.84)
All Others	
3 Disc.	.074-.125 (1.88-3.14)
4 Disc.	.067-.134 (1.70-3.40)
5 Disc.	.075-.152 (1.91-3.86)

REAR CLUTCH
Disassembly

1) Remove large selective snap ring securing pressure plate in clutch retainer. Lift pressure plate, clutch plates and inner pressure plate out of retainer. Pry 1 end of wave spring out of groove in clutch retainer. Remove wave spring, spacer ring (727) and clutch piston spring.

2) Invert clutch piston retainer assembly and bump on wood block to remove piston. Remove seals from piston. If necessary, remove snap ring and press input shaft from clutch piston retainer.

Inspection

1) Inspect plates and discs for flatness; they must not be warped or cone-shaped. Inspect facing material on all drive discs; replace if damaged. Inspect disc and plates for wear on splines or lugs, and check lug grooves in clutch retainer for damage.

2) Make sure check ball in piston moves freely. Check seal ring surfaces in clutch retainer for nicks and scratches. Check neoprene seals for wear, hardness, or deterioration.

3) Inspect interlocking seal rings on input shaft for wear or broken locks; make sure rings turn freely in grooves. Do not remove rings unless replacement is required.

4) Check bushing in input shaft for wear or scores. Measure rear clutch-to-front clutch thrust washer

Fig. 37: Exploded View of Rear Clutch Assembly — All Models Except 727

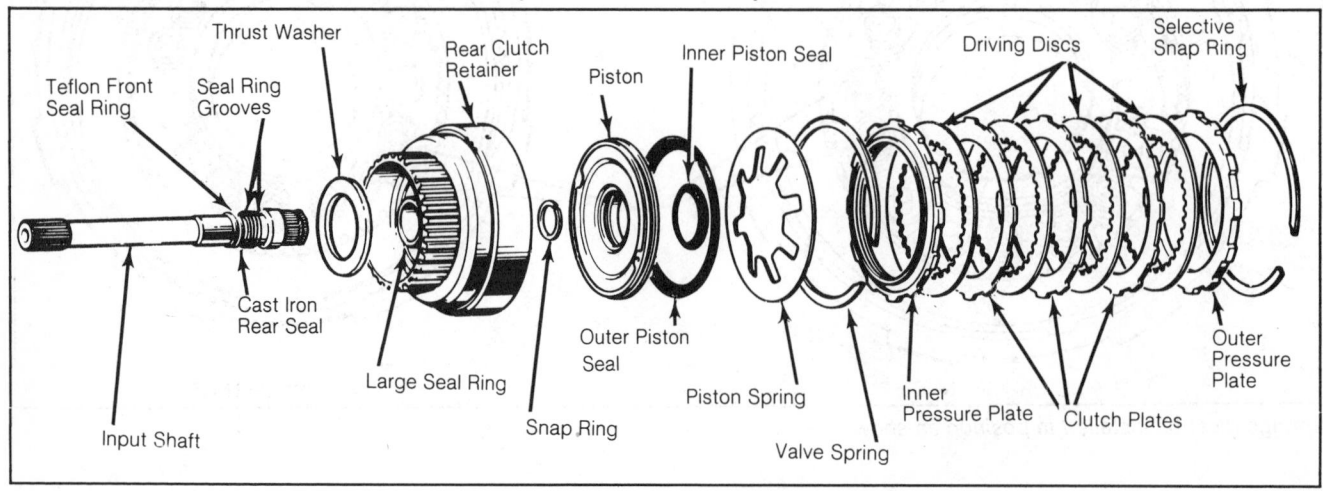

AMERICAN MOTORS, CHRYSLER & JEEP
727, 904, 998 & 999 (Cont.)

Fig. 38: Exploded View of Rear Clutch Assembly — Model 727

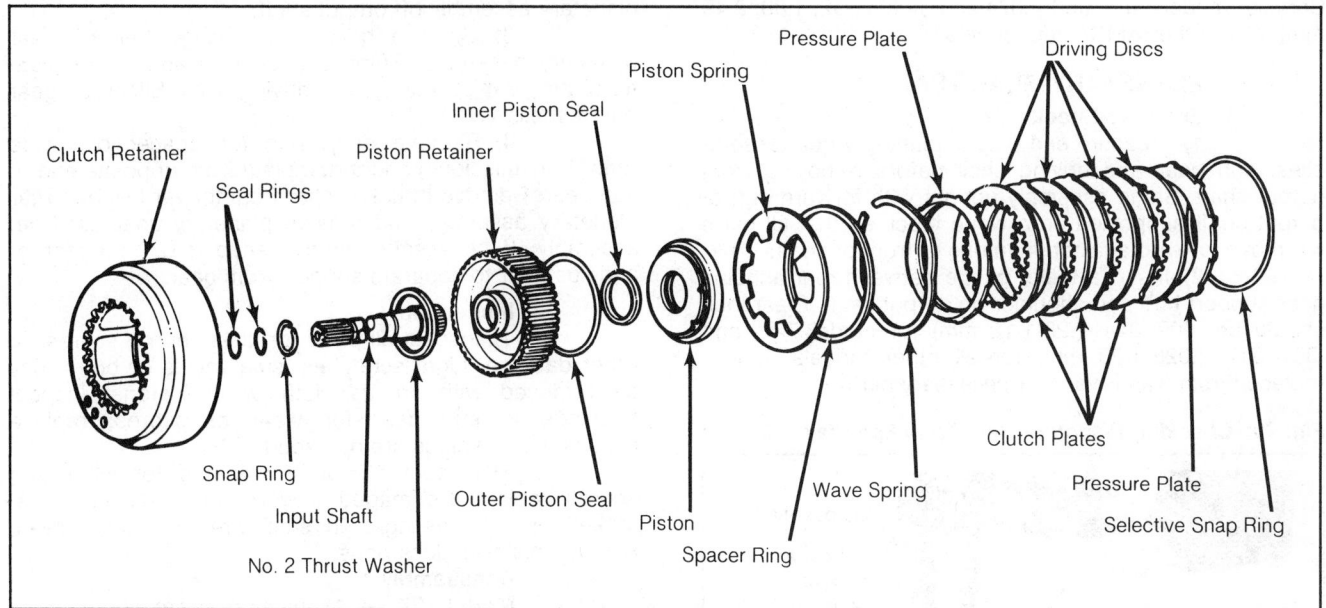

for wear. If washer is not .061-.063" (1.55-160 mm) thick, it should be replaced.

Input Shaft Bushing Replacement — Model 727

1) Clamp input shaft in soft-jawed vise, taking care not to clamp seal ring lands or journals. Thread bushing remover into bushing and withdraw bushing from shaft.

2) Thoroughly clean input shaft to remove any metal chips made by tool. Drive new bushing into place.

Fig. 39: Replacing Input Shaft Bushing

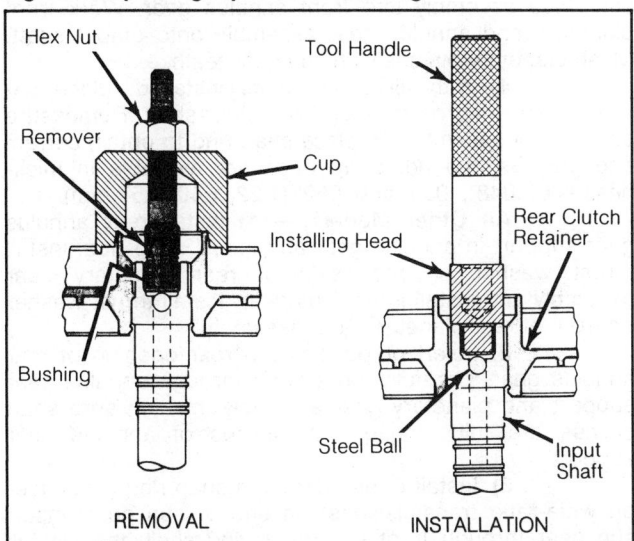

Clean input shaft to remove any metal chips made by tool.

Reassembly

1) If removed, press input shaft into clutch piston retainer and install snap ring. Lubricate and install inner and outer seal rings on clutch piston. Make sure lips of seals face toward head of clutch retainer and are properly seated in grooves.

2) Place piston assembly in retainer and, using a twisting motion, seat piston in bottom of retainer. On 727 transmissions, position clutch retainer over piston retainer splines and support assembly so clutch retainer remains in place.

3) On all models, place piston spring and spacer ring (727) on top of piston. Make sure they are positioned in retainer recess. Start one end of wave spring in retainer groove. Progressively push or tap spring into place. Make sure it is fully seated in groove.

4) Install inner pressure plate in retainer with raised portion of plate against spring. Lubricate all clutch plates, and install 1 faced disc followed by 1 steel plate until all clutch plates are installed. *See Rear Clutch Plate Chart.* Install outer pressure plate and selective snap ring.

REAR CLUTCH PLATE CHART

Application	Steel Plates	Composition Plates
All Models	3	4

5) Measure rear clutch plate clearance by having an assistant press downward firmly on outer pressure plate. Insert a feeler gauge between plate and snap ring.

REAR CLUTCH PLATE CLEARANCE CHART

Application	[1] Clearance Inches (mm)
727	.025-.045 (.64-1.14)
All Others	.032-.055 (.81-1.40)

[1] — Lower limits preferred.

6) If clearance is incorrect it may be adjusted by installing a different size snap ring. Selective snap rings are available in thicknesses of .060", .074", .088" and .106" (1.52, 1.88, 2.24, 2.69 mm) for 727 transmissions,

2-36

Automatic Transmissions
AMERICAN MOTORS, CHRYSLER & JEEP
727, 904, 998 & 999 (Cont.)

.060", .068" and .076" (1.52, 1.73, 1.93 mm) for all other Chrysler models and .060", .074 and .098" (1.52, 1.88, 2.49 mm) for all other AMC/Jeep models.

PLANETARY GEAR TRAIN
End Play Check
1) Measure end play of planetary gear assemblies, sun gear and driving shell before removing from output shaft. Stand assembly upright with forward end of output shaft supported on a wood block so that all parts will move forward against snap ring at front of shaft.

2) Insert a feeler gauge between rear annulus gear support hub and shoulder on output shaft. Clearance should be .009-.044" (.23-1.12 mm) for model 727, and .001-.047" (.025-1.20 mm) for all other models. If not, replace thrust washer and/or necessary parts.

Fig. 40: Checking Planetary Gear Train End Play

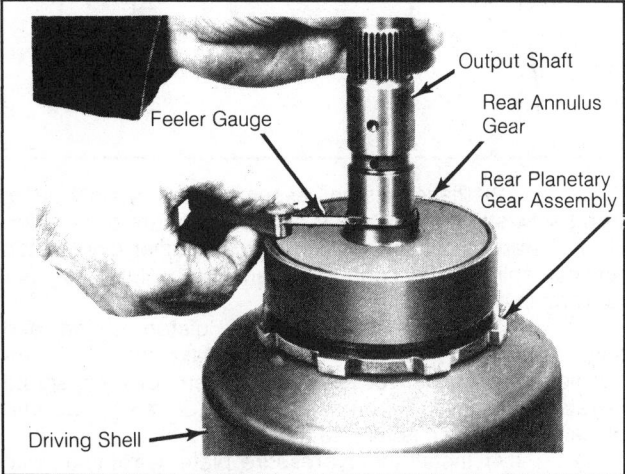

Feeler Gauge

Output Shaft

Rear Annulus Gear

Rear Planetary Gear Assembly

Driving Shell

Measure end play of planetary gear before disassembly.

Disassembly
Model 727 — 1) Remove thrust washer and selective snap ring from forward end of output shaft. Slide front planetary assembly off shaft. Slide front annulus gear off planetary gear set. Remove thrust washer from rear side of gear set.

2) Slide sun gear, driving shell, and rear planetary assembly off output shaft. Lift sun gear and driving shell off rear planetary assembly. Remove thrust washer from inside driving shell.

3) Remove snap ring and steel washer from sun gear (rear side of driving shell) and slide gear out of shell, removing front snap ring from sun gear if necessary. Note that front end of sun gear is longer than rear.

4) Remove thrust washer from forward side of rear planetary assembly. Remove planetary gear set and thrust plate from annulus gear.

All Other Models — 1) Remove thrust washer and selective snap ring from forward end of output shaft. Slide front planetary assembly off of shaft. Remove snap ring and thrust washer from forward hub of front planetary gear assembly. Slide front annulus gear and support off planetary gear set.

2) Remove thrust washer fron front side of planetary gear set, then remove thrust washer from rear side of planetary gear assembly. Separate support from annulus gear, removing snap ring from front of annulus

gear if necessary. Slide sun gear, driving shell and rear planetary assembly off output shaft.

3) Lift sun gear and driving shell off rear planetary assembly. Remove snap ring and thrust plate from sun gear at rear side of driving shell. Slide sun gear out of shell.

4) Remove snap ring (or spacer on "wide ratio" transmissions) and thrust plate from opposite end of sun gear. Remove thrust washer from forward side of rear planetary assembly and remove planetary gear set from assembly. If necessary, remove snap ring from rear of annulus gear to separate support from gear.

Inspection
1) Inspect all parts for nicks, burrs, scores, or other damage. Light scratches, small nicks or burrs may be removed with crocus cloth or fine stone. Inspect bushings in sun gear for wear or scores; replace assembly if bushings are damaged.

2) Inspect all thrust washers for wear and scores; replace if damaged or worn below specifications. Make sure oil passages in shaft are open and clean. Replace distorted lock rings.

Reassembly
Model 727 — 1) Install rear annulus gear on output shaft. Lightly grease thrust plate and place it on shaft, in annulus gear. Make sure teeth are over shaft splines. Position rear planetary gear assembly in rear annulus gear, and install thrust washer on front side of gear assembly.

2) Install snap ring in front groove of sun gear (long end of gear). Insert sun gear through front side of driving shell. Install rear steel washer and snap ring. Slide driving shell and sun gear assembly on output shaft. Engage sun gear teeth with rear planetary pinion teeth.

3) Place thrust washer inside front of driving shell. Place thrust washer on rear hub of planetary gear set. Slide assembly into front annulus gear. Work front planetary and annulus gear assembly onto output shaft. Mesh planetary pinions with sun gear teeth.

4) With all components installed, place selective snap ring on front end of output shaft. Remeasure end play of assembly. Replace snap ring to obtain correct end play as needed. Snap rings are available in thicknesses of .048", .055" and .062" (1.22, 1.40, 1.57 mm).

All Other Models — 1) Install rear annulus gear support in annulus gear and install snap ring. Install thrust washer on rear side of rear planetary gear assembly and install in annulus gear. Install thrust washer on front of rear planetary gear assembly.

2) Insert output shaft in rear opening of rear annulus gear. Carefully work shaft through annulus gear support and planetary gear assembly, making sure shaft splines are fully engaged in splines of annulus gear support.

3) Install thrust plate and snap ring (or spacer on wide-ratio transmissions) on end of sun gear. Insert sun gear through front side of driving shell, then install thrust plate and snap ring on other end.

4) Carefully slide driving shell and sun gear assembly on the output shaft, engaging sun gear teeth with rear planetary pinion teeth. Place front annulus gear support in annulus gear and install snap ring.

5) Place thrust washer on front of front planetary gear assembly and position assembly in front

AMERICAN MOTORS, CHRYSLER & JEEP
727, 904, 998 & 999 (Cont.)

Fig. 41: *Exploded View of Planetary Gear Train and Output Shaft*

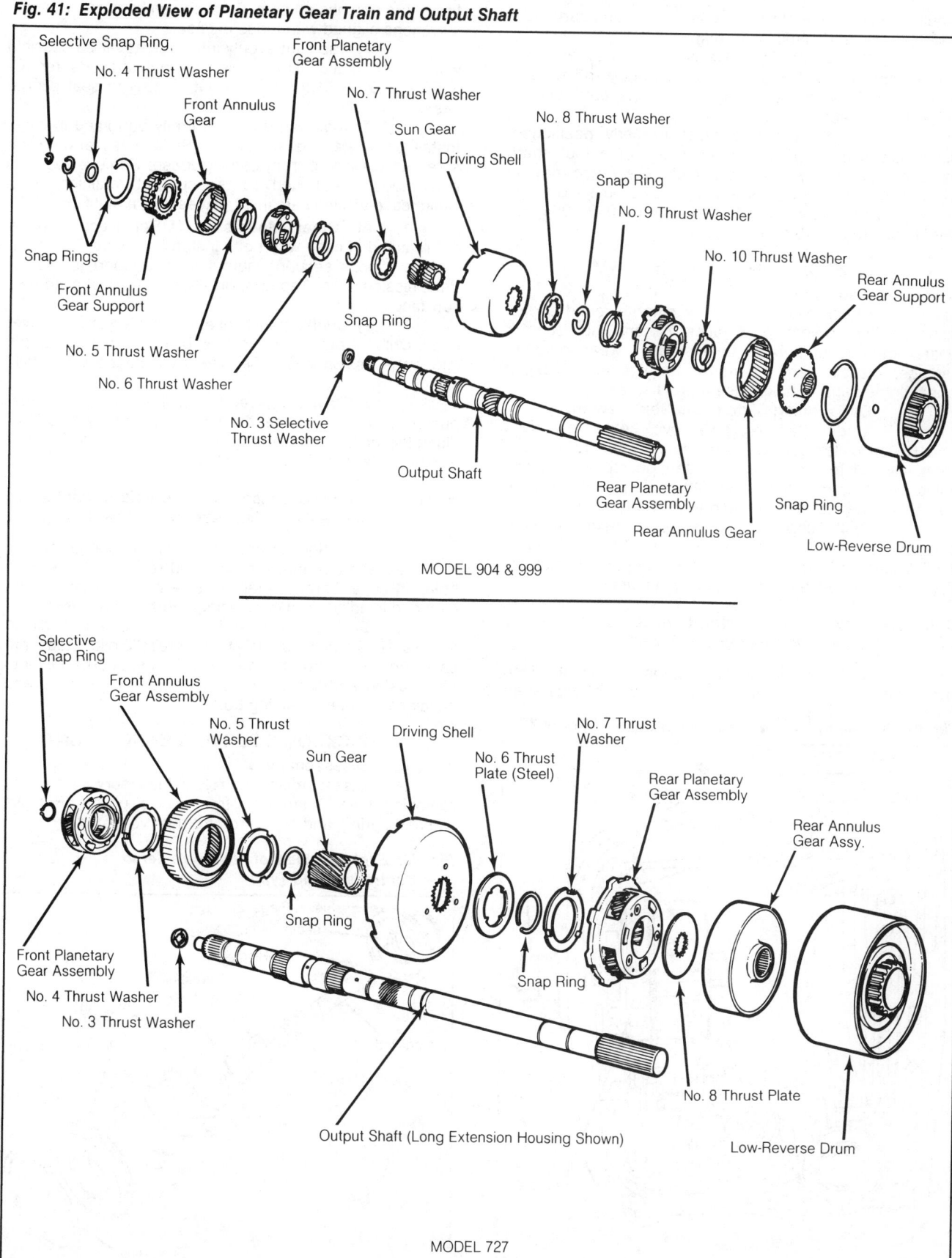

MODEL 904 & 999

MODEL 727

2-38

Automatic Transmissions
AMERICAN MOTORS, CHRYSLER & JEEP
727, 904, 998 & 999 (Cont.)

annulus gear. Place thrust washer over planetary gear assembly hub and install snap ring.

6) Position thrust washer on rear of planetary gear assembly. Carefully work front planetary and annulus gear assembly on output shaft, meshing planetary pinions with sun gear teeth.

7) With all components properly positioned, install selective snap ring on front end of output shaft. Remeasure end play of the assembly. Clearance may be adjusted with various thicknesses of seletive snap rings. Snap rings are available in thicknesses of .042, .064 and .084" (1.02, 1.63, 2.13 mm).

OVERRUNNING CLUTCH

Inspection

Check clutch rollers for smooth round edges. Inspect roller contacting surfaces in cam and race for wear. Check roller springs for distortion, wear, or other damage. Inspect cam set screw for tightness (727); if loose, tighten and restake case around screw.

Overrunning Clutch Cam Replacement

Model 727 — 1) Remove set screw from case (below clutch cam) and remove bolts securing output shaft support to rear of case. Insert punch through bolt holes and drive cam from case. Alternate punch from one hole to another so cam will be driven evenly from case.

2) If support requires replacement, tap support rearward with a soft-faced hammer. To install, screw 2 pilot studs into case and position support over studs. Tap firmly into place using soft-faced hammer.

CAUTION: Output shaft support must be in case to install overrunning clutch cam.

3) Clean all burrs and chips from case. Place spring retainer on cam and make sure retainer lugs snap

Fig. 42: Installing Overrunning Clutch Cam — Model 727

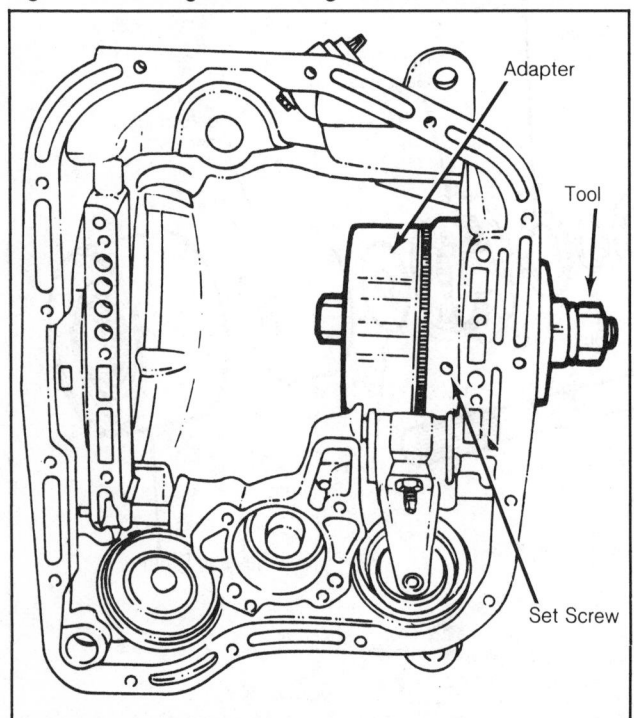

Tighten nut on tool to seat cam in case.

firmly into notches on cam. Position cam in case, with cam serrations aligned with those in case.

4) Tap cam evenly into case as far as possible with a soft mallet. Using aligning tool and adapter (C-3863-A and SP-5124), tighten nut on tool to seat cam in case.

5) Make sure cam is firmly bottomed in case. Install cam retaining set screw. Stake case around set screw to prevent it from coming loose. Remove tool and pilot studs. Install and tighten support retaining bolts. Stake case around cam in 12 places with a blunt chisel.

All Other Models — 1) Replacement parts are retained in case with bolts instead of rivets. To install, remove 4 bolts securing output shaft support to rear of transmission case. Tap support rearward out of case with soft-faced hammer.

2) Center punch rivets in center of each rivet head. Drill out rivet with 3/8" drill, being careful not to drill into transmission case. Remove rivet heads with small chisel.

3) Drive rivets and cam from case with blunt punch. Carefully enlarge rivet holes in case with 17/64" diameter drill. Remove any metal chips, burrs and/or foreign material from case.

NOTE: **Alternate punch from one hole to another so cam will be driven evenly from case.**

4) Install replacement cam and spring retainer into case with bolt holes in cam and retainer aligned with holes in case. Thread retaining screws and washers into cam and install cam in case using soft-faced hammer.

5) Alternately and evenly tighten retaining screws to 100 inch lbs. (11 N.m). Thread 2 pilot studs into case. Position support over studs. Tap support firmly into place using soft-faced hammer. Remove pilot studs and install and tighten retaining bolts.

KICKDOWN SERVO & BAND (FRONT)

Disassembly

Disassemble controlled load servo piston by removing small snap ring from servo piston. Remove washer, spring, and piston rod from servo piston.

Fig. 43: Exploded View of Kickdown Servo — Controlled Load Type

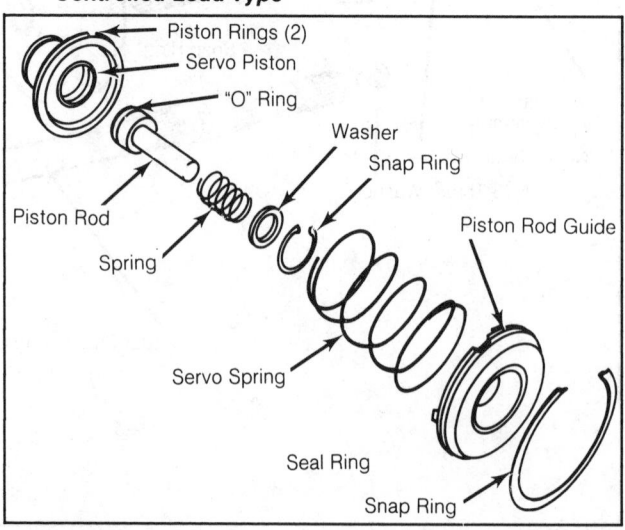

Model 727

AMERICAN MOTORS, CHRYSLER & JEEP
727, 904, 998 & 999 (Cont.)

Inspection

1) Inspect all parts for wear or damage. Be sure piston and guide seal rings turn freely in grooves. Do not remove seal rings unless replacement is required. Inspect piston bore in case for scores or other damage. Inspect fit of guide on piston rod. Check position spring for distortion.

2) If equipped with controlled load servo piston, inspect bore in piston and "O" ring on piston rod. Inspect band lining for wear or damage; if lining is worn so grooves are not visible at ends, or at any portion of band, replace band.

Reassembly

Assemble controlled load servo piston as follows: Grease "O" ring and install on piston rod. Install piston rod into servo piston. Install spring, flat washer and snap ring.

Fig. 44: Exploded View of Kickdown Servo — Non-Controlled Load Type

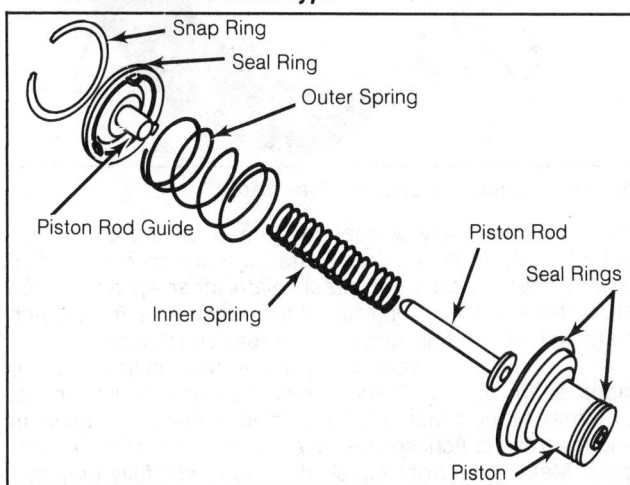

All Except 727

LOW-REVERSE SERVO & BAND (REAR)
Disassembly

Remove snap ring from piston and remove piston plug and spring.

Fig. 45: Exploded View of Low-Reverse Servo

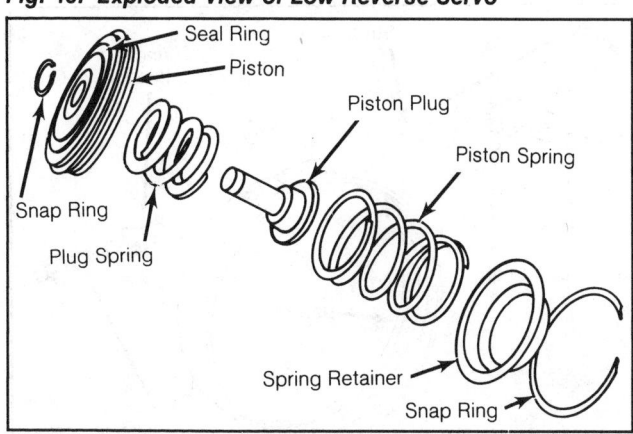

Inspection

1) Inspect seal for wear, deterioration, and hardness. Inspect piston and plug for cracks, burrs, scores, and wear. Piston plug must operate freely in piston. Inspect piston bore for scores or damage.

2) Check springs for distortion. Inspect band lining for wear and bond of lining to band. If lining is worn so grooves are not visible at end or any portion of band, replace band.

Reassembly

Lubricate and insert piston plug and spring in piston. Secure with snap ring.

TRANSMISSION REASSEMBLY

NOTE: Use only Dexron type automatic transmission fluid to lubricate transmission parts during reassembly.

OVERRUNNING CLUTCH

With transmission case in upright position, insert clutch hub inside cam. Install overrunning clutch rollers and springs. *See Fig. 46.*

Fig. 46: Installed View of Overrunning Clutch

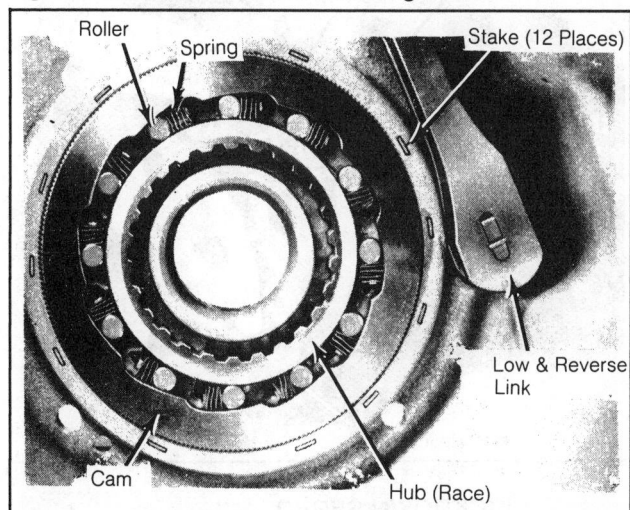

Install parts as shown.

LOW-REVERSE SERVO & BAND (REAR)

1) Carefully work servo piston into case with a twisting motion. Place spring, retainer and snap ring over piston. Compress low-reverse servo piston and install snap ring.

2) On models with double-wrap band, install replacement "O" ring on reaction pin. Insert pin into case until flush with gasket surface. Position band in case so both lugs rest against reaction pin. Install low-reverse drum into rear band. Install operating lever and pivot pin.

3) On all other models, position rear band in case and install short strut. Connect long link and anchor to band. Screw in band adjuster enough to hold strut in place. Install low-reverse drum.

2-40

Automatic Transmissions
AMERICAN MOTORS, CHRYSLER & JEEP
727, 904, 998 & 999 (Cont.)

Fig. 47: Double-Wrap Low-Reverse Band and Linkage

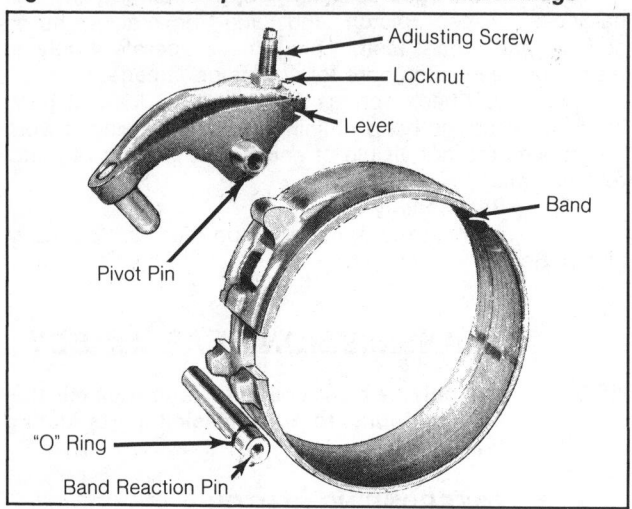

Fig. 48: Double-Wrap Band Linkage Installation

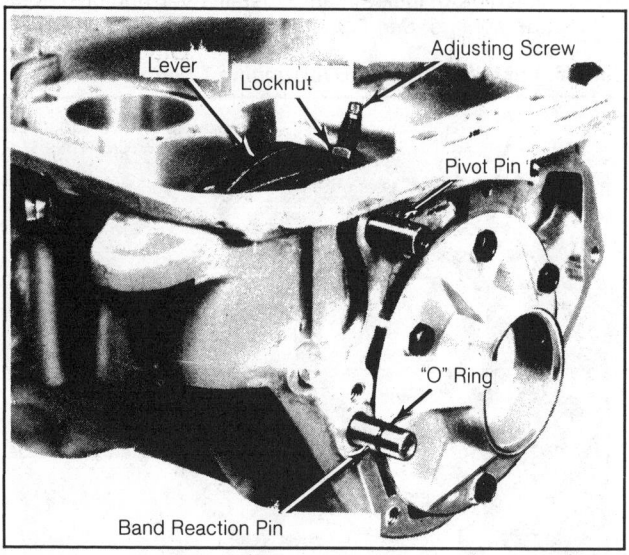

KICKDOWN SERVO

Carefully push servo piston into case bore. Install piston rod, springs and guide. Compress servo piston springs and install snap ring.

PLANETARY GEAR ASSEMBLIES, SUN GEAR & DRIVING SHELL

While supporting assembly in case, insert output shaft through rear support. Carefully work assembly rearward, engaging rear planetary carrier lugs into low-reverse drum slots.

CAUTION: Do not damage machined surfaces on output shaft during installation.

FRONT & REAR CLUTCH ASSEMBLIES

NOTE: Front and rear clutches, front band, oil pump and reaction shaft support are easier to install with transmission in upright position.

Fig. 49: Model 727 Low-Reverse Band and Linkage

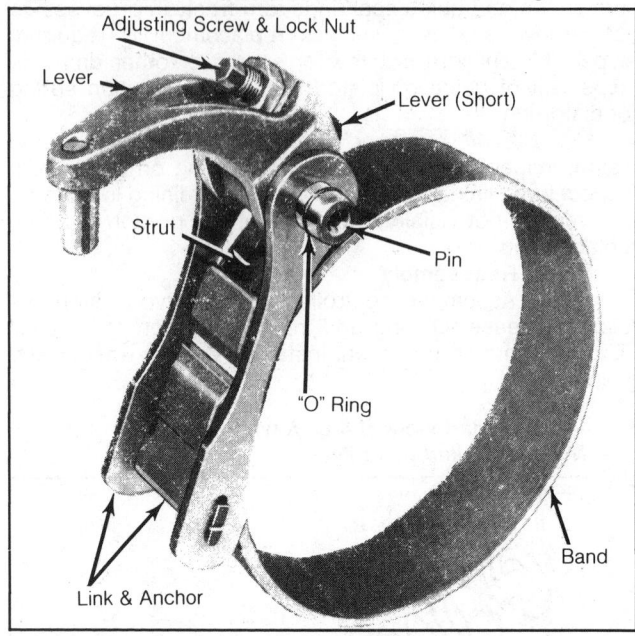

All others similar (except double-wrap).

1) Apply a coat of grease on input shaft-to-output shaft thrust washer. Install washer on front end of output shaft. Align front clutch plate inner splines. Place assembly in position on rear clutch. Make sure front clutch plate splines are fully engaged on rear clutch splines.

2) Align rear clutch plate inner splines. Grasp input shaft by hand and lower assemblies into case. Carefully work clutch assemblies in a circular motion to engage rear clutch splines over splines of front annulus gear. Make sure front clutch drive lugs are fully engaged in slots of driving shell.

KICKDOWN (FRONT) BAND

Slide band over front clutch assembly. Install band strut screw in band adjuster just enough to hold strut and anchor in place.

Fig. 50: Kickdown Band and Linkage

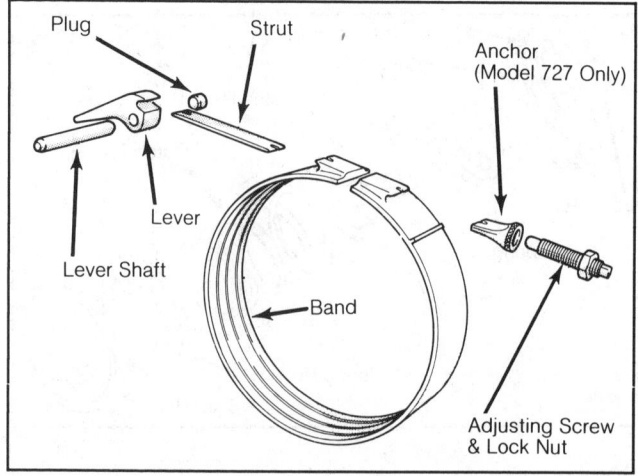

Anchor used on 727 only.

AMERICAN MOTORS, CHRYSLER & JEEP
727, 904, 998 & 999 (Cont.)

THRUST WASHER CHART

Thrust Washer	Thrust Washer No.	A-727 Inches (mm)	Thrust Washer No.	All Others Inches (mm)
Reaction Shaft Support Thrust Washer	1	Selective Natural: .061-.063 (1.55-1.60) Red: .084-.086 (2.13-2.18) Yellow: .102-.104 (2.59-2.64)	1	.061-.063 (1.55-1.60)
Rear Clutch Retainer	2	Natural: .061-.063 (1.55-1.60)	2	.061-.063 (1.55-1.60)
Input Shaft Thrust Plate		....		.024-.026 (.61-.66)
Output Shaft Thrust Washer	3	.062-.064 (1.57-1.63)	3	Selective Tin: .052-.054 (1.32-1.37) Red: .068-.070 (1.73-1.78) Green: .083-.086 (2.11-2.18)
Output Shaft Thrust Plate		.030-.032 (.76-.81)		....
Front Annulus Thrust Washer		....	4	.121-.125 (3.07-3.18)
Front Carrier (To Annulus) Thrust Washer	4	.059-.062 (1.50-1.57)	5	.048-.050 (1.22-1.27)
Drive Shell (To Front Annulus) Thrust Washer	5	.059-.062 (1.50-1.57)		....
Front Carrier (To Drive Shell) Thrust Washer		....	6	.048-.050 (1.22-1.27)
Sun Gear Drive Shell Thrust Plate	6	.... .034-.036 (.86-.91)	7 8	.050-.052 (1.27-1.32) .050-.052 (1.27-1.32)
Rear Carrier (To Drive Shell) Thrust Washer	7	.059-.062 (1.50-1.57)	9	.048-.050 (1.22-1.27)
Rear Carrier (To Annulus) Thrust Plate	8	.034-.036 (.86-.91)		....
Rear Carrier (To Annulus) Thrust Washer		....	10	.048-.050 (1.22-1.27)

OIL PUMP & REACTION SHAFT SUPPORT

NOTE: **If difficulty was encounterd in removing pump assembly due to an exceptionally tight fit, it may be necessary to expand case in pump area with a heat lamp prior to installation.**

1) If input shaft end play was not within specifications, replace thrust washer on reaction shaft support hub with one of proper thickness. *Refer to Thrust Washer Chart.*

2) Screw 2 pilot studs into pump opening in case. Install a new gasket over studs. Place a new rubber seal ring in groove on outer flange of pump housing, make sure seal is not twisted.

3) Coat seal ring with grease. Install pump assembly into case, tapping lightly with a soft mallet if necessary. Remove pilot studs. Install bolts, and snug down evenly.

4) Rotate input and output shafts to see that no binding exists. Tighten pump attaching bolts. Check shafts again for free rotation. Adjust both bands.

GOVERNOR
See SERVICE (IN VEHICLE).

Automatic Transmissions
AMERICAN MOTORS, CHRYSLER & JEEP
727, 904, 998 & 999 (Cont.)

EXTENSION/ADAPTER HOUSING
See SERVICE (IN VEHICLE).

**VALVE BODY ASSEMBLY &
ACCUMULATOR PISTON**
See SERVICE (IN VEHICLE).

TORQUE CONVERTER
See Transmission Removal & Installation in AUTOMATIC TRANSMISSION SERVICING.

TIGHTENING SPECIFICATIONS

Application	Ft. Lbs. (N.m)
Adapter Housing-to-Transmission Case	
Jeep	24 (33)
Extension Housing-to-Transmission Case	
Chrysler Corp	32 (43)
Extension Housing-to-Insulator	50 (68)
Band Adjusting Screw Lock Nut	35 (48)
Converter Drive Plate-to-Crankshaft Bolt	105 (142)
Converter Drive Plate-to-Torque Converter	22 (30)
Cooler Line Nut	25 (34)
Neutral Safety Switch	24 (33)
Output Shaft Flange Nut	175 (238)
Transmission-to-Engine Bolts	30 (41)
	INCH Lbs. (N.m)
Cooler Line Fitting	180 (20)
Governor Body-to-Support Bolts	96 (11)
Kickdown Lever Shaft Plug	156 (18)
Oil Pan Bolts	156 (18)
Output Shaft Support Bolt	156 (18)
Overrunning Clutch Cam Set Screw	36 (5)
Overrunning Clutch Cam Retaining Screws	96 (11)
Pressure Test Take-Off-Plug	108 (12)
Pump Hsg.-to-Transmission Case	180 (20)
Reaction Shaft Support-to-Oil Pump	156 (18)
Valve Body Screws	36 (5)
Valve Body-to-Transmission Case	96 (11)

CHRYSLER CORP. A-404, A-413 & A-470

Chrysler
  E-Class, LeBaron, New Yorker
Dodge
  Aries, Omni, Rampage, 400, 600
Plymouth
  Horizon, Reliant, Scamp

TRANSAXLE IDENTIFICATION

The automatic transaxle identification number is located on a pad just above the oil pan at the rear of the transaxle.

CAUTION: Transaxle operation requirements are different for each vehicle and engine combination, and some internal parts will be different to provide for this. Therefore, when replacing parts, refer to the 7 digit part number stamped on rear of transmission oil pan flange.

DESCRIPTION

The Chrysler Corp. Automatic Transaxles combine a torque converter, fully automatic 3 speed transmission, final drive gearing and differential into a front-wheel-drive system. The torque converter, transmission and differential are housed in an integral aluminum die casting. The differential oil sump is common with the transmission sump.

The transmission consists of 2 multiple disc clutches, an overrunning clutch, 2 servos, a hydraulic accumulator, 2 bands and 2 planetary gear sets to provide 3 forward gear ratios and a reverse ratio. The hydraulic system consists of an oil pump, and a single valve body which contains all of the valves except the governor valve.

Output torque from the transmission is delivered through helical gears to the transfer shaft. This gear set is a factor of the final drive (axle) ratio. The transfer shaft also carries the governor and parking sprag. An integral helical gear on the transfer shaft drives the differential ring gear.

TRANSAXLE APPLICATION

Engine Size	Transaxle Model	Final Drive Ratio
1.7L	A-404	3.50
2.2L		
EFI & Hi. Alt.	A-413	3.02
All Others	A-413	2.78
2.6L		
Hi. Alt. & Fleet	A-470	3.02
All Others	A-470	2.78

LUBRICATION & ADJUSTMENTS

See the appropriate article in AUTOMATIC TRANSMISSION SERVICING Section.

TESTING

ROAD TEST

1) Prior to road testing, be certain that fluid level and condition, and control cable adjustments have been checked and corrected if necessary.

2) During test, transmission should upshift and downshift at approximately the speeds shown in Automatic Shift Speeds and Governor Pressures Chart. All shift speeds may vary somewhat due to production tolerances, rear axle ratio, or tire size. The important factor is the quality of the shifts. All shifts should be smooth, responsive, and with no slipping or engine speed flare-up.

3) Slipping or flare-up in any gear usually indicates clutch, band or overrunning clutch problems. The slipping clutch or band in a particular gear can usually be identified by noting transmission operation in other selector positions and comparing which internal units are applied in those positions.

4) For example, if transmission slips in "D", third gear, either the front or rear clutch is slipping. By selecting another gear which uses 1 of those units, but not both, the clutch which is slipping can be identified. See Clutch and Band Application Chart. Using this example, if transmission slips in reverse also, the front clutch is slipping. If it does not slip in reverse, the rear clutch is slipping.

5) Although this process of elimination can be used to detect any unit which slips and to confirm proper operation of good units, the actual cause of malfunction cannot easily be determined. Practically any condition can be caused by leaking hydraulic circuits or sticking valves. Therefore, unless an obvious condition exists, a transmission should never be disassembled until hydraulic pressure tests have been made.

HYDRAULIC PRESSURE TESTS

Before making pressure tests, be certain that fluid level and condition, and control cable adjustments have been checked and corrected if necessary. Install an engine tachometer, raise vehicle on a hoist which allows front wheels to turn, and position tachometer so it can be read under vehicle. Disconnect throttle cable and shift cable from transmission levers so they can be controlled from under vehicle.

NOTE: See Fig. 3 for location of the various transmission pressure test ports.

Pressure Test (Selector in "1")

1) Attach 150 psi (10.5 kg/cm²) gauges to "line" and "low-reverse servo" ports. Operate engine at 1000 RPM for test. Move selector lever on transaxle all the way rearward ("1" position).

2) Read pressures on both gauges as throttle lever on transaxle is moved from full forward position to full rearward position.

3) Line pressure should read 52-58 psi (3.6-4.1 kg/cm²) with throttle lever forward and gradually increase, as lever is moved rearward, to 80-88 psi (5.6-6.2 kg/cm²). Rear servo pressure should read the same as line pressure within 3 psi (.2 kg/cm²).

4) This tests pump output, pressure regulation, and condition of rear clutch and rear servo hydraulic circuits.

Automatic Transmissions

CHRYSLER CORP. A-404, A-413 & A-470 (Cont.)

Fig. 1: Cutaway View of Chrysler Corp. Automatic Transaxle

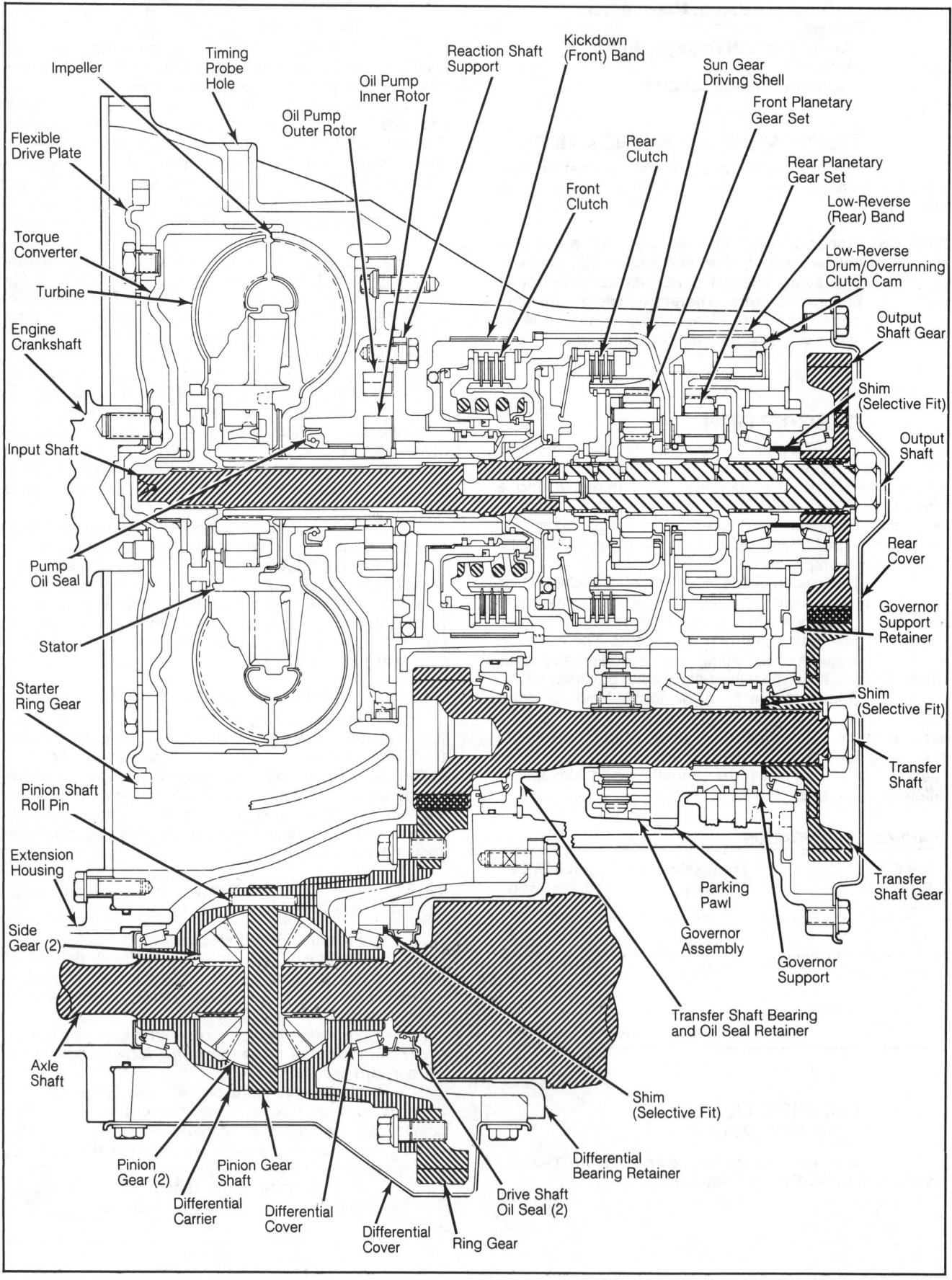

CHRYSLER CORP. A-404, A-413 & A-470 (Cont.)

AUTOMATIC SHIFT SPEEDS & GOVERNOR PRESSURES

Engine	1.7L	2.2L	2.2L
Axle Ratio	3.50	2.78	3.02
Throttle Closed			
1-2 Upshift	11-15	10-14	12-15
2-3 Upshift	16-21	15-20	17-22
3-1 Downshift	11-14	10-13	11-15
Throttle Wide Open			
1-2 Upshift	33-39	37-44	35-39
2-3 Upshift	55-64	63-71	60-70
Kickdown Range			
3-2 Downshift	51-60	58-66	54-64
3-1 Downshift	30-35	31-39	33-36
Governor Pressure [1]			
15 psi	23-26	22-24	26-29
50 psi	54-61	61-68	59-66

[1] — Governor pressure should be from zero to 3.0 psi at stand-still or downshift may not occur.

CLUTCH AND BAND APPLICATION CHART (ELEMENTS IN USE)

Selector Lever Position	Front Clutch	Rear Clutch	Over-running Clutch	Front (Kickdown) Band	Rear (Low-Reverse) Band
D — DRIVE					
First		X	X		
Second		X		X	
Direct	X	X			
2 — SECOND					
First		X	X		
Second		X		X	
1 — LOW (First)		X			X
R — REVERSE	X				X

NEUTRAL OR PARK — All clutches and bands released and/or ineffective.

Pressure Test (Selector in "2")

1) Install a "tee" connection at lower cooler line fitting. Attach 150 psi (10.5 kg/cm²) gauges to "tee" connection and "line pressure" port. Operate engine at 1000 RPM for test.

2) Move selector lever on transaxle 1 detent forward from full rearward position (into selector "2" position). Read pressures on both gauges as throttle lever on transaxle is moved from full forward position to full rearward position.

3) Line pressure should read 52-58 psi (3.6-4.1 kg/cm²) with throttle lever forward and gradually increase, as lever is moved rearward, to 80-88 psi (5.6-6.2 kg/cm²). Lubrication pressure should be 10-25 psi (.7-1.8 kg/cm²) with lever forward and 10-35 psi (.7-2.5 kg/cm²) with lever rearward.

4) This tests pump output, pressure regulation, and condition of rear clutch and lubrication hydraulic circuits.

Pressure Test (Selector in "D")

1) Attach 150 psi (10.5 kg/cm²) gauges to "line" and "kickdown release" ports. Operate engine at 1600 RPM for test.

2) Move selector lever on transaxle 2 detents forward from full rearward position (into selector "D" position). Read pressures on both gauges as throttle lever on transaxle is moved from full forward position to full rearward position.

3) Line pressure should read 52-58 psi (3.6-4.1 kg/cm²) with throttle lever forward, gradually increasing to 80-88 psi (5.6-6.2 kg/cm²) as lever is moved rearward.

4) Kickdown release is pressurized only in direct drive and should be same as line pressure within 3 psi (.2 kg/cm²), up to kickdown point.

5) This tests pump output, pressure regulation, and condition of rear clutch, front clutch and hydraulic circuits.

Pressure Test (Selector in Reverse)

1) Attach a 300 psi (21 kg/cm²) gauge to "low-reverse apply" port. Operate engine at 1600 RPM for test.

2) Move selector lever on transaxle 4 detents forward from full rearward position (into selector "R" position).

Automatic Transmissions

CHRYSLER CORP. A-404, A-413 & A-470 (Cont.)

Fig. 2: Chrysler Corp. Automatic Transaxle Hydraulic Circuits Diagram

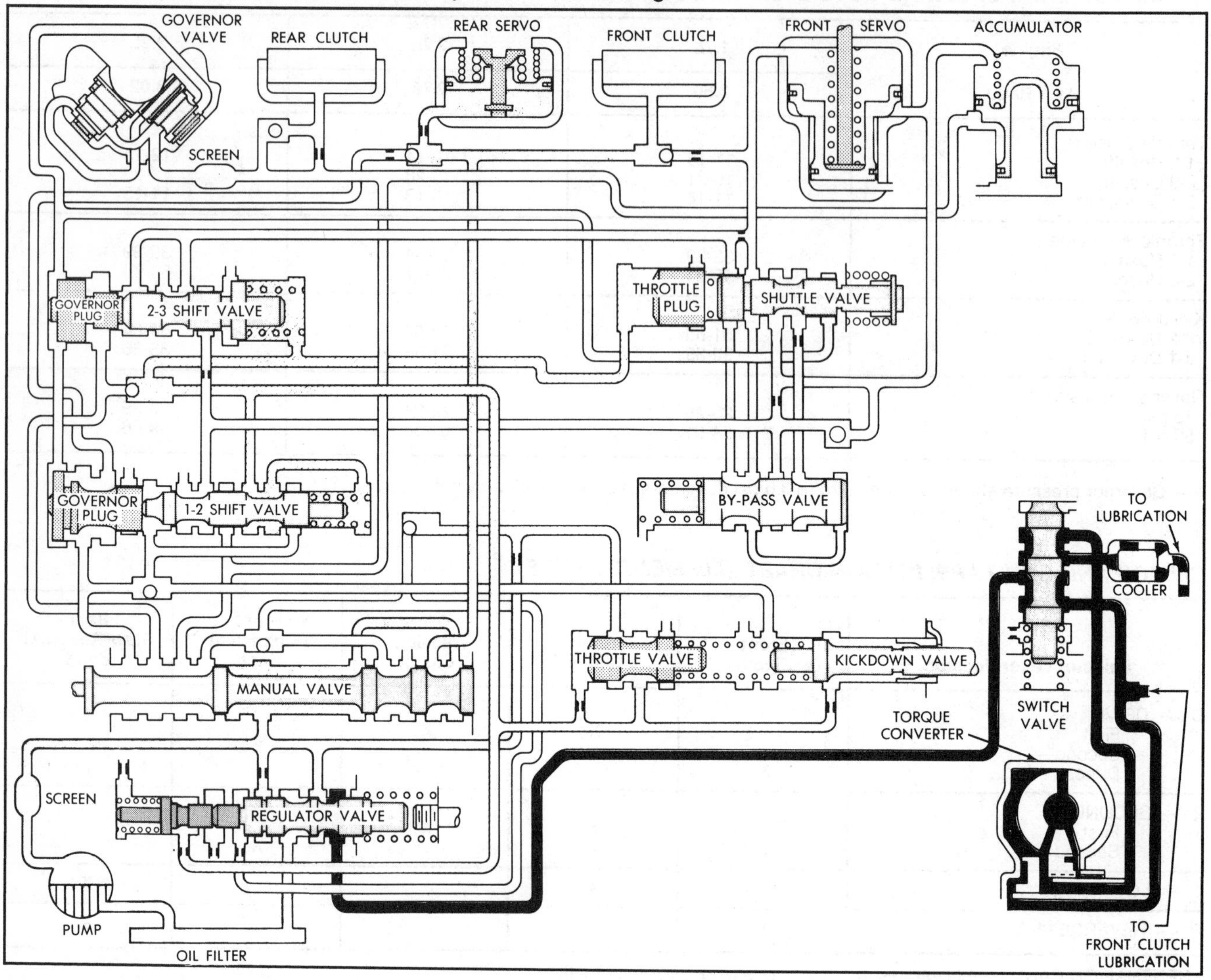

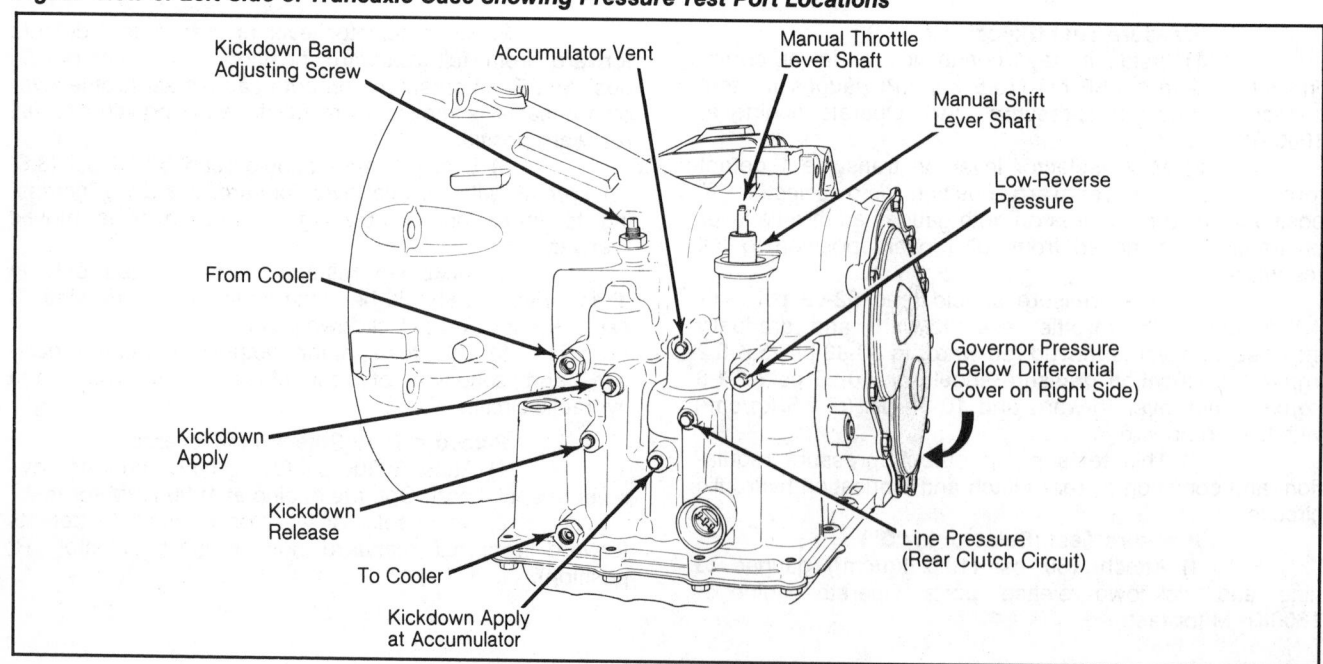

Fig. 3: View of Left Side of Transaxle Case Showing Pressure Test Port Locations

CHRYSLER CORP. A-404, A-413 & A-470 (Cont.)

3) Low-reverse pressure should read 180-220 psi (12.6-15.4 kg/cm²) with throttle lever forward and gradually increase, as lever is moved rearward, to 260-300 psi (18.2-21.0 kg/cm²).

4) This tests pump output, pressure regulation and condition of front clutch and rear servo hydraulic circuits.

5) Move selector lever on transaxle to "D" position to check that rear servo pressure drops to zero.

6) This tests for leakage into rear servo, due to case porosity, which can cause reverse band burn out.

Pressure Test Indications

1) If proper line pressure, minimum to maximum, is found in any test, pump and pressure regulator are working properly.

2) Low pressure in "D", "1" and "2", but correct pressure in "R", indicates rear clutch circuit leakage.

3) Low pressure in "D" and "R", but correct pressure in "1", indicates front clutch circuit leakage.

4) Low pressure in "R" and "1", but correct pressure in "2", indicates rear servo circuit leakage.

5) Low line pressure in all positions indicates a defective pump, clogged filter, or stuck pressure regulator valve.

NOTE: **The following Governor Pressure Test need only be performed if transaxle shifts at wrong vehicle speed with throttle cable correctly adjusted.**

Governor Pressure Test

1) Connect a 150 psi (10.5 kg/cm²) pressure gauge to governor pressure take-off point, located at lower right side of case, below differential cover.

2) Operate transaxle in third gear to read pressures. Compare pressure readings obtained with governor pressures shown in *Automatic Shift Speeds & Governor Pressures* chart.

3) If governor pressures are incorrect at the given vehicle speed, governor valve and/or weights are probably sticking.

4) Governor pressure should respond smoothly to changes in MPH and should return to 0 to 3 psi (0-.2 kg/cm²) when vehicle is stopped. Pressure above 3 psi (.2 kg/cm²) at standstill will prevent transaxle from downshifting.

Throttle Pressure

No gauge port is provided for testing throttle pressure. Incorrect throttle pressure should only be suspected if part throttle upshift speeds are either delayed or occur too early in relation to vehicle speeds. Engine runaway on either upshifts or downshifts can also be an indication of incorrect (low) throttle pressure setting.

CAUTION: **In no case should throttle pressure be adjusted until transmission throttle cable adjustment has been checked and corrected as needed.**

HYDRAULIC PRESSURE ADJUSTMENTS

NOTE: **An incorrect throttle pressure setting will cause incorrect line pressure readings even though line pressure adjustment is correct. Therefore, always inspect and correct throttle pressure adjustment before adjusting line pressure.**

Throttle Pressure

1) Remove valve body from transaxle. Back off throttle lever stop screw approximately 5 turns, then insert the gauge pin of special gauging tool C-3763 between throttle lever cam and kickdown valve.

2) By pushing in on tool, compress kickdown valve against spring so that valve is completely bottomed.

3) As force is being exerted to compress spring, turn throttle lever stop screw until head of screw touches throttle lever tang with throttle lever cam touching tool and the throttle valve bottomed.

CAUTION: **Be sure adjustment is made with spring fully compressed and valve bottomed in valve body bore.**

Line Pressure

1) Turn Allen screw in end of pressure regulator spring bracket so measurement between valve body and inner edge of adjusting nut is 1 5/16" (33.3 mm).

NOTE: **Due to manufacturing tolerances, adjustment can be varied to obtain specified line pressure.**

2) One complete turn of adjusting screw changes closed throttle line pressure about 1 2/3 psi (.12 kg/cm²). Turning adjusting screw counterclockwise increases pressure; clockwise decreases pressure.

STALL TEST

1) Before making test, check transaxle fluid level, bring engine to normal operating temperature, and attach a tachometer to engine.

2) Test consists of determining engine speed obtained at full throttle in "D" (Drive) position. Both parking and service brakes must be fully applied while making test.

CAUTION: **Do not hold throttle open any longer than is necessary to obtain a maximum engine speed reading, and never longer than 5 seconds at a time.**

3) If more than one stall test is required, operate engine at approximately 1000 RPM in neutral for 20 seconds to cool transmission fluid between runs. If engine speed exceeds maximum limits shown, release accelerator immediately since transmission clutch slippage is indicated.

STALL SPEED SPECIFICATIONS

Engine	Transaxle Model	Stall RPM
1.7 Liter	A-404	2300-2500
2.2 Liter	A-413	2200-2410
2.6 Liter	A-470	2400-2630

STALL TEST RESULTS

Stall Speed Above Specification

If stall speed exceeds maximum limits shown by more than 200 RPM, transmission clutch slippage is indicated. Make hydraulic pressure and air pressure checks to determine cause of slippage.

Automatic Transmissions

CHRYSLER CORP. A-404, A-413 & A-470 (Cont.)

Stall Speed Below Specification

1) Low stall speeds (with a properly tuned engine) indicate torque converter stator clutch problems. A road test will be necessary to identify the exact problem.

2) If stall speeds are 250-350 RPM below specifications, and vehicle operates properly at highway speeds, but has poor through-gear acceleration, stator overrunning clutch is slipping.

3) If stall speed and acceleration are normal, but abnormally high throttle opening is required to maintain highway speeds, stator clutch has seized.

4) Both of the preceding stator defects require replacement of the torque converter.

Noise During Stall Test

1) A whining or siren-like noise due to fluid flow is normal during stall operation with some converters; however, loud metallic noises from loose parts or interference within the assembly indicate a defective torque converter.

2) To be sure that noise originates within the converter, raise vehicle on hoist and operate at light throttle in "D" and "N" while listening under transmission bellhousing.

AIR PRESSURE TEST

A "No Drive" condition could exist even with correct fluid pressure, because of inoperative clutches or bands. The inoperative units can be located by applying air pressure to the appropriate case passages after valve body has been removed.

CAUTION: Compressed air supply must be free of dirt and moisture. Use a pressure of 30 psi (2.1 kg/cm²) for tests.

Front Clutch

Direct air pressure into front clutch apply passage. Operation of clutch is indicated by a dull thud which may be heard, or felt. Hold air pressure on for a few seconds and check system for excessive oil leaks.

Rear Clutch

Direct air pressure into rear clutch apply passage. Operation of clutch is indicated by a dull thud which may be heard, or felt. Also, check for excessive leaks.

Kickdown Servo (Front)

Direct air pressure into front servo apply passage. Operation of servo is indicated by a tightening of the front band. Spring tension on servo piston should release the band.

Low-Reverse Servo (Rear)

Direct air pressure into rear servo apply passage. Operation of servo is indicated by a tightening of the rear band. Spring tension of servo piston should release the band.

NOTE: If clutches and servos operate properly, no upshift or erratic shift conditions indicate malfunctions in valve body assembly

Fig. 4: Bottom View of Transmission Case (With Valve Body Removed) Showing Air Pressure Test Points

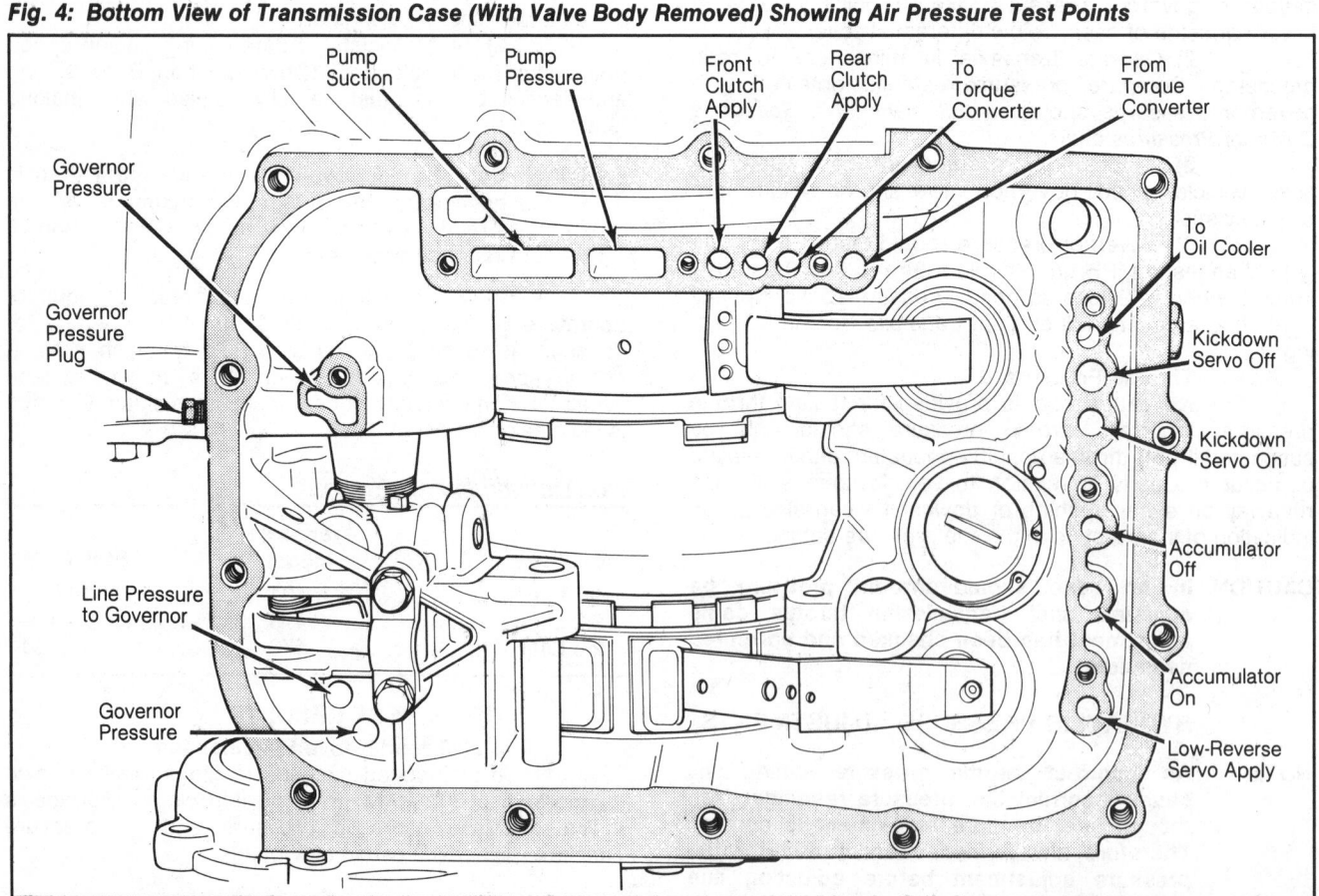

CHRYSLER CORP. A-404, A-413 & A-470 (Cont.)

SERVICE (IN VEHICLE)

NOTE: The valve body, extension housing oil seal, parking sprag, and governor assembly may also be removed from transaxle with transaxle still installed in vehicle. See procedures given in Transaxle Disassembly and Transaxle Reassembly & Adjustments.

SPEEDOMETER PINION GEAR

NOTE: When speedometer pinion adapter is removed for any reason, a new "O" ring must be installed on outside diameter of adapter.

Removal
Remove bolt and washer securing speedometer pinion adapter in extension housing. With cable housing connected, carefully work adapter and pinion out of extension housing. Remove retainer and remove pinion from adapter.

Seal Replacement
1) If transmission fluid is found in cable housing, install a new speedometer pinion and seal assembly.
2) If fluid is found between cable and adapter, replace small "O" ring on cable.

NOTE: Before installing pinion, adapter, and cable assembly make sure adapter flange and its mating areas on extension housing are clean. Dirt or sand will cause misalignment resulting in speedometer pinion gear damage.

Installation
To install, reverse removal procedure. Tighten retainer bolt.

NEUTRAL SAFETY SWITCH
See the appropriate article in AUTOMATIC TRANSMISSION SERVICING Section.

DRIVE AXLE SHAFTS

NOTE: Two different make drive axle shafts are used, GKN and Citroen. Service replacement parts are not interchangeable. To avoid problems, the make of shaft must be determined prior to ordering parts. See Fig. 5.

Fig. 5: Drive Axle Shaft Identification

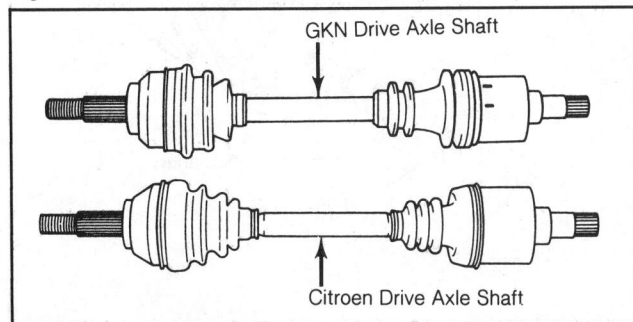

GKN Drive Axle Shaft

Citroen Drive Axle Shaft

Removal
1) Remove cotter key and hub nut lock from end of drive axle shaft, then loosen hub and wheel nuts. Raise and support front of vehicle. Remove hub nut and wheel and tire assembly.

NOTE: Before removing right side axle shaft, remove speedometer pinion assembly. Otherwise, removal procedures for both axles are the same.

2) Remove clamp bolt securing ball joint stud to steering knuckle, then separate ball joint from knuckle by prying against knuckle leg and control arm.

CAUTION: Use care not to damage ball joint or CV joint boots while separating ball joint from steering knuckle.

3) Separate outer CV joint splined shaft from hub by holding CV joint housing while moving knuckle (hub) assembly away. DO NOT pry on or otherwise damage wear sleeve on outer CV joint.

4) Support drive shaft assembly at outer CV joint housings. Remove shaft from transaxle by pulling outward on inner joint housing. DO NOT PULL ON SHAFT.

Disassembly (Inner CV Joint)
1) With axle shaft removed from vehicle, remove clamps and rubber boot. On GKN shafts, bend back retaining tabs and pull housing from shaft. Remove snap ring from retaining groove and tap tripod from shaft using a brass punch.
2) On Citroen shafts, slightly deform retainer ring around tripod and pull housing from shaft. With housing removed, secure tripod rollers and needle bearing in tripod with tape. Remove snap ring from groove in shaft and remove tripod from shaft using a brass punch.

Reassembly (Inner CV Joint)
1) To install new boot, slide small rubber clamp onto shaft (GKN only). Slide small end of boot over shaft.

NOTE: On tubular shafts (right side shaft), position boot lip face in line with mark on the shaft O.D. On solid shafts (left side shaft), position small boot end in machined groove provided.

2) Clamp small boot end by placing rubber clamp over boot groove (GKN) or clamp with metal clamp. Reinstall tripod on shaft with non-chamfered face of tripod body facing shaft retainer groove.
3) Assemble snap ring in groove to lock tripod assembly on shaft. Distribute 2 packets of grease (GKN) or 2/3 tube of grease (Citroen) in axle boot (provided in Boot Joint Kits). Distribute remaining grease in housing.
4) Position spring in spring pocket with spring cup attached to exposed end of spring. Place small amount of grease on spring cup and position housing over tripod.
5) On GKN shafts, bend retaining tabs back to original position and ensure that tripod is retained in housing, against spring. On Citroen models, reform old retaining ring or obtain new ring. Install ring and ensure that tripod is retained in housing, against spring.
6) On GKN shafts, fit metal clamp on boot making sure that boot is properly located on shaft and housing and is not twisted. Locate clamp tangs in slots, making clamp as tight as possible by hand. Clamp bridge with tool and squeeze to complete tightening the clamp.

NOTE: During this operation, care must be taken not to cut through clamp bridge and/or damage the boot.

Automatic Transmissions

CHRYSLER CORP. A-404, A-413 & A-470 (Cont.)

7) On Citroen shafts, wrap special binding strap around boot twice, plus an additional 2 1/2" (65 mm). Pass strap through buckle and fold it back about 1 1/8" (28 mm) on inside of buckle. Put strap around boot with eye of buckle toward you. Wrap boot once more and pass it through buckle, then wrap it around a second time, also passing it through buckle.

8) Fold strap back slightly to prevent it from slipping backwards. Open special tool (C-4653) all the way and place strap in narrow slot approximately 1/2" (12 mm) from buckle. Hold binding strap with left hand and push tool forward and slightly upward, then fit hook of tool into eye of buckle.

9) Tighten strap by closing the tool handles, then rotate tool downward while slowly releasing pressure on tool handles. *See Fig. 6.* Allow tool to open progressively. Open tool entirely and remove. If strap is not tight enough, repeat tightening procedure as many times as necessary, always engaging strap about 1/2" (12 mm) from buckle.

10) When strap is tight enough, trim off all but about 1/8" (3 mm) of the strap and fold back over buckle. Cut end must not extend beyond edge of buckle.

NOTE: When tightening strap, always be careful to see that strap slides in a straight line and without resistance in the buckle.

Fig. 6: *Tightening Boot Binding Strap*

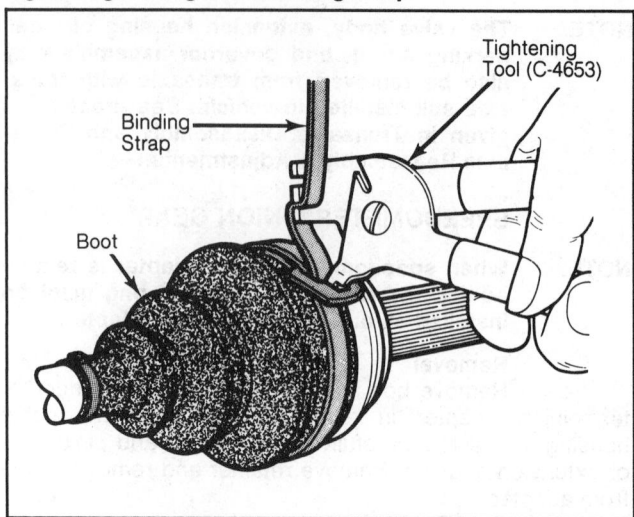

Disassembly (Outer CV Joint)

1) Cut boot clamp on boot and discard. Wipe grease away to expose joint. Support shaft in a soft-jawed vise, support outer joint, and using a soft hammer, give a sharp tap to top of joint body to dislodge joint from internal circlip installed in groove at outer end of shaft.

Fig. 7: *Exploded View of Drive Axle Shaft Components*

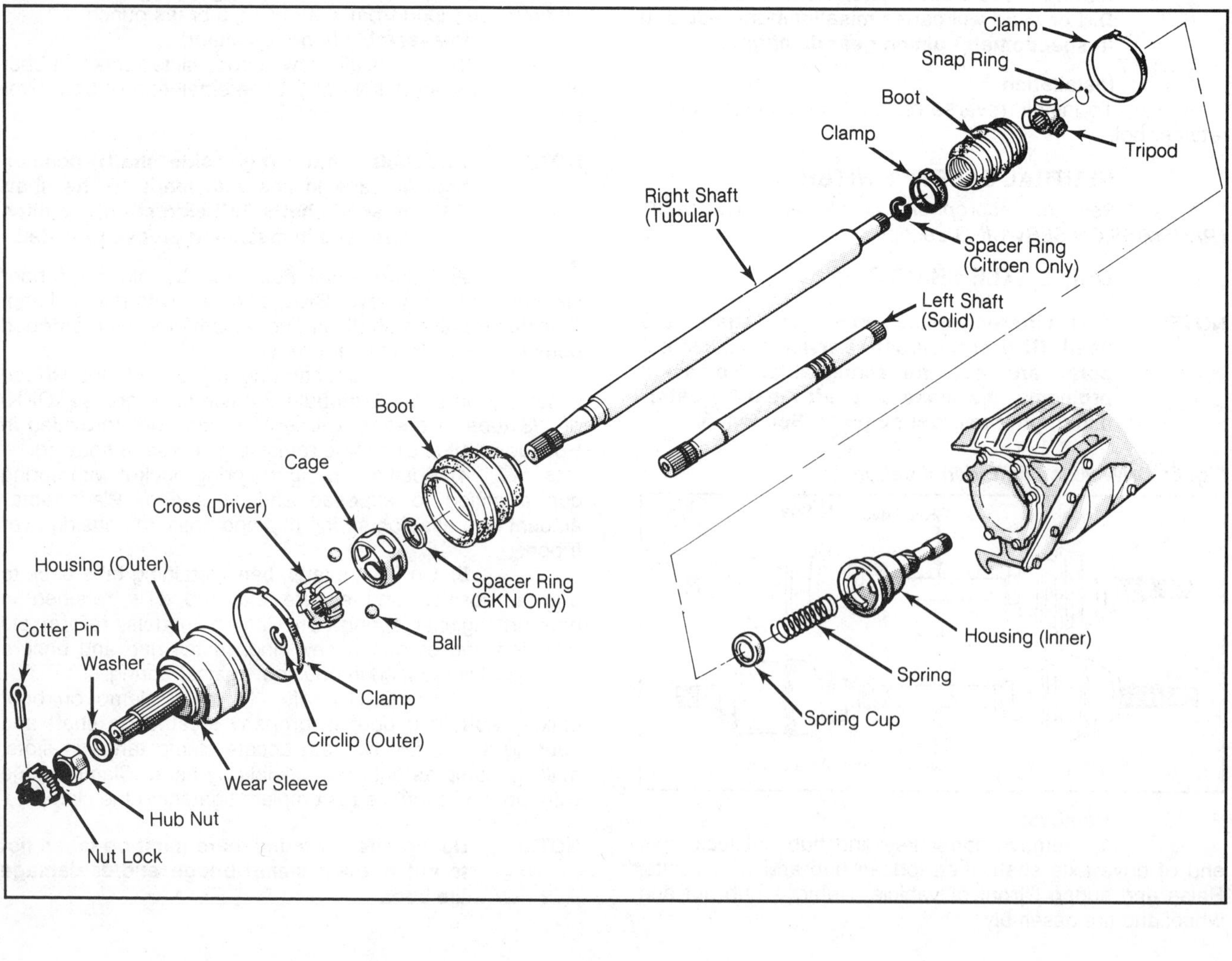

CHRYSLER CORP. A-404, A-413 & A-470 (Cont.)

NOTE: A wear sleeve installed on outer CV joint housing provides a wipe surface for hub bearing seal (installed in steering knuckle). If bent or damaged, carefully pry wear sleeve from CV joint housing.

2) Remove circlip from shaft groove and discard. Unless shaft is damaged and requires replacement, do not remove heavy spacer ring from shaft (GKN only). With joint separated, proceed as follows:

3) If outer CV joint was operating properly and grease does not appear to be contaminated, just replace boot. If outer joint is noisy or badly worn, replace entire unit.

NOTE: Outer CV joint repair kit includes boot, clamps, circlip and lubricant.

4) Wipe off surplus grease and mark relative position of inner cross, cage and housing with a dab of paint. Hold joint vertically in vise by clamping on splined shaft, with soft jaws to prevent damage.

5) Press down on one side of inner race to tilt cage and remove ball from opposite side. If joint is tight, use hammer and brass drift to tap inner race. DO NOT hit cage. Repeat procedure until all 6 balls are removed.

6) Tilt cage and inner race assembly vertically and position the 2 opposing, elongated cage windows in area between ball grooves. *See Fig. 8.* Remove cage and inner race assembly by pulling upward and away from housing.

7) Turn inner cross (driver) 90° to cage and align one of race spherical lands with elongated cage window. Raise land into cage window and remove inner race by swinging out.

Fig. 8: *Removing Cage and Cross Assembly*

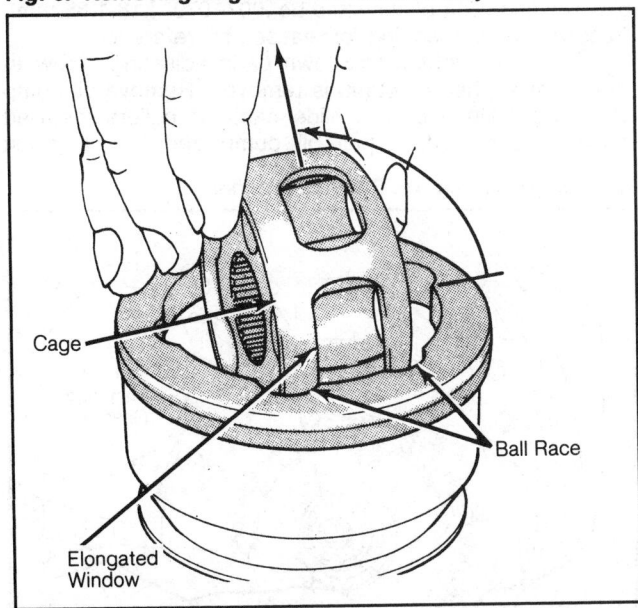

Turn cage 90° to position long openings between ball races, then rotate cage out.

Inspection (Outer CV Joint)
1) Wash all parts in solvent and dry with compressed air. Inspect housing ball races for excessive wear and scoring. Check splined shaft and nut threads for damage.

2) Inspect all 6 balls for pitting, cracks, scoring and wear. Dulling of surface is normal. Inspect cage for excessive wear on inside and outside spherical surfaces, heavy brinelling of cage window, cracks, and chipping.

3) Inspect inner race (cross) for excessive wear or scoring of ball races. If any of the preceding is found, the complete CV joint should be replaced.

NOTE: Polished areas in races (cross and housing) and on cage spheres are normal and do not indicate need for joint replacement unless they are suspected of causing noise and vibration.

Reassembly (Outer CV Joint)
1) If removed, press new wear sleeve on joint housing machined ledge. Lightly oil all components before reassembling outer joint. Align parts according to paint markings made at disassembly.

2) Insert 1 of inner race (cross) lands into an elongated cage window and feed race into cage. Pivot cross 90° to complete cage assembly.

3) Align opposing elongated cage windows with housing land and feed cage assembly into housing. Pivot cage 90° to complete installation. When properly assembled, curved side of cage windows and the inner cross counterbore should face outwards from joint. *See Fig. 9.*

4) Apply lubricant to ball races from packet provided in overhaul kit and distribute equally between all sides of ball groove. One packet is sufficient to lubricate joint. Insert balls into raceway by tilting cage and inner race assembly.

5) Support shaft in a soft-jawed vise, then slip small metal clamp over spacer ring (GKN only) and shaft. Slide small end of boot over spacer ring and shaft and position in machined groove provided.

Fig. 9: *Cutaway View Showing Correct Cage and Cross Installation*

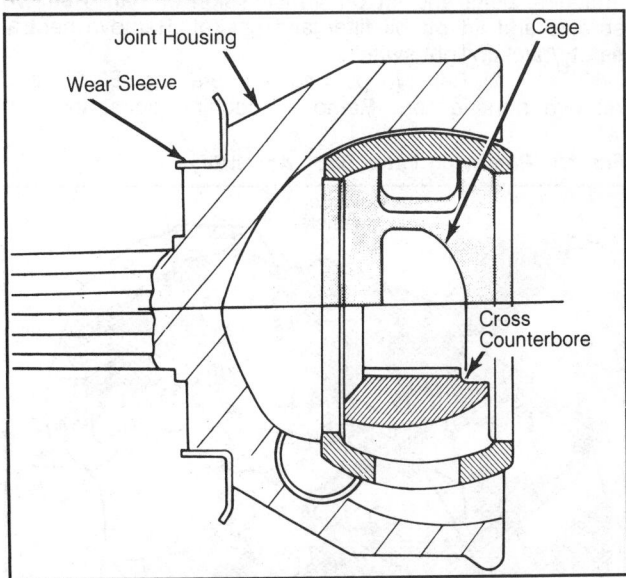

Curved side of elongated window must face out.

NOTE: Citroen units are provided with a vent sleeve. Position this vent sleeve under boot-to-shaft clamp area during boot installation.

Automatic Transmissions

CHRYSLER CORP. A-404, A-413 & A-470 (Cont.)

6) Insert new circlip, provided in kit, in shaft groove using care not to over expand or twist circlip during installation. Position outer joint on splined end, engage splines, and tap sharply with mallet.

7) Ensure that circlip is properly seated by attempting to pull joint from shaft. Position large end of boot over joint housing, checking that boot is not twisted. Install boot clamps as described under *Inner CV Joint Reassembly.*

Installation

1) Hold inner CV joint assembly at housing while aligning and guiding inner joint spline into transaxle. Push hub assembly out and install splined outer CV joint shaft in hub.

2) Reinstall steering knuckle assembly on ball joint stud, then install and tighten ball joint clamp bolt. Install speedometer pinion.

3) Fill differential to bottom of filler plug hole with correct fluid. Install hub nut assembly.

4) If, after attaching the drive axle shaft, the inboard boot appears collapsed or deformed, vent inner boot by inserting a round-tipped, small diameter rod between boot and shaft.

5) If a rubber inner clamp is used, it need not be removed to vent boot. If a metal clamp is used, it must be removed and a NEW clamp installed after venting procedure is complete. Boot will return to original shape during venting procedure.

TRANSAXLE REMOVAL & INSTALLATION

See the appropriate article in *AUTOMATIC TRANSMISSION SERVICING* Section.

TRANSAXLE DISASSEMBLY

1) Place transaxle in a holding fixture. Remove attaching bolts and lift off transmission oil pan. Remove screws and lift off oil filter and gasket. Remove neutral safety/backup light switch.

2) Remove parking rod retaining "E" clip and remove parking rod. Remove attaching bolts, then lift

Fig. 10: Removing Valve Body Assembly

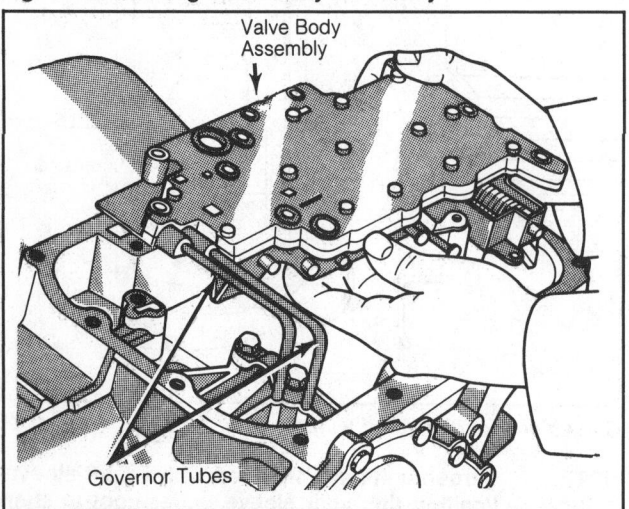

Use care when removing valve body to avoid damage to governor tubes.

valve body assembly from transmission using care not to damage governor tubes.

NOTE: Before continuing disassembly, input shaft end play should be measured. This will usually indicate when a thrust washer change is required, except when major parts are replaced. This thrust washer is located between input and output shafts. Check end play as follows:

3) Attach a dial indicator to transmission bellhousing with its plunger seated against end of input shaft. *See Fig. 11.*

Fig. 11: Measuring Input Shaft End Play

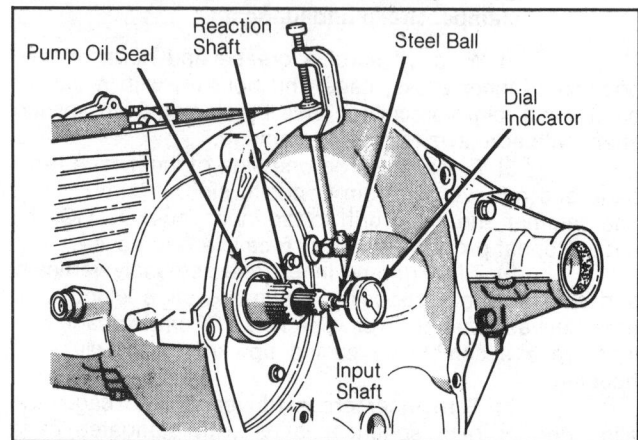

Hold steel ball in place with grease and position dial indicator plunger on ball.

4) Move input shaft in and out to obtain end play reading. End play should be .007-.073" (.18-1.85 mm). Record end play reading for reassembly reference.

5) Tighten kickdown band adjusting screw to retain parts when oil pump is removed. Remove oil pump attaching bolts. Using 2 slide hammer pullers installed opposite each other, pull oil pump and No. 1 thrust

Fig. 12: Removing No. 3 Thrust Washer

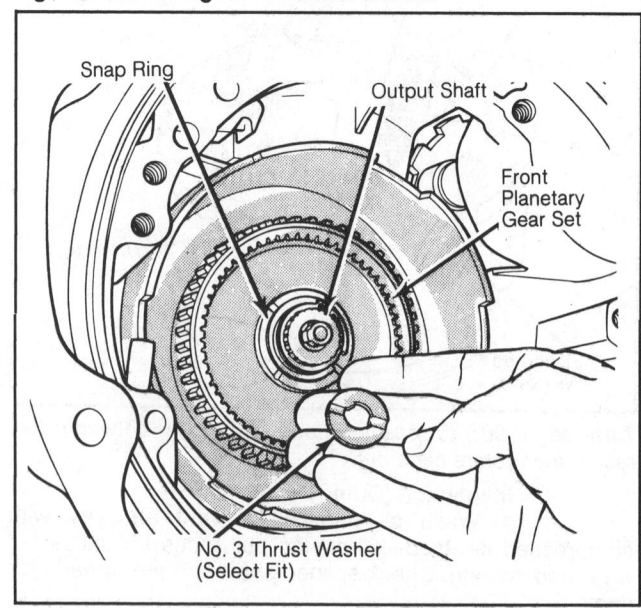

CHRYSLER CORP. A-404, A-413 & A-470 (Cont.)

washer from case. Remove pump-to-case gasket. Loosen kickdown band adjusting screw.

6) Slide kickdown band and strut from case. Remove front clutch assembly. Slide rear clutch assembly out of case by pulling input shaft, then remove thrust washer No. 2 from input shaft and clutch drum.

7) Remove No. 3 thrust washer from end of output shaft. *See Fig. 12.* Remove snap ring retaining front planetary gear assembly in case, then slide out gear assembly.

8) Remove thrust washer No. 6 from sun gear driving shell, then slide out driving shell. Remove thrust washer No. 9 from rear planetary gear set, then remove gear set from case.

NOTE: Thrust washers No. 7 and 8 are assembled with sun gear driving shell assembly.

Fig. 13: Removing Overrunning Clutch Rollers & Springs

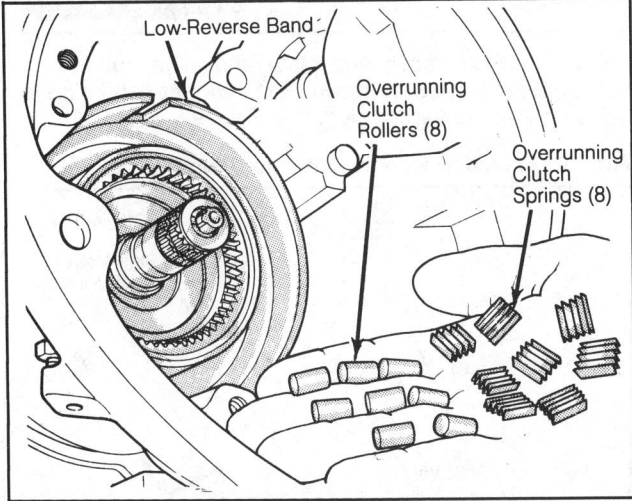

9) Remove thrust washer No. 10, then withdraw overrunning clutch cam assembly. Remove the 8 overrunning clutch rollers and springs. Loosen low-reverse band adjusting screw, then remove band and strut from case. Withdraw thrust washer No. 11 from case.

Fig. 14: Removing Governor from Transfer Shaft

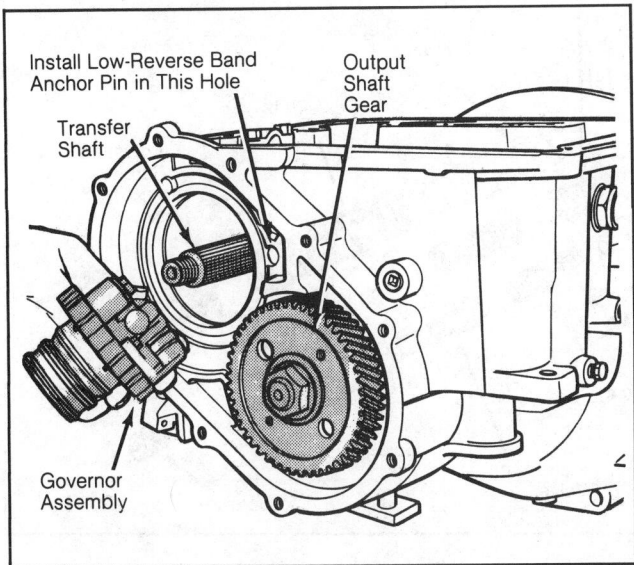

10) Remove attaching bolts and lift off rear cover. Install special holding tool L-4434 (or equivalent) to hold transfer shaft stationary, then remove transfer shaft gear retaining nut and washer.

11) Using gear puller, remove transfer shaft gear and selective fit shim installed behind gear. Remove governor support retainer. Remove low-reverse band anchor pin. Slide governor assembly from transfer shaft.

12) Remove transfer shaft retaining snap ring. Using a slide hammer and adapter, pull transfer shaft and bearing retainer assembly from case.

13) Remove attaching bolts and lift off parking pawl retainer. Slide pivot shaft out, then remove parking pawl and return spring.

Fig. 15: Removing Parking Pawl and Pivot Shaft

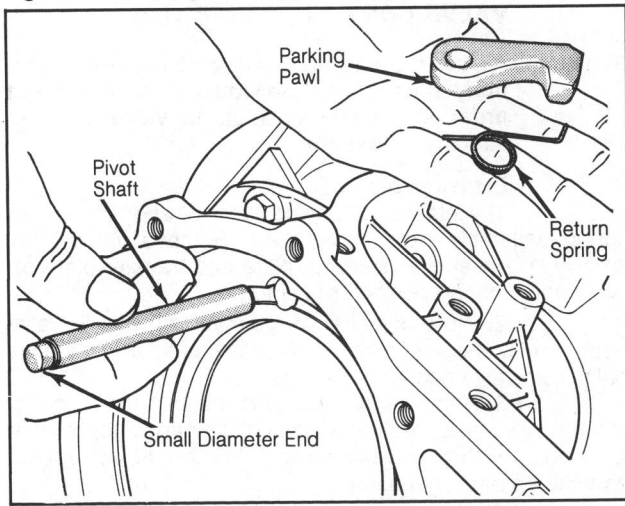

Pivot shaft is installed with small diameter to rear.

14) Hold output shaft stationary with tool (L-4434). Remove output shaft retaining nut and washer. Remove output shaft gear with puller, then slide out selective fit shim installed behind gear. From front of case slide out output shaft and annulus gear.

15) Using a screwdriver, pry oil seal out of extension housing. Remove attaching bolts and lift off differential cover.

Fig. 16: Removing Differential Bearing Retainer

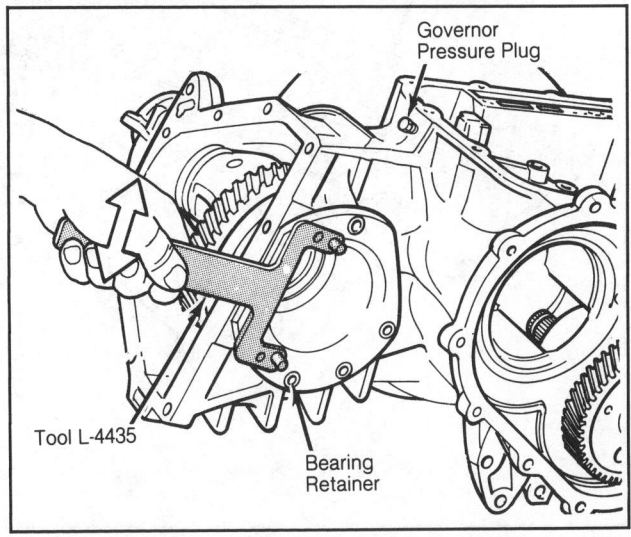

Rock tool back and forth to remove retainer.

CHRYSLER CORP. A-404, A-413 & A-470 (Cont.)

16) Remove differential bearing retainer bolts. Using special removal tool L-4435 (or equivalent), rotate retainer back and forth to remove.

17) Remove extension housing attaching bolts. Rotate housing back and forth to remove. Lift differential assembly out of transaxle case.

CAUTION: Hold onto differential assembly to prevent it from falling out of case when removing extension housing.

COMPONENT DISASSEMBLY & REASSEMBLY

VALVE BODY

NOTE: **As valve trains are removed from each valve body bore, place individual parts in correct order in relative position to valve body to simplify reassembly.**

Disassembly

1) Remove attaching screw and lift detent spring assembly from valve body. Remove valve body screws (16), then lift separator plate and transfer plate off valve body, noting position of screen.

2) Note installation position of the 8 valve body check balls in valve body passages, then remove balls from valve body.

3) Remove "E" clip and washer from end of throttle valve lever assembly, then slide manual valve lever assembly off throttle valve lever. Slide throttle valve lever assembly from valve body.

4) Remove manual valve from valve body. Remove pressure regulator and adjusting screw bracket attaching screws, then lift off bracket and adjusting screws. Slide out pressure regulator and manual control valve trains. *See Fig. 17.*

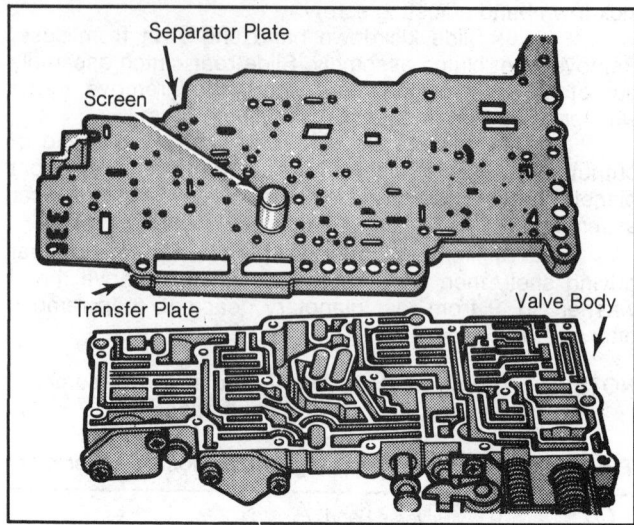

Fig. 18: *Removing Separator and Transfer Plates*

5) Remove end plate and slide out 2-3 shift valve governor plug. Remove next end plate and slide out 1-2 shift valve governor plug. *See Fig. 19.*

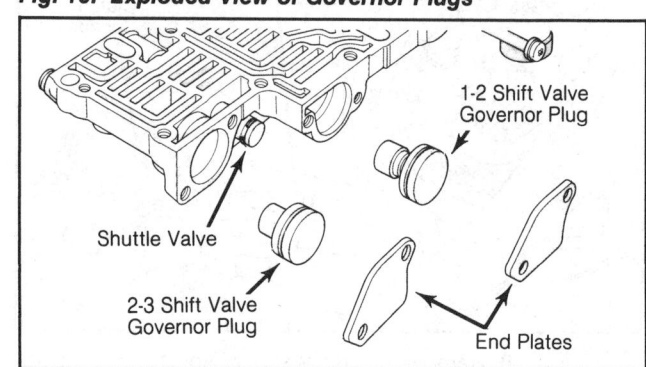

Fig. 19: *Exploded View of Governor Plugs*

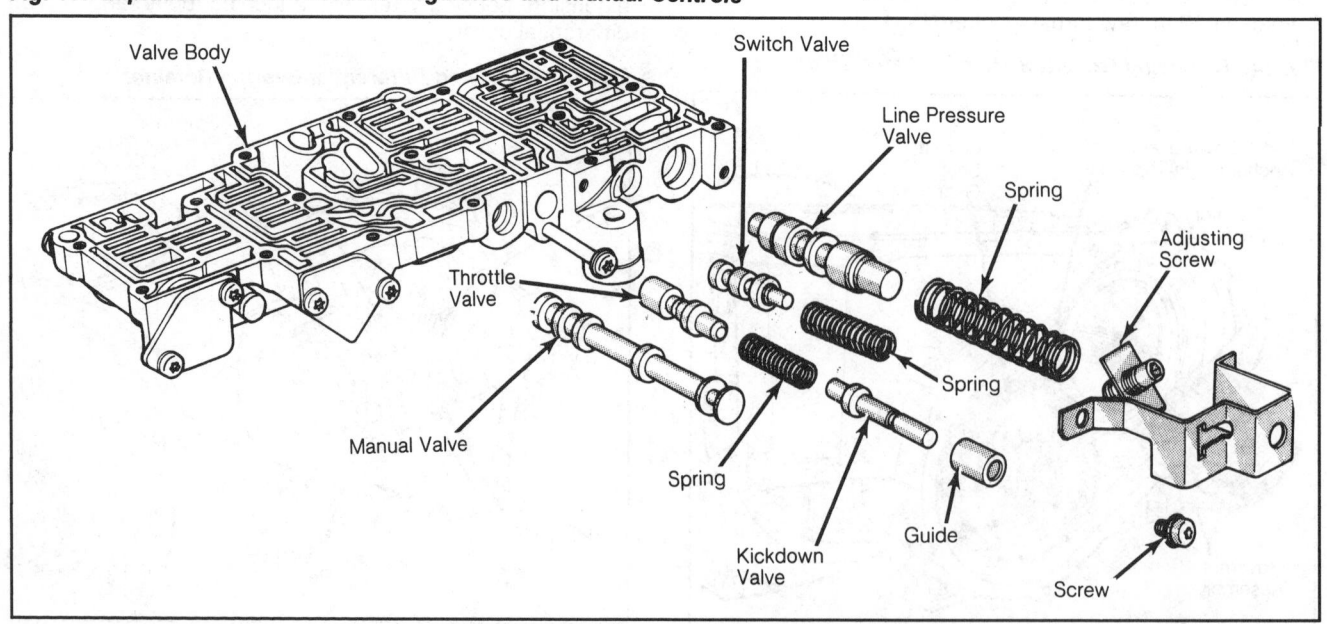

Fig. 17: *Exploded View of Pressure Regulators and Manual Controls*

CHRYSLER CORP. A-404, A-413 & A-470 (Cont.)

6) Remove end plate screws and carefully remove end plate. Remove regulator valve throttle pressure plug spring and regulator valve throttle pressure plug. *See Fig. 20.*

Fig. 20: Exploded View of Regulator Valve Throttle Pressure Plug Assembly

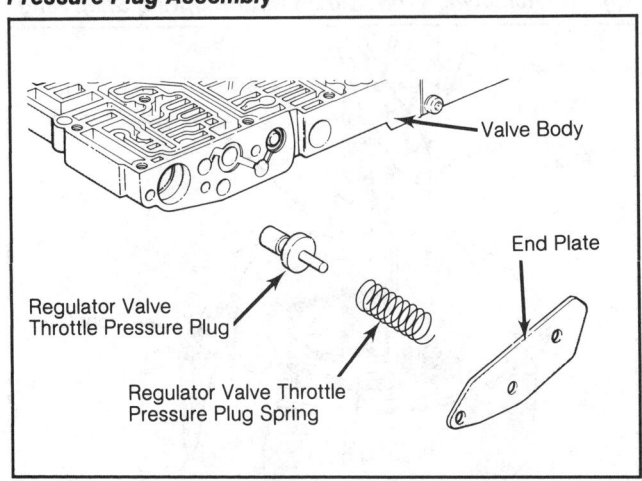

Remove end plate carefully to prevent losing spring.

7) Remove remaining end plate from valve body and remove the following: 1-2 shift valve train, by-pass valve train, shuttle valve train, and 2-3 shift valve train. *See Fig. 21.*

Reassembly
Reverse disassembly using exploded view illustrations as reassembly guides. Ensure that valve body

check balls are installed in the correct passages as shown in *Fig. 22.*

Fig. 22: View of Valve Body Showing Check Ball Locations

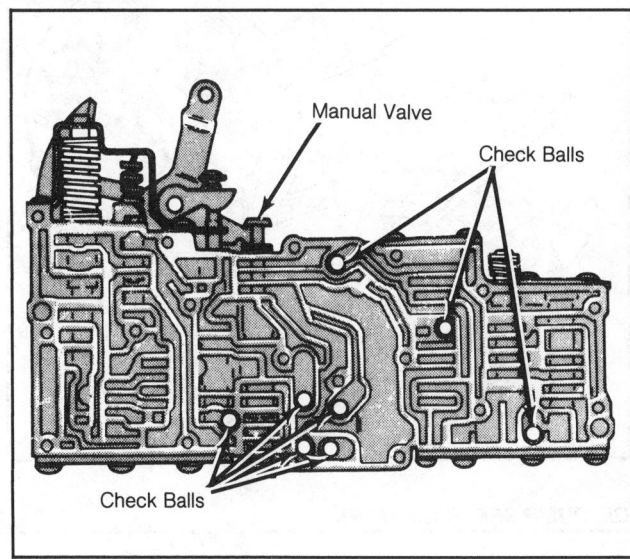

OIL PUMP ASSEMBLY
Disassembly
Remove attaching bolts and separate reaction shaft support from oil pump body. Mark inner and outer pump gears for reassembly reference, then remove gears from pump body.

Fig. 21: Exploded View of Shuttle Valve and Shift Valve Trains

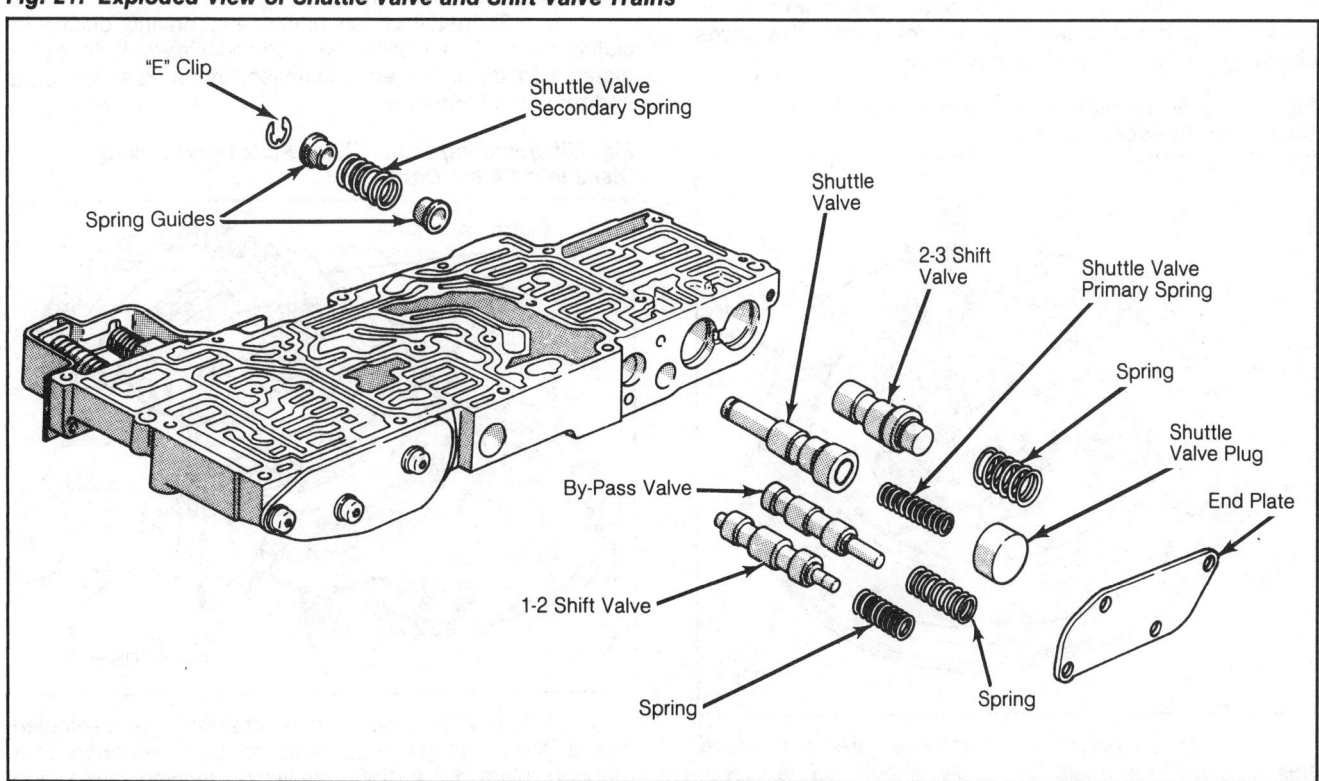

CHRYSLER CORP. A-404, A-413 & A-470 (Cont.)

Fig. 23: Separating Reaction Shaft Support from Oil Pump Housing

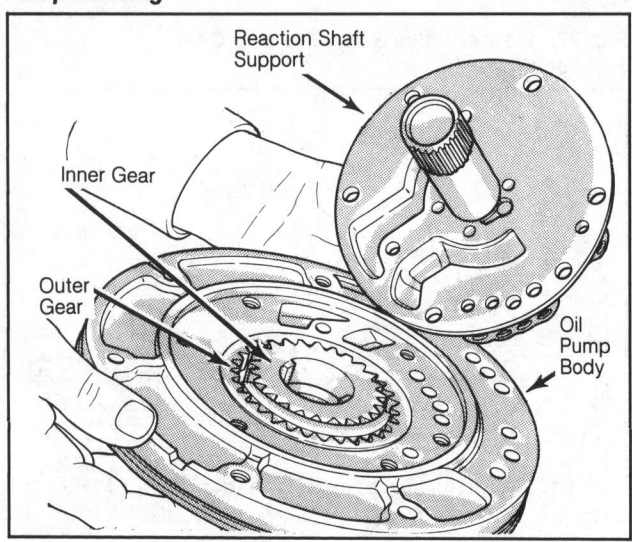

OIL PUMP SPECIFICATIONS

Measurement	Clearance In. (mm)
Outer Gear-to-Pocket	.0018-.0056 (.045-.141)
Outer Gear I.D.-to-Crescent	.0059-.012 (.150-.306)
Outer Gear Side Clearance	.001-.002 (.025-.050)
Inner Gear O.D.-to-Crescent	.0063-.0124 (.160-.316)
Inner Gear Side Clearance	.001-.002 (.025-.050)

Reassembly

1) Install inner and outer gears into pump body. Using feeler gauge measure oil pump clearances shown in *Oil Pump Specifications Table*.

Fig. 24: Using a Feeler Gauge to Measure Oil Pump Outer Gear-to-Pocket Clearance

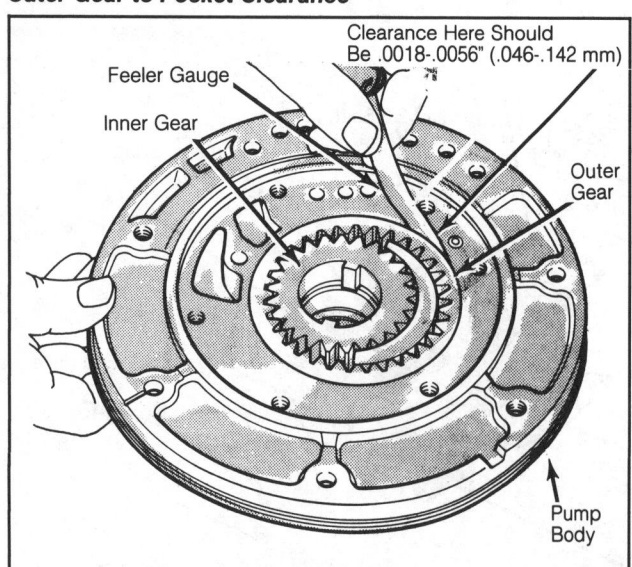

2) If oil pump clearances are not within specifications, oil pump assembly should be replaced. After clearances have been measured, install reaction shaft support-to-pump body and install attaching bolts.

FRONT CLUTCH ASSEMBLY
Disassembly

1) Using a screwdriver, pry waved snap ring from clutch drum. Lift out reaction plate along with clutch plates and driving discs.

Fig. 25: Removing Front Clutch Return Spring Snap Ring

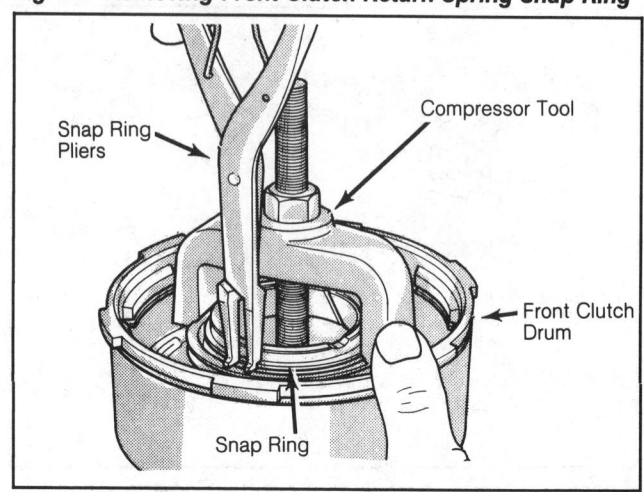

2) Compress clutch return spring with tool and remove retaining snap ring. Remove compressor tool and lift out return spring retainer, return spring and clutch piston.

3) If necessary for replacement, remove lip seals from clutch piston and from inside of clutch drum.

Reassembly

1) Reverse disassembly procedures to assemble clutch, noting the following:

2) Install clutch plates and driving discs into clutch drum. *See Clutch Plate Usage Chart*. With clutch plates and discs correctly installed, install reaction plate and retaining snap ring.

Fig. 26: Installing Front Clutch Plates and Driving Discs into Clutch Drum

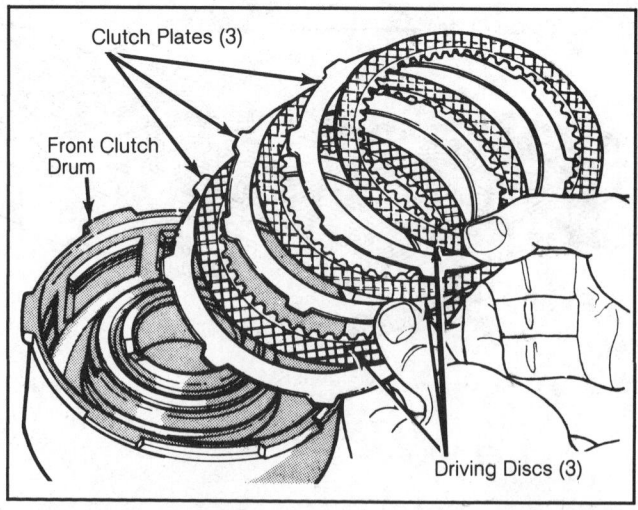

3) With front clutch assembly reassembled, use a feeler gauge and measure the clearance from reaction plate to farthest wave on waved snap ring. Clearance should be .087-.133" (2.2-3.4 mm) on models with 2.2L or 2.6L engines.

CHRYSLER CORP. A-404, A-413 & A-470 (Cont.)

Fig. 27: *Measuring Front Clutch Clearance*

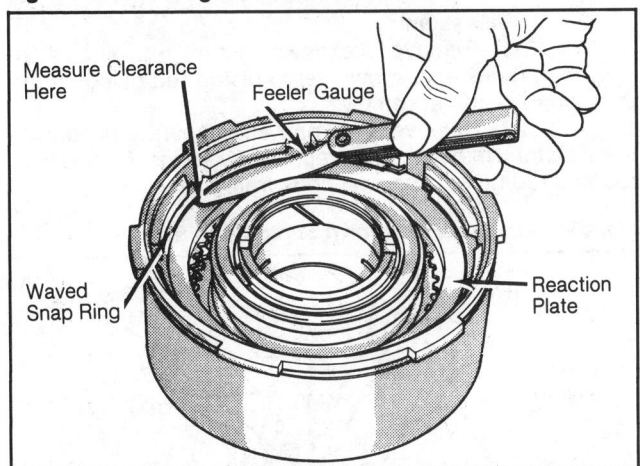

CLUTCH PLATE USAGE CHART

Application	Clutch Plates	Driving Discs
Front Clutch All Models	3	3
Rear Clutch All Models	2	3

REAR CLUTCH ASSEMBLY
Disassembly

1) Pry selective snap ring from rear clutch drum. Lift out reaction plate, clutch plates, driving discs and pressure plate.

2) Pry piston spring waved snap ring from clutch drum. Remove piston spring and piston. If necessary, remove seals from piston.

3) If necessary, remove input shaft snap ring from inside clutch drum, then press input shaft out of drum.

Fig. 28: *Removing Rear Clutch Piston and Spring*

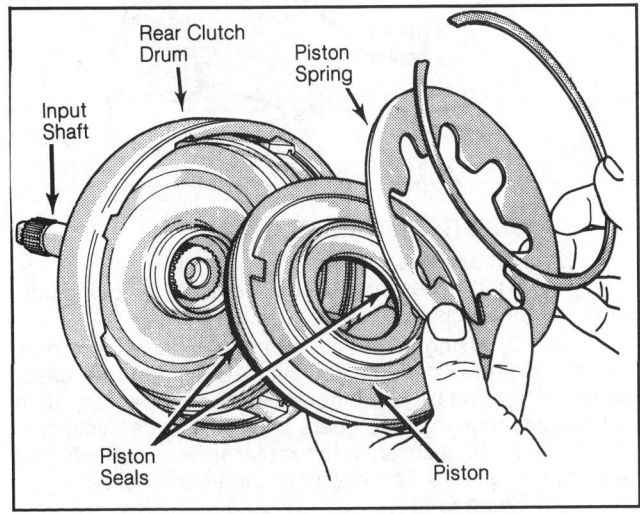

Reassembly

1) Reverse disassembly procedure and note the following:

2) Install clutch plates and driving discs into rear clutch drum as shown in *Fig. 29*. See *Clutch Plate Usage Chart*.

Fig. 29: *Installing Clutch Plates and Driving Discs*

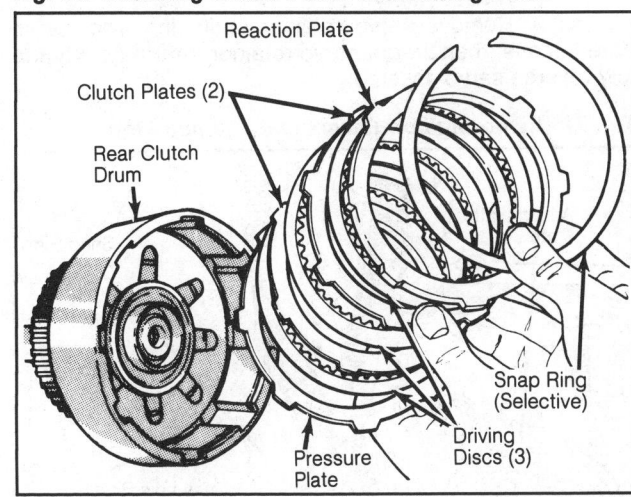

3) With rear clutch reassembled, measure clearance between waved snap ring and reaction plate using a feeler gauge. Clearance should be .023-.037" (.58-.95 mm).

4) If clearance is not within correct limits, install selective snap ring as required to obtain correct clearance. Snap rings are available in thicknesses of .060-.062" (1.52-1.57 mm), .076-.078" (1.93-1.98 mm) and .093-.095" (2.36-2.41 mm).

FRONT PLANETARY & ANNULUS GEAR
Disassembly

1) Remove snap ring retaining front planetary gear set in annulus gear. Remove thrust washer No. 4 which is located under snap ring.

2) Lift planetary gear from annulus gear, then lift out thrust washer No. 5. Remove front snap ring from annulus gear and separate front annulus gear support from annulus gear. Remove rear snap ring.

Fig. 30: *Removing Front Planetary Gear and No. 5 Thrust Washer from Annulus Gear*

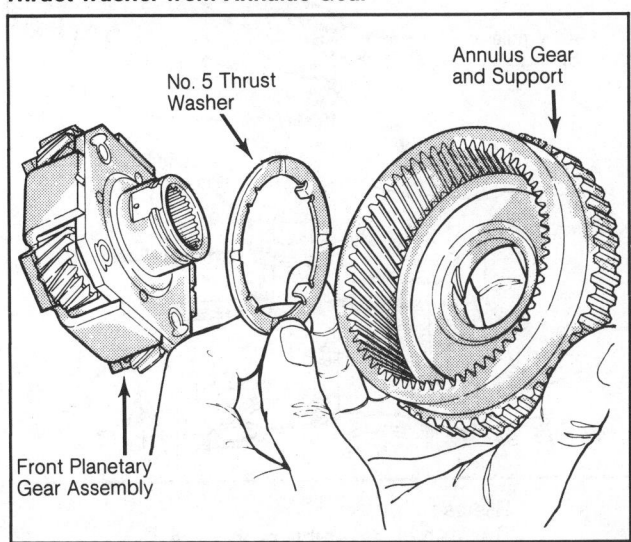

CHRYSLER CORP. A-404, A-413 & A-470 (Cont.)

Reassembly

Reverse disassembly procedure.

LOW-REVERSE SERVO

Disassembly

Remove servo retainer snap ring from servo bore in case, then lift out servo retainer, return spring and low-reverse servo assembly.

Fig. 31: Removing Low-Reverse Servo Snap Ring

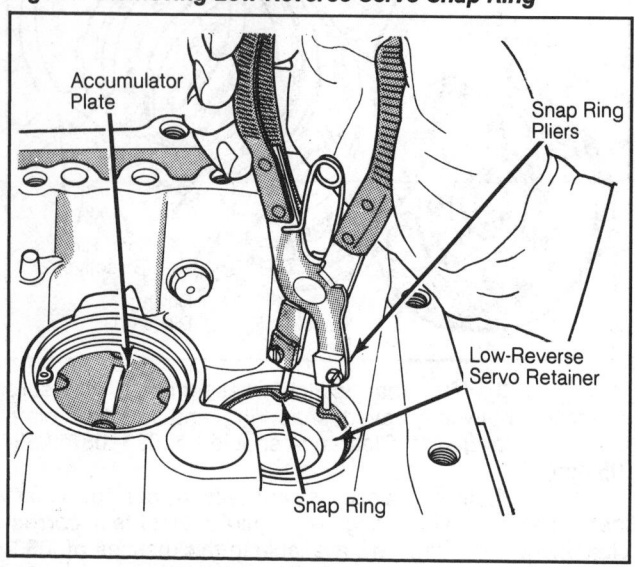

Reassembly

Reverse disassembly procedure. Replace servo assembly lip seal if necessary.

ACCUMULATOR ASSEMBLY

Disassembly

Remove accumulator retaining snap ring, then lift accumulator plate from case bore. Withdraw accumulator spring and piston. If necessary, remove seal rings from piston.

Fig. 32: Removing Accumulator Piston and Spring

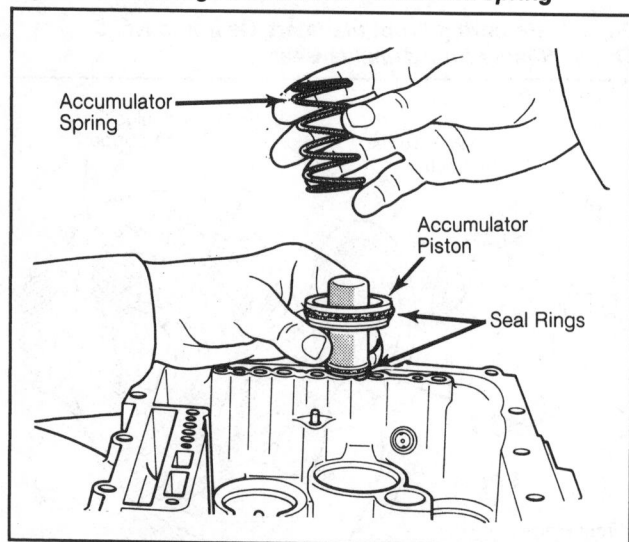

Reassembly

Reverse disassembly procedure.

KICKDOWN (FRONT) SERVO

Disassembly

1) Remove kickdown servo retaining snap ring, then remove kickdown servo piston rod guide, return spring and piston assembly.

2) Remove snap ring and separate piston rod from piston. If necessary, remove "O" rings from piston rod and rod guide, and seal rings from piston.

Fig. 33: Removing Kickdown Servo Snap Ring

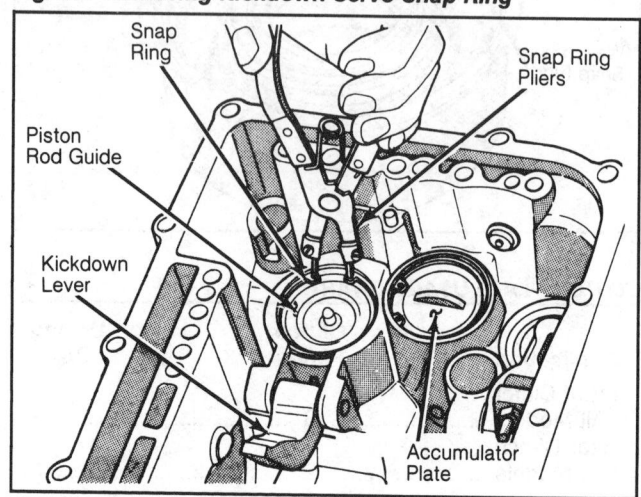

Reassembly

Reverse disassembly procedure.

Fig. 34: Exploded View of Kickdown Servo

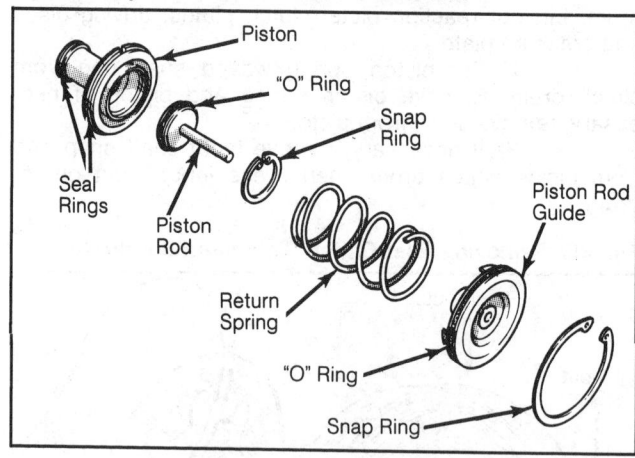

DIFFERENTIAL ASSEMBLY

Disassembly

1) If necessary for replacement, remove differential side bearings from carrier using a puller.

2) Using a punch, remove differential pinion shaft roll pin, then drive pinion shaft from differential case. Rotate pinion gears to differential case opening, then remove pinion gears, side gears and the 4 thrust washers.

3) If necessary for replacement, remove ring gear attaching bolts. Tap ring gear off differential case.

Reassembly

To reassemble, reverse disassembly procedure and note the following: If removed, immerse ring gear in boiling water for 15 minutes before installing on differential case.

CHRYSLER CORP. A-404, A-413 & A-470 (Cont.)

Fig. 35: Exploded View of Differential Gears, Thrust Washers and Pinion Shaft

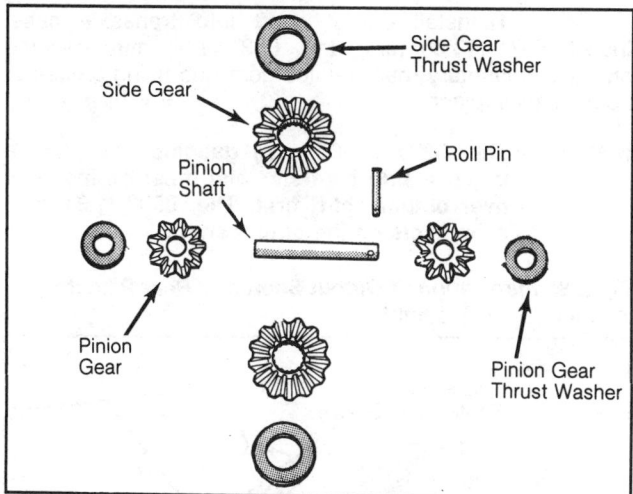

Side Gear Thrust Washer
Side Gear
Pinion Shaft
Roll Pin
Pinion Gear
Pinion Gear Thrust Washer

TRANSAXLE REASSEMBLY & ADJUSTMENT

DIFFERENTIAL ASSEMBLY

Differential bearing preload must be adjusted if any of the following components have been replaced:
- Transaxle Case
- Differential Carrier
- Differential Bearing Retainer
- Extension Housing
- Differential Bearings

If none of these parts are replaced, differential may be reassembled using the original adjusting shims.

1) Remove differential bearing outer race and preload adjusting shim from differential bearing retainer. If differential bearings have been replaced, also replace outer race in extension housing.

2) Reinstall bearing outer race in differential bearing retainer using a .020" (.50 mm) gauging shim. Also, install a new outer race in extension housing if removed.

3) Position differential assembly in transaxle case with ring gear end of carrier installed on bearing retainer side of case.

4) Install extension housing on case and tighten attaching bolts. Install differential bearing retainer and tighten attaching bolts.

5) Position the transaxle assembly vertically in a support stand and install special tool L-4436 into extension housing. Rotate differential at least 1 full turn to ensure tapered roller bearings are fully seated.

NOTE: Special tool L-4436 fits through extension housing and rests on pinion shaft. See Fig. 36.

6) Attach a dial indicator to case as shown in *Fig. 36*. Zero dial indicator. Position indicator tip on end of tool L-4436.

7) Place a large screwdriver to each side of the ring gear and lift. Check the dial indicator for the amount of end play.

CAUTION: Do not damage the transaxle case or the differential cover sealing surface when lifting the ring gear.

8) To determine proper shim combination to use to obtain specified differential bearing preload, select required shim combination from *Differential Bearing Shim Chart*.

DIFFERENTIAL BEARING SHIM CHART

End Play with Gauging Shim Installed Inches (mm)	Required Shim Combination Inches (mm)
.000 (.00)	[1] .020 (.50)
.002 (.05)	.029 (.75)
.004 (.10)	.031 (.80)
.006 (.15)	.033 (.85)
.008 (.20)	.035 (.90)
.010 (.25)	.037 (.95)
.012 (.30)	.039 (1.00)
.014 (.35)	.041 (1.05)
.016 (.40)	.020+.024 (.50+.60)
.018 (.45)	.020+.026 (.50+.65)
.020 (.50)	.020+.027 (.50+.70)
.022 (.55)	.020+.029 (.50+.75)
.024 (.60)	.020+.031 (.50+.80)
.026 (.65)	.020+.033 (.50+.85)
.027 (.70)	.020+.035 (.50+.90)
.029 (.75)	.020+.037 (.50+.95)
.031 (.80)	.020+.039 (.50+1.00)
.033 (.85)	.020+.041 (.50+1.05)
.035 (.90)	.039+.024 (1.00+.60)
.037 (.95)	.039+.026 (1.00+.65)
.039 (1.00)	.039+.027 (1.00+.70)
.041 (1.05)	.039+.029 (1.00+.75)
.043 (1.10)	.039+.031 (1.00+.80)
.045 (1.15)	.039+.033 (1.00+.85)
.047 (1.20)	.039+.035 (1.00+.90)
.049 (1.25)	.039+.037 (1.00+.95)
.051 (1.30)	.039+.039 (1.00+1.00)
.053 (1.35)	.039+.041 (1.00+1.05)
.055 (1.40)	.041+.041 (1.05+1.05)

[1] — Gauging shim.

9) Remove differential bearing retainer, then remove differential bearing outer race and gauging shim from retainer. Install proper shim combination, determined in step **8)**, under bearing race. Make sure oil baffle is installed properly in retainer, below bearing shims and race. Reinstall bearing retainer in case. Use RTV sealant between retainer and case.

10) To check adjustment, oil differential bearings, then insert special tool L-4436 (or equivalent) through extension housing to engage differential assembly.

11) Using an INCH lbs. torque wrench, check differential turning torque. Turning torque with differential bearing preload correctly adjusted, should be 5-18 INCH lbs. (.55-2.0 N.m) If not, install a .002" (.05 mm) thinner shim to decrease torque or a .002" (.05 mm) thicker shim to increase torque.

CHRYSLER CORP. A-404, A-413 & A-470 (Cont.)

Fig. 36: Measuring Differential End Play

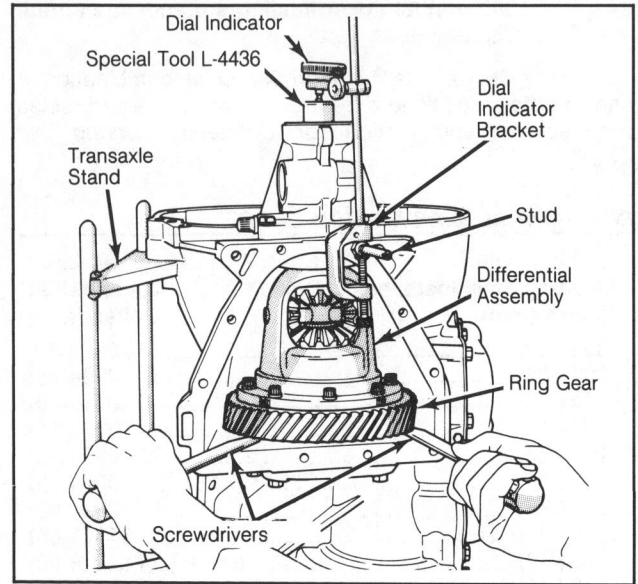

Lift ring gear with 2 large screwdrivers and read end play on dial indicator.

12) When correct torque has been obtained, remove tools, apply 1/8" bead of RTV sealant around differential cover and install cover on case. Install and tighten attaching bolts. Oil and install a new extension housing oil seal.

Fig. 37: Using Special Tool to Measure Differential Turning Torque

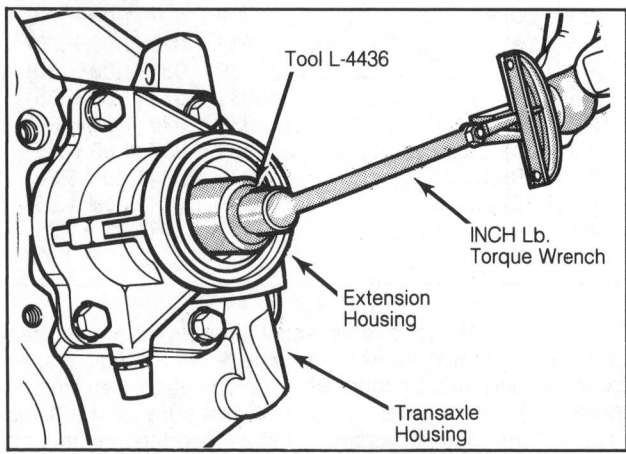

OUTPUT SHAFT ASSEMBLY

The following procedure includes end play adjustment for the output shaft. If any of the following components have been replaced, end play must be checked and adjusted.

- Transaxle Case
- Output Shaft
- Rear Planetary Annulus Gear
- Output Shaft Gear
- Rear Annulus and Output Shaft Gear Bearings or Races
- Overrunning Clutch Races

If none of these components are replaced, and output shaft bearing turning torque is 3-8 INCH lbs. (.3-.9

N.m), reassemble output shaft in case using original adjusting shim (spacer).

1) Install output shaft into transaxle case. Install .537" (13.65 mm) and .053" (1.34 mm) gauging shims on planetary rear annulus gear hub using grease to hold shims in place.

NOTE: The .537" (13.65 mm) gauging shim has a larger inside diameter and must be installed over output shaft first. The .053" (1.34 mm) shim pilots on the output shaft.

Fig. 38: Installation of Output Shaft and Rear Planetary Annulus Gear Assembly

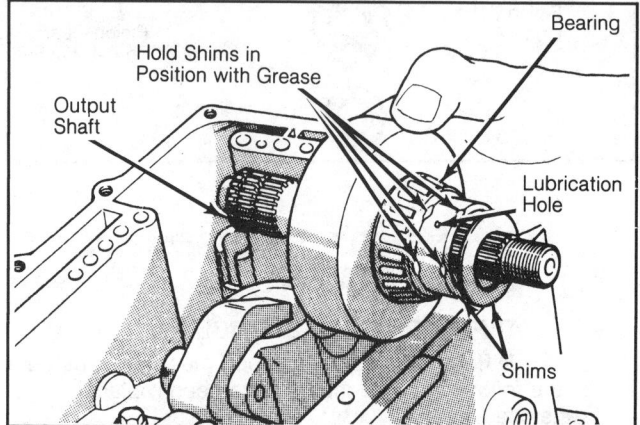

2) Place output shaft gear in position on output shaft, then install washer and retaining nut. Hold output shaft stationary and tighten retaining nut to 200 ft. lbs. (271 N.m).

Fig. 39: Using a Dial Indicator to Measure Output Shaft End Play

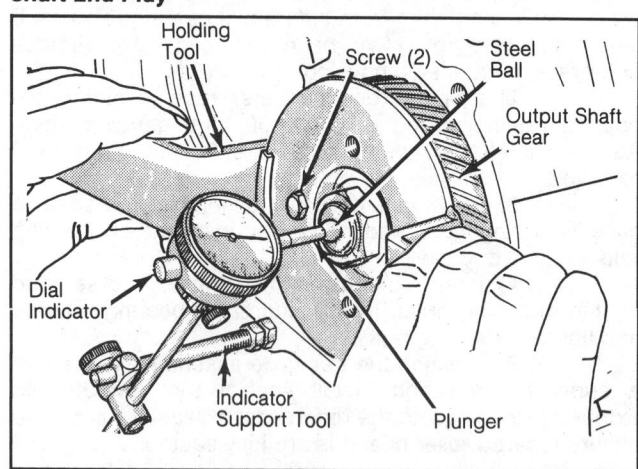

3) Attach holding tool (L-4432) to output shaft gear. Mount a steel ball into end of output shaft and retain in place with grease. Attach a dial indicator to case and position plunger against steel ball. Push and pull gear while rotating back and forth to insure seating of roller bearings.

4) Move output shaft in and out and measure end play. With end play determined, select required output shaft adjusting shim combination from *Output Shaft Bearing Shim Chart.*

CHRYSLER CORP. A-404, A-413 & A-470 (Cont.)

OUTPUT SHAFT BEARING SHIM CHART

End Play with Gauging Shims Installed Inches (mm)	Required Shim Combination Inches (mm)
.000 (.00)	¹ .537 + .053 (13.65 + 1.34)
.002 (.05)	.537 + .049 (13.65 + 1.24)
.004 (.10)	.537 + .047 (13.65 + 1.19)
.006 (.15)	.537 + .045 (13.65 + 1.14)
.008 (.20)	.537 + .043 (13.65 + 1.09)
.010 (.25)	.537 + .041 (13.65 + 1.04)
.012 (.30)	.537 + .039 (13.65 + .99)
.014 (.35)	.537 + .037 (13.65 + .94)
.016 (.40)	.518 + .055 (13.15 + 1.39)
.018 (.45)	.518 + .053 (13.15 + 1.34)
.020 (.50)	.518 + .051 (13.15 + 1.29)
.022 (.55)	.518 + .049 (13.15 + 1.24)
.024 (.60)	.518 + .047 (13.15 + 1.19)
.026 (.65)	.518 + .045 (13.15 + 1.14)
.028 (.70)	.518 + .043 (13.15 + 1.09)
.030 (.75)	.518 + .041 (13.15 + 1.04)
.032 (.80)	.518 + .039 (13.15 + .99)
.034 (.85)	.518 + .037 (13.15 + .94)
.036 (.90)	.498 + .055 (12.65 + 1.39)
.038 (.95)	.498 + .053 (12.65 + 1.34)
.040 (1.00)	.498 + .051 (12.65 + 1.29)
.042 (1.05)	.498 + .049 (12.65 + 1.24)
.044 (1.10)	.498 + .047 (12.65 + 1.19)
.046 (1.15)	.498 + .045 (12.65 + 1.14)
.048 (1.20)	.498 + .043 (12.65 + 1.09)
.049 (1.25)	.498 + .041 (12.65 + 1.04)
.051 (1.30)	.498 + .039 (12.65 + .99)
.053 (1.35)	.498 + .037 (12.65 + .94)

¹ — Gauging shims.

NOTE: The .537" (13.65 mm), .518" (13.15 mm) and .498" (12.65 mm) shims are always installed first. These shims have lubrication slots which are necessary for proper bearing lubrication.

5) With proper shim combination determined, remove output shaft gear from case. Remove gauging shims from annulus gear hub and install correct shims. Hold shims in place with grease. Reinstall output shaft gear and tighten retaining nut.

6) Using an INCH lb. torque wrench, check output shaft bearing turning torque. Turning torque should be 3-8 INCH lbs. (.3-.9 N.m). If torque is not within limits, correct by changing shim thickness in increments of .002" (.05 mm). To reduce torque, increase total shim thickness. To increase torque, decrease shim thickness.

TRANSFER SHAFT, GOVERNOR & PARKING PAWL ASSEMBLIES

1) Position parking pawl and return spring in place in transaxle case. Slide parking pawl pivot shaft (small diameter to rear) through case bore and into parking pawl and spring. Install parking pawl retainer and tighten attaching bolts.

2) If necessary for replacement, install new oil seal and "O" rings on transfer shaft bearing retainer. Slide retainer onto transfer shaft.

3) Using special tool L-4512 (or equivalent), install transfer shaft into transaxle case. Install transfer shaft bearing retainer snap ring and ensure it is fully seated in groove in case.

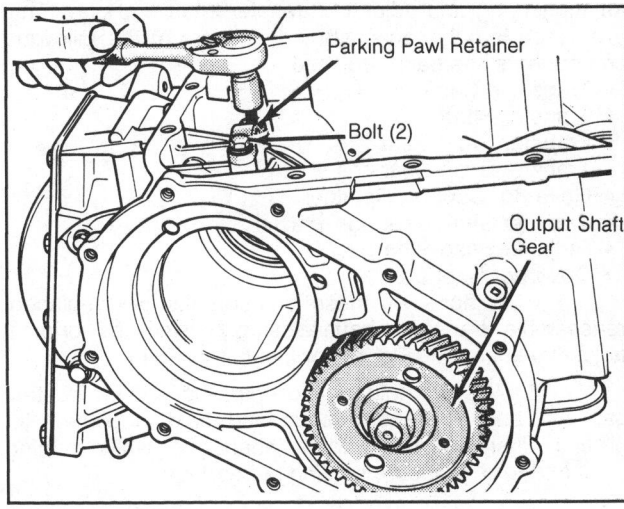

Fig. 40: Parking Pawl Retainer Installation

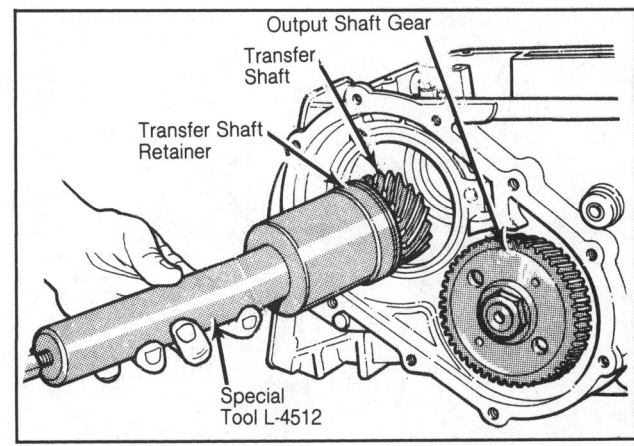

Fig. 41: Using Special Tool to Install Transfer Shaft into Case

4) Slide governor assembly onto transfer shaft. Install low-reverse band anchor pin into bore in transaxle case. Install governor support retainer.

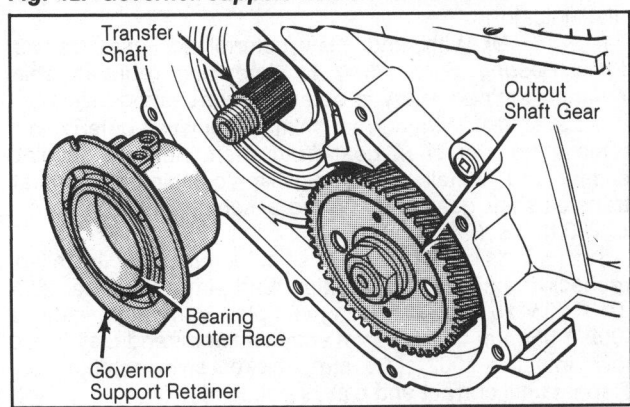

Fig. 42: Governor Support Retainer Installation

5) Install .090" (2.29 mm) and .055" (1.39 mm) gauging shims on transfer shaft, behind governor support. Install transfer shaft gear and bearing assembly.

6) Hold transfer shaft stationary with holding tool. Install gear retaining nut and washer and tighten to 200 ft. lbs. (271 N.m).

CHRYSLER CORP. A-404, A-413 & A-470 (Cont.)

The following 4 steps describe the procedure for measuring and adjusting transfer shaft end play. This procedure is only necessary if 1 or more of the following components has been replaced.

- Transaxle Case
- Transfer Shaft
- Transfer Shaft Gear
- Transfer Shaft Bearings
- Governor Support Retainer
- Transfer Shaft Bearing Retainer
- Retainer Snap Ring
- Governor Support

If none of these components are replaced, reassemble transfer shaft assembly using the original adjusting shim. See *Fig. 44* for location of shim.

7) With holding tool installed, mount a steel ball into end of transfer shaft and hold in place with grease. Push and pull transfer shaft gear while rotating back and forth to insure seating of bearings.

Fig. 43: Using a Dial Indicator to Measure Transfer Shaft End Play

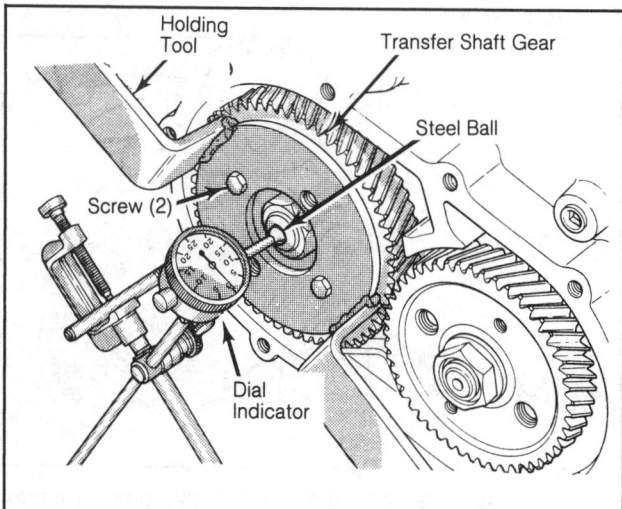

8) Attach a dial indicator to case and position so that plunger contacts steel ball installed in end of transfer shaft. Move shaft in and out and read end play on dial indicator.

9) With end play determined, use *Transfer Shaft Bearing Shim Chart* to determine required shim combination necessary to obtain proper bearing setting.

10) With correct shim combination determined, remove transfer shaft gear from shaft. Remove gauging shims and install selected shim combination. Install transfer shaft gear and bearing assembly and tighten nut to 200 ft. lbs. (271 N.m).

11) With correct shim combination installed, recheck transfer shaft end play. End play should be .002-.010" (.05-.25 mm). If bearing end play is too high, install a .002" (.05 mm) thinner shim combination. If end play is too low, install a .002" (.05 mm) thicker shim combination. Repeat until correct end play is obtained.

12) Apply a continuous bead of RTV sealer on rear cover mounting surface, then position cover on transaxle case. Install and tighten cover attaching bolts.

TRANSFER SHAFT BEARING SHIM CHART

End Play with Gauging Shims Installed Inches (mm)	Required Shim Combination Inches (mm)
.000-.006 (.00-.15)	[1] .090 + .055 (2.29 + 1.39)
.008 (.20)	.090 + .053 (2.29 + 1.34)
.010 (.25)	.090 + .051 (2.29 + 1.29)
.012 (.30)	.090 + .049 (2.29 + 1.24)
.014 (.35)	.090 + .047 (2.29 + 1.19)
.016 (.40)	.090 + .045 (2.29 + 1.14)
.018 (.45)	.090 + .043 (2.29 + 1.09)
.020 (.50)	.090 + .041 (2.29 + 1.04)
.022 (.55)	.090 + .039 (2.29 + .99)
.024 (.60)	.072 + .055 (1.84 + 1.39)
.026 (.65)	.072 + .053 (1.84 + 1.34)
.028 (.70)	.072 + .051 (1.84 + 1.29)
.030 (.75)	.072 + .049 (1.84 + 1.24)
.032 (.80)	.072 + .047 (1.84 + 1.19)
.034 (.85)	.072 + .045 (1.84 + 1.14)
.036 (.90)	.072 + .043 (1.84 + 1.09)
.038 (.95)	.072 + .041 (1.84 + 1.04)
.040 (1.00)	.072 + .039 (1.84 + .99)
.042 (1.05)	.055 + .055 (1.39 + 1.39)
.044 (1.10)	.055 + .053 (1.39 + 1.34)
.046 (1.15)	.055 + .051 (1.39 + 1.29)
.048 (1.20)	.055 + .049 (1.39 + 1.24)
.049 (1.25)	.055 + .047 (1.39 + 1.19)
.050 (1.30)	.055 + .045 (1.39 + 1.14)
.052 (1.35)	.055 + .043 (1.39 + 1.09)
.055 (1.40)	.055 + .041 (1.39 + 1.04)
.057 (1.45)	.055 + .039 (1.39 + .99)
.059 (1.50)	.037 + .055 (.94 + 1.39)
.061 (1.55)	.037 + .053 (.94 + 1.34)
.063 (1.60)	.037 + .051 (.94 + 1.29)

[1] — Gauging shims.

Fig. 44: View of Transfer Shaft with Gear Removed Showing Location of Adjusting Shim

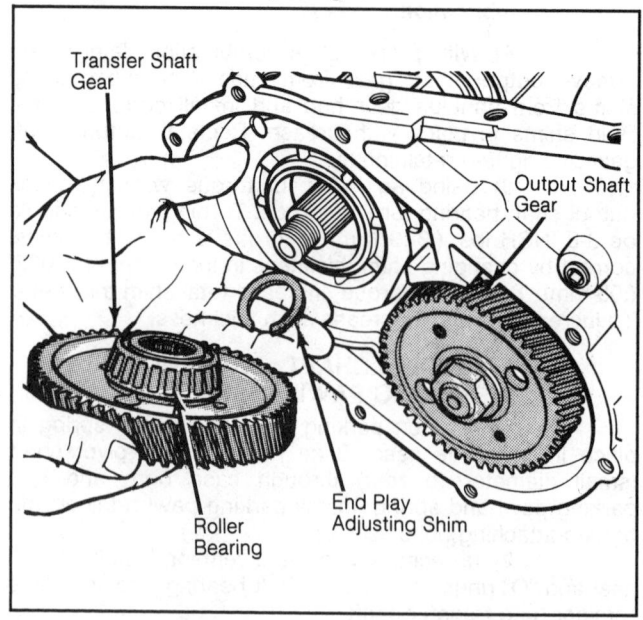

CHRYSLER CORP. A-404, A-413 & A-470 (Cont.)

TRANSMISSION ASSEMBLY

1) Position rollers and springs in overrunning clutch cam using special tool L-4440 (or equivalent) to hold them in place. *See Fig. 45.*

2) Install thrust washer No. 11 into case and over rear planetary annulus gear. Position low-reverse band around annulus gear in case, then install band strut.

Fig. 45: Installing Rollers and Springs in Overrunning Clutch Cam Assembly

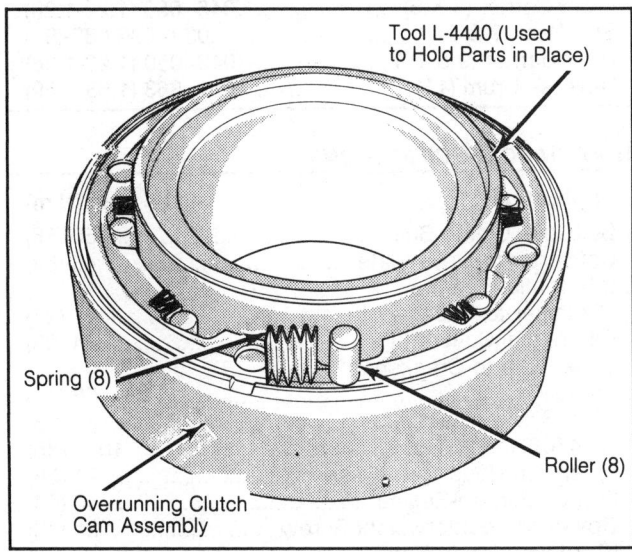

3) Install overrunning clutch cam assembly (with tool L-4440 installed) into case, then remove tool. Install thrust washer No. 10 (with tangs facing out) into position in rear planetary annulus gear.

4) Install rear planetary gear assembly into rear annulus gear. Install thrust washer No. 9 into case and make sure tabs on washer engage slots in planetary assembly.

Fig. 46: Installed View of Rear Planetary Assembly

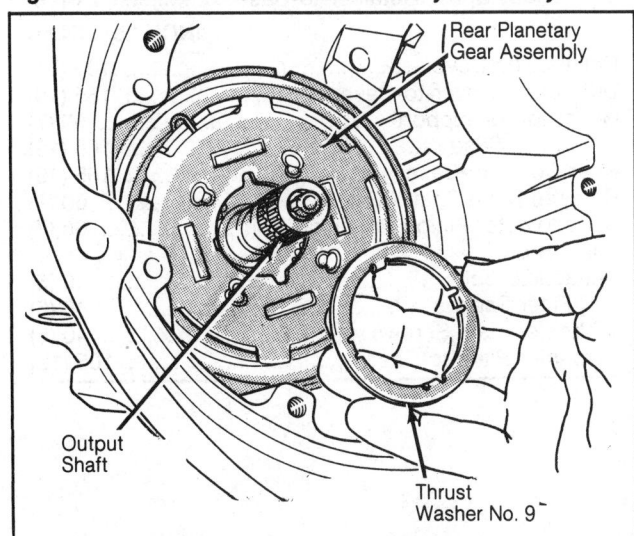

5) Position thrust washer No. 7 inside sun gear driving shell and install sun gear in shell. Install No. 8 thrust washer on back side of driving shell and hold in place with snap ring. Install driving shell into case. Install

thrust washer No. 6 (with tangs facing out) into driving shell.

6) Install front planetary gear assembly into case and make sure it engages tabs of thrust washer No. 6. Install front planetary gear assembly retaining snap ring into groove in output shaft.

Fig. 47: Installation of Front Planetary Gear Assembly Retaining Snap Ring

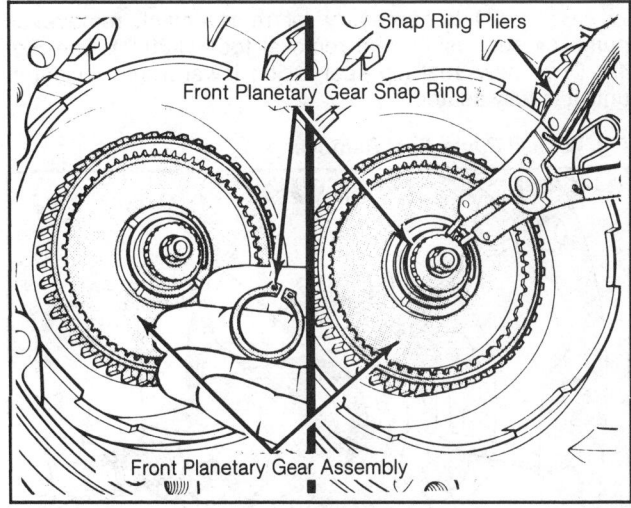

7) Slide thrust washer No. 3 onto end of output shaft. Position thrust washer No. 2 into place in rear clutch drum, then install rear clutch/input shaft assembly into case.

CAUTION: Thrust washer No. 3 controls input shaft end play. If input shaft end play check during Transaxle Disassembly indicated excessive end play, ensure a new thrust washer of correct thickness is installed.

8) Install front clutch assembly into case, and ensure that tabs on front clutch drum engage slots in rear clutch drum.

9) Position kickdown (front) band into place on front clutch drum, then install band strut. Tighten kickdown band adjusting screw just enough to hold parts in place.

Fig. 48: Kickdown (Front) Band and Strut Installation

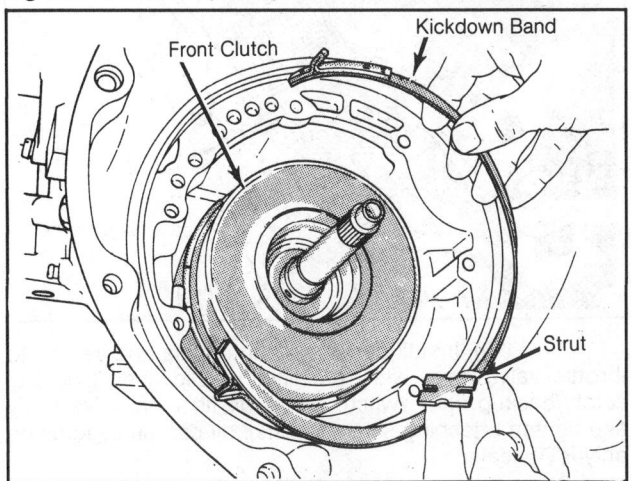

CHRYSLER CORP. A-404, A-413 & A-470 (Cont.)

10) Install oil pump gasket into case, making sure that oil holes in gasket align with holes in case. Install oil pump assembly into case using new attaching bolts.

NOTE: **At this point, input shaft end play should be rechecked to ensure correct thrust washer No. 3 has been installed. See end play checking procedure given during Transaxle Disassembly.**

11) If necessary for replacement, remove oil pump oil seal using seal removal tool (C-3981). *See Fig. 49.* Drive new seal (lip seal facing inward) into oil pump until it is fully seated.

Fig. 49: Oil Pump Seal Removal

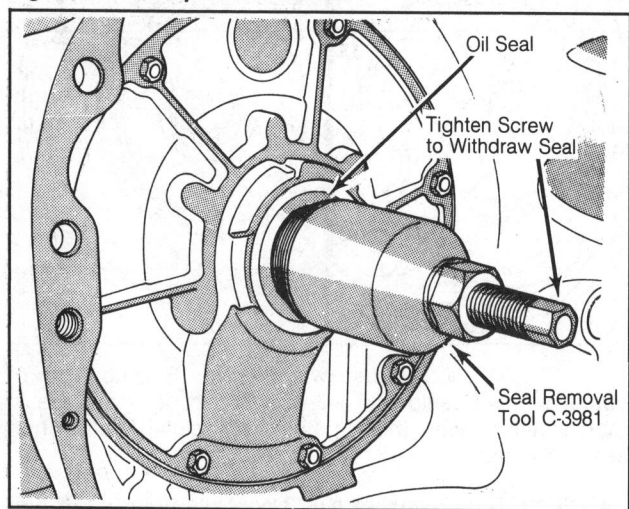

12) Carefully install valve body assembly into case while guiding governor tubes into position. Install valve body attaching bolts and tighten alternately and evenly.

Fig. 50: Parking Rod Installation

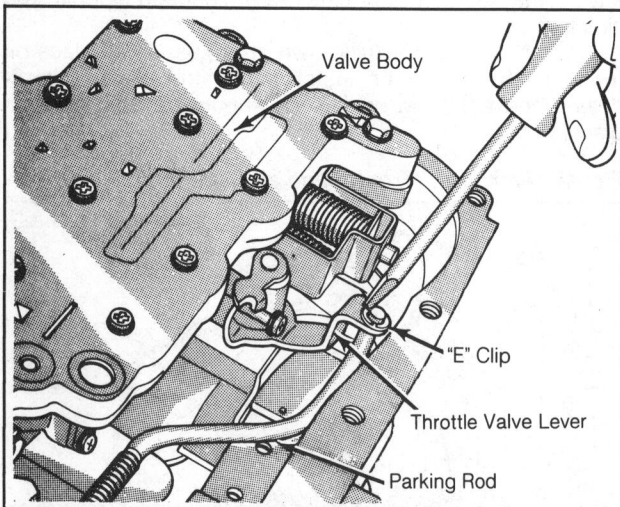

13) Install parking rod into case and secure to throttle valve lever with retaining "E" clip. Install neutral safety/backup light switch. Install oil filter on valve body and tighten attaching screws. Install oil pan on case using only RTV sealer.

THRUST WASHER CHART

Thrust Washer (No.)	Thickness Inches (mm)
Reaction Shaft Support (1)	.061-.063 (1.55-1.60)
Rear Clutch Retainer (2)	.061-.063 (1.55-1.60)
Output Shaft — Selective (3)	.077-.080 (1.98-2.03)
	.085-.087 (2.15-2.22)
	.092-.095 (2.34-2.41)
Front Annulus (4)	.116-.120 (2.95-3.05)
Front Carrier (5 & 6)	.048-.050 (1.22-1.28)
Sun Gear (7 & 8)	.033-.036 (.85-.91)
Rear Carrier (9 & 10)	.048-.050 (1.22-1.28)
Reverse Drum (11)	.061-.063 (1.55-1.60)

TIGHTENING SPECIFICATIONS

Application	Ft. Lbs. (N.m)
Ball Joint Clamp Bolt	50 (68)
Converter-to-Drive Plate	40 (54)
Differential Bearing Retainer-to-Case	21 (28)
Differential Cover Plug	24 (33)
Drive Plate-to-Crankshaft	
A-404	50 (68)
A-413	65 (88)
A-470	100 (136)
Extension Housing-to-Case	21 (28)
Front Mount-to-Engine	40 (54)
Governor Counterweight Screw	21 (28)
Kickdown (Front) Band Adjusting Screw Lock Nut	35 (47)
Oil Pump-to-Case	23 (31)
Output Shaft Gear Nut	200 (271)
Reaction Shaft Bolt	21 (28)
Ring Gear-to-Carrier	70 (95)
Side Mount-to-Engine	40 (54)
Starter-to-Bellhousing	40 (54)
Transaxle-to-Engine	70 (95)
Transfer Shaft Gear Nut	200 (271)
Valve Body Sprag Retainer-to-Case	21 (28)

	INCH Lbs. (N.m)
Bellhousing Cover	105 (12)
Differential Cover-to-Case	165 (19)
Governor-to-Support	60 (7)
Oil Pan-to-Case	165 (19)
Rear Cover-to-Case	165 (19)
Reverse Band Shaft Plug	60 (7)
Speedometer Pinion Retaining Bolt	60 (7)
Valve Body	
Attaching Bolts	40 (5)
Oil Filter Screws	40 (5)
Transfer Plate Screws	40 (5)
Transfer Plate-to-Case	105 (12)

FORD MOTOR CO.
AUTOMATIC OVERDRIVE TRANSMISSION

Continental, Cougar, Crown Victoria, Grand Marquis, LTD, Mark VI, Marquis, Thunderbird, Town Car, E100/350, F100/250

IDENTIFICATION

The Automatic Overdrive Transmission (A.O.T.) is identified by the code letter "T". The identification code letter is found on the lower line of Vehicle Certification Label under "TRANS". This label is attached to the left (driver's) side door lock post.

The transmission model may be identified by a metal tag attached to transmission by the lower extension housing retaining bolt. Top line of tag shows transmission Model Number and Line Shift Code. Bottom line on tag shows the Build Date Code. *See Fig. 1.*

Fig. 1: Service Identification Tag

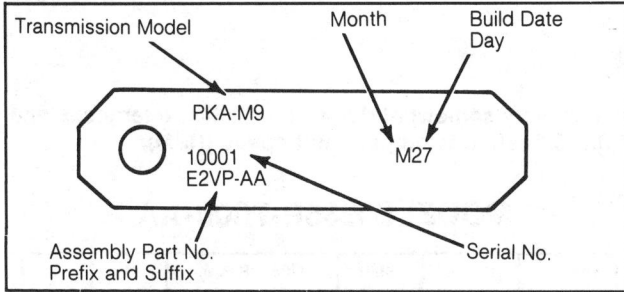

DESCRIPTION

The Automatic Overdrive Transmission (A.O.T.) is a 4 speed, fully automatic transmission which combines automatic shifting with two fuel saving features: An overdrive gear ratio and mechanical lock-out split torque path in 3rd gear. In this range, 40% of the torque is transmitted hydraulically through the torque converter as in conventional automatic transmissions while the remaining 60% of engine torque is transmitted mechanically.

The torque converter operation is similar to other automatics, but has an added damper assembly and an input shaft which is used in 3rd (direct drive) and overdrive gears.

Overdrive is accomplished by band application which locks the reverse sun gear while driving the planet carrier. In this ratio, engine torque flows through the damper assembly and in doing so, by-passes the torque converter. Power flow from the engine into the transmission is then direct.

Transmission consists basically of the torque converter assembly, 4 multi-disc clutches, 2 bands, 2 one-way roller clutches and a hydraulic control system. The hydraulic system differs from that on other Ford automatic transmissions in that the vacuum diaphragm that is normally used for the "engine load" input has been eliminated. In place of this vacuum device, mechanical linkage is employed from the carburetor to the transmission. As a result, throttle (TV) fluid pressure is controlled mechanically rather than by vacuum.

LUBRICATION & ADJUSTMENT

See the appropriate article in AUTOMATIC TRANSMISSION SERVICING Section.

TESTING

ROAD TEST

1) Check minimum throttle upshifts in "O/D". Transmission should start in 1st gear, shift to 2nd then

Fig. 2: Cross-Sectional View of Automatic Overdrive Transmission

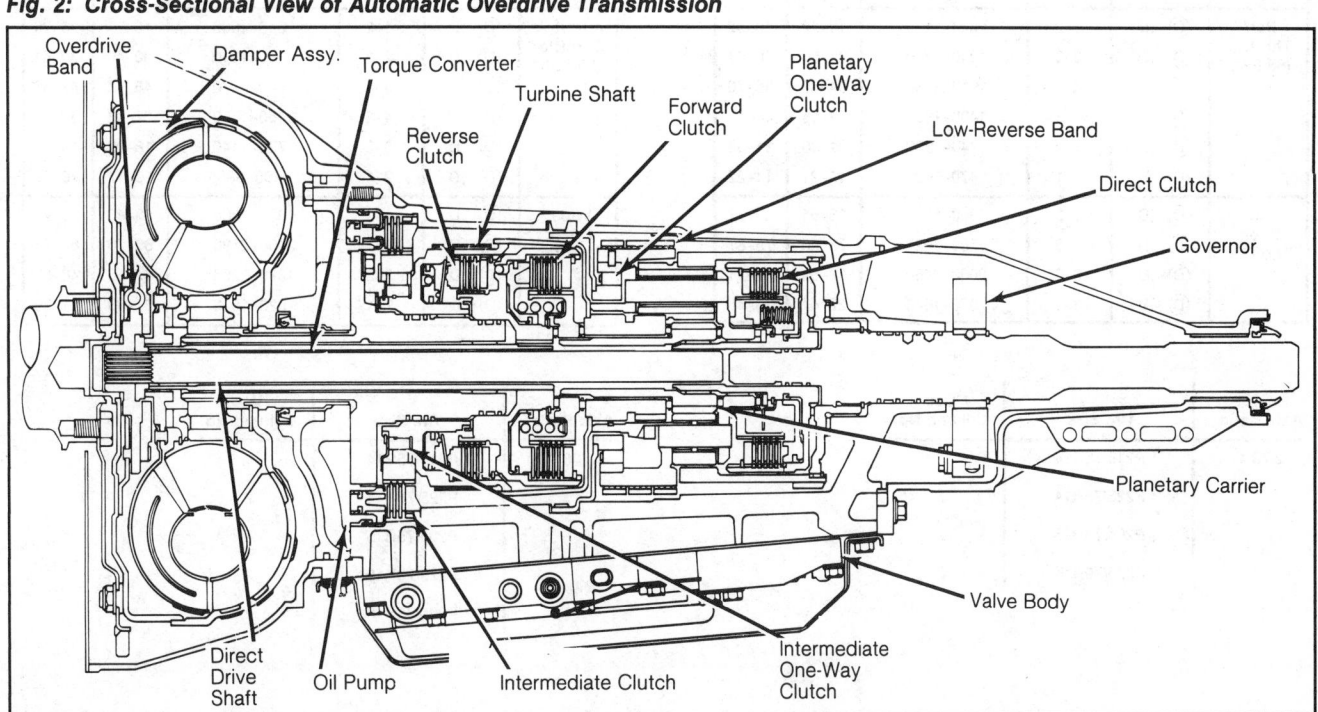

Automatic Transmissions
FORD MOTOR CO.
AUTOMATIC OVERDRIVE TRANSMISSION (Cont.)

shift to 3rd, and finally shift to 4th gear at approximately the speeds shown in *Shift Speed Table*.

NOTE: **Choke must be "OFF" when checking minimum throttle upshifts. If not, shift points will be affected.**

2) Check partial throttle upshifts in "O/D". Transmission should start in 1st gear, shift to 2nd, then shift to 3rd, and finally shift to 4th gear. *See Shift Speed Table*.

3) With transmission in 4th gear (overdrive), depress accelerator pedal to the floor. Transmission should downshift to 3rd or to 2nd gear, depending on vehicle speed. *See Shift Speed Table*.

4) Since closed throttle downshifts are extremely difficult to detect, it will be necessary to attach pressure gauges to forward and direct clutch pressure taps in order to detect 4-3 and 3-2 coast downshifts.

5) With gauges attached, a 4-3 coast (closed throttle) downshift is signified by the application of the forward clutch, and 3-2 coast downshift is signified by the release of the direct clutch. *See Shift Speed Table*.

NOTE: **A 2-1 downshift should not be felt.**

6) With transmission selector lever in "1" (manual low), transmission should operate only in 1st gear.

7) When selector lever is moved from either overdrive or direct drive ranges to "1" position, transmission should downshift into 2nd gear if vehicle speed is above 25 MPH, and into 1st gear is speed is less than 25 MPH.

NOTE: **The Automatic Overdrive Transmission will not shift into 4th gear (overdrive) at wide open throttle. Also, this transmission will not make a 4-1 downshift.**

SHIFT SPEED SPECIFICATIONS (MPH)

NOTE: **Shift speeds shown are approximate. All shift speeds may vary somewhat due to production tolerances and emission control equipment. In the following charts, "O.P.S." refers to output shaft speed (RPM).**

MODELS E3AP-7000-BA, FA

Throttle	Range	Shift	OPS—R.P.M.	1	2
Closed Throttle (Minimum)	Ⓓ ,D	1-2	280-520	8-15	8-15
	Ⓓ ,D	2-3	620-820	18-23	18-24
	Ⓓ	3-4	1140-1630	32-46	33-47
	Ⓓ	4-3	900-1440	25-41	26-42
	Ⓓ ,D	3-2	530-750	15-21	15-22
	Ⓓ ,D	2-1	180-460	5-13	5-13
	1	3-1 2-1	790-1280	22-36	23-37
Part Throttle (60 PSI)	Ⓓ ,D	1-2	660-1120	19-32	19-32
	Ⓓ ,D	2-3	1240-1770	35-50	36-51
	Ⓓ	3-4	1910-2430	54-69	55-70
	Ⓓ	4-3	1490-1930	42-55	43-56
	Ⓓ ,D	3-2	740-1260	21-36	21-36
	Ⓓ ,D	2-1	470-750	13-21	14-22
Wide Open Throttle	Ⓓ ,D	1-2	1360-1960	38-55	39-57
	Ⓓ ,D	2-3	2580-3020	73-85	75-87
	Ⓓ ,D	3-2	2000-2450	57-69	58-71
	Ⓓ ,D	2-1	970-1670	27-47	28-48

MODELS E35P-7000-AA

Throttle	Range	Shift	OPS—R.P.M.	1	2
Closed Throttle (Minimum)	Ⓓ ,D	1-2	320-510	8-13	8-13
	Ⓓ ,D	2-3	610-770	15-19	16-20
	Ⓓ	3-4	1180-1550	30-39	30-40
	Ⓓ	4-3	1000-1370	25-34	26-35
	Ⓓ ,D	3-2	520-700	13-18	13-18
	Ⓓ ,D	2-1	220-450	6-11	6-11
	1	3-1 2-1	730-1150	18-29	19-29
Part Throttle (60 PSI)	Ⓓ ,D	1-2	640-1000	16-25	16-26
	Ⓓ ,D	2-3	1180-1610	30-40	30-41
	Ⓓ	3-4	1840-2270	46-57	47-58
	Ⓓ	4-3	1480-1850	37-46	38-47
	Ⓓ ,D	3-2	720-1140	18-29	18-29
	Ⓓ ,D	2-1	400-690	10-17	10-18
Wide Open Throttle	Ⓓ ,D	1-2	1300-1800	33-45	33-46
	Ⓓ ,D	2-3	2400-2790	60-70	61-71
	Ⓓ ,D	3-2	1870-2250	47-56	48-57
	Ⓓ ,D	2-1	820-1520	21-38	21-39

Axle Ratio	Tire Size	Use Column No.
2.73:1	P215/75R14	1
	P225/75R14	2
	P205/75R15	2
	P225/70R15	2

Axle Ratio	Tire Size	Use Column No.
3.08:1	P215/75R14	1
	P225/75R14	2
	P205/75R15	2
	P225/70R15	2
	P205/75R15	2

FORD MOTOR CO.
AUTOMATIC OVERDRIVE TRANSMISSION (Cont.)

SHIFT SPEED SPECIFICATIONS (Cont.)

MODELS E2VP-7000-BB

Throttle	Range	Shift	OPS—R.P.M.	1	2
Closed Throttle (Minimum)	Ⓓ ,D	1-2	320-510	7-11	7-12
	Ⓓ ,D	2-3	650-810	15-18	15-19
	Ⓓ	3-4	1330-1700	30-38	31-39
	Ⓓ	4-3	1180-1550	27-35	27-36
	Ⓓ ,D	3-2	570-740	13-17	13-17
	Ⓓ ,D	2-1	220-450	5-10	5-10
	1	3-1 2-1	730-1150	16-30	17-26
Part Throttle (60 PSI)	Ⓓ ,D	1-2	700-1100	16-25	16-25
	Ⓓ ,D	2-3	1380-1740	31-39	32-40
	Ⓓ	3-4	1950-2380	44-54	45-55
	Ⓓ	4-3	1610-1960	36-44	37-45
	Ⓓ ,D	3-2	910-1340	21-30	21-31
	Ⓓ ,D	2-1	400-690	9-16	9-16
Wide Open Throttle	Ⓓ ,D	1-2	1440-1850	32-42	33-42
	Ⓓ ,D	2-3	2500-2880	56-65	57-66
	Ⓓ ,D	3-2	2030-2360	46-53	47-54
	Ⓓ ,D	2-1	940-1540	21-35	22-35

Axle Ratio	Tire Size	Use Column No.
3.42:1	P215/75R14	1
	P225/75R14	2
	P205/75R15	2
	P225/70R15	2
	P205/75R15	2

MODELS E35P-7000-CA

Throttle	Range	Shift	OPS—R.P.M.	1	2
Closed Throttle (Minimum)	Ⓓ ,D	1-2	320-510	8-13	8-12
	Ⓓ ,D	2-3	650-810	17-21	16-19
	Ⓓ	3-4	1330-1700	34-43	32-41
	Ⓓ	4-3	1180-1550	30-40	28-37
	Ⓓ ,D	3-2	570-740	15-19	14-18
	Ⓓ ,D	2-1	220-450	6-11	5-11
	1	3-1 2-1	730-1150	19-29	18-28
Part Throttle (60 PSI)	Ⓓ ,D	1-2	660-1000	17-26	16-24
	Ⓓ ,D	2-3	1300-1700	33-43	31-41
	Ⓓ	3-4	1950-2380	50-61	47-57
	Ⓓ	4-3	1610-1960	41-50	39-47
	Ⓓ ,D	3-2	790-1260	20-32	19-30
	Ⓓ ,D	2-1	400-690	10-18	10-17
Wide Open Throttle	Ⓓ ,D	1-2	1370-1820	35-46	33-44
	Ⓓ ,D	2-3	2460-2850	63-73	59-69
	Ⓓ ,D	3-2	1980-2310	51-59	48-56
	Ⓓ ,D	2-1	880-1520	22-39	21-37

Axle Ratio	Tire Size	Use Column No.
3.08:1	P205/75R15	1
3.27:1	P205/75R15	2

MODELS E3VP-7000-AA

Throttle	Range	Shift	OPS—R.P.M.	1
Closed Throttle (Minimum)	Ⓓ ,D	1-2	320-510	8-12
	Ⓓ ,D	2-3	650-810	16-19
	Ⓓ	3-4	1510-1840	36-44
	Ⓓ	4-3	1370-1690	33-41
	Ⓓ ,D	3-2	570-740	14-18
	Ⓓ ,D	2-1	220-450	5-11
	1	3-1 2-1	730-1150	18-28
Part Throttle (60 PSI)	Ⓓ ,D	1-2	660-1000	16-24
	Ⓓ ,D	2-3	1300-1700	31-41
	Ⓓ	3-4	1920-2330	46-56
	Ⓓ	4-3	1690-2000	41-48
	Ⓓ ,D	3-2	790-1260	19-30
	Ⓓ ,D	2-1	400-690	10-17
Wide Open Throttle	Ⓓ ,D	1-2	1370-1820	33-44
	Ⓓ ,D	2-3	2460-2850	59-69
	Ⓓ ,D	3-2	1980-2310	48-56
	Ⓓ ,D	2-1	880-1520	21-37

Axle Ratio	Tire Size	Use Column No.
3.27:1	P205/75R15	1

MODELS E3TP-7000-NA

Throttle	Range	Shift	OPS—R.P.M.	1	2	3	4
Closed Throttle (Minimum)	Ⓓ ,D	1-2	260-500	7-13	7-13	7-14	7-13
	Ⓓ ,D	2-3	600-780	15-20	16-21	17-22	15-20
	Ⓓ	3-4	1310-1670	34-43	35-44	36-46	33-42
	Ⓓ	4-3	1160-1520	30-39	31-40	32-42	29-38
	Ⓓ ,D	3-2	520-700	13-18	14-19	14-19	13-18
	Ⓓ ,D	2-1	100-450	3-12	3-12	3-13	3-11
	1	3-1 2-1	730-1150	19-29	19-31	20-32	18-29
Part Throttle (60 PSI)	Ⓓ ,D	1-2	590-930	15-24	16-25	16-26	15-23
	Ⓓ ,D	2-3	1110-1550	28-40	29-41	31-43	28-39
	Ⓓ	3-4	1900-2320	49-59	50-62	53-64	48-58
	Ⓓ	4-3	1570-1910	40-49	42-51	44-53	39-48
	Ⓓ ,D	3-2	680-1030	17-26	18-27	19-29	17-26
	Ⓓ ,D	2-1	420-620	11-16	11-16	12-17	11-16
Wide Open Throttle	Ⓓ ,D	1-2	1080-1620	28-42	29-43	30-45	27-41
	Ⓓ ,D	2-3	2220-2590	57-66	59-69	62-72	56-65
	Ⓓ ,D	3-2	1680-2050	43-53	45-54	47-57	42-51
	Ⓓ ,D	2-1	750-1360	19-35	20-36	21-38	19-34

Axle Ratio	Tire Size	Use Column No.
3.00:1	P195/75R15SL	1
	P215/75R15SL	2
	P235/75R15XL	3
3.08:1	P195/75R15SL	4
	P215/75R15SL	1
	P235/75R15XL	3

Automatic Transmissions
FORD MOTOR CO.
AUTOMATIC OVERDRIVE TRANSMISSION (Cont.)

SHIFT SPEED SPECIFICATIONS (Cont.)

MODELS E3TP-7000-NA (Truck Models)

Throttle	Range	Shift	OPS—R.P.M.	1	2	3	4	5
Closed Throttle (Minimum)	Ⓓ ,D	1-2	260-500	6-11	6-12	7-13	6-12	6-12
	Ⓓ ,D	2-3	600-780	13-17	14-18	16-20	15-19	15-19
	Ⓓ	3-4	1310-1670	29-37	31-39	34-43	33-41	32-40
	Ⓓ	4-3	1160-1520	26-34	27-35	30-40	29-38	28-37
	Ⓓ ,D	3-2	520-700	12-16	12-16	14-18	13-17	13-17
	Ⓓ ,D	2-1	100-450	2-10	2-10	3-12	2-11	2-11
	1	3-1 2-1	730-1150	16-26	17-27	19-30	18-29	18-28
Part Throttle (60 PSI)	Ⓓ ,D	1-2	590-930	13-21	14-22	15-24	15-23	14-23
	Ⓓ ,D	2-3	1110-1550	25-35	26-36	29-40	28-38	27-38
	Ⓓ	3-4	1900-2320	42-52	44-54	49-60	47-58	46-56
	Ⓓ	4-3	1570-1910	35-43	37-45	41-50	39-47	38-46
	Ⓓ ,D	3-2	680-1030	15-23	16-24	18-27	17-26	16-25
	Ⓓ ,D	2-1	420-620	9-14	10-14	11-16	10-15	10-15
Wide Open Throttle	Ⓓ ,D	1-2	1200-1730	27-39	28-40	31-45	30-43	29-42
	Ⓓ ,D	2-3	2330-2680	52-60	54-60	61-70	58-67	56-65
	Ⓓ ,D	3-2	1770-2150	39-48	41-50	46-56	44-53	43-52
	Ⓓ ,D	2-1	800-1430	18-32	19-33	21-37	20-35	19-35

Axle Ratio	Tire Size	Use Column No.
3.50:1	P205/75R15SL	1
	P225/75R15SL	2
	P235/75R15XL	2
3.54:1	7.50R x 16D	3
	LT215/85R16D	4
	LT235/85R16D	3
	LT235/85R16E	3
	8.00 x 16.5D	2
	8.75 x 16.5D	5
	8.75 x 16.5E	5
	8.75R x 16.5E	5
3.55:1	P195/75R15SL	1
	P215/75R15SL	1
	P235/75R15XL	2

Axle Ratio	Tire Size	Use Column No.
3.55:1	7.50R x 16D	3
	LT215/85R16D	4
	LT235/85R16D	3
	LT235/85R16E	3
	8.00 x 16.5D	2
	8.75 x 16.5D	5
	8.75 x 16.5E	5
	8.75R x 16.5E	5
3.73:1	7.50R x 16D	4
	LT215/85R16D	2
	LT235/85R16D	4
	LT235/85R16E	4

FORD MOTOR CO.
AUTOMATIC OVERDRIVE TRANSMISSION (Cont.)

SHIFT SPEED SPECIFICATIONS (Cont.)

MODELS E3SP-7000-BA

Throttle	Range	Shift	OPS—R.P.M.	1	2
Closed Throttle (Minimum)	Ⓓ ,D	1-2	280-520	7-12	6-11
	Ⓓ ,D	2-3	620-820	15-20	13-17
	Ⓓ	3-4	1570-1940	37-46	33-41
	Ⓓ	4-3	1370-1740	33-42	29-37
	Ⓓ	3-2	530-750	13-18	11-16
	Ⓓ ,D	2-1	180-460	4-11	4-10
	1	3-1 2-1	790-1280	19-30	17-27
Part Throttle (60 PSI)	Ⓓ ,D	1-2	660-1120	16-27	14-24
	Ⓓ ,D	2-3	1240-1770	30-42	26-38
	Ⓓ	3-4	2000-2440	48-58	43-52
	Ⓓ	4-3	1720-2080	41-50	37-44
	Ⓓ ,D	3-2	740-1260	18-30	16-27
	Ⓓ ,D	2-1	470-750	11-18	10-16
Wide Open Throttle	Ⓓ ,D	1-2	1360-1960	32-47	29-42
	Ⓓ ,D	2-3	2580-3020	62-72	55-64
	Ⓓ ,D	3-2	2000-2450	48-58	43-52
	Ⓓ ,D	2-1	970-1670	23-40	21-36

Axle Ratio	Tire Size	Use Column No.
3.08:1	P185/75R14	1
	P195/75R14	1
	P205/70R14	1
	220/55R390	1
	205/60R390	1
	205/70HR14	1
3.45:1	P185/75R14	2
	P195/75R14	2
	P205/70R14	2
	220/55R390	2
	205/60R390	2
	205/70HR14	2

MODELS E3TP-7000-PA

Throttle	Range	Shift	OPS—R.P.M.	1	2	3	4
Closed Throttle (Minimum)	Ⓓ ,D	1-2	260-500	6-11	6-12	6-12	6-12
	Ⓓ ,D	2-3	600-780	13-17	14-18	14-19	15-19
	Ⓓ	3-4	1470-1790	33-40	34-42	35-43	36-43
	Ⓓ	4-3	1340-1650	30-37	31-38	32-39	32-40
	Ⓓ ,D	3-2	520-700	12-16	12-16	12-17	13-17
	Ⓓ ,D	2-1	100-450	2-10	2-10	2-11	2-11
	1	3-1 2-1	730-1150	16-26	17-27	17-27	18-28
Part Throttle (60 PSI)	Ⓓ ,D	1-2	590-930	13-21	14-22	14-22	14-23
	Ⓓ ,D	2-3	1110-1550	25-35	26-36	26-37	27-38
	Ⓓ	3-4	1830-2250	41-50	43-52	44-54	44-54
	Ⓓ	4-3	1620-1930	36-43	38-45	39-46	39-47
	Ⓓ ,D	3-2	680-1030	15-23	16-24	16-25	16-25
	Ⓓ ,D	2-1	420-620	9-14	10-14	10-15	10-15
Wide Open Throttle	Ⓓ ,D	1-2	1080-1620	24-36	25-38	26-39	26-39
	Ⓓ ,D	2-3	2220-2590	49-58	52-60	53-62	54-63
	Ⓓ ,D	3-2	1680-2050	37-46	39-48	40-49	41-50
	Ⓓ ,D	2-1	750-1360	17-30	17-32	18-32	18-33

Axle Ratio	Tire Size	Use Column No.
3.50:1	P205/75R15SL	1
	P225/75R15SL	2
	P235/75R15XL	3
3.54:1	8.00 x 16.5D	2
	8.75 x 16.5D	4
	8.75 x 16.5E	4
	8.75 x 16.5E	3
3.55:1	P195/75R15SL	1
	P215/75R15SL	1
	P235/75R15XL	2
	8.00 x 16.5D	2
3.55:1	8.75 x 16.5D	4
	8.75 x 16.5E	4
	8.75R x 16.5E	3

CONTROL PRESSURE TEST

NOTE: When testing line pressure on the Automatic Overdrive Transmission, two readings must be taken; one at idle position (zero TV) and the other at wide open, full throttle (full TV).

Line Pressure

1) With engine at normal operating temperature, connect a 0-300 psi pressure gauge to line pressure port tap on left side of transmission case just above control levers.

2) With throttle off fast idle cam, check line pressure in all ranges with engine at idle. Pressures should be approximately as shown in *Control Pressure Specifications Table.*

NOTE: T.V. linkage must be properly adjusted when performing line pressure test.

3) Next, apply parking and service brakes. Check line pressure in all ranges with throttle in wide open position. Pressures should be approximately as shown in *Control Pressure Specifications Table.*

CAUTION: Pressure test at wide open throttle position should be taken at Full Stall conditions. Also, this test must be made as quickly as possible to prevent overheating transmission. Run engine at a fast idle in Neutral for cooling between tests.

Throttle Valve Pressure

1) Connect a 0-100 psi pressure gauge to T.V. pressure tap at right side of the transmission case. *See Fig. 3.* Gauge hose must be long enough so that gauge can be read from under the hood.

Automatic Transmissions
FORD MOTOR CO.
AUTOMATIC OVERDRIVE TRANSMISSION (Cont.)

Fig. 3: Right Side of Transmission Case Showing T.V. Limit Pressure Tap

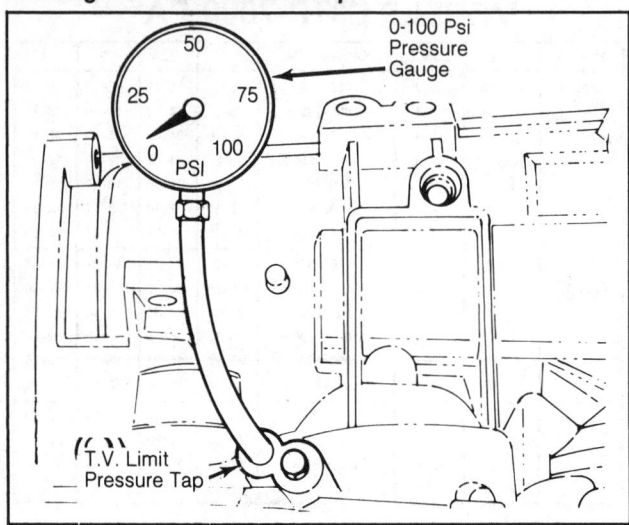

CONTROL PRESSURE SPECIFICATIONS [1]

Throttle Position	Line Pressure psi (kg/cm²)	T.V. Limit Pressure psi (kg/cm²
At Idle		
In "R"	75-90	0
	(5.3-6.3)	0
All Other Ranges	55-65	0
	(3.9-4.6)	
At W.O.T.		
In "R"	250-290	79-91
	(17.5-20.3)	(5.5-6.4)
All Other Ranges	180-215	79-91
	(12.6-15.1)	(5.5-6.4)

[1] — With governor pressure at zero.

NOTE: If pressure cannot be adjusted to specifications, it may be necessary to adjust control rod length at transmission. See Automatic Transmission Servicing article.

2) Make sure throttle lever is at idle stop position (fast idle cam off). Set parking brake firmly, then start engine and let idle in Neutral.

3) Using a 1/16" drill bit, placed between linkage lever adjustment screw and throttle lever, T.V. limit pressure should be 5 psi (.35 kg/cm²) or lower. If pressure is above 5 psi (.35 kg/cm²), throttle linkage is too long. Back off linkage lever adjusting screw 1/2 turn at a time until pressure drops below 5 psi (.35 kg/cm²).

4) Remove 1/16" drill bit and replace it with a 5/16" drill bit. Now, with engine idling in Neutral, T.V. limit pressure must be at least 22 psi (1.5 kg/cm²). If not, turn adjusting screw inward 1/2 turn at a time until pressure is within specifications.

CONTROL PRESSURE TEST RESULTS
Low in "P"
Faulty valve body or low-reverse servo.
Low in "R"
Faulty reverse clutch or low-reverse servo.
Low in "N"
Faulty valve body.
Low in "O/D"
Check for faulty forward clutch, overdrive servo, or for faulty valve body.
Low in "3"
Faulty forward clutch or intermediate servo.
Low in "1"
Faulty forward clutch or low-reverse servo.

CLUTCH AND BAND APPLICATION CHART (ELEMENTS IN USE)

Selector Lever Position	Intermed. Clutch	Intermed. One-Way Clutch	Overdrive Band	Reverse Clutch	Forward Clutch	Planetary One-Way Clutch	Low-Reverse Band	Direct Clutch
O/D — OVERDRIVE								
First Gear					X	X		
Second Gear	X	X			X			
Third Gear	X				X			X
Fourth Gear	X		X					X
3 — OVERDRIVE LOCKOUT								
First Gear					X	X		
Second Gear	X	X			X			
Third Gear	X				X			X
1 — LOW								
First Gear					X	X	X	
Second Gear	X	X	X		X			
R — REVERSE				X			X	
P — PARK							X	

NEUTRAL — All clutches and bands released and/or ineffective.

FORD MOTOR CO.
AUTOMATIC OVERDRIVE TRANSMISSION (Cont.)

Fig. 4: Automatic Overdrive Transmission Hydraulic Circuits Diagram

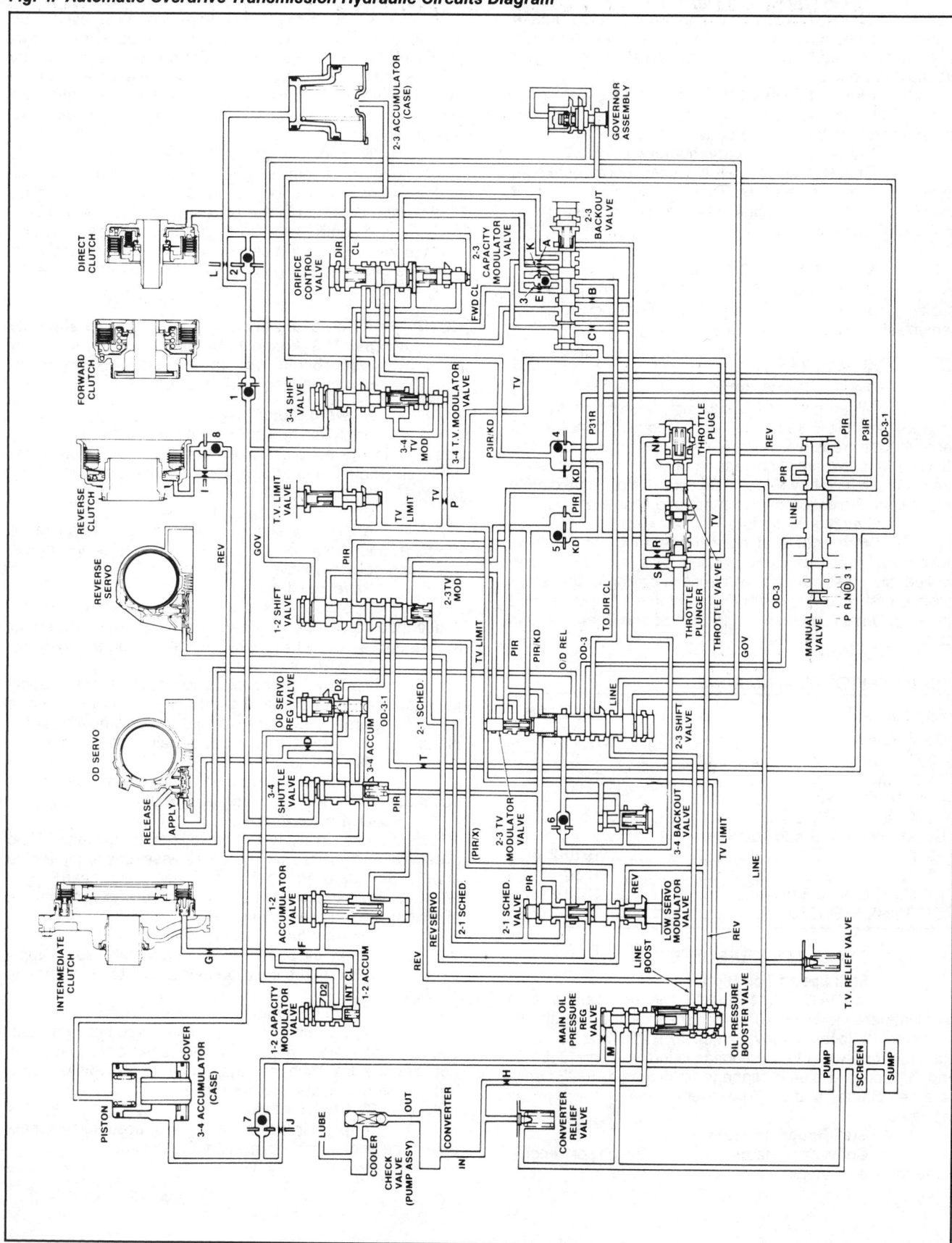

FORD MOTOR CO.
AUTOMATIC OVERDRIVE TRANSMISSION (Cont.)

Low at Idle in All Ranges
Check for low fluid level, restricted intake screen or filter, loose valve body bolts, pump leakage, case leakage, faulty valve body, excessively low engine idle, fluid too hot.

High at Idle in All Ranges
Check throttle valve linkage adjustment and condition and for faulty valve body.

Pressure Okay at Idle but Low at W.O.T.
Check for internal leakage, pump leakage, restricted intake screen of filter, damaged or out of adjustment T.V. valve linkage. Also check for sticking T.V. or T.V. limit valve in valve body.

GOVERNOR CHECK
Accelerate vehicle to 25 MPH and back off throttle completely. If governor is operating properly, transmission will shift to 3rd gear.

STALL TEST
Testing Precautions
When performing stall test, do not hold throttle open longer than 5 seconds. Allow a cooling period of 15 seconds with transmission in Neutral and engine speed at 1000 RPM between each test. If engine speed exceeds maximum limits shown, release accelerator immediately as this is an indication of clutch or band slippage.

Testing Procedure
With engine at normal operating temperature, tachometer installed, and parking and service brakes applied, stall test transmission in each driving range at full throttle, and note maximum RPM obtained. Engine speed should be within limits shown in Stall Speed Specifications table.

STALL SPEED SPECIFICATIONS

Application	Stall RPM
Continental	
3.8L	1952-2247
5.0L	1913-2222
Cougar, Thunderbird	
LTD, Marquis 3.8L	1651-1914
Crown Victoria, Grand Marquis	
5.0L	1910-2250
5.8L	1536-1815
Linclon, Mark VII 5.0L	1888-2187
E100/350, F100/250 5.0L	1924-2169

STALL TEST RESULTS
Stall Speed Too High
In "O/D", "3", "1" and "R"; general transmission problems are indicated and a control pressure test should be made to locate faulty unit(s). In "O/D" and "3" only; planetary one-way clutch slippage is indicated. In "O/D" "3" and "1"; forward clutch slippage is indicated. In "R" only; reverse clutch and/or low-reverse band slippage is indicated.

Stall Speed Too Low
Converter stator one-way clutch or engine performance is faulty.

AIR PRESSURE TESTS
A "No Drive" condition can exist even with correct transmission fluid pressure, because of inoperative clutches or bands. Erratic shifts could be caused by a stuck governor valve. The inoperative units can be located through a series of checks by substituting air pressure for fluid pressure to determine location of malfunction.

To make air pressure checks, loosen oil pan bolts and allow transmission fluid to drain, then remove oil pan and control valve body assembly. Install adapter plate (T82L-7006-A), with adapter plate attaching screws (T82P-7006-C), and control valve body gasket, in place of control valve body. With a rubber tipped air nozzle, apply air pressure at points noted in *Fig. 5* and check unit operation as follows:

NOTE: **Air pressure should be regulated to about 25 psi (1.8 kg/cm²). Compressed air used for test should be filtered and dry to avoid contaminating transmission fluid.**

Forward Clutch
Apply air pressure to the forward clutch apply passage in the adapter plate. A dull thud can be heard when clutch piston is applied, or movement can be felt by placing fingertips on input shell.

Governor
Apply air pressure to line pressure-to-governor passage and listen for sharp clicking or whistling noise, indicating governor valve movement.

Reverse Clutch
Apply air pressure to reverse clutch passage. A dull thud can be heard when clutch piston is applied, or movement can be felt by placing fingertips on clutch drum.

Low-Reverse Servo
Apply air pressure to low-reverse servo apply passage. Low-reverse band should tighten around drum if servo is operating properly. When air is removed, servo piston should be felt to move back against servo cover.

Direct Clutch
Apply air pressure to direct clutch passage. A dull thud can be heard if clutch is operating properly.

Overdrive Servo
First pressurize servo apply passage. Hold pressure and pressurize servo release passage. Piston should be heard to apply band and also heard as it releases against cover when air pressure is removed. A hissing noise indicates a leak.

Intermediate Clutch
Apply air pressure to intermediate clutch apply passage. A dull thud should be heard if clutch is operating properly.

2-3 Accumulator
Apply air pressure to 2-3 accumulator passage. Accumulator piston should unseat and can be detected by inserting a metal rod into 2-3 piston hole. When piston unseats, rod will move.

3-4 Accumulator
Apply air pressure to 2-3 accumulator passage. The accumulator piston should unseat.

FORD MOTOR CO.
AUTOMATIC OVERDRIVE TRANSMISSION (Cont.)

Fig. 5: Air Pressure Test Apply Ports on Adapter Plate

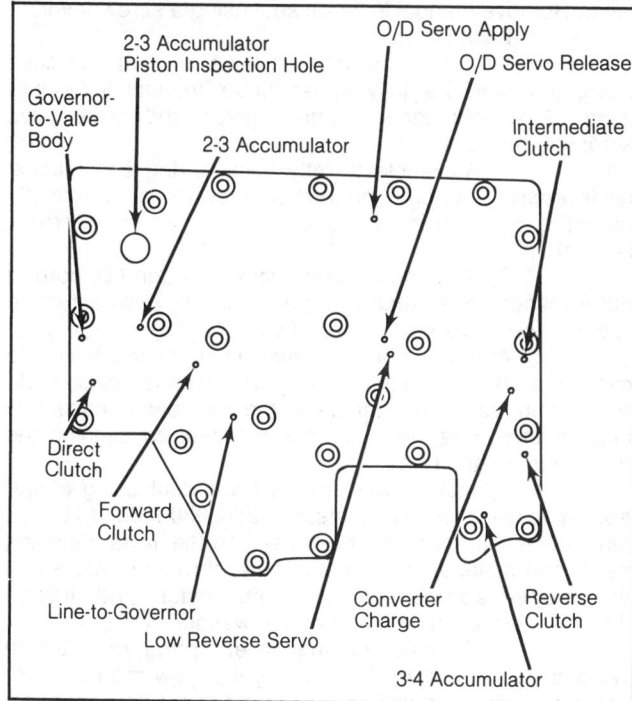

SERVICE IN VEHICLE

VALVE BODY ASSEMBLY

Removal

1) Raise vehicle on a hoist. Loosen oil pan retaining bolts and allow transmission fluid to drain. Remove oil pan and gasket.

2) Remove filter-to-valve body retaining bolts and remove filter, grommet and gasket. Remove detent spring retaining bolt and spring. Remove retaining bolts and remove valve body from transmission.

Installation

1) Using guide pins, position valve body (with new gasket) in case, making sure that inner manual lever and inner T.V. lever are engaged. Install and tighten valve body retaining bolts.

2) Install and tighten detent spring and retaining bolts. Remove guide pins and install remaining 2 valve body retaining bolts. Load throttle lever torsion spring against separator plate. To complete installation, reverse removal procedure using new gaskets on filter and oil pan.

OVERDRIVE SERVO ASSEMBLY

Removal

1) Remove valve body as previously described. Depress overdrive servo piston cover and remove retaining snap ring.

2) Apply air pressure to servo piston release passage to remove piston, cover, and spring. Separate piston from cover and remove rubber seals from piston and cover.

Installation

1) Install new seals on piston and cover. Lubricate piston seals with automatic transmission fluid or petroleum jelly, then install piston into cover.

2) Lubricate cover seals and overdrive servo pocket in transmission case. Assemble spring to piston. Install assembly into case pocket.

3) Depress servo cover and install retaining snap ring. To complete installation, reverse removal procedures.

LOW-REVERSE SERVO ASSEMBLY

Removal

1) Remove valve body assembly as previously described. Depress low-reverse servo piston cover and remove retaining snap ring and cover.

2) Remove piston and spring from case by applying compressed air to low-reverse servo release passage in case.

CAUTION: Low-reverse servo piston may spring free from case when cover is removed.

Installation

To install, reverse removal procedure and note the following: Make sure that servo piston is installed with the same length rod as was removed.

3-4 ACCUMULATOR PISTON

Removal

1) Remove valve body assembly as previously described. Depress 3-4 accumulator cover and remove retaining snap ring.

2) Slowly release pressure on cover and remove cover, piston, and (if equipped) return spring. Remove seals from piston and cover.

NOTE: If necessary, 3-4 accumulator piston can be removed by applying compressed air to hydraulic apply passage.

Installation

To install, reverse removal procedures and note the following: Lubricate rubber seals and accumulator pocket in case prior to accumulator installation. Make sure that accumulator cover is seated snug against retaining snap ring.

2-3 ACCUMULATOR PISTON

Removal

Remove valve body assembly as previously described. Depress 2-3 accumulator piston cover. Remove retaining snap ring, cover, and spring. Remove accumulator piston and seals from piston.

Installation

To install, reverse removal procedure and note the following: Lubricate piston seals and piston pocket in case prior to installation.

EXTENSION HOUSING BUSHING & REAR OIL SEAL

Removal

1) Raise vehicle on a hoist and disconnect propeller shaft from transmission. Remove oil seal using puller (T74P-77248-A).

2) Remove bushing using puller (T77L-7697-A), using care not to damage output shaft splines.

Installation

Install new bushing into extension housing using driver (T80L-77034-A). Install new seal into housing

using driver (T61L-7657-A). Coat inside diameter of rubber portion of seal with a lubricant. Install propeller shaft.

EXTENSION HOUSING
Removal
1) Raise vehicle on a hoist and disconnect parking brake cable from equalizer, (if so equipped). Remove propeller shaft and disconnect speedometer cable from extension housing.

2) Remove engine rear support-to-extension housing retaining bolts.

3) Raise transmission just enough to remove weight from rear support. Remove rear support-to-crossmember retaining bolt and remove rear support.

4) Lower transmission and remove extension housing retaining bolts. Slide housing off output shaft and allow fluid to drain. Remove and discard extension housing-to-case gasket.

Installation
Clean mating surface on transmission and extension housing. Position new gasket on transmission. Slide extension housing into place, install and tighten retaining bolts. To complete installation, reverse removal procedures.

GOVERNOR ASSEMBLY
Removal
1) Remove extension housing as previously described. Remove governor-to-output shaft retaining snap ring. Using a mallet, tap governor assembly off output shaft.

2) Remove governor drive ball. Remove governor-to-counterweight retaining screws and lift governor from counterweight.

Installation
1) Lubricate governor parts with clean transmission fluid and make sure valve moves freely in bore. Position governor body on counterweight with cover facing toward front of vehicle. Install and tighten 2 retaining screws.

2) Position governor drive ball into pocket on output shaft. Align keyway in counter weight with drive ball and drive assembly onto output shaft with mallet. Install governor-to-output shaft retaining snap ring. To complete installation, reverse removal procedures.

INTERNAL & EXTERNAL SHIFT LINKAGE
Removal
1) Raise vehicle on a hoist. Apply penetrating oil to outer throttle lever retaining nut to prevent breaking inner throttle lever.

2) Loosen oil pan retaining bolts and allow fluid to drain. Remove oil pan. Disconnect shift rod and throttle valve linkage at transmission.

3) Disconnect inner throttle lever spring. Remove detent spring. Hold outer throttle lever stationary and remove throttle lever retaining nut and lock washer. Using a small screwdriver, remove outer throttle lever seal.

4) Grasp manual lever roll pin with vise grip pliers and remove pin. Hold manual lever firmly in position and remove manual lever retaining nut using a box wrench. Remove outer manual lever from case.

5) Remove inner throttle lever and spring. Remove inner manual lever and park pawl actuating rod.

Disconnect park pawl actuating rod from inner manual lever. Remove manual lever oil seal using a screwdriver.

Installation
1) Install new manual lever oil seal into case using a driver. Partially install outer manual lever into case. Assemble inner manual lever and park pawl actuating rod together.

2) Assemble throttle lever spring and manual lever retaining nut onto inner throttle lever shaft. Assemble actuating rod and inner manual lever onto inner throttle lever shaft.

3) Slide inner throttle lever through I.D. bore of outer manual lever shaft and position park pawl actuating rod into rod guide cup in rear of case.

4) Push outer manual lever all the way into case and start retaining nut on outer manual lever shaft. Reposition outer manual lever (up or down). Assemble inner manual lever to outer manual lever by aligning the flats, then tighten retaining nut.

5) Install new throttle lever seal using a 3/8" socket to seat the seal. Install seal .030-.060" (.76-1.52 mm) below surface. Install outer throttle lever (aligning flats), and make sure inner and outer throttle levers are in the proper approximate position. Install and tighten throttle lever retaining nut and lock washer.

6) Connect manual lever spring to notch in valve body separator plate. Drive in a new manual lever roll pin. Install detent spring and retaining bolt. Connect transmission manual lever to manual shift linkage making sure that manual lever is in same position as adjustment is necessary.

7) Connect transmission throttle linkage to throttle lever. Install oil pan using a new gasket. Lower vehicle and fill transmission to correct fluid level. Adjust linkage as necessary. *See Automatic Transmission Servicing article for linkage adjustment.*

REMOVAL & INSTALLATION
See the appropriate article in AUTOMATIC TRANSMISSION REMOVAL Section.

TORQUE CONVERTER

LEAKAGE CHECK
See procedures given in Ford C-6 article.

FLUSHING CONVERTER
See procedures given in Ford C-6 article.

TURBINE & STATOR END PLAY CHECK
See procedures given in Ford C-6 article.

STATOR ONE-WAY CHECK
See procedures given in Ford C-6 article.

STATOR INTERFERENCE CHECKS
See procedures given in Ford C-6 article.

TRANSMISSION DISASSEMBLY
1) Mount transmission in a holding fixture. Remove torque converter. Remove retaining bolts and lift

FORD MOTOR CO.
AUTOMATIC OVERDRIVE TRANSMISSION (Cont.)

Fig. 6 Exploded View of Automatic Overdrive Transmission

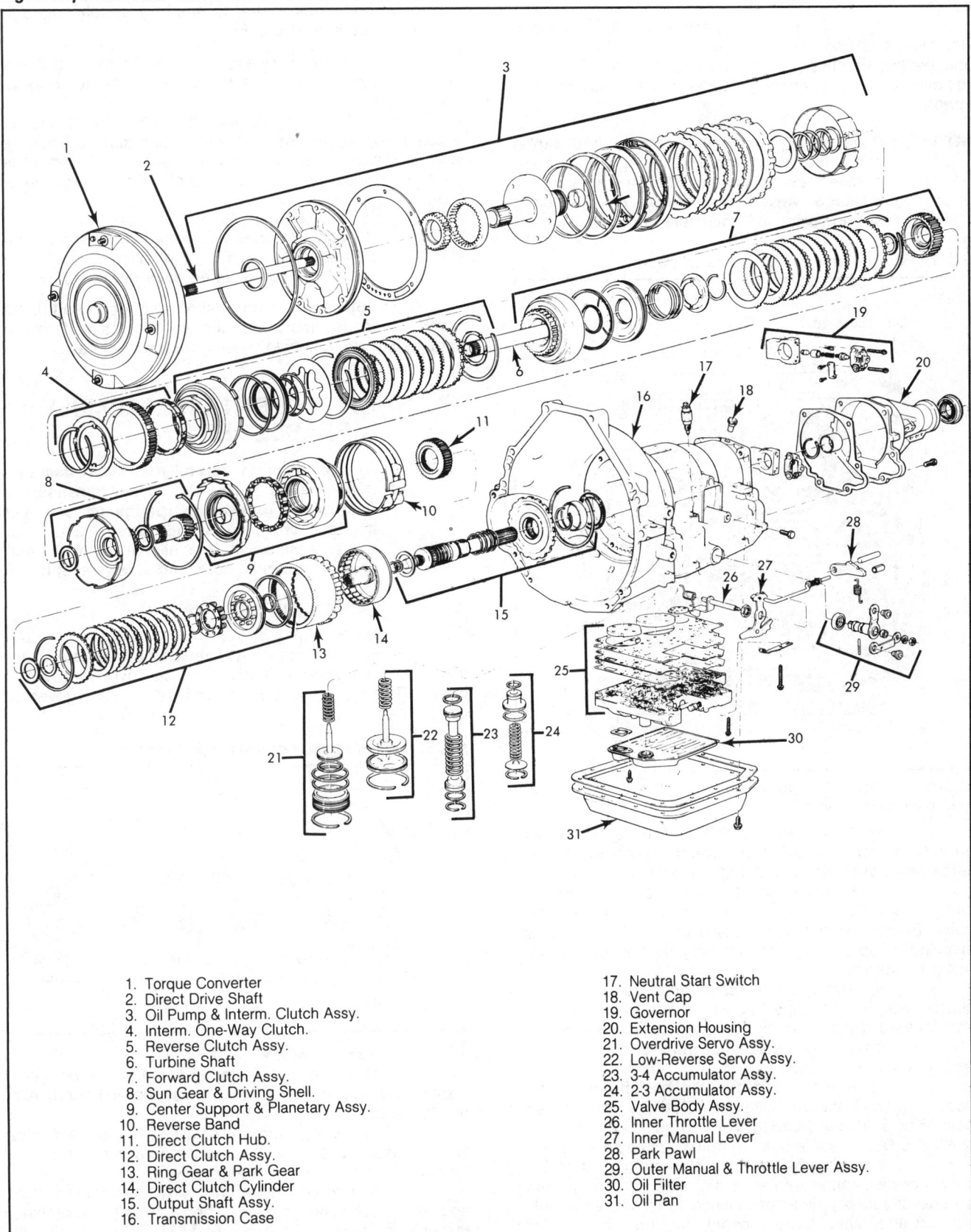

1. Torque Converter
2. Direct Drive Shaft
3. Oil Pump & Interm. Clutch Assy.
4. Interm. One-Way Clutch.
5. Reverse Clutch Assy.
6. Turbine Shaft
7. Forward Clutch Assy.
8. Sun Gear & Driving Shell.
9. Center Support & Planetary Assy.
10. Reverse Band
11. Direct Clutch Hub.
12. Direct Clutch Assy.
13. Ring Gear & Park Gear
14. Direct Clutch Cylinder
15. Output Shaft Assy.
16. Transmission Case

17. Neutral Start Switch
18. Vent Cap
19. Governor
20. Extension Housing
21. Overdrive Servo Assy.
22. Low-Reverse Servo Assy.
23. 3-4 Accumulator Assy.
24. 2-3 Accumulator Assy.
25. Valve Body Assy.
26. Inner Throttle Lever
27. Inner Manual Lever
28. Park Pawl
29. Outer Manual & Throttle Lever Assy.
30. Oil Filter
31. Oil Pan

Automatic Transmissions
FORD MOTOR CO.
AUTOMATIC OVERDRIVE TRANSMISSION (Cont.)

off oil pan and gasket. Remove oil filter, grommet, and gasket.

   2) Remove detent spring and roller assembly. Remove valve body retaining bolts and lift off valve body and gasket. Push down on 3-4 accumulator cover and remove retaining snap ring. Remove cover, piston, and spring.

NOTE: If necessary, accumulator cover and piston can also be removed by applying compressed air to accumulator hydraulic apply passage. Also, some models do not use a spring on the 3-4 accumulator piston.

Fig. 7: Bottom View of Transmission Case

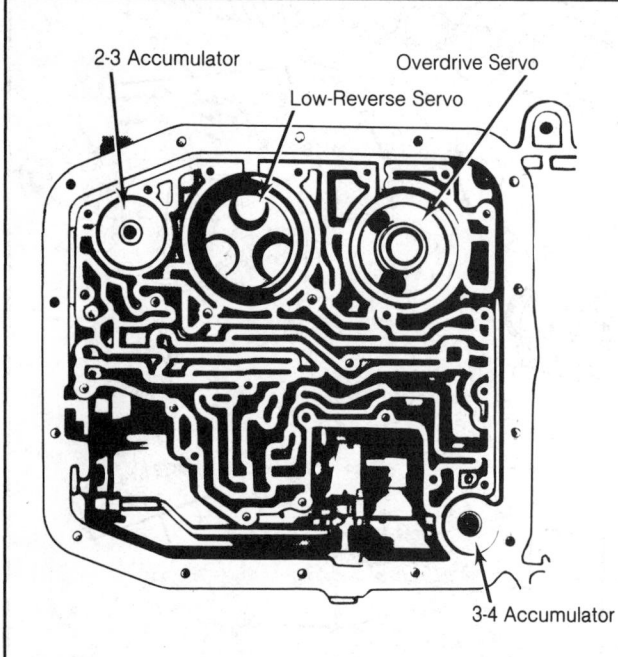

Illustration shows 2-3 and 3-4 accumulators and low-reverse and overdrive servos.

   3) Following the 3-4 accumulator removal procedure, remove 2-3 accumulator assembly, low-reverse servo assembly and overdrive servo assembly.

   4) Remove direct drive shaft by pulling it straight out from case. Remove pump body retaining bolts. Remove pump from case using 2 slide hammers installed in opposite pump retaining bolt holes. Remove pump-to-case gasket.

   5) Grasp turbine shaft and pull intermediate clutch pack, intermediate one-way clutch, reverse clutch, and forward clutch from transmission case as an assembly. Disconnect overdrive band from anchor pin and remove band from case.

   6) Remove forward clutch hub and No. 3 needle bearing as an assembly. Remove forward sun gear, No. 5 needle bearing, reverse sun gear and drive shell, and No. 4 needle bearing from case as an assembly.

   7) Note position of center support snap ring tangs for installation reference. Remove snap ring. Using a screwdriver, pry anti-clunk spring from between center support and case. Remove center support and planetary carrier from case as an assembly.

NOTE: Prior to removal, note installation position of anti-clunk spring to ensure it is reinstalled in the same position.

   8) Remove reverse band from case. If direct clutch hub did not come out with planetary carrier, remove it from direct clutch.

   9) Remove retaining bolts and slide extension housing from transmission. Remove and discard housing-to-case gasket. Remove retaining snap ring and slide governor assembly off output shaft. Remove governor drive ball from output shaft.

NOTE: If transmission is positioned with output shaft pointing up, do not allow shaft assembly to fall through case when governor is removed.

   10) Remove output shaft, ring gear, and direct clutch as an assembly, through front of case. Remove output shaft No. 9 needle bearing from rear of case.

COMPONENT DISASSEMBLY & REASSEMBLY

NOTE: Handle all parts carefully to avoid damage. Lubricate all parts with clean transmission fluid before reassembly (petroleum jelly may be used on gaskets and thrust washers for easier assembly). Use all new gaskets and seals. Tighten all bolts and screws evenly.

GOVERNOR ASSEMBLY
Disassembly
   Remove retaining screws and separate counterweight from governor body. Remove cover screws and cover. Remove plug, sleeve, and valve from governor body.

Fig. 8: Exploded View of Governor Assembly

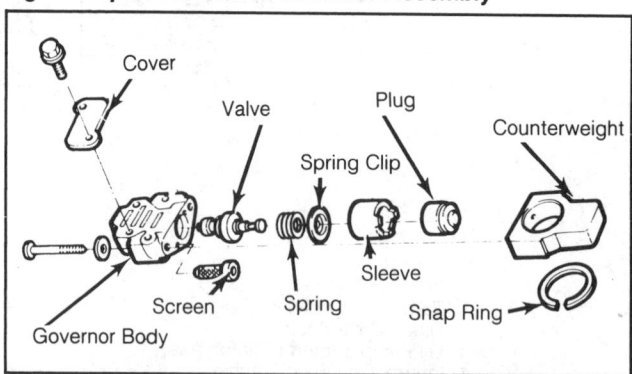

Reassembly
   1) If removed, install clip and spring on valve. Install valve into governor body. Install sleeve in body with points outward.

   2) Install plug in sleeve with knurled face inward. Install cover. Install screen in body with steel band forward and tip of screen facing outward.

   3) Position governor body on counterweight and install retaining screws. When correctly assembled, the finished face of governor body should be flush with face of counterweight.

FORD MOTOR CO.
AUTOMATIC OVERDRIVE TRANSMISSION (Cont.)

INTERMEDIATE ONE-WAY CLUTCH
Disassembly
Remove clutch retaining ring and lift off clutch retaining plate. Remove clutch outer race by lifting on race while turning counterclockwise. Carefully lift one-way clutch from inner race.

Fig. 9: Intermediate One-Way Clutch Assembly

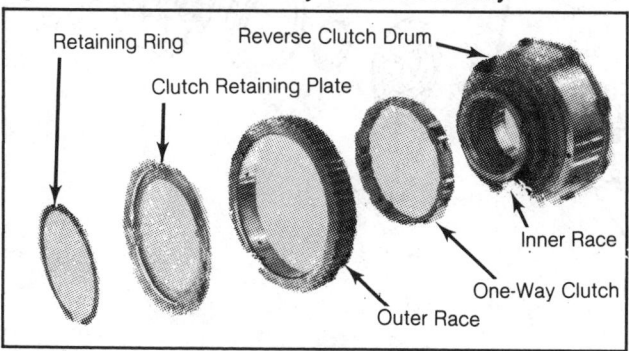

NOTE: If a roller is damaged or lost, entire one-way clutch assembly must be replaced.

Reassembly
Reverse disassembly and make sure outer race is installed over roller clutch with chamfer side facing reverse clutch drum.

OUTPUT SHAFT ASSEMBLY
Disassembly
1) Remove retaining ring and separate output shaft and hub assembly from ring gear. Remove direct clutch from ring gear and No. 8 needle bearing from rear of direct clutch.

2) Remove 4 output shaft seal rings and hub-to-shaft retaining ring. Separate hub from output shaft. Remove the 2 direct clutch seal rings from end of output shaft.

Reassembly
Reverse disassembly procedures.

Fig. 10: Exploded View of Output Shaft Assembly

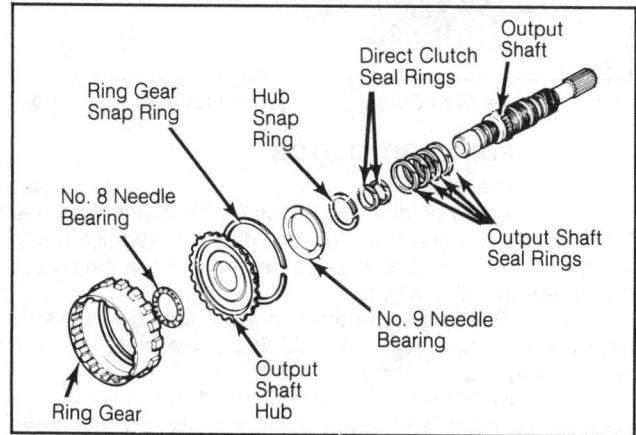

MANUAL & THROTTLE LINKAGE
Disassembly
1) Hold outer throttle lever stationary and remove retaining nut, lock washer, and throttle lever.

Using a small screwdriver, remove oil seal from outer manual lever counterbore.

NOTE: Failure to hold outer throttle lever stationary when removing retaining nut will allow inner throttle lever to rotate against valve body surface, which could result in damage to surface.

2) Using a pair of diagonal cutters, remove manual shaft retaining pin from case. Hold inner manual lever stationary and remove retaining nut. Remove throttle lever. Remove inner throttle lever and torsion spring.

3) Remove inner manual lever and parking pawl actuating rod as an assembly. Separate rod from lever if necessary. Remove manual lever shaft seal from case using a seal puller.

Reassembly
Reverse disassembly procedures. Install new manual lever seal using seal installer (T74P-77498-A). Before installing outer throttle lever, install new seal in outer manual lever using a 13 mm socket. Install seal with identification number facing outward.

DIRECT CLUTCH ASSEMBLY
Disassembly
1) Remove No. 7 direct clutch hub inner needle bearing and bearing support. Using a screwdriver, remove clutch pack selective retaining snap ring and lift out clutch pack.

2) Using a compressor tool, compress piston return springs and remove retaining snap ring. Remove tool and lift spring retainer assembly and piston from clutch drum. Note position and direction of lip seals, remove seals from drum and piston.

NOTE: If necessary, piston can be removed from drum by applying compressed air to lubrication hole in clutch drum.

Fig. 11: Bottom View of Transmission Case

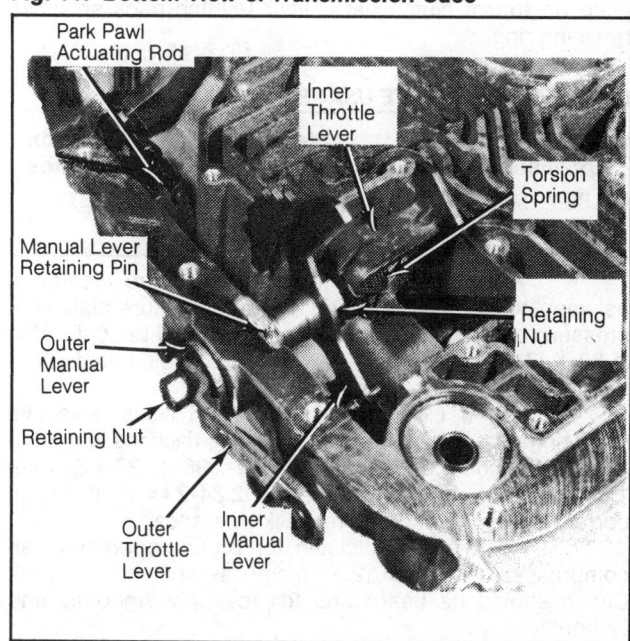

Illustration shows manual and throttle linkage locations.

Fig. 12: *Exploded View of Direct Clutch Assembly*

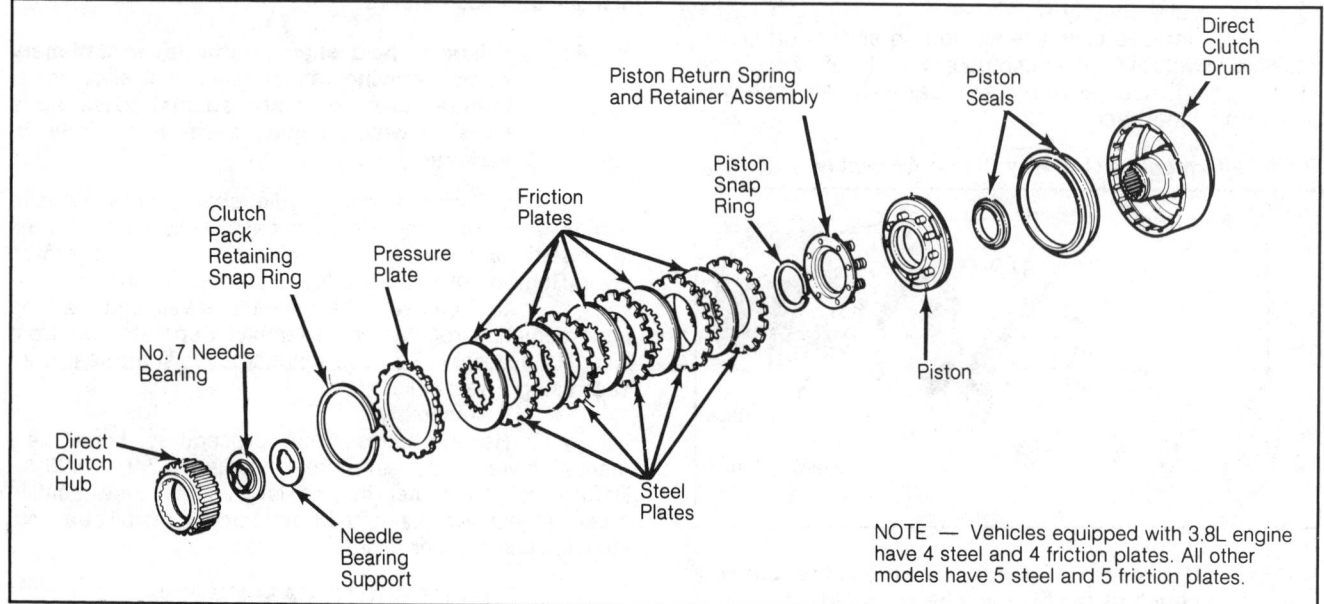

NOTE — Vehicles equipped with 3.8L engine have 4 steel and 4 friction plates. All other models have 5 steel and 5 friction plates.

Reassembly

1) Using a seal protector (T80L-77234-A), install inner seal on clutch drum hub with sealing lip facing down into drum. Install outer piston seal on piston with lip pointing away from spring posts.

NOTE: **Lubricate seals and seal protector with petroleum jelly prior to installation.**

2) Coat piston seals, clutch drum sealing area, and piston inner seal area with petroleum jelly. Install piston into clutch drum using seal protector (T80L-77254-A) to prevent damaging seals.

3) Position piston spring and retainer assembly in clutch drum. Compress assembly and install retaining snap ring. Install clutch pack into drum. Install pressure plate on top of clutch pack. Install clutch pack selective retaining ring.

DIRECT CLUTCH PLATE USAGE CHART

Application	Steel Plates	Friction Plates
3.8L	4	4
All Others	5	5

4) Using a feeler gauge, measure clearance between clutch pack retaining ring and pressure plate with pressure plate held down. Clearance should be .040-.058" (1.02-1.47 mm) if equipped with 3.8L engine and .050-.067" (1.27-1.70 mm) for all others.

5) If clearance is not within limits, selective snap rings are available in the following thicknesses: .050-.054", .064-.068", .078-.082" and .092-.096" (1.27-1.37 mm, 1.63-1.73 mm, 1.98-2.08 mm, and 2.34-2.44 mm). Install correct size snap ring and recheck clearance.

6) To check clutch for proper operation use compressed air 30 psi (2.1 kg/cm²) as shown in *Fig. 13*. Clutch should be heard and felt to apply smoothly and without leakage.

Fig. 13: *Using Compressed Air to Check Direct Clutch Operation*

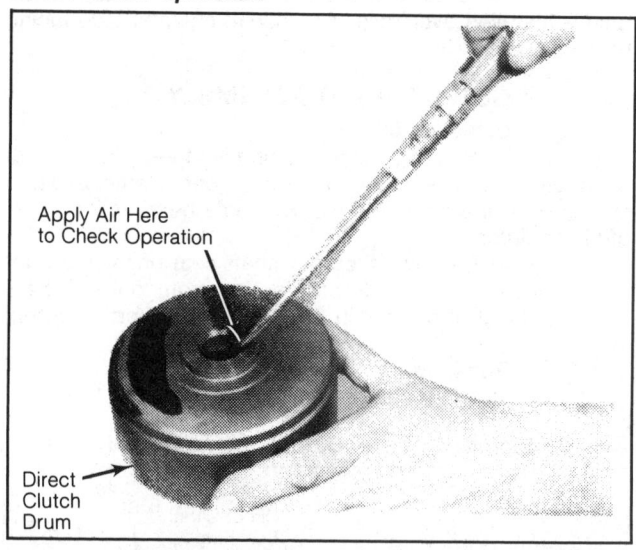

Apply no more than 30 psi (2.1 kg/cm²) to check operation.

FORWARD CLUTCH
Disassembly

1) If not already removed, lift clutch hub and No. 3 needle bearing from forward clutch assembly. Using a screwdriver, pry clutch pack retaining snap ring from drum. Remove clutch pack.

2) Using a compressor tool, compress piston return spring and remove retaining snap ring. Lift out retainer and return spring.

3) Remove clutch piston from drum. Note position of inner and outer piston seals, then remove seals.

Reassembly

1) Lubricate and install inner and outer seals on piston with seal lips facing into clutch drum. Lubricate

FORD MOTOR CO.
AUTOMATIC OVERDRIVE TRANSMISSION (Cont.)

Fig. 14: Exploded View of Forward Clutch Assembly

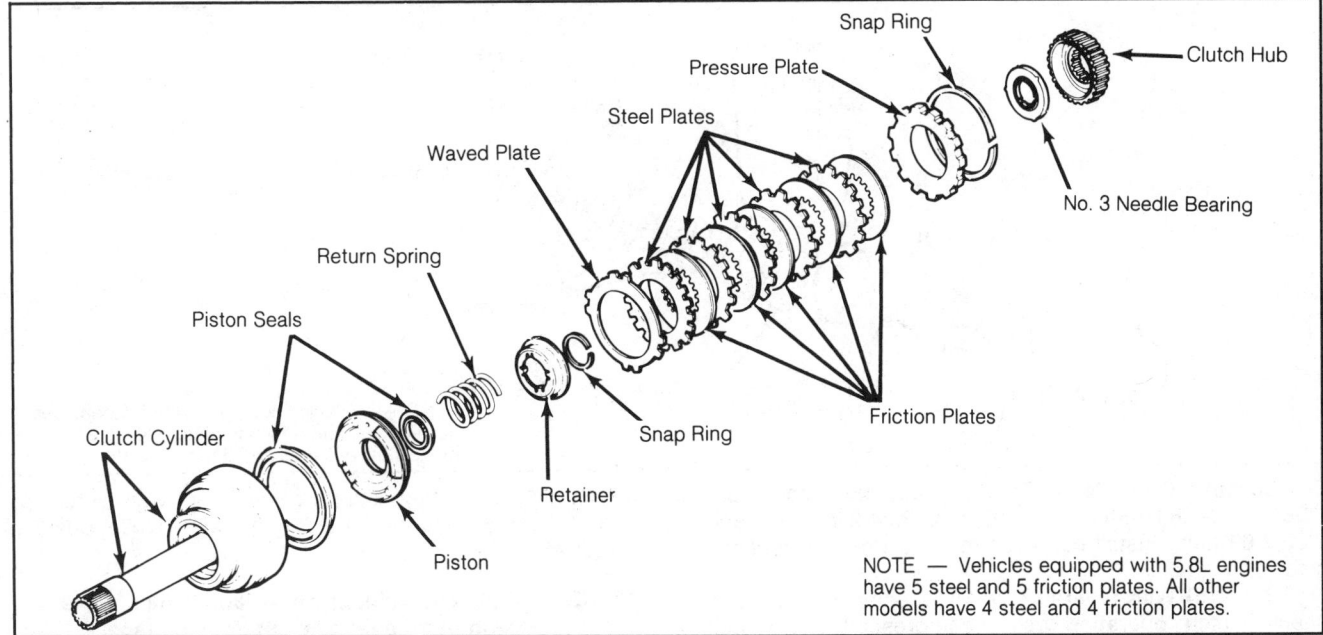

NOTE — Vehicles equipped with 5.8L engines have 5 steel and 5 friction plates. All other models have 4 steel and 4 friction plates.

piston seals and drum sealing area with petroleum jelly. Install piston into drum using a seal protector (T80L-77140-A) to prevent damaging seals.

2) Position return spring and retainer on piston. Compress return spring and install retaining snap ring. Install clutch pack into clutch drum starting with waved plate. Install clutch pack retaining snap ring.

3) Using a feeler gauge, measure clearance between retaining snap ring and pressure plate with pressure plate held downward. Clearance should be .050-.089" (1.27-2.26 mm) if equipped with 5.8L engine, and .040-.071" (1.02-1.80 mm) for all others.

FORWARD CLUTCH PLATE USAGE CHART

Application	Steel Plates	Friction Plates
5.8L Engine	5 [1]	5
All Others	4 [1]	4

[1] — Plus 1 waved plate installed next to piston.

4) If forward clutch clearance is not within limits, selective snap rings are available in the following thicknesses: .060-.064", .074-.078", .088-.092" and .102-.106" (1.53-1.63 mm, 1.88-1.98 mm, 2.24-2.34 mm, and 2.59-2.69 mm). Install correct size snap ring and recheck clearance.

5) With reassembly completed, use compressed air and check forward clutch operation. Clutch should be heard and felt to apply smoothly and without leakage.

REVERSE CLUTCH
Disassembly
1) Remove No. 2 thrust washer. Using a screwdriver, pry clutch pack retaining snap ring from clutch drum. Lift out clutch pack.

2) Compress return spring and remove waved snap ring. Remove return spring and thrust ring. Remove piston from drum. Remove seals from piston.

NOTE: **It may be necessary to apply compressed air to clutch drum lubrication hole to remove piston. Block remaining hole with finger.**

Reassembly
1) Prior to reassembly, make sure that check ball in inner piston seal is free. Install new oil seal on piston. Coat seals and sealing surface in clutch drum with petroleum jelly. Install piston into clutch drum using inner and outer seal protectors (T80L-77403-B and A) to prevent damaging seals.

NOTE: **Seals used on reverse clutch piston are square cut, therefore direction of installation is not important.**

2) Install thrust ring and return spring. Compress return spring and install waved snap ring. Install apply plate into clutch drum with dished side facing piston. Install clutch pack and retaining snap ring.

REVERSE CLUTCH PLATE USAGE CHART

Engine Application	Steel Plates	Friction Plates
5.8L	3	4
All Others	2	3

3) Using a feeler gauge, measure clearance between clutch pack snap ring and pressure plate while pushing down on pressure plate. Clearance should be .040-.075" (1.02-1.91 mm) for 5.8L engine, and .030-.056" (.76-1.42 mm) for all other models.

4) If reverse clutch clearance is not within limits, selective snap rings are available in the following

Fig. 15: *Exploded View of Reverse Clutch Assembly*

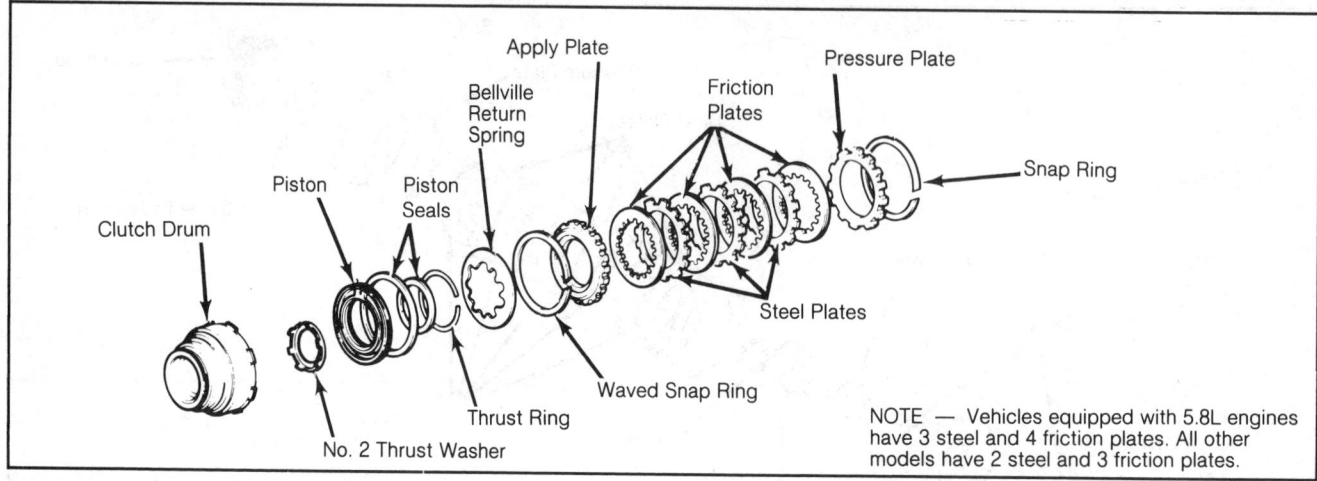

NOTE — Vehicles equipped with 5.8L engines have 3 steel and 4 friction plates. All other models have 2 steel and 3 friction plates.

thicknesses: .060-.064", .074-.078", .088-.092" and .102-.106" (1.52-1.63 mm, 1.88-1.98 mm, 2.24-2.34 mm, and 2.59-2.69 mm). Install correct size snap ring and recheck clearance.

5) With reverse clutch reassembly completed, check clutch operation using compressed air. Clutch should be heard and felt to apply smoothly and without leakage.

CENTER SUPPORT & PLANETARY ONE-WAY CLUTCH
Disassembly
Remove center support from planetary carrier by lifting up on center support while rotating it counterclockwise. Carefully remove planetary one-way clutch from planetary assembly.

NOTE: If a roller from planetary one-way clutch is lost or damaged, entire one-way clutch assembly must be replaced.

Fig. 16: *Center Support and Planetary Assembly*

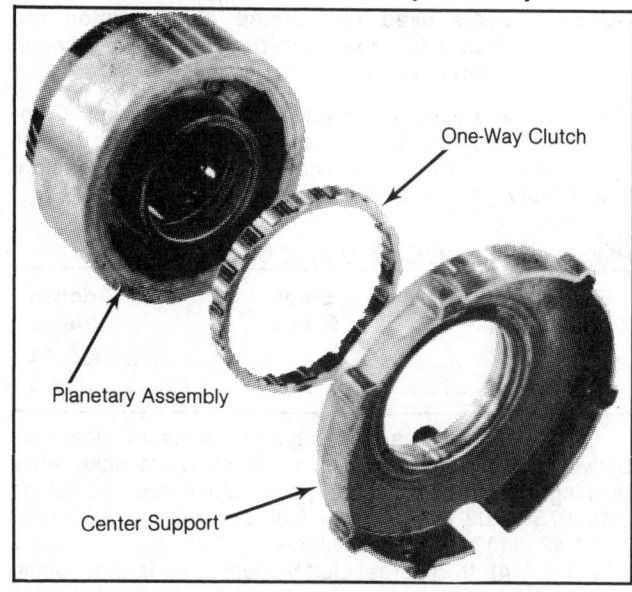

Reassembly
If necessary, assemble one-way clutch as shown in *Fig. 17.* Install one-way clutch in planetary

carrier. Install center support into one-way clutch by rotating center support counterclockwise while pushing rod down.

NOTE: Lubricate clutch races and clutch assembly with petroleum jelly to retain in place.

Fig. 17: *Assembling Planetary One-Way Clutch*

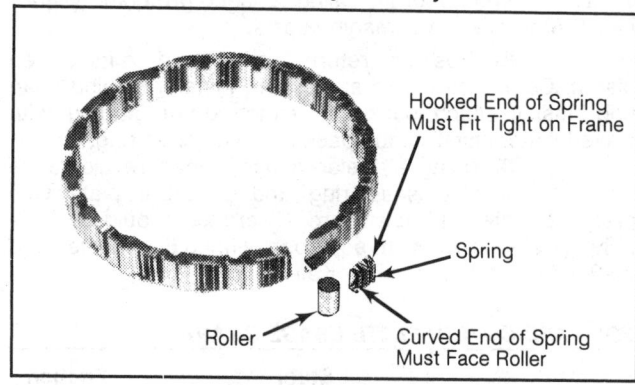

SUN GEAR & DRIVING SHELL
Disassembly
Remove No. 4 needle bearing from driving shell. Remove forward sun gear and No. 5 needle bearing from shell. Remove needle bearing from forward sun gear.
Reassembly
Sun gear and driving shell will be reassembled as part of Transmission Reassembly.

Fig. 18: *Exploded View of Sun Gear and Driving Shell*

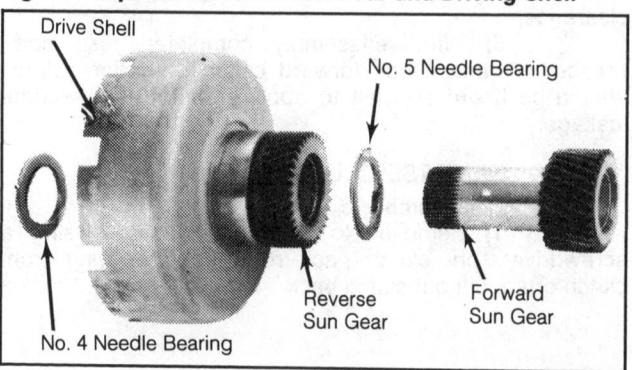

FORD MOTOR CO.
AUTOMATIC OVERDRIVE TRANSMISSION (Cont.)

Fig. 19: Exploded View of Oil Pump and Intermediate Clutch Piston

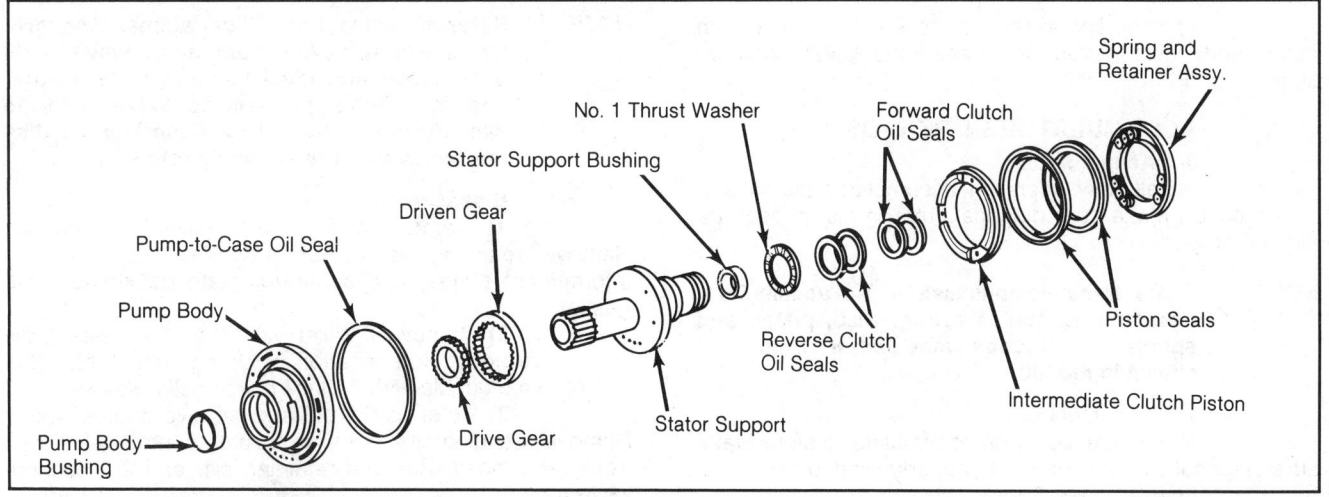

OIL PUMP & INTERMEDIATE CLUTCH PISTON

Disassembly

1) Lift No. 1 thrust washer from stator support. Remove 4 seal rings from stator support. Remove pump body-to-case seal and discard.

NOTE: Reverse clutch seal rings on stator support are larger than forward clutch seal rings.

2) Remove spring retainer assembly by carefully dislodging the tabs. Lift intermediate clutch piston from pump assembly. Remove retaining bolts and separate stator support from pump body. Remove drive and driven gears from pump body.

Reassembly

1) Install drive gear and driven gear into pump body with chamfers on both gears facing into pump body.

2) Position stator support on pump body. Install and tighten retaining bolts. Install pump-to-case seal around outer diameter of pump body.

3) Install new seals on intermediate clutch piston. Seal lips point away from spring posts. Coat piston seal and pump body sealing area with petroleum jelly. Install piston in pump body making sure piston bleed hole

Fig. 20: Exploded View of Accumulator and Servo Assemblies

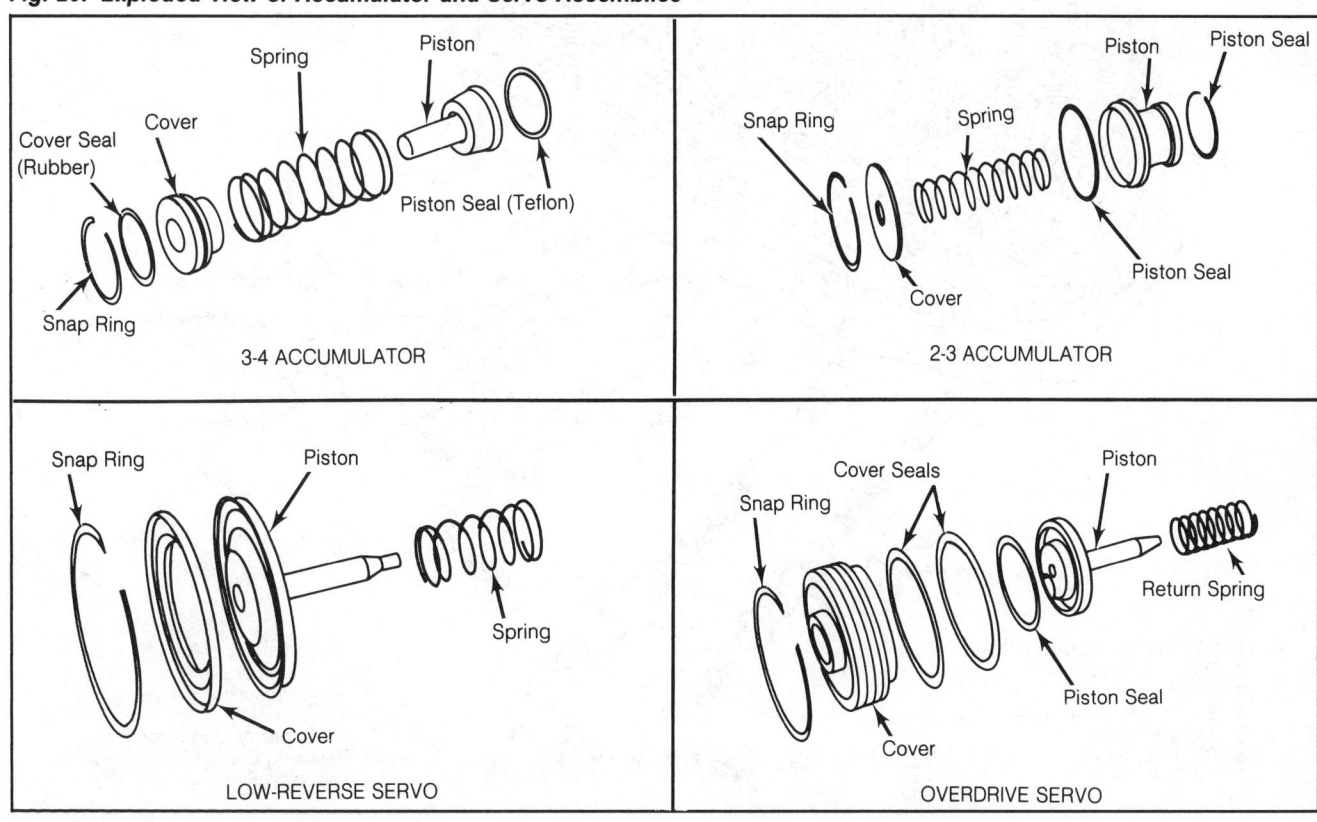

Automatic Transmissions
FORD MOTOR CO.
AUTOMATIC OVERDRIVE TRANSMISSION (Cont.)

is located at 12 o'clock position (toward top of transmission case).

4) Snap spring retainer assembly into place on pump body using even pressure. Install seal rings on stator support.

ACCUMULATORS & SERVOS
3-4 Accumulator
Install new seals on accumulator piston and piston cover. Make sure diagonal cuts on piston seal are aligned properly.

NOTE: **Some transmissions use a 3-4 accumulator assembly without a spring. Also, piston and spring construction may differ from that shown in Fig. 20.**

2-3 Accumulator
Install new seals on accumulator piston. Make sure diagonal cuts on seals are properly aligned.
Low-Reverse Servo
Inspect sealing edge on both servo cover and piston. Replace cover or piston, if necessary.
Overdrive Servo
Separate piston from servo cover. Install new seals on piston and cover. Assemble piston to cover.

VALVE BODY ASSEMBLY

NOTE: **Refer to valve body illustrations. As valve trains are removed from each valve body bore, place individual parts in correct order and in relative position to valve body to simplify reassembly. Tag all springs as they are removed for reassembly reference.**

Disassembly
1) Remove and discard valve body gasket. Remove retaining bolts. Remove separator plate, reinforcement plates, and separator plate gasket. Discard gasket.

2) Remove 2 relief valves and 7 check balls from valve body. Note location of Orange check ball, it is not interchangeable with 6 Black check balls. *See Fig. 22.*

3) Refer to *Fig. 23* and remove manual valve. Remove retaining clip and slide throttle control valve train from valve body. Remove retaining clip and 2-3 backout valve train.

4) Refer to *Fig. 21* and remove retaining clip, retaining plate, 2-3 capacity modulator valve, and orifice control valve trains. Remove retaining clip, 3-4 throttle valve modulator valve, and 3-4 shift valve trains. Remove retaining plate and throttle valve limit valve train.

Fig. 21: Exploded View of Valve Body Valve Trains

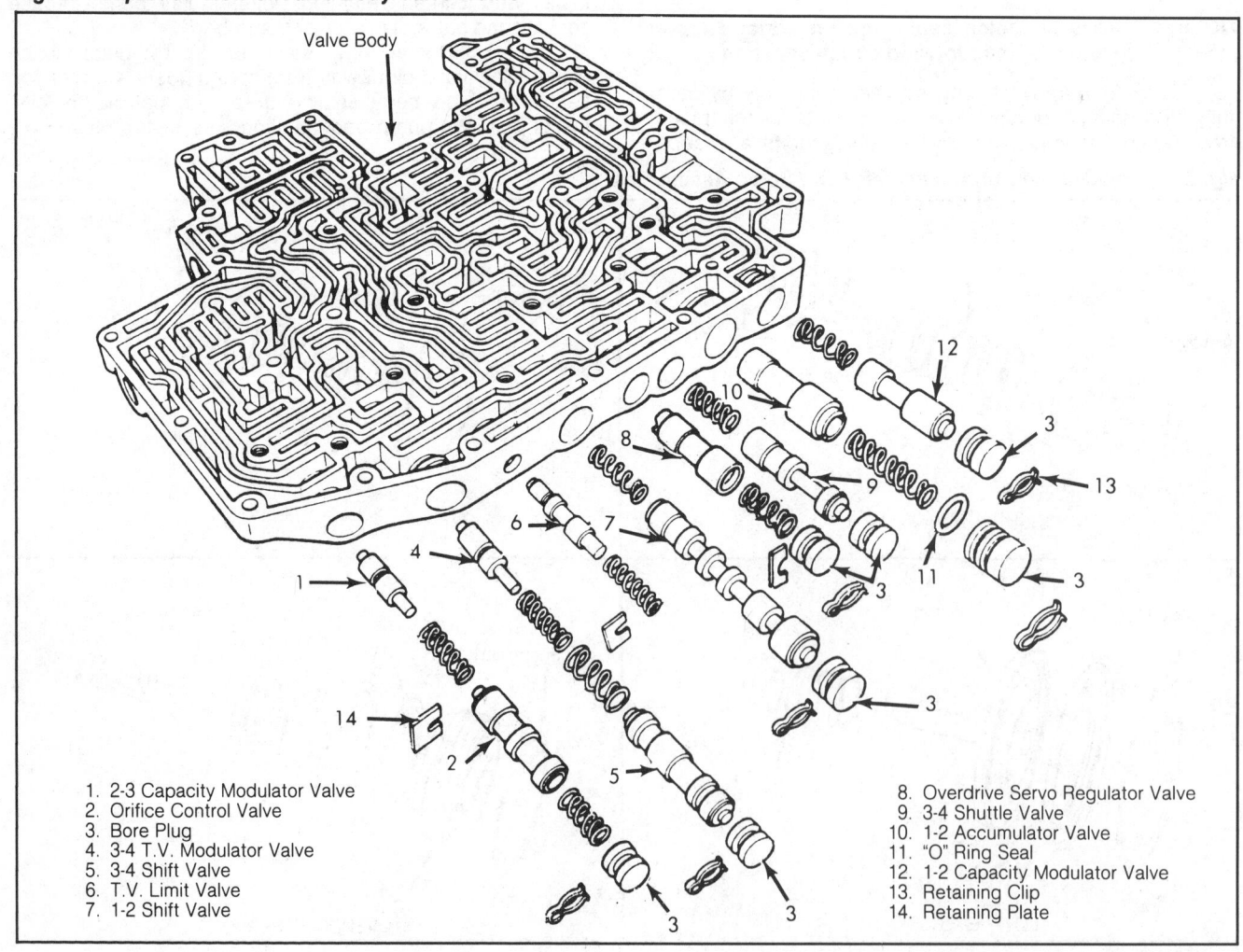

1. 2-3 Capacity Modulator Valve
2. Orifice Control Valve
3. Bore Plug
4. 3-4 T.V. Modulator Valve
5. 3-4 Shift Valve
6. T.V. Limit Valve
7. 1-2 Shift Valve
8. Overdrive Servo Regulator Valve
9. 3-4 Shuttle Valve
10. 1-2 Accumulator Valve
11. "O" Ring Seal
12. 1-2 Capacity Modulator Valve
13. Retaining Clip
14. Retaining Plate

FORD MOTOR CO.
AUTOMATIC OVERDRIVE TRANSMISSION (Cont.)

Fig. 22: View of Transmission Valve Body

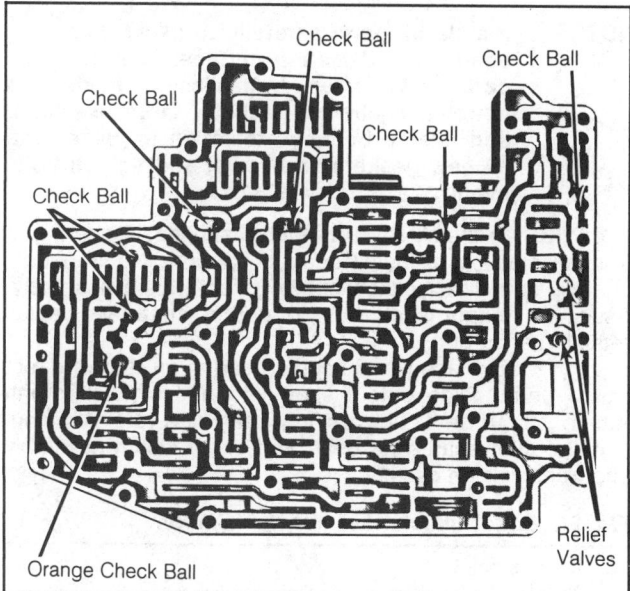

Location of check balls and pressure relief valves are shown.

5) Remove retaining clip, 1-2 shift valve train, retaining plate, and overdrive servo regulator valve train. Remove retaining clip and 3-4 shuttle valve train.

6) Remove retaining clip and 1-2 accumulator valve train. Remove retaining clip and 1-2 capacity modulator valve train.

7) Refer to *Fig. 24* and remove retaining clip and boost valve and main pressure regulator valve trains. Remove 2 retaining plates, 2-1 scheduling valve, and low servo modulator valve trains. Remove retaining plate and 3-4 backout valve train.

8) Remove the retaining clip, 2-3 shift valve, and 2-3 throttle valve modulator valve trains.

Inspection

1) Clean all parts thoroughly in clean solvent, and blow dry with moisture-free compressed air. Inspect

Fig. 23: Exploded View of Manual Valve, Throttle Control Valve Train and 2-3 Backout Valve Train

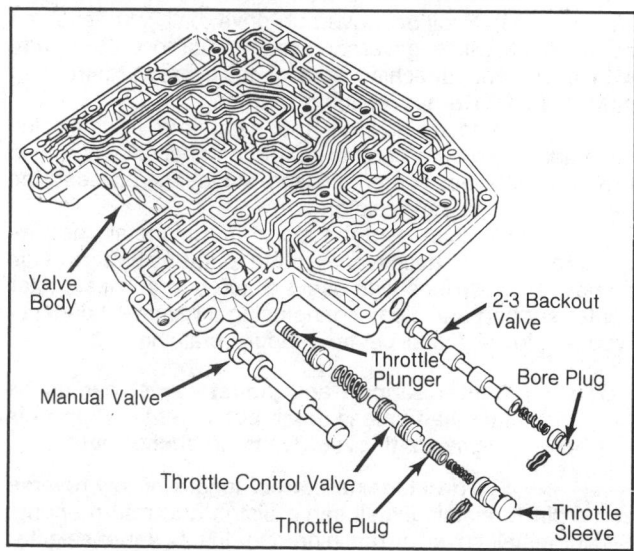

Assemble in same order as removed.

all valves and plug bores for scores. Check all fluid passages for obstructions.

2) Inspect all mating surfaces, plugs, and valves for burrs and scores. If necessary, use crocus cloth to polish valves and plugs.

CAUTION: Avoid rounding off the sharp edges of valves and plugs with the crocus cloth. These edges perform a cleaning action.

3) Inspect all springs for distortion. Check all valves and plugs for free movement in their respective bores. Valves and plugs, when dry, must fall free from their own weight in their respective bores.

Fig. 24: Exploded View of Valve Body Valve Trains

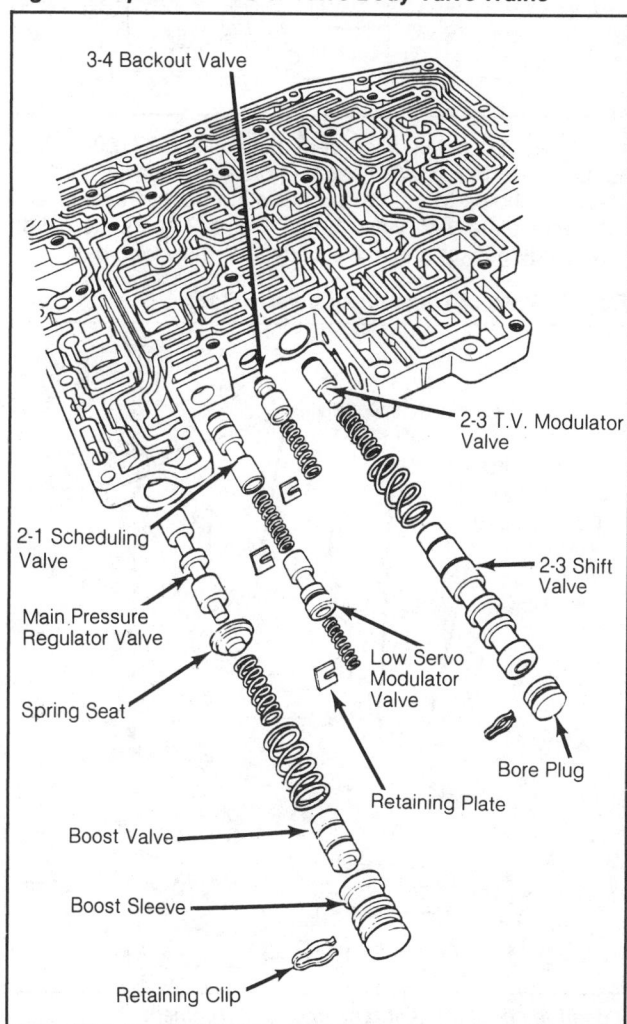

Reassembly

1) Install all valve trains into their respective bores using illustrations as assembly guides, and note that the chamfered stem of throttle control valve faces throttle plunger. Retainer plate used for 2-3 capacity modulator valve is thicker and longer than other retainer plates.

2) The 1-2 accumulator valve and valve body diameters are not the same for all models. Install valve body check balls as shown in *Fig. 21*. Make sure that Orange check ball is correctly installed. This check ball is larger than the others and is not interchangeable. Install pressure relief valves and springs as shown in *Fig. 25*.

Fig. 25: Pressure Relief Valve Installation

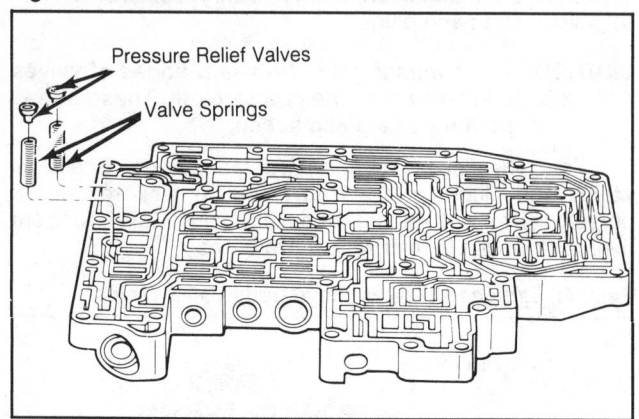

3) Install alignment pins (T80L-77100-A) into holes shown in *Fig. 26*. These 2 holes are smaller than the other bolt holes to assure proper alignment of gasket and separator plate with valve body. These 2 holes also align valve body gasket and valve body assembly with case.

Fig. 26: View of Transmission Valve Body

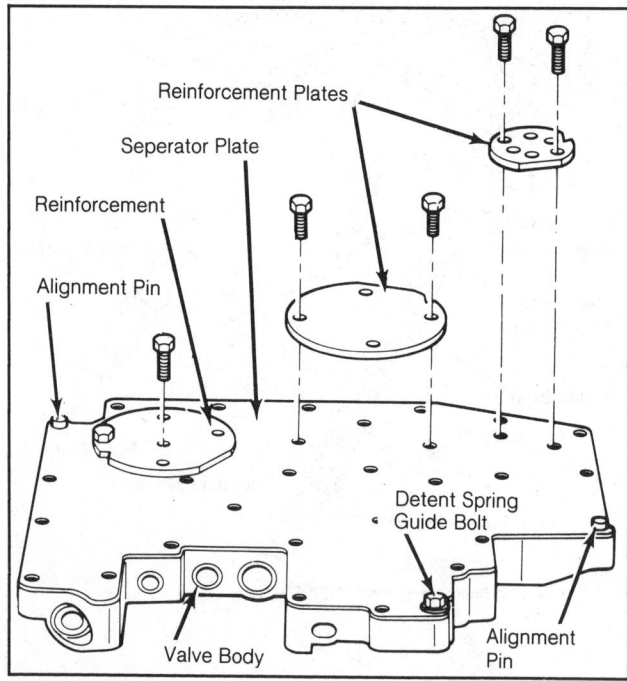

Locations of alignment pins and reinforcement plates are shown.

4) Using a new separator plate gasket, slide plate, and gasket over alignment pins. Position the 3 reinforcement plates and loosely install retaining bolts. Loosely install detent spring guide bolt.

NOTE: Detent spring guide bolt is the same length as short valve body-to-case retaining bolts.

5) Starting at center (large) reinforcement plate and working outward, tighten retaining bolts. Remove alignment pins.

TRANSMISSION REASSEMBLY

NOTE: Handle all parts carefully to avoid damaging bearings and mating surfaces. Lubricate all parts with clean transmission fluid. Use petroleum jelly on gaskets, thrust washers, and needle bearings to retain in place. Use all new gaskets and seals, and tighten bolts evenly.

1) Install No. 9 output shaft needle bearing in transmission case. Install bearing support, No. 7 needle bearing and direct clutch hub in direct clutch assembly. Assemble output shaft hub to output shaft and install retaining snap ring.

2) Place No. 8 needle bearing on rear of direct clutch drum. Slide output shaft into direct clutch drum. Attach output shaft hub to ring gear with retaining ring. Install output shaft, ring gear, and direct clutch assembly into transmission case.

Fig. 27: Direct Clutch Assembly Installation

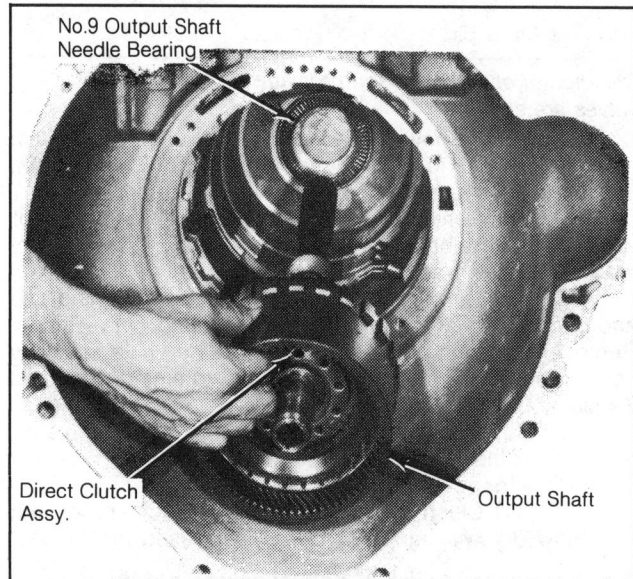

With needle bearings in place, install assembly.

3) Position governor drive ball in pocket on output shaft. Slide governor assembly onto output shaft with cover and attaching screws facing toward front of case. Install governor retaining snap ring.

4) Install low-reverse band into transmission case and make sure band is seated on anchor pins. When properly installed, center of band actuating rod seat can be seen through servo piston bore.

5) Install center support and planetary assembly into case. If necessary, rotate output shaft to align planet carrier splines with direct clutch hub splines. Install center support anti-clunk spring using a hammer handle or wooden dowel. Install center support retaining ring.

NOTE: Center support and planet carrier cannot be installed unless notch cut in center support is aligned with overdrive band anchor pin.

6) To determine correct length of low-reverse servo pin to install, install servo piston and return spring. Do not install cover or retaining ring. Install servo selector

FORD MOTOR CO.
AUTOMATIC OVERDRIVE TRANSMISSION (Cont.)

tool (T80L-77030-A) into servo bore and tighten band apply bolt on tool to 120 INCH lbs. (14 N.m). Attach dial indicator as shown in *Fig. 28* and position indicator stem on flat portion of servo piston. Zero dial indicator.

7) Thread bolt out of selector tool until piston stops against bottom of tool. Read amount of piston travel on dial indicator. If travel is .108"-.241" (2.74-6.12 mm), correct servo pin is installed. If travel is not within specifications, selective pistons are available in lengths of: 2.936" (74.57 mm) identified by 1 groove, 2.989" (75.92 mm) 2 grooves, and 3.043" (77.30 mm) 3 grooves.

8) Length is measured from base of piston to end of rod. Select proper servo pin to bring servo travel within specifications. Remove selector tool and dial indicator.

9) Install selected low-reverse servo piston. Install servo cover and cover retaining snap ring.

Fig. 28: Low-Reverse Servo Pin Selection

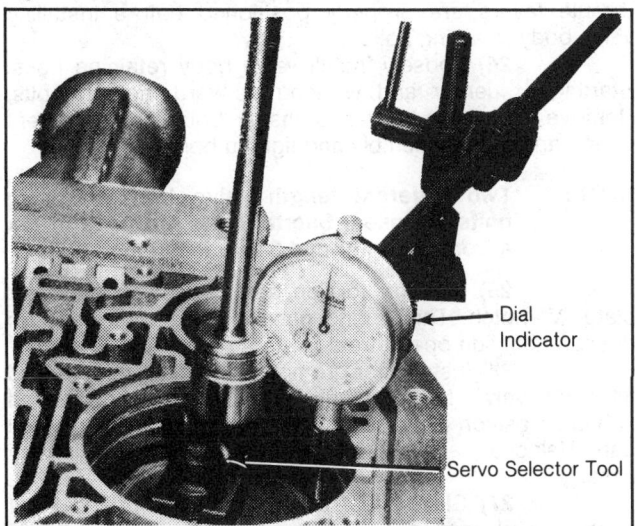

Position indicator stem on flat portion of servo piston.

10) Make sure No. 2 thrust washer is in position in reverse clutch. Assemble reverse clutch on forward clutch. Install No. 3 needle bearing and forward clutch hub in forward clutch. Position No. 4 needle bearing on forward clutch hub.

11) Install drive shell over clutch assemblies. Install No. 5 needle bearing and forward sun gear on drive shell. Install complete assembly into case, rotating output to aid in engaging sun gear with planetary gears.

12) Install overdrive band into case and around drive shell assembly, making sure band anchor is properly positioned on anchor pin. Use a screwdriver to hold overdrive band in position, install overdrive servo.

NOTE: **With overdrive servo installed, inspect band and apply pin for proper position and engagement. If band anchor and apply pin are not properly engaged, remove servo and reposition band as necessary.**

13) Install intermediate clutch pack components into case in the following order: Pressure plate, clutch pack (starting with a friction plate and alternating steel and friction plates) and selective steel plate. Measure intermediate clutch clearance as follows.

14) Intermediate clutch clearance is measured using a depth micrometer and end play checking tool (T80L-77003-A), as shown in *Fig. 29.* Set end play tool across pump case mounting surface. Locate micrometer end play bar and read depth.

15) Check depth again with micrometer at 180° opposite from previous measurement. Depth at intermediate clutch selective steel plate should be 1.629-1.640" (41.38-41.66 mm) if vehicle is equipped with 3.8L engine, and 1.634-1.646" (41.50-41.81 mm) for all other models. Average of the 2 measurements should be within this range.

NOTE: **A downward pressure must be applied to clutch pack while measuring intermediate clutch clearance.**

16) If intermediate clutch clearance is not within tolerance, the following size selective steel plates are available: .067-.071", .077-.081", .087-.091" and .097-.101" (1.70-1.80 mm, 1.96-2.06 mm 2.21-2.31 mm, and 2.46-2.57 mm). Install correct size plate and recheck clearance.

INTERMEDIATE CLUTCH PLATE USAGE

Engine Application	Steel Plates	Friction Plates
3.8L	2	2
All Others	3	3

Fig. 29: Measuring Intermediate Clutch Clearance

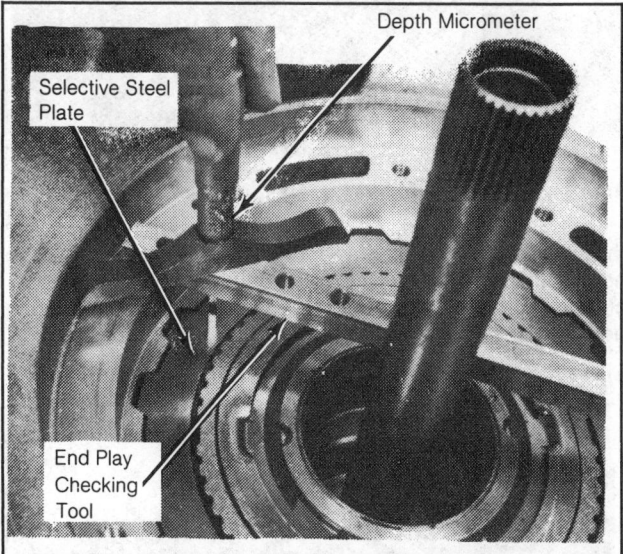

Push down on clutch pack while measuring clearance.

17) Check transmission end play by locating depth micrometer on end play checking tool bar (T80L-77003-A), so that depth is measured at reverse clutch drum thrust face.

18) Check end play 180° opposite to determine average depth. Thrust washer controlling transmission end play is located on stator support which is attached to back of pump housing.

19) Transmission end play can be adjusted using one of the selective thrust washers available for

FORD MOTOR CO.
AUTOMATIC OVERDRIVE TRANSMISSION (Cont.)

service. After measuring depth, select required thrust washer from the *End Play Thrust Washer Selection Chart.*

END PLAY THRUST WASHER SELECTION CHART

Measured Depth	Washer Thickness	Color Code
1.483-1.500" (37.67-38.10)	.050-.054" (1.27-1.37)	Green
1.501-1.517" (38.13-38.53)	.068-.072" (1.73-1.83)	Yellow
1.518-1.534" (38.56-38.96)	.085-.089" (2.16-2.26)	Natural
1.535-1.551" (38.99-39.40)	.102-.106" (2.59-2.69)	Red
1.552-1.568" (39.42-39.83)	.119-.123" (3.02-3.12)	Blue

Fig. 30: Measuring Transmission End Play

After measuring depth, select thrust washer from table.

20) Install selected transmission end play thrust washer on stator support, using petroleum jelly to hold it in place. Install pump alignment dowel, made by cutting the head from a M8-1.25 bolt, into pump mounting bolt hole shown in *Fig. 31.*

Fig. 31: Pump Alignment Dowel Installation

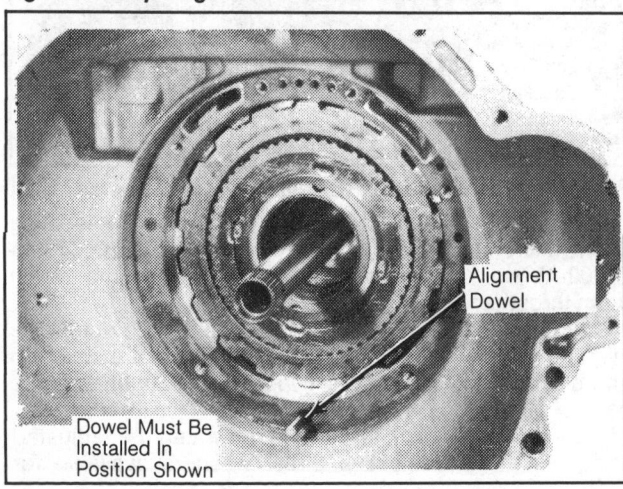

Dowel is made by cutting a MB-1.25 bolt.

21) Install new pump gasket into case. Install pump assembly into case using 2 slide hammers to lower pump into position. Remove alignment dowel and install the pump retaining bolts. Alternately tighten bolts a few turns at a time to draw pump into case.

22) Assemble 3-4 accumulator. Install piston (and spring, if so equipped) into case. Lubricate rubber seal on accumulator cover and top of bore to help cover installation. Install cover and retaining ring. Install 2-3 accumulator assembly.

NOTE: **After installation, 3-4 accumulator cover must be seated firmly against retaining ring. Use air pressure if necessary to seat cover against ring.**

23) Install 2 valve body alignment pins (T80L-77100-A) into valve body. Install valve body gasket and valve body assembly over pins, making sure manual and throttle levers are properly positioned before installing valve body retaining bolts.

24) Loosely install valve body retaining bolts. Starting at center and working outward, tighten bolts. Remove alignment pins and install bolts. Install detent spring and roller assembly and tighten bolts.

NOTE: **Two different length valve body retaining bolts are used. Shorter bolts are used at the 4 front, 1 center and 3 rear locations.**

25) Position torsion spring against separator plate "V" notch. This spring pushes the throttle lever in direction of wide open throttle.

26) Install filter grommet, new filter gasket, and filter on valve body. Install filter attaching bolts and tighten. Position new pan gasket on case and install oil pan. Using a new gasket, install extension housing on case.

27) Slide direct drive shaft into turbine input shaft. Install torque converter, making sure it is fully seated in pump

TIGHTENING SPECIFICATIONS

Application	Ft. Lbs. (N.m)
Stator Support-to-Pump	16-25 (22-34)
Pump-to-Case	16-20 (22-27)
Oil Pan-to-Case	12-16 (16-22)
Extension-to-Case	16-20 (22-27)
Converter-to-Flywheel	20-34 (27-46)
Inner Manual Lever-to-Shaft	30-40 (41-54)
Outer Throttle Lever-to-Shaft	12-16 (16-22)
Cooler Line-to-Case	10-14 (14-19)
Converter Plug-to-Converter	8-23 (11-38)
Pressure Plug-to-Case	6-12 (8-16)
Transmission-to-Engine	40-50 (55-68)
	INCH Lbs (N.m)
Reinforcing Plate-to-Valve Body	80-100 (9-11)
Separator Plate-to-Valve Body	80-100 (9-11)
Valve Body-to-Case	80-100 (9-11)
Filter-to-Valve Body	80-100 (9-11)
Governor Body-to-Counterweight	50-60 (6-7)
Cover-to-Governor Body	20-30 (2.3-3.4)

FORD MOTOR CO. ATX — AUTOMATIC TRANSAXLE

Escort, EXP, LN7, Lynx, Tempo, Topaz

TRANSAXLE IDENTIFICATION

The ATX automatic transaxle can be identified by the code letter "B". The identification code letter is found on the lower line of the Vehicle Certification Label under "TR". The ratio of the ATX automatic transaxle can be determined by the letter code under "AX" of the Vehicle Certification Label. This label is attached to the left (driver's) side door lock panel. In addition, transaxle can be identified by a metal tag attached to the transaxle case. First line on tag shows the build date code and transaxle model number. Bottom line on tag shows the transaxle serial number and assembly part number prefix and suffix. Transaxle codes and corresponding axle ratios are as follows:

TRANSAXLE IDENTIFICATION CODES

Application	Axle Ratio	Code
All Models		
Auto. Trans	3.31:1	3
Auto. Trans	3.59:1	5

DESCRIPTION

The ATX automatic transaxle combines an automatic transmission and differential into a single component designed for front-wheel-drive applications. The transmission and differential are housed in a one-piece light-alloy housing which is bolted to the engine. The automatic transmission uses 3 friction clutches, 1 band and a single one-way clutch. These components are

Fig. 1: Cross-Sectional View of ATX Automatic Transaxle Assembly

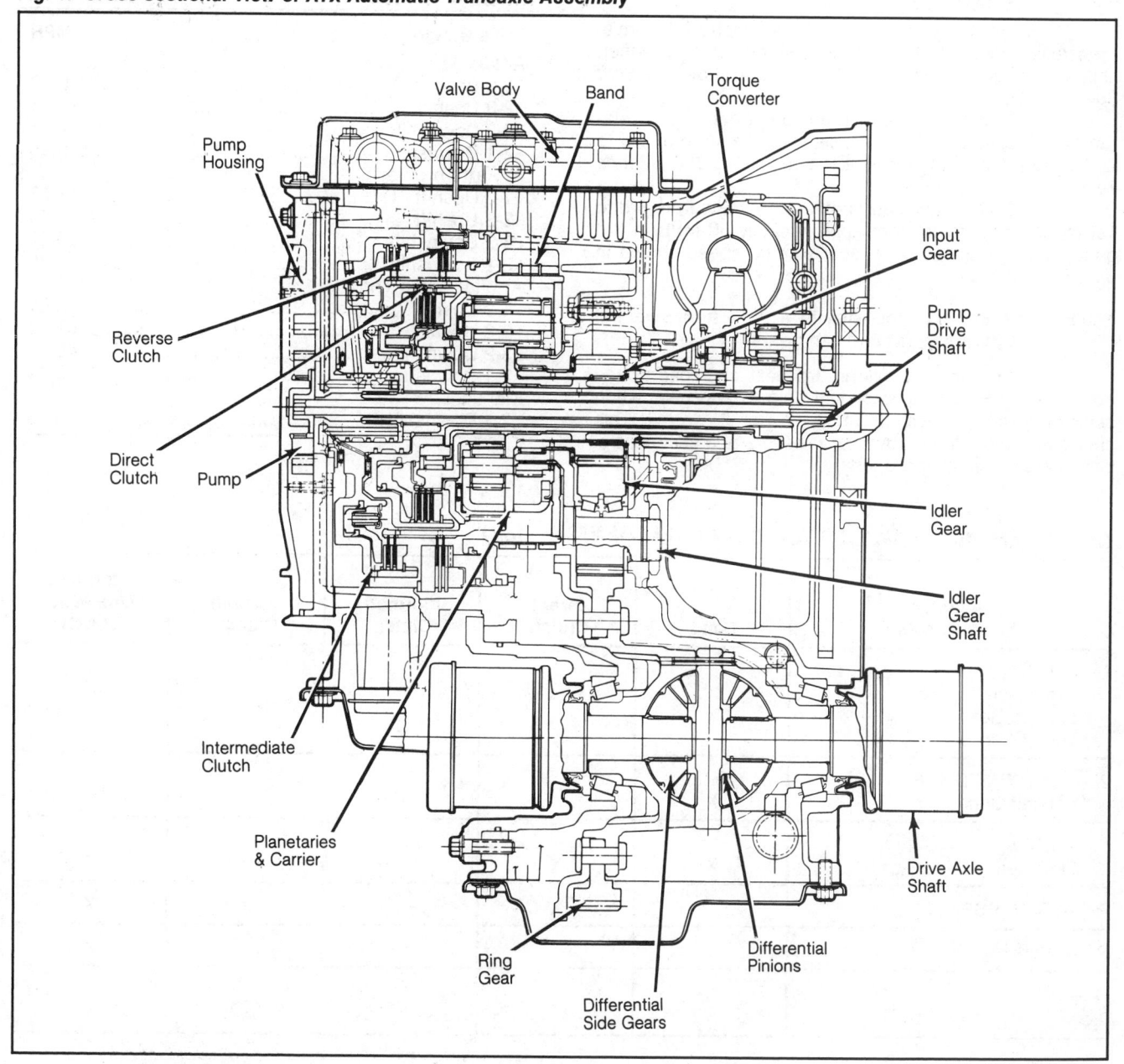

FORD MOTOR CO. ATX — AUTOMATIC TRANSAXLE (Cont.)

applied as necessary to transmit engine torque through a compound planetary gear set. The planetary provides 3 forward gear ratios and 1 reverse. The planetary transmits engine torque to the input gear, which meshes with the differential idler gear. The idler gear meshes with the differential ring gear, which is riveted to the differential case. When power flow reaches the differential, engine torque flows outward to the wheels through the differential gears.

LUBRICATION & ADJUSTMENT

See the appropriate article in AUTOMATIC TRANSMISSION SERVICING Section.

TESTING

ROAD TEST

1) Check minimum throttle upshifts in drive. Transaxle should start in 1st gear, shift to 2nd, and then shift to 3rd at approximately the speeds shown in Shift Speeds Table.

2) With transaxle in 3rd gear, depress accelerator pedal to the floor. Transaxle should shift from 3rd to 2nd or 1st, depending on vehicle speed. See Shift Speeds Table.

3) Check closed throttle downshifts from 3rd to 1st by coasting down from approximately 30 MPH in 3rd gear. Shift should occur at approximate speed shown in Shift Speeds Table.

NOTE: When selector lever is at "2", transaxle will operate in 1st and 2nd gears.

4) With transaxle in 3rd gear and road speed above 30 MPH, transaxle should shift to 2nd gear when selector lever is moved from "Drive" to "2", to "1". This check will determine if governor pressure and shift control valves are functioning properly.

NOTE: The following step is for checking shift speeds with vehicle in the shop. This test will check shift valve operation, governor circuits, shift delay pressures, throttle boost and downshift valve action.

CAUTION: Never exceed 60 MPH speedometer speed when performing the following test.

5) Place transaxle in "Drive" and make a minimum throttle 1-2, 2-3 shift test. At this point of shift, the speedometer needle will make a momentary surge and a driveline bump will be felt.

6) If shift points are within specifications, 1-2 and 2-3 shift valves, and governor are okay. If shift points are incorrect, perform a Governor Check to isolate the problem.

ATX SHIFT SPEEDS

Drive Range	MPH
At Idle	
1-2 Upshift	10-19
2-3 Upshift	15-31
3-2 Downshift	14-25
2-1 Downshift	9-15
At Part Throttle	
1-2 Upshift	11-27
2-3 Upshift	24-45
3-2 Downshift	20-42
2-1 Downshift	13-20
At Wide Open Throttle	
1-2 Upshift	23-51
2-3 Upshift	52-78
3-2 Downshift	49-73
2-1 Downshift	15-44
Manual Low	
2-1 Downshift	20-38

CLUTCH AND BAND APPLICATION CHART (ELEMENTS IN USE)

Selector Lever Position	Band	Direct Clutch	Intermed. Clutch	Reverse Clutch	Intermed. One-Way Clutch
D — DRIVE					
First Gear	X				X
Second Gear	X		X		
Third Gear		X	X		
2 — INTERMEDIATE					
Second Gear	X		X		
1 — LOW					
First Gear	X	X			X
R — REVERSE		X		X	X
P — Park					X
N — Neutral					X

FORD MOTOR CO. ATX — AUTOMATIC TRANSAXLE (Cont.)

LINE PRESSURE SPECIFICATIONS [1]

Selector Position	Pressure (Psi)
At Idle	
"D", "1" & "2"	49-66
"R"	66-111
"P" & "N"	49-66
At Wide Open Throttle	
"D", "1" & "2"	97-122
"R"	205-284
"P" & "N"	95-122

[1] — With governor pressure at zero.

GOVERNOR CHECK

Accelerate vehicle to 30 MPH, then back off throttle completely. If governor is functioning properly, transaxle will shift to 3rd gear.

LINE PRESSURE TEST

1) Connect a 0-300 psi pressure gauge to line pressure test port on transaxle case. *See Fig. 2.* Run engine until normal operating temperature is reached.

2) Apply service and parking brakes. Check line pressure in all selector lever positions with engine at idle and then with engine at wide open throttle. Pressures should be as shown in *Line Pressure Specifications* table.

Fig. 2: View of Transaxle Case Showing Line Pressure Test Port

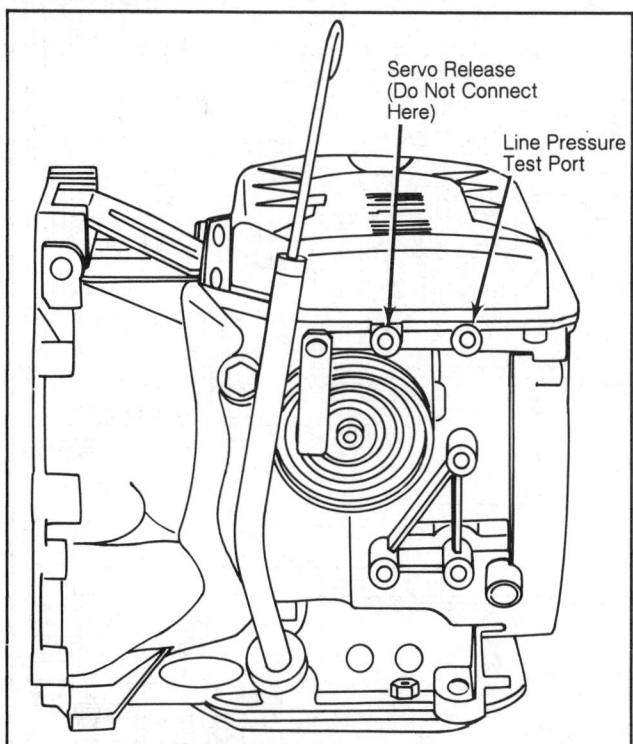

LINE PRESSURE TEST RESULTS

Low at Idle in All Ranges

Check engine EGR system. Check for low fluid level, restricted intake screen or filter, loose valve body or regulator-to-case bolts, loose oil tubes, excessive leakage in oil pump, case, valve body or sticking control pressure regulator valve.

High at Idle in All Ranges

Check engine EGR system, throttle valve or control rod, sticking regulator boost valve(s).

Low in "P" or "N"

Faulty valve body.

Low in "D"

Faulty servo or valve body.

Low in "2"

Faulty valve body and/or intermediate servo.

Low in "1"

Faulty direct clutch and/or valve body.

Low in "R"

Faulty direct clutch and/or reverse clutch. Faulty valve body.

STALL TEST

Testing Precautions

When performing stall test, do not hold throttle open longer than 5 seconds. Allow a cooling period of 15 seconds with transmission in neutral and engine speed at 1000 RPM between each test. If engine speed exceeds maximum limits shown, release accelerator immediately as this is an indication of clutch or band slippage.

Testing Procedure

With engine at normal operating temperature, tachometer installed, and parking and servicing brakes applied, stall test transmission in each driving range at full throttle, and note maximum RPM obtained. Engine speed should be within limits shown in following table:

STALL SPEED SPECIFICATIONS

Range	Stall RPM
Escort, EXP, LN7 & Lynx	
"D" or "2"	2440-2890
"1"	2610-3110
"R"	2750-3160
Tempo & Topaz	
All Ranges	2272-2664

STALL TEST RESULTS

Stall Speed Too High

In "D" and "2"; turbine shaft one-way clutch defective. In "D", "2" and "1"; low-intermediate band or servo defective. In "R"; reverse clutch defective. In all driving ranges; T.V. cable adjustment incorrect or incorrect line pressure.

Stall Speed Too Low

Converter reactor one-way clutch or engine performance is faulty.

AIR PRESSURE TESTS

A "No Drive" condition can exist even with correct transaxle fluid pressure, because of inoperative clutches or band. Erratic shifts could be caused by a stuck governor valve. The inoperative units can be located through a series of checks by substituting air pressure for the fluid pressure to determine location of malfunction.

FORD MOTOR CO. ATX — AUTOMATIC TRANSAXLE (Cont.)

Fig. 3: Air Pressure Test Apply Ports on Adapter Plate

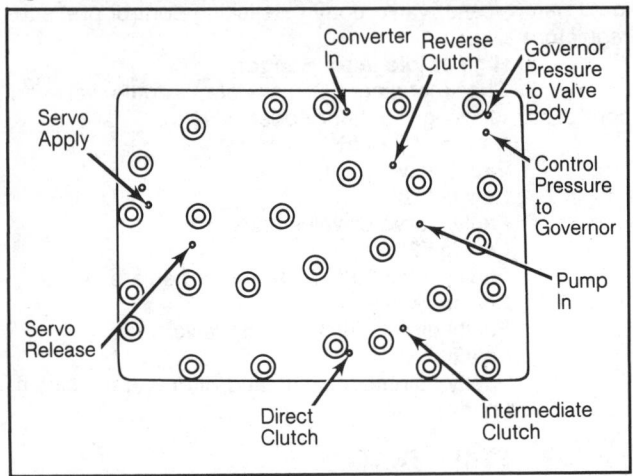

To make air pressure checks, loosen valve body cover bolts, then remove cover and valve body

assembly. Install the special adapter plate (P/N T82P-7006-B) in place of valve body. *See Fig. 3*. The inoperative units can be located by applying air pressure in transaxle case passages, through adapter plate, leading to the clutches, servo and governor. See *Fig. 3* for location of various case passages.

NOTE: **Air pressure test adapter plate should be installed with a new valve body gasket. Torque attaching bolts to 80-100 INCH lbs. (9-11 N.m).**

Band Apply Servo
Apply air pressure to servo apply passage. The band should apply. A dull thud should be heard when air pressure is removed, allowing servo piston to return to release position.

Direct Clutch
Apply air pressure to direct clutch apply passage. A dull thud can be heard or movement of piston can be felt as piston is applied. If direct clutch seals are leaking, a hissing noise will be heard.

Fig. 4: ATX Automatic Transaxle Hydraulic Circuits Diagram

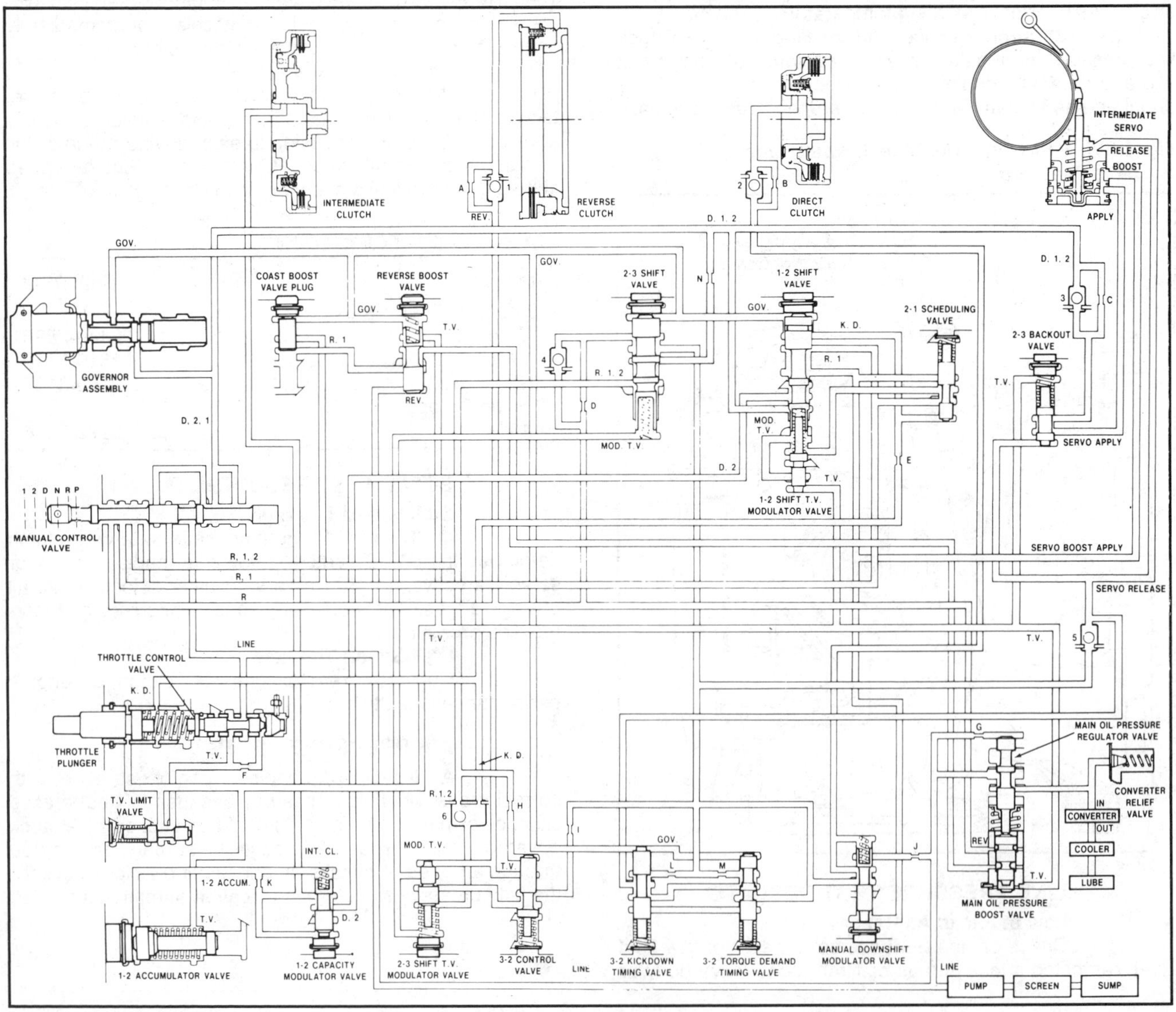

FORD MOTOR CO. ATX — AUTOMATIC TRANSAXLE (Cont.)

Intermediate Clutch

Apply air pressure to intermediate clutch apply passage. A dull thud can be heard or movement of piston can be felt on case as piston is applied. If intermediate clutch seals are leaking, a hissing noise will be heard.

Reverse Clutch

Apply air pressure to reverse clutch apply passage. A dull thud can be heard or movement of piston can be felt on case as piston is applied. If reverse clutch seals are leaking, a hissing noise will be heard.

Converter In

This passage can only be checked for blockage. If passage holds air pressure, remove adapter plate and check for an obstruction or damage.

Control Pressure-to-Governor

Remove governor cover. Apply air pressure to control pressure-to-governor apply passage. Watch for movement of governor valve.

Governor Pressure-to-Valve Body

This passage can only be checked for blockage. If passage holds air pressure, remove adapter plate and check for an obstruction or damage.

Pump In (Bench Test)

With transaxle removed from vehicle and converter removed, apply air pressure to pump in apply passage. Rotation of pump gears should be heard when air pressure is applied.

NOTE: **"Pump In" check is normally performed during the assembly of an overhauled transaxle.**

SERVICE (IN VEHICLE)

VALVE BODY

Removal

1) Apply parking brake. Open hood and remove battery and battery tray. Remove ignition coil and transaxle dipstick. Disconnect supply hoses and vacuum lines from managed air valve, then remove valve from valve body cover.

2) Disconnect neutral safety switch connector. Disconnect fuel evaporator hose at frame rail. Disconnect fan motor and water temperature sending unit wiring.

3) Remove attaching bolts, then lift off valve body cover and gasket. Remove valve body-to-case attaching bolts, then remove valve body assembly and gasket from transaxle case.

Installation

1) Install 2 alignment pins into opposing valve body attaching bolt holes, then install valve body-to-case gasket. Install valve body assembly into case, removing 1 alignment pin to allow attachment of manual valve. Reinstall alignment pin.

NOTE: **Ensure roller on end of throttle valve plunger has engaged cam on end of throttle lever shaft.**

2) Connect throttle valve control spring. Install the 27 valve body attaching bolts, detent spring and oil pressure regulator exhaust plate (baffle plate). Remove alignment pins. Tighten valve body attaching bolts.

3) Install new valve body cover gasket on case, then install and tighten cover attaching bolts, making sure transaxle I.D. tag is installed in its original position.

4) To complete installation, reverse removal procedure and check and adjust transaxle fluid level.

GOVERNOR

Removal

1) Apply parking brake and disconnect battery. Remove the 2 managed air valve supply rear hoses and all vacuum lines from managed air valve. Remove managed air valve supply hose band-to-intermediate shift control bracket attaching bolt.

2) Remove air cleaner. Using a long screwdriver, remove governor retaining clip. Remove governor cover and pull out governor.

Installation

To install governor, reverse removal procedure and note the following: Install a new "O" ring seal on governor cover. Check transaxle fluid level and add fluid if necessary.

SERVO

Removal

1) Apply parking brake and disconnect battery. Disconnect fan motor and water temperature sending unit wiring. If equipped, disconnect FM capacitor wiring.

2) Remove fan shroud-to-radiator attaching nuts, then remove fan and fan shroud assembly. Remove filler tube-to-case attaching bolt using care not to lose service I.D. tag which is attached with bolt. Remove filler tube.

3) From left front mount remove lower left mount-to-case attaching bolt. Using a compressor tool (T81P-70027-A or equivalent), compress servo cover and remove retaining snap ring, then remove cover and servo assembly.

Installation

To install servo, reverse removal procedure and fill transaxle with fluid.

DRIVE AXLE SHAFTS

NOTE: **When removing both axle shafts, shipping plugs (T81P-1177-B) must be installed into differential case. Failure to use these plugs can result in differential side gear becoming mis-aligned. Should the gears become mis-aligned, differential must be removed from transaxle to re-align gears.**

NOTE: **The right hand drive axle shaft must be removed from case first. Driver (T81P-4026-A) is then inserted into transaxle to drive left hand inboard constant velocity (CV) joint from transaxle. If only left axle shaft is to be removed for service, remove right axle shaft only from transaxle.**

CAUTION: **Drive axle shafts should not be removed unless a new hub nut, and a new ball joint-to-steering knuckle attaching bolt and nut are available. These parts must not be reused.**

Removal

1) Before raising vehicle, remove dust cap and loosen hub nut. Raise and support vehicle, remove wheel and tire, then remove hub nut and washer.

FORD MOTOR CO. ATX — AUTOMATIC TRANSAXLE (Cont.)

NOTE: The hub nut must be loosened without unstaking. Use of a chisel may damage spindle threads. Discard hub nut when removed, it must not be reused.

2) Remove bolt attaching brake hose retaining clip to suspension strut. Remove ball joint-to-steering knuckle bolt, then drive bolt out of knuckle using a punch and hammer.

NOTE: Discard ball joint-to-steering knuckle bolt and nut. They are of a torque prevailing design and cannot be reused.

3) Separate ball joint from steering knuckle using a pry bar positioned with the end outside the bushing pocket to prevent damage to bushing. *See Fig. 5.*

NOTE: The plastic disc brake shield must be bent back away from ball joint while prying ball joint from steering knuckle.

4) Using a pry bar, separate drive axle shaft from differential housing. Position bar between housing and shaft and use care not to damage dust deflector between shaft and housing, differential oil seal, joint boot or CV joint dust deflector.

5) Support end of axle shaft with a piece of wire to prevent damage to outboard CV joint. Using a puller, separate outboard CV joint from hub.

CAUTION: Never use a hammer to separate outboard CV joint from hub. Damage to CV joint internal components may result.

6) To remove CV joint and boot from axle shaft, clamp shaft in a vise, making sure vise jaws do not contact boot or clamp. Cut large boot clamp and peel away from boot, then pull boot back over shaft.

7) Separate CV joint from shaft using CV Joint Separator T81P-3514-A (or equivalent) as shown in *Fig. 6.* Cut remaining boot clamp and remove boot from shaft.

Fig. 5: Separating Ball Joint from Steering Knuckle

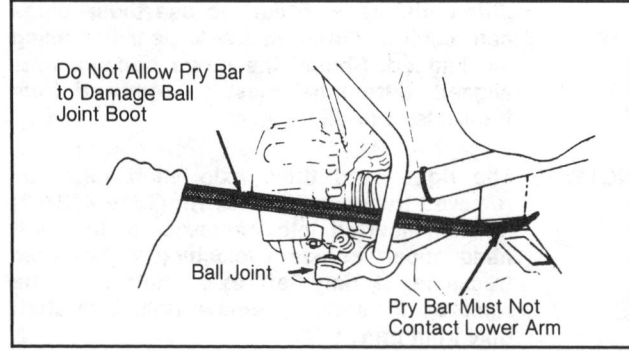

8) Remove snap ring from end of shaft and discard. The stop ring, located just below snap ring, should be removed only if inspection shows it to be damaged or worn.

Disassembly (Outboard CV Joint)
1) Clamp CV joint stub shaft in a vise with bearing facing up. Press down on inner race until it tilts enough to remove ball bearing. With cage tilted, remove ball from cage. Repeat this step until all 6 balls are removed.

NOTE: A tight bearing cage can be tilted by tapping the inner race with a wooden dowel or hammer. Do not hit the cage. Also, if balls are tight use a blunt screwdriver to pry them from cage, using care not to scratch or otherwise damage cage.

Fig. 6: Separating CV Joint from Drive Axle Shaft

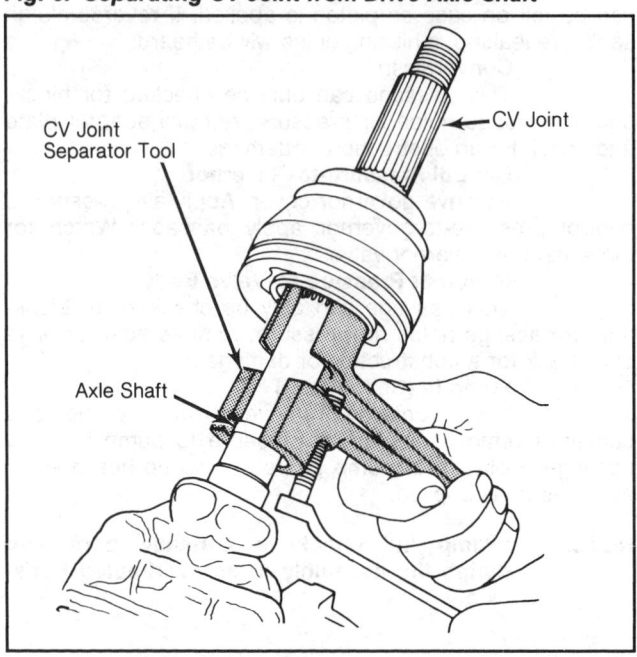

2) Pivot bearing cage and inner race assembly until it is straight up and down in outer race. Align cage windows with outer race lands while pivoting bearing cage, then lift assembly from outer race.

3) To separate inner race from cage, rotate race up and out of cage, if cage has 6 equal size windows. If cage has 4 equal size windows and 2 elongated windows, pivot inner race until it is straight up and down in cage. Align 1 of the inner race bands with 1 of the elongated windows and position race through window, then rotate race up and out of cage.

Reassembly (Outboard CV Joint)
1) Apply a light coating of grease on inner and outer races. Install inner race into cage, then install race and cage into outer race by installing assembly vertically and pivoting 90° into position.

NOTE: When correctly installed, shallow counterbore cut into inner race will be facing up.

2) Align bearing cage and inner race with outer race, then tilt race and cage and install ball bearing. Repeat this step until all 6 ball bearings are installed.

3) After installing bearings, pack CV joint with 1 packet of specified grease (supplied in service kit). Pack grease into joint by forcing it through splined hole in inner race.

Disassembly (Inboard CV Joint)
1) Remove snap ring from end of CV joint stub shaft. Using a pair of side cutters, cut and remove ball retainer. Discard ball retainer when removed. A new retainer is not required for reassembly.

2) Gently tap CV joint on bench until cage and inner race assembly can be removed by hand. Remove

FORD MOTOR CO. ATX — AUTOMATIC TRANSAXLE (Cont.)

Fig. 7: Exploded View of Drive Axle Shaft and CV Joint Assembly (Right Side Assembly Shown; Left Side Similar)

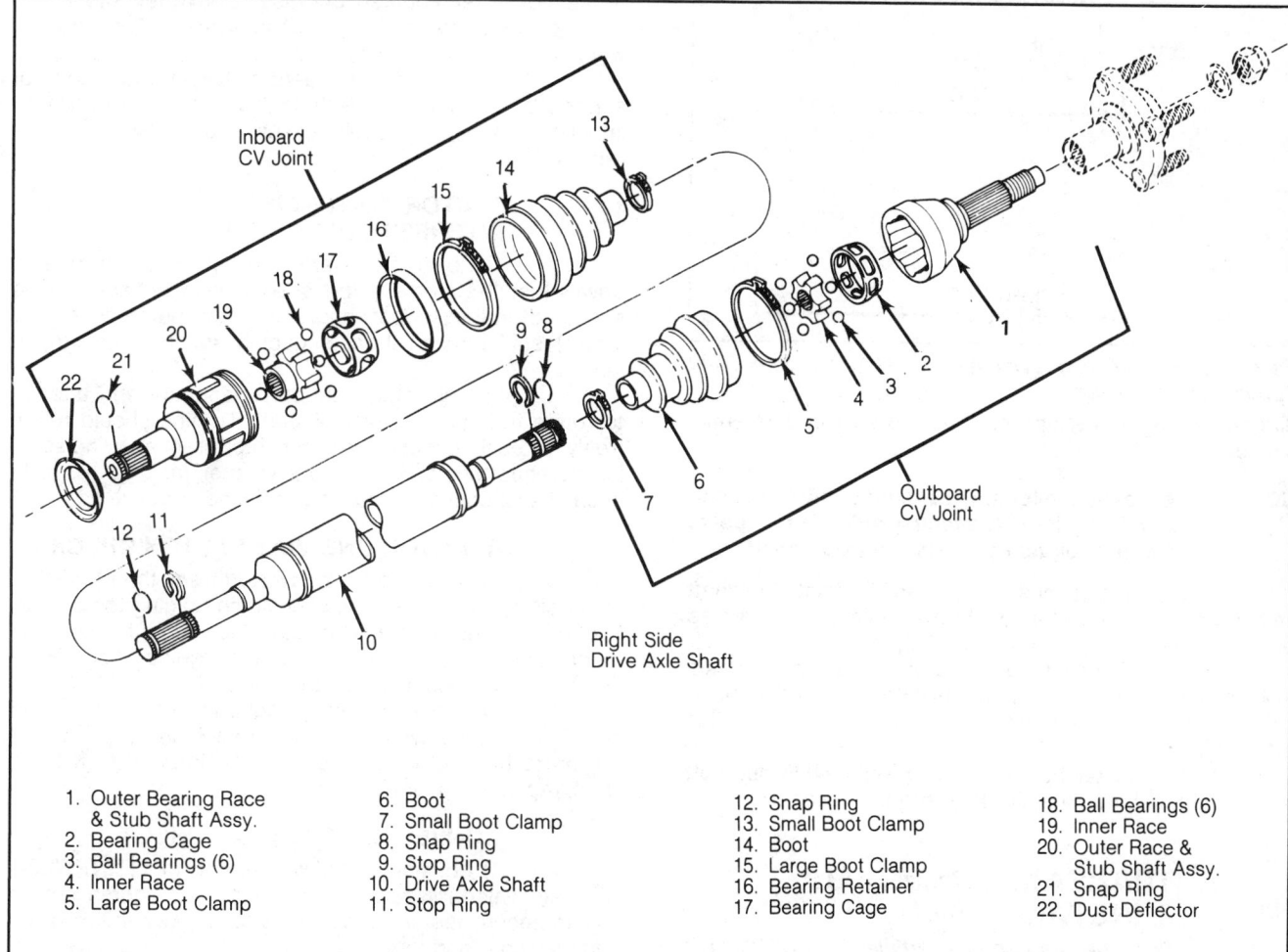

1. Outer Bearing Race & Stub Shaft Assy.	6. Boot	12. Snap Ring	18. Ball Bearings (6)
2. Bearing Cage	7. Small Boot Clamp	13. Small Boot Clamp	19. Inner Race
3. Ball Bearings (6)	8. Snap Ring	14. Boot	20. Outer Race & Stub Shaft Assy.
4. Inner Race	9. Stop Ring	15. Large Boot Clamp	21. Snap Ring
5. Large Boot Clamp	10. Drive Axle Shaft	16. Bearing Retainer	22. Dust Deflector
	11. Stop Ring	17. Bearing Cage	

ball bearings by prying from cage with a blunt screwdriver, using care not to scratch or otherwise damage race and cage spheres.

3) On Escort, EXP, LN7 and Lynx models, rotate inner race to align lands with cage windows. Lift inner race from bearing cage through wider end of cage.

4) On Tempo and Topaz models, with boot peeled back, position CV joint on shaft and tap into position using plastic mallet.

Reassembly (Inboard CV Joint)

1) Install snap ring on stub shaft by starting one end of ring in groove of shaft and then working snap ring over shaft end and into groove. This will avoid over expanding snap ring.

2) Install inner race through large end of cage with race hub facing large end of cage. With inner race and cage properly aligned, press ball bearings through cage with hand.

3) Pack outer race with 2 packets of grease (supplied with service kit). Position inner race and bearing assembly in outer race. Push inner race and bearing assembly into outer race. When properly assembled, inner race hub will face into outer race.

Installation

1) If removed, install a new stop ring into groove on drive axle shaft. Install a new snap ring in groove nearest end of axle shaft, using care not to over

expand it. If removed, install CV joint boot on axle shaft. Make sure boot is seated in groove and clamp in position using crimping pliers.

2) With joint boot peeled back, position CV joint on shaft and tap into position using a plastic mallet. When fully seated, the snap ring locks in groove cut into CV joint inner race.

3) Before positioning boot over CV joint, pack joint and boot with lubricant supplied in service kit. Fill boots of CV joints with 1 packet each. Fill inboard CV joint with 2 packets and outboard CV joint with 1 packet.

4) Remove excess grease from CV joint external surfaces, then position boot over joint. Before installing boot, make sure any air pressure which might have built-up in boot is relieved.

5) Move CV joint in or out, as necessary, to adjust length of drive axle shaft to 15.6" (397 mm) on left side axle shaft or 28.1" (714 mm) on right side axle shaft. *See Fig. 8.*

6) With axle shaft length properly adjusted, ensure boot is seated in groove, then clamp in position using crimping pliers.

7) Install a new snap ring on inboard CV joint stub shaft (outboard joints do not have a snap ring), using care not to over expand snap ring.

8) Carefully align splines of inboard CV joint stub shaft with splines in differential, then push joint into

FORD MOTOR CO. ATX — AUTOMATIC TRANSAXLE (Cont.)

Fig. 8: Drive Axle Shaft Assembled Length

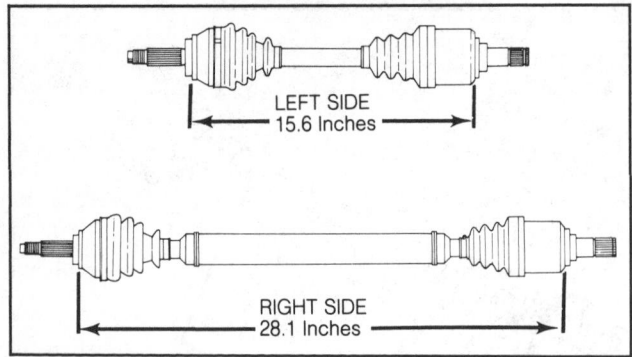

LEFT SIDE
15.6 Inches

RIGHT SIDE
28.1 Inches

Escort, EXP, LN7 and Lynx models shown; Tempo and Topaz models similar.

differential until the snap ring is felt to seat in differential side gear.

NOTE: **A plastic mallet may be used to aid in seating snap ring into differential side gear groove. Tap only on outboard CV joint stub shaft.**

9) Align splines on outboard CV joint stub shaft with splines in hub, then push shaft into hub as far as possible. Use a puller to pull shaft fully into hub.

10) Connect control arm to steering knuckle and install a NEW bolt and nut. Position brake hose routing clip in position on suspension strut and install attaching bolt.

11) Install hub nut washer and a NEW hub nut, then tighten hub nut. Install wheel and tire assembly.

TRANSAXLE REMOVAL & INSTALLATION

See the appropriate article in AUTOMATIC TRANSMISSION REMOVAL Section.

TORQUE CONVERTER

NOTE: **The torque converter is a sealed unit and cannot be disassembled for service. Replace converter if found to be defective. Perform the following tests to be certain converter is defective before replacing unit.**

FLUSHING CONVERTER

Whenever the transaxle has been disassembled to replace worn or damaged parts, or because valve body sticks due to foreign material, converter and oil cooler MUST be cleaned. Use a mechanically agitated cleaner (Rotunda 14-0028 or equivalent).

CAUTION: **Under no circumstances should an attempt be made to clean converters and oil coolers by hand agitation with solvent.**

STATOR-TO-IMPELLER INTERFERENCE CHECK

1) Position stator support assembly on work bench with spline end of stator pointing up. Mount converter on stator support with splines of one-way clutch inner race engaging splines of stator support.

2) Hold stator support stationary, and try to rotate converter counterclockwise. Converter should rotate freely without any signs of interference or scraping within converter assembly.

3) If scraping is heard or felt, trailing edges of stator blades may be interfering with leading edges of impeller blades. In such cases, converter must be replaced.

STATOR-TO-TURBINE INTERFERENCE CHECK

1) Position converter on bench with front side down. Install stator support assembly to engage mating splines of stator support and stator, and pump drive gear lugs. Install turbine shaft, engaging splines with turbine hub.

2) Hold stator support stationary and attempt to rotate turbine with turbine shaft. Turbine should rotate freely in each direction without interference or noise. If interference exists, stator front washer may be worn. In such cases, converter must be replaced.

REACTOR ONE-WAY CLUTCH CHECK

1) Align slot in converter front thrust washer with holding lug. Insert one-way clutch holding tool (T81P-7902-A or equivalent) into holding lug. While holding tool in position, install one-way clutch torquing tool (T81P-7902-B or equivalent) in reactor spline.

2) Continue holding tool and turn torquing tool counterclockwise with a torque wrench. If torquing tool begins to turn before torque wrench reads 10 ft. lbs. (14 N.m), replace converter.

CONVERTER END PLAY CHECK

1) Position end play checking tool (T81P-7902-D or equivalent) in torque converter hub. Tighten nut on tool to secure tool in converter. Mount a dial indicator on end play checking tool.

2) With indicator stylus contacting converter shell and with indicator zeroed, lift on checking tool handles. If indicator reading is above .010-.040" (.254-1.016 mm), replace torque converter.

TRANSAXLE DISASSEMBLY

1) Mount transaxle in a holding stand. Pull torque converter from case, then remove oil pump drive shaft. Remove oil pan attaching bolts, then remove oil pan. Remove attaching bolts and lift out oil filter.

2) Remove differential bearing retainer-to-case attaching bolts, then pry retainer from case. Remove differential bearing preload and tapered shims located under bearing retainer. Remove differential assembly from transaxle case.

3) Remove valve body cover. Remove valve body attaching bolts, baffle plate and detent/roller assembly. Disconnect and remove throttle valve control spring. Disengage "Z" link from manual valve and remove valve body assembly. Lift governor screen from bore in case (located under valve body).

NOTE: **The 7 baffle plate attaching bolts are longer than the other valve body attaching bolts.**

4) Remove cover and pull governor from case. Pry speedometer driven gear retaining pin partially out of

FORD MOTOR CO. ATX — AUTOMATIC TRANSAXLE (Cont.)

case, then remove pin using side cutters. Remove driven gear from case using a hammer handle as shown in *Fig. 9*.

Fig. 9: Removing Speedometer Driven Gear

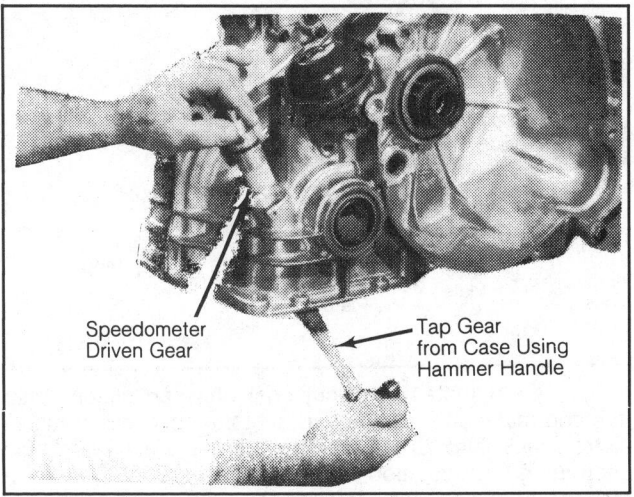

Speedometer Driven Gear

Tap Gear from Case Using Hammer Handle

5) Remove oil pump attaching bolts and washers. Remove pump from case using a slide hammer puller. Remove and discard pump gasket. Remove thrust bearing (needle) from top of intermediate clutch, then remove clutch assembly from case.

6) Remove thrust bearing (needle) from direct clutch, then remove direct clutch from case. Remove intermediate clutch hub and ring gear assembly. Remove thrust bearing (needle) from planetary assembly.

7) Remove large snap ring securing reverse clutch in case, then pull reverse clutch pack from case. Remove planetary assembly and thrust washer from case. Remove reverse clutch return springs and holder assembly, then pull reverse clutch piston from case. Pry reverse clutch drum up to loosen and remove from case.

8) Using a compressor tool, compress servo and remove retaining snap ring. Slowly release spring pressure, then remove compressor tool and servo assembly. Remove band from inside case.

9) Remove sun gear and drum assembly from case, then remove thrust washer from transfer housing at rear of case. Remove transfer housing-to-case attaching

Fig. 10: Removing Idler Gear Shaft Nut

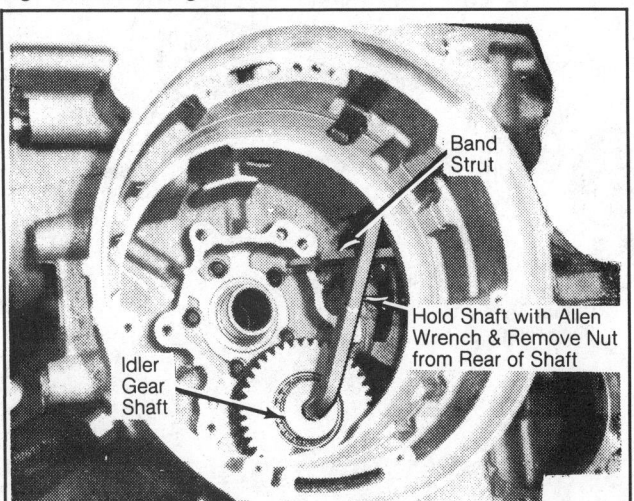

Band Strut

Hold Shaft with Allen Wrench & Remove Nut from Rear of Shaft

Idler Gear Shaft

bolts, then use a screwdriver and pry housing from idler gear shaft and remove from case.

10) Remove thrust bearing (needle) from input gear and remove input gear from case. Remove input gear caged needle bearing and thrust bearing located under it from case.

11) Position a 12 mm Allen wrench in idler gear shaft and allow wrench to catch on band strut as shown in *Fig. 10*. With wrench holding idler gear shaft, remove nut from rear of shaft using a 32 mm, 12 point socket. Tap idler gear shaft with a hammer handle to loosen "O" ring, then remove shaft from case.

COMPONENT DISASSEMBLY & REASSEMBLY

OIL PUMP

Disassembly

1) Remove selective fit thrust washer and oil seal rings from clutch support. Remove pump-to-case oil seal ring from outside diameter of clutch support.

2) Remove clutch support-to-pump body attaching bolts, then separate support from pump body. Remove insert from pump drive gear. Remove driven gear and drive gear from pump body.

Fig. 11: Exploded View of Oil Pump

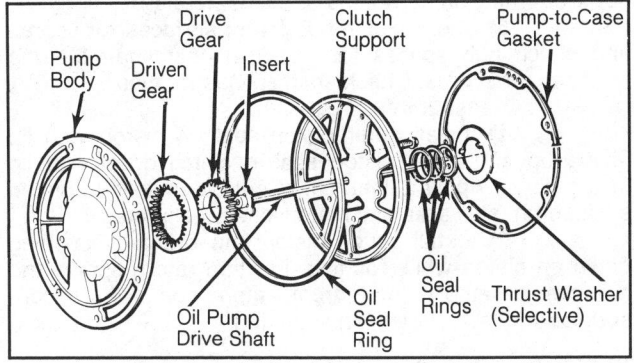

Pump Body

Drive Gear

Driven Gear

Insert

Clutch Support

Pump-to-Case Gasket

Oil Pump Drive Shaft

Oil Seal Ring

Oil Seal Rings

Thrust Washer (Selective)

Reassembly

Reverse disassembly procedure making sure ends of scarf-cut oil seal rings are correctly positioned.

INTERMEDIATE CLUTCH

Disassembly

1) Remove intermediate shaft snap ring, then pull shaft from intermediate clutch drum. If damaged, remove stop ring from intermediate shaft.

2) Remove clutch pack retaining snap ring and withdraw pressure plate and clutch pack. Remove seal rings from clutch drum hub.

3) Using a compressor tool, compress clutch return springs and remove retaining snap ring. Remove tool and lift return spring retainer and spring assembly from clutch drum.

4) Using pliers, remove clutch piston from drum. Remove inner piston seal from clutch drum and outer piston seal from clutch piston.

Inspection

1) Inspect clutch drum thrust surfaces, piston bore and clutch plate serrations for scores or burrs. Minor scores or burrs may be removed with crocus cloth. Replace drum if it is badly scored or damaged.

FORD MOTOR CO. ATX — AUTOMATIC TRANSAXLE (Cont.)

Fig. 12: *Exploded View of Intermediate Clutch Assembly*

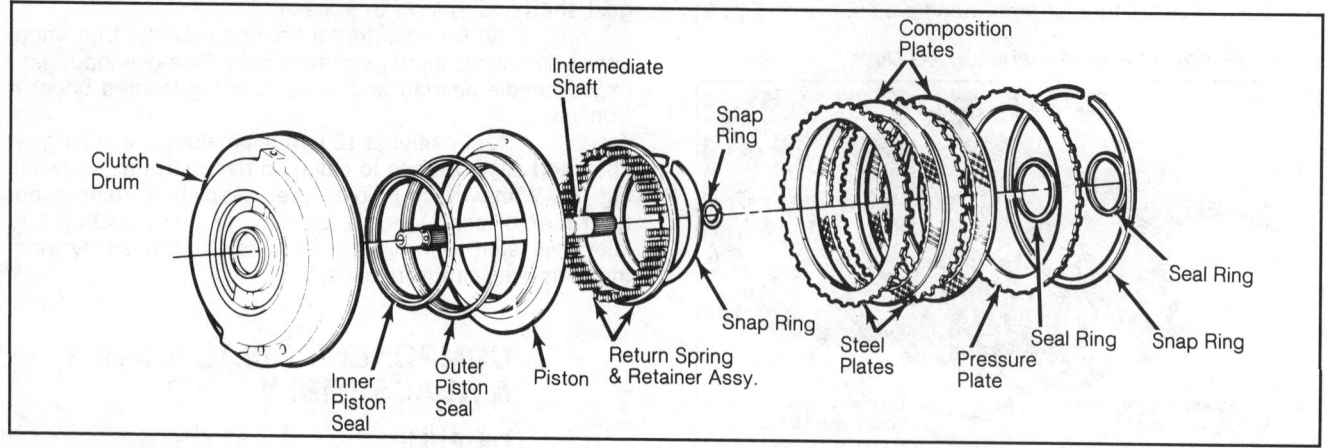

2) Check fluid passage in clutch drum for obstructions. Clean out all passages. Inspect clutch piston for scores and replace if necessary. Inspect piston check ball for freedom of movement and proper seating.

3) Inspect clutch return springs for distortion and cracks. Inspect composition plates, steel plates and pressure plate for worn or scored bearing surfaces. Replace all parts that are deeply scored.

4) Check clutch plates for flatness and fit on clutch drum hub serrations. Replace any plate that does not slide freely on serrations or that is not flat.

5) Check clutch hub thrust surfaces for scores and clutch hub splines for wear. Inspect shaft bearing surfaces for scores. Check shaft splines for wear.

Reassembly

1) Install outer piston seal on piston with lip facing up and inner piston seal in clutch drum with lip facing down. Apply a light film of petroleum jelly to piston seals, drum seal area and piston inner seal area.

2) Install clutch piston into drum by pushing down on piston while rotating. Position return spring and retainer assembly into drum, then compress return springs and install retaining snap ring.

3) Install scarf-cut seal rings on clutch drum hub and make sure seals overlap at the bevel edge. Install clutch pack into drum starting with a steel plate and alternating composition and steel plates until correct number of plates are installed. *See Intermediate Clutch Plate Usage Chart.* Install pressure plate and clutch pack retaining snap ring.

INTERMEDIATE CLUTCH PLATE USAGE CHART

Application [1]	Composition Plates	Steel Plates
Exc. Tempo, Topaz		
PMA-K, PMA-T,		
PMB-A, PMB-B	2	2
PMA-P, PMA-R	3	3
Tempo, Topaz		
PMA-N	3	3

[1] — These codes can be found on the first line of the transaxle identification tag.

Fig. 13: *Exploded View of Direct Clutch Assembly*

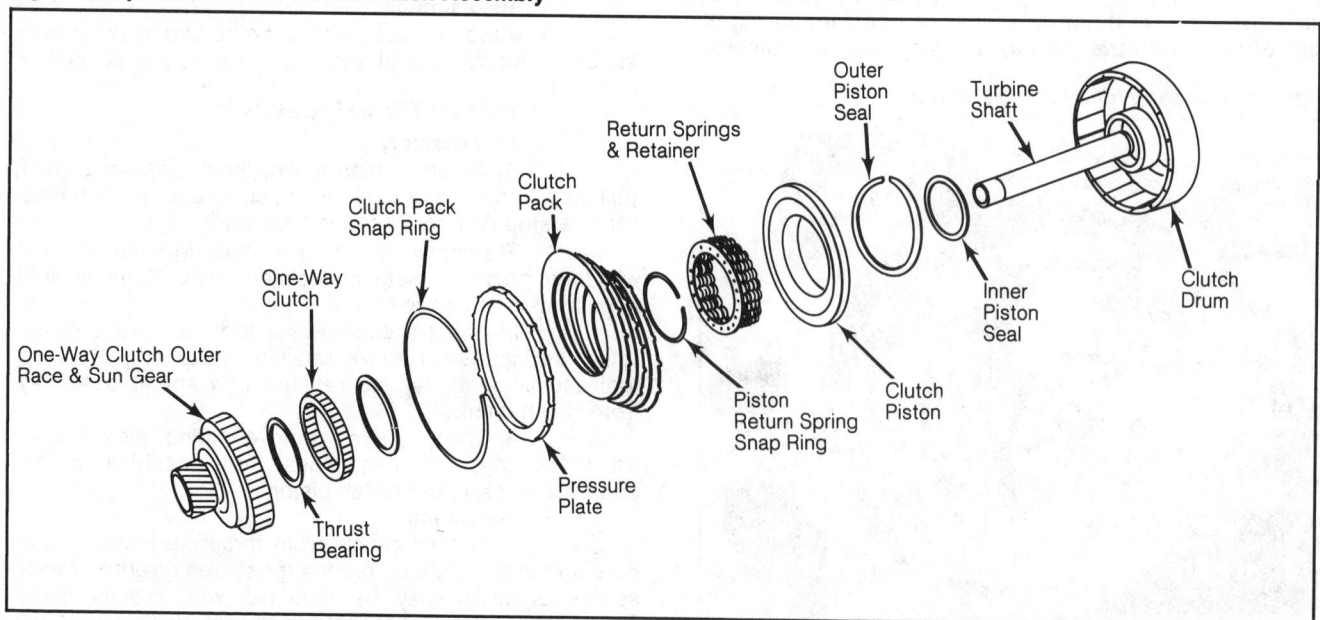

FORD MOTOR CO. ATX — AUTOMATIC TRANSAXLE (Cont.)

4) On Escort, EXP, LN7 and Lynx models, use a feeler gauge to measure clearance between clutch pack retaining snap ring and pressure plate with pressure plate held downward. Clearance should be .022-.035" (.56-.88 mm).

5) On Tempo and Topaz models, use a dial indicator to measure clearance between clutch between clutch pack retaining snap ring and pressure plate with pressure plate held downward. Take 2 readings 180° apart and average the readings. Clearance should be .030-.044" (.75-1.12 mm).

6) On all models, if clearance is not within specifications, selective snap rings are available in the following thicknesses: .049-.053" (1.245-1.346 mm), .059-.063" (1.499-1.600 mm), and .070-.074" (1.778-1.880 mm). Install correct size snap ring and recheck clearance.

7) If removed, install stop ring on intermediate shaft. Install shaft into clutch drum, then install intermediate shaft retaining snap ring.

DIRECT CLUTCH
Disassembly

1) Remove sun gear/one-way clutch race assembly. Remove thrust washer, then withdraw one-way clutch.

2) Remove clutch pack retaining snap ring, then remove pressure plate and clutch pack from clutch drum. Remove thrust bearing. Using a compressor tool, compress piston return spring retainer and remove retaining snap ring. Remove tool and piston return spring retainer.

3) Remove piston from clutch drum using pliers. Remove inner piston seal from clutch drum and outer piston seal from piston.

Inspection
See Intermediate Clutch Assembly Inspection.
Reassembly

1) Install inner seal on clutch drum with seal lip facing down. Install outer piston seal on piston with seal lip facing up. Apply a light film of petroleum jelly to piston seals, then install piston into drum using a rotating motion while applying downward pressure.

2) Position return springs, retainer and retaining snap ring in clutch drum, then compress retainer and install snap ring in groove. Install thrust bearing on top of return spring retainer.

3) Install clutch pack into drum starting with a steel clutch plate and alternating composition clutch plates and steel plates until correct number of clutch plates have been installed. *See Direct Clutch Plate Usage Chart.* Install pressure plate and clutch pack snap ring.

DIRECT CLUTCH PLATE USAGE CHART

Application	Composition Plates	Steel Plates
Exc. Tempo, Topaz		
PMA-K, PMA-T,		
PMB-A, PMB-B	3	3
PMA-P, PMA-R	4	4
Tempo, Topaz		
PMA-N	4	4

4) Install one-way clutch over turbine shaft and into clutch drum. Install thrust washer into drum and ensure that tabs of washer are facing down against shoulder of one-way clutch inner race.

5) Using a feeler gauge or dial indicator, measure clearance between clutch pack retaining snap ring and pressure plate with pressure plate held down. Direct clutch clearance should be .031-.047" (.78-1.20 mm) on 3 plates or .040-.056" (1.01-1.43 mm) on 4 plates.

6) If clearance is not within specified limits, selective fit snap rings are available in the following thicknesses: .050-.054" (1.26-1.36 mm), .062-.066" (1.58-1.68 mm) and .075-.079" (1.90-2.00 mm). Install correct size snap ring and recheck clearance.

7) Install sun gear/one-way clutch outer race assembly over turbine shaft and into clutch drum. Check operation of one-way clutch. When properly assembled the one-way clutch allows sun gear/outer race assembly to rotate in one direction only.

REVERSE CLUTCH

NOTE: **Reverse clutch was disassembled under Transaxle Disassembly and will be reassembled during Transaxle Reassembly. The following procedure is for replacing piston seals.**

Piston Seal Replacement
Remove seals from clutch cylinder and clutch piston. Install new seal on clutch cylinder with seal lips facing up. Install new inner seal on piston with seal lip facing down, then install new outer seal on piston.

NOTE: **The outer piston seal is square-cut, making direction of installation unimportant.**

Inspection
1) Inspect clutch piston bore and piston inner and outer bearing surfaces for scores. Check air bleed ball valve in piston for free movement. Check orifice for obstructions.

2) Check fluid passages for obstructions. All passages must be clean and free of obstructions. Inspect clutch plates for wear, scoring and fit on clutch hub serrations. Replace all plates that are badly scored, worn, or do not fit freely in hub serrations.

3) Inspect clutch pressure plate for scores on clutch plate bearing surface. Check clutch return springs for distortion or collapsed coils.

BAND APPLY SERVO
Disassembly
Remove piston return spring, then separate servo piston from cover. Remove piston rod circlip, then slide piston rod, cushion spring and spring retaining washer from piston. Remove seals from servo cover and piston.

Fig. 14: Exploded View of Band Apply Servo

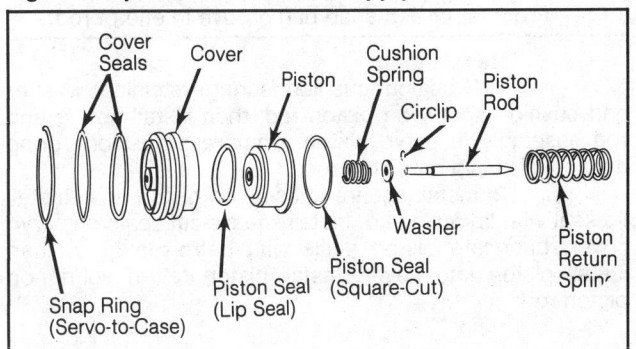

Automatic Transmissions

FORD MOTOR CO. ATX — AUTOMATIC TRANSAXLE (Cont.)

Inspection

1) Inspect servo body for cracks and piston bore for scores. Check fluid passages for obstructions. Inspect band and struts for distortion. Inspect band ends for cracks.

2) Inspect servo spring for distortion. Inspect band lining for excessive wear and bonding to metal band. Replace damaged seals.

NOTE: The following Servo Travel Check needs to be performed only if one of the following components has been replaced:
   - Transaxle Case
   - Band Assembly
   - Drum and Sun Gear Assembly
   - Servo Piston Rod
   - Servo Piston
   - Band Anchor Strut

Servo Travel Check

1) Clean and assemble servo piston without piston seals. Install return spring (T81P-70027-A or equivalent) on piston rod and position piston in case.

2) Install servo piston selector tool (T81P-70023-A) and secure in case using servo cover retaining snap ring, then tighten gauge disc screw to 10 ft. lbs. (14 N.m).

3) Mount a dial indicator and position indicator stylus through hole in gauge disc, making sure stylus contacts servo piston. Zero dial indicator.

4) Back-off gauge disc screw until piston movement stops and read dial indicator. The amount of piston travel shown on indicator will determine piston rod length to install.

5) If piston travel is .203-.247" (5.15-6.28 mm), correct piston rod is installed and no change is required. If travel is less than specifications, piston rod is too long and a shorter rod (more grooves) will have to be installed. If travel is more than specified, rod is too short and a longer rod (less grooves) will have to be installed.

6) Select a new piston rod, if necessary, from the following table, then install selected rod and recheck servo travel.

SERVO PISTON ROD SELECTION

Rod Length [1] In. (mm)	Rod I.D.
6.313-6.324 (160.22-160.52)	No Grooves
6.289-6.300 (159.61-159.90)	1 Groove
6.265-6.276 (159.00-159.30)	2 Grooves
6.240-6.252 (158.39-158.69)	3 Grooves
6.216-6.223 (157.88-158.08)	4 Grooves
6.197-6.209 (157.17-157.47)	5 Grooves

[1] — From far end of snap ring groove to end of rod.

Reassembly

1) Position cushion spring retaining washer and cushion spring on piston rod, then install spring and rod assembly in servo piston. Compress cushion spring and install circlip on piston rod.

2) Install square-cut seal on piston, then install lip seal with lip facing up. Install square-cut seals on servo cover. Lubricate piston seals with petroleum jelly, then install piston into cover. Install piston return spring on piston rod.

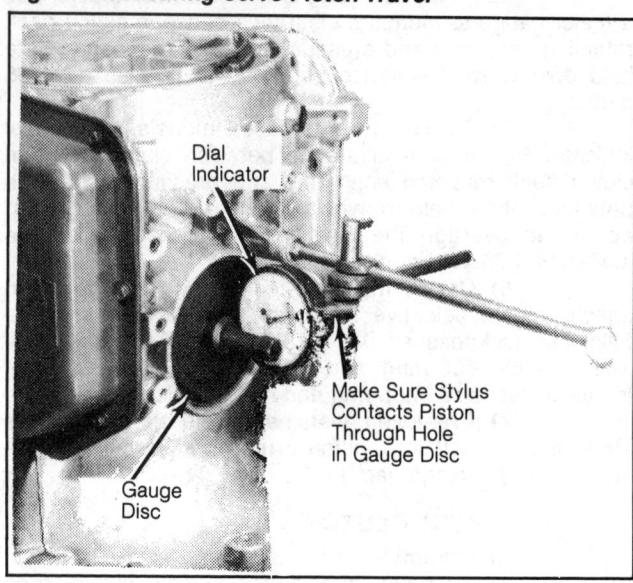

Fig. 15: Measuring Servo Piston Travel

VALVE BODY ASSEMBLY

NOTE: The reference numbers in Fig. 17 apply to the Valve Body Disassembly numbered steps.

Disassembly

1) Remove the 2 separator plate attaching screws and remove separator plate from valve body, then remove check balls and relief valve from valve body cored passages. Compress reverse boost valve plug, remove retainer and slide out valve plug, spring and reverse boost valve.

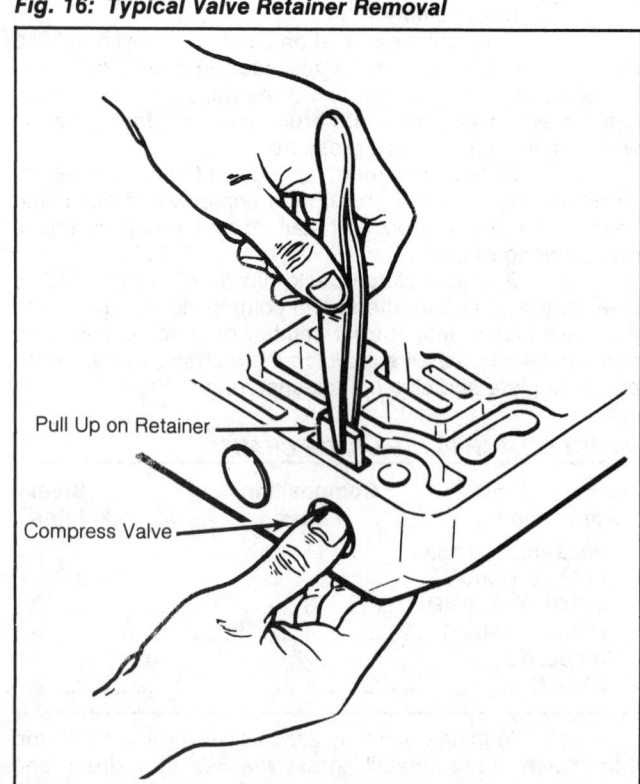

Fig. 16: Typical Valve Retainer Removal

FORD MOTOR CO. ATX — AUTOMATIC TRANSAXLE (Cont.)

2) Compress 2-3 shift valve plug, remove retainer and slide out valve plug, 2-3 shift valve and valve spring.

3) Compress 1-2 shift valve, remove retainer, then slide out valve plug, 1-2 shift valve, modulator valve spring and 1-2 T.V. modulator valve.

4) Compress 2-1 scheduling valve, remove retainer, then slide out valve spring and 2-1 scheduling valve.

5) Compress 2-3 backout valve, remove retainer, then slide out valve plug, valve spring and 2-3 backout valve.

6) Compress main oil pressure regulator, remove retainer, then slide out main oil pressure booster sleeve, main oil regulator boost valve, regulator valve spring, spring retainer and main oil regulator valve.

7) Compress manual low downshift modulating valve, remove retainer, then slide out valve plug, manual low downshift valve and valve spring.

8) Compress 3-2 torque demand timing valve, remove retainer, then slide out valve spring and 3-2 torque demand timing control valve.

9) Compress 3-2 kickdown timing valve, remove retainer, then slide out valve spring and 3-2 kickdown timing valve.

10) Compress 3-2 control valve, remove retainer, then slide out valve spring and 3-2 control valve.

11) Compress 2-3 shift T.V. modulator valve, remove retainer, then slide out valve plug, valve spring and 2-3 shift T.V. modulator valve.

12) Compress 1-2 capacity modulator valve, remove retainer, then slide out valve plug, 1-2 capacity modulator valve and valve spring.

13) Compress 1-2 accumulator valve, remove retainer, then slide out valve plug, 1-2 accumulator valve and valve spring.

14) Compress T.V. limit valve, remove retainer, then slide out valve spring and T.V. limit valve.

15) Compress throttle pressure valve, remove retainer, then slide out throttle valve plunger sleeve, throttle pressure valve, plunger return spring (large), throttle valve spring (small) and small throttle pressure valve. Using a drift, drive out retaining pin and remove throttle pressure adjusting sleeve.

CAUTION: DO NOT turn throttle valve adjusting screw and lock nut. Adjustment screw is set during manufacture and must not be altered.

16) Slide manual control valve from valve body bore.

Fig. 17: Exploded View of Valve Body Valve Trains

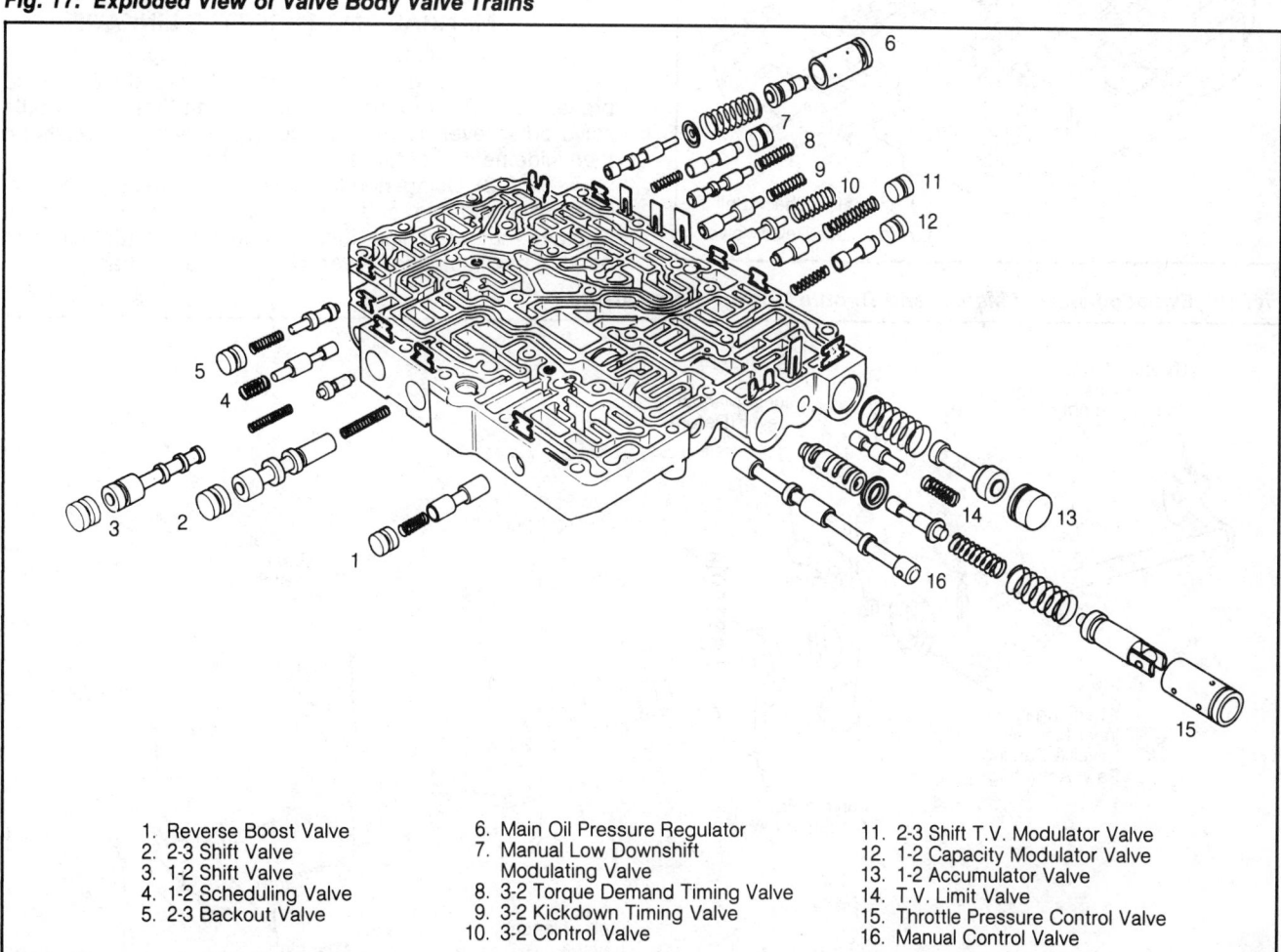

1. Reverse Boost Valve
2. 2-3 Shift Valve
3. 1-2 Shift Valve
4. 1-2 Scheduling Valve
5. 2-3 Backout Valve
6. Main Oil Pressure Regulator
7. Manual Low Downshift Modulating Valve
8. 3-2 Torque Demand Timing Valve
9. 3-2 Kickdown Timing Valve
10. 3-2 Control Valve
11. 2-3 Shift T.V. Modulator Valve
12. 1-2 Capacity Modulator Valve
13. 1-2 Accumulator Valve
14. T.V. Limit Valve
15. Throttle Pressure Control Valve
16. Manual Control Valve

NOTE: See numbered step under Valve Body Disassembly which corresponds to valve train reference number for identification of individual valve train components.

FORD MOTOR CO. ATX — AUTOMATIC TRANSAXLE (Cont.)

Inspection

1) Clean all parts thoroughly in clean solvent, and blow dry with moisture-free compressed air.

2) Inspect all valve and plug bores for scores. Check all fluid passages for obstructions. Inspect all mating surfaces for burrs or distortion. Inspect all plugs and valves for burrs and scores.

NOTE: **If necessary, use crocus cloth to polish valve and plugs. Avoid rounding off sharp edges of valves and plugs with cloth.**

3) Inspect all springs for distortion. Check all valves and plugs for free movement in their bores. Valves and plugs, when dry, must fall from their own weight in their respective bores. Roll manual control valve on a flat surface to check for bent condition.

Fig. 18: View of Valve Body Showing Location of Check Balls and Relief Valve

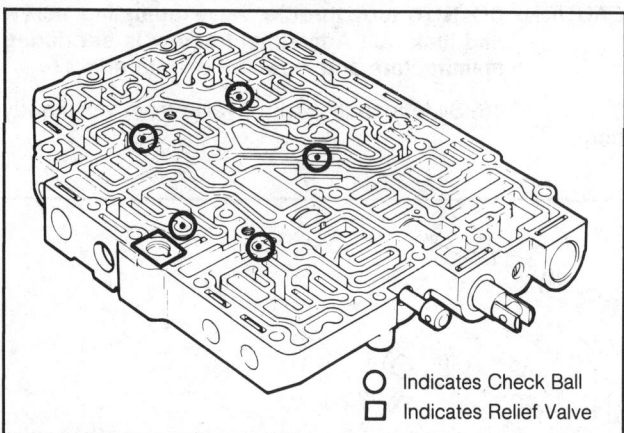

○ Indicates Check Ball
□ Indicates Relief Valve

Reassembly

Reverse disassembly procedure and note the following: Install the 6 check balls and the relief valve into valve body passages shown in *Fig. 18*. Use alignment pins when installing separator plate and gasket to ensure that they are properly aligned with valve body.

GOVERNOR

NOTE: **Governor Disassembly and Reassembly procedures were not available from manufacturer.**

Inspection

1) Inspect governor valve and bore for scores. Minor scores may be removed from valve with crocus cloth. Replace governor if valves or body is deeply scored.

2) Inspect governor screen for obstructions. Screen must be free of foreign material. If contaminated, clean thoroughly in solvent and blow dry with compressed air.

3) Check for free movement of valves in bores. Valves should slide freely of their own weight in bores when dry. Inspect fluid passages in valve body and counterweight for obstructions. All fluid passages must be clean. Inspect governor drive gear and replace it if teeth are broken, chipped or excessively worn.

MANUAL AND THROTTLE LINKAGE

Disassembly

1) Hold outer throttle lever stationary to prevent damage to throttle shaft cam and remove throttle valve outer lever. Remove attaching screws and washers, then slide neutral safety switch from shaft.

2) Using needle nose pliers, remove manual lever retaining pin and parking pawl ratcheting spring. Remove nut attaching inner manual lever (detent) and parking pawl actuating lever to manual lever shaft.

Fig. 19: Exploded View of Manual and Throttle Linkage Components

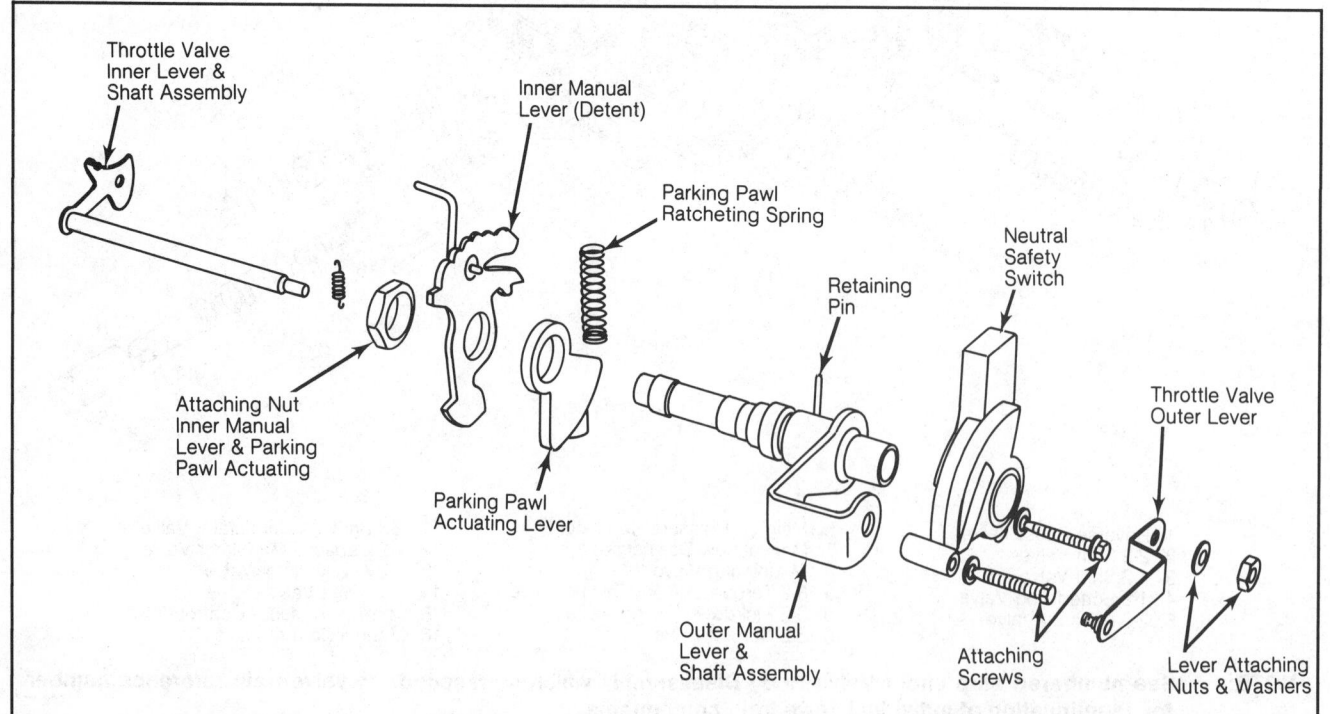

Throttle Valve Inner Lever & Shaft Assembly

Inner Manual Lever (Detent)

Parking Pawl Ratcheting Spring

Retaining Pin

Neutral Safety Switch

Throttle Valve Outer Lever

Attaching Nut Inner Manual Lever & Parking Pawl Actuating

Parking Pawl Actuating Lever

Outer Manual Lever & Shaft Assembly

Attaching Screws

Lever Attaching Nuts & Washers

FORD MOTOR CO. ATX — AUTOMATIC TRANSAXLE (Cont.)

3) Remove manual lever and shaft assembly, then remove throttle valve lever and components on throttle valve lever shaft. Remove parking pawl return spring. Using a screwdriver, pry manual lever shaft oil seal from case and throttle valve lever shaft seal from manual lever.

Reassembly
1) Install new manual lever shaft seal in case. Install new seal on throttle lever shaft. Install parking pawl return spring.

2) Install inner manual lever and parking pawl actuator attaching nut on throttle shaft, then install inner manual lever and parking pawl actuator on shaft. Position throttle shaft in case and install manual lever and shaft assembly.

3) Position parking pawl actuator and inner manual lever on manual shaft, then install and tighten attaching nut. Install parking pawl ratcheting spring. Install manual lever retaining pin.

4) Install neutral safety switch in case. Install, but do not tighten, attaching screws and washers. Adjust neutral safety switch. See appropriate article in Automatic Transmission Servicing for switch adjustment. Tighten attaching screws. Install outer throttle lever. Tighten attaching nut while holding lever stationary to prevent damage to throttle shaft cam.

DIFFERENTIAL ASSEMBLY
Disassembly
1) Using a puller, remove differential side bearings from differential case. Pull speedometer drive gear from case.

2) Remove side gears and thrust washers from differential case by rotating the gears toward case windows. Using a punch, drive out differential pinion gear shaft retaining pin, then remove gears and thrust washers from case.

3) If necessary, remove ring gear from differential case as follows: Using a 5/16" drill, drill formed side of attaching rivets, then remove heads of rivets with a chisel. Using a punch, drive remaining rivet shank from case and remove ring gear.

Inspection
1) Thoroughly clean all parts in new solvent. Do not spin dry bearings using compressed air. Oil side bearings immediately after cleaning to prevent corrosion. Inspect parts for any major defect.

NOTE: When a scored or chipped gear is replaced, transaxle case must be cleaned thoroughly to insure all chips are removed.

2) Examine pinion and side gears for scoring, excessive wear, nicks and chips. Worn, scored and damaged gears must be replaced.

3) Make sure differential case bearing journals are smooth. Inspect case bearing shoulders for damage caused by bearing removal. Check fit (free rotation) of side gears in their cavities.

4) Check bearing races for deep scores, galling or chipping. If races are not damaged, do not remove from transaxle case or differential retainer. If races must be replaced, remove and install with appropriate tools.

5) Check side bearings for smooth rotation in races. Examine bearing roller ends for step wear. If

Fig. 20: Exploded View of Differential Assembly

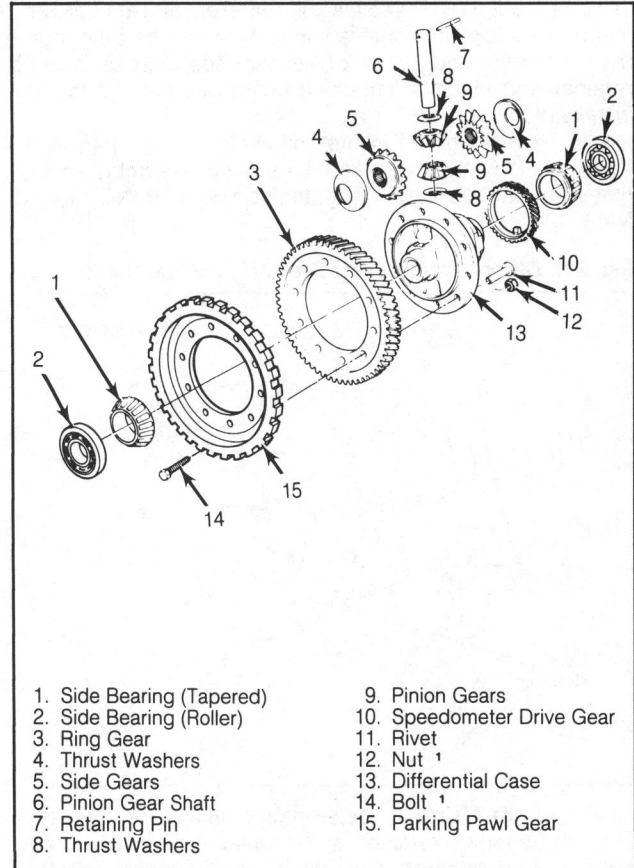

1. Side Bearing (Tapered)
2. Side Bearing (Roller)
3. Ring Gear
4. Thrust Washers
5. Side Gears
6. Pinion Gear Shaft
7. Retaining Pin
8. Thrust Washers
9. Pinion Gears
10. Speedometer Drive Gear
11. Rivet
12. Nut [1]
13. Differential Case
14. Bolt [1]
15. Parking Pawl Gear

[1] — Service replacement for attaching ring gear.

inspection reveals either a damaged race or bearing, both parts must be replaced as they are a matched set.

Reassembly
To reassemble differential assembly, reverse disassembly procedure and note the following:
- Lubricate all thrust washers and thrust surfaces on gears and in case with automatic transmission fluid.
- If removed, press ring gear onto differential case and attach to case with service replacement nuts and bolts. Install bolts with heads on parking pawl gear side of ring gear.

NOTE: Differential side gears must be aligned in case. This alignment must be held while installing differential assembly in transaxle case. Failure to maintain alignment will make it impossible to install axle drive shafts through side gears.

Differential Bearing Preload Adjustment
1) Differential bearing preload is set at the factory and need not be checked or adjusted unless one of the following parts is replaced:
- Transaxle Case
- Differential Case
- Differential Bearings
- Differential Bearing Retainer

2) To adjust preload, install differential assembly into transaxle case. Install differential bearing retainer to case without oil seal or "O" ring seal.

FORD MOTOR CO. ATX — AUTOMATIC TRANSAXLE (Cont.)

3) Install differential bearing preload shim selector tool (T81P-4451-A) in differential retainer and make sure tool is centered in differential bearing outer race. Position gauge bar of selector tool across bearing retainer and install 2 attaching bolts. *See Fig. 21 for tool installation.*

4) Tighten center screw of gauge bar to 10 INCH lbs. (1 N.m), then rotate differential assembly several times to seat bearings. Retighten screw to 10 INCH lbs. (1 N.m).

Fig. 21: Differential Bearing Preload Tool Installation

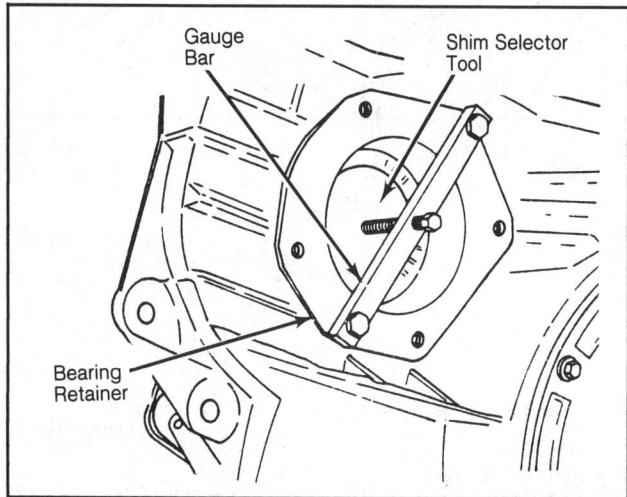

5) Using a feeler gauge, measure clearance between bearing retainer and transaxle case at 3 positions around retainer. Add the 3 measurements together and divide by 3 to obtain the average of all measurements.

6) To determine the shim needed for correct bearing preload, subtract the bearing preload value of .018" (.457 mm) and the tapered shim thickness of .030" (.762 mm) from the average measurement obtained in step **5)**. Resulting sum is the thickness of preload shim to install.

Fig. 22: Installing Tapered Shim

Make Sure Notch in Shim is Installed as Shown

Differential Bearing Tapered Shim

NOTE: Differential bearing preload shims are available in thicknesses of .012"-.051" (.305-1.29 mm) in various increments. If calculations result in shim thickness which falls between 2 available thicknesses, always use the thicker shim.

7) Remove gauge bar, selector tool and bearing retainer. Install new differential oil seal in retainer and new "O" ring on retainer. Position tapered shim and selected preload shim in position on transaxle case, then install bearing retainer by tapping evenly around outside edge of retainer face.

NOTE: Make sure notch in tapered shim is positioned as shown in Fig. 22.

8) Apply sealer to bolt threads, then install differential bearing retainer-to-case attaching bolts. Tighten bolts to specifications.

PINION CARRIERS

NOTE: Individual parts of the planet carrier are not serviceable. If any part is worn or damaged, complete planet carrier must be replaced.

Inspection
Inspect pins and shafts for loose fit and/or complete disengagement. Check shaft welds. Inspect pinion gears for damage or excessively worn teeth. Check for free rotation of pinion gears.

INPUT, IDLER AND FINAL DRIVE GEARS
Inspection
Inspect gear teeth; they should be smooth with a uniform contact pattern without signs of excessive wear. Replace any gear which is cracked, chipped, broken or excessively worn.

TRANSAXLE CASE
Inspection
Inspect case for cracks and stripped threads. Inspect gasket surfaces and mating surfaces for burrs. Check vent for obstructions, and check all fluid passages for obstructions and leakage. Inspect case bushing for scores. Check all parking linkage parts for wear or damage.

NOTE: Service kits are available for repairing damaged case threads.

TRANSAXLE REASSEMBLY

NOTE: Handle all parts carefully to avoid damaging bearings and mating surfaces. Lubricate all parts with clean automatic transmission fluid (use petroleum jelly on gaskets, thrust washers and needle bearings to retain them in place). Use all new gaskets and seals, and tighten bolts evenly.

1) Install a new "O" ring seal on idler gear shaft, then position gear and shaft in transaxle case. Install a 12 mm Allen wrench in idler gear shaft and bring it around until it catches on band anchor strut. Install lock

FORD MOTOR CO. ATX — AUTOMATIC TRANSAXLE (Cont.)

nut and tighten to specifications while holding shaft stationary.

2) Install thrust bearing (needle) into case and over reactor support, then place input gear caged needle bearing over reactor support as shown in *Fig. 23*.

Fig. 23: Installing Thrust Bearing and Caged Needle Bearing

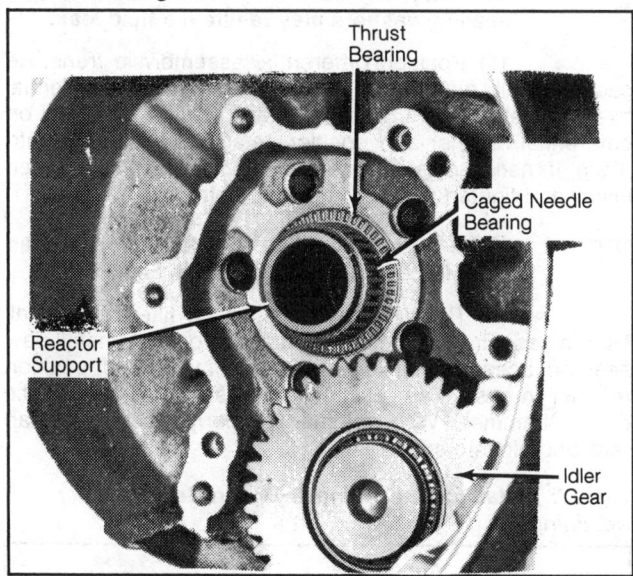

3) Install input gear over reactor support, then install thrust bearing (needle) on input gear. Position transfer housing in case, making sure it is fully seated on alignment dowels. Install and tighten transfer housing-to-transaxle case attaching bolts.

4) Install thrust washer on transfer housing. Install sun gear and drum assembly into transaxle case, then install band into case and around drum, making sure band lug engages strut.

Fig. 24: Measuring Reverse Clutch Clearance

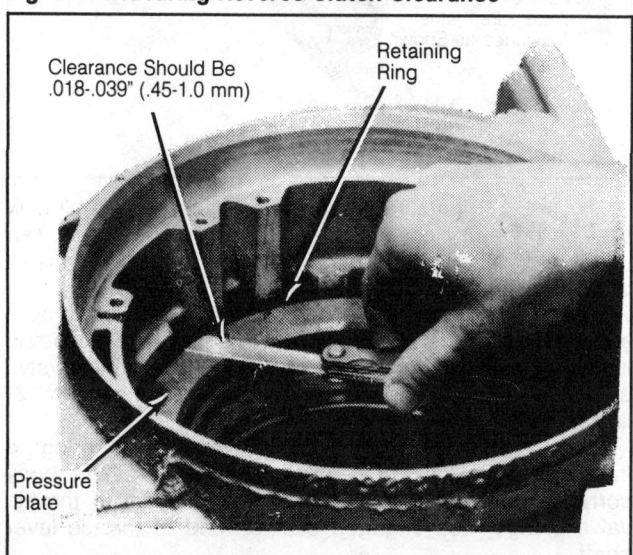

5) Position servo piston in case, then compress servo and install retaining snap ring. Before removing servo compressor tool, make sure servo piston rod has engaged band lug.

6) Position reverse clutch drum in transaxle case. Using a hammer handle, tap drum fully into case. Using a seal protector, install reverse clutch piston into clutch drum. Remove seal protector. Install thrust washer on planetary assembly, then install assembly on sun gear.

NOTE: **Before installing reverse clutch piston return spring and holder assembly, reverse clutch clearance must be checked as follows:**

7) Install clutch pack wave spring, clutch pack and pressure plate, then install clutch pack retaining ring. Using a feeler gauge, measure clearance between retaining ring and pressure plate at 2 places 180 degrees apart.

8) If average clearance is .030-.053" (.76-1.35 mm), clutch clearance is correct. If clearance is less than .030" (.76 mm), install a thinner retaining ring. If clearance is greater than .053" (1.35 mm), install a thicker retaining ring.

NOTE: **Whenever a new retaining ring is installed, repeat clearance check. Reverse clutch retaining rings are available in the following thicknesses: .074-.078" (1.89-1.99 mm), .092-.096" (2.33-2.43 mm), .109-.113" (2.77-2.87 mm) and .126-.130" (3.21-3.31 mm).**

REVERSE CLUTCH PLATE USAGE CHART

Application [1]	Composition Plates	Steel Plates
Exc. Tempo, Topaz		
PMA-K, PMA-T,		
PMB-A, PMB-B	2	2
PMA-P, PMA-R	3	3
Tempo, Topaz		
PMA-N	3	3

[1] — These codes can be found on the first line of the transaxle identification tag.

Fig. 25: Checking Intermediate Clutch for Proper Engagement

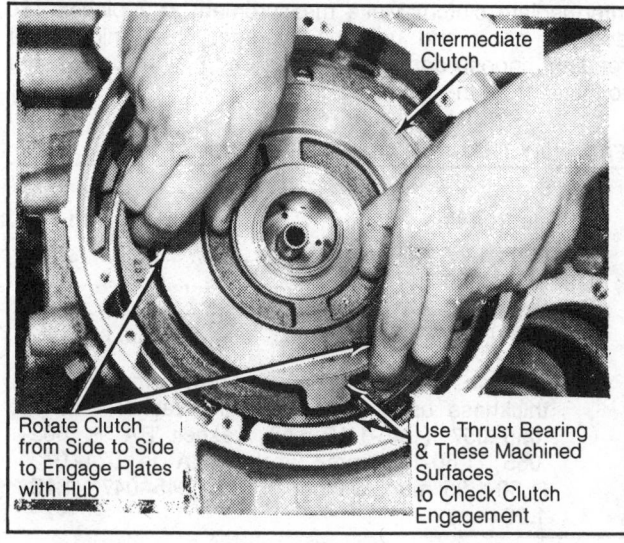

FORD MOTOR CO. ATX — AUTOMATIC TRANSAXLE (Cont.)

9) Remove reverse clutch pack retaining ring, pressure plate, clutch pack and wave spring. Install reverse clutch return spring and holder assembly, then reinstall wave spring, clutch pack, pressure plate and retaining ring.

10) Install thrust bearing (needle) on planetary assembly. Install intermediate clutch hub and ring gear assembly into case. Install direct clutch assembly into case, then position thrust bearing (needle) on direct clutch.

11) Install intermediate clutch assembly into case and check for proper clutch engagement as follows: Position thrust bearing on one of the machined tabs and push it up against the case. If bearing is flush with, or slightly below machined pump housing surface in case, clutch is fully engaged. *See Fig. 25.* Position thrust bearing on clutch drum.

12) Install oil pump alignment pins (T81P-77100-A or equivalent) and pump housing gasket. Position transaxle end play checking tools (T81P-77389-A and T80L-77003-A) in intermediate clutch as shown in *Fig. 26.*

Fig. 26: Assembling Transaxle End Play Measuring Tools

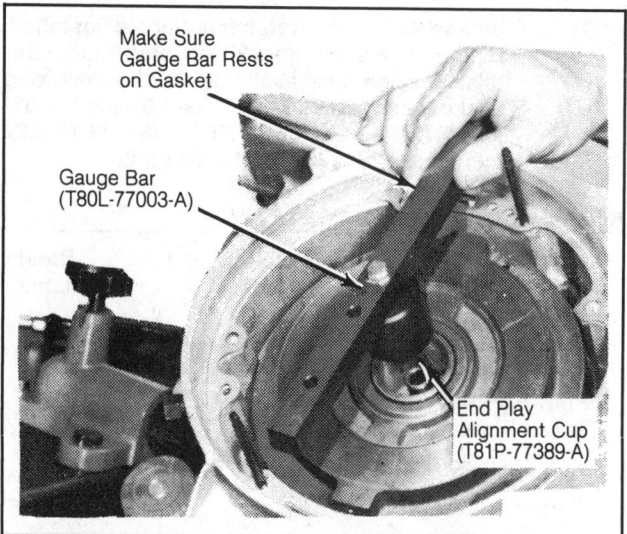

13) Using a micrometer, measure distance from top of gauge bar to top of thrust bearing installed on intermediate clutch. Make measurement at 2 places 180 degrees apart and use the average. From micrometer reading, choose correct thickness end play thrust washer to install from the following chart.

END PLAY THRUST WASHER SELECTION CHART

For This Reading	Use This [1] Washer Part I.D.
.070-.079" (1.77-2.00 mm)	AA
.079-.087" (2.00-2.20 mm)	BA
.087-.095" (2.20-2.41 mm)	CA
.057-.070" (1.46-1.77 mm)	EA

[1] — If washer thickness is not known, measure its thickness using a micrometer. Washer "AA" is .055-.057" (1.40-1.45 mm); washer "BA" is .063-.065" (1.60-1.65 mm); washer "CA" is .071-.073" (1.80-1.85 mm); washer "EA" is .045-.047" (1.15-1.20 mm).

14) Install selected transaxle end play thrust washer on oil pump, then position pump in case and tap into place using a hammer handle. Remove pump alignment pins and install pump attaching bolts and washers.

CAUTION: Attaching bolt washers provide the bolt seal and must not be substituted. Failure to use sealing washers may result in a fluid leak.

15) Position differential assembly in transaxle case. Install differential tapered shim and differential bearing preload shim on case. Install new "O" ring seal on differential retainer and position retainer in case (tap into place if necessary). Apply sealer to bolt threads, then install and tighten retainer attaching bolt.

NOTE: Make sure that notch in differential tapered shim is positioned as shown in Fig. 22.

16) Position new seal on oil filter and install filter in case. Install oil pan using a new gasket. Install new seal on speedometer driven gear retainer and position retainer in case. Tap retainer into position using a plastic tipped hammer. With retainer properly positioned, tap retaining pin into case.

Fig. 27: Installing Speedometer Driven Gear Retainer Retaining Pin

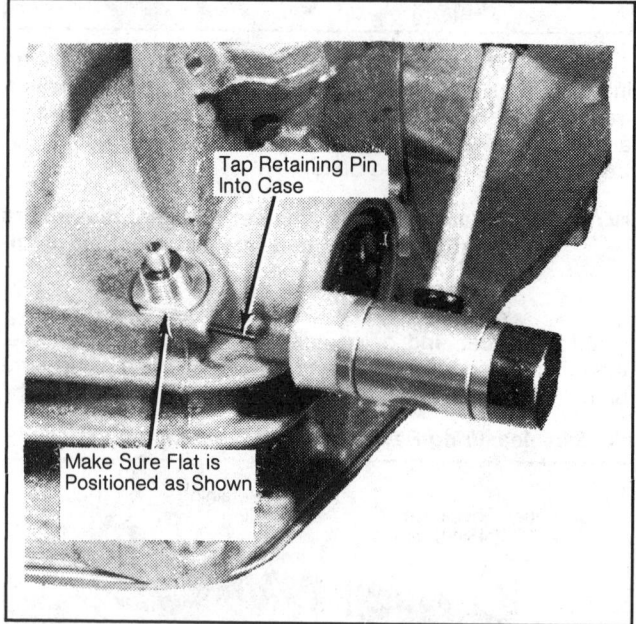

17) Install governor into case, then install new seal on governor cover and position cover on case. Tap cover into place using a plastic tipped hammer and install cover retaining wire.

18) Position governor screen into case bore shown in *Fig. 29.* Position valve body gasket on case and install alignment pins to hold gasket in place. Place valve body in position in case and at the same time connect "Z" link to manual valve.

19) Connect throttle valve control spring to inner lever cam and to separator plate. With valve body correctly positioned, make sure roller on end of throttle valve plunger has engaged cam on end of throttle lever shaft.

FORD MOTOR CO. ATX — AUTOMATIC TRANSAXLE (Cont.)

Fig. 28: Exploded View of ATX Automatic Transaxle Assembly

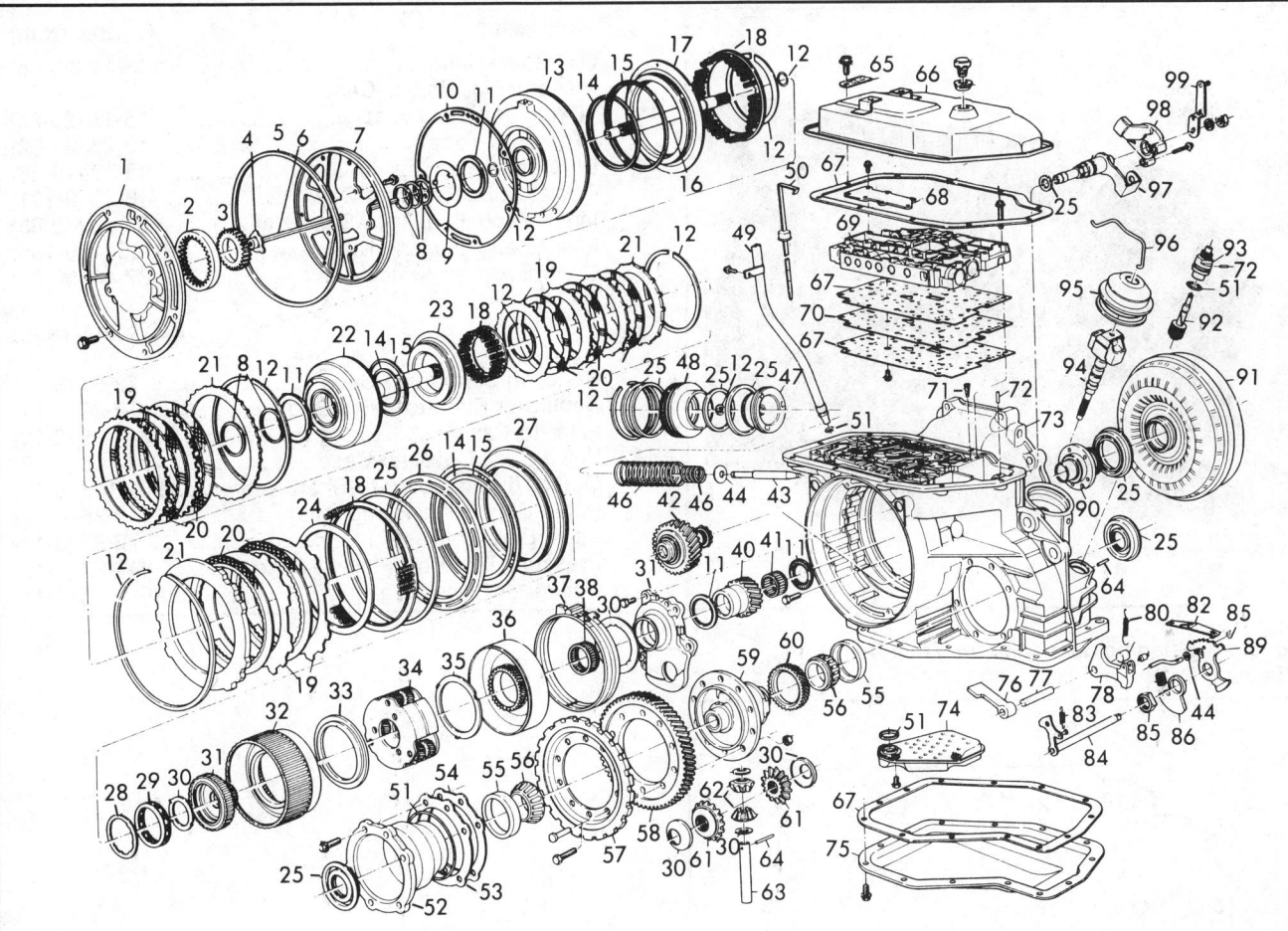

1. Oil Pump Body	26. Reverse Clutch Piston	51. "O" Ring	76. Band Anchor Strut
2. Pump Driven Gear	27. Reverse Clutch Drum	52. Differential Retainer	77. Park Pawl Shaft
3. Pump Drive Gear	28. One-Way Clutch Bearing	53. Tapered Shim	78. Park Pawl
4. Pump Gear Insert	29. Spring & Roller Assy.	54. Side Bearing Preload Shim	79. Cup Plug
5. Oil Pump Seal	30. Thrust Washer	55. Outer Race	80. Pawl Return Spring
6. Oil Pump Shaft	31. Race & Sun Gear Assy.	56. Differential Side Bearing	81. Pawl Roller Pin
7. Clutch Support	32. Interm. Clutch Hub & Ring Gear	57. Parking Pawl Gear	82. Manual Valve Detent Spring
8. Teflon Oil Seals	33. Planet Rear Thrust Bearing	58. Ring Gear	83. TV Lever Control Spring
9. End Play Thrust Washer	34. Planetary Assy.	59. Differential Case	84. TV Lever Actuating Shaft
10. Pump Gasket	35. Planet Front Thrust Washer	60. Speedometer Drive Gear	85. Nut
11. Thrust Bearing	36. Sun Gear & Drum Assy.	61. Side Gears	86. Park Pawl Actuating Lever
12. Snap Ring	37. Band	62. Pinion Gears	87. Park Pawl Ratcheting Spring
13. Interm. Clutch Drum	38. Transfer Hsg. Bearing	63. Pinion Gear Shaft	88. Manual Lever Actuator
14. Inner Piston Seal	39. Transfer Housing	64. Retaining Pin	89. Manual Valve Inner Lever
15. Outer Piston Seal	40. Input Gear	65. Transaxle I.D. Tag	90. Reactor Support
16. Interm. Clutch Shaft	41. Input Gear Bearing	66. Valve Body Cover	91. Torque Converter
17. Interm. Clutch Piston	42. Idler Gear	67. Gasket	92. Speedometer Driven Gear
18. Return Spring Assy.	43. Servo Rod	68. Baffle Plate	93. Speedometer Gear Retainer
19. Steel Clutch Plates	44. Washer	69. Valve Body Assy.	94. Governor
20. Composition Clutch Plates	45. Cushion Spring	70. Separator Plate	95. Governor Cover
21. Pressure Plate	46. Piston Spring	71. Governor Screen	96. Retainer Wire
22. Direct Clutch Drum	47. Servo Piston	72. Dowel Pin	97. Manual Lever
23. Direct Clutch Piston	48. Servo Cover	73. Transaxle Case	98. Neutral Safety Switch
24. Wave Spring	49. Oil Filler Tube	74. Oil Filter	99. TV Outer Lever
25. Seal	50. Dipstick	75. Oil Pan	

FORD MOTOR CO. ATX — AUTOMATIC TRANSAXLE (Cont.)

Fig. 29: Installing Governor Screen

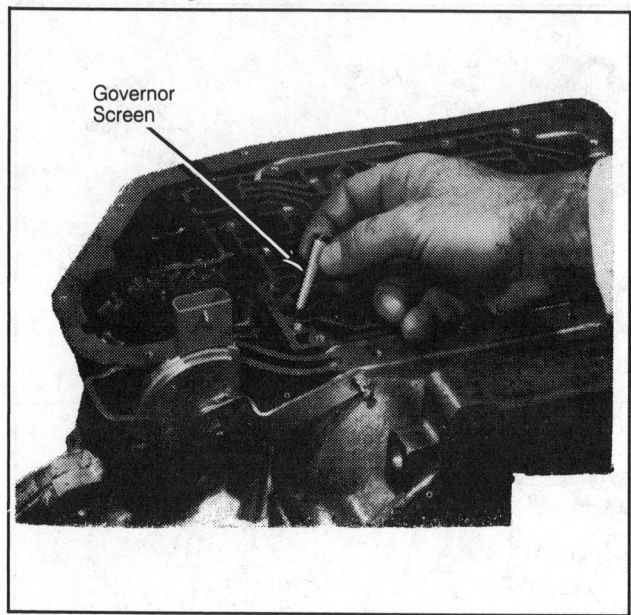

TIGHTENING SPECIFICATIONS

Application	Ft. Lbs. (N.m)
Oil Pan-to-Case	15-19 (20-26)
Transfer Housing-to-Case	
Exc. Tempo & Topaz	15-19 (20-26)
Tempo & Topaz	18-23 (24-32)
Differential Retainer-to-Case	15-19 (20-26)
Cooler Tube Fitting-to-Case	18-23 (24-31)
Inner Manual Lever-to-Shaft Nut	32-48 (43-65)
Idler Shaft Attaching Nut	80-100 (108-136)
Control Arm-to-Knuckle	37-44 (50-60)

	INCH Lbs. (N.m)
Reaction Support-to-Case	72-96 (8-11)
Separator Plate-to-Valve Body	72-96 (8-11)
Filter-to-Case	84-108 (9-12)
Valve Body Cover-to-Case	84-108 (9-12)
Outer Throttle Lever-to-Shaft Nut	90-114 (10-13)
Pump Support-to-Pump Body	72-96 (8-11)
Valve Body-to-Case	72-96 (8-11)
Pressure Test Port Plug-to-Case	84-132 (9-15)
Converter Drain Plug	96-144 (10-16)

Fig. 30: Tightening Sequence for Valve Body Attaching Bolts

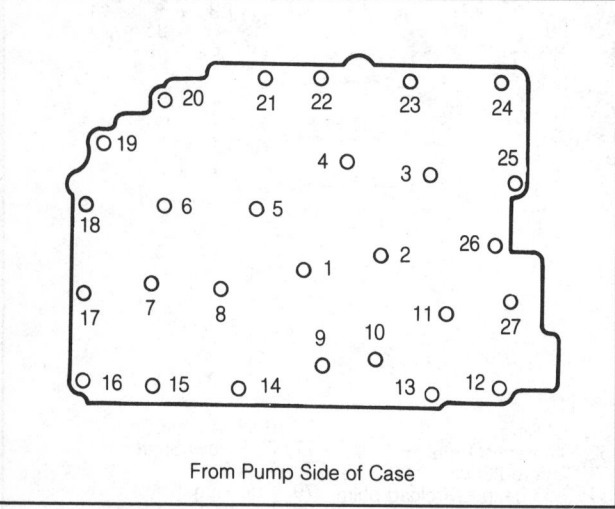

From Pump Side of Case

20) Install detent roller assembly, baffle plate and the remaining valve body attaching bolts. Tighten valve body attaching bolts using sequence shown in *Fig. 30.* Position a new valve body cover gasket on case, then install cover and tighten attaching bolts.

21) Install oil pump shaft. Using lifting handles (T81P-7902-C or equivalent), install torque converter into transaxle case.

FORD C-3

**Bronco II, Capri, Fairmont, LTD,
Marquis, Mustang, Ranger, Zephyr**

IDENTIFICATION

The C-3 automatic transmission is identified by the code letter "V", which is shown on lower line of Vehicle Certification Label under "TRANS". This label is attached to the left front door lock pillar.

The transmission model may be identified by a metal tag attached to transmission by the lower extension housing retaining bolt. Top line of tag shows transmission Model Number and Line Shift Code. Bottom line on tag shows the Build Date Code. *See Fig. 1.*

Fig. 1: Service Identification Tag

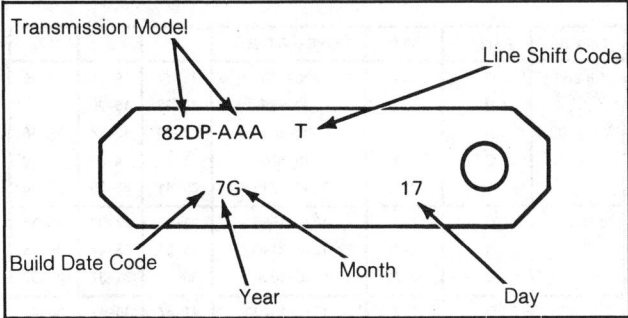

Tag is attached to transmission by housing bolt.

The C-3 transmission may be visually identified by location of vacuum diaphragm (modulator). Diaphragm unit is located at right center of case, just rearward of the intermediate (front) servo.

DESCRIPTION

Transmission is a 3 speed unit capable of providing automatic upshifts and downshifts through 3 forward gear ratios, and is also capable of providing manual selection of first and second gears.

Transmission consists of a torque converter, planetary gear train, 2 multiple disc clutches, 2 servos and bands, a one-way clutch, and a hydraulic control system. The only adjustment required is on the front band.

LUBRICATION & ADJUSTMENT

See the appropriate article in AUTOMATIC TRANSMISSION SERVICING Section.

TESTING

ROAD TEST

1) Check minimum throttle upshifts in "D" position. Transmission should start in first gear, shift to second, and then shift to third gear as speed increases. *See Shift Speeds Table.*

Fig. 2: Cutaway View of C-3 Automatic Transmission Assembly

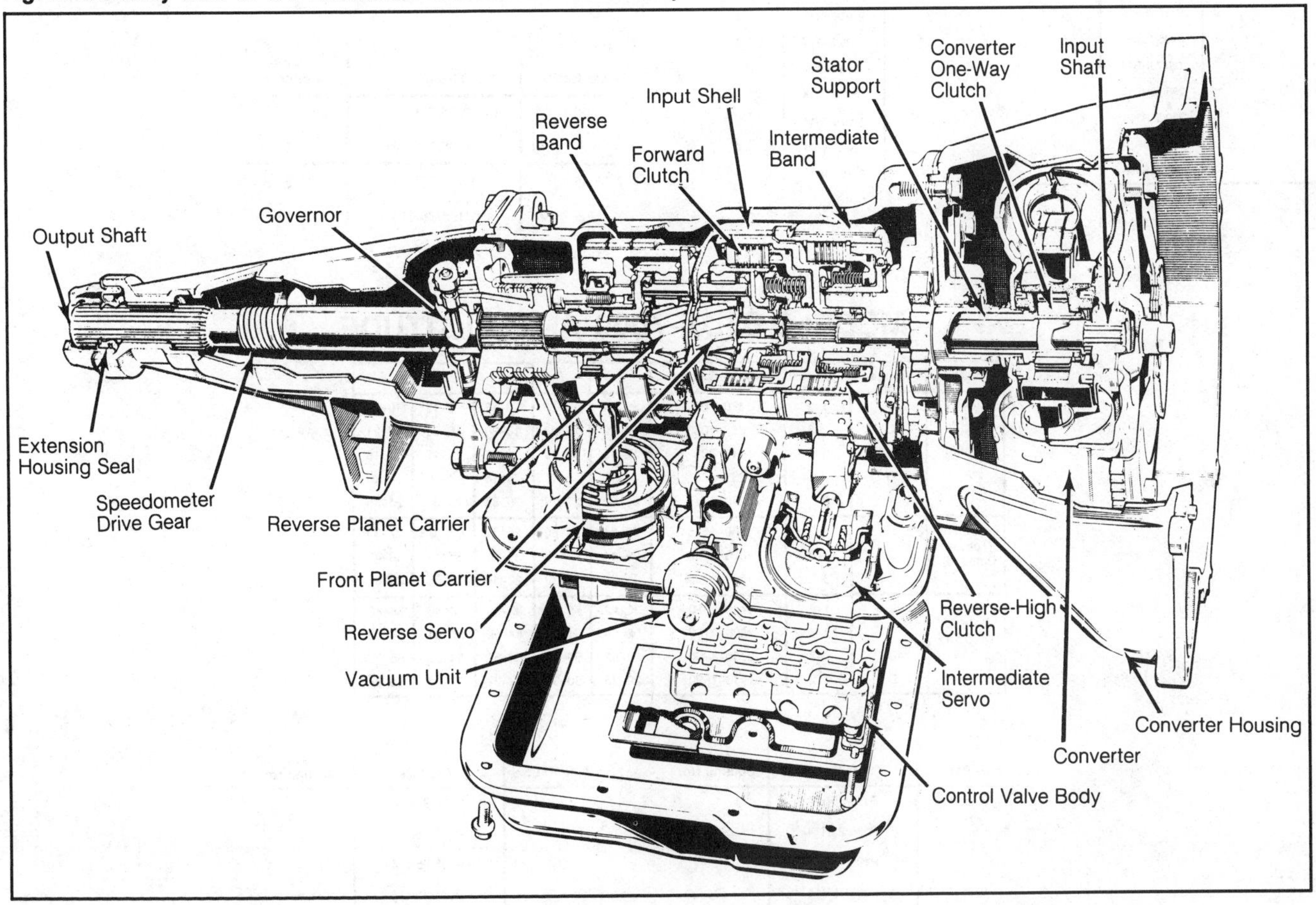

Automatic Transmissions
FORD C-3 (Cont.)

2) With transmission in third gear, depress accelerator through detent (to floor). Transmission should shift from third to second, or third to first, depending on vehicle speed. *See Shift Speeds Table.*

3) Check closed throttle downshift from third to first by coasting down from about 30 MPH in third gear. Shift should occur as shown in table. *See Shift Speeds Table.*

4) With transmission selector lever in "2" position, transmission should operate only in second gear.

5) With transmission in third gear and road speed over 30 MPH, transmission should downshift to second gear when selector lever is moved from "D" to "2" or "1". When same manual shift is made below 25 MPH, transmission should shift from second or third to first.

SHIFT SPEEDS (MPH)

NOTE: Figures given below are approximate. All shift speeds may vary somewhat due to production tolerances, rear axle ratio, or emission control equipment.

MODELS 83DT-7000-AAB/ABB

Throttle	Range	Shift	OPS—R.P.M.	1	2	3	4	5
Closed (Above 17" Vacuum)	D	1-2	428-640	10-15	9-13	9-14	8-13	9-14
	D	2-3	770-1070	18-25	16-22	17-24	15-21	17-23
	D	3-2	480-741	11-17	10-15	11-17	9-15	10-16
	D	2-1	218-480	5-11	4-10	5-11	4-9	4-10
	1	2-1	1439-1875	34-44	30-39	33-43	29-38	31-41
To Detent (Torque Demand)	D	1-2	1455-1712	34-40	31-36	33-39	29-35	32-37
	D	2-3	1969-2226	47-53	41-47	45-51	40-45	43-49
	D	3-2	1626-1883	38-45	34-40	37-43	33-38	35-41
Through Detent (W.O.T.)	D	1-2	1926-2183	46-52	41-46	44-50	39-44	42-48
	D	2-3	3000-3253	71-77	63-69	69-75	61-66	66-71
	D	3-2	2825-3082	67-73	60-65	65-71	57-63	62-67
	D	3-1 2-1	1584-1840	37-44	33-39	36-42	32-37	34-40

Axle Ratio	Tire Size	Use Column No.
3.08:1	P185/75R14	1
	P195/75R14	1
	P205/70HR14	1
	195/70HR14	1
	205/70HR14	1
	220/55R390	1
	P175/75R14	3
	190/65R390	3
3.27:1	P195/75R14	3
	P185/75R14	5

Axle Ratio	Tire Size	Use Column No.
3.45:1	P185/75R14	2
	P195/75R14	2
	P205/70R14	2
	190/65R390	2
	195/70R14	2
	205/70R14	2
	220/55R390	2
	P175/75R14	4

MODELS 83DT-7000-AGB/AHB

Throttle	Range	Shift	OPS—R.P.M.	1	2	3
Closed (Above 17" Vacuum)	D	1-2	470-730	11-17	9-15	10-15
	D	2-3	730-985	17-23	15-20	15-21
	D	3-2	600-860	14-20	12-18	12-18
	D	2-1	215-470	5-11	4-9	4-10
	1	2-1	1280-1715	30-41	26-35	27-36
To Detent (Torque Demand)	D	1-2	1330-1585	31-37	27-33	28-33
	D	2-3	1840-2140	44-51	38-44	39-45
	D	3-2	1540-1800	36-43	32-37	32-38
Through Detent (W.O.T.)	D	1-2	1715-1970	41-47	35-41	36-42
	D	2-3	2825-3080	67-73	58-64	60-65
	D	3-2	2780-3040	66-72	58-63	59-64
	D	3-1 2-1	1415-1670	33-39	29-34	30-35

Axle Ratio	Tire Size	Use Column No.
3.08:1	P185/75R14	1
	P195/75R14	1
3.45:1	P185/75R14	2
	P195/75R14	3

MODELS 83DT-7000-AMB-ALTITUDE

Throttle	Range	Shift	OPS—R.P.M.	1	2	3	4	5
Closed (Above 17" Vacuum)	D	1-2	470-700	9-14	10-15	9-13	9-13	9-14
	D	2-3	850-1080	17-22	18-23	16-20	16-21	17-21
	D	3-2	610-895	12-18	13-19	11-17	12-17	12-18
	D	2-1	235-520	4-10	5-11	4-10	4-10	4-10
	1	2-1	1270-1740	26-36	27-38	23-33	25-34	25-35
To Detent (Torque Demand)	D	1-2	1360-1645	28-34	29-36	26-31	27-32	27-33
	D	2-3	1880-2160	39-44	41-47	36-41	37-42	38-43
	D	3-2	1500-1790	31-37	32-39	28-34	29-35	30-36
Through Detent (W.O.T.)	D	1-2	1740-2020	36-42	38-44	33-38	34-40	35-40
	D	2-3	2820-3100	58-64	61-67	54-59	55-61	57-62
	D	3-2	2730-3000	56-62	59-65	52-57	54-59	55-60
	D	3-1 2-1	1410-1690	29-35	30-37	27-32	28-33	28-34

Axle Ratio	Tire Size	Use Column No.
3.45:1	P175/75R14	1
	P185/75R14	1
	P195/75R14	2
	P205/75R14	2

Axle Ratio	Tire Size	Use Column No.
3.73:1	P175/75R14	3
	P185/75R14	3
	P195/75R14	4
	P205/75R14	5

FORD C-3 (Cont.)

NOTE: The preceding step will determine if governor pressure and shift control valves are operating properly.

6) Slipping or engine speed flare-up in any gear usually indicates clutch or band problems. In most cases, the clutch or band that is slipping can be determined by noting transmission operation in all selector positions, and comparing which internal units are applied in those positions. *See Clutch & Band Application Chart.*

CONTROL PRESSURE TEST

1) With engine at normal operating temperature, connect a tachometer to engine. Connect a 0-400 psi pressure gauge to control pressure port, and install a vacuum gauge (using a "T") into vacuum line at vacuum diaphragm unit. *See Fig. 3.*

Fig. 3: Gauge Hook-Up for Pressure Testing

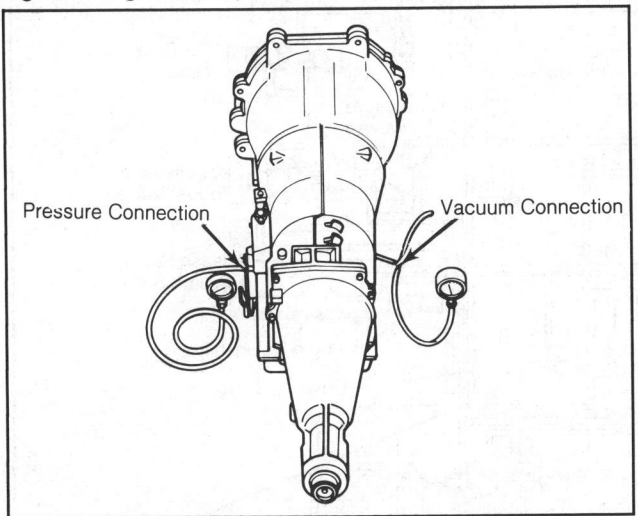

Pressure Connection

Vacuum Connection

2) Before proceeding with control pressure test, check vacuum supply at diaphragm unit. If vacuum is steady and acceptable at properly adjusted idle speed, quickly open and close throttle while observing gauge.

3) Reading must drop rapidly at acceleration and return immediately upon releasing throttle. If vacuum is slow to drop or return, check for a restriction or poor vacuum connection.

4) If vacuum at idle is not acceptable, check for a restriction or poor vacuum connection, vacuum diaphragm leak, or poor engine vacuum.

5) If vacuum is satisfactory, proceed as follows: With parking and service brakes applied, and while engine is idling, shift transmission through all ranges. Read and record control pressure in each selector postition.

6) Place selector lever in "D" position and accelerate engine until vacuum gauge reads 10 in. Hg. Read and record control pressure at 10 in. Hg.

7) The control pressure test at 1 in. Hg requires the throttle to be wide open (through detent). Read and record control pressure in "D" and "R".

CAUTION: Release throttle immediately if slippage is indicated. Also, after each test, shift transmission into Neutral and run engine at 1000 RPM for 15-20 seconds to cool transmission.

CONTROL PRESSURE SPECIFICATIONS (psi)

Transmission Model	Range	Idle		
		15" & Above	10"	WOT Stall Thru Detent
83DT-AAB/ABB/ ACB/ADB	* D,2,1 R P,N	50-60 66-78 50-60	74-94 129-148	165-195 278-316
83DT-ALB/AMB/ AGB/AHB	* D,2,1 R P,N	50-70 75-109 50-70	90-113 158-178	167-195 282-316
83DT-ACB/ADB	@ D,2,1 R P,N	50-60 66-78 50-60	50-75 94-116	144-177 244-282
83DT-AMB/AHB	@ D,2,1 R P,N	50-60 66-78 50-60	70-93 122-145	144-177 247-282

* Absolute barometric pressure (ABP) 29.0-30.0
@ Absolute barometric pressure (ABP) 24.0-25.0

6) Compare pressures obtained in test with pressures given in *Control Pressure Table.*

CONTROL PRESSURE RESULTS

If control pressures are not within specifications, use the following to determine cause of trouble:

CLUTCH AND BAND APPLICATION CHART (ELEMENTS IN USE)

Selector Lever Position	Intermediate Band	Low-Reverse Band	Forward Clutch	Reverse-High Clutch	One-Way Clutch
D — DRIVE First Gear Second Gear Third Gear	X X		X X X	X	X
2 — INTERMEDIATE Second Gear	X		X		
1 — LOW (First)		X	X		
R — REVERSE		X		X	
NEUTRAL OR PARK — All clutches and bands released and/or ineffective.					

Automatic Transmissions

FORD C-3 (Cont.)

Fig. 4: C-3 Automatic Transmission Hydraulic Circuits Diagram

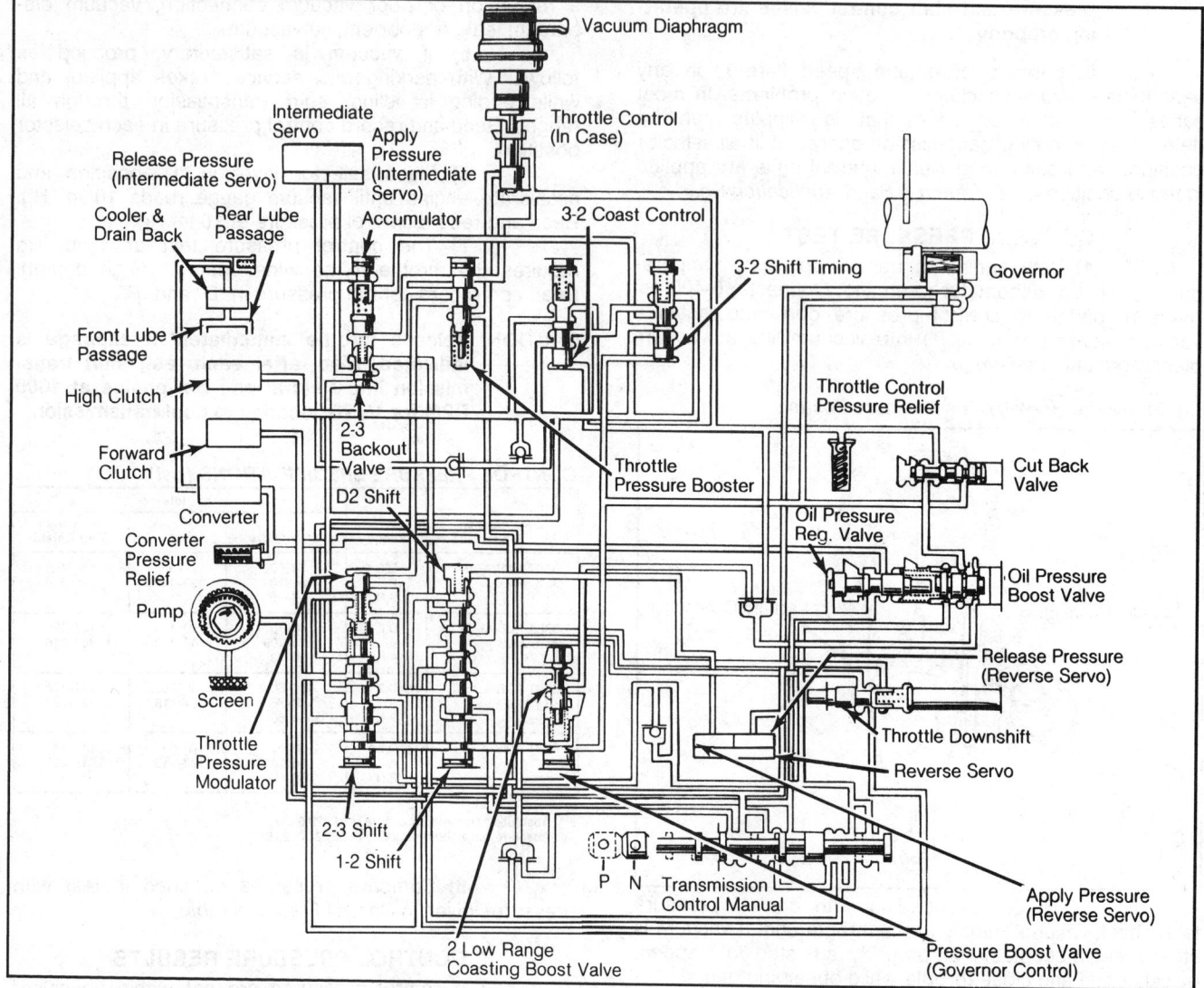

High in All Ranges

Check the engine EGR system, vacuum diaphragm unit, and manifold vacuum line. Also check throttle valve or control rod and regulator boost valve for sticking.

Low at Idle in All Ranges

Check the engine EGR system. Check fluid level. Check for restricted intake screen or filter. Check for loose oil tubes, loose valve body or regulator to case bolts. Check for excessive leakage in oil pump. Check for defective control valve body. Check control pressure regulator valve for sticking.

Control Pressure OK at Idle in All Ranges, But Low at 10 in. Hg

Check vacuum diaphragm unit. Control rod or throttle valve stuck.

Control Pressure OK at Idle in All Ranges, OK at 10 in. Hg, But Low at 1 in. Hg

Check for excessive leakage, low pump capacity, or restricted oil pan screen.

Control Pressure Low in "D"

Check for faulty forward clutch.

Control Pressure Low in "2"

Check forward clutch and/or front servo.

Control Pressure Low in "1"

Check forward clutch and/or rear servo.

Control Pressure Low in "R"

Check reverse-high clutch and/or rear servo.

GOVERNOR PRESSURE TEST

NOTE: **Governor can be checked at the same time control pressure test is performed and in the same manner.**

1) Raise vehicle and support, so that rear wheels are free to turn. Disconnect and plug vacuum line to vacuum diaphragm unit. Connect a hand-held vacuum pump to diaphragm unit.

CAUTION: Never exceed 60 MPH speedometer speed during governor pressure test.

2) Place transmission in manual "2", with no load on engine and apply 10 in. Hg to diaphragm unit. Increase speed slowly and watch speedometer for speed at which control pressure cut-back occurs. It should occur between 10-20 MPH.

FORD C-3 (Cont.)

NOTE: After each test, move selector lever to Neutral and run engine at 1000 RPM to cool transmission.

3) Decrease vacuum to 0-2 in. Hg and repeat test. Control pressure cut-back should occur between 30-50 MPH.

4) Governor is okay if cut-back occurs as specified. If not, check shift speeds to verify that problem is in governor and not a stuck cut-back valve, then repair or replace governor.

STALL TEST

Testing Precautions

1) Hold accelerator down just long enough to get a stable tachometer reading. Do not floor accelerator for more than 5 seconds. Do not exceed maximum specified RPM for vehicle.

2) Before shifting into each selector position, run engine in Neutral at 1000 RPM for 15 to 20 seconds to cool transmission.

CAUTION: If engine speed exceeds upper specification, release accelerator immediately as this is an indication of clutch or band slippage.

Testing Procedure

1) Connect a tachometer to engine, apply parking and service brakes firmly. Place selector lever in "D" position, and push accelerator completely to floor.

2) Record tachometer reading. Engine speed should be within specifications given in *Stall Speed Specifications Table*. Repeat procedure in "2", "1", and "R" positions.

STALL SPEEDS

Application	Stall RPM
2.3L	
Capri, Fairmont, LTD,	
Marquis, Mustang, Zephyr	2256-2654
2.3L	
Bronco II, Ranger 2WD	2381-2760

STALL TEST RESULTS

Stall Speed Low in All Ranges
Poor engine performance. Faulty torque converter stator one-way clutch.

Stall Speed High in All Ranges
General transmission problems are indicated. Perform control pressure tests.

Fig. 5: Bottom View of Transmission Case

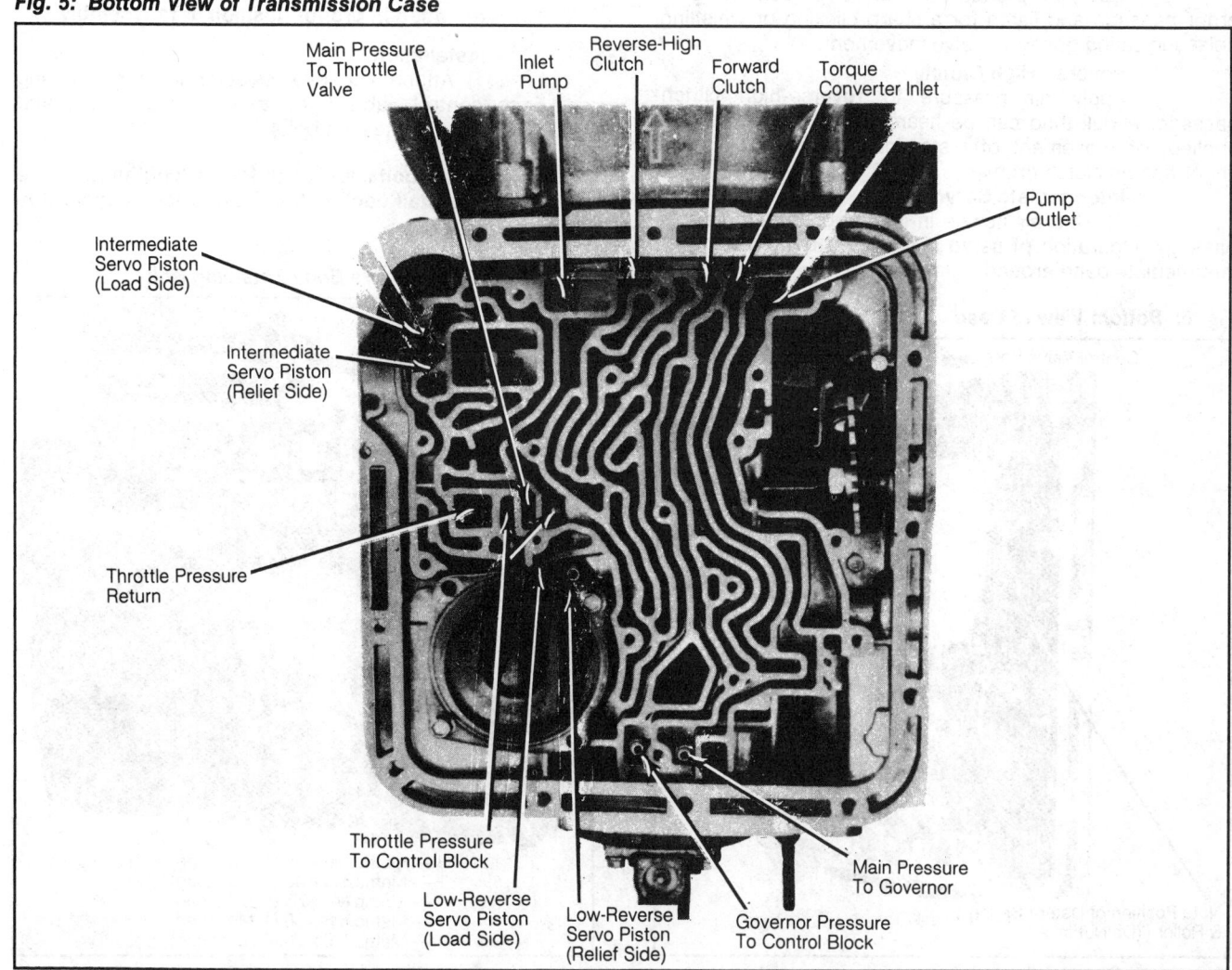

FORD C-3 (Cont.)

Stall Speed High in "D" Only
Planetary one-way clutch faulty.
Stall Speed High in "D", "2" & "1"
Forward clutch faulty.
Stall Speed High in "R" Only
Reverse-High clutch faulty and/or the reverse band is faulty.

AIR PRESSURE CHECKS

1) A "No Drive" condition can exist, even with correct transmission fluid pressure, because of inoperative clutches or bands. Erratic shifts could be caused by a stuck governor valve.

2) The inoperative units can be located through a series of checks by substituting air pressure for the fluid pressure to determine location of malfunction.

3) To make air pressure checks, loosen oil pan bolts and allow transmission fluid to drain, then remove oil pan and control valve body. Apply air at points noted in *Fig. 5.* Check unit operation as follows:

Forward Clutch
Apply air pressure to forward clutch passage. A dull thud can be heard when clutch piston is applied, or movement of the piston can be felt by placing finger tips on input shell.

Governor
Apply air pressure to control pressure-to-governor passage and listen for a sharp clicking or whistling noise indicating governor valve movement.

Reverse-High Clutch
Apply air pressure to reverse-high clutch passage. A dull thud can be heard when clutch piston is applied, or movement of piston can be felt by placing finger tips on clutch drum.

Intermediate Servo
1) Hold air nozzle in intermediate servo apply passage. Operation of servo is indicated by tightening of intermediate band around drum.

2) While continuing to apply air pressure at servo apply passage, apply air pressure to intermediate servo release passage. Intermediate servo should then release band against the applied pressure.

Low-Reverse Servo
Apply air pressure to low-reverse servo apply passage. Low-reverse band should tighten around drum if servo is operating properly.

NOTE: **If air pressure applied to either clutch passages fails to operate clutch, or operates both clutches at once, remove and, with air pressure, check fluid passages in case and oil pump to detect obstructions.**

SERVICE (IN VEHICLE)

CONTROL VALVE BODY

Removal
Remove oil pan, filter screen, and gasket. Remove rear servo cover and gasket. Remove valve body retaining bolts. Carefully ease valve body from case while unlocking and detaching selector lever connecting rod.

NOTE: **Note size and location of valve body retaining bolts. Bolts are of different sizes and must be replaced in proper position at reassembly.**

Installation
1) Attach and lock selector lever connecting rod. Ease control valve body to the case. Install and tighten valve body retaining bolts.

CAUTION: **Since bolts are of different lengths, be sure to install each bolt in its correct location. See Fig. 7.**

Fig. 7: Location of Valve Body Retaining Bolts

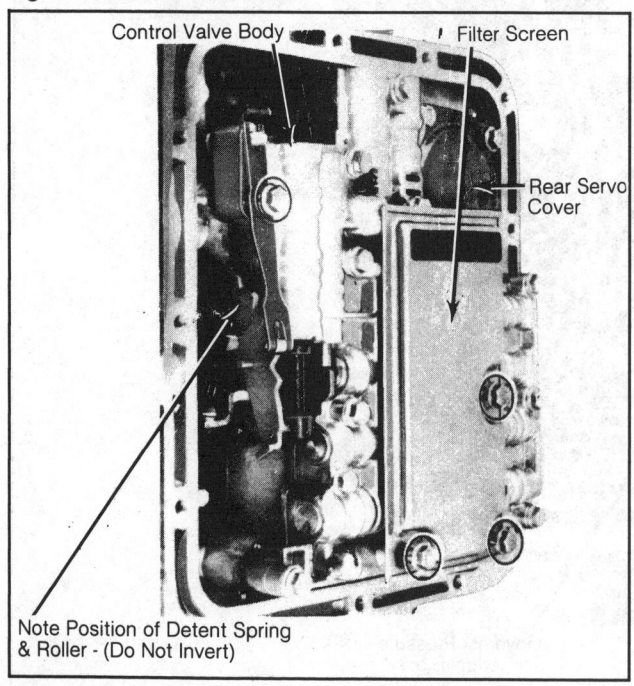

Fig. 6: Bottom View of Case

Control Valve Body — Filter Screen

Rear Servo Cover

Note Position of Detent Spring & Roller - (Do Not Invert)

Illustration shows valve body and filter screen position

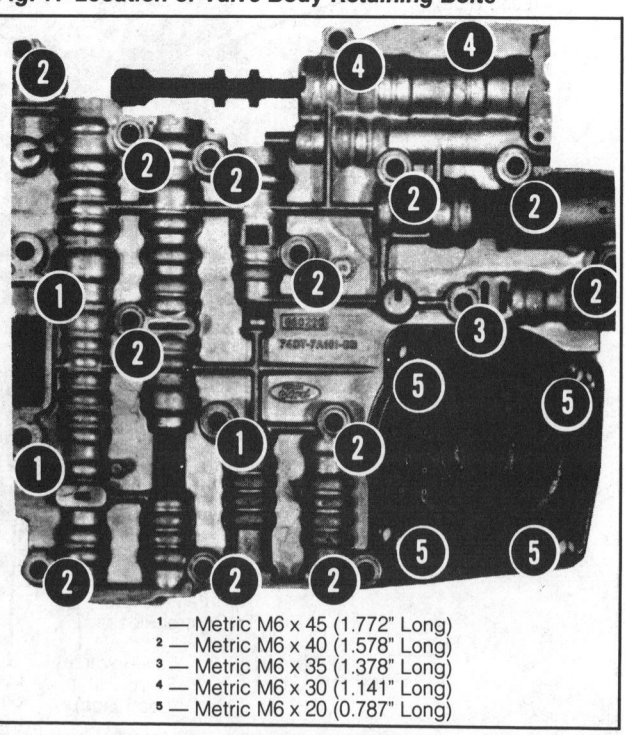

¹ — Metric M6 x 45 (1.772" Long)
² — Metric M6 x 40 (1.578" Long)
³ — Metric M6 x 35 (1.378" Long)
⁴ — Metric M6 x 30 (1.141" Long)
⁵ — Metric M6 x 20 (0.787" Long)

Bolts must be returned to original locations.

FORD C-3 (Cont.)

2) Install rear servo cover with a new gasket. Clean filter screen. Install filter screen and gasket.

CAUTION: When installing filter screen and gasket, DO NOT use spacers as control pressure would be reduced, resulting in transmission malfunction or failure.

3) Install oil pan using a new gasket. Install and tighten pan bolts. Lower vehicle and fill transmission with fluid.

REAR SERVO
Removal

With oil pan and filter screen removed, remove rear servo cover retaining bolts, cover, gasket, servo piston, and spring.

NOTE: Force of servo spring will raise cover.

Installation
Reverse removal procedures.

Fig. 8: Bottom View of Transmission Case

Spring Force Will Raise Assembly

Illustration shows rear servo separated.

EXTENSION HOUSING REAR SEAL & BUSHING
Removal

1) Raise and support vehicle. Mark propeller shaft end yoke and rear axle companion flange for reassembly reference. Remove propeller shaft.

Fig. 9: Removing Extension Housing Oil Seal & Bushing

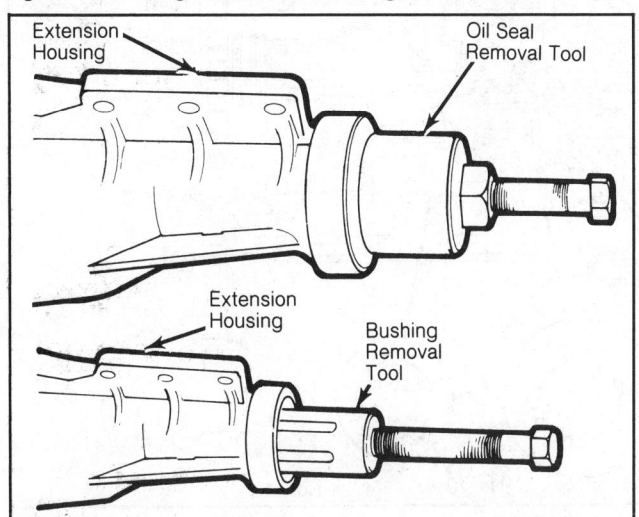

Extension Housing

Oil Seal Removal Tool

Extension Housing

Bushing Removal Tool

2) Remove extension housing rear oil seal and bushing using pullers (T71P-7657-A for seal and T77L-7697-E for bushing). *See Fig. 9.*

Installation
Drive new bushing and oil seal into extension housing using a driver. Install propeller shaft, aligning reference marks made at removal.

EXTENSION HOUSING
Removal

1) Raise and support vehicle. Mark propeller shaft for installation reference. Remove shaft. Disconnect speedometer cable from extension housing.

2) Remove rear support-to-crossmember bolts. Raise transmission slightly and remove rear support from extension housing.

3) Loosen extension housing retaining bolts and allow transmission fluid to drain. Remove bolts and slide extension housing off output shaft.

Installation
Using a new gasket, position extension housing on case, paying special attention to correctly seating the operating rod parking notch. Install and tighten bolts. To complete installation, reverse removal procedures.

GOVERNOR
Removal

Remove extension housing as previously described. Remove governor body-to-oil collector body retaining bolts. Remove governor body, valve, spring, and weight from collector body.

CAUTION: Components are not retained once governor body bolts have been removed. It is therefore necessary to hold body and components while removing and installing governor.

Fig. 10: Removing Governor Assembly

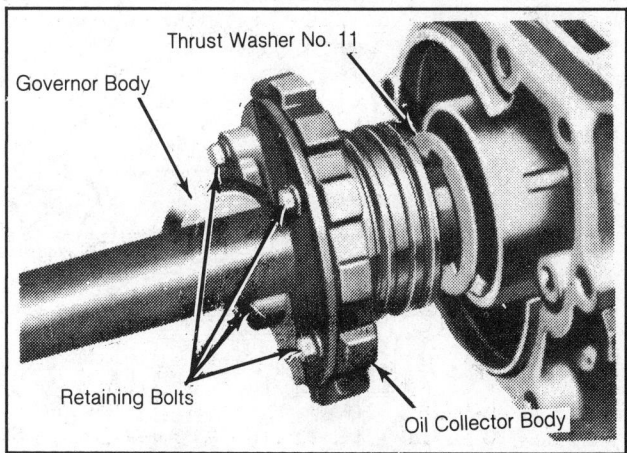

Thrust Washer No. 11

Governor Body

Retaining Bolts

Oil Collector Body

Installation
Assemble governor body and components. Position body over oil feed holes of oil collector body. Install retaining bolts. Install extension housing.

VACUUM DIAPHRAGM ASSEMBLY
Removal

Disconnect hoses from unit. Remove retaining bracket (do no pry or bend bracket). Remove vacuum diaphragm, actuating pin and throttle valve from case. Remove "O" ring from assembly.

Automatic Transmissions

FORD C-3 (Cont.)

Fig. 11: Side View of Transmission Case

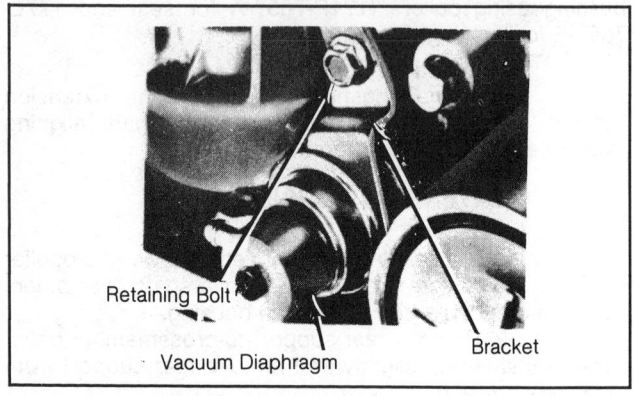

Illustration shows vacuum diaphragm installed.

Installation

Install a new "O" ring. Install throttle valve, actuating pin and vacuum diaphragm (with tubes pointing rearward). Install retaining bracket and tighten bolt.

REMOVAL & INSTALLATION

See the appropriate article in AUTOMATIC TRANSMISSION REMOVAL Section.

TORQUE CONVERTER

LEAKAGE CHECK

See procedures given in Ford C-6 article.

FLUSHING CONVERTER

See procedures given in Ford C-6 article.

TURBINE & STATOR END PLAY CHECK

See procedures given Ford C-6 article.

STATOR ONE-WAY CLUTCH CHECK

See procedures given Ford C-6 article.

STATOR INTERFERENCE CHECKS

See procedures given in Ford C-6 article.

TRANSMISSION DISASSEMBLY

NOTE: **Ten thrust washers are used in this transmission, with No. 1 at front pump and No. 11 at governor. Note that No. 6, while performing a thrust function, is actually a bearing. This adds one to thrust washer count. Because this bearing is part of the staked portion of planet assembly, it is not removable. Refer to Fig. 12 for identification and location of thrust washers.**

Rear Servo, Valve Body, and Oil Pump

1) Remove torque converter, input shaft, and oil pan. Remove oil filter screen, gasket, and 3 spacers (if so equipped). Remove interlock spring.

2) Remove rear servo cover and gasket (spring force will raise cover). Remove bolts from valve body, note

Fig. 12: Cutaway View of Transmission Showing Thrust Washer Identification and Location

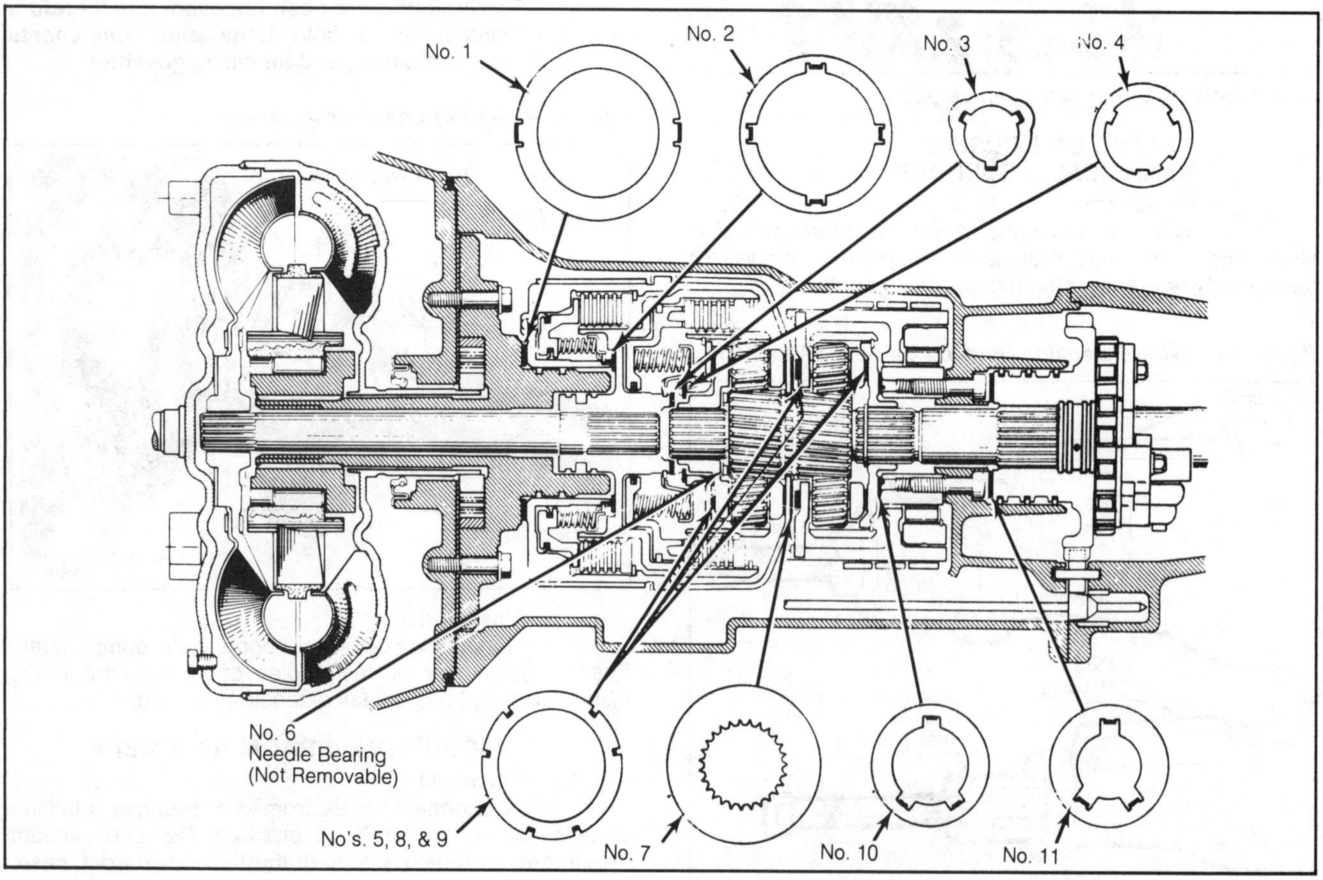

FORD C-3 (Cont.)

size, length, and location of bolts for reassembly reference.

3) While easing valve body out of transmission, unlock and detach selector lever connecting link. Remove valve body and gasket.

4) Remove converter housing bolts. Remove housing and oil pump as an assembly. Remove the No. 1 thrust washer and gasket. Remove oil pump seal with puller (T74P-77248-A).

5) Remove oil pump fron converter housing. Remove steel plate (behind oil seal) with "O" ring.

NOTE: Before continuing with disassembly, transmission end play should be measured as follows:

Transmission End Play Check

1) Install oil pump (without gasket) and existing No. 1 thrust washer into transmission case. Make sure pump body is below the case gasket surface.

2) Mount dial indicator on oil pump with plunger resting on transmission housing. See Fig. 13. Set dial gauge to zero, then swing gauge around so plunger contacts oil pump.

Fig. 13: Tool Set-Up for Transmission End Play Check

Dial Indicator

3) Check reading on dial and note for future reference. Move dial indicator assembly to opposite side of pump and again make an end play check. Find average of 2 readings; the average must be between .001-.025" (.025-.635 mm).

4) If end play exceeds limits, replace thrust washer No. 1 with one that will bring end play within specifications.

SELECTIVE THRUST WASHER NO. 1

ID Number	Thickness Inches (mm)
"1"	.0488-.0507 (1.24-1.29)
"2"	.0610-.0630 (1.55-1.60)
"3"	.0768-.0787 (1.95-1.99)
"4"	.0929-.0949 (2.36-2.41)
"5"	.1091-.1110 (2.77-2.82)

5) After end play check has been completed, remove oil pump and selective thrust washer No. 1. Mark installed position of oil pump gears in relation to one another and remove.

Front Brake and Front Servo Assemblies

1) Loosen lock nut, back out adjustment screw, and remove struts. Remove front brake and front assembly, including thrust washer No. 8.

Fig. 14: Front Band Removal

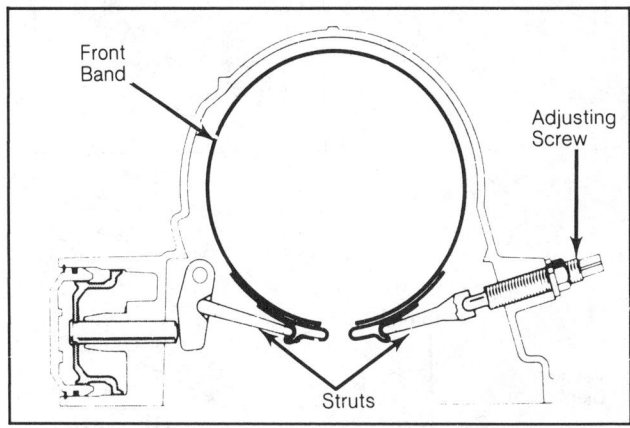
Front Band
Adjusting Screw
Struts

2) Press inward slightly on front servo cover and remove snap ring. Carefully force out servo piston assembly with compressed air. See Fig. 15.

Fig. 15: Bottom View of Transmission Case

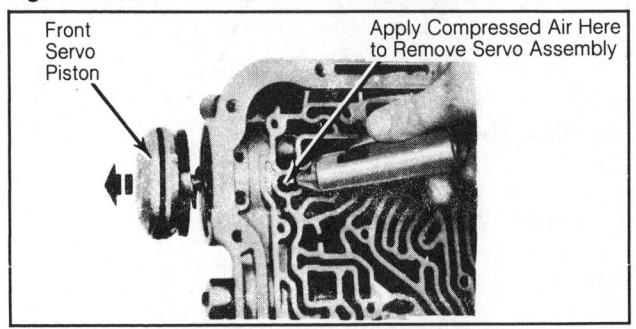
Front Servo Piston
Apply Compressed Air Here to Remove Servo Assembly

Illustration shows front servo piston removal

Case and Extension Housing Parts

1) Remove extension housing bolts. Remove housing and gasket. Remove return spring and parking pawl. Remove large snap ring from planet gear carrier (rear).

2) Remove planet gear carrier with thrust washer No. 5 from case. Remove small snap ring from

Fig. 16: Locations of Planet Gear Carrier Snap Rings

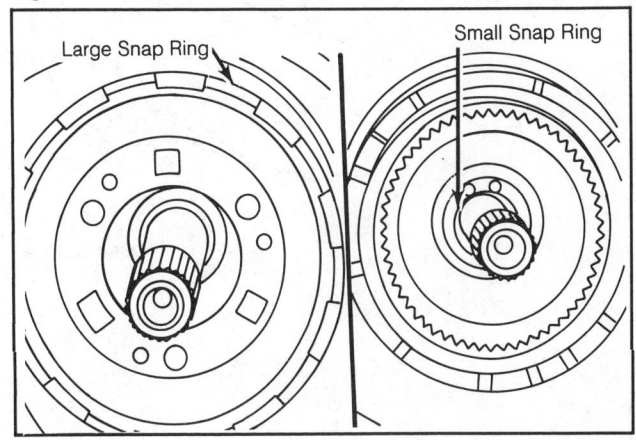
Large Snap Ring
Small Snap Ring

Automatic Transmissions
FORD C-3 (Cont.)

Fig. 17: Exploded View of C-3 Automatic Transmission Assembly

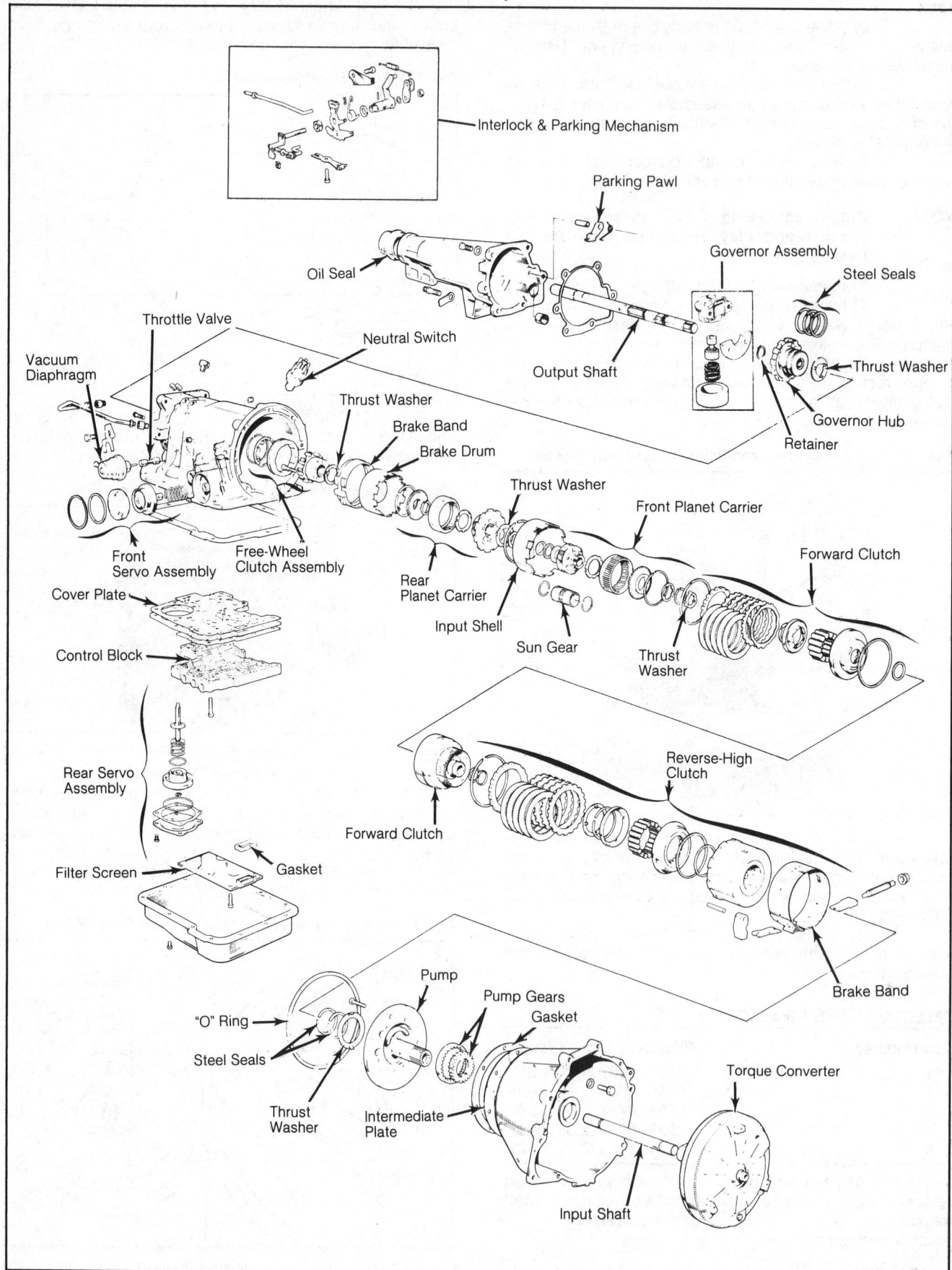

Interlock & Parking Mechanism

Parking Pawl

Governor Assembly

Steel Seals

Oil Seal

Neutral Switch

Output Shaft

Thrust Washer

Governor Hub

Retainer

Throttle Valve

Vacuum Diaphragm

Thrust Washer

Brake Band

Brake Drum

Thrust Washer

Front Planet Carrier

Forward Clutch

Front Servo Assembly

Free-Wheel Clutch Assembly

Rear Planet Carrier

Input Shell

Sun Gear

Thrust Washer

Cover Plate

Control Block

Rear Servo Assembly

Reverse-High Clutch

Forward Clutch

Filter Screen

Gasket

Brake Band

"O" Ring

Pump

Pump Gears

Gasket

Steel Seals

Thrust Washer

Intermediate Plate

Input Shaft

Torque Converter

FORD C-3 (Cont.)

output shaft. Remove output shaft and governor with thrust washer No. 11.

3) Remove internal gear, No. 10 thrust washer, and intermediate brake drum. Remove rear band assembly. If necessary, due to wear or damage, remove the one-way clutch inner race. Remove vacuum diaphragm unit. Remove neutral safety switch.

CAUTION: Use a thin-walled socket to remove neutral safety switch. An open-end wrench will crush switch.

Fig. 18: Interior View of Transmission Case

Illustration shows one-way clutch inner race

4) If necessary, replace shift lever oil seal as follows: Press inward on downshift lever and remove "O" ring. Remove shift lever roll pin from case. Remove shift lever nut (outside). Remove parking pawl actuating rod.

5) Remove selector lever from outside and downshift lever shaft from inside case. Remove shift lever oil seal with a screwdriver. Install a new oil seal using a seal driver (T74P-77498-A).

6) Install downshift lever inside case and shift lever outside. Install nuts and parking pawl actuating rod. Install roll pin, new "O" ring, and downshift lever.

COMPONENT DISASSEMBLY & REASSEMBLY

FRONT ASSEMBLY

Disassembly

Remove input shell and sun gear. Remove planet gear carrier with internal gear and thrust washer No. 5. If necessary, remove sun gear from input shell after removing retainer. Replace thrust washer No. 7 if it is damaged. Remove forward drive clutch and thrust washer No. 2.

NOTE: Front assembly will be reassembled at the end of Component Disassembly and Reassembly.

REVERSE-HIGH CLUTCH

Disassembly

1) Remove snap ring. Remove pressure plate and clutch pack. Using spring compressor (T65L-77515-A), compress piston springs and remove snap ring. Carefully release pressure on springs.

2) Remove spring retainer and springs. Turn clutch body over and carefully force out piston with compressed air. *See Fig. 21.* Remove "O" rings from piston and clutch body.

Reassembly

1) Inspect all parts for wear, damage, or effects of overheating. If new clutch plates are to be used, soak in transmission fluid for 30 minutes before installing.

2) Install new "O" rings on piston and clutch body. Carefully install clutch piston, using seal protector (T74P-77404-A) to protect inner seal.

3) Install 20 piston springs and spring retainer. Compress springs, with tool used at disassembly, install snap ring and remove compressor tool.

4) Install clutch plates, starting with a steel plate and alternating composition, and steel plates until all clutch plates are installed. *See Clutch Plate Usage Chart.* Install pressure plate and secure with snap ring.

Fig. 19: Exploded View of Forward Part of Transmission Gear Train

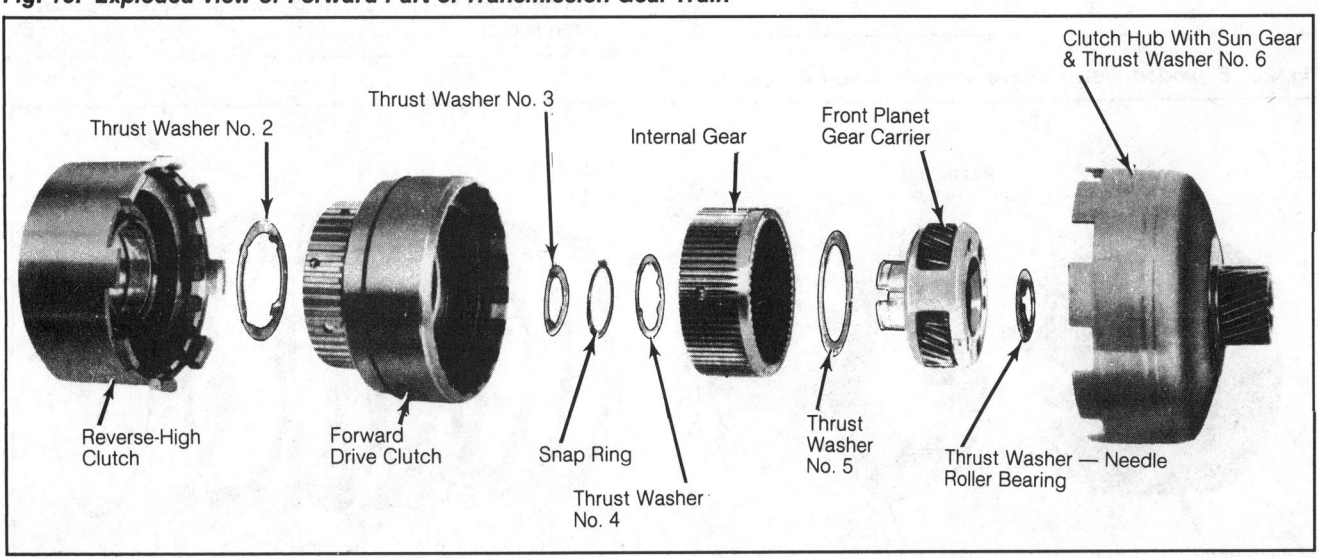

Automatic Transmissions

FORD C-3 (Cont.)

Fig. 20: *Removing Reverse-High Piston Springs Retaining Snap Ring*

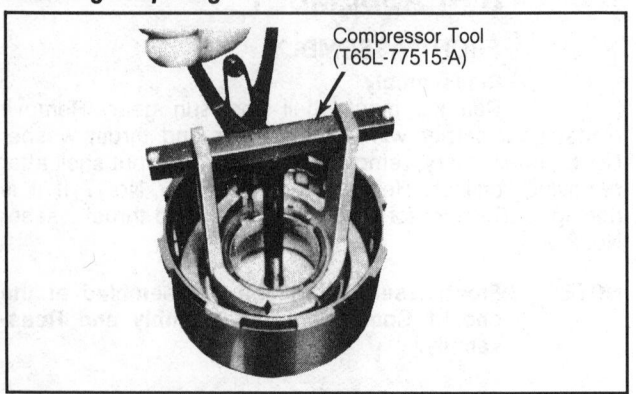

5) Using feeler gauge, measure clearance between pressure plate and snap ring while pushing down on plate. Clearance should be .051-.079" (1.29-2.01 mm). If clearance is not within specifications, install correct thickness selective snap ring.

NOTE: Reverse-High clutch selective snap rings are available in the following thicknesses: .054", .068", .082", and .096" (1.37, 1.73, 2.08, and 2.44 mm).

Fig. 21: *Using Compressed Air to Remove Reverse-High Clutch Piston*

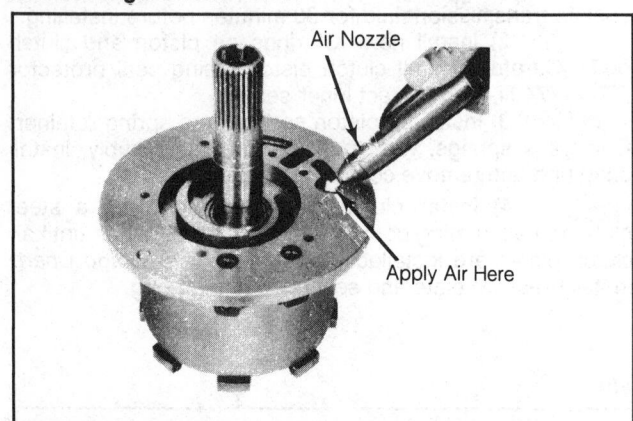

Fig. 22: *Exploded View of Reverse-High Clutch Assembly*

Fig. 23: *Reverse-High Clutch Piston Installation*

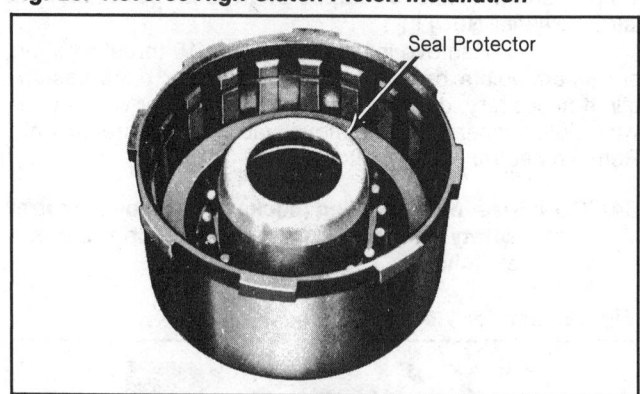

Installed position of seal protector.

Fig. 24: *Clutch Pressure Plate Clearance*

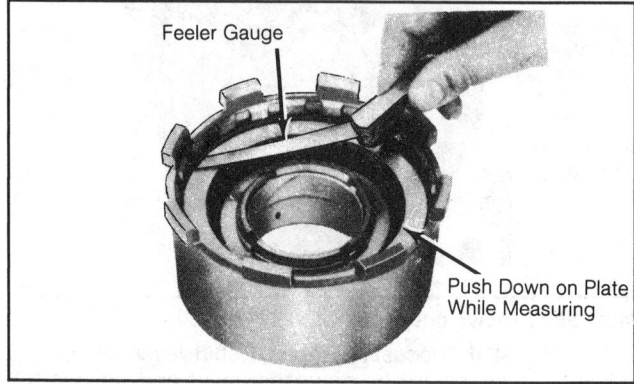

Use a feeler gauge to measure clearance.

CLUTCH PLATE USAGE CHART

Application	Composition Plates	Steel Plates
2.3L Engine		
Forward Clutch	5	5
High Clutch	4	4
3.3L Engine		
Forward Clutch	5	5
High Clutch	5	5

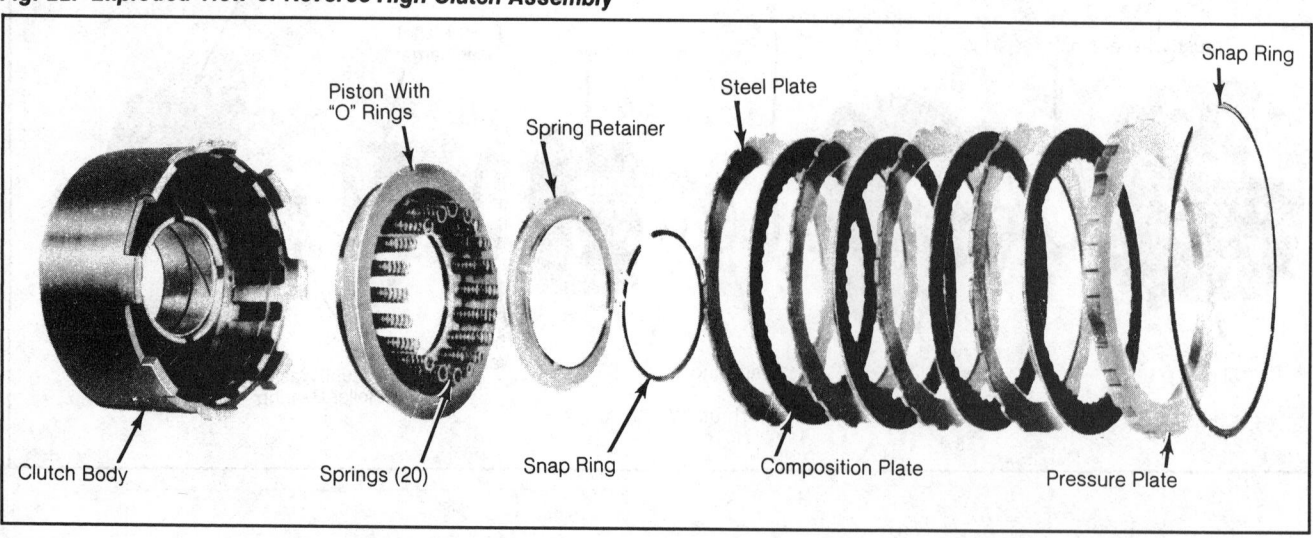

FORD C-3 (Cont.)

Fig. 25: Exploded View of Forward Clutch Assembly

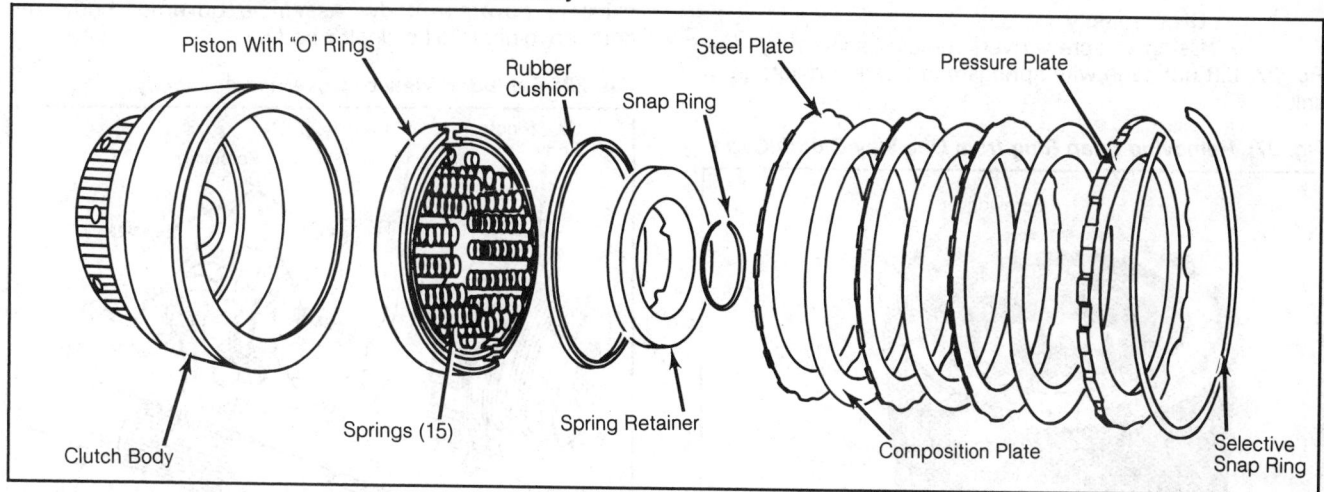

Piston With "O" Rings · Rubber Cushion · Steel Plate · Pressure Plate · Snap Ring · Clutch Body · Springs (15) · Spring Retainer · Composition Plate · Selective Snap Ring

FORWARD CLUTCH

Disassembly

1) Remove snap ring, lift out pressure plate, clutch pack, and rubber cushion spring. Using a spring compressor, compress piston return springs and remove retaining snap ring.

2) Carefully release pressure on springs. Remove spring retainer and springs. Using compressed air, carefully force clutch piston from clutch body. Remove "O" rings from piston and clutch body.

Reassembly

1) Inspect all parts for wear, damage, or effects of overheating. If new clutch plates are to be used, soak in transmission fluid for 30 minutes before installing.

2) Use protective tool (T74P-77548-A & B) to prevent damage to inner and outer seals. Install new "O" rings, apply petroleum jelly to rings and to shoulder at clutch stub, carefully install piston.

3) Install 15 piston springs and spring retainer. Compress springs with tool used at disassembly, install snap ring, and remove tool.

4) Install rubber cushion spring. Install clutch plates, starting with a steel plate and alternating composition and steel plates until all clutch plates are installed. *See Clutch Plate Usage Chart.*

Fig. 26: Positioning of Seal Protectors for Forward Clutch Piston Installation

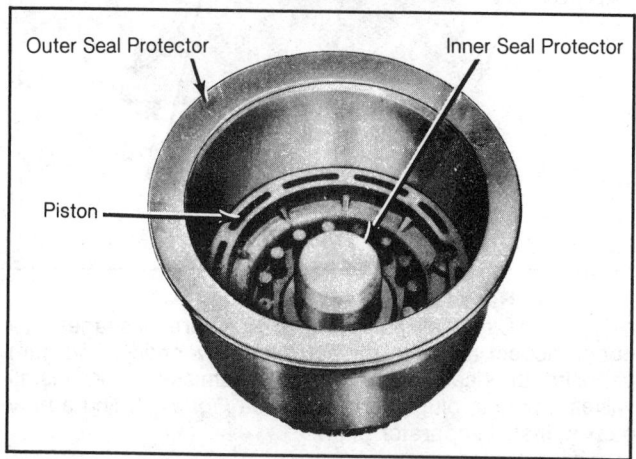

Outer Seal Protector · Inner Seal Protector · Piston

5) Install pressure plate and retaining snap ring. Measure clearance between snap ring and pressure plate following procedures given for Reverse-High clutch. Clearance for forward clutch should be .051-.079" (1.29-2.01 mm). Install new steel seals on clutch hub.

NOTE: Forward clutch selective snap rings are available in the following thicknesses: .054", .068", .082", and .096" (1.37, 1.73, 2.08, and 2.44 mm).

INTERNAL GEAR & PLANET GEAR ASSEMBLY

Disassembly

Remove snap ring, planet gear carrier internal gear, and thrust washer No. 4. Separate planet gear carrier from internal gear and remove thrust washer No. 5.

Reassembly

Insert planet gear carrier with thrust washer No. 5 into internal gear. Position thrust washer No. 4 in place and secure with a new snap ring.

NOTE: The needle roller bearing (No. 6 washer) can only be replaced complete, with planet gear carrier. If thrust washer needle bearing is removed, washer must be positioned with collar pointing toward the rear.

FRONT ASSEMBLY

NOTE: Refer to Fig. 19: Exploded View of Forward Part of Transmission Gear Train for identification of parts.

Reassembly

1) Place reverse-high clutch assembly vertically on a bench. Install thrust washer No. 2 and forward gear clutch assembly. Position thrust washer No. 3 on planet gear carrier and retain with petroleum jelly.

2) Install internal gears and planet gear assembly. Assemble input shell with sun gear to planet gear carrier. Install unit to reverse-high clutch.

FORD C-3 (Cont.)

ONE-WAY CLUTCH

Disassembly

Using a screwdriver, remove snap ring. *See Fig. 27.* Lift out cage with springs and bearing rollers as a unit.

Fig. 27: *Removing Snap Ring from One-Way Clutch Cage*

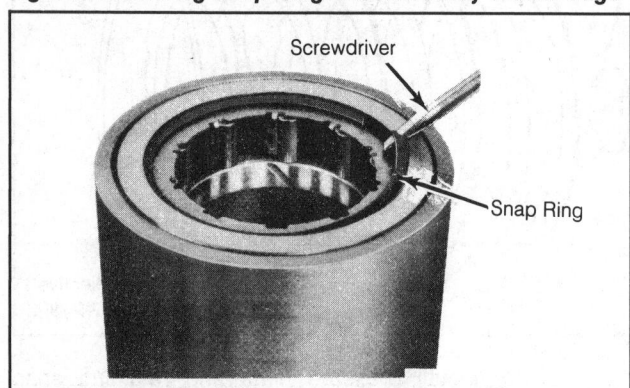

Use a screwdriver to remove snap ring.

Reassembly

Inspect all parts for wear or damage. Install cage with springs. Insert bearing rollers one by one, using a screwdriver to compress springs. Install snap ring.

Fig. 28: *Installing One-Way Clutch Bearing Rollers*

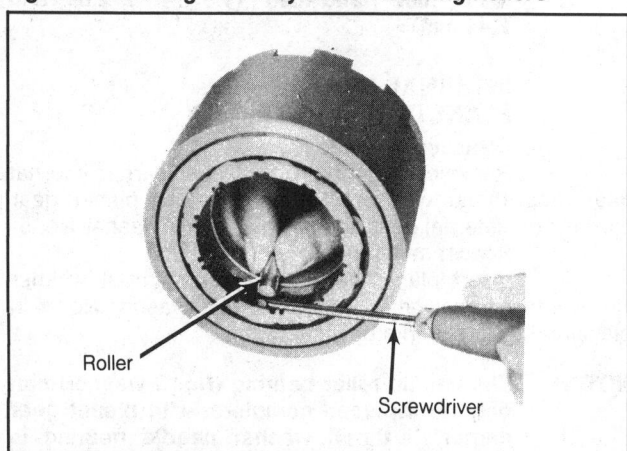

Use a screwdriver to install rollers.

GOVERNOR

Disassembly

Remove governor body to oil collector body retaining bolts. Remove components from governor body. Remove counterweight.

CAUTION: When governor-to-collector bolts are removed, governor components are no longer retained in position in governor body. Care must be taken not to drop governor body and components when bolts are removed.

Reassembly

1) Clean all parts and replace any that are worn or damaged. If necessary, remove 3 rubber seals from oil collector. Carefully install new seals without over stretching.

2) Assemble counterweight spring and primary valve in governor body. Assemble governor body and counterweight to oil collector body.

Fig. 29: *Exploded View of Governor Assembly*

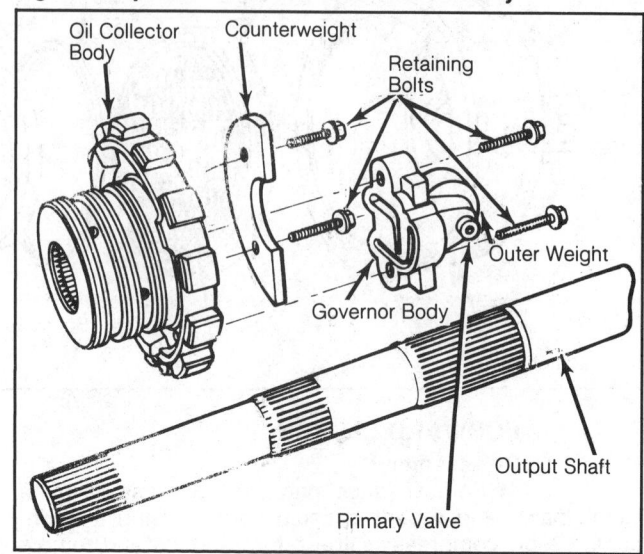

CONTROL VALVE BODY

NOTE: As valve trains are removed from each valve body bore, place individual parts in correct order, and in relative position to valve body to simplify reassembly. Tag all springs as they are removed for reassembly reference.

Disassembly

Remove separator plate bolts and lift off separator plate and gasket. Remove the 4 check balls, 1 check puck and both relief valves with springs. *Refer to Fig. 31 for correct placement.* Remove retaining plates, dowels, plugs, and valves with springs from valve body.

Fig. 30: *Valve Body Separator Plate and Bolt Locations*

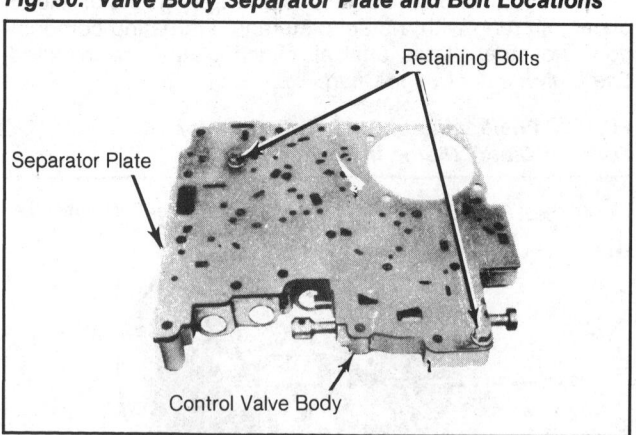

Reassembly

Clean all parts and make sure passages are open. Inspect all parts for burring, unevenness, and gum deposits. Lubricate all parts with transmission fluid. Install valves, springs, plugs, and pins. *See Fig. 31.* Using a new gasket, install separator plate.

FORD C-3 (Cont.)

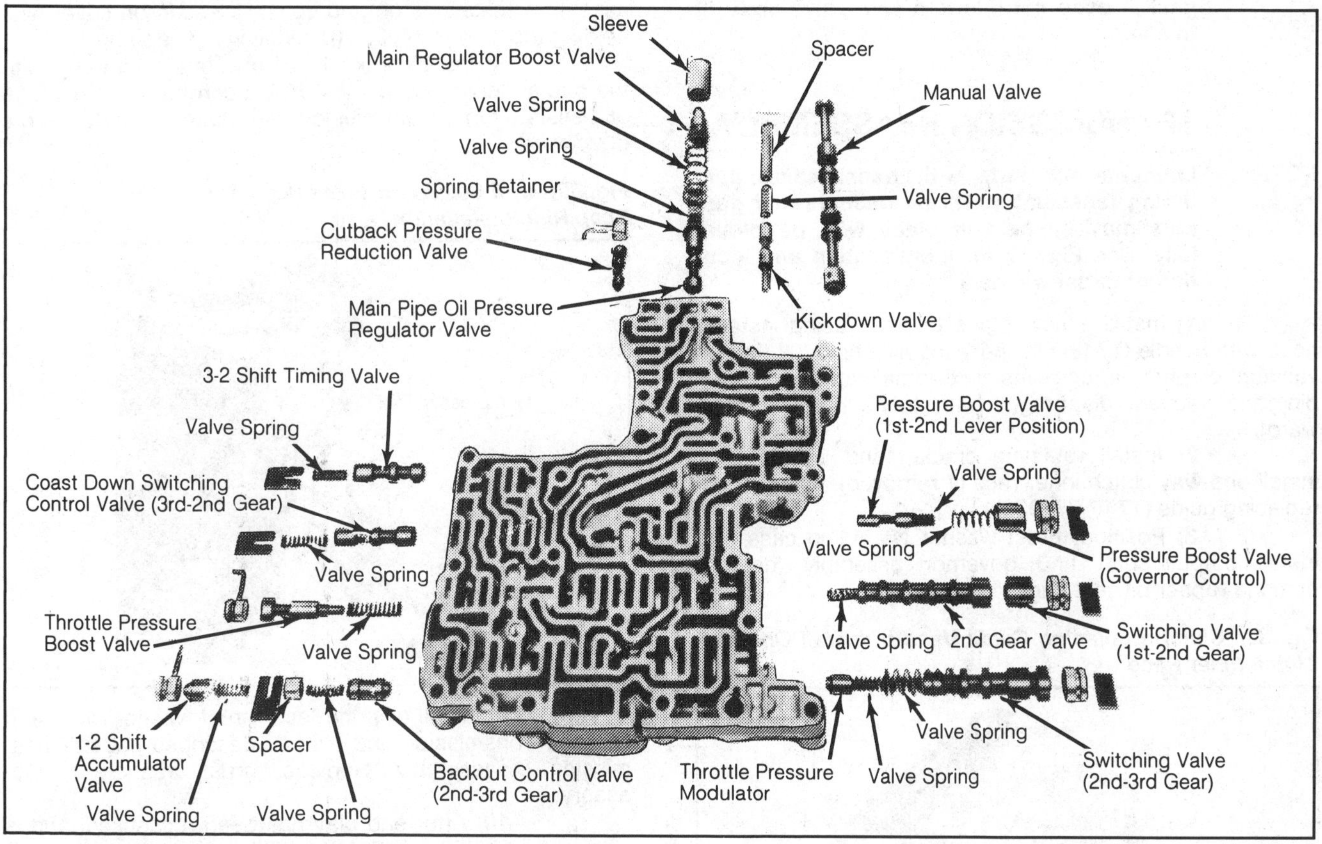

Fig. 31: Exploded View of Valve Body Assembly

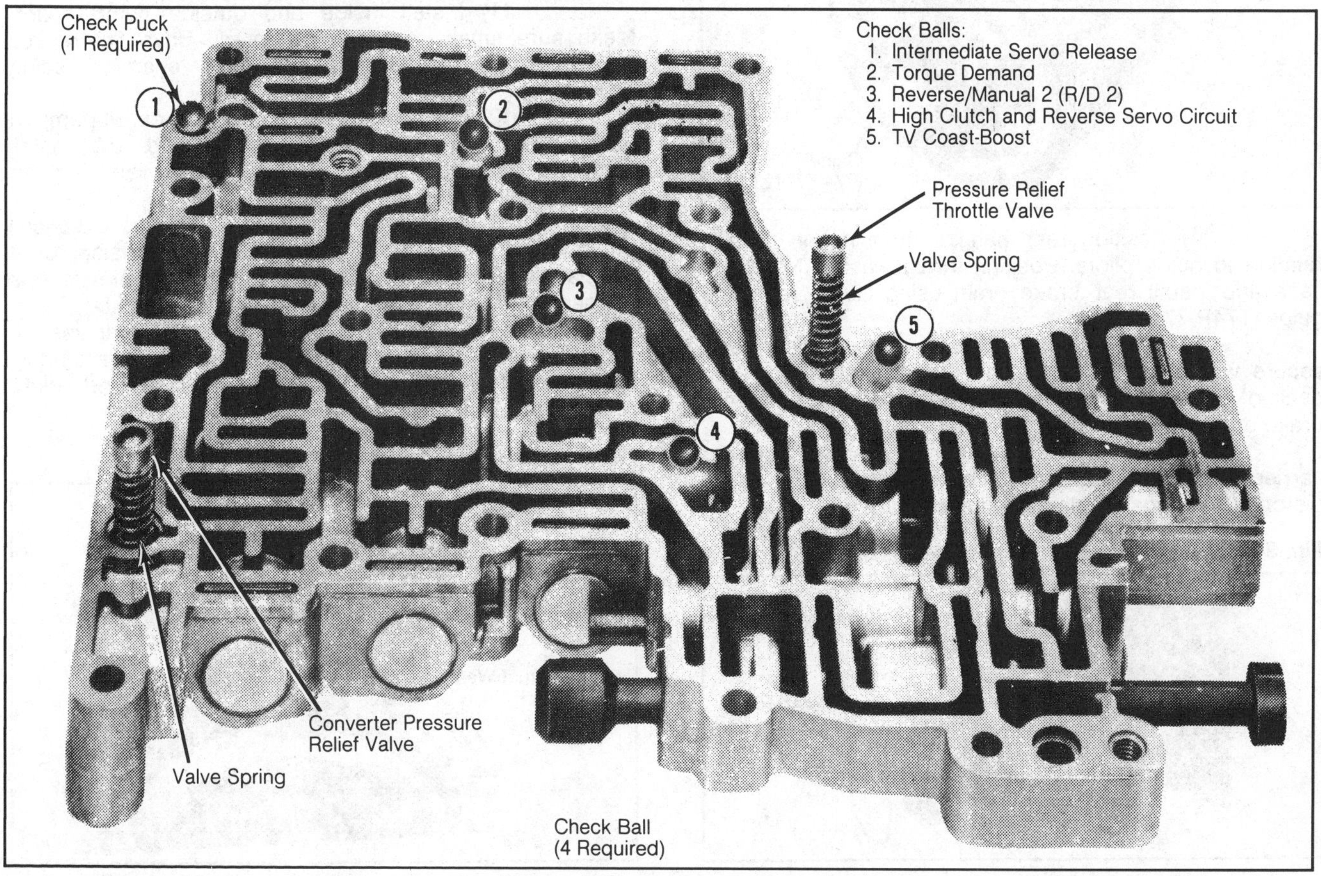

Sleeve
Main Regulator Boost Valve
Valve Spring
Valve Spring
Spring Retainer
Cutback Pressure Reduction Valve
Main Pipe Oil Pressure Regulator Valve
Spacer
Manual Valve
Valve Spring
Kickdown Valve

3-2 Shift Timing Valve
Valve Spring
Coast Down Switching Control Valve (3rd-2nd Gear)
Valve Spring
Throttle Pressure Boost Valve
Valve Spring
1-2 Shift Accumulator Valve
Spacer
Valve Spring
Valve Spring
Backout Control Valve (2nd-3rd Gear)
Throttle Pressure Modulator

Pressure Boost Valve (1st-2nd Lever Position)
Valve Spring
Valve Spring
Pressure Boost Valve (Governor Control)
Valve Spring
2nd Gear Valve
Switching Valve (1st-2nd Gear)
Valve Spring
Valve Spring
Switching Valve (2nd-3rd Gear)

Fig. 32: Locations of Check Ball and Pressure Relief Valve in Valve Body

Check Puck (1 Required)

Check Balls:
1. Intermediate Servo Release
2. Torque Demand
3. Reverse/Manual 2 (R/D 2)
4. High Clutch and Reverse Servo Circuit
5. TV Coast-Boost

Pressure Relief Throttle Valve
Valve Spring

Converter Pressure Relief Valve
Valve Spring

Check Ball (4 Required)

FORD C-3 (Cont.)

NOTE: Make sure that ID tag on separator plate gasket does not interfere with valve body fit to case.

TRANSMISSION REASSEMBLY

NOTE: Lubricate all parts with transmission fluid during reassembly. Thrust washers and gaskets may be held in place with petroleum jelly. See Fig. 12 for identification and location of thrust washers.

1) Install a new pump oil seal, using installer head with handle (T74P-77248-B). Install a new "O" ring on vacuum diaphragm unit. Install throttle valve, actuating pin, and vacuum diaphragm (with tubes pointing rearward).

2) Install retaining bracket and tighten bolt. Install one-way clutch inner race (if removed), using clutch replacing guide (T74P-77193-A).

3) Position thrust washer No. 11 in case and install output shaft and governor assembly (do not damage rubber oil seal rings).

Fig. 33: Clutch Replacing Guide Used to Install One-Way Clutch Inner Race

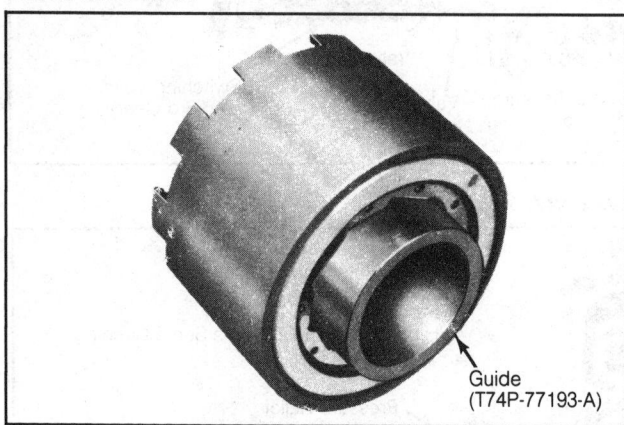

Guide
(T74P-77193-A)

4) Position rear band in housing, in correct relation to guide pilots. Position thrust washer No. 10 in case and install rear brake drum using clutch replacing guide (T74P-77193-A).

5) Remove guide, install internal gear, and secure with snap ring. Position thrust washer No. 9 to back of planet carrier. Install carrier and secure to rear brake drum with snap ring.

6) Position thrust washer No. 8 on planet gear carrier and install front assembly. Replace front servo piston or "O" rings at this time, if necessary.

Fig. 34: Exploded View of Front Servo Assembly

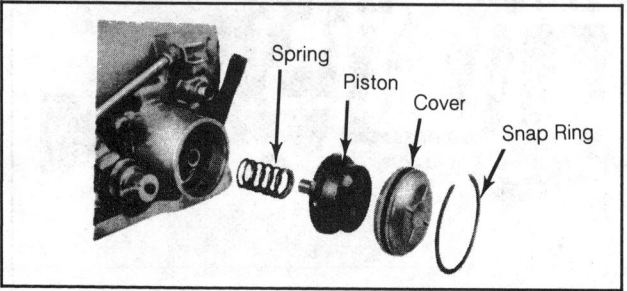

Spring   Piston   Cover   Snap Ring

7) Install spiral spring on front servo piston assembly. Install piston and cover; press in on cover with holding tool (T74P-77028-A). Install with snap ring.

8) Install brake band and struts, starting with the one at servo piston lever. Being careful not to damage oil seals, turn transmission so output shaft points downward.

Fig. 35: Tool Set-Up for Front Servo Snap Ring Installation

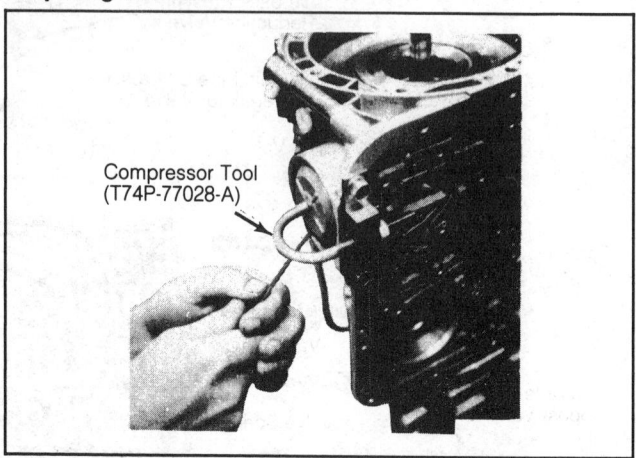

Compressor Tool
(T74P-77028-A)

9) Install oil pump and thrust washer No. 1 and recheck transmission end play as described under Transmission Disassembly. Replace thrust washer, if necessary.

10) After end play has been rechecked, and is within limits of .001-.025" (.025-.635 mm), remove oil pump and thrust washer again.

11) Install inside and outside pump gears. Make sure small gear has I.D. pump drive flat recess facing upward, and large gear has chamfer facing downward.

12) Position steel adapter plate on oil pump in exact position required as shown in *Fig. 37*. Install complete assembly to converter housing and tighten retaining bolts finger tight.

13) Front pump alignment requires a special pump aligning tool (T74P-77103-X). Tool consists of 4 special sleeves and a handle. The O.D. of each sleeve is the same, however, each sleeve has a different I.D.

14) Centering pump support and gear assembly in converter housing is critical. Select the smallest I.D. sleeve which will fit COMPLETELY over support shaft. Assemble selected sleeve to handle.

Fig. 36: Installing Pump Into Case

Thrust Washer

FORD C-3 (Cont.)

15) Slide tool down over shaft until tool bottoms against pump. The outside diameter of sleeve will then automatically center pump in converter housing. Tighten retaining bolts and remove centering tool.

NOTE: **Use care not to damage alignment sleeve tools. Damage to sleeve gauging surfaces may result in incorrect pump to converter housing alignment, pump seal leakage, or bushing failure.**

Fig. 37: Correct Positioning of Adapter Plate on Housing

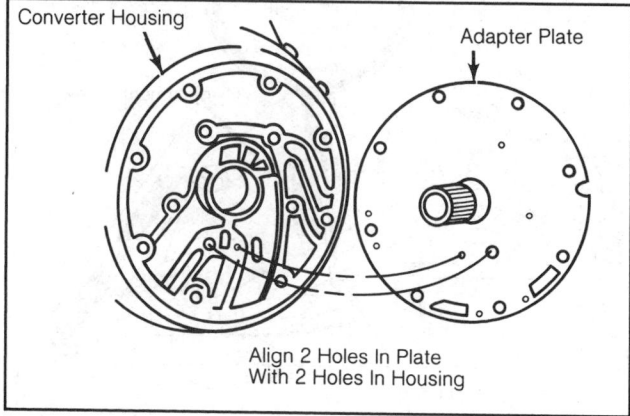

Fig. 38: Special Front Pump Alignment Tool

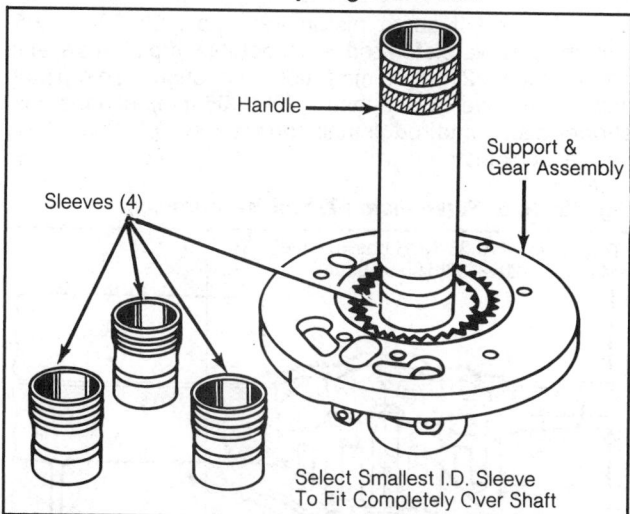

Tool T74P-77103-X consist of 4 sleeves and a handle.

16) Install input shaft into pump. Install converter into pump gears. Rotate converter to check for free movement. Remove converter and input shaft.

17) Position selected No. 1 thrust washer to pump housing and retain with petroleum jelly. Install a new "O" ring. Carefully install converter housing with pump using a new gasket (do not damage the steel oil seals).

18) Install bolts using NEW aluminum washers and tighten. Adjust front band. Perform air pressure tests to ensure proper transmission operation as described under Testing in this article.

19) Install parking pawl and its return spring in extension housing and preload. Using a new gasket, install extension housing. Make sure to correctly seat the operating parking rod in extension guide cup. Install and

Fig. 39: Front View of Converter Housing.

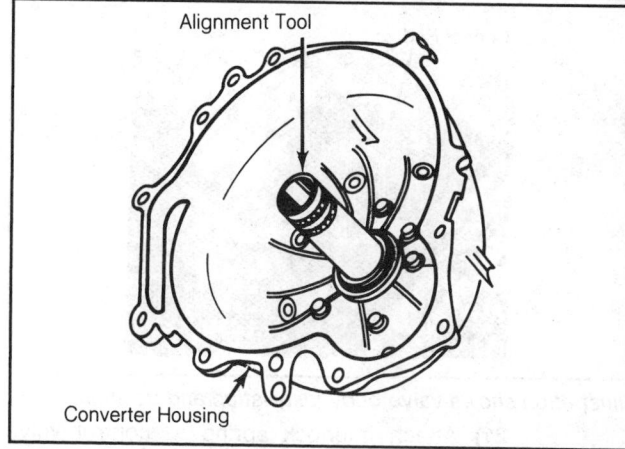

Illustration shows position of pump alignment tools.

tighten bolts. If necessary, replace extension housing oil seal.

Fig. 40: Interior View of Extension Housing

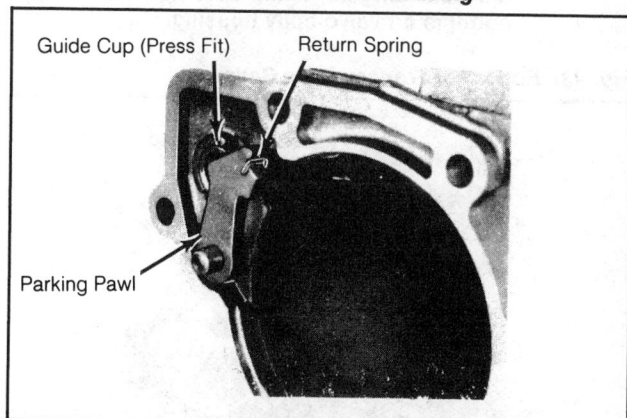

Illustration shows correct installation of parking pawl.

Fig. 41: Rear of Transmission Housing

Illustration shows proper installation of extension housing.

20) Using a new gasket, place control valve body in position. Attach and lock connecting rod or link to manual valve. Install and tighten retaining bolts.

FORD C-3 (Cont.)

Fig. 42: Interior View of Transmission Case

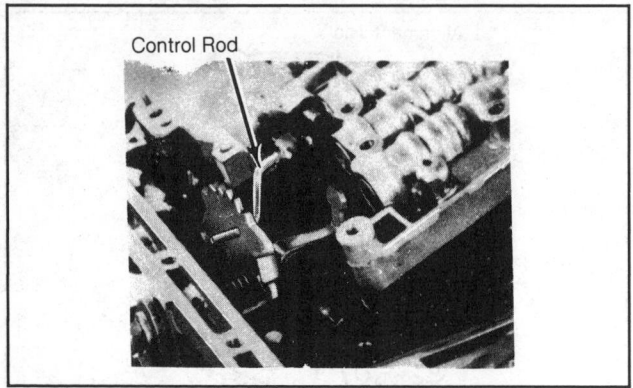

Control Rod

Illustration shows valve body installation and position.

21) Attach interlock spring to control valve housing. Before proceeding further, make sure inner downshift lever is seated between stop and downshift valve as shown in *Fig. 43.*

CAUTION: Because valve body retaining bolts are of different lengths, make sure each bolt head bottoms on valve body housing.

Fig. 43: Bottom of Transmission Case

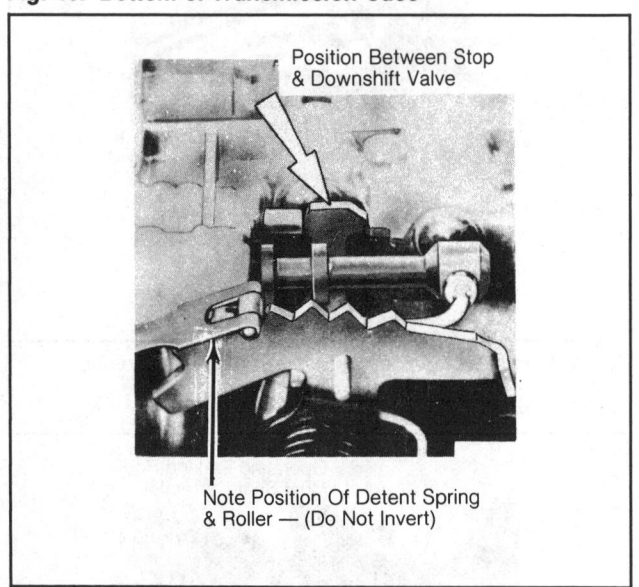

Position Between Stop & Downshift Valve

Note Position Of Detent Spring & Roller — (Do Not Invert)

Illustration shows inner downshift lever position.

22) Insert a screwdriver through rear servo rod bore in case to make sure servo rod pocket or rear band end is centered with bore in case.

23) Assemble servo piston rod, servo piston and spring. In addition, install a reverse servo piston spring to check piston travel only.

24) Install piston assembly and springs into rear servo bore. Make sure piston rod is correctly seated in reverse band apply end.

25) Install Servo Rod Selecting Guide (T74P-77190-A) using a new servo cover gasket. Install and tighten 3 retaining bolts (servo cover bolts are not long enough to attach tool to case; use 3 M6x30 valve body retaining bolts).

26) Tighten tool adjusting screw to 36 INCH lbs. (4 N.m). Install a dial indicator on case and position

indicator pointer on one of the servo piston pads accessible through cutout of tool.

27) Zero dial indicator and back out tool adjusting screw until servo piston bottoms out on tool. Record distance servo piston moved.

Fig. 44: Tool Set-Up for Rear Servo Pin Selection

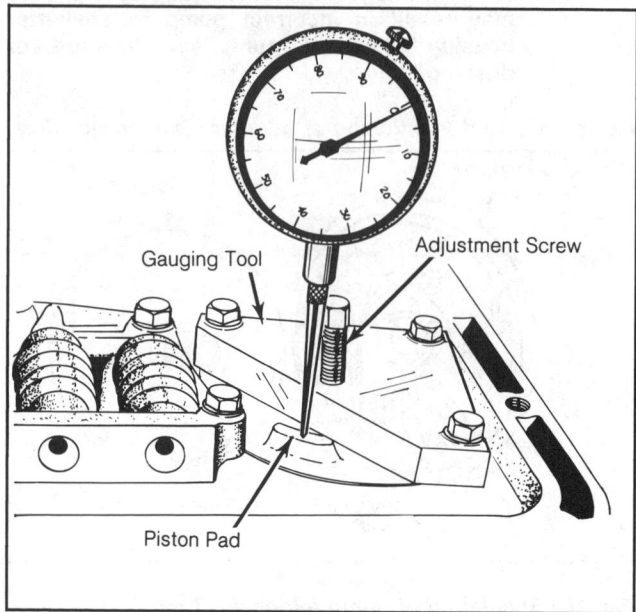

Gauging Tool

Adjustment Screw

Piston Pad

28) If servo piston travel is .120-.220" (3.05-5.59 mm), servo piston rod is acceptable. If piston travel is greater than .220" (5.59 mm), use next longer servo piston and rod. If travel is less than .120" (3.05 mm), use the next shorter piston and rod. Install correct servo piston and rod and recheck piston travel.

Fig. 45: Rear Servo Piston Travel Measurement

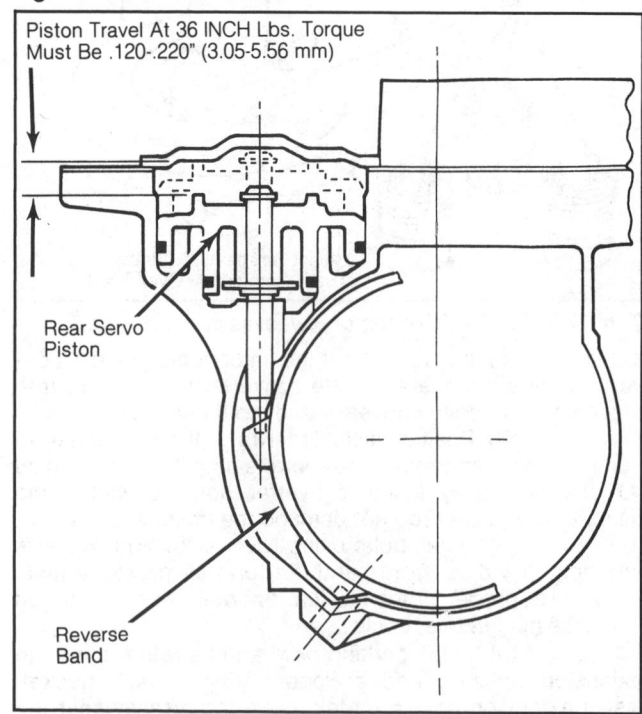

Piston Travel At 36 INCH Lbs. Torque Must Be .120-.220" (3.05-5.56 mm)

Rear Servo Piston

Reverse Band

FORD C-3 (Cont.)

NOTE: Servo piston rods are available in 3 sizes and identified by grooves on rod. Rod sizes and I.D. are as follows: 2.085-2.112" (1 groove), 1.986-2.014" (no groove), and 1.888-1.915" (2 grooves).

29) Remove servo adjusting tool and additional reverse servo spring (used for checking piston travel). Reinstall servo assembly. Install servo cover and bolts.

30) Install oil pan, using a new gasket. Tighten pan bolts to specifications in 2 steps. Install neutral switch. Install input shaft and torque converter.

TIGHTENING SPECIFICATIONS

Application	Ft. Lbs. (N.m)
Converter Drain Plug	20-30 (27-41)
Converter Housing-to-Case	27-39 (37-53)
Converter Housing-to-Engine	28-38 (38-52)
Connector-to-Case	10-15 (14-20)
Converter-to-Flywheel	27-49 (37-67)
Downshift Lever Outer Nut	7-11 (10-15)
Extension Housing-to-Case	27-39 (37-53)
Flywheel-to-Crankshaft	48-53 (65-72)
Front Band Adjusting Screw Lock Nut	35-45 (48-61)
Governor-to-Collector Body	7-10 (10-14)
Oil Cooler Line or By-Pass Tube-to Connector	7-10 (10-14)
Oil Pan-to-Case	12-17 (16-23)
One Way Clutch Inner Race-to-Case	7-10 (10-14)
Pump-to-Converter Housing	7-10 (10-14)
Rear Servo Cover-to-Case	7-10 (10-14)
Separator Plate-to-Valve Body	7-9 (10-12)
Valve Body-to-Case	6-8 (8-11)

Automatic Transmissions

FORD C-5

Bronco II, Capri, Cougar, Fairmont, Granada, Mustang, Ranger, Thunderbird, XR7, Zephyr, F100/150 Pickups

IDENTIFICATION

Transmission Type

The C-5 automatic transmission is identified by a code letter on the Identification Tag. The tag is located under lower front intermediate servo cover bolt. The first line on tag shows transmission model prefix and suffix. A number appearing after the suffix indicates that internal parts have been changed after initial production start up.

TRANSMISSION IDENTIFICATION CODES

Application	Code
Bronco II, Ranger, F100/150 Pickups	"W"
All Other Models	"C"

DESCRIPTION

The C-5 transmission is a fully automatic 3 speed unit capable of providing automatic upshifts and downshifts through 3 forward gear ratios and also capable of providing manual selection of first and second gears.

The unit consists essentially of a converter clutch torque converter, a compound planetary gear train controlled by 2 bands, 2 disc clutches, a one-way clutch and a hydraulic control system.

LUBRICATION & ADJUSTMENT

See the appropriate article in AUTOMATIC TRANSMISSION SERVICING Section.

TESTING

STALL TEST

Testing Precautions

1) When making test, do not hold throttle open longer than 5 seconds. Allow a cooling period of I5 seconds with transmission in Neutral and engine speed at 1000 RPM between each test.

2) If engine speed exceeds maximum limits shown, release accelerator immediately as this is an indication of clutch or band slippage.

Testing Procedure

1) Install tachometer and fully apply parking and service brakes. Start engine and run at curb idle and at normal operating temperature.

2) Stall test transmission in each driving range at full throttle. Note maximum RPM obtained. Engine speed should be within limits shown in *Stall Speeds Table.*

Fig. 1: Cutaway View of Ford Motor Co. C-5 Automatic Transmission Assembly

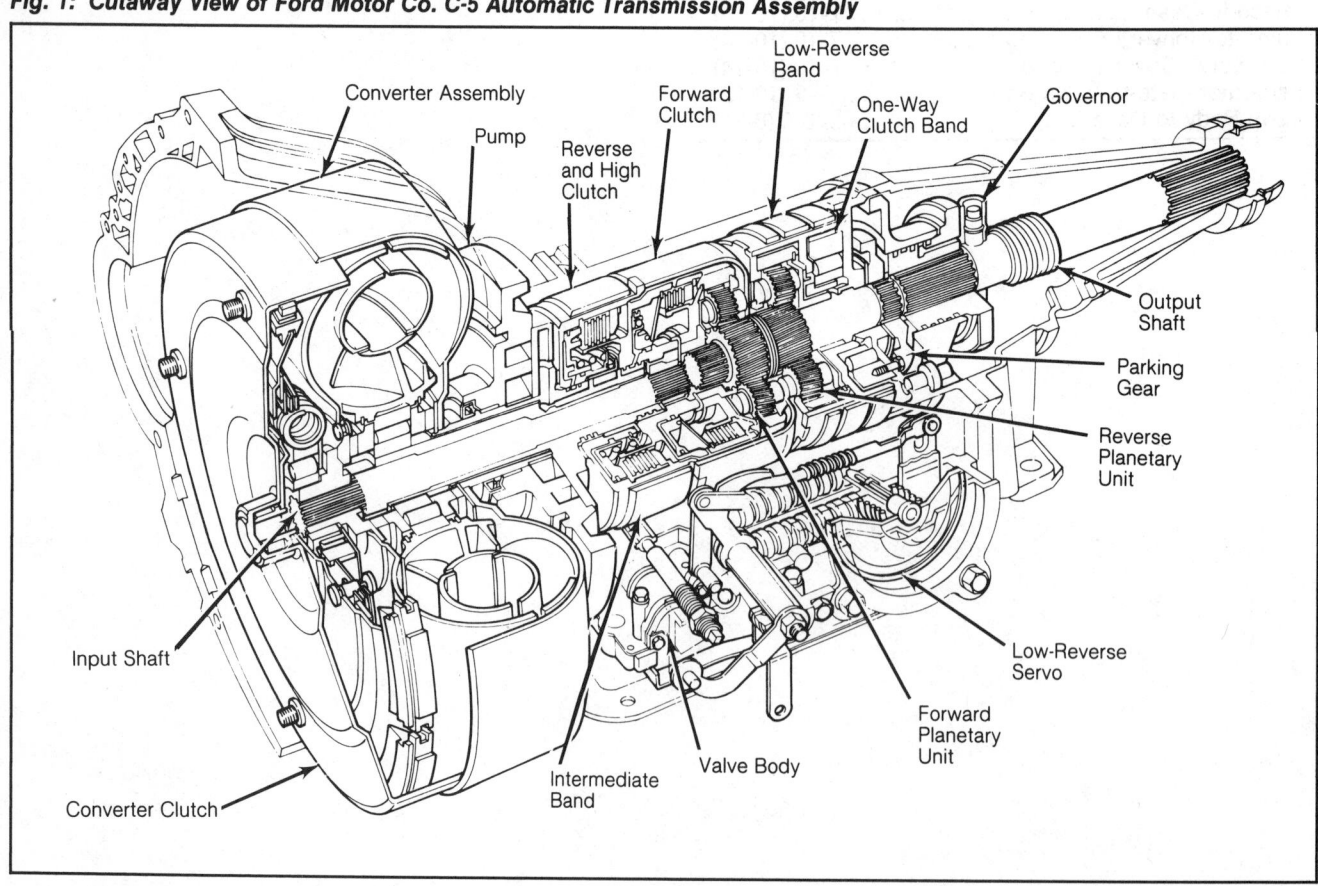

FORD C-5 (Cont.)

Fig. 2: C-5 Automatic Transmission Hydraulic Circuits Diagram

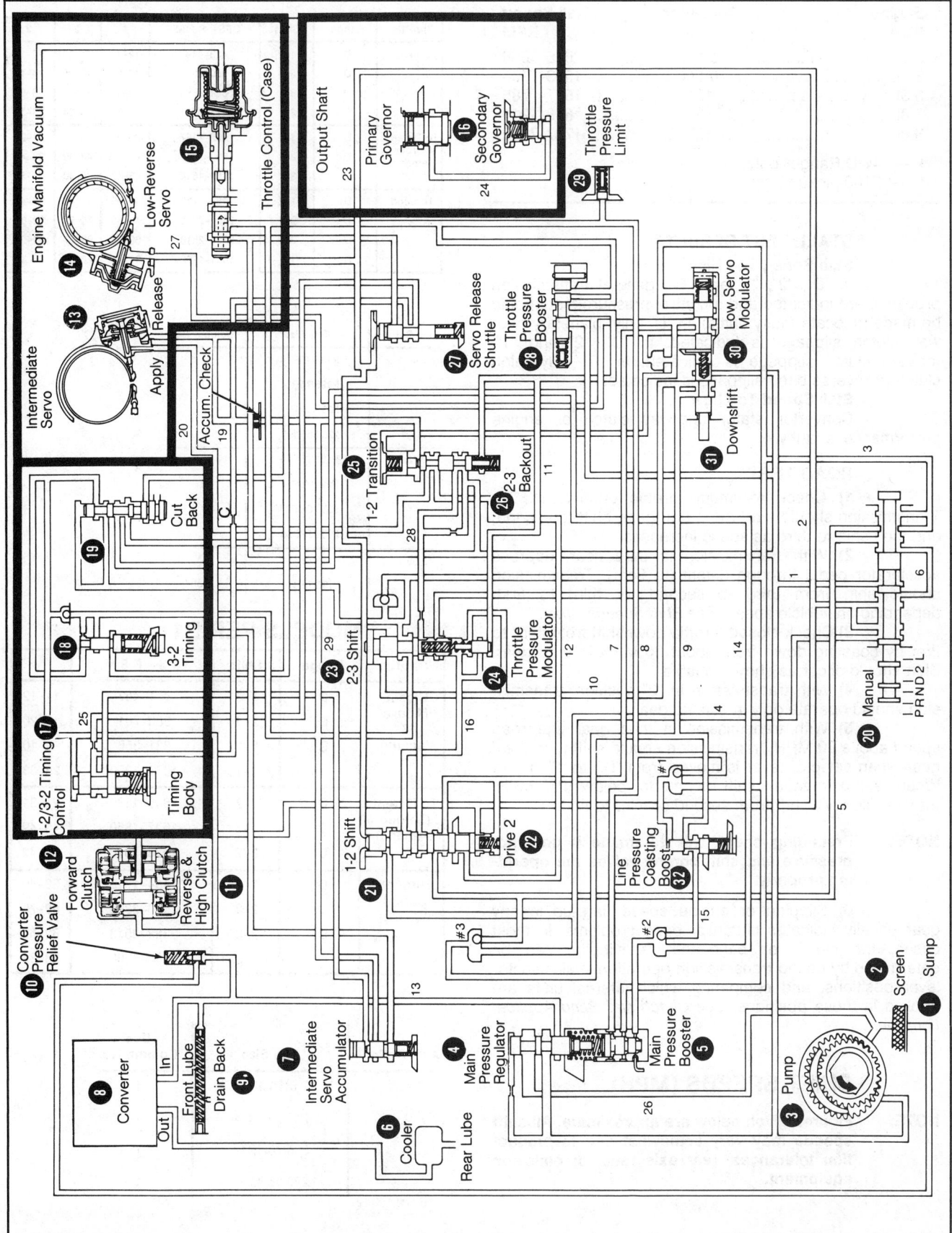

Automatic Transmissions

FORD C-5 (Cont.)

STALL SPEED SPECIFICATIONS

Engine Size	Converter Size	Stall Speed RPM
2.3L [1]	10 1/4"	2675-3068
3.3L	10 1/4"	1503-1760
3.3L	12"	1527-1785
3.8L	12"	1648-1911
3.8L [2]	12"	1737-2022

[1] — 4WD Ranger only.
[2] — F100 pickup only.

STALL TEST RESULTS

Stall Speed Too High

In "D", "2", "1" and "R", general transmission problems are indicated and a control pressure test should be made to locate faulty unit(s). In "D" only, planetary one-way clutch slippage is indicated. In "D", "2" and "1", forward clutch slippage is indicated. In "R" only, high clutch or reverse band slippage is indicated.

Stall Speed Too Low

Converter stator one-way clutch or engine performance is faulty.

ROAD TEST

1) Check minimum throttle upshifts in "D". Transmission should start off in first gear, shift to second, and then shift to third as speed increases.

2) With transmission in third gear, depress accelerator pedal through detent (to floor). Transmission should shift from third to second, or third to first, depending on vehicle speed. See *Shift Speeds Chart.*

3) Check closed throttle downshift from third to first by coasting down from about 30 MPH in third gear. Shift should occur as shown in table.

4) With transmission in "2" position, transmission should operate only in second gear.

5) With transmission in third gear and road speed above 30 MPH, transmission should shift to second gear when selector lever is moved from "D", to "2" or "1". When same manual shift is made below 25 MPH, transmission will shift from second or third to first.

NOTE: **Preceding check will determine if governor pressure and shift control valves are operating properly.**

6) Slipping or engine speed flare-up in any gear usually indicates clutch or band problems. In most cases, the clutch or band that is slipping can be determined by noting transmission operation in all selector lever positions, and comparing which internal units are applied in those positions. See *Clutch and Band Application Chart.*

SHIFT SPEEDS (MPH)

NOTE: **Figures given below are approximate. All shift speeds may vary somewhat due to production tolerances, rear axle ratio, or emission equipment.**

MODELS PEP-R, PEP-W

Throttle	Range	Shift	OPS—R.P.M.	1	2	3
Closed (Above 17" Vacuum)	D	1-2	413-456	12-13	11-13	10-11
	D	2-3	580-761	17-22	15-20	14-18
	D	3-1	331-366	10-11	9-10	8-9
	1	2-1	1074-1271	31-37	29-34	25-30
To Detent (Torque Demand)	D	1-2	907-1187	26-35	24-32	21-28
	D	2-3	1600-1852	47-54	43-49	38-44
	D	3-2	1459-1614	43-47	39-43	34-38
Through Detent (W.O.T.)	D	1-2	1480-1718	43-50	39-46	35-40
	D	2-3	2621-2901	76-85	70-77	62-68
	D	3-2	2359-2516	69-73	63-67	56-59
	D	3-1 2-1	1061-1292	31-38	28-34	25-30

Axle Ratio	Tire Size	Use Column No.
2.47:1	P185/75R14	1
	P195/75R14	1
	205/70HR14	1
	220/55R390	1
2.73:1	P185/75R14	2
	P195/75R14	2
	205/70HR14	2
	220/55R390	2
3.08:1	P185/75R14	3
	P195/75R14	3

MODELS PEP-B1

Throttle	Range	Shift	OPS—R.P.M.	1
Closed (Above 17" Vacuum)	D	1-2	411-457	11-12
	D	2-3	580-761	15-20
	D	3-1	331-366	9-10
	1	2-1	1074-1269	28-33
To Detent (Torque Demand)	D	1-2	845-1185	22-31
	D	2-3	1527-1850	40-49
	D	3-2	1436-1610	38-42
Through Detent (W.O.T.)	D	1-2	1464-1716	39-45
	D	2-3	2600-2898	68-76
	D	3-2	2338-2513	62-66
	D	3-1 2-1	1046-1290	28-34

Axle Ratio	Tire Size	Use Column No.
2.73:1	P185/75R14	1
	P195/75R14	1
	205/70HR14	1
	220/55R390	1

FORD C-5 (Cont.)

SHIFT SPEEDS (MPH) (Cont.)

MODELS PEP-V

Throttle	Range	Shift	OPS—R.P.M.	1	2
Closed (Above 17" Vacuum)	D	1-2	421-467	12-14	12-14
	D	2-3	586-807	17-23	17-24
	D	3-1	331-366	10-11	10-11
	1	2-1	1091-1313	32-38	32-39
To Detent (Torque Demand)	D	1-2	831-1193	24-35	25-35
	D	2-3	1496-1845	44-54	44-55
	D	3-2	1330-1542	39-45	40-46
Through Detent (W.O.T.)	D	1-2	1506-1769	44-51	45-53
	D	2-3	2655-2971	77-87	79-89
	D	3-2	2387-2582	69-75	71-77
	D	3-1 2-1	1080-1332	31-39	32-40

Axle Ratio	Tire Size	Use Column No.
2.47:1	P185/75R14	1
	P195/75R14	2
	P205/70R14	1
	220/55R390	1
	205/60R390	1

MODELS PEN-P, G, S, U, Y, Z, CA

Throttle	Range	Shift	OPS—R.P.M.	1	2
Closed (Above 17" Vacuum)	D	1-2	399-446	10-11	11-12
	D	2-3	585-847	15-22	15-22
	D	3-1	331-366	8-9	9-10
	1	2-1	1091-1317	28-34	29-35
To Detent (Torque Demand)	D	1-2	492-964	13-25	13-25
	D	2-3	1107-1551	29-40	29-41
	D	3-2	1040-1515	27-39	27-40
Through Detent (W.O.T.)	D	1-2	1514-1775	39-46	40-47
	D	2-3	2683-3008	69-78	71-80
	D	3-2	2426-2633	63-68	64-70
	D	3-1 2-1	1094-1344	28-35	29-35

Axle Ratio	Tire Size	Use Column No.
2.73	P175/75R14	1
	190/65R390	
2.73	P185/75R14	2
	P195/75R14	2
	P205/70R14	2
	195/70HR14	2

MODELS PEN-AA, AB, BA

Throttle	Range	Shift	OPS—R.P.M.	1	2
Closed (Above 17" Vacuum)	D	1-2	398-449	10-12	10-12
	D	2-3	582-854	15-22	15-23
	D	3-1	331-366	8-9	9-10
	1	2-1	1091-1317	28-34	29-35
To Detent (Torque Demand)	D	1-2	490-994	13-26	13-26
	D	2-3	1085-1589	28-41	29-42
	D	3-2	978-1545	35-40	26-41
Through Detent (W.O.T.)	D	1-2	1506-1781	39-46	40-47
	D	2-3	2673-3016	69-78	71-80
	D	3-2	2416-2641	62-68	64-70
	D	3-1 2-1	1087-1348	28-35	29-36

Axle Ratio	Tire Size	Use Column No.
2.73	P175/75R14	1
	190/65R390	
2.73	P185/75R14	2
	P195/75R14	2
	P205/70R14	2
	195/70HR14	2

MODELS PEA-CR1

Throttle	Range	Shift	OPS—R.P.M.	1	2	3
Closed (Above 17" Vacuum)	D	1-2	409-444	11-12	12-13	13-14
	D	2-3	655-864	19-24	19-25	20-27
	D	3-1	331-366	9-10	10-11	10-11
	1	2-1	1104-1303	31-37	32-38	34-40
To Detent (Torque Demand)	D	1-2	490-910	14-26	14-27	15-28
	D	2-3	1079-1489	30-42	31-45	33-46
	D	3-2	1017-1498	29-42	30-44	31-46
Through Detent (W.O.T.)	D	1-2	1513-1751	43-49	44-51	46-54
	D	2-3	2682-2975	76-84	78-87	82-91
	D	3-2	2435-2610	69-74	71-76	75-80
	D	3-1 2-1	1100-1329	31-38	32-39	34-41

Axle Ratio	Tire Size	Use Column No.
2.73:1	P195/75R15SL	1
	P215/75R15SL	2
	P235/75R15XL	3

FORD C-5 (Cont.)

SHIFT SPEEDS (MPH) (Cont.)

MODELS PEJ-AE1

Throttle	Range	Shift	OPS—R.P.M.	1	2	3	4	5	6
Closed (Above 17" Vacuum)	D	1-2	405-440	8-9	8-9	8-9	8-9	8-9	8-9
	D	2-3	880-1116	18-23	18-24	19-24	17-21	17-22	18-22
	D	3-1	331-366	6-7	7-8	7-8	6-7	6-7	6-7
	1	2-1	1478-1724	30-35	31-37	32-37	28-33	29-34	30-35
To Detent (Torque Demand)	D	1-2	831-1441	17-30	18-30	18-31	16-28	16-28	17-29
	D	2-3	1477-2004	30-41	31-43	32-44	28-38	29-39	30-40
	D	3-2	1458-1740	30-36	31-37	32-38	28-33	29-34	29-35
Through Detent (W.O.T.)	D	1-2	1977-2283	40-47	42-49	43-50	38-44	39-45	40-46
	D	2-3	3071-3438	63-70	65-73	67-75	59-66	66-68	62-69
	D	3-2	2743-2965	56-60	58-63	60-65	53-57	54-58	55-60
	D	3-1 2-1	1485-1768	30-36	32-38	32-39	28-34	29-35	30-36

Axle Ratio	Tire Size	Use Column No.
3.45	185/75R14SL	1
	195/75R14SL	2
	P205/75R14SL	3
	P205/75R14XL	3
3.73	185/75R14SL	4
	195/75R14SL	5
	P205/75R14SL	6
	P205/75R14XL	6

CONTROL PRESSURE TEST
Engine Vacuum Method
    1) Attach a tachometer to engine, and install a vacuum gauge (using a "T") into manifold vacuum line or vacuum diaphragm unit. Attach a 0-400 psi gauge to control pressure take-off point at transmission. *See Fig. 4.*
    2) Apply both parking and service brakes. Start engine, read and record control pressure in all selector positions at specified manifold vacuum. *See Control Pressure Table.*

Fig. 3: Vacuum Gauge Installation

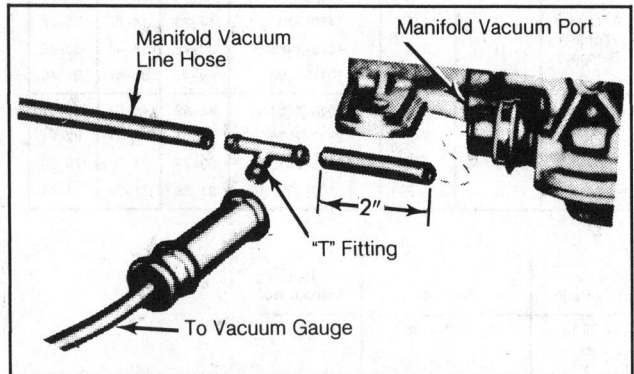

Manifold Vacuum Line Hose

Manifold Vacuum Port

2"

"T" Fitting

To Vacuum Gauge

Pressure gauges affect shift quality of transmission.

Vacuum Pump Method
    1) Attach tachometer to engine. Attach a 0-400 psi pressure gauge to control pressure take-off point at transmission.
    2) Disconnect and temporarily plug manifold vacuum line at vacuum diaphragm unit. Connect a remote vacuum source, such as the vacuum pump provided in a distributor tester.
    3) Apply both parking and service brakes. Start engine and vacuum pump. Set vacuum at 15 in. Hg, read and record control pressure in all shift selector position. See *Control Pressure Table.*

Fig. 4: View of Left Side of Transmission Case

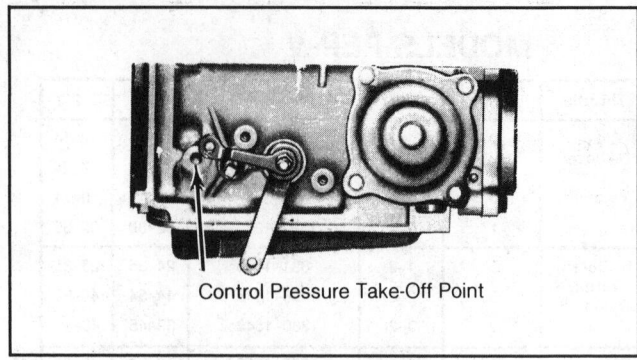

Control Pressure Take-Off Point

Illustration shows location of pressure test point

CONTROL PRESSURE SPECIFICATIONS

Transmission Model	Range	Idle 15" & Above	Idle 10"	WOT Stall Thru Detent
PEN-G,P,S,U,Y,Z	D	55-70	94-107	162-174
	2,1	107-119	100-112	162-174
	R	91-117	156-178	271-291
	P,N	55-70	94-107	162-174
PEN-AA,AB	D	54-72	92-109	161-176
	2,1	107-119	100-112	161-176
	R	90-121	154-182	268-293
	P,N	54-72	92-109	161-176
PEP-V	D	64-68	86-97	160-169
	2,1	105-114	100-109	160-169
	R	76-96	144-162	267-281
	P,N	64-68	86-97	160-169
PEP-R	D	67-80	99-110	157-165
	2,1	102-112	99-110	157-165
	R	113-133	166-184	261-275
	P,N	67-80	99-110	157-165
PEP-B @	D	66-81	97-111	153-165
	2,1	102-112	103-111	153-165
	R	110-134	162-174	256-274
	P,N	66-81	97-111	153-165
PEJ-AE,AG	D	60-64	83-94	157-165
	2,1	101-111	97-106	157-165
	R	70-90	139-156	262-275
	P,N	60-64	83-94	157-165
PEJ-AF, AH @	D	60-64	82-96	155-167
	2,1	102-110	97-106	155-167
	R	69-94	137-160	259-278
	P,N	60-94	82-96	155-167
PEJ-AJ	D	57-61	83-93	157-165
	2,1	101-111	97-106	157-165
	R	70-90	139-156	262-275
	P,N	57-61	83-93	157-165
PEJ-AK @	D	57-61	82-96	155-167
	2,1	102-110	97-106	155-167
	R	69-94	137-147	259-279
	P,N	57-61	83-93	157-167
PEA-CR	D	64-68	83-94	163-172
	2,1	109-117	104-114	163-172
	R	79-85	139-157	272-287
	P,N	64-68	83-94	163-172

CONTROL PRESSURE RESULTS
    If control pressures are not within specification, use the following to determine cause of trouble:
    Control Pressure Low at Idle in All Ranges
    1) Check engine EGR system. Check for low fluid level or restricted intake screen or filter. Check for loose oil tubes or loose valve body.
    2) Check for loose regulator to case bolts, excessive leakage in front pump, case, control valve body, or a sticking control pressure regulator valve.

FORD C-5 (Cont.)

Control Pressure High at Idle in All Ranges

Check engine EGR system. Check vacuum diaphragm unit, manifold vacuum line, throttle valve, and control rod. Check for sticking regulator boost valve(s).

Control Pressure OK at Idle in All Ranges, But Low at 10 in. Hg

Check vacuum diaphragm unit. Control rod or throttle valve are stuck.

Control Pressure OK at Idle in All Ranges, OK at 10 in. Hg, But Low at 1 in. Hg

Check for excessive leakage, low pump capacity, or restricted oil pan screen.

Control Pressure Low In "2"

Check forward clutch and/or front servo.

Control Pressure Low In "D"

Check for faulty forward clutch.

Control Pressure Low In "1"

Check forward clutch and/or rear servo.

Control Pressure Low In "R"

Check reverse-high clutch and/or rear servo.

GOVERNOR CHECK

1) Raise vehicle and support, so that rear wheels are clear of floor. Disconnect and plug vacuum line to vacuum diaphragm unit. Connect hose from a remote vacuum pump to vacuum diaphragm unit.

2) Attach tachometer to engine. Attach a 0-400 psi pressure gauge to control pressure take-off point at transmission.

CAUTION: Do not exceed 60 MPH speedometer speed during governor pressure test.

3) Place transmission in manual "2", no load on engine, and apply 10 in. Hg to vacuum diaphragm unit. Increase speed slowly and watch speedometer. Check MPH at which control pressure cutback occurs. It should occur between 10-20 MPH.

NOTE: After each test, shift into Neutral and run engine at 1000 RPM to cool transmission.

4) Decrease vacuum at vacuum diaphragm to 0-2 in. Hg, and repeat check. Control pressure cutback should occur between 30-50 MPH. Governor is good if cutback occurs within these specifications.

5) If cutback does not occur within specifications, check shift speeds to verify that it is the governor and not a stuck cutback valve, then repair or replace governor.

VACUUM DIAPHRAGM CHECK

Vacuum Supply to Diaphragm Unit

1) Check supply by disconnecting vacuum line at vacuum unit and connect it to a vacuum gauge. With engine idling, gauge must show steady acceptable vacuum.

2) If reading is low, check for vacuum leak or poor engine vacuum. If reading is OK, rapidly accelerate engine momentarily. Reading must drop rapidly at acceleration and return immediately upon release of accelerator.

3) If reading does not change or changes slowly, transmission vacuum line is plugged, restricted, or connected to a reservoir supply. Correct as necessary.

Vacuum Diaphragm Unit

1) Remove unit from transmission. Use a distributor tester equipped with a vacuum pump. Start pump and set regulator knob so that vacuum gauge reads 18 in. Hg, with end of hose blocked off.

2) Connect vacuum hose to manifold vacuum port. If gauge still reads 18 in. Hg, vacuum unit diaphragm is not leaking. If reading does not hold at 18 in. Hg, but drops, diaphragm is leaking and unit must be replaced.

3) As hose is removed from vacuum unit, hold a finger over end of control rod. When hose is removed, the internal spring of vacuum unit should push control rod outward.

4) Check also for presence of transmission fluid in vacuum side of diaphragm or in vacuum hose. If fluid is present, diaphragm is leaking and must be replaced.

AIR PRESSURE CHECKS

1) A "No Drive" condition can exist, even with correct transmission fluid pressure, because of inoperative clutches or bands. Erratic shifts could be caused by a stuck governor valve.

2) The inoperative units can be located through a series of checks by substituting air pressure for the fluid pressure to determine location of malfunction.

3) To make air pressure checks, loosen oil pan bolts and allow transmission to drain. Remove oil pan and control valve body. Apply air to fluid passages to ensure that unit operation is as follows:

Forward Clutch

Apply air pressure to forward clutch passage. A dull thud can be heard when clutch piston is applied, or movement of the piston can be felt by placing finger tips on input shell.

Governor

Apply air pressure to control pressure-to-governor passage and listen for a sharp clicking or whistling noise indicating governor valve movement.

Reverse-High Clutch

Apply air pressure to reverse-high clutch passage. A dull thud can be heard when clutch piston is applied, or movement of piston can be felt by placing finger tips on clutch drum.

Intermediate Servo

1) Hold air nozzle in intermediate servo apply passage. Operation of servo is indicated by tightening of intermediate band around drum.

2) While continuing to apply air pressure at servo apply passage, apply air pressure to intermediate servo release passage. Intermediate servo should release band against the applied pressure.

Low-Reverse Servo

Apply air pressure to low-reverse servo apply passage. Low-Reverse band should tighten around drum if servo is operating properly.

NOTE: If air pressure applied to either of the clutch passages fails to operate a clutch or operates both clutches at once, remove and, with air pressure, check fluid passages in case and oil pump to detect obstructions.

Automatic Transmissions

FORD C-5 (Cont.)

SERVICE (IN VEHICLE)

CONTROL VALVE BODY

Removal

1) Raise and support vehicle. Drain transmission fluid. Remove oil pan retaining bolts, pan and gasket. Shift transmission manual lever to "P" position and remove 2 bolts retaining detent spring to valve body and case.

2) Remove filter retaining bolt and remove filter. Remove remaining valve body-to-case retaining bolts. Hold manual valve in valve body to prevent damaging valve. Remove valve body from case.

NOTE: The nylon plug will be found in transmission pan, it is used to retain transmission fluid within transmission during shipment and should be discarded when oil pan is removed.

Installation

1) Place manual lever in "P" position. Position valve body in case. Place inner downshift lever between downshift lever stop and downshift valve.

2) Make sure that the 2 lands on end of manual valve engage actuating pin on manual detent lever. Install 7 body-to-case bolts, but do not tighten at this time.

3) Position detent spring on lower valve body. Install spring-to-case bolt finger tight. Hold detent spring roller in center of manual lever and install detent spring-to-lower valve body bolt. Tighten retaining bolt.

4) Tighten all control body-to-case retaining bolts. Position filter and install retaining bolt and tighten. Position gasket on pan and install pan and retaining bolts and tighten.

INTERMEDIATE SERVO

Removal

Raise and support vehicle. Remove servo cover retaining bolts. Remove identification tag. Remove servo cover, gasket, piston and piston return spring. Remove piston from cover and seals from piston.

NOTE: On some models it may be necessary to remove crossmember and/or oil cooler lines to gain access to servo cover bolts.

Installation

1) Install new seals on piston, lubricate seals with transmission fluid. Install piston into cover. Install return spring into case. Install new gasket to cover.

2) Install piston and cover into transmission case. Use two 5/16-18 x 1 1/4 bolts, 180° apart to position cover against case. Install identification tag and 2 retaining bolts. Remove aligning bolts.

3) Install remaining retaining bolts and tighten. Install crossmember and adjust intermediate band. Check fluid level.

NOTE: If band cannot be adjusted properly, band struts are not in position. Remove oil pan and valve body, install struts. Reinstall valve body and pan. Adjust band and check fluid level.

LOW-REVERSE SERVO

Removal

1) Raise vehicle on a hoist, loosen reverse band adjusting screw lock nut. Tighten band adjusting screw to l0 ft. lbs. (14 N.m) to prevent band strut from falling down when servo is removed.

2) Remove servo cover-to-case retaining bolts, servo cover and seal. Remove servo piston from case.

NOTE: On some models it may be necessary to remove crossmember and support transmission to gain access to Low Reverse Servo. The piston seal cannot be replaced without replacing piston. Seal is bonded to piston.

Installation

1) Install piston into case. Install a new seal on cover. Install cover by using two 5/16-18 x 1 1/4" bolts, 180° apart to position servo cover on case. Install 2 cover retaining bolts.

2) Remove aligning bolts and install remaining 2 retaining bolts. Tighten all retaining bolts. Adjust low-reverse band. Lower vehicle and check transmission fluid level.

NOTE: If band cannot be adjusted properly, low-reverse band struts are not in position. Remove oil pan and valve body. Install struts, valve body and oil pan. Adjust band. Refill transmission with fluid.

EXTENSION HOUSING BUSHING & SEAL

Removal

Raise vehicle and support. Disconnect propeller shaft from transmission. Remove seal using a tapered chisel or seal remover tool. Remove bushing using a puller.

CAUTION: When bushing is installed, the fluid return drain hole must face downward in alignment with extension housing fluid return groove.

Installation

1) Install new bushing using a driver. Inspect sealing surface of universal joint yoke. If damaged, replace yoke. Remove any scores in counter bore of housing with a crocus cloth.

2) Using a driver, install new seal into extension housing. Lubricate seal, yoke and splines. Install propeller shaft.

EXTENSION HOUSING

Removal

1) Raise and support vehicle. Disconnect propeller shaft and speedometer cable from transmission. Support transmission with a jack.

2) Remove rear support-to-crossmember retaining bolts and nuts. Raise transmission and remove rear support from extension housing.

3) Remove extension housing-to-case retaining bolts and vacuum tube clip. On "cable" floor shift models, remove retainer from extension housing. On all models, remove extension housing.

FORD C-5 (Cont.)

Installation
To install, reverse removal procedures. Tighten all bolts and adjust fluid level.

GOVERNOR
Removal
With extension housing removed, remove governor housing-to-governor distributor retaining bolts. Remove housing from distributor.
Installation
To install, reverse removal procedures. Tighten all bolts, and adjust fluid level.

REMOVAL & INSTALLATION
See the appropriate article in AUTOMATIC TRANSMISSION REMOVAL Section.

TORQUE CONVERTER

LEAKAGE CHECK
See procedures given in Ford C-6 article.

FLUSHING CONVERTER
See procedures given in Ford C-6 article.

TURBINE & STATOR END PLAY CHECK
See procedures given in Ford C-6 article.

STATOR ONE-WAY CHECK
See procedures given in Ford C-6 article.

STATOR INTERFERENCE CHECKS
See procedures given in Ford C-6 article.

TRANSMISSION DISASSEMBLY

NOTE: **Ten thrust washers are used in this transmission, with No.1 located at the front pump and No. 10 located at the parking pawl ring gear. It is important that each thrust washer be installed in the correct position during reassembly.**

1) Remove converter assembly. Mount transmission to holding fixture. Loosen transmission oil pan retaining bolts and allow fluid to drain. Remove oil pan bolts, pan, and gasket.

2) Remove filter retaining bolt and filter. Remove valve body retaining bolts and lift valve body out of transmission case. Remove filter screen from pick-up passage.

3) Remove converter housing retaining bolts and detach housing from case. Insert a large screwdriver between input shell and reverse planet carrier, and pry input shell forward until pump can be removed from case.

Fig. 5: Exploded View of C-5 Valve Body Assembly

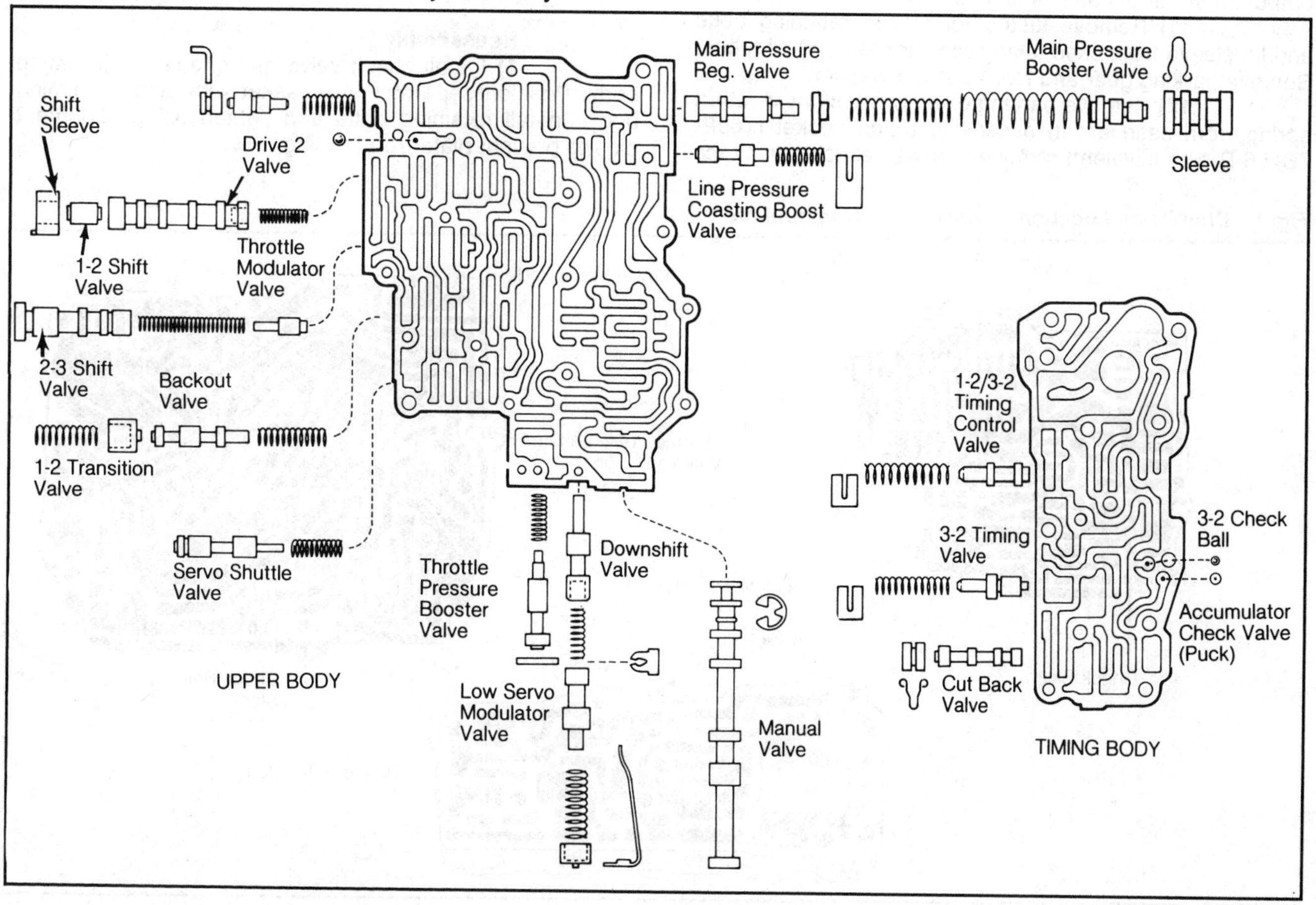

Automatic Transmissions

FORD C-5 (Cont.)

NOTE: **Check stator support for No. 1 thrust washer. If washer is not present, remove it from top of reverse-high clutch.**

4) Loosen intermediate band adjusting screw lock nut, thread adjusting screw out of case, and remove band struts. Turn intermediate band counterclockwise until band lugs are aligned with clearance relief provided in case.

5) Remove band, clutch packs, front planetary, and input shell as an assembly. Remove reverse planetary assembly. Loosen low-reverse band adjusting screw lock nut, thread adjusting screw out of case, and remove band struts.

6) Remove lock nut from adjusting screw and discard lock nut. Rotate low-reverse band until lugs are aligned with clearance relief provided in case. Remove band. Remove extension housing retaining bolts, vacuum diaphragm and throttle valve.

7) Remove extension housing and gasket. Remove and discard rubber shipping plug from output shaft. Remove governor retaining bolts and slide governor off output shaft.

8) Using a magnet, lift governor filter out of governor distributor body. Using snap ring pliers, remove snap ring retaining reverse ring gear and hub assembly to output shaft.

9) Remove reverse ring gear hub and assembly. To gain access to snap ring, it may be necessary to push the output shaft forward.

10) Remove low-reverse drum and detach No. 8 thrust washer from drum. Lift governor distributor and output shaft out of case as an assembly.

11) Remove distributor sleeve retaining bolts and lift sleeve from case taking care not to bend oil tubes. Remove parking gear and No. 10 thrust washer.

12) Remove parking pawl, pivot pin, and return spring from case as an assembly. Using socket (T65P-7B456-B or equivalent) remove one-way clutch outer race

retaining bolts, positioning one hand in case to catch clutch assembly before last bolt is removed.

COMPONENT DISASSEMBLY & REASSEMBLY

NOTE: **Handle all parts carefully to avoid damaging bearing or mating surfaces. Lubricate all internal parts with clean automatic transmission fluid only (gaskets and thrust washers may be held in place with petroleum jelly). Use all new gaskets, and tighten all bolts evenly.**

CONTROL VALVE BODY
Disassembly
1) Remove timing body retaining bolts. Remove timing body and relief valve from lower body. Remove timing body separator plate retaining screw, separator plate, check valve, and check ball from timing body.

2) Remove upper body to lower body retaining bolts, turn valve body over and remove lower body to upper body retaining bolts. Hold separator plate against lower body and lift lower body half away from upper body half.

3) Turn lower body over and place it on a bench with separator plate facing up. Remove separator plate and gasket from body and discard gasket.

4) Remove check balls and pressure limit valve from lower body half. Remove the check ball from upper body half.

Reassembly
1) Install check valve and check ball in timing body. Position separator and gasket with plate on timing body. Install retaining bolts and tighten using alignment pins to prevent plate from turning.

Fig. 6: Check Ball Location in Valve Body Components

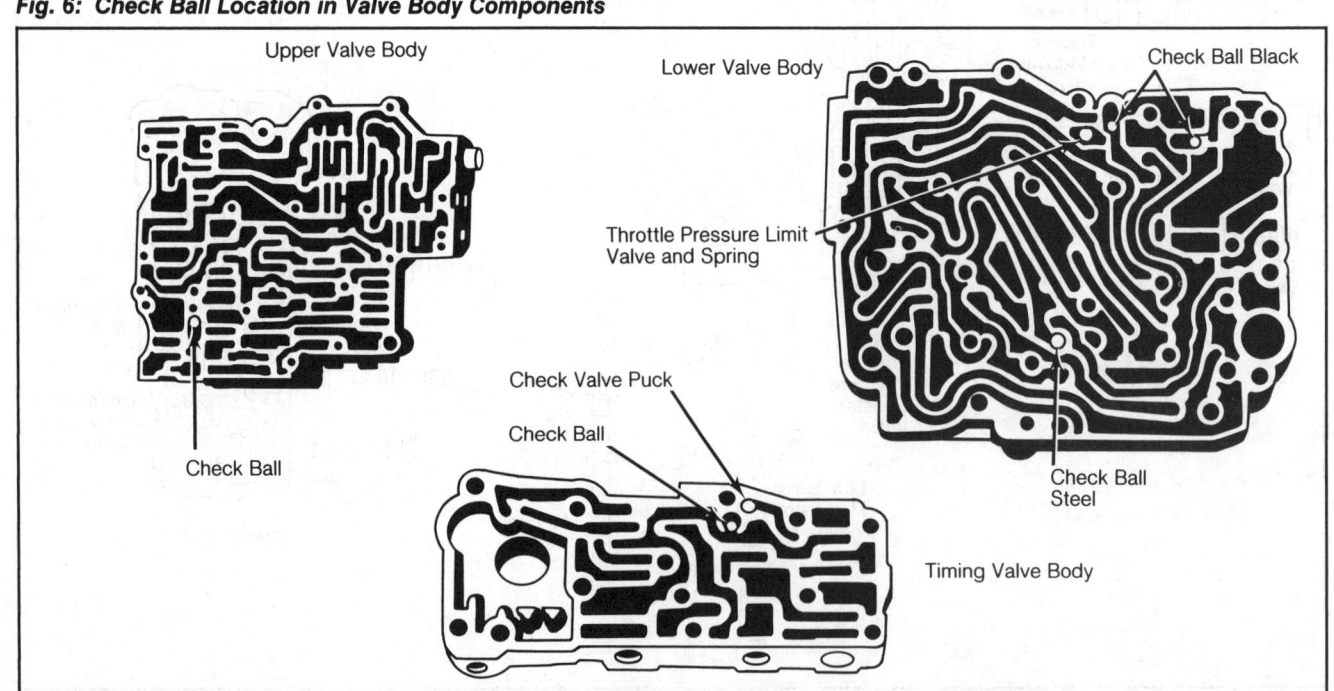

FORD C-5 (Cont.)

2) Install check balls and pressure limit valve in lower half of valve body. The steel ball is larger than other check balls and must be positioned as shown in *Fig. 6*.

3) Install gasket and separator plate on lower body half. Install check ball in upper body half. Hold separator plate firmly against lower body half while turning it over.

4) Position lower body half on upper body half. Install retaining bolts and tighten. Turn valve body over and install upper to lower body retaining bolts and tighten.

5) Install detent spring and roller assembly on lower body half. Position a drift punch in valve body to hold assembly in alignment. Install retaining bolt and tighten.

6) Install check valve in lower body half and position timing body on lower body half. Install timing body retaining bolts and tighten.

INTERMEDIATE SERVO
Disassembly
Remove servo cover, gasket, piston, and return spring. Remove seal rings from piston and servo piston cover. Using snap ring pliers, remove snap ring and remove piston rod from piston.

Reassembly
Reverse disassembly procedures.

Fig 7: *Exploded View of Intermediate Servo*

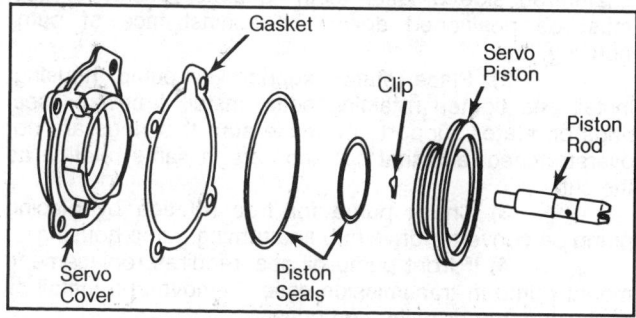

LOW-REVERSE SERVO
Disassembly
Remove servo cover, cover seal, piston, and piston return spring from transmission case.

Reassembly
Reverse disassembly procedures.

Fig. 8: *Exploded View of Low-Reverse Servo*

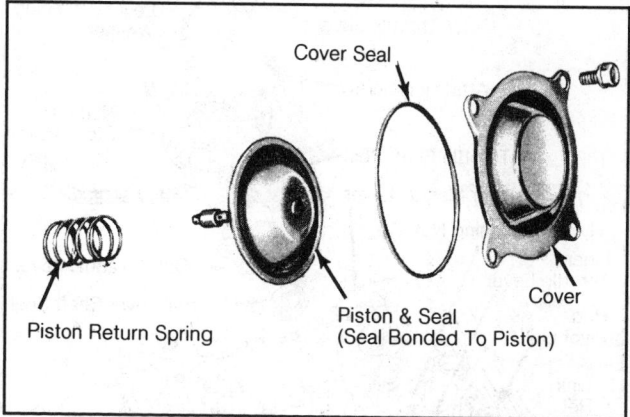

GOVERNOR
Disassembly
Remove snap ring from governor bore. Remove primary valve spring, spring seat washer, and primary valve. Remove secondary valve spring retaining plate. Remove secondary valve and spring from governor bore.

Reassembly
Reverse disassembly procedures.

MANUAL & THROTTLE LINKAGE
Disassembly
1) Remove outer throttle lever retaining nut and lock washer. Remove lever from shaft. Remove inner lever and shaft assembly.

NOTE: **Shaft seal is located in the neutral safety switch and will be removed when shaft is pulled out of case.**

2) Remove retaining bolts and slide neutral safety switch off outer manual lever. Remove inner manual lever retaining nut and lever. Remove outer manual lever and shaft assembly.

Fig. 9: *Exploded View of Governor Assembly*

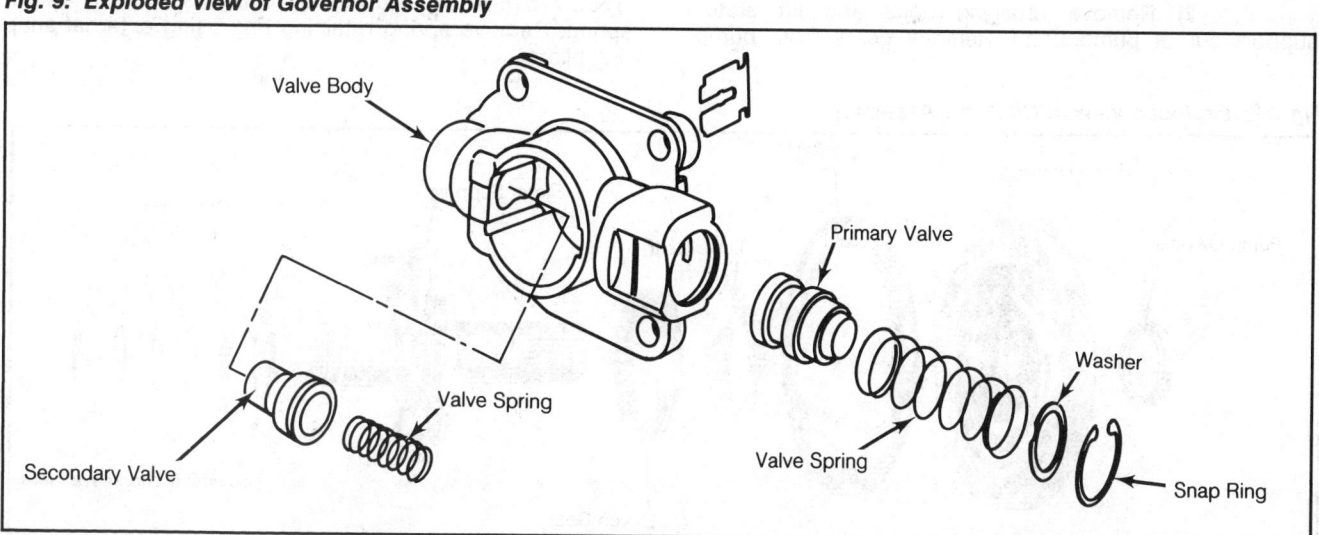

Automatic Transmissions

FORD C-5 (Cont.)

Fig. 10: *Exploded View of Manual and Throttle Linkage*

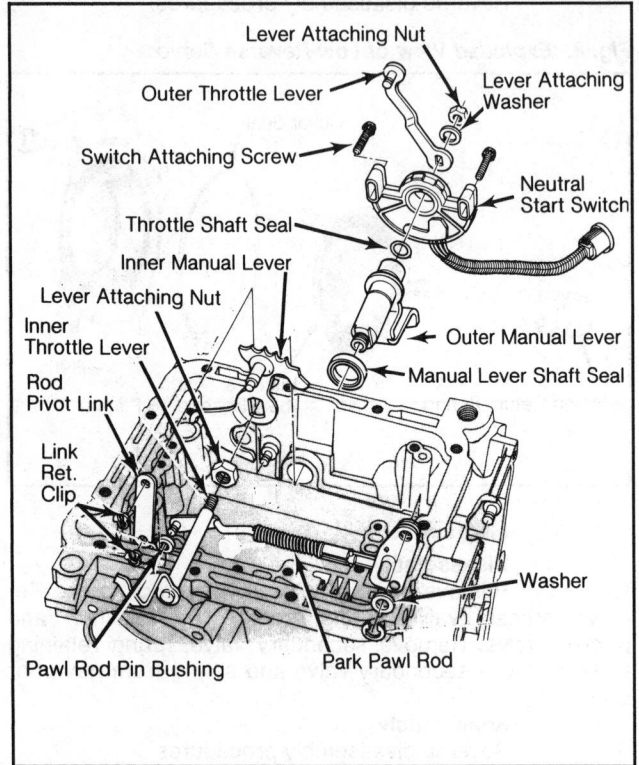

3) Using large screwdriver, pry out manual lever shaft seal from case. Remove front parking pawl linkage retaining clip. Remove rear parking pawl linkage retaining clip, flat washer and linkage.

Reassembly

Install manual lever shaft seal using seal installer (T74P-77498-A or equivalent). If tool is not available, a socket can also be used. Reverse disassembly procedures to complete reassembly.

FRONT PUMP

Disassembly

1) Remove No. 1 and 2 thrust washers from stator support. Remove the teflon and cast iron seal rings from stator support.

2) Remove retaining bolts and lift stator support out of pump body. Remove gears from pump body. Using hammer and punch, drive out converter hub seal from pump body.

Pump Housing Bushing Replacement

1) If bushing is worn or damaged, press old bushing out, using bushing remover (T66L-7003-B9). Press new bushing in place, using bushing installer (T66L-7003-B5) and tool handle.

2) Make sure bushing is installed with slot and groove positioned to rear of pump body and 60° below horizontal centerline as shown in *Fig. 11.*

Fig. 11: *View of Oil Pump Housing*

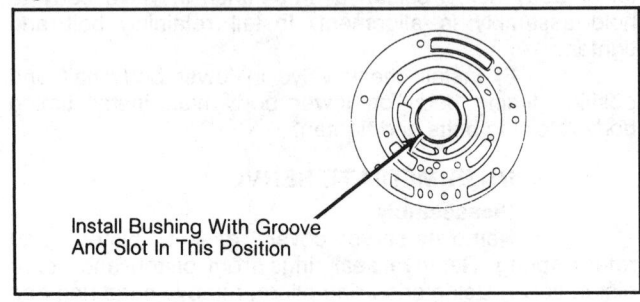

Install Bushing With Groove And Slot In This Position

Illustration shows correct bushing installation

Reassembly

1) Install drive and driven gears into pump housing. Each pump gear has an identification mark on chamfered side of gear teeth. Chamfered side of gear must be positioned downward against face of pump housing.

2) Place stator support in pump housing. Install and tighten retaining bolts. Install 4 new oil seal rings on stator support and make sure that rings are not overstretched, and that cut ends are in same relation as the cut.

3) Check pump for free rotation by placing pump on converter drive hub and turning pump housing.

4) If front pump oil seal requires replacement, mount pump in transmission case. Remove and install oil seal using proper puller and driver.

REVERSE-HIGH CLUTCH

Disassembly

1) Remove clutch pack retaining ring and clutch pack from drum. Using clutch spring compressor (T65L-77515-A or equivalent), compress piston return spring. Remove spring retaining ring using external snap ring pliers.

Fig. 12: *Exploded View of Oil Pump Assembly*

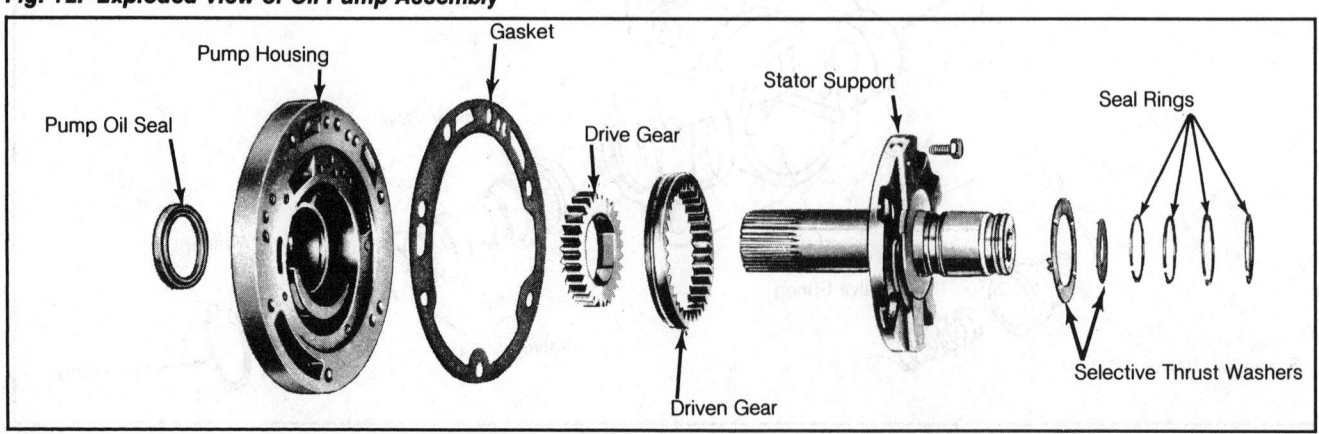

FORD C-5 (Cont.)

Fig. 13: Exploded View of Reverse-High Clutch Assembly

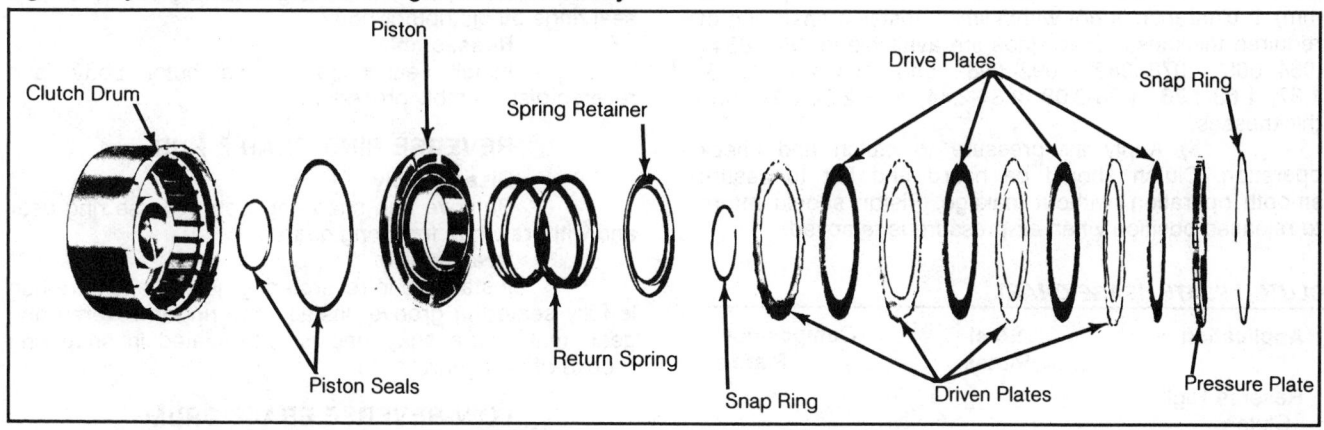

2) Remove clutch piston. If piston is difficult to remove, air pressure can be used to help remove piston. Remove clutch piston seal and inner seal from clutch drum hub.

Reassembly

1) To complete reassembly, reverse disassembly procedures. If old composition plates are to be used, clean by wiping with a lint-free cloth.

2) If new composition plates are to be installed, soak in transmission fluid for 15 minutes before installing.

3) To check clutch pack clearance, install steel plate in clutch drum. Install composition and steel plates alternately until 2 composition plates remain.

4) Install remaining 2 composition plates, disc spring and pressure plate (thicker steel plate). Install retaining ring.

NOTE: **This is not correct plate installation sequence. This sequence is only used to check clutch pack clearance.**

5) Using a feeler gauge, check the clearance between pressure plate and retaining ring. If clearance exceeds .025-.050" (.64-1.35 mm), install a snap ring of required thickness. Snap rings are available in .050-.054", .064-.068", .078-.082" and .092-.096" (1.35-1.37, 1.63-1.73, 1.98-2.08, 2.34-2.44, and 2.64-2.74 mm) thicknesses.

6) After clearance has been checked and proper snap ring selected, remove clutch plates from clutch drum and reinstall as follows: install a steel plate, then alternately install composition and steel plates. Install pressure plate and disc spring with splines facing snap ring. Install retaining ring.

NOTE: **Using air pressure, check clutch for proper operation. Clutch should be heard and felt to assure smooth operation, without leakage. Piston should return to released position when air pressure is removed.**

FORWARD CLUTCH

Disassembly

1) Remove clutch pack retaining ring and remove clutch plates from drum. Using a screwdriver, disengage piston retaining ring from clutch drum ring groove.

2) Remove piston retaining ring, piston return spring, and thrust ring. Remove clutch piston outer seal from piston and inner seal from clutch drum hub.

Reassembly

1) If new clutch plates are installed, they must be soaked in transmission fluid for 15 minutes before clutch pack is assembled.

2) Starting with a composition plate, then alternately install composition and steel plates. The last plate to be installed is the rear pressure plate.

3) Install clutch pack retaining ring. Using a feeler gauge, check clearance between pressure plate and retaining ring. Hold pressure plate down when making measurement.

Fig. 14: Exploded View of Forward Clutch Assembly

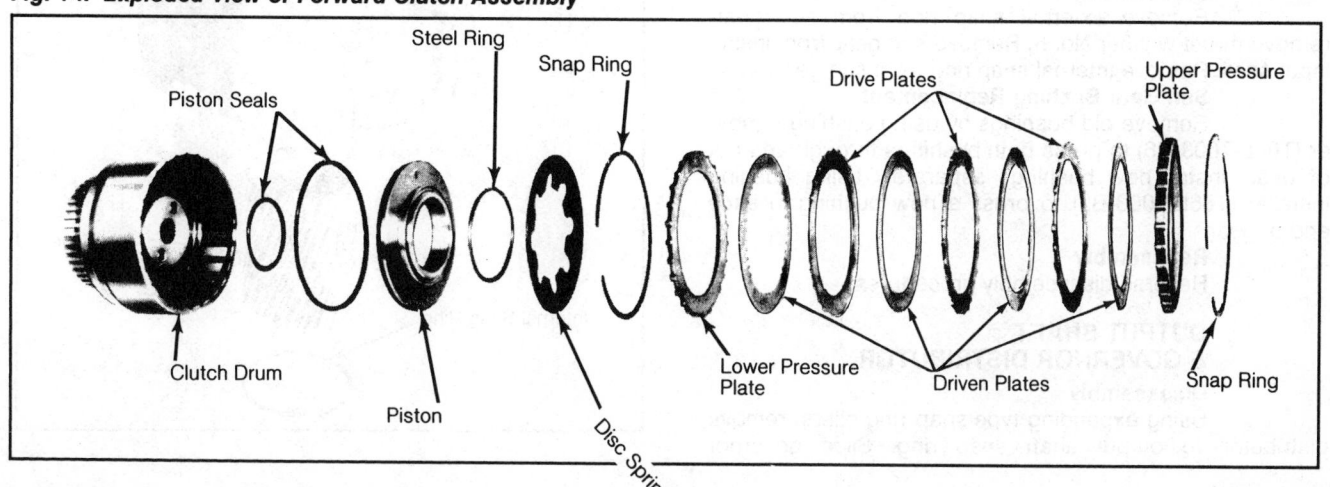

FORD C-5 (Cont.)

4) Clearance should be .025-.050" (.64-1.35 mm). If clearance is not within limits, install a snap ring of required thickness. Snap rings are available in .050-.054", .064-.068", .078-.082", .092-.096", and .104-.108" (1.35-1.37, 1.63-1.73, 1.98-2.08, 2.34-2.44, and 2.64-2.74 mm) thicknesses.

5) Apply air pressure to clutch and check operation. Clutch should be heard and felt to assure smooth operation, without leakage. Piston should return to released position when air pressure is removed.

CLUTCH PLATE USAGE CHART

Application	Steel Plates	Composition Plates
Reverse-High Clutch		
All Models	3	3
Forward Clutch		
All Models (Exc. Ranger)	4	5
Ranger	3	4

FORWARD CLUTCH HUB & RING GEAR
Disassembly
Remove forward clutch hub snap ring and withdraw hub from ring gear. If necessary, remove and install clutch hub bushing using bushing drivers.
Reassembly
Install forward clutch hub in ring gear, make sure hub is bottomed in groove of gear. Install clutch hub snap ring, being sure snap ring is fully seated in groove of ring gear.

Fig. 15: View of Forward Clutch Hub and Ring Gear

Snap Ring — Ring Gear — Forward Clutch Hub

INPUT SHELL & SUN GEAR
Disassembly
Remove external snap ring from sun gear, remove thrust washer No. 5. Remove sun gear from inside input shell. Remove internal snap ring from sun gear.
Sun Gear Bushing Replacement
Remove old bushings by using bushing remover (T66L-7003-B6) to press both bushings through and out of gear. Install new bushings separately using bushing installer (T66L-7003-B2) to press a new bushing in each end of gear.
Reassembly
Reverse disassembly procedures.

OUTPUT SHAFT & GOVERNOR DISTRIBUTOR
Disassembly
Using expanding type snap ring pliers, remove distributor to output shaft snap ring. Slide governor

distributor off output shaft. Using snap ring pliers, remove seal rings on distributor body.
Reassembly
Install seal rings on distributor body, and reverse disassembly procedures.

REVERSE RING GEAR & HUB
Disassembly
Remove hub snap ring from reverse ring gear and withdraw hub from ring gear.
Reassembly
Install hub in reverse ring gear, make sure hub is fully seated in groove. Install snap ring in reverse ring gear, make sure snap ring is fully seated in snap ring groove of ring gear.

LOW-REVERSE BRAKE DRUM BUSHING REPLACEMENT
To remove bushing, use a cape chisel and cut along bushing seam until chisel breaks through bushing wall. Pry loose ends of bushing up with an awl and remove bushing. Use bushing driver (T66L-7003-B6) to install new bushing.

TRANSMISSION REASSEMBLY

NOTE: Handle all parts carefully to avoid damaging bearing and mating surfaces. Lubricate all parts with clean automatic transmission fluid only (gaskets and thrust washers may be held in place with petroleum jelly). Use all new gaskets and seals. Tighten all bolts evenly.

Fig. 16: Input Shell and Sun Gear Assembly

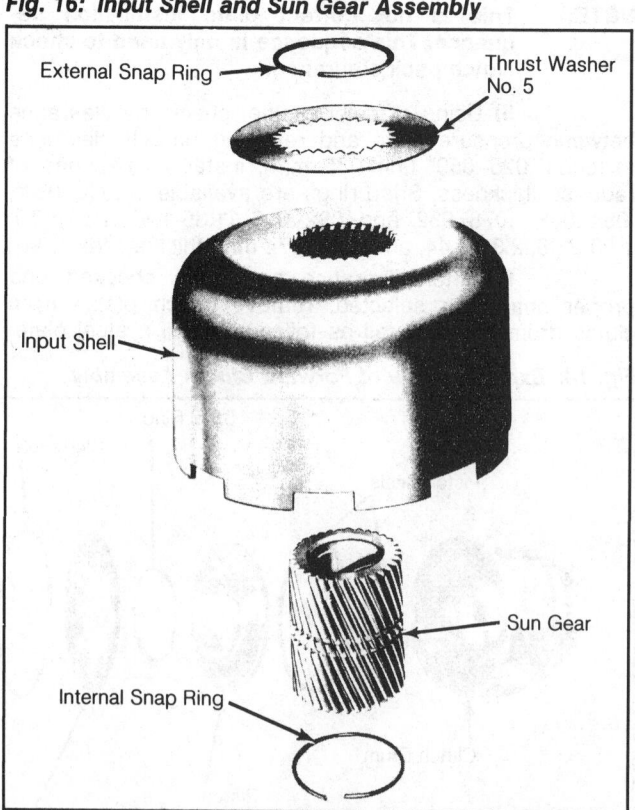

External Snap Ring — Thrust Washer No. 5 — Input Shell — Sun Gear — Internal Snap Ring

FORD C-5 (Cont.)

1) Install low-reverse servo piston and return spring in transmission case. Place a new seal on servo cover and position cover on case, install bolts and tighten.

2) Position new gasket on intermediate servo cover, make sure that notch in gasket will align with fluid port in case. Install servo cover, piston, and return spring as an assembly. Install cover bolts and tighten.

Fig. 17: Reverse Ring Gear and Hub

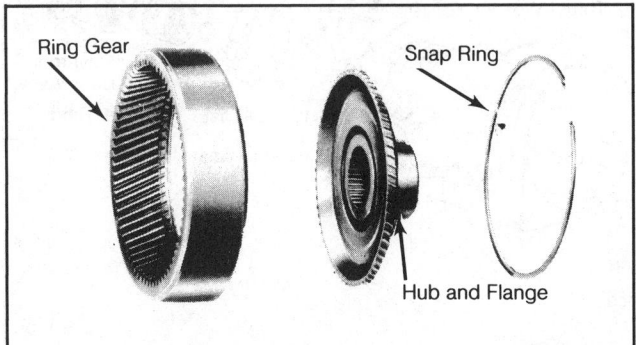

3) Lightly coat No. 9 thrust washer with petroleum jelly and position washer in case. Position one-way clutch in case. Install bolts and tighten. Install parking pawl, pivot pin, and return spring in case as an assembly.

4) Position No. 10 thrust washer and parking gear in case. Install pawl spring by looping the bend in spring over spring seat provided in case.

5) Install distributor sleeve on case, make sure oil tubes are properly seated in case fluid passages. Install distributor sleeve retaining bolts and tighten.

6) Install governor and output shaft in case as an assembly. Coat No. 8 thrust washer with petroleum jelly, and position it on low-reverse drum. Install low-reverse drum in case.

SELECTIVE THRUST WASHER CHART

Washer No. & Color	Thickness In. (mm)	Combined Thickness In. (mm)
1 Red	.053-.058 (1.35-1.46)	
1 Red & #2		.109-.116 (2.77-2.934)
1 Green	.070-.075 (1.78-1.90)	
1 Green & #3		.143-.150 (3.63-3.80)
1 Natural (White) [1]	.087-.092 (2.21-2.32)	
1 Natural & #2 [1]		.175-186 (4.45-4.71)
1 Natural [1]	.087-.092 (2.21-2.34)	
1 Natural & #3 [1]		.192-.203 (4.88-5.72)

[1] — Spacer must be installed next to stator support to obtain correct end play. Plus spacer .036-.0915" (.91-2.32 mm)

NOTE: **Check one-way clutch for proper operation by turning low-reverse drum both counterclockwise and clockwise. Drum should turn when rotated clockwise and lock-up when turned counterclockwise.**

7) Install reverse ring gear and hub assembly. Using external snap ring pliers, install reverse ring gear and hub assembly retaining ring. If necessary, push output shaft forward to gain access to snap ring groove.

8) Align band lugs with clearance provided in case. Install low-reverse band, make sure the double lug faces adjuster screw.

9) Install band struts, use new lock nut on adjuster screw, and thread screw into case tightening it enough to hold band in place. Install governor screen in governor distributor body.

10) Slide governor over output shaft, install retaining bolts, and tighten. Position extension housing on case. Install throttle valve, valve rod, and altitude compensating modulator.

11) Install extension housing retaining bolts and tighten. Lightly coat No. 6 and No. 7 thrust washer with petroleum jelly and install a washer on each side of reverse planetary assembly.

12) Install reverse planetary assembly in case, making sure that lugs are fully engaged in low-reverse drum slots. Install forward clutch in reverse-high clutch drum. Lightly coat No. 3 thrust washer with petroleum jelly. Position washer on forward clutch hub.

13) Lightly coat No. 4 thrust washer with petroleum jelly. Position washer on front planetary assembly. Install planetary assembly in forward clutch hub.

14) Install forward clutch hub and ring gear in forward clutch. Install input shell and sun-gear assembly on reverse-high clutch. Rotate input shaft to ensure proper assembly of clutch packs.

15) Position clutch packs, front planetary, and input shell as an assembly in case. Align intermediate band lugs with relief clearance provided in case. Install band and struts.

16) Install new lock nut on adjuster screw and thread into case, tightening enough to hold band in position. Position new gasket on front pump assembly.

17) Place pump assembly in case, install converter housing-to-pump retaining bolts, and tighten. Install input shaft. Mount a dial indicator on case and position indicator stylus against end of input shaft.

18) Position a screwdriver against lug on reverse-high clutch and push gear train rearward by tapping on screwdriver handle. Make sure that input shaft is fully seated, then zero indicator.

19) Position a screwdriver blade between input shell and reverse planetary assembly. Pry input shell forward and observe dial indicator.

20) If end play is greater than .008-.042" (.20-1.07 mm), No. 1 and No. 2 thrust washers must be changed. Thrust washers should be replaced in pairs to obtain proper clearance.

21) If end play was within specifications, remove dial indicator and bolts holding front pump assembly in case. Position converter housing on case. Install housing-to-pump retaining bolts and tighten.

Automatic Transmissions
FORD C-5 (Cont.)

Fig. 18: Exploded View of Transmission Showing Main Components

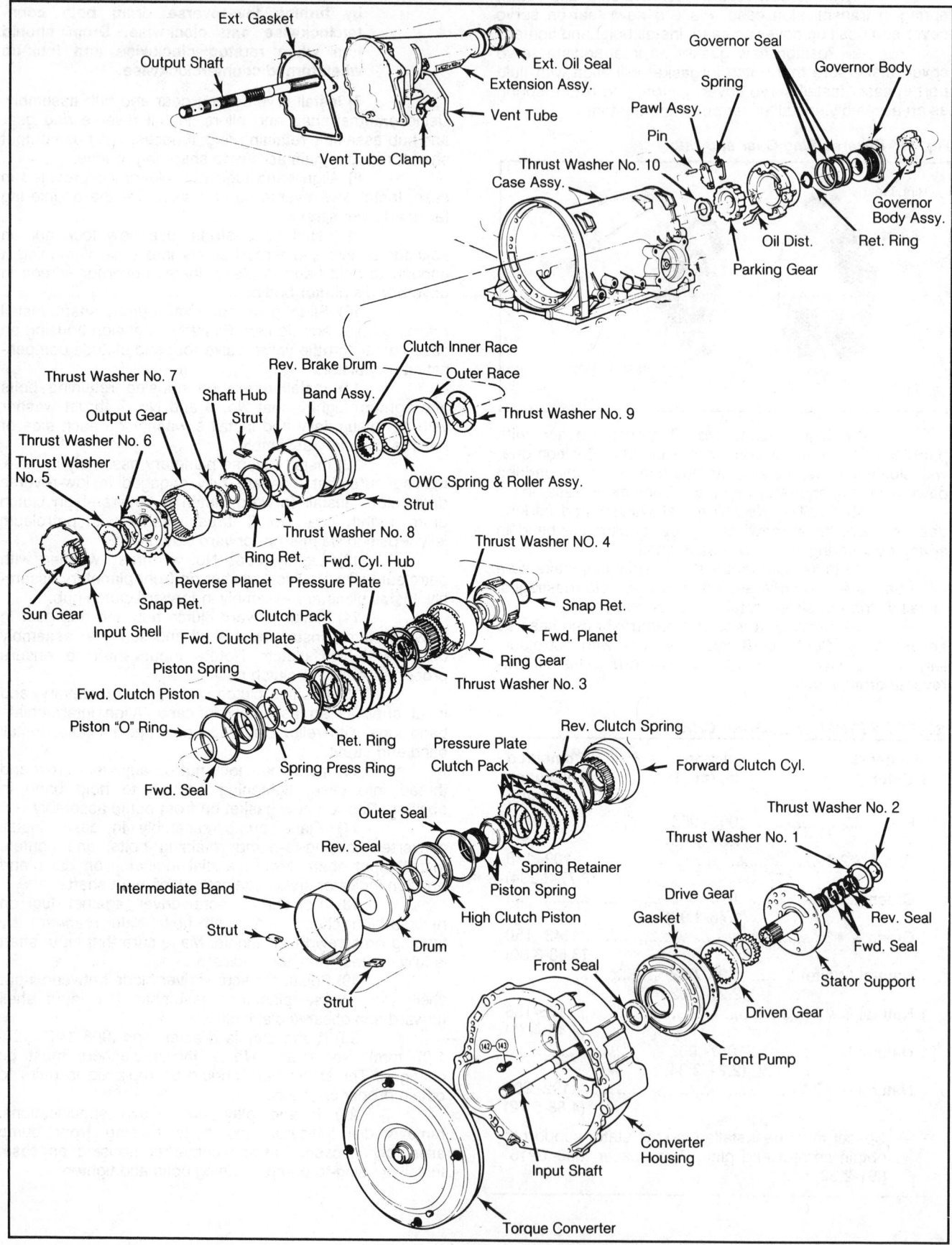

FORD C-5 (Cont.)

Fig. 19: Measuring Transmission End Play

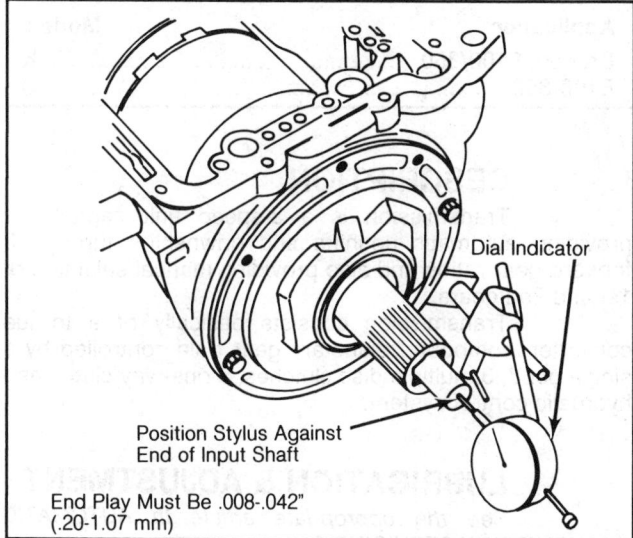

Dial Indicator

Position Stylus Against
End of Input Shaft

End Play Must Be .008-.042"
(.20-1.07 mm)

NOTE: If end play measurement was not within specifications, it will be necessary to remove front pump assembly and install proper thrust washers to obtain proper clearance. Install dial indicator and recheck end play measurement.

22) Adjust intermediate and low-reverse bands. See *Automatic Transmission Servicing Section.* Check transmission for proper assembly by turning output shaft using a slip yoke.

23) Output shaft should turn in both directions. Using shift linkage, place transmission in "P" position, grasp yoke and attempt to turn output shaft. Output shaft should not turn in either direction.

Fig. 20: Air Pressure Test Locations on Case

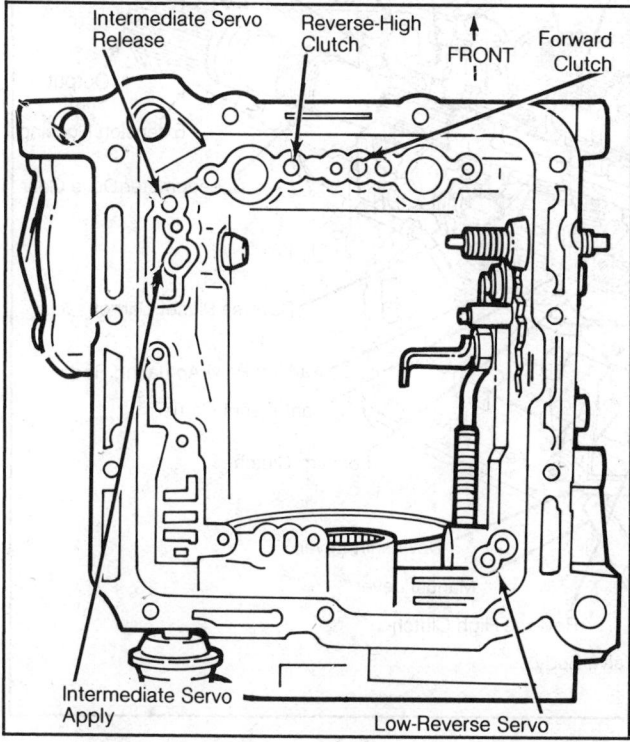

Intermediate Servo
Release

Reverse-High
Clutch

FRONT

Forward
Clutch

Intermediate Servo
Apply

Low-Reverse Servo

24) Using air pressure regulated at 25 psi, apply air to proper hydraulic circuit to ensure proper assembly of clutch packs and band servos. Clutches should be heard and felt, and should operate smoothly.

25) Check for leakage and ensure that clutch returns to released position when air pressure is removed. When air pressure is applied, it is possible to see servos in operation, and to see them release when air is removed.

26) Install inlet pump filter in case. Install valve body in case, make sure manual valve engages the manual lever. Make sure that the throttle lever is positioned to engage the throttle valve.

27) Note location of the 2 longer valve body retaining bolts, install all bolts, and tighten. Make sure filter seal is properly positioned on filter. Place filter on valve body. Install retaining bolts and tighten.

28) Position a new gasket on oil pan. Install pan on transmission housing. Install oil pan bolts and tighten. Install input shaft with oil groove end first.

29) Position torque converter on shaft making sure that it is fully seated. Make sure input shaft, stator support, and pump drive gear engage.

TIGHTENING SPECIFICATIONS

Application	Ft. Lbs. (N.m)
Oil Line-to-Transmission	18-23 (24-31)
Overrunning Clutch Race-to-Case	13-20 (18-27)
Oil Pan-to-Case	12-16 (17-21)
Reactor Support-to-Pump	12-20 (17-27)
Converter Hsg. Cover-to-Converter Hsg.	12-16 (17-21)
Converter Hsg.-to-Case	28-40 (38-55)
Pump-to-Case	28-40 (38-55)
Engine Rear Cover Plate-to-Trans.	12-16 (17-21)
Rear Servo Cover-to-Case	16-22 (22-29)
Oil Distributor Sleeve-to-Case	12-20 (17-27)
Extension Housing-to-Case	28-40 (38-54)
Engine-to-Trans. 3.8L	28-38 (38-51)
Trans.-to-Engine 4.2L & 3.3L	40-50 (54-67)
Outer Throttle Lever-to-Shaft	12-16 (17-21)
Inner Manual Lever-to-Shaft	30-40 (41-54)
Inter. & Reverse Lock Nut	35-45 (47-61)
Drain Plug-to-Converter Cover	12-17 (16-23)

	INCH Lbs. (N.m)
End Plates-to-Body	25-40 (2.8-4.5)
Separator Plate-to-Timing Body	25-40 (2.8-4.5)
Lower Body & Detent-to-Upper Body	40-60 (4.5-6.7)
Pan Screen-to-Timing Valve Body	25-40 (2.8-4.5)
Governor-to-Oil Collector	80-120 (9.0-12.5)
Pump Assembly-to-Case	28-38 (3.2-3.9)
Main Control-to-Case	80-120 (9.0-13.5)
Neutral Switch-to-Case	55-75 (6.2-8.5)
Upper Body-to-Lower Body (Long)	80-120 (9.0-12.5)
Upper Body-to-Lower Body (Short)	40-60 (4.5-6.7)
3-2 Timing Valve Body-to-Upper Body	40-60 (4.5-6.7)
Detent Spring & Lower Body-to-Upper Body	40-60 (4.5 6.7)
3-2 Timing Valve Body-to-Lower Body 5/16" Bolts	40-60 (4.5-6.7)
3/8" Bolts	75 (8.5)

Automatic Transmissions

FORD C-6

**Bronco, E100/350, F100/350,
F150/350 4WD**

IDENTIFICATION

An identification tag is located under lower front intermediate servo cover bolt. A number appearing after the suffix indicates internal parts in transmission have been changed after initial production start-up.

For example, a PJA-AL 15 model transmission that has been changed internally would read PJA-AL 16. See Fig. 1.

Fig. 1: C-6 Transmission Identification Tag

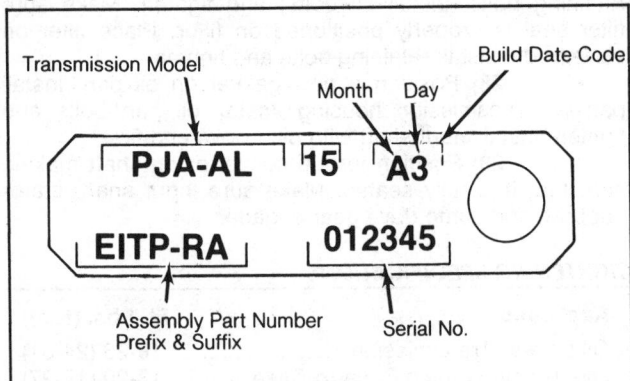

Tag is located under lower front intermediate servo cover bolt.

TRANSMISSION IDENTIFICATION CODES

Application	Models
Bronco, F100/350	K
E100/350	G

DESCRIPTION

Transmission is a 3-speed unit capable of providing automatic upshifts and downshifts through 3 forward gear ratios and also providing manual selection of 1st and 2nd gears.

Transmission consists basically of a torque converter, compound planetary gear train controlled by a single band, 3 multiple disc clutches, a one-way clutch and hydrualic control system.

LUBRICATION & ADJUSTMENT

See the appropriate article in AUTOMATIC TRANSMISSION SERVICING Section.

TESTING

ROAD TEST

1) Check minimum throttle upshift in "D". Transmission should start in 1st gear, shift to 2nd, and then shift to 3rd as speed increases. See Shift Table.

Fig. 2: Sectional View of Ford C-6 Automatic Transmission Assembly

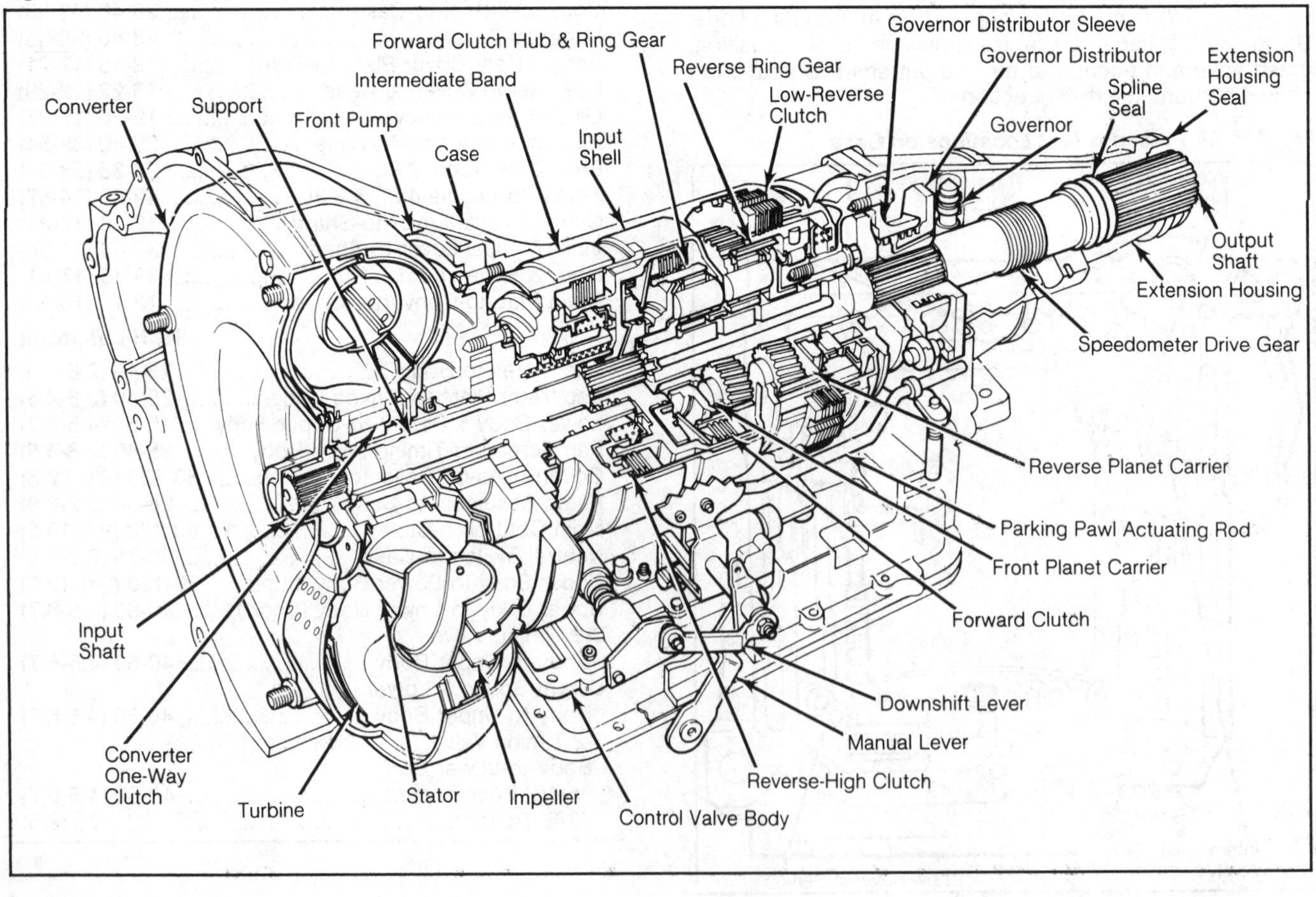

FORD C-6 (Cont.)

Fig. 3: Ford C-6 Automatic Transmission Hydraulic Circuits Diagram

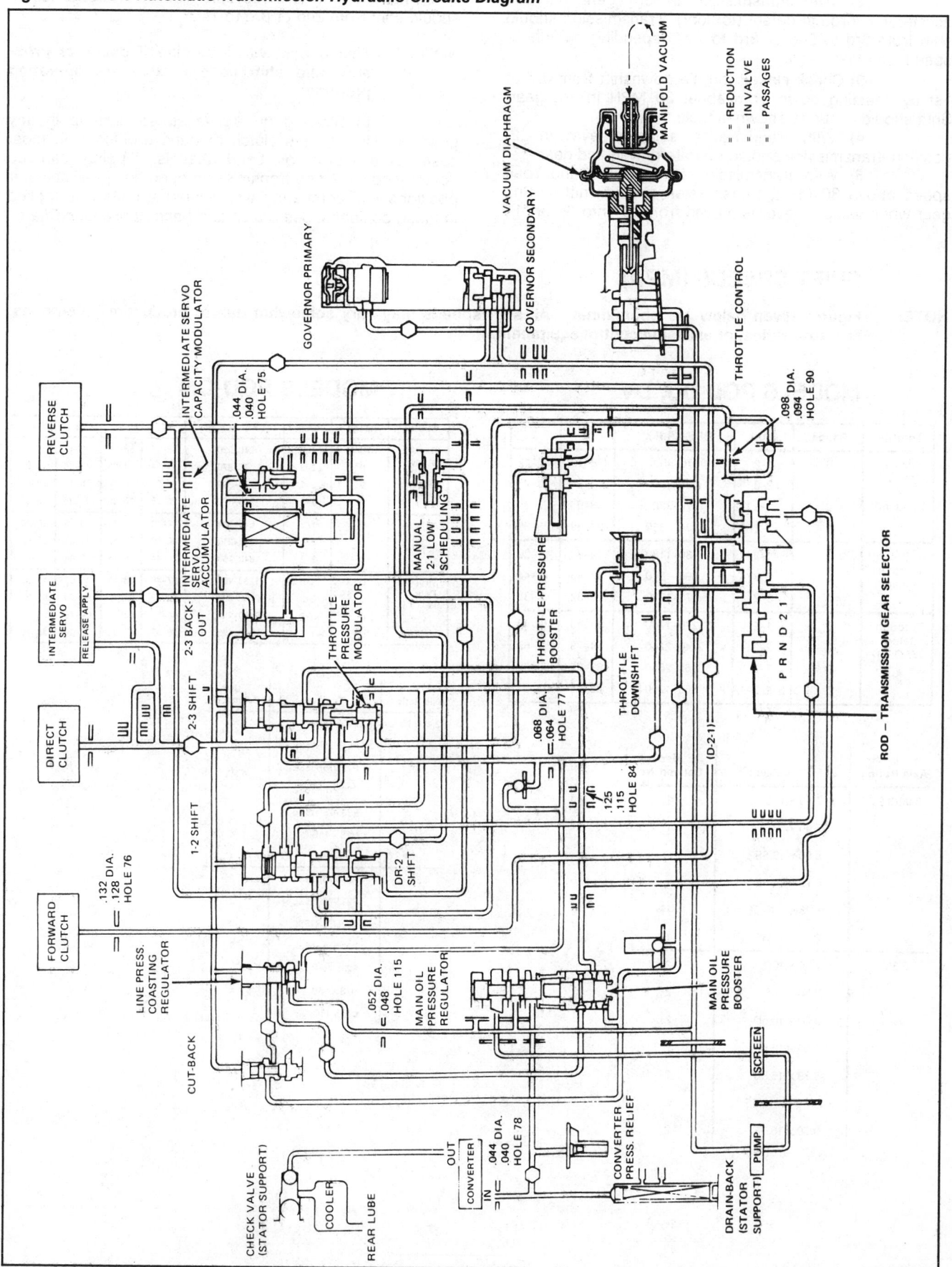

Automatic Transmissions

FORD C-6 (Cont.)

2) With transmission in 3rd gear depress accelerator through detent (to floor). Transmission should shift from 3rd to 2nd or 3rd to 1st, depending on vehicle speed. *See Shift Table.*

3) Check closed throttle downshift from 3rd to 1st by coasting down from about 30 MPH in 3rd gear. Shift should occur as shown in table.

4) With transmission selector lever in "2" position, transmission should operate only in 2nd gear.

5) With transmission in 3rd gear and road speed above 30 MPH, transmission should shift to 2nd gear when selector lever is moved from "D" into "2" or "1".

When manual shift is made below 30 MPH, transmission should shift from 2nd or 3rd to 1st.

NOTE: **This check will determine if governor pressure and shift control valve are operating properly.**

6) Slipping or engine speed flare-up in any gear usually indicates clutch or band problems. In most cases, the clutch or band that is slipping can be determined by noting transmission operation in all selector positions and comparing which internal units are applied in those positions. *See Clutch and Band Application Chart.*

SHIFT SPEEDS (MPH)

NOTE: **Figures given below are approximate. All shift speeds may vary somewhat due to production tolerances, rear axle ratios, or emission control equipment.**

MODELS PGD-DU, DV

Throttle	Range	Shift	OPS—R.P.M.	1	2
Closed (Above 17" Vacuum)	D	1-2	270-460	8-13	7-12
	D	2-3	330-920	11-24	10-23
	D	3-1	270-330	8-9	7-8
	1	2-1	930-1330	27-39	25-36
To Detent (Torque Demand)	D	1-2	430-1180	12-31	11-29
	D	2-3	690-1610	17-43	16-41
	D	3-2	270-1260	8-32	7-30
Through Detent (W.O.T.)	D	1-2	1270-1700	37-49	36-47
	D	2-3	2240-2740	64-79	59-69
	D	3-2	2160-2640	63-75	59-62
	D	3-1 2-1	860-1290	26-36	23-32

Axle Ratio	Tire Size	Use Column No.
3.00/3.25	7.50 × 16D	1
	7.50 × 16E	1
	8.00 × 16.5E	1
	8.75 × 16.5E	1
	8.75R × 16.5E	1
	9.50 × 16.5E	1
3.33	7.50 × 16D	2
	7.50 × 16E	2
	8.00 × 16.5D	2
	8.00 × 16.5E	2
	8.75 × 16.5E	2
	8.75R × 16.5E	2
	9.50 × 16.5E	2

MODELS PGD-CM

Throttle	Range	Shift	OPS—R.P.M.	1	2	3	4
Closed (Above 17" Vacuum)	D	1-2	270-520	8-16	8-17	8-17	8-18
	D	2-3	375-870	11-24	11-26	11-26	12-27
	D	3-1	270-330	8-9	8-10	8-10	8-10
	1	2-1	860-1200	25-35	26-36	27-38	28-39
To Detent (Torque Demand)	D	1-2	640-1440	18-42	19-43	19-45	20-46
	D	2-3	1070-2130	30-60	31-63	32-65	33-67
	D	3-2	840-1530	24-44	25-45	25-46	26-48
Through Detent (W.O.T.)	D	1-2	1280-1640	37-48	38-49	39-51	40-52
	D	2-3	2190-2620	63-75	64-77	66-79	68-82
	D	3-2	2100-2510	60-72	62-74	64-76	66-78
	D	3-1 2-1	890-1250	26-37	27-38	28-39	28-40

Axle Ratio	Tire Size	Use Column No.
2.47/2.75	P205/75R15SL	1
	P215/75R15SL	1
	P225/75R15SL	2
	P235/75R15SL	3
	P235/75R15XL	3
	H78 × 15B	4
	L78 × 15C	4
3.25	P205/75R15SL	2
	P215/75R15SL	2
	P225/75R15SL	2
	P235/75R15SL	3
	P235/75R15XL	3
	H78 × 15B	4
	L78 × 15C	4

FORD C-6 (Cont.)

SHIFT SPEEDS (MPH) (Cont.)

MODELS PGD-BD-BN

Throttle	Range	Shift	OPS—R.P.M.	1	2	3	4	5	6	7
Closed (Above 17" Vacuum)	D	1-2	270-420	8-15	8-15	7-13	7-13	7-13	7-12	6-12
	D	2-3	375-830	11-24	11-25	11-24	10-22	10-21	9-20	9-19
	D	3-1	270-330	8-10	8-10	8-9	7-9	7-8	7-8	6-8
	1	2-1	860-1200	26-36	27-38	25-35	23-33	23-32	21-30	20-29
To Detent (Torque Demand)	D	1-2	620-1310	19-40	20-41	19-39	17-36	17-35	16-33	15-31
	D	2-3	1030-1910	30-56	31-58	29-55	27-50	26-49	25-47	24-44
	D	3-2	900-1460	26-43	27-44	26-42	24-38	23-37	22-36	21-34
Through Detent (W.O.T.)	D	1-2	1270-1590	38-47	39-49	37-46	34-43	33-42	31-40	30-38
	D	2-3	2190-2560	64-75	66-78	62-73	57-67	56-66	53-62	51-60
	D	3-2	2120-2470	62-73	64-75	61-71	56-65	54-63	52-60	49-57
	D	3-1 2-1	900-1220	25-35	28-38	26-36	24-33	24-32	22-30	21-29

Axle Ratio	Tire Size	Use Column No.
2.47/2.75	P195/75R15SL	1
	P205/75R15SL	1
	P215/75R15SL	1
	P235/75R15XL	2
	H78 x 15B	2
	L78 x 15C	2
3.00	P195/75R15SL	5
	P205/75R15SL	5
	P215/75R15SL	4
	P235/75R15XL	3
	H78 x 15B	3
	L78 x 15C	3
3.25	P215/75R15SL	2
	P225/75R15SL	2
	P235/75R15XL	2

Axle Ratio	Tire Size	Use Column No.
3.33	7.50 x 16D	3
	7.50 x 16E	3
	8.00 x 16.5D	4
	8.00 x 16.5E	4
	8.75 x 16.5E	4
	8.75R x 16.5E	4
	9.50 x 16.5E	4
3.54	7.50 x 16D	5
	7.50 x 16E	5
	8.00 x 16.5D	6
	8.00 x 16.5E	6
	8.75 x 16.5E	6
	8.75R x 16.5E	6
	9.50 x 16.5E	6
3.73	7.50 x 16D	6
	7.50 x 16E	6
	8.00 x 16.5D	7
	8.00 x 16.5E	7
	8.75 x 16.5E	7
	8.75R x 16.5E	7
	9.50 x 16.5E	7

Automatic Transmissions
FORD C-6 (Cont.)

SHIFT SPEEDS (MPH) (Cont.)

MODELS PGD-BE, BF, DC, EA

Throttle	Range	Shift	OPS—R.P.M.	1	2	3	4	5	6	7
Closed (Above 17" Vacuum)	D	1-2	270-460	8-16	8-16	8-15	7-14	7-14	7-13	6-12
	D	2-3	375-920	11-28	11-27	11-26	10-24	10-24	9-22	8-21
	D	3-1	270-330	8-10	8-10	8-9	7-9	7-8	7-8	6-8
	1	2-1	930-1330	29-41	28-40	27-39	25-36	25-35	23-33	22-32
To Detent (Torque Demand)	D	1-2	680-1450	22-45	21-44	20-43	19-39	18-38	17-36	17-35
	D	2-3	1120-2100	33-63	33-62	32-60	29-55	29-54	27-51	26-49
	D	3-2	980-1610	29-49	29-47	28-46	26-42	25-41	24-39	23-37
Through Detent (W.O.T.)	D	1-2	1390-1760	43-54	41-53	35-51	37-47	36-46	34-44	33-42
	D	2-3	2390-2820	72-85	70-83	68-81	63-74	61-72	58-69	56-66
	D	2-3	2310-2720	70-82	68-80	68-78	61-72	59-70	56-66	54-63
	D	3-1 2-1	1000-1380	30-42	29-41	28-39	26-36	26-35	24-34	23-32

Axle Ratio	Tire Size	Use Column No.
2.75	P195/75R15SL	2
	P205/75R15SL	2
	P215/75R15SL	2
	P235/75R15XL	1
	P235/75R15SL	1
	H78 × 15B	1
	L78 × 15C	1
3.00	P195/75R15SL	5
	P205/75R15SL	5
	P215/75R15SL	4
	P235/75R15SL	3
	P235/75R15XL	3
	H78 × 15B	3
	L78 × 15B	3
3.00/3.25	7.50 × 16D	3
	7.50 × 16E	3
	8.00 × 16.5D	4
	8.00 × 16.5E	4
	8.75 × 16.5E	4
	8.75R × 16.5E	4
	9.50 × 16.5E	4

Axle Ratio	Tire Size	Use Column No.
3.54/3.33	7.50 × 16D	5
	7.50 × 16E	5
	8.00 × 16.5D	6
	8.00 × 16.5E	6
	8.75 × 16.5E	6
	8.75R × 16.5E	6
	9.50 × 16.5E	7

Automatic Transmissions

FORD C-6 (Cont.)

SHIFT SPEEDS (MPH) (Cont.)

MODELS PGD-A, AW, DB, DL, DK, DP, DW, EC, EG, EK

Throttle	Range	Shift	OPS—R.P.M.	1	2	3	4	5	6	7
Closed (Above 17" Vacuum)	D	1-2	270-560	8-16	8-17	8-16	7-15	7-14	7-14	6-14
	D	2-3	375-870	11-26	11-26	11-25	10-23	10-22	9-21	9-21
	D	3-1	270-330	8-10	8-10	8-9	7-9	7-8	7-8	6-8
	1	2-1	890-1260	26-37	27-38	25-36	23-33	23-32	21-31	20-29
To Detent (Torque Demand)	D	1-2	760-1390	22-41	23-42	22-40	20-37	19-36	19-34	18-32
	D	2-3	1320-2080	39-61	40-63	38-59	35-55	34-53	32-51	31-48
	D	3-2	820-1600	24-47	25-48	23-46	22-42	21-41	20-39	19-37
Through Detent (W.O.T.)	D	1-2	1250-1590	37-47	38-48	36-45	33-42	32-41	30-39	29-38
	D	2-3	2190-2570	64-76	66-78	63-73	58-68	56-66	53-63	51-60
	D	3-2	1990-2340	59-69	60-71	57-67	52-62	51-60	49-57	46-54
	D	3-1 2-1	840-1200	25-35	25-36	24-34	22-32	22-31	20-29	20-28

Axle Ratio	Tire Size	Use Column No.
2.47/2.75	P195/75R15SL	1
	P205/75R15SL	1
	P215/75R15SL	1
	P235/75R15XL	2
	H78 × 15B	2
	L78 × 15C	2
3.00/3.07	P195/75R15SL	5
	P205/75R15SL	5
	P215/75R15SL	4
	P235/75R15XL	3
	H78 × 15B	3
	L78 × 15C	3
3.25	P215/75R15SL	2
	P235/75R15SL	2
	P235/75R15XL	2

Axle Ratio	Tire Size	Use Column No.
3.33	7.50 × 16D	3
	7.50 × 16E	3
	8.00 × 16.5D	4
	8.75 × 16.5E	4
	8.75R × 16.5E	4
	9.50 × 16.5E	4
3.73	7.50 × 16D	6
	7.50 × 16E	6
	8.00 × 16.5D	7
	8.00 × 16.5E	7
	8.75 × 16.5E	7
	8.75R × 16.5E	7
	9.50 × 16.5E	7

Automatic Transmissions

FORD C-6 (Cont.)

SHIFT SPEEDS (MPH) (Cont.)
MODELS PGD-EF

Throttle	Range	Shift	OPS—R.P.M.	1	2	3	4
Closed (Above 17" Vacuum)	D	1-2	270-640	8-17	8-18	8-18	8-19
	D	2-3	375-930	11-24	11-26	11-26	12-27
	D	3-1	270-330	8-9	8-10	8-10	8-10
	1	2-1	890-1260	25-35	26-36	27-38	28-39
To Detent (Torque Demand)	D	1-2	770-1520	18-42	19-43	19-45	20-46
	D	2-3	1330-2330	30-60	31-63	32-65	33-67
	D	3-2	730-1640	24-44	25-45	25-46	26-48
Through Detent (W.O.T.)	D	1-2	1250-1630	37-48	38-49	39-51	40-52
	D	2-3	2200-2630	63-75	64-77	66-79	68-82
	D	3-2	1980-2380	60-72	62-74	64-76	66-78
	D	3-1 2-1	830-1230	76-37	27-38	28-39	28-40

Axle Ratio	Tire Size	Use Column No.
3.00	P205/75R15SL	
	P215/75R15SL	
	P225/75R15XL	
	P235/75R15SL	
	P235/75R15XL	
	L78 × 15B	
	L78 × 15C	
3.25	P225/75R15XL	
	P235/75R15SL	
	P235/75R15XL	
	L78 × 15B	
	L78 × 15C	

MODELS PJD-W, Z, BA, BB, BC

Throttle	Range	Shift	OPS—R.P.M.	1	2	3
Closed (Above 17" Vacuum)	D	1-2	270-690	6-15	6-16	6-17
	D	2-3	375-890	8-19	9-20	9-21
	D	3-1	270-330	6-7	6-8	6-8
	1	2-1	880-1210	19-26	20-28	21-29
To Detent (Torque Demand)	D	1-2	1110-1570	24-34	25-36	26-37
	D	2-3	1830-2430	40-53	42-55	44-58
	D	3-2	1100-1640	24-36	25-37	26-39
Through Detent (W.O.T.)	D	1-2	1320-1600	28-35	30-37	31-38
	D	2-3	2230-2560	48-55	51-58	53-61
	D	3-2	1940-2260	42-49	44-51	46-54
	D	3-1 2-1	870-1170	19-25	20-27	21-28

Axle Ratio	Tire Size	Use Column No.
3.73/4.10	8.00 × 16.5D	1
	8.00 × 16.5E	2
	9.50 × 16.5E	3
	8.75 × 16.5D	2
	8.75 × 16.5E	2

CLUTCH AND BAND APPLICATION CHART (ELEMENTS IN USE)

Selector Lever Position	Intermediate Band	Reverse Clutch	Forward Clutch	High Clutch	One-Way Clutch
D — DRIVE					
First Gear			X		X
Second Gear	X		X		
Third	X		X	X	
2 — INTERMEDIATE					
Second Gear	X		X		
1 — LOW (First)		X	X		
R — REVERSE		X		X	

NEUTRAL OR PARK — Band and all clutches released and/or ineffective.

CONTROL PRESSURE TEST
Engine Vacuum Method
1) Attach tachometer to engine. Install vacuum gauge (using "T") into manifold vacuum line at vacuum diaphragm unit. Attach a 0-400 psi gauge to control pressure take-off point at transmission. See Fig. 4 and 5.

2) Apply both parking and service brakes. With engine at curb idle speed and normal operating temperature. Read and record control pressure in all selector positions at specified manifold vacuum. Compare control pressures obtained in tests with pressures given in Control Pressure Table.

Fig. 4: Side View of Transmission Case

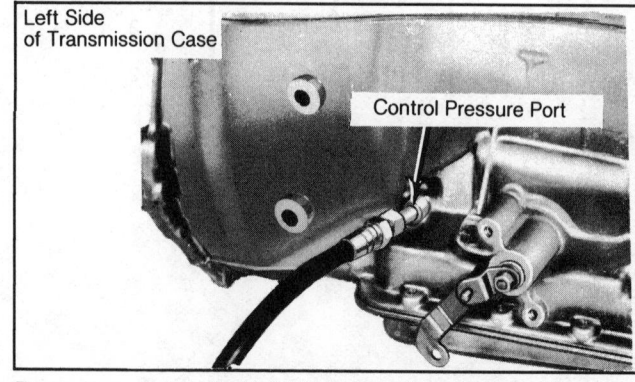

Left Side of Transmission Case

Control Pressure Port

Pressure gauges affect shift quality of transmission.

FORD C-6 (Cont.)

CAUTION: Release throttle immediately if slippage is indicated. Also shift transmission to Neutral and run engine at 1000 RPM to cool transmission fluid between tests.

Fig. 5: Connecting Vacuum Gauge for Pressure Test

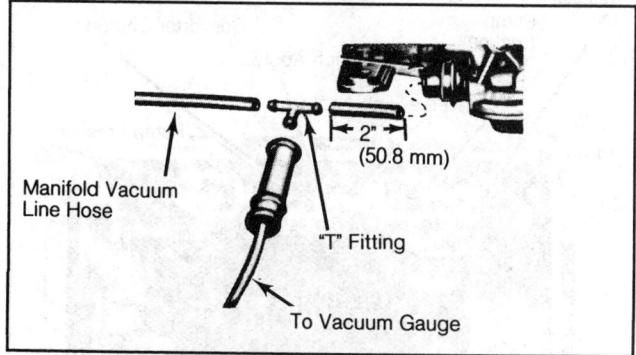

Manifold Vacuum Line Hose

2" (50.8 mm)

"T" Fitting

To Vacuum Gauge

This is for the engine vacuum test method

Vacuum Pump Method

1) Attach tachometer to engine and a 0-400 psi gauge to pressure take-off point at transmission. Disconnect and plug manifold vacuum line at diaphragm unit.

2) Connect vacuum source (vacuum pump in distributor tester). Apply both parking and service brakes. Start engine and vacuum pump, setting vacuum to 15 in. Hg. Read and record control pressure in all shift selector positions.

3) Increase engine to 1000 RPM, and reduce vacuum to 10 in. Hg. Read and record control pressure in "D", "2" and "1" shift selector positions.

4) With engine still at 1000 RPM, reduce vacuum to 1 in. Hg. Read and record control pressure in "D", "2", "1" and "R". Compare control pressures obtained in tests with pressures given in *Control Pressure Table*.

NOTE: Governor can be checked at same time as Control Pressure Test is performed.

5) With vehicle raised, place selector lever in "2", no load on engine and apply 10 in. Hg. Increase speed slowly while watching speedometer, check speed at which control pressure cutback occurs. It should occur between 10-20 MPH.

6) Decrease vacuum to 0.2 in. Hg and repeat test. Control pressure cutback should occur between 30-50 MPH. If cutback does not occur within specifications, check shift speeds to make sure that it is the governor and not a stuck cutback valve.

CAUTION: Do not exceed 60 MPH speedometer speed during test. If control pressures are not within specifications, proceed to Control Pressure Test Results to determine problems.

CONTROL PRESSURE TEST RESULTS

Low at Idle in All Ranges:

Check for low fluid level, restricted intake screen or filter, and loose oil tubes. Check for loose valve body or regulator-to-case bolts. Check for excessive leakage in front pump, case, or control valve body. Check for sticking control pressure regulator valve.

OK at Idle in All Ranges, But Low at 10 in. Hg:

Check vacuum diaphragm unit. Check if control rod or throttle valve is stuck.

High at Idle in All Ranges:

Check vacuum diaphragm unit, manifold vacuum line, throttle rod, and control rod. Check for sticking regulator boost valve(s).

OK at Idle in All Ranges, OK at 10 in. Hg, But Low at 1 in. Hg:

Check for excessive leakage, low pump capacity, or restricted oil pan screen.

Low In "P":

Check valve body pressure regulator.

Low in "R":

Check high clutch and/or reverse clutch.

Low in "N":

Check valve body for correct operation.

Low in "D":

Check for faulty forward clutch operation.

Low in "2":

Check forward clutch and servo.

Low in "1":

Check forward clutch and/or reverse clutch.

CONTROL PRESSURE SPECIFICATIONS

Transmission Model	Range	Idle 15" & Above	Idle 10"	WOT Stall Thru Detent
PGD,CM,DU,DV, EE,EF	D,2,1	50-80		150-185
	R	66-122		235-285
	P,N	50-80		
PJD,W,Z,BA, BB,BC	D,2,1	55-95		155-180
	R	87-142		245-275
	P,N	55-95		
PGD,A,AW,BD, BE,BF,DB,DC, DK,DL,DN,DP, DW,EA,EC	@ D,2,1	50-65		155-180
	R	66-99		245-275
	P,N	50-65		

VACUUM DIAPHRAGM UNIT

Vacuum Supply Check

1) Disconnect vacuum line at vacuum unit and connect vacuum gauge. With engine idling, gauge must show a steady acceptable vacuum. If reading is low, check for vacuum leak and/or poor engine vacuum.

2) If reading is acceptable, rapidly accelerate engine momentarily, vacuum must drop rapidly at acceleration and return immediately upon deceleration. If vacuum reading does not change or changes slowly, vacuum line is plugged, restricted or connected to reservoir supply. Repair as required.

Vacuum Diaphragm Unit Check

1) Remove unit from transmission. Use tester equipped with vacuum pump. Start pump and set regulator knob so vacuum gauge reads 18 in. Hg with end of hose blocked off.

2) Connect vacuum hose to port on unit. If gauge still reads 18 in. Hg, unit is not leaking. If vacuum does not hold at 18 in. Hg, unit is leaking and must be replaced.

3) When hose is removed from unit, hold finger over end of control rod. Internal spring of unit should push control rod outward. Also, check for presence of transmission fluid in vacuum side of diaphragm or in vacuum hose. If fluid is present, unit is leaking and must be replaced.

STALL SPEED TEST

CAUTION: Do not hold throttle open longer than 5 seconds at a time during testing. If engine speed exceeds maximum limit of stall speed, release throttle immediately as clutches or bands are slipping.

Automatic Transmissions

FORD C-6 (Cont.)

Testing Procedure

Install tachometer and fully apply parking and service brakes. Start engine and run at curb idle and at normal operating temperature. Stall test transmission in each driving range at full throttle. Note maximum RPM obtained. Engine speed should be within limits shown in *Stall Speeds Table*.

NOTE: Allow a cooling period of 15 seconds with transmission in Neutral and engine speed at 1000 RPM between each test.

STALL TEST RESULTS

Stall Speed Too High

In "D", "2", "1", & "R"; general transmission problems are indicated and a control pressure test should be made to locate faulty unit(s). In "D" only; planetary one-way clutch slippage is indicated. In "D", "2", & "1"; forward clutch slippage is indicated. In "R" only; high and/or reverse clutch slippage indicated.

Stall Speed Too Low

Converter stator one-way clutch faulty.

CAUTION: Make sure engine performance is satisfactory before condemning converter assembly. Converter cannot be overhauled and must be replaced if defective.

STALL SPEEDS

Application	Stall RPM
4.9L 6-Cyl.	
Bronco, E100/350, F100/350	1616-1871
5.0L V8	
Bronco, E100/250, F100/250	1616-1871
5.8L V8	
Bronco, E100/350	1569-1729
6.9L V8 Diesel	
E250-350, F250/350	1715-1966
7.5L V8	
E250/350, F250/350	1610-1891

AIR PRESSURE CHECKS

1) A "No Drive" condition can exist, even with correct transmission fluid pressure, because of inoperative clutches or bands. Erratic shifts could be caused by stuck governor valve.

2) The inoperative units can be located through a series of checks by substituting air pressure for the fluid pressure to determine location of malfunction.

3) To make air pressure checks, loosen oil pan bolts and allow transmission to drain. Remove oil pan and control valve body. Apply air at points noted. *See Fig. 6.* Check unit operations as follows:

Forward Clutch

Apply air pressure to transmission case forward clutch passage. A dull thud can be heard when clutch piston is applied, or movement of piston can be felt by placing a finger on input shell.

Governor

Apply air pressure to control pressure-to-governor passage and listen for sharp clicking or whistling noise, indicating governor valve movement.

Reverse-High Clutch

Apply air pressure to reverse-high clutch passage, dull thud should be heard when clutch piston is

applied. If not, place finger tips on clutch drum, movement should be felt.

Fig. 6: Bottom View of Transmission Case

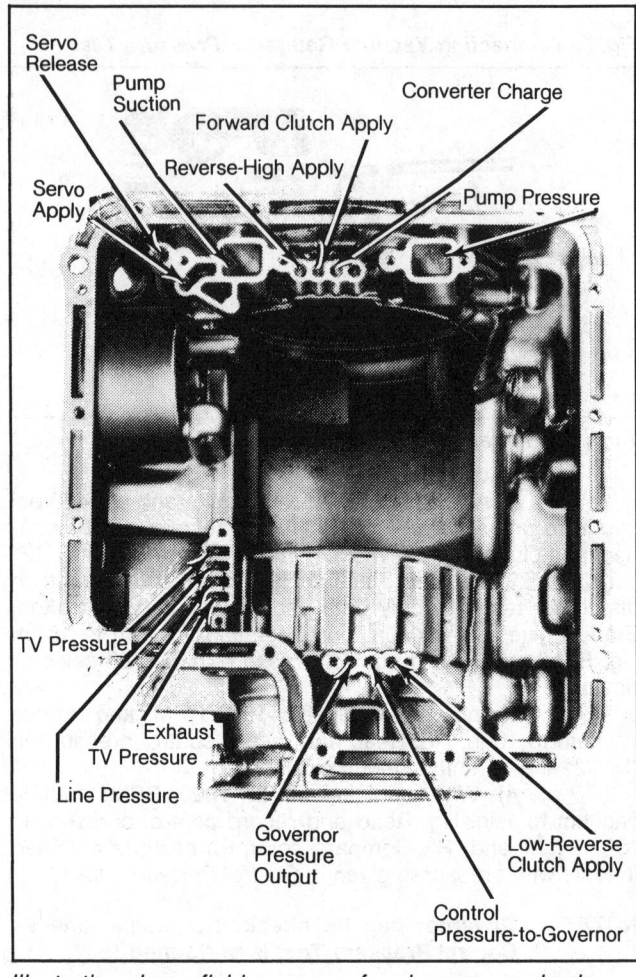

Illustration shows fluid passages for air pressure checks

Intermediate Servo

Hold air nozzle in intermediate servo apply passages. Operation of servo will be indicated by tightening of intermediate band around drum. With air still applied at apply passage, use 2nd air nozzle to apply air at the servo release passage. Band should now release (combination of air pressure and spring on release side of piston should overcome apply pressure).

Low-Reverse Clutch

Apply air pressure to reverse clutch apply passage. A dull thud should be heard if clutch is operating properly.

SERVICE (IN VEHICLE)

VALVE BODY

Removal

1) Loosen oil pan retaining bolts, tap pan to break it loose allowing fluid to drain. Remove oil pan and gasket. Remove and discard nylon shipping plug from filler tube hole.

FORD C-6 (Cont.)

NOTE: This plug is used to retain fluid in transmission during shipment and should be discarded when oil pan is removed.

2) Remove valve body retaining bolts and lower valve body from transmission case.

Installation

Position valve body to case, ensure selector and downshift levers are engaged. Install and tighten retaining bolts evenly. Install oil pan with new gasket, and tighten retaining bolts evenly.

INTERMEDIATE SERVO

Removal

Remove engine rear support-to-crossmember bolt. Remove crossmember-to-frame retaining bolts, and remove crossmember. Disconnect muffler inlet pipe from exhaust manifolds and allow pipe to hang. Place a drain pan under servo, remove cover retaining bolts. Remove cover, piston, spring, and gasket.

NOTE: As piston is being removed, screw in band adjusting screw. This keeps tension on band, keeping struts properly engaged in band end notches as piston is removed.

Fig. 7: Disassembled View of Intermediate Servo

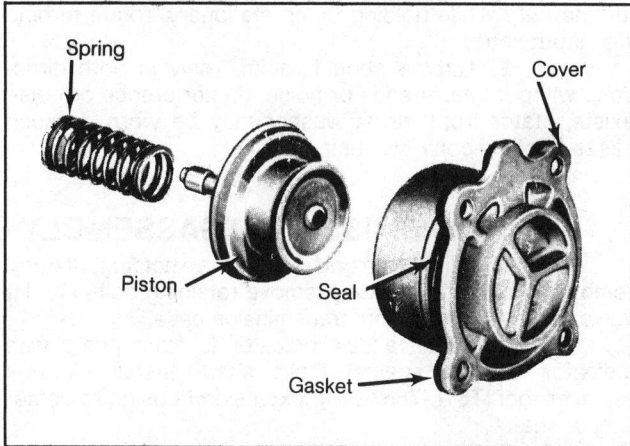

Seal Replacement

1) Apply air pressure to port in servo cover and remove piston and rod. Remove seal from cover. Replace complete piston and rod assembly if piston or piston sealing lips are damaged.

2) Dip new seal in transmission fluid and install on cover. Coat 2 new gaskets with petroleum jelly and install on cover. Dip piston in transmission fluid and install in cover.

Installation

To install, reverse removal procedures. Install service identification tag and back off band adjusting screw as servo cover bolts are being tightened. Adjust intermediate band and refill transmission to correct fluid level.

EXTENSION HOUSING
SEAL & BUSHING

Removal

Disconnect propeller shaft at transmission. Using a tapered chisel, carefully remove rear seal. Using a bushing remover tool, withdraw bushing from extension housing.

NOTE: Use tool carefully so that spline seal is not damaged.

Installation

1) Install bushing into extension housing using a bushing driver. Before installing a new seal, inspect sealing surface of propeller shaft yoke for wear or damage. If scores are found, replace yoke.

2) Using a seal driver, install seal in extension housing, ensure that it is fully seated in bore. Coat inside of seal and yoke spline with wheel bearing grease, and install propeller shaft.

EXTENSION HOUSING & GOVERNOR

Removal

1) Remove propeller shaft. Remove transfer case (if equipped), and speedometer cable. Remove engine rear support-to-extension housing bolts. Raise transmission with jack to take weight off support and remove support from crossmember.

2) Place drain pan under rear of transmission and remove extension housing-to-case bolts. Slide housing off output shaft. Remove governor housing-to-flange bolts and separate governor from flange.

Installation

To install, reverse removal procedures. Tighten all nuts and bolts. Make sure all mating surfaces are kept clean and refill transmission to correct fluid level.

REMOVAL & INSTALLATION

See the appropriate article in AUTOMATIC TRANSMISSION REMOVAL Section.

TORQUE CONVERTER

NOTE: Converter is a sealed unit and cannot be disassembled for service. Replace if found defective. Make the following tests to be certain converter is defective before replacing unit.

FLUSHING CONVERTER

Whenever transmission has been disassembled to replace worn or damaged parts or because valve body sticks due to foreign material, converter and oil cooler must be cleaned using a mechanically agitated cleaner (Rotunda 140028 or equivalent). Under no conditions should converter or oil cooler be cleaned by hand agitation using solvent.

LEAK TEST

NOTE: If torque converter welds indicate leakage, assemble Torque Converter Leak Detector (Rotunda 720004 or equivalent) to converter and follow detector kit instructions.

TURBINE & STATOR END PLAY CHECK

1) Insert test tool (T80L-7902-D) into converter pump drive hub until it bottoms. Expand sleeve in turbine spline by tightening threaded inner post of test tool until tool is securely locked into spine.

Automatic Transmissions

FORD C-6 (Cont.)

Fig. 8: Checking Torque Converter Turbine and Stator End Play

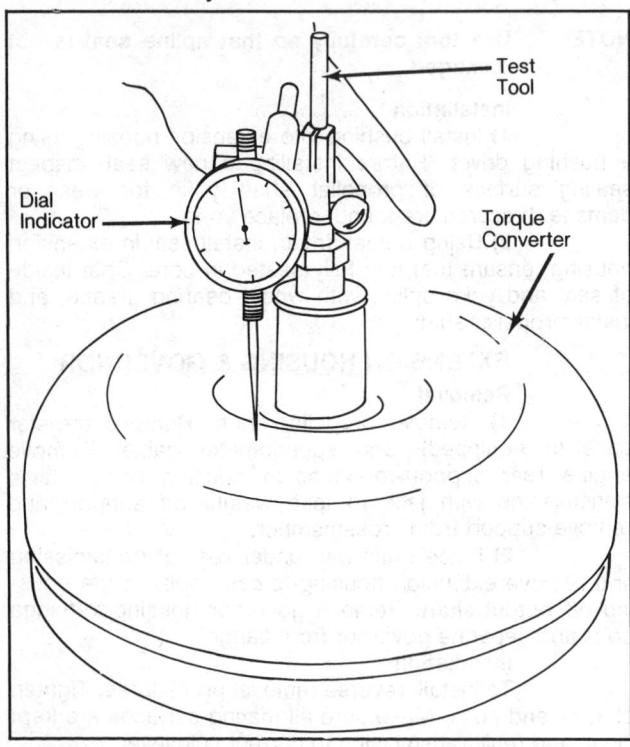

With test tool (T80L-7902-D) inserted and secured in hub check end play.

2) Attach a dial indicator to tool with button on indicator on converter pump drive hub. Zero dial face. Lift tool upward as far as it will go and note indicator reading.

3) Reading is total end play of turbine and stator. If end play exceeds .021" (.53 mm) new or rebuilt converter, or .040" (1.02 mm) used converter, replace torque converter assembly.

STATOR ONE-WAY CLUTCH CHECK

1) Insert one-way clutch holding tool into one of the grooves in the stator thrust washer. Insert clutch

Fig. 9: Stator One-Way Clutch Check

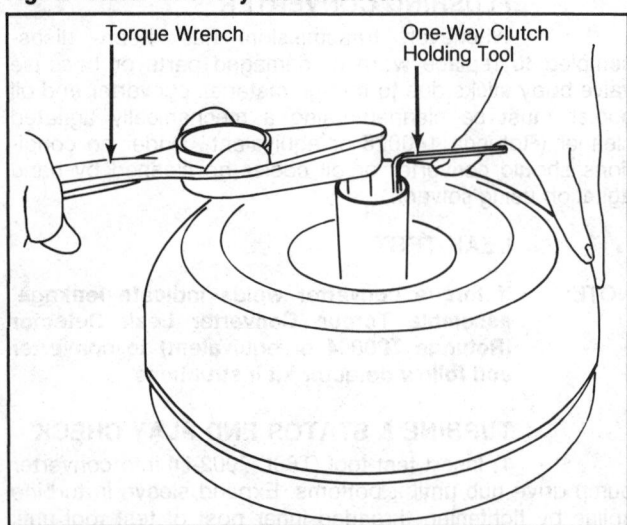

Use torquing tool (T77L-7902-A) check stator one-way clutch.

torquing tool (T83L-7902-A1) in converter pump drive hub so as to engage one-way clutch inner race.

2) Attach a torque wrench to torquing tool. With clutch holding tool held stationary, turn torque wrench counterclockwise. The converter one-way clutch should lock-up and hold a 10 ft. lb. (14 N.m) force. One-way clutch should rotate freely in a clockwise direction.

3) Repeat lock-up test in at least 5 different locations around torque converter. If clutch fails to lock-up and hold, replace torque converter.

STATOR INTERFERENCE CHECK

Stator to Impeller Interference Check

1) Position front pump assembly on bench with spline end of stator shaft pointing up. Mount converter on pump so splines of one-way clutch inner race engage splines of stator support, and converter hub engages pump drive gear.

2) While holding pump stationary, rotate converter counterclockwise. Converter should rotate freely without interference or scraping within assembly. Should this condition exist, replace converter unit.

Stator To Turbine Interference Check

1) Place converter on bench, front side down. Install front pump assembly to engage mating splines of stator support, stator, and pump drive gear lugs.

2) Install input shaft, engaging the splines with turbine hub. While holding pump stationary, rotate turbine with input shaft.

3) Turbine should rotate freely in both directions without interference or noise. If interference or noise exists, stator front thrust washer may be worn. In such cases, replace converter unit.

TRANSMISSION DISASSEMBLY

1) With transmission in a holding fixture, remove oil pan and gasket. Remove retaining bolts and lift valve body assembly from transmission case.

2) Attach a dial indicator to front pump with indicator contact against input shaft. Install oil seal replacer tool (T61L-7657-B) in extension housing to center output shaft.

3) Check transmission end play as follows: Pry gear train to rear of case. Press input shaft inward until bottomed. Zero dial indicator.

4) Pry gear train forward, read and record end play for reassembly reference. Remove checking tools from transmission. *See Fig. 10.*

5) Remove vacuum diaphragm, rod, and primary throttle valve from case, slide input shaft from front pump. Remove front pump retaining bolts, pry gear train forward and remove pump.

6) Loosen band adjusting screw and remove 2 band struts. Rotate band 90° counterclockwise to align band ends with slot in case. Remove band from reverse-high clutch drum.

7) Remove forward part of gear train from transmission as an assembly. Remove servo cover retaining bolts, servo cover, piston, spring and gasket from case. Remove large snap ring securing reverse planet carrier in low-reverse clutch hub.

8) Lift carrier from drum. Remove snap ring securing reverse ring gear and hub on output shaft and slide assembly from shaft. Rotate low-reverse hub in clockwise direction and remove from case.

FORD C-6 (Cont.)

Fig. 10: Checking Transmission End Play

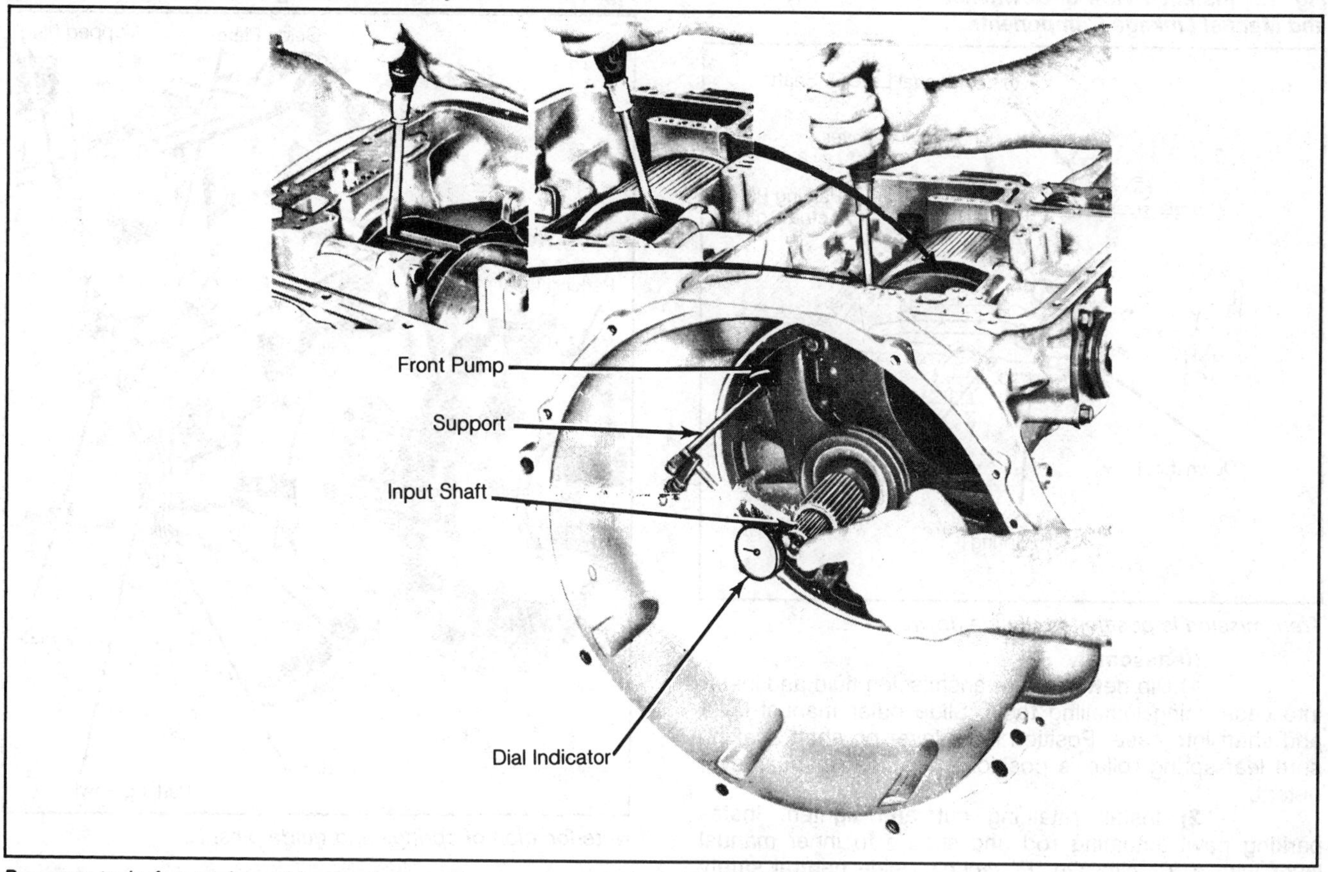

Front Pump

Support

Input Shaft

Dial Indicator

Pry gear train forwards and backwards, and measure end play with dial indicator.

Fig. 11: Removing Forward Part of Gear Train

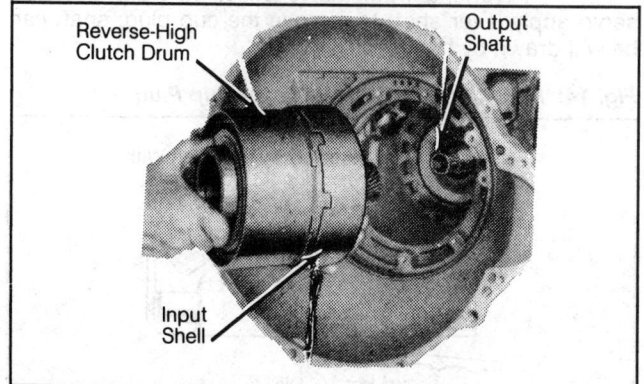

Reverse-High Clutch Drum

Output Shaft

Input Shell

Remove reverse-high clutch as shown.

9) Remove reverse clutch snap ring and withdraw clutch discs, plates and pressure plate from case. Remove extension housing retaining bolts and vent tube from case.

10) Remove extension housing and gasket. Slide output shaft asssembly from case. Remove distributor sleeve retaining bolts. Remove sleeve, parking pawl gear, and thrust washer.

NOTE: **If thrust washer is staked in place, use a sharp chisel and cut off metal from behind thrust washer. Remove any metal particles from case.**

11) Compress reverse clutch piston release spring, remove snap ring and lift out springs and retainer assembly.

12) Remove one-way clutch inner race retaining bolts from rear of case and remove inner race. Remove reverse clutch piston by applying air pressure to low-reverse apply passage in case.

NOTE: **See Fig. 6 for location of low-reverse apply passage.**

COMPONENT DISASSEMBLY & REASSEMBLY

DOWNSHIFT & MANUAL LINKAGE
Disassembly

1) On all models, remove nut and lock washer securing outer downshift lever to transmission, and remove lever. Slide downshift lever out from inside case, remove seal from recess in manual lever shaft.

2) On "E" models, remove neutral safety switch bolts and remove switch. On all models, remove "C" clip securing parking pawl actuating rod to manual lever. Remove rod from case.

3) Remove nut retaining inner manual lever to shaft. Remove inner lever from shaft, slide outer lever and shaft from case. Remove seal from case using a puller and slide hammer.

Automatic Transmissions

FORD C-6 (Cont.)

Fig. 12: _Installed View of Downshift and Manual Linkage Components_

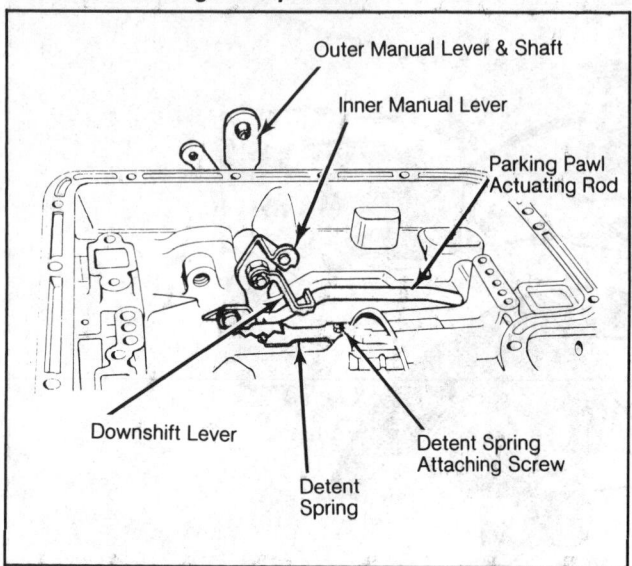

Transmission is positioned upside down.

Reassembly

1) Dip new seal in transmission fluid and install into case using installing tools. Slide outer manual lever and shaft into case. Position inner lever on shaft, making sure leaf spring roller is positioned in inner manual lever detent.

2) Install retaining nut and tighten. Install parking pawl actuating rod and secure to inner manual lever with a "C" clip. On "E" models, slide neutral safety switch on outer shaft lever.

3) Install retaining bolt. With manual lever in neutral, rotate switch and install gauge pin (No. 43 drill) into gauge pin hole. Tighten switch retaining bolt.

4) Install a new downshift lever seal in outer lever shaft recess. Slide downshift lever and shaft into position. Place outer downshift lever on shaft. Install and tighten lock washer and nut.

PARKING PAWL LINKAGE
Disassembly

1) Remove bolts retaining parking pawl guide plate to case. Remove plate. Remove spring, parking pawl and shaft from case.

2) Working from pan mounting surface, drill a 1/8" hole through center of cupped plug. Pull plug from case with a wire hook.

3) Unhook end of spring from park plate slot. Thread a 1/4-20 x 1 1/4" or 8-32 x 1 1/4" screw into park plate shaft. Pull shaft from case with screw. Remove spring and park plate.

Reassembly

1) Position spring and park plate in case and install shaft. Place end of spring into slot of park plate. Install a new cupped plug to retain shaft. Install parking pawl shaft in case.

2) Slip parking pawl and spring into place on shaft. Position guide plate on case, make sure actuating rod is seated in slot of plate. Secure plate with 2 bolts and lock washers.

Fig. 13: _Installed View of Parking Pawl Linkage Assembly_

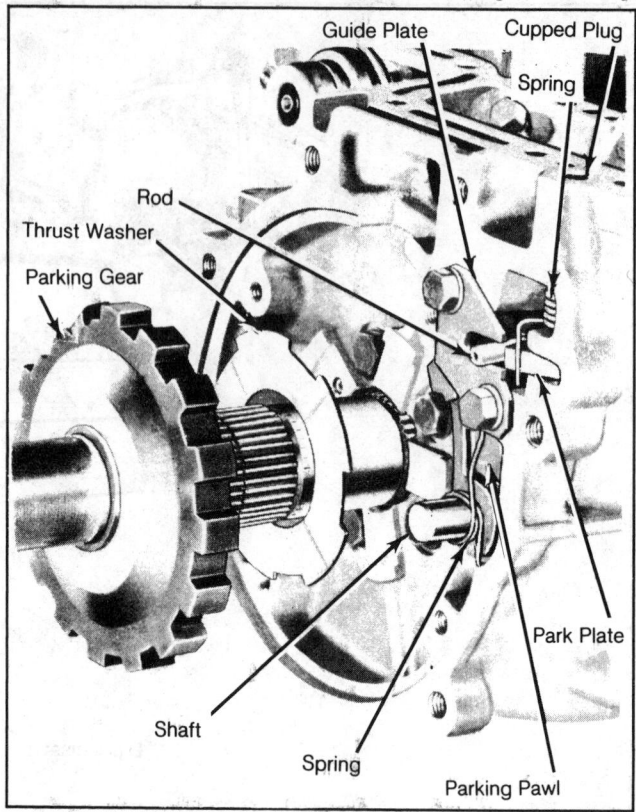

Note location of springs and guide pins.

SERVO APPLY LEVER
Disassembly

Working from inside case, carefully drive on servo apply lever shaft to remove the cup plug; shaft can be withdrawn by hand.

Fig. 14: _Installing Servo Apply Lever Cup Plug_

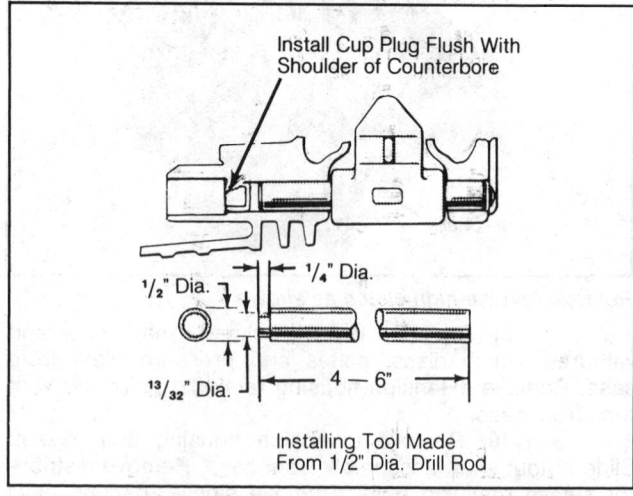

Using shop fabricated tool, drive cup plug into position.

Reassembly

Hold servo apply lever in position and install shaft. Using fabricated shop tool shown in _Fig. 14_, drive

FORD C-6 (Cont.)

Fig. 15: Exploded View of Upper Valve Body Assembly

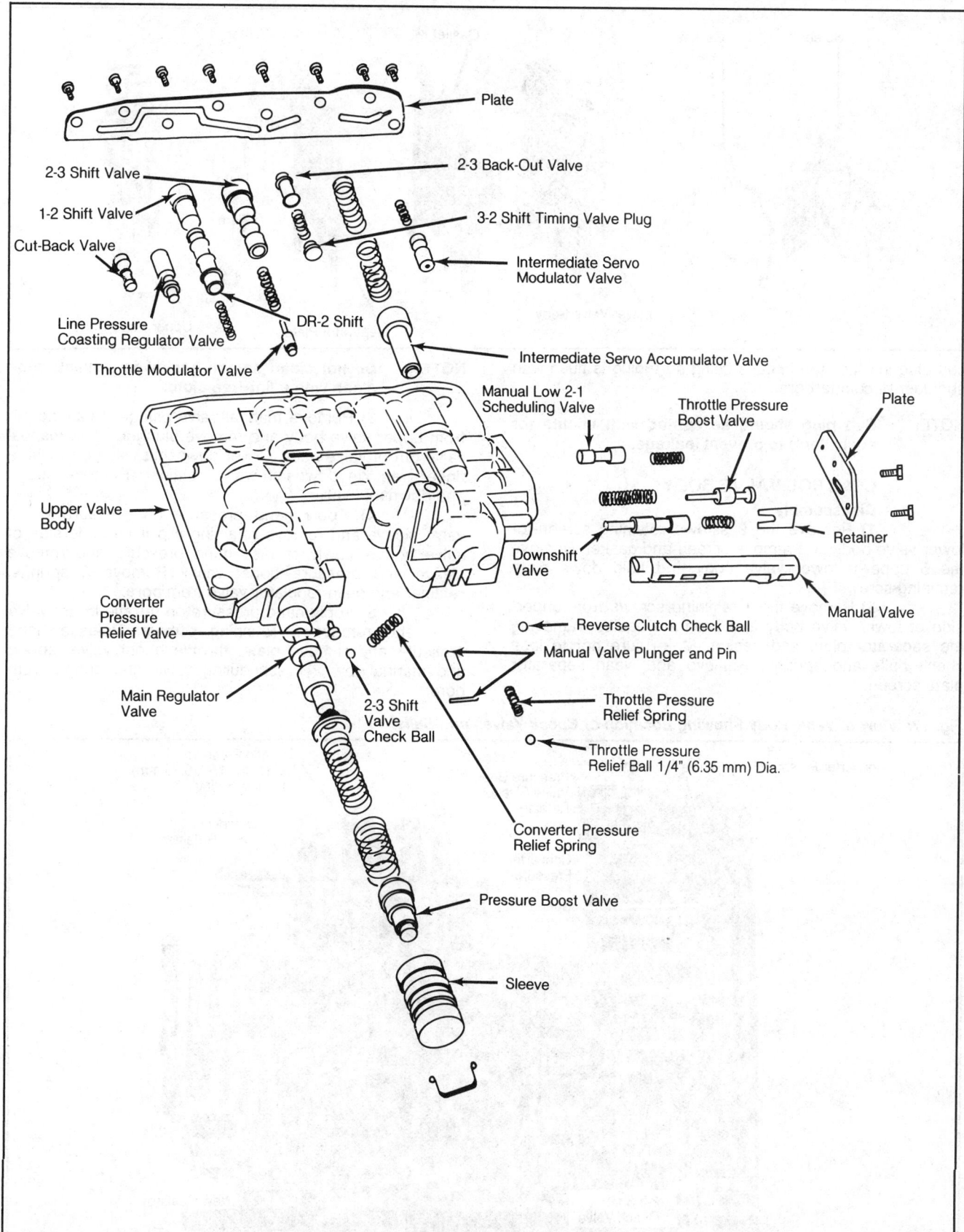

Automatic Transmissions
FORD C-6 (Cont.)

Fig. 16: Exploded View of Control Valve Body Assembly

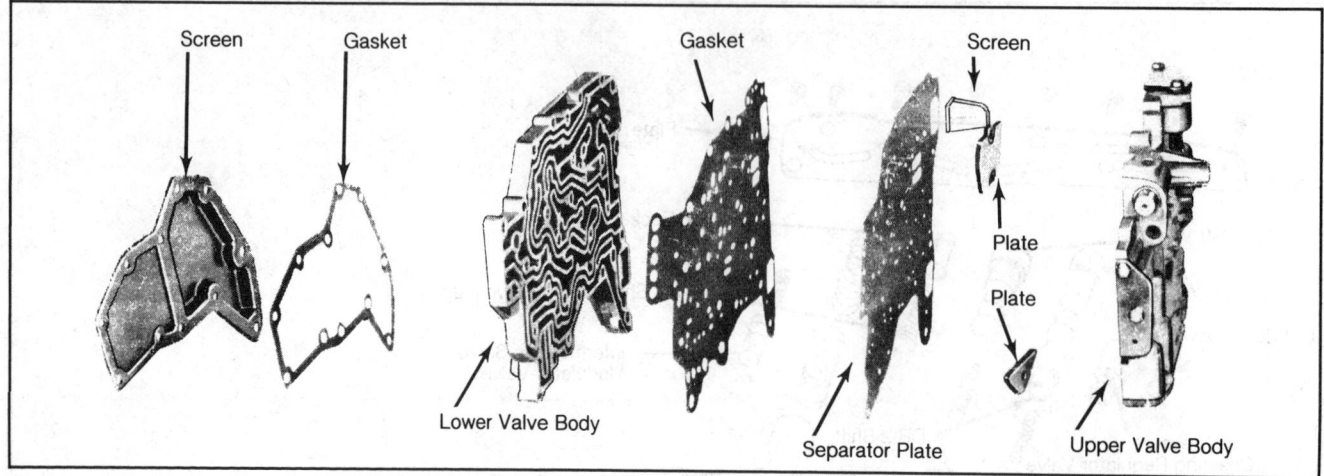

cup plug into positon in case being sure plug is flush with shoulder of counterbore.

NOTE: **Cup plug should be coated with Loctite (or equivalent) to prevent leakage.**

CONTROL VALVE BODY
Disassembly

1) Remove the 9 screws retaining screen-to-lower valve body and remove screen and gasket. Remove the 5 upper-to-lower valve body and hold down plate retaining screws.

2) Remove the 7 retaining screws from underside of lower valve body and separate bodies, removing the separator plate and gasket. Make sure not to lose check balls and springs. Remove and clean separator plate screen.

NOTE: **Do not clean screen gasket in solvent; wipe clean with a lint-free cloth.**

3) Remove manual valve plunger retaining pin from upper valve body and remove plunger. Slide manual valve out of valve body. Cover downshift valve port with a finger, remove downshift valve retainer. Remove spring and downshift valve.

4) Apply hand pressure on pressure boost valve sleeve and remove retaining clip from underside of valve body. Slowly release hand pressure and remove sleeve and pressure boost valve. Remove 2 springs, retainer and main regulator valve from bore.

5) Apply hand pressure on throttle boost valve plate and remove 2 retaining screws. Release hand pressure and remove plate, throttle boost valve, spring and manual low 2-1 scheduling valve and spring from bore.

Fig. 17: View of Valve Body Showing Location of Check Valves and Balls

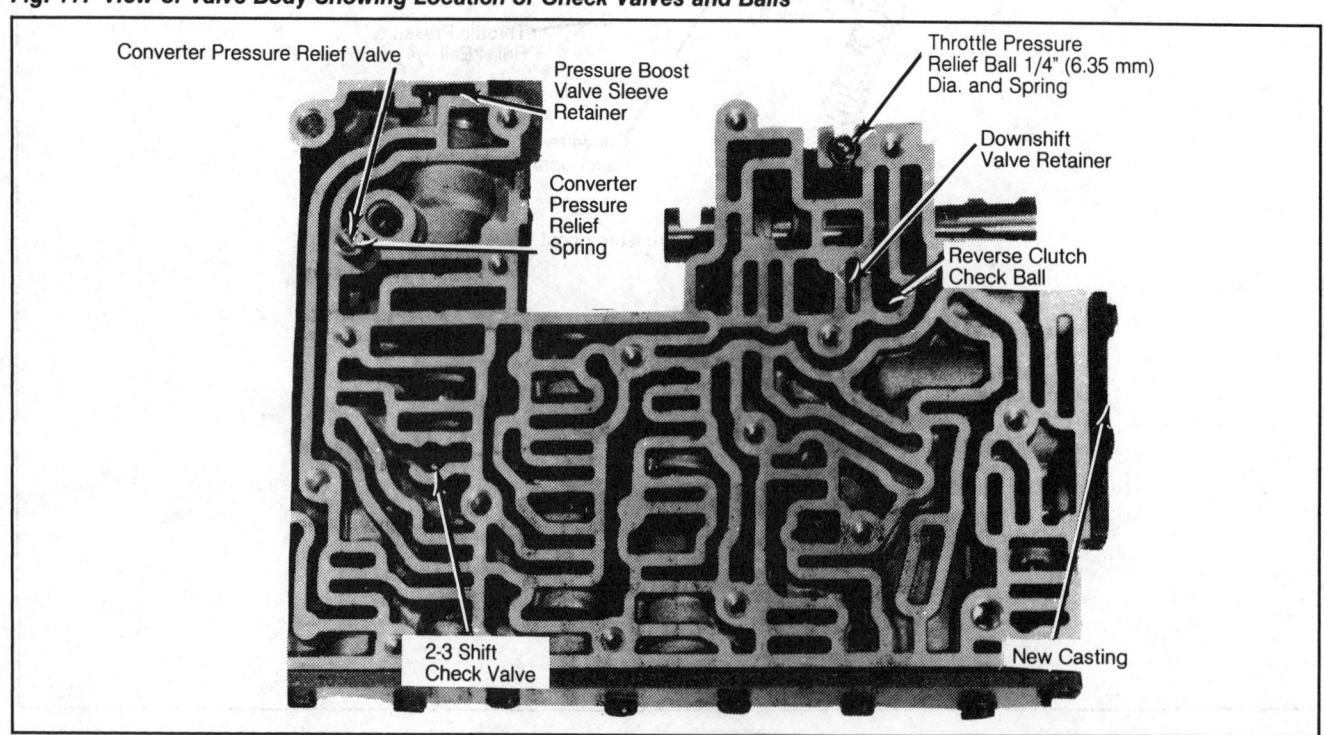

FORD C-6 (Cont.)

Fig. 18: Exploded View of Transmission Case and Drive Train Assembly

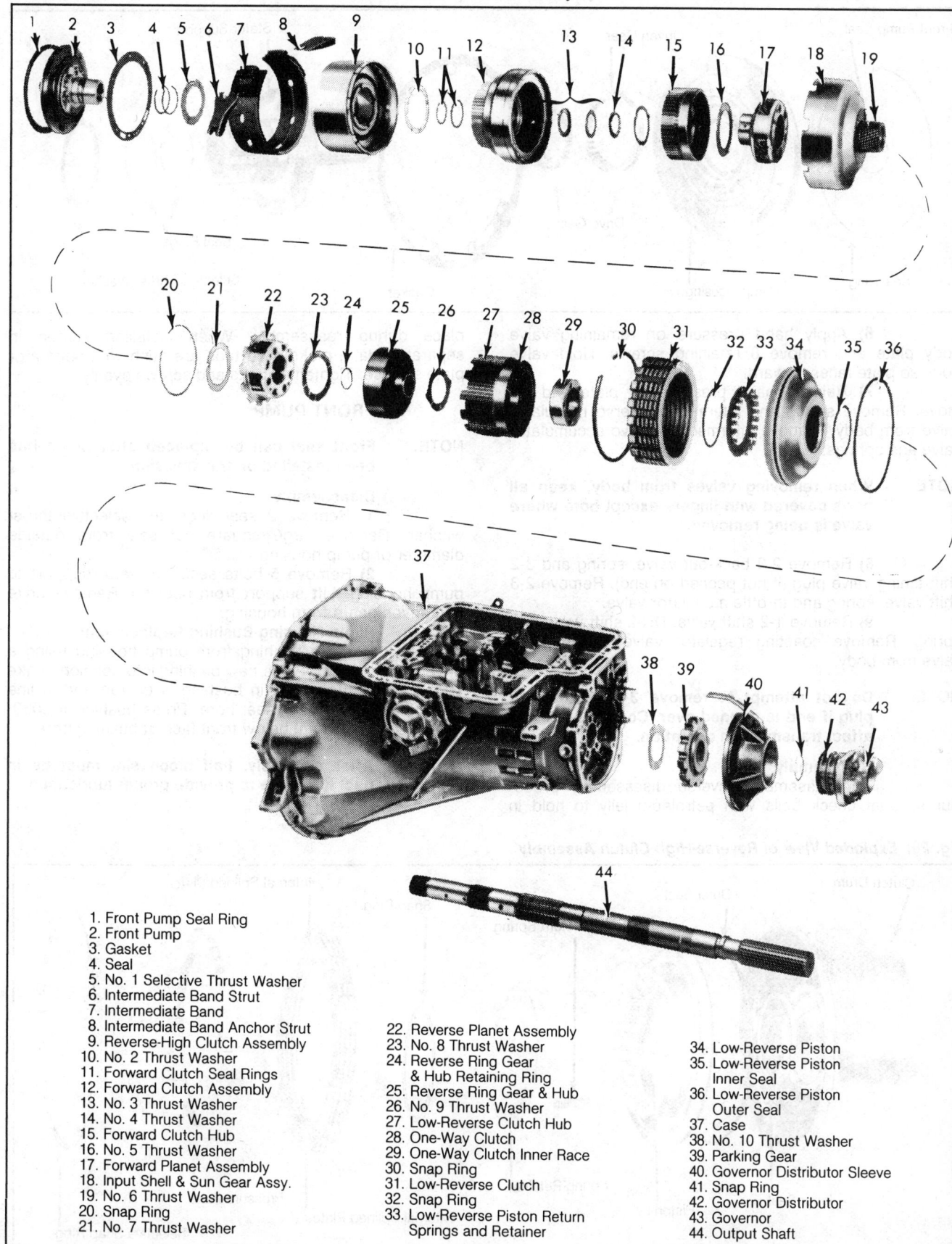

1. Front Pump Seal Ring
2. Front Pump
3. Gasket
4. Seal
5. No. 1 Selective Thrust Washer
6. Intermediate Band Strut
7. Intermediate Band
8. Intermediate Band Anchor Strut
9. Reverse-High Clutch Assembly
10. No. 2 Thrust Washer
11. Forward Clutch Seal Rings
12. Forward Clutch Assembly
13. No. 3 Thrust Washer
14. No. 4 Thrust Washer
15. Forward Clutch Hub
16. No. 5 Thrust Washer
17. Forward Planet Assembly
18. Input Shell & Sun Gear Assy.
19. No. 6 Thrust Washer
20. Snap Ring
21. No. 7 Thrust Washer

22. Reverse Planet Assembly
23. No. 8 Thrust Washer
24. Reverse Ring Gear
    & Hub Retaining Ring
25. Reverse Ring Gear & Hub
26. No. 9 Thrust Washer
27. Low-Reverse Clutch Hub
28. One-Way Clutch
29. One-Way Clutch Inner Race
30. Snap Ring
31. Low-Reverse Clutch
32. Snap Ring
33. Low-Reverse Piston Return
    Springs and Retainer

34. Low-Reverse Piston
35. Low-Reverse Piston
    Inner Seal
36. Low-Reverse Piston
    Outer Seal
37. Case
38. No. 10 Thrust Washer
39. Parking Gear
40. Governor Distributor Sleeve
41. Snap Ring
42. Governor Distributor
43. Governor
44. Output Shaft

Automatic Transmissions

FORD C-6 (Cont.)

Fig. 19: *Exploded View of Front Pump Assembly*

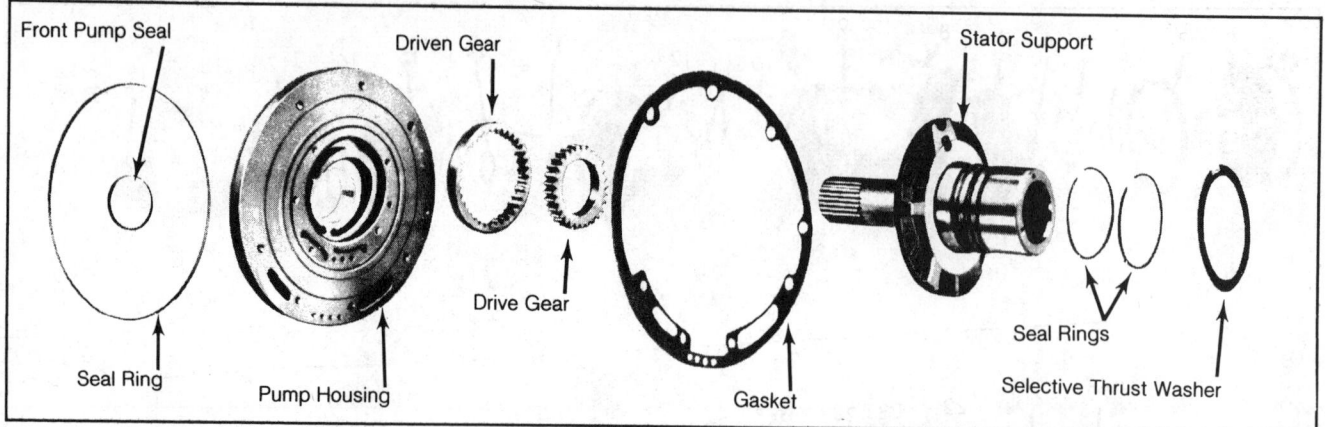

6) Apply hand pressure on remaining valve body plate and remove 8 retaining screws. Hold valve body so plate faces upward.

7) Release hand pressure on plate and remove. Remove spring and intermediate servo modulator valve from body. Remove intermediate servo accumulator valve and springs.

NOTE: **When removing valves from body, keep all parts covered with fingers except bore where valve is being removed.**

8) Remove 2-3 back-out valve, spring and 3-2 shift timing valve plug (if not peened on end). Remove 2-3 shift valve, spring and throttle modulator valve.

9) Remove 1-2 shift valve, DR-2 shift valve and spring. Remove coasting regulator valve and cutback valve from body.

NOTE: **Do not attempt to remove 3-2 shift timing plug if end is peened over. Condition will not affect transmission operation.**

Reassembly

To reassemble, reverse disassembly procedures. Coat check balls with petroleum jelly to hold in place during reassembly. When installing screen in separator plate, make sure tabs are flush with separator plate surface. Tighten all bolts and screws evenly.

FRONT PUMP

NOTE: **Front seal can be replaced after pump has been installed on transmission.**

Disassembly

1) Remove 2 seal rings and selective thrust washer. Remove large square cut seal from outside diameter of pump housing.

2) Remove 5 bolts securing stator support to pump housing. Lift support from housing. Remove drive and driven gears from housing.

Pump Housing Bushing Replacement

Remove bushing from pump housing using a driver and hammer. Place new bushing into position, make sure the half moon slot in bushing is on top and in line with oil lube hole near seal bore. Press bushing in .060-.080" (15.24-2.03 mm) below front face of bushing bore.

NOTE: **After assembly, half moon slot must be in past lube hole to provide proper lubrication.**

Fig. 20: *Exploded View of Reverse-High Clutch Assembly*

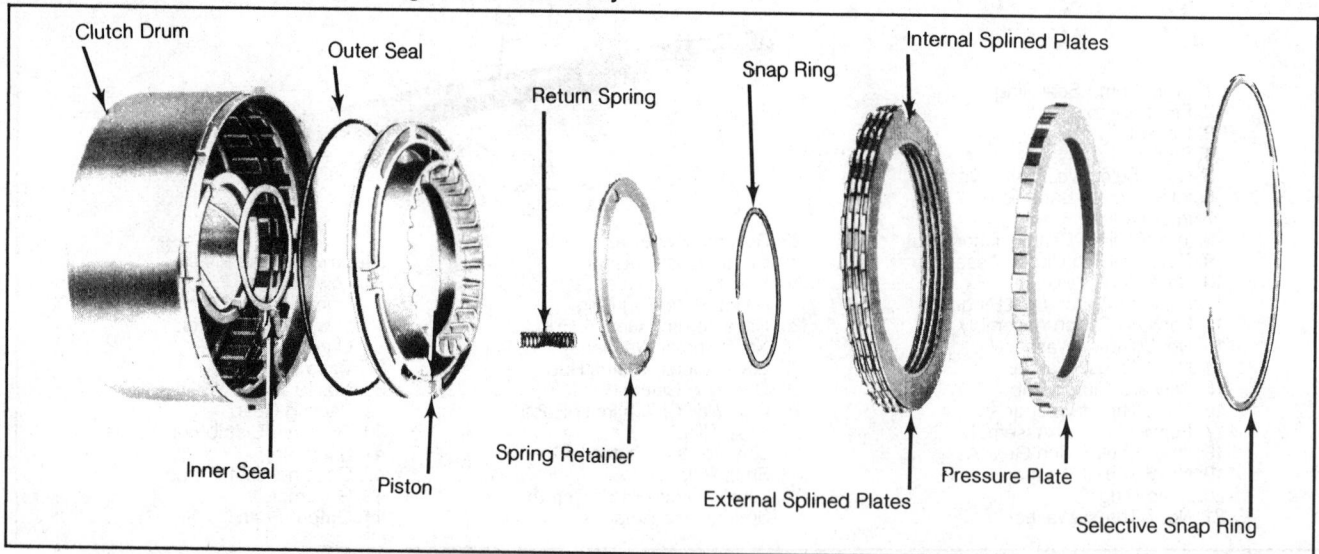

FORD C-6 (Cont.)

Reassembly

1) Install drive and driven gear in pump housing with identification mark or chamfered surface of each gear installed toward front of pump housing. Position stator support in pump housing. Install and tighten retaining bolts.

2) Carefully install 2 new seal rings on stator support. Make sure ends of rings are engaged to lock them in place. Install a new square cut seal on outside diameter of pump housing.

3) Install selective thrust washer. Place pump on torque converter, make sure that the drive gear engages converter hub. Rotate pump to ensure that gears rotate freely.

DRIVE TRAIN

Separate drive train into subassembly components. *See Fig. 18.*

NOTE: **Different clutch assemblies are used in various models. When disassembling clutches, note number and location of plates used for reassembly reference**

REVERSE-HIGH CLUTCH
Disassembly

1) Remove pressure plate snap ring by prying up with a screwdriver. Remove pressure plate, drive, and driven plates. Using clutch spring compressor tool (T65L-77515-A), compress piston return springs.

2) Remove snap ring, spring retainer, and springs. Apply air pressure to piston apply hole in drum and remove piston. Remove piston outer seal from piston, and inner seal from clutch drum.

Bushing Replacement

To remove front bushing, use a cape chisel and cut along bushing seam until chisel breaks through bushing wall. Pry loose ends of bushing up to remove. Remove rear bushing using a press ram and bushing adapter. Install bushings using bushing drivers.

Reassembly

1) Dip new seals in transmission fluid and install one seal on piston and one in drum. Install piston into clutch drum. Position return springs in pockets as shown. Place spring retainer over springs. Using compressor tool, compress springs and install snap ring. *See Fig. 22.*

Fig. 22: View of Reverse-High Clutch Piston Return Springs

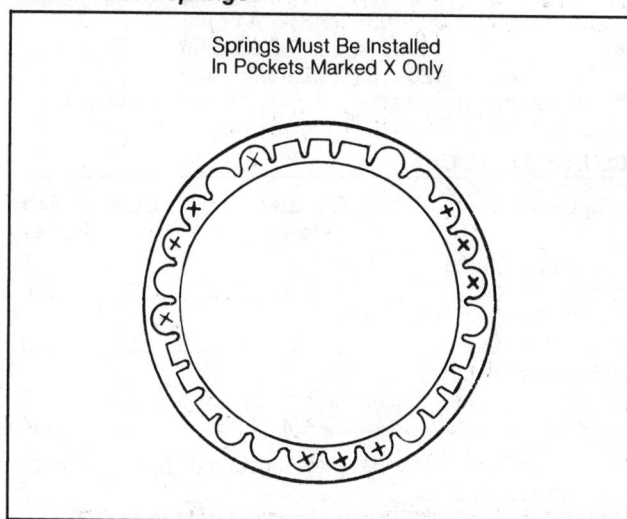

Springs Must Be Installed In Pockets Marked X Only

Ensure that springs are in correct pockets.

NOTE: **Before releasing tool, make sure snap ring is seated inside 4 snap ring guides on spring retainer.**

2) Install clutch plates alternately starting with a steel drive plate. If new clutch plates are being installed, composition plates must be soaked in transmission fluid for 15 minutes before installation.

3) Install pressure plate and retaining snap ring. See *Clutch Plate Chart* for the number of clutch plates required.

4) Using a feeler gauge, check clearance between pressure plate and snap ring. Hold pressure plate downward while measuring. Clearance should be .022-.036" (.56-.91 mm).

Fig. 21: Exploded View of Forward Clutch Assembly

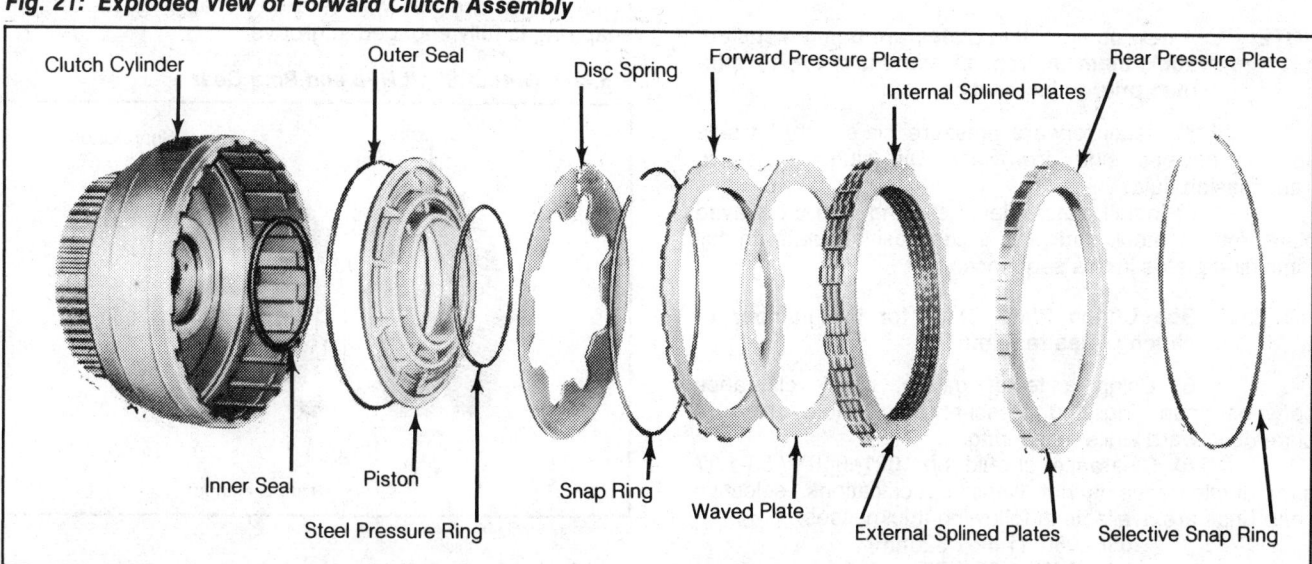

Clutch Cylinder — Outer Seal — Disc Spring — Forward Pressure Plate — Rear Pressure Plate — Internal Splined Plates — Inner Seal — Piston — Snap Ring — Steel Pressure Ring — Waved Plate — External Splined Plates — Selective Snap Ring

5) If clearance is not within specifications, selective snap rings are available in the following thicknesses:

.056-.060" (1.42-1.52 mm)
.065-.069" (1.65-1.75 mm)
.074-.078" (1.88-1.98 mm)
.083-.087" (2.11-2.21 mm)
.092-.096" (2.34-2.44 mm)
.110-.114" (2.79-2.90 mm)
.128-.132" (3.25-3.35 mm)

Install correct thickness snap ring and recheck clearance.

CLUTCH PLATE CHART

Application	Flat Steel Plates	Composition Plates
Forward Clutch		
PGD, PJD	[1] 4	4
High Clutch		
PGD, PJD	3	3
Reverse Clutch		
PJD	[2] 5	5
PGD	[2] 4	4

[1] - Plus one WAVED plate installed next to inner pressure plate.
[2] - Plus one WAVED plate installed next to piston.

FORWARD CLUTCH
Disassembly

1) Remove clutch pressure plate retaining snap ring. Remove rear pressure plate, drive and driven plates, and forward pressure plate from clutch drum.

2) Remove snap ring securing disc spring in drum and remove disc spring. Apply air pressure to clutch apply passage in drum and remove piston. Remove seals from piston and drum.

Reassembly

1) Dip 2 new seals in transmission fluid. Install smaller seal on clutch hub and other seal on piston. Install clutch piston in cylinder.

2) Make sure steel pressure ring is in groove on piston. Place disc spring in clutch drum with dished face downward. Secure in place with retaining snap ring.

NOTE: If new composition plates are being installed, soak them in transmission fluid for 15 minutes prior to installation.

3) Install forward pressure plate with flat side up and beveled side downward. Dip clutch plates in transmission fluid.

4) Install clutch plates starting with the waved plate, then a steel plate and a composition plate. Install remaining plates in this sequence.

NOTE: See Clutch Plate Chart for the number of clutch plates required.

5) Using a feeler gauge, check clearance between snap ring and pressure plate. Hold pressure plate downward while measuring.

6) Clearance should be .021-.046" (.53-1.17 mm). If clearance is not within specifications, selective snap rings are available in following thicknesses:

.056-.060" (1.42-1.52 mm)
.065-.069" (1.65-1.75 mm)

.074-.078" (1.88-1.98 mm)
.083-.087" (2.11-2.21 mm)
.092-.096" (2.34-2.44 mm)
.110-.114" (2.79-2.90 mm)
.128-.132" (3.25-3.35 mm).

Install correct thickness snap ring and recheck clearance.

INPUT SHELL & SUN GEAR
Disassembly

Remove rear (external) snap ring from sun gear and remove thrust washer from sun gear and input shell. Working inside input shell, remove sun gear. Remove internal (forward) snap ring from gear.

Reassembly

Install forward snap ring on short end of sun gear. Working inside input shell, slide sun gear and snap ring into place, making sure longer end of gear is at rear. Place thrust washer on rear end of input shell and sun gear. Install rear snap ring.

Fig. 23: Exploded View of Input Shell & Sun Gear

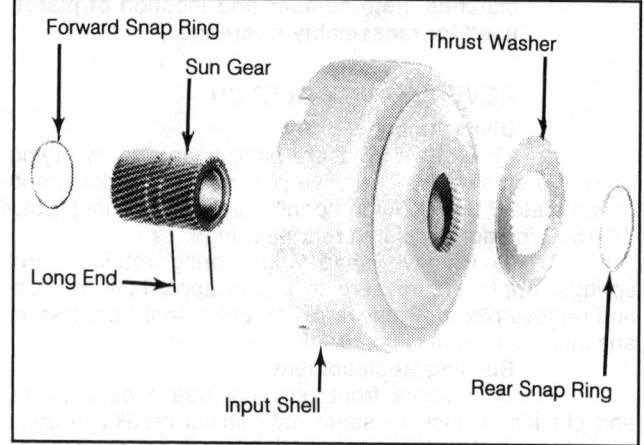

OUTPUT SHAFT HUB & RING GEAR
Disassembly & Reassembly

If necessary to remove these parts, remove hub retaining snap ring and lift hub from ring gear. When installing, secure hub with retaining snap ring, make sure snap ring is fully engaged in groove.

Fig. 24: Output Shaft Hub and Ring Gear

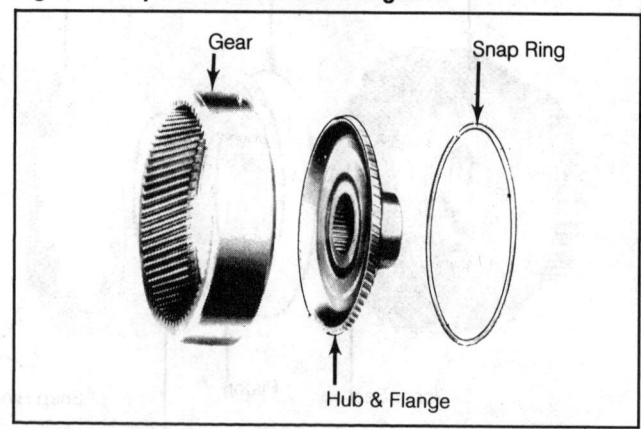

FORD C-6 (Cont.)

ONE-WAY CLUTCH

Disassembly

Remove snap ring and bushing from rear of low-reverse clutch hub. Remove rollers from spring assembly. Lift spring assembly from hub. Remove remaining snap ring from hub.

Reassembly

1) Install snap ring in forward groove of low-reverse clutch hub. Place hub on bench with forward end down. Install spring assembly on top of snap ring.

2) Install a roller into each spring assembly compartment. Install bushing on top of spring assembly. Install remaining snap ring at rear of clutch hub to secure assembly.

Fig. 25: Exploded View of One-Way Clutch Assembly

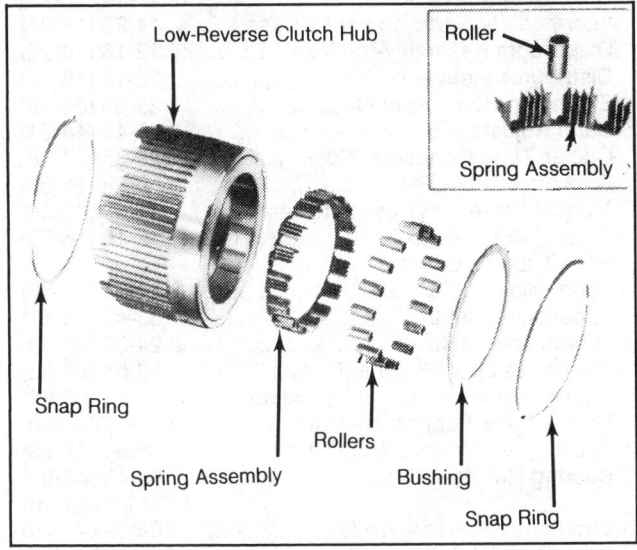

INTERMEDIATE SERVO

Disassembly

Apply air pressure to port in servo cover and remove piston assembly. Remove seal from cover.

NOTE: **Piston and rod are serviced as an assembly, replace if piston or sealing lips are damaged.**

Reassembly

Dip new seal in transmission fluid and install on cover. Dip piston assembly in transmission fluid and install in cover.

LOW-REVERSE CLUTCH PISTON

NOTE: **Clutch is assembled as part of transmission reassembly; replace seals as follows:**

Remove inner and outer seals from clutch piston. Dip new seals in transmission fluid and install on piston.

GOVERNOR

Disassembly

Remove governor retaining bolts and governor. Remove snap ring securing governor distributor to output shaft. Slide distributor off front of shaft. Remove seal rings from governor distributor.

Reassembly

1) Carefully install new seal rings on distributor. Working from front end of output shaft, slide governor distributor into place on shaft.

2) Secure in place with snap ring. Make sure snap ring is fully seated in groove. Position governor on distributor, install and tighten retaining screws.

TRANSMISSION REASSEMBLY

1) With transmission mounted in fixture, tap low-reverse clutch piston into case with a soft mallet. Hold one-way clutch inner race in position, then install and tighten retaining bolts.

2) Install low-reverse clutch return spring and retainer assembly in clutch piston. Position snap ring on one-way clutch inner race. Compress return spring and retainer and seat snap ring in groove.

3) Place transmission case on bench with front end facing downward. Position parking gear thrust washer and gear on case. It is not necessary to restake thrust washer. Position oil distributor and tubes on rear of case.

4) Install and tighten retaining bolts. Install output shaft and governor as an assembly. Place a new gasket on rear of case, install extension housing and retaining bolts. Tighten bolts to specifications. Install vent tube.

5) Coat 2 new servo cover gaskets with petroleum jelly and position them on servo cover. Place servo spring on piston rod and install in case.

6) Install retaining bolts, make sure identification tag is under one of the cover bolts and tighten. Align low-reverse clutch hub and one-way clutch with inner race at rear of case.

Fig. 26: Exploded View of Output Shaft and Governor Assembly

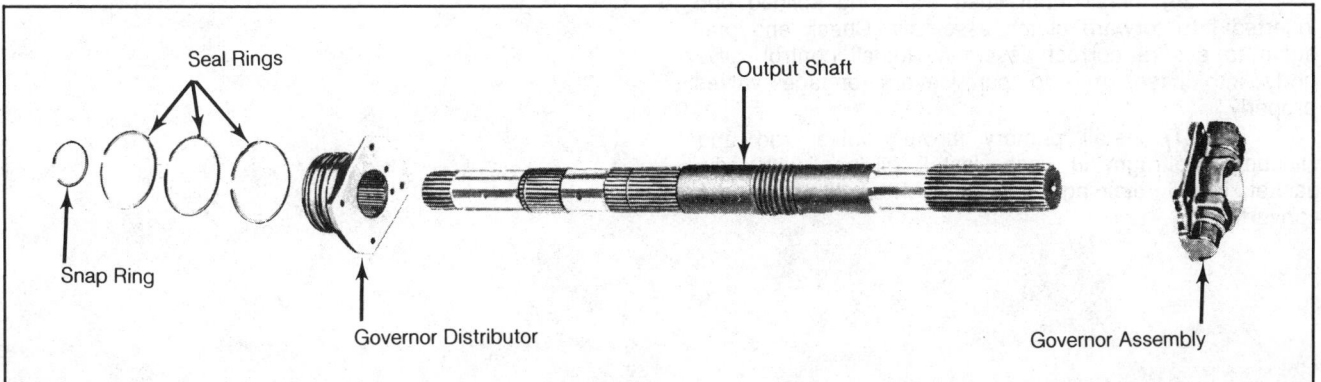

Automatic Transmissions

FORD C-6 (Cont.)

7) Rotate low-reverse clutch hub clockwise while applying pressure to seat it on inner race. Install low-reverse clutch plates, starting with the waved plate next to piston and follow with a steel, then a composition plate until all plates are installed.

8) Retain plates with petroleum jelly. Install pressure plate and snap ring. Test operation of low-reverse clutch assembly by applying air pressure to clutch pressure apply hole in case.

9) Install reverse planet ring gear thrust washer, ring gear and hub assembly. Install snap ring in groove of output shaft. Install front and rear thrust washers onto reverse planet assembly using petroleum jelly to retain.

10) Install assembly into ring gear and install snap ring. Place reverse-high clutch on bench with front end facing downward. Install thrust washer on rear end of assembly and retain with petroleum jelly.

11) Install splined end of forward clutch into open end of reverse-high clutch with splines engaging direct clutch plates. Install thrust washer on front end of forward planet ring gear and hub. Retain with petroleum jelly.

12) Install ring gear into forward clutch and install thrust washer on front end of forward planet assembly and retain with petroleum jelly.

13) Install assembly into ring gear. Install input shell and sun assembly. Install reverse-high clutch, forward clutch, forward planet assembly, input shell and sun gear as an assembly into case.

14) Install intermediate band around direct clutch drum. Install band struts and tighten band adjusting screw enough to retain band.

15) Place selective bronze thrust washer on rear shoulder of stator support and retain with petroleum jelly.

16) If end play was not within specifications when disassembled, replace washer at this time with one of correct thickness.

17) Using 5/16 x 3" bolts, make 2 alignment studs by cutting the heads off and grinding a taper on the cut end. Install the studs opposite each other in case mounting holes.

18) Slide a new gasket onto studs. Position pump on case, being careful not to damage seal on pump housing, and remove studs. Install 6 of the mounting bolts and tighten.

19) Tighten intermediate band adjusting screw to 10 ft. lbs. (14 N.m) Back off screw exactly 1 1/2 turns. Hold adjusting screw in this position and tighten lock nut to specifications.

20) Install input shaft with long splined end inserted into forward clutch assembly. Check end play again to ensure correct assembly. Install control valve body into case, making sure levers engage valves properly.

21) Install primary throttle valve, rod and vacuum diaphragm in case. Install oil pan with new gasket, install retaining bolts and tighten. Install torque converter.

SELECTIVE THRUST WASHERS

Color Code	Thickness In. (mm)
Blue	.056-.060 (1.42-1.52)
Natural (White)	.073-.077 (1.85-1.96)
Red	.088-.092 (2.24-2.34)

TIGHTENING SPECIFICATIONS

Application	Ft. Lbs. (N.m)
Converter-to-Flywheel	20-34 (27-46)
Front Pump-to-Case	16-30 (22-41)
Overrunning Clutch Race-to-Case	18-25 (24-34)
Stator Support-to-Pump	12-16 (16-22)
Converter Cover-to-Housing	12-16 (16-22)
Guide Plate-to-Case	12-16 (16-22)
Intermediate Servo Cover-to-Case	14-20 (19-27)
Diaphragm Assembly-to-Case	12-16 (16-22)
Distributor Sleeve-to-Case	12-16 (16-22)
Extension Housing-to-Case	25-35 (34-48)
Band Adjusting Screw Lock Nut	35-45 (48-61)
Cooler Tube Connector Lock	20-35 (27-48)
Converter Drain Plug	8-28 (11-38)
Manual Valve Inner Lever-to-Shaft	30-40 (41-54)
Downshift Lever-to-Shaft	12-16 (16-22)
Filler Tube-to-Engine	
Econoline - 5.0L, 5.8L, 7.5L	40-50 (54-68)
Econoline - 4.9L	33-42 (45-57)
Econoline - 6.9L	24-35 (33-48)
Transmission-to-Engine (Diesel)	50-65 (68-88)
Transmission-to-Engine (Gasoline)	40-50 (54-68)
Rear Engine Support-to-Trans.	60-80 (82-109)
Ext. Hsg.-to-Bearing Ret. Stud	35-50 (48-68)
Bearing Ret.-to-Ext. Housing	35-45 (48-61)
	INCH Lbs. (N.m)
End Plates-to-Valve Body	20-40 (2.5-4.5)
Inner Downshift Lever Stop	20-45 (2.5-5.0)
Reinforcement Plate-to-Valve Body	20-45 (2.5-5.0)
Screen & Lower-to-Upper Valve Body	40-55 (4.5-6.2)
Shift Valve Plate-to-Upper Body	20-45 (2.5-5.0)
Upper-to-Lower Body	40-55 (4.5.0-6.2)
Cover Housing-to-Cover Housing	
7.5L Engine Only	30-60 (3.5-6.5)
Control Assy.-to-Case	95-125 (11.0-14.0)
Governor Body-to-Collector Body	90-120 (10.5-13.5)
Detent Spring-to-Case	80-120 (9.5-13.5)
Neutral Switch-to-Case	55-75 (6.2-8.0)
Yoke-to-Output Shaft 4WD Only	130 (15.0)

GENERAL MOTORS TORQUE CONVERTER CLUTCH

All GM Automatic Transmissions and Transaxles except THM 400

DESCRIPTION

The torque converter clutch assembly consists of a 3-element torque converter with the addition of a converter clutch. The converter clutch is an internal mechanism with friction material attached to the front face. It is splined to the turbine assembly in the converter. When in operation, the clutch applies against the converter cover, providing a mechanical direct drive coupling of the engine to the transmission planetary gears. Applying the converter clutch eliminates converter slippage, resulting in improved fuel economy and reduced fluid operating temperatures. When the converter clutch is released, the assembly operates as a conventional torque converter.

Converter clutch apply and release is controlled by several factors. On 4WD vehicles one of these is drive range selection. When transfer case is shifted from 2H to 4L or 4H, circuit to TCC system is opened. In this position (4L or 4H) converter clutch will not apply. When transfer case is shifted back to 2H, TCC system operates in normal manner. If vehicle does not shift out of 4L or 4H, converter clutch will not apply.

Converter clutch apply and release is controlled by the position of the converter clutch apply valve, located in oil pump on THM 180C and 200C, valve body on THM 200-4R, 325-4L and 700-R4, and in auxiliary valve body on THM 125C, 250C and 350C. Apply valve operation is controlled by a solenoid.

In order for the torque converter clutch to engage, the transmission must be operating in 3rd gear (3rd or 4th on 4-speed models) and vehicle speed must be over a specific level (typically 30-35 MPH). In addition, several other controls may be incorporated in the vacuum/electrical system to aid in the apply and release of the converter clutch. Specific additional component use is determined by whether or not the vehicle is equipped with the Computer Command Control (CCC) system, and some other factors. On vehicles with the CCC system, operation of the apply solenoid is controlled by the Electronic Control Module (ECM). On systems without CCC, the solenoid control signal is routed through whatever additional controls are used, any of which may break the circuit if specific operating conditions are not met. These controls are external to the transmission and operate as described.

The following components supply engine condition information to the ECM on CCC equipped vehicles:

Brake Release Switch

Used on all engines, this switch releases the converter clutch when the brakes are applied.

Throttle Position Sensor

Provides the ECM with throttle position information. Converter clutch operation is prevented below a specific signal level.

Engine Coolant Temperature Sensor

Not used on all models, this sensor provides the ECM with engine coolant temperature information. The ECM will not allow clutch operation until the signal from this sensor indicates a coolant temperature higher than about 165°F (75°C).

Vacuum Sensor

Used on models which do not use the Engine Coolant Temperature Sensor, this sensor provides the ECM with engine vacuum (load) information.

Third Gear Switch

Used on some models, this switch prevents TCC operation until direct drive (3rd gear) is obtained.

NOTE: On systems using the ECM of the CCC system for solenoid control, the emission control system of the vehicle must be in perfect operating condition to guarantee proper TCC function.

The following components are used on vehicles without the CCC system. Not all components will be present on all vehicles.

Brake Release Switch

Used on all engines, switch releases converter clutch when brakes are applied to prevent engine stalling.

High Vacuum Switch

Used on vehicles with diesel engines, switch releases converter clutch during closed throttle deceleration.

Fig. 1: Exploded View of General Motors Torque Converter Clutch

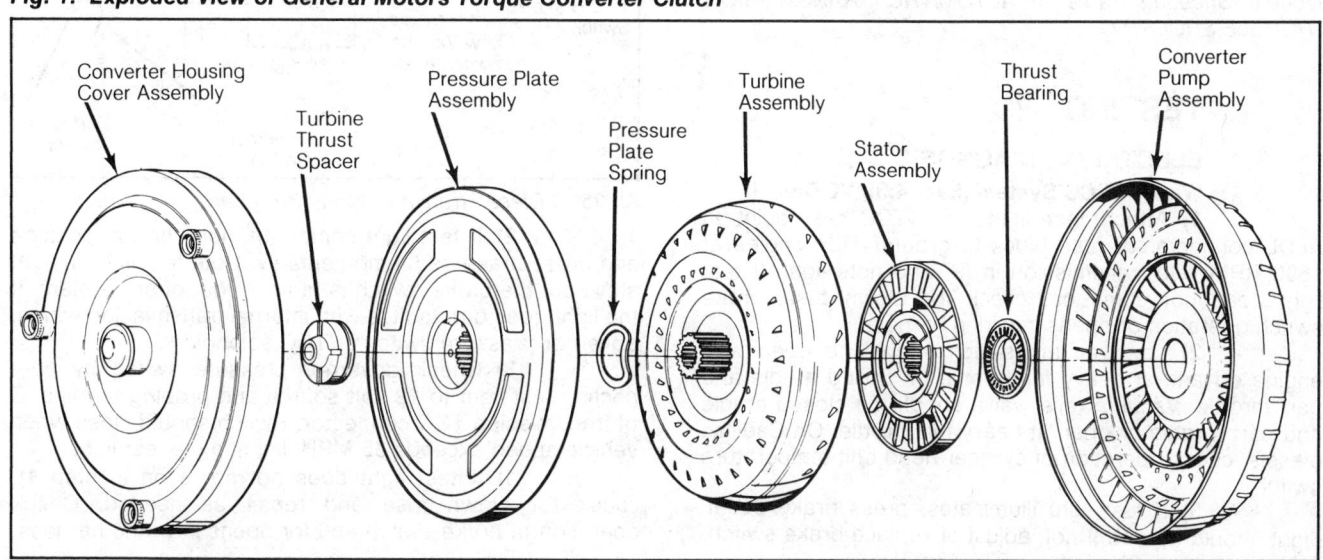

Low Vacuum Switch

Releases converter clutch when vacuum signal drops below about 1.5-3.0 in. Hg during moderate acceleration and prior to a part throttle or detent downshift.

Thermal Vacuum Valve

Used with most gasoline engines to prevent converter clutch operation below a specific engine coolant temperature, typically 130°F (55°C).

Vacuum Delay Valve

Used with some gasoline engines to slow vacuum switch response to sudden changes in engine vacuum.

Third Gear Switch

Signals TCC Delay Module that transaxle is operating in direct drive (3rd gear). Prevents TCC operation in 1st and 2nd gear.

Governor Pressure Switch

Completes ground circuit for TCC and EGR solenoids at or above specific vehicle speed, typically about 35 MPH.

TCC Delay Module

Delays TCC engagement to prevent TCC and direct clutch application at the same time, causing an audible "thump".

Vacuum Regulator Valve

Opens at about 3/4 or more throttle to disengage TCC during heavy acceleration.

Engine Coolant Fan Temperature Switch

A 2-position switch that closes when coolant temperature exceeds about 250°F (120°C). This increases fan speed and bypasses delay feature in TCC Delay Module. Does not prevent TCC operation when Governor Pressure Switch is closed.

A/C High Pressure Switch

Switch closes when A/C high side pressure reaches or exceeds 370 psi (26 kg/cm²). This increases fan speed and bypasses delay feature in TCC Delay Module. Does not prevent TCC operation when Governor Pressure Switch is closed.

TROUBLE SHOOTING

See General Motors Torque Converter Clutch Trouble Shooting Table in AUTOMATIC TRANSMISSION TROUBLE SHOOTING.

TESTING

ELECTRICAL DIAGNOSIS

Without CCC System (Exc. 4.3L V6 Diesel)

1) Attach test light from TCC test point in ALDL connector or fuse block to ground. Run engine at 1500 RPM with transmission in "P" and note light. If test light does not come on, check for blown fuse, brake switch operation or opens in wiring harness.

2) Low vacuum switch should be open with engine off and at heavy full throttle or closed at idle and part throttle. Vacuum relief valve should be closed at idle and part throttle or open at heavy full throttle. On Cadillac diesels, check operation of cylinder head bolt temperature switch.

3) If test light illuminates, press brake pedal. Light should go out. If not, adjust or replace brake switch.

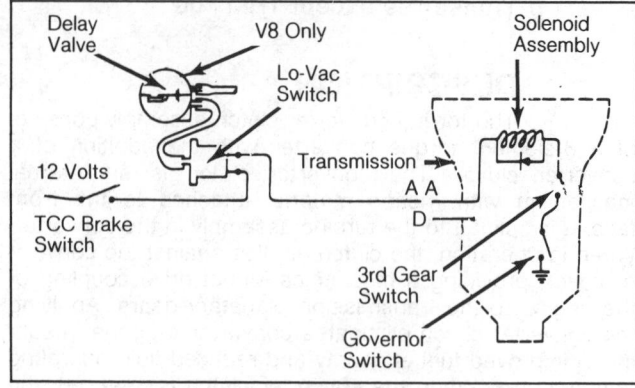

Fig. 2: Torque Converter Clutch System Schematic

Typical for all without CCC system (except 350C Diesel). Transmission in 3rd gear.

If light goes out, disconnect light from ground and connect to 12-volt source at fuse block. If light comes on, internal transmission wiring, switches and/or solenoid may be grounded.

4) If light stays off when attached to power source, raise drive wheels off floor and run engine with transmission in gear at 50-55 MPH. Press brake pedal briefly while observing test light. If light comes on electrical function is normal. Check mechanical function of solenoid and TCC valve. If light remains off, check for open in internal transmission circuitry.

4.3L V6 Diesel

1) If TCC does not engage, connect test light from ALCL terminal F to ground and raise rear wheels of vehicle off ground. Start engine, place transmission in "D" and accelerate until transmission shifts to 3rd gear. Note test light. If light does not come on, go to step **4)**.

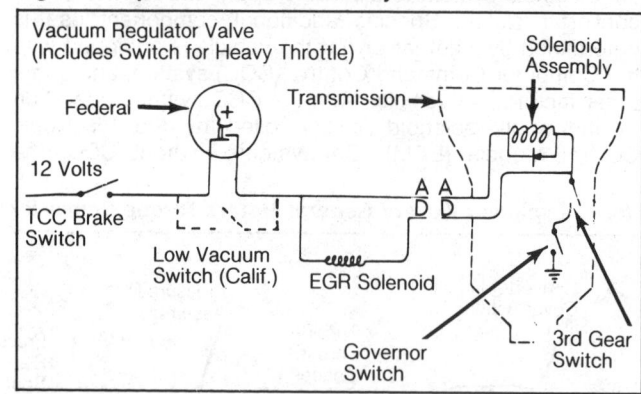

Fig. 3: Torque Converter Clutch System Schematic

All 350C Diesel, transmission in 3rd gear.

2) If test light comes on, hold throttle position and press brake pedal momentarily. Note test light. If light stays on, the brake switch is faulty or out of adjustment. If the light goes out, fault is with internal transmission wiring, governor pressure switch or TCC solenoid.

3) Check governor pressure switch by connecting test light to 12 volt source and probing terminal D of transmission TCC connector. Switch should close when vehicle speed exceeds 35 MPH, lighting the test light.

4) If test light does not come on in step **1)**, check for blown fuse and repair as needed. Check operation of brake switch and for opens in wiring harness.

Fig. 4: Transmission Connector Terminal Identification

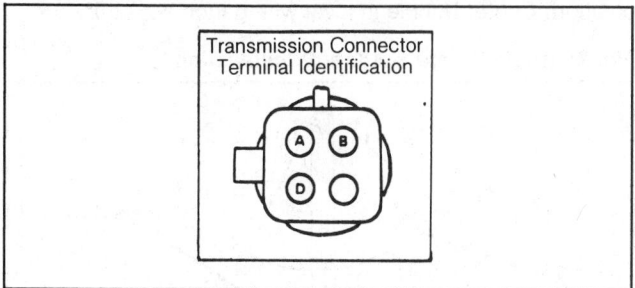

Check for proper third gear switch operation. Switch should be open with transmission in third gear.

5) Check continuity of VRV switch with test light. There should be continuity up to 3/4 throttle. Check ground to VRV. If all checks in this step and step **4)** are OK, replace delay module assembly.

6) If TCC operates in second gear, perform the following test. With ignition key "ON" and engine off, attach test light from ALCL terminal F to ground. If the test light does not come on, TCC solenoid, TCC control valve or the torque converter itself is faulty. If the test light comes on, check for engine overheating and/or excessive A/C high pressure. Repair as needed and check TCC operation.

7) If TCC still engages in 2nd gear, check operation of 3rd gear switch. Connect test light to 12 volt source and remove harness connector at transmission. Probe terminal B of connector. If test light comes on, replace delay module assembly. If not, replace 3rd gear switch or repair faulty wiring to switch.

With CCC System (Exc. Olds 4-Cyl EFI)

1) Disconnect fan cut-out if present. Connect test light from terminal F of ALCL connector (FWD Chevrolet, Camaro, Corvette and Pontiac) or test point in ALDL (all others) to ground. With drive wheels off floor and transmission in gear, increase speed to 25 MPH. If test light comes on, go to step **5)**.

2) If light does not come on, check for blown fuse. If fuse is OK, disconnect connector at transmission and connect test light from connector A to D. With ignition "ON", engine stopped and throttle opened slightly (3.0L V6 only), note test light.

3) If light is on, check for ground in wire to ECM terminal P (FWD Buick, FWD Chevrolet, Corvette, Camaro, Pontiac) or F (all others). If not grounded, replace ECM. If light is off, connect test light from terminal A to ground. If light does not come on, adjust brake switch or repair open in circuit. On 3.0L V6, check TCC relay.

4) If test light comes on, remove it and reconnect between harness connectors A and D. If light does not come on, repair open in wire from transmission to test point. If light comes on, check for faulty connection at transmission, solenoid circuit or ECM connector.

5) If light comes on in step **1)**, momentarily press brake pedal and light should go out. If not, adjust or replace brake switch. If OK, increase speed to 50-55 MPH and, on RWD vehicles only, lightly apply parking brake while maintaining speed for 5 seconds. If test light goes out, go to step **6)**. If the light stays on, go to step **10)**.

6) On 3-speed transmissions, check throttle position switch (TPS) adjustment and, on 3.0L V6, check TCC relay. If OK, no electrical problem is indicated. On 4-speed transmissions turn engine off and, with ignition in

"ON" position, check voltage from ECM terminal H (FWD Pontiac and Cavalier) or N (17 if used) to ground.

7) If over 6 volts, check for open in wire between ECM terminal N (FWD Chevrolet, Camaro, Corvette, Olds exc. 2.8 and 3.0L, Pontiac) or H (all others) and transmission connector terminal B (C for terminal 17). If no open is found, transmission switch or connector at transmission is faulty.

8) If voltage from step **6)** is under 6 volts, start engine and bring speed to 50-55 MPH with transmission in "D". If voltage is now above 6 volts, check TPS adjustment. If OK, there is no electrical problem. If voltage is below 6 volts, stop engine, leave ignition in "ON" position and disconnect transmission connecter. Check voltage from terminal B to ground (C for terminal 17).

9) If voltage reading is over 6 volts, transmission switch is either grounded or not opening. Repair or replace as needed. If reading is below 6 volts, check for grounded wire to ECM terminal N (or 17). If not grounded, ECM connector or ECM is faulty. Replace as needed.

10) If light from step **5)** is on, check voltage from ECM terminal 2 to ground with digital voltmeter, engine stopped, ignition "ON" and throttle wide open. If less than 1 volt, check for ground in wire to ECM terminal 2. If no ground, replace ECM.

11) If more than 1 volt in step **10)**, stop engine but leave ignition "ON". Check voltage from terminal 16 to ground while turning a drive wheel by hand, with other drive wheel on floor. Voltage should alternate from below 3 to over 10 volts.

Fig. 5: Torque Converter Clutch System Schematic

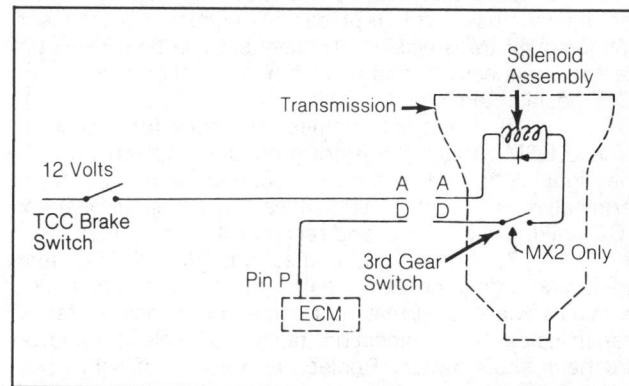

All 3-speed with CCC system, transmission in 3rd gear.

Fig. 6: Torque Converter Clutch System Schematic

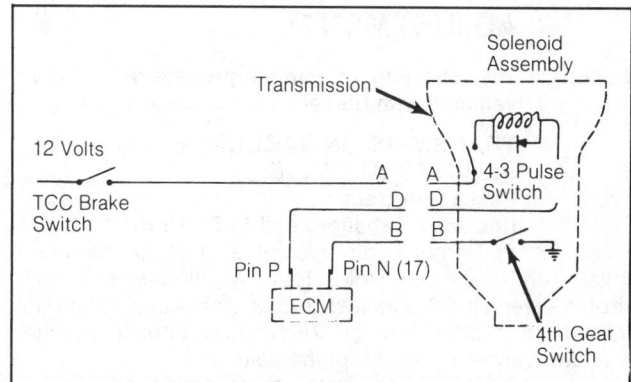

All 4-speed with transmission in 3rd or 4th gear.

12) If voltage fluctuation is incorrect, check for faulty speed sensor. If voltage fluctuation is correct, check and adjust TPS as needed. Check for low coolant level and above normal resistance in coolant sensor circuit. Check TCC solenoid resistance.

13) If resistance is less than 20 ohms, replace solenoid and ECM. If resistance is above 20 ohms, ECM connection or ECM is faulty. Replace as needed.

Oldsmobile 4-Cyl. EFI

1) With engine at normal operating temperature, connect test light from terminal F of ALCL connector to ground. Raise and support drive wheels several inches off ground, start engine and let idle in neutral.

2) If test light comes on, transmission 3rd gear apply switch is faulty and should be replaced. If test light does not come on, increase vehicle speed to 30 MPH with transmission in "D". If test light remains off, go to step **5)**. If light comes on, press brake pedal lightly and watch test light.

3) If test light stays on, brake switch should be adjusted or replaced. If light goes out, increase speed to 45 MPH. If light remains off, TCC system is OK. If light comes on, turn off engine and return key to "ON" position. Probe White ECM connector terminal 2 with a voltmeter while turning one drive wheel with the other wheel on the ground.

4) Voltage reading should alternate from below 3 to over 10. If not, check speed sensor. If voltage reading is correct, check for low coolant level and/or excessive coolant sensor circuit resistance. If OK, ECM connector or ECM is faulty.

5) If test light remained off in step **2)**, check for blown fuse and replace as needed. Disconnect connector at transmission and connect test light between harness connector A and D. With engine off and ignition in "ON" position, observe test light.

6) If test light comes on, check for ground in wire to ECM circuit 422. If not grounded, replace ECM. If the light does not come on, connect test light from terminal A to ground. If light does not come on, inspect TCC brake switch circuit and repair or adjust as needed.

7) If test light comes on, ground TCC test point and again connect test light between connector terminals A and D. If test light comes on, check for faulty transmission TCC connection, faulty TCC solenoid and/or 3rd gear apply switch. Replace as needed. If light goes out, repair open in wire from transmission to terminal F of ALCL connector.

ADJUSTMENT

NOTE: The following adjustment procedures apply to vehicles with diesel engines, only.

TRANSMISSION VACUUM REGULATOR VALVE
Passenger Cars
(Includes Caballero and El Camino)

1) Remove air crossover. Install screened covers on intake manifold. Remove throttle rod from throttle lever on V8 engines; throttle cable and detent/TV cable from throttle lever on V6 engines. Loosen vacuum regulator valve-to-injection pump bolts.

2) Install carburetor angle gauge adapter (J-26701-15) on injection pump throttle lever and place angle gauge on adaptor. Rotate throttle lever to wide open position. Center bubble in level with gauge set at 0°.

Fig. 7: Angle Gauge & Adapter Installation

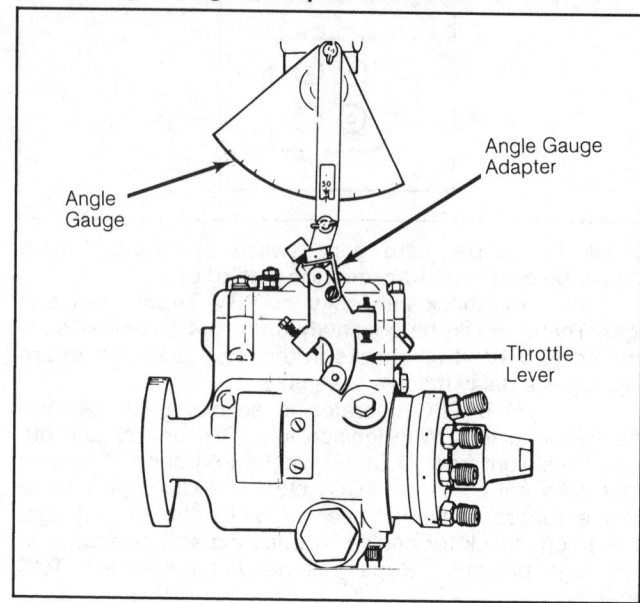

File tool as needed to fit on thicker V6 throttle lever.

3) Set gauge to 58° (V8) or 49° (V6) and rotate throttle lever until bubble is centered. Attach vacuum pump to regulator port "A" and a vacuum gauge to port "B". Apply 18-24 in. Hg of vacuum at port "A".

Fig. 8: Vacuum Regulator Valve Port Locations

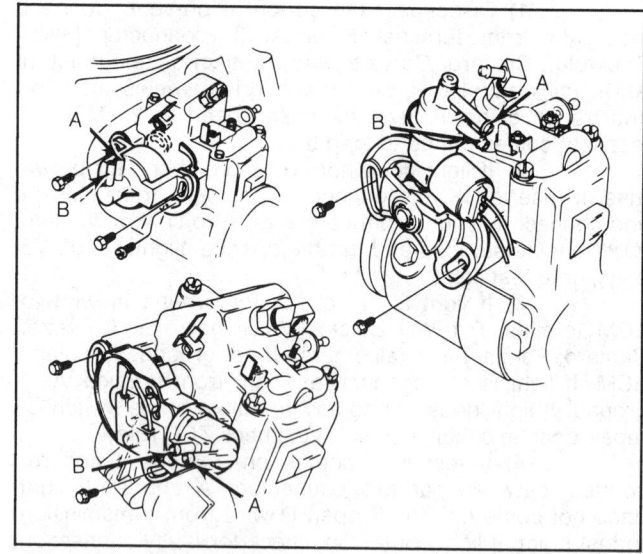

Attach vacuum pump to port "A", gauge to port "B".

4) Rotate vacuum valve clockwise until vacuum gauge reads 10.6 in. Hg and tighten valve mounting bolts. Remove vacuum source and gauge. Install throttle rod or throttle cable and detent/TV cable to pump throttle lever. Remove screened covers and install air crossover.

Trucks

1) Loosen vacuum regulator valve-to-injection pump bolts enough to allow for regulator valve rotation. Attach vacuum pump to bottom vacuum port of valve; vacuum gauge to top port.

GENERAL MOTORS TORQUE CONVERTER CLUTCH (Cont.)

2) Insert measuring gauge bar (.646" thick) between gauge boss on injection pump and wide open stop screw on throttle lever. *See Fig. 9.* Rotate throttle shaft against bar.

Fig. 9: Adjusting Vacuum Regulator Valve

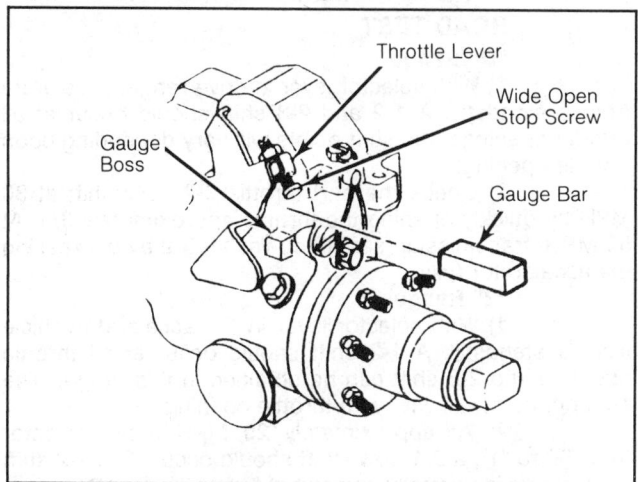

Insert gauge bar between gauge boss and wide open throttle stop screw.

3) Apply 18-21 in. Hg of vacuum with vacuum pump. Slowly rotate vacuum regulator valve body clockwise (facing valve) until vacuum gauge reads 7-9 in. Hg. Hold valve body in this position and tighten mounting screws.

NOTE: Valve MUST be set while rotating in a clockwise direction.

4) Check adjustment by allowing throttle shaft to return to idle position, then rotate shaft back against gauge bar. If vacuum gauge reading is not 7-9 in. Hg, re-adjust valve.

HIGH VACUUM SWITCH

NOTE: The high vacuum switch MUST be adjusted whenever throttle rod, vacuum regulator valve or high idle speed adjustment is changed.

1) Disconnect high vacuum switch electrical connector. Connect one lead of self-powered test light to either terminal of high vacuum switch. Connect test light probe to other switch terminal.

2) Start engine and run at high idle speed. Energize fast idle solenoid by disconnecting Pink/Green wire connector from coolant switch (on left rear of intake manifold). Remove seal cap on back of high vacuum switch.

3) High vacuum switch contacts must be closed (test light on) before making adjustment. If contacts are open (test light off), turn switch adjustment screw clockwise until contacts close.

4) Adjust vacuum switch by slowly turning adjustment screw counterclockwise until switch contacts just open (test light "OFF"). Do not turn past this point.

5) Reinstall seal cap on back of switch, reconnect vacuum switch electrical connector and coolant temperature switch connector.

Fig. 10: High Vacuum Switch Adjustment

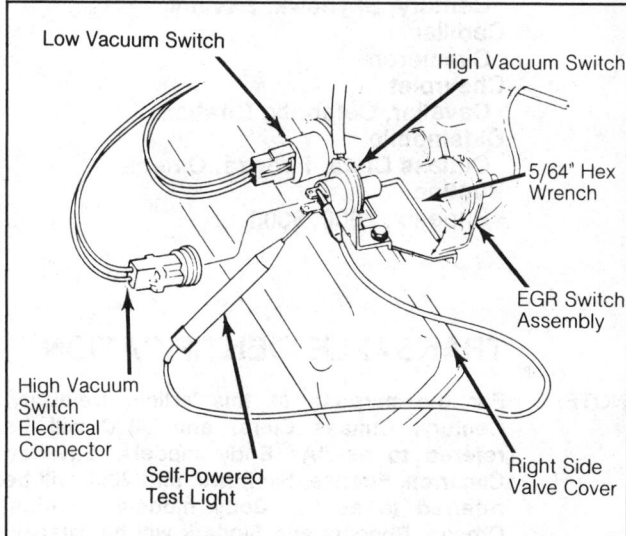

Adjust switch whenever throttle rod, vacuum regulator valve or high idle speed is adjusted.

NOTE: If air cleaner is removed when making high vacuum switch adjustment, EGR solenoid port to EGR valve MUST be plugged to prevent vacuum leak at EGR solenoid

Automatic Transmissions
GENERAL MOTORS
TURBO HYDRA-MATIC 125C TRANSAXLE

Buick
  Century, Skyhawk, Skylark
Cadillac
  Cimmaron
Chevrolet
  Cavalier, Celebrity, Citation
Oldsmobile
  Cutlass Ciera, Firenza, Omega
Pontiac
  Phoenix, 2000, 6000

TRANSAXLE IDENTIFICATION

NOTE: For the purpose of this article Celebrity, Century, Cutlass Ciera, and 6000 will be refered to as "A" Body models. Cavalier, Cimmaron, Firenza, Skyhawk, and 2000 will be referred to as "J" Body models. Citation, Omega, Phoenix and Skylark will be referred to as "X" Body models.

The transaxle identification code is stamped on a machined pad located to the rear of the valve body cover and to the right of the dipstick tube.

TRANSAXLE CODES

Final Drive Ratio	Code Letters
2.39:1	HW, H6, OP, PK, PW, PZ
2.53:1	BL, CD, CE
2.84:1	AL, CL, HS, PD
2.97:1	BF
3.06:1	CT
3.18:1	CB, HY, PG
3.32:1	AC, RD, 3SB, 3SC
3.33:1	P3
3.43:1	CA
3.65:1	BD, 3SD, 3SF
3.73:1	HC, CF

DESCRIPTION

The THM-125C transaxle combines a torque converter, fully automatic 3-speed transmission, final drive gearing and differential into a front wheel drive system. The 4-element torque converter couples the engine crankshaft to the planetary gear set through a dual sprocket and drive link assembly.

The 4-element torque converter consists of a pump, a turbine, a pressure plate splined to the turbine and a stator assembly. The pressure plate, when applied, provides a mechanical direct drive coupling between the engine and the planetary gear set.

Three multi-disc clutches, a roller clutch and a single band provide the friction elements required to obtain the desired function of the planetary gear sets.

The differential is integral with the transmission. Power transfer to the differential is by direct mesh of final drive sun gear to final drive sun gear pinions, located in the differential housing. An internal gear, held stationary by the case, provides the pinion track that forces rotation of final drive assembly.

LUBRICATION & ADJUSTMENT

See the appropriate article in AUTOMATIC TRANSMISSION SERVICING Section.

TESTING

ROAD TEST

"D" Range

1) With selector lever in drive range, accelerate from a standstill. A 1-2 and 2-3 shift should occur at all throttle openings (the shift points will vary depending upon throttle opening).

2) Check the part throttle 3-2 downshift at 30 MPH by quickly opening the throttle approximately 3/4. At 50 MPH, transmission should downshift 3-2 by depressing the accelerator fully.

"2" Range

1) With selector lever in "2", accelerate vehicle from a standstill. A 1-2 shift should occur at all throttle openings (no 2-3 shift can be obtained in this range). The 1-2 shift point will vary with throttle opening.

2) At approximately 20 MPH move selector from "2" to "1", a 2-1 downshift should occur. The 1-2 shift in "2" range is normally somewhat firmer than in "D" range.

3) With selector lever in "D" range and vehicle speed at approximately 50 MPH, release accelerator and move selector lever to "2" range. A 3-2 downshift should occur accompanied by an increase in engine speed and an engine braking effect.

"1" Range

1) With selector lever in "1" range, accelerate vehicle from a standstill. No upshift should occur in this range. At 40 MPH with throttle closed, move selector lever to "1".

2) A 2-1 downshift should occur between approximately 25 to 45 MPH, depending on valve body calibration. A 2-1 downshift at closed throttle should be accompanied by increased engine speed and an engine braking effect.

Converter Clutch

Install a tachometer and bring engine to normal operating temperature. With vehicle speed between 40-45 MPH, in third gear, the converter clutch should apply. Observing tachometer, a drop of 200 RPM's will occur when clutch is applied.

LINE PRESSURE TESTS

CAUTION: Parking and service brakes must be applied at all times during test. Total duration for portion of test with selector in driving ranges should not exceed 2 minutes.

1) Before making line pressure tests, ensure that fluid level, condition and control linkage adjustments have been checked and corrected as necessary.

2) Install a tachometer to engine and a pressure gauge to line pressure take-off point on transaxle case. Line pressure tap is on bell housing side of transmission, above valve body cover.

Minimum T.V. Pressure Check

With T.V. cable properly adjusted to specifications, check line pressure in ranges and at RPM indicated on chart.

Maximum T.V. Pressure Check

With T.V. cable supported at full extent of its travel, check line pressure in ranges and at RPM indicated in chart.

GENERAL MOTORS
TURBO HYDRA-MATIC 125C TRANSAXLE (Cont.)

Fig 1: *Cutaway View of Turbo Hydra-Matic I25C Automatic Transaxle*

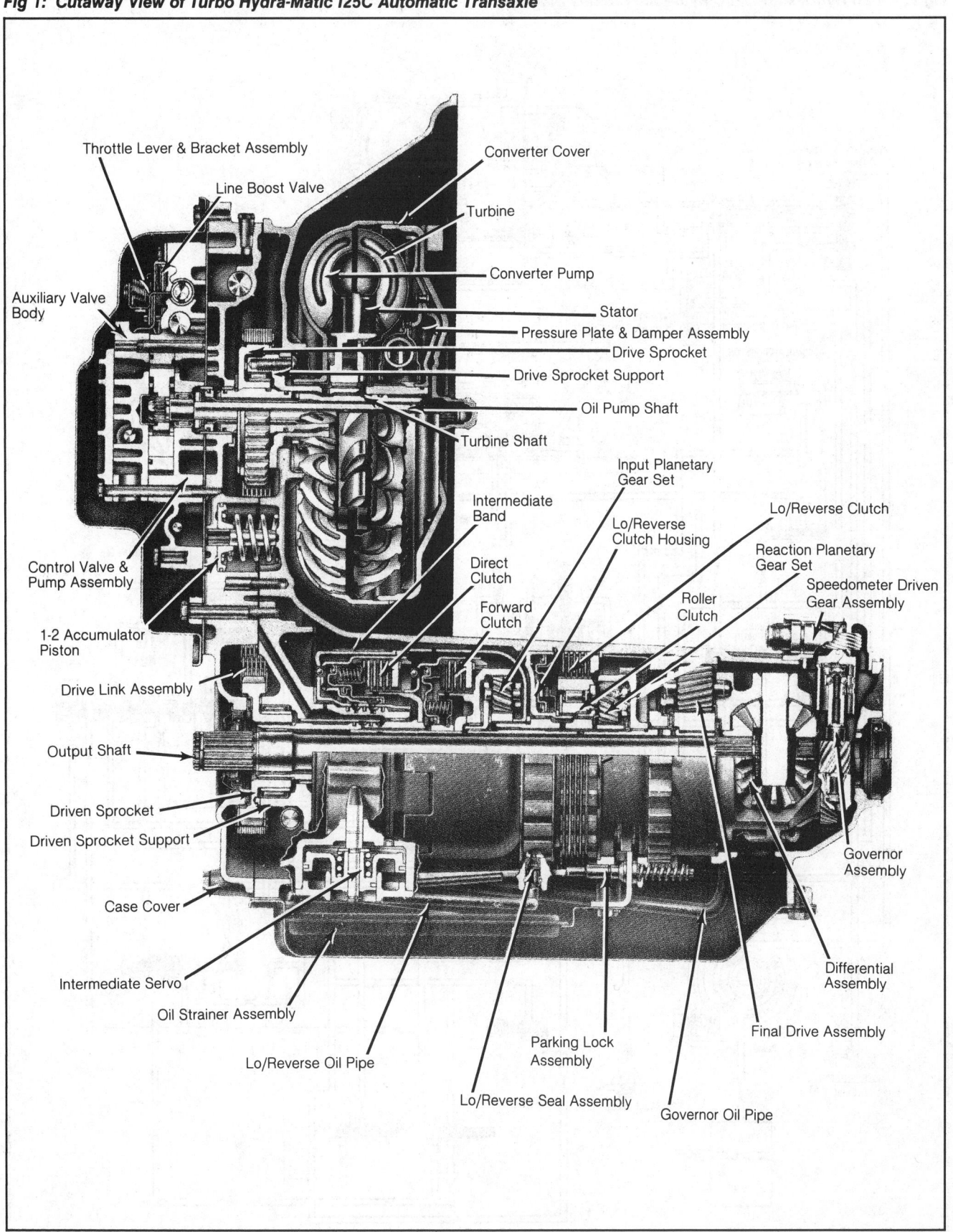

Automatic Transmissions
GENERAL MOTORS
TURBO HYDRA-MATIC 125C TRANSAXLE (Cont.)

Fig 2: Turbo Hydra-Matic 125C Hydraulic Circuits Diagram

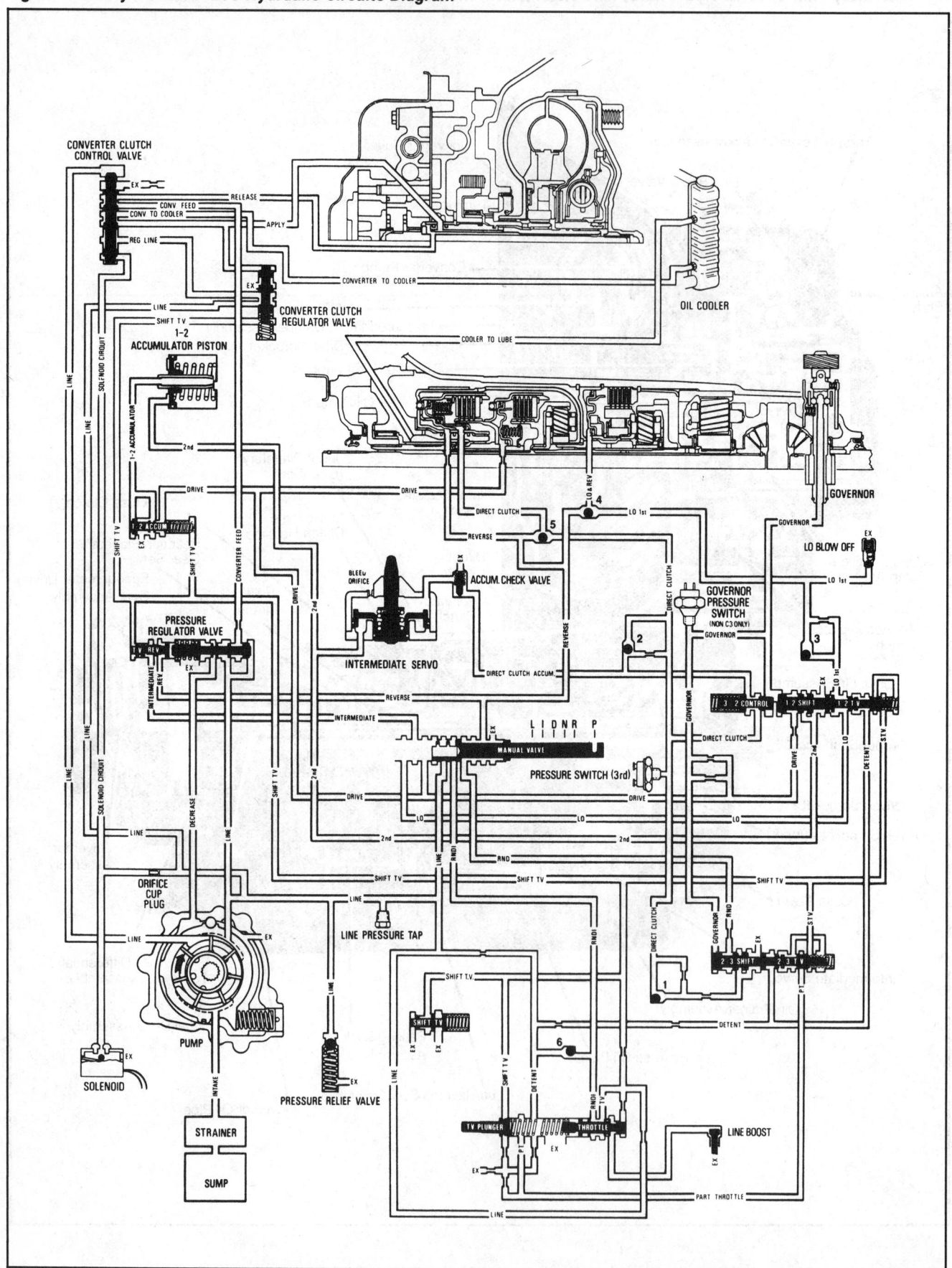

GENERAL MOTORS
TURBO HYDRA-MATIC 125C TRANSAXLE (Cont.)

Fig 3: Inside View of Case Cover Showing Oil Passages

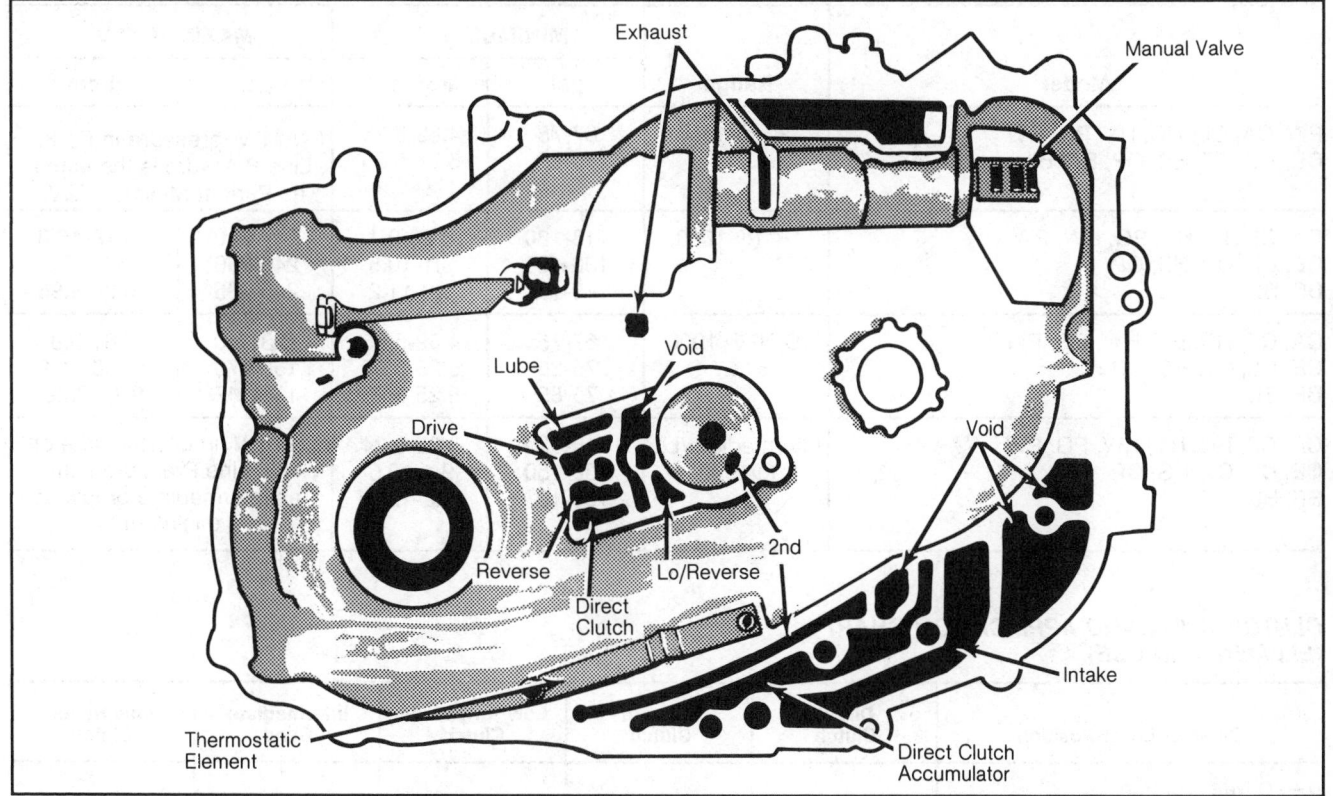

Fig 4: Outside view of Case Cover Showing Oil Passages

1. Reverse	22. Direct Clutch
2. T.V. Exhaust	23. Direct Clutch Accumulator
3. Line	24. Intake
4. T.V.	25. To Cooler
5. Exhaust	26. Cooler to Lube
6. Drive	27. Lo
7. 1-2 Accumulator	28. Void
8. Drive	29. Converter Feed
9. Lube	30. Exhause
10. 1-2 Accumulator	31. Void
11. Shift T.V.	32. Shift T.V.
12. Direct Clutch	33. Part Throttle
13. Lo/Reverse	34. Detent
14. Lo/1st	35. Lo
15. 2nd	36. Intermediate
16. Void	37. Drive
17. Lo/1st	38. Void
18. Drive	39. Line
19. Governor	40. RND1
20. Drive	41. RND
21. 2nd	42. Void

← Check Balls

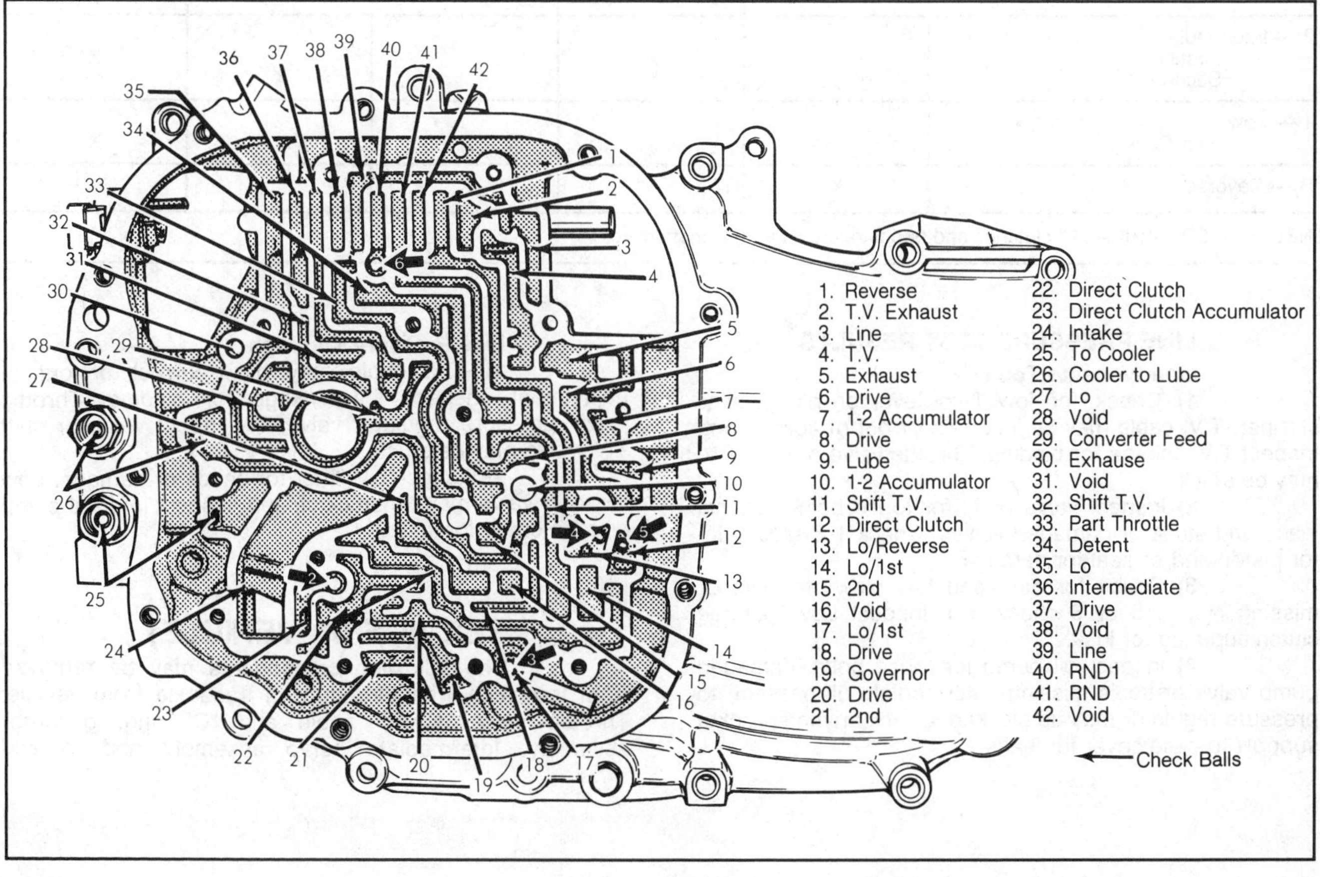

Automatic Transmissions
GENERAL MOTORS
TURBO HYDRA-MATIC 125C TRANSAXLE (Cont.)

THROTTLE VALVE LINE PRESSURE CHECK

Model	Range	MINIMUM T.V.		MAXIMUM T.V.	
		psi	kg/cm²	psi	kg/cm²
PW, CA, CF, HC, HY, PG, HW CE, CL, CT, HS, OP, BF, BL	"P" @ 1000	67-75 75-85	4.69-5.25 5.25-5.95	No T.V. pressure in Park. Line Pressure is the same as Park at Minimum T.V.	
CA, CF,HC, HY, PG, HW, PW CE, CL, CT, HS, OP BF, BL	"R" @ 1000	118-130 130-150 140-160	8.26-9.1 9.1-10.5 9.8-11.2	217-240 240-290 240-285	15.19-16.8 16.8-20.3 16.8-19.95
CA, CF, HC, HY, HW, PG, PW CE, CL, CT, HS, OP BF, BL	"D/N" ® 1000	67-75 75-85 75-85	4.69-5.25 5.25-5.95 5.25-5.95	123-140 150-170 130-147	8.61-9.8 10.50-11.9 9.1-10.29
CA, CF, HC, HY, HW, PG, PW CE, CL, CT, HS, OP BF, BL	Intermediate/Lo @1000	115-132 130-150 160-183	8.05-9.24 9.1-10.5 11.2-12.81	No T.V. in intermediate or low. Line Pressure same as intermediate or low at minimum.	

CLUTCH AND BAND APPLICATION CHART
(ELEMENTS IN USE)

Selector Lever Position	Direct Clutch	Forward Clutch	Low & Reverse Clutch	Intermediate Band	Low Roller Clutch
D — Drive					
First Gear		X			X
Second Gear		X		X	
Third Gear	X	X			
2 — Intermediate					
First Gear		X			X
Second Gear		X		X	
1 — Low					
First Gear		X	X		X
R — Reverse	X		X		

NEUTRAL OR PARK — All clutches and bands released and/or ineffective.

LINE PRESSURE TEST RESULTS
Line Pressure Too Low
1) Check for low fluid level or plugged oil strainer. T.V. cable may be incorrect or out of adjustment. Inspect T.V. linkage for binding. Throttle valve or shift T.V. may be stuck.

2) Inspect valve body for loose bolts, internal leaks and stuck or damaged valves. Check 1-2 accumulator piston and/or seal for damage.

3) Check for damaged low blow-off valve or missing No. 4, 5 or 6 check ball. Inspect Low-Reverse clutch cup plug for leak.

4) Inspect oil pump for loose bolts, damaged pump valve or seals missing. Intermediate oil passage to pressure regulator may be blocked. Check driven sprocket support-to-case cover for leaks.

Line Pressure Too High
1) T.V. cable may be incorrect or out of adjustment. Inspect T.V. linkage for binding. Throttle valve, pressure regulator valve, T.V. boost valve or shift T.V. valve may be stuck.

2) Inspect T.V. lifter for bends or damage. Low blow-off valve may be stuck closed. Inspect internal pump or case cover for leaks.

SERVICE (IN VEHICLE)
The following components may be removed from transaxle without removing transaxle from vehicle: Throttle valve control cable and "O" ring, governor assembly, intermediate servo assembly and lo and

reverse oil pipe and seal assembly, speedometer drive gear assembly.

The following may also be removed without removing the transaxle: Oil pan, direct clutch accumulator check valve, control valve assembly and cover, throttle lever and bracket and oil pump drive shaft and parking pawl.

For removal and installation procedures of components other than drive axles, see procedures given in Transaxle Disassembly and Transaxle Reassembly.

DRIVE AXLE SHAFTS

NOTE: Removal, Inspection and Installation procedures apply to either side drive axle assembly.

Removal

1) Raise and support front of vehicle. Remove hub nut, wheel nuts, wheel and tire. Use a boot seal protector (J-28712) as shown in *Fig. 5* to protect boot seals. Remove brake caliper and rotor and support out of way.

2) On "A" and "X" series vehicles, mark strut-to-steering knuckle relation to insure proper camber alignment on reassembly. Remove strut-to-steering knuckle attaching bolts and separate strut from knucle.

3) Using a slide hammer type puller and special tool (J-28468) as shown in *Fig. 5*, pull inner CV joint from transaxle. Using puller (J-28733), separate axle shaft from spindle hub and bearing assembly.

Fig. 5: Removing Drive Axles From Transaxle

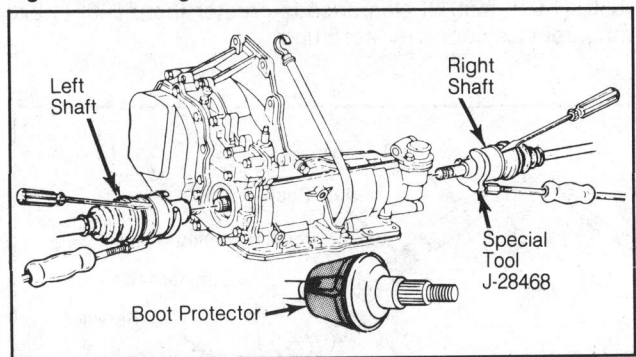

Do not damage boot seals during removal.

Disassembly

1) Procedure is similar for inner and outer CV joints. *See Figs. 6 and 7.* Cut seal clamp on small end of

seal and discard. Using brass drift, tap lightly around edge of seal retainer to remove retainer from CV joint assembly. Spread snap ring and pull shaft from joint assembly.

2) For outer CV joint, use brass drift to tap lightly on bearing cage until it tilts enough to remove one ball bearing. Rotate cage and repeat procedure to remove remaining balls from cage.

3) On inner CV joint, remove ball retaining ring and balls will come out when cage and inner race are removed from outer race.

4) On outer CV joint, pivot cage and inner race until 90° to normal installed position (cage windows will align with lands of outer race). *See Fig. 7.* Lift cage and inner race from outer race. Then, rotate inner race upward and out of cage.

Inspection

1) Wash all parts in solvent and dry with compressed air. Inspect outer ball races for excessive wear and scoring. Inspect splined stub shaft for wear, cracks and twisted splines.

2) Inspect all 6 balls for pitting, cracking or scoring. Dulling of surface is normal. Inspect cage for excessive wear on inside and outside spherical surfaces. Look for heavy brinelling of cage windows and for cracks or chips.

3) Inspect inner race for excessive wear or scoring. If any damage is found, replace entire CV joint assembly. Polished areas in races and on cage spheres are normal and do not require joint replacement.

Reassembly

1) Apply a light coat of grease on ball grooves of inner and outer races. Install inner race into cage using a rotating action opposite of removal. Inner race snap ring should face axle side.

2) On inner CV joints, be sure ball bearing retaining ring is installed on inner race side facing small end of cage. Align windows of cage with outer racelands, and pivot cage with inner race into tilted position (opposite of removal).

3) Install ball bearings one at a time into outer CV joint as cage is tilted and rotated. On inner CV joint, insert ball bearings through cage windows. After balls are installed into cage of outer joint, pivot cage and inner race into installed position.

4) Slide new seal clamp for small end of boot seal, boot seal and seal retainer onto axle shaft. Coat inside lip (large diameter end) of seal with grease. Slide seal retainer on end of seal.

5) Spread ears of bearing race snap ring, and slide CV joint onto axle shaft until snap ring seats in

Fig. 6: Exploded View of Drive Axle Assembly

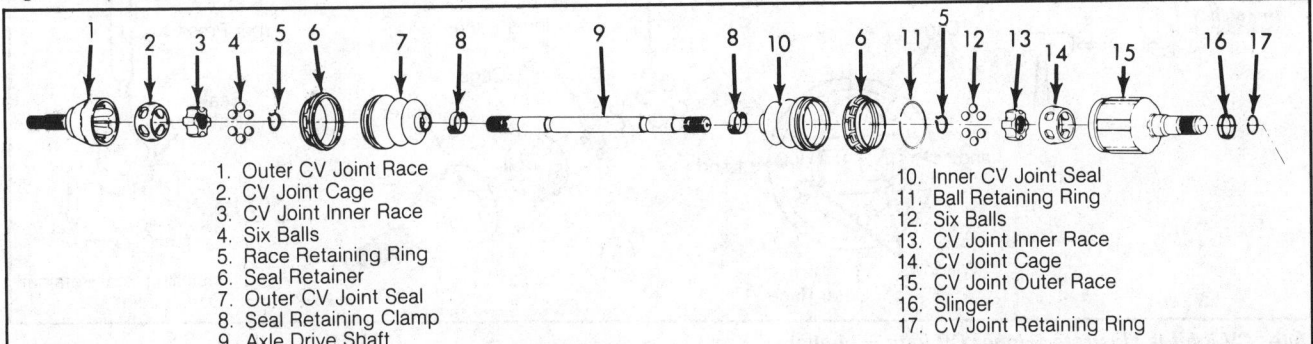

1. Outer CV Joint Race
2. CV Joint Cage
3. CV Joint Inner Race
4. Six Balls
5. Race Retaining Ring
6. Seal Retainer
7. Outer CV Joint Seal
8. Seal Retaining Clamp
9. Axle Drive Shaft

10. Inner CV Joint Seal
11. Ball Retaining Ring
12. Six Balls
13. CV Joint Inner Race
14. CV Joint Cage
15. CV Joint Outer Race
16. Slinger
17. CV Joint Retaining Ring

Automatic Transmissions
GENERAL MOTORS
TURBO HYDRA-MATIC 125C TRANSAXLE (Cont.)

groove. Pack joint with approximately one-half grease provided in seal kit. Apply remaining grease inside seal.

6) Slide seal toward joint until small end of seal is in groove in axle shaft. Position small clamp over small end of seal and into groove and tighten.

7) Place assembly vertically into an arbor press, with CV joint up so seal retainer is supported. See Fig. 7. Press CV joint down onto retainer. Make sure seal stays on retainer during reassembly.

Installation

1) Position drive axle loosely into steering knuckle and transaxle. Install steering knuckle onto strut bracket and tighten strut bracket bolts finger tight only. Install rotor and brake caliper and tighten attaching bolts.

2) Install drive axle through steering knuckle. Install hub nut and torque to 70 ft. lbs. (100 N.m). When shaft begins to turn, insert a drift in rotor slot to prevent hub from turning.

3) Seat drive axle at the transaxle using a screwdriver in the groove provided on the inner retainer. See Fig. 5. Tap screwdriver until shaft is seated.

TORQUE CONVERTER

NOTE: **Torque converter is a sealed unit and cannot be disassembled for service or repair.**

LEAKAGE CHECK

Install pressure test plug tool (J-21369-B) into converter hub and tighten tool to expand it. Install safety strap to prevent tool from blowing out when air pressure is applied. Apply 80 psi (5.6 kg/cm²) air pressure to air

valve in tool. Submerge converter in water and check for air bubbles in water indicating leaks.

CAUTION: After leak checking converter, bleed air pressure from test tool before removing tool from converter hub.

Fig. 8: Installing Converter Leakage Test Tools

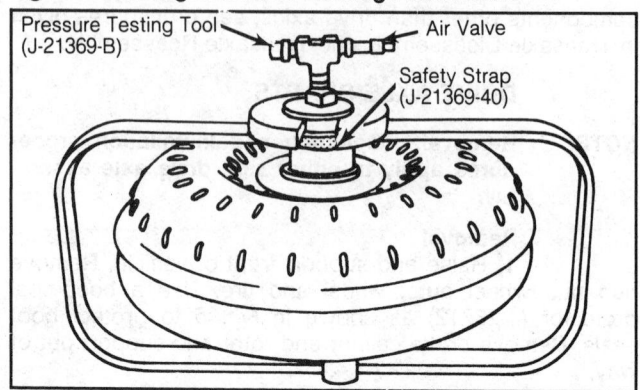

Apply 80 psi (5.6 kg/cm²) air pressure to air valve.

END CLEARANCE CHECK

1) Install end clearance checking tool (J-29830) into converter hub and hand tighten counterclockwise. Mount a dial indicator onto hub of tool collet so dial indicator plunger rests on converter. Zero dial indicator.

2) Lift up on tool and read clearance at dial indicator. Converter end clearance should be less than .050" (1.270 mm). If clearance is greater than .050" (1.270 mm), replace converter assembly.

Fig. 7: Disassembly of Drive Axle and CV Joints

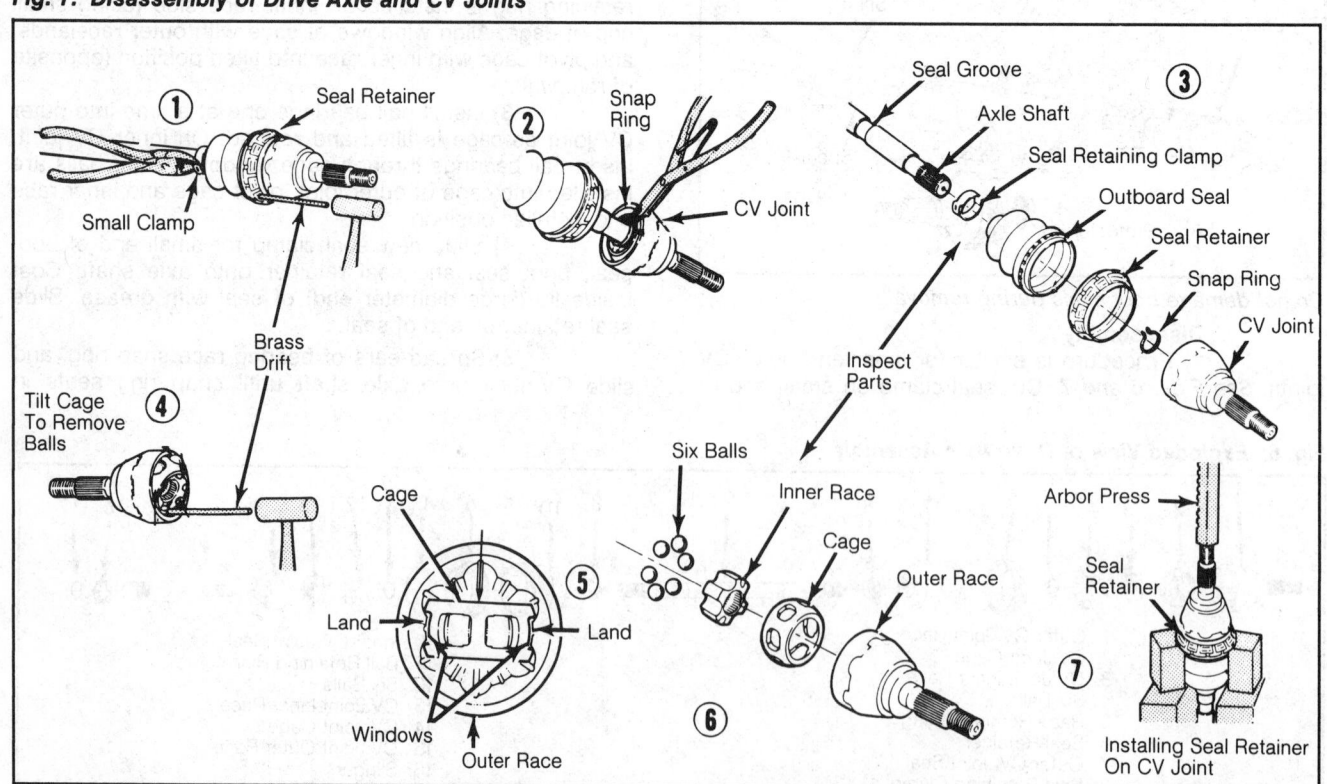

Outer CV joint is illustrated, inner CV joint is similar.

GENERAL MOTORS
TURBO HYDRA-MATIC 125C TRANSAXLE (Cont.)

Fig. 9: Measuring Converter End Play

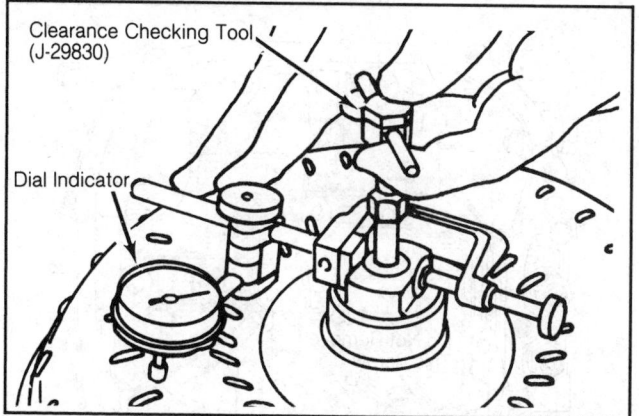

End play must not exceed .050" (1.270 mm).

TRANSAXLE DISASSEMBLY

Before disassembling unit, throughly clean the exterior. Remove torque converter by pulling it straight out. Place transaxle in holding fixture. Position so right side axle end is down to drain fluid.

SPEEDOMETER DRIVE GEAR & GOVERNOR ASSEMBLY

Reposition transaxle to normal position. Remove speedometer driven gear attaching bolt and withdraw driven gear assembly from governor cover. Remove governor cover bolts and lift off cover. Lift out governor and speedometer drive gear as an assembly.

INTERMEDIATE SERVO ASSEMBLY

1) Position transaxle so oil pan is up. Remove oil pan and oil strainer from lower case assembly. Remove and discard oil strainer "O" ring.

Fig. 10: Removing Intermediate Servo Assembly

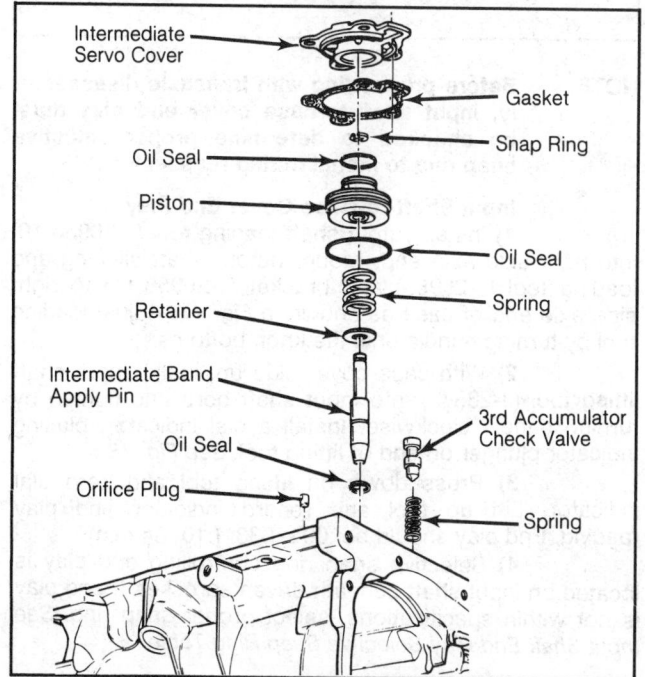

2) Remove bolt holding reverse oil pipe retaining bracket to servo cover. Remove remaining servo cover bolts. Lift off servo cover and gasket. Withdraw intermediate servo assembly. Remove 3rd accumulator check valve and spring. See Fig. 10.

Fig. 11: Removing 3rd Accumulator Check Valve and Spring

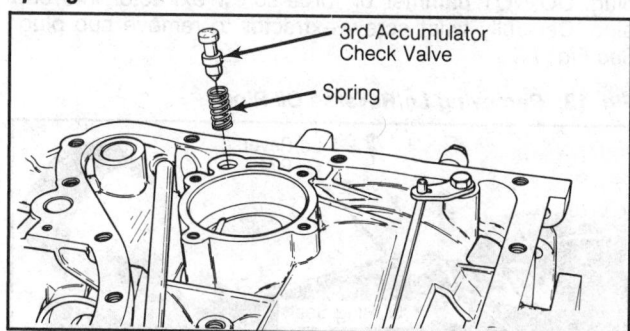

NOTE: Make intermediate band apply pin selection check at this time to determine correct pin to use during reassembly.

Band Apply Pin Selection Check

1) Install special band apply pin selection gauge (J-28535-1) over intermediate servo bore and retain with 2 servo cover bolts. See Fig. 12.

2) Remove band apply pin from intermediate servo assembly. Install band apply pin gauge extension (J-28535-4) onto servo piston end of band apply pin. Install band apply pin and gauge extension into gauge on servo bore.

Fig. 12: Checking for Proper Band Apply Pin

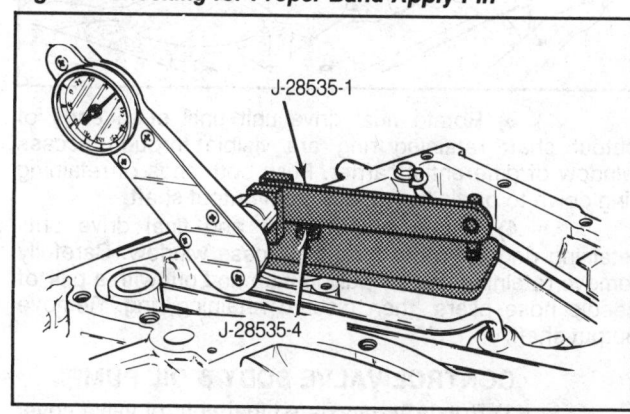

3) Apply 100 INCH lbs. (11.2 N.m) of torque to hex nut on selection gauge to compress band. White line, on gauge extension, should appear in window on selection gauge to indicate proper pin installed.

4) If White line cannot be seen, change the band apply pin (longer or shorter as necessary) and recheck. See Intermediate Band Apply Pin Table.

INTERMEDIATE BAND APPLY PIN TABLE

Length	Identification
Short	2 Grooves
Medium	1 Groove
Long	No Grooves

2-176

Automatic Transmissions
GENERAL MOTORS
TURBO HYDRA-MATIC 125C TRANSAXLE (Cont.)

OUTPUT SHAFT

1) Remove dipstick stop and parking lock bracket from above parking pawl and parking pawl actuator rod. Remove Lo/Reverse oil pipe, oil pipe seal back-up washer and seal.

2) Grind approximately 3/4" from end of No. 4 screw extractor. Insert ground end into Lo/Reverse cup plug. DO NOT hammer or force screw extractor into cup plug. Carefully twist screw extractor to remove cup plug. *See Fig. 14.*

Fig. 13: Removing Lo/Reverse Oil Pipe

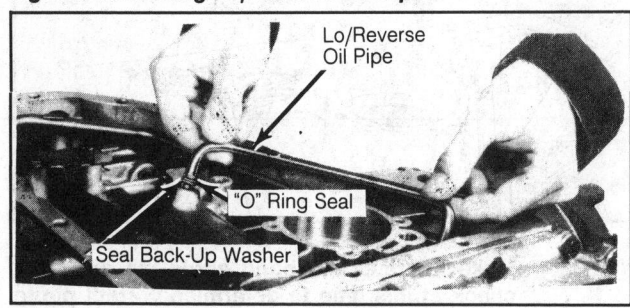

Fig. 14: Removing Lo/Reverse Seal Assembly

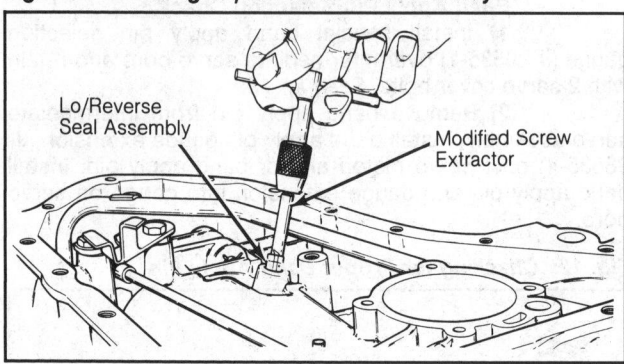

3) Rotate final drive unit until open ends of output shaft retaining ring are visible through access window of differential carrier. Push both ends of retaining ring down to partially dislodge from output shaft.

4) Rotate output shaft and final drive until retaining ring is visible through access window. Carefully remove retaining ring by pulling it up and out with a pair of needle nose pliers, then discard retaining ring. Remove output shaft.

CONTROL VALVE BODY & OIL PUMP

1) Rotate transaxle so that control valve cover is up. Remove control valve cover and gasket. Remove 2 bolts securing throttle lever and bracket assembly to control valve. Lift off throttle lever and bracket assembly using care not to bend throttle lever link.

2) Remove the auxiliary valve body screws EXCEPT for the lower left screw. *See Fig. 15.* Remove remaining control valve assembly bolts. Carefully lift off control valve assembly. Place it on the bench with the machined surface up.

3) Remove No. 1 check ball from direct clutch passage on spacer plate. Lift out oil pump drive shaft. Carefully remove spacer plate and spacer plate gaskets. Remove the 5 check balls from the case cover. *See Fig. 16.*

Fig. 15: Removing Control Valve & Pump Assembly Bolts

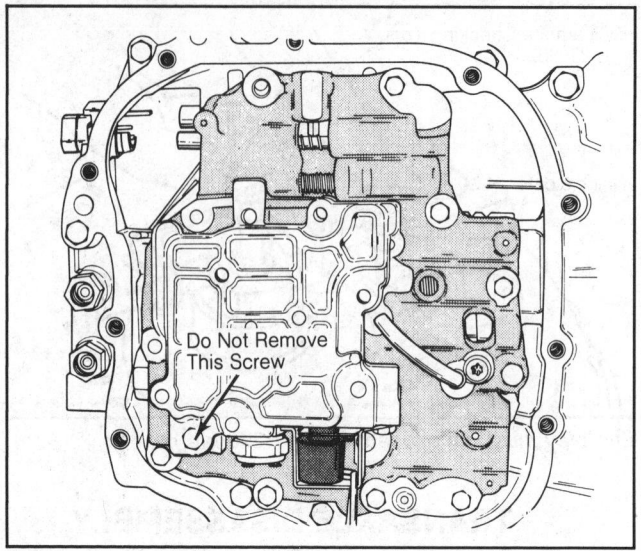

Fig. 16: Check Ball Locations in Case Cover

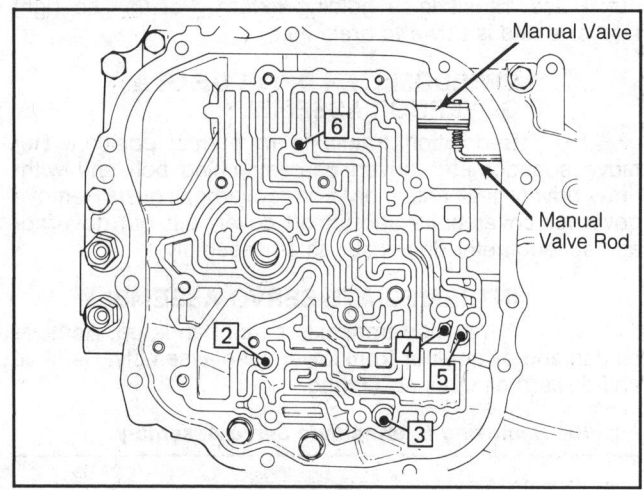

NOTE: Before proceeding with transaxle disassembly, input shaft-to-case cover end play must be checked to determine proper selective snap ring to install during reassembly.

Input Shaft-to-Case Cover End Play

1) Install output shaft loading tool (J-26958-10) into right side axle end. Mount output shaft aligning and loading tool (J-26958) and bracket (J-26958-11) to right side axle end of case as shown in *Fig. 17.* Adjust loading tool by turning handle until the knob bottoms.

2) With case cover side up, install input shaft lifting tool (J-28544) into input shaft bore and tighten by turning handle clockwise. Install a dial indicator, placing indicator plunger on end of lifting tool. *See Fig. 18.*

3) Press down on lifting tool and zero dial indicator. Lift up tool and record indicator end play reading. End play should be .004-.033" (.10-.84 mm).

4) Selective snap ring controlling end play is located on input shaft beneath driven sprocket. If end play is not within specifications, select proper snap ring. *See Input Shaft End Play Selective Snap Ring Table.*

Fig. 17: Positioning Output Shaft Aligning and Loading Tool on Transaxle.

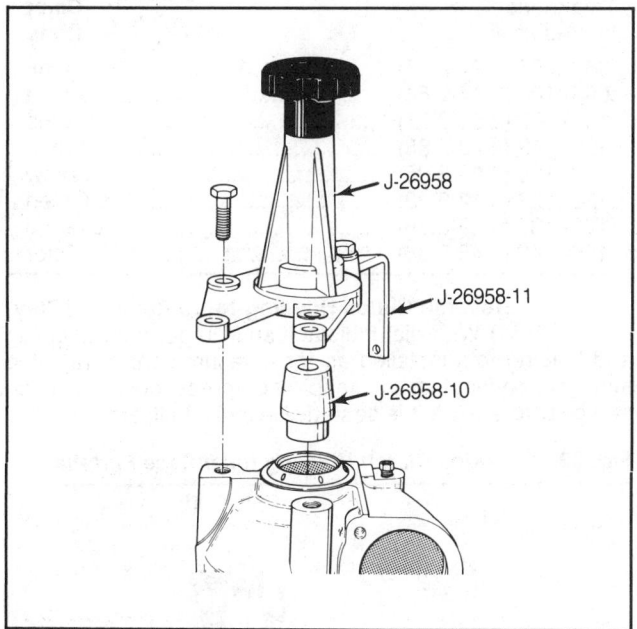

Fig 18: Checking Input Shaft-to-Cover End Play

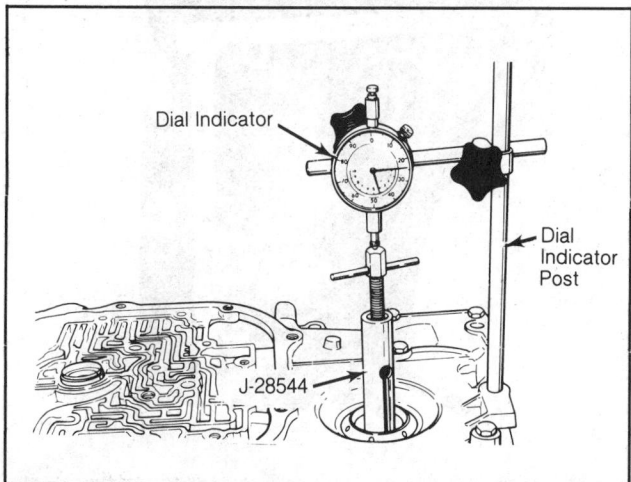

End play should be .004-.033" (.10-.84 mm).

INPUT SHAFT END PLAY SELECTIVE SNAP RINGS

Thickness In. (mm)	Color Code
.071-.076 (1.83-1.93)	White
.078-.084 (2.03-2.13)	Blue
.088-.092 (2.23-2.33)	Brown
.095-.099 (2.43-2.53)	Yellow
.103-.107 (2.63-2.73)	Green

CAUTION: Oil soaked snap rings may tend to discolor so that it will be necessary to measure snap ring for its actual thickness.

CASE COVER & INPUT UNIT

1) Disconnect manual valve rod from manual valve. See Fig. 16. Remove remaining case cover attach-ing bolts. Install 2 M12 x 1.75 x 50 bolts into the case cover dowel pin holes. See Fig. 19.

Fig. 19: Removing Case Cover

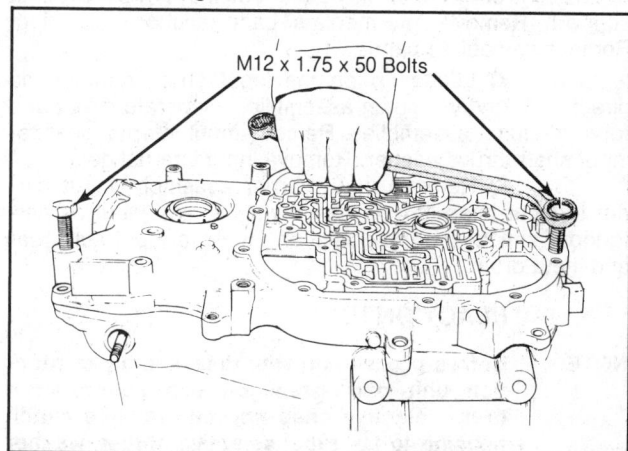

Install bolts in case cover dowel pin holes.

NOTE: 1-2 accumulator pin may drop out of case cover during removal.

2) The bolts will self-tap, bottom out on the dowel pins and separate the case cover from the case. DO NOT pry the cover from the case.

3) Remove 1-2 accumulator spring and center case-to-cover gasket. Remove case cover-to-drive sprocket thrust washer and driven sprocket thrust bearing assembly. The case cover-to-drive sprocket thrust washer may have come off with case cover.

4) Lift off drive sprocket, driven sprocket and chain as an assembly. Remove drive and driven sprocket-to-support thrust washers. These washers may have come off with sprockets.

5) Using 3/16" drift, remove detent lever-to-manual shaft pin. Remove manual shaft-to-case retaining pin. Withdraw manual shaft from case and lift out manual

Fig. 20: Removing Manual Shaft and Driven Sprocket Support

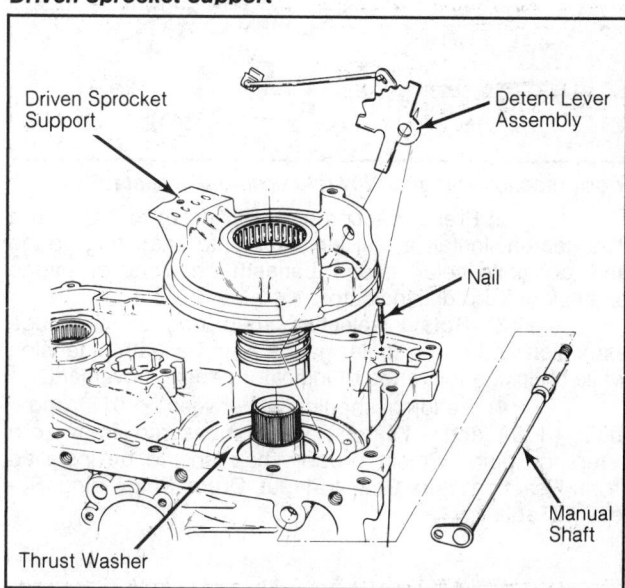

GENERAL MOTORS
TURBO HYDRA-MATIC 125C TRANSAXLE (Cont.)

vave rod and detent lever assembly. Remove park lock actuator rod.

6) Remove driven sprocket support and thrust washer. Thrust washer may come out with driven sprocket support. Remove intermediate band anchor hole plug. Remove immediate band.

7) Lifting up on the input shaft, remove the direct and forward clutch assemblies. Separate direct and forward clutch assemblies. Remove input internal gear-to-input shaft thrust washer. Remove input internal gear.

8) Remove input carrier assembly, input carrier-to-input internal gear thrust washer and input carrier-to-input sun gear thrust washer. Remove input sun gear and input drum.

REACTION UNIT

NOTE: Before proceeding with disassembly of reaction unit parts, reaction sun gear-to-input drum selective snap ring and reverse clutch housing-to-Lo race selective thrust washer end play measurements should be taken to determine correct snap ring and thrust washer to install during reassembly.

Reaction Sun Gear-to-Input Drum End Play

1) With output shaft aligning and loading tool installed (in fully loaded position), install reaction sun gear snap ring gauge (J-28588) to case using 2 case cover bolts. Position gauge extension between open ends of selective snap ring. *See Fig. 22.*

Fig. 21: Reaction Sun Gear-to-Input Drum End Play

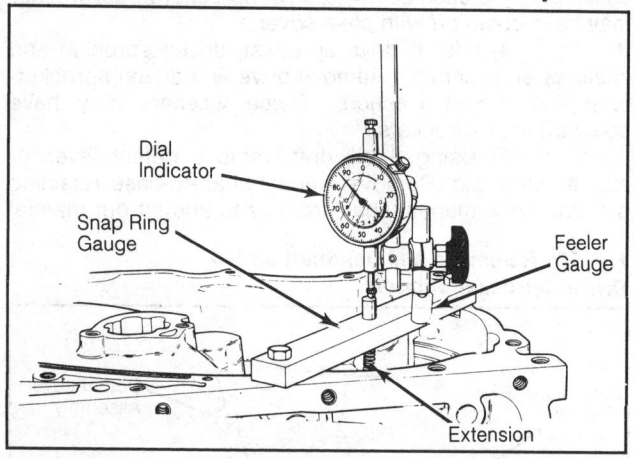

Press reaction sun gear down to ensure it is seated.

2) Press reaction sun gear down to make sure it is seated. Install a dial indicator onto snap ring gauge and position feeler gauge beneath shoulder of gauge extension. Zero dial indicator.

3) Rotate selective snap ring under gauge extension and swing feeler gauge from beneath extension while checking full range of indicator needle movement.

4) Reading should be between +.013" and -.005" (+.33 and -.13 mm) when measured from zero reference point. Select proper snap ring to be installed from Reaction Sun Gear-to-Input Drum Snap Ring Selection Table.

REACTION SUN-TO-INPUT DRUM SNAP RING SELECTION

Thickness Inches (mm)	Color Code
.089-.093 (2.27-2.37)	Pink
.096-.100 (2.44-2.54)	Brown
.103-.107 (2.61-2.71)	Lt. Blue
.109-.113 (2.78-2.88)	White
.116-.120 (2.95-3.05)	Yellow
.123-.127 (3.12-3.22)	Lt. Green
.129-.133 (3.29-3.39)	Orange
.136-.140 (3.46-3.56)	No Color

Reverse Clutch Housing-to-Lo Race End Play

1) With dial indicator and output shaft aligning and loading tool installed as for measurement of reaction sun gear-to-input drum snap ring, press down reaction sun gear to ensure it is seated. Zero dial indicator.

Fig. 22: Checking Clutch Housing-to-Lo Race End Play

Do Not Pry On Spacer

2) Place a screwdriver through parking pawl case opening and lift reaction internal gear and read resulting end play. DO NOT rest screwdriver on spacer in parking pawl case opening when prying reaction internal gear. Damage to spacer will result.

3) End play should be .003"-.046" (.08-1.17 mm). Selective washer controlling end play is located between the Lo/Reverse clutch housing and the lo roller clutch assembly. Select proper thrust washer from *Reverse Clutch Housing-to-Lo Race Washer* table.

4) Remove dial indicator, gauge and output shaft loading and aligning tool. Leave output shaft loading tool adapter in place for use when final drive-to-case end play is measured.

GENERAL MOTORS
TURBO HYDRA-MATIC 125C TRANSAXLE (Cont.)

REVERSE CLUTCH HOUSING-TO-LO RACE WASHER

Thickness Inches (mm)	Identification Code
.039-.043 (1.00-2.20)	1
.056-.060 (1.42-1.52)	2
.072-.076 (1.84-1.94)	3
.089-.093 (2.26-2.36)	4
.105-.109 (2.68-2.78)	5
.122-.126 (3.10-3.20)	6

5) Remove reaction sun gear. Sun gear will lift straight out. Remove Lo/Reverse clutch housing-to-case snap ring. Snap ring is .092" (2.36 mm) thick. Using lifting tool (J-28542), lift out Lo/Reverse Clutch housing. *See Fig. 23*

Fig. 23: Removing Lo/Reverse Clutch Housing

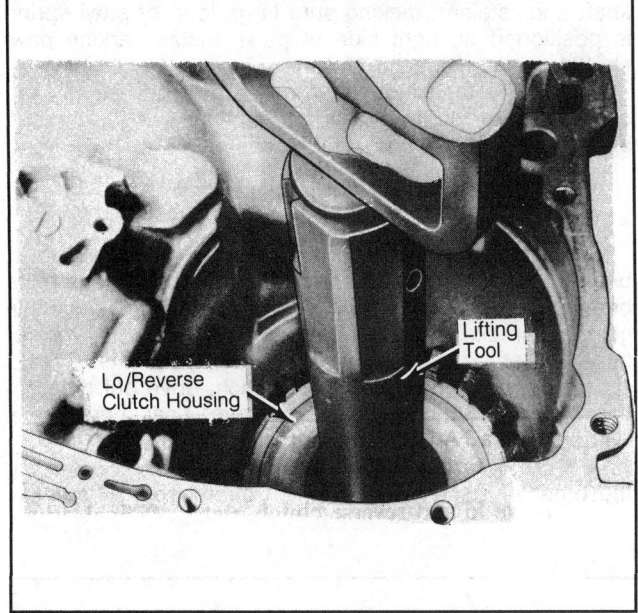

6) Remove Lo/Reverse clutch housing-to-case spacer ring from groove in case. Spacer ring is .042" (1.07 mm) thick. Lift out final drive sun gear shaft and reaction gear set as an assembly.

FINAL DRIVE UNIT

NOTE: **Before proceeding with transaxle disassembly, final drive-to-case end play should be checked to determine proper final drive differential-to-case selective thrust washer to install during reassembly. Also, case bushing should be inspected for wear and replaced if necessary.**

Final Drive-to-Case End Play

1) With output shaft loading tool adapter (J-26958-10) in place, press down on adapter to fully seat final drive onto final drive internal gear-to-case snap ring. Install dial indicator onto case so plunger rests on top of adapter. Zero dial indicator. *See Fig. 24.*

2) Insert a large screwdriver into transaxle governor bore and lift final drive by prying up on governor drive gear. Read end play at dial indicator. End play should be .005" to .032" (.12-.82 mm).

Fig. 24: Checking Final Drive-to-Case End Play

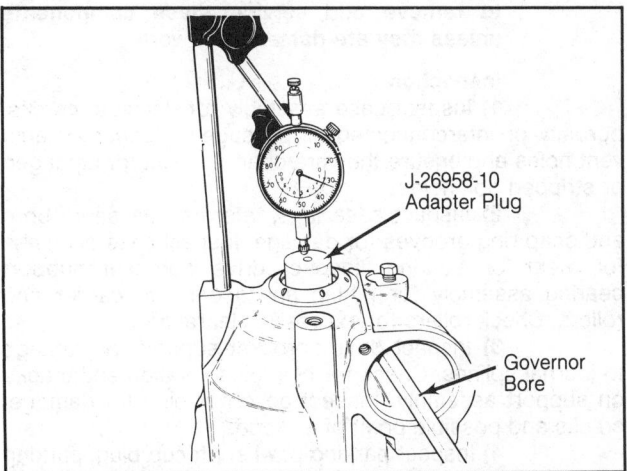

3) Selective washer controlling end play is located between differential carrier and differential carrier case thrust bearing assembly. Select correct thrust washer from *Final Drive-to-Case End Play table.*

FINAL DRIVE-TO-CASE END PLAY

Thickness Inches (mm)	Identification Code
.055-.059 (1.40-1.50)	0
.059-.062 (1.50-1.60)	1
.062-.066 (1.60-1.70)	2
.066-.070 (1.70-1.80)	3
.070-.074 (1.80-1.90)	4
.074-.078 (1.90-2.00)	5
.078-.082 (2.00-2.10)	6
.082-.086 (2.10-2.20)	7
.086-.091 (2.20-2.30)	8
.091-.095 (2.30-2.40)	9

4) Remove dial indicator, indicator post and loading and aligning tool adapter. Remove final drive internal gear spacer snap ring. The snap ring is .092" (2.36 mm) thick. Remove final drive internal gear spacer. Lift final drive unit from case.

5) Remove final drive differential-to-case thrust washer (selective) and differential carrier-to-case thrust roller bearing assembly from final drive or case.

COMPONENT DISASSEMBLY & REASSEMBLY

NOTE: **When reassembling transaxle unit, lubricate all bushings, seals, thrust bearings and internal mating surfaces with transmission fluid. Use petroleum jelly to lubricate and retain all thrust washers.**

Automatic Transmissions
GENERAL MOTORS
TURBO HYDRA-MATIC 125C TRANSAXLE (Cont.)

CASE

NOTE: Disassembly procedures include drive sprocket support, drive sprocket roller bearing, 3rd oil cup plug, parking pawl and governor oil pipe removal. It is not necessary to remove and service these components unless they are damaged or worn.

Inspection

1) Inspect case assembly for damage, cracks, porosity or interconnected oil passages. Inspect exhaust vent holes and ensure they are open. Inspect for damaged or stripped bolt holes.

2) Inspect case lugs, intermediate servo bore and snap ring grooves for damage. Inspect case bushings for wear or scoring. Inspect drive sprocket support bearing assembly for pitting and scoring to carrier and rollers. Check rollers for excessive clearance.

3) Inspect drive sprocket support for damage to journal splines. Check for heat discoloration and cracks on support assembly. Inspect governor pipe for damage, cracks and possible point of leakage.

4) Inspect parking pawl shaft cup plug, parking pawl shaft and parking pawl for damage and excessive wear. Inspect 3rd oil cup plug for tightness in bore or damage. Use a straight edge to check all sealing and mating surfaces for straightness.

Disassembly

1) Using a slide hammer equipped with internal jaws, remove drive sprocket support roller bearing (from case cover side). Inspect roller bearing race on drive sprocket for wear. From inside torque converter housing, unbolt and remove drive sprocket support.

2) Using a 3/8" drift, remove parking pawl shaft cup plug from oil pan side of case. Remove parking pawl shaft retainer, parking pawl shaft, parking pawl and return spring from case.

3) Remove governor oil pipe clamp screw and clamp. Pry right side end up first, then pry left side end of pipe from case. Remove pipe.

4) Grind approximately 1/2" (13 mm) from end of No. 3 easy out and install into 3rd oil cup plug. Twist easy out counterclockwise and remove cup plug. Remove manual valve seal, axle seal and torque converter seal from case.

Reassembly

1) Install new 3rd cup plug using a 1/4" drift. Cup plug will seat in bore when fully installed. Install new manual shaft oil seal with sealing lip facing up. Install new axle seal being careful not to damage seal guard.

2) Coat ends of governor oil pipe with sealing compound (Loctite), to seal against leakage. Install governor pipe and retaining clamp. Lightly tap pipe into place to secure against leakage.

3) Install parking pawl and spring, parking pawl shaft and retainer, making sure large loop of pawl spring is positioned on right side of pawl. Install parking pawl shaft cup plug using a 3/8" drift.

4) Install drive sprocket support. Lightly tap drive sprocket support bearing in place using a bearing installer. Install new converter oil seal.

DIFFERENTIAL & FINAL DRIVE
Disassembly & Inspection

1) Remove final drive internal gear and thrust bearing. Lift out final drive sun gear and sun gear roller bearing. Inspect final drive internal gear and final drive sun gear for cracks, damage, heat discoloration and worn or missing teeth.

2) Using a 3/16" pin punch, drive out differential pinion shaft retaining pin from final drive side. Withdraw differential pinion shaft.

3) Rotate 1 differential side gear while holding the other in place to push pinion gears from differential.

Fig. 25: Exploded View of Differential and Final drive Unit

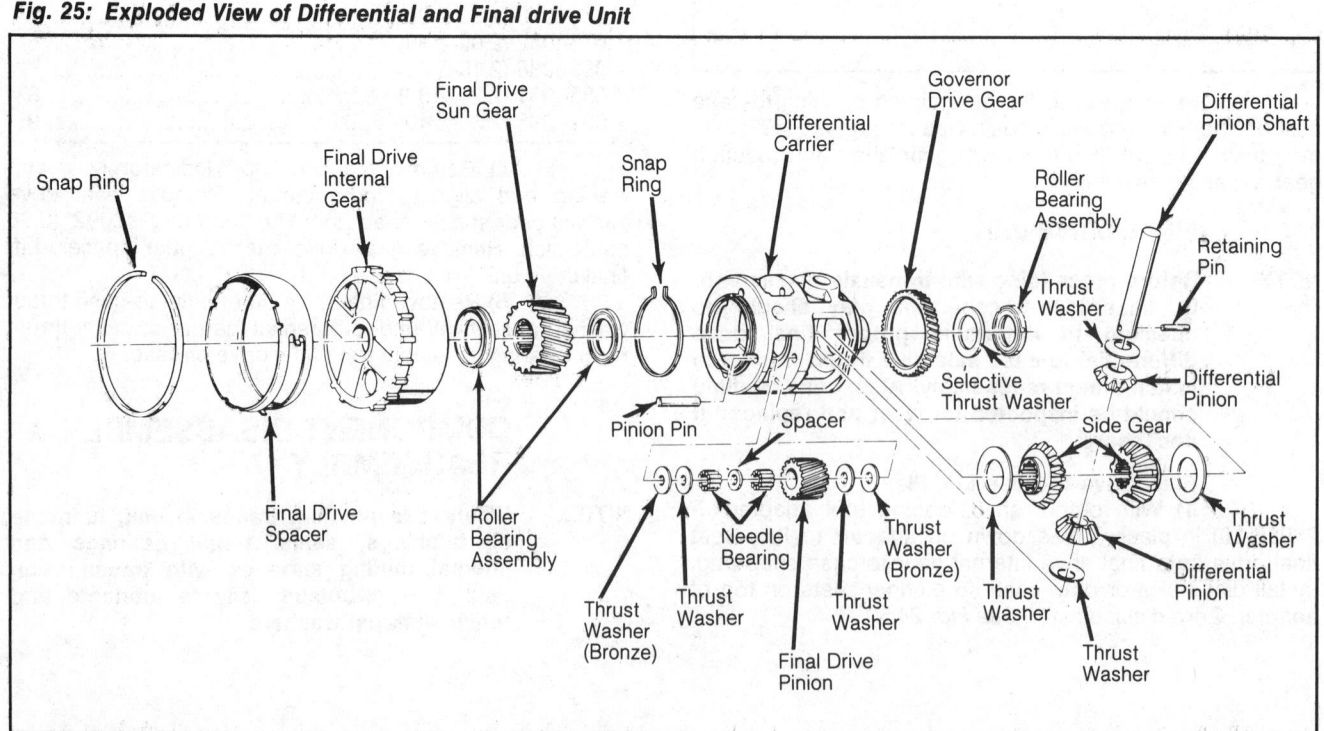

Make sure dished pinion thrust washers are removed with pinion gears.

NOTE: Pinion shaft retaining pin can be removed and installed from one end of retaining pin bore only. The pin MUST exit carrier assembly toward the governor drive gear and MUST be installed from the governor drive gear end toward the final drive end of carrier.

4) Slide 1 differential side gear toward center of carrier and remove, then remove other gear in same manner. Remove side gear thrust washers, making sure they are kept with gear from which they were removed.

5) Inspect side gear and pinion thrust washers for scoring, elongated inside diameter, heat discoloration and flattened outer edges.

6) Check final drive pinion end play by inserting a feeler gauge between the carrier and the final drive pinion. See Fig. 26. End play should be .009 to .025" (.24-.63 mm).

7) Remove pinion snap ring and withdraw pinion pins. Carefully remove pinion gears and thrust washers together to prevent dropping needle roller bearings. Remove 36 needle bearings from each pinion gear and inspect all parts for damage.

Fig. 26: Checking Pinion End Play

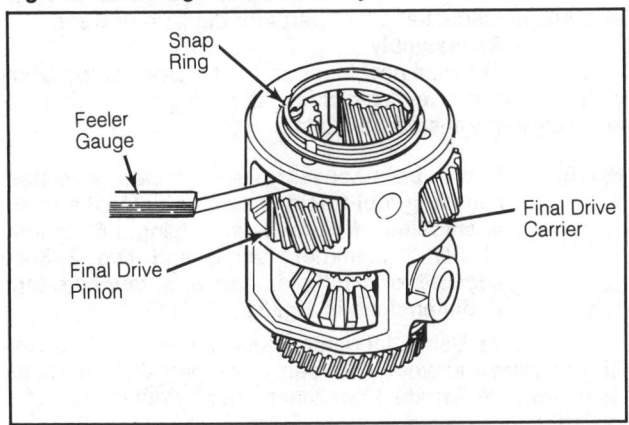

End play must be .009-.025" (.24-.63 mm).

NOTE: It is not necessary to remove governor drive gear for inspection or repair of differential and final drive unit. Remove gear only if replacement is necessary.

8) Using a puller and a heavy flat washer positioned on end of carrier assembly (to protect carrier when puller ram is tightened), pull governor drive gear from differential.

Reassembly
1) With a plastic mallet, lightly tap governor drive gear into place. Lube pinion pin with petroleum jelly and slide 1 steel thrust washer onto end of pin. Install 18 needle bearings onto pin against steel thrust washer.

2) Install needle bearing spacer onto pin and install remaining 18 needle bearings to pin on opposite side of spacer. See Fig. 27. Push needle bearing and pinion pin assembly into pinion gear.

3) Install steel pinion thrust washer onto end of pin (side without first thrust washer). Install 1 bronze pinion thrust washer to each end of pin. Slide pinion pin from assembly (keeping bearings intact in gear).

Fig. 27: Assembling Pinion Pin Prior to Installation

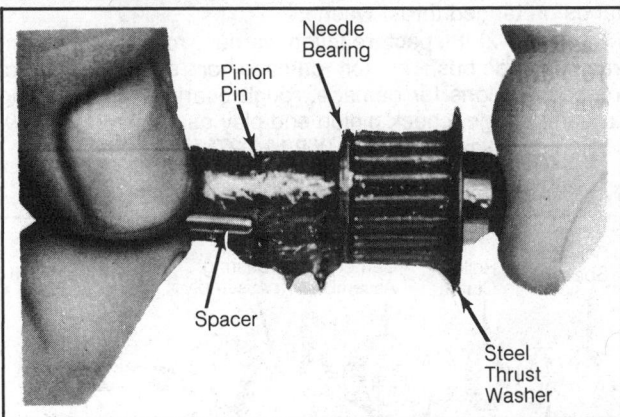

4) Install pinion ear assembly into final drive carrier. Install pinion pin (stepped end last) into carrier through pinion gear assembly. Repeat this procedure for remaining final drive pinion gears. Install pinion pin snap ring.

NOTE: Install pinion pin so that step is to the outside.

5) Install differential side gear thrust washers and side gears. Retain in place with petroleum jelly. Coat side gear pinion dished thrust washers with petroleum jelly and install onto side gear pinions. Install pinion gears in differential carrier windows.

6) Slide differential pinion shaft through both pinion gears to align. Remove shaft, without disturbing pinion location, and rotate pinions into place. Install pinion shaft into carrier through both pinion gears and install pinion shaft retaining pin.

7) Install final drive sun gear-to-differential carrier thrust bearing outer race against carrier. Install sun gear with step side up.

8) Install sun gear-to-final drive internal gear thrust bearing, cupped race side onto final drive internal gear and retain with petroleum jelly. Install internal gear on final drive carrier.

9) Install the differential selective thrust washer onto the differential carrier. Install the case-to-differential roller bearing thrust washer with the inner race against the differential selective thrust washer.

REACTION INTERNAL GEAR
Inspection
Inspect reaction internal gear splines, teeth and bearing surface for wear, cracks and damage. Inspect the reaction internal gear-to-reaction sun gear roller thrust bearing for damage.

Inspect the reverse clutch housing-to-lo race selective washer for wear. Inspect parking pawl lugs for cracks or damage.

ROLLER CLUTCH & REACTION CARRIER
Disassembly
Remove roller clutch race, then pull roller clutch from reaction carrier. Lift reaction carrier-to-roller clutch thrust washer from carrier.

Inspection
1) Inspect roller clutch race and splines for scoring or wear. Inspect roller clutch bearings, cage and springs for wear, heat discoloration and damage. Inspect

Automatic Transmissions
GENERAL MOTORS
TURBO HYDRA-MATIC 125C TRANSAXLE (Cont.)

thrust washers for scoring, excessive wear and distorted tangs on tanged thrust washer.

2) Inspect reaction carrier, roller clutch cam ramps and bushing for damage or scoring. Inspect reaction pinions for damage, rough bearings or tilt. Using a feeler gauge, check pinion end play as shown in *Fig. 29.* Pinion end play should be .009 to .027" (.24-.69 mm).

Fig. 28: Exploded View of Reaction Gear Set

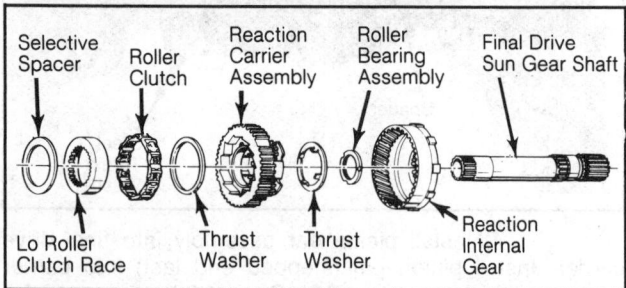

Fig. 29: Checking Reaction Carrier Pinion End Play

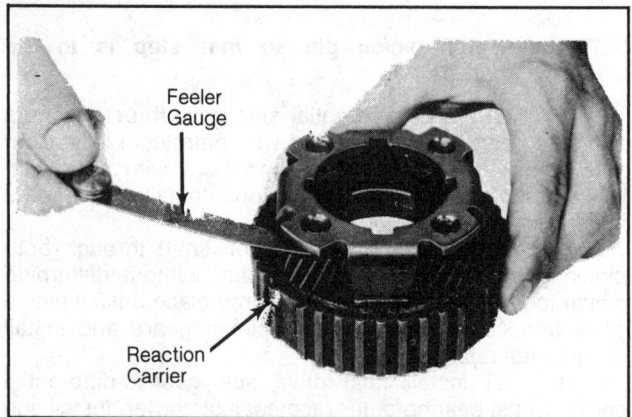

Reassembly
1) Install thrust washer into reaction carrier. Install rollers that may have come out of roller clutch cage by compressing energizing spring with finger and inserting roller from outer edge.

2) Install roller clutch into carrier, then install clutch race, (splined side out) and rotate race clockwise

into position. Install tanged thrust washer onto reaction carrier assembly, aligning tangs into slot on pinion side of carrier and retain with petroleum jelly.

3) Install reaction internal gear onto final drive sun gear shaft. Install reaction internal gear-to-reaction sun gear roller thrust bearing onto shaft.

4) Install reaction carrier and roller clutch assembly into the reaction internal gear. Install Lo/Reverse clutch housing-to-Lo roller clutch race selective washer.

LO/REVERSE CLUTCH HOUSING

NOTE: **Some models may not be equipped with an apply ring.**

Disassembly
Compress Lo/Reverse clutch spring retainer, remove snap ring, then lift out retainer. Remove waved spring and clutch piston from housing. Remove inner and outer piston seals and clutch apply ring.

Inspection
Inspect clutch housing for damage, scoring or plugged feel hole. Inspect clutch splines and snap ring groove for damage or burrs. Remove any burrs on splines or snap ring groove.

Inspect piston and apply ring for distortion, cracks or damage. Inspect clutch plates for signs of wear or burning. Inspect all other parts for damage or wear.

Reassembly
1) Install new inner and outer seals onto piston with lips facing away from clutch apply ring side. Lubricate seal lips with transmission fluid.

NOTE: **It will be necessary to fabricate a piston installing tool to aid in proper installation and positioning of clutch seals. Using a 6" length of 3/16" diameter tubing and two 2 3/4" sections of .015" diameter wire, fabricate tool to dimensions in Fig. 31.**

2) Using fabricated tool, install clutch piston into housing and work inner seal down partially, then outer seal down. Alternate from inner seal to outer seal until piston is fully seated.

3) Install waved spring and spring retainer (cupped side down). Compress retainer and install snap ring.

Fig. 30: Exploded View of Lo/Reverse Clutch Assembly

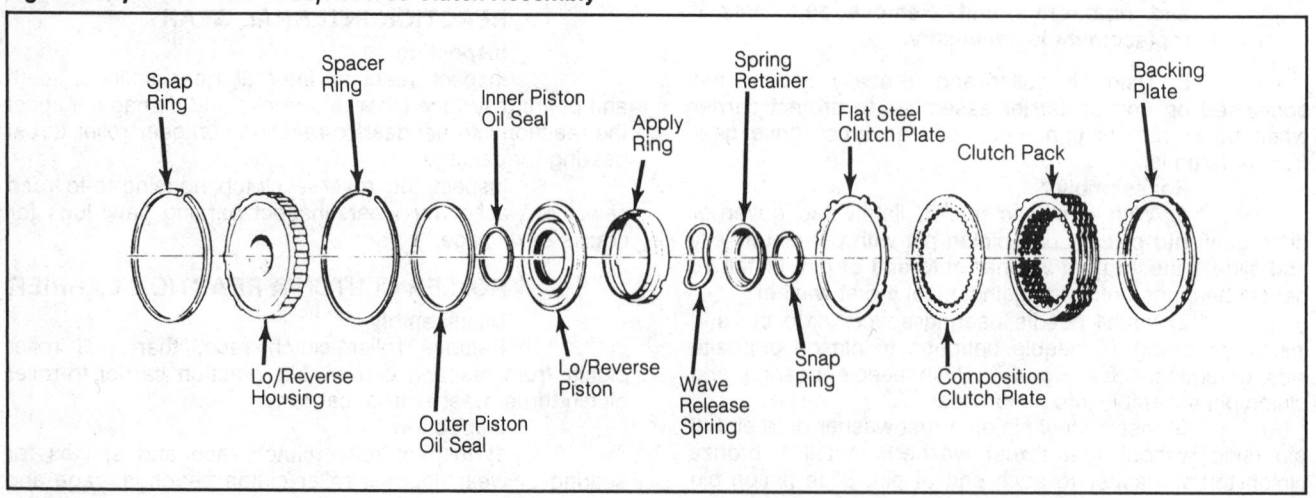

GENERAL MOTORS
TURBO HYDRA-MATIC 125C TRANSAXLE (Cont.)

Fig. 31: Piston Seal Installing Tool

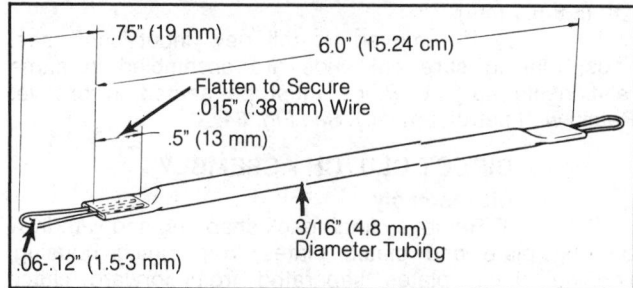

REACTION SUN GEAR & INPUT DRUM
Inspection
Check reaction sun gear (shaft) for cracks, splits, spline damage, gear-to-journal wear and for plugged lubrication passages. Inspect input drum for distortion, damaged splines and pins. Angle of roll pins is normal. DO NOT attempt to straighten pins.

INPUT CARRIER, SUN GEAR & INTERNAL GEAR
Inspection
1) Check all parts for pitting, scoring, damaged gear teeth and cracks. Make sure all lubrication holes are open. Check input carrier thrust washers for wear and distortion of tangs.

Fig. 32: Exploded View of Input Unit

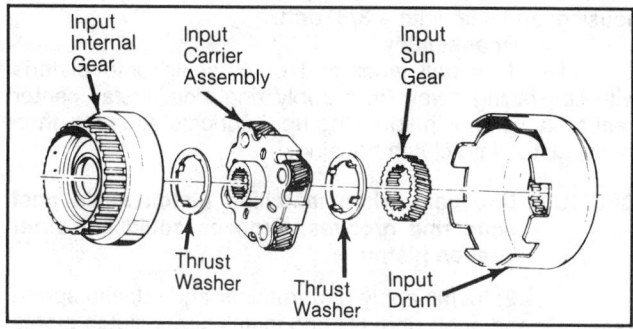

2) Check carrier pinion pins for tightness. Pin should not rotate. Using a feeler gauge, check input carrier pinion end play. End play should be .009-.027" (.24-.69 mm).

FORWARD CLUTCH ASSEMBLY
NOTE: Some models may not be equipped with an apply ring.

Disassembly
1) Place forward clutch housing in a holding fixture, clutch pack facing up. Remove clutch pack retaining snap ring, then remove backing plate and clutch plates from housing.

2) Using a compressor tool, compress retainer and spring assembly and remove snap ring. Remove tool, then lift retainer and spring assembly from clutch housing. Remove piston from housing and seals from piston.

NOTE: Do not remove clutch apply ring from piston unless piston or apply ring requires replacement.

Inspection
1) Inspect oil seals on input shaft for free fit in grooves and damage. Do not remove seals unless replacement is necessary. Inspect clutch plate for signs of wear or burning. Inspect backing plate for scratches and damage.

2) Inspect release spring retainer for distortion and release springs for collapsed coils. Inspect piston and clutch apply ring assembly for cracks and damage. Apply ring width should be .470" (11.9 mm).

3) Check snap ring groove in clutch housing for damage or burrs. Inspect input shaft splines and journals for distortion or damage. Input shaft sleeve must be secure and aligned with hole in input shaft.

Reassembly
1) If removed, install apply ring on piston. Install new inner and outer seals on piston with lips facing away from apply ring side. Lubricate seals and install piston into clutch housing using tool fabricated for Lo/Reverse clutch piston installation.

Fig. 33: Exploded View of Forward Clutch Assembly

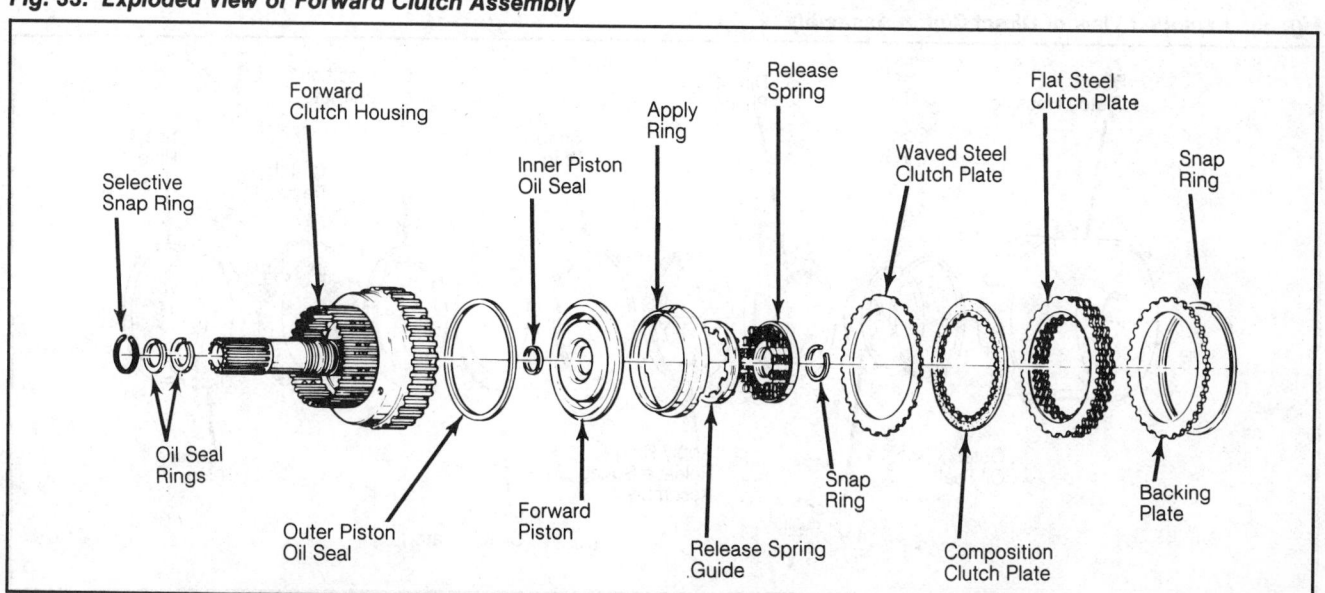

2-184

Automatic Transmissions
GENERAL MOTORS
TURBO HYDRA-MATIC 125C TRANSAXLE (Cont.)

2) Position spring guide, retainer and spring assembly into clutch housing. Compress retainer and spring assembly past snap ring groove and install snap ring. Remove compressor tool.

3) Lubricate and install forward clutch plates into housing. Start with waved steel plate, then install a composition plate. Waved steel plate should be .06" (1.6 mm) thick. Alternate until 4 composition and 3 flat steel plates are installed. *See Forward Clutch Plate Usage Table.*

FORWARD CLUTCH PLATE USAGE TABLE

Application	Flat Steel	Composition
All Models	[1] 3	4

[1] — Plate thickness is .08" (1.9 mm)

4) Install clutch backing plate into housing with identification side up. Install snap ring. Make sure composition clutch plates turn freely.

5) Measure clearance between backing plate and snap ring with a feeler gauge. DO NOT compress waved clutch plate.

6) If clearance is not within .04-.07" (1.0-1.5 mm), choose a selective thickness backing plate to correct clearance. Backing plates are available in the following

Fig. 34: Installing Input Shaft Seal Ring

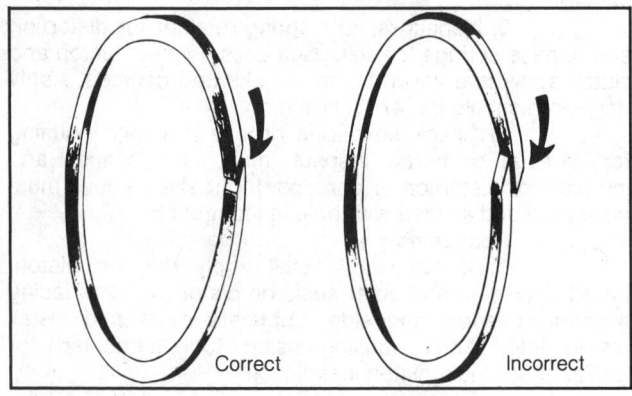

Correct   Incorrect

sizes: .18-.19" (4.6-4.8 mm), .20-.2l" (5.1-5.3 mm) and .23-.24" (5.8-6.1 mm).

7) If removed, install new input shaft seal rings, making sure cut ends are assembled in same relationship as cut. Rings must be seated in groove. Retain with petroleum jelly. *See Fig. 34.*

DIRECT CLUTCH ASSEMBLY
Disassembly

1) Remove clutch pack snap ring and withdraw backing plate and clutch plates from clutch housing, keeping clutch plates separated from forward clutch plates (if foward clutch disassembled).

2) Remove snap ring holding apply ring and release spring assembly. Withdraw apply ring and release assembly from housing. Remove direct piston from clutch housing, then remove inner and outer seals from piston. Remove center seal from clutch housing.

Inspection

1) Inspect composition plates, steel plates and backing plate for wear, burning or scoring. Inspect apply ring, retainer and release spring assembly for damage, collapsed springs and proper apply ring width. Apply ring width should be .750".

2) Inspect direct clutch piston for distortion, cracks or damage. Inspect clutch housing for excessive wear, distortion and damaged check ball capsule.

3) If necessary, drive check ball capsule (toward direct clutch side of housing) from housing, using a 3/8" drift. Install new capsule, from direct clutch side of housing, and seat with a 3/8" drift.

Reassembly

1) Install inner and outer seals onto pistons with lips facing away from apply ring side. Install center seal on housing wih lip facing up. Lubricate all seals, then install piston into clutch housing.

CAUTION: Use care when installing piston seals past snap ring grooves. Grooves could cut outer seal on piston.

2) Install apply ring, retainer and release spring assembly and snap ring. Oil and install direct clutch plates into housing, starting with a flat steel plate and alternating

Fig. 35: Exploded View of Direct Clutch Assembly

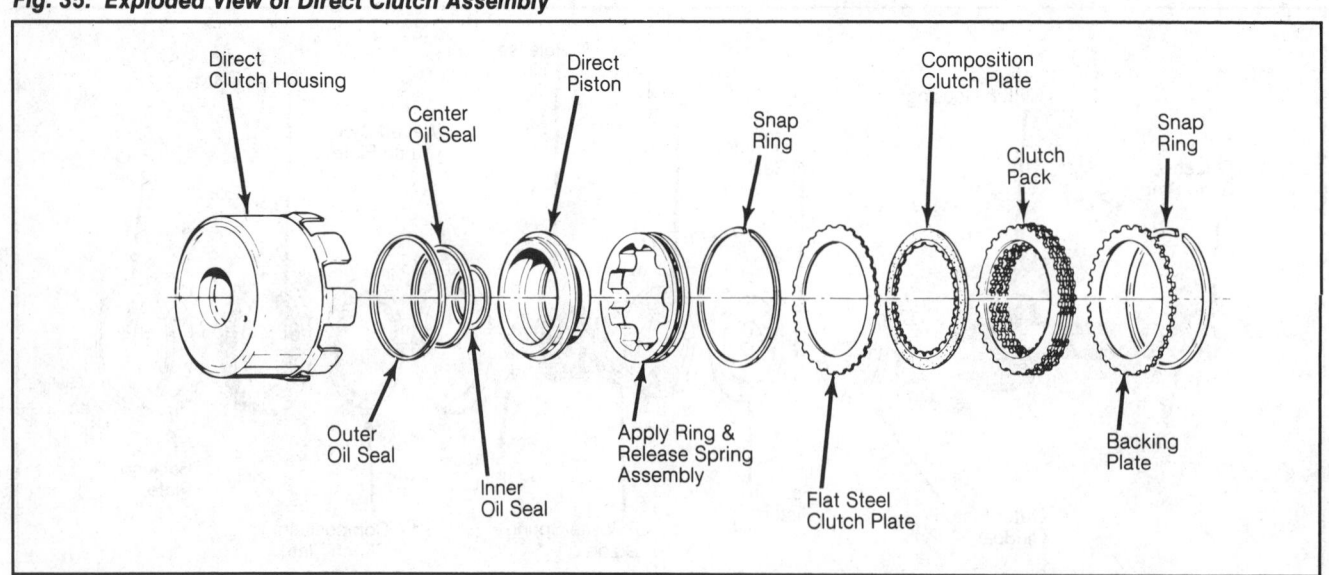

GENERAL MOTORS
TURBO HYDRA-MATIC 125C TRANSAXLE (Cont.)

4 composition and 4 flat steel plates. *See Direct Clutch Plate Usage Table.*

    3) Install backing plate into housing with flat side up. Backing plate thickness should be .19" (4.92 mm). Install snap ring. Ensure composition plates turn freely.

DIRECT CLUTCH PLATE USAGE TABLE

Application	Flat Steel	Composition
All Models	[1] 4	4

[1] — Plate thickness is .09" (2.3 mm).

DRIVEN SPROCKET SUPPORT
Inspection

    1) Inspect driven sprocket support and sleeve for cracks, burrs or damage. It must be tight in its bore and align with holes in support. Inspect driven sprocket support bushings and bearing assembly for damage and excessive wear. Inspect seal rings for nicks and cuts.

    2) If necessary to replace bearing assembly, install bearing with manufacturing identification facing up. Also, bearing race on driven sprocket must be checked. If race requires replacement, driven sprocket support must be replaced.

MANUAL SHAFT
Inspection

    1) Inspect manual valve rod, rod retainer, detent lever and manual shaft for damage. Inspect parking lock actuator rod for damage or broken retainer lugs.

    2) The manual shaft and detent lever assembly are made as a matched set. They must be replaced as an assembly.

DRIVE LINK, DRIVE & DRIVEN SPROCKETS
Inspection

    1) Inspect drive link for damage or loose links. Inspect driven gear thrust bearing race. If damaged, replace driven gear, drive gear and drive support bearing assembly.

    2) Inspect drive sprocket teeth for nicks, burrs, scoring or wear. Inspect turbine shaft, turbine shaft seal rings and grooves for damage. If turbine shaft seal removal is necessary, proceed as follows:

Turbine Shaft Oil Seal Replacement

    1) Carefully remove old seals from turbine shaft. Place seal installer over the turbine shaft and lubricate the installer with petroleum jelly.

    2) Use seal installer (J-29569-1) on the 2 seals on the valve body side of the sprocket. Use seal installer on (J-29829-1) on the 1 seal on the case side of sprocket.

CASE COVER
Inspection

    1) Inspect case cover for damage, cracks, porosity or damaged threads in any threaded hole. Inspect vent assembly for damage and clogging. Check manual valve for damage and freedom of movement.

    2) Inspect manual detent spring and roller assembly for damage. Inspect case cover sleeve, making sure hole in sleeve aligns with case cover passages that intersect case cover (pump shaft) bore.

    3) Inspect 1-2 accumulator piston seals for damage and for free fit in grooves. Inspect thermostatic element for damage or distortion.

NOTE: Do not disassemble case cover unless repair or replacement of cover and/or components is necessary.

Disassembly

    1) Remove detent spring and roller assembly. Remove 2 thermostatic roll pin washers. Remove thermostatic element and plate. Remove axle seal.

    2) Using a drift, drive out manual valve cup plug as shown in *Fig. 36*. Carefully withdraw manual valve. DO NOT use manual valve to drive out cup plug.

Fig. 36: Removing Manual Valve Cup Plug

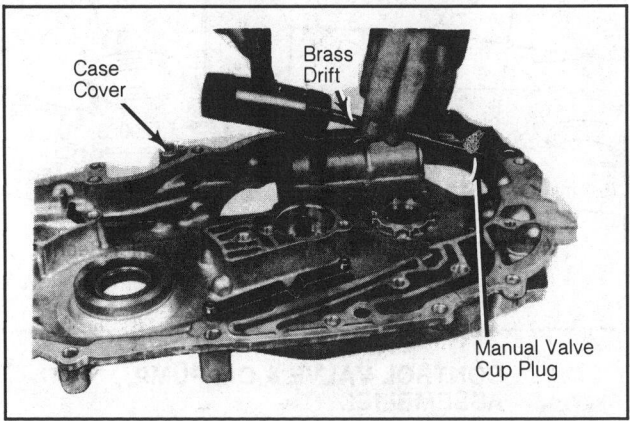

Do not use manual valve to drive out cup plug.

Reassembly

    1) Replace axle seal. Install detent spring and roller assembly. If 1-2 accumulator piston seal was removed, install new seal ring as shown in *Fig. 34*. Install 1-2 accumulator piston (flat side down). Install 1-2 accumulator piston pin.

    2) Install manual valve assembly. Using a 3/8", drift replace manual valve cup plug. Coat cup plug with sealant before installing.

    3) If removed, install thermostatic element roll pins into case and adjust installed height of capped roll pin to .240" (6.0 mm). *See Fig. 37*. Install thermostatic element plate.

Fig. 37: Measuring Thermostatic Element Capped Roll Pin Installed Height

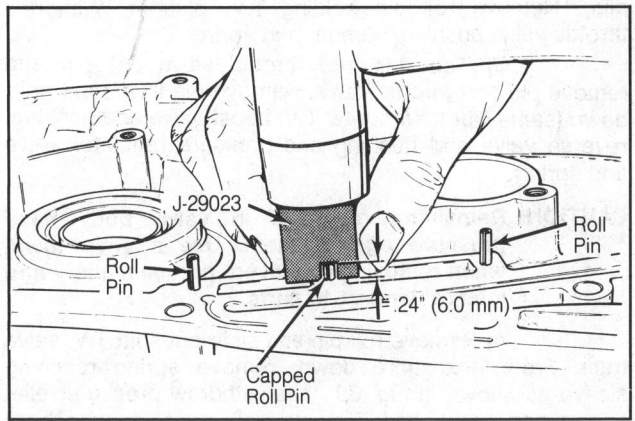

GENERAL MOTORS
TURBO HYDRA-MATIC 125C TRANSAXLE (Cont.)

4) Install thermostatic element onto roll pins. Place gauge (J-29023) against roll pin, between case surface and thermostatic element. Gauge should be .210" (5.24 mm) thick.

5) Install roll pin washers and tap them down onto roll pins until element contacts gauge. *See Fig. 38.*

NOTE: This adjustment is important for thermostatic element operation. Thermostatic element controls fluid level in control valve cover oil sump.

Fig. 38: Adjusting Thermostatic Element Height

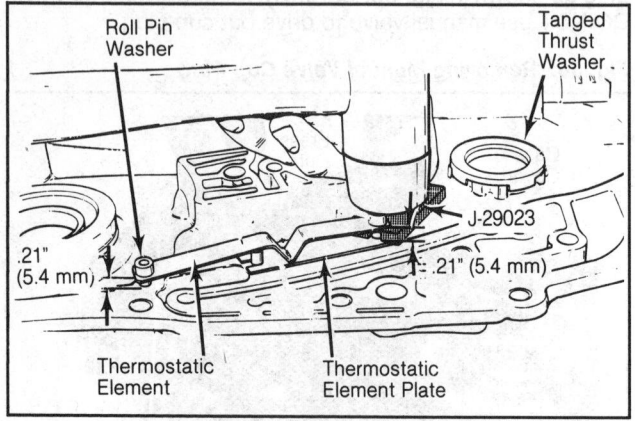

CONTROL VALVE & OIL PUMP ASSEMBLIES

NOTE: As valve train assemblies are removed from their bore in valve body, place individual parts in correct order in relative position to valve body to simplify reassembly. Valves, bushings and springs are not interchangeable, and all parts must be installed in correct order in proper valve body bore. Remove all roll pins by pushing through from case side of body, except for blind hole roll pins.

Disassembly

1) Position control valve body with cored face up and line boost valve at the top. Grind a taper to one end of a No. 49 (.073") drill. This will be used to remove all blind hole roll pins from valve body.

2) Lightly tap drill into line boost valve roll pin. Pull out drill and roll pin. Remove line boost valve and plug. Remove roll pin holding T.V. plunger. Withdraw throttle valve bushing, plunger and spring.

3) Tap drill into throttle valve roll pin and remove pin and throttle valve. Remove pin from next bore down (same side). Withdraw T.V. boost valve and bushing, reverse valve and bushing and pressure regulator valve and spring.

CAUTION: Remaining roll pins in valve body have pressure against them. Use a shop towel when removing to prevent personal injury and loss or damage to parts.

4) Remove roll pin and slide out shift T.V. valve train. From next bore down, remove spring retaining sleeve as shown in *Fig. 39*, then withdraw pressure relief spring and check ball. Remove roll pin from next bore down and withdraw 1-2 accumulator valve train.

Fig. 39: Removing Pressure Relief Check Ball and Spring Retaining Sleeve

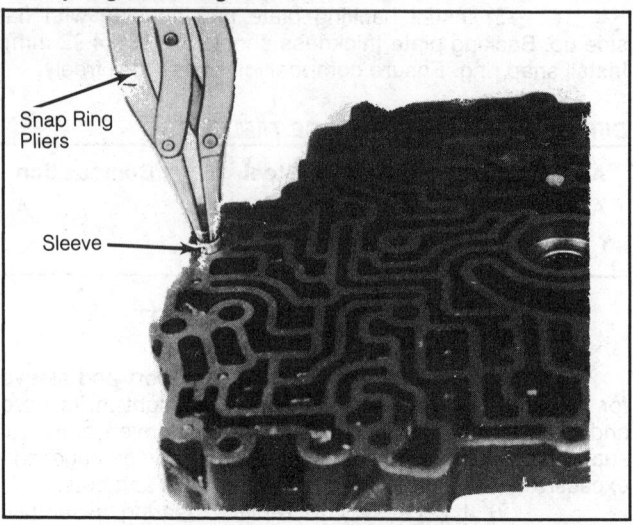

5) Remove roll pin from next bore down and remove 2-3 throttle valve train. Remove roll pin from next bore down and remove 1-2 throttle valve train and 1-2 shift valve.

6) Remove spring retaining sleeve from 3-2 control valve bore. Remove 3-2 control valve and spring. Using a 1/4" punch, remove lo-blowoff spring, plug assembly and ball.

NOTE: The lo-blowoff assembly must be removed if valve body is washed in solvent.

7) Turn control valve body so oil pump side is facing up. Remove roll pin from oil pump priming spring bore. Remove priming spring cup plug and priming spring.

8) Remove auxiliary valve body cover screw, auxiliary valve body, gasket and cover. Remove pump slide, rotor, vanes (7) and vane rings (2).

CAUTION: DO NOT attempt to service the oil pump rotor if the pump pocket or the auxiliary valve body/pump cover surfaces are scored. Servicing of oil pump rotor and slide should be performed ONLY if the selective pump rotor, pump drive shaft or pump slide show signs of wear.

Inspection

1) Inspect control valve/oil pump body for cracks, damage or scoring of valve bores, pump pocket and pump cover. Inspect pump shaft bearing for smooth operation.

2) If necessary to replace bearing, drive bearing out toward pump pocket and install new bearing from pump cover side. Install bearing until race is .040-.048" (1.00-1.20 mm) ABOVE pump pocket face.

3) Inspect valve bushings for cracks and scoring of bore. Inspect bore plugs, pump slide, pump rotor, pump vanes and pump vane rings for damage, cracks or wear. Inspect springs for distortion or collapsed coils.

Pump Rotor & Slide Replacement

1) If pump rotor and/or slides are defective, the replacement parts must provide the same end play originally built into the transaxle. Use the following

GENERAL MOTORS
TURBO HYDRA-MATIC 125C TRANSAXLE (Cont.)

procedure to obtain an end clearance of .0026-.0036" (.066-.092 mm).

2) Use a micrometer to measure the pump/rotor or slide thickness. Measure on flat, undamaged surface. Using the original measurement, order replacement part using *Selective Pump Rotor and Slide Tables.*

3) Hone both sides of the replacement rotor and/or slide to remove any burrs. After assembly, the pump drive shaft should turn freely. If not, recheck the pump rotor and slide.

Reassembly

1) Install pump slide into pump pocket. Install pump slide seal and seal support and retain with petroleum jelly. Install pump slide pivot pin, vane ring and pump rotor.

2) Install vanes (7) into pump making sure vane wear pattern is against center ring and each vane is flush with rotor.

3) Install top vane ring, slide "O" ring seal, pump slide-to-auxiliary valve body oil seal ring, auxiliary valve body, gasket and cover (make sure to align pump rotor step with valve body sleeve).

4) To complete reassembly, reverse disassembly procedures, using *Fig. 40* as a guide. Care must be taken during reassembly of remaining components to avoid damage to valve bores and control valve body-to-case cover mating surfaces.

Fig. 40: *Exploded View of Control Valve Body and Oil Pump Assembly*

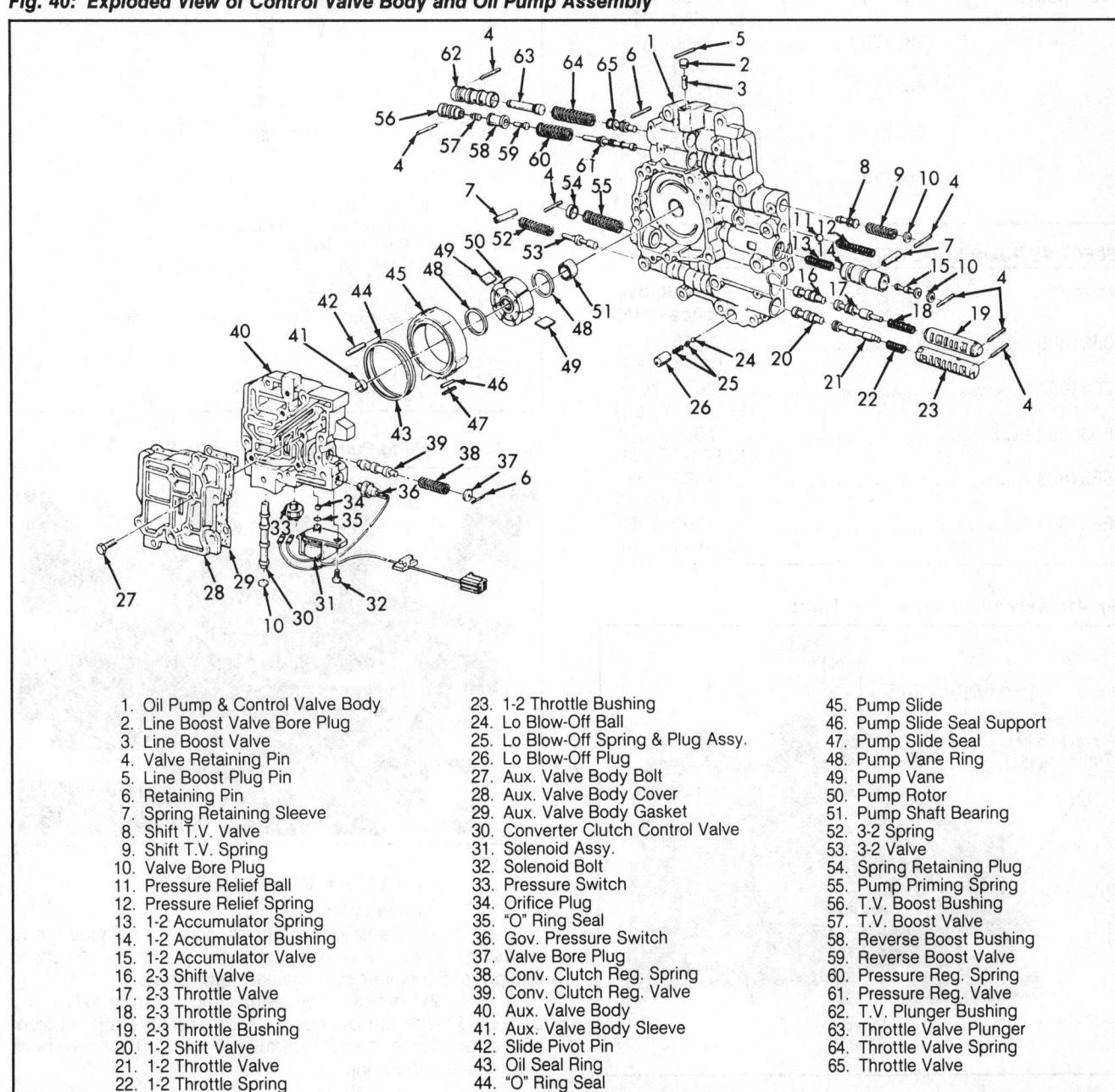

1. Oil Pump & Control Valve Body	23. 1-2 Throttle Bushing	45. Pump Slide
2. Line Boost Valve Bore Plug	24. Lo Blow-Off Ball	46. Pump Slide Seal Support
3. Line Boost Valve	25. Lo Blow-Off Spring & Plug Assy.	47. Pump Slide Seal
4. Valve Retaining Pin	26. Lo Blow-Off Plug	48. Pump Vane Ring
5. Line Boost Plug Pin	27. Aux. Valve Body Bolt	49. Pump Vane
6. Retaining Pin	28. Aux. Valve Body Cover	50. Pump Rotor
7. Spring Retaining Sleeve	29. Aux. Valve Body Gasket	51. Pump Shaft Bearing
8. Shift T.V. Valve	30. Converter Clutch Control Valve	52. 3-2 Spring
9. Shift T.V. Spring	31. Solenoid Assy.	53. 3-2 Valve
10. Valve Bore Plug	32. Solenoid Bolt	54. Spring Retaining Plug
11. Pressure Relief Ball	33. Pressure Switch	55. Pump Priming Spring
12. Pressure Relief Spring	34. Orifice Plug	56. T.V. Boost Bushing
13. 1-2 Accumulator Spring	35. "O" Ring Seal	57. T.V. Boost Valve
14. 1-2 Accumulator Bushing	36. Gov. Pressure Switch	58. Reverse Boost Bushing
15. 1-2 Accumulator Valve	37. Valve Bore Plug	59. Reverse Boost Valve
16. 2-3 Shift Valve	38. Conv. Clutch Reg. Spring	60. Pressure Reg. Spring
17. 2-3 Throttle Valve	39. Conv. Clutch Reg. Valve	61. Pressure Reg. Valve
18. 2-3 Throttle Spring	40. Aux. Valve Body	62. T.V. Plunger Bushing
19. 2-3 Throttle Bushing	41. Aux. Valve Body Sleeve	63. Throttle Valve Plunger
20. 1-2 Shift Valve	42. Slide Pivot Pin	64. Throttle Valve Spring
21. 1-2 Throttle Valve	43. Oil Seal Ring	65. Throttle Valve
22. 1-2 Throttle Spring	44. "O" Ring Seal	

Automatic Transmissions
GENERAL MOTORS
TURBO HYDRA-MATIC 125C TRANSAXLE (Cont.)

SELECTIVE PUMP ROTOR REPLACEMENT TABLE

Rotor	Part No.	Thickness In. (mm)
20 Tooth	8631495	.7065-.7069 (17.943-17.955)
	8631496	.7070-.7074 (17.956-17.968)
	8631497	.7075-.7079 (17.969-17.981)
	8631514	.7080-.7084 (17.982-17.994)
	8631515	.7085-.7089 (17.995-18.008)
15 Tooth	8637768	.7055-.7059 (17.917-17.929)
	8637769	.7060-.7064 (17.930-17.942)
	8637178	.7065-.7069 (17.943-17.955)
	8637179	.7070-.7074 (17.956-17.968)
	8637180	.7075-.7079 (17.969-17.981)

SELECTIVE PUMP SLIDE REPLACEMENT TABLE

Part No.	Thickness Inches (mm)
8631800	.7070-.7074 (17.955-17.967)
8631801	.7075-.7079 (17.968-17.980)
8631802	.7080-.7084 (17.981-17.993)
8631803	.7085-.7089 (17.994-18.006)
8631804	.7090-.7094 (18.007-18.020)

Fig. 41: Assembled View of Oil Pump

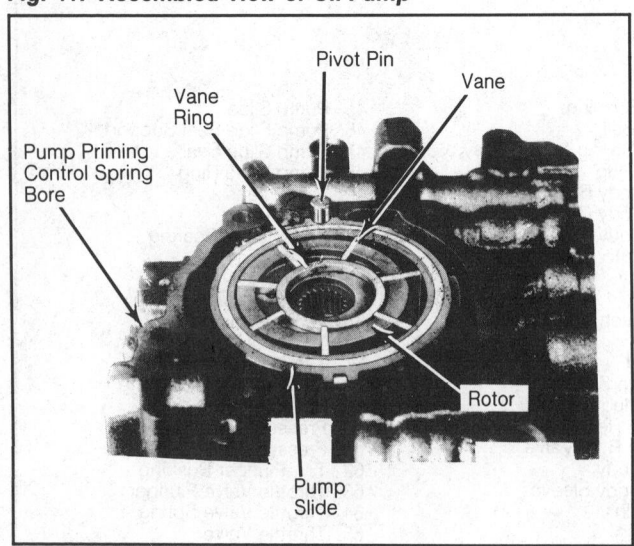

Fig. 42: Exploded View of Auxiliary Valve Body

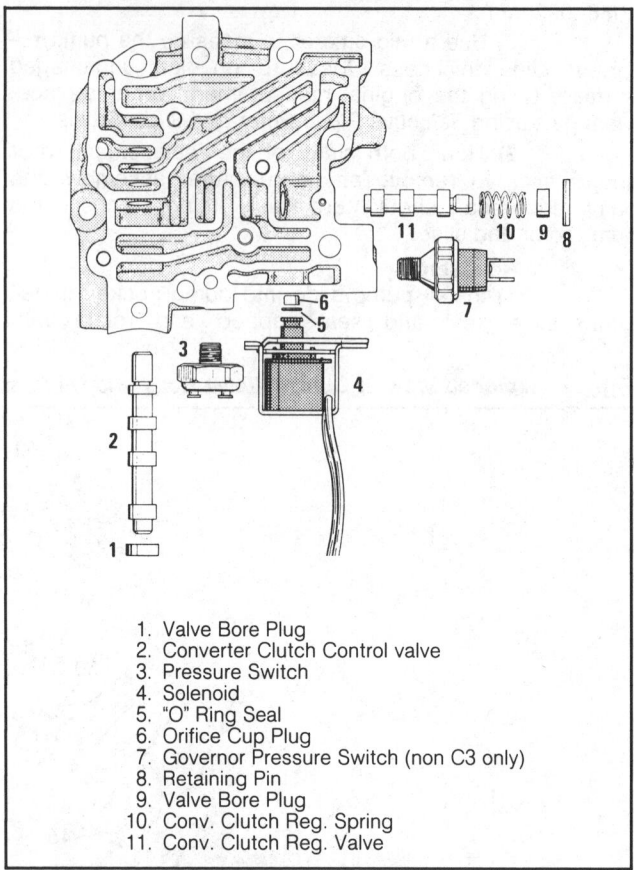

1. Valve Bore Plug
2. Converter Clutch Control valve
3. Pressure Switch
4. Solenoid
5. "O" Ring Seal
6. Orifice Cup Plug
7. Governor Pressure Switch (non C3 only)
8. Retaining Pin
9. Valve Bore Plug
10. Conv. Clutch Reg. Spring
11. Conv. Clutch Reg. Valve

Fig. 43: Installing Pump Slide "O" Ring Seals

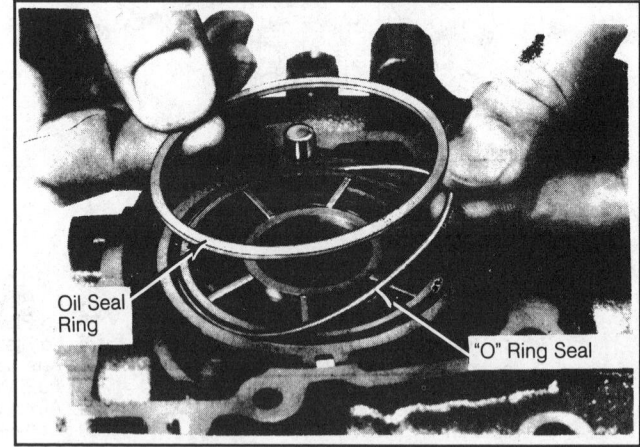

AUXILIARY VALVE BODY
Disassembly

1) Remove solenoid screw, solenoid and pressure switch. Remove governor pressure switch, if equipped. Remove cover, gasket and screw.

2) Remove converter clutch control valve and bore plug. With rag over end of bore, remove roll pin from converter clutch control regulator valve. Remove bore plug, valve and spring.

GENERAL MOTORS
TURBO HYDRA-MATIC 125C TRANSAXLE (Cont.)

Inspection

1) Wash all valve body parts except solenoid. Inspect valves and valve body for cracks, scoring and other damage. Inspect spring for distortion or collapsed coils.

2) Make sure orifice cup plugs are present in solenoid bore and pressure switch parts. Inspect solenoid "O" ring and bore plug for damage.

3) To prevent oil exhausting from vent after reassembly, check length of auxiliary valve body bolts. Bolts must be M6 x 1.0 x 20mm. Tighten to 8 ft. lbs. (11 N.m).

Reassembly

1) Install converter clutch control regulator valve, spring and bore plug. Compress spring and install roll pin.

2) Install converter clutch control valve and bore plug. Install pressure switches. Install solenoid and new "O" ring. Install cover gasket and screw.

INTERMEDIATE SERVO

Inspection

Remove snap ring and disassemble servo. See Fig. 44. Inspect all parts for damage, cracks, scoring and distortion. Reassemble servo using new inner and outer oil seals on piston and proper apply ring (proper apply pin size determined during disassembly).

Fig. 44: Exploded View of Intermediate Servo Assembly

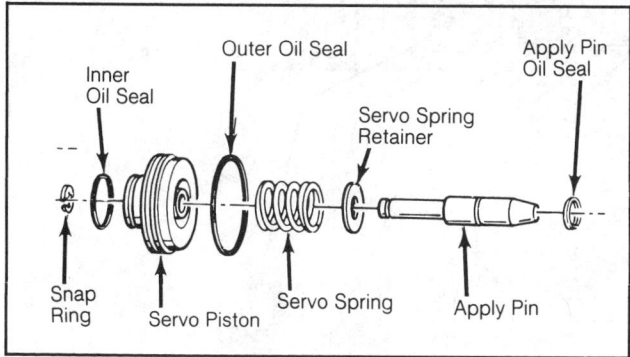

GOVERNOR ASSEMBLY

Inspection

1) If necessary, remove speedometer drive gear from governor shaft and inspect gear for nicks or damage. Check governor cover for damage or distortion of mating surface.

2) Inspect governor driven gear for nicks or damage. Check governor shaft seal rings for cuts, damage and free fit in groove. Check for free operation of governor weights. Check for damaged, mispositioned or tilted springs.

CAUTION: When servicing any "CB" or "HY" transaxle built prior to serial number 83-CB-29532 and 83-HY-3199, REMOVE the primary spring from the governor assembly. This will prevent an erratic 2nd gear start-out condition.

3) Inspect for presence of 2 check balls. Inspect governor shaft and thrust washer for damage. If seal ring is being replaced, make sure cut ends of seal are assembled in the same relationship as cut. See Fig. 34.

Fig. 45: Sectional View of Governor Assembly

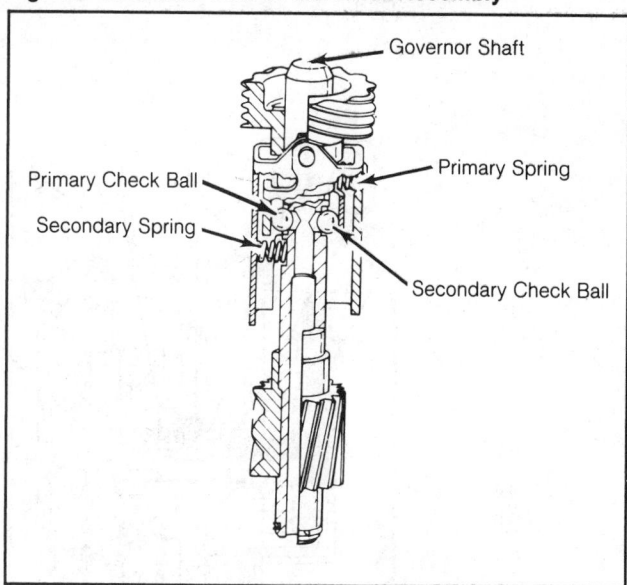

TRANSAXLE REASSEMBLY

NOTE: All selective snap ring and thrust washer measurements taken during disassembly should be rechecked at appropriate stage of reassembly. Follow procedures given in Transaxle Disassembly.

1) Turn transaxle so case cover end is up. Install proper final drive-to-case thrust washer and thrust bearing assembly to final drive unit (inner race of bearing against selective washer). Install differential and final drive assembly into case.

2) Install final drive internal gear spacer (cupped side against final drive internal gear), making sure opening in spacer aligns with parking pawl opening in case. Check to see that parking pawl passes through spacer freely.

3) Install final drive spacer-to-case snap ring with ring gap away from parking pawl opening in case. Install reaction sun gear set into case.

4) Install Lo/Reverse clutch backing plate (stepped side down) into case, then install clutch plates,

Fig. 46: Installing Thrust Washer and Bearing to Final Drive Assembly

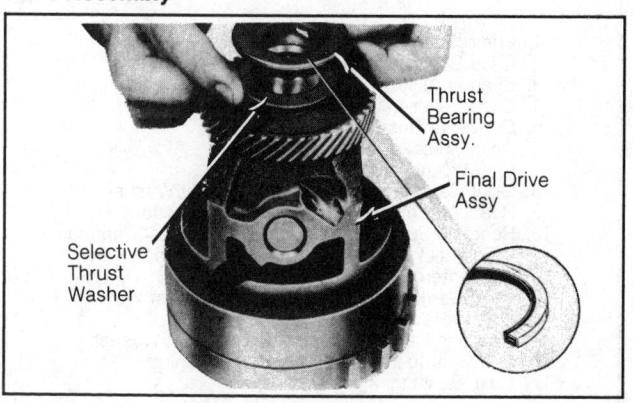

Automatic Transmissions
GENERAL MOTORS
TURBO HYDRA-MATIC 125C TRANSAXLE (Cont.)

Fig. 47: Thrust Bearing, Thrust Washer and Bushing Locations

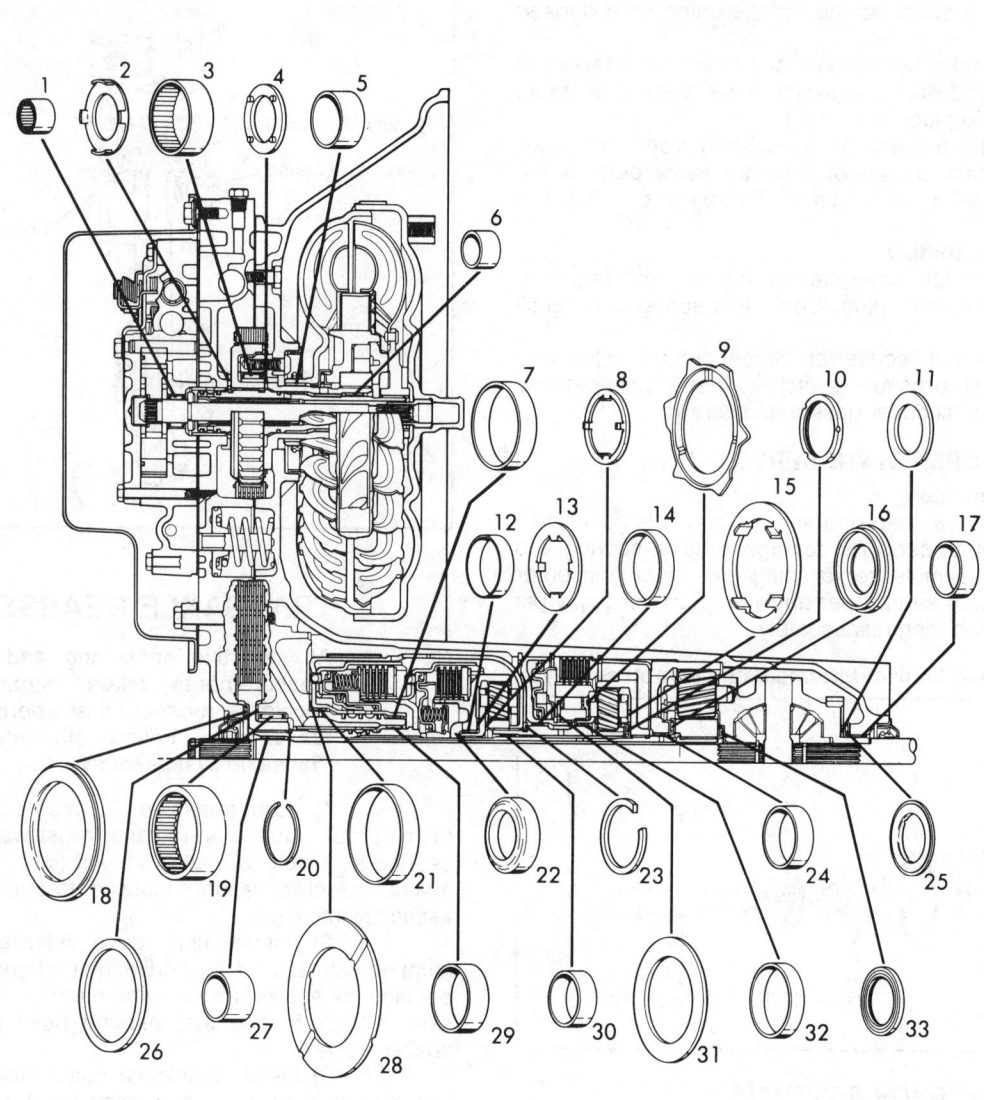

1. Pump Shaft Bearing Assy.
2. Case Cover-to-Driven Sprocket Thrust Washer
3. Bearing Assy.
4. Case Cover-to-Drive Sprocket Thrust Washer
5. Converter Bushing
6. Drive Sprocket Support Bushing
7. Direct Clutch Drum Bushing
8. Input Carrier-to-Input Sun Gear Thrust Washer
9. Reaction Carrier-to-Lo Race Thrust Washer
10. Reaction Sun Gear-to-Internal Gear Thrust Bearing
11. Differential Carrier-to-Case Selective Thrust Washer
12. Input Internal Gear Bushing
13. Input Carrier-to-Input Internal Gear Thrust Washer
14. Lo and Reverse Clutch Housing Bushing
15. Reaction Carrier-to-Internal Gear Thrust Washer
16. Sun Gear-to-Internal Gear Thrust Bearing
17. Case Bushing
18. Driven Sprocket Thrust Bearing Assy.
19. Bearing Assy.
20. Selective Snap Ring
21. Direct Clutch Bushing
22. Input Shaft Thrust Washer
23. Selective Snap Ring
24. Final Drive Internal Gear Bushing
25. Differential Case Thrust Bearing Assy.
26. Driven Sprocket Support Thrust Washer
27. Input Shaft Bushing
28. Thrust Washer
29. Driven Sprocket Support Bushing
30. Reaction Sun Gear Bushing
31. Reverse Housing-to-Lo Race Selective Thrust Washer
32. Reaction Carrier Bushing
33. Sun Gear-to-Carrier Thrust Bearing

GENERAL MOTORS
TURBO HYDRA-MATIC 125C TRANSAXLE (Cont.)

starting with a composition plate and alternating steel and composition plates until all plates are installed. *See Lo/Reverse Clutch Plate Usage Table.*

LO/REVERSE CLUTCH PLATE USAGE TABLE

Application	Flat Steel	Composition
All Models	4	5

5) Install Lo/Reverse clutch housing-to-case spacer ring. This case spacer ring is .042" (1.07 mm) thick. Install Lo/Reverse clutch housing into transaxle case, making sure clutch feed hole in housing lines up with clutch feed hole in case.

6) Install proper selective snap ring onto reaction sun gear and install reaction sun gear onto final drive sun gear shaft in transaxle. Rotate reaction sun gear while pushing down on the Lo/Reverse clutch housing until clutch housing drops below snap ring groove in case.

7) Install Lo/Reverse clutch housing-to-case snap ring. This snap ring is .092" (2.36 mm) thick. Install input drum onto reaction sun gear. Install input sun gear into input drum. Install input carrier-to-input sun gear tanged thrust washer to pinion side of carrier.

8) Install input carrier-to-input internal gear tanged thrust washer to internal gear side of carrier (input carrier-to-input internal gear thrust washer is larger of 2). Install input pinion carrier onto input sun gear. Install input internal gear over input carrier.

9) Place forward clutch assembly on bench with input shaft up. Install direct clutch assembly over input shaft onto the forward clutch housing.

10) When clutch housings are fully seated together, it should be about 1 7/32" (31 mm) from tang end of direct clutch housing to end of forward clutch housing drum. *See Fig. 48.*

Fig. 48: Measuring Forward Clutch-to-Direct Clutch Assembled Height

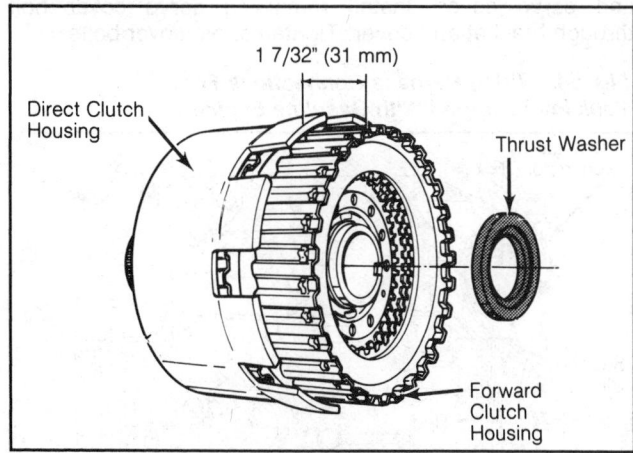

11) Install input shaft-to-input internal gear thrust washer, with rounded side against input shaft and stepped side facing outward, onto forward and direct clutch assembly.

12) Install direct and forward clutch assemblies into case. Rotate clutch assemblies, without pushing down, until they drop into fully seated position in case. When correctly installed, case face-to-direct clutch housing measurement should be 1-1/6" (27 mm). *See Fig. 49.*

13) Install intermediate band, locating eye of band into case and aligning lugged end with apply pin bore. Install band anchor hole plug (use new design hole plug with securing tab attached).

14) Install driven sprocket support-to-direct clutch housing thrust washer. Install driven sprocket support. *See Fig. 20.*

NOTE: Manual shaft and detent lever assemblies are made as a matched set. Replacement of complete set is required if either part is damaged.

Fig. 49: Checking Installed Position of Direct and Forward Clutch Assemblies

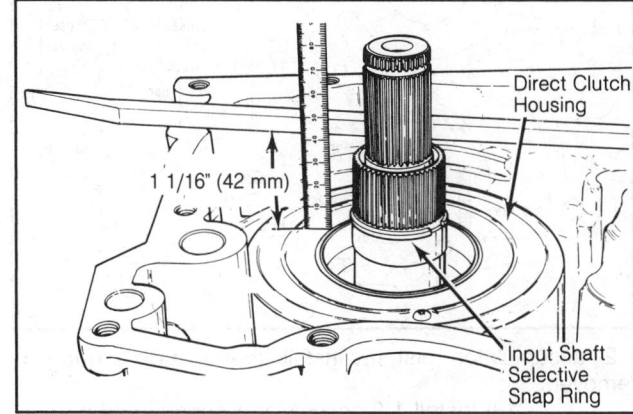

15) Install manual shaft and parking lock actuator rod into case through driven sprocket support. Install detent lever on manual shaft (hub side away from driven sprocket support) and push manual shaft in place.

16) Install detent lever-to-manual shaft retaining nail. Install manual shaft-to-case retaining pin. *See Fig. 20.*

Fig. 50: Case Cover Bolt Locations

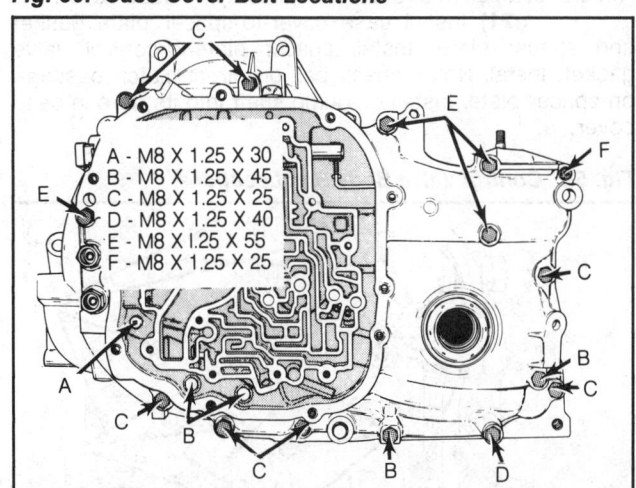

17) Assemble drive and driven sprockets with link assembly and install drive and driven thrust washers to sprockets. Install drive link assembly onto transaxle. The colored guide link, which has numerals, must face the case cover.

18) Install case cover-to-driven sprocket roller bearing thrust washer (outer race against sprocket). Install

2-192

Automatic Transmissions
GENERAL MOTORS
TURBO HYDRA-MATIC 125C TRANSAXLE (Cont.)

Fig. 51: View of Spacer Plate Showing Passage Location

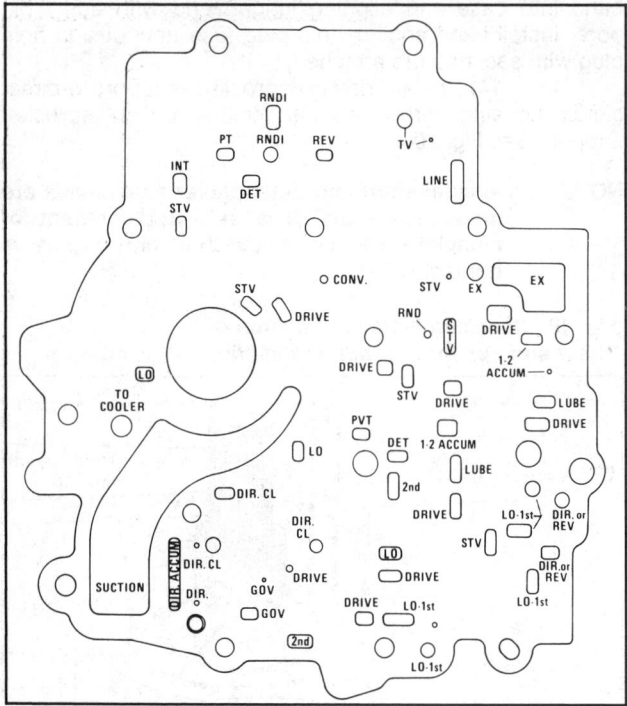

1-2 accumulator piston. Install thermostatic spring if removed.

19) Install 1-2 accumulator spring in its bore in case. Install inner and outer case-to-cover gaskets and case cover. Install 2 case cover bolts from inside torque converter housing (M8 x 1.25 x 14). Install remaining case cover bolts using *Fig. 50* as a guide.

20) Connect manual valve rod to manual valve. Using *Fig 16* as a guide, install No. 2 check ball into direct clutch accumulator passage, No. 3 check ball in circular Lo/First passage, No. 4 check ball in Lo/Reverse slot and No. 5 check ball in direct clutch passage in case cover.

21) Install case cover-to-spacer plate gasket and spacer plate. Install spacer plate-to-control valve gasket. Install No. 1 check ball on direct clutch passage on spacer plate. Install oil pump shaft into its bore in case cover.

Fig. 52: Control Valve Body Bolt Locations

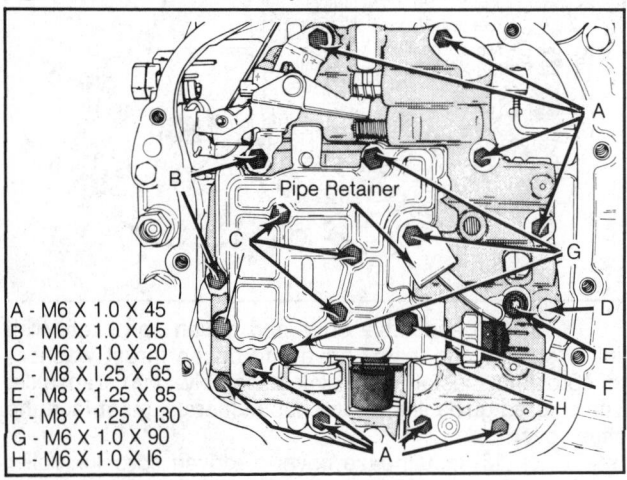

A - M6 X 1.0 X 45
B - M6 X 1.0 X 45
C - M6 X 1.0 X 20
D - M8 X 1.25 X 65
E - M8 X 1.25 X 85
F - M8 X 1.25 X 130
G - M6 X 1.0 X 90
H - M6 X 1.0 X 16

22) Install two 6mm guide pins (M6 x 1.0 x 75) in case cover-to-valve body bolt holes. These will aid in positioning valve body down onto case cover.

23) Install control valve body with bolts and tighten. Install valve body wiring harness as shown in *Fig. 55*. Connect lever link to T.V. bracket. Install T.V. bracket onto valve body.

24) Remove guide bolts used to install valve body and install remaining 2 valve body bolts. Thoroughly clean valve body cover and install using new gasket.

25) Turn transaxle so oil pan side is up. Install output shaft into transaxle. Rotate final drive so retaining ring groove is visible through access window in case. Install new retaining ring onto shaft groove.

Fig 53: Installing Output Shaft Retaining Ring

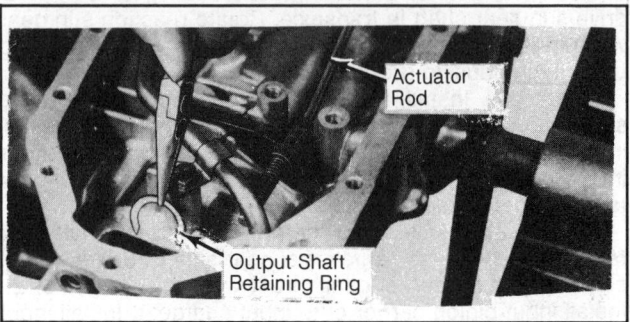

26) Install parking lock bracket and dipstick stop. Using a 3/8" drift, install new Lo/Reverse oil pipe seal assembly. Install "O" ring back-up washer and "O" ring seal onto end of Lo/Reverse pipe. Install pipe, plain end in first, then "O" ring end. Install retainer bracket.

27) Install intermediate servo piston assembly. Install 3rd accumulator check valve and spring into check valve bore next to servo piston. Install intermediate servo cover and 3 bolts.

28) Install reverse oil pipe bracket to oil pipe and servo cover. Install remaining servo cover bolt through bracket and cover. Tighten servo cover bolts.

Fig. 54: Wiring Harness Connections For Vehicles Equipped With Gasoline Engine

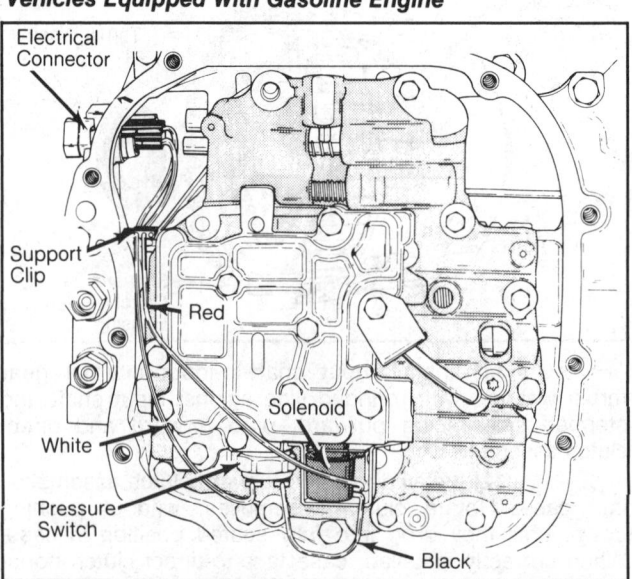

Automatic Transmissions

GENERAL MOTORS
TURBO HYDRA-MATIC 125C TRANSAXLE (Cont.)

2-193

Fig. 55: Exploded View of Transaxle Case and Related Components

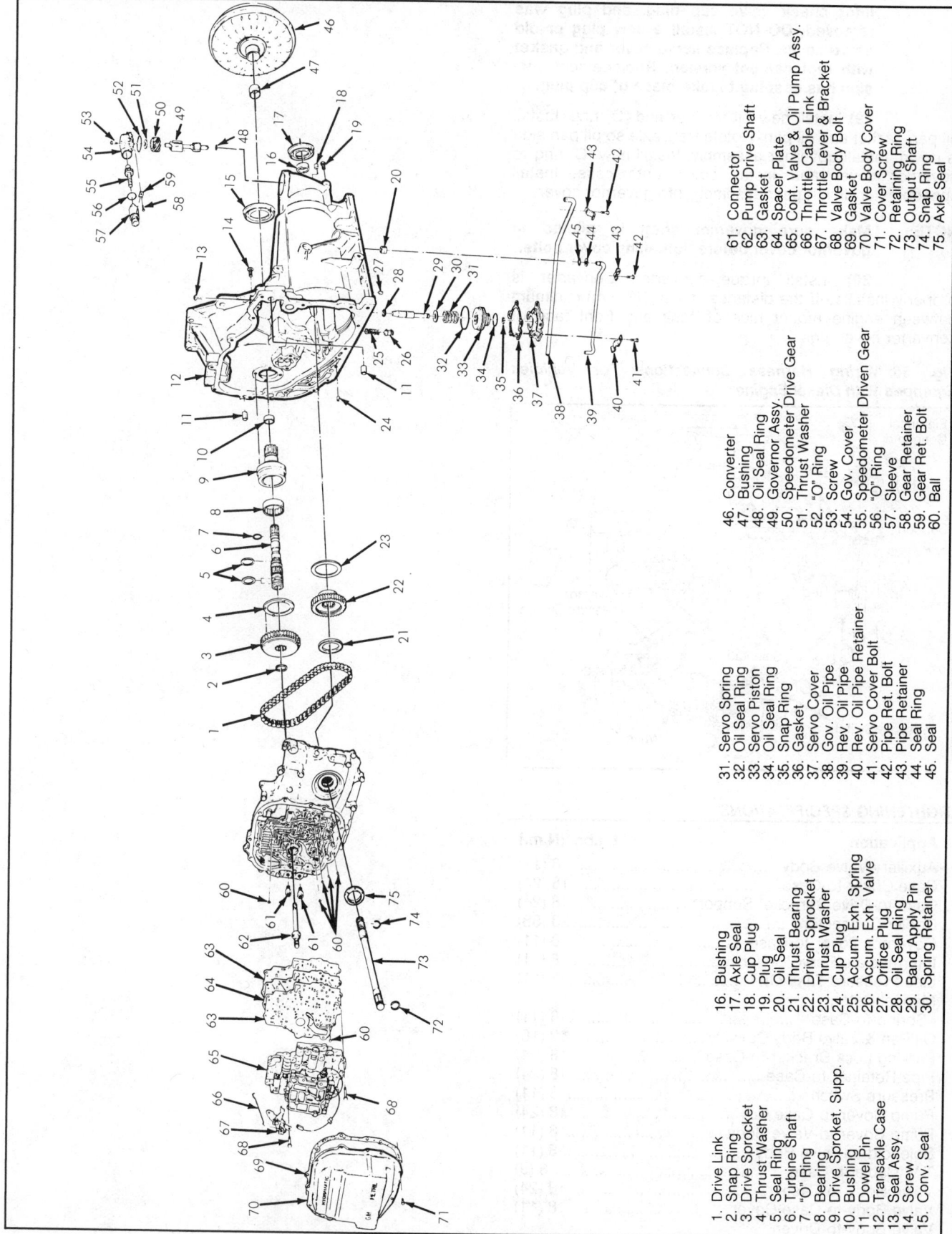

1. Drive Link
2. Snap Ring
3. Drive Sprocket
4. Thrust Washer
5. Seal Ring
6. Turbine Shaft
7. "O" Ring
8. Bearing
9. Drive Sproket. Supp.
10. Bushing
11. Dowel Pin
12. Transaxle Case
13. Seal Assy.
14. Screw
15. Conv. Seal

16. Bushing
17. Axle Seal
18. Cup Plug
19. Plug
20. Oil Seal
21. Thrust Bearing
22. Driven Sprocket
23. Thrust Washer
24. Cup Plug
25. Accum. Exh. Spring
26. Accum. Exh. Valve
27. Orifice Plug
28. Oil Seal Ring
29. Band Apply Pin
30. Spring Retainer

31. Servo Spring
32. Oil Seal Ring
33. Servo Piston
34. Oil Seal Ring
35. Snap Ring
36. Gasket
37. Servo Cover
38. Gov. Oil Pipe
39. Rev. Oil Pipe
40. Rev. Oil Pipe Retainer
41. Servo Cover Bolt
42. Pipe Ret. Bolt
43. Pipe Retainer
44. Seal Ring
45. Seal

46. Converter
47. Bushing
48. Oil Seal Ring
49. Governor Assy.
50. Speedometer Drive Gear
51. Thrust Washer
52. "O" Ring
53. Screw
54. Gov. Cover
55. Speedometer Driven Gear
56. "O" Ring
57. Sleeve
58. Gear Retainer
59. Gear Ret. Bolt
60. Ball

61. Connector
62. Pump Drive Shaft
63. Gasket
64. Spacer Plate
65. Cont. Valve & Oil Pump Assy.
66. Throttle Cable Link
67. Throttle Lever & Bracket
68. Valve Body Bolt
69. Gasket
70. Valve Body Cover
71. Cover Screw
72. Retaining Ring
73. Output Shaft
74. Snap Ring
75. Axle Seal

2-194

Automatic Transmissions
GENERAL MOTORS
TURBO HYDRA-MATIC 125C TRANSAXLE (Cont.)

NOTE: If transaxle was equipped with a 3rd accumulator check valve cup plug, and plug was removed, DO NOT install a new plug or old servo cover. Replace servo cover and gasket with replacement version. Replacement version has cast lug to take place of cup plug.

29) Install new oil strainer and "O" ring. Install oil pan gasket and oil pan. Rotate transaxle so oil pan side is down. Install governor assembly. Install new "O" ring to governor cover and install cover onto case. Install speedometer driven gear assembly into governor cover.

NOTE: Make sure governor shaft is piloted in governor cover before tightening cover bolts.

30) Install torque converter. Converter is properly installed if the distance is 1/2" (13 mm) minimum between engine mount face of case and front face of converter cover lugs.

Fig. 56: Wiring Harness Connections For Vehicles Equipped With Diesel Engine

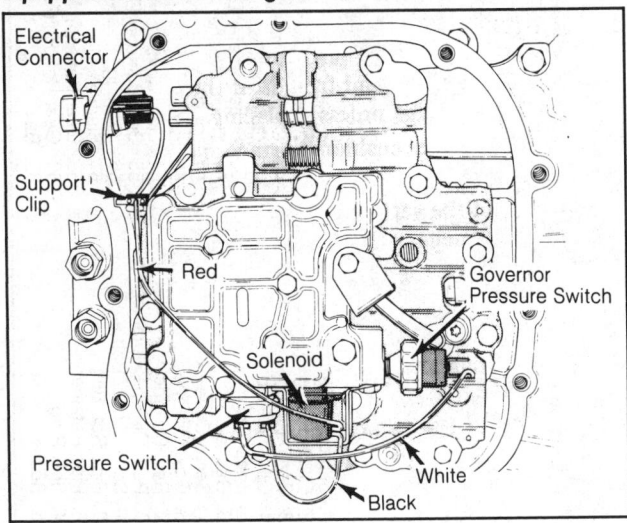

TIGHTENING SPECIFICATIONS

Application	Ft. Lbs. (N.m.)
Auxiliary Valve Body	8 (11)
Case Cover-to-Case	18 (24)
Case-to-Drive Sprocket Support	18 (24)
Cooler Connector	23 (38)
Governor Cover-to-Case	8 (11)
Intermediate Servo Cover	8 (11)
Line Pressure Take-Off	8 (11)
Manual Detent	
Spring-to-Case	8 (11)
Oil Pan & Valve Body Cover	12 (16)
Parking Lock Bracket-to-Case	18 (24)
Pipe Retainer-to-Case	18 (24)
Pressure Switch	8 (11)
Pump Cover-to-Case Cover	18 (24)
Pump Cover-to-Valve Body	8 (11)
Solenoid-to-Valve Body	8 (11)
T.V. Cable-to-Case	6 (9)
Valve Body-to-Case	18 (24)
Valve Body-to-Case Cover	8 (11)
Valve Body-to-Driven	
Sprocket Support	18 (24)

GENERAL MOTORS TURBO HYDRA-MATIC 180C

**Chevrolet Chevette
Pontiac T1000**

TRANSMISSION IDENTIFICATION

The transmission identification code and serial number are stamped on a Blue tag on right side of transmission case on forward edge of torque converter housing.

DESCRIPTION

The Turbo Hydra-Matic 180C transmission is a fully automatic unit consisting primarily of a 4-element torque converter with the addition of a converter clutch and a compound planetary gear set. Three multiple-disc clutches, a roller clutch and a band provide the friction of the compound plantary gear set. A hydraulic system pressurized by a gear type pump provides the working pressure required to operate the friction elements and automatic controls.

LUBRICATION & ADJUSTMENTS

See Automatic Transmission Servicing.

TESTING

ROAD TEST

Drive Range ("D")

With selector lever in "D" range, accelerate vehicle from a standstill. A 1-2 and 2-3 shift should occur at all throttle openings (shift points will vary with throttle openings). As vehicle speed decreases to zero MPH, a 3-2 and 2-1 downshift should occur.

Intermediate Range ("L2")

Place selector lever in "L2" and accelerate vehicle from a standstill. A 1-2 shift should occur at all throttle openings. No 2-3 shift can be obtained in this range. The 1-2 shift point will vary with throttle opening. As vehicle speed decreases to zero MPH, a 2-1 downshift should occur.

Low Range ("L1")

Place selector lever in "L1" and accelerate vehicle from a standstill. No upshift should occur in this range.

2nd Gear ("L2") Overrun Braking

With selector lever in "D" range, lift foot off accelerator and move selector lever to intermediate range ("L2"). An increase in engine RPM and an engine braking effect should be noted.

Fig. 1: Cutaway View of Turbo Hydra-Matic 180C Automatic Transmission

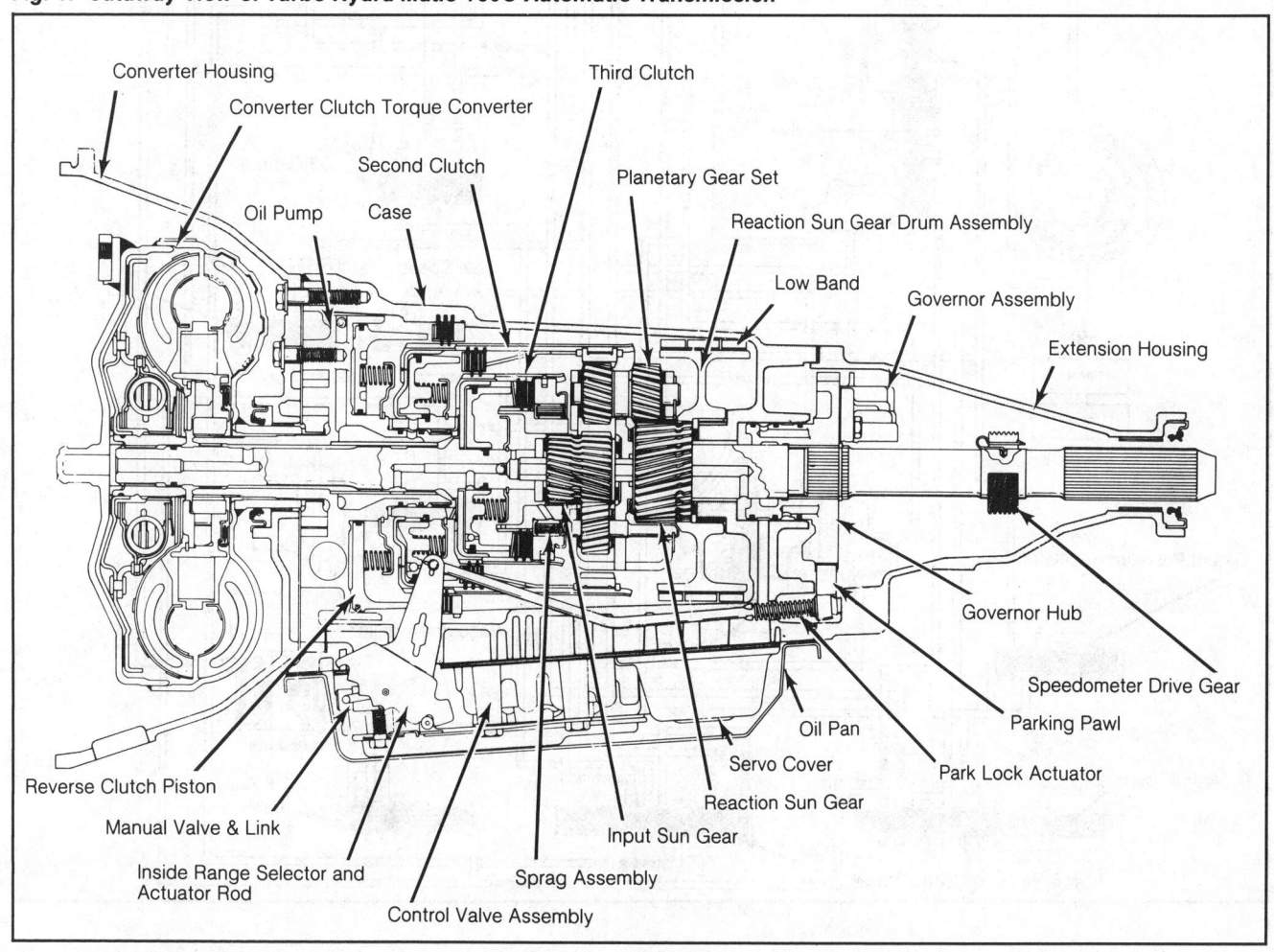

Automatic Transmissions

GENERAL MOTORS TURBO HYDRA-MATIC 180C (Cont.)

Fig. 2: *Turbo Hydra-Matic 180C Hydraulic Circuits Diagram (Torque Converter ON)*

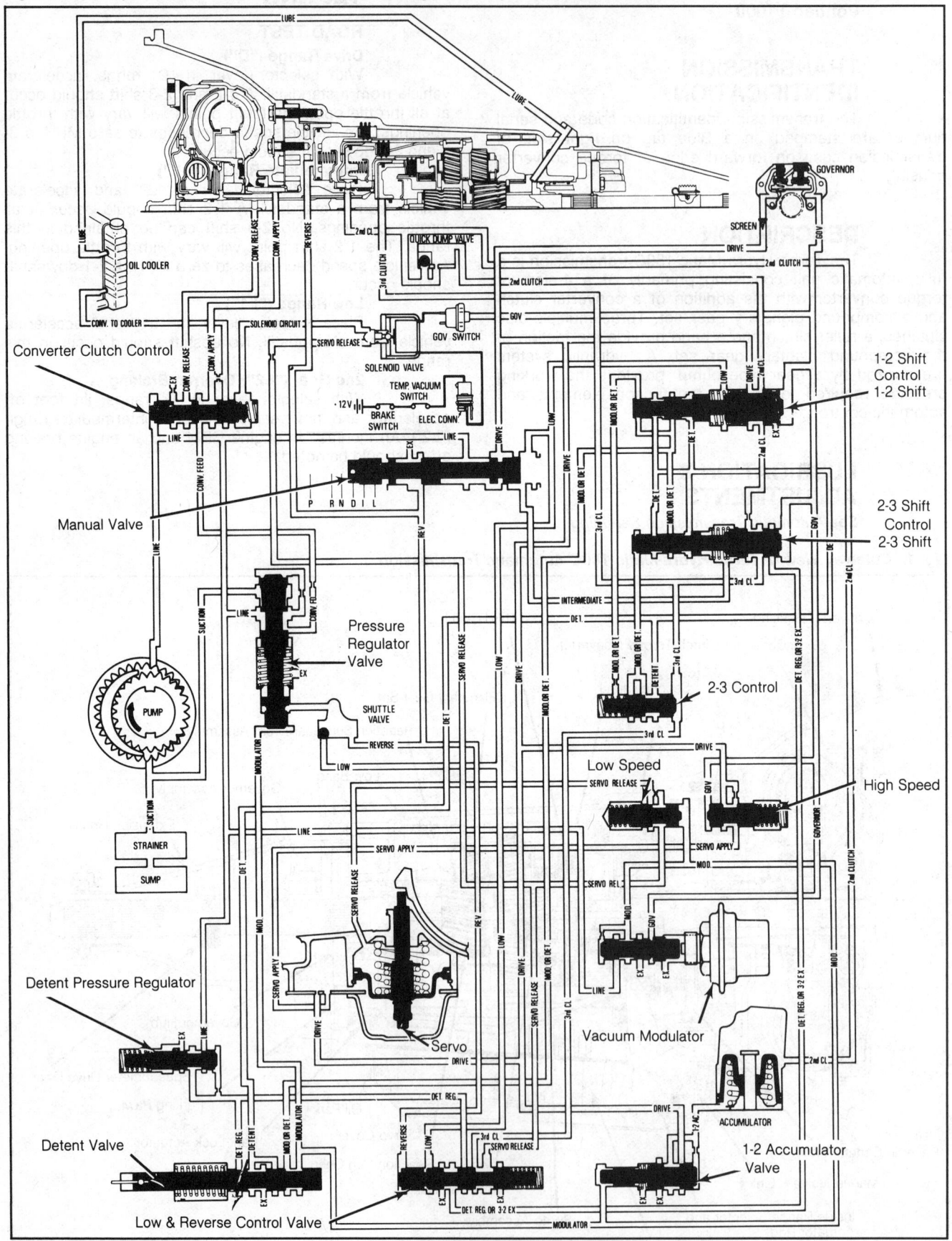

GENERAL MOTORS TURBO HYDRA-MATIC 180C (Cont.)

CLUTCH AND BAND APPLICATION CHART (ELEMENTS IN USE)

Selector Lever Position	Reverse Clutch	Second Clutch	Third Clutch	Sprag Clutch	Low Band
D — DRIVE					
First Gear				X	X
Second Gear		X			X
Third Gear		X	X	X	
L2 — INTERMEDIATE					
Second Gear		X			X
L1 — LOW			X	X	X
R — REVERSE	X		X	X	

NEUTRAL OR PARK — All clutches, brakes, and bands released and/or ineffective.

1st Gear ("L1") Overrun Braking

With selector lever in "L2" range, and vehicle speed approximately 30 MPH at constant throttle, move selector lever to "L1" range. An increase in engine RPM and an engine braking effect should be noted.

CONTROL PRESSURE TEST

Connect a tachometer to engine and a pressure gauge to line pressure take-off point on left side of transmission case. With transmission fluid at correct level and operating temperature, pressure can be checked by road testing or by running engine with vehicle on a hoist as follows:

NOTE: **It will be necessary to remove rear transmission crossmember side bolts and lower transmission slightly to gain access to line pressure take-off point.**

Stationary Test (Modulator Disconnected)

Make test with vehicle stationary, service brakes applied, engine speed set at 1500 RPM, vacuum modulator line disconnected, and pressure gauge installed. Transmission line pressure should be approximately as shown in following table:

CONTROL PRESSURES

(Vacuum Modulator Disconnected)	
Shift Lever Position	[1] **Psi**
Drive ("D")	118
Intermediate ("L2")	118
Low ("L1")	160

[1] — Maximum pressure.

Coasting Check (Modulator Connected)

With vehicle coasting at 30 MPH (foot off throttle), pressure gauge installed and vacuum modulator line connected, transmission line pressure should be approximately as shown in following table.

CONTROL PRESSURES

(Vacuum Modulator Connected)	
Shifter Position	[1]1 **Psi**
Drive ("D")	65
Intermediate ("L2")	65
Low ("L1")	95

[1] — Minimum pressure.

CONTROL PRESSURE TEST RESULTS

Control Pressure Too Low
- Low oil level.
- Clogged suction screen.
- Leak in oil pump suction circuit.
- Leak in oil pressure circuit.
- Pressure regulator valve mulfunction.
- Sealing ball in valve body dropped out

Control Pressure Too High
- Modulator vacuum line leaking or interrupted.
- Failed vacuum modulator.
- Vacuum leak in engine or accessory vacuum system.
- Pressure regulator valve malfunction.

SERVICE (IN VEHICLE)

The following components may be removed from transmission for inspection or repair, without removing transmission from vehicle:
- Governor Cover, Seals & Assembly
- Governor Pressure Switch (Diesel Only)
- Intermediate Servo Cover, Seal & Assembly
- Oil Pan & Screen Assembly
- Control Valve Assembly
- Check Balls & Valve Body Space Plates & Gaskets
- Inside Detent Range Lever
- Manual Detent Roller & Spring Assembly
- Throttle Lever & Bracket Assembly
- TV Detent Cable & "O" Ring

GENERAL MOTORS TURBO HYDRA-MATIC 180C (Cont.)

- Parking Pawl Actuator Rod
- Parking Pawl & Bracket
- Manual Shift & Seal
- Manual Valve
- Manual Valve Link
- Extension Housing, Gasket & Rear Seal
- 1-2 Accumulator Assembly
- Vacuum Modulator
- Cooler Fittings
- Oil Filter Pipe & "O" Ring
- Speedometer Driven Gear & Assembly
- Converter Clutch Solenoid
- Solenoid Wire Clips
- Electrical Connectors
- Governor Feed Screen
- Modulator Valve
- Low Band Adjustment

NOTE: For removal and installation procedures on these components, see Transmission Disassembly and Transmission Reassembly.

REMOVAL & INSTALLATION

See the appropriate article in AUTOMATIC TRANSMISSION REMOVAL Section.

TORQUE CONVERTER

NOTE: Torque converter is a sealed unit and cannot be disassembled for service.

LEAKAGE CHECK

See procedure given in G.M. Turbo Hydra-Matic 400 article in this section.

NOTE: For additional information on the Torque Converter Clutch (TCC) system used with this transmission see General Motors Torque Converter Clutch (TCC) System article in this section.

TRANSMISSION DISASSEMBLY

TORQUE CONVERTER & CONVERTER HOUSING OIL SEAL

1) Remove oil filler tube. Remove converter by pulling straight out. Install transmission in a holding fixture with oil pan up.

2) If converter housing oil seal replacement is necessary, remove oil seal using puller and slide hammer.

OIL PAN, VALVE BODY & SERVO PISTON

1) Remove attaching bolts and lift off oil pan. Remove oil pan gasket.

2) Remove manual detent roller and spring (retained by 2 bolts). Remove attaching bolt, then remove oil strainer and discard gasket.

3) Remove transfer plate reinforcement attaching bolts and remove reinforcement. Remove servo cover attaching bolts and remove cover and gasket.

4) Remove remaining bolts attaching valve body to case. Carefully remove valve body with gasket, and transfer plate.

Fig. 3: Removing Manual Detent Spring

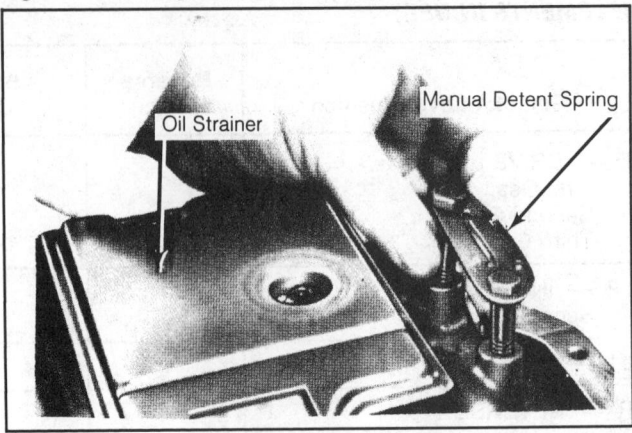

Fig. 4: Removing Valve Body from Transmission

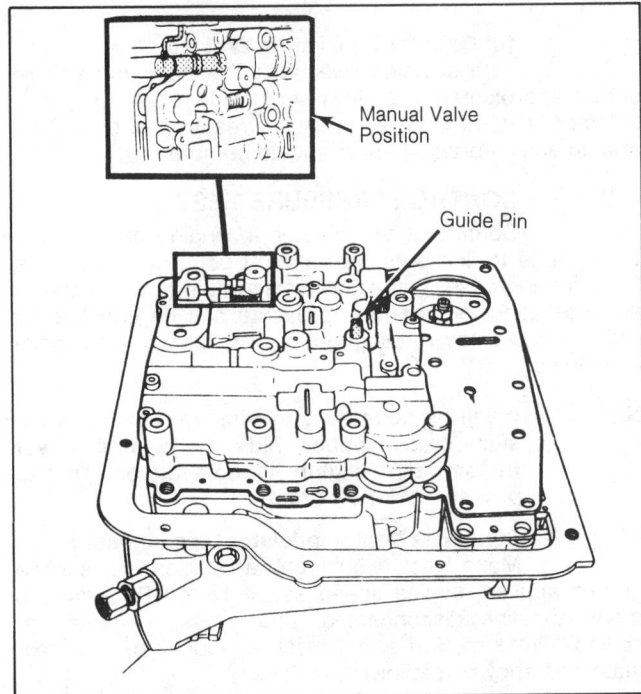

Care must be taken so that manual valve and link are not damaged or lost during valve body removal.

Fig. 5: Location of Check Balls in Case Oil Passages

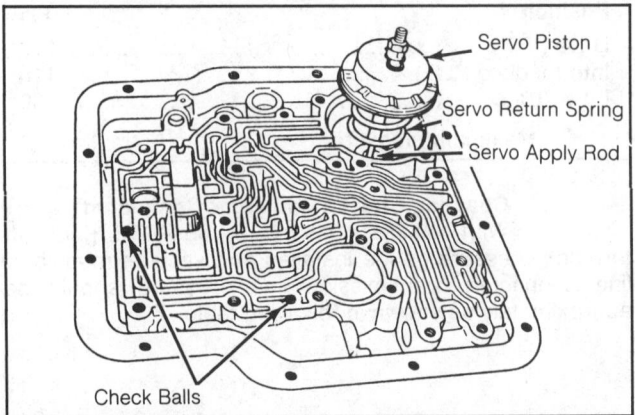

Arrows indicate check ball location.

GENERAL MOTORS TURBO HYDRA-MATIC 180C (Cont.)

5) Remove 2 bolts holding transfer plate to valve body, then remove plate and gasket. Remove 2 check balls located in oil passages in transmission case.

NOTE: Location of these 2 check balls must be noted to ensure that they are reinstalled correctly. See Fig. 5.

6) Using a compressor tool, compress servo piston and remove retaining snap ring. Remove tool and servo piston assembly.

Fig. 6: Compressing Servo Piston to Remove Snap Ring

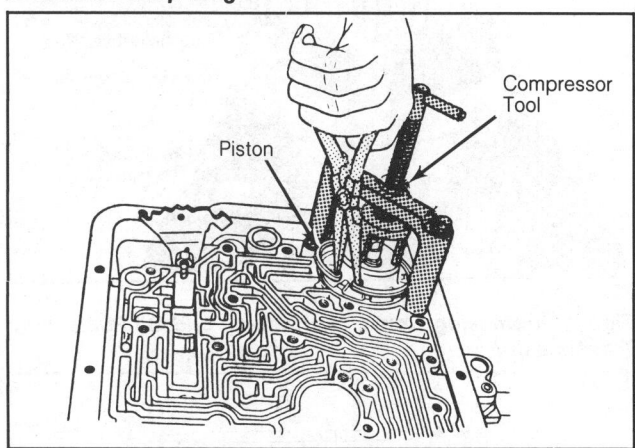

Compressor Tool

Piston

Servo is under high spring tension.

MODULATOR ASSEMBLY

1) Remove vacuum modulator from transmission case. Use care not to lose the modulator plunger.

2) Remove modulator valve and sleeve from case. Remove "O" ring seal, by using internal snap ring pliers.

SELECTOR LEVER, SHAFT & DETENT VALVE ASSEMBLY

1) Remove lock nut securing inner lever to selector shaft, then remove inner lever. Remove selector lever shaft spring pin by pulling upwards with small pliers as shown in Fig. 7.

Fig. 7: Removing Selector Lever Shaft Spring Pin

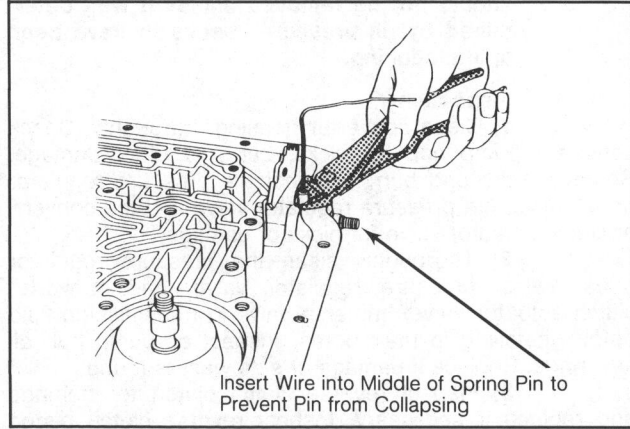

Insert Wire into Middle of Spring Pin to Prevent Pin from Collapsing

Insert wire into middle of spring to prevent pin from collapsing.

2) Remove selector lever shaft. Remove selector lever shaft oil seal. Discard oil seal.

3) Remove detent valve spring pin using pliers. Push on spring seat of detent valve assembly from front of case and remove detent valve, sleeve, spring, and spring seat from rear of case.

EXTENSION HOUSING & SPEEDOMETER DRIVEN GEAR

1) Remove bolt holding speedometer driven gear housing retainer. Carefully remove retainer and pull driven gear assembly from extension housing bore.

2) Remove extension housing attaching bolts. Slide extension housing and gasket from case, while noting position of parking pawl in housing. Remove parking pawl actuator lever and actuator rod from transmission case as shown in Fig. 8.

Fig. 8: Removing Parking Pawl Actuator Rod

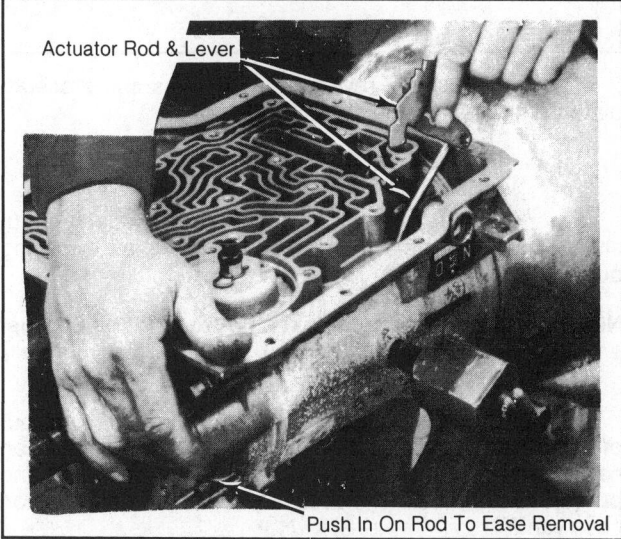

Actuator Rod & Lever

Push In On Rod To Ease Removal

Push in on rod to ease removal.

SPEEDOMETER DRIVE GEAR, GOVERNOR BODY & HUB

1) Depress speedometer drive gear retaining clip and slide gear off output shaft.

2) Remove 4 attaching bolts from governor body, slide governor body off output shaft. Remove governor hub retaining snap ring, and slide hub from output shaft.

CONVERTER HOUSING, OIL PUMP, REVERSE CLUTCH & SECOND CLUTCH ASSEMBLY

1) Turn transmission in holding fixture so that converter housing is facing up. Remove the 7 converter housing attaching bolts. Loosen, but do not remove, the 5 oil pump attaching bolts. See Fig. 9.

2) Remove converter housing with oil pump, reverse clutch and second clutch assemblies. Use care not to lose selective thrust washer, located between oil pump hub and second clutch drum.

NOTE: Second clutch assembly may remain in case when removing converter housing.

GENERAL MOTORS TURBO HYDRA-MATIC 180C (Cont.)

Fig. 9: View of Converter Housing Showing Housing and Oil Pump Attaching Bolts

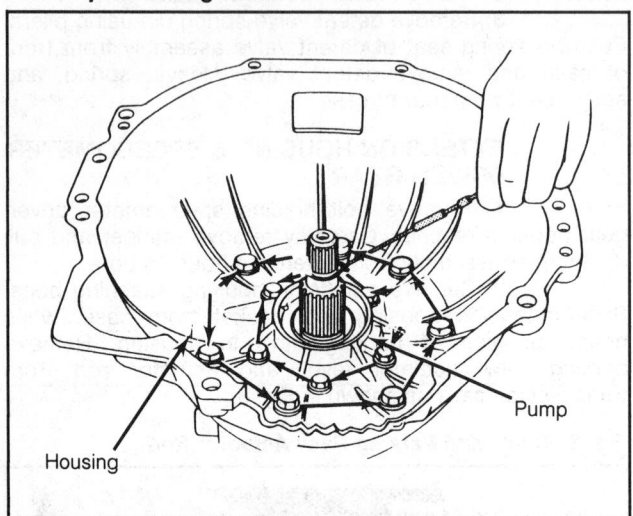

Housing

Pump

3) Remove reverse clutch plates and pressure plate from transmission case.

THIRD CLUTCH, PLANETARY CARRIER, REACTION SUN GEAR & LOW BAND

1) Lift out third clutch assembly and input shaft. Remove planetary carrier and output shaft by sliding out.

NOTE: Care should be taken not to lose the 2 thrust bearings and 1 thrust washer from planetary carrier assembly.

2) Pull reaction sun gear and drum straight out of case. Remove thrust bearing from rear of transmission case. Remove low band by slightly compressing band and pulling straight out. If necessary, remove transmission case vent.

NOTE: If transmission case vent is removed, a new vent must be installed. DO NOT attempt to reinstall old vent.

COMPONENT DISASSEMBLY & REASSEMBLY

CONVERTER HOUSING, OIL PUMP & REVERSE CLUTCH

Disassembly
1) Remove second clutch assembly from oil pump shaft. Remove selective washer from oil pump shaft.
2) Remove oil pump outer seal. Remove oil pump bolts from converter housing. Separate oil pump from housing. Remove oil pump wear plate. *See Fig. 11.*
3) Remove converter housing oil seal, and if necessary, remove housing bushing using a bushing driver. Mark relative location of oil pump gears and remove gears from oil pump body.
4) Using a compressor tool, compress reverse clutch return springs and remove snap ring. Remove reverse clutch retaining ring and 24 return springs. Remove reverse clutch piston.

Fig. 10: Separating Second Clutch from Converter Housing

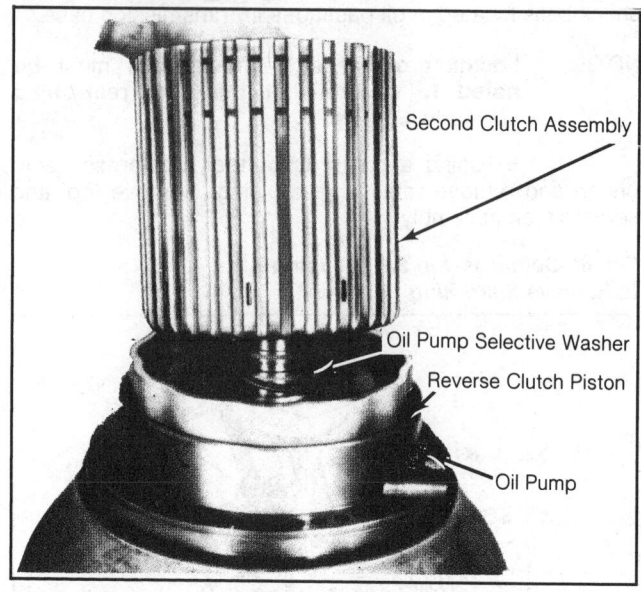

Second Clutch Assembly

Oil Pump Selective Washer

Reverse Clutch Piston

Oil Pump

Fig. 11: Removing Converter Housing and Oil Pump from Transmission

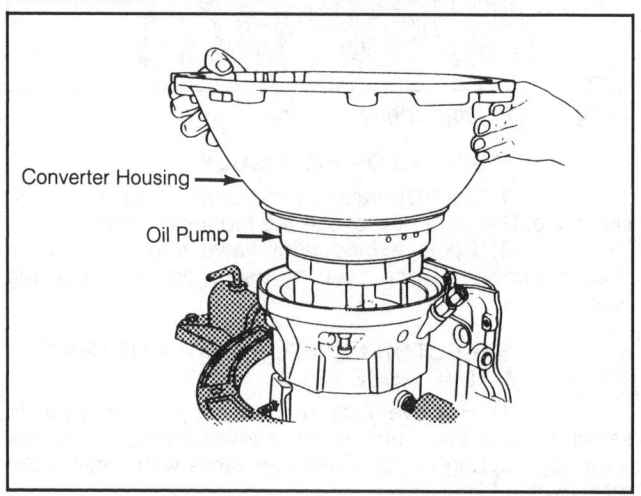

Converter Housing

Oil Pump

NOTE: Pressure regulator valve and boost valve should not be removed unless it was determined by oil pressure checks to have been malfunctioning.

Inspection
1) Clean converter housing thoroughly. Check converter pump hub for nicks, burrs or other damage. Remove nicks and burrs. Inspect the pressure regulator boost valve, the pressure regulator valve and the converter clutch actuator valve for nicks or damage.
2) Thoroughly clean the pressure regulator boost valve, pressure regulator valve, and converter clutch actuator valve. Immerse valve in transmission fluid before installing in their bores. Inspect oil pump hub oil seal rings. Replace if damage or side wear is found.
3) Inspect reverse clutch piston for damage and replace if necessary. Inspect reverse clutch piston springs for wear or distortion and replace as necessary.

GENERAL MOTORS TURBO HYDRA-MATIC 180C (Cont.)

Fig. 12: Exploded View of Valves in Oil Pump

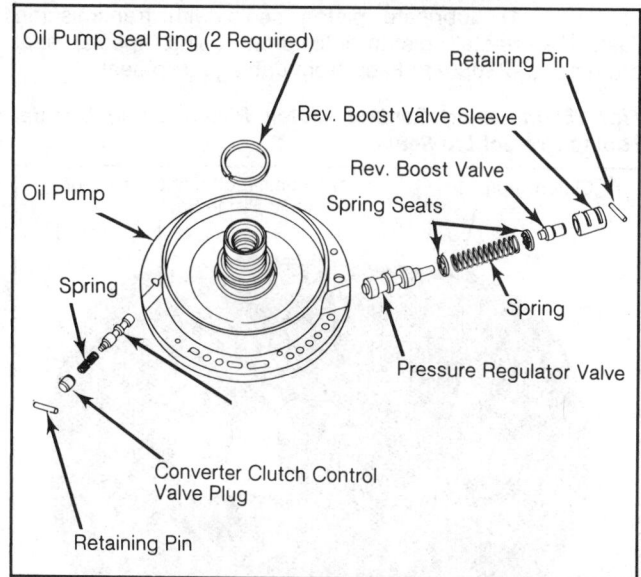

NOTE: Use rag or cloth to protect oil pump face when pressing out bushing.

2) Clean pump body, including all holes and pockets thoroughly. With oil pump shaft hole "A" (*Fig. 13*) facing downward, scribe an alignment mark on oil pump shaft inner diameter at the center of oil groove to right of hole "A".

3) Scribe mark on outer edge of bushing through centers of small and large drilled holes "B". Place bushing into oil pump shaft with small hole up, and align scribe marks on bushing with those made in oil pump shaft.

4) Use arbor press to drive bushing into oil pump shaft until seated in bore.

CAUTION: Care must be taken so that bushing is pressed in straight, using scribe marks as a guide until firmly seated.

Reassembly

1) If removed, install a new converter housing bushing using a driver. Install bushing flush with front face of housing. Install new converter housing oil seal.

2) Immerse pressure regulator valve in transmission fluid, install valve in oil pump body bore. Install pressure regulator spring, 2 spring seats, boost valve and sleeve into pump bore. Depress regulator boost valve sleeve until back end lines up with pin holes. Install retaining spring pin.

3) Install 2 new oil seals on reverse clutch piston. Install reverse clutch piston onto rear face of oil pump using a liberal amount of transmission fluid.

4) Install 24 reverse clutch piston return springs, then install retaining seat. Compress return springs and seat and install retaining snap ring.

CAUTION: DO NOT air check reverse clutch as the clutch is not complete and damage to return spring retaining seat may occur.

5) Turn oil pump and reverse clutch assembly so that oil pump face is up. Install oil pump gears using location marks made at disassembly. Install oil pump wear plate onto oil pump.

4) Inspect oil pump and gears for any signs of wear or damage, and replace as necessary. Install gears into oil pump and check end clearance of both gears as follows:

5) Using a straightedge and feeler gauge, measure clearance between face of gears and pump face. Clearance should be .0005-.0035" (.013-.089 mm).

6) Next, measure clearance between drive gear and crescent while rotating gears one complete revolution. Clearance should be .005-.009" (.127-.229 mm).

7) Measure clearance between outside of driven gear and housing. Clearance here should be .003-.007" (.076-.178 mm). Finally, measure between inside of driven gear and crescent segment. Rotate gear one revolution. Clearance should be a minimum of .005" (.127 mm).

8) Inspect oil pump hub bushing for wear or damage. If replacement is necessary, proceed as follows:

Oil Pump Hub Bushing Replacement

1) Thread a 3/4" standard pipe tap into bushing. Using a drift on tap, press oil pump bushing out with arbor press.

Fig. 13: Installation of Oil Pump Hub Bushing

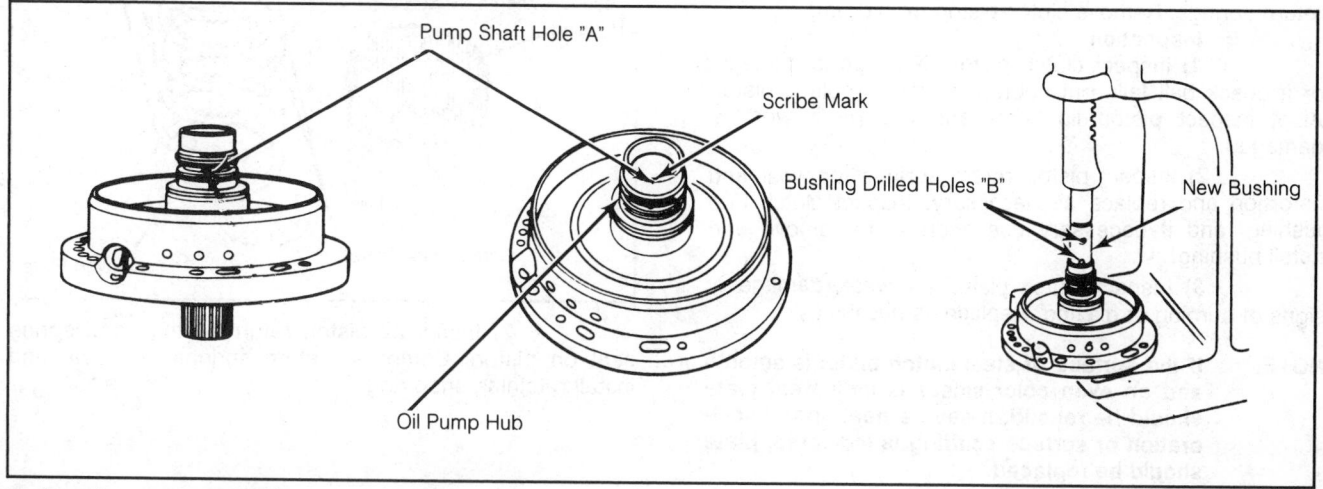

Scribe alignment marks on pump hub and bushing.

6) Insert guide pin into oil pump for alignment of converter housing and lower housing onto pump. Loosely install bolts into converter housing.

7) Use a aligning tool (J-23082-01) to align converter housing to pump. *See Fig. 14.* Tool should bottom on oil pump gear.

Fig. 14: Using Special Tool to Align Converter Housing to Oil Pump

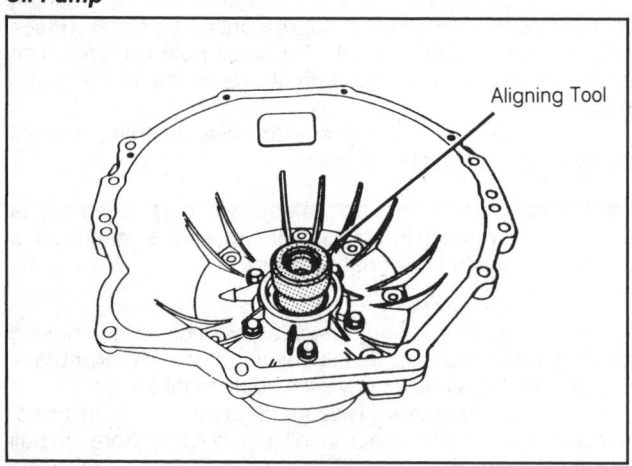

When correctly installed tool should bottom on oil pump gear.

8) Tighten oil pump attaching bolts in two stages to specified torque. Remove aligning tool. Install new converter housing-to-case rubber oil seal.

SECOND CLUTCH ASSEMBLY
Disassembly
1) Remove ring gear retaining ring from second clutch drum, then pull ring gear from drum. Remove second clutch spacer plate retaining ring, then remove spacer plate, steel and composition clutch plates from clutch drum.

NOTE: **Keep clutch plates in same sequence as they were installed in clutch drum.**

2) Remove second clutch-to-third clutch thrust washer. Using a compressor tool, compress second clutch return springs and remove retaining snap ring. Remove tool and withdraw spring retaining seat and return springs. Remove clutch piston from drum.

Inspection
1) Inspect clutch piston. If piston is damaged or if check ball falls out upon inspection, replace piston. Also, inspect piston lip seals and replace if worn or damaged.

2) Inspect piston return springs for wear and distortion and replace as necessary. Inspect clutch hub bushing, and if necessary use a driver to remove and install bushing.

3) Inspect clutch plates for wear, damage or signs of burning or glazing. Replace as necessary.

NOTE: **If the surface of steel clutch plate; is smooth and an even color smear is indicated, plate should be reused. If severe heat spot discoloration or surface scuffing is indicated, plate should be replaced.**

Reassembly
1) Lubricate piston seals with transmission fluid, then install piston into drum using special seal protector (J-23080) to keep from damaging lip seals.

Fig. 15: Installing Second Clutch Piston Using Special Tool to Protect Lip Seals

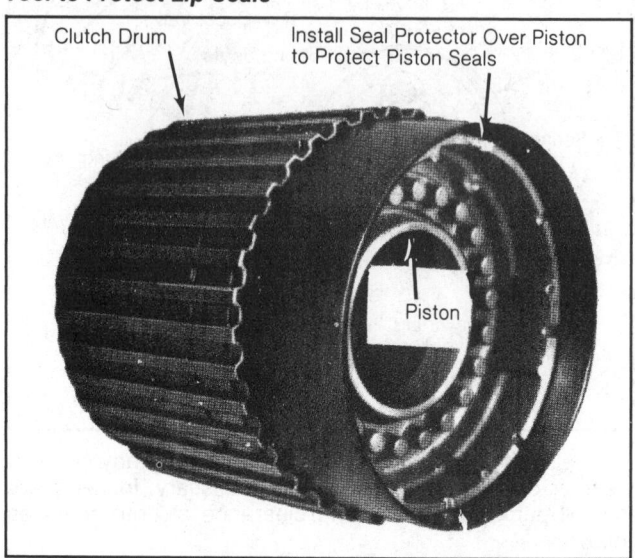

Install seal protector over piston to protect piston seals.

Fig. 16: Exploded View of Second Clutch Assembly

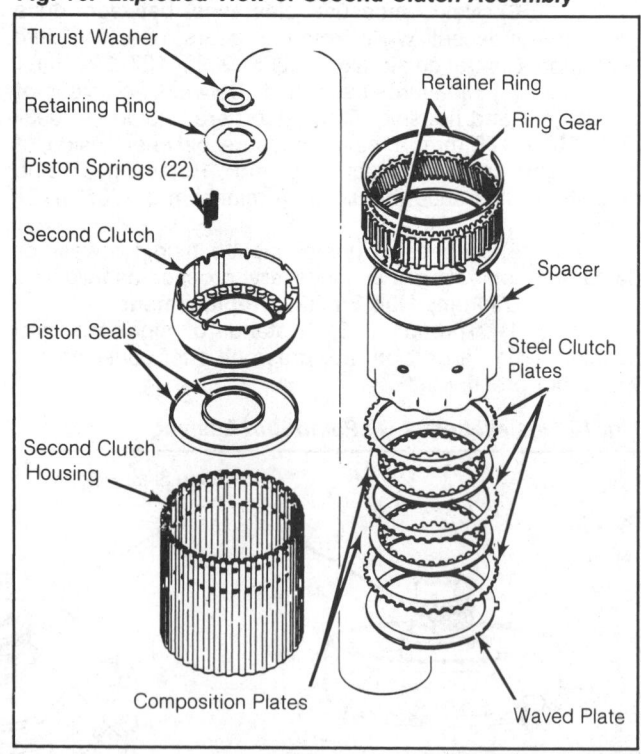

2) Install 22 piston return springs and spring seat on piston. Compress return springs and seat and install retaining snap ring.

GENERAL MOTORS TURBO HYDRA-MATIC 180C (Cont.)

Fig. 17: Exploded View of 180C Automatic Transmission THM 180C

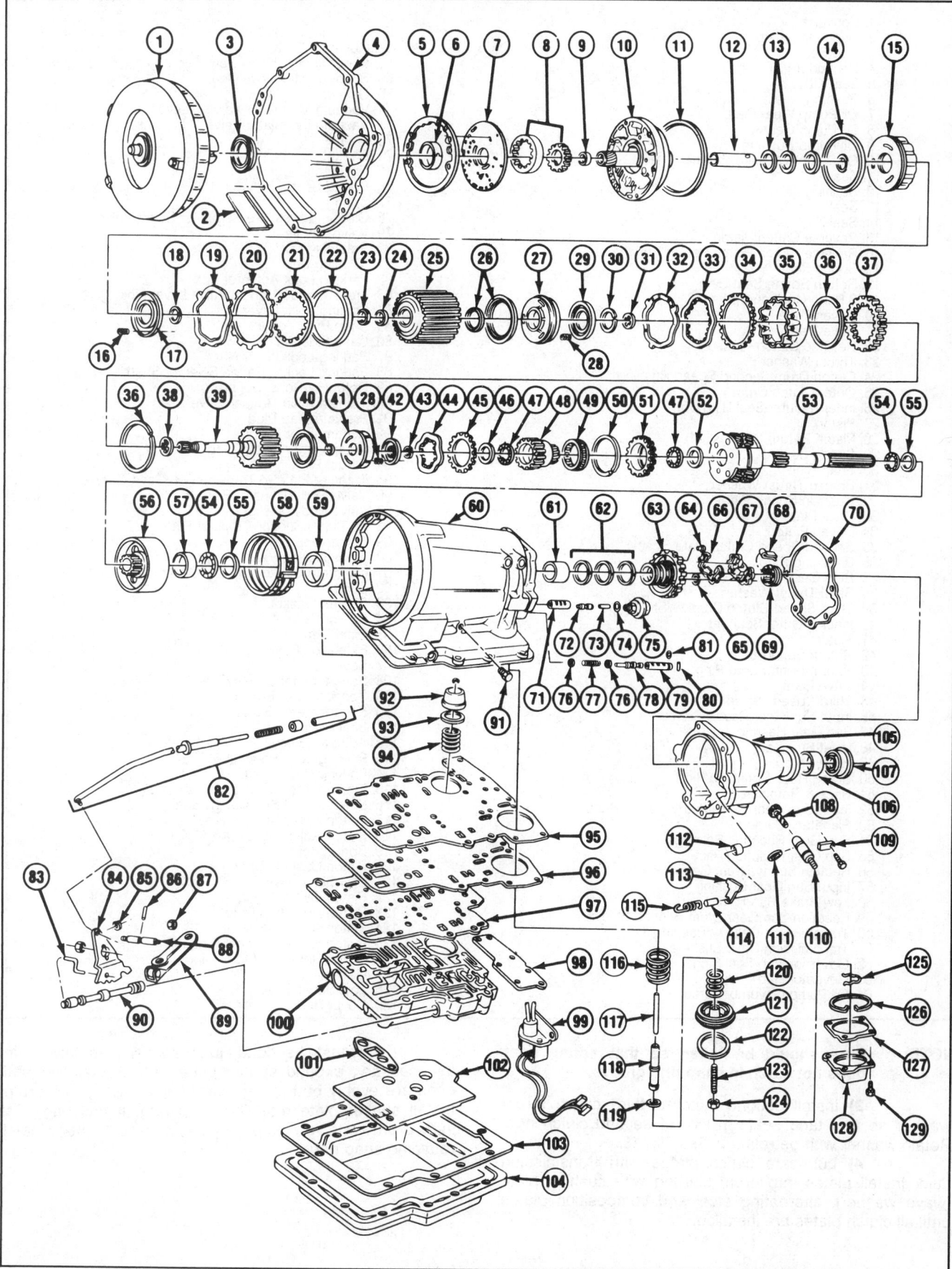

Automatic Transmissions

GENERAL MOTORS TURBO HYDRA-MATIC 180C (Cont.)

Automatic Transmission Components (Use With Fig. 17)

1. Converter	65. Snap Ring
2. Inspection Plate	66. Governor Gasket
3. Hub Seal	67. Governor Body
4. Converter Housing	68. Speedometer Drive Gear Clip
5. Seal Kit	69. Speedometer Drive Gear
6. Bushing	70. Gasket
7. Oil Pump Wear Plate	71. Vacuum Modulator Valve Sleeve
8. Oil Pump Gear	72. Vacuum Modulator Valve
9. Oil Pump Bushing	73. Sleeve
10. Oil Pump w/Gasket & Wear Plate	74. Gasket
11. Seal Kit	75. Vacuum Modulator
12. Bushing	76. Spring Seat
13. Seal	77. Spring
14. Seal Kit	78. Oil Pump Pressure Regulator Boost Valve
15. Reverse Clutch Piston	79. Valve Sleeve
16. Reverse Clutch Piston Return Springs (24)	80. Retainer Pin
17. Spring Seat	81. "O" Ring Seal
18. Return Spring Seat Ring	82. Parking Lock Actuator
19. 3 Pong Cushion Spring	83. Transmission Manual Valve Lever Link
20. Driven Plate	84. Parking Lock Lever Nut
21. Drive Plate	85. Snap Ring
22. Reverse Clutch Pressure	86. Case Side Pin
23. Thrust Washer	87. Parking Lock Lever Nut
24. Clutch Drum Second Speed Bushing	88. Parking Lock & Range Selector Shaft
25. Outer Clutch Drum	89. Detent w/Roller Spring
26. Inner & Outer Seal Ring Set	90. Transmission Manual Valve
27. Piston	91. Pressure Tap Plug
28. Piston Return Springs (24)	92. Accumulator Piston
29. Spring Seat	93. Accumulator Piston Ring
30. Snap Ring	94. Thrust Ring
31. Bronze Thrust Washer	95. Transfer Plate to Transmission Case Gasket
32. Cushion Spring Plate	96. Valve Body Transfer Plate
33. Drive Plate	97. Valve Body Gasket
34. Driven Plate	98. Oil Pump Suction Transfer Plate
35. Second Speed Clutch Plate Spacer	99. Solenoid
36. Retaining Ring	100. Transmission Valve Body
37. Ring Gear	101. Oil Pump Suction Screen Gasket
38. Steel Thrust Washer	102. Screen
39. Third Speed Clutch Drum w/Shaft	103. Oil Pan Gasket
40. Inner & Outer Seal Set	104. Oil Pan
41. Piston	105. Extension
42. Return Spring Seat	106. Extension Bushing
43. Return Spring Seat Ring	107. Seal
44. Drive Plate	108. Speedometer Driven Gear
45. Third Speed Driven Plate	109. Speedometer Bracket
46. Input Sun Gear Race	110. Speedometer Guide
47. Sun Gear Bearing	111. Seal Ring
48. Input Sun Gear	112. Actuator Sleeve
49. Input Sprag	113. Parking Lock Pawl
50. Sprag Race Retaining Ring	114. Parking Pawl Shaft
51. Race & Retainer	115. Parking Pawl Disengaging Spring
52. Input Sun Gear to Planetary Carrier Race	116. Low Servo Piston Return Spring
53. Planetary Carrier	117. Piston Apply Rod
54. Sun Gear Reaction Bearing	118. Piston Adjusting Sleeve
55. Sun Gear Reaction Race	119. Spring Seat
56. Rection Sun w/Drum Gear	120. Piston Cushion Spring
57. Input Sun Gear Bushing	121. Low Servo Piston
58. Low Brake Band	122. Piston Oil Seal Ring
59. Reaction Sun Gear Drum Bearing Sleeve	123. Piston Adjusting Stud
60. Transmission Case w/Bushing	124. Piston Adjusting Nut
61. Transmission Case Bushing	125. Piston Retaining Inner Ring
62. Governor Hub Seal Ring	126. Piston Retaining Outer Ring
63. Governor Hub	127. Gasket
64. Oil Pump Governor Screen	128. Low Servo Cover
	129. Cover Bolt

NOTE: **Care should be taken so that spring seat does not catch in snap ring groove.**

3) Install second clutch-to-third clutch thrust washer so that tang seats in slot of second clutch hub. Retain washer with petrolatum. *See Fig. 18.*

4) Lubricate clutch plates with transmission fluid. Install plates into drum starting with cushion plate (wave washer), alternating steel and composition plates until all clutch plates are installed.

5) Install second clutch spacer plate into drum. If necessary, expand spacer plate with screwdriver until ends are evenly butted together seating tightly into drum. Install spacer plate retaining snap ring. Install ring gear into drum with grooved edge facing up, then install retaining snap ring.

GENERAL MOTORS TURBO HYDRA-MATIC 180C (Cont.)

Fig. 18: *Installing Second Clutch-to-Third Clutch Thrust Washer*

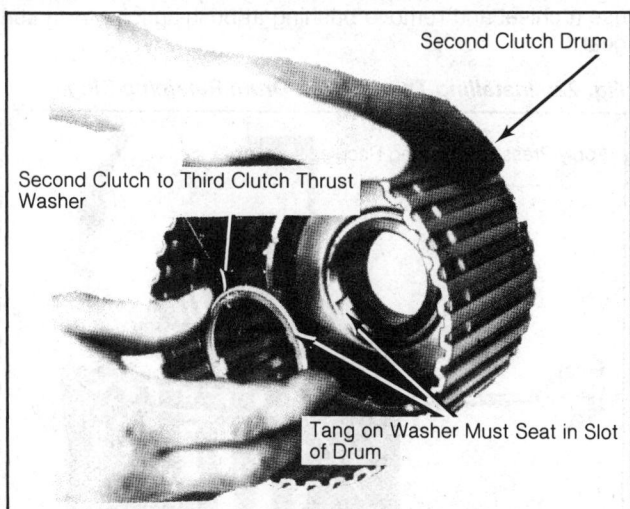

THIRD CLUTCH ASSEMBLY, SPRAG & INPUT SUN GEAR

Disassembly

1) Mount third clutch assembly in vise at a 90 degree angle. Position the 5 pins of sprag retaining ring removal tool (J-29351) into elongated slots of third clutch drum as shown in *Fig. 19*.

NOTE: Do not put a pin into slot if the internal retaining ring is not visible in that slot.

2) Slide compressing ring of removal tool over pin cage to compress retaining ring. Pull up on removal tool to withdraw sprag assembly from clutch drum. Remove input shaft-to-input sun gear thrust washer and thrust bearing from clutch drum.

NOTE: If sprag retaining ring hangs up on one side causing clutch hub to cock, insert a punch in slot to compress ring.

Fig. 19: *Installing Retaining Ring Removal Tool on Third Clutch Assembly*

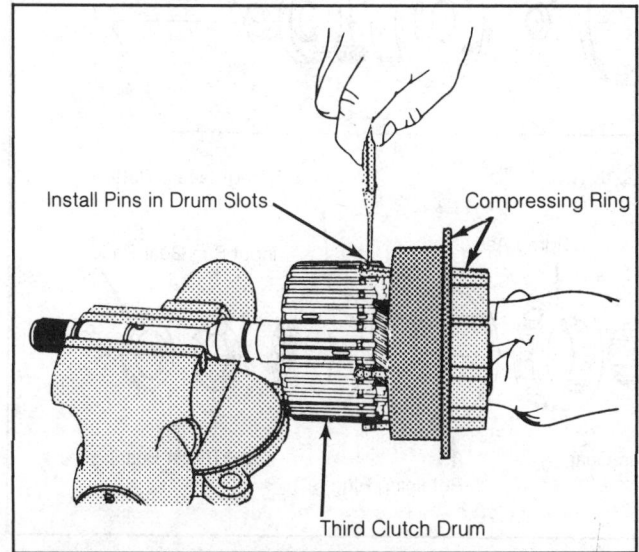

Insert punch in slot only if ring is visible.

3) Lift clutch plates from drum, noting the number and installation sequence for reassembly reference.

4) Remove input sprag race and retainer assembly from clutch hub and input sun gear assembly. *See Fig. 20.*

Fig. 20: *Sprag Assembly*

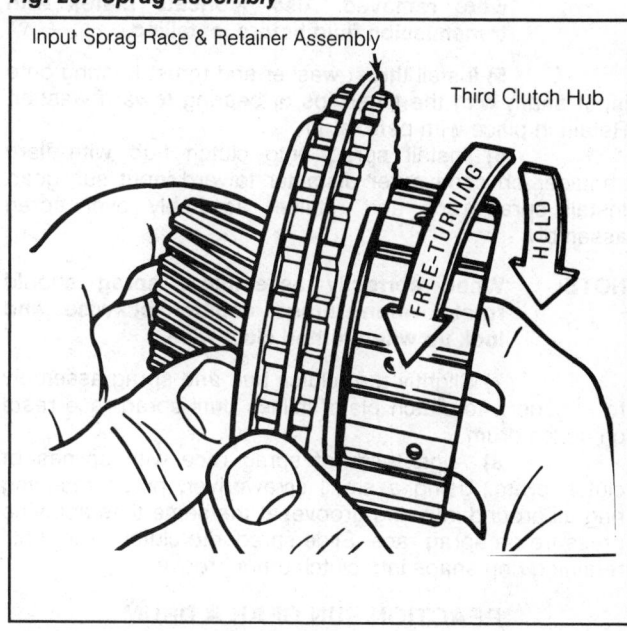

Check sprag for correct operation.

5) Push sprag assembly and retaining rings from sprag race and retainer.

6) Using a compressor tool, compress third clutch piston return springs and remove snap ring. Remove retaining seat and 12 piston return springs. Remove piston from drum.

Inspection

1) Inspect piston return springs for wear and distortion. Replace as necessary.

2) Inspect clutch piston for wear, damage and condition of check ball. If check ball is missing or falls out upon inspection, replace piston.

3) Inspect steel thrust washer on front face of third clutch drum. Replace if scored or damaged. Inspect all other thrust washers and thrust bearing for wear or damage and replace as necessary.

4) Inspect condition of composition and steel clutch plates. Replace as necessary.

5) Inspect sprag assembly for wear, damage or sprags that fall freely out of cage. Inspect input sun gear for chipped or nicked teeth or abnormal wear. Replace as necessary.

Reassembly

1) Lubricate and install new lip seals on clutch piston. Carefully install new oil seal on input shaft inside third clutch drum, with lip pointing downward.

2) Install piston into drum using care not to damage lip seals. Install 12 piston return springs onto piston, then install spring seat over springs.

3) Using a compressor tool, compress return springs and seat and install retaining snap ring.

NOTE: Care must be taken so that spring seat does not catch in snap ring groove when compressing springs.

4) Install the third clutch plate on the hub in the following order: steel plate, compostion plate, steel plate, composition plate, steel plate, and conical steel plate. When installed correctly, the I.D. of the conical plate will touch the steel plate below it but, the O.D. will not.

NOTE: Install the same number of clutch plates as were removed. Also, lubricate plates with transmission fluid before installing.

5) Install thrust washer and thrust bearing onto input shaft, with the inner lips of bearing toward washer. Retain in place with petrolatum.

6) Install sprag onto clutch hub with flare shoulder on cage outer diameter toward input sun gear. Install sprag race and retainer assembly over sprag assembly.

NOTE: When correctly assembled, sprag should rotate when turned counterclockwise and lock up when turned clockwise.

7) Slightly turn clutch hub and sprag assembly to engage it to clutch plate splines until sprag race rests on clutch drum.

8) Align teeth of sprag race with splines of clutch drum. Using a small screwdriver, press retaining ring all around into ring groove, at the same time applying pressure on sprag race. Slide sprag into clutch drum until retaining ring snaps into clutch drum groove.

REACTION SUN GEAR & DRUM
Inspection
1) Inspect reaction sun gear for chipped or nicked teeth and inspect sun gear for scoring. If necessary, replace complete assembly.

2) Inspect reaction sun gear, drum and bushing for wear or damage. If bushing requires replacement, use a chisel and remove bushing at bushing joint from sun gear.

Fig. 22: Installing Third Clutch Drum Retaining Ring

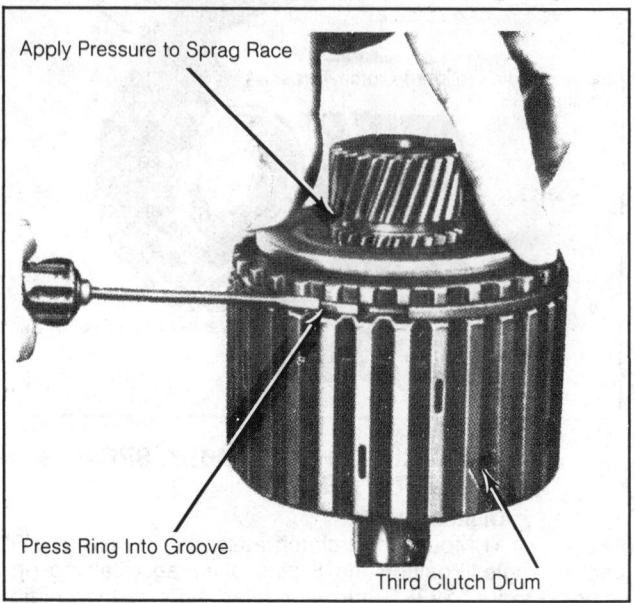

Press ring into groove.

3) Thoroughly clean drum. Install new bushing using a driver. Bushing should be installed flush with rear face of sun gear drum hub.

Fig. 21: Exploded View of Third Clutch Assembly, Sprag and Input Sun Gear Assembly

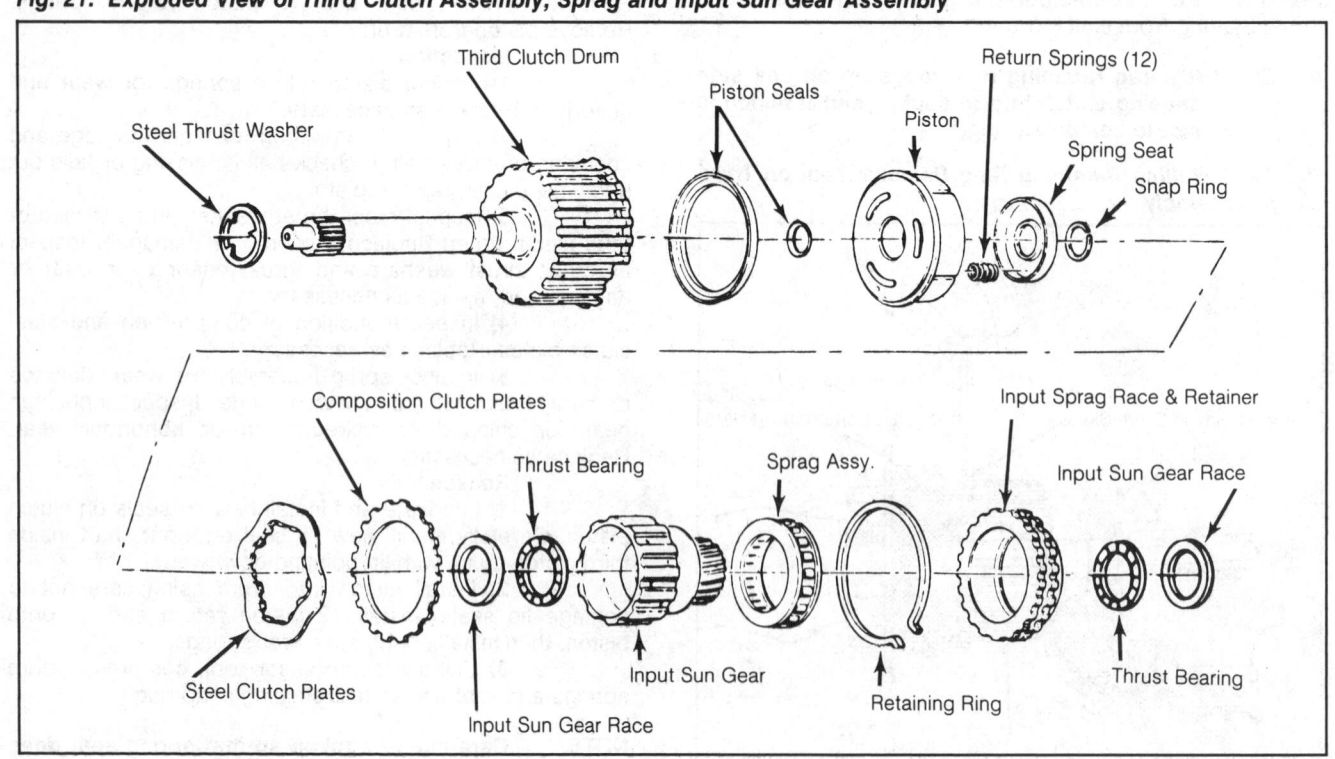

GENERAL MOTORS TURBO HYDRA-MATIC 180C (Cont.)

PLANETARY CARRIER

Inspection

1) Inspect planetary carrier and output shaft for distortion or damage. Inspect planetary pinions for excessive wear or damage, such as chipped teeth.

2) Check end play of all planetary pinions using a feeler gauge at points "A" and "B" in *Fig. 23.* End play should be .005-.035" (.127-.89 mm). If end play is not as specified, replace complete planetary carrier.

3) Tighten planetary carrier lock plate retaining screws to 20-35 ft. lbs. (27-48 N.m.)

GOVERNOR BODY

Disassembly

1) Depress secondary valve spring with small screwdriver and remove secondary valve spring retainer.

Fig. 23: Planetary Carrier and Pinion End Play

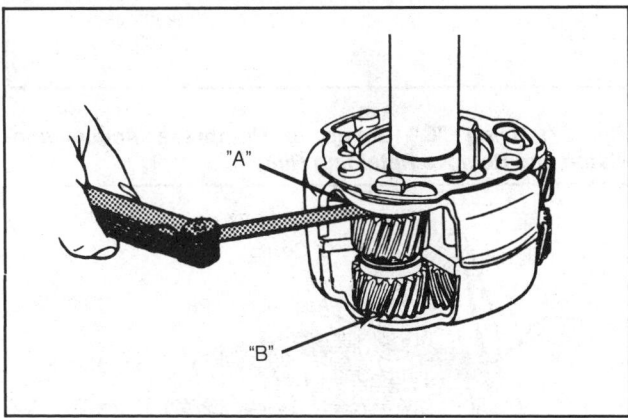

Check both "A" and "B".

Fig. 24: Removing Governor Assembly Secondary Valve Spring Retainer

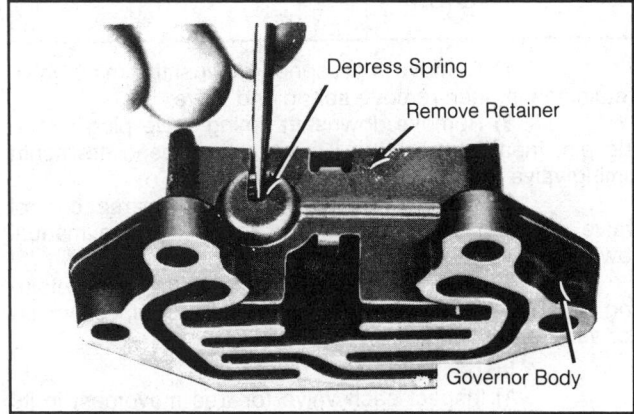

2) Remove secondary valve spring, secondary valve and primary valve from governor body.

Inspection

1) Inspect primary and secondary valves for nicks, burrs and other damage. If necessary, use crocus cloth to remove small burrs.

NOTE: **Do not remove the sharp edges of the valve since these edges perform a cleaning action within the valve bore.**

2) Inspect secondary valve spring for distortion or breakage. Clean governor body in solvent and below out all passages with compressed air. Replace governor body if damaged or worn.

Reassembly

NOTE: **Lubricate governor valves with transmission fluid before installation.**

Install primary valve in governor, small end first. Install secondary valve (small end first) into governor body. Install secondary valve spring, then depress spring and install retainer.

Fig. 25: Exploded View of Governor Body

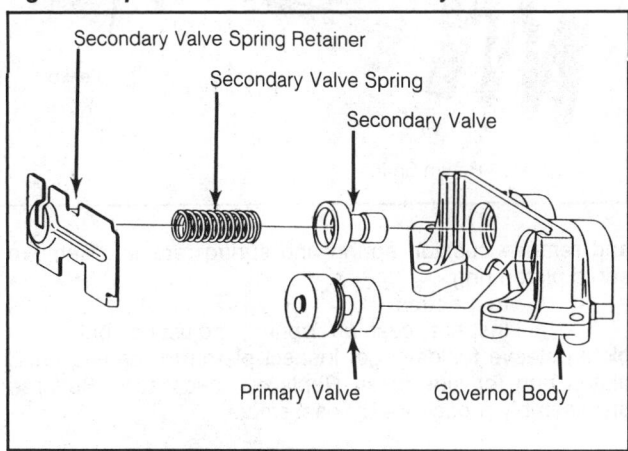

GOVERNOR HUB

Inspection

1) Inspect governor hub oil seal rings for wear or damage, and if necessary replace. Remove governor hub oil screen, using care not to lose or damage screen.

2) Inspect screen and clean with solvent and air dry. Install governor screen flush with hub.

3) Inspect governor hub splines for cracks or chipped teeth in splines. Replace governor hub if required.

EXTENSION HOUSING

Inspection

1) Inspect extension housing for damage and replace housing if necessary. Check parking pawl and spring for damage and replace as necessary.

2) If extension housing rear seal requires replacement, use a screwdriver and pry seal from housing. If bushing requires replacement, use a driver and drive bushing from housing.

3) Clean housing of dirt and foreign matter. Install new housing bushing into housing using a bushing driver until bushing is flush with shoulder of extension housing. Install new oil seal into rear of housing.

SERVO PISTON

Disassembly

1) Remove servo piston apply rod. Holding servo piston sleeve at flat portion of sleeve with wrench, loosen adjusting bolt lock nut and remove.

2) Depress servo piston sleeve and remove piston sleeve retaining ring. Push sleeve through piston

Fig. 26: Exploded View of Servo Piston Assembly

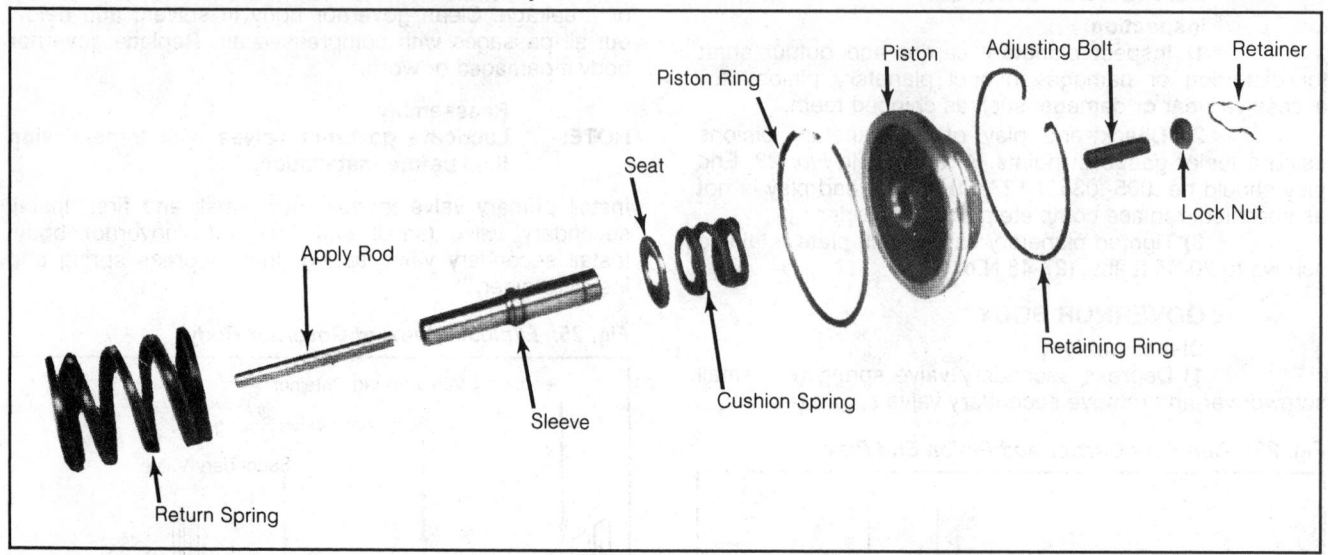

and remove cushion spring and spring retainer. Remove servo piston ring.

Inspection

Inspect cushion spring, adjusting bolt, and piston sleeve for damage. Inspect piston for damage and piston ring for side wear. Replace if necessary. Reverse disassembly procedure to reassemble.

VALVE BODY ASSEMBLY

NOTE: **As valve trains are removed from each valve body bore, place individual parts in correct order and in relative postion to valve body to simplify reassembly. Valves and springs are not interchangeable, all parts must be re-installed in correct order in proper valve body bore. Use valve body exploded view illustration as a disassembly and reassembly guide.**

Disassembly

1) Remove manual valve and link from valve body. Turn valve body so that transfer plate is facing upward and remove the two bolts attaching plate to valve body. Remove transfer plate and gasket.

2) Using a small "C" clamp. See Fig. 27. Compress accumulator piston and remove retaining ring. Carefully loosen "C" clamp as accumulator is under spring tension, then remove accumulator piston, oil ring and spring.

3) Remove retaining pin then slide out 1-2 shift control valve sleeve, control valve, 1-2 shift valve spring and valve.

NOTE: **It may be necessary to remove burrs in valve body bores made by retaining pin prior to removal of sleeves and valves.**

4) Remove 2-3 shift control valve retaining pin and sleeve, then slide out 2-3 shift control valve, spring seat, spring and 2-3 shift valve.

5) Remove 3-2 control valve retaining pin and plug. Remove 3-2 control valve spring and control valve.

6) Remove detent pressure regulator valve retaining pin, then remove spring and detent pressure regulator valve.

Fig. 27: Using "C" Clamp to Compress Accumulator Piston and Remove Retaining Ring

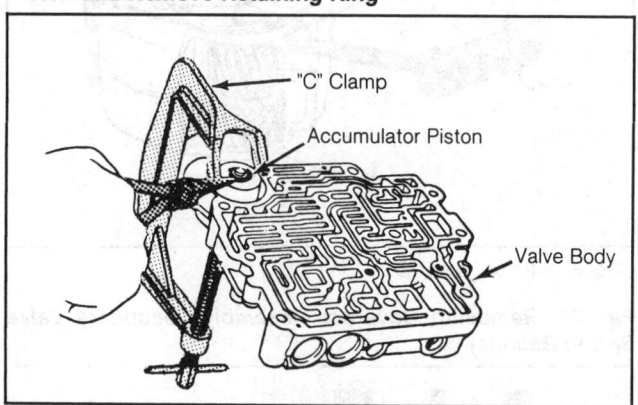

7) Remove high speed downshift timing valve retaining pin, then remove spring and valve.

8) Remove downshift timing valve plug retaining pin, then remove plug. Remove low speed downshift timing valve and spring.

9) Remove manual low and reverse control valve retaining pin, then remove spring and the manual low control valve and the reverse control valve.

10) Remove the 1-2 accumulator valve retaining pin and remove 1-2 accumulator valve plug, accumulator valve and spring.

Inspection

1) Inspect each valve for free movement in its respective bore. If necessary, use crocus cloth to remove small burrs on valves.

CAUTION: Do not remove the sharp edges of the valves as these edges perform a cleaning action within the bore.

2) Inspect valve springs for distortion or collapsed coils. Replace the complete valve body assembly if any part is damaged.

3) Inspect transfer plate for dents or distortion. Replace transfer plate if necessary.

GENERAL MOTORS TURBO HYDRA-MATIC 180C (Cont.)

Fig. 28: Exploded View of Valve Body Assembly

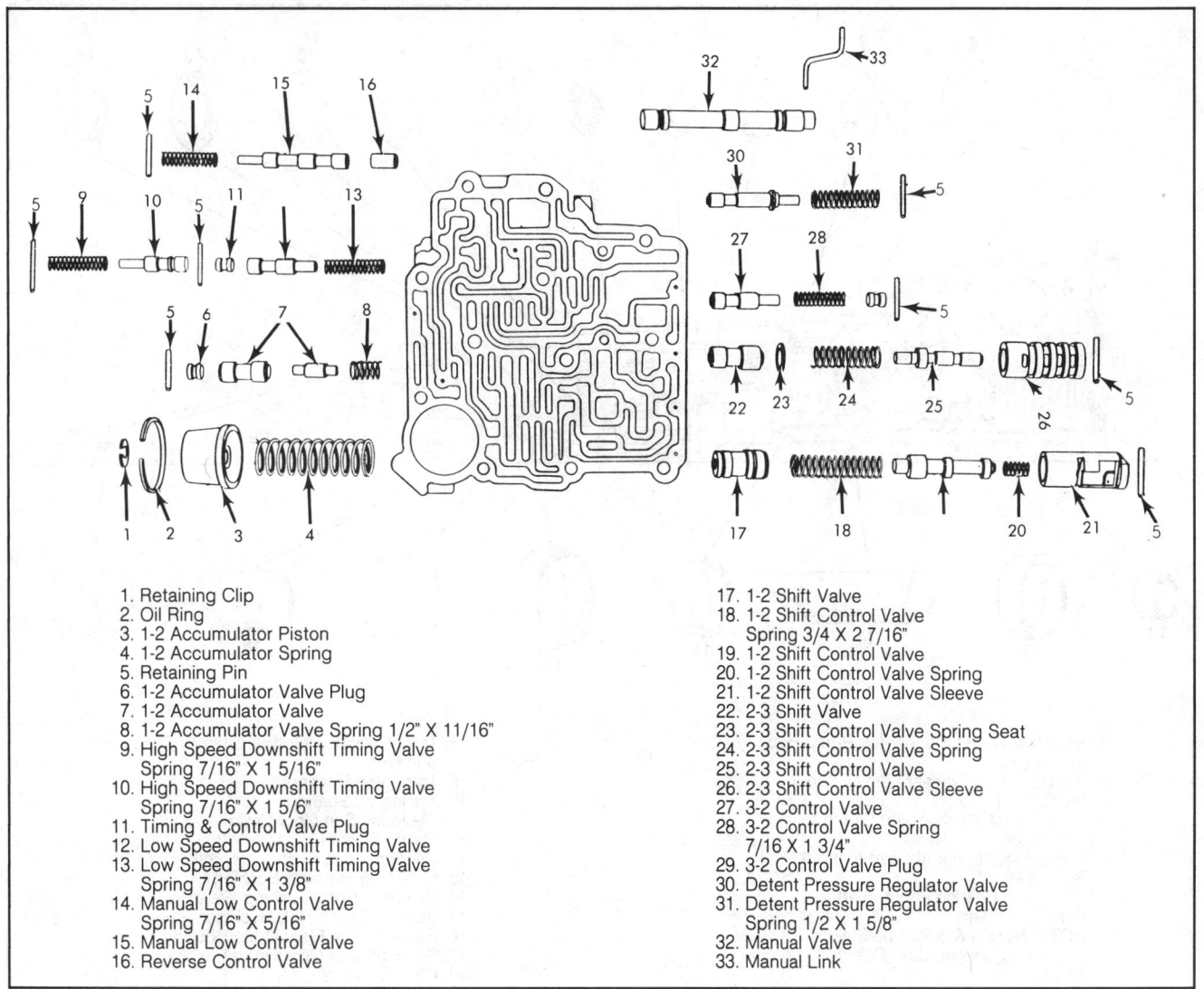

1. Retaining Clip
2. Oil Ring
3. 1-2 Accumulator Piston
4. 1-2 Accumulator Spring
5. Retaining Pin
6. 1-2 Accumulator Valve Plug
7. 1-2 Accumulator Valve
8. 1-2 Accumulator Valve Spring 1/2" X 11/16"
9. High Speed Downshift Timing Valve
   Spring 7/16" X 1 5/16"
10. High Speed Downshift Timing Valve
    Spring 7/16" X 1 5/6"
11. Timing & Control Valve Plug
12. Low Speed Downshift Timing Valve
13. Low Speed Downshift Timing Valve
    Spring 7/16" X 1 3/8"
14. Manual Low Control Valve
    Spring 7/16" X 5/16"
15. Manual Low Control Valve
16. Reverse Control Valve

17. 1-2 Shift Valve
18. 1-2 Shift Control Valve
    Spring 3/4 X 2 7/16"
19. 1-2 Shift Control Valve
20. 1-2 Shift Control Valve Spring
21. 1-2 Shift Control Valve Sleeve
22. 2-3 Shift Valve
23. 2-3 Shift Control Valve Spring Seat
24. 2-3 Shift Control Valve Spring
25. 2-3 Shift Control Valve
26. 2-3 Shift Control Valve Sleeve
27. 3-2 Control Valve
28. 3-2 Control Valve Spring
    7/16 X 1 3/4"
29. 3-2 Control Valve Plug
30. Detent Pressure Regulator Valve
31. Detent Pressure Regulator Valve
    Spring 1/2 X 1 5/8"
32. Manual Valve
33. Manual Link

Reassembly

Reverse disassembly procedure using a liberal amount of transmission fluid on all valves, plugs and springs.

TRANSMISSION CASE

Inspection

1) Inspect case for damage. Clean oil passages with cleaning solvent and air.

2) Check for good retention of band anchor pins. Inspect all threaded holes for thread damage. Inspect detent valve and modulator valve bores for scratches or scoring.

3) Inspect case bushing inside case at rear. If damaged, remove and install bushing using a driver. Install bushing flush with rear of case.

4) Inspect reaction sun gear drum bushing sleeve inside case at rear for scoring. If necessary, replace sleeve before installing new case bushing.

CAUTION: Care must be used when removing sleeve in order that aluminum case is not damaged.

TRANSMISSION REASSEMBLY

SELECTOR LEVER & SHAFT

1) Install new selector lever shaft oil seal in case, with grooved end (with metric threads) outside of case. Insert selector shaft through case from outside.

NOTE: Use care not to damage oil seal when installing shaft.

2) Insert spring pin in case to secure selector lever shaft. Guide selector lever over shaft and secure with lock nut. Insert parking pawl actuator rod from front of case and through hole in rear of case, then install retaining ring.

LOW BAND, REACTION SUN GEAR & DRUM

1) Turn transmission case so that front of case is upward. Place band in case and locate onto anchor pins in case.

GENERAL MOTORS TURBO HYDRA-MATIC 180C (Cont.)

Fig. 29: *Cutaway View of Transmission Case Showing Location of Washers and Bushings*

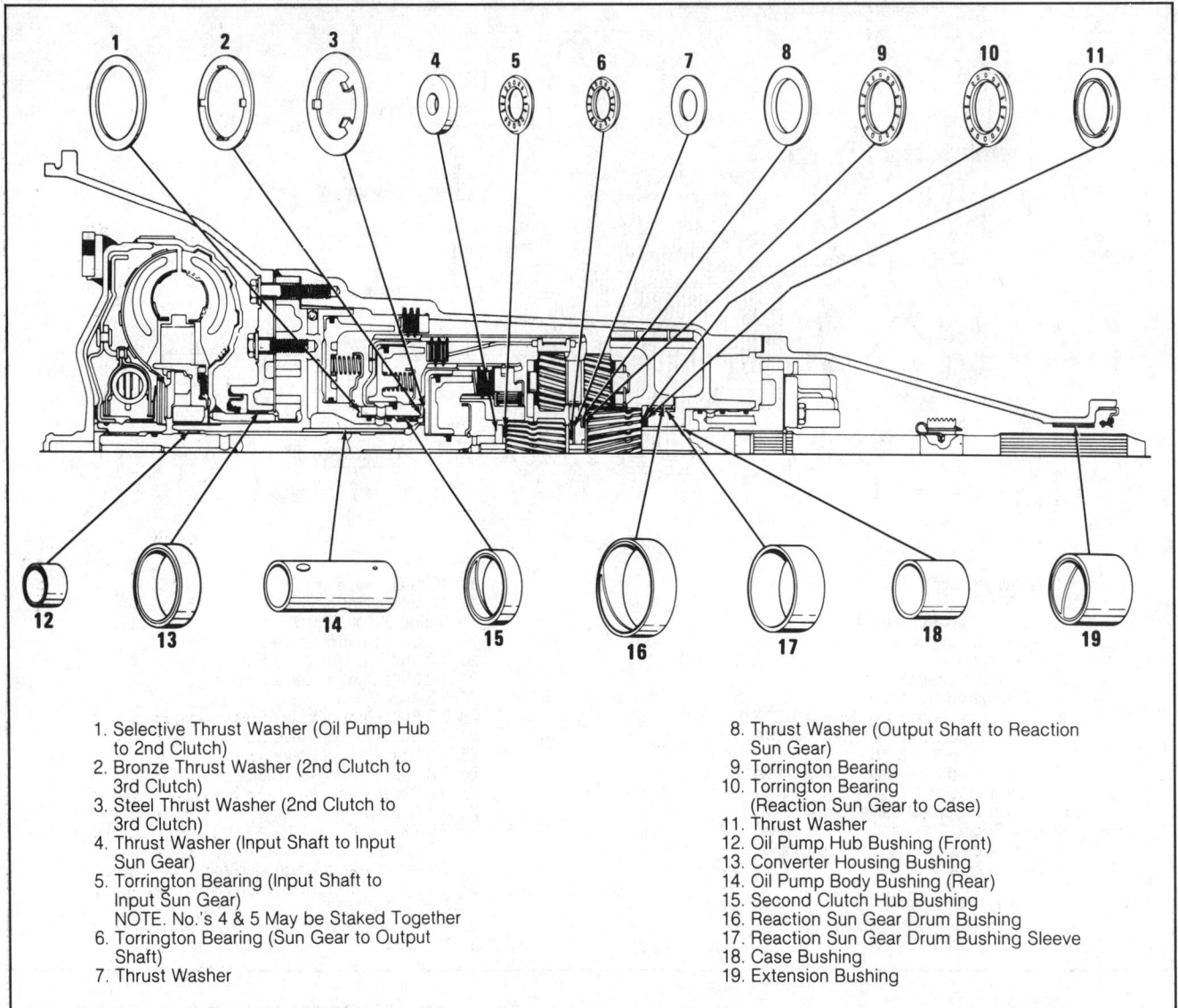

1. Selective Thrust Washer (Oil Pump Hub to 2nd Clutch)
2. Bronze Thrust Washer (2nd Clutch to 3rd Clutch)
3. Steel Thrust Washer (2nd Clutch to 3rd Clutch)
4. Thrust Washer (Input Shaft to Input Sun Gear)
5. Torrington Bearing (Input Shaft to Input Sun Gear)
   NOTE. No.'s 4 & 5 May be Staked Together
6. Torrington Bearing (Sun Gear to Output Shaft)
7. Thrust Washer
8. Thrust Washer (Output Shaft to Reaction Sun Gear)
9. Torrington Bearing
10. Torrington Bearing (Reaction Sun Gear to Case)
11. Thrust Washer
12. Oil Pump Hub Bushing (Front)
13. Converter Housing Bushing
14. Oil Pump Body Bushing (Rear)
15. Second Clutch Hub Bushing
16. Reaction Sun Gear Drum Bushing
17. Reaction Sun Gear Drum Bushing Sleeve
18. Case Bushing
19. Extension Bushing

2) Place thrust bearing into case and retain with petrolatum. The case bushing acts as a guide to center bearing.

3) Insert reaction sun gear and drum into low band with reaction sun gear facing upward. Install thrust bearing onto sun gear and hold in place with petrolatum.

OUTPUT SHAFT & PLANETARY CARRIER

1) Install thrust washer and Torrington bearing into planetary carrier. Retain in place with petrolatum.

2) Insert output shaft and planetary carrier from front of case. Ensure that planetary carrier engages reaction sun gear.

SECOND & THIRD CLUTCH ASSEMBLIES

1) With second clutch assembly on bench, align drive plates in drum. Insert third clutch drum and input shaft through top of second clutch drum, seating third clutch drum splines with second clutch plate splines.

2) Holding clutch assemblies by input shaft, lower into transmission case, indexing second clutch drum ring gear with long planetary pinion gear teeth.

REVERSE CLUTCH PLATES

1) Install aluminum pressure plate into transmission case with flat side up. Make sure that the lug on pressure plate engages with one of the narrow notches in case.

2) Lubricate steel and composition reverse clutch plates with transmission fluid. Install clutch plates into transmission case starting with a steel plate and alternating composition and steel clutch plates until all plates are installed.

3) Install reverse clutch cushion plate (wave washer) into case, so that all three of its lugs are engaged into narrow notches in case.

GENERAL MOTORS TURBO HYDRA-MATIC 180C (Cont.)

SELECTING TRANSMISSION END PLAY SELECTIVE THRUST WASHER

1) Place special gauging tool (J-23085) on case flange and against input shaft as shown in *Fig. 31*. Loosen thumb screw on tool to allow inner shaft of tool to drop onto second clutch drum hub.

2) Tighten thumb screw and remove gauging tool. Compare thickness of selective thrust washer No. "1" removed during transmission disassembly with protruding portion of gauging tool inner shaft.

3) Selective thrust washer used in reassembly should be the thickest washer available without exceeding the dimension of shaft protruding from tool.

Fig. 30: Converter Housing Oil Passages

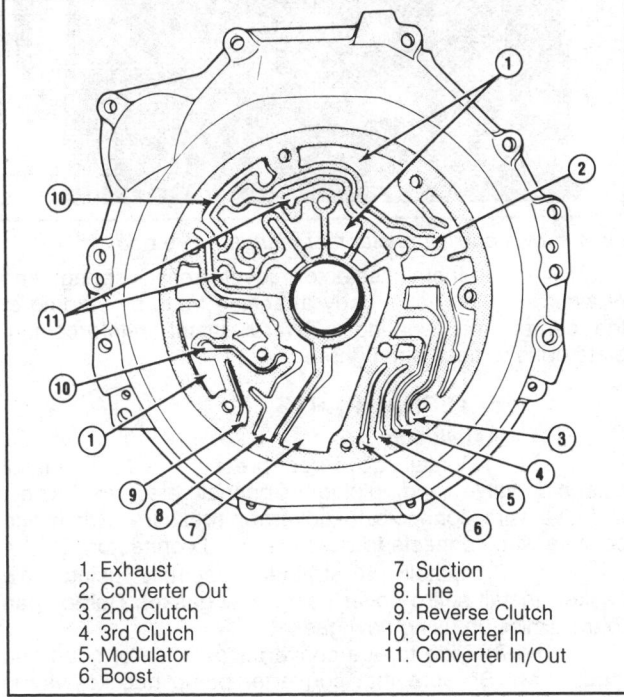

1. Exhaust	7. Suction
2. Converter Out	8. Line
3. 2nd Clutch	9. Reverse Clutch
4. 3rd Clutch	10. Converter In
5. Modulator	11. Converter In/Out
6. Boost	

Fig. 31: Using Special Gauging Tool to Select Transmission End Play Thrust Washer

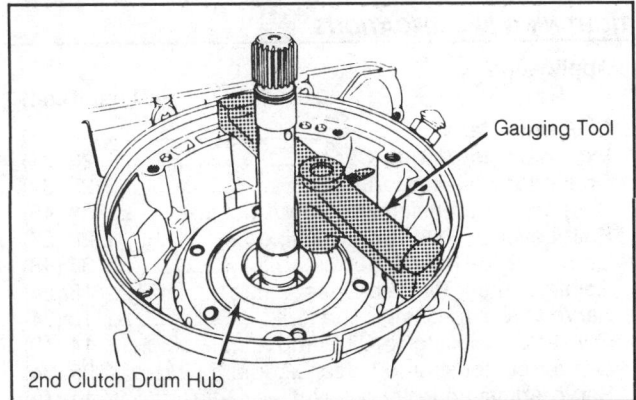

Gauging Tool

2nd Clutch Drum Hub

NOTE: **The dimension of thrust washer selected should be equal to or slightly less than inner shaft dimension for correct transmission end play. Selective thrust washers for end play**

are available in the following thicknesses: .069-.074", .075-.079", .080-.084", .085-.089", .090-.094", and .095-.100" (1.7-1.8 mm, 1.9-2.0 mm, 2.0-2.1 mm, 2.2-2.3 mm, 2.3-2.4 mm, and 2.4-2.5 mm).

4) If correct thickness thrust washer has been installed, transmission end play should be .014-.031" (.36-.79 mm).

Fig. 32: Aligning Converter Housing and Pump with Transmission Case

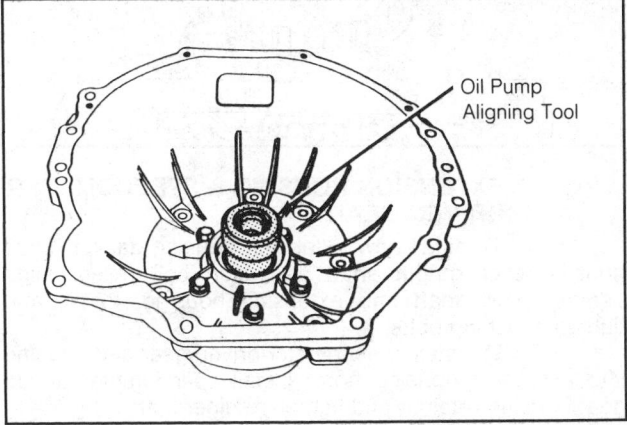

Oil Pump Aligning Tool

When correctly installed, tool should bottom on oil pump gear.

CONVERTER HOUSING, OIL PUMP & REVERSE CLUTCH ASSEMBLY

1) Install new oil pump flange gasket. Place transmission end play thrust washer, as previously determined, onto oil pump shaft and retain with petroleum jelly.

2) Install 2 guide pins in case and lower converter housing and oil pump into case. Use oil pump aligning tool (K-23082) to align converter housing with oil pump and case, then install and tighten converter housing attaching bolts.

3) Check for correct assembly by turning input shaft by hand. Shaft should rotate freely without binding.

GOVERNOR ASSEMBLY & SPEEDOMETER DRIVE GEAR

1) Turn transmission so that bottom face is upward. Lubricate governor hub seal rings with transmission fluid, then slide hub onto output shaft until it seats in case. Install snap ring into output shaft groove to lock hub in place.

2) Install new governor body gasket. Install governor body to governor hub, then install and tighten attaching bolts.

NOTE: **Ensure governor valves move freely after governor body is installed on hub.**

3) Install speedometer drive gear retaining clip into hole in output shaft. While depressing retaining clip, slide drive gear over output shaft and onto retaining clip.

GENERAL MOTORS TURBO HYDRA-MATIC 180C (Cont.)

Fig. 33: Installing Speedometer Drive Gear and Governor Body

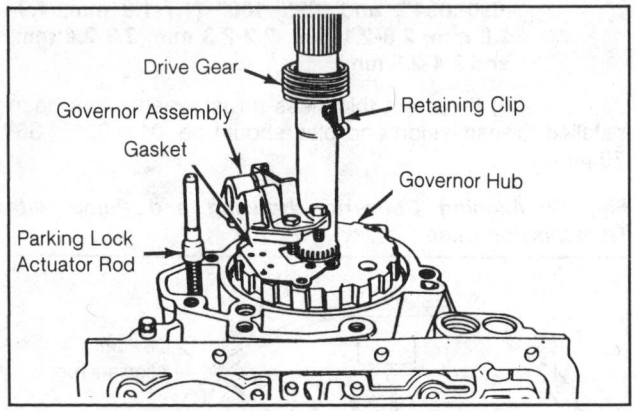

EXTENSION HOUSING & SPEEDOMETER DRIVEN GEAR

1) Install new extension housing gasket. Slide housing over output shaft and align bolt holes. Align parking pawl shaft into extension housing. Install and tighten attaching bolts.

2) Install speedometer driven gear and housing into extension housing bore. Install speedometer driven gear housing retainer and tighten retainer bolt.

DETENT VALVE, MODULATOR VALVE & MODULATOR ASSEMBLY

1) Lubricate with transmission fluid, then install detent valve, sleeve, spring and spring seat into case bore. Depress detent valve spring and insert spring pin to secure valve assembly.

NOTE: Detent valve sleeve must be installed with slot facing oil pan. Also, care should be taken so that spring pin is inserted into groove provided in sleeve and not into oil passage slots in sleeve.

2) Install modulator valve and sleeve into case with small end of valve installed first. Use a new "O" ring on modulator, then install plunger and thread modulator into case and tighten.

SERVO ASSEMBLY

1) Install servo apply rod, spring and piston into case using a liberal amount of transmission fluid. Compress servo piston spring and install retaining ring while lightly tapping piston until piston is seated.

2) To adjust servo, use a 3/16" hex head wrench on servo adjusting bolt and tighten bolt to 40 INCH lbs. Back off bolt EXACTLY 5 turns. Hold adjusting bolt stationary and tighten lock nut.

VALVE BODY ASSEMBLY

1) Position steel check balls into case oil passages. *See Fig. 5.*

2) Locate guide pins in case as shown in *Fig. 34* for correct alignment of valve body and transfer plate. Install new transfer plate-to-case gasket. Install bolts holding transfer plate to valve body.

3) Install manual valve into valve body bore using liberal amount of transmission fluid. Install long side of manual valve link into valve, then install short end of

link into selector lever as valve body and transfer plate are installed over guide pins.

Fig. 34: Positioning of Guide Pins for Valve Body Installation

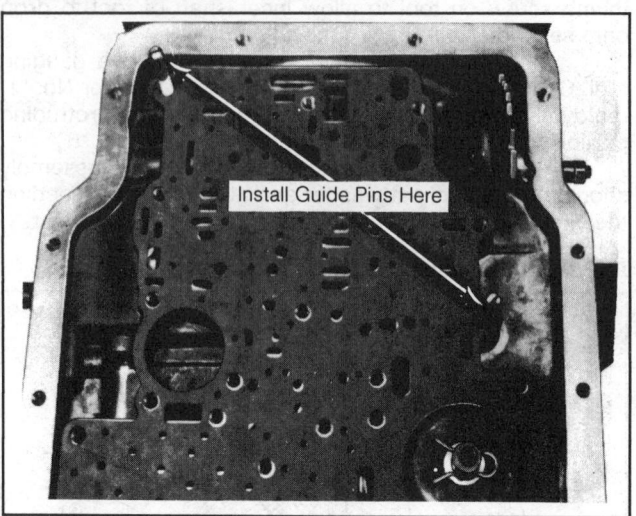

Inset shows correct position of manual valve body.

4) Install selector lever roller spring and retainer. Tighten valve body attaching bolts by starting at the center and working outward. Install reinforcement plate bolts to case and tighten.

EXTERNAL PARTS

Installation

1) Install governor pressure switch. Install solenoid valve and piping. Connect electrical wires, negative wire connects to governor pressure switch and positive wire connects to case electrical connector.

2) Install oil strainer assembly using new gasket. Install servo cover using new gasket. Bolt oil pan to transmission using new gasket.

3) Slide torque converter over stator shaft and input shaft. Be sure that converter pump hub keyway is seated into oil pump drive lugs. With converter properly seated, distance between engine mounting face of case and the front face of converter cover straps should be 1".

TIGHTINING SPECIFICATIONS

Application	Ft. Lbs. (N.m.)
Oil Pan-to-Case	8 (11)
Extension Housing-to-Case	23 (31)
Converter Housing-to-Engine	25 (34)
Support-to-Extension Housing	33 (45)
Shift Lever-to-Extension Housing	20 (27)
Converter-to-Drive Plate	35 (48)
Reinforcement Plate-to-Case	18 (24)
Servo Cover-to-Case	18 (24)
Converter Housing-to-Oil Pump	14 (19)
Converter Housing-to-Case	25 (34)
Servo Adjusting Bolt Lock Nut	14 (19)
	INCH Lbs.
Converter Inspection Cover	84 (10)
Transfer Plate-to-Valve Body	84 (10)
Oil Pressure Tap	72 (8)
Selector Lever Lock Nut	108 (12)
Governer Body-to-Hub	72 (8)

GENERAL MOTORS TURBO HYDRA-MATIC 200C

Buick
Chevrolet
GMC
Oldsmobile
Pontiac

TRANSMISSION IDENTIFICATION

Transmission model may be identified by the production code number, located on an identification plate attached to right side of transmission case. Number consists of a year code, 2 letter model code, and a build date code. Transmission model codes and their application are as follows:

TRANSMISSION MODEL CODES

Application	Code
All Models	CN,CZ,HB,HF,HH,HL, JE,JH,JJ,JY,OR,PS

DESCRIPTION

The Turbo Hydra-Matic 200C automatic transmission is a fully automatic unit consisting primarily of a 3-element hydraulic torque converter with the addition of a converter clutch and a compound planetary gear set. Three multiple-disc clutches, a roller clutch and a band provide friction elements required to obtain the desired function of the compound planetary gear set. A hydraulic system pressurized by a gear type pump provides the working pressure required to operate the friction elements and automatic controls.

The 3-element torque converter consists of a pump or driving member, a turbine or driven member, and a stator assembly. The stator assembly is mounted on a one-way roller clutch which will allow stator to turn clockwise but not counterclockwise. The converter clutch is splined to the turbine assembly, and when operated, applies against the converter cover, providing mechanical direct drive coupling of the engine to the transmission planetary gears. When converter clutch is released, the assembly operates as a normal torque converter.

NOTE: **See General Motors Torque Converter Clutch System article in this section for information on the torque converter clutch system used in the THM 200C.**

LUBRICATION & ADJUSTMENT

See the appropriate article in AUTOMATIC TRANSMISSION SERVICING Section.

TESTING

ROAD TEST

Drive Range

Position selector lever in Drive range and accelerate vehicle. A 1-2 and 2-3 shift should occur at all throttle openings (shift points will vary with throttle opening). Check part throttle 3-2 downshift at 30 MPH by quickly opening throttle approximately three-fourths, transmission should downshift 3-2. Check for 3-2 downshifts at 50 MPH, by depressing accelerator fully.

Fig. 1: Sectional View of Turbo Hydra-Matic 200C Automatic Transmission

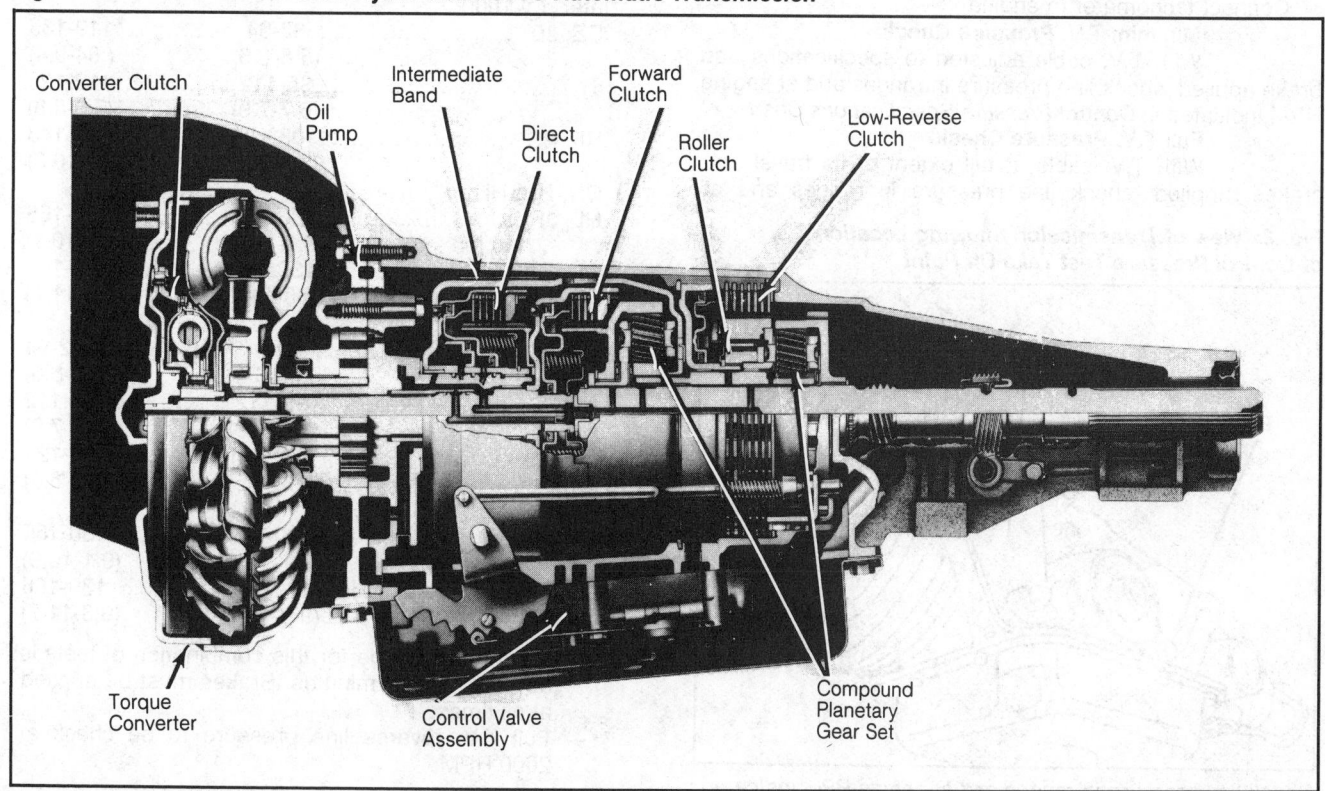

GENERAL MOTORS TURBO HYDRA-MATIC 200C (Cont.)

Intermediate Range

Position selector lever in Intermediate range and accelerate vehicle. A 1-2 shift should occur at all throttle openings (shift point will vary with throttle opening). No 2-3 shift can be obtained in this range. Check detent 2-1 downshift at 20 MPH. Transmission should downshift 2-1.

Low Range

Position selector lever in Low range and accelerate vehicle. No upshift should occur in this range.

Intermediate Range Overrun Braking

Position selector lever in Drive range and with vehicle speed at approximately 50 MPH, with closed throttle, move selector lever to Intermediate range. Transmission should downshift to 2nd. An increase in engine RPM and an engine braking effect should be noticed.

Low Range Overrun Braking

At 40 MPH, with throttle closed, move selector lever to Low. A 2-1 downshift should occur in speed range of approximately 40-25 MPH, depending on axle ratio and control valve assembly calibration. The 2-1 downshift at closed throttle will be accompanied by increasing engine RPM and an engine braking effect should be noticed.

Reverse Range

Position selector lever in Reverse range and check for reverse operation.

CONTROL PRESSURE TEST

Preliminary Checking Procedure

Perform the following prior to making control pressure test:
- Check transmission fluid level.
- Check and adjust T.V. cable.
- Check and adjust outside manual linkage.
- Check engine tune.
- Install oil pressure gauge. *See Fig. 2.*
- Connect tachometer to engine

Minimim T.V. Pressure Check

With T.V. cable adjusted to specifications and brake applied, check line pressure in ranges and at engine RPM indicated in *Control Pressure Specifications Chart.*

Full T.V. Pressure Check

With T.V. cable at full extent of its travel and brakes, applied, check line pressure in ranges and at engine RPM indicated in *Control Pressure Specifications Chart.*

CONTROL PRESSURE SPECIFICATIONS

Range @ RPM (Model Code)	Minimum T.V. Pressure psi (kg/cm²)	Full T.V. Pressure psi (kg/cm²)
"P" @ 1000		
CZ, JE	58-64 (4.1-4.5)	None
CN, HB, HF, HH, HL, JH, JJ, PS	66-64 (4.5-5.2)	None
OR	76-85 (5.3-6.0)	None
"R" @ 1000 [1] [2]		
CZ, JE	107-145 (7.5-10.2)	169-214 (11.8-15.0)
JY	107-145 (7.5-10.2)	161-206 (11.3-14.5)
CN, HF, HH, JH, PS	115-155 (8.1-10.9)	176-223 (12.3-15.6)
HB, HL, JJ	144-217 (10.1-15.3)	205-264 (14.4-18.6)
OR	153-229 (10.8-16.1)	197-279 (14.0-20.0)
"D" & "N" @ 1000 [1]		
CZ, JE	59-69 (4.1-4.8)	119-133 (8.4-9.4)
JY	58-69 (4.1-4.8)	112-125 (7.9-8.8)
HB, HF, HH, HL, CN, JH, JJ, PS	66-79 (4.6-5.6)	127-143 (9.0-10.0)
OR	76-90 (5.3-6.3)	120-135 (8.4-9.5)
"Inter" @ 1000 [1]		
CZ, JE	82-94 (5.8-6.6)	119-133 (.84-9.4)
JY	95-112 (6.7-7.9)	112-125 (7.9-8.8)
HF, PS	103-121 (7.2-8.5)	127-143 (9.0-10.0)
CN, HB, HH, HL, JH, JJ	130-155 (9.1-10.1)	130-155 (9.1-10.1)
OR	139-166 (9.8-11.7)	139-166 (9.8-11.7)
"L" @ 1000 [1]		
CZ, JE	82-94 (5.8-6.6)	82-94 (5.8-6.6)
JY	95-112 (6.7-7.9)	95-112 (6.7-7.9)
HF, PS	103-121 (7.2-8.5)	103-121 (7.2-8.5)
CN, HB, HH, HL, JH, JJ	130-155 (9.1-10.9)	130-155 (9.1-10.9)
OR	139-166 (9.8-11.7)	139-166 (9.8-11.7)

[1] — Total running time for this combination of tests is not to exceed 2 minutes. Brakes must be applied at all times.

[2] — Full T.V. reverse line pressure to be check at 2000 RPM.

Fig. 2: View of Transmission Showing Location of Control Pressure Test Take-Off Point

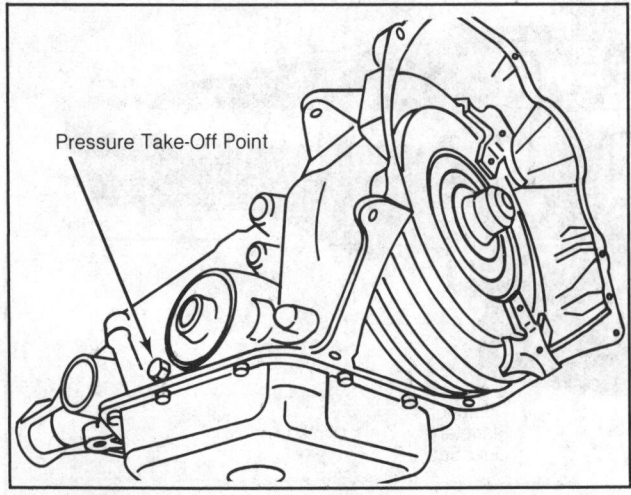

Pressure Take-Off Point

Check line pressure in ranges and at engine RPM indicated.

GENERAL MOTORS TURBO HYDRA-MATIC 200C (Cont.)

*Fig. 3: Turbo Hydra-Matic 200C Hydraulic Circuits Diagram
(All Except Diesel Models)*

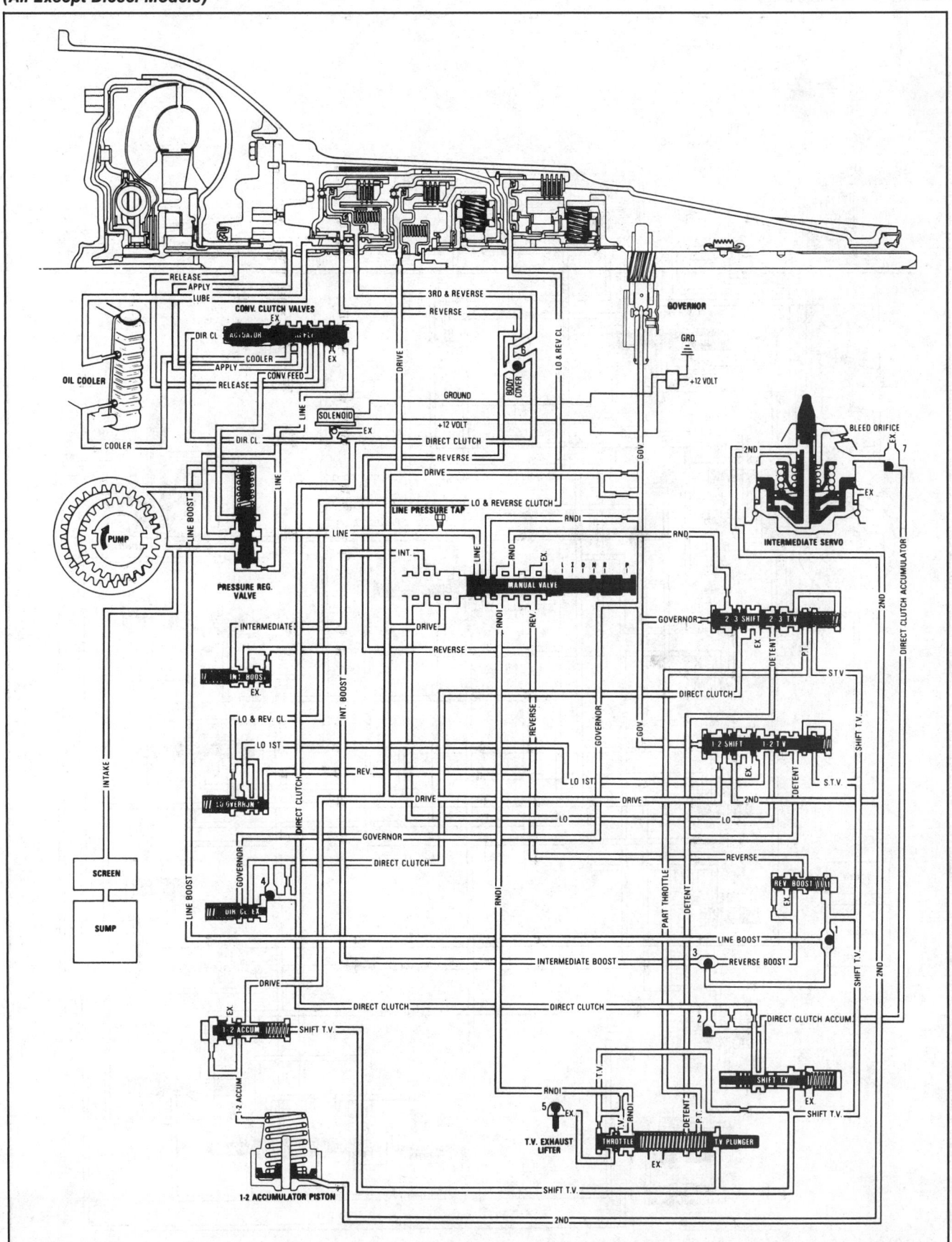

Automatic Transmissions

GENERAL MOTORS TURBO HYDRA-MATIC 200C (Cont.)

**Fig. 4: Turbo Hydra-Matic 200C Hydraulic Circuits Diagram
(Models With Diesel Engines)**

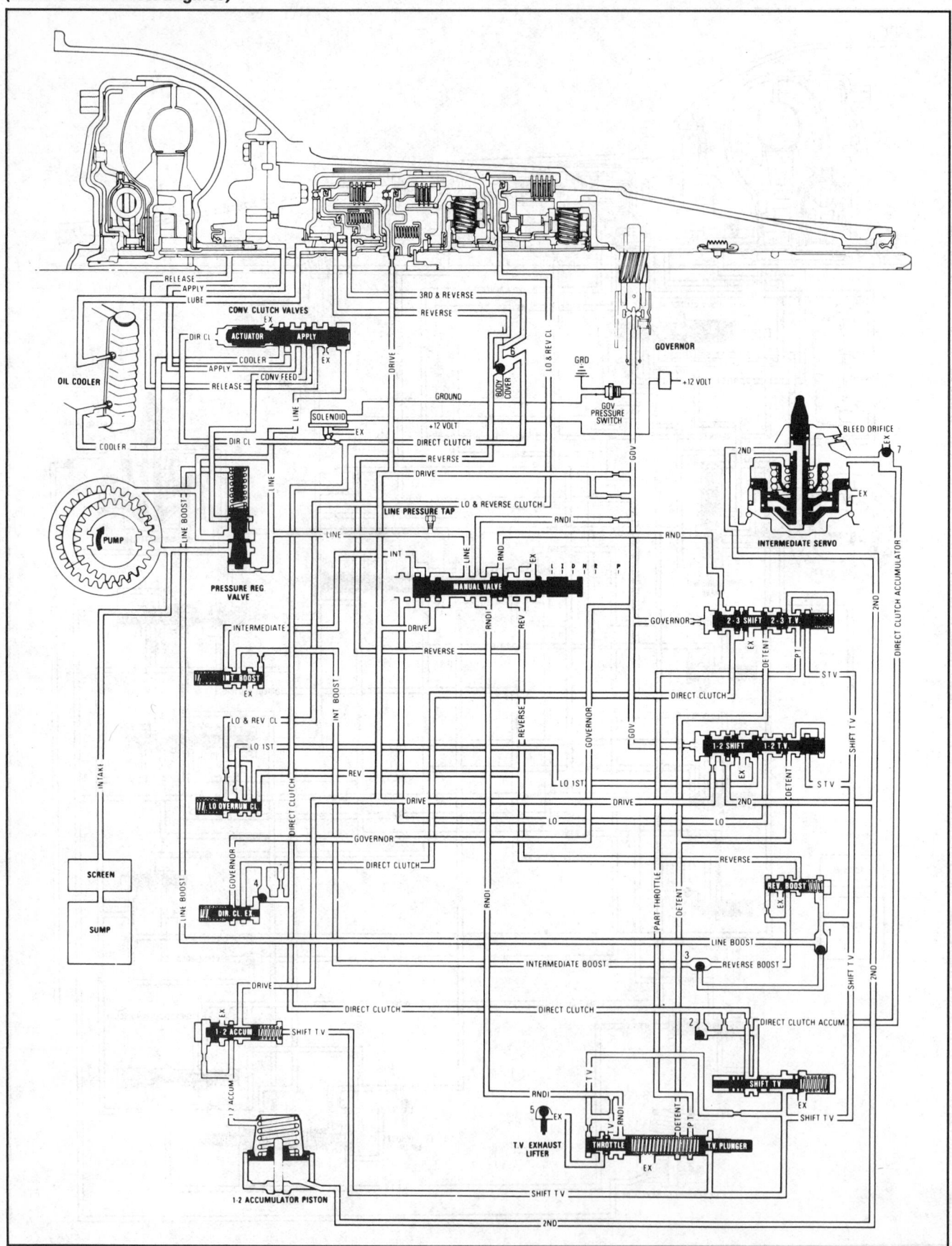

GENERAL MOTORS TURBO HYDRA-MATIC 200C (Cont.)

CONTROL PRESSURE RESULTS

High Or Low Oil Pressures

- T.V. cable misadjusted, binding, unhooked or broken.
- Throttle lever and bracket assembly binding, unhooked or mispositioned.
- Throttle valve or plunger binding.
- Shift T.V. valve binding.
- No. 1 check ball missing or leaking.
- Pressure regulator valve binding.
- Wrong pressure regulator valve spring installed.
- Oil pressure control orifice in pump cover plugged (causes high oil pressure).
- Pressure regulator bore plug leaking.
- Manual valve not connected.
- Intermediate boost valve binding (pressure will be low in intermediate and low ranges only).
- Orifice in spacer plate at end of intermediate boost valve plugged.
- Reverse boost valve binding (pressures will be incorrect in reverse only).
- Orifice in spacer plate at end of reverse boost valve plugged.

SERVICE (IN-VEHICLE)

The following components may be removed from transmission without removing transmission from vehicle.

- Governor Assembly.
- Governor Pressure Switch (Diesel Only).
- Intermediate Servo Assembly.
- Oil Pan and Oil Screen (Intake Pipe) Assembly.
- 3rd Accumulator Check Valve Assembly.
- Control Valve Body Assembly.
- Check Balls and Valve Body Spacer Plate and Gaskets.
- Pressure Regulator Parts.
- Inside Detent/Range Lever.
- Manual Detent and Roller Assembly.
- Throttle Lever and Bracket Assembly.
- T.V. Cable and "O" Ring.
- Parking Pawl Actuator Rod, Bracket, and Parking Pawl.
- Manual Shaft and Seal.

- Manual Valve.
- Rear Seal.
- 1-2 Accumulator and Spring.
- Low-Reverse Clutch Cup Plug.
- Cooler Fittings.
- Oil Filter Pipe & "O" Ring.
- Speedometer Driven Gear Assembly.
- Solenoid Wire Clips.
- Electrical Connector

For removal and installation of these components, see *Transmission Disassembly* and *Transmission Reassembly*.

REMOVAL & INSTALLATION

See the appropriate article in AUTOMATIC TRANSMISSION REMOVAL Section.

TORQUE CONVERTER

NOTE: Torque converter is a sealed unit and cannot be disassembled for service.

LEAKAGE CHECK

See procedure given in G.M. Turbo Hydra-Matic 400 article.

END CLEARANCE CHECK

See procedure given in G.M. Turbo Hydra-Matic 400 article.

CONVERTER FLUSHING

See procedure given in G.M. Turbo Hydra-Matic 400 article.

NOTE: For additional information on the Torque Converter Clutch (TCC) system used on the THM 200C transmission, see General Motors Torque Converter Clutch System article in this section.

CLUTCH AND BAND APPLICATION CHART (ELEMENTS IN USE)

Selector Lever Position	Direct Clutch	Forward Clutch	Low & Reverse Clutch	Intermediate Band	Low Roller Clutch
D — DRIVE					
First Gear		X			X
Second Gear		X		X	
Third Gear	X	X			
S or L2 — INTERMEDIATE					
First Gear		X			X
Second Gear		X		X	
L or L1 — LOW					
First Gear		X	X		
R — REVERSE	X		X		

NEUTRAL OR PARK — Band and clutches released and/or ineffective.

GENERAL MOTORS TURBO HYDRA-MATIC 200C (Cont.)

TRANSMISSION DISASSEMBLY

EXTERNAL PARTS

1) Mount transmission in a holding fixture and remove torque converter by pulling straight out. Remove oil pan and discard gasket. Remove oil screen and discard gasket.

NOTE: The two oil screen attaching bolts are about 3/8" (10 mm) longer than valve body attaching bolts, and they are not interchangeable.

2) On diesel models, remove governor pressure switch lead wire from switch and wire clips. Remove pressure switch using a 1 1/16" oil sending unit socket.

Fig. 5: Removing Throttle Valve and Bracket Assy.

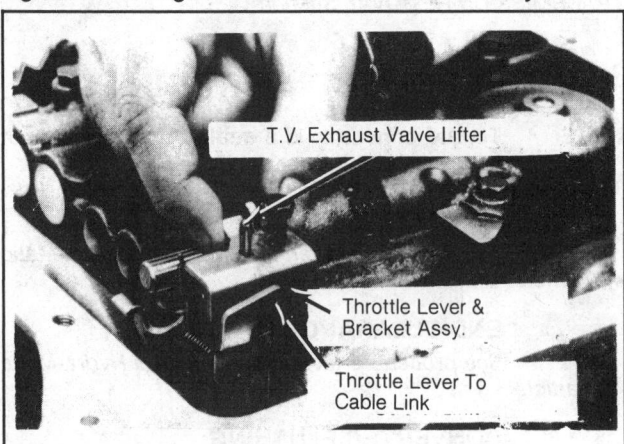

T.V. Exhaust Valve Lifter

Throttle Lever & Bracket Assy.

Throttle Lever To Cable Link

Do not bend throttle linkage.

3) On all models, remove throttle lever and bracket assembly, using care not to bend throttle lever link. T.V. exhaust valve lifter and spring may separate from lever and bracket assembly.

4) Remove manual detent roller and spring assembly and remaining valve body attaching bolts. Holding manual valve with finger, remove valve body assembly, spacer plate, and gaskets together, to prevent dropping the 4 check balls located in valve body.

Fig. 6: Removing Fifth Check Ball From Transmission Case

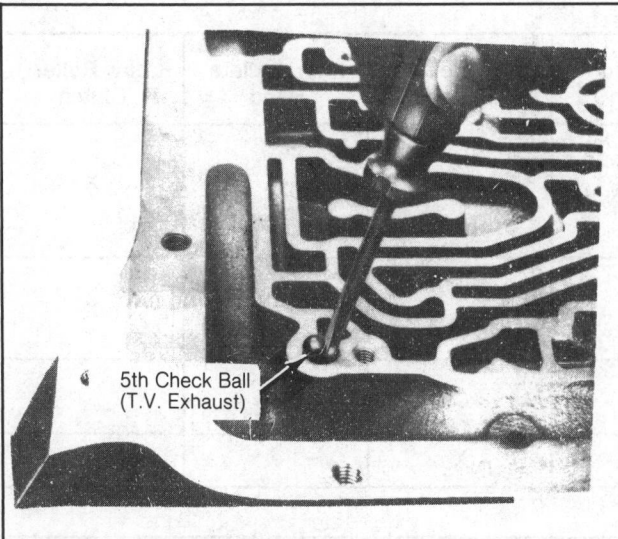

5th Check Ball (T.V. Exhaust)

5) Remove 1-2 accumulator spring. Remove fifth check ball from bore in transmission case. *See Fig. 6.* Using a small screwdriver, remove governor cover retaining ring, then remove cover using pliers and discard cover seal rings. Remove governor assembly and governor-to-case washer.

NOTE: It may be necessary to rotate output shaft counterclockwise while removing governor. Do not use any type of pliers to remove governor.

6) Remove lead wire from case electrical connector and solenoid wire clip, then compress fingers on connector sleeve and withdraw connector.

7) Depress intermediate servo cover and remove retaining ring. Using pliers, pull servo cover from case and discard cover seal ring. Remove intermediate servo piston and band apply pin assembly.

NOTE: Before continuing with Transmission Disassembly, check for proper intermediate band apply pin as follows:

Band Apply Pin Selection

1) Install band apply pin selection gauge (J-25014) into intermediate servo bore and retain with servo cover retaining ring. Align retaining ring gap in case slot. Install selection gauge tapered pin (J-25014-1) into gauge as shown in *Fig. 7.*

NOTE: Make sure tapered pin end is properly located against band apply lug. Also, make sure band anchor pin is properly located in case and band anchor lug.

2) Install dial indicator and position indicator pointer on top of selection gauge zero post. Set indicator to zero. Make sure selection gauge is squarely seated against servo retaining ring and stepped side of tapered pin is aligned with torquing arm of gauge. Arm must stop against step in tapered pin.

NOTE: If band selection pin does not register between the high and low limits, look for possible problem with intermediate band, direct clutch or case.

Fig. 7: Intermediate Band Apply Pin Selection

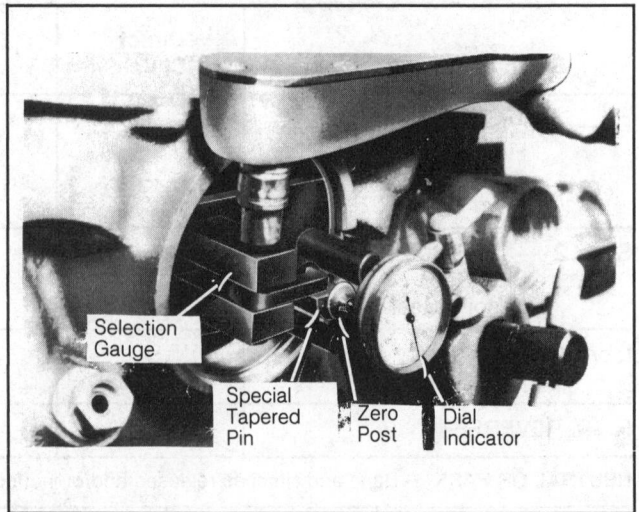

Selection Gauge

Special Tapered Pin

Zero Post

Dial Indicator

GENERAL MOTORS TURBO HYDRA-MATIC 200C (Cont.)

3) Apply 100 INCH lbs. (11 N.m) torque to hex nut on side of gauge. Slide dial indicator over tapered pin and read dial indicator travel. Select correct band apply pin from the following chart:

NOTE: Dial indicator travel is reversed, making the indicator readings backwards. On an indicator that ranges from 0-100, a .020" (.51 mm) travel will read .080" (2.03 mm), a .060" (1.52 mm) travel will read .040" (1.02 mm).

INTERMEDIATE BAND APPLY PIN SELECTION CHART

Indicator Reading In. (mm)	[1] Apply Pin Identification
.0-.029 (.0-.72)	1 Ring
.029-.057 (.72-1.44)	2 Rings
.057-.086 (1.44-2.16)	3 Rings
.086-.114 (2.16-2.88)	Wide Band

[1] — Identification ring(s) or band is located on band end of apply pin.

4) Remove apply pin selection tools. Inspect third accumulator valve for the following: Missing check ball; Check ball binding or stuck in tube; Oil feed slot in tube missing or restricted; Improperly assembled, loose fitting or not fully seated in case. If third accumulator check valve assembly requires replacement, proceed as follows:

Fig. 8: Third Accumulator Check Valve Assembly

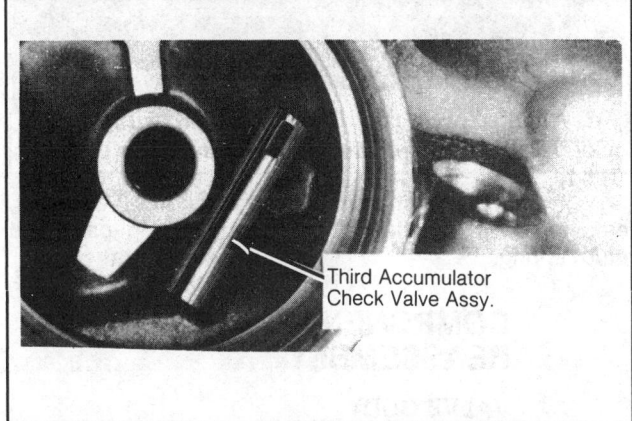

Fig. 9: Removing Third Accumulator Check Valve

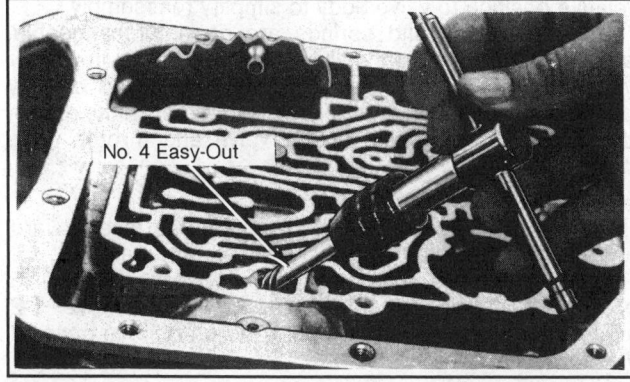

Remove check valve assembly from case by turning and pulling.

Third Accumulator Check Valve Replacement

1) Using a No. 4 easy-out, remove check valve assembly from case by turning and pulling straight out. *See Fig. 9.*

2) Install new check valve assembly, small end first, into case. Position oil feed slot in tube so it faces servo cover. Using a 3/8" diameter metal rod and hammer, drive assembly in until it is flush or below surface of third accumulator case hole.

OIL PUMP & FRONT UNIT COMPONENTS

NOTE: Prior to removing oil pump and front unit components, check front unit end play to determine correct end play thrust washer for use at reassembly. See Front Unit End Play Check under Transmission Reassembly.

1) Turn transmission so oil pump faces upward. If necessary, remove and discard pump oil seal. Remove oil pump-to-case attaching bolts and washers, then withdraw oil pump and gasket from case using a puller.

2) Grasp turbine shaft and pull direct and forward clutch assemblies from transmission case. Pull direct clutch assembly off forward clutch assembly.

NOTE: Direct-to-forward clutch thrust washer may stick to end of direct clutch housing.

3) Remove intermediate band assembly and anchor pin from case. Withdraw output shaft-to-turbine shaft front selective thrust washer.

NOTE: Output shaft-to-turbine shaft selective thrust washer may be stuck to end of turbine shaft.

FRONT INTERNAL GEAR

NOTE: At this time, check rear unit end play to determine correct end play thrust washer for use at reassembly. See Rear Unit End Play Check under Transmission Reassembly.

Fig. 10: Removing Front Internal Gear

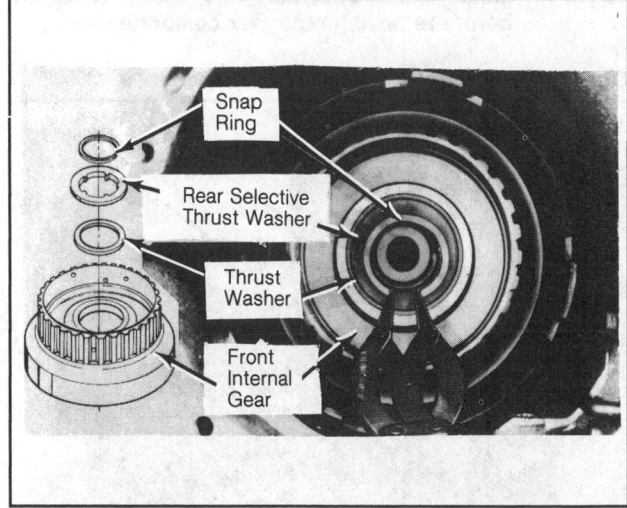

The front sun gear-to-front carrier thrust bearing may come out with front carrier.

GENERAL MOTORS TURBO HYDRA-MATIC 200C (Cont.)

Using snap ring pliers, remove output shaft-to-selective washer snap ring, then withdraw front internal gear, rear selective thrust washer, and thrust washer. Remove front carrier assembly and front internal gear-to-front carrier thrust bearing assembly. Remove front sun gear, and front sun gear-to-front carrier thrust bearing assembly.

INPUT DRUM, REAR SUN GEAR & LOW-REVERSE CLUTCH HOUSING

1) Remove input drum and rear sun gear from case. Remove the 4-tanged input drum-to-reverse clutch housing thrust washer from rear of input drum or from reverse clutch housing.

2) Grind approximately 3/4" from end of a No. 4 easy-out to remove housing-to-case cup plug. Remove cup plug assembly by turning easy-out 2 or 3 turns and pulling straight out. Discard cup plug and seal. *See Fig. 11.*

3) Remove low-reverse clutch housing-to-case beveled snap ring. Flat side of snap ring should have been against housing with beveled side up. Withdraw low-reverse clutch housing assembly from case. Remove clutch housing-to-case spacer ring.

Fig. 11: Removing Low-Reverse Clutch Housing To Case Cup Plug

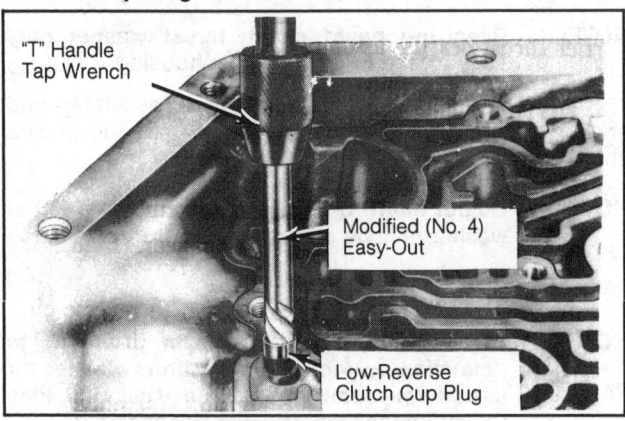

REAR GEAR COMPONENTS

NOTE: Make sure governor has been removed before removing rear gear components.

Fig. 12: Removing Rear Internal Gear Components

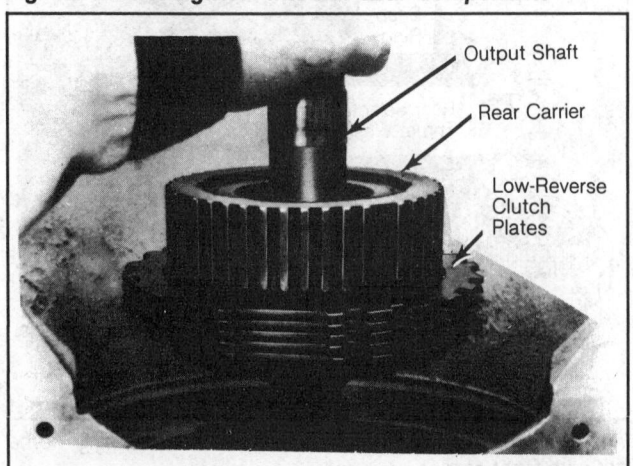

1) Grasp output shaft and lift out rear unit parts and lay them down in a horizontal position. Slide roller clutch and rear carrier assembly off output shaft. Remove 4-tanged rear carrier-to-rear internal gear thrust washer off end of rear carrier, or inside rear internal gear.

2) Remove low-reverse clutch plates from output shaft. Remove rear internal gear-to-rear sun gear thrust bearing assembly from rear internal gear. Remove rear internal gear from output shaft.

MANUAL SHAFT & PARKING LINKAGE

1) Remove hex nut holding inside detent lever to manual shaft, then remove parking actuator rod and detent lever. Remove manual shaft retaining pin from case and slide manual shaft out. If necessary, pry manual shaft seal from case.

2) Remove parking lock bracket. Remove parking pawl shaft retaining pin. Grind approximately 3/4" from end of a No. 4 easy-out. Remove parking pawl cup plug and discard. *See Fig. 13.*

Fig. 13: Removing Parking Pawl Shaft Cup Plug

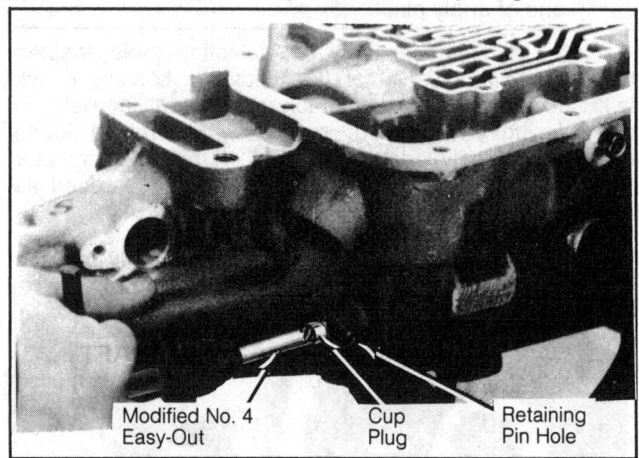

3) Using sheet metal screw or No. 3 easy-out, remove parking pawl shaft. Remove parking pawl and return spring.

COMPONENT DISASSEMBLY & REASSEMBLY

VALVE BODY

As valve trains are removed from each valve body bore, place individual parts in correct order in relative position to valve body to simplify reassembly.

Valves and springs are not interchangeable, and all parts must be installed in correct order in proper valve body bore. *See Fig. 14.* Remove all coiled pins by pushing through from rough case surface of body, except the 2 pins which retain throttle valve and throttle valve plunger.

Disassembly

1) Position valve body with cored face upward and 1-2 accumulator pocket at lower left. *See Fig. 15.* Remove four check balls from cored passages of valve body (5th check ball is in case), then remove 1-2 accumulator piston. From upper bore, remove manual valve.

GENERAL MOTORS TURBO HYDRA-MATIC 200C (Cont.)

Fig. 14: Exploded View of Turbo Hydra-Matic 200C Valve Body Assembly

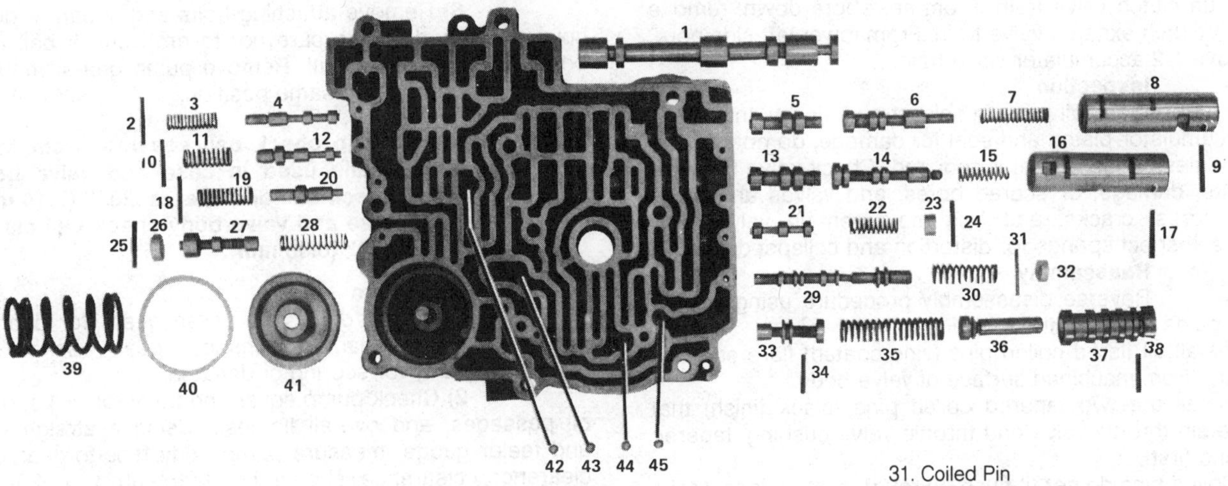

1. Manual Valve
2. Coiled Pin
3. Intermediate Boost Spring
4. Intermediate Boost Valve
5. 2-3 Shift Valve
6. 2-3 Throttle Valve
7. 2-3 Throttle Spring
8. 2-3 Throttle Bushing
9. Coiled Pin
10. Coiled Pin
11. Low Overrun Clutch Spring
12. Low Overrun Clutch Valve
13. 1-2 Shift Valve
14. 1-2 Throttle Valve
15. 1-2 Throttle Spring

16. 1-2 Throttle Bushing
17. Coiled Pin
18. Coiled Pin
19. Direct Clutch Exhaust Spring
20. Direct Clutch Exhaust Valve
21. Reverse Boost Valve
22. Reverse Boost Spring
23. Reverse Boost Bore Plug
24. Coiled Pin
25. Coiled Pin
26. 1-2 Accumulator Bore Plug
27. 1-2 Accumulator Valve
28. 1-2 Accumulator Spring
29. Shift T.V. Valve
30. Shift T.V. Spring

31. Coiled Pin
32. Shift T.V. Bore Plug
33. Throttle Valve
34. Coiled Pin
35. Throttle Valve Spring
36. Throttle Valve Plunger
37. Throttle Valve Plunger Bushing
38. Coiled Pin
39. 1-2 Accumulator Spring
40. 1-2 Accumulator Piston Seal
41. 1-2 Accumulator Piston
42. Check Ball No. 4
43. Check Ball No. 3
44. Check Ball No. 2
45. Check Ball No. 1
   (NOTE: 5th Check Ball in Case)

CAUTION: Some coiled pins in valve body assembly have pressure against them. Hold a shop towel over bore while removing pin to prevent losing bore plug or spring.

2) From upper right side bore, remove the 2-3 valve train. From next bore down, remove the 1-2 valve train. From next bore down, remove the reverse boost valve train.

NOTE: Some valves and springs may be inside valve bushings.

3) If necessary to remove shift T.V. valve train, remove coiled pin and place valve body with rough casting surface up. Use needle nose pliers and push in on valve, then hold in place with a small screwdriver. Position a 1/4" diameter rod, 3/8" long against end of valve, pry on rod with a screwdriver, remove small screwdriver, and remove plug, spring, and valve.

4) From lower right side bore, remove outer coiled pin and withdraw throttle valve bushing, plunger and spring. Remove throttle valve detent pin. Using a 1/16" Allen wrench, with sides ground to fit inside pin, remove inner coiled pin, and then withdraw throttle valve.

Fig.15: Removing Shift T.V. Valve Train

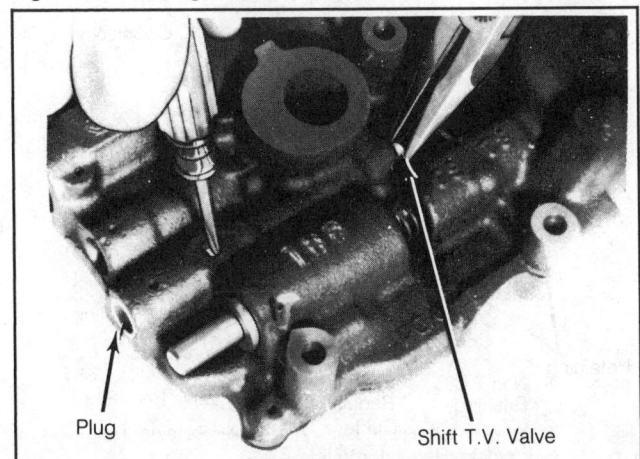

Valves and valve springs are not interchangeable.

Fig. 16: Removing Throttle Valve Inner Pin

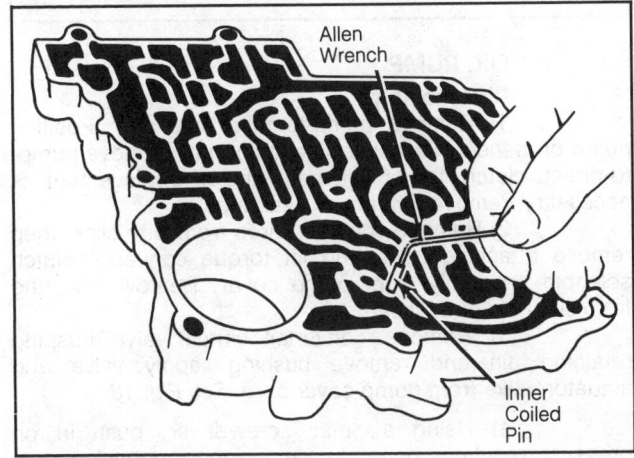

Use modified Allen Wrench.

GENERAL MOTORS TURBO HYDRA-MATIC 200C (Cont.)

5) From upper left side bore, remove intermediate boost valve train. From next bore down, remove low overrun clutch valve train. From next bore down, remove direct clutch exhaust valve train. From lower left side bore, remove 1-2 accumulator valve train.

Inspection

Wash all parts in solvent and air dry. Inspect 1-2 accumulator piston and seal for damage; do not remove seal unless replacement is required. Check valve body for cracks, damage, or scored bores, and valves and plugs for scores, cracks, and free movement in valve body bores. Inspect springs for distortion and collapsed coils.

Reassembly

Reverse disassembly procedure using *Fig. 14* as a guide and note the following:
- Install all flared coiled pins (zinc coated) flare end out, and from machined surface of valve body.
- Install the two tapered coiled pins (black finish) that retain throttle valve and throttle valve bushing, tapered end first.
- Coiled pins do not fit flush on rough casting face. Make sure pins are flush at machined face.
- When installing 1-2 throttle bushing and 2-3 throttle bushing, align in bores, so that coiled pins can be installed in pin slot. *See Fig. 17.*
- Install manual valve with inside detent lever pin groove to the right.

Fig. 17: *Installing Throttle Valve Bushings*

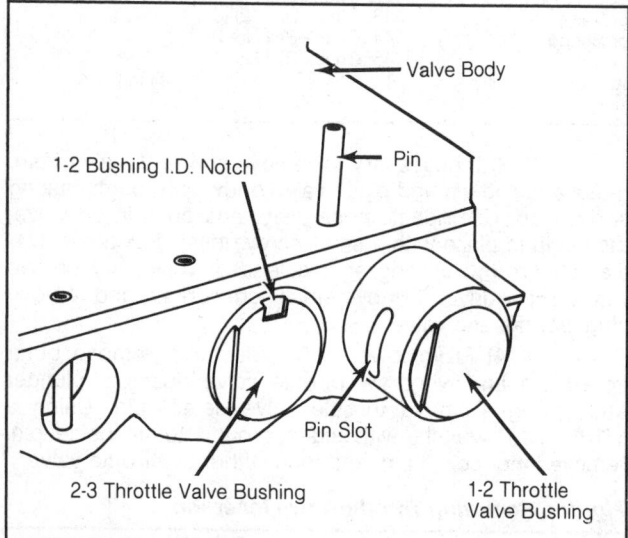

OIL PUMP

Disassembly

1) Remove pump-to-case seal ring. Position pump on bench with cover side facing up. Remove pump-to-direct clutch thrust washer, and if replacement is necessary, remove 3 teflon oil seal rings.

2) Remove solenoid wires from wire clips, then remove attaching bolts and lift torque converter clutch solenoid assembly from pump cover. Remove "O" ring from solenoid and discard.

3) Remove converter clutch valve bushing retaining pin and remove bushing, apply valve and actuator valve from pump cover bore. *See Fig. 18.*

4) Using a small screwdriver, push in on pressure regulator bore plug and remove retaining ring.

Release spring tension slowly and remove pressure regulator valve train.

5) Remove attaching bolts and separate pump cover from body using care not to drop check ball from body. Remove check ball. Remove pump gears, marking them for reassembly in same position.

NOTE: **Keep pump check ball separate from the 5 check balls used in case and valve body. Pump check ball diameter is .281" (7.14 mm), while case and valve body check ball diameter is .250" (6.35 mm).**

Inspection

1) Check drive and driven gears for scoring, galling, or other damage. Inspect gear pocket and crescent in body for scoring or damage.

2) Check pump cover and body for nicks, open oil passages, and overall flatness. Using a straightedge and feeler gauge, measure pump body face-to-gear face clearance; clearance should be .0007-.0021" (.020-.055 mm).

Fig. 18: *Removing Converter Clutch Valve Assembly*

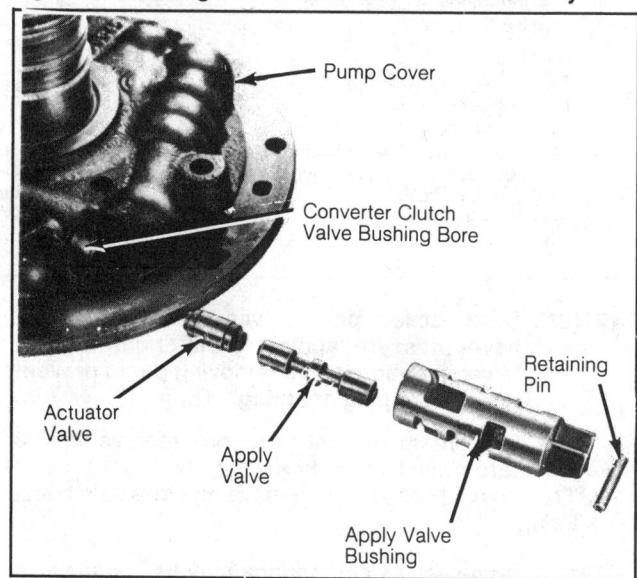

Fig. 19: *Exploded View of Oil Pump Assembly*

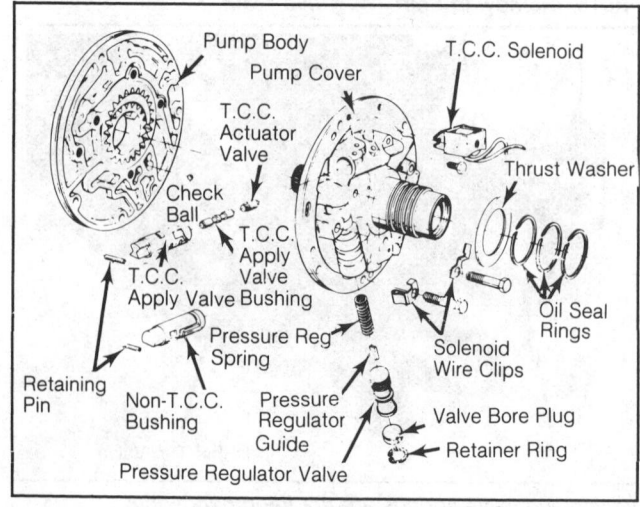

GENERAL MOTORS TURBO HYDRA-MATIC 200C (Cont.)

3) Inspect torque converter clutch solenoid wires for loose connections and damaged or cut insulation. Inspect solenoid assembly ball check valve for nicks or damage. Check for defective ball or ball seat as follows:

- Blow air into ball seat with solenoid de-energized; air should pass through ball seat.
- Noting polarity, energize solenoid with +12 volts D.C. and again blow air into ball seat; air should not pass through ball seat.

NOTE: **Do not use compressed air to check ball and ball seat. The use of compressed air may cause a false reading.**

4) Inspect converter clutch apply and actuator valves for nicks or damage. Check valves for free operation in bushing bore.

5) Grind approximately 1/2" from end of a No. 4 easy-out and, using modified easy-out, remove and discard cup plug from pump body. *See Fig. 21.* Discard cup plug. Withdraw screen from plug bore.

6) Clean screen in clean solvent and air dry, then reinstall screen in pump body bore. Install new cup plug, small diameter end first, into hole in pump body. Using a 5/16" diameter metal rod and hammer, drive cup plug until just below surface of hole.

Fig. 20: Removing Cup Plug From Pump Body

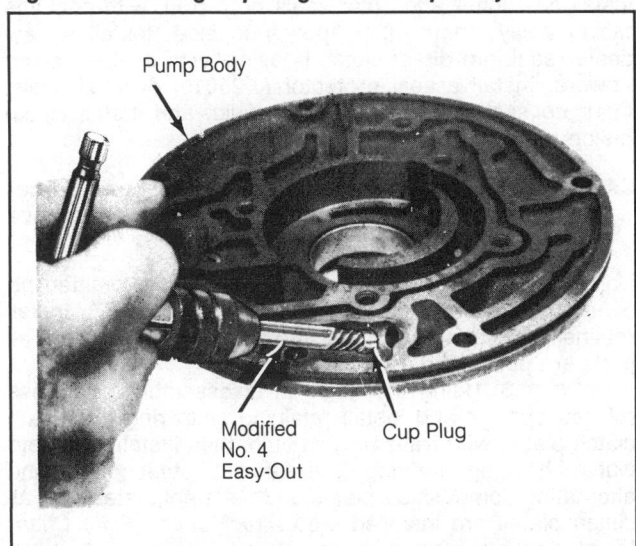

7) Inspect pressure regulator valve bore in pump cover and pressure regulator valve assembly for wear or damage, and make sure parts operate freely in bore. Inspect the 6 cup plugs in pump cover for damage or leaks. If necessary, replace cup plug as follows:

Pump Cover Cup Plug Replacement

Remove old cup plugs using care not to damage pump cover. Drive new cup plugs to 1/32" below top of hole, using a 1/4" diameter rod on smaller plug and a 5/16" rod on the 5 larger plugs. Stake top of hole in 2 places, directly opposite each other, to retain plugs.

Reassembly

1) Install driven gear into pump body with identification mark down against gear pocket. *See Fig. 22.* Install drive gear into pump body with identification marks on tangs up. *See Fig. 23.* Place check ball into pocket in pump body as shown in *Fig. 21.* Retain with petrolatum.

Fig. 21: Pump Body Oil Passages

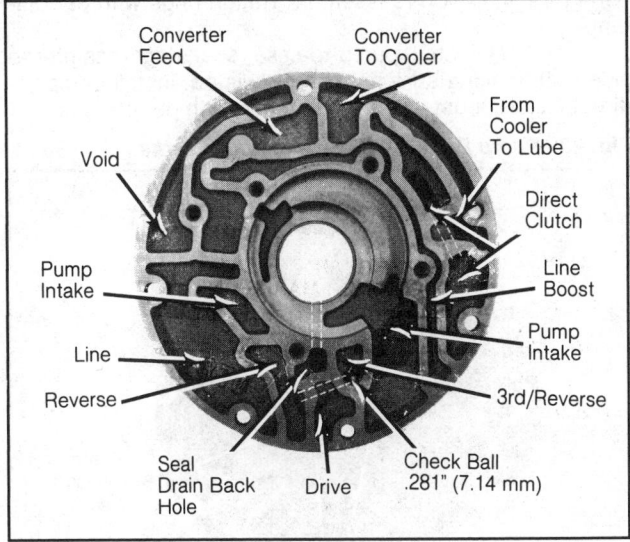

Make sure all castings are clean and true.

Fig. 22: Pump Driven Gear Identification Marks

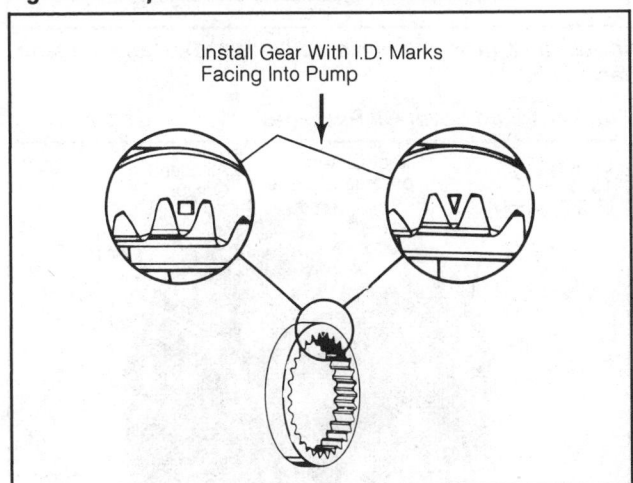

Install gear with I.D. marks facing into pump.

2) Assemble pump cover and body using alignment strap (J-25015) and lace bolt or screwdriver through pump-to-case bolt hole. Install and tighten pump cover attaching bolts and remove strap.

3) Install pressure regulator spring, spring guide, valve (stem end out), and bore plug (hole end out) into pump cover bore. Compress pressure regulator valve assembly and install retaining ring.

4) Install actuator valve into bushing bore of pump cover. Install apply valve into bushing, then install bushing into cover. Install apply valve bushing retaining pin and pin clip and bolt. *See Fig. 18.*

5) Install new pump-to-case gasket on pump and retain with petrolatum. Lubricate with petrolatum and install new "O" ring on solenoid assembly, then install solenoid on pump and tighten attaching bolts. Install solenoid wires into wire clip.

6) If removed, install 3 new oil seal rings on pump cover stator shaft, making sure cut ends are assembled in the same relationship as cut. Also, make

Automatic Transmissions

GENERAL MOTORS TURBO HYDRA-MATIC 200C (Cont.)

sure rings are seated in grooves to prevent damage during transmission reassembly. Retain rings with petrolatum.

7) Install pump-to-case seal ring (chamfered side out), making sure ring is not twisted. Install pump-to-direct clutch thrust washer and retain with petrolatum.

Fig. 23: Pump Drive Gear Identification Marks

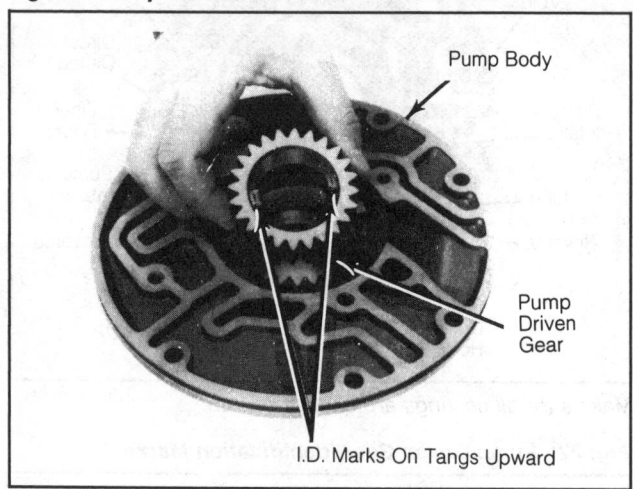

Install drive gear into pump body with I.D. marks on tangs facing up.

Fig. 24: Pump Cover Oil Passages

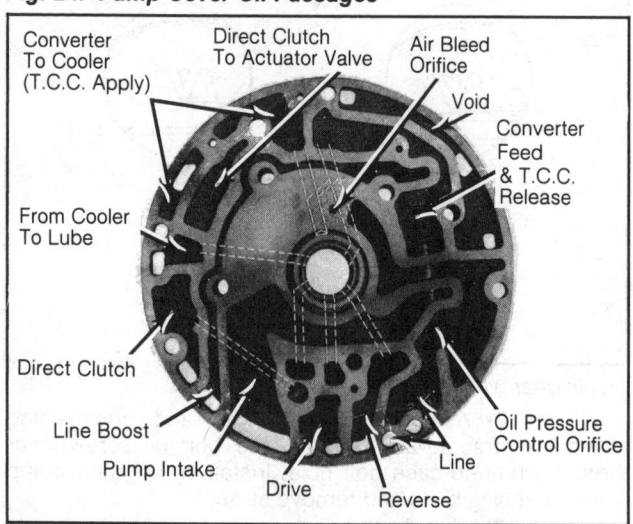

Make sure castings are clean.

DIRECT CLUTCH
Disassembly

1) Remove clutch pack snap ring. Remove backing plate from clutch housing. Remove clutch plates from housing and keep them separate from the forward clutch plates.

2) Using a compressor tool, compress retainer and spring assembly and removed snap ring. Remove tool and lift retainer and spring assembly from clutch housing.

3) Remove release spring guide from clutch housing. Remove clutch piston from housing. Remove inner and outer seals from piston and center seal from housing.

NOTE: **Do not separate apply ring from clutch piston unless ring or piston requires replacement.**

Inspection

Inspect composition plates, steel plates, and backing plate for wear, burning, or scoring. Check release springs and retainer for damage or a collapsed condition. Inspect clutch piston for distortion, cracks and free operation of check ball. Check clutch housing for cracks, wear, and open passages, and for free operation of check ball. Inspect snap ring grooves and bushing in housing for wear or damage.

Reassembly

1) Install apply ring on clutch piston, then install new inner and outer seals on piston, with seal lips facing away from clutch apply ring side. Install a new center seal into direct clutch housing, with seal lip facing upward. Install a seal protector (J-25010) over oil seals, lubricate seals with transmission fluid, and install clutch piston.

CAUTION: **Use care when installing piston past larger snap ring groove in clutch housing as groove could cut outer seal on piston.**

2) Install release spring guide with omitted rib over check ball in piston as shown in *Fig. 27*. Install retainer and spring assembly into housing, making sure all parts are positioned correctly.

3) Using tool used at disassembly, compress release springs and install retaining snap ring. Lubricate clutch plates with transmission fluid, then install them into clutch housing starting with a flat steel plate and alternating composition plates and flat steel plates until all clutch plates are installed. *See Direct Clutch Plate Chart.* Install backing plate with chamfered side up and clutch pack retaining snap ring.

Fig. 25: Exploded View of Direct Clutch Assembly

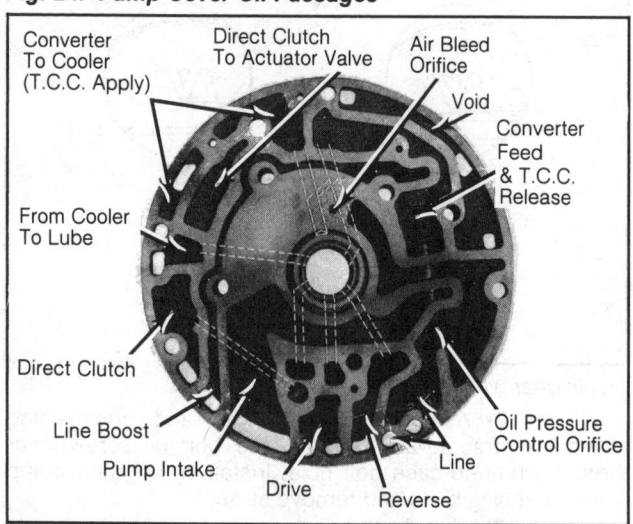

GENERAL MOTORS TURBO HYDRA-MATIC 200C (Cont.)

Fig. 26: Assembling Release Spring Guide to Piston

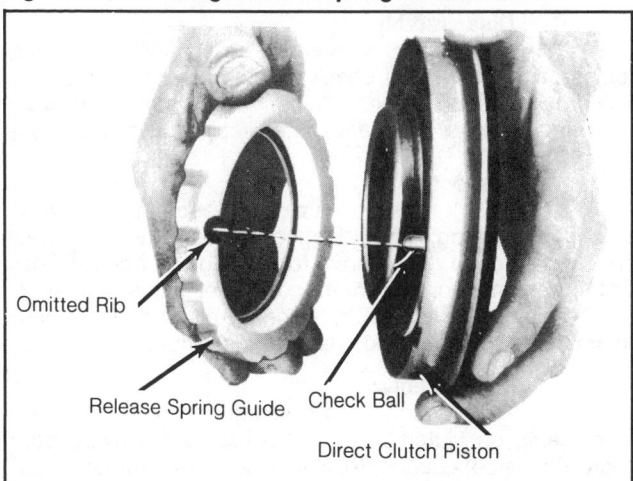

Install release spring guide with omitted rib over check ball in piston.

NOTE: **After reassembly is completed, ensure that composition faced clutch plates turn freely.**

DIRECT CLUTCH PLATE USAGE CHART

Model Application	Flat Steel [1]	Composition
CN, CZ, HF, HH, JE, JH, JY, PS	4	4
HB, HL, JJ, OR	5	5

[1] — Plate thickness is .091" (2.31 mm).

FORWARD CLUTCH

Disassembly
1) Remove forward clutch-to-direct clutch thrust washer. If replacement is required, remove teflon oil seal rings from turbine shaft. Remove clutch pack snap ring and lift out backing plate and clutch plates.

NOTE: **Keep forward clutch plates separate from direct clutch plates.**

2) Using an arbor press, compress retainer and spring assembly and remove retaining snap ring. Release arbor press slowly, then remove retainer and spring assembly. Remove piston from clutch housing, then remove inner and outer seals from piston.

NOTE: **Do not remove clutch apply ring from piston unless piston or apply ring requires replacement.**

Inspection
Inspect composition plates, steel plates, and backing plate for wear, scores or other damage. Check spring retainer and release springs for distortion or collapse. Inspect piston and housing for cracks, distortion, open oil passages, or other damage. Inspect snap ring grooves for wear or damage, and make sure ball check in housing operates freely. Check turbine shaft for open passages on both ends of shaft, and check journals for damage. Inspect clutch housing cup plug and if damaged, remove using a No. 3 easy-out (grind to fit). Install new cup plug to .039" (1.0 mm) below surface.

Reassembly
1) Install clutch apply ring on piston, then install new inner and outer seals on piston, with seal lips facing away from apply ring side. Lubricate seals with transmission fluid, then install piston into housing. Install retainer and spring assembly into housing, compress retainer and springs, and install retaining snap ring.

CAUTION: Use care when installing piston past large snap ring groove as groove could cut outer piston seal.

2) Lubricate with transmission fluid then install forward clutch plates into housing starting with the waved steel plate then alternating composition plates and flat steel plates until all clutchplates are installed. *See Forward Clutch Plate Chart.* Install backing plate (chamfered side up) and clutch pack snap ring. If removed, install new turbine shaft seal rings and forward clutch-to-direct clutch thrust washer.

NOTE: **After reassembly is completed, ensure that composition faced clutch plates turn freely.**

Fig. 27: Exploded View of Forward Clutch Assembly

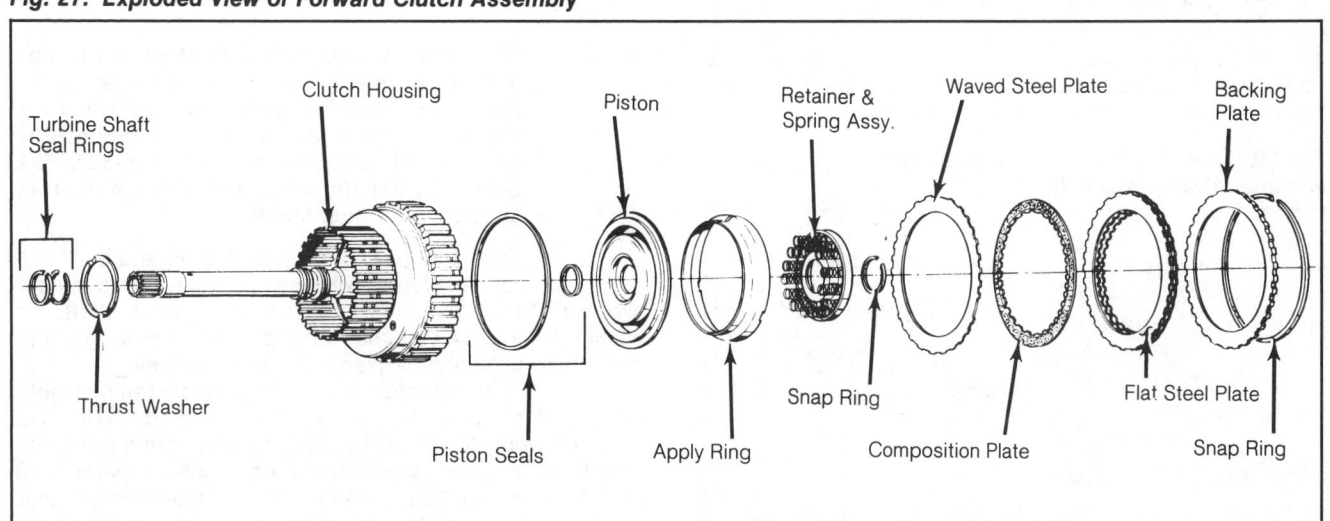

FORWARD CLUTCH PLATE USAGE CHEAT

Model Application	Flat Steel [1]	Composition
CN, CZ, HF, HH, JE, JH, JY, PS	2 [2]	3
HB, HL, JJ, OR	3 [2]	4

[1] — Plate thickness is .077" (1.96 mm).
[2] — Plus 1 WAVED steel plate .062" (1.57 mm) installed first.

FRONT CARRIER, SUN GEAR & INTERNAL GEAR

Inspection

Check all parts for pitting, scoring, damaged gear teeth, and cracks. Make sure all lubrication holes are open. Check front internal gear thrust washers for wear or other damage, and front carrier roller thrust bearing for roughness and pitting. Check pinion end play of front carrier; end play should be .009-.027" (.23-.69 mm).

Fig. 28: Using Feeler Gauge to Measure Front Carrier Pinion End Play

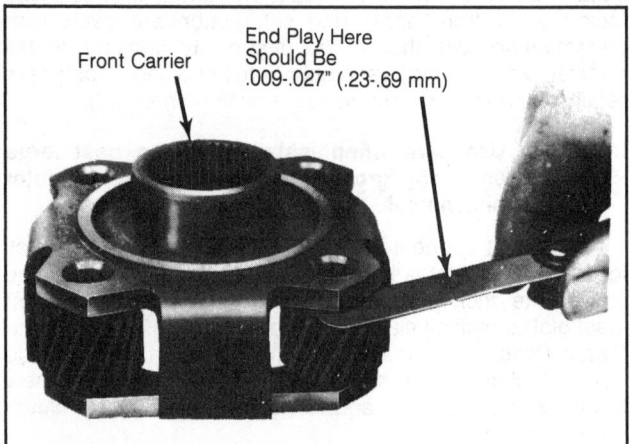

Front Carrier

End Play Here Should Be .009-.027" (.23-.69 mm)

If not within specifications, replace.

REAR SUN GEAR & INPUT DRUM

Inspection

Check rear sun gear for cracks, splits, spline damage, gear or journal wear, and for plugged lubrication holes. If necessary, remove snap ring and separate sun gear from input drum and inspect drum splines for damage. Check input drum-to-low-reverse clutch housing thrust washer for scoring or distorted tangs.

Fig. 29: Exploded View of Rear Sun Gear and Input Drum Assembly

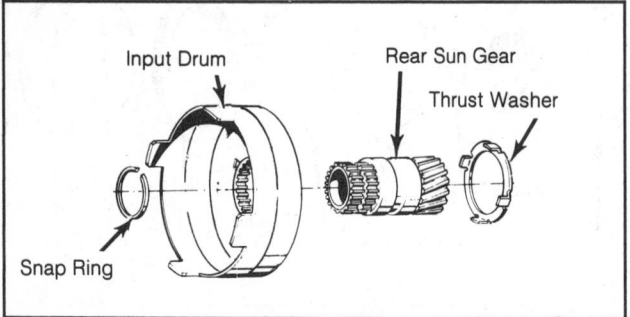

Input Drum

Rear Sun Gear

Thrust Washer

Snap Ring

LOW-REVERSE CLUTCH

Disassembly

Compress low-reverse clutch spring retainer, remove snap ring, and check for damage and distortion. Withdraw retainer, waved spring, and clutch piston from housing. Remove inner and outer seals and clutch apply ring from piston.

Inspection

Check clutch housing for scoring or wear, damaged bushing, and plugged oil feed hole. Inspect splines and snap ring groove for damage or burrs. Check piston assembly or distortion, cracks, or damage. Inspect clutch plates for signs of scoring or burning. Check retainers and spring for damage or distortion.

Reassembly

1) Install clutch apply ring and new inner and outer seals on clutch piston (seal lips facing away from apply ring side). Lubricate clutch seal with transmission fluid and place a seal protector into clutch housing.

2) Using a flat tip screwdriver to start seal into housing, install clutch piston, rotating while pushing down into bore. Remove seal protector, then install waved spring, retainer (cupped side down), and snap ring.

REAR CARRIER, ROLLER CLUTCH & INTERNAL GEAR

Inspection

Check rear internal gear splines, teeth, bearing surface, and parking pawl lugs for wear, cracks, or other damage. Inspect roller clutch race and spline for scoring or wear, and roller bearings, cage and springs for wear, scoring, distortion, or collapse. Inspect thrust washers for excessive wear or damaged tangs. Check rear carrier roller clutch cam ramps and bushing for scoring or other damage. Inspect planet pinions for damage, rough bearings, tilt, and correct end play; end play should be .009-.027" (.23-.69 mm).

OUTPUT SHAFT

Inspection

Inspect journals and snap ring grooves for wear or damage. Check lubrication holes for being plugged or damaged. Inspect shaft splines and governor drive gear for rough or damaged surfaces. Check speedometer drive gear and retaining clip for wear or damage.

NOTE: **The service replacement output shaft has one speedometer drive gear clip hole at the front speedometer gear location which is about 1/4" diameter and opposite this hole is another clip hole which is about 5/32". The shaft also has the same size holes at the rear speedometer gear location.**

Speedometer Drive Gear Replacement

1) If equipped with a nylon gear, depress gear clip and slide drive gear and clip off output shaft. To install, place gear clip with tanged end in correct hole in shaft, then align slot of gear with slip and install gear.

2) If equipped with a steel gear, remove gear using puller. To install, position front end of shaft on a block of wood to prevent damaging shaft during installation. Position gear (large chamfered inside diameter first) over rear end of output shaft. Using a driver, drive gear

GENERAL MOTORS TURBO HYDRA-MATIC 200C (Cont.)

Fig. 30: Exploded View of Low-Reverse Clutch Assembly

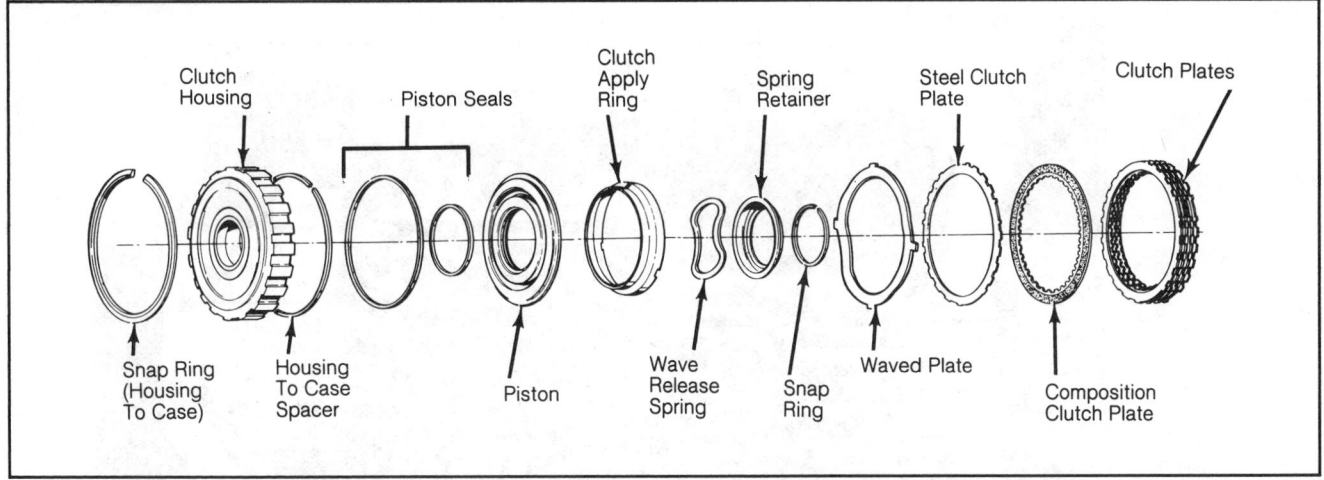

onto shaft until distance from rear end of shaft to rear face of gear is 6 5/32" (156.37 mm).

Fig. 31: Exploded View of Rear Carrier and Roller Clutch Assembly

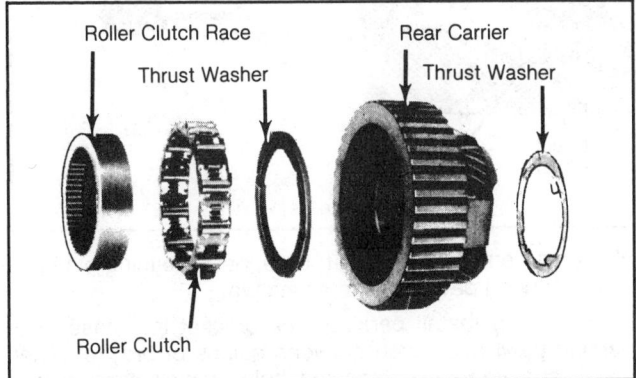

Fig. 32: Output Shaft and Speedometer Drive Gear

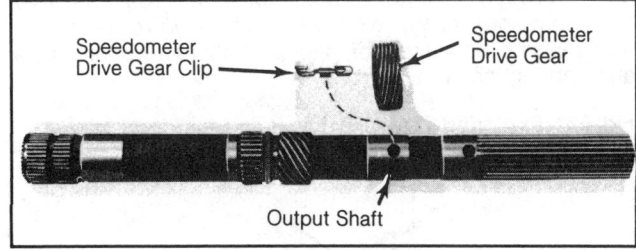

Align slot of gear with clip and install gear.

INTERMEDIATE SERVO

Disassembly

Compress intermediate servo piston spring. Using small flat edge screwdriver, remove servo pin-to-piston snap ring. Separate band apply pin, spring and washer from servo piston.

Inspection

1) Check intermediate servo pin for wear or damage, and for proper fit in case bore. Inspect inner and outer seal rings. for damage, and proper fit in seal ring grooves of piston.

CAUTION: Do not remove seal rings from piston unless replacement is required.

2) Check servo piston and cover for cracks or other damage. Inspect servo spring for collapsed coils or distortion.

Reassembly

1) Install retainer on band apply pin and install snap ring. Install band apply pin (retainer end first) through servo pistons. If removed, install new inner and outer seal rings on piston, making sure seal ring ends are assembled in the same relationship as cut and seal rings are seated in grooves.

2) Lubricate with petrolatum and install new seal ring on intermediate servo cover. Install servo piston assembly into servo cover.

Fig. 33: Exploded View of Intermediate Servo Assembly

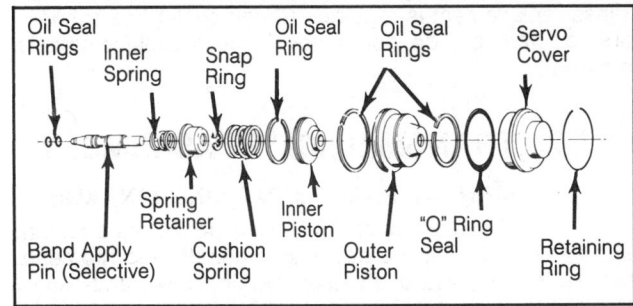

GOVERNOR ASSEMBLY

Inspection

1) Inspect governor cover for damage, scored or worn bore, or plugged oil passage. Wash governor assembly in cleaning solvent and blow out oil passage. Inspect governor driven gear, weights, springs, shaft and washer for wear or damage.

2) Check governor shaft seal ring for cuts, damage, and for free fit in groove. If damaged, cut ring off shaft, and install new seal ring. Lubricate seal with petrolatum. Inspect for presence of two check balls.

TRANSMISSION CASE

Inspection

Check case assembly for cracks, porosity, and interconnected oil passages. Inspect reverse clutch lugs, governor bore, intermediate servo bore, speedometer bore, and snap ring grooves for wear and other damage. Make sure all vents and passages are open and clear.

Automatic Transmissions

GENERAL MOTORS TURBO HYDRA-MATIC 200C (Cont.)

Fig. 34: *Bottom of Transmission Case Showing Oil Passages*

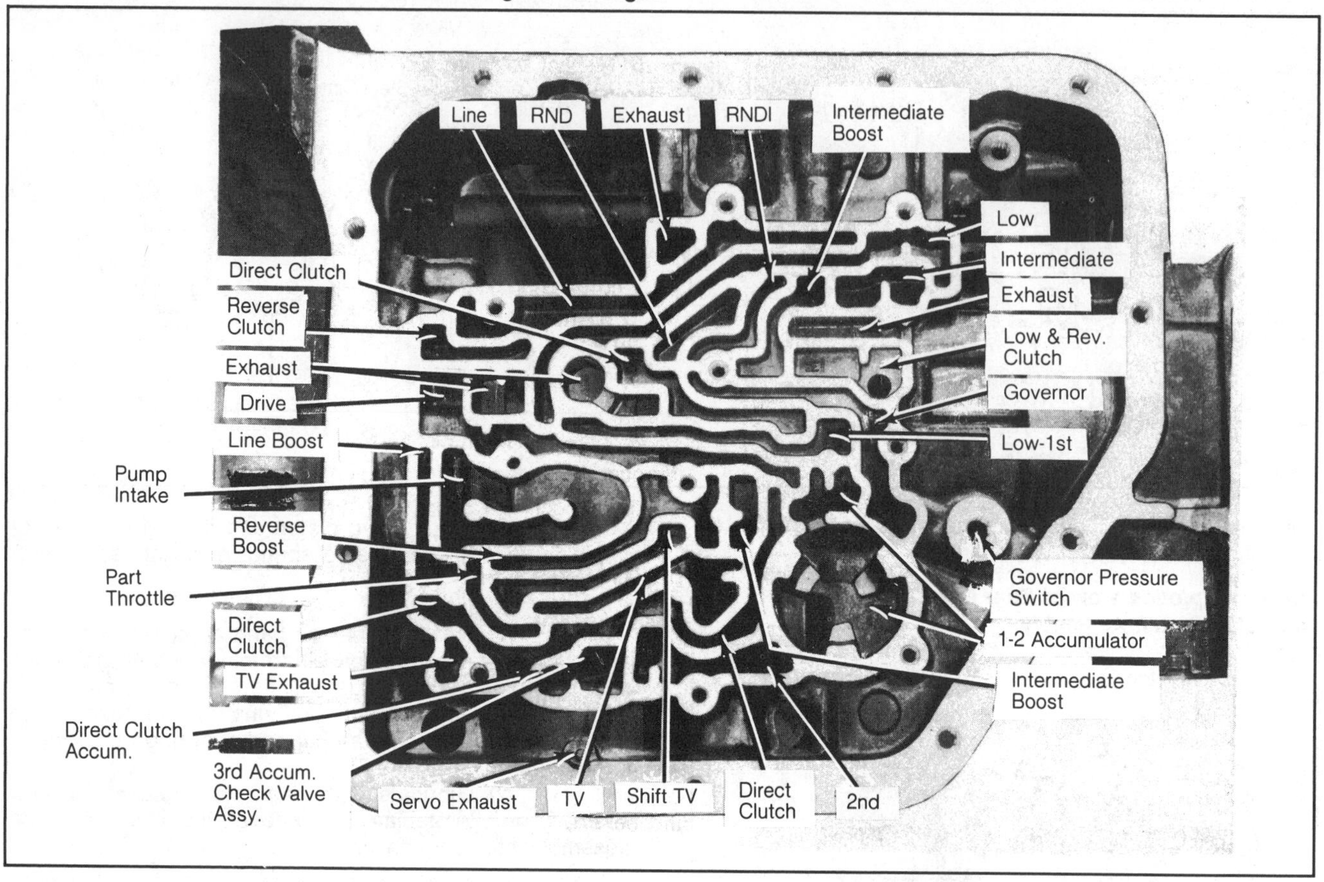

Line | RND | Exhaust | RNDI | Intermediate Boost

Direct Clutch
Reverse Clutch
Exhaust
Drive
Line Boost
Pump Intake
Reverse Boost
Part Throttle
Direct Clutch
TV Exhaust
Direct Clutch Accum.
3rd Accum. Check Valve Assy.

Low
Intermediate
Exhaust
Low & Rev. Clutch
Governor
Low-1st
Governor Pressure Switch
1-2 Accumulator
Intermediate Boost

Servo Exhaust | TV | Shift TV | Direct Clutch | 2nd

Inspect vent assembly in case for damage; do not remove unless replacement is required. Check cooler line connectors for damage; do not remove unless replacement is required.

TRANSMISSION REASSEMBLY

MANUAL SHAFT & PARKING LINKAGE

1) Place transmission in a horizontal position, oil pan side up. Install a new manual shaft seal into case, seal lip facing inward. Position parking pawl and return spring into case, making sure pawl tooth faces inside of case, spring is positioned under pawl tooth, and spring ends locate against case pad. Align pawl and spring with shaft bore in case, then install pawl shaft (tapered end first). Using a 3/8" diameter rod, install a new shaft cup

plug (open end out) into shaft bore, past retaining pin hole. Install parking pawl shaft retaining pin.

2) Install parking lock bracket into case, with parking pawl positioned between guides of bracket. Then install and tighten 2 attaching bolts. Install parking lock actuator rod into inside detent lever (on pin side), locating lever between actuator rod tangs. Install rod and lever assembly into case, with lever pin toward center of transmission and actuator plunger between parking pawl and parking lock bracket.

Fig. 36: *Exploded View of Manual and Parking Linkage*

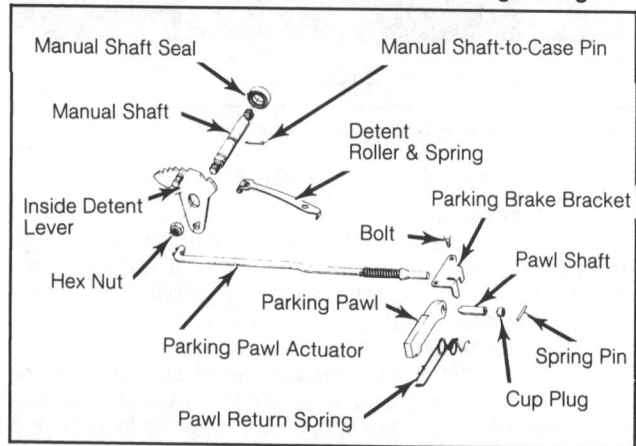

Manual Shaft Seal
Manual Shaft
Inside Detent Lever
Hex Nut
Manual Shaft-to-Case Pin
Detent Roller & Spring
Parking Brake Bracket
Bolt
Parking Pawl
Parking Pawl Actuator
Pawl Return Spring
Pawl Shaft
Spring Pin
Cup Plug

Fig. 35: *Installing Parking Actuator Rod*

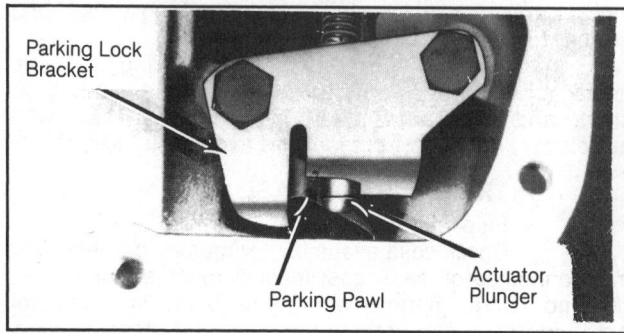

Parking Lock Bracket
Parking Pawl
Actuator Plunger

Be careful not to bend rod during installation.

NOTE: File any burrs or raised edges off manual shaft that could damage seal during installation of shaft.

GENERAL MOTORS TURBO HYDRA-MATIC 200C (Cont.)

3) Install manual shaft (small I.D. ring groove first) through case. Install manual shaft-to-case retaining pin, indexing with larger groove on manual shaft. Align inside detent lever with flats on manual shaft, position lever on shaft, then install and tighten nut on manual shaft.

OUTPUT SHAFT & REAR INTERNAL GEAR

If removed, install a new rear internal gear-to-output shaft snap ring into groove on output shaft, then install rear internal gear (hub end first) onto shaft. Position rear internal gear-to-rear sun gear roller thrust bearing assembly over shaft by placing small diameter race against rear internal gear.

ROLLER CLUTCH & REAR CARRIER

1) Install rear internal gear, hub end first, on output shaft. Install internal gear-to-rear sun gear roller thrust bearing assembly into internal gear by placing small diameter race over output shaft.

2) Install roller clutch-to-rear carrier thrust washer into rear carrier. Install rollers that may have come out of roller clutch cage, by compressing energizing spring with forefinger and inserting roller from outer edge. Install roller clutch assembly into roller clutch cam.

3) Install roller clutch race, spline side out, and rotate clutch race counterclockwise into position. Install 4 tanged rear carrier-to-rear internal gear thrust washer onto carrier and align tangs into slots of carrier. Retain washer with petrolatum. Install roller clutch and carrier assembly into rear internal gear on output shaft.

4) Install a output shaft support tool (J-25013) on rear of transmission as follows: Place sleeve (J-25013-1) into rear of case, open end first. Then bolt bracket and screw assembly (J-25013-5) into rear mount bolt holes on extension housing. Turn case to a vertical position, pump end upward. Install rear unit parts (output shaft, rear internal gear, and rear carrier previously assembled) into transmission case and into support sleeve (J-25013-1), indexing rear internal gear parking pawl lugs to pass by parking pawl tooth.

Fig. 37: Installing Output Shaft Support Tools

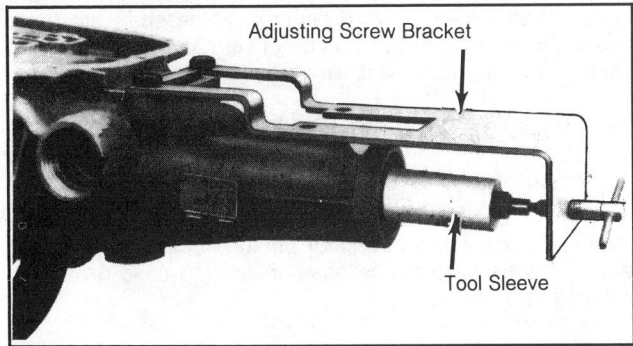

Adjusting Screw Bracket

Tool Sleeve

5) Using adjusting screw on tool bracket (J-25013-5) and looking through parking pawl case slot, adjust height of the rear internal gear parking pawl lugs to align flush with the parking pawl tooth.

CAUTION: With rear internal gear parking pawl lugs correctly aligned, make sure speedometer drive gear is visible through speedometer gear bore of case. If gear is not visible, it may be located on wrong journal of output shaft.

LOW-REVERSE CLUTCH

1) Lubricate with transmission fluid then install low-reverse clutch plates, starting with a flat steel plate, and alternating composition and flat steel plates until all clutch plates are installed. See Low-Reverse Clutch Plate Chart. Install waved steel clutch plate on top of last flat steel plate.

2) Install low-reverse clutch housing-to-case spacer ring into case, then install low-reverse clutch housing assembly, aligning housing oil feed hole with case oil feed passage. If housing does not seat past snap ring groove, proceed as follows: Install input drum and rear sun gear assembly into case and rotate back and forth to align roller clutch race and low-reverse clutch hub splines, then remove input drum and sun gear.

LOW-REVERSE CLUTCH PLATE USAGE CHART

Model Application	Flat Steel	Composition
CM, CZ, HF, HH, JE, JH, JY, PS	5 [1]	4
HB, HL, JJ, OR	7 [1]	6

[1] — Plus 1 WAVED steel plate .077" (1.96 mm) thick, installed last.

Fig. 38: Installing Low-Reverse Clutch Housing To Case Snap Ring

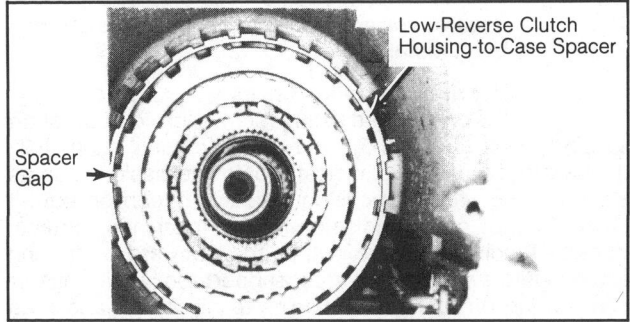

Low-Reverse Clutch Housing-to-Case Spacer

Spacer Gap

Align housing oil feed hole with case oil feed passage.

3) Repeat preceding step if low-reverse clutch housing still is not seated past case snap ring groove. With parts properly seated, install low-reverse clutch housing-to-case snap ring, with flat side of ring against housing (beveled side upward). Locate snap ring gap opposite parking pawl rod.

NOTE: It may be necessary to loosen adjusting screw on output shaft support tool to install low-reverse clutch housing-to-case snap ring.

REAR SUN GEAR, INPUT DRUM & FRONT SUN GEAR

Position thrust washer (four tangs) on input drum over sun gear end, align washer tangs with slots in drum, and retain with petrolatum. Install rear sun gear and input drum assembly into case. Install front sun gear, with drill spot or groove on face against input drum-to-rear sun gear snap ring. Install front sun gear-to-front carrier thrust bearing and race assembly with roller thrust bearing against front sun gear.

NOTE: The front sun gear-to-front carrier thrust bearing requires only 1 thrust race.

GENERAL MOTORS TURBO HYDRA-MATIC 200C (Cont.)

Fig. 39: Front Sun Gear Identification Marks

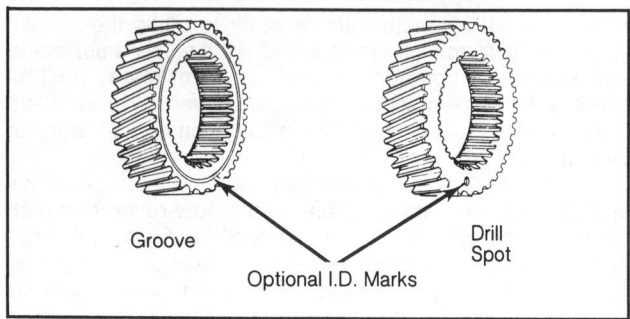

Groove

Drill Spot

Optional I.D. Marks

FRONT CARRIER

Position front carrier-to-front internal ring gear thrust bearing assembly on front carrier, with small diameter race against carrier and retain in place with petrolatum. Install front carrier and thrust bearing assembly into case, engaging front sun gear.

FRONT INTERNAL GEAR

Install thrust washer on front internal gear and retain with petrolatum, then install front internal gear into case. Install rear unit selective thrust washer on top of internal gear thrust washer, then install output shaft-to-thrust washer snap ring and make sure snap ring is fully seated in output shaft groove.

NOTE: At this time, measure rear unit end play to ensure correct selective thrust washer has been installed.

Rear Unit End Play Check

1) Loosen adjusting screw on output shaft support tool (J-25013-5) and push output shaft fully downward. Mount a dial indicator on transmission case as shown in *Fig. 40* and position indicator button on output shaft. Do not clamp indicator to any machined surface. Zero dial indicator. Move output shaft upward by turning adjusting screw on output shaft support tool, until white or scribed line on tool sleeve begins to disappear and read resulting end play on indicator.

2) Rear unit end play should be .004-.025" (.10-.64 mm); if not, the selective thrust washer located between front internal gear thrust washer and output shaft

Fig. 40: Checking Rear Unit End Play

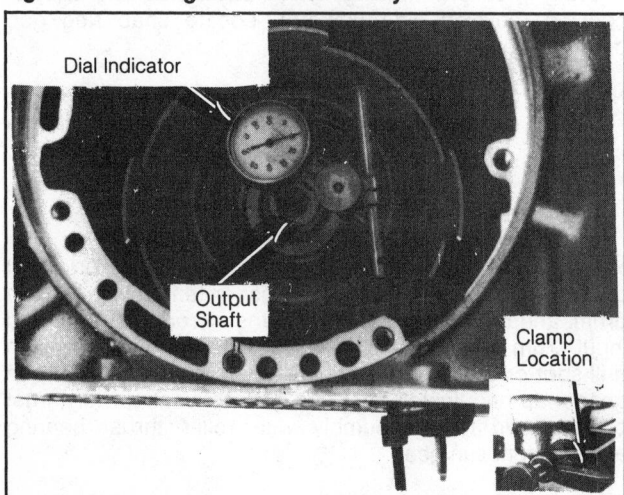

Dial Indicator

Output Shaft

Clamp Location

Dial indicator is located on output shaft.

snap ring must be changed. *See Rear Unit Thrust Washer Chart for thicknesses.* Install correct thickness thrust washer (with I.D. number toward front of case), then reinstall output shaft snap ring, making sure it is fully seated in groove.

3) Remove dial indicator assembly and loosen adjusting screw on output shaft support tool. Install output shaft-to-turbine shaft front selective thrust washer, locating in output shaft and retain with petrolatum.

REAR UNIT SELECTIVE THRUST WASHER CHART

Washer Thickness In. (mm)	I.D. Number	I.D. Color
.114-.119 (2.90-3.01)	1	Orange
.121-.126 (3.08-3.19)	2	White
.128-.133 (3.26-3.37)	3	Yellow
.135-.140 (3.44-3.55)	4	Blue
.143-.147 (3.62-3.37)	5	Red
.150-.154 (3.80-3.91)	6	Brown
.157-.161 (3.98-4.09)	7	Green
.164-.168 (4.16-4.27)	8	Black
1.71-.175 (4.34-4.45)	9	Purple

DIRECT CLUTCH, FORWARD CLUTCH & INTERMEDIATE BAND

NOTE: Align direct clutch composition clutch plate teeth one above the other to make forward clutch assembly easier to install.

1) Position direct clutch over hole in bench with clutch plate end upward. Make sure forward clutch-to-direct clutch thrust washer is still in place on forward clutch, then install forward clutch (turbine shaft first) into direct clutch. Hold direct clutch housing and rotate forward clutch back and forth until forward clutch is seated.

NOTE: When properly seated, end of forward clutch drum will be approximately 5/8" (15.88 mm) from tang end of direct clutch housing.

2) Position intermediate band into case, locating band apply lug and anchor pin lug in case slots. Install direct and forward clutch assemblies into case as a unit, rotating into position.

NOTE: When correctly seated, the direct clutch housing will be approximately 1 5/16" (33.34 mm) from pump face in case.

OIL PUMP

1) Install new pump-to-case gasket on pump and retain with petrolatum. Install 2 pump-to-case alignment pins in case, 180° opposite each other.

NOTE: Before installing pump, ensure intermediate band anchor pin lug is aligned with band anchor pin hole in case.

GENERAL MOTORS TURBO HYDRA-MATIC 200C (Cont.)

Fig. 41: Checking Forward Clutch Engagement

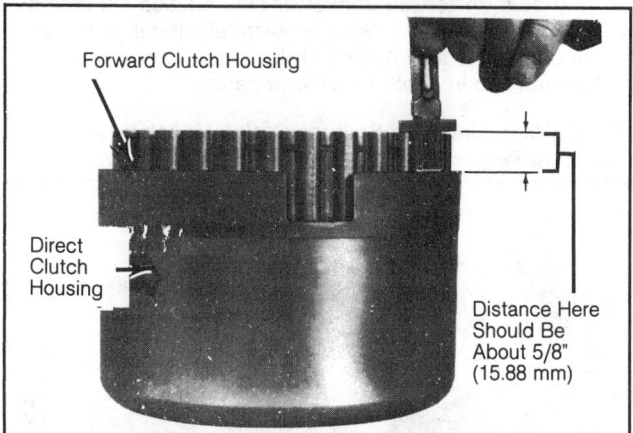

Fig. 42: Checking for Proper Installation of Direct and Forward Clutch Assemblies

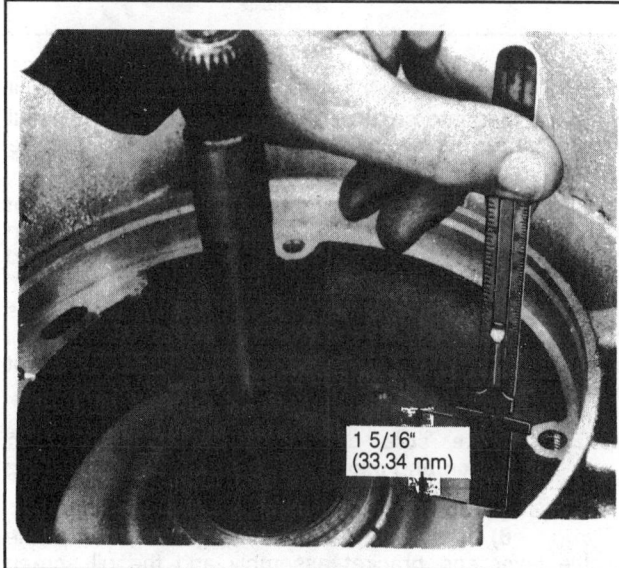

Assembly must be completely seated before measuring.

2) Install pump assembly and finger start pump-to-case bolts and new washers, except 1 bolt which will be used to make front unit end play check.

CAUTION: If turbine shaft cannot be rotated as pump is pulled into place, forward or direct clutch housings have not been installed properly to index with all clutch plates. This condition must be corrected before pump is pulled fully into place.

3) Remove alignment pins and install 2 pump attaching bolts and new washers. Tighten pump-to-case bolts evenly and make sure turbine shaft rotates freely.

Front Unit End Play Check
1) With transmission in a vertical position (pump side up), install an 11" long bolt into pump attaching bolt hole. Push turbine shaft downward.

NOTE: Output shaft support tool (J-25013-5 and J-25013-1) should still be attached to rear of transmission; if not, reinstall using procedure given in Roller Clutch and Rear Carrier section of Transmission Reassembly.

2) Install end play gauging fixture and adapter (J-24773 and J-25022) on end of turbine shaft. *See Fig. 43.* Mount dial indicator on bolt and position indicator button against cap nut of gauging fixture. Move output shaft upward by turning adjusting screw on output shaft support tool until white or scribed line on sleeve begins to disappear, then zero dial indicator. Pull turbine shaft upward and read end play on indicator. Front unit end play should be .022-.051" (.56-1.30 mm).

Fig. 43: Checking Front Unit End Play

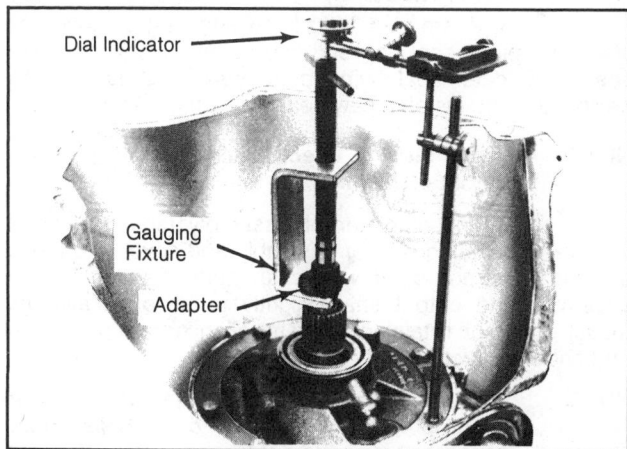

3) Selective thrust washer controlling front unit end play is located between output shaft and turbine

FRONT UNIT SELECTIVE THRUST WASHER CHART

Washer Thickness In. (mm)	I.D. Number	I.D. Color
.065-.070 (1.66-1.77)	1	....
.070-.075 (1.79-1.90)	2	....
.076-.080 (1.92-2.03)	3	Black
.081-.085 (2.05-2.16)	4	Light Green
.086-.090 (2.18-2.29)	5	Scarlet
.091-.095 (2.31-2.42)	6	Purple
.096-.100 (2.44-2.55)	7	Cocoa Brown
.101-.106 (2.57-2.68)	8	Orange
.106-.111 (2.72-2.81)	9	Yellow
.111-.116 (2.83-2.94)	10	Light Blue
.117-.121 (2.96-3.07)	11	Blue
.122-.126 (3.09-3.20)	12	....
.127-.131 (3.22-3.33)	13	Pink
.132-.136 (3.35-3.46)	14	Green
.137-.141 (3.48-3.59)	15	Gray

shaft. If more or less washer thickness is required to bring end play within specifications, remove oil pump and forward and direct clutch assemblies, and install correct thickness washer on end of output shaft. *See Front Unit Thrust Washer Chart for washer thickness and identification.*

4) Remove front unit end play checking tools. Install remaining pump-to-case bolt and tighten. Remove output shaft support tools.

GOVERNOR

1) If removed, install new seal ring on governor shaft and place seal ring end into governor cover to size seal. Lubricate seal with petrolatum. Lubricate with petrolatum and install 2 new seal rings on governor cover.

NOTE: **Make sure 2 check balls are in governor before installation.**

2) Install governor assembly (seal end first) into cover. Install governor assembly and cover into case, aligning governor shaft with shaft hole in case. Rotate assembly and output shaft slightly to ease installation. Install governor retaining ring and align ring gap with an end showing in case slot.

NOTE: **If retaining ring cannot be installed, governor shaft is not aligned with case hole. Also, governor cover fits tight in case bore the last 1/16" (1.59 mm).**

BAND ANCHOR PIN & INTERMEDIATE SERVO

Install anchor pin (stem end first) into case, making sure stem locates in hole of intermediate band lug. Install servo assembly into case and make sure tapered end of band apply pin is properly located against band apply lug. Compress servo cover and install retaining ring. Align ring gap with an end showing in case slot.

Fig. 44: Installing Intermediate Band Anchor Pin

Band Anchor Pin

VALVE BODY

1) Install new low-reverse clutch housing-to-case cup plug and seal assembly, with seal end first, into hole in case. *See Fig. 45.* Using a 3/8" diameter metal rod and hammer, drive plug and seal assembly into case until it seats against low-reverse clutch housing.

2) Lubricate with petrolatum and install new "O" ring seal on torque converter clutch electrical connector. Connect solenoid lead wire to electrical connector. Install connector into case with lock tabs facing into case and locator tab in notch on side of case.

Fig. 45: Installing Low-Reverse Clutch Housing to Case Cup Plug and Seal Assembly

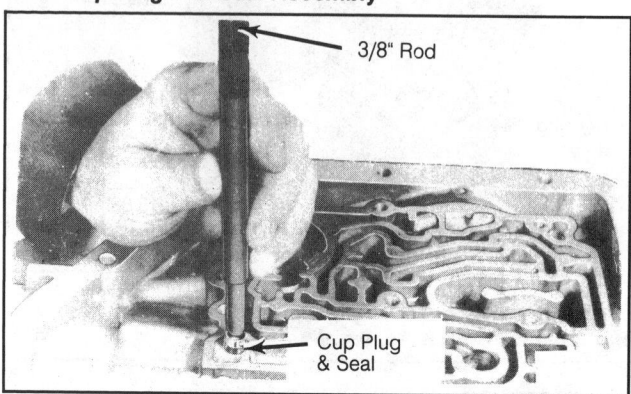

3/8" Rod

Cup Plug & Seal

3) Install 1-2 accumulator spring into case pocket. Install fifth check ball into case. *See Fig. 6.* Install two guide pins into case to align valve body parts. Install remaining four check balls into ball seat pockets in valve body and retain with petrolatum. *See Fig. 14.*

4) Position valve body-to-spacer plate gasket (marked "VB") on valve body, then place spacer plate on top of gasket. Place spacer plate-to-case gasket (marked "C") on top of spacer plate.

5) Insert two valve body attaching bolts through valve body, gaskets and spacer plate, then install valve body assembly, aligning manual valve with detent lever pin.

NOTE: **Make sure check balls, 1-2 accumulator piston and manual valve do not fall out during valve body installation.**

6) Start valve body attaching bolts, except the throttle lever and bracket assembly and the oil screen attaching bolts. Remove guide pins and replace with bolts and inside manual detent roller and spring assembly, locating tang in valve body assembly, and the roller on inside detent lever.

7) If removed, install spring on top of throttle lever and bracket assembly lifter, then place lifter and spring into throttle bracket. Install link on throttle lever, making sure link is hooked. *See Fig. 47.*

8) Install lever and bracket assembly, locating slot in bracket with coiled pin, aligning lifter through valve body hole and link through T.V. linkage case bore. Install attaching bolts. Tighten all valve body attaching bolts evenly.

9) On diesel models, install governor pressure switch using a 1 1/16" oil pressure sending unit socket. Connect long solenoid lead wire to governor pressure switch terminal. Press solenoid lead wires into wire clip.

OIL SCREEN, OIL PAN & SPEEDOMETER DRIVEN GEAR

Install a new screen gasket on oil screen, retain with petrolatum, then install screen on valve body and install and tighten attaching bolts. Position a new pan

GENERAL MOTORS TURBO HYDRA-MATIC 200C (Cont.)

Fig. 46: *Cutaway View of Transmission Showing Location of Thrust Washers, Thrust Bearings and Bushings*

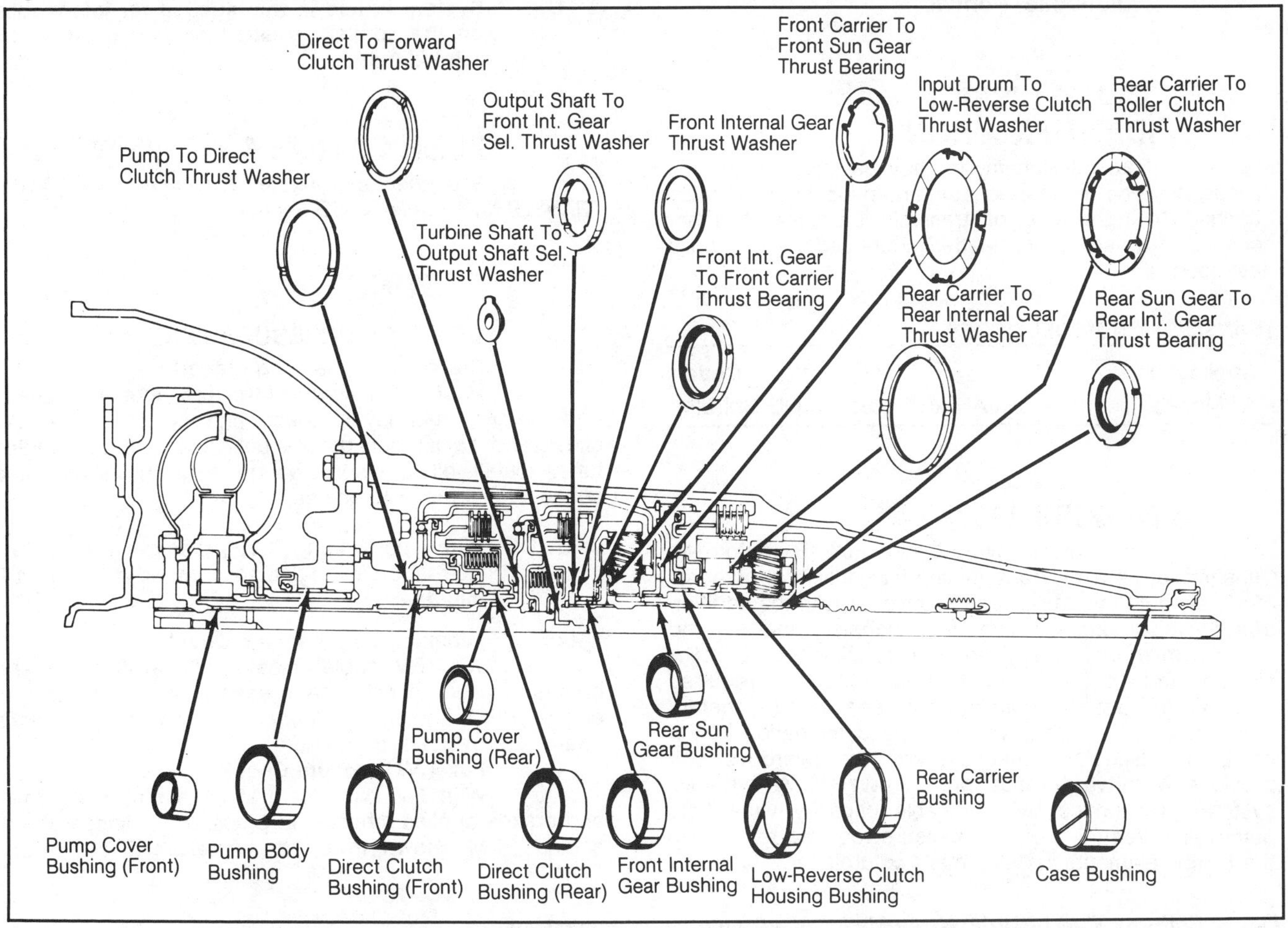

Direct To Forward
Clutch Thrust Washer

Output Shaft To
Front Int. Gear
Sel. Thrust Washer

Front Carrier To
Front Sun Gear
Thrust Bearing

Front Internal Gear
Thrust Washer

Input Drum To
Low-Reverse Clutch
Thrust Washer

Rear Carrier To
Roller Clutch
Thrust Washer

Pump To Direct
Clutch Thrust Washer

Turbine Shaft To
Output Shaft Sel.
Thrust Washer

Front Int. Gear
To Front Carrier
Thrust Bearing

Rear Carrier To
Rear Internal Gear
Thrust Washer

Rear Sun Gear To
Rear Int. Gear
Thrust Bearing

Pump Cover
Bushing (Rear)

Rear Sun
Gear Bushing

Rear Carrier
Bushing

Pump Cover
Bushing (Front)

Pump Body
Bushing

Direct Clutch
Bushing (Front)

Direct Clutch
Bushing (Rear)

Front Internal
Gear Bushing

Low-Reverse Clutch
Housing Bushing

Case Bushing

gasket on case, install oil pan and attaching bolts, and tighten. If necessary, install a new "O" ring seal on speedometer driven gear housing, install housing into case, then install retainer and attaching bolt, aligning slot in housing with retainer.

TORQUE CONVERTER

Install torque converter into pump assembly, making sure converter hub drive slots are fully engaged

with pump drive gear tangs, and that converter is fully installed towards rear of transmission.

NOTE: **When properly installed, the distance between engine mounting face of transmission case and front face of converter cover drive lugs will be at least 1".**

Fig. 47: *Throttle Lever and Bracket Assembly*

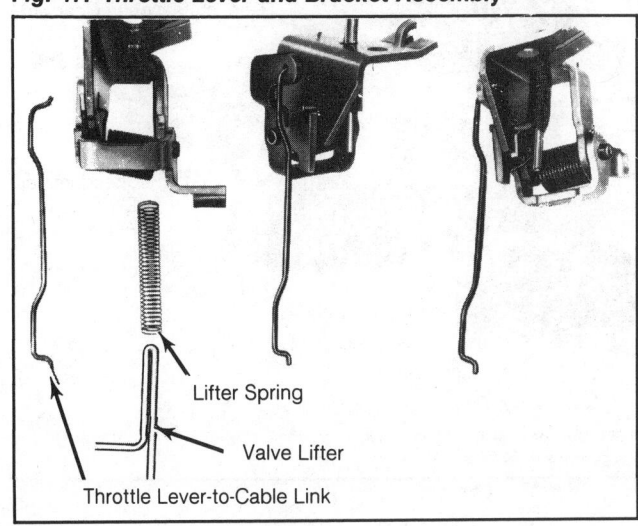

Lifter Spring

Valve Lifter

Throttle Lever-to-Cable Link

TIGHTENING SPECIFICATIONS

Application	Ft. Lbs. (N.m)
Transmission-to-Engine	
4-Cyl. (1.9L)	25 (34)
V6 (2.8L)	55 (75)
All Others	35 (47)
Converter-to Flywheel	35 (47)
Pump Body-to-PumpCober	15-20 (20-27)
Pump-to-Case	15-20 (20-27)
Park Lock Bracket-to-Case	15-20 (20-27)
Manual Shaft-to-Detent Lever	20-25 (27-34)
	INCH Lbs. (N.m)
Oil Pan-to-Case	124-160 (14-18)
Line Perssure Take Off	62-124 (7-14)
Throttle Lever Bracket-to-Case	115-151 (13-17)
Valve Body-to-Case	115-151 (13-17)
Oil Screen-to-Case	115-151 (13-17)
Speedo Driven Gear Retainer-to-Case	71-124 (8-14)
Governor Pressuer Switch (Diesel)	62-124 (7-14)
T.C.C. Solenoid-to-Pump	27-44 (3-5)

GENERAL MOTORS TURBO HYDRA-MATIC 200-4R

**Buick, Cadillac, Chevrolet,
Oldsmobile, Pontiac**

TRANSMISSION IDENTIFICATION

Transmission model may be identified by the production code number, located on an identification plate attached to right side of transmission case. Number consists of a year code, 2-letter model code, and a build date code.

TRANSMISSION MODEL CODES

Application	Code
All Models	AA,AH,AP,BR,BY,HE,OG,OM,ZR

DESCRIPTION

The Turbo Hydra-Matic 200-4R automatic transmission is a fully automatic unit consisting primarily of a 3-element hydraulic torque converter with the addition of a converter clutch, a compound planetary gear set and an overdrive unit. Five multiple-disc clutches, 2 roller clutches and a band provide the friction elements required to obtain the desired function of the compound planetary gear set and the overdrive unit. The combination of the compound planetary gear set and the overdrive unit provides 4 forward ratios and 1 reverse. A hydraulic system, pressurized by a variable capacity vane type pump, provides the working pressure required to operate the friction elements and automatic controls.

NOTE: See General Motors Torque Converter Clutch System article in this section for information on the converter clutch system used in the THM 200-4R.

LUBRICATION & ADJUSTMENT

See the appropriate article in AUTOMATIC TRANSMISSION SERVICING Section.

TESTING

CONTROL PRESSURE TEST

Preliminary Checking Procedure
Prior to making control pressure test: check transmission fluid level, check and adjust T.V. cable, check and adjust outside manual linkage, check engine tune, install oil pressure gauge to transmission and connect tachometer to engine.

CAUTION: When performing T.V. pressure checks, DO NOT sustain engine test speed more than 2 minutes.

Minimum T.V. Pressure Check
With T.V. cable adjusted to specifications and brakes applied, check line pressure in ranges and at engine RPM shown in *Control Pressure Specifications Chart.*

Full T.V. Pressure Check
With T.V. cable held at full extent of its travel and brakes applied, check line pressure in ranges and at engine RPM shown in *Control Pressure Specifications Chart.*

Fig. 1: Cutaway View of Turbo Hydra-Matic 200-4R Automatic Transmission

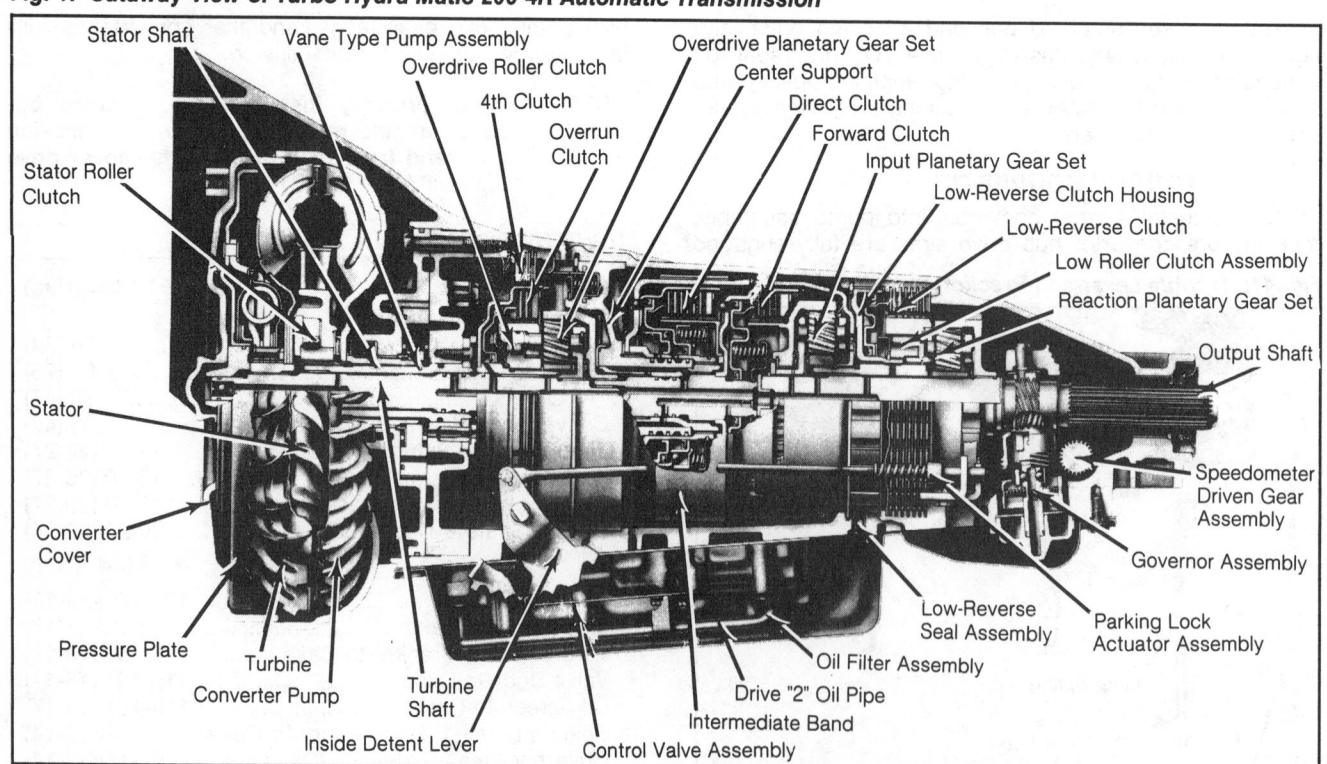

GENERAL MOTORS TURBO HYDRA-MATIC 200-4R (Cont.)

CONTROL PRESSURE SPECIFICATIONS CHART (psi)

Range @ RPM (Model Code)	Minumum T.V. Pressure	Full T.V. Pressure
"P" & "N" @ 1000		
OM	55-65	110-127
OG,AA,AP,BY,HE	55-65	123-140
AH	55-65	140-160
BR	55-65	145-170
ZR	65-75	160-190
Reverse @ 1000		
OM	105-120	220-235
OG,AA,AP,BY,HE	105-120	230-260
AH	105-120	260-297
BR	105-120	275-315
ZR	120-140	293-350
"D" & 3rd @ 1000		
OM	55-65	110-127
OG,AA,AP,BY,HE	55-65	123-140
AH	55-65	140-160
BR	55-65	145-170
ZR	65-75	160-190
"L" & 2nd @ 1000		
OM	122-140	122-140
OG,AA,AP,BY,HE	122-140	122-140
AH	122-140	122-140
BR	122-140	122-140
ZR	140-160	140-160

CONTROL PRESSURE TEST RESULTS
High or Low Oil Pressures
- T.V. cable out of adjustment, binding, unhooked, broken, or wrong link.
- Throttle lever and bracket assembly binding, unhooked or mispositioned.
- Throttle valve or plunger valve binding.
- Pressure regulator valve binding.
- T.V. Boost valve binding, or wrong valve installed (causing low oil pressure only).
- Reverse Boost valve binding.
- Manual valve unhooked, or mispositioned.
- Pressure relief valve ball missing or spring damaged.
- Oil pump slide stuck, or slide seal missing or damaged.
- Pump decrease air bleed orifice missing or damaged (causing low oil pressure only).
- Pump decrease air bleed orifice plugged (causing low oil pressure only).
- T.V. Limit valve binding.
- Line Bias valve binding in open position (causing high oil pressure).
- Line Bias valve binding in closed position (causing low oil pressure).

SERVICE (IN-VEHICLE)
The following components can be removed from transmission without removing transmission from vehicle:
- Governor Assembly
- Intermediate Servo Piston Assembly
- Oil Pan and Screen
- Control Valve Assembly
- Check Balls and Valve Body Spacer Plate and Gaskets
- Pressure Regulator Parts
- Inside Detent/Range Lever
- Manual Detent Roller and Spring Assembly
- Throttle Lever and Bracket Assembly

CLUTCH AND BAND APPLICATION CHART (ELEMENTS IN USE)

Selector Lever Position	Overrun Clutch	Inter-mediate Band	Overdrive Roller Clutch	Direct Clutch	Low Roller Clutch	4th Clutch	Forward Clutch	Low-Reverse Clutch
D — DRIVE								
First Gear			X		X		X	
Second Gear		X	X				X	
Third Gear			X	X			X	
Overdrive				X	X	X		
3 — MANUAL THIRD	X			X			X	
2 — MANUAL SECOND	X	X					X	
1 — MANUAL LOW	X						X	X
R — REVERSE			X	X				X
NEUTRAL or PARK			X					

Automatic Transmissions

GENERAL MOTORS TURBO HYDRA-MATIC 200-4R (Cont.)

Fig. 2: *Turbo Hydra-Matic 200-4R Hydraulic Circuits Diagram*

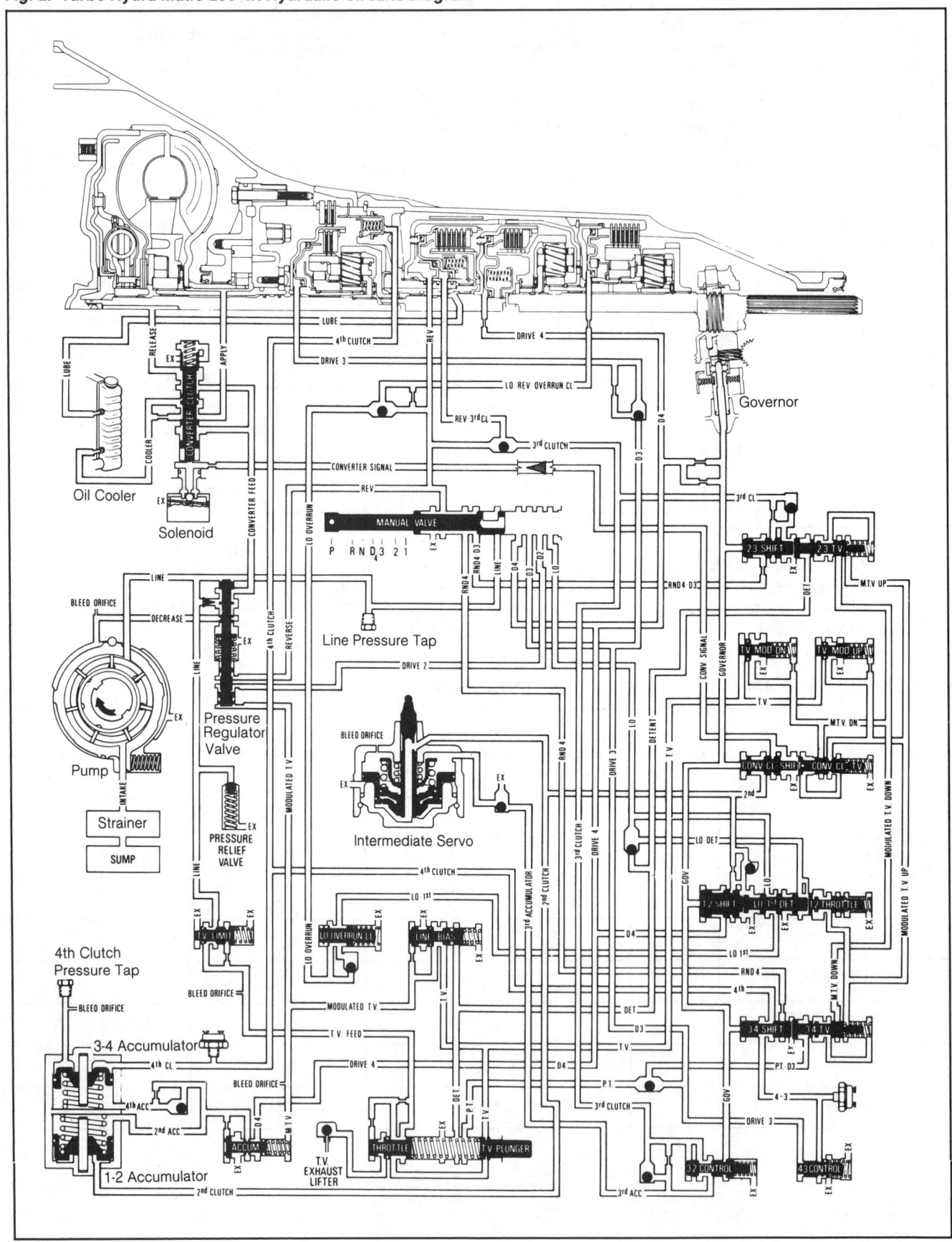

GENERAL MOTORS TURBO HYDRA-MATIC 200-4R (Cont.)

- T.V. Cable and "O" Ring
- T.V. Boost Valve and Bushing
- Parking Pawl Actuator Rod, Bracket and Pawl
- Manual Shaft and Seal
- Manual Valve and Link
- Rear Seal
- 1-2 Accumulator Assembly
- 3-4 Accumulator Assembly
- Low-Reverse Cup Plug
- Reverse Boost Valve and Bushing
- Stop Valve
- Intermediate Band Anchor Pin
- 4-3 Pressure Switch
- 4th Clutch Pressure Switch
- Speedometer Driven Gear Assembly
- Converter Clutch Valve and Spring
- Converter Clutch Solenoid
- Solenoid Wire Clips
- Electrical Connectors
- Cooler Fittings
- Oil Filter Pipe and "O" Ring

For removal and installation of these components, see *Transmission Disassembly* and *Transmission Reassembly* procedures in this article.

TRANSMISSION REMOVAL & INSTALLATION

See the appropriate article in *AUTOMATIC TRANSMISSION REMOVAL* Section.

TORQUE CONVERTER

NOTE: **The torque converter is a sealed unit and cannot be disassembled for service.**

LEAKAGE CHECK

See procedure given in *G.M. Turbo Hydra-Matic 400* article.

END CLEARANCE CHECK

See procedure given in *G.M. Turbo Hydra-Matic 400* article.

CONVERTER FLUSHING

See procedure given in *G.M. Turbo Hydra-Matic 400* article.

NOTE: **For additional information on the Torque Converter Clutch (TCC) system used on this transmission, see General Motors Torque Converter Clutch System article in this section.**

TRANSMISSION DISASSEMBLY

EXTERNAL PARTS

1) Mount transmission in a holding fixture and remove torque converter. Rotate transmission so that oil pan is facing up. Remove oil pan and gasket. Remove oil filter intake pipe and "O" rings. "O" rings may be located in pump bore.

2) Disconnect wire leads at electrical connector and pressure switches. See Fig. 3. Using a 3/4" box wrench to compress connector tangs, withdraw electrical connector and "O" ring from case. Remove converter clutch solenoid assembly bolts, clips and solenoid.

Fig. 3: Bottom View of Transmission Case Showing Location of Solenoid and Pressure Switches

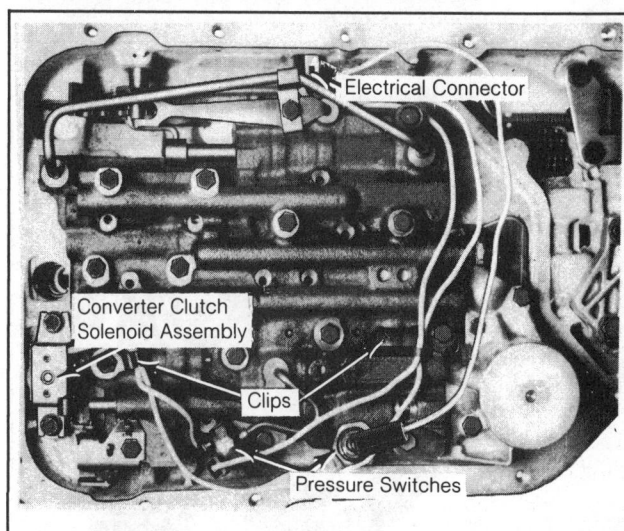

3) Using care not to bend throttle lever link, remove throttle lever and bracket assembly. T.V. exhaust valve lifter and spring may separate from lever and bracket assembly. Remove manual detent roller and spring assembly, signal (Drive "2") oil pipe retaining clip and oil pipe.

4) Remove 4-3 pressure switch and retaining bolt, then remove remaining valve body attaching bolts. Hold manual valve in bore and carefully lift control valve assembly from case. Care must be taken as 3 check balls are located on top of spacer plate-to-valve body gasket. Remove check balls.

Fig. 4: Location of Check Balls on Spacer Plate Gasket

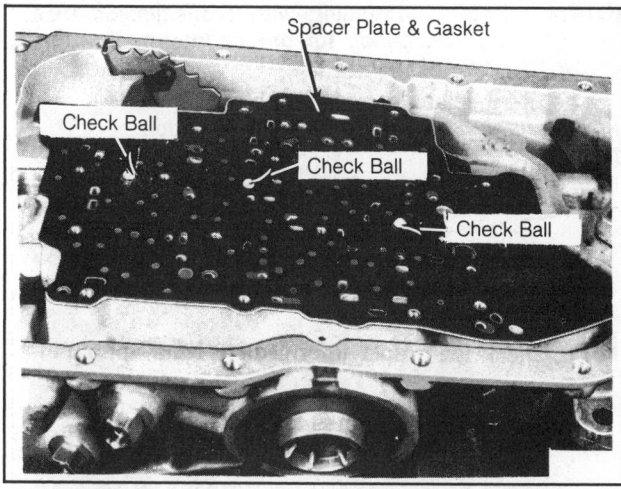

5) Remove 1-2 accumulator housing, then withdraw spring, gasket, plate and piston from housing. It may be necessary to apply low air pressure (approximately 3 psi) to orifice in accumulator housing passage to remove piston.

Automatic Transmissions

GENERAL MOTORS TURBO HYDRA-MATIC 200-4R (Cont.)

6) Remove control valve assembly gaskets and spacer plate from transmission case. Withdraw 3-4 accumulator spring, piston and pin from bore in case. It may be necessary to apply low air pressure (approximately 3 psi) to orifice in case core passage to remove piston. See Fig. 5.

Fig. 5: View of Case Core Passage Showing Orifice for 3-4 Accumulator Piston Removal

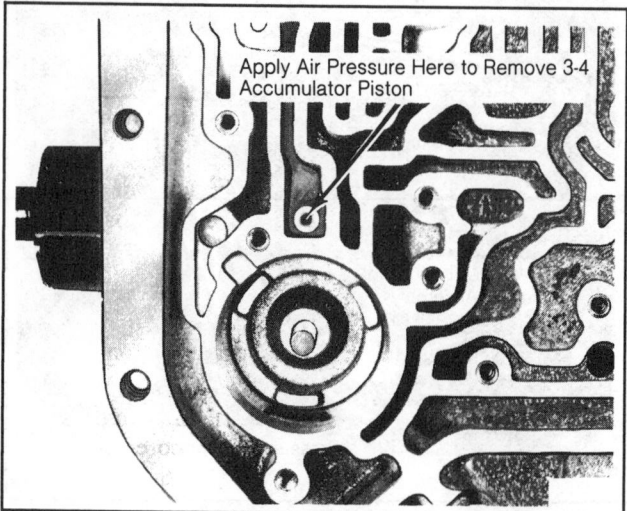

Use approximately 3 psi (2 kg/cm²) to remove piston.

7) Remove 8 check balls from core passages in case. Remove governor cover and gasket from case, then remove governor assembly while rotating output shaft counterclockwise to ease removal.

CAUTION: Do not use any type of pliers to remove governor assembly.

8) Pry intermediate servo cover retaining ring from groove in case. Remove servo cover and discard seal ring. Remove servo piston and band apply pin from bore in case.

NOTE: Before continuing with Transmission Disassembly, check for proper intermediate band apply pin as follows.

Fig. 6: Intermediate Band Apply Pin Selection

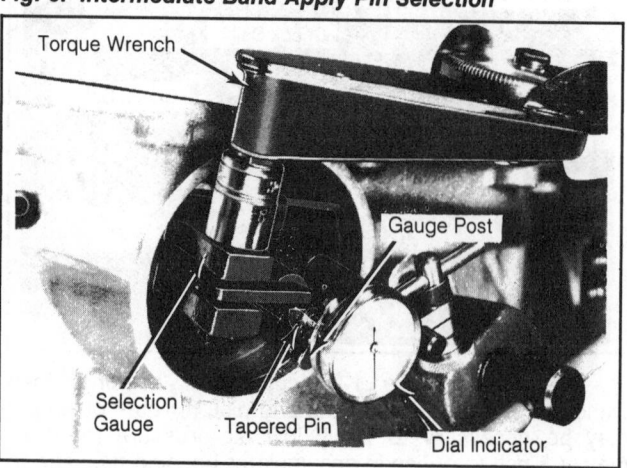

Intermediate Band Apply Pin Selection

1) Install band apply pin selection gauge (J-25014-2) in intermediate servo bore and retain with servo cover retaining ring, aligning ring with gap at case slot. Install selection gauge tapered pin (J-25014-1) into gauge. See Fig. 6.

NOTE: Make sure tapered pin end is properly located against band apply lug. Also, make sure band anchor pin is properly located in case and band anchor lug.

NOTE: If band selection tapered pin does not register between the high and low limits, look for possible problem with intermediate band, direct clutch housing or transmission case.

2) Install dial indicator and position indicator point on top of selection gauge post. Set indicator to zero. Make sure selection gauge is squarely seated against servo retaining ring and stepped side of tapered pin is aligned with torquing arm of gauge.

NOTE: Dial indicator travel is reversed, making the indicator readings backwards. On indicators that range from 0-100, a .020" (.51 mm) travel will read .080" (2.03 mm), a .060" (1.52 mm) travel will read .040" (1.02 mm).

INTERMEDIATE BAND APPLY PIN SELECTION CHART

Indicator Reading In. (mm)	Apply Pin I.D.
0-.029 (0-.74)	1 Groove
.029-.057 (.74-1.45)	2 Grooves
.057-.086 (1.45-2.18)	3 Grooves
.086-.114 (2.18-2.89)	None

3rd Accumulator Check Valve Replacement

1) Inspect 3rd accumulator check valve for the following conditions: Missing check ball; check ball binding or stuck in tube; oil feed slot in tube missing or restricted; improperly assembled, loose fitting or not fully seated in case. If check valve requires replacement, go to step **2)**.

Fig. 7: 3rd Accumulator Check Valve Assembly

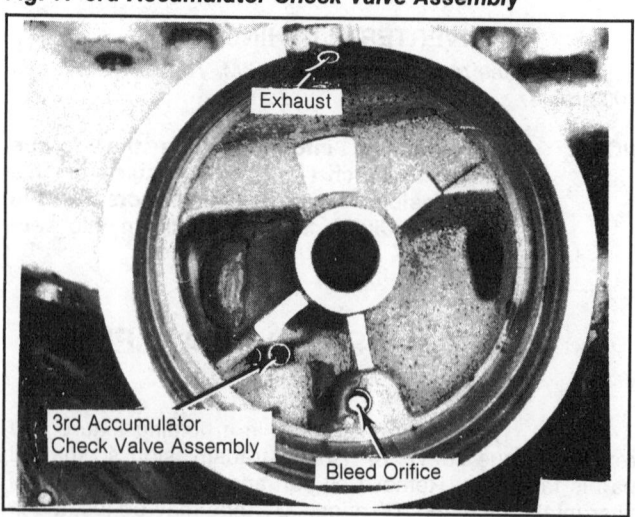

GENERAL MOTORS TURBO HYDRA-MATIC 200-4R (Cont.)

2) Using a No. 4 screw extractor, remove check valve assembly from case by turning and pulling straight out. *See Fig. 8.*

3) Install new check valve assembly, small end first, into case. Position oil feed slot in tube so it faces servo. Using a 3/8" diameter metal rod and hammer, drive assembly until it is seated in case hole.

Fig. 8: Removing 3rd Accumulator Check Valve

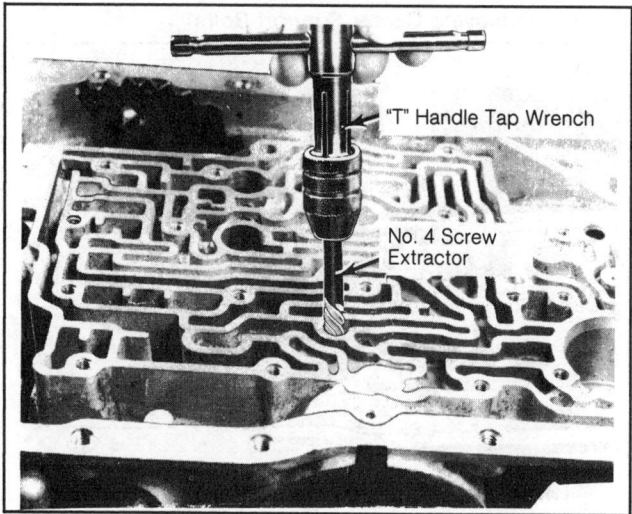

OVERDRIVE UNIT PARTS

NOTE: **Prior to removing overdrive unit parts, check overdrive unit end play to determine correct end play thrust washer for use at reassembly.**

Overdrive End Play Checking
1) Install output shaft loading fixture (J-29332) and support sleeve (J-25013-1) to output shaft. *See Fig. 9.* Turn transmission to vertical position, pump side up.

Fig. 9: Installing Output Shaft Loading Tools

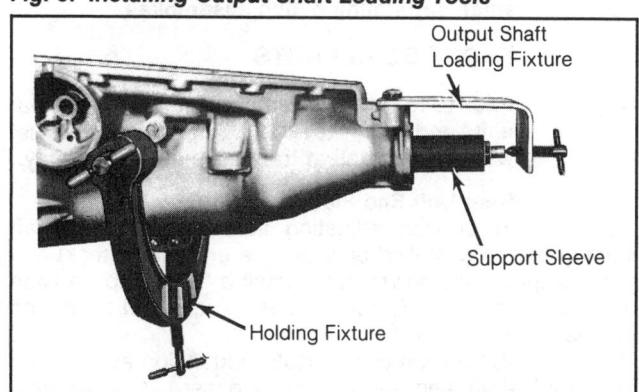

2) Remove 1 pump-to-case bolt and washer and install an 11" long bolt into pump bolt hole. Attach overdrive end play checking tool (J-25022) and oil pump removal tool (J-24773-5) to turbine shaft. *See Fig. 10.*

3) Mount a dial indicator, and clamp assembly on long bolt, positioning indicator point cap on top of pump removal tool. Lift upward on removal tool with approximately 3 lbs. force and zero indicator while maintaining the upward force.

NOTE: **The preceding step must be performed to eliminate the tolerance difference between turbine shaft snap ring and overdrive carrier.**

4) With dial indicator zeroed, increase upward force to approximately 20 lbs. (9.1 kg) and read end play on indicator. Overdrive unit end play should be .004-.027" (.10-.69 mm). The selective thrust washer controlling this end play is located between pump cover and overdrive clutch housing. If more or less washer thickness is required to bring end play within specification, select washer from the *Overdrive Unit End Play Washer Selection Chart.*

OVERDRIVE UNIT END PLAY WASHER SELECTION CHART

Washer Thickness	I.D. Number	I.D. Color
.167-.171"	0	Scarlet
.172-.176"	1	White
.177-.180"	2	Brown
.181-.185"	3	Gray
.186-.190"	4	Yellow
.191-.195"	5	Lt. Blue
.196-.200"	6	Pink/Purple
.201-.204"	7	Black/Orange
.205-.209"	8	Green

Fig. 10: Checking Overdrive Unit End Play

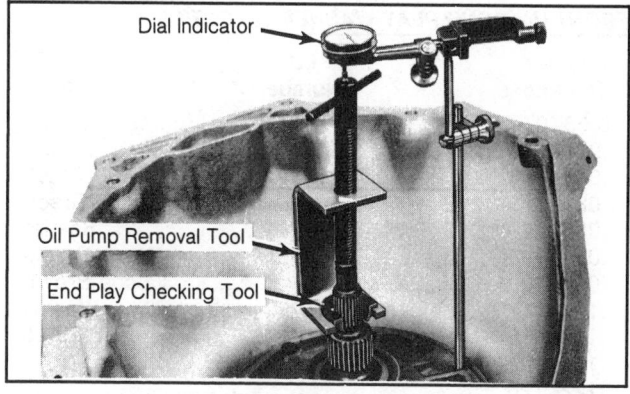

Component Removal
1) If necessary, pry oil pump seal from pump. Remove pump-to-case bolts and washers. Install oil pump removal tool (J-24773-A) on turbine shaft. *See Fig. 10.* Remove oil pump assembly from case. Remove pump-to-case gasket and tanged oil deflector plate located under pump.

2) Remove 4th clutch plate-to-case snap ring, then grasp turbine shaft and lift overdrive assembly and 4th clutch plates from case. Remove clutch plates from overdrive assembly and the remaining steel plate from case.

3) Remove overdrive internal gear-to-carrier thrust washer from inside internal gear. Remove internal gear and internal gear-to-support thrust washer from case.

4) Using a spring compressor tool, compress 4th clutch spring and retainer assembly. Remove support-to-clutch snap ring, spring and retainer tool. Remove compressor tool from retainer assembly. Lift 4th clutch piston from case.

GENERAL MOTORS TURBO HYDRA-MATIC 200-4R (Cont.)

FRONT UNIT PARTS

NOTE: Prior to removing front unit parts, check front unit end play to determine correct thrust washer to install at reassembly.

Front Unit End Play

1) Push forward clutch shaft downward, then install forward and direct clutch removal tool (J-29337) in end of shaft. Mount dial indicator and clamp assembly. *See Fig. 11.* Position indicator point on top of clutch removal tool.

NOTE: Perform this check with output shaft loading fixture and support sleeve in place.

2) Move output shaft upward by turning adjusting screw on output shaft loading fixture. Move shaft upward until White or scribed line on support sleeve begins to disappear. Zero dial indicator.

3) Pull clutch removal tool upward and read resulting end play on dial indicator. Front unit end play should be .022-.051" (.56-1.30 mm). Selective thrust washer controlling this end play is located between output shaft and forward clutch shaft. If more or less washer thickness is required to bring end play within specification, select proper washer from the *Front Unit End Play Washer Selection Chart.*

FRONT UNIT END PLAY WASHER SELECTION CHART

Washer Thickness	I.D. Number	I.D. Color
.065-.070"	1	
.070-.075"	2	
.076-.080"	3	Black
.081-.085"	4	Lt. Green
.086-.090"	5	Scarlet
.091-.095"	6	Purple
.096-.100"	7	Cocoa Brown
.106-.111"	9	Yellow
.111-.116"	10	Lt. Blue
.117-.121"	11	
.122-.126"	12	
.127-.131"	13	Pink
.132-.136"	14	Green
.137-.141"	15	Gray

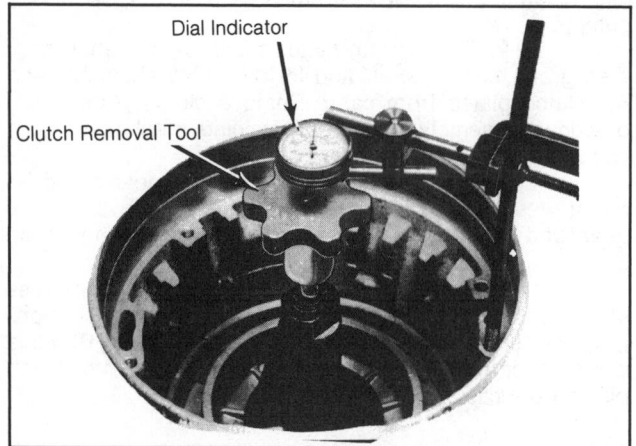

Fig. 11: Checking Front Unit End Play

Component Removal

1) Remove 2 center support-to-case bolts. *See Fig. 12.* From inside case, remove center support-to-case beveled snap ring and lift center support from case. Remove support-to-direct clutch thrust washer.

NOTE: Center support-to-direct clutch thrust washer may be stuck to back of direct clutch.

Fig. 12: Removing Center Support Bolts

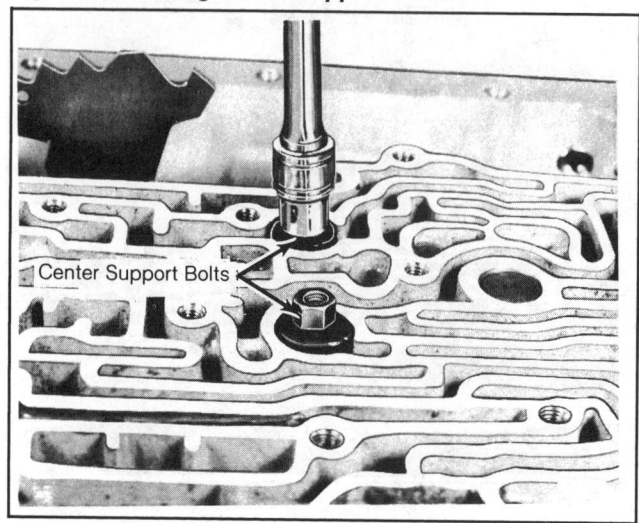

Center Support Bolts

2) Install direct and forward clutch removal tool (J-29337) in end of forward clutch shaft. *See Fig. 11.* Grasp removal tool and pull direct and forward clutch assemblies from case. Separate direct clutch from forward clutch. Remove intermediate band assembly and band anchor pin from case. Remove output shaft-to-forward clutch shaft selective thrust washer.

NOTE: The direct-to-forward clutch thrust washer may stick to end of direct clutch housing when separating clutch assemblies.

FRONT GEAR PARTS

NOTE: Prior to removing front gear parts, check rear unit end play to determine correct thrust washer to install at transmission reassembly.

Rear Unit End Play Checking

1) Loosen adjusting screw on output shaft loading fixture (installed at overdrive end play check) and push output shaft downward. Install a "C" clamp on case as shown in *Fig. 13,* then mount a dial indicator and extension on "C" clamp.

2) Position dial indicator extension against end of output shaft and set indicator to zero. Move output shaft upward by turning screw on loading fixture until White or scribed line on support sleeve begins to disappear, then read indicator end play.

3) Rear unit end play should be .004-.025" (.10-.64 mm). Selective thrust washer controlling this end play is located between front internal gear thrust washer and output shaft snap ring. If more or less thrust washer thickness is required to bring end play within specification, select proper washer from the *Rear Unit End Play Washer Selection Chart.* Remove dial indicator and "C" clamp.

GENERAL MOTORS TURBO HYDRA-MATIC 200-4R (Cont.)

REAR UNIT END PLAY WASHER SELECTION CHART

Washer Thickness	I.D. Number	I.D. Color
.097-.102"	0	.....
.114-.119"	1	Orange
.121-.126"	2	White
.128-.133"	3	Yellow
.135-.140"	4	Blue
.143-.147"	5	Red
.150-.154"	6	Brown
.157-.161"	7	Green
.164-.168"	8	Black
.171-.175"	9	Purple

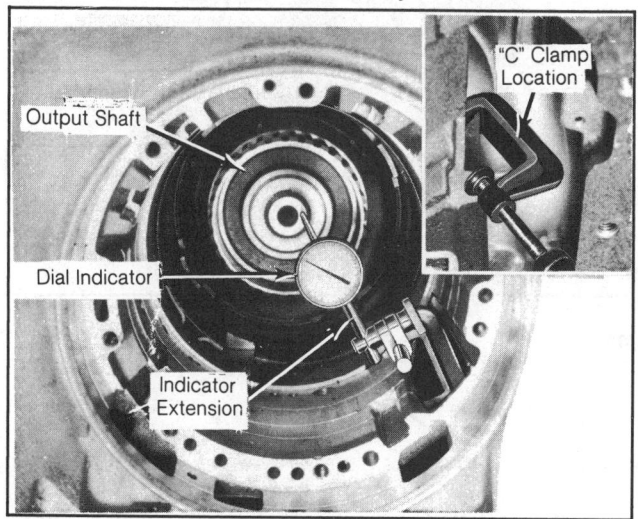

Fig. 13: Checking Rear Unit End Play

Component Removal

1) Remove output shaft-to-selective washer snap ring, then lift front internal gear, rear selective washer and thrust washer from case and remove washers from front internal gear.

2) Remove front carrier assembly and front internal gear-to-front carrier thrust bearing assembly. If it did not come out with front carrier, remove front sun gear and sun gear-to-front carrier thrust bearing assembly.

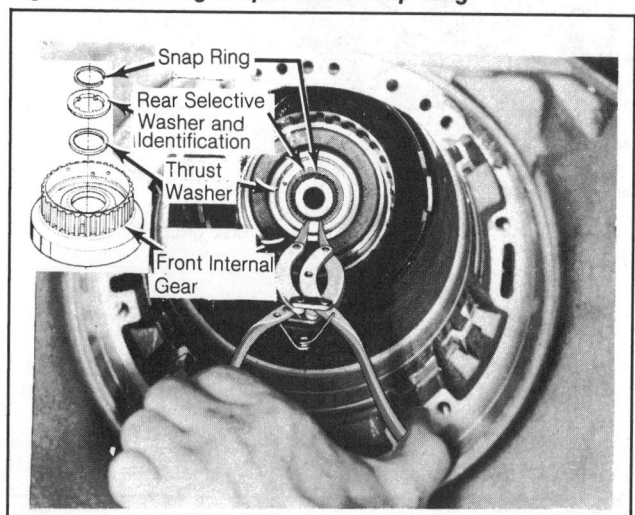

Fig. 14: Removing Output Shaft Snap Ring

NOTE: The front sun gear-to-front carrier thrust bearing requires only 1 race.

3) Remove input drum and rear sun gear. Remove the 4-tanged input drum-to-reverse clutch housing thrust washer from rear of drum or front clutch housing.

4) Grind approximately 3/4" from end of a No. 4 screw extractor. Insert screw extractor into low-reverse clutch housing-to-case cup plug. Turn screw extractor 2 or 3 turns and pull out cup plug. Remove low-reverse clutch-to-case beveled snap ring. Lift clutch assembly from case. Remove low-reverse clutch housing-to-case spacer ring.

NOTE: Do not reuse low-reverse clutch housing cup plug and seal assembly.

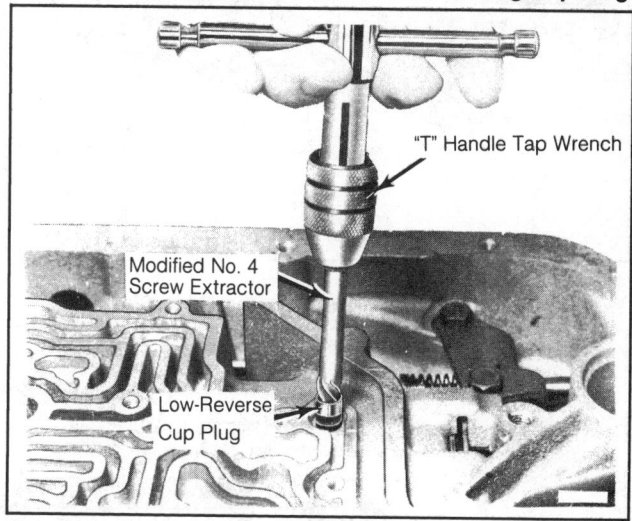

Fig. 15: Removing Low-Reverse Clutch Housing Cup Plug

REAR GEAR PARTS

NOTE: Make sure governor assembly has been removed before removing rear gear parts.

1) Grasp output shaft and lift out remaining rear unit parts and lay down in a horizontal position. Remove roller clutch and rear carrier from output shaft. Remove the 4-tanged rear carrier-to-rear internal gear thrust washer from end of carrier or from inside rear internal gear.

2) Pull low-reverse clutch plates from output shaft. Remove rear internal gear-to-rear sun gear thrust bearing assembly from internal gear, then remove internal gear from output shaft. If necessary, remove rear oil seal from transmission case.

MANUAL SHAFT & PARKING PAWL PARTS

1) Turn transmission to a horizontal position, oil pan side up. If necessary, remove manual shaft and parking pawl linkage.

2) Remove hex nut securing inside detent lever to manual shaft. Remove parking lock actuator rod and inside detent lever. Remove manual shaft retaining pin from case and slide shaft out. If damaged, pry manual shaft oil seal from case.

3) Remove parking lock bracket. Remove parking pawl shaft retaining pin, then remove parking pawl

GENERAL MOTORS TURBO HYDRA-MATIC 200-4R (Cont.)

cup plug using a No. 4 screw extractor with 3/4" ground from end. Using a No. 4 screw extractor, remove parking pawl shaft from case. Remove parking pawl and spring.

Fig. 16: Removing Parking Pawl Cup Plug

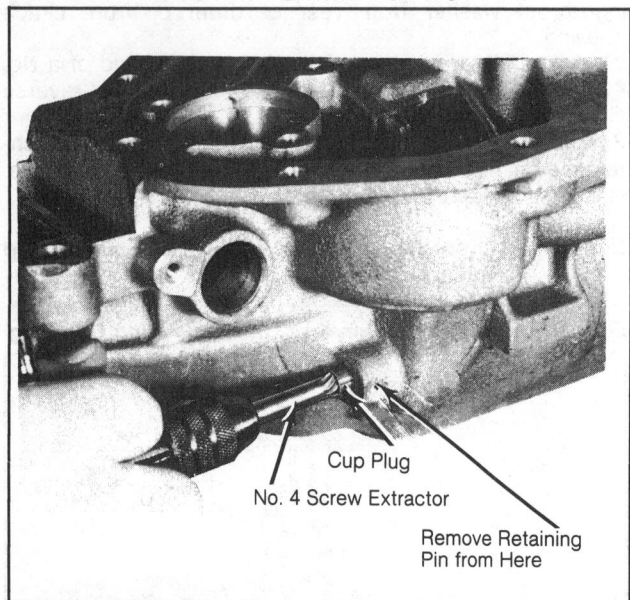

COMPONENT DISASSEMBLY & REASSEMBLY

TRANSMISSION CASE
Inspection

1) Inspect case assembly for damage, cracks, porosity or interconnected oil passages. Inspect orifice plug in intermediate servo bore. If plug requires replace-

Fig. 17: Front View of Transmission Case Showing Oil Passages

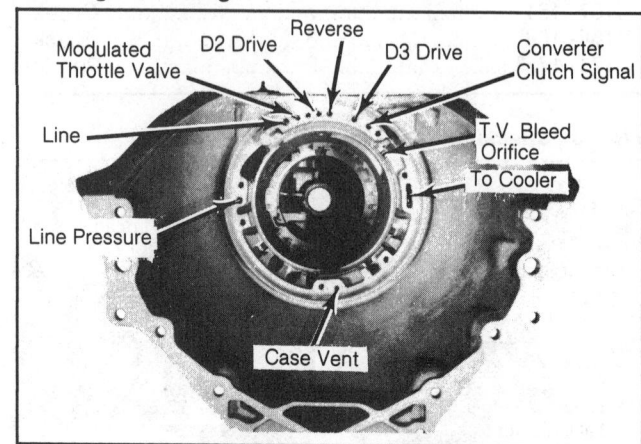

Fig. 18: Bottom View of Transmission Case Showing Oil Passages

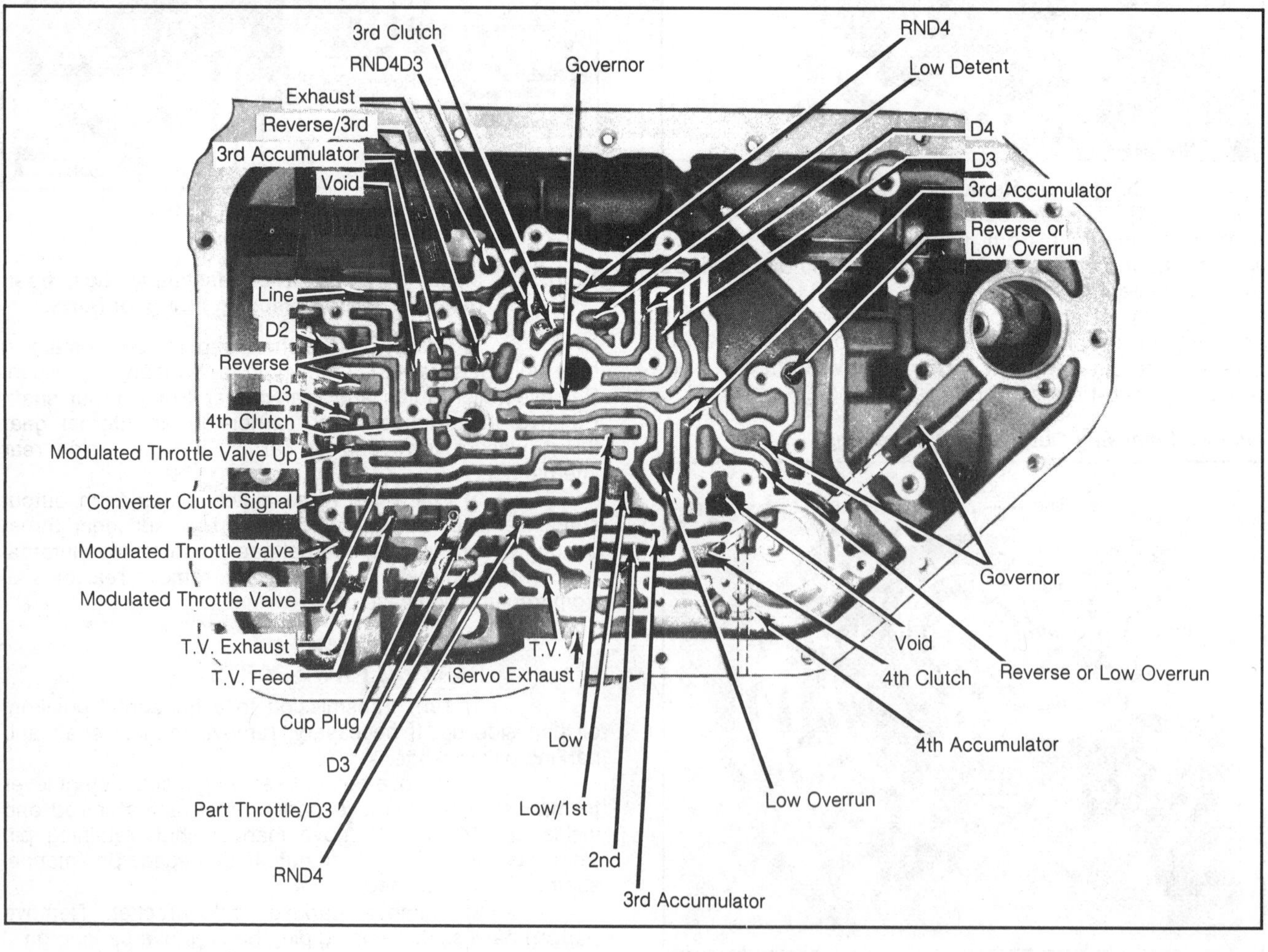

GENERAL MOTORS TURBO HYDRA-MATIC 200-4R (Cont.)

ment, install new plug, orifice end first, flush to slightly below top of plug hole.

2) Inspect case exhaust passages for restrictions. Inspect reverse clutch lugs, governor, intermediate servo bore, speedometer bore, and snap ring grooves for damage. Inspect all bolt holes for damage or stripped holes. Inspect case bushing for damage and scoring.

REAR GEAR PARTS
Inspection

1) Inspect output shaft journals, snap ring groove and splines for wear or damage. Check lubrication passages for damage or obstructions. Check governor drive gear for rough or damaged teeth.

2) Inspect rear internal gear splines, teeth and bearing surface for wear, cracks or damage. Inspect parking pawl lugs for cracks or damage. Thoroughly clean, air dry and inspect rear internal gear-to-rear sun gear thrust bearing assembly for pitted or rough conditions.

ROLLER CLUTCH & REAR CARRIER ASSEMBLY
Disassembly

Remove roller clutch inner race and lift roller clutch assembly from rear carrier. Remove rear carrier-to-clutch thrust washer (4 tangs) from rear of carrier and roller clutch-to-rear carrier thrust washer from inside carrier.

Inspection

1) Inspect roller clutch race and spline for scoring or wear. Inspect roller clutch bearings, cage and springs for damage or wear. Inspect thrust washers for signs of scoring or excessive wear and check tanged thrust washer for bent tangs.

2) Inspect rear carrier for damage to roller clutch cam ramps. Inspect bushing for damage and scoring. Inspect planet pinions for damage, rough bearings or tilt. Check pinion end play using a feeler gauge inserted between carrier and pinion gears. End play should be .009-.024" (.23-.61 mm).

Reassembly

1) Position roller clutch-to-carrier thrust washer in rear carrier. Install rollers that may have come out of

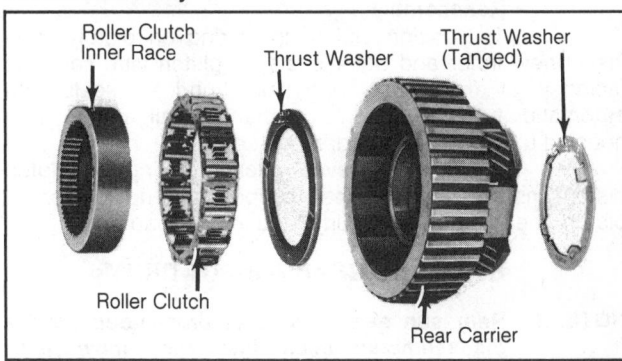

Fig. 19: *Disassembled View of Roller Clutch and Rear Carrier Assembly*

roller cage by compressing energizing spring with forefinger and inserting roller from outer edge. Install roller clutch into rear carrier.

2) Install roller clutch race, spline side out, into roller clutch and rotate it into position. Install 4-tanged rear carrier-to-rear internal gear thrust washer. Align tangs into slots of rear carrier and retain with petroleum jelly.

LOW-REVERSE CLUTCH
Disassembly

Compress low-reverse clutch spring retainer and remove snap ring. Remove waved spring from top of piston, then remove piston from housing. Remove inner and outer seals from piston. Remove clutch apply ring.

NOTE: **Low-reverse clutch assembly clutch plates and disc were removed during Transmission Disassembly.**

Inspection

1) Inspect composition, steel and waved clutch plates for signs of wear or burning. Check spring retainer and waved spring for damage or distortion. Inspect clutch housing for damage or plugged feed hole. Inspect clutch housing bushing for damage or scoring.

2) Inspect clutch housing splines and snap ring groove for damage or burrs. Remove burrs with crocus cloth. Inspect clutch piston and apply ring assembly for

Fig. 20: *Exploded View of Low-Reverse Clutch Assembly*

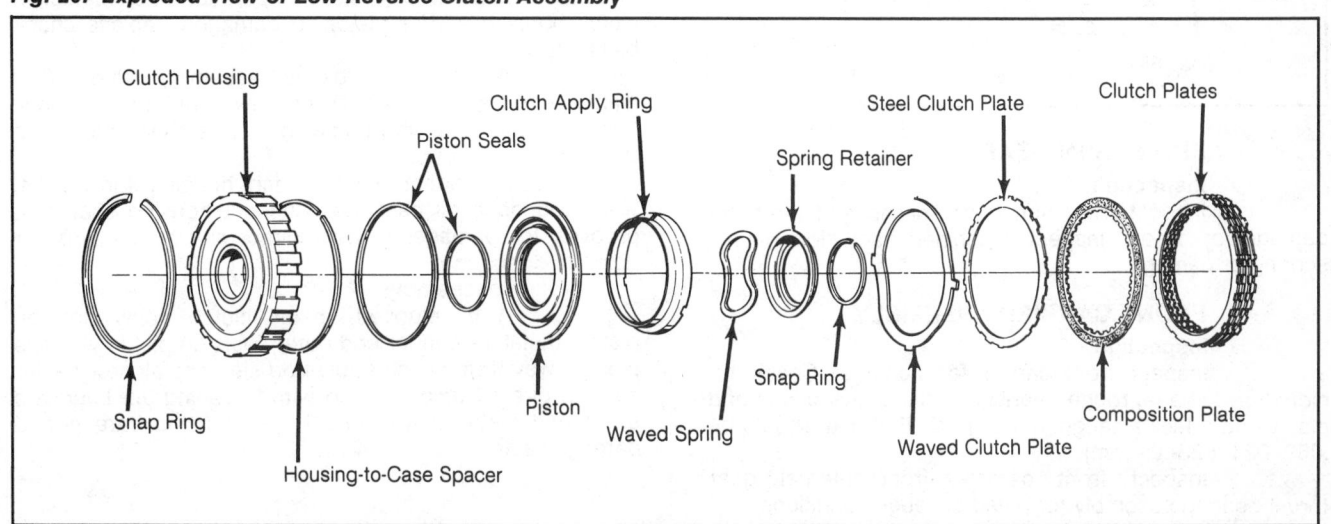

distortion, cracks or damage. Inspect clutch housing-to-case spacer ring for damage.

Reassembly

1) Position clutch apply ring on piston, then install new inner and outer seals on piston with seal lips facing away from apply ring side. Lubricate seals with automatic transmission fluid, then install piston into housing using care not to damage seals.

2) Position waved release spring on clutch piston. Install spring retainer, cupped face up, on top of piston, then compress retainer and install snap ring.

REAR SUN GEAR & INPUT DRUM

NOTE: Rear sun gear and input drum need not be disassembled unless inspection shows it to be necessary.

Inspection

Inspect rear sun gear for cracks, splits, damaged spline, worn gear or journals and plugged lubrication holes. Inspect sun gear bushing for damage or scoring. Inspect input drum for damage. Inspect 4-tanged input drum-to-low and reverse clutch housing thrust washer for scoring or distorted tangs. If damaged, replace sun gear-to-input drum snap ring.

Disassembly

Remove input drum-to-rear sun gear snap ring. Separate sun gear from input drum. Remove tanged thrust washer from drum.

Reassembly

Install sun gear into input drum, spline side first, and retain with snap ring. Install 4-tanged thrust washer on drum over sun gear end. Align tangs into drum and retain with petroleum jelly.

Fig. 21: Disassembled View of Rear Sun Gear and Input Drum Assembly

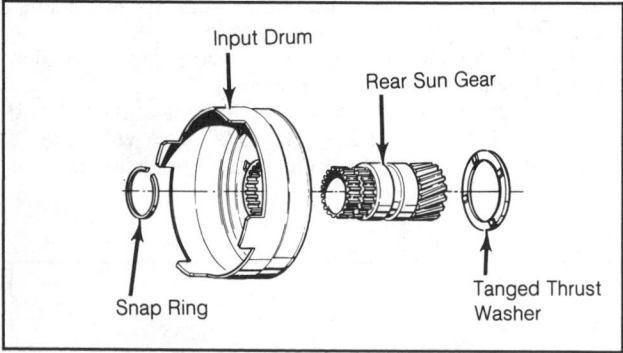

Input Drum
Rear Sun Gear
Snap Ring
Tanged Thrust Washer

FRONT SUN GEAR

Inspection

Inspect front sun gear splines and teeth for damage or wear. Inspect machined face for pitting, scoring or damage.

FRONT CARRIER ASSEMBLY

Inspection

Inspect front carrier for damage. Check pinions for damage, rough bearings or tilt. Check pinion end play using a feeler gauge. See Fig. 22. End play should be .009-.024" (.23-.61 mm).

Inspect front carrier-to-front internal gear thrust bearing assembly for pitted or rough conditions.

Fig. 22: Checking Front Carrier Pinion End Play

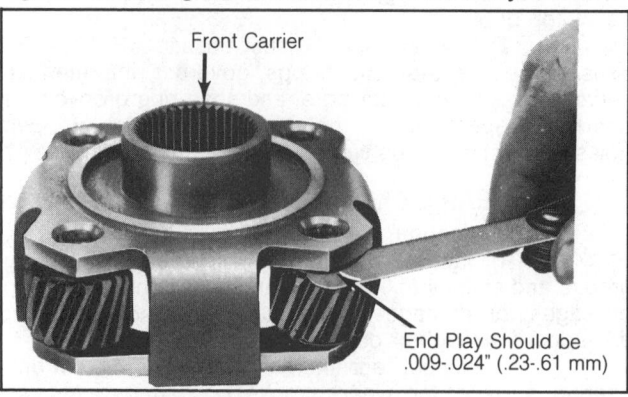

Front Carrier

End Play Should be .009-.024" (.23-.61 mm)

FRONT INTERNAL GEAR

Inspection

Inspect forward clutch hub for worn splines and restricted lubrication holes. Inspect internal gear for cracks, damage and worn gear teeth. Check bushing for damage or scoring. Inspect front internal gear-to-selective thrust washer for scoring or damage. See Fig. 14.

DIRECT CLUTCH ASSEMBLY

Disassembly

1) Remove snap ring and lift out clutch backing plate, composition clutch plates and steel clutch plates. Keep clutch plates separated from forward clutch plates.

2) Compress retainer and spring assembly and remove snap ring. Withdraw retainer and spring assembly from clutch housing. Remove release spring guide. Remove piston from housing and remove seals from piston. Remove center seal from housing.

NOTE: Do not remove apply ring from clutch piston unless piston or apply ring require replacement.

Inspection

1) Inspect clutch plates for wear or signs of burning. Inspect backing plate for scoring or damage. Inspect retainer and release springs for being collapsed. Inspect release spring guide for damage.

2) Inspect clutch piston for distortion, cracks or other damage. Check for free operation of check ball in clutch housing and/or piston. If damaged, replace check ball as follows:

3) Remove check ball assembly using a 3/8" diameter rod as a punch. Place new check ball in check ball hole, and using the same rod, drive check ball down into hole until it bottoms.

4) Inspect direct clutch housing for cracks, wear and open oil passages. Inspect housing snap ring grooves for damage. Inspect direct clutch bushings for damage or scoring.

Reassembly

1) If removed, install clutch apply ring on piston. Install new inner and outer seals on piston with lips facing away from clutch apply ring side. Install new center seal on direct clutch housing with lip facing up. Lubricate seals and install piston into housing using care not to damage seals.

GENERAL MOTORS TURBO HYDRA-MATIC 200-4R (Cont.)

Fig. 23: Exploded View of Direct Clutch Assembly

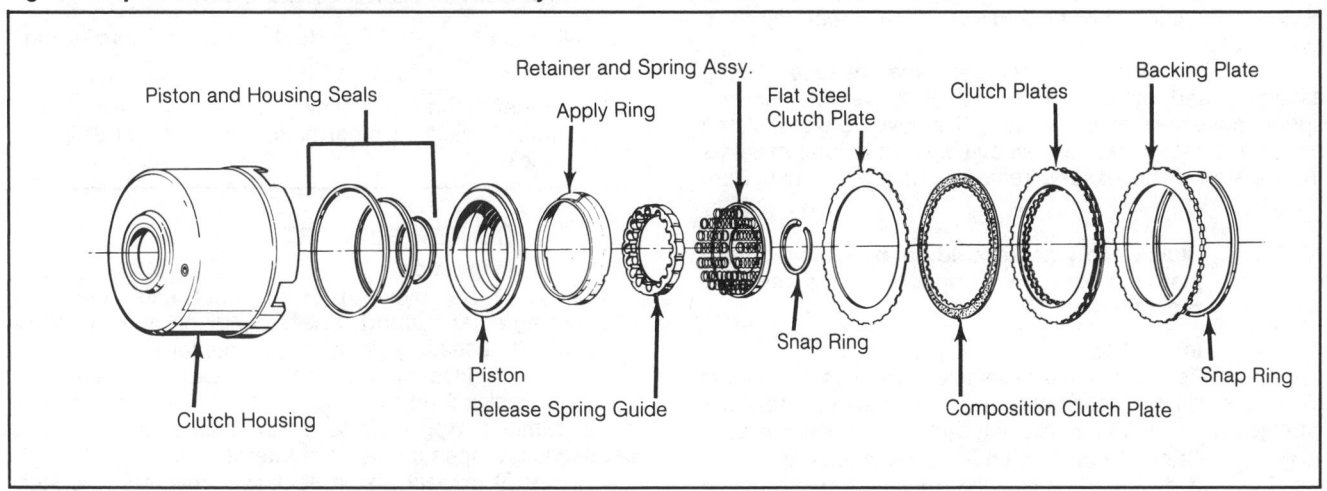

CAUTION: Use care when installing piston into clutch housing. Large snap ring groove in housing could cut outer piston seal.

Fig. 24: Installing Direct Clutch Release Spring Guide

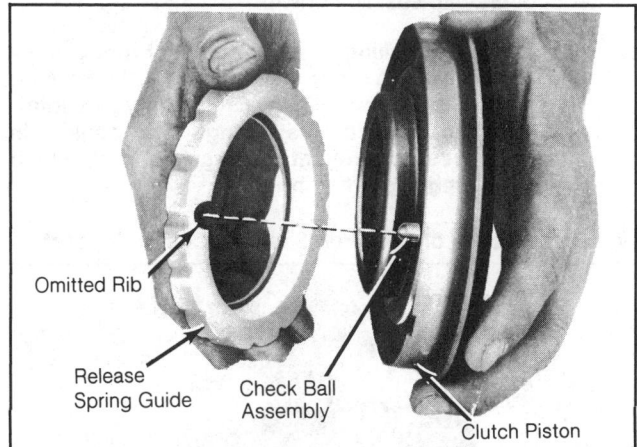

2) Install release spring guide with the omitted rib over check ball in piston. *See Fig. 24.* Install retainer and spring assembly, compress springs and install snap ring.

3) Oil and install clutch plates into clutch housing. Start with a flat steel and alternate composition and flat steel clutch plates. *See Direct Clutch Plate Usage Chart.* Install backing plate, micro-finish down. Install clutch pack retaining snap ring. Make sure composition clutch plates turn freely.

DIRECT CLUTCH PLATE USAGE CHART

Application	Steel	Composition
All Models	6	6

FORWARD CLUTCH ASSEMBLY
Disassembly

1) If damaged, remove Teflon oil seal rings from forward clutch shaft. Remove forward clutch-to-direct clutch thrust washer. Remove retaining snap ring

Fig. 25: Exploded View of Forward Clutch Assembly

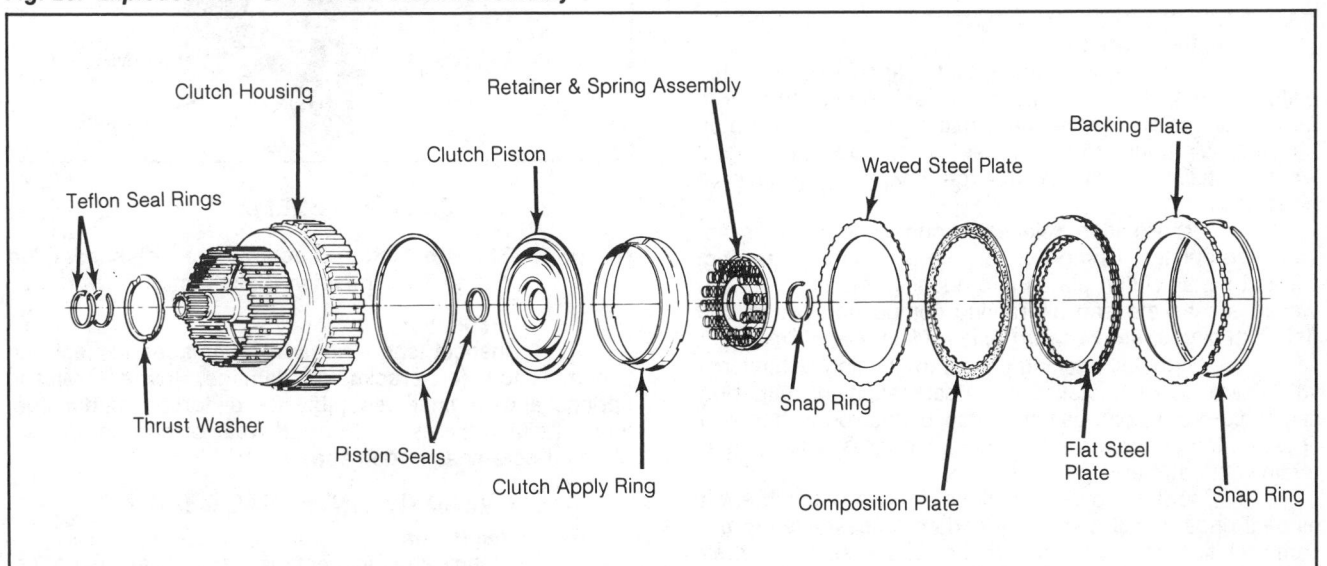

GENERAL MOTORS TURBO HYDRA-MATIC 200-4R (Cont.)

and withdraw backing plate, composition plates and steel plates from clutch housing and keep them separated from direct clutch plates.

2) Compress retainer and release spring assembly and remove snap ring. Remove retainer and spring assembly from housing. Remove forward clutch piston from housing, then remove inner and outer oil seals from piston. If necessary, remove clutch apply ring from piston.

NOTE: **Clutch apply ring should not be removed from piston unless apply ring or piston requires replacement.**

Inspection

Forward clutch assembly inspection is identical to direct clutch assembly inspection except for the changes noted in *Clutch Housing Cup Plug Replacement*.

Clutch Housing Cup Plug Replacement

If damaged or missing, replace forward clutch housing cup plug. Remove plug using a No. 3 screw extractor (grind to fit). Install new cup plug .039" (1 mm) below surface.

Fig. 26: View of Forward Clutch Housing Showing Location of Check Ball and Cup Plug

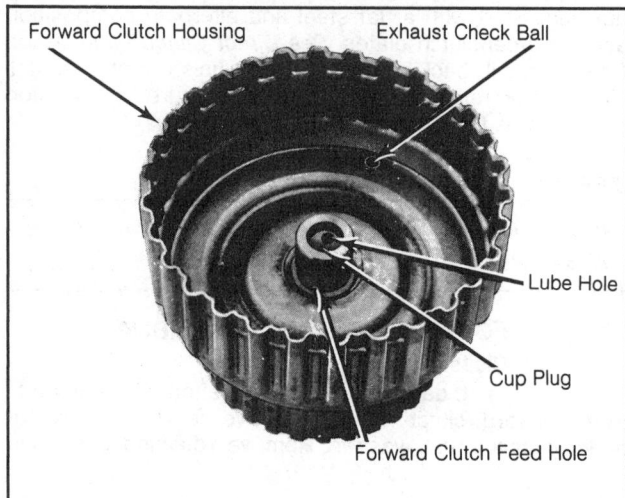

Reassembly

1) If removed, install clutch apply ring on clutch piston. Install new inner and outer seals on clutch piston. Lubricate piston seals and install piston into clutch housing using care to prevent seals from being damaged when installing piston past large snap ring groove in housing.

2) Position release springs and retainer assembly on piston. Compress retainer and install snap ring. Oil and install clutch plates into housing, starting with the waved steel plate and alternating compostion plates and flat steel plates. *See Forward Clutch Plate Usage Chart.*

3) Install backing plate into housing with microfinish side down. Install clutch pack retaining snap ring and make sure composition clutch plates rotate freely in housing. Install forward-to-direct clutch thrust washer and retain with petroleum jelly.

4) If removed, install new forward clutch shaft oil seal rings, making sure cut ends are assembled in the same relationship as cut and that rings are seated in their groove. Retain with petroleum jelly.

FORWARD CLUTCH PLATE USAGE CHART

Application	Steel	Composition
All Models	4 [1]	4

[1] — Installed first is 1 waved steel plate .062" (1.57 mm) thick. Flat steel plates are .077" (1.96 mm) thick.

CENTER SUPPORT
Inspection

1) Remove 4th clutch inner and outer seal rings from center support. Check condition of cast iron oil rings, and if necessary, remove from center support.

2) Inspect bushings for scoring, wear or galling. Check oil ring grooves and oil rings for nicks or other damage. Apply air to oil passages to make sure passages are open and are not interconnected.

3) Inspect piston sealing surfaces for scratches. Inspect support for cracks or porosity. Inspect support for burrs or raised edges. If present, remove with fine stone or fine abrasive paper.

4) If removed, install cast iron oil seal rings on center support. Install new inner and outer seal rings on center support with seal lips down.

NOTE: **When installing cast iron oil seal rings, make sure ends overlap and interlock. Make sure ends are flush with each other when interlocked, and oil seal rings are seated in grooves to prevent damage to ring during assembling of mating parts.**

Fig. 27: Location of Cast Iron Seals on Center Support

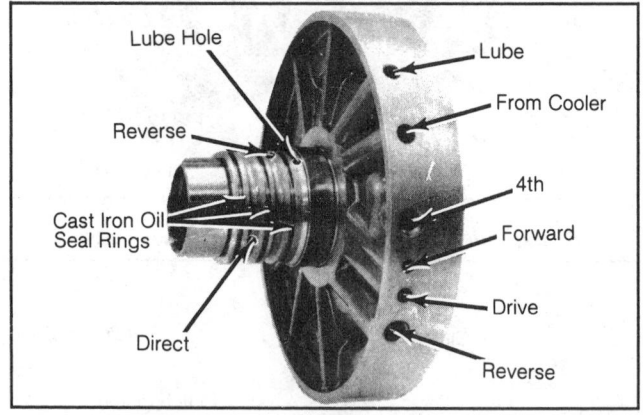

4TH CLUTCH ASSEMBLY

NOTE: **The 4th clutch assembly was disassembled during Transmission Disassembly.**

Inspection

Inspect snap rings for damage. Inspect 4th clutch piston for cracks or damage. Inspect release springs and retainer assembly for distortion or damage. Inspect clutch plates for signs of wear or burring. Inspect plate for scratches or damage.

OVERDRIVE INTERNAL GEAR
Inspection

Clean and inspect internal gear-to-support thrust washer and overdrive carrier-to-sun gear thrust

GENERAL MOTORS TURBO HYDRA-MATIC 200-4R (Cont.)

bearing assembly. Inspect gear, splines, teeth and bearing surface of overdrive gear for wear, cracks or damage.

OVERRUN CLUTCH & OVERDRIVE CARRIER ASSEMBLY
Disassembly
Remove snap ring and slide turbine shaft from overdrive carrier assembly. Remove carrier from overrun clutch assembly. Remove sun gear from clutch assembly.

NOTE: Reassembly of this unit follows the disassembly and reassembly of the individual components.

OVERRUN CLUTCH ASSEMBLY
Disassembly
1) Remove retaining snap ring and lift backing plate, steel clutch plates and composition clutch plates from overrun clutch housing. Keep clutch plates separated from the other plate assemblies.

2) Using snap ring pliers, remove overrun clutch hub snap ring. Lift overdrive roller clutch cam assembly from housing, then separate roller clutch from cam assembly.

3) Remove retainer and wave spring assembly from clutch housing. Remove overrun clutch piston from housing, then remove inner and outer seals from piston.

Fig. 28: Removing Overdrive Roller Clutch Cam Assembly

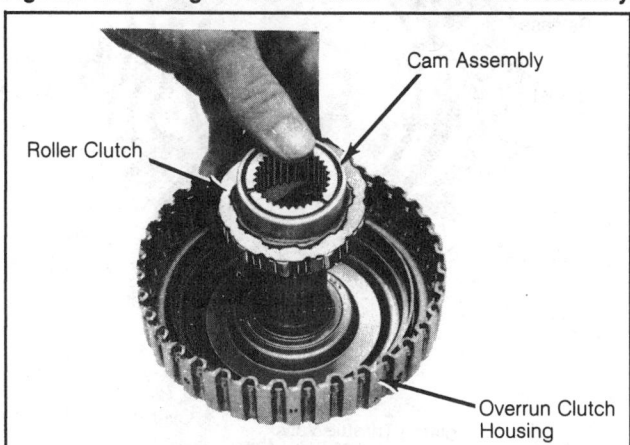

Inspection
1) Inspect clutch plates for signs of wear or burning. Inspect roller clutch cam ramps for damage. Check roller bearings, cage and springs of roller clutch for wear or damage.

2) Inspect retainer and wave spring for damage. Inspect clutch piston for distortion, cracks and damage. Inspect housing for cracks, wear and open oil passages. Check clutch housing snap ring groove and bushing for damage or scoring.

Reassembly
1) Install new inner and outer seals on piston with seal lips facing away from clutch apply ring side. Lubricate seals and install piston into clutch housing using care not to damage seals. Position overrun clutch waved release spring and spring retainer (cupped face down) on clutch piston.

2) Install roller clutch cam on roller clutch assembly. Locating tangs on roller clutch must set on

roller clutch cam. Install roller clutch assembly on overrun clutch hub. Compress spring and retainer assembly by pushing down on roller clutch assembly and install narrow snap ring.

3) Oil and install overrun clutch plate into housing. Start with a flat steel and alternate compostion and flat steel plates. *See Overrun Clutch Plate Usage Chart.* Install backing plate, chamfered side up. Install retaining snap ring. Make sure composition clutch plates rotate freely.

OVERRUN CLUTCH PLATE USAGE CHART

Application	Flat Steel	Composition
All Models	2 [1]	2

[1] — Plate thickness is .077" (1.96 mm).

OVERDRIVE CARRIER
Inspection
1) Inspect locating splines for damage and roller clutch race for scratches and wear. Inspect carrier housing for cracks and wear.

2) Inspect pinions for damage, rough bearings or tilt. Using a feeler gauge, measure pinion end play between pinion and carrier. End play should be .009-.024" (.23-.61 mm). If necessary to disassemble carrier, go to disassembly procedure.

Disassembly
1) Remove overdrive carrier snap ring. Using pliers, remove pinion pins. Remove pinions, thrust washers and roller bearings. Inspect pinion pocket thrust faces for burrs, remove if present.

2) Remove overdrive sun gear-to-overdrive carrier thrust bearing assembly. Thoroughly clean, air dry and closely inspect thrust bearing assembly for pitting or rough condition.

Fig. 29: Assembling Overdrive Carrier Pinions

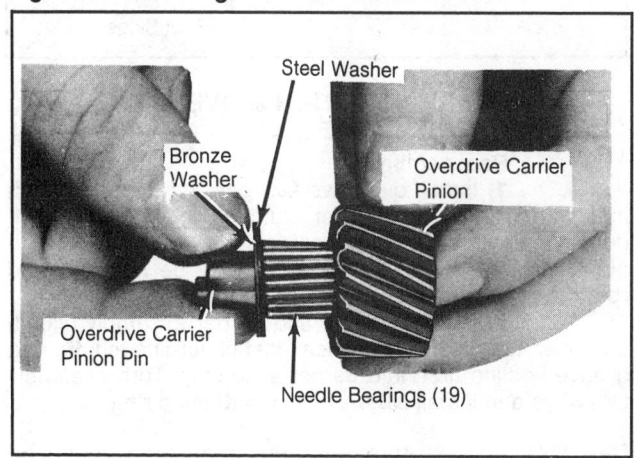

Reassembly
1) Install thrust bearing into carrier housing with small diameter race down. Retain bearing in place with petroleum jelly. Install 19 needle bearings into each pinion and hold them in place. Place a bronze and steel thrust washer on each side of pinion so that steel washer is against pinion. Hold washers in place with petroleum jelly.

GENERAL MOTORS TURBO HYDRA-MATIC 200-4R (Cont.)

2) Install a pinion assembly in place in housing and use a pilot shaft to align parts. Push pinion pin into place while rotating pinions from the side. Repeat procedure for remaining pinions. Install overdrive carrier snap ring to retain pinion pins.

TURBINE SHAFT

Inspection

1) Inspect Teflon oil seals on turbine shaft for damage and free fit in grooves. Do not remove seal unless replacement is necessary. Inspect snap ring for damage. Check journals and snap ring grooves for wear or damage.

2) Inspect both ends of turbine shaft for open oil passages. Inspect journals for damage. Check for free operation of check ball in end of shaft. If check ball is damaged, go to step **3)**.

3) Straighten tangs of retainer and check valve assembly capsule in end of shaft. Remove check ball. Use a No. 4 screw extractor to remove check valve retainer from turbine shaft by turning and pulling straight out.

4) Install new check valve assembly, check valve seat first, into turbine shaft. Using a 3/8" diameter rod, drive retainer and check valve assembly until it is 1/8" below top surface of turbine shaft.

Fig. 30: Turbine Shaft Assembly

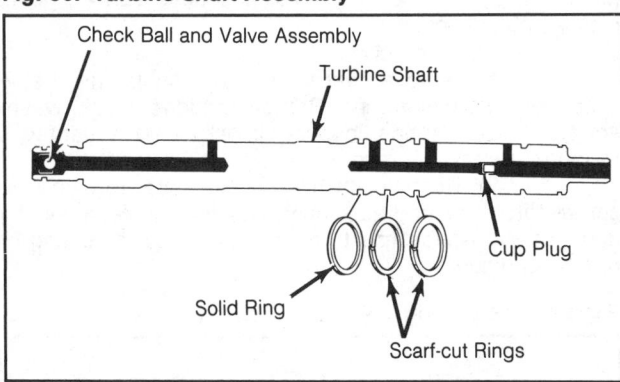

OVERRUN CLUTCH & OVERDRIVE CARRIER ASSEMBLY

Reassembly

1) Install overdrive sun gear on overrun clutch hub with groove up. Center clutches in overrun clutch housing. Position overdrive carrier in overrun clutch with pinion side of carrier facing up. It may be necessary to rotate carrier counterclockwise to seat it.

2) Position clutch and carrier assembly (clutch up) over hole in work bench. Install turbine shaft, ring grooved spline first, into carrier assembly. Turn assembly sideways and install NEW turbine shaft snap ring.

CAUTION: A new turbine shaft snap ring must be installed as damage to unit may occur if old snap ring is used.

PUMP ASSEMBLY

Disassembly

1) Remove pump-to-case seal ring. Remove pump cover-to-pump body attaching bolts and separate cover from body. Remove stator shaft-to-overrun selective thrust washer.

2) Push in on T.V. boost valve bushing, compressing pressure regulator spring, and remove retaining snap ring. Release spring tension slowly and remove valve train.

3) Push in on converter clutch stop valve, compressing converter clutch valve spring, and remove snap ring. Release spring tension slowly and remove stop valve and converter clutch valve. Using a punch, remove pressure relief spring retaining pin. Remove relief spring and ball.

4) If replacement of stator shaft and flange assembly is required, remove attaching screws and press stator shaft until it is removed from pump cover bore.

5) Place shop towel over pump slide spring (spring is under high pressure) and using a screwdriver, remove spring from pump body. Remove pump slide, slide-to-wear plate oil seal and back-up "O" ring seal, rotor, rotor guide, 7 vanes and 2 vane rings, pump slide seal support and seal. Remove pivot slide pin and spring.

Fig. 31: View of Pump Cover and Body Showing Hydraulic Passages

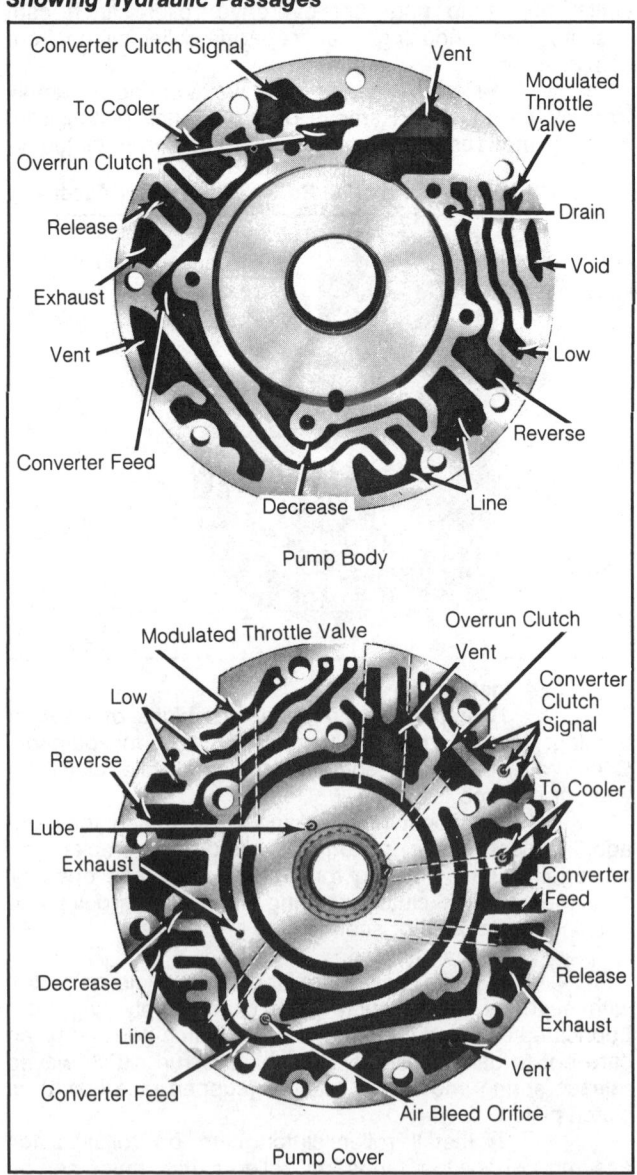

GENERAL MOTORS TURBO HYDRA-MATIC 200-4R (Cont.)

Fig. 32: Exploded View of Pump Assembly

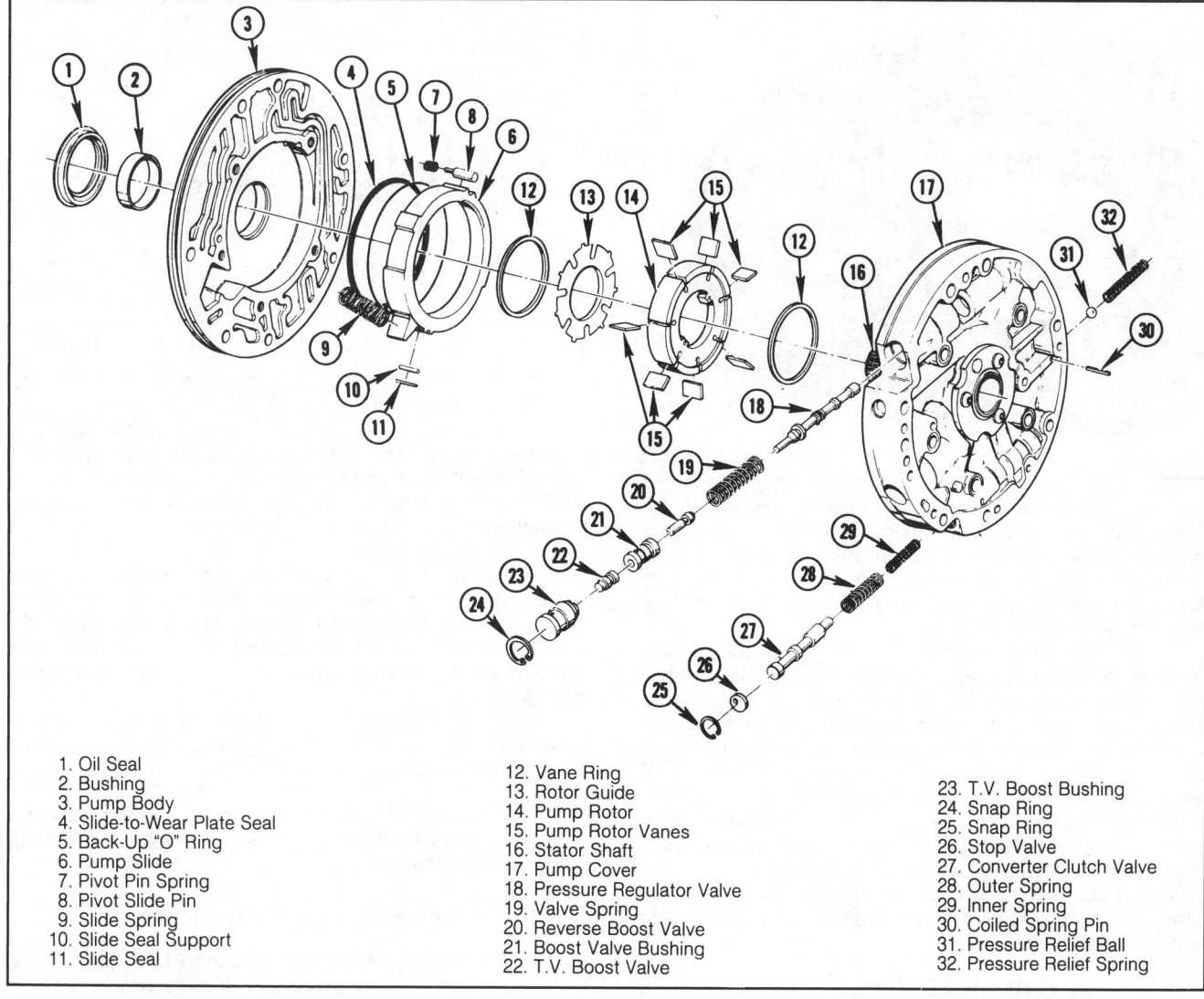

1. Oil Seal	12. Vane Ring	23. T.V. Boost Bushing
2. Bushing	13. Rotor Guide	24. Snap Ring
3. Pump Body	14. Pump Rotor	25. Snap Ring
4. Slide-to-Wear Plate Seal	15. Pump Rotor Vanes	26. Stop Valve
5. Back-Up "O" Ring	16. Stator Shaft	27. Converter Clutch Valve
6. Pump Slide	17. Pump Cover	28. Outer Spring
7. Pivot Pin Spring	18. Pressure Regulator Valve	29. Inner Spring
8. Pivot Slide Pin	19. Valve Spring	30. Coiled Spring Pin
9. Slide Spring	20. Reverse Boost Valve	31. Pressure Relief Ball
10. Slide Seal Support	21. Boost Valve Bushing	32. Pressure Relief Spring
11. Slide Seal	22. T.V. Boost Valve	

Inspection

1) Inspect pump-to-case seal ring groove in pump body for damage. Inspect stator shaft-to-overrun selective washer for wear and damage. Wash pump body, springs, pump slide, rotor, vanes, vane rings and rotor guide. Do not put pump seals in solvent.

2) Inspect pump pocket and pump body for damage or scoring. Check pump body bushing for wear or scoring. Inspect springs for damage or distortion and pump slide for damage, cracks or wear. Check rotor for damage, cracks or wear. Inspect vanes and vane rings for damage, cracks or wear. Inspect pump body face for nicks and overall flatness and open oil passages.

3) Inspect T.V. boost valve, reverse boost valve, stop valve and converter clutch valve for nicks or damage. Check valves for free operation in bushing or cover bore. Inspect all springs for damage or distortion. Inspect stator shaft and flange assembly for damaged splines or bushing. Check stator shaft for damaged or missing orifice cup plug in dowel pin. Do not remove cup plug unless damaged.

4) Inspect pump cover for open oil passages. Check pump cover face for nicks and overall flatness.

Inspect for chips in pressure regulator, pressure relief and converter clutch bores. Inspect cup plugs and orifice plugs in cover and if damaged, replace plugs.

Pump Cover Cup Plug Replacement

If cup plug is missing, drive a new plug to 1/32" below top of hole, using a 9/32" diameter rod on the 2 smaller plugs, a 5/16" rod on the line-to-case cup plug, and a 7/16" rod on the large plug. Stake top of hole in 2 places, directly opposite each other, to retain plug.

Pump Cover Orifice Plug Replacement

If plugs require replacement, place new plug, orifice end first, into plug hole from rough casting side of cover. Drive new plug flush to .100" below top of hole, on rough casting side. Stake top of hole in 2 places to retain plug.

Reassembly

1) Turn pump body so that pump pocket side is up. Install slide "O" ring and slide-to-wear plate oil seal in slide and retain with petroleum jelly. Install slide into pump pocket with seal side down. Install slide seal support and pump slide seal. *See Fig. 33.* Retain with petroleum jelly. Install pivot pin and spring into bore in pump body (opposite pivot pin and spring).

GENERAL MOTORS TURBO HYDRA-MATIC 200-4R (Cont.)

Fig. 33: Installing Slide Seal and Support

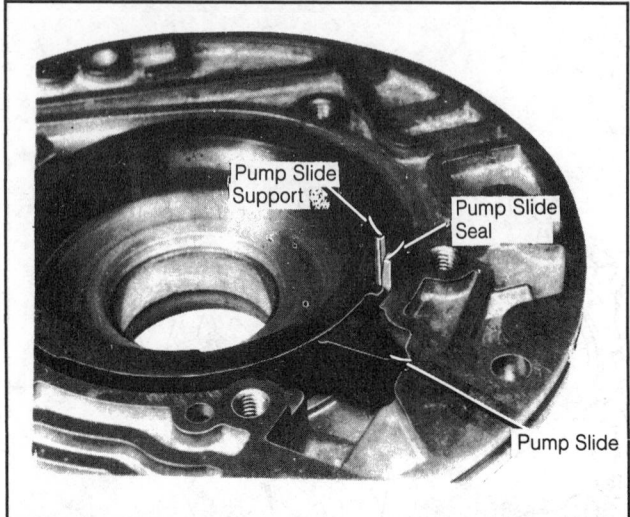

Fig. 34: Exploded View of Intermediate Servo

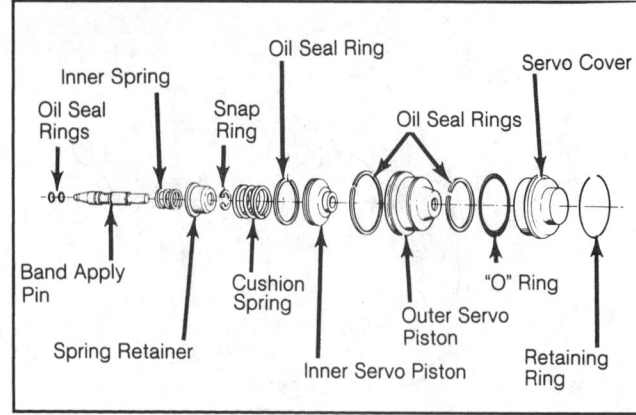

2) Install a vane ring in pump pocket. Install rotor guide in pump rotor, then install rotor into pump pocket. Center and seat rotor on guide so rotor is flush with pump slide. Install 7 vanes into pump and make sure vane pattern is installed against vane ring. Install top vane ring. Install pump slide spring.

3) If stator shaft and flange assembly was removed from pump cover, install as follows: Align dowel pin of stator shaft with hole in pump cover. Using a press, press stator shaft into cover until fully seated on cover. Install stator shaft and flange assembly attaching bolts.

4) Install all valve trains in reverse order of removal. *See Fig. 3.* Assemble pump cover to pump body and install attaching bolts finger tight. Align cover to body using alignment strap (J-25015) and tighten attaching bolts. Install pump-to-case seal ring, chamfered side out, making sure seal is not twisted. Install stator shaft-to-overrun clutch selective thrust washer and retain with petroleum jelly.

GOVERNOR ASSEMBLY
Inspection
1) Inspect governor cover for damage, plugged oil passage, scored or worn bore. Inspect governor driven gear for nicks or damage. If replacement is necessary, remove retaining ring and slide gear and thrust washer from shaft.

CAUTION: **Care must be taken after removing driven gear to keep governor in a vertical position to retain governor weight pin in its holding position.**

2) Inspect governor shaft seal ring for cuts, damage and free fit in groove. Inspect for free operation of weights. Weights must operate freely and independently of each other. Check spring for damage and correct installation. Check for presence of 2 check balls. Inspect shaft for damage.

INTERMEDIATE SERVO ASSEMBLY
Disassembly
Using a small screwdriver, remove intermediate pin-to-retainer snap ring. Separate band apply pin, spring and washer from servo pistons.

Inspection
Inspect pin oil seal rings for damage and replace if necessary. Inspect pin for damage and fit in case. Inspect inner and outer piston seal rings for damage and free fit in grooves; do not replace unless damaged. Inspect spring for damage and distortion.

Reassembly
1) Install retainer on band apply pin, then install snap ring. Install apply pin, retainer end first, through servo pistons. If removed, install new inner and outer piston seal rings, making sure cut ends are assembled in same relationship as cut, and retain with petroleum jelly.

2) Lubricate with petroleum jelly and install new seal ring on intermediate servo cover. Install servo piston into servo cover.

CAUTION: **Intermediate servo cover seal rings must be well lubricated to prevent damage or cutting of ring.**

CONTROL VALVE ASSEMBLY

NOTE: **As valve trains are removed from each valve body bore, place individual parts in correct order in relative position to valve body to simplify reassembly. Valves, bushings and springs are not interchangeable, and all parts must be installed in correct order in proper valve body bore. Remove all roll pins and spring retaining sleeves by pushing through from rough case surface side of valve body, except for the blind hole roll pins.**

Disassembly
1) Lay control valve assembly with machined face up and manual valve at upper left corner. If not removed at Transmission Disassembly, remove 3 check balls from cored passages of valve body. From upper left corner bore, remove manual valve.

CAUTION: **Some roll pins in valve body have pressure against them. Hold a shop towel over bore while removing pin, to prevent possibly losing a bore plug or spring.**

2) From bore beneath manual valve, remove roll pin and slide out 2-3 throttle valve and 2-3 shift valve train. The 2-3 throttle valve spring and valve may be inside bushing.

GENERAL MOTORS TURBO HYDRA-MATIC 200-4R (Cont.)

3) From next bore down, remove roll pin and withdraw converter clutch valve train. Converter clutch valve spring and converter clutch throttle valve may be inside bushing. On Computer Command Control models, clutch throttle valve and spring have been eliminated.

4) From next bore down, remove outer roll pin and remove 1-2 throttle valve train and low 1st/detent valve. Remove inner roll pin and slide out low 1st/detent valve bushing and 1-2 shift valve.

5) Cover the next bore down to prevent loss of spring, then remove outer spring retaining sleeve. Remove

Fig. 35: Removing Throttle Valve Inner Roll Pin

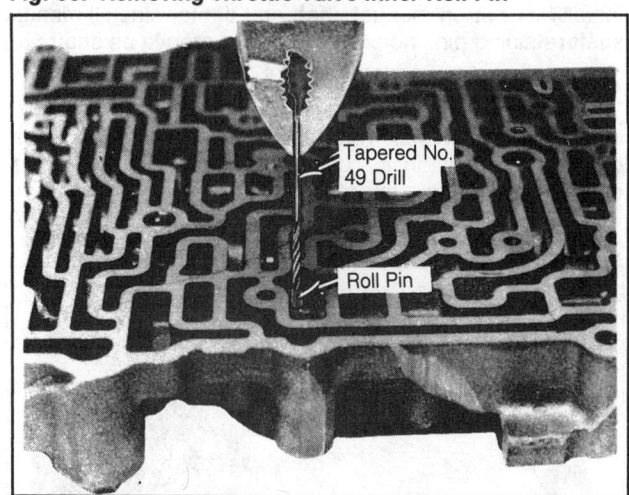

bore plug and 4-3 control valve and spring. Remove inner spring retaining sleeve and withdraw low/overrun clutch valve spring and valve.

6) From next bore down, remove roll pin and slide out 3-4 throttle valve train. From last bore down, remove roll pin and bore plug and withdraw accumulator valve train.

7) From upper right corner, remove roll pin and remove line bias valve train. From next bore down, remove roll pin and 3-2 control valve train.

8) From next bore down, remove roll pin, then remove T.V. modulator upshift valve train. From next bore down, remove roll pin and T.V. modulator downshift valve train.

9) Cover the next bore down to prevent loss of spring, then remove spring retaining sleeve and withdraw T.V. limit valve train.

10) From last bore, remove outer roll pin, then remove throttle valve bushing, plunger and spring. Remove inner pin as follows: Grind a taper to end of a No. 49 drill. Lightly tap tapered end of drill into roll pin, then pull drill and roll pin out. Remove throttle valve.

Inspection

1) Wash control valve body, springs, valves and other parts in clean solvent and air dry. Inspect valves for scoring, cracks and free movement in their bores.

2) Inspect bushings for cracks and scored bores. Inspect valve body for cracks, damage or scored bores. Inspect springs for distortion or collapsed coils. Inspect bore plugs for damage.

Fig. 36: Exploded View of Control Valve Assembly

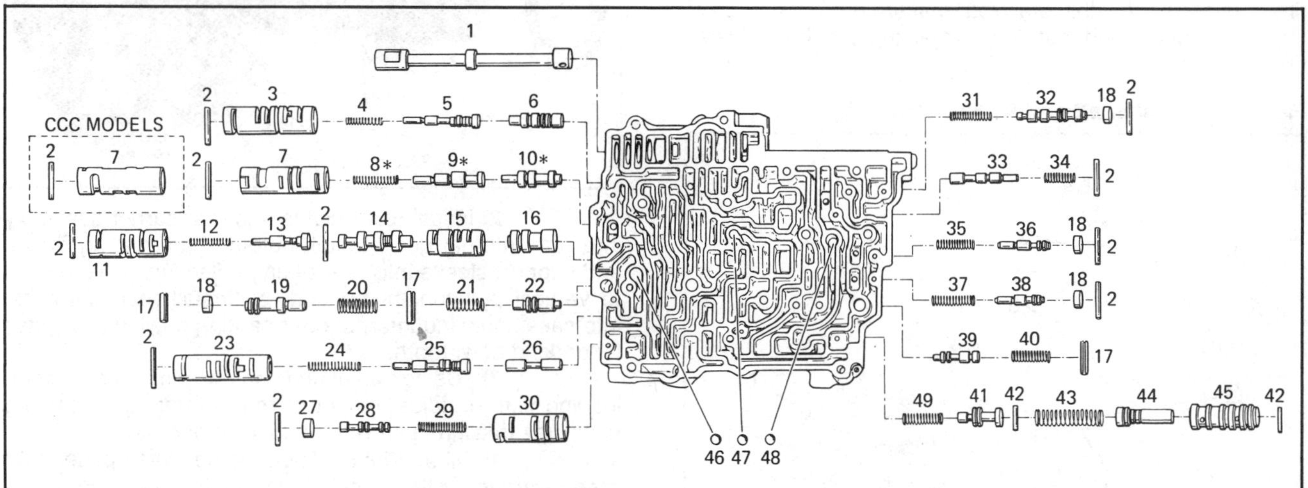

1. Manual Valve
2. Roll Pin (Zinc)
3. 2-3 Throttle Valve Bushing
4. 2-3 Throttle Vave Spring
5. 2-3 Throttle Valve
6. 2-3 Shift Valve
7. Converter Clutch Throttle Bushing
8. Converter Clutch Throttle Valve Spring
9. Converter Clutch Throttle Valve
10. Converter Clutch Shift Valve
11. 1-2 Throttle Valve Bushing
12. 1-2 Throttle Valve Spring
13. 1-2 Throttle Valve
14. Low 1st/Detent Valve
15. Low 1st/Detent Valve Bushing
16. 1-2 Shift Valve
17. Spring Retaining Sleeve

18. Bore Plug (.50")
19. Low/Overrun Clutch Valve
20. Low/Overrun Clutch Valve Spring
21. 4-3 Control Valve Spring
22. 4-3 Control Valve
23. 3-4 Throttle Valve Bushing
24. 3-4 Throttle Valve Spring
25. 3-4 Throttle Valve
26. 3-4 Shift Valve
27. Bore Plug (.560")
28. Accumulator Valve
29. Accumulator Valve Spring
30. Accumulator Valve Bushing
31. Line Bias Valve Spring
32. Line Bias Valve
33. 3-2 Control Valve
34. 3-2 Control Valve Spring

35. T.V. Modulator Upshift Valve Spring
36. T.V. Modulator Upshift Valve
37. T.V. Modulator Downshift Valve Spring
38. T.V. Modulator Downshift Valve
39. T.V. Limit Valve
40. T.V. Limit Valve Spring
41. Throttle Valve
42. Roll Pin (Black)
43. Throttle Valve Spring
44. Throttle Valve Plunger
45. Throttle Valve Plunger Bushing
46. "D3" Check Ball
47. 1-2 Shift Check Ball
48. Low/1st Check Ball

* Items 8, 9 & 10 are not used on C.C.C. models.

GENERAL MOTORS TURBO HYDRA-MATIC 200-4R (Cont.)

Reassembly

Reassembly is the reverse of disassembly procedure. Reassemble Control Valve Assembly using exploded view as a guide. Note the following:

- Install all flared roll pins (zinc coated) flared end out, and from machined face of valve body.
- Install the 2 tapered roll pins (black finish) that retain throttle valve and throttle valve bushing, tapered end first.
- Roll pins do not fit flush on rough casting face. Make sure that all roll pins are flush at machined face or damage to transmission will occur.
- Make sure all spring retaining sleeves are installed from machined face and that they are level with or below machined surface.
- Install all bore plugs with hole out.
- Install all valve sleeves so that slot in sleeve aligns with roll pin hole in valve body.

TRANSMISSION REASSEMBLY

MANUAL SHAFT & PARKING PAWL PARTS

1) Turn transmission to horizontal position with oil pan side up. If removed, install new manual shaft seal with lip facing into case using a 9/16" socket to seat seal. Install parking pawl and spring into case with tooth toward inside of case and spring under pawl tooth with spring ends toward inside of case. Make sure spring ends locate against case pad.

2) Align parking pawl and spring with case shaft hole, then install parking pawl shaft, tapered end first. Using a 3/8" diameter rod, install new parking pawl cup plug, open end out, past retaining pin hole. Install retaining pin.

Fig. 37: Manual Shaft and Parking Parts

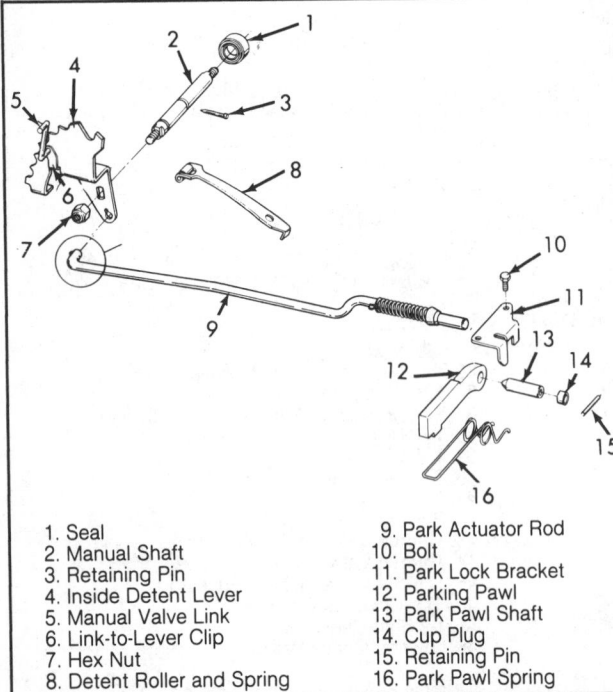

1. Seal
2. Manual Shaft
3. Retaining Pin
4. Inside Detent Lever
5. Manual Valve Link
6. Link-to-Lever Clip
7. Hex Nut
8. Detent Roller and Spring
9. Park Actuator Rod
10. Bolt
11. Park Lock Bracket
12. Parking Pawl
13. Park Pawl Shaft
14. Cup Plug
15. Retaining Pin
16. Park Pawl Spring

3) While holding parking pawl toward center of transmission, install parking lock bracket and tighten attaching bolts. Assemble parking actuator rod on pin side of inside detent lever, locating lever between actuator rod tangs. Install rod and detent lever into case with detent lever pin toward center of transmission and actuator plunger between parking pawl and parking lock bracket.

NOTE: File any burrs or raised edges off manual shaft that could damage manual shaft seal during installation of shaft.

4) Install manual shaft, small identification ring groove first, through case. Align inside detent lever with flats on shaft, then install detent lever on manual shaft. Install hex nut on manual shaft and tighten. Install manual shaft retaining pin, indexing with large groove on shaft.

REAR GEAR PARTS

1) Install rear internal gear, hub end first, onto output shaft. Install rear internal gear-to-rear thrust bearing assembly, inside diameter race against gear, over output shaft and into internal gear.

Fig. 38: Rear Internal Gear & Thrust Bearing Installation

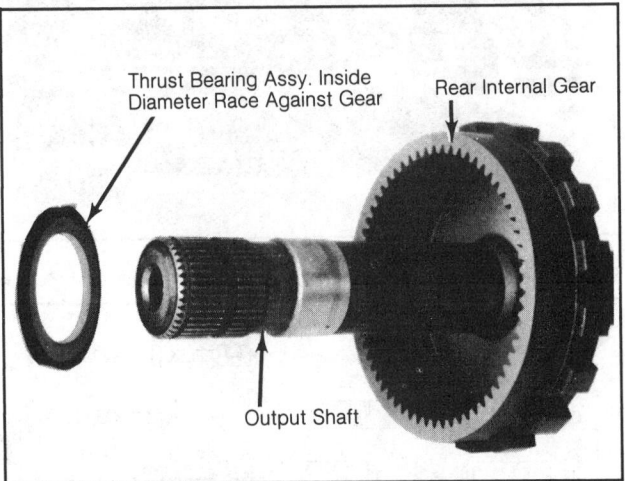

Thrust Bearing Assy. Inside Diameter Race Against Gear

Rear Internal Gear

Output Shaft

2) Install roller clutch and rear carrier assembly into rear internal gear. Install output shaft loading fixture and support sleeve into rear of case. *See Fig. 9.* Turn case to vertical position, pump end up. Install rear unit parts into case, indexing internal gear parking pawl lugs to pass by parking pawl tooth.

3) Using adjusting screw on output shaft loading fixture, adjust height of rear internal gear parking pawl lugs to align flush with parking pawl tooth.

4) Oil and install low-reverse clutch plates into case starting with a flat steel plate and alternating composition and flat steel clutch plates. *See Low-Reverse Clutch Plate Usage Chart.* Next, install the waved steel plate on top of last flat steel plate. Install low-reverse clutch housing-to-case spacer ring in case.

5) Install low-reverse clutch housing into case, aligning feed hole in housing with reverse clutch feed passage in case. If clutch housing does not seat past case snap ring groove, install input drum and rear sun gear into case.

6) Rotate sun gear back and forth, tapping lightly with input drum to align roller clutch race with low-reverse clutch hub splines. Remove input drum and rear sun gear assembly.

GENERAL MOTROS TURBO HYDRA-MATIC 200-4R (Cont.)

7) Install low-reverse clutch-to-case snap ring with flat side against clutch (beveled side up). Position snap ring groove on opposite side of parking pawl rod.

LOW-REVERSE CLUTCH USAGE CHART

Application	Steel	Composition
All Models	7 [1]	6

[1] — Installed last is 1 waved steel plate .077" (1.96 mm) thick.

NOTE: It may be necessary to loosen adjusting screw on output shaft loading fixture to install clutch-to-case snap ring.

8) If removed, install new low-reverse clutch housing-to-case cup plug and seal. Use a 3/8" diameter rod to drive cup plug and seal assembly into case until it seats against clutch housing. *See Fig. 39.*

Fig. 39: Installing Low-Reverse Clutch Housing Cup Plug and Seal Assembly

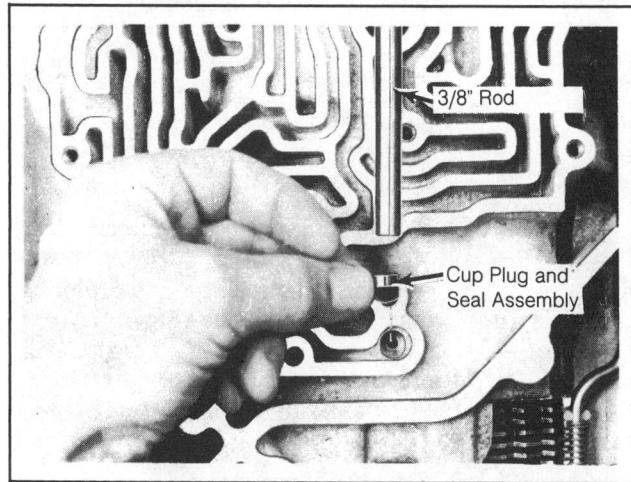

FRONT GEAR PARTS

1) Install 4-tanged thrust washer on input drum over sun gear end; align tangs into input drum and retain with petroleum jelly. Install rear sun gear and input drum assembly into case.

2) Install front sun gear into case and input drum with face of gear having identification groove against input drum. Install front sun gear-to-front carrier thrust bearing and race assembly into case with needle bearings against sun gear.

3) Install front carrier-to-front internal gear thrust bearing assembly on carrier with small diameter race against carrier. Install front carrier and thrust bearing assembly into transmission.

4) Install thrust washer on front internal gear and retain with petroleum jelly. Install front internal gear and thrust washer into case. Install rear unit end play selective washer into case with identification number on washer toward front of transmission. Install wide retaining snap ring. *See Fig. 14.*

NOTE: At this time, recheck rear unit end play to make sure correct selective thrust washer has been installed. See Rear Unit End Play Checking in Transmission Disassembly.

5) Install output shaft-to-forward clutch shaft selective thrust washer into case and position washer. *See Fig. 40.*

Fig. 40: Installing Front Selective Washer

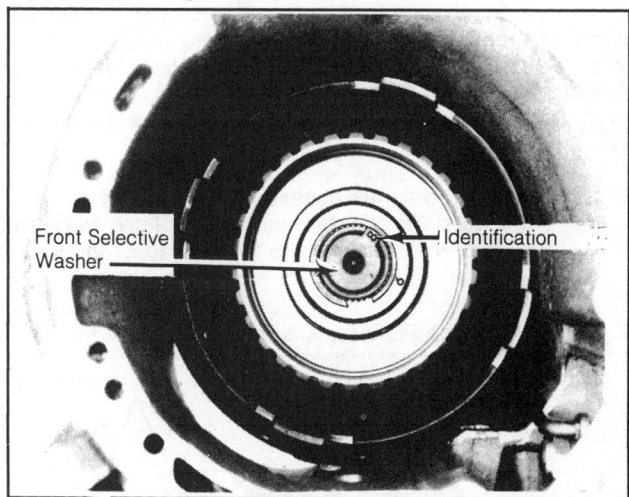

Front Selective Washer — Identification

FRONT UNIT PARTS

1) Install intermediate band into case, locating band apply lug and anchor pin lug in case slot. Install band anchor pin.

2) Position direct clutch assembly, clutch plate end up, over hole in work bench. Align teeth of composition plates in direct clutch, then install forward clutch assembly, shaft first, into direct clutch assembly. Hold direct clutch and rotate forward clutch back and forth until fully seated.

NOTE: When forward clutch is fully seated, it will be approximately 5/8" from tang end of direct clutch housing to end of forward clutch drum.

3) Install direct and forward clutch assemblies into case and rotate into position. When assemblies are correctly installed, it will be approximately 4 1/8" from pump face in case to direct clutch housing.

4) Install center support-to-direct clutch thrust washer on center support. Visually align center support with case bolt holes and install center support into case. Install, but do not tighten, center support attaching bolts. Install center support-to-case snap ring with beveled side up. Tighten center support attaching bolts.

NOTE: At this time, recheck front unit end play to make sure correct front selective washer has been installed. See Front Unit End Play Checking in Transmission Disassembly.

OVERDRIVE UNIT PARTS

1) Install 4th clutch outer and inner seals on center support with lips facing down, apply petroleum jelly to seals. Install 4th clutch piston into case, aligning piston tab with wide case spline. Position return spring and retainer assembly on piston, then compress retainer assembly and install support-to-4th clutch spring snap ring.

NOTE: The 4th clutch inner seal, installed on center support, is identified by a white stripe.

GENERAL MOTORS TURBO HYDRA-MATIC 200-4R (Cont.)

2) Install internal gear-to-support thrust washer into case with tangs down. Install overdrive internal gear, hub end first, on forward clutch shaft. Install overdrive carrier-to-sun gear thrust bearing assembly into overdrive internal gear with large diameter race against carrier.

3) Grasp turbine shaft and lower overrun clutch and overdrive carrier assembly into case and rotate into position. Oil and install 4th clutch plates into case. *See Fig. 41 and 4th Clutch Plate Usage Chart.* Install clutch pack retaining snap ring. Install oil deflector plate into case with tangs facing up.

CAUTION: Note the installation order of 4th clutch plates. The center has 2 steel plates together and the thick plate is on top. Incorrect installation sequence will cause damage.

Fig. 41: 4th Clutch Plate Installation Sequence

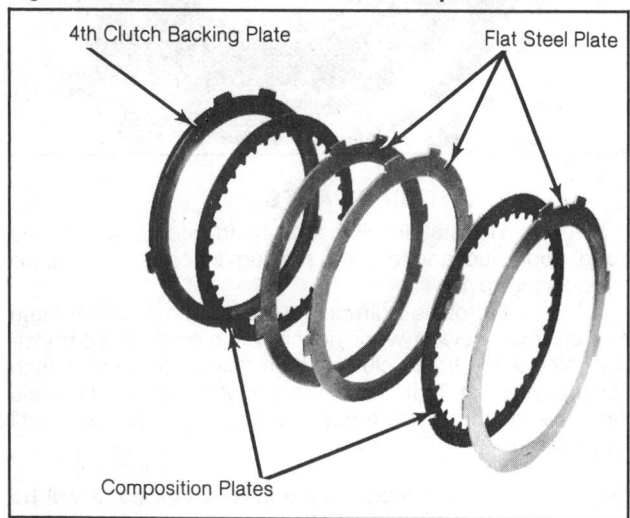

4th Clutch Backing Plate   Flat Steel Plate

Composition Plates

4th CLUTCH PLATE USAGE CHART

Application	Steel	Composition
All Models	3	2

4) Install a new pump-to-case gasket on pump and retain with petroleum jelly. Install 2 alignment pins into pump attaching bolt holes opposite each other. Install pump assembly in case. Install pump attaching bolts with NEW washers. Remove alignment pins and install remaining bolts and washers. Tighten oil pump attaching bolts.

NOTE: At this time, recheck overdrive unit end play to make sure correct overdrive end play thrust washer has been installed. See Overdrive Unit End Play Checking in Transmission Disassembly.

EXTERNAL PARTS

1) Remove output shaft loading fixture and support sleeve tools from rear of transmission case. Turn transmission to horizontal position with oil pan side up. If removed, install new oil seal ring on governor shaft. Install governor assembly into case, then install governor cover and tighten attaching bolts.

CAUTION: Make sure governor shaft is piloted in governor cover before tightening cover attaching bolts.

2) With correct band apply pin installed, as determined during Transmission Disassembly, install intermediate servo assembly into case. Make sure tapered end of apply pin is properly located against band apply lug. Install servo cover retaining ring and align ring gap with end showing in case slot.

NOTE: Intermediate servo cover seal rings must be well lubricated with petroleum jelly to prevent damage or cutting of ring.

3) Lubricate with petroleum jelly and install new "O" rings on case electrical connector. Install electrical connector with lock tabs facing into case, positioning locator tab in notch on side of case.

4) Install a new Teflon seal on 3-4 accumulator piston. Install accumulator pin in case, then install accumulator piston and spring. *See Fig. 42.*

Fig. 42: Installing 3-4 Accumulator Assembly

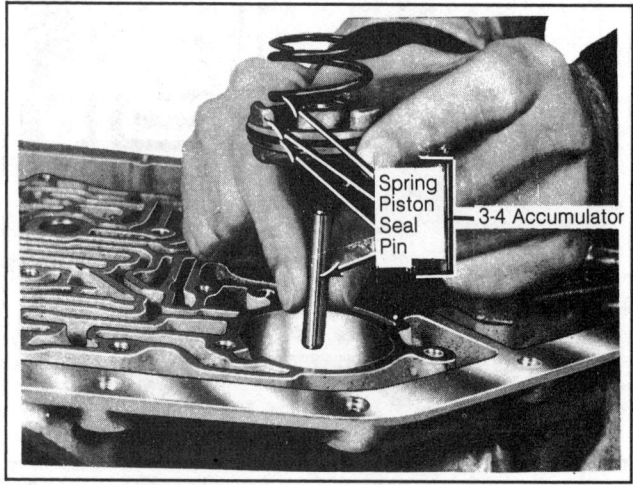

Spring
Piston
Seal
Pin
— 3-4 Accumulator

5) Install 9 check balls into locations in case. *See Fig. 43.* Install 2 valve body alignment pins into opposing bolt holes. Install spacer plate-to-case gasket (marked "C") on case, then install spacer plate.

6) Install valve body assembly-to-spacer plate gasket (marked "VB") on spacer plate. Position 1-2 accumulator plate and gasket in place on case, install accumulator spring on plate. Install a new teflon seal on 1-2 accumulator piston, install piston in accumulator housing with dome up. Install 1-2 accumulator assembly, then install and tighten 5 attaching bolts.

7) Position remaining 3 check balls in valve body. *See Fig. 36.* Retain with petroleum jelly. Remove alignment pins. Install valve body assembly making sure to align manual valve with detent lever.

CAUTION: It is possible during reassembly to position manual valve too far into valve body and still connect the selective lever link to it. This will prevent valve body from fitting properly in case.

GENERAL MOTORS TURBO HYDRA-MATIC 200-4R (Cont.)

Fig. 43: Location of Check Balls in Bottom of Case

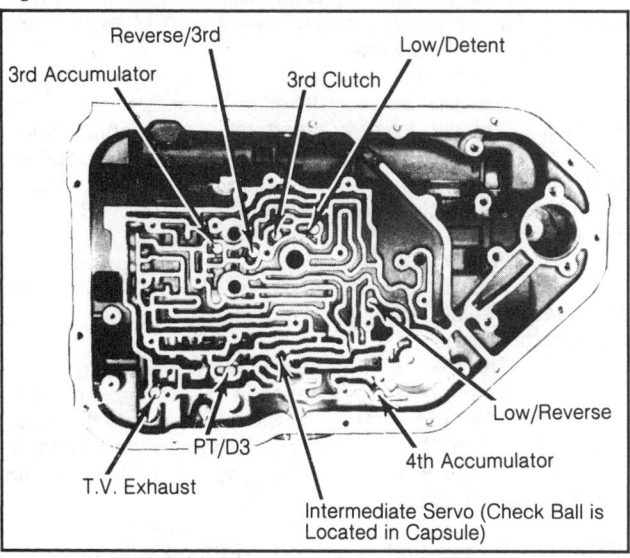

Fig. 45: Throttle Lever and Bracket Installation

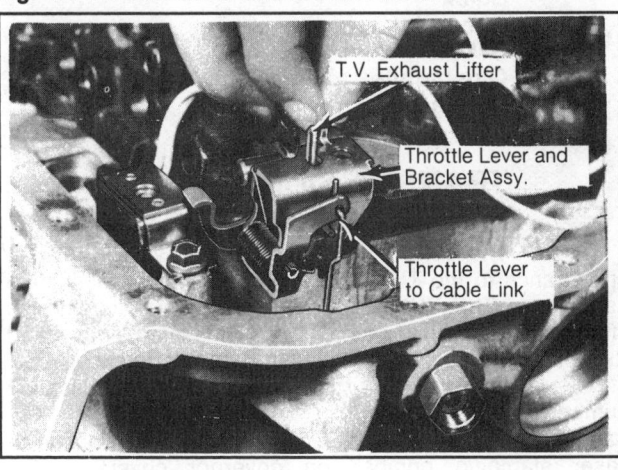

Fig. 44: Proper Positioning of Manual Valve and Selective Lever Link in Valve Body

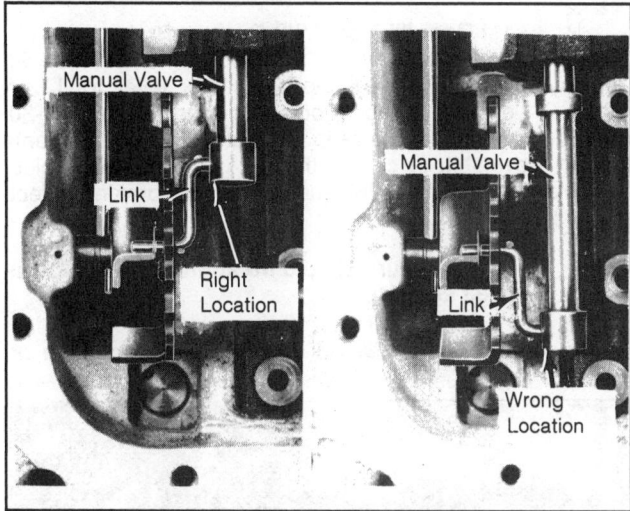

TIGHTENING SPECIFICATIONS

Application	Ft. Lbs. (N.m)
Case-to-Center Support	15-20 (20-27)
Converter-to-Flywheel	35 (47)
Cooler Connector	26-30 (35-40)
Governor Cover-to-Case	15-20 (20-27)
Manual Shaft-to-Lever Nut	20-25 (27-34)
Oil Pan-to-Case	10-13 (14-18)
Park Lock Bracket-to-Case	15-20 (20-27)
Pump Body-to-Pump Cover	15-20 (20-27)
Pump-to-Case	15-20 (20-27)
Transmission-to-Engine	35 (47)
	INCH Lbs. (N.m)
Accumulator Housing-to-Case	84-120 (10-14)
Pressure Switch	60-120 (7-14)
Pressure Take Off Plugs	60-120 (7-14)
Solenoid-to-Case	84-120 (10-14)
Speedo Retainer-to-Case	84-120 (10-14)
Stator Shaft-to-Pump Cover	84-120 (10-14)
Valve Body-to-Case	84-120 (10-14)

8) Start 15 of 20 valve body attaching bolts. DO NOT thread the following bolts at this time: Throttle lever and bracket assembly, manual detent roller and spring assembly and clip retaining bolts. Install signal oil pipe in valve body assembly.

9) Install manual detent roller and spring assembly, locating tang in valve body and roller on inside detent lever. If removed, install throttle and bracket assembly spring on top of lifter. Install link on throttle. Make sure link is hooked. *See Fig. 45.* Install throttle lever and bracket assembly, locating slot in bracket with roll pin and aligning lifter through valve body hole and link through T.V. linkage case bore. Install retaining bolt.

10) With locating pipe in hole, install 4-3 pressure switch (on non Computer Command Control models only) and attaching bolt. Install filter intake pipe "O" ring on pipe and coat with petroleum jelly. Install filter in pump bore. Install oil pan using a new gasket and tighten attaching bolts.

Automatic Transmissions

GENERAL MOTORS TURBO HYDRA-MATIC 250C

Buick
Chevrolet
GMC
Oldsmobile
Pontiac

TRANSMISSION IDENTIFICATION

The THM 250C transmission, while similar in appearance to the THM 350 and 350C, may be identified as follows: The THM 250C case will have an external intermediate band adjustment screw located above and forward of the 1-2 accumulator (at right side of case).

In addition, the transmission identification number can be located in 1 of 3 positions on the transmission. Locations are: Identification plate on side of case; stamping number on governor cover; or ink stamping on bell housing. Transmission model codes and applications are as follows:

TRANSMISSION MODEL CODES

Application	Code
All Models	WX,XD,XH,XK,XL,XN,XP

DESCRIPTION

The Turbo Hydra-Matic 250C transmission is a fully automatic unit consisting primarily of a 3 element hydraulic torque converter and 2 planetary gear sets. Three multi-disc clutches, one roller clutch, and an adjustable intermediate band provide friction elements required to obtain desired function of 2 planetary gear sets. A hydraulic system pressurized by a gear type pump provides working pressure required to operate friction elements and automatic controls.

In addition, a torque converter clutch has been added to this transmission. The converter clutch assembly consists of a 3 element torque converter with the addition of a converter clutch. The converter clutch is splined to the turbine assembly, and when operated, applies against converter cover, providing mechanical direct drive coupling of engine-to-transmission planetary gears. When converter clutch is released, assembly operates as a normal torque converter.

NOTE: See General Motors Torque Converter Clutch System article in this section for information on the torque converter clutch system used in this transmission.

LUBRICATION & ADJUSTMENT

See the appropriate article in AUTOMATIC TRANSMISSION SERVICING Section.

TESTING

ROAD TEST
"D" Range
Position selector lever in "D" range and accelerate vehicle from a standstill. A 1-2 shift should occur at all throttle openings. Shift points will vary with throttle opening. As vehicle speed decreases to 0 MPH, 3-2 and 2-1 downshifts should occur.

"1" or "L1" Range
Position selector lever in "1" or "L1" range and accelerate vehicle from a standstill. A 1-2 shift should occur at all throttle openings. No 2-3 shift can be obtained in this range. The 1-2 shift point will vary with throttle opening. As vehicle speed decreases to 0 MPH, a 2-1 downshift should occur.

"L" or "L2" Range
Position selector lever in "L" or "L2" range and accelerate vehicle from a standstill. No upshift should occur in this range.

2nd Gear ("1" or "L1") Overrun Braking
Position selector lever in "D" range, and with vehicle speed approximately 35 MPH, move selector lever to "1" or "L1" range. Transmission should downshift to 2nd. An increase in engine RPM and an engine braking effect should be noticed.

NOTE: If road test is being performed with pressure gauge attached, line pressure should change from approximately 60 psi (4.22 kg/cm²) to approximately 90 psi (6.33 kg/cm²) in 2nd.

1st Gear ("L" or "L2") Overrun Braking
With selector lever in "1" or "L1" range at 30-50 MPH, with throttle closed, move selector lever to "L" or "L2". A 2-1 downshift should occur at approximately 45-30 MPH (depending on axle ratio and valve body calibration). The 2-1 downshift at closed throttle will be accompanied by increased engine RPM and an engine braking effect should be noticed.

NOTE: Line pressure should be approximately 90 psi (6.33 kg/cm²).

Fig. 1: View of Transmission Case Showing Location of Pressure Taps

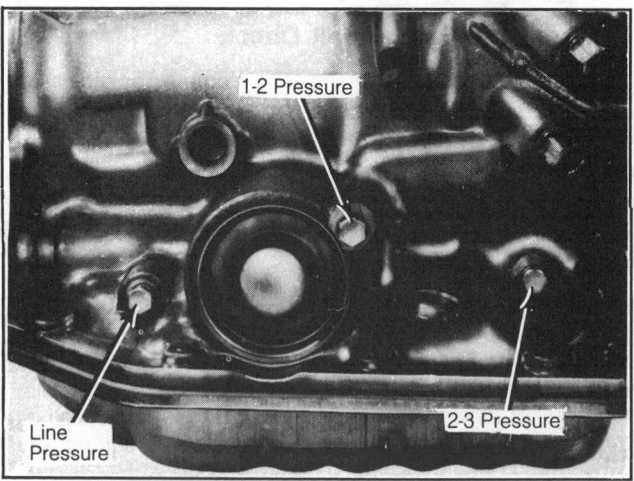

CONTROL PRESSURE CHECK
Connect tachometer to engine, and a 0-300 psi (0-21 kg/cm²) pressure gauge at line pressure take-off point. See Fig. 1. With transmission fluid at correct level and operating temperature, proceed as follows:

GENERAL MOTORS TURBO HYDRA-MATIC 250C (Cont.)

Fig. 2: Sectional View of Turbo Hydra-Matic 250C Automatic Transmission

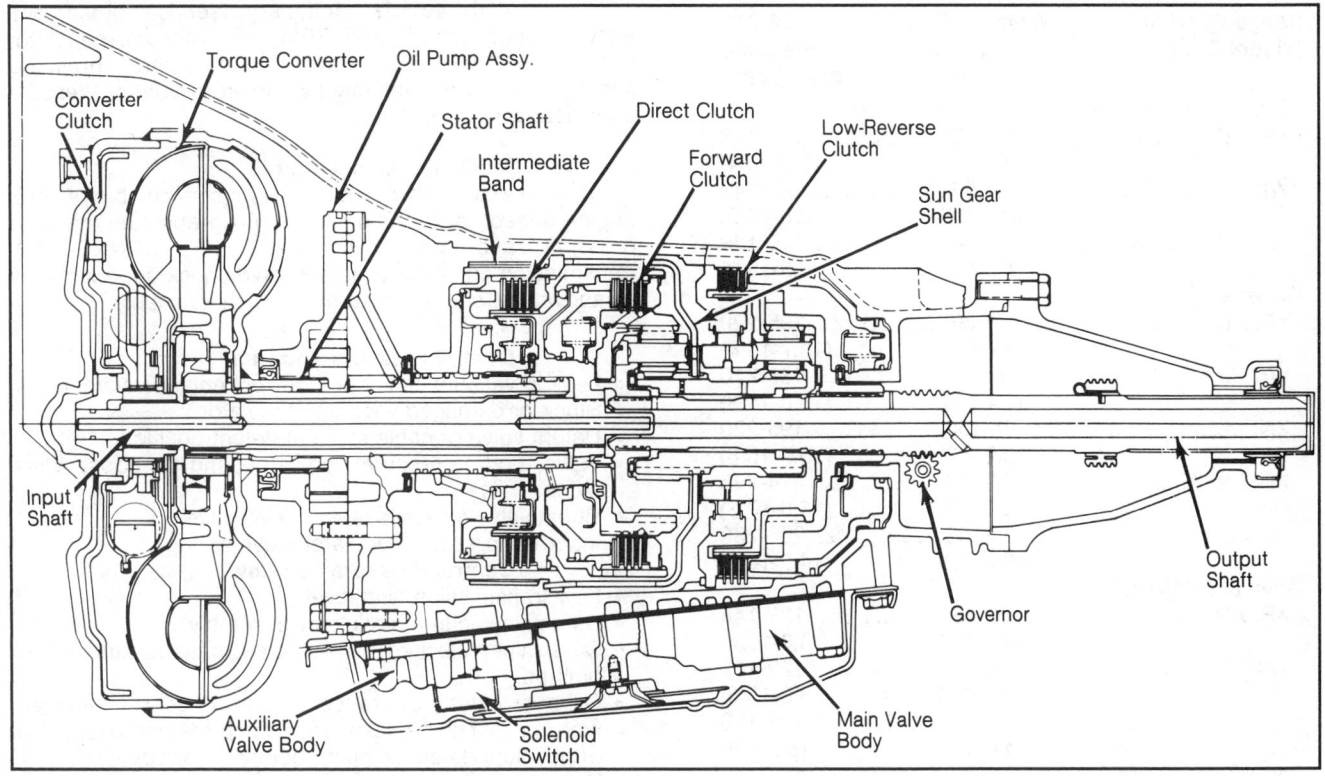

Fig. 3: Turbo Hydra-Matic 250C Hydraulic Circuits Diagram (Shown With Torque Converter Clutch Applied)

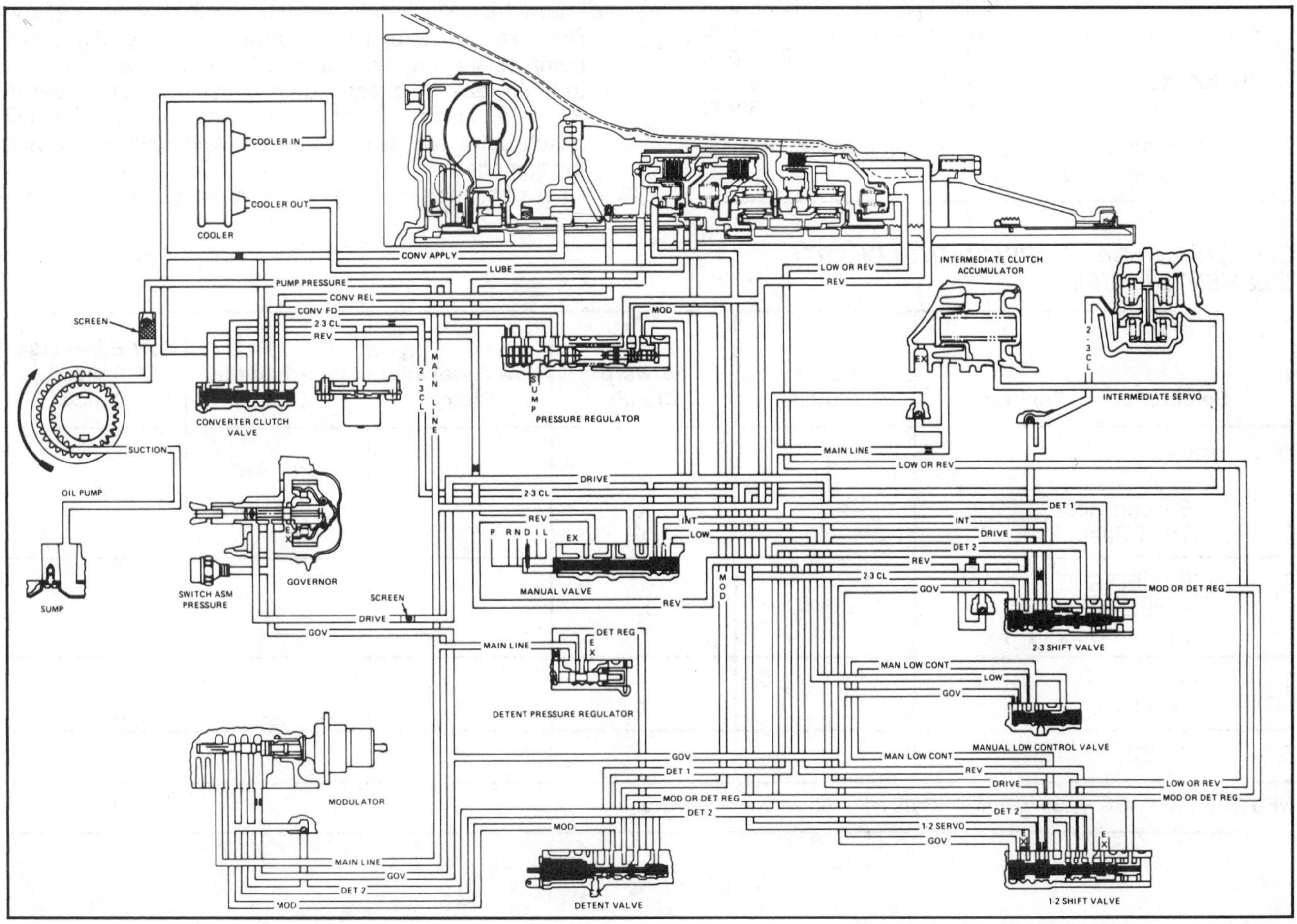

GENERAL MOTORS TURBO HYDRA-MATIC 250C (Cont.)

CONTROL PRESSURE SPECIFICATIONS

Range @ RPM (Model Code)	Minimum T.V. Pressure psi(kg/cm²)	Full T.V. Pressure psi(kg/cm²)
"P" & "N"@1000 ¹		
XP, XD	51-58 (3.6-4.1)	128-148 (9.0-10.4)
WK	51-58 (3.6-4.1)	122-142 (8.6-10.0)
XH, XK, XL, XN	55-64 (4.0-4.5)	119-139 (8.3-10.0)
Reverse @ 1000 ¹		
XP, XD	77-89 (5.4-6.4)	195-220 (13.7-15.6)
WK	77-89 (5.4-6.3)	185-210 (13.0-14.8)
XN	88-103 (6.2-7.2)	195-220 (13.7-15.6)
XH, XK	88-103 (6.2-7.2)	214-246 (15.0-17.3)
XL	88-103 (6.2-7.2)	206-230 (14.5-16.2)
Drive & 3rd@1000 ¹		
XP, XD	51-58 (3.6-4.1)	128-148 (9.0-10.4)
WK	51-58 (3.6-4.1)	122-142 (8.6-10.0)
XN, XH, XK, XL	55-64 (4.0-4.5)	119-139 (8.3-9.8)
2nd & Low @ 1000 ¹		
XP, XD	73-85 (5.1-6.0)	131-151 (9.2-10.6)
WK	73-85 (5.1-6.0)	126-146 (8.9-10.3)
XH, XK, XL, XN	82-95 (5.8-6.8)	119-139 (8.3-9.8)

¹ — Total running time for this combination of tests not to exceed 2 minutes.

Modulator Disconnected

With vehicle stationary (service brake on), engine speed set to 1200 RPM, and vacuum modulator tube DISCONNECTED, transmission control pressure should check approximately as shown in Control Pressure Specifications table.

Modulator Connected

With vehicle stationary (service brake on), engine speed set to maintain 16 in. Hg absolute manifold pressure, and vacuum modulator tube CONNECTED, transmission control pressure should check approximately as shown in Control Pressure Specifications table.

Control Pressure Too High

- Leak in vacuum circuit or incorrect engine vacuum.
- Stuck or damaged vacuum modulator.
- Detent valve or cable stuck in detent position.
- Valve body pressure regulator and/or boost valve stuck.
- Boost valve sleeve broken or defective.
- Incorrect pressure regulator valve spring.

Control Pressure Too Low

- Low transmission fluid level.
- Defective vacuum modulator assembly.
- Oil strainer blocked or restricted, gasket damaged or omitted.
- Oil pump gear clearance incorrect; gears damaged, worn or installed backwards; pump-to-case gasket out of position; defective pump body and/or cover.
- Valve body pressure regulator or boost valve stuck.
- Pressure regulator valve spring too weak.
- Internal leak in forward clutch circuit (pressure low in Drive range, normal in Neutral and Reverse); check pump oil seal rings and forward clutch seals.
- Internal leak in direct clutch circuit (pressure low in Reverse, normal in all other ranges); check direct clutch outer seal and 1-2 accumulator piston and ring for damage.
- Check ball missing from cored passages in case face.

CLUTCH AND BAND APPLICATION CHART (ELEMENTS IN USE)

Selector Lever Position	Direct Clutch	Forward Clutch	Low & Reverse Clutch	Intermediate Band	Low & Reverse Roller Clutch
D — DRIVE					
First Gear		X			X
Second Gear		X		X	
Third Gear	X	X			
2 — INTERMEDIATE					
First Gear		X			X
Second Gear		X		X	
1 — LOW					
First Gear		X	X		X
R — REVERSE	X		X		

NEUTRAL OR PARK — Band and clutches released and/or ineffective.

GENERAL MOTORS TURBO HYDRA-MATIC 250C (Cont.)

GOVERNOR PRESSURE TEST

1) With vehicle on a hoist (rear wheels off ground), disconnect vacuum line to modulator. Install a tachometer to engine and a pressure gauge to line pressure take-off point on transmission case. See Fig. 1.

2) Start engine, keep foot off brake, move selector lever to Drive range, and check line pressure with engine speed at 1000 RPM. Slowly increase engine speed to 3000 RPM and determine if a pressure drop to 7 psi minimum (.5 kg/cm²) occurs.

3) If no pressure drop takes place, inspect governor for a stuck valve or weight, or a restricted orifice in governor valve. Check governor feed system for a plugged or restricted screen in control valve assembly, restrictions in feed line, or scored governor bore.

VACUUM MODULATOR CHECK

See procedure given in G.M. Turbo Hydra-Matic 400 article.

TORQUE CONVERTER CLUTCH TEST

See Testing in G.M. Torque Converter Clutch System article.

SERVICE (IN VEHICLE)

VACUUM MODULATOR & VALVE

Removal

Disconnect vacuum hose from modulator and remove modulator attaching screw and retainer. Remove modulator and its "O" ring seal from case. Remove modulator valve from case.

Installation

Reverse removal procedure. Install with a new "O" ring seal and adjust fluid level.

GOVERNOR

Removal

Raise vehicle and disconnect speedometer cable at transmission. Remove retainer wire and carefully pry off governor cover. Remove governor. Inspect governor weights and valve for freeness.

Installation

Install governor into transmission case. Apply a anaerobic sealant (Loctite Cup Plug Sealant II or equivalent) to cover, then install cover using a brass drift around outside flange. Install cover retainer wire. Connect speedometer cable, lower vehicle and check transmission fluid level.

SPEEDOMETER DRIVE GEAR

Removal

1) Raise vehicle and support transmission with jack. Remove propeller shaft. Disconnect speedometer cable.

2) Disconnect transmission rear mount from frame crossmember. Remove 2 bolts at each end of crossmember and remove crossmember. Remove extension housing. Depress retaining clip and remove speedometer drive gear.

Installation

Place speedometer drive gear retaining clip into hole in output shaft, then install gear on output shaft, aligning slot in gear with clip. To complete installation, reverse removal procedure.

EXTENSION HOUSING OIL SEAL

Removal

Remove propeller shaft. Pry oil seal from extension housing using a screwdriver or small chisel.

Installation

Coat outer casting of new lip oil seal with nonhardening sealer, then drive seal into place. Install propeller shaft. Check and adjust transmission fluid level.

1-2 ACCUMULATOR

Removal

Remove 2 transmission oil pan bolts below the 1-2 accumulator cover. Install compressor tool (J-23069) in place of bolts removed. Press in on cover and remove retaining ring. Remove cover, "O" ring seal, spring and 1-2 accumulator.

Installation

Reverse removal procedure and note that rotating piston slightly when installing will aid in getting rings started in bore. Adjust fluid level.

VALVE BODY & AUXILIARY VALVE BODY ASSEMBLY

Removal

1) Drain transmission fluid from oil pan, then remove oil pan and strainer. Remove detent spring and roller assembly from valve body. Remove valve body and auxiliary valve body attaching bolts.

2) Remove valve body assembly while disconnecting manual control valve link from range selector inner lever and removing detent control valve link from range selector inner lever and removing detent control valve link from detent actuating lever. Remove manual valve and link assembly from valve body assembly.

Installation

Reverse removal procedure. Install with new gasket and adjust fluid level.

Fig. 4: View Showing Components To Be Removed for Valve Body Assembly Removal

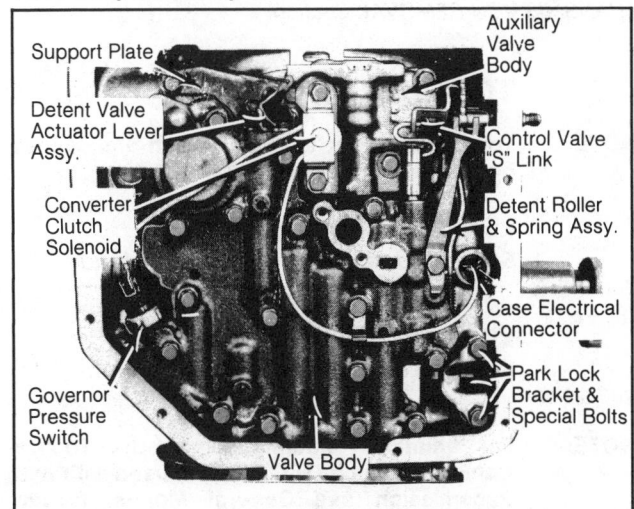

GENERAL MOTORS TURBO HYDRA-MATIC 250C (Con't.)

MANUAL SHAFT, RANGE SELECTOR INNER LEVER AND PARKING LINKAGE ASSEMBLIES

Removal

1) Loosen oil pan and allow fluid to drain, then remove oil pan and strainer. Remove valve body assembly and discard gasket.

Fig. 5: Removing Manual Shaft-to-Case Retainer

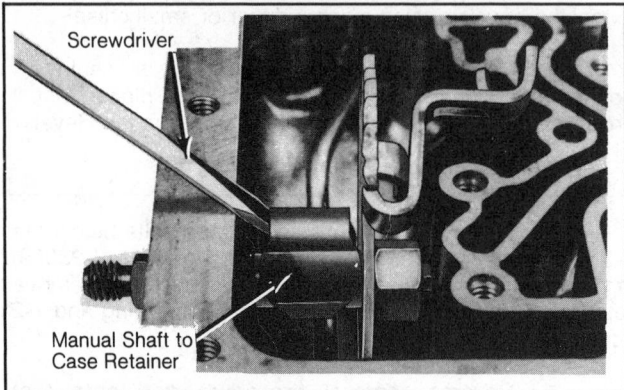

2) Remove manual shaft-to-case retainer and loosen jam nut holding range selector inner lever to manual shaft. *See Fig. 5.* Remove jam nut and manual shaft from case.

NOTE: Do not remove manual shaft lip seal unless replacement is necessary.

3) Remove parking pawl actuating rod and range selector inner lever from case. Remove bolts and parking lock bracket. Remove parking pawl disengaging spring and, if necessary to replace park pawl or shaft, clean bore in case and remove shaft retaining plug, park pawl shaft and pawl.

Installation

Reverse removal procedure and note the following: Install new shaft retaining plug, manual shaft lip seal and gaskets. Adjust fluid level.

REMOVAL & INSTALLATION

See the appropriate article in AUTOMATIC TRANSMISSION REMOVAL Section.

TORQUE CONVERTER

NOTE: Torque converter is a sealed unit and cannot be disassembled for service.

LEAKAGE CHECK

See procedure given in G.M. Turbo Hydra-Matic 400 article.

END CLEARANCE CHECK

See procedure given in G.M. Turbo Hydra-Matic 400 article.

NOTE: For additional information on the Torque Converter Clutch (TCC) system used with this transmission see General Motors Torque Converter Clutch (TCC) System article in this section.

TRANSMISSION DISASSEMBLY

NOTE: During disassembly, all parts should be throughly cleaned in cleaning fluid and then air dried. Wiping cloths or rags should NOT be used to dry parts. DO NOT use solvents which could damage rubber seals or clutch facings.

CONVERTER, MODULATOR ASSEMBLY & SPEEDOMETER DRIVEN GEAR

With transmission in a holding fixture, remove torque converter assembly. Remove vacuum modulator attaching bolt and retainer, then remove modulator, "O" ring seal, and modulator valve from case. Remove speedometer driven gear retainer bolt, retainer, driven gear and "O" ring seal on input shaft.

EXTENSION HOUSING, GOVERNOR, OIL PAN & STRAINER

1) Remove attaching bolts, then remove extension housing and square cut "O" ring seal from case. If necessary, pry rear oil seal from extension housing.

2) Remove governor cover retainer using a screwdriver. Gently tap along governor cover lip with a screwdriver and hammer to remove cover and "O" ring seal.

CAUTION: Do not pry screwdriver between case and governor cover as case damage may result.

3) Remove governor assembly from case and check governor bore and sleeve for scoring. Remove oil pan attaching bolts, oil pan and gasket. Remove oil strainer and gasket from valve body.

VALVE BODY & LINKAGE

NOTE: Refer to Fig. 4 for location of components.

1) Remove detent roller and spring assembly from valve body. Remove actuator valve lever and remove control wire. Disconnect wire from governor pressure switch and case connector and remove torque converter clutch solenoid. If replacement is required, remove pressure switch.

2) Using a screwdriver, pry manual shaft retaining clip from shaft, then slide manual shaft outward to disconnect manual valve link. Remove link.

Fig.6: Removing Auxiliary Valve Body

GENERAL MOTORS TURBO HYDRA-MATIC 250C (Cont.)

3) Remove valve body attaching bolts and valve body. Remove auxiliary valve body and support plate.

NOTE: **Intermediate servo cannot be removed at this time. Intermediate band must be removed first.**

4) Remove spacer plate and gasket. Note location for reassembly reference, then remove 5 check balls from case. Remove oil pump screen and governor feed screen from case. *See Fig. 7.*

NOTE: **It may be necessary to use a screw extractor to remove governor feed screen.**

5) Remove park lock attaching bolts and park lock. If necessary to remove internal linkage proceed as follows:

- Loosen attaching nut holding range selector inner lever to manual shaft. Pull on shaft and remove nut, then remove manual shaft.
- Remove range selector lever parking pawl actuator rod from case and separate lever from rod.
- Remove manual shaft-to-case lip seal.
- Remove parking pawl disengaging spring.
- Remove parking pawl shaft retaining plug using a bolt extractor, then remove shaft and parking pawl.

6) Remove case electrical connector by compressing tabs on sleeve. Remove and discard case connector "O" ring seal.

Fig. 7: View of Case Showing Location of Check Balls, Oil Pump Screen and Governor Feed Screen.

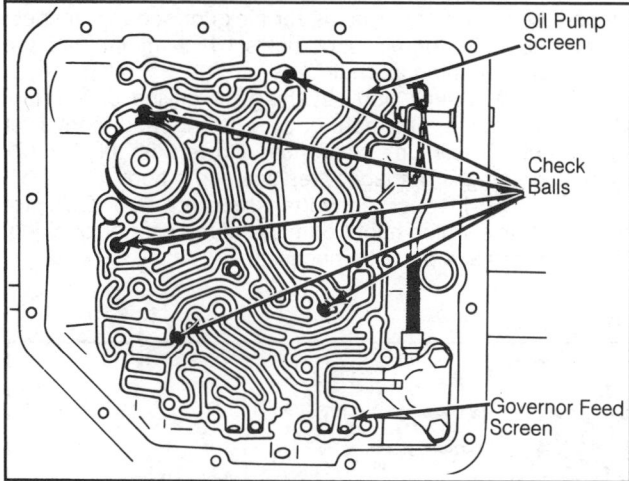

OIL PUMP & INTERNAL CASE COMPONENTS

1) Remove oil pump attaching bolts with washer type seals. Remove oil pump assembly using 2 slide hammers installed in opposite pump attaching bolt holes.

2) Loosen nut and intermediate band anchor bolt. Remove direct and forward clutch assemblies and intermediate band from case. Remove intermediate servo, cushion spring and washer from case.

3) Remove front input ring gear thrust washer (washer has 3 tangs) and input ring gear. Remove output carrier-to-output shaft snap ring. Remove input ring gear (output carrier) thrust washer. Remove output carrier assembly and sun gear driving shell assembly.

4) Remove low-reverse roller clutch support-to-case retaining ring, then remove low-reverse clutch support and race assembly and anti-clunk spring (clutch retainer spring).

5) Remove reaction carrier assembly, output ring gear and shaft assembly and clutch plates from case. Remove reaction carrier from output ring gear and shaft assembly. Remove carrier-to-ring gear needle bearing. Remove output ring gear-to-case needle bearing assembly.

6) Compress low-reverse clutch piston spring retainer and remove retaining ring, spring retainer and springs. Apply compressed air to case passage shown in *Fig. 8* and remove low-reverse clutch piston from case. Remove seals from piston.

7) Compress 1-2 accumulator piston cover and remove retaining ring, then remove cover, piston spring and piston assembly from case. Remove "O" ring seal from cover and remove scarf cut teflon oil seals from piston ONLY if damaged.

COMPONENT DISASSEMBLY & REASSEMBLY

VALVE BODY ASSEMBLY

NOTE: **As valve trains are removed from each valve body bore, place individual parts in correct order and in relative position to valve body to simplify reassembly. Valves and springs are not interchangeable, and all parts must be installed in correct order in proper valve body bore.**

Fig. 8: Low-Reverse Clutch Piston Removal

Apply Air Pressure Here to Remove Low-Reverse Clutch Piston

Position valve body assembly with cored face up and direct clutch accumulator piston pocket positioned as shown in *Fig. 10*, then remove valve trains as follows:

- Remove manual valve from lower left hand bore.
- From lower right hand bore, remove retaining pin, sleeve, intermediate boost valve, reverse and modulator boost valve, spring, and pressure regulator valve.
- From next bore up, remove retaining pin, sleeve, spring, 2-3 shift control valve, spring and 2-3 shift valve.
- From next bore up, remove retaining pin, sleeve, spring, 1-2 shift control valve and 1-2 shift valve.

Automatic Transmissions

GENERAL MOTORS TURBO HYDRA-MATIC 250C (Cont.)

- From next bore up, remove retaining pin, plug, spring and manual low control valve.
- From top right hand bore, remove retaining pin, spring, spring seat and detent regulator valve.
- From bore on opposite side, remove detent actuating lever bracket bolt, bracket, stop, spring retainer, seat, outer spring, inner spring, washer and detent valve.

Reassembly

Reverse disassembly procedure, using *Fig. 10* as a guide, tighten detent actuating lever bracket bolt to 52 INCH lbs. (6 N.m).

AUXILIARY VALVE BODY

Disassembly

Position valve body with cored face up. Remove retaining pin, seat, spring and converter clutch apply valve from valve body bore.

Fig. 9: Exploded View of Turbo Hydra-Matic 250C Auxiliary Valve Body

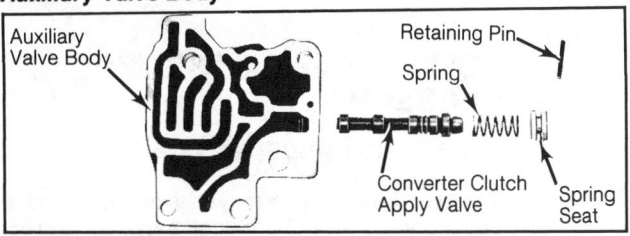

Inspection

Inspect apply valve for scoring, cracks, and free movement' in bore. Inspect valve body for cracks, scored bores, interconnected oil passage, and flatness of mounting surface. Check spring for distortion.

Reassembly

Reverse disassembly procedure.

OIL PUMP ASSEMBLY

Disassembly

1) Remove attaching bolts and separate pump cover and stator shaft assembly from pump body. If damaged, remove 2 forward clutch-to-pump hub scarf cut oil seal rings and 3 direct clutch-to-pump hub oil rings.

Check steady rest ring. If cut or frozen in bore, remove and replace.

2) Mark pump drive and driven gears to ensure reassembly in same position, then remove gears from pump body. Remove pump outside diameter-to-case square cut "O" ring seal.

Fig. 11: View of Stator Shaft Showing Oil Seal Rings and Steady Rest Ring

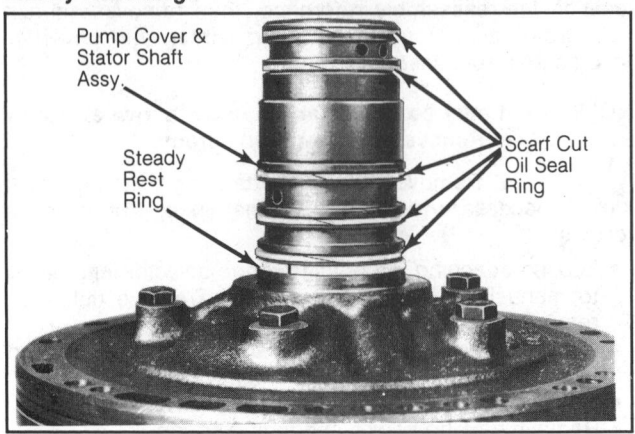

Inspection

1) Wash all parts in cleaning solvent and blow out all oil passages. Do not use cloth or paper to dry parts; air dry parts only.

NOTE: Solvents may be harmful to rubber seals.

2) Inspect pump gears for nicks or damage. Inspect body and cover faces for nicks or scoring. Inspect cover hub O.D. for nicks or burrs which might damage clutch drum bushing journal.
3) Check body bushing for galling or scoring. Check clearance between body bushing and converter pump hub. Maximum clearance allowed is .005" (.127 mm). If bushing is damaged, replace pump body.
4) Inspect converter housing hub O.D. for nicks or burrs which might damage pump seal or bushing. Repair or replace parts as necessary.

Fig. 10: Exploded View of Turbo Hydra-Matic 250C Valve Body Assembly

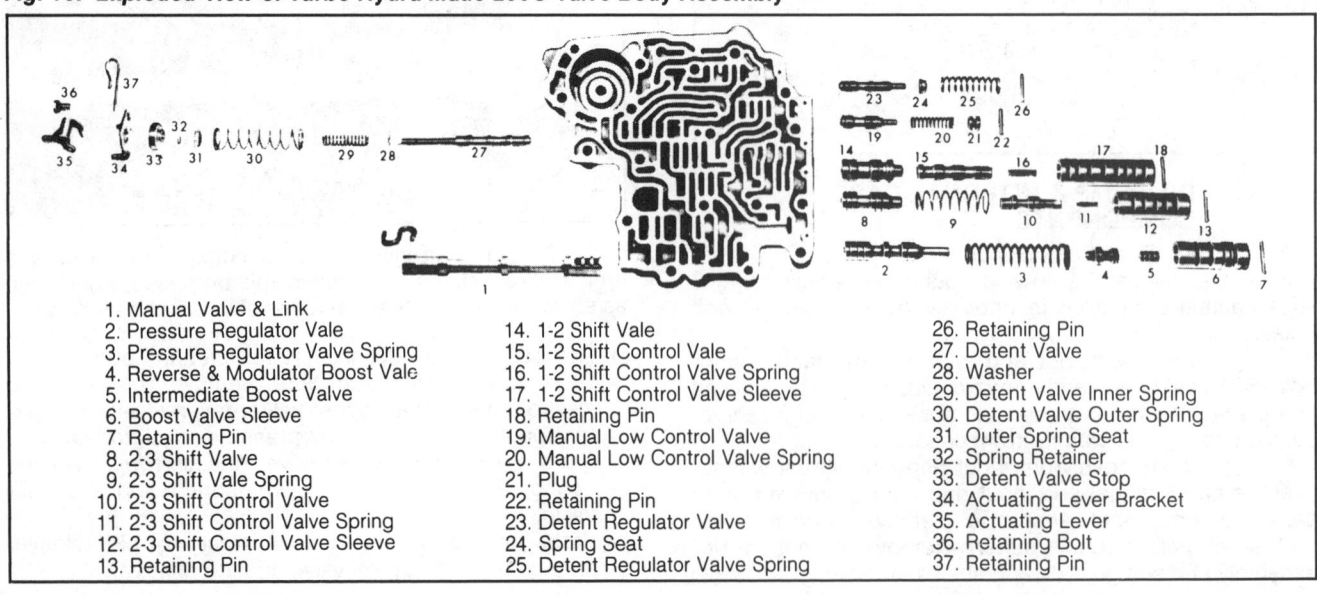

1. Manual Valve & Link
2. Pressure Regulator Vale
3. Pressure Regulator Valve Spring
4. Reverse & Modulator Boost Vale
5. Intermediate Boost Valve
6. Boost Valve Sleeve
7. Retaining Pin
8. 2-3 Shift Valve
9. 2-3 Shift Vale Spring
10. 2-3 Shift Control Valve
11. 2-3 Shift Control Valve Spring
12. 2-3 Shift Control Valve Sleeve
13. Retaining Pin
14. 1-2 Shift Vale
15. 1-2 Shift Control Vale
16. 1-2 Shift Control Valve Spring
17. 1-2 Shift Control Valve Sleeve
18. Retaining Pin
19. Manual Low Control Valve
20. Manual Low Control Valve Spring
21. Plug
22. Retaining Pin
23. Detent Regulator Valve
24. Spring Seat
25. Detent Regulator Valve Spring
26. Retaining Pin
27. Detent Valve
28. Washer
29. Detent Valve Inner Spring
30. Detent Valve Outer Spring
31. Outer Spring Seat
32. Spring Retainer
33. Detent Valve Stop
34. Actuating Lever Bracket
35. Actuating Lever
36. Retaining Bolt
37. Retaining Pin

GENERAL MOTORS TURBO HYDRA-MATIC 250C (Cont.)

Fig. 12: Pump Gear Installation

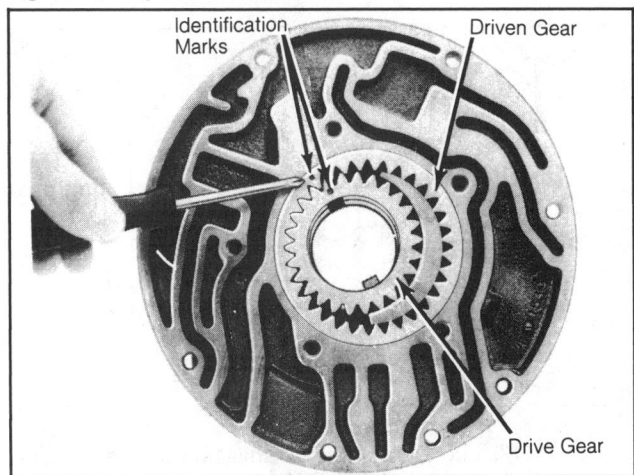

Fig. 14: Oil Pump Body and Cover Oil Passages

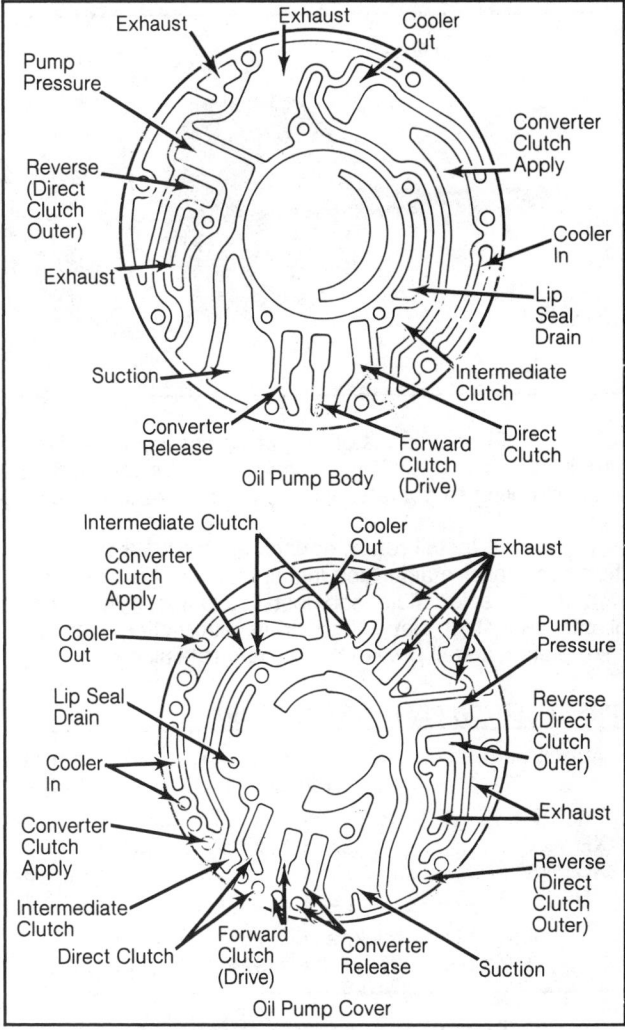

5) Check condition of pump-to-converter hub lip seal and replace if damaged. With parts clean and dry, install gears in pump body and check pump body face-to-gear face clearance. Using a feeler gauge and straight-edge. Clearance should be .0005-.0015" (.013-.038 mm).

Reassembly

1) Install drive and driven gears in pump body making sure they are installed in position noted at disassembly and that identifications marks are face up and aligned as shown in *Fig. 12*.

2) Install direct clutch drum-to-pump cover needle bearing over pump cover delivery sleeve. If removed, install 3 direct clutch-to-pump hub oil seal rings and 2 forward clutch-to-pump hub oil seal rings.

3) Check pump cover and body oil passages to make sure they are not restricted. *See Fig. 13.* Install pump outside diameter-to-case square cut "O" ring seal. Align pump body to cover and install and tighten attaching bolts.

DIRECT CLUTCH

Disassembly

1) Remove pressure plate-to-clutch drum retaining ring and lift out pressure plate, lined drive plates, steel driven plates and cushion spring.

2) Using a compressor tool, compress piston return spring retainer and remove retaining ring. Remove tool, spring retainer and return springs from clutch drum.

3) Remove piston assembly from clutch drum, then remove inner and outer seals from piston. Remove center piston seal from clutch drum.

Inspection

1) Inspect drive and driven clutch plates for signs of burning, scoring or wear. Inspect return springs for distortion or collapsed coils.

2) Inspect piston for cracks. Check clutch housing for wear, scoring, open oil passages and proper operation of check ball.

Reassembly

1) Install new inner and outer seals on piston. Install new piston center seal on clutch drum with lip facing upward.

Fig. 13: Exploded View of Direct Clutch Assembly

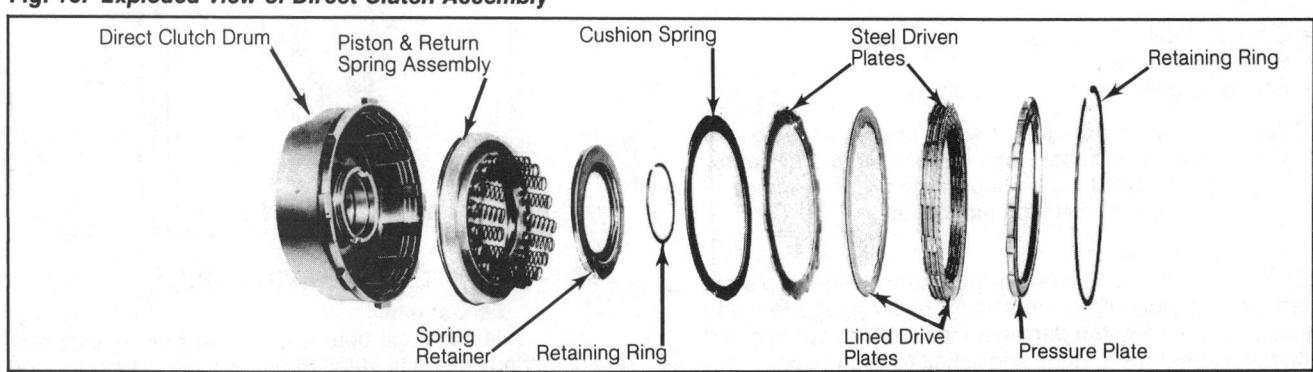

GENERAL MOTORS TURBO HYDRA-MATIC 250C (Cont.)

Fig. 15: Exploded View of Forward Clutch Assembly

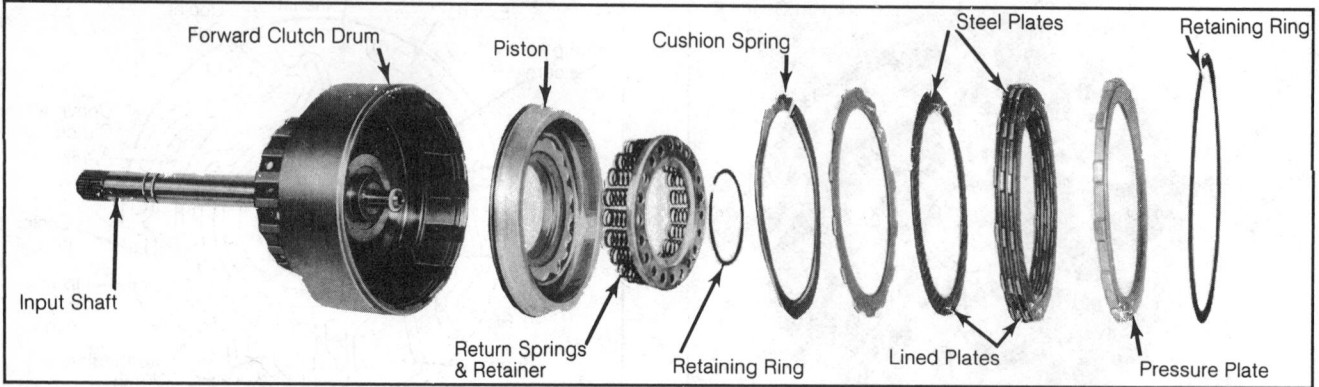

2) Install piston clutch drum using a feeler gauge or piece of .020" (.51 mm) piano wire crimped into copper tubling to guide seals into drum without damaging them.

3) Install return springs and retainer on piston, then compress retainer and install retaining ring. Lubricate with transmission fluid and install cushion spring, lined places and steel plates into drum, alternating steel and lined plates. Install pressure plate and retaining ring.

DIRECT CLUTCH PLATE USAGE CHART

Application	Steel Plates	Lined Plates
XL, XK	4 [1]	4
XP	3 [2]	3
XD, WK	3 [2]	3
XH	4 [1]	4

[1] — Clutch piston thickness is .755" (19.18 mm).
[2] — Clutch piston thickness is .926" (23.52 mm).

FORWARD CLUTCH

Disassembly
1) Remove direct clutch drum-to-forward clutch housing needle bearing. Remove forward clutch retaining ring and pressure plate, then lift out lined plates, steel plates and cushion spring.

2) Using a compressor tool, compress retainer and remove retaining ring. Remove piston return spring retainer and springs. Remove piston from clutch drum, then remove seals from piston.

Inspection
Following inspection procedures for Direct Clutch and, in addition, inspect input shaft for the following:

- Open lubrication passages at each end
- Splines for damage
- Ground bushing journals for damage

NOTE: **Input shaft and forward clutch housing are serviced separately. Make certain that center of forward clutch housing is properly supported when removing input shaft.**

Reassembly
1) Install new inner and outer seals on piston, then install piston into drum using a feeler gauge to guide seals into drum without damage. Install return springs and retainer. Compress springs and install retaining ring.

2) Lubricate with transmission fluid and install cushion spring, lined plates and steel plates, starting with cushion spring and alternating steel and lined plates.

3) Install forward clutch pressure plate and retaining ring. Pressure plate is selective fit. To check for correct pressure plate, proceed as follows:

FORWARD CLUTCH PLATE USAGE CHART

Application	Steel Plates	Lined Plates
All Models	4 [1]	4

[1] — Clutch piston thickness is 1.445" (36.70 mm).

4) Measure distance from top of cutch pack to top of clutch drum (dimension "A" in *Fig. 16*. Next, measure distance from lower edge of notch on inner surface of drum to end of drum (dimension "B"). Subtract "B" from "A" to obtain thickness of pressure plate to install (dimension "C").

5) If dimension "C" is .016-.052" (.41-1.32 mm) use pressure plate (6261072); if dimension "C" is .052-.083" (1.32-2.11 mm) use pressure plate (6261349); if dimension "C" is .083-.1218" (2.11-3.09 mm) use pressure plate (6261350). Install correct pressure plate and recheck measurement.

Fig. 16: Determining Forward Clutch Pressure

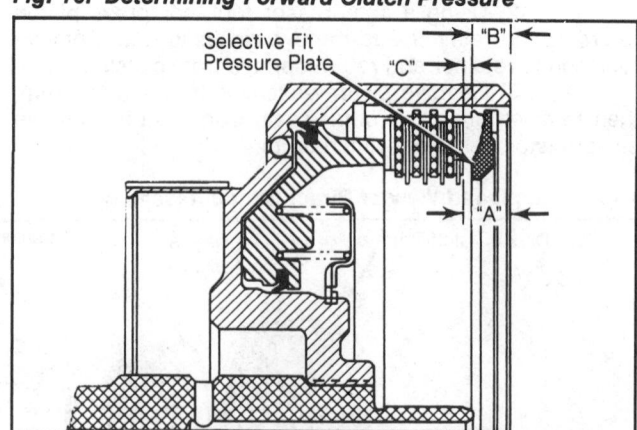

SUN GEAR & DRIVING SHELL
Disassembly
Remove sun gear-to-sun gear driving shell rear retaining ring and flat steel thrust washer. Remove sun

GENERAL MOTORS TURBO HYDRA-MATIC 250C (Cont.)

Fig. 17: Exploded View of Planetary Gear Train

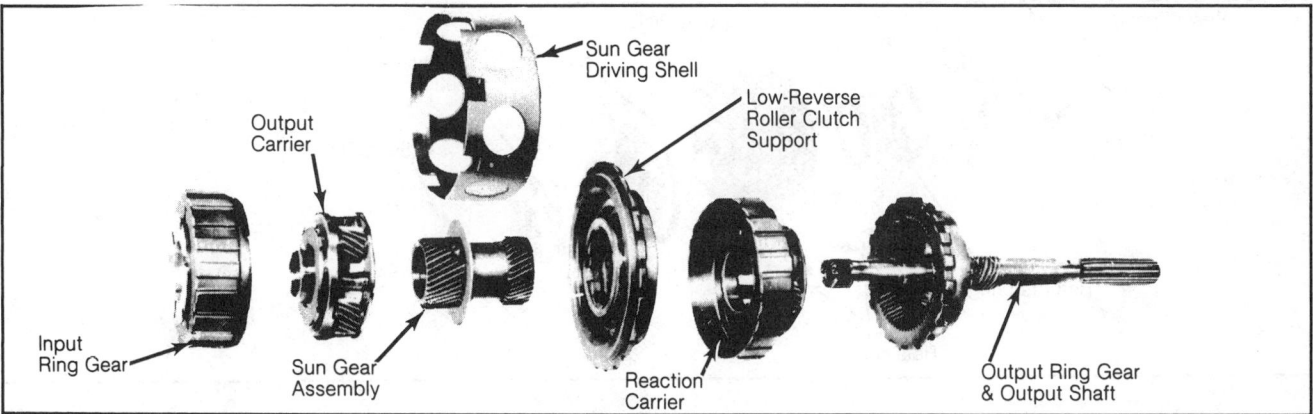

gear from driving shell, then remove front retaining ring from gear.

Reassembly

Install new front retaining ring on sun gear, then install gear into driving shell. Position rear thrust washer on shell and install a new rear retaining ring.

NOTE: **Do not overstress front and rear retaining rings at installation.**

LOW-REVERSE ROLLER CLUTCH

Disassembly

Remove low-reverse clutch-to-sun gear shell thrust washer. Remove overrun clutch inner race from support. Remove retaining ring, then remove roller clutch from support.

Fig. 18: Exploded View of Low-Reverse Roller Clutch

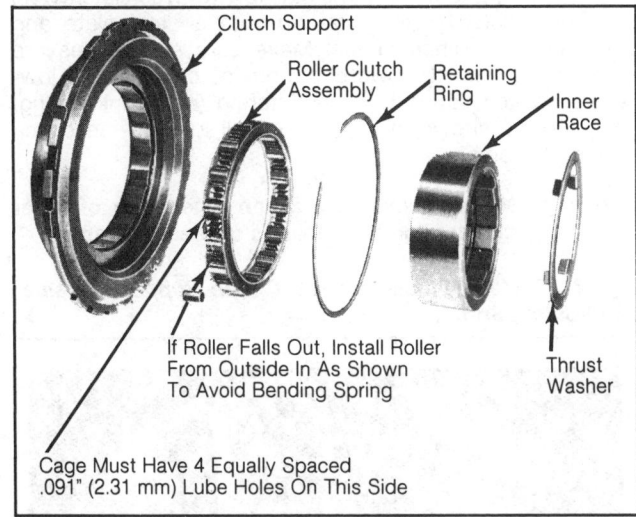

Inspection

Inspect roller clutch inner and outer race for scratches and indentations. Inspect rollers for wear and roller springs for distortion.

Reassembly

Install roller clutch assembly to outer race with oil holes toward rear of transmission. Install inner race into roller clutch, then install retaining ring. Install roller clutch-to-sun gear thrust washer. *See Fig. 18.*

NOTE: **When properly assembled, low-reverse roller clutch should free wheel in clockwise direction only.**

INTERMEDIATE SERVO

Disassembly

Compress servo piston and remove "E" ring retainer, then remove apply piston, spring and pilot. Compress cushion piston and remove "E" ring retainer, then slide piston, spring and servo retainer from servo apply rod.

NOTE: **With servo disassembled, inspect oil seal rings on pistons and remove them ONLY if replacement is required.**

Reassembly

Reverse disassembly procedure, making sure oil seal is properly installed into apply piston pilot.

GOVERNOR ASSEMBLY

NOTE: **Governor, including driven gear, is serviced as a complete assembly; however, driven gear may be serviced separately. Governor disassembly is necessary to replace driven gear. Disassembly may also be necessary due to improper operation.**

Disassembly

Cut off one end of each governor weight pin and remove pins, thrust cap, weights and springs. Remove governor valve from sleeve using care not to damage valve.

NOTE: **Governor weights are interchangeable from side to side and need not be identified.**

Inspection

1) Wash all parts in cleaning solvent, air dry and blow out all passages. Inspect governor sleeve for nicks, burrs, scoring or galling. Check sleeve for free operation in bore of transmission case.

2) Inspect valve for nicks, burrs, scoring, galling and for free operation in bore of sleeve. Inspect gear for nicks, burrs, damage, and for looseness on sleeve.

Automatic Transmissions

GENERAL MOTORS TURBO HYDRA-MATIC 250C (Cont.)

Fig. 19: Exploded View of Intermediate Servo Assembly

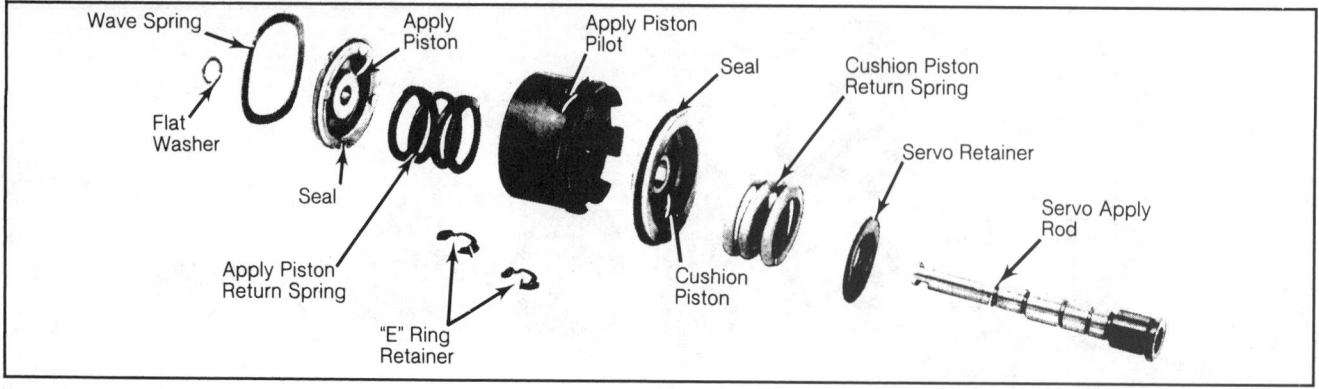

3) Inspect weight springs for distortion or damage. Check weights for free operation in their retainers. Check valve opening at entry and exhaust .020" minimum (.51 mm).

Governor Driven Gear Replacement

1) Drive out governor gear retaining pin using a small punch. Support governor on 3/16" plates installed in exhaust slots of sleeve, place in arbor press, and with a long punch, press gear from sleeve. Carefully clean metal chips from sleeve.

2) Support governor with plates installed in exhaust slots, position new gear in sleeve and, with a small socket, press gear into sleeve until nearly seated. Clean metal chips that may have shaved off gear, then press gear in until bottomed on shoulder.

3) Locate a new retaining pin hole position 90° from existing hole, center punch and then, while supporting governor in press, drill a new 1/8" (3.18 mm) hole through gear and sleeve. Install retaining pin and wash governor assembly throughly to remove any chips that may have collected.

Reassembly

1) Install governor valve (large land end first) into bore of sleeve. Install weights and springs, and thrust cap on sleever.

2) Align pin holes in thrust cap, weight assemblies and sleeve, and install new pins. Crimp both ends of pins to prevent them from falling out. Check governor weights and valve for free movement.

Fig. 20: Exploded View of Governor Assembly

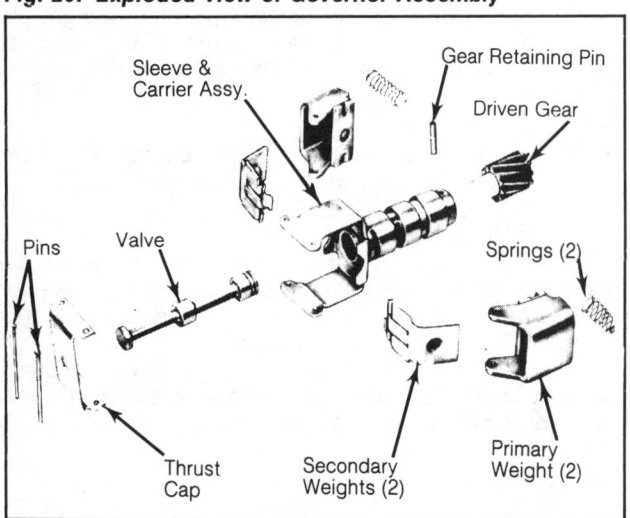

TRANSMISSION REASSEMBLY

NOTE: **When reassembling transmission, use only ATF or petroleum jelly as lubricants to retain bearings or races. Lubricate all bearings, seal rings and clutch plates prior to reassembly.**

INTERNAL CASE COMPONENTS

1) Install low-reverse clutch piston assembly into case, making sure to index piston lug into slot in case and that piston is fully seated. Install piston return spring and retainer, then compress retainer and install retaining ring.

2) Install output ring gear rear thrust bearing into case. Assemble output ring gear on output shaft, then install reaction carrier-to-output ring gear bearing into ring gear support with tanged race (black side) up. Position output shaft assembly in case and install reaction carrier assembly into ring gear and shaft assembly.

3) Lubricate and install low-reverse clutch steel and lined clutch plates, starting with a steel plate and alternating with lined plates. Make sure steel plates are installed with notch toward bottom of case. Install low-reverse clutch support retainer spring (anti-clunk spring) into case as shown in *Fig. 21*. Install low-reverse clutch support assembly.

NOTE: **Make certain splines on inner race of roller clutch align with splines of reaction carrier.**

Fig. 21: Installing Low-Reverse Clutch Support Retainer (Anti-Clunk) Spring

GENERAL MOTORS TURBO HYDRA-MATIC 250C (Cont.)

LOW-REVERSE CLUTCH PLATE USAGE CHART

Application	Steel Plates	Lined Plates
All Models	4 [1]	 4

[1] — Clutch piston thickness is 3.146" (80 mm).

4) Install low-reverse clutch support-to-case snap ring with anti-clunk spring between gap. Install sun gear thrust washer onto roller clutch race. Install sun gear driving shell assembly.

5) Install output carrier assembly. Install input ring gear rear thrust washer. Install input ring gear-to-output shaft snap ring, then install input ring gear and front thrust washer.

NOTE: Do not overstress input ring gear-to-output shaft snap ring; damage may result.

6) Install needle bearing to forward clutch assembly. Assemble direct clutch assembly to forward clutch assembly, then install clutch assemblies into case. Make sure tangs on direct clutch drum are installed into slots in sun gear driving shell.

7) Position cushion spring into intermediate servo bore in case and retain in place with petroleum jelly. Make sure washer is in place on intermediate servo rod and install servo assembly into case.

8) Install intermediate band into case and make sure band ends are properly located on adjusting screw and servo rod ends. Turn adjusting screw into case until end of screw is against band lug. Align slotted band end on notched end of servo rod.

END PLAY CHECK & OIL PUMP ASSEMBLY

NOTE: Check for proper thickness of selective fit shim between oil pump cover and direct clutch assembly as follows:

1) Install original number of shims (remove during transmission disassembly) or pump cover. Position oil pump gasket in position and using guide studs, install oil pump and secure to case with 2 attaching bolts. Install dial indicator as shown in *Fig. 22*. Zero indicator.

2) Lift up on transmission output shaft and read resulting end play on dial indicator. End play should be .010-.044" (.25-1.12 mm). If end play is not within specifications, add or remove shims as necessary to correct.

Fig. 22: Measuring Transmission End Play

Slide Hammer Bolt

Dial Indicator Set

End Play Should Be .010-.044" (.25-1.12 mm)

CAUTION: If input shaft cannot be rotated as pump is pulled into place, direct and forward clutch housings have not been properly installed to index lined plates with respective parts. This condition must be corrected before pump is pulled into place.

3) With pump assembly completely installed, adjust intermediate band. Tighten adjusting screw to 30 INCH lbs. (3.4 N.m), and then back-off 3 complete turns. Hold adjusting screw stationary and tighten lock nut. Install new "O" ring seal on input shaft.

SPEEDOMETER DRIVE GEAR & EXTENSION HOUSING

1) Place speedometer drive gear retaining clip into hole in output shaft. Align slot in drive gear with retaining clip and install gear onto shaft.

NOTE: If necessary for installation, speedometer drive gear may be heated using a heat lamp.

2) Install extension housing-to-case square cut "O" ring seal. Attach extension housing to case and tighten attaching bolts. If necessary, replace extension housing rear oil seal.

MANUAL LINKAGE

1) If necessary, install new manual shaft-to-case lip seal using a 3/4" diameter rod and make sure seal is fully seated in case. Install parking pawl (tooth toward inside of case) into case. Install parking pawl shaft into case and through parking pawl.

2) Install parking pawl shaft retainer plug. Drive plug into case, using a 3/8" diameter rod, until plug is .130-.170" (3.30-4.32 mm) below face of case, then stake in 3 places.

3) Install parking pawl disengaging spring, and hook square end on pawl. Install parking lock bracket, using 2 special bolts (G.M. 300M, 6 marks on head) and tighten bolts to specifications.

4) Install range selector inner lever to parking pawl actuator rod, then install rod under park lock bracket and parking pawl. Install manual shaft through case and range selector inner lever, then install and tighten shaft retaining nut.

VALVE BODY, AUXILIARY VALVE BODY & SOLENOID

1) Install oil pump pressure screen and governor feed screen into case passages indicated in *Fig. 7*. If removed, install case electrical connector with new "O" ring. Install 5 check balls into proper transmission case pockets. *See Fig. 7.*

2) Install valve body spacer plate and gasket. Install auxiliary valve body and support plate. Install valve body assembly and tighten attaching bolts in a random sequence.

3) Install manual valve to range selector link, then install manual shaft retainer. Connect detent control valve wire to detent valve actuating lever, then attach lever to valve body.

4) Install solenoid and connect wires. If removed, install governor pressure switch. Install detent roller and spring assembly to valve body. Align lube hole in suction screen and valve body and install gasket and oil screen.

Automatic Transmissions

GENERAL MOTORS TURBO HYDRA-MATIC 250C (Cont.)

CAUTION: Be sure lube holes in screen match up with those in valve body.

GOVERNOR & VACUUM MODULATOR

Install governor assembly, "O" ring and cover seal, then install retainer wire. Install vacuum modulator valve into case, then install vacuum modulator and retainer clip.

1-2 ACCUMULATOR & OIL PAN

Install 1-2 accumulator piston assembly and spring. Install new "O" ring seal in case groove, then install accumulator cover and retaining ring. Install oil pan using a new gasket.

TIGHTENING SPECIFICATIONS

Application	Ft. Lbs. (N.m)
Transmission-to-Engine	35 (47)
Converter-to-Flywheel	35 (47)
Oil Pan-to-Case	13 (18)
Oil Pump-to-Case	20 (27)
Vacuum Modulator Retainer	12 (16)
Valve Body-to-Case	13 (18)
Pump Body-to-Pump Cover	15 (20)
Park Lock Bracket-to-Case	29 (39)
Extension Housing-to-Case	35 (47)
Manual Shaft Nut	30 (41)
Band Adjusting Screw Lock Nut	15 (20)

GENERAL MOTORS
TURBO HYDRA-MATIC 325-4L — TRANSAXLE

Buick Riviera
Cadillac Eldorado & Seville
Oldsmobile Toronado

TRANSMISSION IDENTIFICATION

The Transmission Identification Number is stamped on a plate attached to left side of torque converter housing. In addition, since this is a metric designed transmission, the word "Metric" is stamped on the bottom of the oil pan. Transmission code letters are as follows:

TRANSMISSION CODES

Application	Codes Letters
All Models	AJ,AL,AM,BE,BJ,OE,OK

DESCRIPTION

The Turbo Hydra-Matic 325-4L transaxle is a fully automatic unit consisting of a 4-element hydraulic torque converter and a compound planetary gear set. 5 multiple-disc clutchs, 2 roller clutches and a band provide the friction elements required to obtain the desired function of the planetary gear set. The torque converter couples the engine to the overdrive unit and planetary gears through oil and hydraulically provides additional torque multiplication when required. A hydraulic system pressurized by a gear type pump provides the working pressure required to operate the friction elements and automatic controls.

LUBRICATION & ADJUSTMENTS

See the appropriate article in AUTOMATIC TRANSMISSION SERVICING section.

TESTING

ROAD TEST
"D" Range
With selector lever in drive range, accelerate vehicle from a standstill. A 1-2, 2-3, and 3-4 shift should occur at all throttle openings (shift points will vary with throttle openings). As vehicle speed decreases to zero MPH, 4-3, 3-2 and 2-1 downshifts should occur.
"L2" or "S" Range
With selector level in intermediate range, accelerate vehicle from a standstill. A 1-2 shift should occur at all throttle openings (No 2-3 shift can be obtained in this range). The 1-2 shift point will vary with throttle opening. As vehicle speed decreases to zero MPH, a 2-1 downshift should occur.
"L1" of "L" Range
Place selector lever in low range and accelerate vehicle from a standstill. No upshift should occur in this range.

1st Gear ("L1" of "L") Overrun Braking
With selector lever in intermediate range, and vehicle speed approximately 30 MPH at constant throttle, move selector lever to low range ("L1" or "L"). An increase in engine RPM and an engine braking effect should be noted.
2nd Gear ("L2" or "S") Overrun Braking
With selector lever in drive range, lift foot off accelerator and move selector lever to intermediate range ("L2" or "S"). An increase in engine RPM and an engine braking effect should be noted.

OIL PRESSURE TESTS
Before making oil pressure tests, ensure that fluid level and condition and control linkage adjustments have been checked and corrected if necessary. Install a tachometer to engine, and an oil pressure gauge to pressure take-off point on transmission case. Check oil pressure as follows:
Minimum T.V. Line Pressure Check
With T.V. cable properly adjusted and brakes applied, take line pressure readings in ranges and at engine RPM shown in the *Control Pressure Table*.
Full T.V. Line Pressure Check
With T.V. cable held fully open and brakes applied, take line pressure readings in ranges and at engine RPM shown in the *Control Pressure Table*.

CONTROL PRESSURE SPECIFICATIONS (psi)

Range@RPM (Model Code)	Minimum T.V. Pressure	Full T.V. Pressure
N, D4, D3@1000		
AJ, AL, OK	64-77	129-155
AM, BE	64-77	113-135
OE	55-65	121-130
BJ	55-65	108-124
D2, D1@1000		
AJ, AL, OK	126-153	126-153
AM, BE	148-179	148-179
OE, BJ	128-152	128-152
Reverse@1000		
AJ, AL, OK	91-109	184-220
AM, BE	126-152	224-268
OE	109	239-284
BJ	109-129	229-254

OIL PRESSURE TEST RESULTS

Oil Pressure Too Low
- Oil level low
- T.V. cable out of adjustment
- T.V. linkage damaged
- Throttle valve stuck
- Shift T.V. valve stuck
- Oil screen plugged
- Oil screen "O" ring leaking
- Control valve assembly bolts loose
- Pressure regulator valve stuck or wrong size
- Control valve assembly check balls No.1 and 3, missing or out of position
- M.T.V. Boost valve and plunger stuck

Automatic Transmissions
GENERAL MOTORS
TURBO HYDRA-MATIC 325-4L — TRANSAXLE (Cont.)

Fig. 1: *Cutaway View of Turbo Hydra-Matic 325-4L Automatic Transaxle*

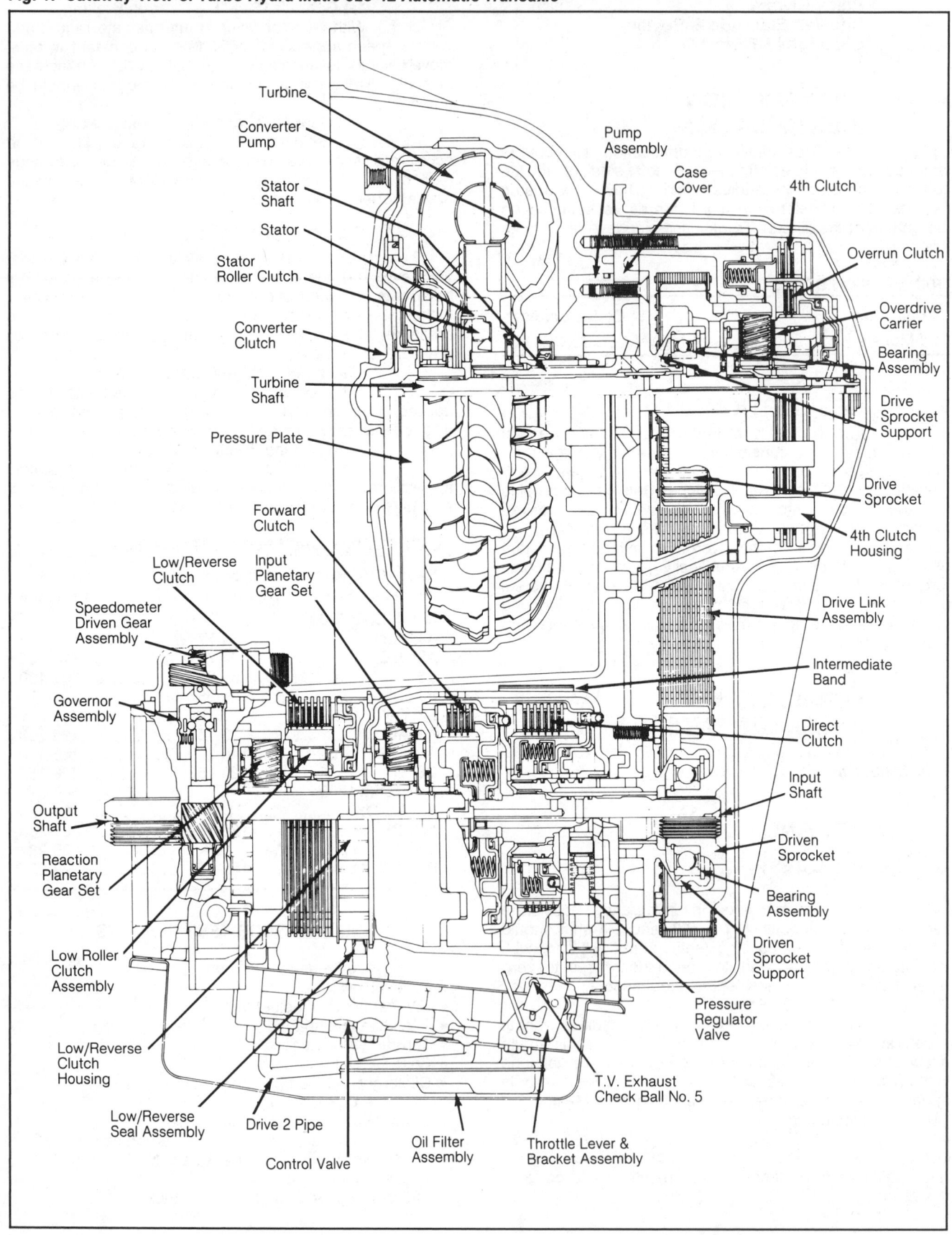

Automatic Transmissions
GENERAL MOTORS
TURBO HYDRA-MATIC 325-4L — TRANSAXLE (Cont.)

2-271

Fig. 2: Turbo Hydra-Matic 325-4L Hydraulic Circuits Diagram (PARK)

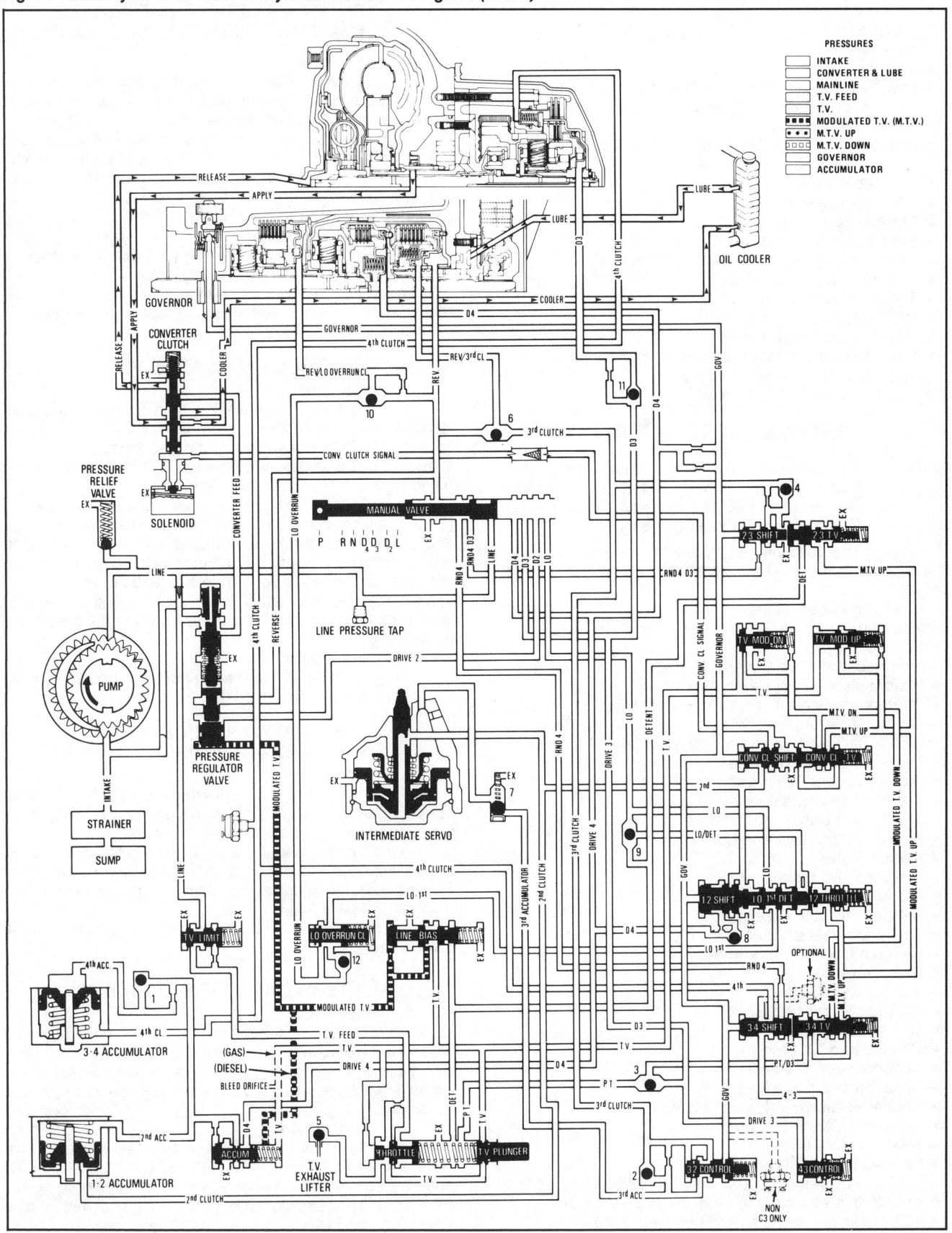

GENERAL MOTORS
TURBO HYDRA-MATIC 325-4L — TRANSAXLE (Cont.)

- Intermediate boost valve stuck
- Reverse Boost valve stuck
- 1-2 accumulator piston missing, seal cut, leaking or missing
- Internal leaks
- Low/Reverse clutch housing-to-case seal and cup plug leaking (pressure low in Reverse only)
- Pump gears broken
- Line boost passage blocked
Oil Pressure Too High
- T.V. cable out of adjustment
- T.V. cable damaged
- Throttle valve stuck
- Shift T.V. valve stuck
- Pressure regulator valve stuck or wrong size
- T.V. valve and plunger stuck
- Shift T.V. valve stuck
- Intermediate boost valve stuck
- Reverse boost valve stuck
- Reverse boost orifice in spacer plate plugged (pressure low in Reverse only)
- Internal pump or case leaks

SERVICE (IN VEHICLE)

NOTE: **For Drive Axles, Output Shafts and Right Output Shaft Support and Bearing Service Procedures, see the General Motors Turbo Hydra-Matic – Final Drive article.**

The following components may be removed from transmission without removing transmission from vehicle:
- Governor Cover, Seals and Assembly
- Governor Pressure Switch (Diesel Only)
- Governor Pipe
- Intermediate Servo Cover and Seal
- Intermediate Servo Piston Assembly
- Oil Pan and Screen, Intake Pipe Assembly
- Control Valve Assembly
- Check Balls and Valve Body Space Plates and Gaskets
- Pressure Regulator Parts
- Manual Detent Roller and Spring Assembly
- Throttle Lever and Bracket Assembly
- T.V./Detent Cable and "O" Ring
- M.T.V. Boost Valve and Bushing
- Manual Valve
- Manual Valve Link
- 1-2 Accumulator Assembly
- 3-4 Accumulator Assembly
- Low and Reverse Clutch Cup Plug
- Reverse Boost Valve and Bushing
- Stop Valve
- 4-3 Pressure Switch
- 4th Clutch Pressure Switch
- Cooler Fittings
- Oil Pipe and "O" Ring
- Speedometer Driven Gear Assembly
- Speedometer Drive Gear
- Converter Clutch Valve and Springs
- Converter Clutch Solenoid
- Solenoid Wire Clips
- Electrical Connectors

For removal and installation procedures not covered in this section, see procedures given in Transmission Disassembly and Transmission Reassembly.

PRESSURE REGULATOR, REVERSE BOOST & MODULATOR THROTTLE BOOST VALVE (M.T.V.) ASSEMBLIES
Removal
1) Drain fluid from transmission, then remove oil pan and screen. Using a small screwdriver, push in on valve assemblies and compress spring.
2) Remove valve assemblies retaining ring, then slowly release tension on spring. Remove M.T.V. Boost Valve and Bushing. Remove Reverse Boost Bushing and Valve, remove spring, then remove pressure regulator and bushing assembly.
Installation
Install all valves in reverse order of disassembly. Push M.T.V. Boost assembly into case bore past retaining ring groove by compressing spring. Install retaining ring, then install screen, gasket and oil pan. Fill transmission with fluid.

CONTROL VALVE ASSEMBLY
Removal
1) Drain transmission fluid from oil pan, then remove pan and screen. Remove screw and washer securing cable to transmission and disconnect T.V. cable.
2) Remove throttle lever and bracket assembly using care not to bend throttle lever link.
3) Disconnect Torque Converter Control (T.C.C.) wiring connector. Remove oil transfer pipes (4) and hold down brackets. Support valve assembly and remove retaining bolts. Lay control valve assembly down with spacer plate side up and note location of check ball in valve body. Note location check balls and then remove spacer plate. Note location of check balls in the accumulator housing.
Installation
To install, reverse removal procedure using *Fig. 7* for location of check balls.

SPEEDOMETER DRIVE GEAR & GOVERNOR ASSEMBLY
Removal
1) Disconnect speedometer cable. Remove speedometer driven gear attaching bolt and retainer, then withdraw driven gear assembly from case.
2) Remove attaching bolts and lift off governor cover. Remove governor and speedometer drive gear assembly. Remove drive gear from governor assembly.
Installation
Reverse removal procedure and tighten all bolts evenly.

INTERMEDIATE SERVO ASSEMBLY
Removal
Using a compressor tool, compress servo cover and remove cover retaining ring. Remove tool. Using pliers, remove servo cover and discard seal rings. Remove intermediate servo piston and band apply pin assembly.
Installation
1) Install new inner and outer servo piston seal rings and ensure they are seated in grooves. Retain seal rings with petrolatum. Install servo piston into servo cover.
2) Lubricate with petrolatum and install new seal ring on servo cover. Install intermediate servo

GENERAL MOTORS
TURBO HYDRA-MATIC 325-4L — TRANSAXLE (Cont.)

assembly into case, tapping with a plastic hammer if necessary.

NOTE: **Make sure the tapered end of band apply pin in properly located against band apply lug.**

3) Compress servo cover. Install retaining ring and align ring end with gap showing in case slot.

REMOVAL & INSTALLATION

See the appropriate article in AUTOMATIC TRANSMISSION REMOVAL Section.

TORQUE CONVERTER

NOTE: **Torque converter is a sealed unit and cannot be disassembled for service.**

LEAKAGE CHECK

See procedure given in G.M. Turbo Hydra-Matic 400 article.

END CLEARANCE CHECK

See procedure given in G.M. Turbo Hydra-Matic 400 article.

CONVERTER FLUSHING

See procedure given in G.M. Turbo Hydra-Matic 400 article.

TRANSMISSION DISASSEMBLY

1) Position transmission in a holding fixture. Remove torque converter by pulling it staight out. Rotate transmission so that oil pan is facing up, then remove oil pan, gasket, oil screen assembly and intake pipe "O" ring.

2) Disconnect the wire leads at case electrical connector and at pressure switches. Remove electrical connector and "O" ring seal from case. Use a small screwdriver to depress connector tangs while pushing out on connector. Remove solenoid assembly attaching bolts, solenoid and "O" ring seal.

3) Remove pressure regulator assembly retaining snap ring. Remove T.V. boost valve busing and valve, the reverse boost valve bushing and valve, the pressure regulator spring and pressure regulator busing and valve.

4) Remove converter clutch apply valve retaining snap ring. Remove converter clutch valve bushing, valve and then spring. Remove D2 signal, reverse signal and overrun pipe retainers. Remove remaining oil pipes and solenoid assembly.

5) Remove throttle lever and bracket assembly. Remove control valve assembly attaching bolts and disconnect manual valve. Do not drop valve. Remove control valve assembly, noting the location of the check balls on spacer plate. Remove check ball. *See Fig. 7.* Remove 1-2 and 3-4 accumulator housing bolts, accumulator housing and 1-2 spring. One check ball will be exposed on top of the spacer plate to valve body gasket. Remove check ball. *See Fig. 7.*

Fig. 3: Transmission Case and Valve Body Oil Passages

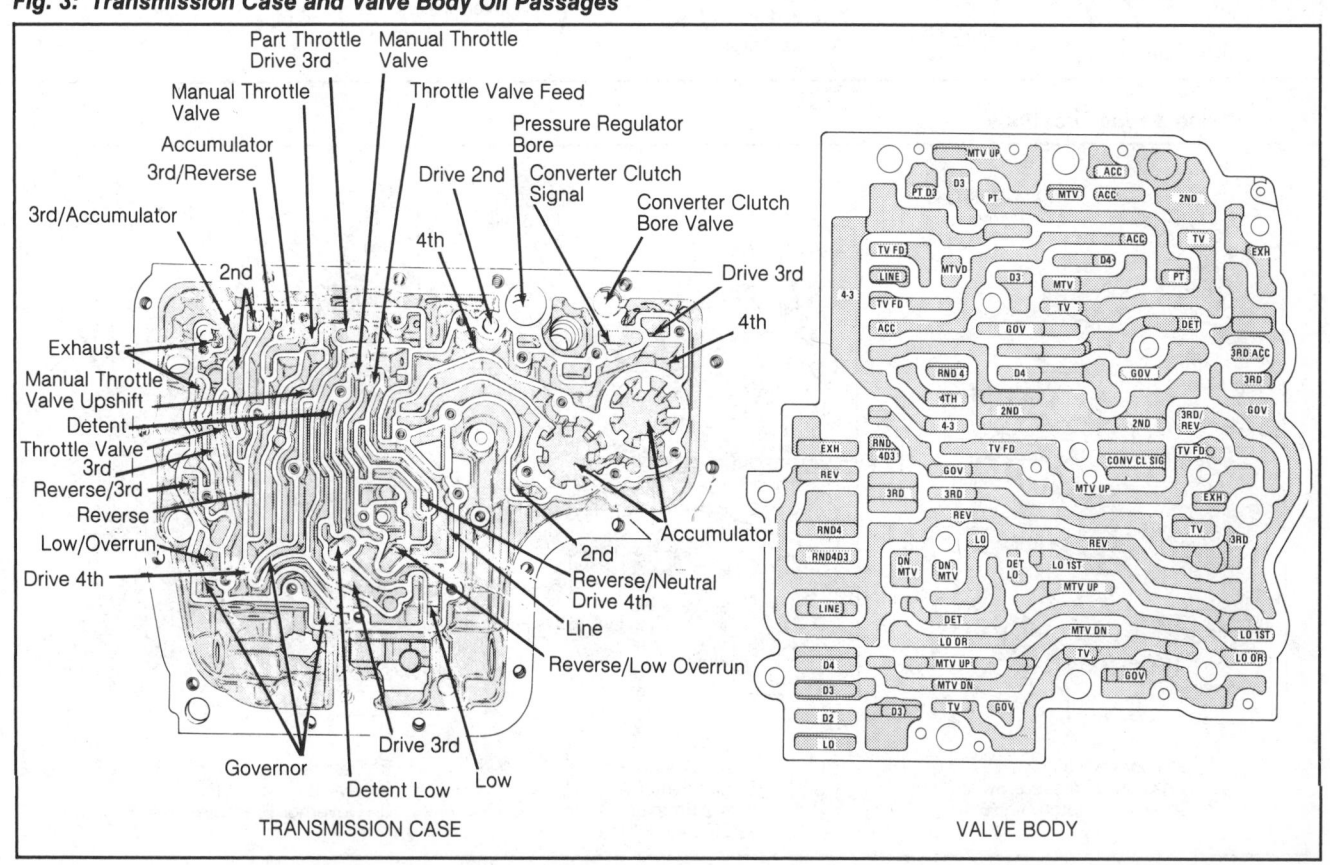

TRANSMISSION CASE VALVE BODY

Automatic Transmissions
GENERAL MOTORS
TURBO HYDRA-MATIC 325-4L — TRANSAXLE (Cont.)

Fig. 4: *Front View of Case Showing Oil Passages*

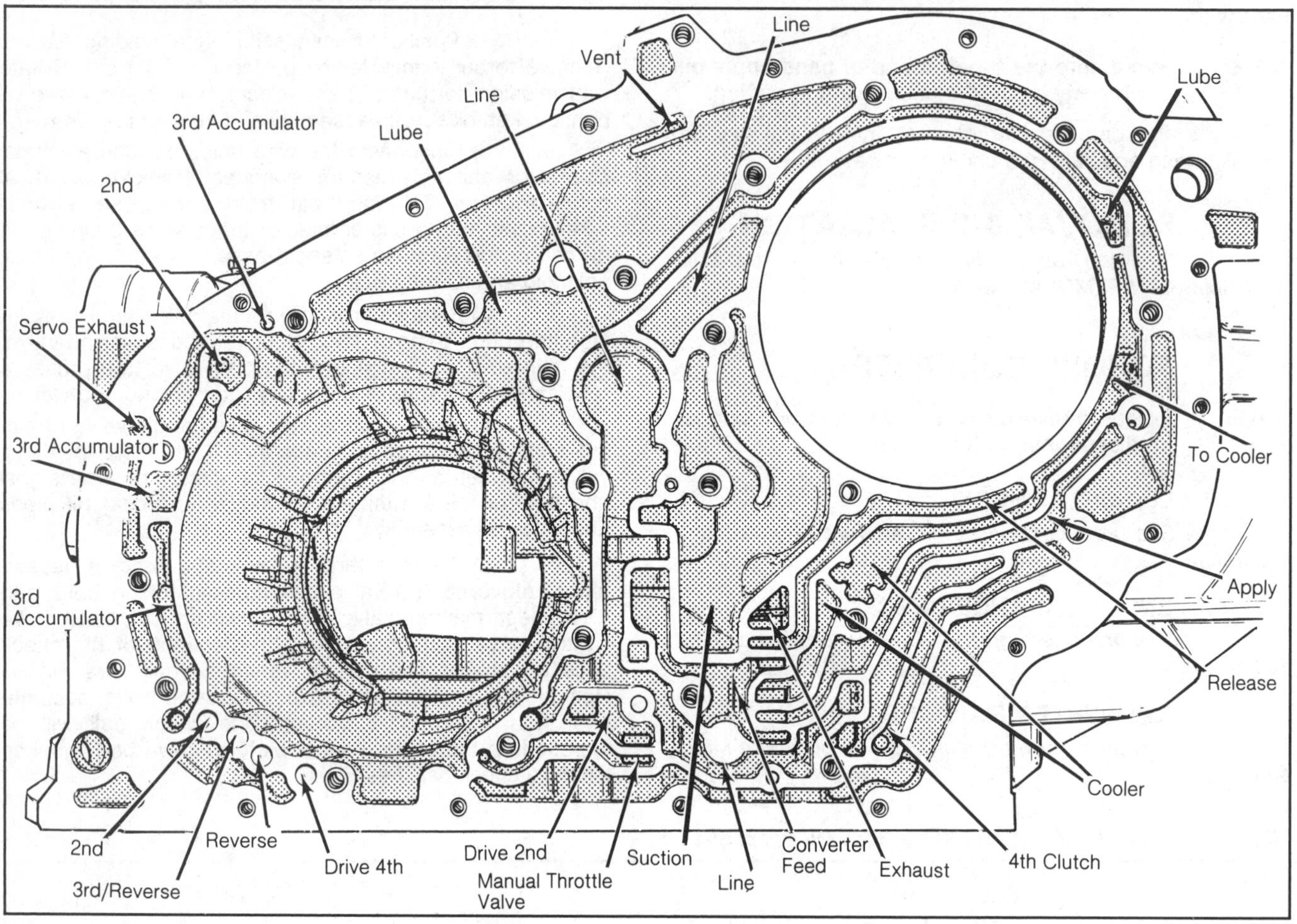

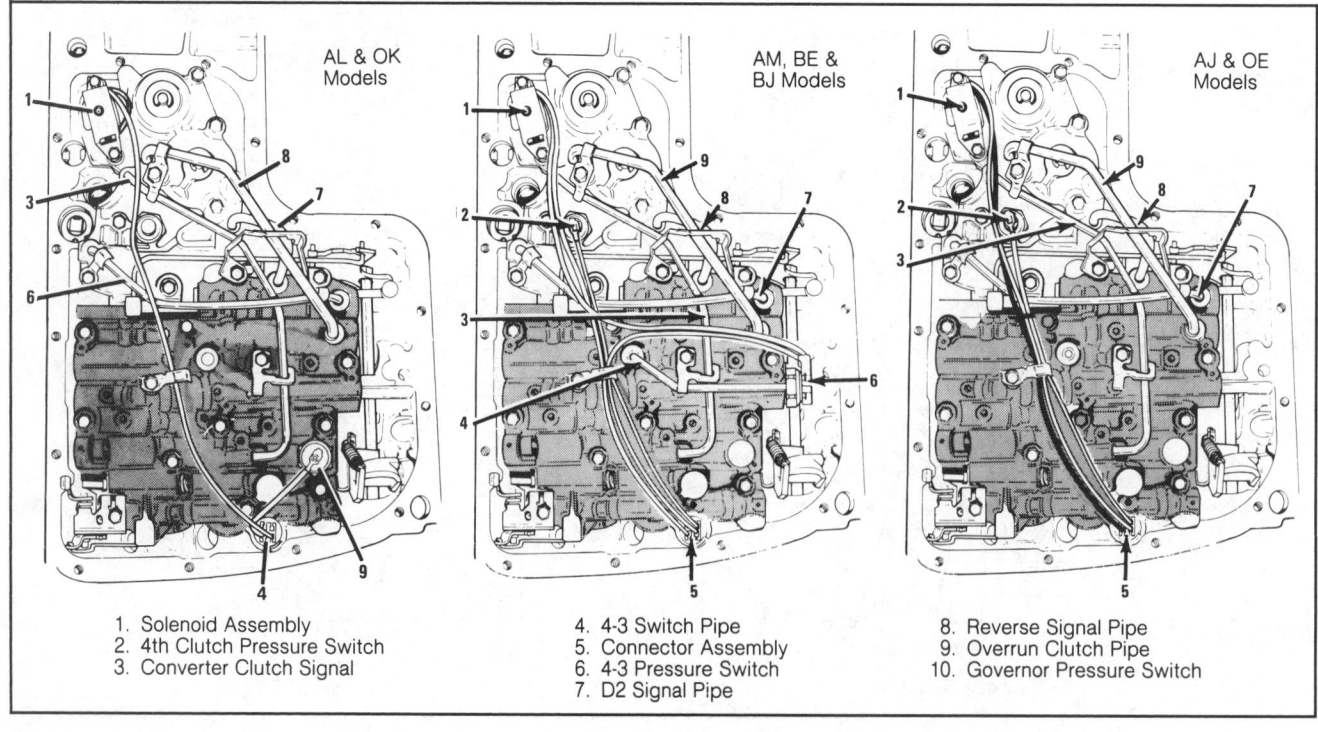

Fig. 5: *Wiring & Pipe Locations*

1. Solenoid Assembly
2. 4th Clutch Pressure Switch
3. Converter Clutch Signal
4. 4-3 Switch Pipe
5. Connector Assembly
6. 4-3 Pressure Switch
7. D2 Signal Pipe
8. Reverse Signal Pipe
9. Overrun Clutch Pipe
10. Governor Pressure Switch

Fig. 6: Converter Clutch Valve Exploded View

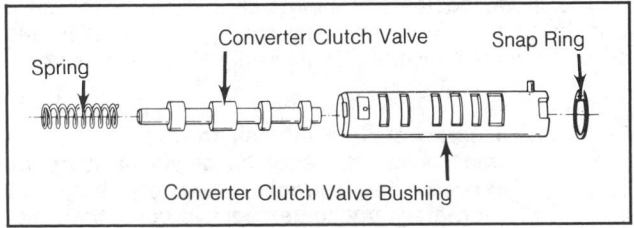

6) Remove accumulator housing assembly gasket and spacer plate. Remove check balls from case passages.

7) Rotate transmission in holding fixture so that oil pan side is down. Remove speedometer driven gear attaching bolt and retainer clip, then lift driven gear assembly from governor cover. Remove governor cover attaching bolts and lift off cover. Remove governor, thrust washer and speedometer drive gear from case.

NOTE: **The governor thrust washer may come out with governor cover.**

8) Using a compressor tool, compress intermediate servo cover and remove retaining ring. Using pliers, remove servo cover. Remove servo piston and band apply pin assembly.

NOTE: **If intermediate servo cover cannot be removed easily, apply air pressure into intermediate servo exhaust port to force assembly from case.**

NOTE: **Before proceeding with transmission disassembly, band apply pin selection check should be made to determine correct pin for use at reassembly.**

9) Install special band apply pin selection gauge (J-25014-2) in intermediate servo bore and retain

with servo cover retaining ring, aligning ring with gap at case slot.

Fig. 8: Using Compressed Air To Remove Intermediate Servo Assembly

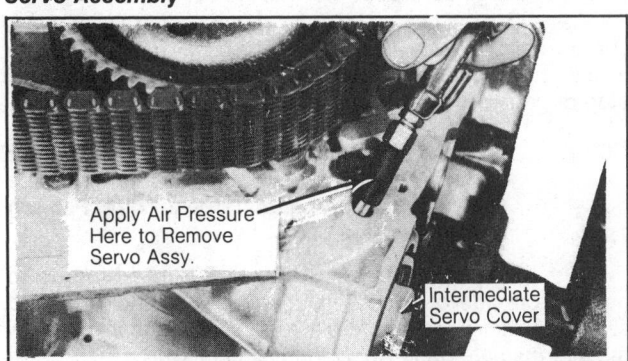

Fig. 9: Intermediate Band Apply Pin Selection

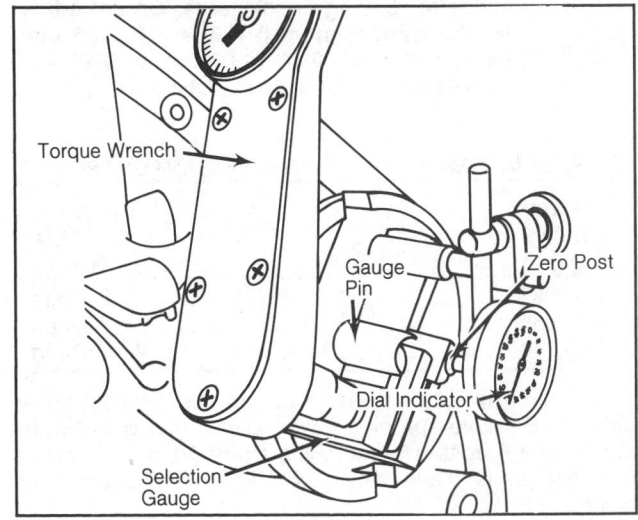

Fig. 7: Location of Check Balls

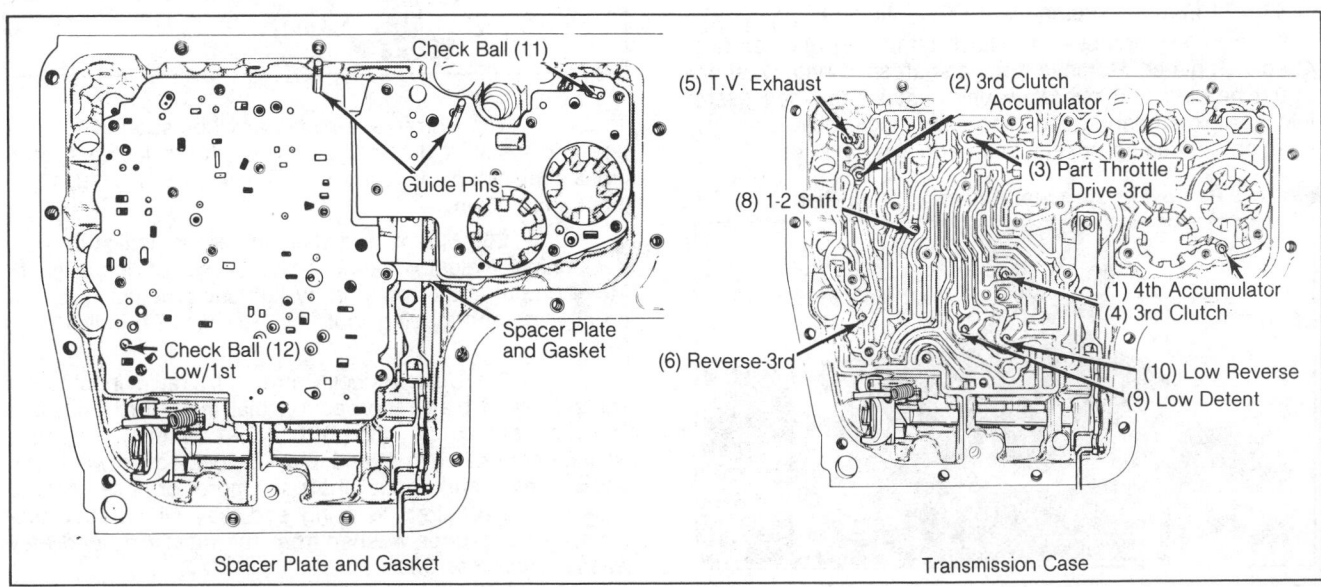

GENERAL MOTORS
TURBO HYDRA-MATIC 325-4L — TRANSAXLE (Cont.)

10) Install gauge pin (J-25014-1) into selection gauge and make sure tapered end of pin is properly located against band apply lug. Install a dial indicator as shown in *Fig. 9* and position indicator point on top of selection gauge zero post. Set dial indicator to zero.

11) Seat selection gauge squarely against servo retaining ring. Align stepped side of gauge pin with torquing arm of selection gauge. Arm must stop against step of gauge pin.

NOTE: If band selection pin does not register between high and low limits, look for possible problem with intermediate band, direct clutch or transmission case.

12) Apply 108 INCH lbs. (12 N.m) of torque to hex nut on side of section gauge pin. Read indicator and select correct band apply pin to use at reassembly from the *Intermediate Band Apply Pin Selection Chart*.

NOTE: Dial indicator travel is reversed, making the indicator readings backwards. On an indicator that ranges from 0-100, a .020" (.5 mm) travel will read .080" (2.0 mm), a .060" (1.5 mm) travel will read .040" (1.0 mm).

INTERMEDIATE BAND APPLY PIN SELECTION CHART

Indicator Reading	Apply Pin I.D.
0-.029"	1 Ring
.029-.057"	2 Rings
.057-.086	3 Rings
.086-.114	Wide Band

13) Rotate transmission to the sprocket cover side up. Remove sprocket cover. Diesel model transmissions have 5 bolts with mounting studs. Note the location of these bolts. Remove cover and clean sealant from cover.

14) Check and record the overdrive unit end play. End play should be .004"-.029" (.10-.74 mm). Overdrive unit washers are available in sizes .063"-.144" (1.63-3.71 mm) in increments of .003" (.08 mm).

15) Remove 4th clutch snap ring and remove 4th clutch plates. Remove turbine shaft snap ring, washer, thrust bearing and overdrive unit. Install snap ring pliers into sprocket bearing retaining snap rings located under drive and driven sprockets, and remove snap rings.

Fig. 10: Removing Sprocket Retaining Snap Ring

Snap Ring Pliers

16) Remove sprockets, drive link bearings and turbine shaft together by alternately pulling on the drive and driven sprockets until bearings are out of drive and driven support housings. Remove drive link from sprockets.

NOTE: If sprockets are difficult to remove, place a small piece of masonite, or similar material, between the sprocket and pry bar, and alternately pry under each sprocket. Do not pry on links or the aluminum case. Pry only on the sprockets.

17) Remove 2 opposite pump attaching flat head screws from drive sprocket support and install two 5/16-18x4" guide pins or bolts. Remove remaining pump attaching screws from support. With 1 hand, hold underside of pump, then gently tap guide pins until pump is removed from case.

18) Before proceeding wih disassembly of transmission, check input unit end play as follows: Install output shaft aligning and loading tool J-26958 to output end of transmission as shown in *Fig 11*.

Fig. 11: Installation of Output Shaft Aligning and Loading Tool

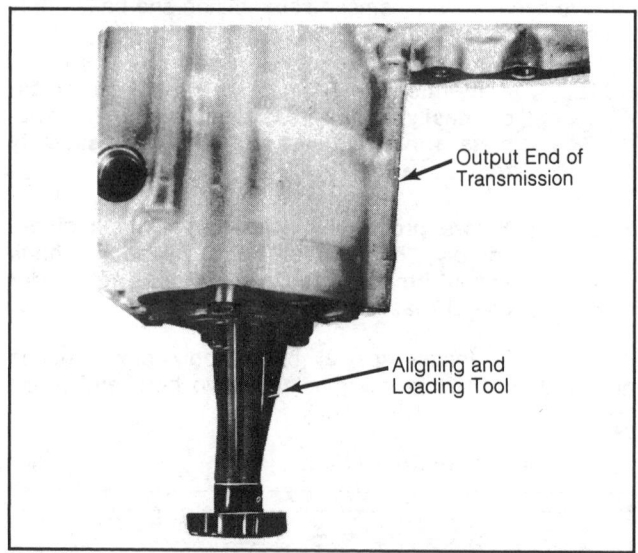

Output End of Transmission

Aligning and Loading Tool

19) Remove driven sprocket support-to-case bolt and install a dial indicator post. Next, install special input shaft lifter bar (J-28494) as shown in *Fig 12*. Push input shaft down.

20) Mount a dial indicator on indicator post positioning indicator point against end of input shaft. Move output shaft upwards by tightening adjusting screw on aligning and loading tool until it stops. Set indicator to zero.

21) Using special lifter bar, raise input shaft and read end play recorded on dial indicator. Input unit end play should be .022-.051" (.56-1.29 mm). Selective washer controlling the end play is located between the output shaft and input shaft. If more or less washer thickness is required to bring end play within specifications, select proper washer from the *Input Unit End Play Washer Thickness Chart*.

GENERAL MOTORS
TURBO HYDRA-MATIC 325-4L — TRANSAXLE (Cont.)

Fig. 12: Checking Input Unit End Play

Fig. 13: Checking Reaction Unit End Play

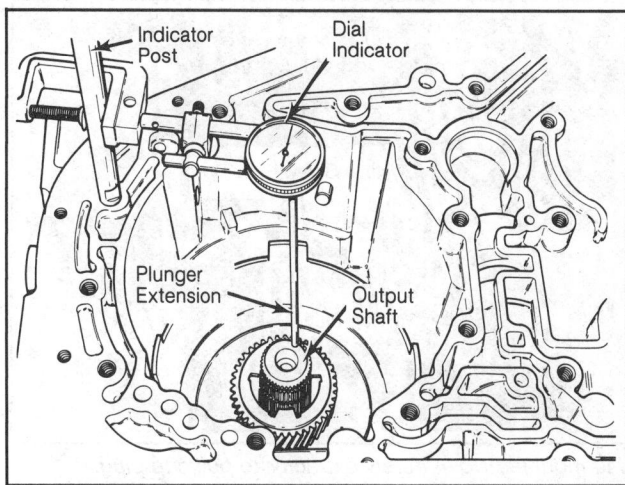

INPUT UNIT END PLAY WASHER THICKNESS CHART

Thickness In. (mm)	Identification No. And/Or Color
.065-.070 (1.66-1.77)	1
.070-.075 (1.79-1.90)	2
.076-.080 (1.93-2.03)	3 — Black
.081-.085 (2.05-2.16)	4 — Light Green
.086-.090 (2.18-2.29)	5 — Scralet
.091-.095 (2.31-2.42)	6 — Purple
.096-.100 (2.44-2.55)	7 — Cocoa Brown
.101-.106 (2.57-2.68)	8 — Orange
.106-.111 (2.70-2.81)	9 — Yellow
.111-.116 (2.83-2.94)	10 — Light Blue
.117-.121 (2.96-3.07)	11
.122-.126 (3.09-3.20)	12
.127-.131 (3.22-3.33)	13 — Pink
.132-.136 (3.35-3.46)	14 — Green
.137-.141 (3.48-3.59)	15 — Gray

22) Remove dial indicator, indicator post and input shaft lifter bar. Do not remove output shaft aligning and loading tool at this time.

23) Remove case cover attaching bolts, but do not remove the driven sprocket support bolts at this time. Remove case cover and gasket. Remove thrust washer from hub of sprocket support.

24) Pull direct and forward clutch assemblies from transmission case. Lift direct clutch assembly from forward clutch assembly. Lift intermediate band from case.

NOTE: The direct-to-forward clutch thrust washer may stick to end of direct clutch housing when it is removed from forward clutch housing.

25) Remove output shaft-to-input shaft selective thrust washer. Check reaction unit end play as follows: Loosen adjusting screw on output shaft aligning and loading tool (J-26958) which was installed during input unit end play check. Push output shaft downward.

26) Position dial indicator post and dial indicator with plunger extension (J-28667) on transmission case as shown in *Fig. 13*. Position plunger extension against end of output shaft and zero dial indicator.

27) Move output shaft upward by turning adjusting screw on aligning tool until it stops. Read and record end play on dial indicator. Reaction unit end play should be .004-.025" (.10-.64 mm).

28) The selective washer controlling reaction unit end play is located between input internal gear thrust washer and output shaft snap ring. If more or less washer thickness is required to bring end play within specifications, select proper washer from the *Reaction Unit End Play Washer Selection Chart*.

REACTION UNIT END PLAY WASHER SELECTION CHART

Thickness In. (mm)	I.D. Number And Color
.114-.119 (2.90-3.01)	1 — Orange
.121-.126 (3.08-3.19)	2 — White
.128-.133 (3.26-3.37)	3 — Yellow
.135-.140 (3.44-3.55)	4 — Blue
.143-.147 (3.62-3.73)	5 — Red
.150-.154 (3.80-3.91)	6 — Brown
.157-.161 (3.98-4.09)	7 — Green
.164-.168 (4.16-4.27)	8 — Black
.171-.175 (4.34-4.45)	9 — Purple

29) Remove dial indicator and post, but leave output shaft aligning and loading tool installed. Remove output shaft-to-selective washer snap ring. Tighten adjusting screw on output shaft tool to remove snap ring.

30) Remove input internal gear, reaction selective thrust washer and tanged thrust washer from end of output shaft. Remove input carrier assembly and input internal gear-to-input carrier thrust bearing assembly.

31) Remove input sun gear-to-input carrier thrust bearing if it did not come out with carrier, then remove input sun gear. Remove input drum and reaction sun gear from case. Remove tanged input drum-to-low-reverse clutch housing thrust washer from rear of input drum or from low-reverse clutch housing.

32) Grind approximately 3/4" from end of a No. 4 screw extractor, then use screw extractor to remove low/reverse cup plug. See *Fig. 14*. Remove low/reverse clutch-to-case beveled snap ring. Remove low/reverse clutch housing assembly from case. Remove low/reverse clutch housing-to-case spacer.

Fig. 14: Removing Low/Reverse Clutch Cup Plug

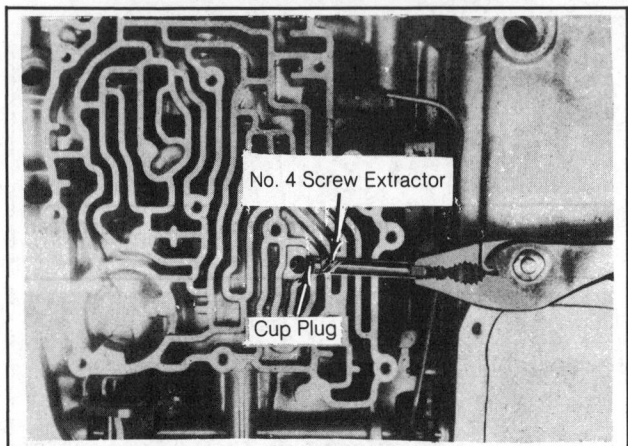

Use modified No. 4 screw extractor to pull cup plug.

33) Ensure governor valve assembly has been removed. Grasp output shaft and pull reaction unit parts from case. Remove roller clutch and reaction carrier assembly from output shaft. Remove tanged thrust washer from end of reaction carrier or inside reaction internal gear.

34) Pull low/reverse clutch plates off output shaft. Remove reaction internal gear-to-sun gear thrust bearing from internal gear, then remove internal gear from output shaft. Remove governor drive gear from output shaft.

Fig. 15: View of Output Shaft Showing Governor Drive Gear Removal

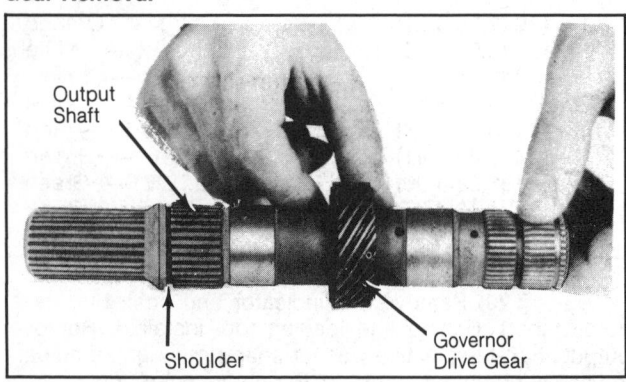

35) Rotate transmission in holding fixture so that oil pan side is up, then remove output shaft aligning and loading tool. If necessary, remove manual shaft and parking linkage from case as follows:

36) Remove manual detent roller and spring assembly. Remove parking strut shaft retaining ring. Grind approximately 3/4" from end of a No. 4 screw extractor, then use screw extractor to remove parking strut shaft cup plug as shown in *Fig. 16*.

37) Using sheet metal screws or No. 3 screw extractor, pull parking strut shaft from case. Remove parking lock spring, strut and lever. Remove parking lock cam.

38) Remove hex nut which holds inside detent lever to manual shaft, then remove shaft and lever assembly. If damaged, pry manual shaft seal from case bore using a screwdriver. Using sheet metal screw or No.

3 screw extractor, pull parking pawl shaft from case. Remove parking pawl and return spring.

Fig. 16: Removing Parking Strut Shaft Cup Plug

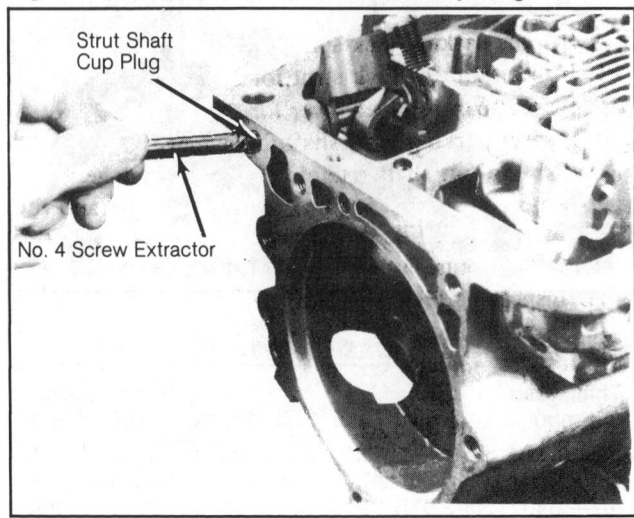

Use modified No. 4 screw extractor to pull cup plug.

Fig. 17: Exploded View of Manual Shaft and Parking Linkage

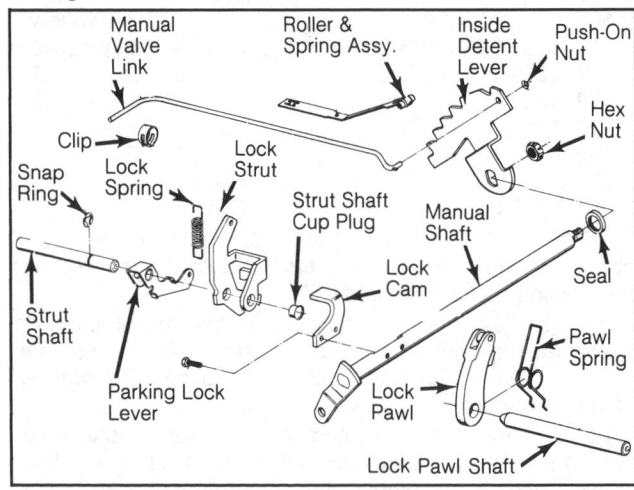

COMPONENT DISASSEMBLY & REASSEMBLY

TRANSMISSION CASE
Inspection
1) Inspect case assembly for damage, cracks, porosity or interconnected oil passages. Inspect orifice plug in case cover face. Inspect exhaust passages for blockage.

2) Inspect reverse clutch lugs, governor bore, intermediate servo bore and snap ring grooves for damage. Inspect low and reverse clutch seal and intermediate band anchor pin for damage.

3) Inspect vent assembly in case for damage. Do not remove vent unless replacement is necessary. Inspect cup plugs for damage or leaks.

GENERAL MOTORS
TURBO HYDRA-MATIC 325-4L — TRANSAXLE (Cont.)

NOTE: If vent was removed, apply Loctite Primer "T" (or equivalent) to outside diameter of the vent that locates in case and Loctite 35 (or equivalent) to the vent hole in case. Install vent using a rubber or plastic hammer.

MANUAL SHAFT & PARKING LINKAGE
Inspection

1) Inpsect parking pawl for cracks or damage and for free rotation of roller. Inspect return spring for deformed end or coils. Inspect pawl shaft for damage.

2) Check parking lock spring, strut, lever, shaft and shaft snap ring for damage. Inspect manual shaft for damaged threads and the flat for raised edges (file down any raised edges).

3) Inspect outisde manual lever, parking lock cam and inside detent lever for damage. Check manual detent spring for cracks and properly working roller. Inspect manaul valve link for damage, or broken retainer lugs.

OUTPUT SHAFT & REACTION INTERNAL GEAR
Inspection

1) Inspect output shaft journals and snap ring grooves for wear or damage. Inspect shaft lubrication passages for restrictions or damage. Inspect splines for damage and governor drive gear for rough or damaged teeth.

2) Inspect reaction internal gear splines, teeth and bearing surface for wear, cracks or damage. Inspect parking pawl lugs for cracks or damage.

ROLLER CLUTCH & REACTION CARRIER
Disassembly

Remove roller clutch race, then pull roller clutch from reaction carrier. Lift reaction carrier-to-roller clutch thrust washer from carrier.

Fig. 18: Exploded View of Roller Clutch and Reaction Carrier

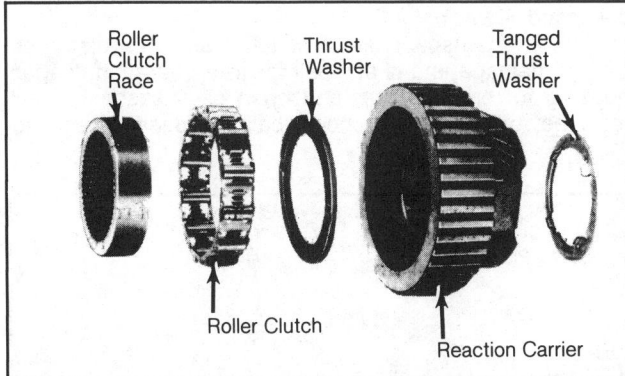

Roller Clutch Race · Thrust Washer · Tanged Thrust Washer · Roller Clutch · Reaction Carrier

Inspection

1) Inspect roller clutch race and spline for scoring or wear. Inspect roller clutch bearings, cage and springs for damage or wear. Inspect thrust washers for signs of scoring or excessing wear, and distorted tangs on tanged thrust washer.

2) Inspect reaction carrier, roller clutch cam ramps and bushing for damage or scoring. Inspect

planetary pinions for damage, rough bearings or tilt. Using a feeler gauge, check pinion end play as shown in *Fig. 19*. Pinion end play should be .009-.027." (.23-.69 mm).

Fig. 19: Measuring Planetary Pinion End Play

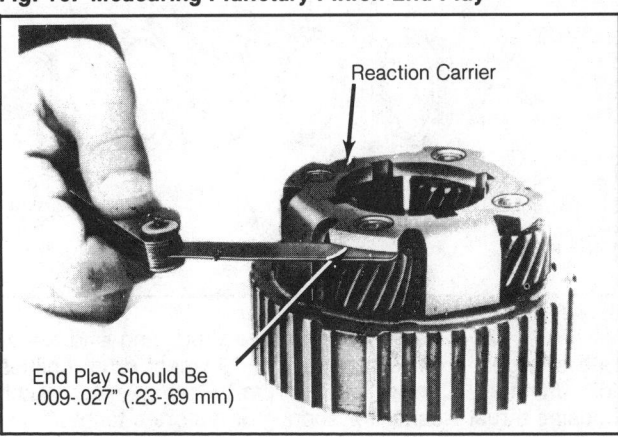

Reaction Carrier

End Play Should Be .009-.027" (.23-.69 mm)

Reassembly

1) Install thrust washer into reaction carrier. Install rollers that may have come out of roller clutch cage, by compressing energizing spring with forefinger and inserting roller from outer edge.

2) Install roller clutch into carrier, then install clutch race (spline side out) and rotate race clockwise into position. Install tanged thrust washer, aligning tangs into slots of reaction carrier and retain with petrolatum.

LOW/REVERSE CLUTCH HOUSING
Disassembly

Compress low/reverse clutch spring retainer, remove snap ring, then lift out retainer. Remove waved spring and clutch piston from housing. Remove inner and outer piston seals and clutch apply ring.

Inspection

Inspect clutch housing for damage, scoring or plugged feed hole. Inspect clutch splines and snap ring groove for damage or burrs. Remove any burrs on splines or snap ring groove. Inspect piston and apply ring for distortion, cracks or damage. Inspect all other parts for damage or excessive wear.

Reassembly

1) Install clutch apply ring on clutch piston. Install new inner and outer seals on piston with lips facing away from clutch apply ring side. Install a suitable seal protector over positon seals to prevent damage to seals during piston installation.

NOTE: Apply transmission fluid to all clutch seals before reassembly.

2) Using a small, flat edged screwdriver, install low/reverse clutch piston, while rotating and pushing down into place in clutch housing. Remove seal protector. Install waved spring and spring retainer (cupped face down), then compress retainer and install snap ring.

REACTION SUN GEAR & INPUT DRUM
Inspection

1) Check reaction sun gear for cracks, splits, spline damage, gear or journal wear, and for plugged lubrication holes.

Fig. 20: Exploded View of Low/Reverse Clutch Assembly

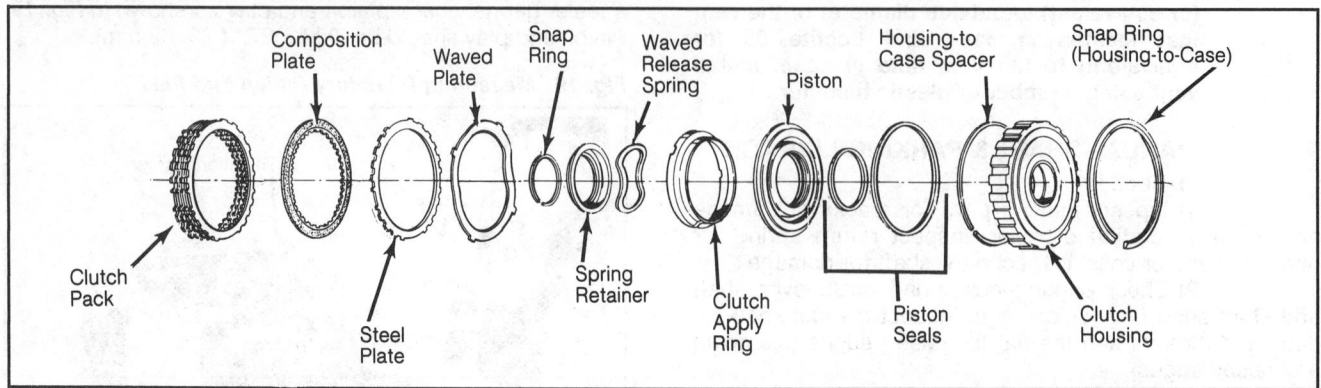

2) If necessary, remove snap ring and separate sun gear from input drum and inspect drum splines for damage. Check input drum-to-low/reverse clutch housing thrust washer for scoring or distorted tangs.

Fig. 21: Exploded View of Reaction Sun Gear and Input Drum Assembly

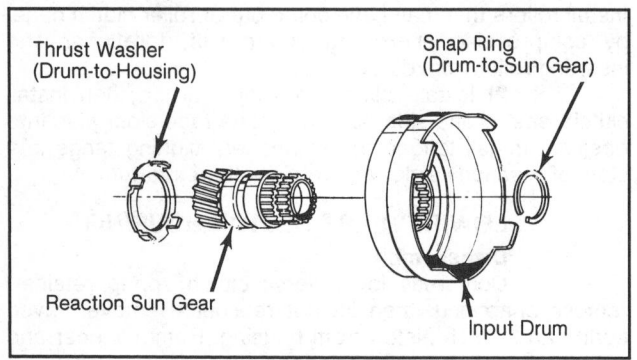

INPUT CARRIER, SUN GEAR & INTERNAL GEAR
Inspection

1) Check all parts for pitting, scoring, damaged gear teeth, and cracks. Make sure all lubrication holes are open.

2) Check internal gear thrust washers for wear or other damage, and input carrier thrust bearing for roughness and pitting. Using a feeler gauge, check input carrier pinion end play. End play should be .009-.027" (.24-.69 mm).

DIRECT CLUTCH ASSEMBLY
Disassembly

1) Remove clutch pack snap ring and withdraw backing plate and clutch plates from clutch housing, keeping clutch plates separated from forward clutch plates.

2) Using a compressor tool, compress retainer and spring assembly and remove snap ring. Remove compressor tool. Remove retainer and spring assembly from clutch housing.

3) Remove release spring guide. Remove direct piston from clutch housing, then remove inner and outer seals from piston. Remove center seal from clutch housing.

NOTE: **Do not remove clutch apply ring from piston unless piston or apply ring requires replacement.**

Inspection

1) Inspect composition plates, steel plates and backing plate for wear, burring or scoring. Check retainer and spring assembly for damage, distortion or for being collapsed.

2) Inspect direct clutch piston for distortion, cracks, damage and check ball for free operation. Inspect housing for cracks, wear and open oil passages. Check for free operation of check balls. Closely check for

Fig. 22: Exploded View of Direct Clutch Assembly

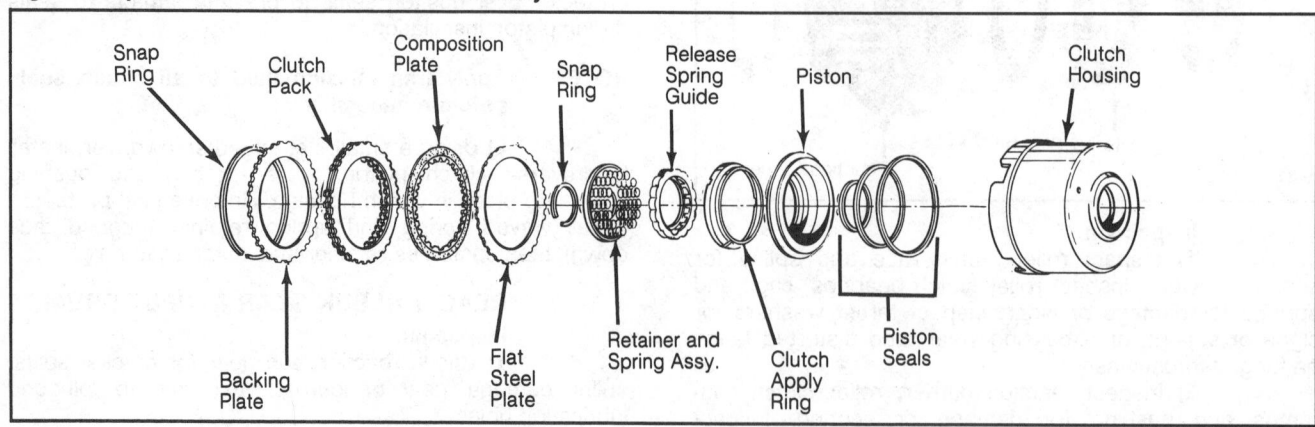

GENERAL MOTORS
TURBO HYDRA-MATIC 325-4L — TRANSAXLE (Cont.)

damaged check ball capsule. Inspect snap ring grooves and bushing in housing for wear or damage.

Reassembly

1) If removed, install clutch apply ring on piston. Install new inner and outer seals on piston with seal lips facing away from apply ring side. Install new center seal on clutch housing wih lip facing up. Install a seal protector over piston seals.

CAUTION: **Use care when installing direct clutch piston past larger clutch snap ring groove. Groove could cut outer seal on piston.**

2) Lubricate seals and install piston into clutch housing, then remove seal protector. Install release spring guide with the omitted rib over check ball in piston. See Fig. 23. Install retainer and spring assembly into clutch housing using care to guide retainer past snap ring groove.

Fig. 23: Installing Release Spring Guide

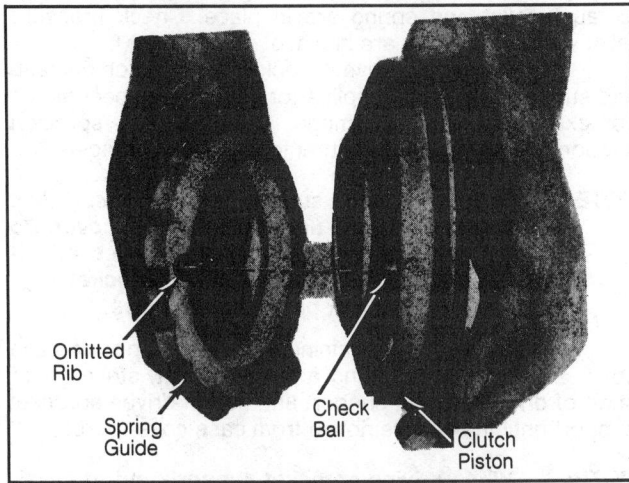

3) Compress retainer and spring assembly and install snap ring. Oil and install clutch plates into direct clutch housing, starting with a flat steel and alternating composition and flat steel clutch plates until correct number of clutch plates are installed. See Direct Clutch Plate Usage Chart.

4) Install backing plate into housing with polished side down. Install snap ring and ensure that composition plates turn freely.

DIRECT CLUTCH PLATE USAGE CHART

Application	Flat Steel [1]	Composition
All Models	6	6

[1] — Plate thickness is .091" (2.3 mm).

FORWARD CLUTCH ASSEMBLY
Disassembly

1) Remove forward clutch-to-direct clutch thrust washer. Remove clutch pack retaining snap ring, then remove backing plate and clutch plates from clutch housing.

2) Using a compressor tool, compress retainer and spring assembly and remove snap ring. Remove tool,

then lift retainer and spring assembly from housing. Remove piston from housing and seals from piston.

NOTE: **Do not remove clutch apply ring from piston unless piston or apply ring requires replacement.**

Inspection

1) Inspect oil seals on input shaft for damage and free fit in grooves. Do not remove seals unless replacement is necessary. Inspect clutch plates for signs of wear or burning. Inspect backing plate for scratches or damage.

2) Inspect release spring retainer for distortion and release springs for collapsed coils. Inspect piston and clutch apply ring assembly for cracks or damage.

3) Inspect clutch housing for cracks, opened oil passages or other damage. Check for free operation of clutch housing check ball and ensure that check ball capsule is not damaged. Check snap ring groove in housing for damage or burrs.

Fig. 24: View of Forward Clutch Housing Showing Points for Inspection

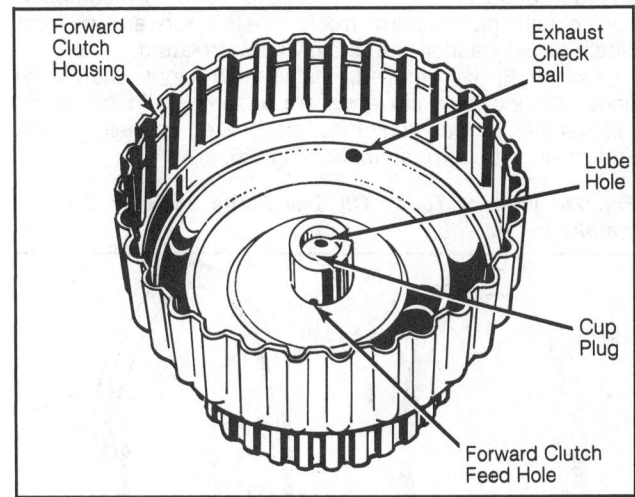

4) Inspect input shaft for open oil passages on both ends of shaft and journals for damage. Inspect cup plug in clutch housing for damage, and if necessary, remove from housing using a No. 3 screw extractor (grind to fit). Install new cup plug to .039" (1.0 mm) below surface.

Reassembly

1) If removed, install apply ring on piston. Install new inner and outer seals on piston with lips facing away from clutch apply ring side. Lubricate seals and install piston into clutch housing.

CAUTION: **Use care when installing piston past large forward clutch snap ring groove in clutch housing. Groove could cut outer seal on piston.**

2) Position retainer and spring assembly in clutch housing using care to guide assembly past snap ring groove. Compress retainer and spring assembly and install snap ring.

3) Oil and install forward clutch plates into housing, starting with the waved steel plate and alternat-

2-282

Automatic Transmissions
GENERAL MOTORS
TURBO HYDRA-MATIC 325-4L — TRANSAXLE (Cont.)

Fig. 25: Exploded View of Forward Clutch Assembly

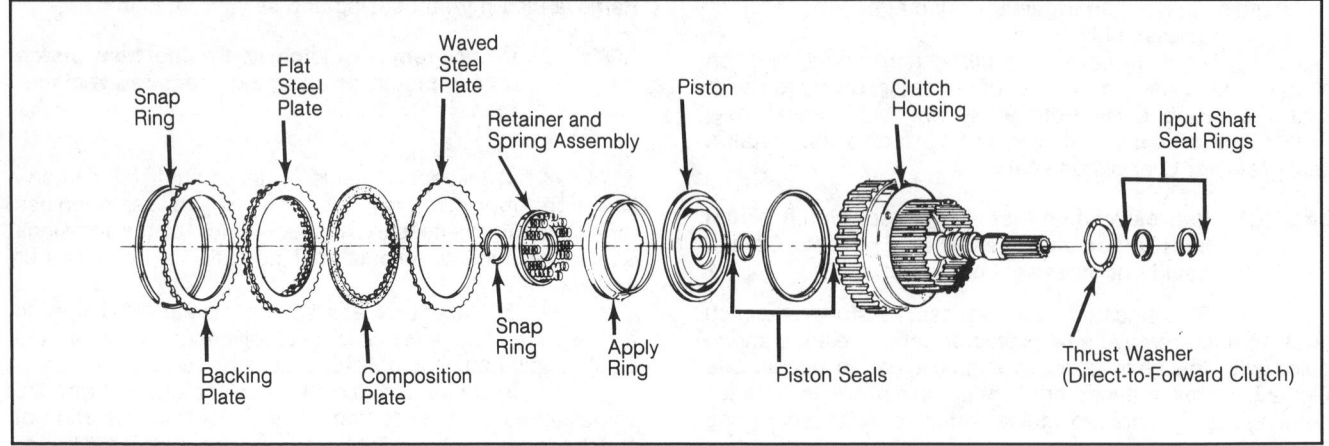

ing composition and flat steel plates until correct number of clutch plates are installed. *See Forward Clutch Plate Usage Chart.*

4) Install clutch backing plate into housing with chamfered side up. Install snap ring. Make sure composition clutch plates turn freely. Install forward-to-direct clutch thrust washer and retain with petrolatum.

5) If removed, install new input shaft seal rings, making sure cut ends are assembled in the same relationship as cut and rings are seated in their groove and retain with petrolatum. *See Fig. 26.*

Fig. 26: View of Teflon Oil Seal Rings Showing Correct Installation Position

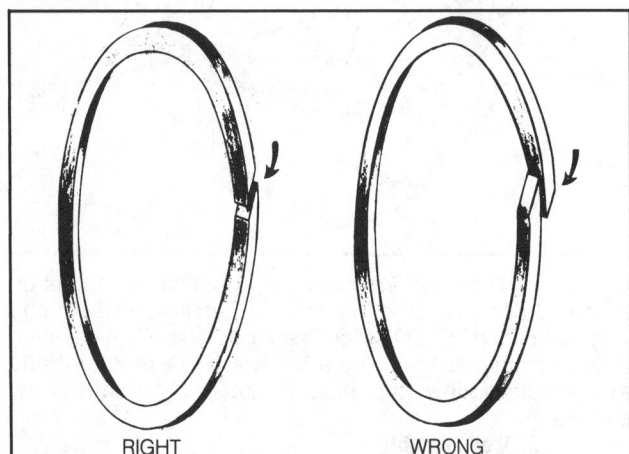

RIGHT   WRONG

FORWARD CLUTCH PLATE USAGE CHART

Application	Flat Steel [1]	Composition
All Models	3 [2]	4

[1] — Plate thickness is .077" (1.96 mm)
[2] — Plus 1 waved steel plate .062" (1.57 mm) thick, installed first.

CASE COVER, DRIVE & DRIVEN SPROCKET SUPPORTS
Inspection
1) Inspect case cover for cracks and damage. Check machined surface of cover for flatness. Check cover for interconnected oil passages. Inspect cup plugs for damage or leaks. Make certain 3rd accumulator exhaust pellet and spring are in place. Check pressure relief valve and spring are in place.

2) Inspect drive sprocket support for damage and support stator shaft spline for damage. Inspect driven sprocket support for damage. Check driven sprocket support oil seal rings, do not remove unless damaged.

NOTE: **Drive and driven support housing assemblies are pressed into and removed with cover. Do not remove them unless it is necessary. If replacement of case cover or sprocket supports is required, proceed as follows:**

3) Remove remaining sprocket support-to-case cover attaching bolts. Using a plastic mallet, strike stator shaft of drive sprocket support and hub of driven sprocket support until they are removed from case cover bores.

NOTE: **When driving sprocket supports out of cover, avoid damaging or distorting stator shaft or ring grooves in hub of driven support.**

4) Remove and discard sprocket support-to-cover gaskets. Remove and inspect converter out check valve from pump cover and check for interconnected oil passages.

Fig. 27: Installing Converter Out Check Valve

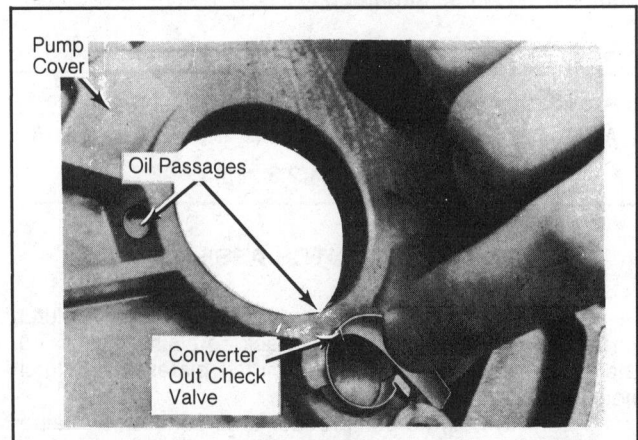

GENERAL MOTORS
TURBO HYDRA-MATIC 325-4L — TRANSAXLE (Cont.)

5) To install, position converter out check valve into pump cover (tanged end first), and coil remainder of valve within itself. *See Fig. 27.* Install drive support-to-case cover gasket, then install support into cover by using a plastic mallet to seat the housing. Use flathead screws for guides.

6) Install driven sprocket support-to-case cover gasket. Install driven sprocket support-to-cover bolts for gasket guides, then drive support into case cover using a plastic mallet. Install driven support-to-cover attaching bolts and tighten evenly.

OIL PUMP
Disassembly
Remove drive and driven gears from pump body. Remove and discard pump body-to-case "O" ring seal.

Inspection
1) Inspect gear pocket and crescent for nicks, burrs, scoring or galling. Check pump body-to-gear face clearance. *See Fig. 28.* Clearance should be .0013-.0035" (.033-.089 mm).

Fig. 28: Checking Pump Body-to-Gear Face Clearance

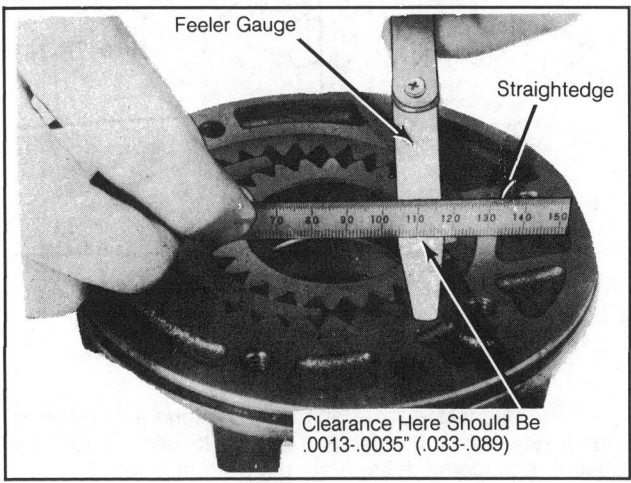

Feeler Gauge

Straightedge

Clearance Here Should Be
.0013-.0035" (.033-.089)

2) Check face of pump body for nicks, burrs, scoring or galling. Inspect bushing for nicks, burrs, scoring, galling, out-of-round, or excessive wear. Install pump body on converter hub and look for out-of-round condition between pump bushing and converter hub. Check front seal for damage and replace if necessary.

NOTE: Use a non-hardening sealing compound on outside of front pump seal before installing it into pump.

Reassembly
Install driven gear into pump with identification mark down against gear pocket. Install drive gear into pump body with identification mark on drive tang up. *See. Fig. 29 for identification.* Install a new pump-to-case "O" ring seal.

DRIVE LINK, DRIVE & DRIVEN
SPROCKETS & SPROCKET COVER
Inspection
Inspect drive link for damage. Check sprockets for nicks, burrs, scoring or galling. Inspect bearings for

Fig. 29: Pump Driven Gear Identification Mark

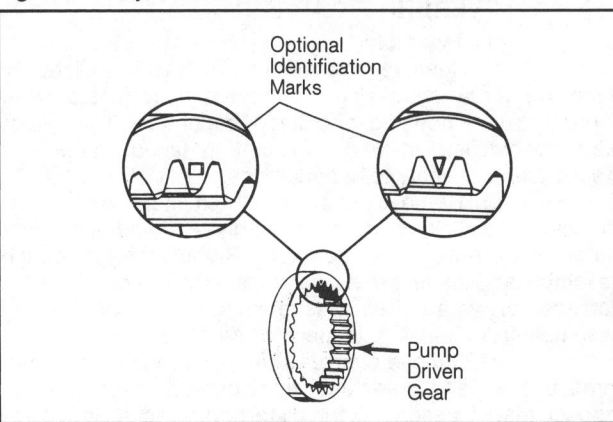

Optional
Identification
Marks

Pump
Driven
Gear

pitted or rough condition. If bearing removal is necessary, proceed as follows:
Sprocket Bearing Replacement
1) Remove sprocket-to-bearing snap ring. Mount sprocket, bearing side down, on 2 pieces of wood. With a hammer and brass rod, drive inner race alternately through each of the access openings, until bearing is removed from sprocket hub.

2) To install, place sprocket-to-bearing snap ring around sprocket hub. Place bearing on hub, then using a driver, drive bearing onto hub until it is resting on bearing seat. Install snap ring into groove of sprocket hub.

CAUTION: When installing drive sprocket bearing, align bearing race groove with locating pin of sprocket hub.

FOURTH CLUTCH ASSEMBLY

Inspection
1) Inspect housing for burrs, raised edges, cracks or porosity. Inspect piston sealing surfaces for scratches. Air check clutch oil passages to be sure it is open and not interconnected. Inspect snap ring, release spring and retainer assembly for distortion or damage.

2) Inspect composition faced and steel plates for signs of wear or burning. Inspect backing plate for scratches or damage.

Reassembly
1) Install 4th clutch outer and inner seals on clutch housing with lips facing down and apply petrolatum. Inner seal is identified by a white stripe. Install clutch piston into housing. Install 4th clutch spring and retainer assembly. Using press and 4th clutch spring and retainer compressor, compress spring and retainer assembly and install snap ring.

2) If 4th clutch housing "O" ring seal was removed or is remaining on housing replace with new "O" ring. Install 4th clutch housing and attaching bolts and tighten.

OVERDRIVE INTERNAL GEAR
Thoroughly clean, air dry and inspect closely, the overdrive carrier to sprocket thrust bearing assembly for pitted or rough conditions. Install overdrive carrier to sprocket thrust bearing assembly by placing large diameter race against carrier.

2-284

Automatic Transmissions
GENERAL MOTORS
TURBO HYDRA-MATIC 325-4L — TRANSAXLE (Cont.)

OVERRUN CLUTCH ASSEMBLY & OVERDRIVE CARRIER

Disassembly

1) Remove overrun clutch backing plate by removing large snap ring. Remove clutch plates from overrun clutch housing and keep separated from other plate assemblies. Inspect composition faced plates and steel plates for wear, or heat damage.

2) Remove overrun clutch hub snap ring. Remove roller clutch cam assembly and inspect roller clutch cam ramps for damage. Remove roller clutch assembly and inspect roller bearings, cage and springs for damage or wear. Remove retainer and wave spring assembly from housing, inspect for damage.

3) Remove overrun clutch piston assembly and remove inner and outer seal from overrun clutch piston. Inspect piston assembly for distortion, cracks and damage. Inspect housing for cracks, wear and open oil passages. Check snap ring groove and bushing for damage or scoring.

4) Inspect overdrive carrier for worn or damaged parts. Check pinion end play with a dial indicator. End play should be .009-.024" (.24 .60 mm).

Reassembly

1) Install new inner and outer seals on piston with lips facing away from clutch apply ring side. Install seal protector (J-29335). Lubricate seals and install the overrun clutch piston. Remove seal protector and install overrun clutch waved release spring retainer, cupped faced positioned down.

2) Install roller clutch cam on roller clutch assembly. The locating tangs on roller must set on roller clutch cam. Install roller clutch assembly on overrun clutch hub and push down to install narrow snap ring. Lubricate and install overrun clutch plates into housing, starting with a flat steel and alternating composition faced and flat steel clutch plates. *See Overrun Clutch Usage Chart.*

OVERRUN CLUTCH USAGE CHART

Application	Flat Steel [1]	Composition
All Models	2	2

[1] — Plate thickness is .077" (1.96 mm).

3) Install backing plate, micro-finish down. Install snap ring. Make sure the composition clutch plates turn freely.

GOVERNOR AND SPEEDOMETER DRIVE GEAR

Inspection

1) If necessary, remove speedometer drive gear from governor shaft and inspect gear for damage or nicks. Check governor cover for damage, then wash in cleaning solvent and blow out oil passages.

2) Inspect governor driven gear for nicks or damage. Check governor shaft seal rings for cuts, damage and free fit in groove. Check for free operation of governor weights. Check for damaged, mispositioned, or tilted springs.

3) Inspect for presence of 2 check balls. Inspect governor shaft for damage. Inspect governor thrust washer for damage. If seal is damaged, cut seal

Fig. 30: Cross-Section of Governor Assembly

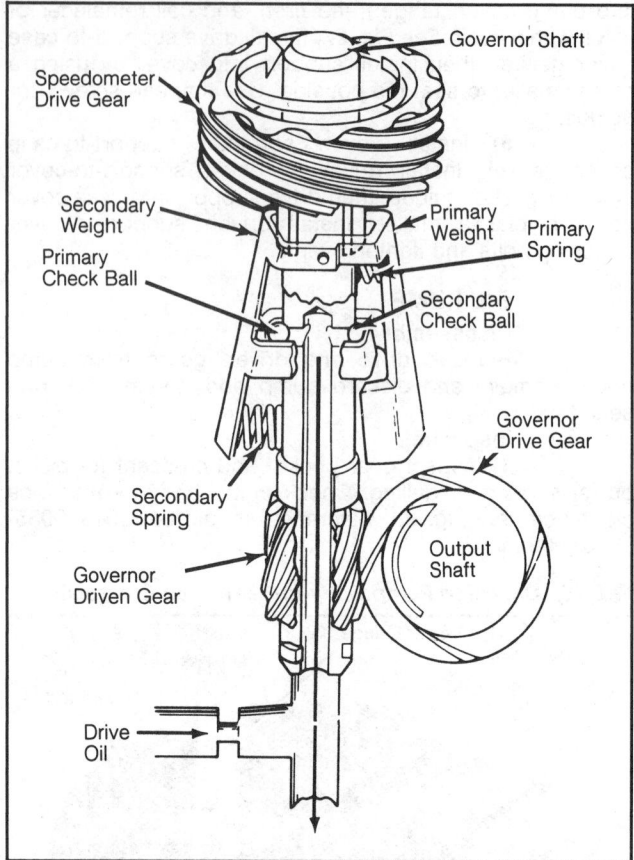

ring off governor shaft, using care not to damage seal ring groove.

INTERMEDIATE SERVO

Disassembly

Separate inner and outer pistons, inner spring, spring retainer and cushion spring. If band apply pin requires replacement, separate pin from retainer.

Fig. 31: Exploded View of Intermediate Servo Assembly

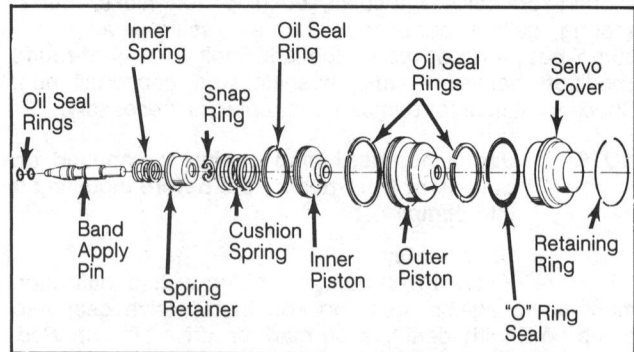

Inspection

1) Check band apply pin for damage and for proper fit in case. Check apply pin seal rings for damage; do not remove seal rings unless replacement is necessary.

2) Inspect inner and outer piston seal rings for damage and for free fit in grooves; do not remove seals

from piston unless replacement is necessary. Inspect springs and retainer for damage.

Reassembly

Install retainer on band apply pin, then install retaining snap ring. If removed, install new seal rings on pistons and apply pin and make sure cut ends are assembled in the same relationship as cut. To complete reassembly, reverse disassembly procedure.

CONTROL VALVE ASSEMBLY

NOTE: As valve trains are removed from each valve body bore, place individual parts in correct order in relative position to valve body to simplify reassembly. Valves, bushings and springs are not interchangeable, and all parts must be installed in correct order in proper valve body bore. Remove all roll pins and spring retaining sleeves by pushing through from the rough case surface side of the control valve pump assembly, except for the blind hole pin.

Disassembly

1) Lay control valve assembly machined face up, with the manual valve at the top. Remove 1 check ball if it is still in place. Remove the manual valve from the upper bore.

CAUTION: Some roll pins in valve body assembly have pressure against them. Therefore, hold a shop towel over bore while removing pin, to prevent possibly losing a bore plug, spring, etc.

2) Remove roll pin from upper left bore, then remove 2-3 valve train. From next bore down, remove spring retaining sleeve, valve bore plug, T.V. modulator downshift valve and T.V. modulator downshift valve spring.

3) From next bore down, remove outer roll pin. Remove 1-2 throttle valve bushing, spring, throttle valve and low 1st/detent valve. Remove inner roll pin holding low 1st/detent valve bushing and 1-2 shift valve.

Fig. 32: Removing Throttle Valve Inner Roll Pin

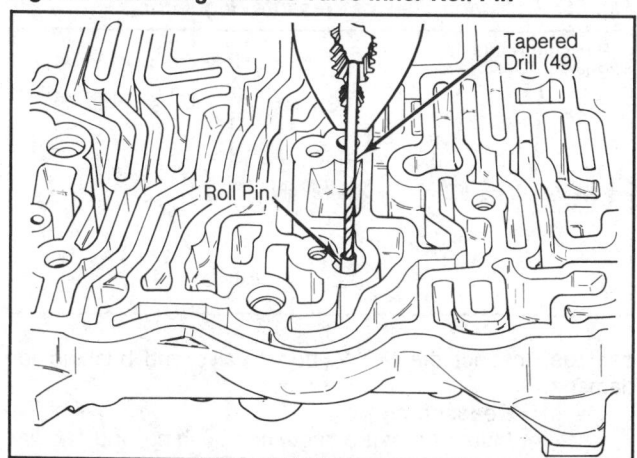

4) From next bore down, remove spring retaining sleeve, valve bore plug, T.V. upshift valve and spring.

5) From next bore down, remove roll pin. Remove converter clutch throttle bushing, valve spring, valve, and converter clutch shift valve.

6) From last bore down, remove roll pin. Remove bore plug, low/overrun clutch valve spring. From same bore, remove inner spring retaining sleeve. Remove 3-2 control valve spring and 3-2 control valve.

7) From the upper right bore, remove spring retaining sleeve. Remove T.V. limit valve spring and T.V. limit valve.

8) From next bore down, remove roll pin. Remove 3-4 throttle valve bushing, 3-4 valve spring, 3-4 valve and 3-4 shift valve.

9) From next bore down, remove roll pin. Remove 4-3 control valve spring and 4-3 control valve.

10) From next bore down remove spring retaining sleeve, valve bore plug, line bias valve and valve spring.

11) From next bore down, remove roll pin and bore plug. Remove accumulator valve bushing, valve and accumulator spring.

12) From the last bore, remove outer roll pin from the rough casting side, throttle valve plunger bushing, plunger and throttle valve spring. Remove inner roll pin as follows: Grind a taper to one end of a No. 49 drill. Insert tapered end into roll pin. Pull drill and coil retaining pin out. Remove throttle valve.

Inspection

Wash control valve body, valves, springs, and other parts in clean solvent and air dry. Inspect valves for scoring, cracks, and free movement in their bores. Inspect bushings and valve body for cracks, damage or scored bores. Inspect springs for distortion or collapsed coils. Inspect bore plugs for damage.

NOTE: Install all flared roll pins (zinc coated), flared end out, and from machined face of control valve assembly. Install the 2 tapered roll pins (black finish) that retain throttle valve and bushing, tapered end first. Roll pins do not fit flush on rough casting face. Make sure that all roll pins are flush at machined face.

Fig. 33: Installing Throttle Valve Bushing Roll Pin

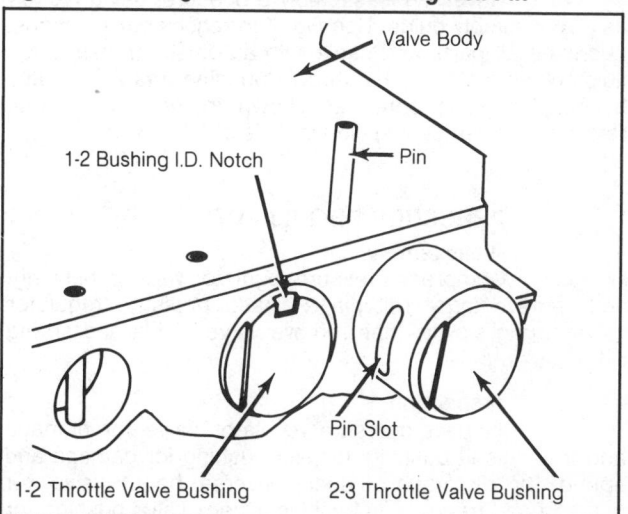

Automatic Transmissions
GENERAL MOTORS
TURBO HYDRA-MATIC 325-4L — TRANSAXLE (Cont.)

Fig. 34: Exploded View of 325-4L Control Valve Assembly

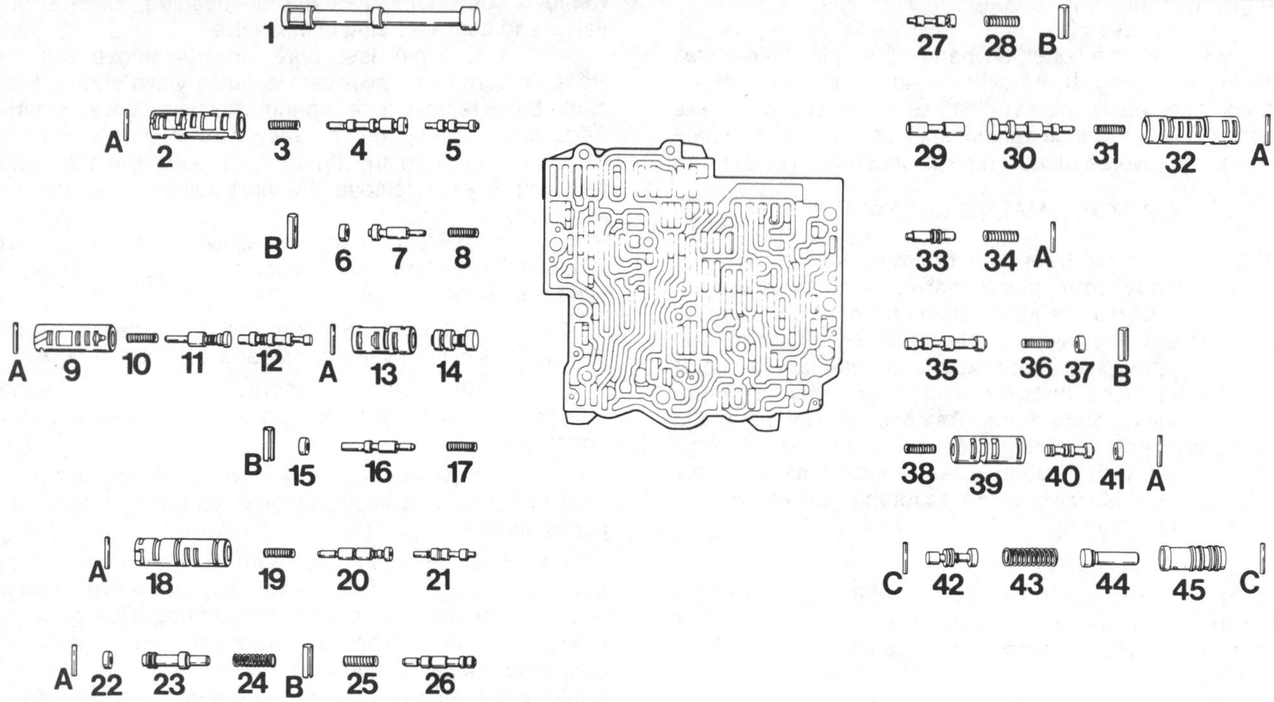

1. Manual Valve
2. 2-3 Throttle Valve Bushing
3. 2-3 Valve Spring
4. 2-3 Throttle Valve
5. 2-3 Shift Valve
6. Bore Plug
7. M.T.V. Downshift Valve
8. M.T.V. Spring
9. 1-2 Throttle Valve Bushing
10. 1-2 Valve Spring
11. 1-2 Throttle Valve
12. Low-1st Detent
13. Low-1st Detent Valve Bushing
14. 1-2 Shift Valve
15. Bore Plug
16. M.T.V. Upshift Valve

17. M.T.V. Upshift Valve Spring
18. Converter Clutch Throttle Valve Bushing
19. Converter Clutch Throttle Valve Spring
20. Converter Clutch Throttle Valve
21. Converter Clutch Shift Valve
22. Bore Plug
23. Low/Overrun Clutch Valve
24. Low/Overrun Clutch Valve Spring
25. 3-2 Control Valve Spring
26. 3-2 Control Valve
27. T.V. Limit Valve
28. T.V. Limit Valve Spring
29. 3-4 Shift Valve
30. 3-4 Throttle Valve
31. 3-4 Throttle Valve Spring
32. 3-4 Throttle Valve Bushing

33. 4-3 Control Valve
34. 4-3 Control Valve Spring
35. Line Bias Valve
36. Line Bias Valve Spring
37. Bore Plug
38. Accumulator Valve Spring
39. Accumulator Valve Bushing
40. Accumulator Bushing
41. Bore Plug
42. Throttle Valve
43. Throttle Valve Spring
44. Throttle Valve Plunger
45. Throttle Valve Plunger Bushing
   A. Coiled Spring Pin/Zinc
   B. Coiled Spring Pin/Plain
   C. Spring Retaining Sleeve

Reassembly

Reverse disassembly procedure, using *Fig. 34* as a reassembly guide. Use *Fig. 7* for check ball locations. Lubricate all parts and seals with automatic transmission fluid. When installing 1-2 throttle bushing and 2-3 throttle bushing, align in bores as shown in *Fig. 23*, so that retaining pin can be installed in pin slot.

PRESSURE REGULATOR
Disassembly

Compress pressure regulator valve in bushing, and remove inner roll pin. Release pressure regulator valve spring slowly, then remove valve, guide and spring from bushing.

Inspection

Inspect pressure regulator valve for damage and freeness in bushing. Inspect bushing for damage and spring for distortion. Inspect reverse boost valve for damage and freeness in bushing. Check valve bushing for

Fig. 35: Exploded View of Pressure Regulator

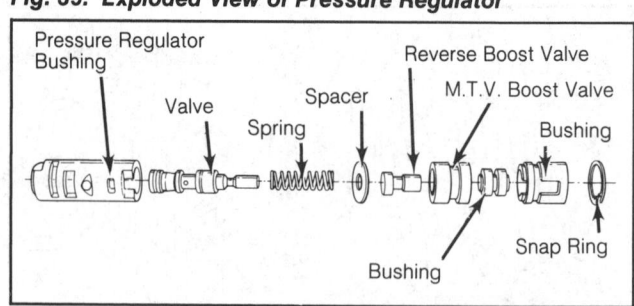

damage. Inspect the M.T.V. boost valve and bushing for damage.

Reassembly

Install pressure regulator bushing and regulator spring into case, then install valve bushing spacer. Install reverse boost valve into reverse boost valve bushing, small end first. Install reverse boost valve and bushing into case. Install M.T.V. boost valve into bushing.

GENERAL MOTORS
TURBO HYDRA-MATIC 325-4L — TRANSAXLE (Cont.)

Install M.T.V. valve and bushing into case and install snap ring.

CONVERTER CLUTCH VALVE
Inspection
Inspect converter valve and bushing for damage and check for freeness in bushing. Inspect spring for distortion or collapsed coils.

TRANSMISSION REASSEMBLY

1) Turn transmission in holding fixture so that oil pan side is up. If removed, install new manual shaft seal with lip facing inward into case using a 9/16" (14 mm) socket to seat seal. Install parking pawl and return spring with tooth toward inside of case and parking pawl return spring under pawl tooth with spring ends toward inside of case and ensure spring ends locate in case slot.

2) Align parking pawl and return spring with case shaft bore, then install parking pawl shaft, tapered end first. File any burrs or raised edges off manual shaft that could damage seal, then install shaft and inside detent lever assembly into case, making sure that shaft flats align with lever hole. Install hex nut on manual shaft and tighten.

NOTE: **If disassembly of manual valve link from inside detent lever is necessary, reassemble with a new push-on nut.**

3) Install parking lock cam and tighten bolts. Start strut shaft into case. Align parking lock strut and lever with parking shaft bore in case and make sure lower strut arm is positioned between lever tangs. Install strut shaft completely into case and install retaining ring. Install parking lock spring. Using a 3/8" (9.5 mm) rod, install new parking strut shaft cup plug, open end out, flush with face. Install manual detent roller and spring assembly and tighten bolt. Check for proper operation of parking lock assembly.

4) Install reaction internal gear, hub end first, on output shaft. Install internal gear-to-reaction sun gear thrust bearing assembly into internal gear by placing the small diameter race over output shaft. See Fig. 36.

Fig. 36: Installing Reaction Internal Gear Thrust Bearing

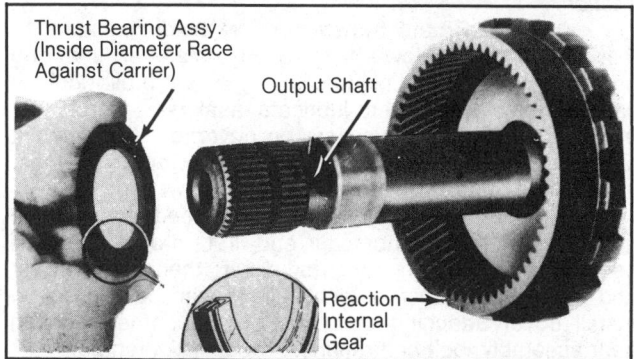

5) Install roller clutch and reaction carrier assembly into reaction internal gear. Install output shaft aligning and loading tool (J-26958) onto output end of case as shown in Fig. 11. Turn case so that case cover end is up.

6) Install reaction unit parts into case and output shaft tool, indexing internal gear parking pawl lugs to pass by parking pawl tooth. Using adjusting screw on output shaft tool, adjust height of internal gear parking pawl lugs to align flush with top of parking pawl tooth.

7) Oil and install low/reverse clutch plates into transmission case, starting with a flat steel plate and alternating composition and flat steel plates until correct number of plates are installed. The last plate installed should be the waved plate. See Low/Reverse Clutch Plate Usage Chart. Install low/reverse clutch housing-to-case spacer into case.

LOW/REVERSE CLUTCH PLATE USAGE CHART

Application	Flat Steel	Composition
All Models	7 [1]	6

[1] — Plus 1 waved steel plate installed on top of last flat steel plate.

8) Install low/reverse clutch housing into case, aligning reverse clutch housing feed hole to reverse clutch case feed passage. If housing does not seat past case snap ring groove, proceed as follows:

9) Using reaction sun gear and input drum as a tool, install input drum and sun gear in case. Rotate reaction sun gear back and forth, tapping lightly with input drum, to align roller clutch race and low/reverse clutch hub splines. Remove drum and sun gear. If necessary repeat this procedure until clutch housing is fully seated. Install clutch housing-to-case snap ring, flat side against housing.

Fig. 37: Installing Low/Reverse Clutch-to-Transmission Case Spacer

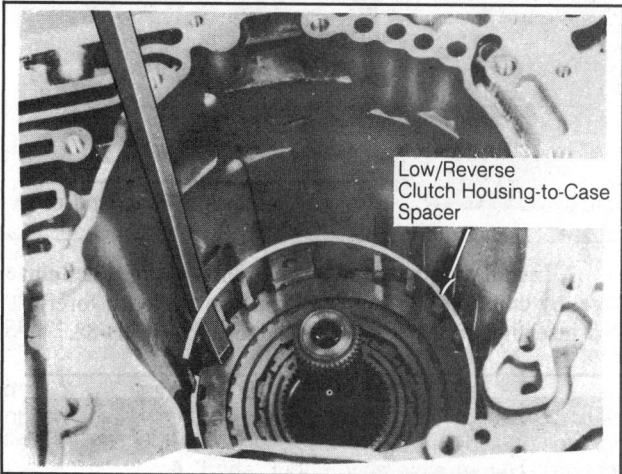

Low/Reverse Clutch Housing-to-Case Spacer

NOTE: **It may be necessary to loosen adjusting screw on output shaft loading tool to install snap ring.**

10) Install reaction sun gear into input drum, spline side first and retain wih snap ring. Install tanged thrust washer on input drum over sun gear end aligning tangs into input drum and retain with petrolatum. Install reaction sun gear and input drum assembly.

11) Install input sun gear, with the identification mark (a drill spot or groove) against input drum-to-reaction

2-288

Automatic Transmissions
GENERAL MOTORS
TURBO HYDRA-MATIC 325-4L — TRANSAXLE (Cont.)

sun gear snap ring. Install sun gear-to-front carrier thrust bearing and race assembly with thrust bearing against sun gear.

12) Position input carrier-to-input internal gear thrust bearing assembly on carrier with smaller diameter race against carrier and retain in place with petrolatum. Install input carrier and thrust bearing assembly into case.

13) Install thrust washer on input internal gear and hold in place with petrolatum. Install internal gear into case. Install reaction selective thrust washer into case with identification number (hardened side) facing snap ring side. Install output shaft-to-reaction selective thrust washer snap ring on output shaft and ensure it is fully seated in output shaft groove.

NOTE: It may be necessary to move output shaft upward by tightening output shaft loading tool adjusting screw to install snap ring.

14) Before proceeding with transmission reassembly, recheck reaction unit end play to ensure that correct reaction selective thrust washer has been installed. *See Reaction Unit End Play checking procedure under Transmission Disassembly.*

Fig. 38: Installing Output Shaft-to-Reaction Selective Thrust Washer

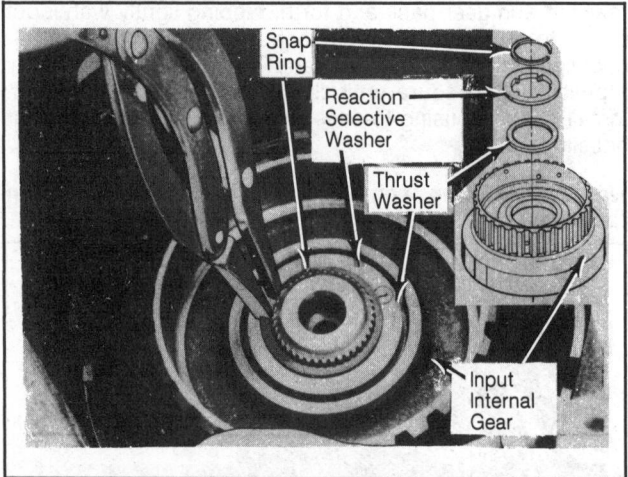

15) Install output shaft-to-input shaft selective thrust washer on end of output shaft and retain with petrolatum. Install intermediate band into case, locating anchor pin lug on anchor pin and apply lug in case slot.

16) Position direct clutch assembly (clutch plate end up) over hole in work bench and align composition plate teeth one above the other. Install forward clutch assembly (input shaft first) into direct clutch. Hold direct clutch and rotate forward clutch back and forth until seated.

NOTE: When forward clutch is seated, it will be approximately 5/8" (15.8 mm) from tang end of direct clutch housing to the end of forward clutch drum.

17) Install direct and forward clutch assemblies into case and rotate into position. When correctly installed, the direct clutch housing will be approximately 7/16" (11 mm) from case cover face.

18) Install thrust washer on hub of driven sprocket support and ensure tabs on washer engage holes in hub. Retain washer in place with petrolatum. If removed, install oil seal rings into grooves in hub of driven sprocket support. Install case cover assembly on transmission using a new gasket, then install and tighten attaching bolts.

CAUTION: If input shaft cannot be rotated as case cover is bolted into place, the forward or direct clutch housing has not been installed properly to index with the clutch plates. This condition must be corrected before case cover is pulled fully into place.

19) Recheck input unit end play at this time to ensure correct output shaft-to-input shaft selective thrust washer has been installed. *See Input Unit End Play checking procedure under Transmission Disassembly.* Remove output shaft aligning and loading tool from rear of case.

20) Mount 2 guide pins into opposing pump attaching bolt holes. Align guide pins with bolt holes in pump body, then install pump assembly into case. Install and tighten pump attaching bolts.

21) If removed, install new oil seal rings on turbine shaft. Place drive link around drive and driven sprockets so that links engage teeth of sprockets, colored guide link which has etched numerals facing sprocket cover.

NOTE: Turbine shaft may appear not to be pressed fully into the sprockets. Do not attempt pressing shaft into sprockets further as a specific length dimension is held during initial assembly.

22) Place drive link and sprocket assembly into sprocket support. Using a plastic mallet, gently seat sprocket bearing assemblies into sprocket supports. Install sprockets-to-sprocket support snap ring. Install the 4th clutch housing and attaching bolts.

23) Install overdrive internal gear, overrun clutch and overdrive carrier assembly units into 4th clutch housing. Install sprocket cover, thrust washers, snap ring and 4th clutch snap ring. Recheck overdrive unit end play. *See Overrun Clutch and Overdrive Carrier Assembly Section.*

24) Rotate transmission in holding fixture so that oil pan side is down. If removed, install new seal ring on governor shaft and place seal ring end into pilot hole in case to size seal, then lubricate seal wih petrolatum. Install speedometer drive gear on governor shaft (weight side) and make sure slot in gear aligns with pin in shaft. Install drive gear-to-governor cover thrust washer.

25) Install governor and speedometer drive gear assembly (governor gear end first) into case. Install new "O" ring seal on governor cover, then install cover and make sure governor shaft aligns with hole in cover. Install cover attaching bolts. Install speedometer driven gear assembly, bolt and retaining clip and tighten bolt.

26) Install intermediate servo piston assembly into servo cover. Lubricate with petrolatum and install new seal rings on cover. Install servo assembly into case, tapping lightly with a plastic mallet, if necessary. Using a compressor tool, compress servo cover and install retaining ring.

GENERAL MOTORS
TURBO HYDRA-MATIC 325-4L — TRANSAXLE (Cont.)

NOTE: When installing servo assembly into case, make sure tapered end of band apply pin is properly located against band apply lug.

27) Place a new low/reverse clutch housing-to-case cup plug (rubber end first) into hole in case. *See Fig. 14 for location of cup plug hole.* Using a 3/8" (9.5 mm) diameter by 6" metal rod and hammer, drive plug until it seats against low/reverse clutch housing.

28) Install check balls in proper locations, then install 2 guide pins. Position spacer plate to case gasket, on case. Place valve body spacer plate on gasket marked "CB."Place spacer plate to control valve assembly gasket marked "VB" on valve body.

29) Install 1 check ball into ball seat pocket in control valve assembly and retain with petrolatum. Install control valve assembly using the 2 pins as guides. Start 2 case bolts and remove guide pins. Install 1-2 accumulator piston with new seal on piston. Install 3-4 accumulator piston with new seal on piston. Install manual valve link into manual valve. Install throttle lever and bracket assembly.

30) Install wiring and oil pipes. All pipes must be fully seated. Install electrical connectors with lock tabs facing into case. Install remaining control valve assembly retaining bolts and torque to specifications.

31) Install pressure regulator,bushing and spring assembly, reverse boost valve and bushing and M.T.V. boost valve and bushing into case. Compress all 3 valve assemblies and install retaining snap ring.

32) Install the clutch converter valve, short stem first into valve bushing. Install spring and valve assembly into case. Retain with snap ring.

33) Install new "O" ring seal on intake pipe of oil screen and lubricate "O" ring with petrolatum. Install oil screen assembly into case. Using a new gasket, install oil pan on case and tighten attaching bolts.

TIGHTENING SPECIFICATIONS

Application	Ft. Lbs. (N.m)
Converter-to-Flywheel	35 (48)
Final Drive-to-Transmission	30 (41)
Transmission-to-Engine	35 (48)
Valve Body-to-Case	11 (15)
Detent Spring Assy.-to-Case	11 (15)
Manual Shaft-to-Inside Detent Lever	23 (31)
Case Cover-to-Case	18 (24)
Driven Sprocket-to-Case Cover	18 (24)
Oil Pan-to-Case	12 (16)
Cooler Connector	28 (38)
4th Clutch Housing-to-Case	18 (24)
	INCH Lbs. (N.m)
Cam-to-Manual Shaft	120 (14)
Sprocket Cover-to-Case	108 (13)
Governer Cover-to-Case	96 (11)
Line Pressure Take-Off	120 (14)
Pressure Switch	120 (14)

Fig. 39: Throttle Lever and Bracket Assembly

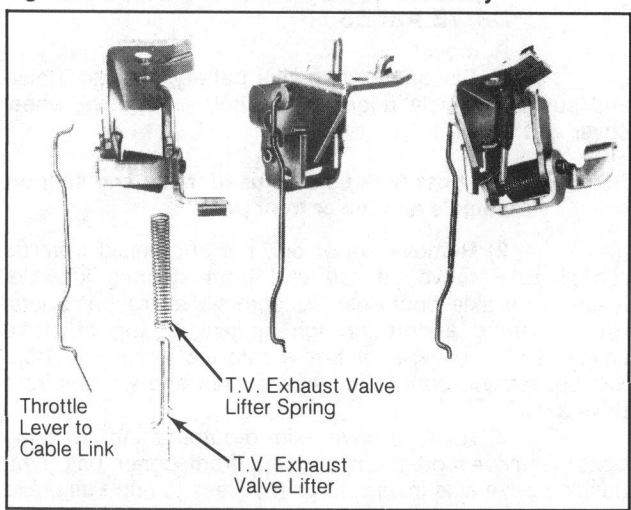

Throttle Lever to Cable Link

T.V. Exhaust Valve Lifter Spring

T.V. Exhaust Valve Lifter

Fig. 40: Installing Throttle Valve and Bracket

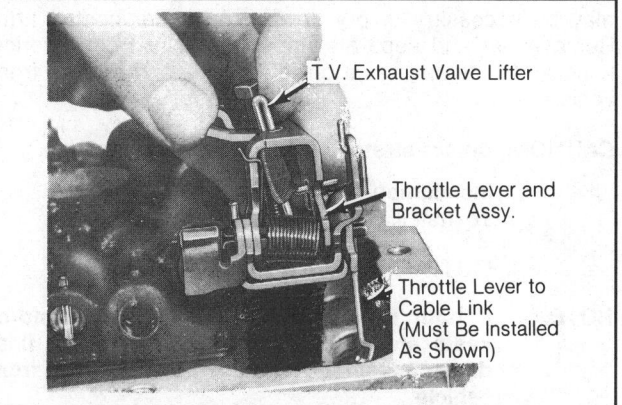

T.V. Exhaust Valve Lifter

Throttle Lever and Bracket Assy.

Throttle Lever to Cable Link (Must Be Installed As Shown)

Automatic Transmissions
GENERAL MOTORS
TURBO HYDRA-MATIC 325-4L — FINAL DRIVE

Buick Riviera
Cadillac Eldorado & Seville
Oldsmobile Toronado

DESCRIPTION

Front wheel final drive assembly is mounted on and splined directly to the automatic transmission. Unit consists of a pinion drive gear, ring gear and differential case assembly.

Torque from final drive unit is transmitted to output shafts, which are connected to drive axles. Output shafts are splined to final drive side gears. Drive axles are flexible assemblies consisting of axle shafts and inner and outer constant velocity joints.

AXLE RATIO & IDENTIFICATION

Axle ratio code and build date are stamped on left side of housing cover mounting surface. Ratio is identified by the 2 letters following the number "4".

AXLE RATIO IDENTIFICATION

Axle Ratio	Code	No. of Teeth [1] Ring/Pinion
Buick and Cadillac		
2.73:1	4MC/4ML	15-41
2.93:1	4MH/4MK	14-41
3.15:1	4ME/4MM	13-41
3.36:1	4MJ/4MN	14-47
Oldsmobile		
2.73:1	4MC/4ML	15-41
2.93:1	4MH/4MK	14-41
3.15:1	4ME/4MM	13-41

[1] — Ring gear is 8" (204 mm) on all models.

Fig. 1: Axle Ratio Code Location

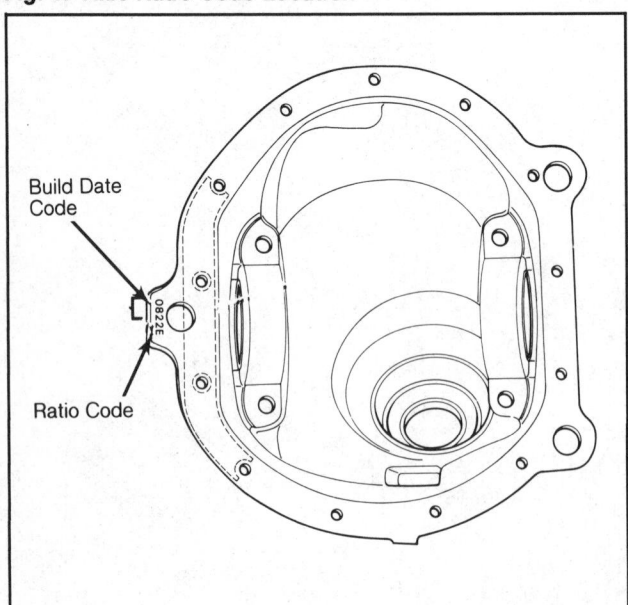

Build Date Code

0822E

Ratio Code

Fig. 2: General Motors Front Wheel Final Drive Assembly

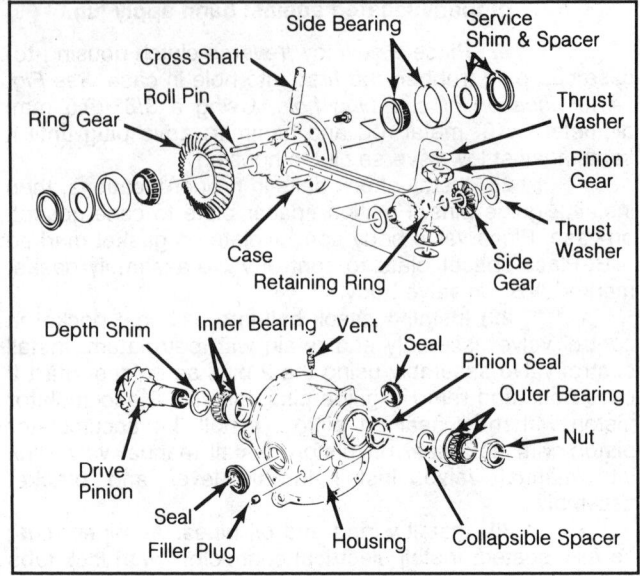

Cross Shaft — Side Bearing — Service Shim & Spacer — Roll Pin — Ring Gear — Thrust Washer — Pinion Gear — Thrust Washer — Case — Retaining Ring — Side Gear

Depth Shim — Inner Bearing — Vent — Seal — Pinion Seal — Outer Bearing — Nut — Drive Pinion — Seal — Filler Plug — Housing — Collapsible Spacer

SERVICE (IN VEHICLE)

DRIVE AXLES

Removal

1) Disconnect negative battery cable(s). Raise and support vehicle under frame horns. Remove wheel cover and wheel.

NOTE: If 2-post type hoist is used, raise and support vehicle and lower front post.

2) Remove cotter pin, nut and shield from tie rod pivot. Remove tie rod end from steering knuckle. Install drive axle boot seal protectors over rubber boots. After inserting a drift through opening in top of brake caliper and into vane of brake rotor to keep axle from turning, remove cotter pin, retainer, nut and washer from drive axle.

3) Remove drive axle-to-output shaft attaching bolts. Remove cotter pin and nut from upper ball joint, pushing drive axle inward to gain access to nut. Pull brake hose clip off of ball joint stud and loosely reinstall nut.

4) Using hammer and brass drift, pound downward on steering knuckle to unseat ball joint stud. It may be necessary to pry upward on upper control arm. Remove nut and separate upper ball joint from steering knuckle. Guide drive axle out of knuckle and remove from vehicle.

CAUTION: Do not stretch or damage brake hose.

Installation
To install, reverse removal procedure.

OUTPUT SHAFTS

NOTE: If both right and left output shafts and/or seals are to be removed or replaced, final drive assembly should be removed from vehicle.

GENERAL MOTORS
TURBO HYDRA-MATIC 325-4L — FINAL DRIVE (Cont.)

Removal

1) Remove drive axle. On right output shaft, remove 2 bolts attaching battery cable retainer to support and 2 bolts attaching output shaft support to engine. On both output shafts, remove front nut and bolt from frame brace. Rotate frame brace outward for access.

2) Use a hammer and a large brass drift to tap on flanged end of output shaft until it "pops" out of retaining ring. Carefully guide shaft out of vehicle. Use pry bar to remove shaft seal from housing and discard seal.

NOTE: Pry seal at 2 or 3 different locations to avoid cocking seal and damaging housing.

Installation

1) Install new output shaft seal, and apply clean wheel bearing grease between seal lips. Being careful not to damage seal, index output shaft splines with side gear splines and use a soft hammer to tap on center of flanged end of shaft until shaft "snaps" into place.

NOTE: Check spline fit to ensure there will be no drive line clunk. Do not let shaft and support assembly hang in final drive unit or align shaft off center in seal, as seal may be damaged.

2) On right output shaft, align shaft support with holes in engine block, loosely install bolts and washers. Move flanged end of shaft up and down and back and forth to find center location, then fully tighten bolts. Install battery cable retainer to support with 2 bolts. On both output shafts, install drive axle and restore frame brace to original position.

RIGHT OUTPUT SHAFT SUPPORT BEARING

Removal

Remove right output shaft and support assembly from vehicle. Remove 3 self-tapping bolts attaching bearing retainer to support. Slide split halves of bearing remover between flanged end of output shaft and flat area of shaft support and tighten bolts. Press shaft support, bearing, retainer and slinger off of output shaft as an assembly.

Fig. 3: Right Output Shaft and Support Bearing Assembly

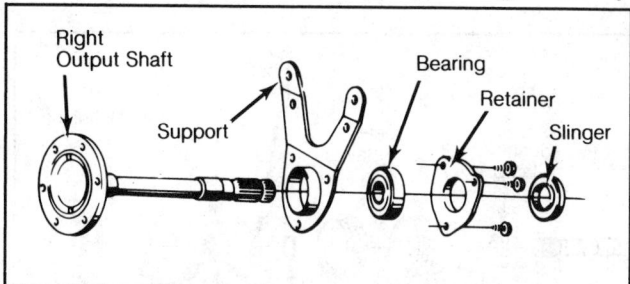

Installation

Pack bearing with wheel bearing grease and install in output shaft support. Install retainer and secure with 3 self-tapping bolts. Place assembled parts and slinger on output shaft. Press bearing and assembled parts on shaft until seated. Check for free bearing rotation and install output shaft and support on vehicle.

FINAL DRIVE ASSEMBLY
Removal

1) Disconnect negative battery cable. Raise and support vehicle under frame horns. Remove right and left frame brace front attaching bolts and rotate braces outward to gain access. Loosen final drive cover bolts, drain lubricant; then remove bolts and cover. Install drive axle boot seal protectors.

NOTE: If 2-post type hoist is used, raise and support vehicle and lower front post.

2) Remove drive axle-to-output shaft attaching bolts and separate output shaft and drive axle flanges to provide clearance for final drive removal. Remove 2 bolts attaching battery cable retainer to right output shaft support and 2 bolts attaching support to engine. Rotate support downward for removal clearance.

3) Remove final drive-to-transmission bolt attaching rear of final drive shield to transmission and loosen final drive support bracket screw attaching front of shield to final drive. Then, slide shield outward and forward and remove from vehicle.

Fig. 4: Attachment of Final Drive Assembly

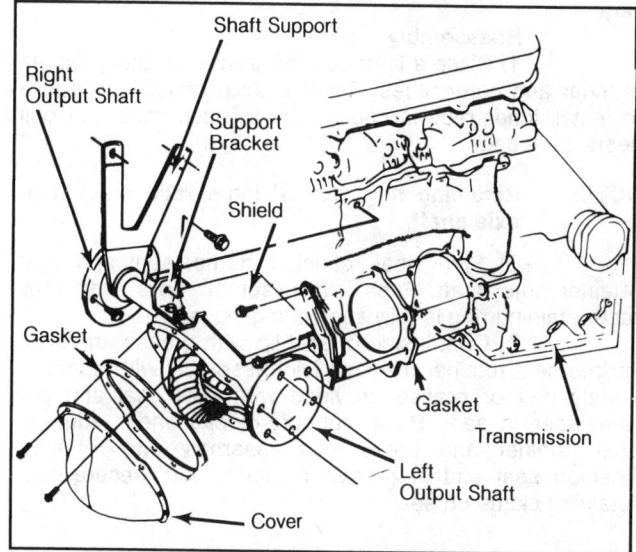

4) Remove final drive support bracket-to-engine block bolt and 5 remaining final drive-to-transmission bolts. Separate steering linkage intermediate shaft from pitman and idler arms, and push linkage toward front of vehicle. With aid of helper or transmission jack, slide final drive assembly forward, off of splined shaft and remove from vehicle with output shafts attached.

CAUTION: Do not use output shafts as "handles" to maneuver or support final drive assembly. Damage to splines or seals may occur.

Installation

Reverse removal procedure and note the following:
- Position new final drive-to-transmission gasket on final drive. Do not use grease, oil or sealer on gasket.
- Tie arm of right hand output shaft support to the hole in shaft flange closest to twelve o'clock position.

2-292

Automatic Transmissions
GENERAL MOTORS
TURBO HYDRA-MATIC 325-4L — FINAL DRIVE (Cont.)

• To ensure proper alignment of right output shaft, loosely install support bolts, move output shaft flange end up and down and back and forth to find central location, and tighten bolts.

COMPONENT DISASSEMBLY & REASSEMBLY

CONSTANT VELOCITY JOINTS

Disassembly (Outer Joint)

1) Clamp mid-part of axle shaft in a vise. Use cutters to remove seal retaining clamp. Using a hammer and brass drift, tap lightly and evenly all around seal retainer to remove it from joint assembly and slide seal down shaft.

2) Using snap ring pliers to spread retaining ring ears apart, remove joint assembly front shaft. Pull shaft out of joint assembly.

3) Using a hammer and brass drift, gently tap on cage until tilted enough to remove one ball. Continue until all balls are removed. Pivot cage and inner race 90°, align cage windows with lands of outer race and lift out cage and inner race. Pivot inner race 90° in cage, align lands with cage windows and remove inner race from cage.

Reassembly

1) Place a light coat of grease on ball grooves of inner and outer races. Reverse disassembly procedure to install inner race in cage, cage in outer race and ball bearings in cage.

NOTE: Retaining ring side of inner race must face axle shaft.

2) Slide seal retaining clamp, seal and seal retainer onto shaft. Push joint assembly onto shaft until race retaining ring is fully seated in groove.

3) Coat inside of seal lip with grease and slide lip into seal retainer. Repack joint assembly with approximately half of grease provided with new seal and put remainder in seal. Place support blocks under edge of seal retainer and press joint assembly into retainer. Position seal end in groove on shaft and secure seal retaining clamp on seal.

Disassembly (Inner Joint)

1) Clamp mid-part of axle shaft in a vise. Use cutters to remove seal retaining clamp. Using a hammer and brass drift, tap lightly and evenly all around seal retainer to remove it from housing and slide seal down shaft. Pull housing off of shaft.

2) Using snap ring pliers to slide spacer ring back, remove spider assembly from shaft. Slide spider assembly back to expose shaft retaining ring, remove ring and pull spider assembly off shaft.

Reassembly

1) Slide seal retaining clamp, seal and seal retainer onto shaft. Repack housing with approximately half of grease provided with new seal and put remainder in seal.

2) Slide spacer ring onto shaft about 4". Hold spider assembly with counterbore facing away from shaft and slide assembly onto shaft beyond shaft retaining ring groove on end of shaft. Install shaft retaining ring in groove; then, slide spider assembly back toward end of shaft until it locks in place over retaining ring. Slide spacer ring toward end of shaft until it contacts spider and seat it in groove.

NOTE: Raised ring on spider assembly must face axle shaft.

3) Slide housing over spider assembly. Coat inside of seal lip with grease and slide lip into seal retainer. Repack joint assembly with approximately half of grease provided with new seal and put remainder in seal.

4) Place support blocks under edge of seal retainer and press housing into retainer. Position seal end in groove on shaft and using band installer, secure retaining clamp on seal.

FINAL DRIVE

Disassembly

1) Remove final drive assembly from vehicle. Mount assembly on holding fixture.

NOTE: Before disassembling unit, check and record ring gear-to-pinion backlash, total drive pinion preload torque and ring gear runout.

Fig. 5: Front Drive Axle Assembly

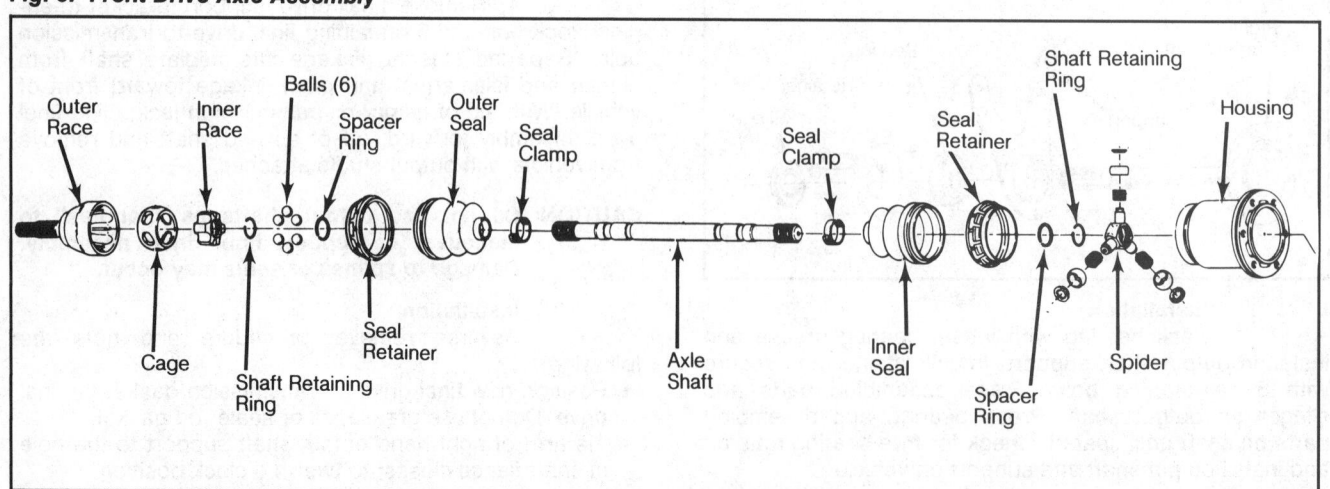

GENERAL MOTORS
TURBO HYDRA-MATIC 325-4L — FINAL DRIVE (Cont.)

2) Mark bearing caps for reassembly reference; then, remove cap bolts and bearing caps. Using pry bar, remove differential case by prying against ring gear bolt. Mark shims for reassembly reference.

3) Remove all but 2 ring gear-to-case bolts, leaving them loosely installed 180° apart. Remove ring gear from case by alternately tapping on these 2 bolts.

4) If differential side bearings are to be replaced, remove using a puller or press. Using a punch and hammer, drive pinion cross shaft roll pin out of differential case and remove pinion cross shaft. Remove pinion gears, side gears and washers by rotating gears to opening in case and removing. Mark pinion gears, side gears and washers for installation in original positions.

5) Check pinion bearing preload using spline adapter and 3/8" drive torque wrench. Record reading. To remove pinion nut, hold nut while turning pinion CLOCKWISE with spline adapter. Remove pinion by threading original nut partially onto pinion to protect threads and tap with hammer to free pinion. *See Fig. 6.*

6) Remove nut, outer bearing, collapsible spacer and pinion. Using hammer and drift, drive pinion seal out of housing toward inside of housing. Drive outer bearing race out from inside of housing.

NOTE: **Ensure drain hole is not plugged when replacing pinion oil seal.**

7) Remove inner bearing race by installing bearing cup remover between housing bore and race. Tap race out with slide hammer. Using bearing remover, press pinion shaft out of inner bearing and note thickness of pinion depth shim.

Fig. 6: Removing or Installing Pinion Nut

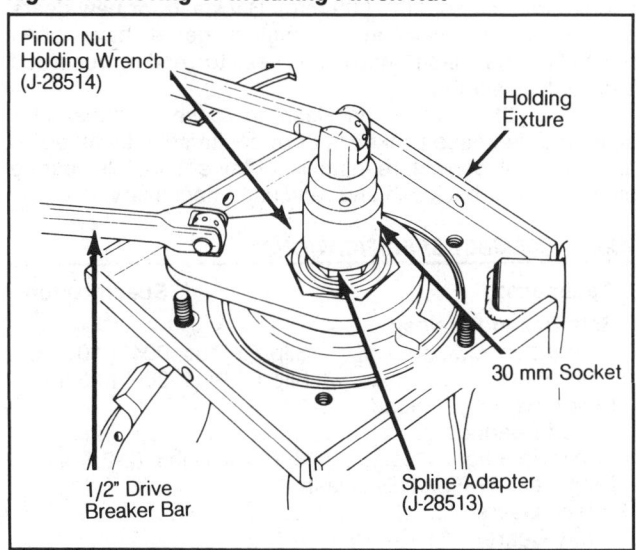

Pinion Nut Holding Wrench (J-28514)

Holding Fixture

30 mm Socket

1/2" Drive Breaker Bar

Spline Adapter (J-28513)

Cleaning & Inspection
Wash all parts in solvent or mineral spirits. Dry thoroughly using dry, compressed air. Using a clean cloth, wipe inside of housing clean. Inspect all parts for chips, nicks, and excessive wear. Replace parts as necessary.

Reassembly
Pinion Depth Setting
1) If original ring gear, pinion and inner pinion bearing are to be reinstalled, the original shim thickness may be used. If installing new components, perform the following procedure.

CAUTION: **Inner pinion bearing race is used as stop gauge for pinion oil seal installing tool. Inner race MUST be installed before pinion seal. If race is not correctly seated, seal may leak.**

2) Clean housing assembly and all gauge parts to ensure accurate measurements. If removed, install pinion bearing races; then, install lubricated pinion bearings in their races.

NOTE: **Use pinion gauge set J-21777-75 to obtain proper pinion depth setting.**

3) Position inner bearing pilot on short threaded end of preload stud. Thread gauge plate onto stud and tighten against pilot. Insert stud through inner and outer bearings, install outer bearing pilot and nut. Rotate bearings to ensure proper seating. Tighten nut until 20 INCH lbs. are required to rotate bearings.

4) Mount side bearing gauging discs on ends of arbor with smaller steps out. Place assembly in housing, making sure discs are properly seated. Install bearing caps and bolts finger tight to prevent movement.

5) Position dial indicator on mounting post of arbor with contact button resting on top of surface plunger. Preload dial indicator 1/2 revolution and tighten in this position.

Fig. 7: Pinion Depth Gauge Set

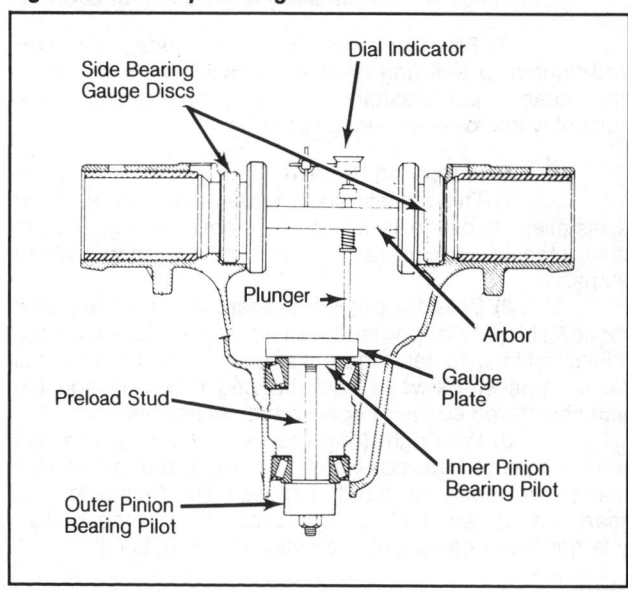

Side Bearing Gauge Discs

Dial Indicator

Plunger

Arbor

Gauge Plate

Preload Stud

Inner Pinion Bearing Pilot

Outer Pinion Bearing Pilot

6) Rotate gauge plate until plunger rests squarely on flat surface of plate. Rock plunger rod slowly back and forth across plate until indicator reads greatest deflection; then, set indicator to zero. Repeat rocking action several times to verify setting. Once zero reading is obtained, swing plunger until it is removed from gauge plate. Dial indicator will now read required pinion shim thickness.

7) Remove bearing caps and gauging tools from housing. Place selected shim pack on pinion and install lubricated bearing onto pinion shaft using a press.

2-294

Automatic Transmissions
GENERAL MOTORS
TURBO HYDRA-MATIC 325-4L — FINAL DRIVE (Cont.)

Pinion Installation & Preload Adjustment

1) Install pinion seal in housing and lubricate with transmission fluid. Lubricate inner bearing with differential lube, install seal protector on pinion, and position pinion in housing. Lubricate outer pinion bearing with transmission fluid and install new collapsible spacer, outer pinion bearing and nut (finger tight) on pinion shaft.

NOTE: Nut can only be partially installed due to nylon coating on threads.

2) Using spline adapter and holding wrench, tighten pinion nut until end play begins to be taken up. (Turning spline adapter COUNTERCLOCKWISE tightens nut). *See Fig. 6.*

3) When no further end play is felt, use spline adapter and 3/8" drive torque wrench to check preload. Continue tightening nut and checking preload until specified preload is obtained.

CAUTION: If preload is exceeded, a new collapsible spacer must be installed and nut retightened to obtain proper preload.

Case Reassembly

1) Install pinions and thrust washers into case; then, install pinion shaft and roll pin. If removed, install side bearings onto case.

NOTE: All ring gear bolts (except those with serrated heads on bottom side) require use of Loctite.

2) Place ring gear into case, install new bolts and tighten to pull ring gear into position on case. Place side gear thrust washers over side gear hubs. Install assembly into case in original positions.

Side Bearing Preload

1) This adjustment is to be made before pinion is installed. If pinion is installed, remove ring gear from case. Measure thickness of original side bearing preload shims.

2) Select a service spacer .170" (4.3 mm) and service shims with a total thickness slightly less than the original shims. Install differential case in housing. Install service spacer between each bearing race and housing with chamfered edges of spacer against housing.

3) With right (ring gear side) bearing race and spacer against housing, install both right and left service shims (previously selected) between left (opposite ring gear) bearing race and service spacer. Insert progressively larger feeler gauges until a noticeable drag is felt.

NOTE: To obtain correct reading, push feeler gauge downward until end of gauge contacts housing bore.

4) Remove differential case and install ring gear (if removed). Remove service shims from left side. Select 2 shims of equal thickness with a total thickness equal to service shim thickness plus feeler gauge reading. Install case in housing.

5) Insert selected shims between bearing race and service spacer on both right and left sides. Adjust differential backlash. Then, preload bearings by replacing right and left service shims with shims .004" (total .008")

thicker on Toronado and .003" (total .006") thicker on all other models.

NOTE: Do not attempt to reinstall original production shims as they will break when tapped into place. Previously installed service shims and spacers may be re-used.

Fig. 8: *Determining Side Bearing Shim Requirements*

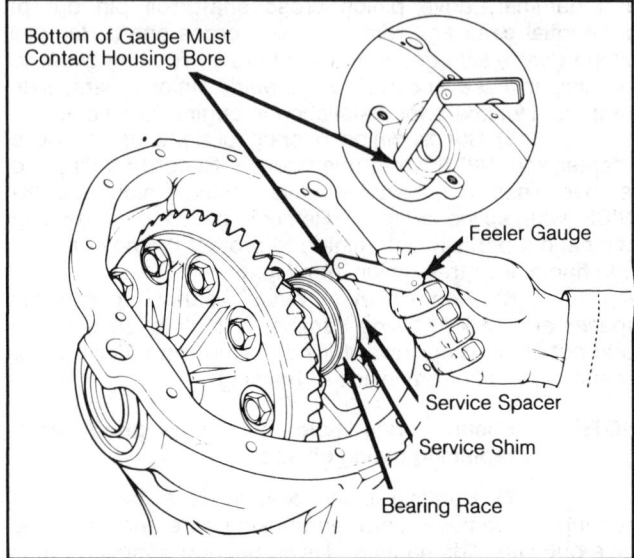

Ring Gear & Pinion Backlash

1) Mount dial indicator on axle housing and check backlash at 4 locations around ring gear. Variation should not exceed .002" (.05 mm). Backlash for new gears should be as specified. If original gears have been reinstalled, backlash should be reset to reading recorded before disassembly.

2) To adjust backlash, increase thickness of 1 shim and decrease thickness of opposite shim by an equal amount until correct reading is obtained. Install bearing caps, recheck backlash and readjust if necessary.

AXLE ASSEMBLY SPECIFICATIONS

Application	Specification
Side Bearing Preload	
Toronado	[1] Slip Fit Plus .004" (.10 mm)
All Others	[2] Slip Fit Plus .006" (.15 mm)
Pinion Bearing Preload	
Used Bearings	[3]
New Bearings	18-24 INCH lbs. (2-2.7 N.m)
Ring Gear-to-Pinion Backlash	
Used Gears	[4]
New Gears	
Toronado	.005-.007" (.13-.18 mm)
All Others	.005-.009" (.13-.23 mm)
Capacity	3.2 Pts. (1.5L)

[1] — Add .004" (.10 mm) to each side after backlash is set.

[2] — Add .003" (.08 mm) to each side after backlash is set.

[3] — Pre-disassembly reading plus 5 INCH lbs. (.6 N.m)

[4] — Restore to pre-disassembly reading.

GENERAL MOTORS
TURBO HYDRA-MATIC 325-4L — FINAL DRIVE (Cont.)

TIGHTENING SPECIFICATIONS

Application	Ft. Lbs. (N.m)
Drive Axle-to-Output Shaft Bolts	61 (82)
Drive Axle Nut	176 (238)
Output Shaft Support-to-Engine Bolts	50 (68)
Final Drive Support Bracket-to-Engine	
All Except 4.1L V8	70 (95)
4.1L V8	35 (47)
Final Drive Support Bracket-to-Housing	33 (45)
Final Drive-to-Transmission Bolts	30 (41)
Upper Control Arm Bushing Bolt	
Toronado	50 (68)
All Others	70 (95)
Lower Control Arm Bushing Bolt	
Toronado	70 (95)
All Others	86 (125)
Tie Rod-to-Steering Knuckle Nut	
Toronado	30 (41)
Riviera	40 (54)
Eldorado & Seville	40 (54)
Ring Gear-to-Case Bolts	
Eldorado & Seville	96 (130)
Riviera	96 (130)
Toronado	80 (110)
Bearing Cap Bolts	41 (56)
Housing Cover Bolts	7 (10)

GENERAL MOTORS TURBO HYDRA-MATIC 350C

Buick
Cadillac
Chevrolet
GMC
Oldsmobile
Pontiac

TRANSMISSION IDENTIFICATION

Transmission identification code is stamped on the right vertical surface of the oil pan or governor, or inked on the bell housing. The Vehicle Identification Number is also stamped on the lower right side of case, in the front.

NOTE: If the I.D. number is stamped on governor cover, the number must be stamped on new cover if the original cover is replaced.

TRANSMISSION MODEL CODES

Application	Model Code
All Manufacturers	KA, KC, KE, KN, LB, LJ, LN, V4, WD, WE, WH, WJ

DESCRIPTION

The Turbo Hydra-Matic 350C transmission is a fully automatic unit consisting primarily of a 4-element torque converter and 2 planetary gear sets. Four multiple-disc clutches, 2 roller clutches and an intermediate overrun band provide the friction elements required to obtain the desired function of the 2 planetary gear sets.

A hydraulic system pressurized by a gear type pump provides the working pressure required to operate the friction elements and automatic controls. The torque converter clutch assembly consists of a 3 element torque converter with the addition of a converter clutch.

The converter clutch is splined to the turbine assembly, and when operated, applies against the converter cover, providing mechanical direct drive coupling of the engine to the transmission planetary gears. When the converter clutch is released, the assembly operates as a normal torque converter.

NOTE: See General Motors Torque converter Clutch (TCC) System article in this section for information on the torque converter clutch system used in the THM 350C transmission.

LUBRICATION & ADJUSTMENT

See the appropriate article in AUTOMATIC TRANSMISSION SERVICING Section.

Fig. 1: Sectional View of Turbo Hydra-Matic 350C Automatic Transmission

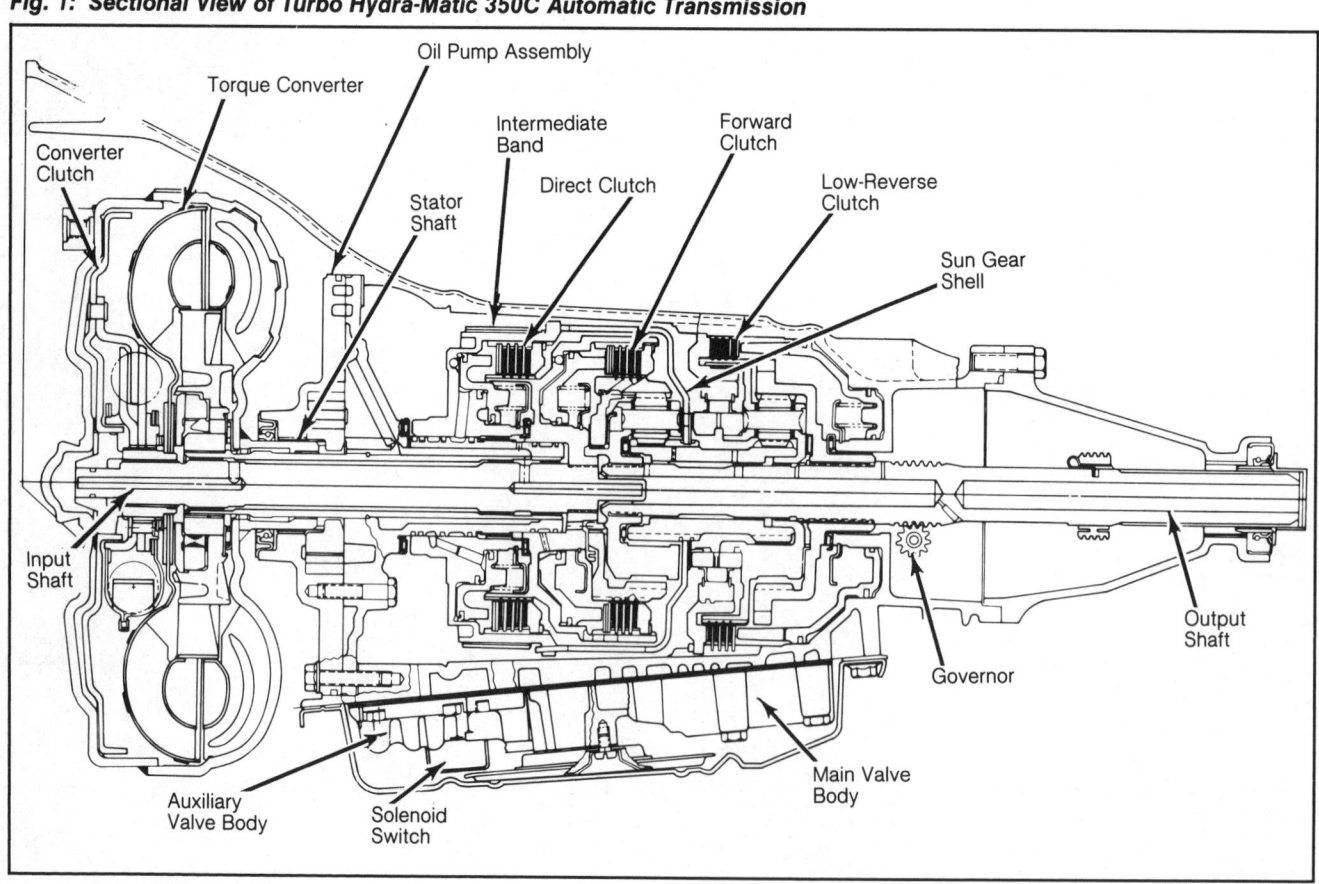

GENERAL MOTORS TURBO HYDRA-MATIC 350C (Cont.)

TESTING

ROAD TEST

Drive Range

With selector lever in "D", accelerate vehicle from zero MPH. A 1-2 and 2-3 shift should occur at all throttle openings. (Shift points will vary with throttle openings.) As vehicle speed decreases to zero MPH, 3-2 and 2-1 shifts should occur.

"2" – Forward Range (L2)

Place selector lever in "2" and accelerate vehicle from zero MPH. A 1-2 shift should occur at all throttle openings. (No 2-3 shift can be obtained in this range.) The 1-2 shift point will vary with throttle opening. As vehicle speed decreases to zero MPH, a 2-1 shift should occur. The 1-2 shift in intermediate range is somewhat firmer than a drive range. This is normal.

Low Range (L1)

Place selector in "L" and accelerate vehicle from zero MPH. No upshift should occur in this range.

2nd Gear (L2) – Overrun Braking

With selector lever in "D", and vehicle speed at approximately 35 MPH with foot off accelerator, move selector lever to "2" position. Transmission should downshift to second gear. An increase in engine RPM and an engine braking effect should be noticed.

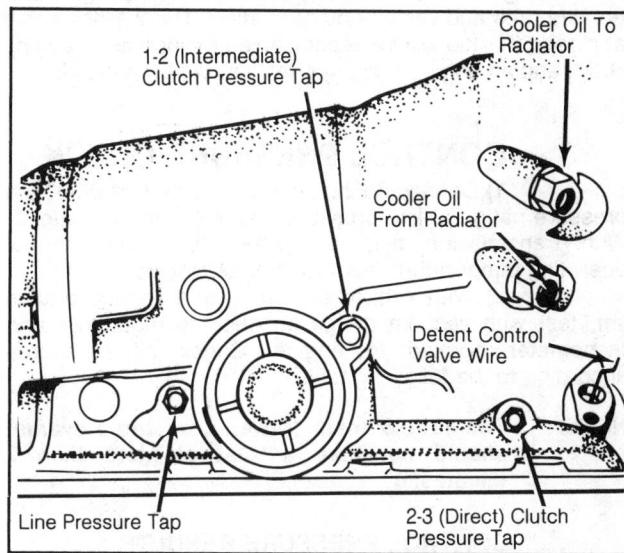

Fig. 2: Pressure Take-Off Points

1st Gear (L-1) – Overrun Braking

With selector lever in "2" position, throttle closed, and vehicle speed at approximately 30 to 50 MPH, move selector lever to "L". A 2-1 downshift should occur in

CONTROL PRESSURE SPECIFICATIONS — psi (kg/cm²)

Range	Models	Modulator [1] Line Connected	Modulator [2] Line Disconnected
DRIVE — BRAKES APPLIED [3]	WD, WH, WJ, WE, KE	57-63 (4.0-4.4)	125-135 (8.8-9.5)
	KA, KC, KN, V4	57-63 (4.0-4.4)	145-165 (10.2-11.6)
	LB, LJ	64-70 (4.5-4.9)	120-130 (8.4-9.1)
	LD	64-70 (4.5-4.9)	140-152 (9.8-10.7)
L2 or L1 — BRAKES APPLIED [3]	WD, WH, WJ, WE, KE	85-93 (5.9-6.5)	125-135 (8.8-9.5)
	KA, KC, KN, V4	83-91 (5.8-6.4)	145-165 (10.2-11.6)
	LB, LJ	79-87 (5.6-6.1)	120-130 (8.4-9.1)
	LD	95-105 (6.7-7.4)	140-152 (9.8-10.7)
REVERSE — BRAKES APPLIED [3]	WD, WH, WJ, WE, KE	88-96 (6.2-6.7)	225-245 (15.8-17.2)
	KA, KC, KN, V4	85-96 (6.0-6.7)	230-280 (16.2-19.7)
	LB, LJ	95-106 (6.7-7.5)	205-220 (14.4-15.5)
	LD	98-108 (6.7-7.4)	230-245 (16.2-17.2)
NEUTRAL — BRAKES APPLIED	WP, WH, WJ, WE, KE	55-64 (3.9-4.5)	119-139 (8.4-9.8)
	KA, KC, V4, KN	57-63 (4.0-4.4)	145-165 (10.2-11.6)
	LB, LJ	64-70 (4.5-4.9)	120-130 (8.4-9.1)
	LD	64-70 (4.5-4.9)	140-152 (9.8-10.7)
DRIVE IDLE SET ENGINE IDLE TO SPECIFICATIONS BRAKES APPLIED	WD, WH, WJ, WE, KE	57-63 (4.0-4.4)	....
	KA, KC, V4, KN	57-63 (4.0-4.4)	....
	LB, LJ	64-70 (4.5-4.9)	....
	LD	64-70 (4.5-4.9)	....
DRIVE — 30 MPH CLOSED THROTTLE OR ON HOIST	WD, WH, WJ, WE, KE	57-63 (4.0-4.4)	....
	KA, KC, V4, KN	57-63 (4.0-4.4)	....
	LB, LJ	64-70 (4.5-4.9)	....
	LD	64-70 (4.5-4.9)	....

[1] — MODULATOR LINE CONNECTED: Run engine to 1,000 RPM, close throttle and check PSI.

[2] — MODULATOR LINE DISCONNECTED: Check PSI at 1,000 RPM, throttle open.

[3] — Total elapsed time for DRIVE, LOW and REVERSE tests not to exceed 2 minutes.

GENERAL MOTORS TURBO HYDRA-MATIC 350C (Cont.)

speed range of approximately 45 to 30 MPH, depending on axle ratio and valve body calibration. The 2-1 downshift at closed throttle will be accompanied by increased engine RPM, and an engine braking effect should be noticed.

CONTROL PRESSURE CHECK

1) Connect tachometer to engine and 0-300 psi pressure gauge at line pressure take-off point. *See Fig. 2.* With transmission fluid at correct level and normal operating temperature, perform test as follows:

2) With vehicle stationary and service brakes set, test with vacuum gauge attached to modulator and tachometer hooked to engine. Check oil pressures according to the following table.

NOTE: The first 3 tests (Drive, Low and Reverse) should not take a total of more than 2 minutes.

CONTROL PRESSURE RESULTS

Control Pressure Too High

- Vacuum leak or improper engine vacuum
- Vacuum modulator valve stuck; water in modulator; modulator valve damaged or not operating properly
- Detent valve or cable stuck in detent position
- Valve body pressure regulator and/or boost valve stuck; boost valve sleeve broken or defective; incorrect pressure regulator valve spring; 2-3 shift control valve and sleeve installed in pressure regulator bore; pressure regulator exhaust hole blocked or not drilled

Control Pressure Too Low

- Low transmission fluid level
- Defective vacuum modulator assembly
- Oil screen blocked or restricted, or gasket omitted or damaged
- Incorrect oil pump gear clearance; pump gears damaged, worn or installed backwards; pump-to-case gasket out of position; defective pump body and/or cover; bottom seal ring on pump cover hub omitted or damaged; priming valve in pump omitted
- Valve body pressure regulator or boost valve stuck; pressure regulator valve spring too weak; No. 1 check ball omitted from valve body; loose valve body bolts; valve body spacer plate support omitted; reverse and modulator boost valve stuck
- Internal leak in forward clutch circuit (pressure low in Drive, normal in Neutral and Reverse); check pump oil seal rings and forward clutch seals
- Internal leak in direct clutch circuit (pressure low in Reverse, normal in other ranges); direct clutch outer seal and 1-2 and 2-3 accumulator pistons and rings damaged or missing
- Intermediate servo piston seal ring broken or omitted
- Check ball missing from cored passage in transmission case face

No Control Pressure

- Flashing blocking suction cavity in case
- Priming valve in pump omitted
- Front pump drive gear lugs sheared off
- Vacuum modulator valve omitted
- Pump-to-case gasket incorrectly installed

GOVERNOR PRESSURE CHECK

1) With vehicle on a hoist (rear wheels off ground), disconnect vacuum line to modulator, then install a tachometer to engine and a pressure gauge to line pressure take-off point on transmission case. *See Fig. 2.*

2) Start engine, keep foot off brake, move shift lever to Drive range, and check line pressure with engine speed at 1000 RPM. Slowly increase engine speed to 3000 RPM and determine if a pressure drop occurs (7 psi or more).

3) If no pressure drop takes place, inspect governor for a stuck valve or weight, or a restricted orifice in governor valve. Check governor feed system for a plugged or restricted screen in control valve assembly, restrictions in feed line, or scored governor bore.

CLUTCH AND BAND APPLICATION CHART (ELEMENTS IN USE)

Selector Lever Position	Intermed. Clutch	Direct Clutch	Forward Clutch	Low & Reverse Clutch	Intermed. Overrun Roller Clutch	Low & Reverse Roller Clutch	Intermed. Overrun Band
D — DRIVE							
First Gear			X			X	
Second Gear	X		X		X		
Third Gear	X	X	X				
2 — INTERMEDIATE							
Second Gear	X		X		X		X
1 — LOW (First)			X	X		X	
R — REVERSE		X		X			

NEUTRAL OR PARK — All clutches and bands released and/or ineffective.

GENERAL MOTORS TURBO HYDRA-MATIC 350C (Cont.)

Fig. 3: *Turbo Hydra-Matic 350C Hydraulic Circuits Diagram*

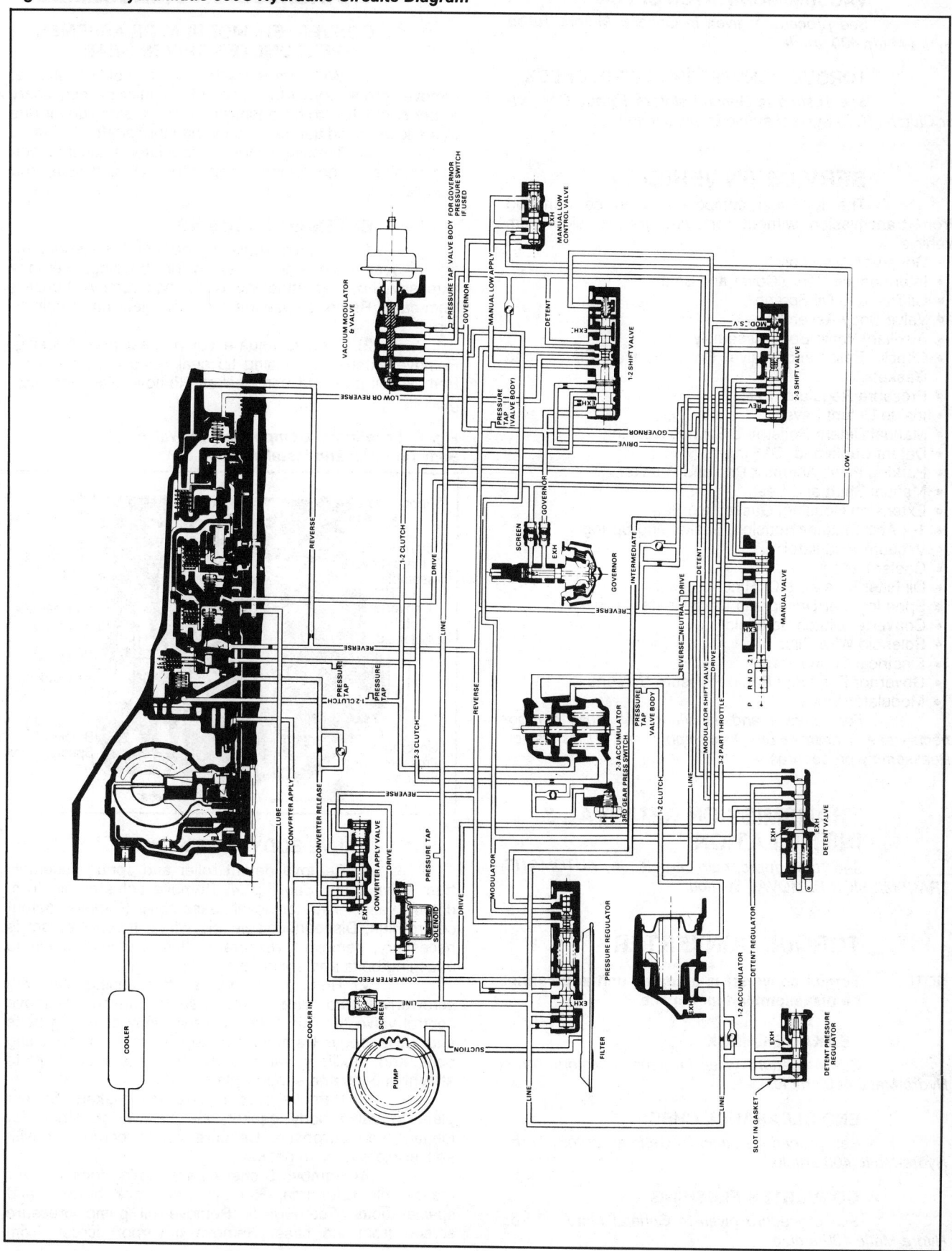

GENERAL MOTORS TURBO HYDRA-MATIC 350C (Cont.)

VACUUM MODULATOR CHECK

See procedure given in General Motors Turbo Hydra-Matic 400 article.

TORQUE CONVERTER CLUTCH CHECK

See Testing in General Motors Torque Converter Clutch (TCC) System article in this section.

SERVICE (IN VEHICLE)

The following components can be removed from transmission without removing transmission from vehicle:

- Governor Assembly
- Intermediate Servo Cover and Seals
- Oil Pan and Oil Screen
- Valve Body Assembly
- Auxiliary Valve Body Assembly
- Check Balls and Valve Body Spacer Plates and Gaskets
- Pressure Regulator Parts
- Inside Detent Lever
- Manual Detent Roller and Spring Assembly
- Detent Cable and "O" Ring
- Parking Pawl, Actuator Rod and Bracket
- Manual Shaft and Seal
- Extension Housing, Gasket and Seal
- 1-2 Accumulator Housing, Gasket and Spring
- Vacuum Modulator
- Cooler Fittings
- Oil Filter Pipe and "O" Ring
- Speedometer Driven and Drive Gears
- Converter Clutch Solenoid
- Solenoid Wire Clips
- Electrical Connectors
- Governor Feed and Pump Pressure Screens
- Modulator Valve

For removal and installation of these components, see Transmission Disassembly and Transmission Reassembly procedures.

TRANSMISSION REMOVAL & INSTALLATION

See the appropriate article in AUTOMATIC TRANSMISSION REMOVAL Section.

TORQUE CONVERTER

NOTE: **Torque converter is a sealed unit and cannot be disassembled for service.**

LEAKAGE CHECK

See procedure given in General Motors Turbo Hydra-Matic 400 article.

END CLEARANCE CHECK

See procedure given in General Motors Turbo Hydra-Matic 400 article.

CONVERTER FLUSHING

See procedure given in General Motors Turbo Hydra-Matic 400 article.

TRANSMISSION DISASSEMBLY

CONVERTER, MODULATOR ASSEMBLY & SPEEDOMETER DRIVEN GEAR

1) With transmission in a holding fixture, remove torque converter assembly. It may be necessary to pry converter from transmission with a screwdriver due to a suction condition caused by the input shaft "O" ring.

2) Remove vacuum modulator attaching bolt and retainer, then remove modulator, "O" ring seal, and modulator valve from case.

EXTENSION HOUSING

1) Remove retaining bolt and speedometer driven gear from side of extension housing. Remove extension housing attaching bolts then remove housing from case. Remove speedometer drive gear and retaining clip.

2) Remove square cut oil seal from housing. Remove extension housing lip seal using a screwdriver. Remove oil pan and pan gasket. Remove filter and filter gasket.

Fig. 4: Location of Components for Valve Body Removal and Installation

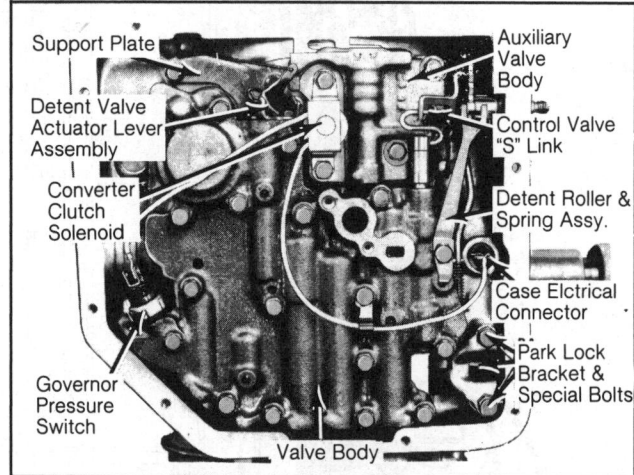

VALVE BODY ASSEMBLY

1) Remove detent roller and spring assembly from valve body. *See Fig. 4.* Remove actuator pin from detent valve actuator lever assembly. Remove detent control link. Disconnect solenoid wires. If replacement is necessary, remove pressure switch. Remove solenoid attaching bolts and solenoid.

2) Remove manual shaft retaining clip with screwdriver and slide manual shaft outward. Remove control valve "S" link. Remove valve body attaching bolts and valve body. Remove auxiliary valve body attaching bolts and auxiliary valve body. Remove support plate attaching bolts and support plate.

3) Remove spacer plate and gaskets. Spacer plate to valve body gasket has Yellow ink stripe for identification purposes. Be sure not to confuse it with spacer plate to case gasket.

4) Remove 5 check balls, noting locations for reassembly reference. Remove park lock bracket and special bolts. *See Fig. 5.* Remove oil pump pressure screen from the case. Remove governor screen from

GENERAL MOTORS TURBO HYDRA-MATIC 350C (Cont.)

case. Remove case electrical connector and "O" ring by depressing tabs.

Fig. 5: Location of Check Balls, Oil Pump Screen and Governor Feed Screen

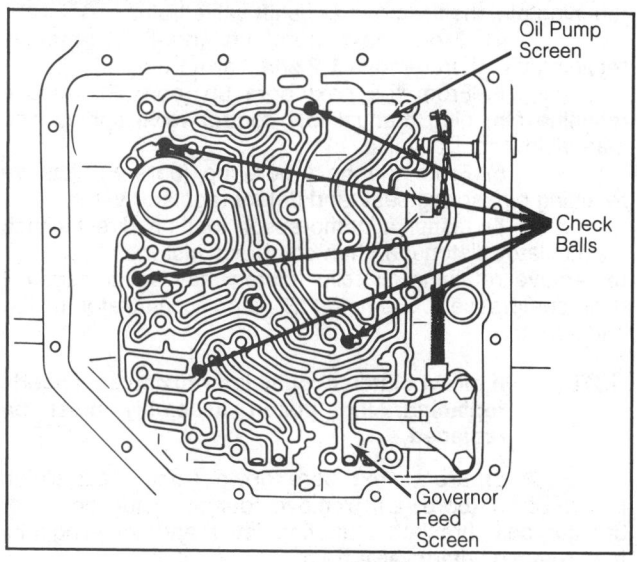

MANUAL SHAFT & PARKING PAWL

1) Remove jam nut holding range selctor lever inner lever to manual shaft. Remove manual shaft from case. Remove range selector inner lever and parking pawl actuating rod. Remove manual shaft to case lip seal, if necessary.

Fig. 6: Bottom View of Transmission Showing Parking Pawl Assembly

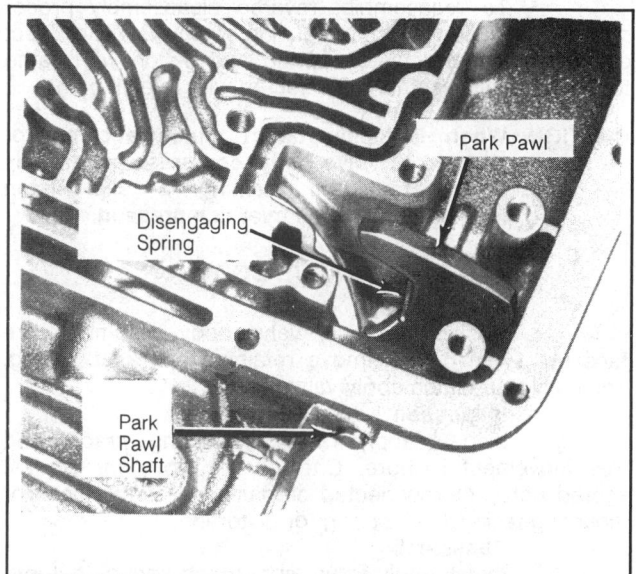

2) Remove parking pawl retaining plug, parking pawl shaft, parking pawl and disengaging spring. See Fig. 6. Remove intermediate servo piston, washer, spring seat, and apply pin. See Fig. 7. If piston or seal needs replacement, both will have to be replaced as an assembly.

Fig. 7: Intermediate Servo Removal

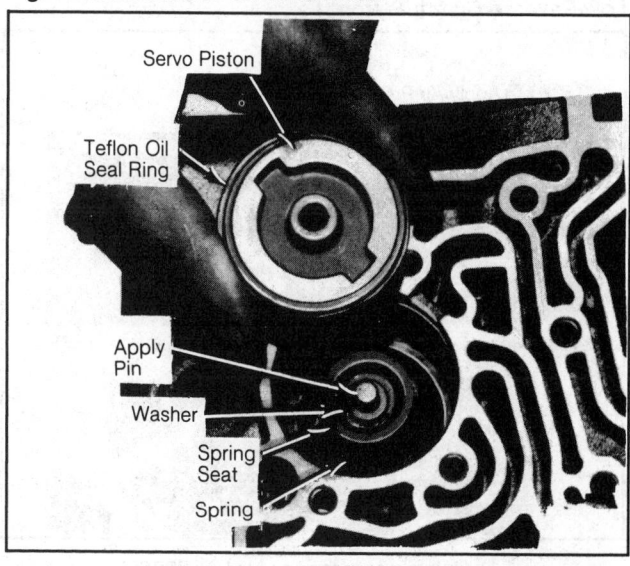

OIL PUMP & INTERNAL COMPONENTS

1) Remove oil pump to case attaching bolts with washer type seals, then discard seals. Install 2 slide hammers into threaded holes in pump body, tighten jam nuts and remove pump from case. Remove and discard gasket.

2) Remove intermediate clutch cushion spring, faced clutch plates, steel separator plates, wave spring and pressure plate from case. Remove intermediate overrun brake band. Grasp input shaft and pull direct and forward clutches from case as an assembly.

3) Remove forward clutch housing-to-input ring gear front thrust washer. Remove input ring gear and ring gear-to-output carrier needle thrust bearing. Remove output carrier-to-output shaft snap ring and remove output carrier.

4) Remove sun gear driving shell assembly. Remove low and reverse roller clutch support-to-case snap ring. Grasp output shaft and pull up until low and reverse roller clutch and support assembly clears retainer spring. Then remove suport assembly from case. Remove retainer (anti-clunk) spring.

5) Remove low and reverse clutch faced plates and steel separator plates, noting number and position of plates used for reassembly reference. Remove reaction carrier assembly from output ring gear and shaft assembly, then remove output ring gear and shaft assembly from case. Remove reaction carrier-to-output ring gear needle thrust bearing.

6) Remove output ring gear to case needle bearing assembly from output shaft assembly or case. If necessary, remove ring gear to output shaft snap ring, then remove output ring gear from ouput shaft. Using a compressor tool, compress low and reverse clutch piston spring retainer.

7) Remove piston retaining ring, spring retainer and springs. Remove low and reverse clutch piston assembly by applying air pressure to oil passage in case. See Fig. 8. Remove seals from low and reverse clutch piston.

GENERAL MOTORS TURBO HYDRA-MATIC 350C (Cont.)

Fig. 8: Using Compressed Air to Remove
Low-Reverse Clutch Piston

Apply Air Pressure Here to
Remove Low-Reverse Piston

8) Using compressor tool (J-23069), compress intermediate clutch accumulator piston cover and remove retaining ring. Remove cover, "O" ring seal, accumulator piston spring, and piston assembly.

NOTE: Do not remove accumulator piston teflon oil seal rings. If seal rings are damaged, the piston assembly must be replaced.

Fig. 9: Exploded View of Intermediate
Accumulator Assembly

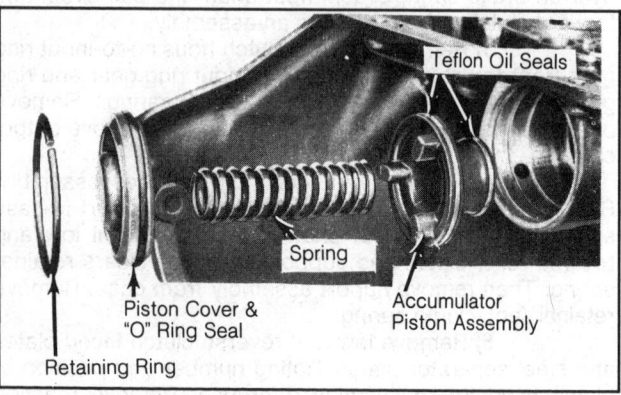

Teflon Oil Seals

Spring

Piston Cover &
"O" Ring Seal

Accumulator
Piston Assembly

Retaining Ring

COMPONENT DISASSEMBLY & REASSEMBLY

VALVE BODY

NOTE: As valve trains are removed from each valve body bore, place individual parts in correct order and in relative position to valve body to simplify reassembly. Valves and springs are not interchangeable, and all parts must be installed in correct order in proper valve body bore.

Disassembly

1) Position valve body assembly with cored face up and direct clutch accumulator piston pocket positioned at upper left. Remove manual valve from lower left hand bore (bore J).

2) From lower right hand bore (bore A) remove retaining pin, then remove pressure regulator valve train.

3) From next bore up (bore B), remove retaining pin, then remove 2-3 shift valve train.

4) From next bore up (bore C), remove retaining pin, then remove 1-2 shift valve train.

5) From the next bore up (bore E), remove retaining pin, plug manual low control valve spring, and manual low control valve.

6) From the next bore up (bore F), remove retaining pin, spring seat, and detent regulator valve.

7) Install a compressor tool on direct clutch accumulator piston (G), then compress piston only enough to remove retaining "E" clip (piston may be damaged if over compressed). Remove "E" clip, accumulator piston and spring.

NOTE: If direct clutch accumulator piston seal needs replacing, the piston assembly must be replaced.

8) From next bore down from direct clutch accumulator (bore D), remove detent actuating lever bracket bolt, bracket, actuating lever and retaining pin, then remove detent valve train.

Inspection

Wash all parts in cleaning solvent, air dry and blow out all passages. Inspect all valves for scoring, cracks, and free movement in their bores. Inspect sleeves for cracks, scratches, or distortion. Inspect valve body for cracks, scored bores, interconnected oil passages and flatness of mounting face. Check all springs for distortion or collapsed coils.

Reassembly

To reassemble, reverse disassembly procedure. Align piston and oil seal ring when installing direct clutch accumulator piston spring and piston with same tool used at disassembly and secure with retaining ring.

CAUTION: When installing direct clutch accumulator piston into valve body, compress piston only enough to install retaining "E" clip. Piston may be damaged if over compressed.

AUXILIARY VALVE BODY

Disassembly

Position auxiliary valve body assembly core face up. From bore, remove retaining pin, seat, spring, and converter clutch apply valve.

Inspection

Inspect apply valve for scoring, cracks and free movement in bore. Check valve body for cracks, scored bore, interconnected oil passage, and flatness of mounting face. Check spring for distortion.

Reassembly

Install apply valve, spring and spring seat into bore. Install retaining pin.

OIL PUMP

Disassembly

1) Remove pump cover-to-body attaching bolts. Remove intermediate clutch return springs and retainer assembly and clutch piston assembly from pump cover. Remove inner and outer seals from piston.

GENERAL MOTORS TURBO HYDRA-MATIC 350C (Cont.)

Fig. 10: Exploded View of Valve Body Assembly

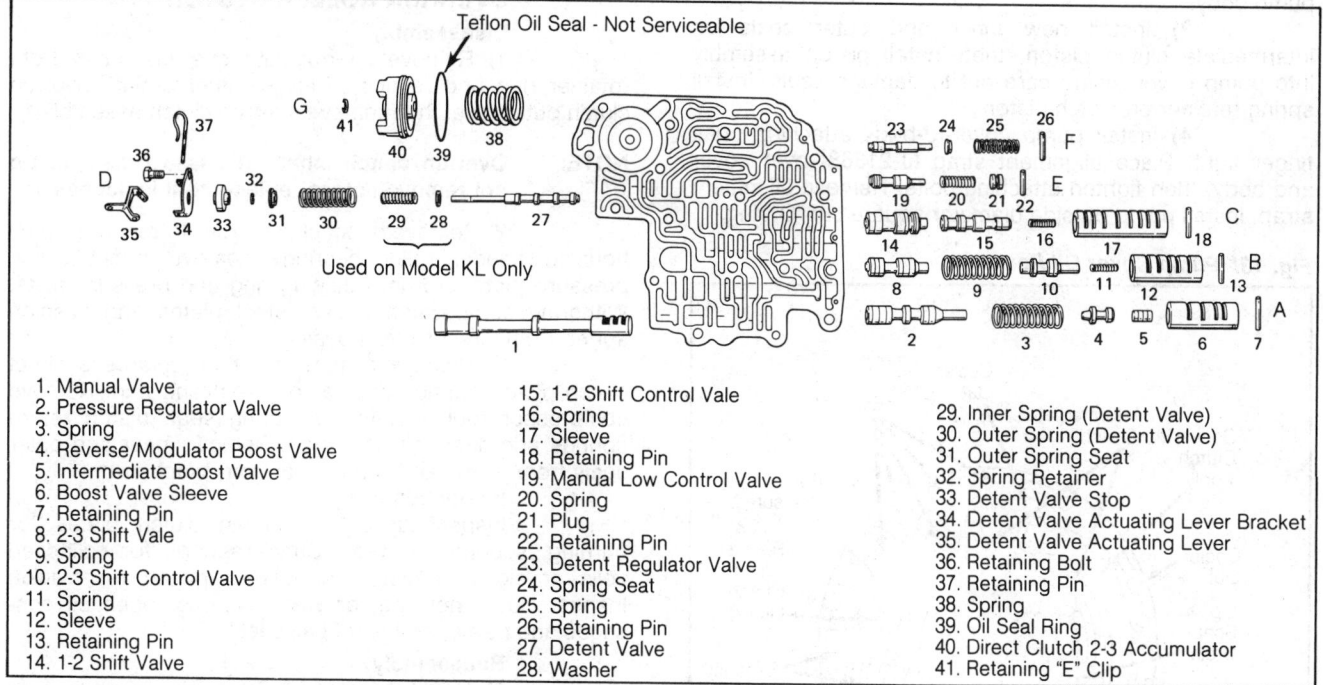

1. Manual Valve
2. Pressure Regulator Valve
3. Spring
4. Reverse/Modulator Boost Valve
5. Intermediate Boost Valve
6. Boost Valve Sleeve
7. Retaining Pin
8. 2-3 Shift Vale
9. Spring
10. 2-3 Shift Control Valve
11. Spring
12. Sleeve
13. Retaining Pin
14. 1-2 Shift Valve

15. 1-2 Shift Control Vale
16. Spring
17. Sleeve
18. Retaining Pin
19. Manual Low Control Valve
20. Spring
21. Plug
22. Retaining Pin
23. Detent Regulator Valve
24. Spring Seat
25. Spring
26. Retaining Pin
27. Detent Valve
28. Washer

29. Inner Spring (Detent Valve)
30. Outer Spring (Detent Valve)
31. Outer Spring Seat
32. Spring Retainer
33. Detent Valve Stop
34. Detent Valve Actuating Lever Bracket
35. Detent Valve Actuating Lever
36. Retaining Bolt
37. Retaining Pin
38. Spring
39. Oil Seal Ring
40. Direct Clutch 2-3 Accumulator
41. Retaining "E" Clip

Fig. 11: Auxiliary Valve Body Exploded View

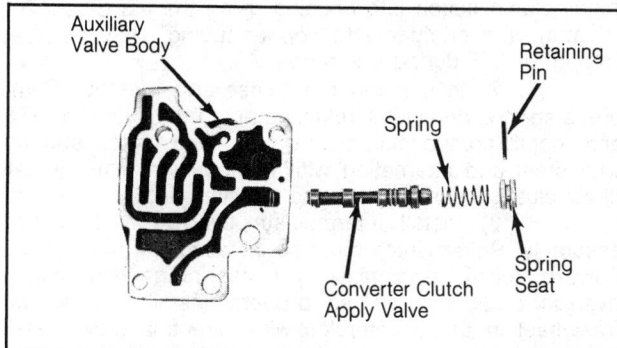

Fig. 12: Oil Pump Body Oil Passages

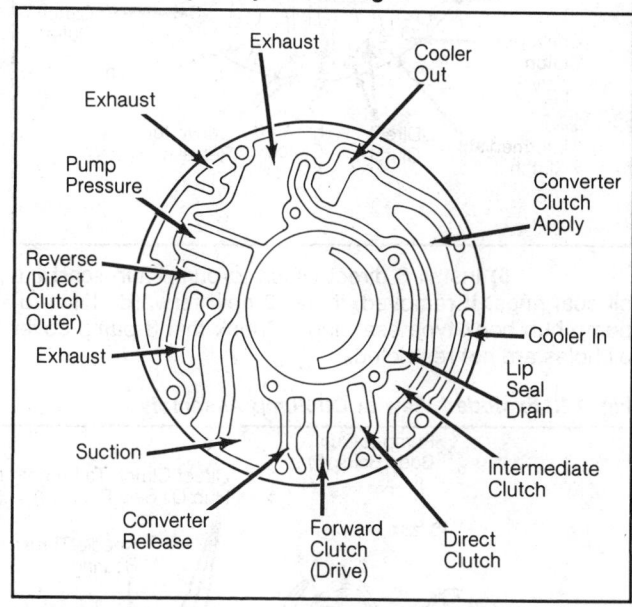

2) Remove 3 direct clutch-to-pump hub oil rings. If damaged, remove 2 forward clutch-to-pump hub teflon oil seal rings. Remove pump cover-to-direct clutch drum needle thrust bearings and, if equipped, remove input shaft end play adjusting shim.

NOTE: If replacement of forward clutch-to-pump hub teflon oil seal rings is necessary, use 2 metal hook-type service replacement rings.

3) Check steady ring. If cut or frozen in groove, remove and replace with a new ring of the same color. The different colors compensate for groove depth. ALWAYS replace this ring with a new ring of the same color.

4) Separate pump cover and stator shaft assembly from pump body. Remove pump drive gear and driven gear from pump body. Remove pump to case square cut "O" ring seal. If required, remove pump body-to-converter hub lip seal.

Inspection

1) Wash all parts in cleaning solvent, blow out all passages and air dry. Do not use rags to dry parts. Inspect pump drive and driven gears, gear packet and crescent for nicks, scoring, or other damage. Inspect pump body and cover for nicks or scoring.

2) Inspect pump cover hub outer diameter for nicks or burrs which might damage direct clutch drum bushing. Check pump cover and hub lubrication holes for restrictions. If replacement of forward clutch teflon seal rings is necessary, replace with 2 metal hook type rings.

Reassembly

1) If pump body oil seal was removed, place pump body on wood blocks, coat outside diameter of new seal with a non-hardening sealer, then install seal fully into its counterbore.

2) Install pump drive and driven gear. Drive gear has offset tangs. Assemble with tang face up to

GENERAL MOTORS TURBO HYDRA-MATIC 350C (Cont.)

prevent damage to converter. Assemble pump cover to pump body.

3) Install new inner and outer seals on intermediate clutch piston, then install piston assembly into pump cover, using care not to damage seals. Install spring retainer on clutch piston.

4) Install pump cover-to-body attaching bolts finger tight. Place alignment strap (J-21368) over cover and body, then tighten attaching bolts. Remove alignment strap. Install pump outside diameter square cut "O" ring.

Fig. 13: Pump Cover Oil Passages

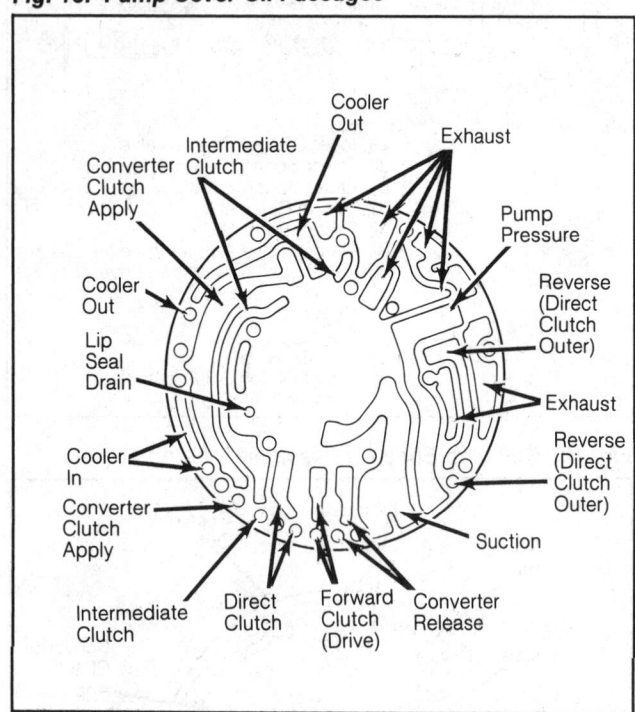

5) Install 3 direct clutch-to-pump hub scarf cut oil seal rings. If removed, install 2 new forward clutch-to-pump hub hook-type seal rings. Check that 3 pump cover oil holes are not restricted.

DIRECT CLUTCH & INTERMEDIATE OVERRUN ROLLER CLUTCH

Disassembly

1) Remove intermediate overrun clutch front retainer ring and retainer. Remove intermediate overrun clutch outer race, then remove overrun clutch assembly.

NOTE: Overrun clutch inner race is a press fit. Do not remove unless replacement is necessary.

2) Remove direct clutch drum-to-forward clutch housing needle roller bearing. Remove direct clutch pressure plate-to-drum retaining ring and pressure plate. Withdraw composition plates, steel plates and cushion spring from direct clutch housing.

3) Using a compressor tool, compress direct clutch piston springs and remove retaining ring. Remove compressor tool and lift out spring seat, piston return springs and direct clutch piston. Remove inner and outer seals from piston and center seal from clutch drum.

Inspection

Inspect drive and driven clutch plates for burning, scoring, or wear. Check springs for collapsed coils or signs of distortion. Inspect piston for cracks. Inspect clutch housing for wear, scoring, open oil passages and free operation of ball check.

Reassembly

1) Install inner and outer seals (lips down) on clutch piston. Install center seal (lip up) in clutch drum, and install clutch piston into housing using the aid of a .020" (.5 mm) wire crimped into copper tubing. Use a liberal amount of ATF during assembly.

2) Install spring retainer and springs. Compress springs and install retaining ring. Lubricate with ATF and install composition plates and steel plates starting with steel and alternating with composition plate. Install direct clutch pressure plate and retaining ring.

3) Install intermediate overrun roller clutch assembly. Roller clutch must be installed with 4 holes up (toward front of transmission). Install intermediate clutch overrun outer race. When properly installed, it should freewheel in the counterclockwise direction only. Install intermediate overrun clutch retainer and retaining ring.

Fig. 14: Exploded View of Oil Pump Assembly

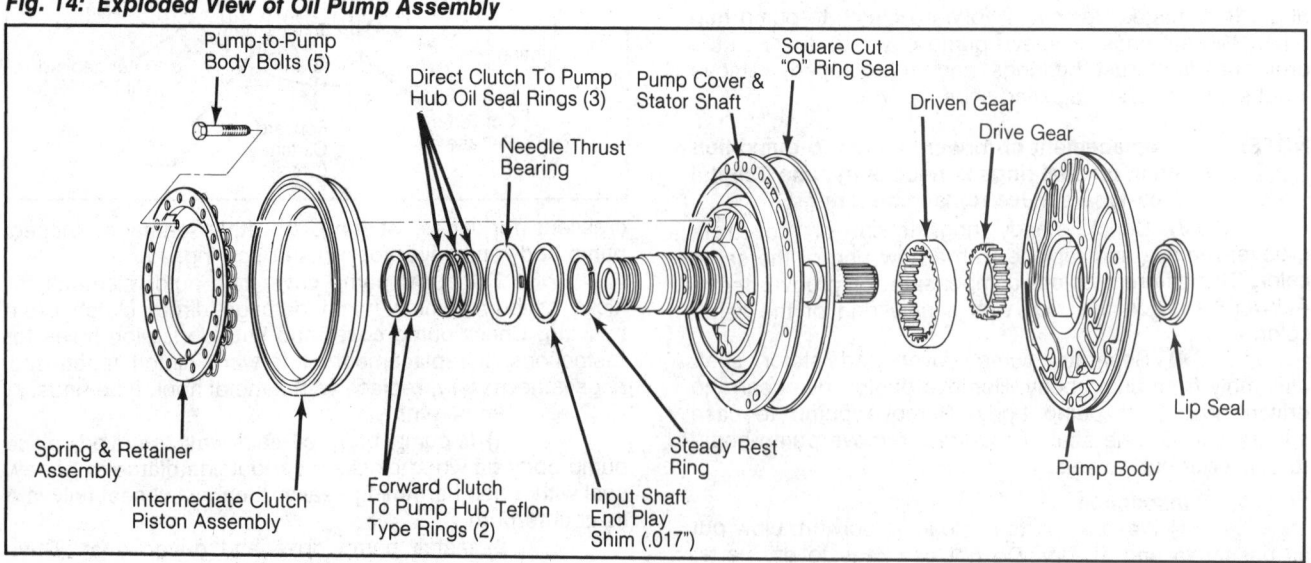

GENERAL MOTORS TURBO HYDRA-MATIC 350C (Cont.)

Fig. 15: Exploded View of Direct Clutch Assembly

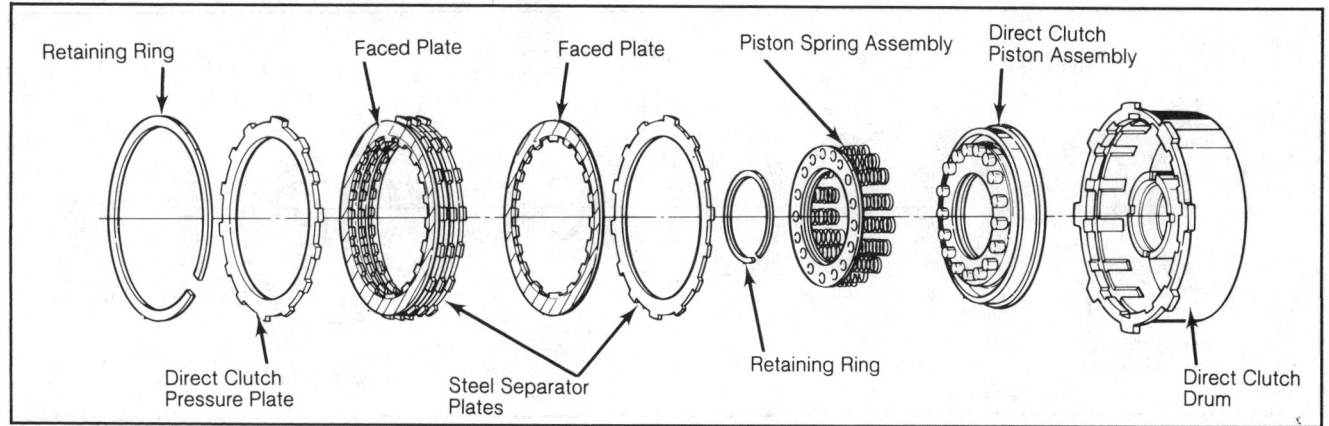

DIRECT & INTERMEDIATE CLUTCH PLATE USAGE

Trans. Code	Faced Plates	Steel Plates
Direct Clutch		
KA, KC, KE, KN [1]	3	3
All Others [2]	4	4
Intermediate Clutch		
KA, KC, KE, KN [3]	2	2
All Others [4]	3	3

[1] — Clutch piston thickness 1.014" (25.75 mm).
[2] — Clutch piston thickness .833" (21.16 mm).
[3] — Clutch piston thickness 1.184" (30.07 mm).
[4] — Clutch piston thickness .992" (25.20 mm).

Fig. 16: Exploded View of Intermediate Overrun Roller Clutch Assembly

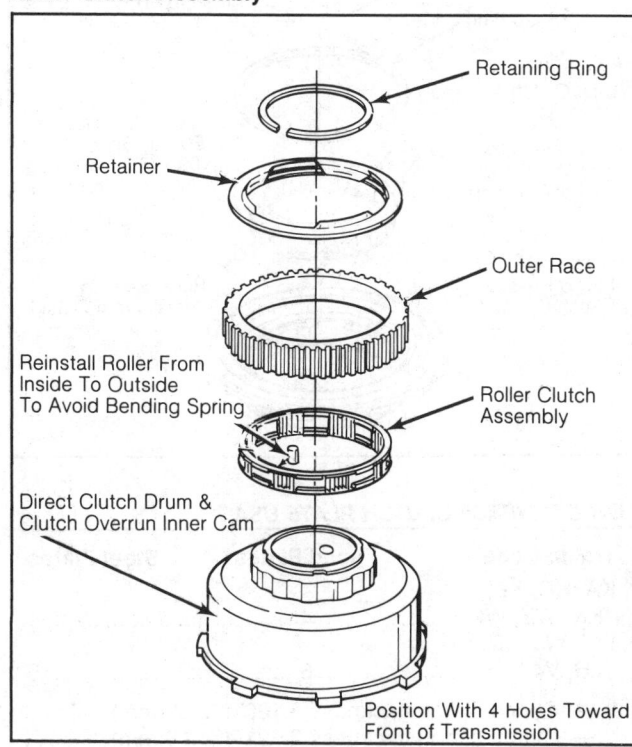

FORWARD CLUTCH

Disassembly

1) Remove forward clutch drum-to-pressure plate retaining ring, then remove pressure plate. Remove faced plates, steel separator plates and cushion spring, noting position and number used.

2) Using a ram compressor, compress forward clutch piston return spring and seat assembly and remove retaining ring. Remove tool, and lift out return springs, seat assembly, and forward clutch piston assembly.

3) Remove inner and outer seals from piston. If required, use wood blocks for support and press input shaft out of forward clutch housing.

NOTE: **When pressing the input shaft into the forward clutch housing, care must be taken not to place excessive force on the input shaft as damage may result.**

Inspection

1) Inspect lined and steel separator plates for signs of burning, scoring or wear. Inspect piston return springs for collapsed coils or signs of distortion or overheating. Inspect piston for cracks. Inspect clutch housing for wear, scoring, open oil passages and free operation of exhaust check ball.

2) Inspect input shaft for open lubrication passages at ends, damaged splines, damaged ground bushing journals, and cracks or distortion.

Reassembly

1) Install the forward clutch inner piston seal and outer piston seal, (if removed). Install the forward clutch piston assembly using a thin feeler gauge. Install spring retainer and springs. Compress spring retainer with an arbor or ram press.

2) Lubricate with ATF and install cushion spring, faced spring, faced plates and steel separator plates, starting with cushion spring and alternating steel and faced plates.

3) Using a feeler gauge, check clearance between forward clutch pressure plate and faced plate. Desired clearance is .011-.082" (.27-2.08 mm). Three thicknesses of pressure plates are available, identified by the number of tangs having markings. If necessary, select a replacement plate to give the desired clearance.

GENERAL MOTORS TURBO HYDRA-MATIC 350C (Cont.)

Fig.17: Exploded View of Forward Clutch Assembly

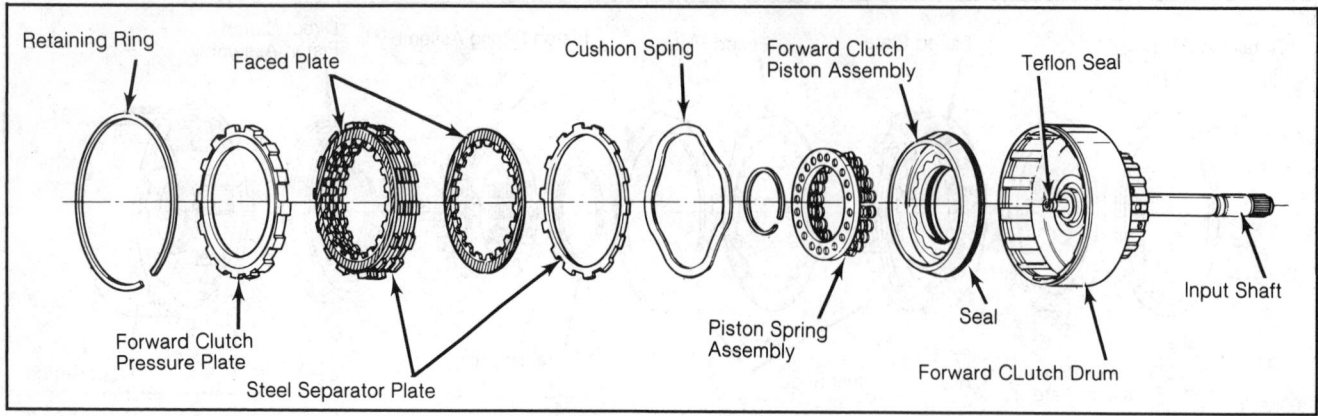

FORWARD CLUTCH PLATE USAGE

Trans. Code	Faced Plates	Steel Plates
KA, KC, KE, KN [1]	4	4
WE, WJ, V4 [2]	5	5
WD, WH [3]	4	4
LD, LB [4]	5	5

[1] — Clutch piston thickness 1.391" (35.33 mm).
[2] — Clutch piston thickness 1.223" (31.06 mm).
[3] — Clutch piston thickness 1.405" (35.68 mm).
[4] — Clutch piston thickness 1.221" (31.01 mm).

FORWARD CLUTCH PRESSURE PLATE THICKNESS

No. of Marks	In. (mm)
None	.245-.255 (6.22-6.47)
1 Mark	.275-.285 (6.98-7.23)
2 Marks	.306-.316 (7.77-8.02)

SUN GEAR & SUN GEAR DRIVE SHELL
Disassembly
Remove and discard sun gear to sun gear drive shell rear retaining ring. Remove sun gear to drive shell flat rear steel thrust washer. Remove sun gear assembly from drive shell, then remove and discard front retaining ring.

Reassembly
Install new front retaining ring on sun gear. Install sun gear into sun gear shell. Install sun gear to drive shell flat steel thrust washer. Install new sun gear to sun gear shell drive retaining ring.

NOTE: Do not overstress front and rear sun gear retaining rings when installing.

LOW & REVERSE ROLLER CLUTCH ASSEMBLY
Disassembly
Remove low-reverse clutch to sun gear shell thrust washer. Remove low-reverse overrun clutch inner race. Remove low-reverse roller clutch retaining ring. Remove low reverse roller clutch assembly.

Reassembly
1) Install low and reverse roller clutch assembly to inner race. Install overrun roller clutch assembly and inner race into low and reverse clutch support with 4 holes down or to rear of transmission. When properly installed, inner race should freewheel in clockwise direction only.

2) Install low and reverse clutch-to-cam retaining ring. Install low and reverse-to-sun gear driving shell thrust washer.

Fig. 18: Exploded View of Low and Reverse Clutch Support and Overrun Roller Clutch Assembly

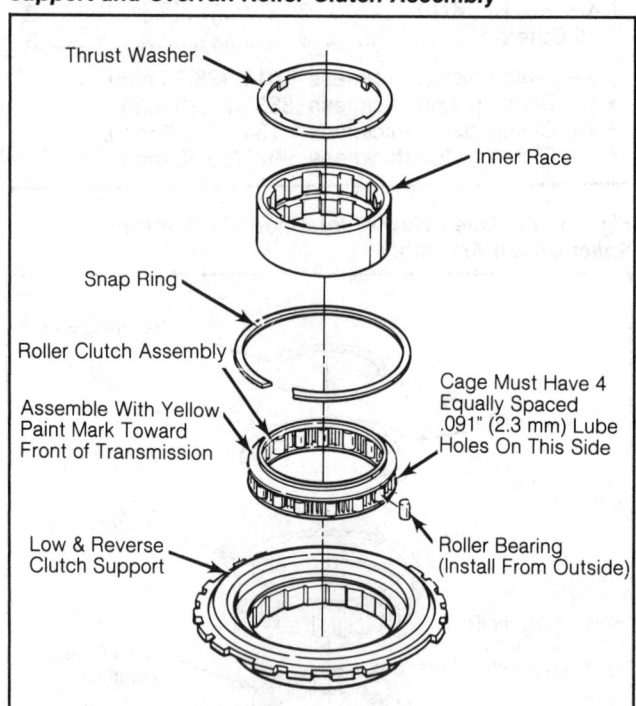

LOW & REVERSE CLUTCH PLATE USAGE

Trans. Code	Faced Plates	Steel Plates
KA, KC, KE, KN, WE, WH [1]	4	4
WE, WJ, LD, LB, V4 [2]	5	5

[1] — Clutch piston thickness 3.106" (78.89 mm).
[2] — Clutch piston thickness 2.921" (74.19 mm).

GENERAL MOTORS TURBO HYDRA-MATIC 350C (Cont.)

GOVERNOR ASSEMBLY

Governor, including driven gear, is serviced as a complete assembly. Driven gear, however, may be serviced separately. Disassembly is necessary to replace a driven gear. Disassembly may also be necessary due to improper operation.

Disassembly

Cut off one end of each governor weight pin and remove pins, thrust cap, weights and springs. Remove governor valve from governor sleeve.

NOTE: Governor weights are interchangeable from side to side and need not be identified.

Inspection

1) Wash all parts, air dry, and blow out all passages. Inspect governor sleeve for nicks, burrs, scoring or galling. Check governor sleeve for free operation in bore of case. Inspect valve for nicks, burrs, scoring or galling and for free operation in bore of governor sleeve.

2) Inspect driven gear for nicks, burrs, damage or looseness on governor sleeve. Inspect springs for distortion or damage. Check weights for free operation in their retainers. Check valve opening at entry and exhaust. It should be .020" (.5 mm) minimum.

Fig. 19: Exploded View of Governor Assembly

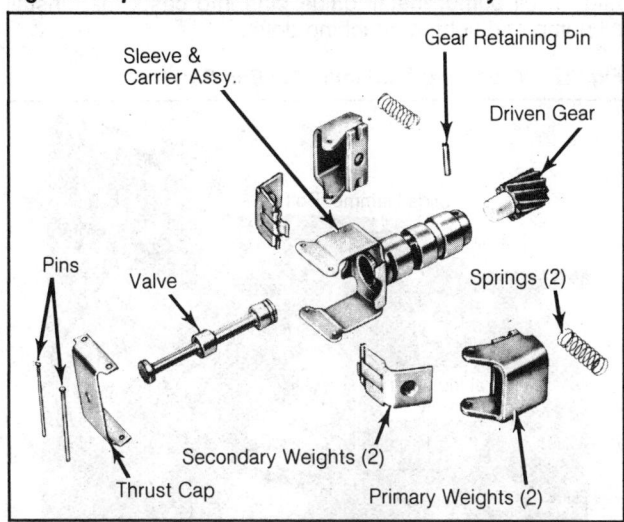

Driven Gear Replacement

1) Drive split retaining pin out of gear. Support governor on 3/16" plates installed in exhaust slots of governor sleeve, place in an arbor press, and with a long punch, press gear out of sleeve. Wash all parts to remove metal chips.

2) Support governor on 3/16" plates installed in exhaust slots of sleeve. Position new gear in sleeve, and using a socket, press gear into sleeve until nearly seated. Remove any chips that may have shaved off gear hub, then press gear in until it bottoms on shoulder.

3) Locate a new pin hole position 90 degrees from existing hole. Make hole with center punch and while supporting governor in press, drill a new 1/8" hole through sleeve and gear. Install split retaining pin. Wash governor assembly thoroughly to remove any metal clips.

Reassembly

1) Install governor valve in bore of sleeve (large land end first). Install weights and springs, and

thrust cap on governor sleeve. Align pin holes in thrust cap, weight assemblies and governor sleeve.

2) Install new pins and crimp both ends of pins to keep them from falling out. Check weight assemblies for free operation on pins. Check governor valve for free movement in governor sleeve.

TRANSMISSION REASSEMBLY

NOTE: When reassembling transmission, use only transmission fluid or petroleum jelly as lubricants to retain bearings or races. Lubricate all bearings, bushings, seal rings and clutch plates prior to reassembly.

INTERNAL COMPONENTS

1) Install inner, outer, and center seals on low and reverse clutch piston. Install piston into transmission case with notch on piston adjacent to parking pawl. Install piston return springs and spring retainer, compress retainer and install retaining snap ring.

NOTE: As spring retainer is compressed, make sure inner edge of retainer does not hang up in snap ring groove.

2) Install output ring on output shaft and retain with a new snap ring. Install reaction carrier-to-output ring gear needle thrust bearing with lip side face up. Install output ring gear-to-case needle thrust bearing assembly with lip on inner race pointing toward rear of transmission.

3) Install reaction carrier assembly into output ring gear and shaft assembly. Install output shaft and reaction carrier assembly into case. Oil and install low and reverse clutch plates, starting with a steel plate and alternating with faced plates.

4) Make sure notch in steel plates is placed toward bottom of case. Install low and reverse clutch support retainer (anti-clunk) spring. See Fig. 21. Install low and reverse clutch support assembly into case, pushing firmly until support assembly is seated past top of low and reverse support retainer spring. Install support-to-case retaining ring.

NOTE: Make sure splines on inner race of roller clutch align with splines on reaction carrier.

5) Install low-reverse clutch support inner race-to-sun gear drive shell thrust washer and install drive shell. Install output carrier assembly. Install input ring gear-to-output carrier needle thrust bearing (lip side face down), then install a new output carrier-to-output shaft snap ring.

6) Install input ring gear into case, then install forward clutch-to-input ring gear front thrust washer. Washer has 3 tangs. Install direct clutch drum-to-forward clutch housing needle roller bearing. Install direct clutch assembly to forward clutch assembly.

7) Install assemblies into case making sure forward clutch faced plates are positioned over input ring gear and tangs on direct clutch housing are installed into slots on sun gear drive shell. Install intermediate overrun brake band with anchor lug and apply lug positioned properly. Install intermediate clutch pressure plate.

8) After lubricating with transmission fluid, install intermediate clutch plates, starting with a faced

GENERAL MOTORS TURBO HYDRA-MATIC 350C (Cont.)

Fig. 20: Exploded View of Planetary Gear Train

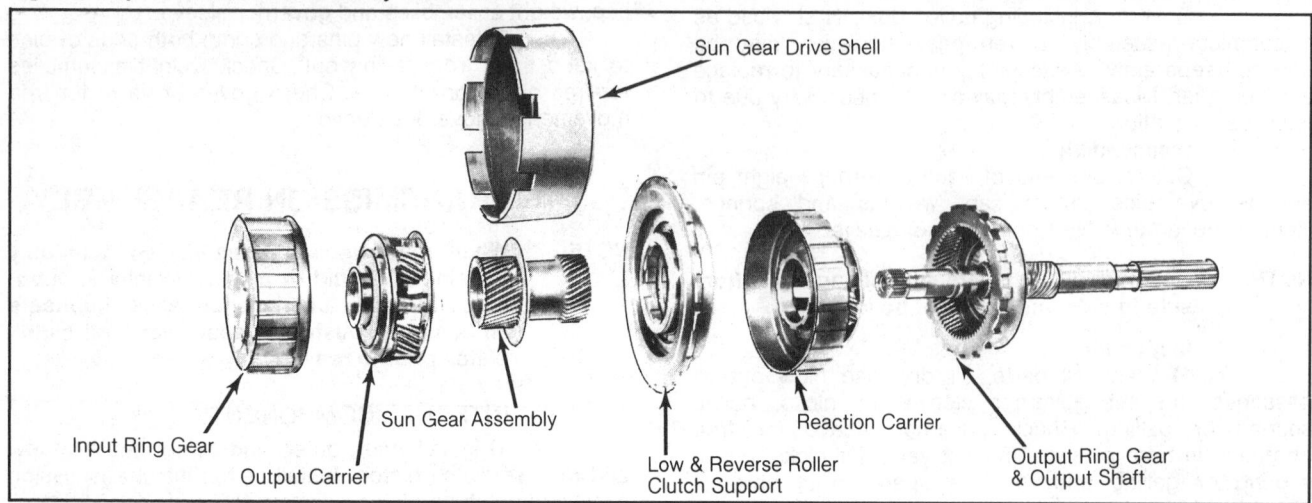

Sun Gear Drive Shell

Input Ring Gear

Output Carrier

Sun Gear Assembly

Low & Reverse Roller Clutch Support

Reaction Carrier

Output Ring Gear & Output Shaft

Fig. 21: Installing Low and Reverse Clutch Support Retainer (Anti-Clunk) Spring

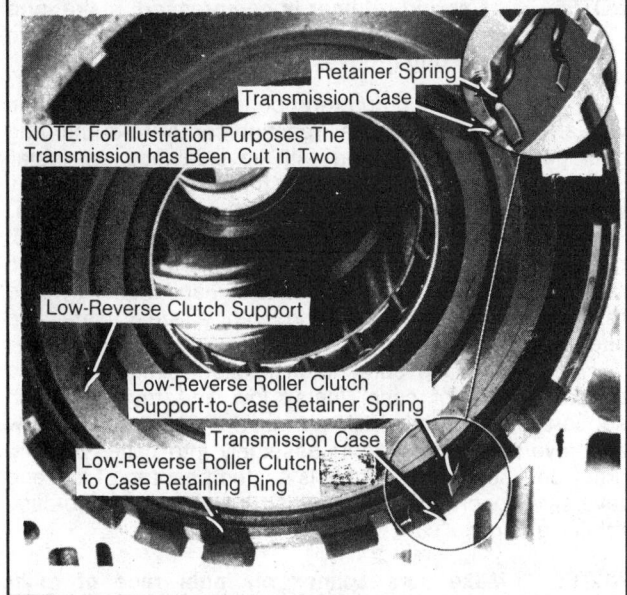

Retainer Spring
Transmission Case

NOTE: For Illustration Purposes The Transmission has Been Cut in Two

Low-Reverse Clutch Support

Low-Reverse Roller Clutch Support-to-Case Retainer Spring

Transmission Case

Low-Reverse Roller Clutch to Case Retaining Ring

plate, then alternating steel and faced plates. Install intermediate clutch cushion spring.

9) Install .017" (.43 mm) shim, and needle thrust bearing face down on pump cover hub. Before installation, coat both sides of shims and bearing with petroleum jelly. Lubricate oil pump bore in case, then install a new pump-to-case gasket. Install guide pins to case.

10) Install pump into case bore, remove guide pins and install 4 pump-to-case attaching bolts. Using new washer type seals, tighten bolts. If input shaft cannot be rotated as the pump is being pulled into place, the direct and forward clutch housings have not been properly installed to index the composition plates with their respective parts. Correct this condition before proceeding.

11) Install a slide hammer bolt into threaded hole in pump, then push input shaft rearward. Attach a dial indicator to slide hammer bolt, place indicator pointer on end of input shaft, and zero dial indicator. Push on end of output shaft and read resulting end play on indicator.

12) End play should be .010-.044" (.25-1.12 mm). If end play is not within specification, add or subtract .017" (.43 mm) adjusting shims, located between pump-to-direct clutch needle thrust bearing and oil pump.

13) Remove pump assembly and install correct thickness adjusting shim(s). Install a new square cut "O" ring on oil pump. Install guide pins into case, then install oil pump and tighten attaching bolts.

Fig. 22: Measuring Transmission End Play

Slide Hammer Bolt

Dial Indicator Assembly

SPEEDOMETER GEARS & EXTENSION HOUSING

1) Place speedometer drive gear retaining clip into hole in output shaft. Align slot in speedometer drive gear with retaining clip and install.

2) Position square-cut "O" ring seal on extension housing, mount extension housing to case, and install and tighten attaching bolts. Install speedometer driven gear and retainer. Install and tighten retainer bolt.

MANUAL LINKAGE

1) Install parking pawl into case, with tooth toward inside of case. Install parking pawl shaft into case through disengaging spring, install spring on parking pawl, and slide shaft through parking pawl.

2) Using a 3/8" diameter rod, drive a new shaft retaining plug into case until plug is flush to .010" (.25 mm)

GENERAL MOTORS TURBO HYDRA-MATIC 350C (Cont.)

below face of case. Stake plug in 3 places to retain in case.

Fig. 23: *Exploded View of Manual Shaft and Parking Pawl Components*

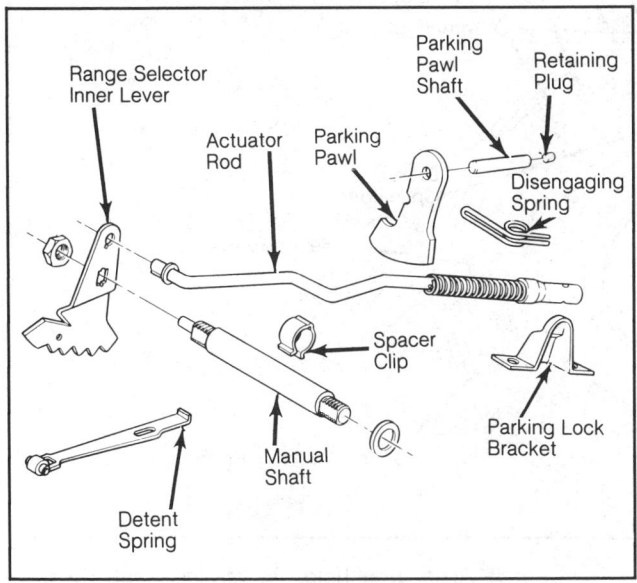

3) Install parking lock bracket and tighten bolts. Install actuator rod under parking lock bracket and parking pawl. If removed, install a new manual shaft-to-case lip seal. Install manual shaft through case and range selector inner lever. Install and tighten manual shaft jam nut. Install manual shaft-to-case spacer clip.

VALVE BODY & OIL PAN

1) Install intermediate servo piston, apply pin, spring and spring seat. Install check balls into correct transmission case pockets. *See Fig. 5.* Clean and install oil pump pressure screen (open end towards, front of case) and governor feed screen into case pockets. *See Fig. 5.*

NOTE: **If number "1" check ball is omitted or incorrectly positioned, transmission failure will result due to minimum line pressure.**

2) Install valve body spacer plate-to-case gasket, valve body spacer plate, and spacer plate-to-valve body gasket (Yellow stripe). Install spacer plate support plate and tighten attaching bolts. Install auxiliary valve body and tighten attaching bolts.

3) On all models, install valve body. Connect manual control valve link to range selector inner lever. Install manual shaft retaining clip. Tighten valve body attaching bolts in random sequence, leaving detent roller and spring bolt loose.

Fig. 24: *Bottom View of Transmission Case Showing Oil Passages*

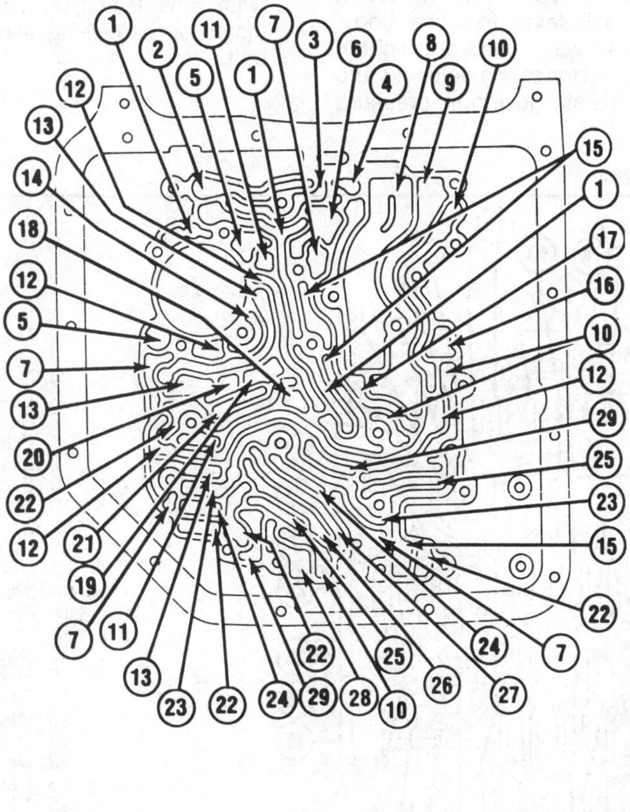

1. Direct Clutch (2-3)
2. Cooler In
3. Converter Apply
4. Converter Release
5. Intermediate Clutch (1-2)
6. Drive Forward Clutch
7. Drain
8. Suction
9. Pump Pressure
10. Reverse
11. Void
12. Intermediate Servo Release (R, N, D)
13. Line
14. 2-3 Clutch
15. Drive
16. Exhaust
17. Converter Feed
18. Exhaust Feed
19. Modulator or Detent Regulator
20. Exhaust Intermediate Clutch
21. Detent Regulator
22. Governor
23. Modulator
24. Detent 2
25. Low
26. Detent Modulator
27. Modulator Thru Detent Valve
28. Low Reverse Clutch
29. Manual Low Control

Automatic Transmissions

GENERAL MOTORS TURBO HYDRA-MATIC 350C (Cont.)

Fig. 25: Front View of Transmission Case Showing Oil Passages

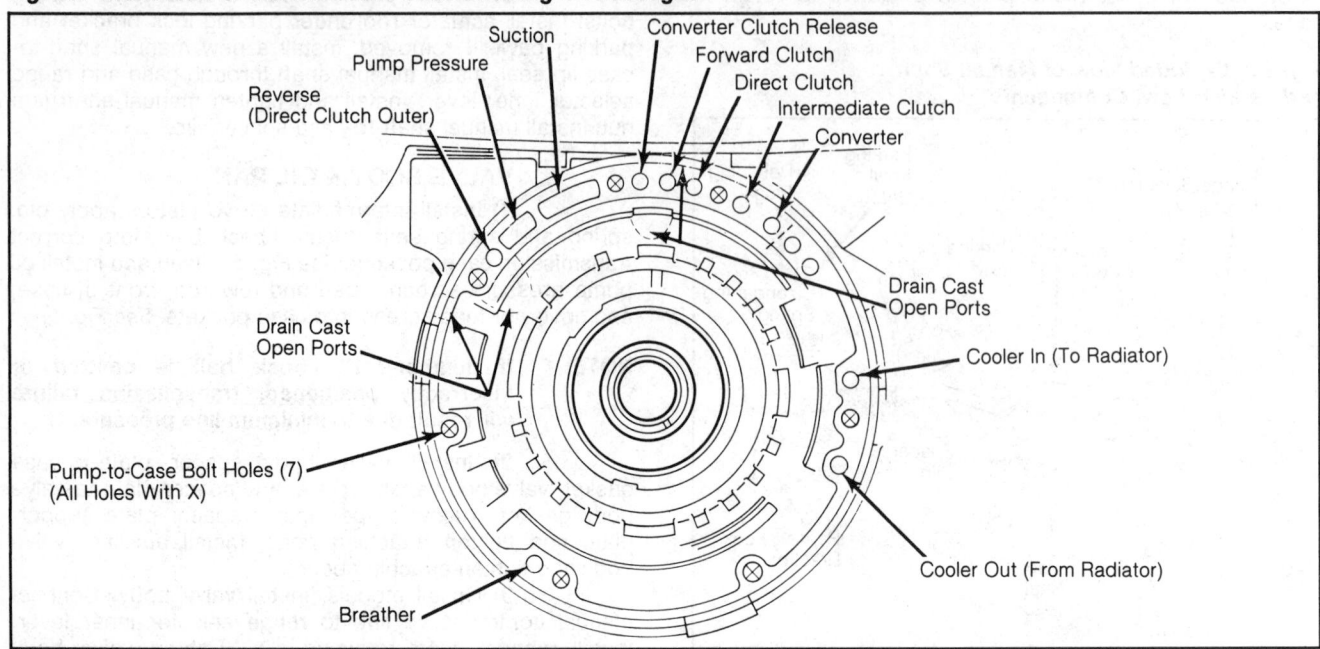

NOTE: **When handling valve body assembly do not touch sleeves as retainer pins may fall into transmission.**

4) Install detent control valve wire to detent valve actuating lever, then attach lever to valve body. Install detent roller and spring to valve body and tighten attaching bolt. Install torque converter clutch solenoid and connect wires. If removed, install governor pressure switch.

5) Align lube holes in strainer with those in valve body and install strainer assembly gasket and strainer. Lubricate new "O" ring seal with petroleum jelly and install on case electrical connector. Install connector (with tabs facing into case) and connect solenoid wire. Install oil pan using a new gasket and tighten attaching bolts.

Fig. 26: Valve Body Oil Passages

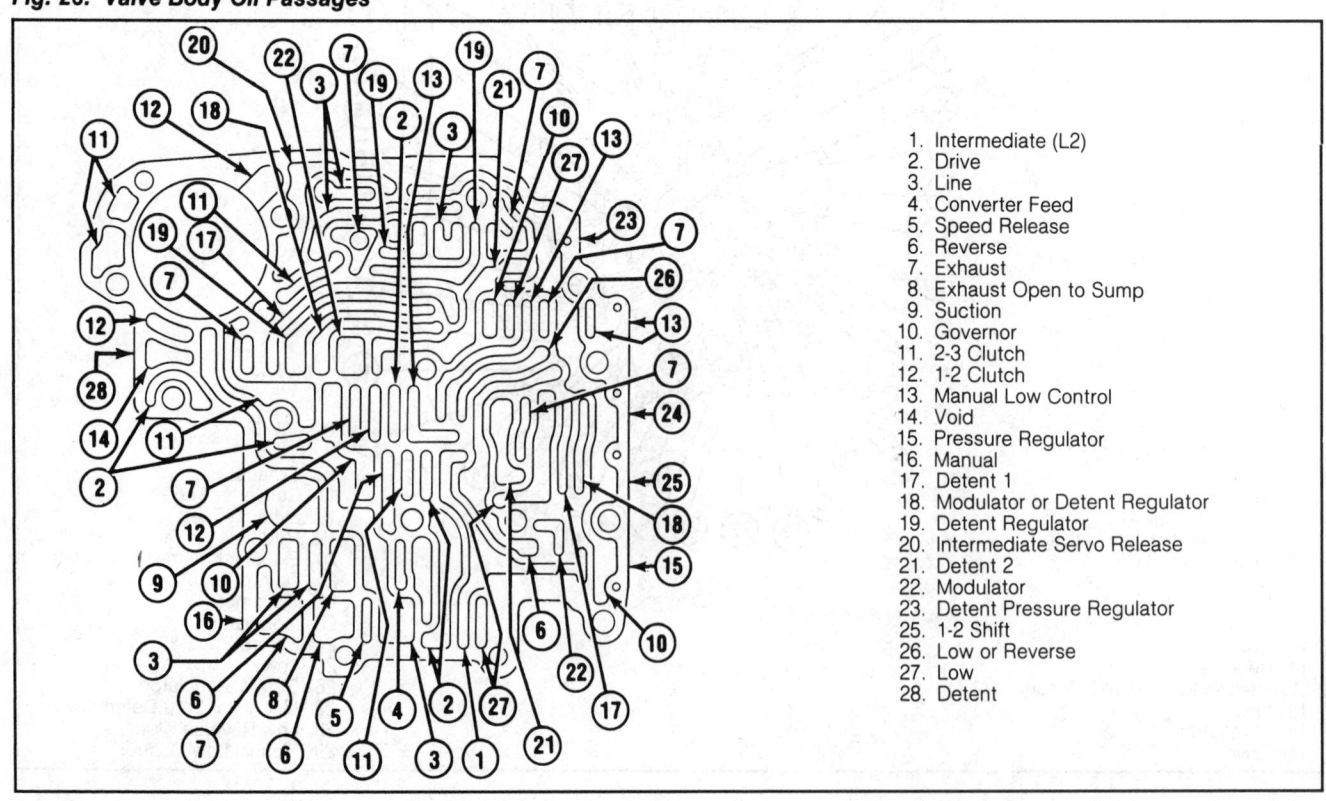

1. Intermediate (L2)
2. Drive
3. Line
4. Converter Feed
5. Speed Release
6. Reverse
7. Exhaust
8. Exhaust Open to Sump
9. Suction
10. Governor
11. 2-3 Clutch
12. 1-2 Clutch
13. Manual Low Control
14. Void
15. Pressure Regulator
16. Manual
17. Detent 1
18. Modulator or Detent Regulator
19. Detent Regulator
20. Intermediate Servo Release
21. Detent 2
22. Modulator
23. Detent Pressure Regulator
25. 1-2 Shift
26. Low or Reverse
27. Low
28. Detent

GENERAL MOTORS TURBO HYDRA-MATIC 350C (Cont.)

GOVERNOR & VACUUM MODULATOR

1) Install governor assembly, and uniformly apply sealant (Loctite Cup Plug Sealant II or equivalent) to governor cover outside diameter. Install by gently tapping into place with a plastic or rawhide hammer.

NOTE: **If governor cover is damaged, it must be replaced.**

2) Install vacuum modulator valve and modulator. Position vacuum modulator retainer with tangs pointing toward modulator. Lubricate "O" ring seal to prevent damage, then install retaining clip. Tighten bolt to specifications.

INTERMEDIATE CLUTCH ACCUMULATOR

Install intermediate clutch accumulator piston assembly and spring into case bore. Install new "O" ring seal on accumulator piston cover. Insall cover into case. Compress cover with a compressor tool (J-23069). Install retaining ring and remove tool.

Fig. 27: Installing Intermediate Clutch Accumulator Retaining Ring

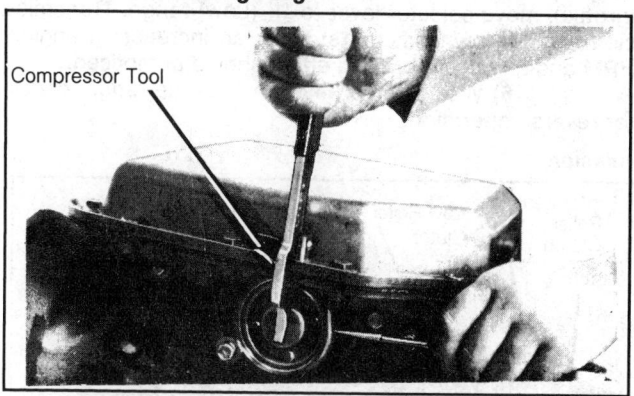

Compressor Tool

TIGHTENING SPECIFICATIONS

Application	Ft. Lbs. (N.m)
Oil Pan-to-Case	13 (18)
Pump-to-Case	20 (27)
Modulator-to-Case	12 (16)
Valve Body-to-Case	13 (18)
Oil Channel Support Plate-to-Case	13 (18)
Pump Body-to-Pump Cover	15 (20)
Extension Housing-to-Case	35 (48)
Inside Shift Nut	30 (41)
External Test Plugs	8 (11)
Manual Shift Nut	20 (27)
Converter-to-Flywheel	35 (48)
Transmission-to-Engine	35 (48)

Automatic Transmissions

GENERAL MOTORS TURBO HYDRA-MATIC 400

Chevrolet, GMC

TRANSMISSION IDENTIFICATION

Transmission may be identified by a serial number, located on an identification plate attached to right side of transmission case. Number consists of a year code, a 2 letter model code, and a production serial number. To further identify transmission, a derivitive of the Vehicle Identification Number is stamped on left side of transmission case, to rear of manual lever shaft.

DESCRIPTION

Transmission is a fully automatic unit consisting primarily of a 3 element hydraulic torque converter and a compound planetary gear set. Three multiple disc clutches, 2 roller clutches, and 2 bands provide friction elements required to obtain desired function of planetary gear set. A hydraulic system pressurized by a gear type pump provides working pressure required to operate friction elements and automatic controls.

LUBRICATION & ADJUSTMENT

See the appropriate article in AUTOMATIC TRANSMISSION SERVICING Section.

TESTING

ROAD TEST

1) Place selector lever in Drive range and accelerate vehicle from a standstill. A 1-2 and 2-3 shift should occur at all throttle openings (shift points will vary with throttle openings). As vehicle speed decreases to 0 MPH, a 3-2 and 2-1 downshift should occur.

2) Place selector lever in "2" (Intermediate) range and accelerate from a standstill. A 1-2 upshift should occur at all throttle openings (shift point will vary with throttle opening), and no 2-3 shift should occur. As vehicle speed decreases to 0 MPH, a 2-1 downshift should occur.

3) Place selector lever in "1" (Low) range and accelerate vehicle from a standstill. No upshifts should occur regardless of throttle opening.

4) With selector lever in Drive range, and vehicle speed approximately 35 MPH, move selector lever to "2" (Intermediate) range. Transmission should downshift to 2nd gear; an increase in engine RPM and an engine braking effect should be noticed.

5) With selector lever in "2" (Intermediate) range and vehicle speed approximately 30 MPH (constant throttle), move selector lever to "1" (Low) range. Transmission should downshift to 1st gear; an increase in engine RPM and an engine braking effect should be noticed.

6) With selector lever in Reverse range, check for reverse operation.

Fig. 1: Cutaway View of Turbo Hydra-Matic 400 Automatic Transmission

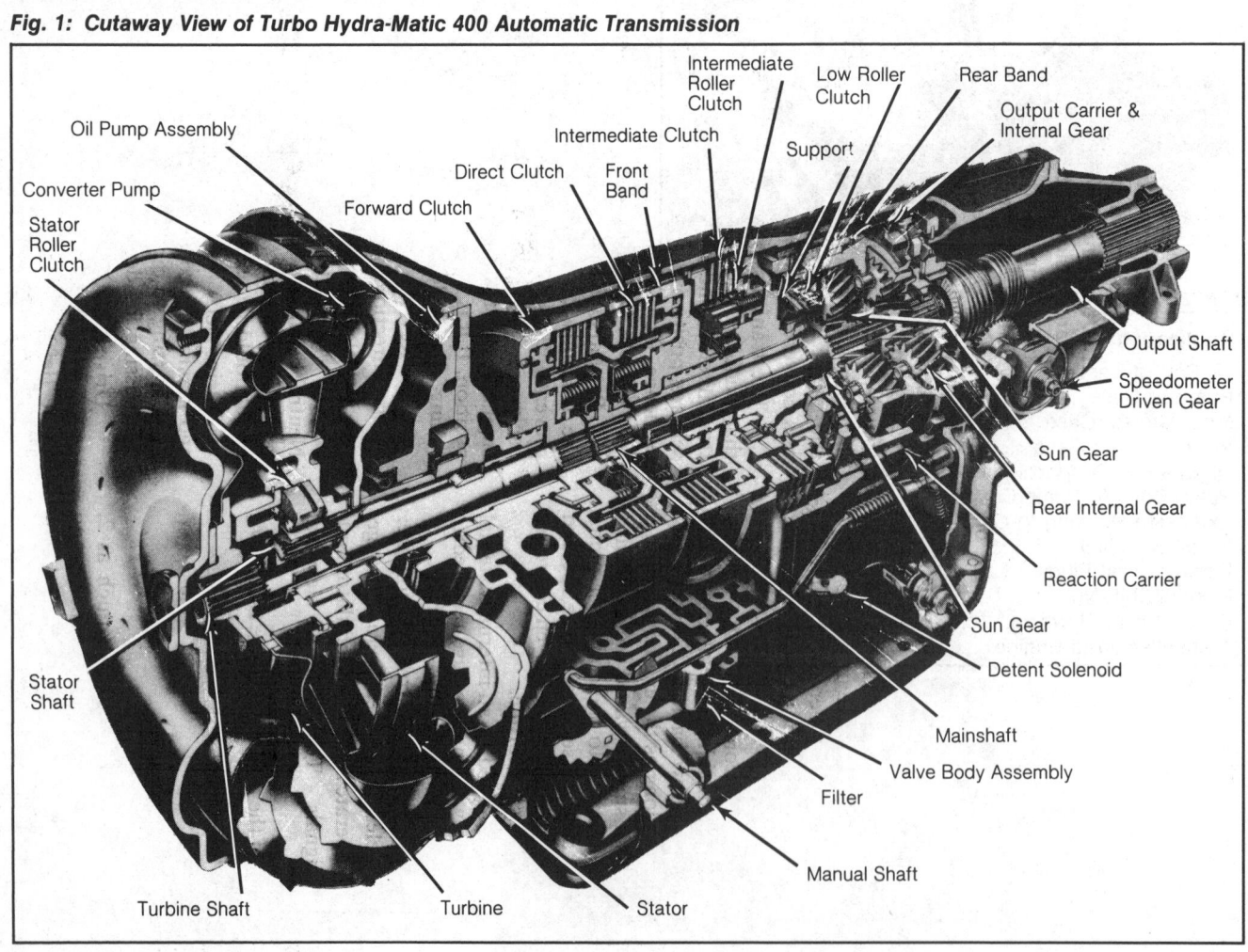

GENERAL MOTORS TURBO HYDRA-MATIC 400 (Cont.)

Fig.2: Turbo Hydra-Matic 400 Hydraulic Circuits Diagram

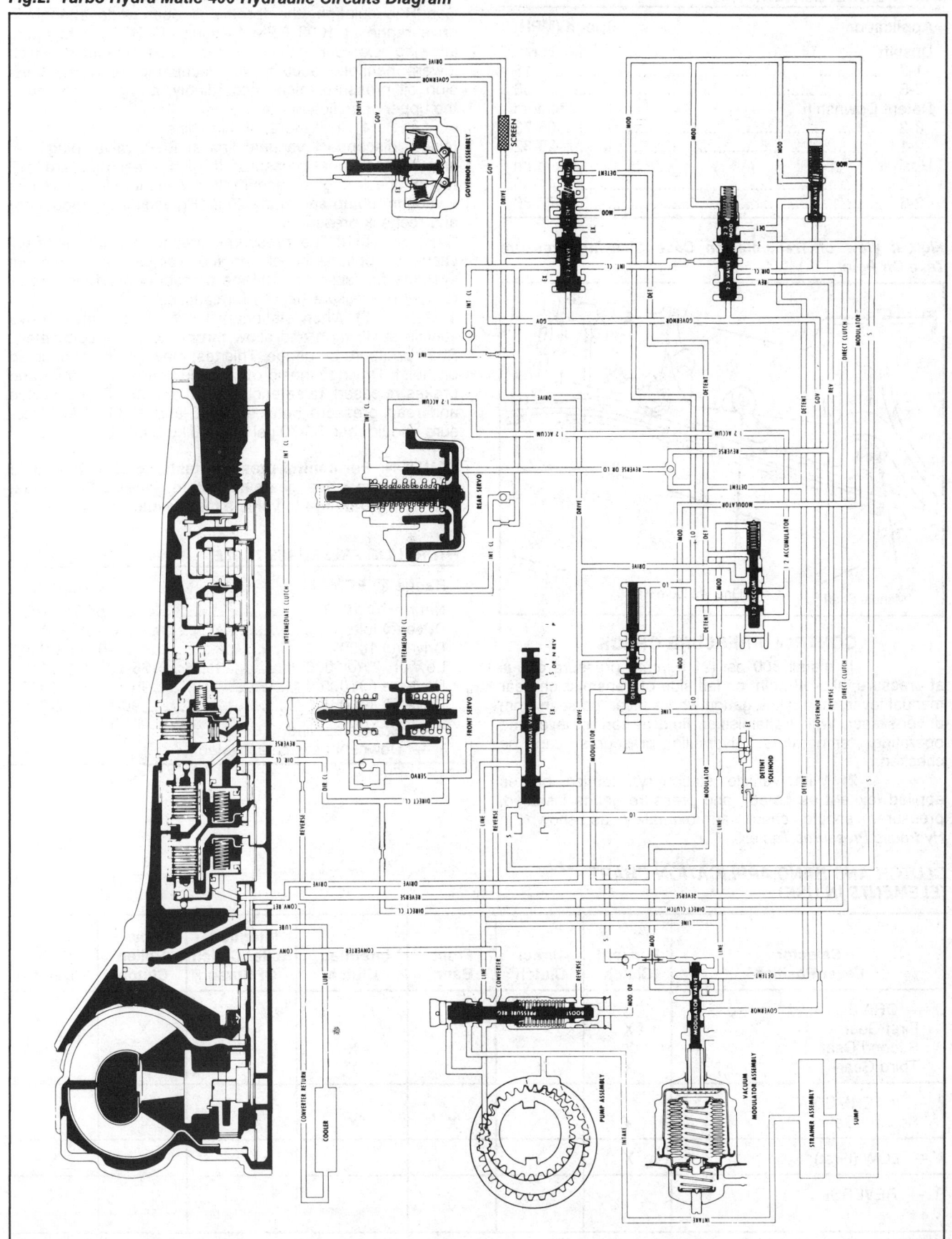

GENERAL MOTORS TURBO HYDRA-MATIC 400 (Cont.)

SHIFT POINT SPECIFICATIONS

Application	Speed (MPH)
Upshift	Minimum
1-2	15
2-3	30
Detent Downshift	Minimum
3-2	68-73
2-1	28-32
Upshift	Maximum
1-2	44-48
2-3	77-83

Fig. 3: View of Transmission Case Showing Pressure Take-Off Point

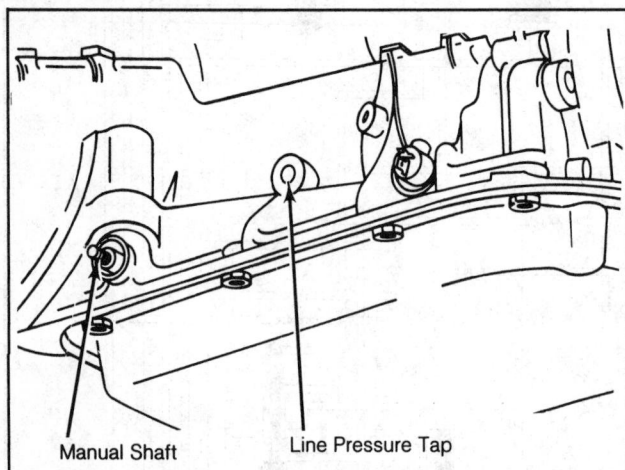

Manual Shaft   Line Pressure Tap

CONTROL PRESSURE CHECK

1) Install 300 psi (21 kg/cm²) pressure gauge at pressure take-off point on left side of transmission near manual lever, then place gauge where it can be seen from driver's seat. With transmission fluid at correct level and operating temperature, hydraulic pressures can be checked.

2) With vehicle stationary, service brakes applied (except as noted), and pressure gauge installed, pressures should check approximately as shown in *Hydraulic Pressures Table.*

3) On some engines equipped with Exhaust Gas Recirculation, the throttle is open wide enough in drive range at 1000 RPM to cause EGR valve to open, allowing exhaust gas to enter intake manifold which lowers manifold vacuum. With vacuum lowered, transmission oil pressure raises accordingly, and may go above the upper specification limit.

4) Therefore, if high line pressures are obtained, disconnect vacuum line at EGR valve, plug line, and recheck line pressure. If high pressures are still found, check engine vacuum. If low vacuum is found, use a vacuum pump and apply 20 in. Hg vacuum to modulator and recheck pressures.

5) If line pressures are normal with external vacuum applied, check engine vacuum and vacuum systems for leaks. If high line pressures are found, refer to *Control Pressure Results* for causes.

6) When stationary testing is complete, drive vehicle at 30 mph and allow throttle to close completely. Read pressure on gauge. This test may also be conducted on hoist: Driving wheels off ground, selector in drive and brakes released, raise engine RPM to 3000. Close throttle and read pressure between 2000 and 1200 RPM. Pressure should read 55-70 psi (3.8-4.9 kg/cm²).

CAUTION: For control pressure tests, total running time in drive gears is not to exceed 2 minutes. Damage to vehicle may result.

HYDRAULIC PRESSURES TABLE

Range @ RPM	psi (kg/cm²)
Neutral @ 1000	55-70 (4-5)
Drive @ Idle	60-85 (4.2-6)
Drive @ 1000 [1]	60-90 (4.2-6.3)
Low or "2" @1000 [1]	135-160 (9.5-11.2)
Reverse @1000 [1]	95-150 (6.7-10.5)
Drive @ 1000 [1][2]	90-110 (6.3-7.7)

[1] — Brakes applied.
[2] — Downshift switch activated.

CLUTCH AND BAND APPLICATION CHART (ELEMENTS IN USE)

Selector Lever Position	Forward Clutch	Direct Clutch	Front Band	Intermed. Clutch	Intermed. Roller Clutch Or Sprag	Low Roller Clutch	Rear Band
D — DRIVE							
First Gear	X					X	
Second Gear	X			X	X		
Third Gear	X	X		X			
2 — INTERMEDIATE							
Second Gear	X		X	X	X		
1 — LOW (First)	X					X	X
R — REVERSE		X					X

NEUTRAL OR PARK — All clutches and bands released and/or ineffective.

GENERAL MOTORS TURBO HYDRA-MATIC 400 (Cont.)

CONTROL PRESSURE RESULTS

Line Pressure Too Low

- Transmission fluid level low, faulty vacuum modulator assembly. Oil filter blocked or restricted, "O" ring on filter intake pipe omitted or damaged, intake pipe split or leaking.
- Not enough spacers in oil pump pressure regulator. Pressure regulator spring too weak. Oil pump gear clearance incorrect, oil pump damaged or worn.
- Internal leak in direct clutch circuit (pressure normal in neutral, low, intermediate and drive, but low in reverse).
- Internal leak in forward clutch circuit (pressure normal in neutral and reverse, low in drive).

Line Pressure Too High

- Vacuum system leak or improper engine vacuum. Water in vacuum modulator. Modulator valve not operating properly or defective. Defective EGR valve.
- Detent switch actuated or shorted, detent solenoid stuck open. Detent feed orifice in spacer plate blocked, detent solenoid loose. Detent valve bore plug damaged. Detent regulator valve pin too short.
- Oil pump pressure regulator and/or boost valve stuck. Incorrect pump pressure regulator spring. Pressure boost valve installed backward. Too many oil pump pressure regulator valve spacers. Oil pump casting defective.
- Control valve assembly-to-spacer gasket out of proportion, control valve assembly gaskets switched

GOVERNOR CHECK

1) With vehicle on a hoist (rear wheels off ground), disconnect vacuum line to modulator. Connect pressure gauge to transmission and tachometer to engine.

2) Start engine, keep foot off brake pedal, move selector lever to drive range, and check line pressure at 1000 RPM. Slowly increase engine speed to 3000 RPM and determine if a pressure drop of 10 psi (.7 kg/cm²) or more occurs.

3) If no pressure drop occurs, inspect governor for stuck valve or weight, or a restricted orifice in valve. Check governor feed system for plugged or restricted screen(s), or for restrictions in governor pipe.

4) If pressure drop of 10 psi (.7 kg/cm²) or more occurs, and transmission is malfunctioning, disassemble, clean and inspect control valve assembly.

VACUUM MODULATOR CHECK

Vacuum Diaphragm Leak Check

Insert a pipe cleaner into vacuum connector pipe as far as possible and check for presence of transmission oil. If oil is found, replace modulator.

NOTE: Gasoline or water vapor may settle in vacuum side of modulator. If this is found without presence of oil, modulator should not be changed.

Atmospheric Leak Check

1) Apply a liberal coating of soap buble solution to vacuum connector pipe seam (the crimped upper-to-lower housing seam).

2) Using a short piece of rubber hose, apply air pressure to vacuum pipe by blowing into hose and check for leak bubbles. If bubbles appear, replace modulator.

CAUTION: DO NOT use any method other than human lung power for applying air pressure. Pressures over 6 psi (.4 kg/cm²) may damage modulator.

Bellows Comparison Check

1) Using a comparison gauge (BT6733 or J-2446), compare load of vacuum modulator in question with a known good modulator (same part number). See Fig. 4.

Fig. 4: Dimensions for Bellows Comparision Gauge

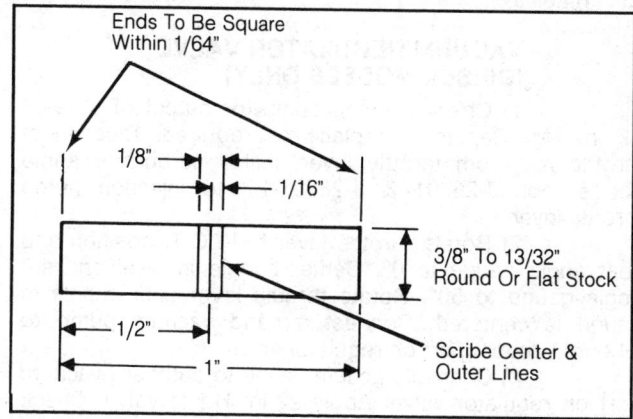

Ends of gauge must be square.

2) Install good modulator on either end of gauge. Install modulator in question on opposite end of gauge. Holding modulators in a horizontal position, bring them together under pressure until either modulator sleeve end just touches the line in center of gauge. See Fig. 5.

Fig. 5: Vacuum Modulator Bellows Comparision Check

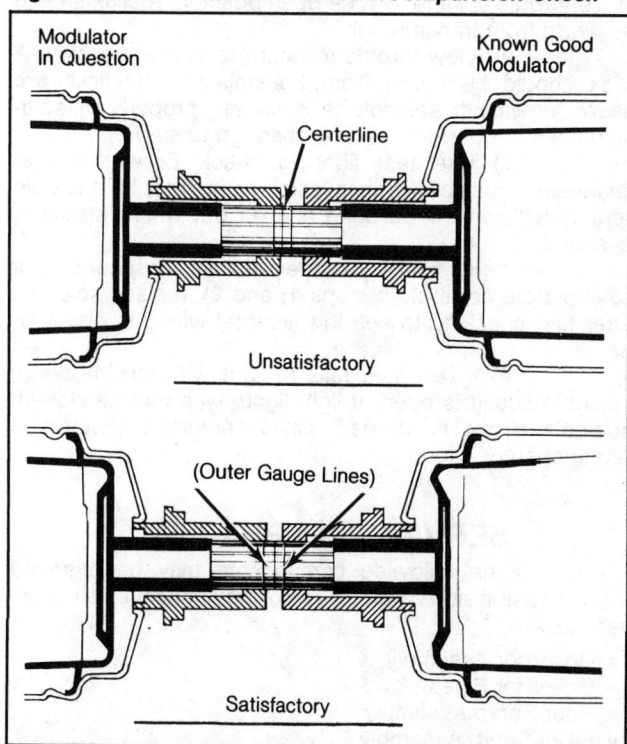

Ends must be equal in length.

GENERAL MOTORS TURBO HYDRA-MATIC 400 (Cont.)

3) If bad, modulator in question will reach center line of comparison gauge before the known good modulator lines up with outer gauge line.

4) If modulator in question is good, both modulator assemblies will be within the outer gauge lines as the assemblies are slowly brought together.

Sleeve Alignment Check

Roll main body of modulator on a flat surface and observe the sleeve for concentricity to the can. If sleeve is concentric and plunger is free, modulator is acceptable.

VACUUM REGULATOR VALVE (DIESEL MODELS ONLY)

1) Check vacuum pump for output of at least 22 in. Hg. Repair or replace as required. Disconnect throttle rod from throttle lever. Install carburetor angle gauge tool (J-26701 & J-26701-15) to injection pump throttle lever.

2) Rotate throttle lever to W.O.T. position and seat angle gauge to 0°. Center bubble in level and set angle gauge to 50°. Rotate throttle lever until bubble in gauge is centered. Connect a hand vacuum pump to inboard vacuum port on regulator valve.

3) Connect vacuum gauge to outboard vacuum port on regulator valve. Apply 22 in. Hg to valve. Check vacuum gauge reading for 7-8 in. Hg. If not, loosen regulator valve attaching bolts, rotate valve clockwise until vacuum reads 7-8 in. Hg and tighten valve attaching bolts to 60 INCH lbs. (6.7 N.m). Remove gauges, reconnect vacuum hoses and throttle rod to throttle lever.

DOWNSHIFT SOLENOID CHECK

1) Place selector lever in "P". Turn ignition to "ON", but do not start engine. From under hood, slowly move throttle linkage to wide open position. A click should be heard from transmission.

2) Allow throttle to return to closed position. A click should be heard from transmission. If clicks are heard, downshift solenoid is operating properly. If solenoid does not perform as described, go to step **3)**.

3) Use test light to check Brown wire at connector on side of transmission case. Test light should light with throttle wide open and go out when throttle is released.

4) If test light operates as described, but solenoid did not click in steps **1)** and **2)**, replace solenoid after first checking to see that internal wiring is operational.

5) If test light fails to light with throttle open, solenoid circuit is open. If light lights with throttle closed, solenoid circuit is shorted. Check solenoid circuit and repair open or short.

SERVICE (IN VEHICLE)

The following components may be removed from transmission without removing transmission from vehicle.

- Governor Assembly
- Governor Pipes
- Rear Servo Assembly
- Front Servo Assembly
- Oil Pan and Oil Screen (Intake Pipe) Assembly
- Valve Body Assembly

- Check Balls and Valve Body Spacer Plates and Gaskets
- Pressure Regulator Parts
- Inside Detent/Range Lever
- Manual Detent Roller and Spring
- Parking Pawl Actuator Rod
- TV/Detent Cable and "O" Ring
- Parking Pawl Bracket and Parking Pawl
- Manual Shaft and Seal
- Extension Housing and Gasket
- Rear Seal
- Vacuum Modulator
- Oil Filler Pipe and "O" Ring
- Speedometer Drive Gear
- Cooler Fittings
- Downshift Solenoid
- Electrical Connectors
- Governor Feed Screen
- Modulator Valve

REMOVAL & INSTALLATION

See the appropriate article in AUTOMATIC TRANSMISSION REMOVAL Section.

TORQUE CONVERTER

LEAKAGE CHECK

Install pressure test plug tool (J-21369) into converter hub and tighten tool to expand it. Install safety strap to prevent tool from blowing out when air pressure is applied. Apply 80 psi (5.6 kg/cm²) air pressure to air valve in tool. Submerge converter in water and check for leaks.

CAUTION: After leak checking converter, bleed air pressure from test tool before removing tool from converter.

Fig. 6: Assembling Pressure Test Plug to Converter

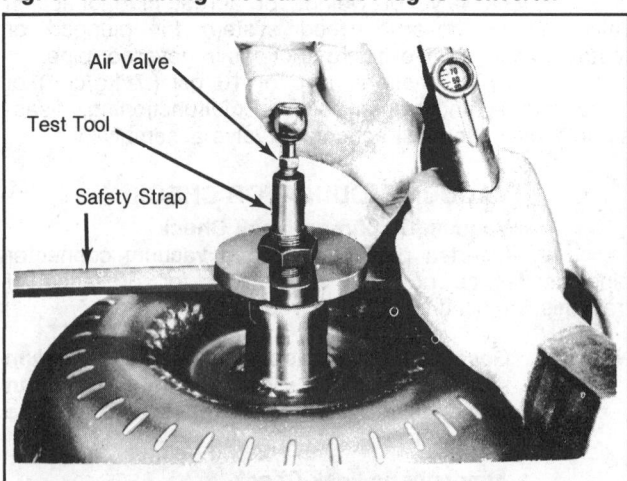

Apply 80 psi (5.6 kg/cm²) to check for leakage.

CLEARANCE CHECK

1) Install end clearance checking tool (J-21371). Place into converter hub until collet end of tool

GENERAL MOTORS TURBO HYDRA-MATIC 400 (Cont.)

bottoms. Tighten tool cap nut to expand collet. Install support collar of checking tool on converter hub and tighten hex nut.

    2) Install a dial indicator on support collar so that indicator contact bears against test tool cap nut. Zero dial indicator. *See Fig. 7.* Loosen hex nut while holding cap nut stationary. With hex nut loose and checking tool firmly against converter hub, the reading obtained on indicator will be converter end clearance.

    3) Converter end clearance should be less than .050" (1.27 mm). If clearance is greater than specified, replace torque converter assembly.

Fig. 7: Assembling Measuring Tools to Converter

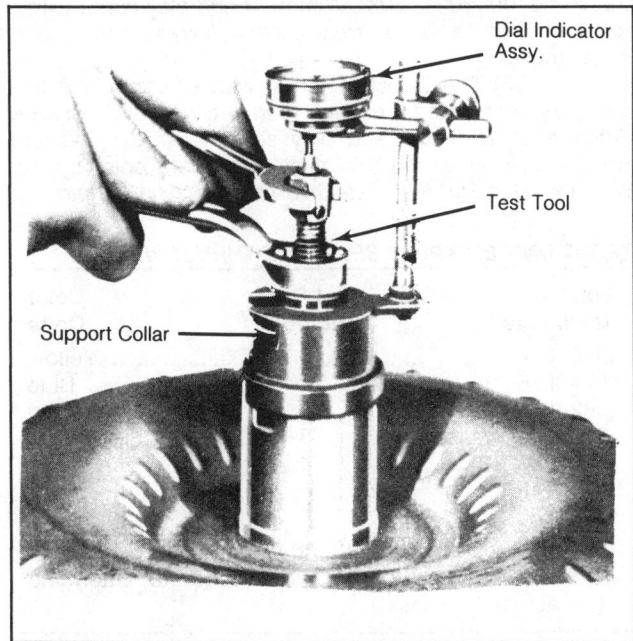

Assembly is used to check converter end clearance.

TRANSMISSION DISASSEMBLY

VACUUM MODULATOR & VALVE

    Remove vacuum modulator attaching screw and retainer. Remove modulator and "O" ring seal from case. Discard "O" ring. Withdraw modulator valve from bore in case.

GOVERNOR

    Remove attaching screws, cover, and gasket, then remove governor assembly by pulling straight out of case.

SPEEDOMETER DRIVEN GEAR

    Remove attaching screw and retainer, then apply slight pressure to remove sleeve and speedometer driven gear assembly from case.

INTAKE PIPE, FILTER & OIL PAN

    Remove pan attaching bolts and remove oil pan. Remove filter retaining bolt, withdraw intake pipe and filter assembly, then discard filter and "O" ring seal from intake pipe.

Fig. 8: Removing Intake Pipe and Filter Assembly

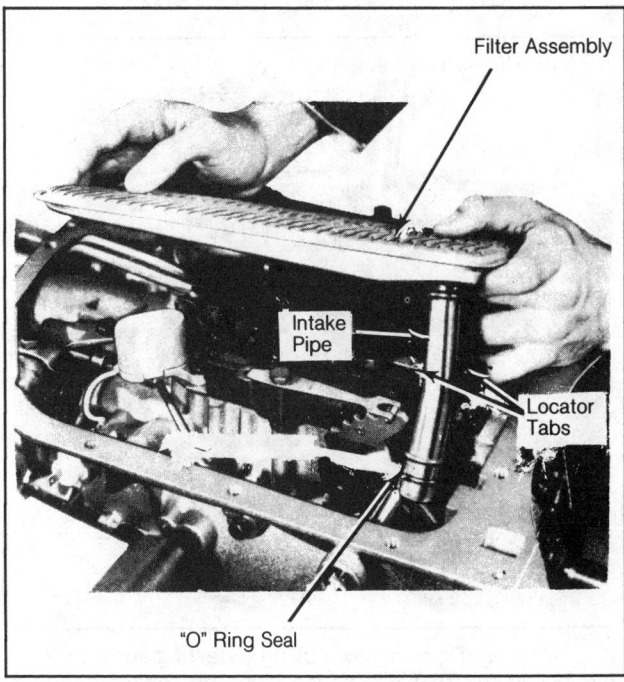

CONTROL VALVE ASSEMBLY

    1) Remove control valve assembly attaching bolts and detent roller and spring assembly (do not remove solenoid attaching screws).

NOTE: **If transmission is in vehicle, front servo parts may drop out as control valve assembly is removed.**

    2) Remove control valve assembly and governor pipes, using care not to drop manual valve as control valve assembly is removed. Remove governor screen assembly from governor feed pipe hole in case or from end of feed pipe.

    3) Remove governor pipes from control valve assembly. Governor pipes are interchangeable and need not be identified. Disconnect detent solenoid wire from electrical connector.

REAR SERVO

    Remove servo cover and gasket and discard gasket. Remove servo assembly and accumulator spring. Make a band apply pin selection check at this time to determine correct pin for use at reassembly. This is equivalent to band adjustment.

Band Apply Pin Selection Check

    1) Position Ban Apply Pin Selection Gauge (J-21370) on transmission case over rear servo bore. *See Fig. 9.* Install gauge with hex nut on side facing toward parking brake linkage. The smaller diameter end of Gauge Pin (J-21370-5) fits in servo pin bore.

    2) Secure gauge with 2 attaching screws, and tighten screws to 18 ft. lbs. (24 N.m). Make sure stepped gauge pin is free to move up and down in both tool and servo pin bore. Stepped side of pin must face front of transmission case.

GENERAL MOTORS TURBO HYDRA-MATIC 400 (Cont.)

Fig. 9: Using Special Gauge to Select Rear Band Apply Pin

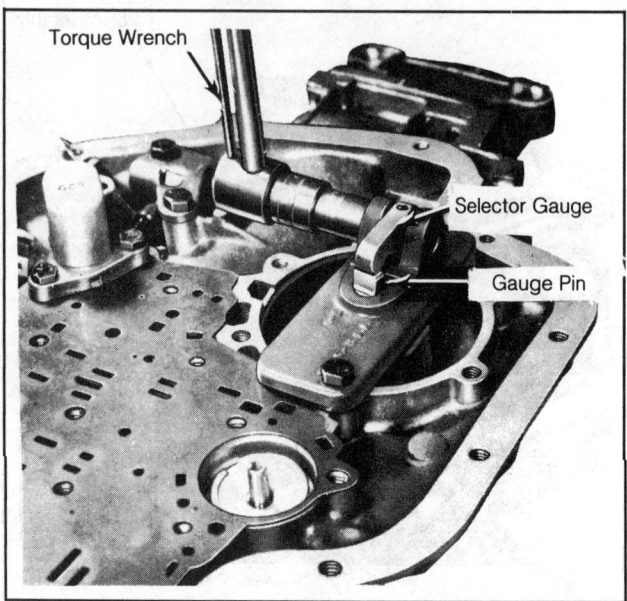

3) Tighten hex nut on side of gauge to 25 ft. lbs. (34 N.m). This will cause lever on top of gauge to depress stepped gauge pin into servo pin bore, simulating actual operating conditions. Note relation of steps on gauge pin and machined surface on top of gauge. To determine proper size pin, go to step **4)**.

4) If machined surface on top of gauge is even with or above steps on gauge pin, long size pin (3 rings), must be installed. If machined surface is between upper and lower steps on pin, medium size pin (2 rings), must be installed. If machined surface is even with or below steps on pin, short size pin (1 ring), must be installed.

NOTE: **Band apply pins are furnished in 3 sizes and identified by rings on band lug end of pin. Long size pin has 3 rings, medium size pin has 2 rings, and short size pin has 1 ring.**

5) If new band apply pin is required, make note of pin size for reassembly reference. Remove selection gauge from transmission case.

DETENT SOLENOID, CONTROL VALVE SPACER & FRONT SERVO

Remove attaching screws and lift off detent solenoid assembly and gasket. Compress connector tangs, and withdraw case sleeve connector and "O" ring seal. Discard seal. Remove control valve spacer plate and gasket. Remove 6 check balls from cored passages in case. Remove front servo piston, retainer ring, servo pin, retainer and spring from case.

CAUTION: **If transmission is installed in vehicle, be careful when detent solenoid is removed to prevent spacer plate, gasket and check balls from dropping out.**

REAR OIL SEAL & EXTENSION HOUSING

If replacement is necessary, pry rear oil seal from extension housing. Remove attaching bolts and remove extension housing and gasket from transmission.

NOTE: **Check front end end play before proceeding with transmission disassembly. Record end play for later reassembly.**

FRONT UNIT END PLAY CHECK

1) With transmission removed, remove 1 oil pump attaching bolt and bolt seal at either 10 o'clock or 5 o'clock position. Install slide-hammer bolt into bolt hole in pump. Mount a dial indicator on rod and index indicator to register with end of turbine shaft.

2) Push turbine shaft rearward and output shaft forward. Zero dial indicator, then pull turbine shaft forward and read resulting end play on indicator. End play should be .003-.024" (.08-.61 mm). If end play is not within specified limits, select correct thickness washer for use at reassembly.

3) The selective thrust washer controlling this end play is located between pump cover and forward clutch housing. Front end play selective thrust washers are available in varing thicknesses and are color coded. *See Front Unit End Play Selective Thrust Washers Chart.*

FRONT UNIT END PLAY SELECTIVE THRUST WASHERS

Washer Thickness [1]	I.D. Number	Color Code
.060-.064"	0	Yellow
.071-.075"	1	Blue
.082-.086"	2	Red
.093-.097"	3	Brown
.104-.108"	4	Green
.115-.119"	5	Black
.126-.130"	6	Purple

[1] — Oil soaked washers tend to discolor. Therefore, it is necessary to measure washer to determine actual thickness.

Fig. 10: Measuring Front Unit End Play

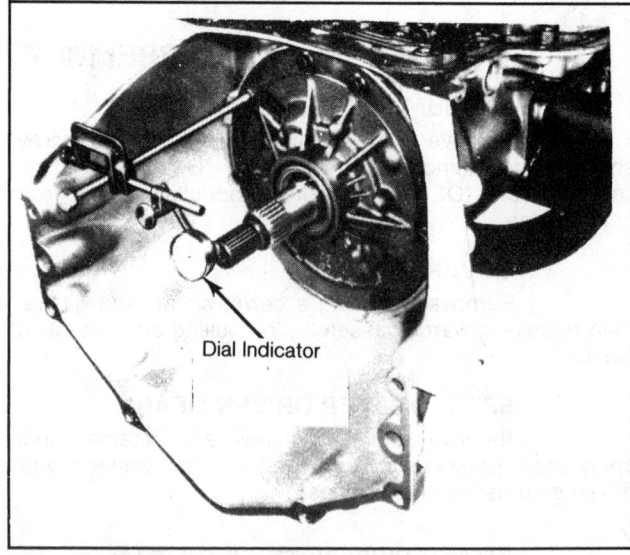

Dial Indicator

Shown with 3/8" rod in bolt hole.

OIL PUMP

If front seal requires replacement, pry seal out before removing pump assembly. Remove pump attaching bolts, install 2 slide hammers into 2 opposite pump bolt

GENERAL MOTORS TURBO HYDRA-MATIC 400 (Cont.)

holes, bump outward evenly on hammers and remove pump assembly from case. Remove and discard pump-to-case seal ring and gasket.

Fig. 11: Using Slide Hammers to Remove Oil Pump

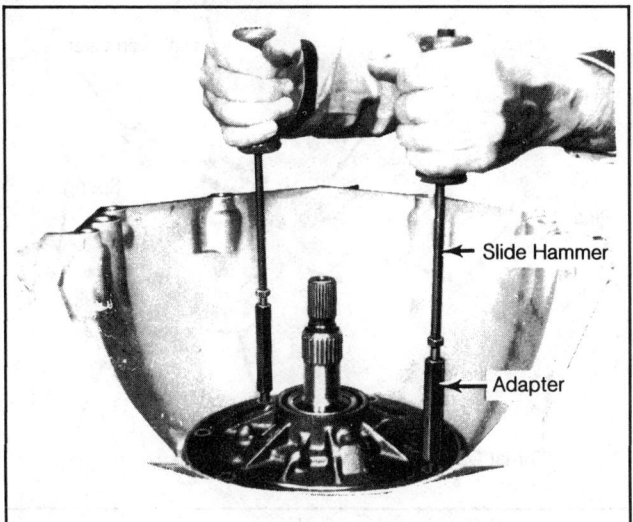

Operate hammers equally and together when removing pump.

TURBINE SHAFT, FORWARD & DIRECT CLUTCH ASSEMBLIES, SUN GEAR SHAFT & FRONT BAND

Remove forward clutch and turbine shaft assembly from case, then remove forward clutch hub-to-direct clutch housing thrust washer. Remove direct clutch and intermediate roller assembly, then remove sun gear shaft and front band.

DETENT LEVER, MANUAL LEVER, SHAFT & PARKING LINKAGE

1) If necessary for parts replacement, remove manual linkage. Loosen jam nut holding detent lever to manual shaft. Remove manual shaft retaining pin from case. Remove jam nut and detent lever from manual shaft. Remove manual shaft.

Fig. 12: Exploded View of Manual Linkage

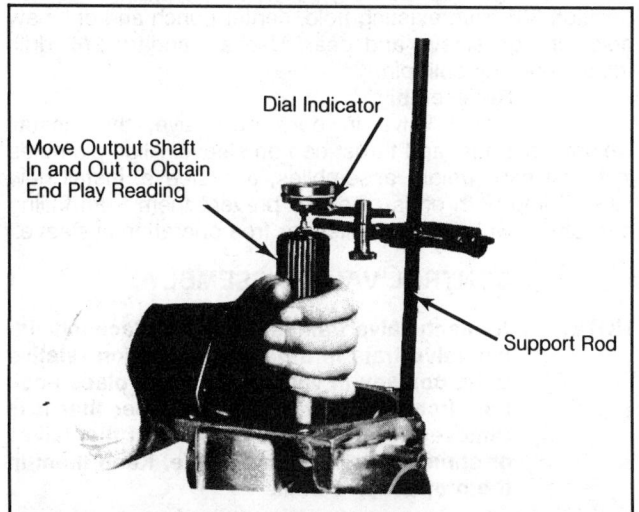

2) Remove parking pawl actuator rod and detent lever assembly. Remove attaching bolts and parking bracket. Remove parking pawl return spring. Remove parking pawl shaft retainer. Remove parking pawl shaft cup plug. Pry outward to remove plug. Remove parking pawl shaft and parking pawl.

REAR UNIT END PLAY CHECK

1) Install the threaded end of a 3/8"-16 rod into one of the extension housing bolt holes in rear of case. Install a dial indicator on rod with button engaging flat surface on end of output shaft. Zero indicator dial, then move output shaft in and out and note end play reading. End play should be .007-.019" (.18-.48 mm). If end play needs adjustment, select a thrust washer that will bring end play within specifications.

2) The selective thrust washer controlling rear unit end play is a steel washer having 3 tabs. It is located between output shaft thrust washer and rear face of transmission case. Notches and/or numerals on tabs of washer identify thickness. *See Selective Thrust Washers Chart.*

Fig. 13: Measuring Rear Unit End Play

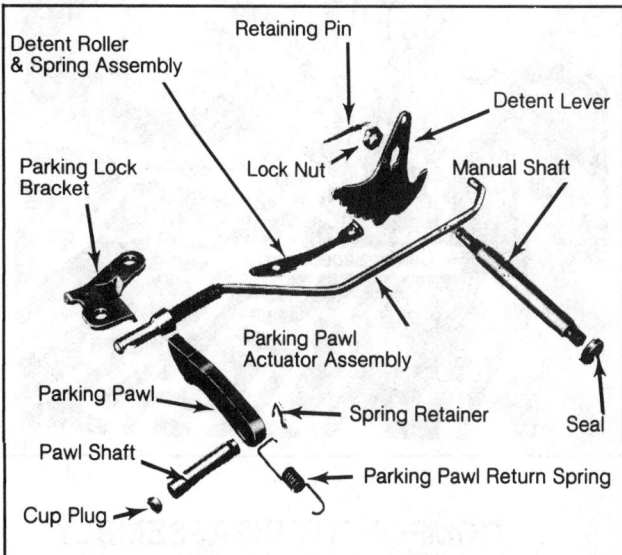

Set dial indicator at zero then pull up on shaft and read indicator.

SELECTIVE THRUST WASHERS
(REAR UNIT END PLAY)

Washer Thickness	I.D. Notches	I.D. Numeral
.074-.078"	None	1
.082-.086"	1 Tab Side	2
.090-.094"	2 Tabs Side	3
.098-.102"	1 Tab O.D.	4
.106-.110"	2 Tabs O.D.	5
.114-.118"	3 Tabs O.D.	6

CENTER SUPPORT, REAR BAND & GEAR UNIT ASSEMBLIES

1) Remove center support bolt from case using a 3/8", 12-point thin wall deep socket. Remove intermediate clutch backing plate-to-case snap ring. Withdraw backing plate and clutch plates.

GENERAL MOTORS TURBO HYDRA-MATIC 400 (Cont.)

2) Remove center support-to-case snap ring. Install special removal tool (J-21795) on end of mainshaft so that tangs engage groove in shaft. Tighten screw on tool to secure tool on shaft. This prevents movement of roller clutch during gear unit removal.

NOTE: **Install a piece of pipe over output shaft to be used as a handle and to prevent spline damage to case bushing when removing gear unit, center support and reaction carrier.**

3) With transmission case in a horizontal position, shift complete assembly forward and remove from case. Remove output shaft-to-case thrust washer from shaft or case. Remove near unit selective washer from transmission case. Rotate rear band lugs away from pins and pull band assembly from case.

Fig. 14: Removing Center Support-to-Case Bolt

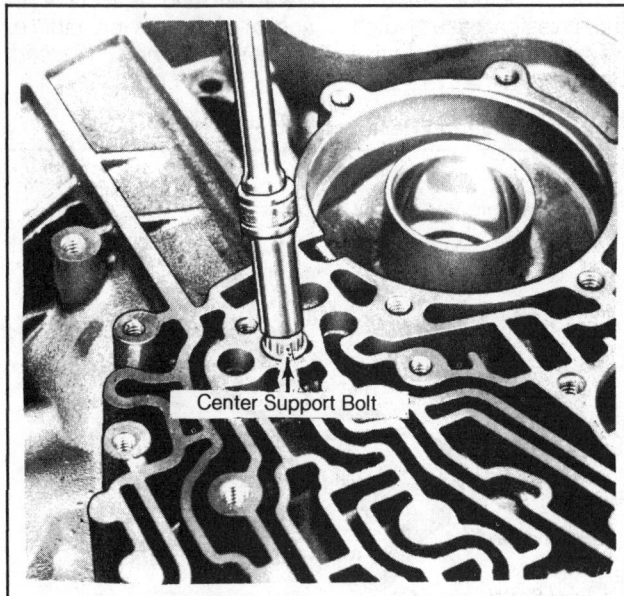

Center Support Bolt

COMPONENT DISASSEMBLY & REASSEMBLY

NOTE: **When reassembling transmission units, lubricate all bushings, seals, thrust bearings, and mating surfaces with transmission fluid. Use petroleum jelly to lubricate and retain thrust washers.**

GOVERNOR

NOTE: **Governor, including driven gear, is serviced as a complete assembly. The driven gear may be serviced separately and requires disassembly of governor for gear replacement.**

Disassembly

Governor weights are interchangeable from side to side and need not be identified for reassembly. Cut off one end of each governor weight pin and remove pins, governor thrust cap, governor weights and springs. Remove governor valve from governor sleeve using care not to damage valve.

Fig. 15: Exploded View of Governor Assembly

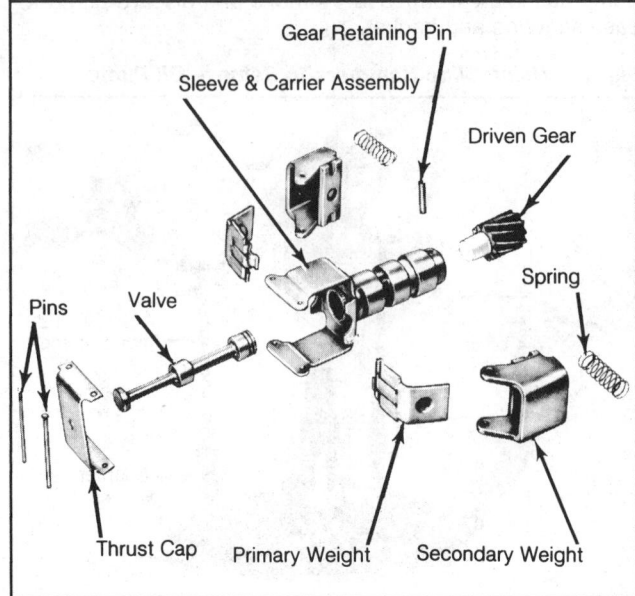

Gear Retaining Pin
Sleeve & Carrier Assembly
Driven Gear
Pins
Valve
Spring
Thrust Cap
Primary Weight
Secondary Weight

Inspection

Wash all parts in solvent and air dry. Inspect sleeve for wear or damage and check for free operation in case bore. Inspect valve for wear or damage and for free operation in sleeve bore. Check driven gear for wear or damage and for looseness on sleeve. Inspect springs for distortion and weights for free operation in retainers. Check valve opening at entry and exhaust .020" (.51 mm) minimum.

Driven Gear Replacement

1) With governor disassembled, drive out gear retaining split pin. Support assembly on 3/16" plates installed in exhaust slots of sleeve. Place assembly in an arbor press and press gear out of sleeve. Carefully clean governor sleeve of chips that remain from original gear installation.

2) To install new gear, support governor assembly in same manner as for gear removal. Press gear into sleeve until nearly seated. Remove any chips that may have been shaved off gear. Press gear in until bottomed on sleeve.

3) A new pin hole must be drilled through sleeve and gear. Support governor in press. Locate hole position 90° from existing hole, center punch and drill new hole through sleeve and gear. Use a standard 1/8" drill. Install retaining split pin.

Reassembly

Install valve in bore of sleeve, then install weights, springs, and thrust cap on sleeve. Align pin holes in thrust cap, weight assemblies, and sleeve. Install new pins. Crimp both ends of pin to prevent them from falling out. Check weight assemblies for free operation in sleeve.

CONTROL VALVE ASSEMBLY

NOTE: **As each valve train is removed, place individual valve train in a separate location relative to its position in valve body. Also, place each part from each valve train in order that it is removed from valve bore. None of the valves or springs are interchangeable. Keep them in the proper valve train.**

GENERAL MOTORS TURBO HYDRA-MATIC 400 (Cont.)

Disassembly

1) Position control valve assembly with cored face up and accumulator pocket at bottom. Remove manual valve from upper bore. Install compressor tool on accumulator piston, compress piston and remove "E" ring, then remove piston and spring.

NOTE: Steps 2) & 3) require using a pin punch to remove retaining pin.

2) From upper right hand bore, remove 1-2 valve train. From center right hand bore, remove 2-3 valve train. From lower right hand bore, remove 3-2 valve train.

3) From upper left hand bore, remove detent valve train. From lower left hand bore, remove 1-2 accumulator valve train.

Inspection

1) Inspect all valves and bushing carefully to make sure they are free from dirt and are not damaged in any way. If burrs are present, remove with a fine stone or fine grade crocus cloth and light oil.

CAUTION: When removing burrs from valves, use care not to round off shoulders of valves.

2) Test all valves and bushings in their bores to make sure they slide freely of their own weight. Manual valve is only valve that can be serviced separately. If other valves require replacement, complete valve body assembly should be replaced.

3) Inspect valve body for cracks or scored bores. Check all springs for distortion or collapsed coils. Inspect accumulator piston and oil ring for damage.

NOTE: Do not remove teflon oil seal from front accumulator piston unless seal needs replacing. For service, the oil seal ring is cast iron.

Reassembly

1) Install front accumulator spring and piston into valve body, then compress piston and spring and install retaining "E" clip.

2) In lower left bore, install 1-2 accumulator primary spring (if required) and 1-2 accumulator valve, stem end out, then install bore plug. Install retaining pin from cast surface side of valve body, with grooves of pin installed last. Tap pin until it is flush with cast surface of valve body

Fig. 16: Exploded View of Control Valve Assembly

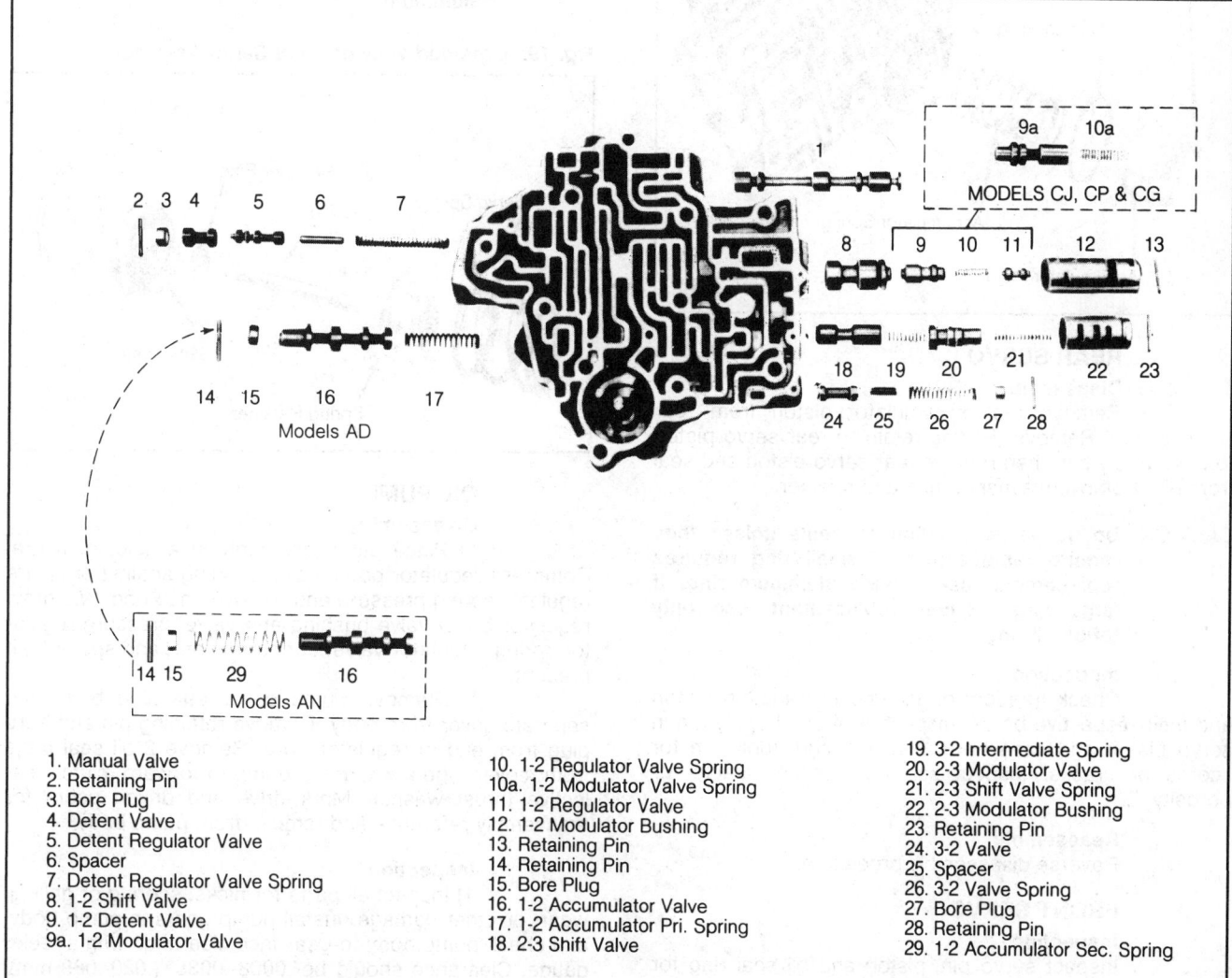

1. Manual Valve
2. Retaining Pin
3. Bore Plug
4. Detent Valve
5. Detent Regulator Valve
6. Spacer
7. Detent Regulator Valve Spring
8. 1-2 Shift Valve
9. 1-2 Detent Valve
9a. 1-2 Modulator Valve
10. 1-2 Regulator Valve Spring
10a. 1-2 Modulator Valve Spring
11. 1-2 Regulator Valve
12. 1-2 Modulator Bushing
13. Retaining Pin
14. Retaining Pin
15. Bore Plug
16. 1-2 Accumulator Valve
17. 1-2 Accumulator Pri. Spring
18. 2-3 Shift Valve
19. 3-2 Intermediate Spring
20. 2-3 Modulator Valve
21. 2-3 Shift Valve Spring
22. 2-3 Modulator Bushing
23. Retaining Pin
24. 3-2 Valve
25. Spacer
26. 3-2 Valve Spring
27. Bore Plug
28. Retaining Pin
29. 1-2 Accumulator Sec. Spring

GENERAL MOTORS TURBO HYDRA-MATIC 400 (Cont.)

3) Install detent regulator spring and spacer in upper left bore, compress spring and retain in place using a .005-.015" (.13-.38 mm) feeler gauge or small screwdriver. Install detent regulator valve (stem end out) and detent valve (narrow land first). Install bore plug with open end out and install retaining pin. Remove tool.

4) Install 3-2 valve in lower right bore, then install spacer, valve spring, bore plug (open end out) and retaining pin. In next bore up, install 2-3 shift valve (hole end out) and 3-2 intermediate spring. Install 2-3 modulator valve into bushing and install both parts into valve bore. Install 2-3 valve spring, then install retaining pin.

5) In next bore, install 1-2 valve (stem end out). Install 1-2 regulator valve (large stem first), spring and 1-2 detent valve (hole end first) into 1-2 modulator bushing, aligning spring in bore of detent valve and install parts into valve body bore. Compress bushing against spring and install retaining pin. Install manual valve with detent pin groove to the right.

Fig. 17: Disassembled View of Front Accumulator

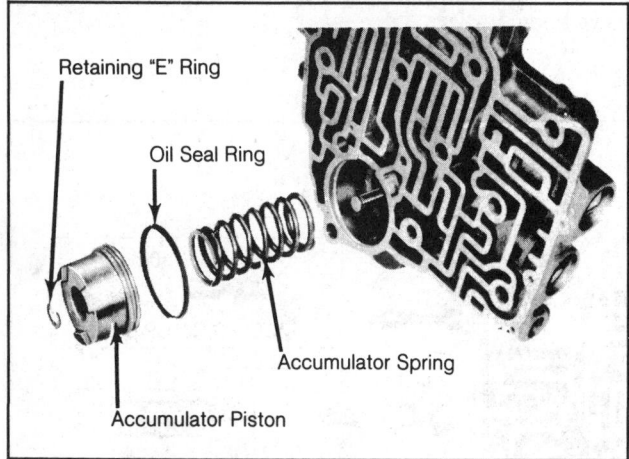

REAR SERVO

Disassembly
Remove rear accumulator piston from rear servo piston. Remove "E" ring retaining rear servo piston to band apply pin, then remove rear servo piston and seal from pin. Remove washer, spring and retainer.

CAUTION: Do not remove teflon oil seals unless they require replacement. If small ring requires replacement, use service aluminum ring. If large ring requires replacement, use only teflon oil ring.

Inspection
Check freedom of accumulator rings in piston and their respective bores. Inspect fit of band apply pin in servo piston and case bore. Inspect band apply pin for scores or cracks. Inspect servo piston for cracks or porosity.

Reassembly
Reverse disassembly procedure.

FRONT SERVO

Inspection
Inspect servo pin, piston and oil seal ring for wear or damage. Check fit of servo pin in piston and in case bore.

Fig. 18: Exploded View of Rear Servo Assembly

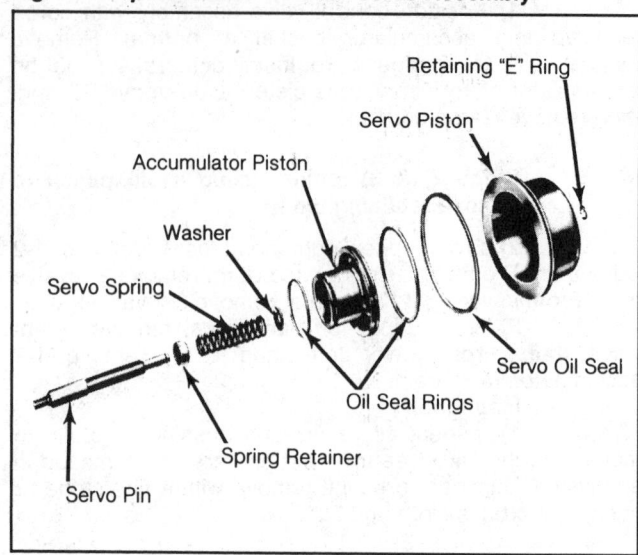

NOTE: Do not remove teflon oil seal ring from servo piston unless seal ring requires replacement. For service, replacement oil seal ring is aluminum.

Fig. 19: Exploded View of Front Servo Assembly

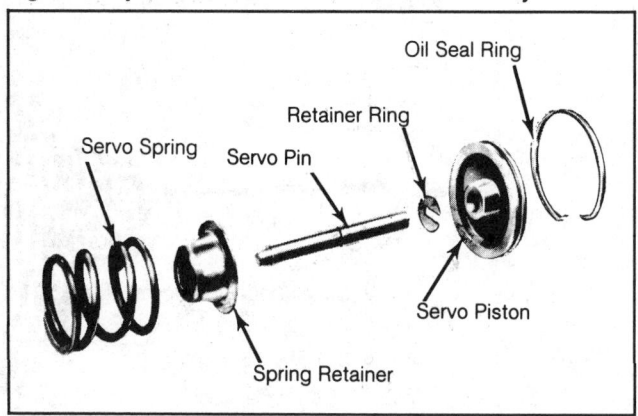

OIL PUMP

Disassembly
1) Place pump assembly in a holding fixture. Compress regulator boost valve bushing against pressure regulator spring pressure and remove snap ring. Withdraw regulator boost valve bushing and valve, pressure regulator spring, regulator valve, spring retainer, and spacer(s) if present.

2) Remove pump cover attaching bolts and separate cover from body. Remove retaining pin and bore plug from end of regulator bore. Remove 2 oil seal rings from cover, then withdraw pump-to-forward clutch selective thrust washer. Mark drive and driven gears for reassembly reference and remove from pump body

Inspection
1) Inspect all parts for nicks, scoring or galling, wear, or other damage. Install pump gears in pump body, and check pump body-to-gear face clearance with a feeler gauge. Clearance should be .0008-.0035" (.020-.089 mm). Check overall flatness of pump body face.

GENERAL MOTORS TURBO HYDRA-MATIC 400 (Cont.)

Fig. 20: Exploded View of Oil Pump Cover and Pressure Regulator Valve

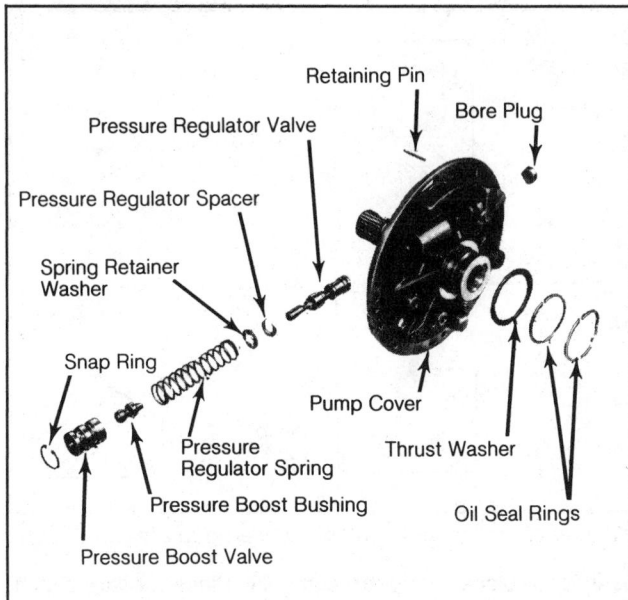

2) To replace stator shaft rear bushing, thread bushing removal tool (J-21465-15) into bushing. Attach a slide hammer to removal tool and remove bushing. To install, place new bushing on shoulder of installer tool (J-21465-2), then drive bushing squarely into bore to a depth of 19/32" (15 mm).

3) To replace stator shaft front bushing, thread bushing removal tool (J-21465-15) into bushing. Attach slide hammer to removal tool. Mount slide hammer in vise, and pull on stator shaft to remove bushing. To install, support hub on wood blocks and drive bushing squarely into bore.

Fig. 21: Pump Cover Used With Pressure Regulator Valve

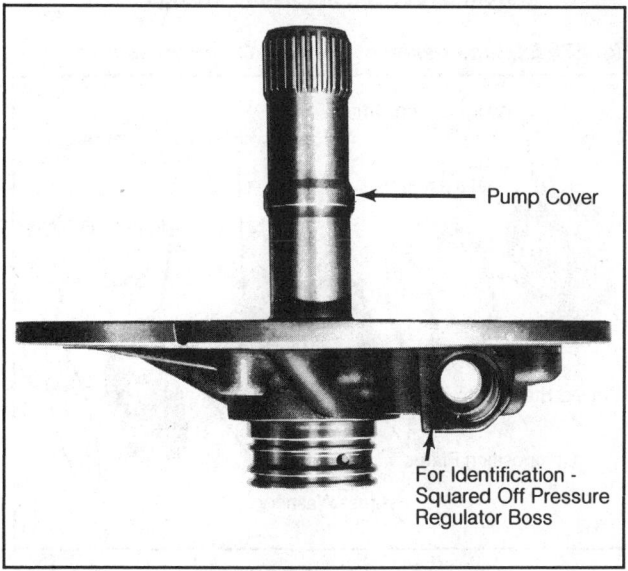

Pump is without orifice holes or cup plug.

2) Inspect pump attaching bolt seals for damage and replace if necessary. Make certain all passages are clear and open. Make sure pressure regulator and boost valves are free in bore. Install pump cover oil seal rings in counterbore of forward clutch housing and check for proper fit.

NOTE: Several different pump covers are used in service. The current production solid type pressure regulator valve does not contain oil holes and an orifice cup plug as did previous models. This new type valve must be used ONLY in a pump cover with the squared-off pressure regulator boss. The previous pressure regulator valve (with oil holes and orifice cup plug) may be used to service either type pump cover.

Reassembly

Reverse disassembly procedure and note the following:

1) When installing front unit selective thrust washer, make sure it is the proper thickness as determined at Transmission Disassembly. When installing gears in pump body, ensure marks made at disassembly are aligned. If correct, converter tangs on drive gear should be upward.

2) When installing pump cover attaching bolts, leave bolts one turn loose, install alignment strap (J-21368) to align cover and body, then tighten attaching bolts.

NOTE: On some models, pump driven gear has a rectangular or triangular identification mark on the face of a tooth. On these models, gear must be installed with mark down.

Bushing Replacement

1) To replace pump body bushing, support body on wood blocks. Using driver, press bushing from body. To install, press bushing squarely into bore until it is .010" (.25 mm) below gear pocket face.

Fig. 22: Compressing Forward Clutch Piston

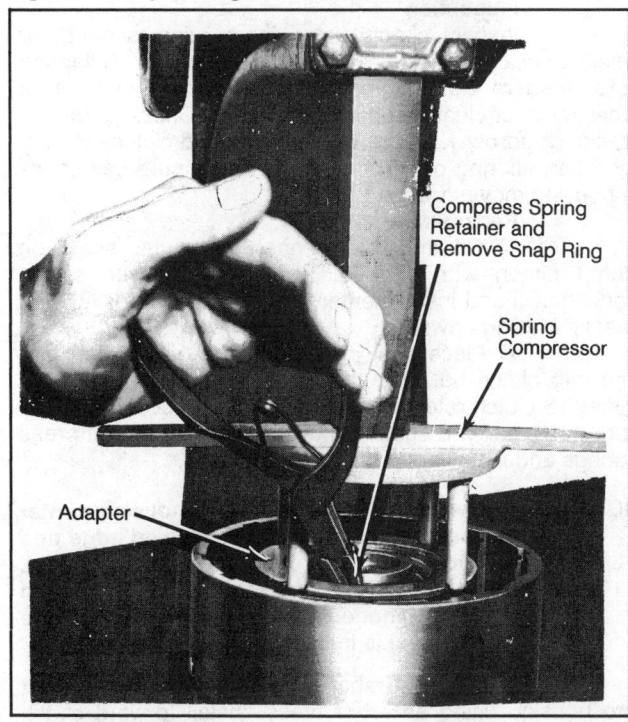

Compress piston to remove snap ring from hub.

GENERAL MOTORS TURBO HYDRA-MATIC 400 (Cont.)

FORWARD CLUTCH

Disassembly

1) Remove forward clutch housing-to-direct clutch hub snap ring and withdraw hub. Remove forward clutch hub and thrust washers from each side of hub. Withdraw composition and steel clutch plates.

2) If necessary, place clutch housing in an arbor press and press turbine shaft out of housing. Using a compressor tool, compress spring retainer and remove snap ring. Remove tool and lift out spring retainer and 16 clutch release springs.

NOTE: Keep forward clutch release springs separate from direct clutch release springs.

Fig. 23: Exploded View of Forward Clutch Assemby

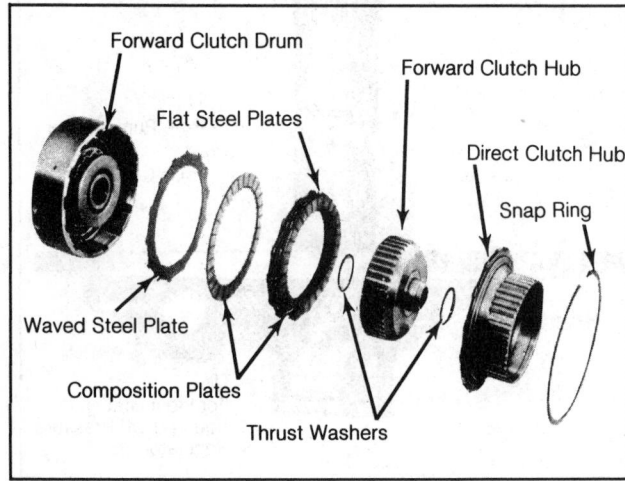

3) Remove forward clutch piston from housing. Remove inner and outer seals from piston and center seal from clutch housing.

Inspection

Inspect clutch plates for burning, scoring, or wear. Check release springs for distortion or collapsed coils. Inspect clutch hubs for worn splines and thrust faces, and for clear lubrication passages. Check piston for cracks or porosity. Check turbine shaft and clutch housing for wear, scoring or other damage. Make sure ball check in housing moves freely.

Reassembly

1) Oil and install inner and outer seals on clutch piston with seal lips facing away from spring pockets. Oil and install center seal on clutch housing with seal lips facing upward.

2) Place seal protector tools over clutch hub and into clutch housing, then install piston into housing. Install 16 clutch release springs into piston pockets, place spring retainer and snap ring over springs, then compress springs and install snap ring into groove.

NOTE: A new type of forward clutch housing center seal is being used. It has a beveled edge and is interchangeable with the old type seal. However, the old type seal cannot be used in the later model transmissions. Make sure correct seal is installed.

3) If turbine shaft was removed, install shaft into housing using an arbor press. Install forward clutch hub thrust washers. Make sure bronze washer is installed on side of hub facing forward clutch housing. Retain

Fig. 24: Forward Clutch Housing Center Seal Application

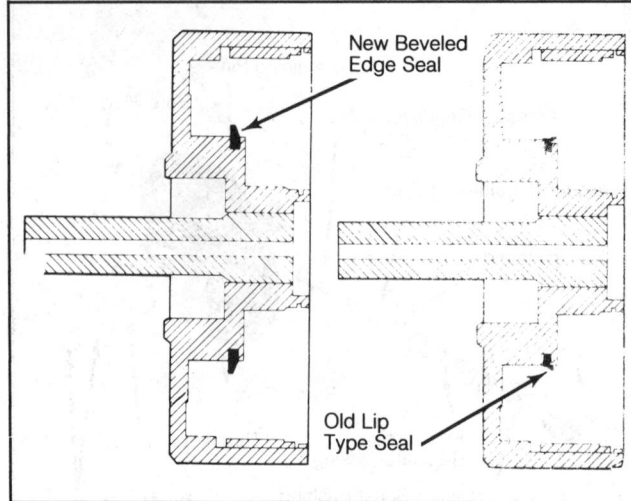

Note difference in new seal lip compared to old seal.

washers in place with petroleum jelly. Place forward clutch hub into clutch housing.

4) Lubricate with transmission fluid and install clutch plates, starting with a waved steel plate (plate with "U" notch), then alternating composition and flat steel plates (plate with "V" notch) until all clutch plates are installed. *See Forward Clutch Plate Chart.*

5) Install direct clutch hub and retaining snap ring. Place forward clutch housing on oil pump delivery

FORWARD CLUTCH PLATE CHART

Application	Flat Steel	Composition
All Models	4 [1]	5

[1] — Steel plates are .077" (1.96 mm) thick for all models except AD and AM. Plates in these transmissions are .095" (2.51 mm) thick.

Fig. 25: Checking Operation of Forward Clutch

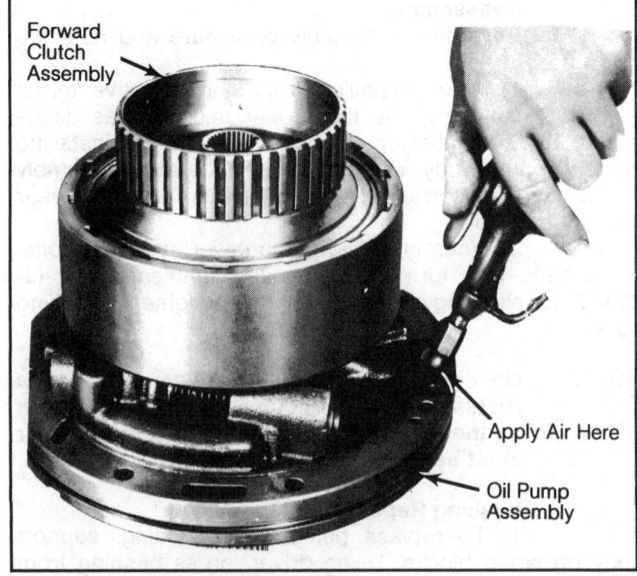

Compressed air must be clean and dry.

GENERAL MOTORS TURBO HYDRA-MATIC 400 (Cont.)

sleeve. Air check operation of forward clutch by applying air through forward clutch passage in pump to actuate piston and move forward clutch. See Fig. 25.

DIRECT CLUTCH & INTERMEDIATE ROLLER ASSEMBLY

Disassembly

1) Remove intermediate roller assembly retainer snap ring and retainer. Remove roller outer race and roller assembly. Turn unit over and remove backing plate-to-direct clutch housing snap ring. Remove direct clutch backing plate and clutch pack.

2) Using a compressor tool, compress spring retainer in arbor press and remove snap ring. Remove retainer and piston and 16 clutch release springs. Remove direct clutch piston from clutch housing, then remove inner and outer seals from piston. Remove center piston seal from direct clutch housing.

NOTE: Keep springs separate from forward clutch release springs.

Inspection

1) Inspect roller assembly for popped or loose rollers. Inspect inner cam and outer race for scratches or wear. Inspect clutch housing for cracks, wear, proper opening of oil passages or wear on clutch plate drive lugs. Inspect clutch plates for wear or burning.

2) Inspect backing plate for scratches or damage. Inspect clutch piston for cracks. Inspect clutch housing for free operation of check ball. Check springs for collapsed coils and distortion.

Reassembly

1) Lubricate seals with transmission fluid and install new inner and outer seals on clutch piston with seal lips facing away from spring pockets. Install new center seals on clutch hub with seal lip facing upward. Place seal protector tool over clutch hub and into clutch housing, then install clutch piston into housing with a rotating motion.

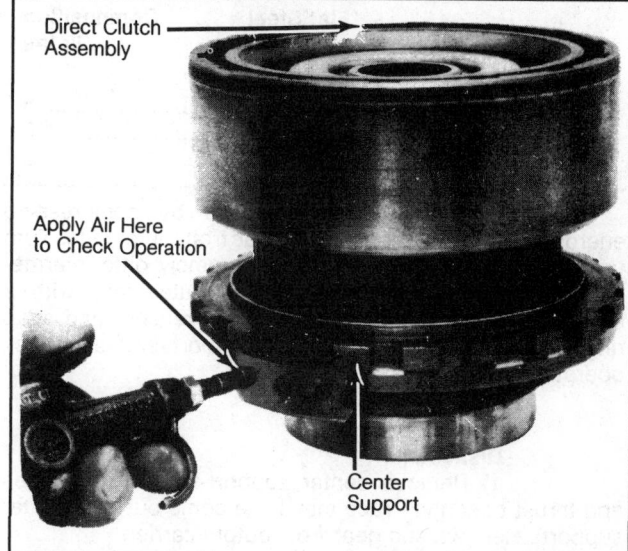

Fig. 27: Checking Operation of Direct Clutch Assembly

Compressed air must be clean and dry.

2) If production clutch release springs are being used, install 14 springs into spring pockets of piston, leaving 2 opposite pockets with no springs. If service replacement springs are used, install all 16 springs into spring pockets. Place spring retainer on top of springs and snap ring on top of retainer. Using tool used at disassembly, compress springs and install snap ring.

3) Lubricate clutch plates with transmission fluid. Install plates into clutch housing starting with a waved steel plate (if used). Alternate composition and flat steel plates until all plates are installed. See Direct Clutch Plate Usage Chart. Install backing plate and retaining snap ring.

NOTE: Do not use radially grooved composition plates in direct clutch.

Fig. 26: Exploded View of Direct Clutch and Intermediate Roller Clutch Assembly

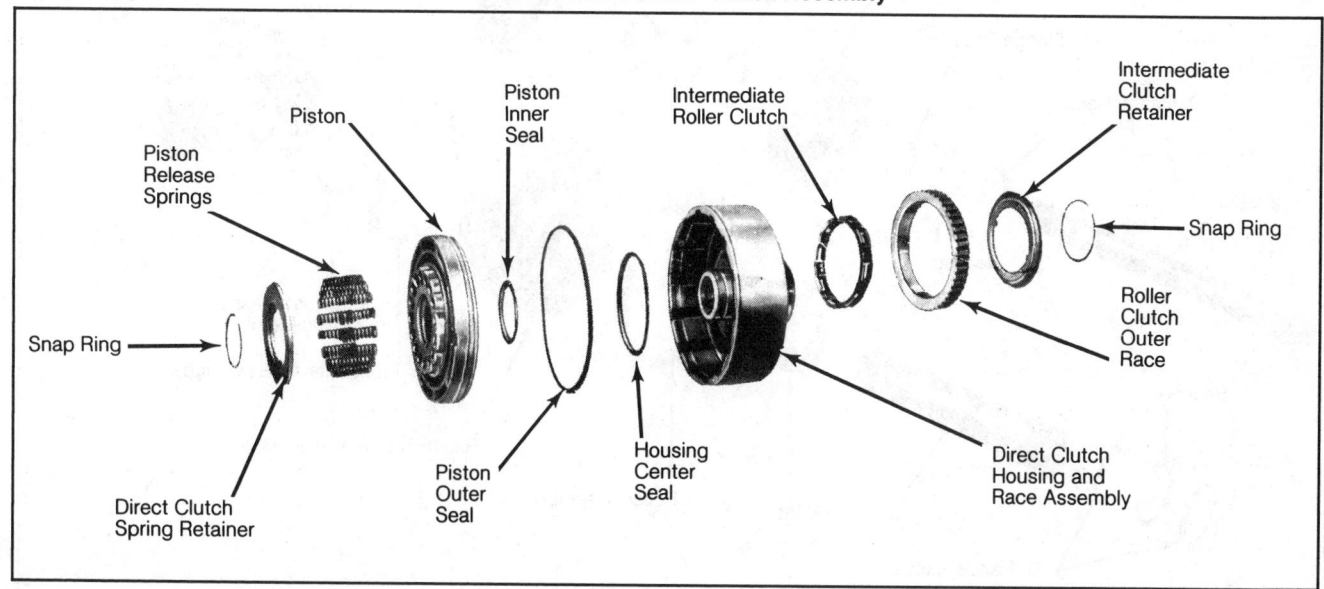

GENERAL MOTORS TURBO HYDRA-MATIC 400 (Cont.)

DIRECT CLUTCH PLATE CHART

Application	Flat Steel Plates	Composition Plates
Models AA, AB, AC, AE, AH	5	5
Model AM	6	6
Model AD	4	5

4) Install rollers in case by compressing energizing spring and inserting roller from outer side. Turn unit over and install roller clutch assembly onto intermediate clutch inner cam, then install outer race with a clockwise turning motion. Install clutch retainer and snap ring. Place assembly on center support and air check operation of clutch.

GEAR UNIT
Disassembly
1) Remove center support-to-sun gear races and thrust bearing (1 race may have come out with center support). Remove sun gear from output carrier.

2) Remove reaction carrier-to-output carrier thrust washer. Remove front internal gear ring from output carrier assembly. Lift roller clutch assembly out of carrier.

3) Remove "O" ring from output shaft (if equipped). Remove output shaft-to-output carrier snap ring and remove output shaft. Remove output shaft-to-rear internal gear thrust bearing and 2 races. Remove rear internal gear and mainshaft.

4) Remove rear internal gear-to-sun gear thrust bearing and 2 races. If necessary, remove rear internal gear-to-mainshaft snap ring to remove mainshaft.

Inspection
1) If reaction carrier is equipped with a spacer ring in an undercut at bottom of roller cam ramps, inspect ring for wear or damage. Inspect reaction carrier bushing for damage; if bushing is damaged, carrier must be replaced.

2) Check pinions for damage, rough bearings, or tilt. Check pinion end play; end play should be .009-.024" (.23-.61 mm). Inspect band surface on reaction carrier for burning or scoring. Check all other parts for wear, scoring, or other damage. Make sure all lubrication holes are open.

NOTE: **If mainshaft is replaced, make sure that the orifice cup plug in replacement mainshaft is removed before installation.**

Speedometer Drive Gear Replacement
1) If equipped with a nylon speedometer gear, depress retaining clip and slide gear off shaft. To install, place retaining clip (square end toward flange of shaft) into hole in shaft, align slot in gear with clip, and install gear.

NOTE: **Nylon speedometer drive gear is installed at factory only; all replacement gears are steel.**

Fig. 28: Exploded View of Planetary Gear Unit

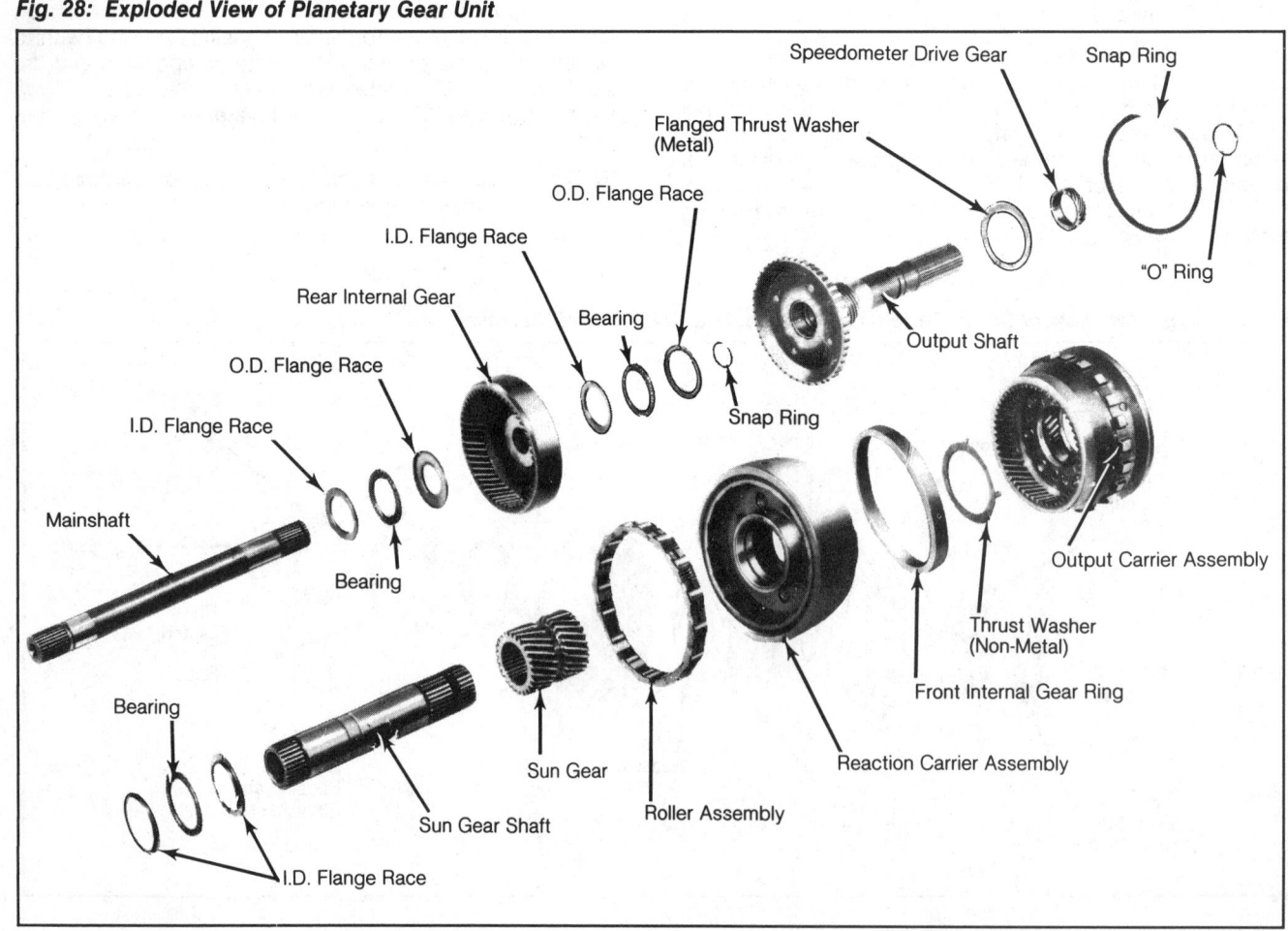

GENERAL MOTORS TURBO HYDRA-MATIC 400 (Cont.)

2) If equipped with a steel gear, use a puller and remove gear from shaft. To install, support output shaft on front face and use driver tool to drive gear onto shaft.

3) Drive speedometer gear onto shaft until distance from rear face of gear to end of output shaft is 5 21/32" (83.34 mm).

Output Shaft Bushing Replacement

If bushing is worn or galled, thread bushing remover (J-21465-16) into bushing, attach slide hammer, and withdraw bushing. Place new bushing on driver (J-21465-1) and drive into place until tool bottoms. Output flange bushing must be installed with oil hole in flange aligned with oil hole in hub and notch in bushing facing outward.

Sun Gear Shaft Bushing Replacement

With sun gear shaft properly supported in a soft-jawed vise, thread a bushing remover into bushing, attach slide hammer and remove bushing. Place new bushing on driver (J-21465-5) and drive into place until tool bottoms.

Pinion Gear Replacement

1) Support carrier assembly on its front face. Using a 1/2" drill, remove stake marks from end of pinion pin(s) to be replaced. This will reduce the possibility of cracking carrier when pressing out pins. Using a tapered punch, drive or press pinion pins out of carrier. Remove pinion gears, thrust washers and needle bearings. Inspect pinion pocket faces for burrs and remove if present.

2) Install 18 needle bearings into each pinion, using pinion pin as a guide, and petroleum jelly to hold bearings in place. Place a bronze and a steel washer on each side of pinion so steel washer is against pinion.

3) Place pinion assembly in carrier, then install a pilot shaft through rear face of assembly to hold parts in place. Drive a new pinion pin into place while rotating pinion from front.

4) Make sure headed end is flush or below face of carrier. Use a punch held in a bench vise for an anvil. Place carrier over punch and stake pinion pin in 3 places.

NOTE: Both ends of pinion pins must lie below face of carrier or interference may occur.

Fig. 29: Exploded View of Pinion Assembly

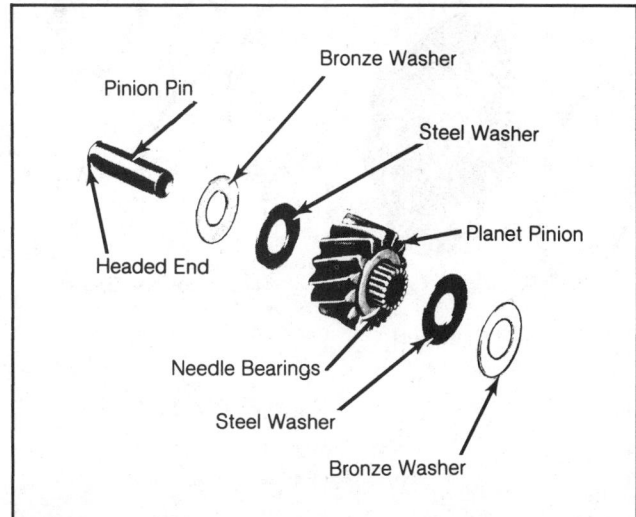

Reassembly (Complete Gear Assembly)

1) Install rear internal gear on end of mainshaft (end with snap ring groove) and install snap ring. Install sun gear-to-internal gear thrust races and bearing against inner face of rear internal gear. Retain with petroleum jelly.

2) Place large race against internal gear with flange facing forward or upward, place thrust bearing against race, then place small race against bearing with inner flange into bearing or downward.

3) Install output carrier over mainshaft so pinions mesh with rear internal gear. With mainshaft in downward position, install rear internal gear to output shaft thrust races and bearings. Retain with petroleum jelly.

4) Place small diameter race against internal gear with center flange facing up. Place bearing on race, then place second race on bearing with outer flange cupped over bearing. Install output shaft into output carrier assembly. Install output shaft to output carrier snap ring.

5) Install output shaft "O" ring (if required). With output shaft in a downward position, install reaction carrier to output carrier thrust washer with tabs facing down in pockets, and retain with petroleum jelly.

6) Install sun gear with chamfer down. Install gear ring over output carrier. Install sun gear shaft with long splined-end down. Install reaction carrier.

NOTE: When a new output carrier and/or reaction carrier is being installed, and if front internal gear ring prevents assembly of carrier, replace front internal gear ring with service gear ring. Front internal gear ring is a selective fit at the factory but not in service.

7) Install center support-to-sun thrust races and bearing (retain with petroleum jelly). Install large race over sun gear shaft with center flange upward, install thrust bearing against race, then install second race with center flange upward.

8) Install rollers that may have come out of roller case by compressing energizing spring with forefinger and inserting roller from outer side. Install roller clutch into reaction carrier outer race.

9) Install center support-to-reaction carrier thrust washer into recess in center support and retain with petroleum jelly. Install center support into reaction carrier and roller clutch assembly.

NOTE: With reaction carrier held stationary, center support should rotate counterclockwise only.

10) Install a holding tool (J-21795) to keep units in place, then install output shaft-to-case thrust washers (bent tabs in pockets) and retain with petroleum jelly.

CENTER SUPPORT & INTERMEDIATE CLUTCH

Disassembly

If necessary, remove 4 center support oil seal rings. Compress spring retainer and remove snap ring. Remove spring retainer and 3 clutch release springs. Remove intermediate clutch spring guide and clutch piston from center support. Remove inner and outer piston seals from piston.

GENERAL MOTORS TURBO HYDRA-MATIC 400 (Cont.)

CAUTION: DO NOT remove the 3 screws retaining roller clutch inner race to center support.

Bushing Replacement

If center support bushing requires replacement, use a driver and remove bushing. To install new bushing, align elongated slot in bushing with drilled hole in oil delivery sleeve closest to piston on front side of center support. Drive bushing squarely into bore until bushing is .010" (.25 mm) below top of delivery sleeve.

Fig. 30: Checking Operation of Intermediate Clutch Piston

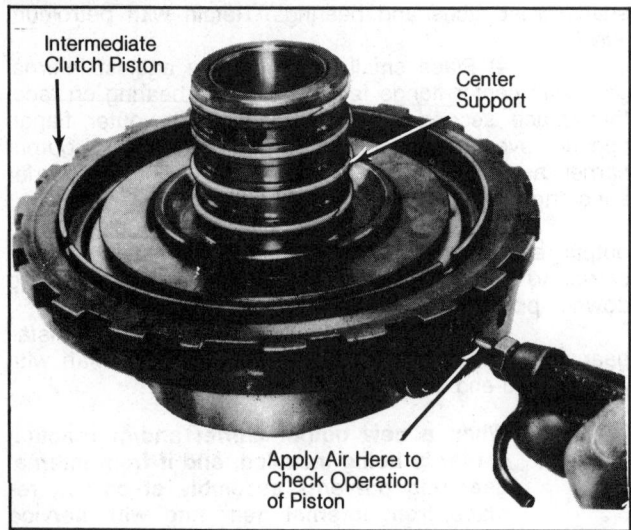

Intermediate Clutch Piston

Center Support

Apply Air Here to Check Operation of Piston

Air must be clean and dry.

Inspection

1) Check all parts for wear, scoring or damage. Inspect release springs for distortion or collapsed coils. Check oil ring grooves and oil rings for wear or damage. Rings should fit freely in grooves.

2) Make sure all passages, lubrication grooves and holes are clear of obstructions. Check roller clutch inner race for scratches and indentations. Make sure constant bleed orifice is open .020" (.51 mm).

Reassembly

1) Lubricate and install inner and outer seals on piston with seal lips facing away from spring pockets. Place a seal protector tool over center support hub. Install piston indexing spring pockets in drum and piston.

2) Install spring guide and evenly space 3 release springs in spring guides. Place spring retainer and snap ring over springs, then compress springs and install snap ring in groove.

3) If removed, install 4 oil seal rings on center support. Air check operation of intermediate clutch piston by applying air through center oil feed hole to actuate clutch piston. *See Fig. 30.*

NOTE: When installing teflon oil seal rings on center support, be sure split ends are assembled in the same relation as cut.

TRANSMISSION CASE

Inspection

Inspect case for cracks, porosity, or interconnected passages. Check governor and modulator valve bores for scratches or scoring. Check band anchor pins for retention, and intermediate clutch driven plate lugs for damage. Inspect snap ring grooves for damage. See that intermediate clutch cup plug is properly staked and sealed.

CAUTION: If case assembly requires replacement, make sure that the center support-to-case spacer and name plate are removed from old case and installed in new case.

Fig. 31: Exploded View of Center Support Assembly

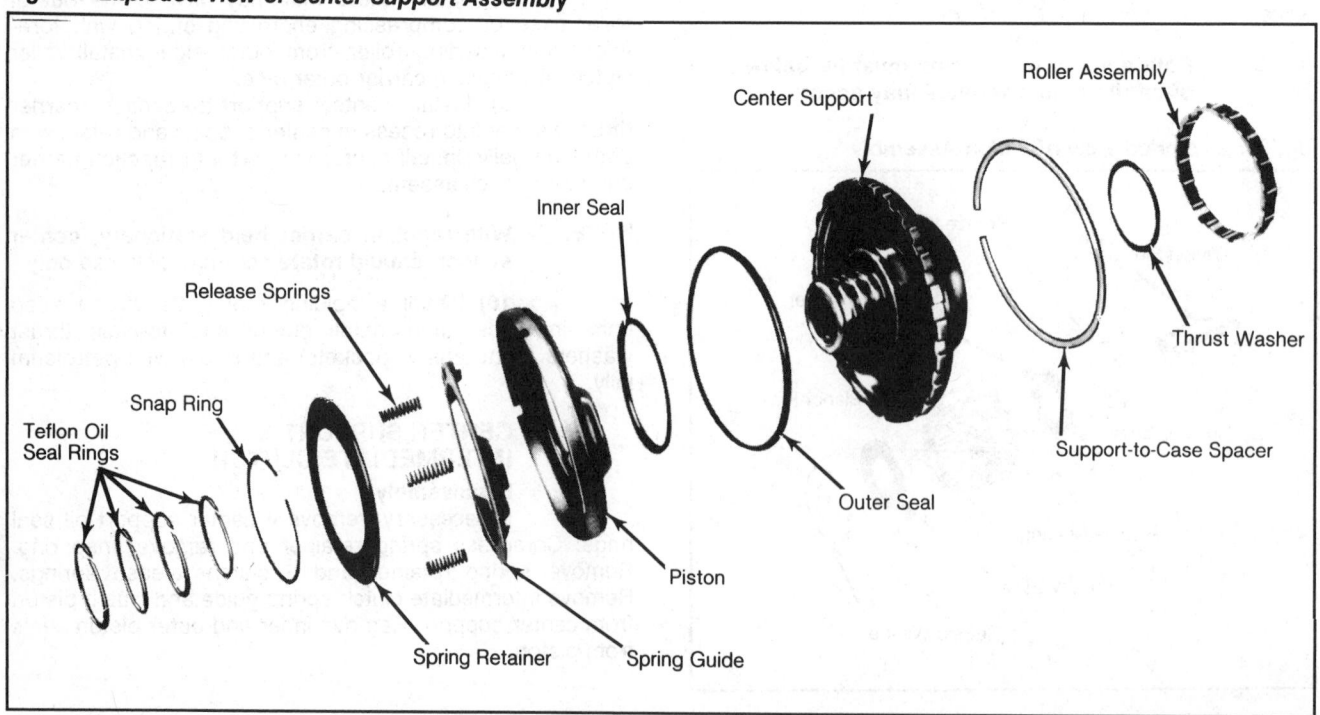

Center Support

Roller Assembly

Inner Seal

Release Springs

Snap Ring

Thrust Washer

Teflon Oil Seal Rings

Outer Seal

Support-to-Case Spacer

Piston

Spring Retainer

Spring Guide

GENERAL MOTORS TURBO HYDRA-MATIC 400 (Cont.)

Case Bushing Replacement

1) With converter end of transmission case downward, use bushing driver (J-21465-8) and a soft-faced hammer to drive bushing out of case.

2) Invert case, install new bushing from front of case using tools (J-21465-8 and J-21465-9). Drive bushing squarely into bore until it is .040-.055" (1.02-1.4 mm) above selective thrust washer surface. Stake bushing in place, staking in lube grooves.

EXTENSION HOUSING

Inspection

Check housing for cracks or porosity. Inspect gasket mounting face for burrs or other damage. Make sure rear seal drain-back part is not obstructed. Check rear bushing for wear or damage. Replace as necessary.

Bushing Replacement

Using a driver tool, drive or press bushing from extension housing. Use same tool and drive or press bushing into housing, .010" (.25 mm) below oil seal counterbore. Stake bushing in place using tool (J-21465-10). Stake marks must be in lube grooves.

NOTE: Staking in production bushings may or may not be in lubrication groove. Production equipment does not distort bushing surface making location of stakes optional.

TRANSMISSION REASSEMBLY

PARKING PAWL

Install parking pawl, tooth toward inside of case, then install parking pawl shaft and shaft retainer. Install a new cup plug using a 3/8" diameter rod, and drive plug into case until shaft bottoms on case rib. Install parking pawl return spring, with square end hooked on pawl and other end on case. Install parking pawl bracket with guides over parking pawl, then install and tighten attaching bolts.

Fig. 32: Bottom View of Transmission Case Showing Oil Passages

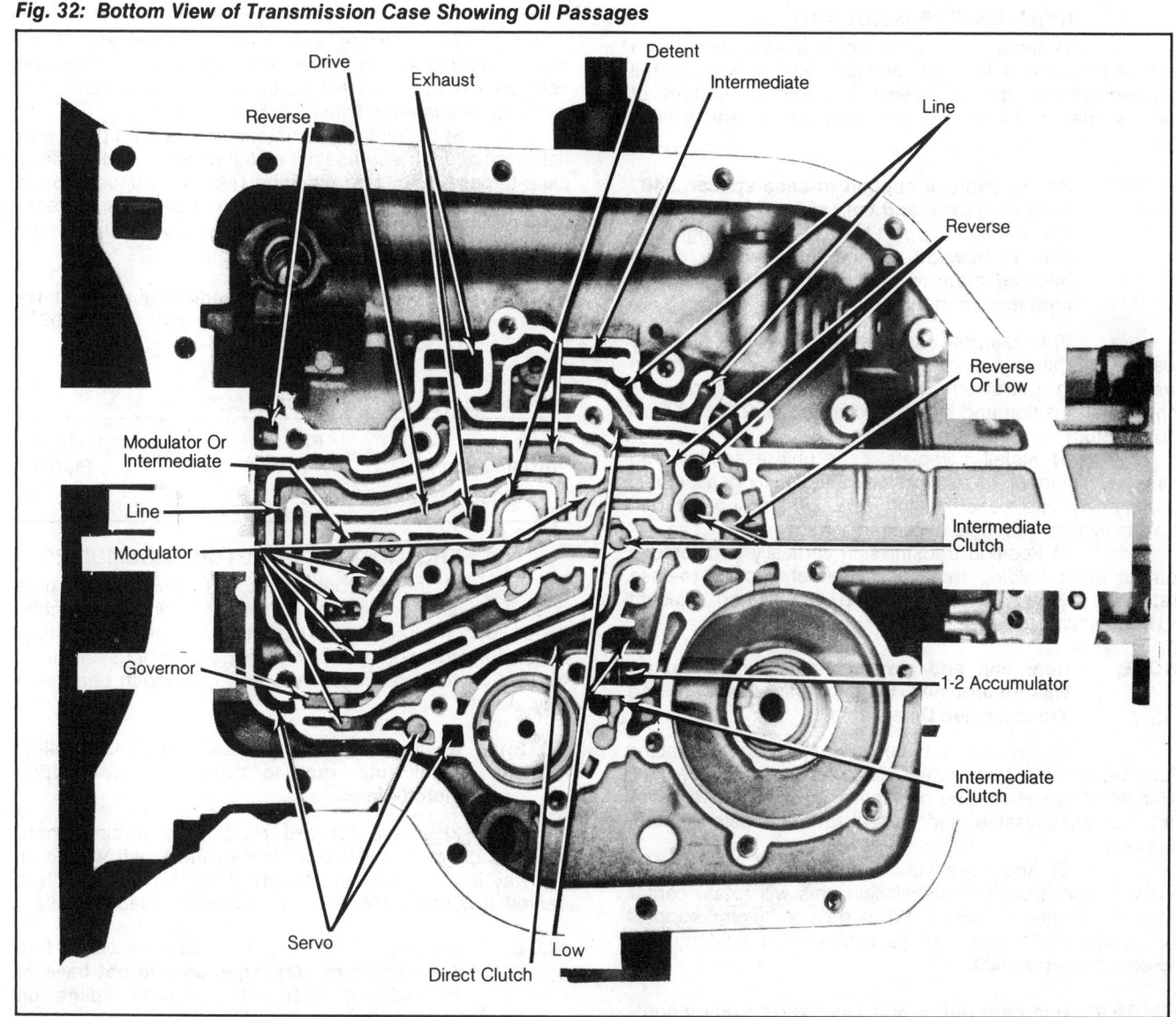

GENERAL MOTORS TURBO HYDRA-MATIC 400 (Cont.)

Fig. 33: Front View of Transmission Case Showing Oil Passages

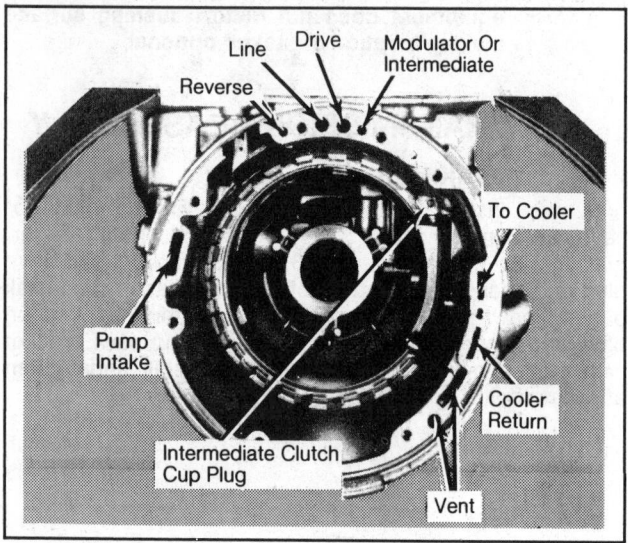

Fig. 34: Using Locating Tool to Install Center Support-to-Case Bolt

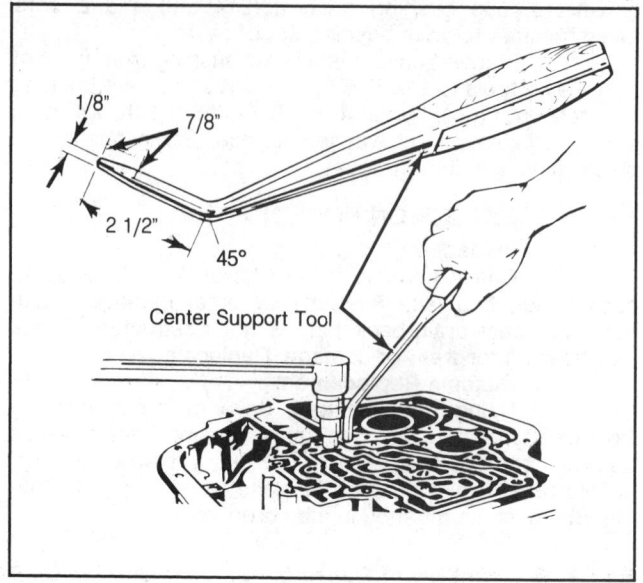

REAR BAND & GEAR UNIT

1) Install rear band so that lugs index with anchor pins and make sure band is seated on lugs. Install support-to-case spacer against shoulder at bottom of case splines and with ring gap adjacent to band anchor pin.

NOTE: Do not confuse support-to-case spacer .040" (1.02 mm) thick and both sides flat with either the center support-to-case snap ring, one side is beveled, or the intermediate clutch backing plate-to-case snap ring, .093" (2.36 mm) thick and both sides flat.

2) Install previously selected rear unit end play washer into slots provided inside rear of case and retain washer with petroleum jelly. Place transmission in a horizontal position and install holding tool (J-21795-02) on output shaft.

3) Install complete gear unit assembly into case by lining up slots and carefully guiding assembly horizontally into case making sure center support bolt hole is aligned with hole in case.

4) Position transmission vertically and remove output shaft holding tool. Install center support-to-case retaining ring, with beveled side up. Locate gap adjacent to band anchor pin.

NOTE: Rear unit end play selective thrust washer was determined by end play check during Transmission Disassembly.

5) Install case to center support bolt by placing locating tool into case direct clutch passage. *See Fig. 34.* Handle of tool should be pointing to right, as viewed from front of transmission, and parallel to bell housing mounting face.

6) Apply pressure downward on tool handle. Viewed from front of transmission, this will rotate center support counterclockwise. While holding center support firmly counterclockwise against case splines, tighten case-to-center support bolt.

CAUTION: Use care not to burr case valve body mounting surface when using locating tool.

7) Lubricate and install intermediate clutch plates, starting with a waved steel plate, then alternating composition and flat steel plates until all clutch plates are installed. *See Intermediate Clutch Plate Chart.*

8) Install intermediate clutch backing plate with flat machined surface against clutch plates. Install backing plate-to-case snap ring, locating ring gap opposite band anchor pin. Before proceeding with transmission reassembly, recheck rear unit end play. *See Transmission Disassembly.*

NOTE: Both sides of the intermediate backing plate-to-case snap ring are flat, and ring is .093" (2.36 mm) thick.

INTERMEDIATE CLUTCH PLATE CHART

Application	Flat Steel Plates	Composition Plates
All Models	3	3

FRONT BAND & CLUTCH ASSEMBLIES

1) Install front band with band anchor hole over band anchor pin and apply lug facing servo hole. Install direct clutch and intermediate roller assembly. Install forward clutch hub to direct clutch housing thrust washer on forward clutch hub and retain with petroleum jelly.

NOTE: It will be necessary to twist housing to allow roller outer race to index with composition clutch plates.

2) Install forward clutch and turbine shaft, indexing direct clutch hub so end of mainshaft will go all the way into forward clutch hub. When forward clutch is seated, it will be 1 1/4" from pump mounting face in case.

NOTE: Missing internal splines in forward clutch hub are lubrication passages and do not have to be indexed with any particular spline on mainshaft.

GENERAL MOTORS TURBO HYDRA-MATIC 400 (Cont.)

OIL PUMP

1) Install new gasket on oil pump and retain in place with petroleum jelly. Lubricate turbine shaft journals and pump oil seal rings. Install pump assembly into case.

2) Install pump attaching bolts with new seals (omit 1 bolt for end play check), tighten bolts evenly.

CAUTION: If turbine shaft cannot be rotated as pump is being pulled into place, forward or direct clutch housings have not been installed properly to index with all clutch plates. Correct this condition before pulling pump fully into place.

3) Recheck front unit end play as described in Transmission Disassembly. If necessary, adjust end play by changing thrust washer located between pump cover and forward clutch housing.

4) Remove dial indicator and install remaining pump attaching bolt. Apply a non-hardening sealer to outside of new front oil seal. Install seal into pump using a driver.

PARKING LINKAGE, DETENT LEVER & MANUAL SHAFT

If removed, install a new manual shaft seal into transmission case using a 3/4" diameter rod to seat seal. Install actuator rod into manual detent lever from side opposite pin. Install actuator rod plunger under parking bracket and over parking pawl. Install manual shaft through case and detent lever. Install detent retaining lock nut on manual shaft and tighten. Install retaining pin, indexing with groove in manual shaft.

NOTE: It may be necessary to bend manual shaft retaining pin to install. Straighten pin as it is installed.

EXTENSION HOUSING

1) Install a new gasket on extension housing and retain with petroleum jelly. Install housing on transmission case and tighten attaching bolts. If applicable, check "O" ring on output shaft for any nicks or flattening and replace ring if necessary.

2) Apply a non-hardening sealer to outside diameter of rear oil seal, position on extension housing, then seat seal in housing using driver.

CONTROL VALVE SPACER & DETENT SOLENOID

1) Install 2 guide pins opposite each other into 2 control valve assembly attaching bolt holes. Install 5 check balls into ball seat pockets in case. If transmission is installed in vehicle, install check balls in pockets of spacer plate. See Figs. 36 and 37.

CAUTION: During reassembly, omit the direct clutch exhaust check ball. This check ball is non-functional.

2) Install control valve spacer plate-to-case gasket, gasket with extension for detent solenoid and marked with a "C". Install control valve spacer plate and control valve-to-spacer plate gasket, marked with a "VB". Install detent solenoid gasket, then install solenoid with connector facing outer edge of case. Do not tighten bolts at this time.

3) Install "O" ring seal on solenoid connector. Compress connector tangs and install in case with locator tab in notch on side of case. Connect detent solenoid wire to connector terminal.

Fig. 36: *Location of Check Balls in Transmission Case*

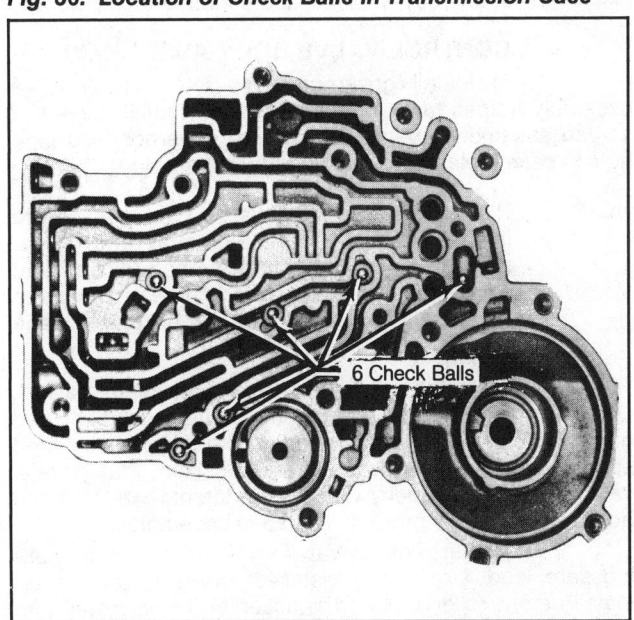

FRONT SERVO

Install front servo spring and spring retainer into transmission case. Install retainer ring in front servo pin groove and install pin in case so tapered end contacts band. Make sure retainer ring is still installed in groove. Install seal ring on piston. Install piston on pin with flat side of piston positioned toward oil pan.

Fig. 35: *View of Oil Pump Cover Passages*

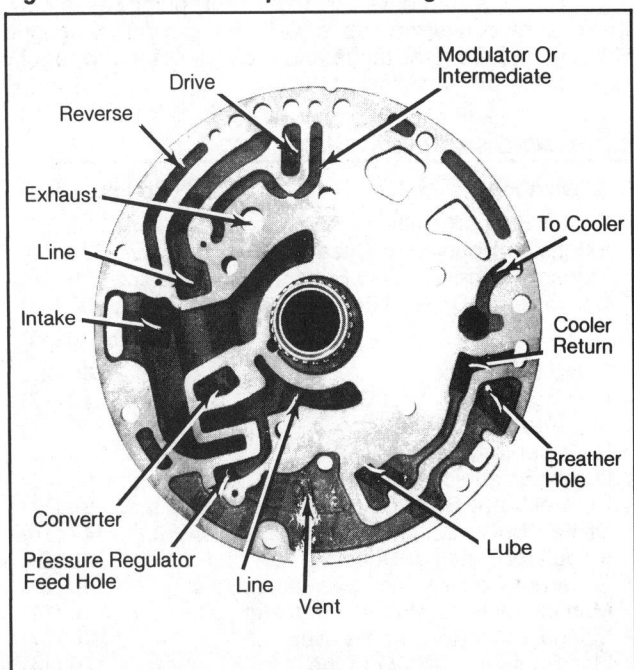

Showing oil passage locations.

GENERAL MOTORS TURBO HYDRA-MATIC 400 (Cont.)

Fig. 37: *Location of Check Balls in Spacer Plate (In Vehicle Installation)*

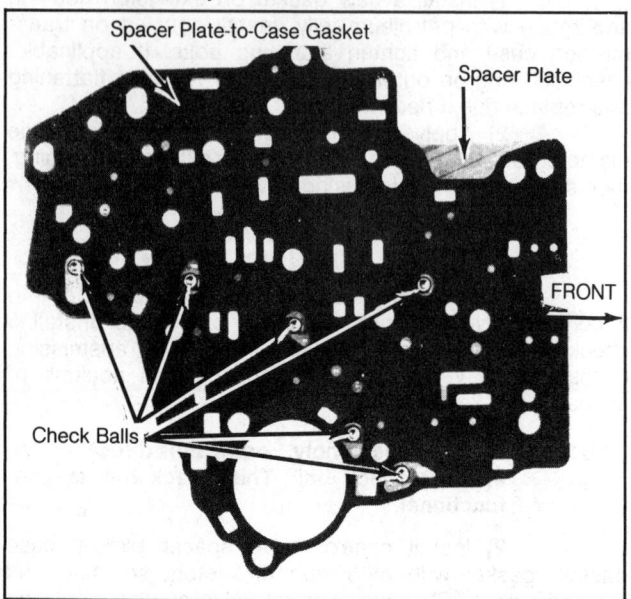

Fig. 38: *Installing Detent Roller and Spring*

tangs in sleeve positioning bosses. Install and tighten attaching bolt.

INTAKE PIPE, FILTER & OIL PAN

Install case-to-intake pipe "O" ring seal on intake pipe. Install pipe into filter assembly. Place filter and intake pipe in case, install retaining bolt and tighten. Install oil pan with new gasket. Install and tighten attaching screws.

VACUUM MODULATOR & VALVE

Install modulator valve into case with stem end out. Install new "O" ring seal on vacuum modulator. Install modulator into case with vacuum hose pipe facing front and angled 5° toward top of case. Install modulator retainer with curved side of tangs inboard. Install and tighten attaching bolt.

CONVERTER ASSEMBLY

Install converter into front pump assembly. Make sure converter hub drive slots are fully engaged with pump drive gear tangs and converter is installed fully toward rear of transmission.

REAR SERVO

1) Before installing servo, check band apply pin. *See Band Apply Pin Selection Check in Transmission Disassembly*. Also, make certain that rear band apply lug is aligned with servo pin bore in transmission case.

2) Lubricate inner and outer rear servo bores in case with transmission fluid, then install rear accumulator spring in servo inner bore. Install rear servo assembly, install gasket and cover. Install and tighten attaching bolts.

CONTROL VALVE BODY ASSEMBLY

1) Install governor pipes into control valve assembly (pipes are interchangeable). Install governor screen assembly (open end first) into governor feed pipe hole in case (hole nearest center of transmission).

NOTE: **If transmission is installed in vehicle, before installing control valve assembly and governor pipes, insert governor screen (closed end first) into governor feed pipe. This pipe locates in governor feed pipe hole in case nearest center of transmission.**

2) Install valve body-to-spacer plate gasket. Using 2 guide pins, install control valve assembly and governor pipes on transmission. Make sure gasket and spacer plate are not moved out of position, that manual valve is indexed properly with pin on detent lever, and that governor pipes are properly seated in case holes.

3) Start control valve body-to-case bolts making sure lead wire clip is installed. Remove guide pins, install detent roller and spring assembly, then install and tighten remaining attaching bolts.

GOVERNOR

Install governor assembly into case. Install cover with new gasket and tighten attaching bolts.

SPEEDOMETER DRIVEN GEAR

If removed, install driven gear into sleeve. Install driven gear assembly into case. Install retainer with

TIGHTENING SPECIFICATIONS

Application	Ft. Lbs. (N.m)
Center Support Bolts	25 (34)
Extension Housing-to-Case Bolts	23 (32)
Transmission-to-Engine Bolts	35 (48)
Converter-to-Drive Plate Bolts	35 (48)

	INCH Lbs. (N.m)
Pump Cover Bolts	240 (27)
Parking Pawl Bracket Bolts	240 (27)
Pump-to-Case Bolts	240 (27)
Rear Servo Cover Bolts	240 (27)
Detent Solenoid Bolts	84 (10)
Control Valve Body Bolts	96 (11)
Oil Pan Bolts	144 (16)
Modulator Retainer Bolts	240 (24)
Governor Cover Bolts	240 (24)
Manual Lever-to-Manual Shaft Nut	96 (11)
Manual Lever-to-Detent Lever	240 (27)
Line Pressure Take-Off Plug	120 (14)
Filter Retainer Bolt	120 (14)

Automatic Transmissions

GENERAL MOTORS TURBO HYDRA-MATIC 700-R4

Chevrolet, GMC, Pontiac

TRANSMISSION IDENTIFICATION

Transmission model may be identified by the production code number, located on identification plate attached to right side of transmission case. Number consists of a year code, 2 letter model code, and a build date code.

DESCRIPTION

The 700-R4 is a fully automatic transmission consisting of a 3-element hydraulic torque converter with the addition of a converter clutch. Two planetary gear sets, 5 multiple-disc clutches, 2 roller clutches and a band are used to provide the friction elements necessary to produce 4 forward speeds, the last of which is overdrive. The torque converter, through oil, couples engine power to gear sets and provides additional torque multiplication when required. The converter clutch drive and driven members operate as one unit when applied, providing mechanical drive from engine through transmission. A hydraulic system, pressurized by a variable capacity vane type pump, provides working pressure required to operate friction elements and automatic controls.

NOTE: See General Motors Torque Converter Clutch System article in this section for additional information on the converter clutch system used in the 700-R4 transmission.

LUBRICATION & ADJUSTMENT

See the appropriate article in AUTOMATIC TRANSMISSION SERVICING Section.

TESTING

CONTROL PRESSURE TEST
Preliminary Checking Procedure
Perform the following prior to making control pressure test:
- Check transmission fluid level.
- Check and adjust T.V. cable.
- Check and adjust outside manual linkage.
- Check engine tune.
- Install oil pressure gauge to transmission.
- Connect tachometer to engine.

Minimum T.V. Pressure Check
With T.V. cable adjusted to specifications and brakes applied, check line pressure in appropriate range at specified engine RPM. See Control Pressure Specifications Chart.

Full T.V. Pressure Check
With T.V. cable held at full extent of its travel and brakes applied, check line pressure in appropriate range at specified engine RPM. See Control Pressure Specifications Chart.

CONTROL PRESSURE TEST RESULTS
High or Low Oil Pressures
- Pump assembly pressure regulator valve binding, dirty or broken spring.

Fig. 1: Cutaway View of General Motors 700-R4 Automatic Transmission

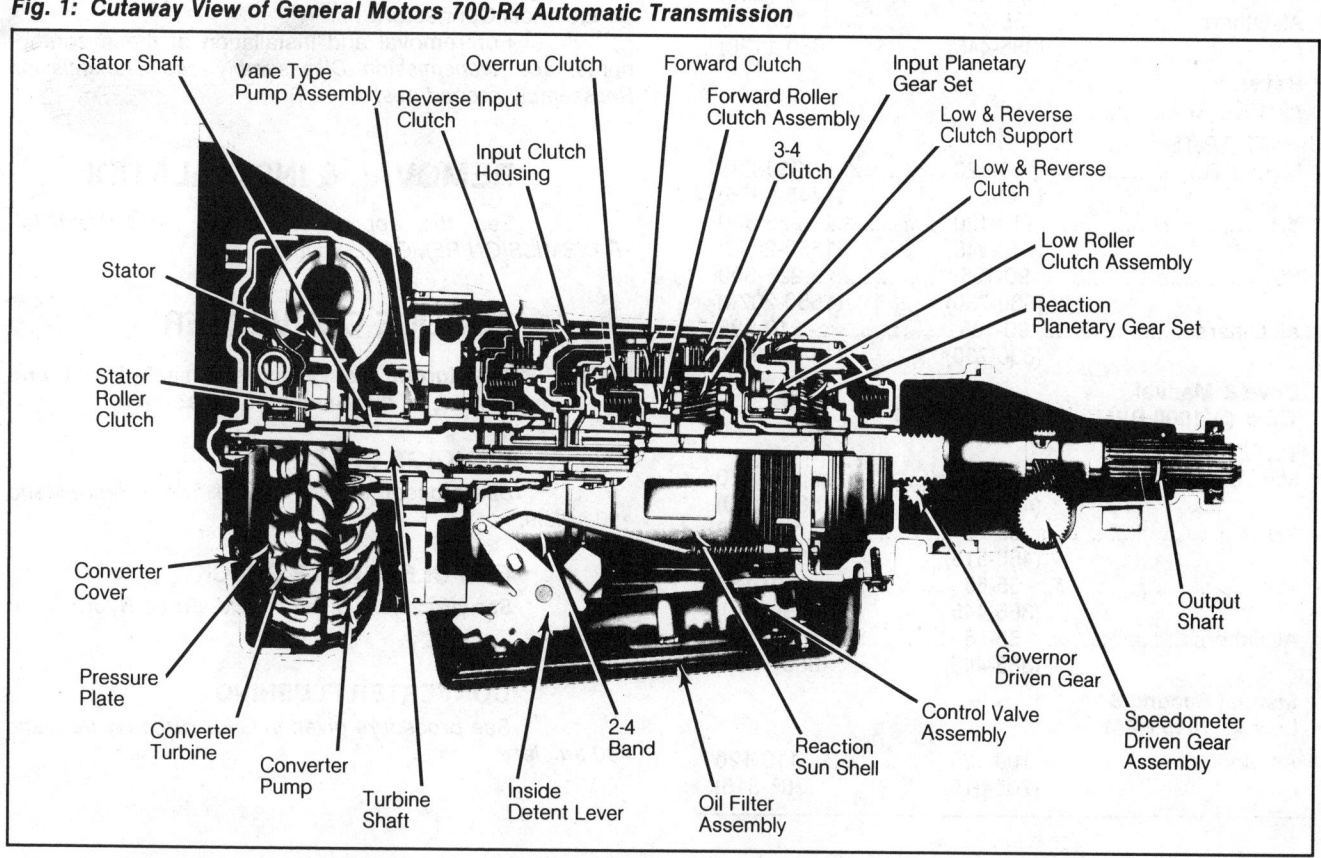

GENERAL MOTORS TURBO HYDRA-MATIC 700-R4 (Cont.)

- Pump assembly T.V. and reverse boost plugs and bushings dirty, sticking, damaged or assembled incorrectly.
- Pump assembly pressure relief ball not seated or damaged.
- Pump assembly slide sticking.
- Pump assembly not regulating.
- Pump assembly excessive rotor clearance.
- Manual valve not engaged or damaged.
- T.V. exhaust valve binding or damaged.
- Throttle lever and bracket assembly binding, damaged, incorrectly assembled or check valve missing.
- Throttle valve or plunger sticking in valve body.
- T.V. limit valve sticking in valve body.
- Throttle link not engaged, damaged, incorrect link, burr on upper end or hanging on T.V. sleeve.
- Oil filter restricted, missing "O" ring or hole in intake pipe.

CONTROL PRESSURE SPECIFICATIONS CHART

Application	Oil Pressure Minumum T.V. psi (kg/cm²)	Oil Pressure Maximum T.V. psi (kg/cm²)
Park & Neutral @ 1000 RPM		
T8,TZ,TP, TS,MH,VJ,TL	65-75 (450-515)	130-170 (880-1190)
YH	65-75 (450-515)	140-180 (965-1240)
Y9	55-65 (385-445)	140-180 (965-1240)
All Others	55-65 (385-445)	137-170 (880-1190)
Reverse @ 1000 RPM		
T8,TZ,TP,TS, MH,VJ,TL,	110-120 (740-845)	210-285 (1445-1955)
YH	110-120 (740-845)	225-300 (1550-2070)
Y9	90-105 (630-730)	225-300 (1550-2070)
All Others	90-105 (630-730)	210-285 (1445-1955)
Drive & Manual Third @ 1000 RPM		
T8,TZ,TP,TS, MH,VJ,TL	65-75 (450-515)	130-170 (880-1190)
YH	65-75 (450-515)	140-180 (965-1240)
Y9	55-65 (385-445)	140-180 (965-1240)
All Others	55-65 (385-445)	130-170 (880-1190)
Manual Second & Low @ 1000 RPM		
All Models	100-120 (705-815)	110-120 (705-815)

SERVICE (IN-VEHICLE)

The following components can be removed from transmission without removing transmission from vehicle:

- Governor Cover and Seals
- Governor Assembly
- Governor Pressure Switch (Diesel Only)
- Intermediate Servo Cover and Seal
- Intermediate Servo Piston Assembly
- 3rd Accumulator Check Valve Assembly
- Oil Pan and Oil Screen (Intake Pipe) Assembly
- Control Valve Assembly (Valve Body)
- Check Balls and Valve Body Spacer Plates and Gaskets
- Inside Detent/Range Lever
- Manual Detent Roller and Spring Assembly
- Throttle Lever and Bracket Assembly
- TV/Detent Cable and "O" Ring
- Parking Pawl Actuator Rod
- Parking Pawl Bracket
- Parking Pawl
- Manual Shaft and Seal
- Manual Valve
- Manual Valve Link
- Extension Housing and Gasket
- Rear Seal
- 1-2 Accumulator Assembly
- Intermediate Band Anchor Pin
- Cooler Fittings
- Oil Filter Pipe and "O" Ring
- Speedometer Driven Gear Assembly
- Speedometer Drive Gear
- Converter Clutch Solenoid
- Solenoid Wire Clips
- Electrical Connectors

For removal and installation of these components, see Transmission Disassembly and Transmission Reassembly procedures.

REMOVAL & INSTALLATION

See the appropriate article in AUTOMATIC TRANSMISSION REMOVAL Section.

TORQUE CONVERTER

NOTE: The torque converter is a sealed unit and cannot be disassembled for service.

LEAKAGE CHECK

See procedure given in G.M. Turbo Hydra-Matic 400 article.

END CLEARANCE CHECK

See procedure given in G.M. Turbo Hydra-Matic 400 article.

CONVERTER FLUSHING

See procedure given in G.M. Turbo Hydra-Matic 400 article.

GENERAL MOTORS TURBO HYDRA-MATIC 700-R4 (Cont.)

Fig. 2: *General Motors 700-R4 Hydraulic Circuits Diagram*

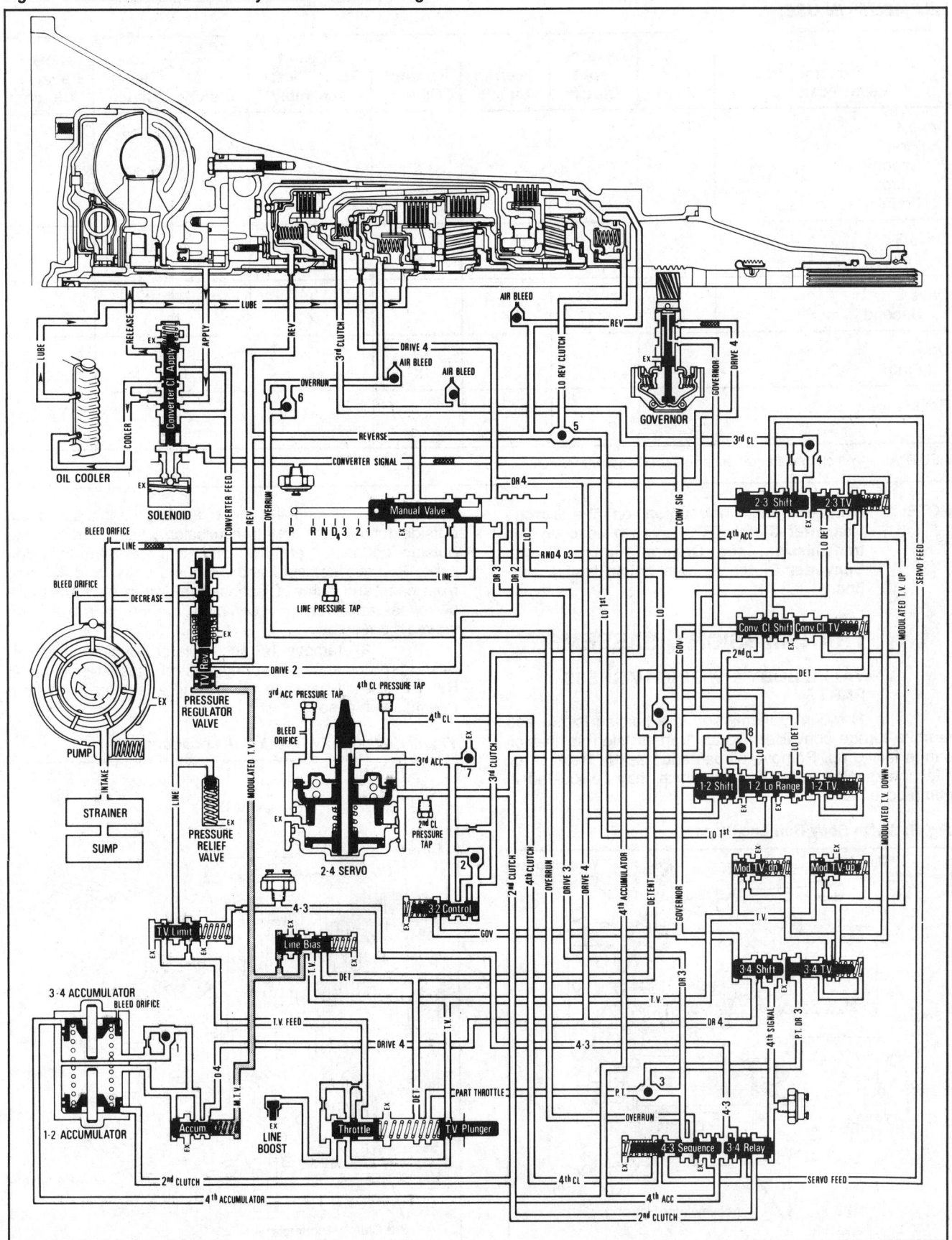

GENERAL MOTORS TURBO HYDRA-MATIC 700-R4 (Cont.)

**CLUTCH AND BAND APPLICATION CHART
(ELEMENTS IN USE)**

Selector Lever Position	2-4 Band	Reverse Input Clutch	Overrun Clutch	Forward Clutch	Forward Sprag Clutch Assembly	3-4 Clutch	Low Roller Clutch	Low Reverse Clutch
Drive 4								
First				X	X		X	
Second	X			X	X			
Third				X	X	X		
Fourth	X			X		X		
Drive 3								
Third			X	X	X	X		
Drive 2								
Second	X		X	X	X			
Drive 1								
First			X	X	X		X	X
Reverse		X						X

NEUTRAL — All clutches and bands released and/or ineffective.

NOTE: For additional information on the Torque Converter Clutch (TCC) system used on this transmission, see General Motors Torque Converter Clutch System article in this section.

TRANSMISSION DISASSEMBLY

VALVE BODY & WIRING HARNESS PARTS

1) Mount transmission in a holding fixture and remove torque converter. Rotate transmission so that oil pan is facing up. Remove oil pan and gasket. Remove oil filter intake pipe and "O" rings which may be located in pump bore.

2) Disconnect inner harness connector at the outside location of the transmission case. Remove the outside connector and "O" ring seal from transmission case. Remove solenoid and attaching bolts, and "O" ring from case and pump. Disconnect all wires from pressure switches and remove complete wiring harness and solenoid assembly.

3) Remove 1-2 accumulator housing, attaching bolts, 1-2 accumulator spring, piston, gasket and plate. Remove the oil passage cover, and attaching bolts from transmission case.

Fig. 3: Valve Body Bolt Locations

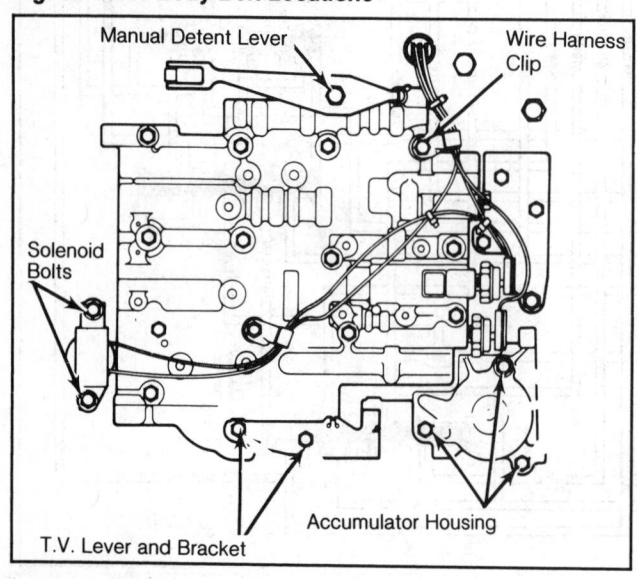

Fig. 4: Valve Body Check Ball Locations

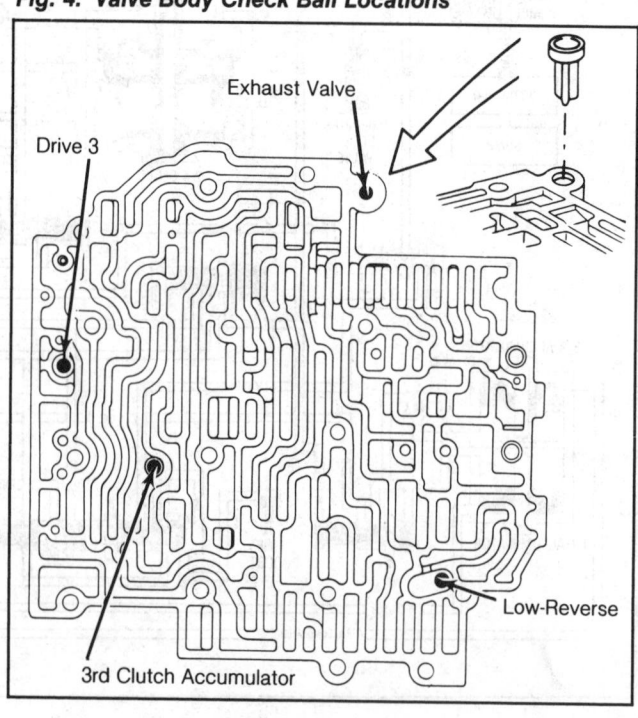

GENERAL MOTORS TURBO HYDRA-MATIC 700-R4 (Cont.)

Fig. 5: Model 700-R4 Case Attaching Parts

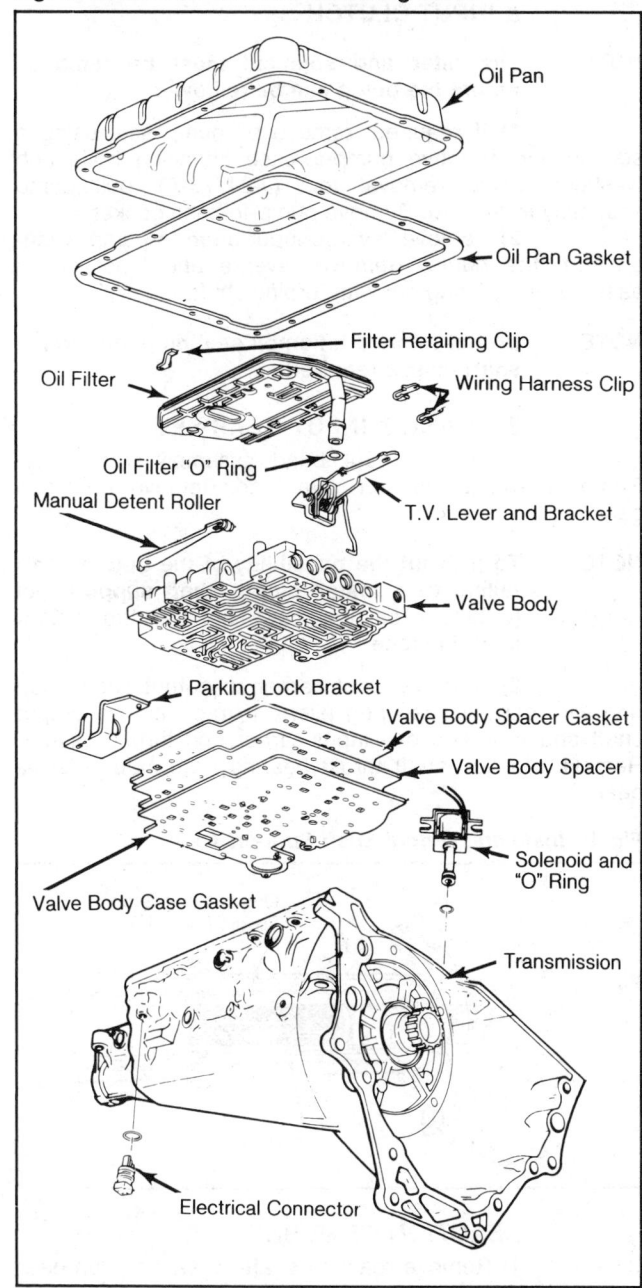

GOVERNOR & EXTERNAL PARTS

1) Remove governor and cover. If rear seal requires replacement, remove with a screwdriver and install a new seal using a seal driver. Remove extension housing and attaching bolts. Remove sleeve and "O" ring from output shaft, then remove speedometer gear and clip.

2) Compress 2-4 servo cover and remove retaining ring. Remove servo cover and "O" ring by applying compressed air to servo apply hole in case. Remove 4th gear apply piston and "O" ring. Remove 2nd servo piston assembly. Remove inner servo piston assembly and oil seal ring, and release spring.

Fig. 6: 1-2 and 3-4 Accumulator Assembly

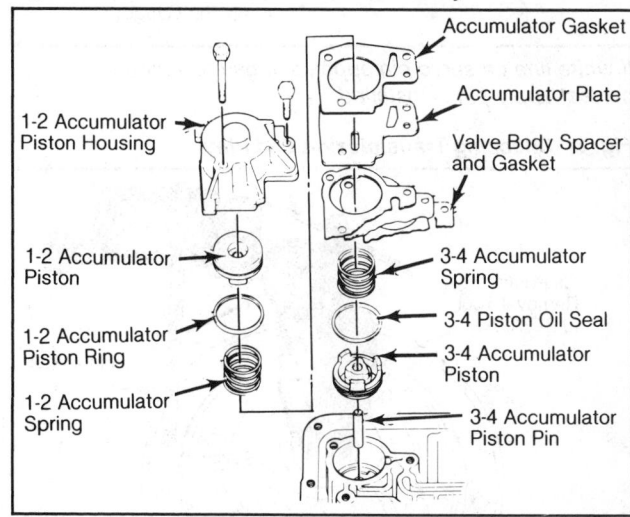

NOTE: Before continuing with Transmission Disassembly, check for correct 2-4 Servo Apply Pin.

2-4 Servo Apply Pin Selection

1) Install servo apply pin selection gauge (J-33037) into servo bore and retain in place with snap ring, locating snap ring gap in case slot. Dissemble 2-4 servo assembly. Insert servo pin into selection gauge. Locate end of pin on band anchor lug.

2) Apply 100 INCH Lbs. (11.2 N.m) torque to hex nut on selection gauge. If any part of white line on servo pin appears in window of gauge, correct pin is installed. If white line cannot be seen, select another pin until correct pin is obtained.

NOTE: Apply pin for 2-4 servo is available in 4 different lengths.

TRANSMISSION END PLAY CHECK

1) Position transmission with oil pump facing up. Remove one oil pump attaching bolt and washer and install an 11" bolt and lock nut in its place. Position oil pump removal tool (J-24773-A) and end play checking adapter (J-25022) on end of turbine shaft. *See Fig. 8.*

2) Clamp a dial indicator on long bolt and position indicator point cap nut on top of pump removal tool. Zero dial indicator. Pull up on removal tool and read resulting end play.

4) Remove manual detent roller assembly and attaching bolt. Remove wire harness retaining clips and attaching bolts. Remove throttle lever bracket assembly and T.V. link. Remove retaining valve body attaching bolts. Disconnect manual valve retaining clip at inside detent lever and remove valve body assembly, spacer plate and gaskets.

NOTE: There are 3 check balls located in the valve body that can and will fall free.

5) Remove 3-4 accumulator spring, piston and pin from transmission case. Remove the 5 check balls and check valve from case passages. Remove converter clutch and governor screens from case.

GENERAL MOTORS TURBO HYDRA-MATIC 700-R4 (Cont.)

Fig. 7: 2-4 Apply Pin Selection

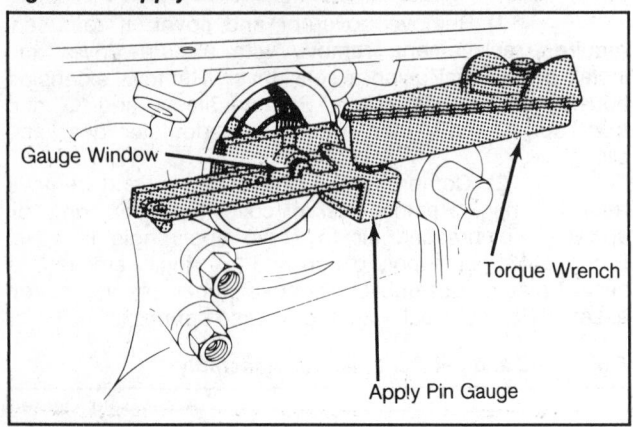

If white line on servo pin appears in gauge window, correct apply pin is installed.

Fig. 8: Checking Transmission End Play.

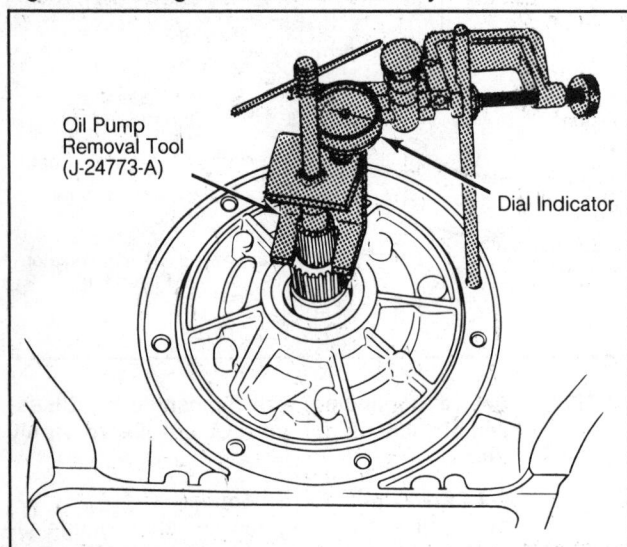

End play should be .005-.036" (.13-.92 mm).

TRANSMISSION END PLAY WASHER SELECTION CHART

I.D. Number	Washer Thickness In. (mm)
67	.074-.078 (1.88-1.98)
68	.080-.084 (2.03-2.13)
69	.087-.091 (2.21-.231)
70	.094-.098 (2.39-2.49)
71	.100-.104 (2.54-2.64)
72	.107-.111 (2.72-2.82)
73	.113-.118 (2.87-3.00)
74	.120-.124 (3.05-3.15)

3) Transmission end play should be .005-.036" (.13-.91 mm). The selective thrust washer controlling transmission end play is located between input housing and thrust washer on the pump hub. If end play is not within specifications, select proper thrust washer from *Transmission End Play Washer Selection Chart*. Remove dial indicator and tools.

OIL PUMP, REVERSE CLUTCH & INPUT CLUTCH

NOTE: The filter and solenoid must be removed before the pump can be removed.

1) If required, remove oil pump seal using a screwdriver. Remove pump-to-case attaching bolts and washers. Using removal tool (J-24773-A), pull pump assembly from case. Remove pump-to-case gasket.

2) Remove reverse input drum-to-pump washer from the pump. Remove reverse and input clutch assemblies by lifting out with turbine shaft.

NOTE: Do not remove teflon oil seal rings on turbine shaft unless required.

2-4 BAND & INPUT GEAR SET

1) Remove 2-4 band assembly from case. Remove band anchor pin from case. Remove input sun gear.

NOTE: To prevent the possibility of the output shaft falling free, install output shaft support tool (J-29837) on the case holding the output shaft in place.

2) Remove input carrier to output shaft snap ring with narrow snap ring pliers. If free, remove output shaft and tool. Remove input carrier and thrust washer. Remove reaction shaft thrust bearing from input internal gear.

Fig. 9: Installing Output Shaft Support Tool

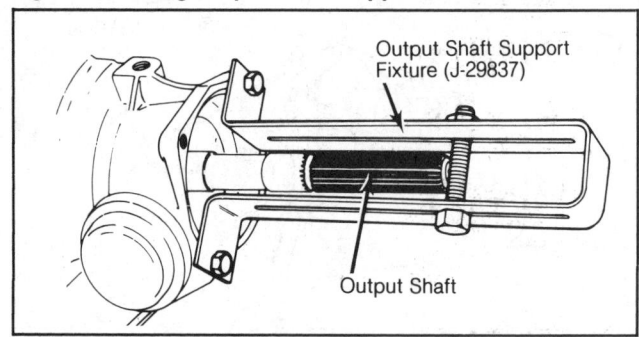

REACTION GEAR SET

1) Remove reaction shaft-to-reaction sun gear washer and reaction shell. Remove reaction shell-to-inner race washer. Remove low and reverse support-to-case retaining ring and support spring. Remove reaction sun gear.

2) Remove low and reverse inner race, roller assembly, support assembly and reaction carrier assembly. Remove low and reverse clutch composition plates and steel plates. Remove reaction internal gear, output shaft (if not previously removed) and bearing assembly. Remove support bearing assembly from case hub.

LOW/REVERSE CLUTCH

1) Remove parking lock bracket and 2 attaching bolts. Position parking lock pawl inboards. Using a compressor tool, compress low/reverse clutch spring retainer.

GENERAL MOTORS TURBO HYDRA-MATIC 700-R4 (Cont.)

compressor tool, compress low/reverse clutch spring retainer.

2) Remove spring retaining ring and low/reverse spring assembly. Remove tools. Remove low/reverse clutch piston by applying air pressure in the case apply passage.

INNER MANUAL LINKAGE

1) Rotate transmission to a horizontal position and loosen manual shaft retaining nut and move inboard on manual shaft. Move inner detent lever and connected actuator rod assembly and manual shaft retainer inboard.

2) Tap manual shaft outboard until retaining nut is free. If necessary, install a retaining nut on outside end of manual shaft. Using a screwdriver, remove manual shaft retainer and connect inner detent lever and actuator rod. Remove manual shaft and nut.

3) If necessary, remove inside detent lever from actuator rod by rotating rod and indexing notches in rod with hole in lever. If required, remove manual shaft seal by driving outwards from case.

PARKING PAWL & RETURN SPRING

Using a screw extractor, remove parking pawl shaft and return spring.

3RD ACCUMULATOR CHECK VALVE REPLACEMENT

1) Inspect 3rd accumulator check valve for the following: missing check ball, check ball binding or stuck in tube, oil feed slot in tube missing or restricted, improperly assembled, loose fitting or not fully seated in case. If check valve requires replacement, proceed to step **2)**.

2) Using a No. 4 screw extractor, remove check valve assembly from case by turning and pulling straight out. *See Fig. 10.*

3) Install new check valve assembly, small end first, into case. Position oil feed slot in tube so it faces servo. On a 3/8" diameter metal rod, scribe a mark 1 41/64" (42 mm) from one end. Drive check valve assembly until mark is flush with machined surface of case.

Fig. 10: Installing 3rd Accumulator Check Valve Assembly

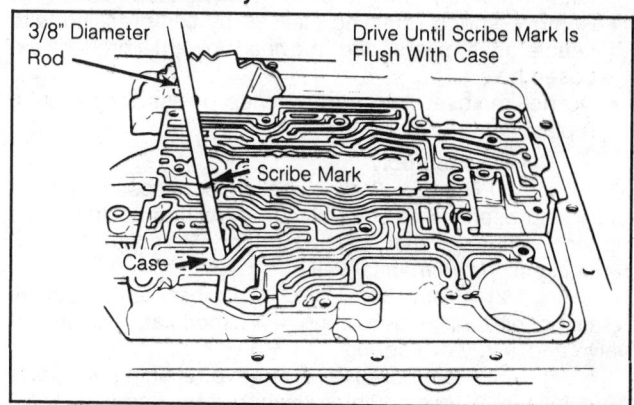

Remove using a No. 4 screw extractor.

COMPONENT DISASSEMBLY & REASSEMBLY

VALVE BODY ASSEMBLY

NOTE: As valve trains are removed from each valve body bore, place individual parts in correct order in relative position to valve body to simplify reassembly. Valves and springs are not interchangeable, and all parts must be installed in correct order in proper valve body bore.

Fig. 11: Exploded View of Model 700-R4 Valve Body Assembly

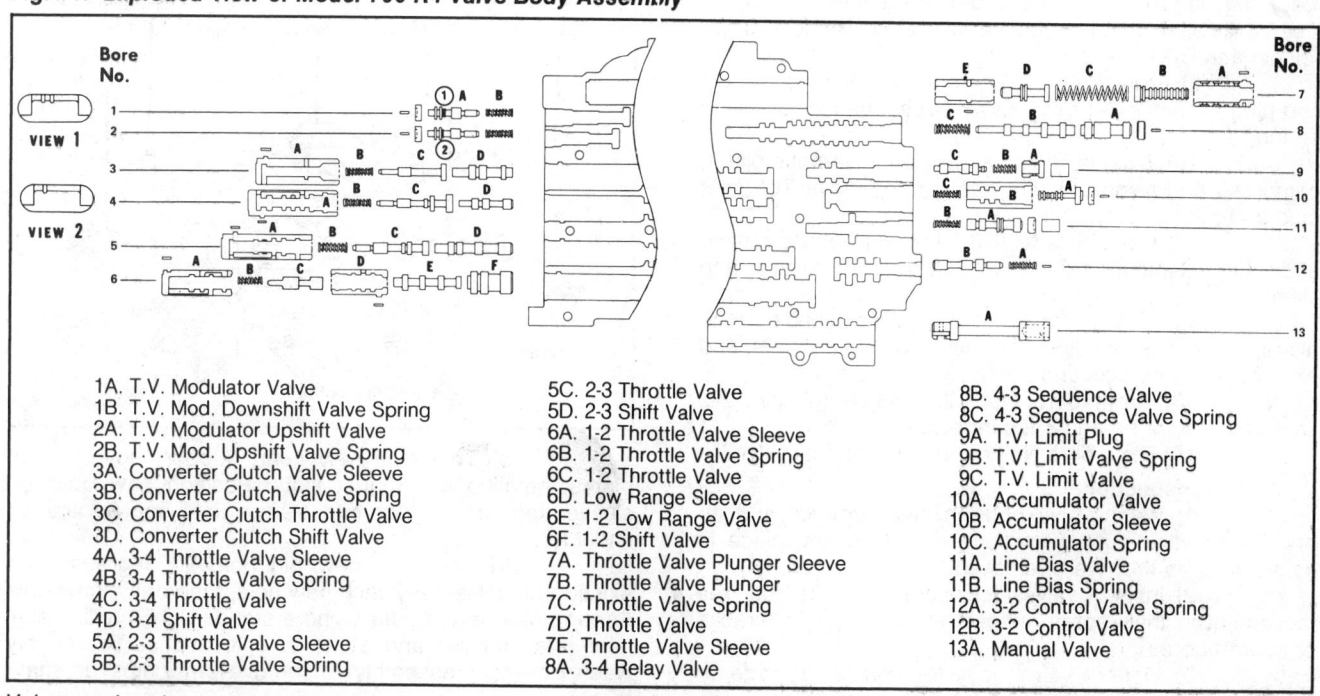

1A. T.V. Modulator Valve
1B. T.V. Mod. Downshift Valve Spring
2A. T.V. Modulator Upshift Valve
2B. T.V. Mod. Upshift Valve Spring
3A. Converter Clutch Valve Sleeve
3B. Converter Clutch Valve Spring
3C. Converter Clutch Throttle Valve
3D. Converter Clutch Shift Valve
4A. 3-4 Throttle Valve Sleeve
4B. 3-4 Throttle Valve Spring
4C. 3-4 Throttle Valve
4D. 3-4 Shift Valve
5A. 2-3 Throttle Valve Sleeve
5B. 2-3 Throttle Valve Spring

5C. 2-3 Throttle Valve
5D. 2-3 Shift Valve
6A. 1-2 Throttle Valve Sleeve
6B. 1-2 Throttle Valve Spring
6C. 1-2 Throttle Valve
6D. Low Range Sleeve
6E. 1-2 Low Range Valve
6F. 1-2 Shift Valve
7A. Throttle Valve Plunger Sleeve
7B. Throttle Valve Plunger
7C. Throttle Valve Spring
7D. Throttle Valve
7E. Throttle Valve Sleeve
8A. 3-4 Relay Valve

8B. 4-3 Sequence Valve
8C. 4-3 Sequence Valve Spring
9A. T.V. Limit Plug
9B. T.V. Limit Valve Spring
9C. T.V. Limit Valve
10A. Accumulator Valve
10B. Accumulator Sleeve
10C. Accumulator Spring
11A. Line Bias Valve
11B. Line Bias Spring
12A. 3-2 Control Valve Spring
12B. 3-2 Control Valve
13A. Manual Valve

Valves and springs are not interchangeable.

GENERAL MOTORS TURBO HYDRA-MATIC 700-R4 (Cont.)

During disassembly, note the following:
• Remove all outside roll pins by pushing through from rough casting side of valve body.
• Remove inner roll pins by grinding a taper on one end of a 1/16" drill, then tap drill into pin and pull straight out.
• Some roll pins are spring loaded and care should be taken when removing to prevent losing them.
• Remove spring retaining sleeves by compressing with needle-nose pliers and moving upward through exposed hole.
• Do not remove pressure switches unless they require replacement.

Disassembly
1) Remove 3 check balls from passage side of body (if present). Position valve body with machined face up and manual valve at lower right. Remove link and retaining clip from manual valve.

2) From bore No. 1 (upper left), remove retaining pin, valve bore plug, T.V. modulator downshift valve and T.V. valve spring.

3) From bore No. 2, remove retaining pin, valve bore sleeve, T.V. modulator upshift valve and T.V. valve spring.

4) From bore No. 3, remove retaining pin, converter clutch throttle sleeve, converter throttle valve spring and valve. Remove converter clutch shift valve.

5) From bore No. 4, remove retaining pin, 3-4 throttle valve sleeve, 3-4 valve spring, 3-4 throttle valve and shift valve.

6) From bore No. 5, remove retaining pin, 2-3 throttle valve sleeve, 2-3 valve spring, 2-3 valve and 2-3 shift valve.

7) From bore No. 6, remove outer roll pin, 1-2 throttle valve sleeve, 1-2 valve spring, 1-2 valve and low range valve. Remove inner retaining pin and remove low range valve sleeve and 1-2 shift valve.

8) From bore No. 7 (upper right), remove outer roll pin from rough casting side, throttle valve plunger sleeve, throttle plunger and valve spring. Remove inner roll pin and valve.

9) From bore No. 8, remove retaining roll pin and plug. Remove 3-4 relay valve, 4-3 sequence valve and spring.

10) From bore No. 9, using needle nose pliers, compress and remove spring retainer. Remove T.V. limit plug and spring valve.

11) From bore No. 10, remove retaining roll pin and plug. Remove 1-2 accumulator valve, spring and sleeve.

12) From bore No. 11, using needle nose pliers, compress the line bias valve spring retainer and remove plug, line bias and spring.

13) From bore No. 12, remove roll pin, 3-2 control valve spring and 3-2 control valve.

14) From bore No. 13, remove manual valve.

Inspection
1) Wash valve body in clean solvent and air dry. Clean valve train parts one at a time and place in same order as they were removed.

2) Inspect valves for scoring, cracks and free movement in their bores. Inspect all bushings for cracks or scored bores.

3) Inspect valve body for cracks, damage or scored bores. Lands should be flat with no cross leaks.

Reassembly
1) Install all parts in reverse order of removal. Assemble all bore plugs against retaining pins with recessed holes outboard. All roll pins must be installed so they do not extend above flat, machined face of valve body pad.

2) Install all flared coiled pins with the flared end out. Ensure all retaining or roll pins are installed into proper slots in the sleeves, not in oil passage holes.

NOTE: **The bushing for the 1-2 accumulator valve train must be assembled with small hole for roll pin facing rough casting side of valve body.**

GOVERNOR ASSEMBLY
Disassembly
Cut off one end of each governor weight pin and remove pins, primary weights and secondary weights. Remove governor valve from sleeve.

Inspection
1) Wash all parts in clean solvent, air dry and blow out passages. Inspect governor body and valve for free operation, nicks, burrs, scoring or galling. Inspect springs for distortion.

2) Inspect driven gear for nicks, damage, or excessive looseness. If driven gear requires replacement, proceed as follows:

Governor Driven Gear Replacement
1) Drive out driven gear retaining pin using a small punch. Support governor assembly on plates installed in exhaust slots of governor sleeve.

2) Place assembly in an arbor press. With a long punch, press driven gear out of sleeve. Clean sleeve of any chips that may be present.

Fig. 12: Governor Assembly Exploded View

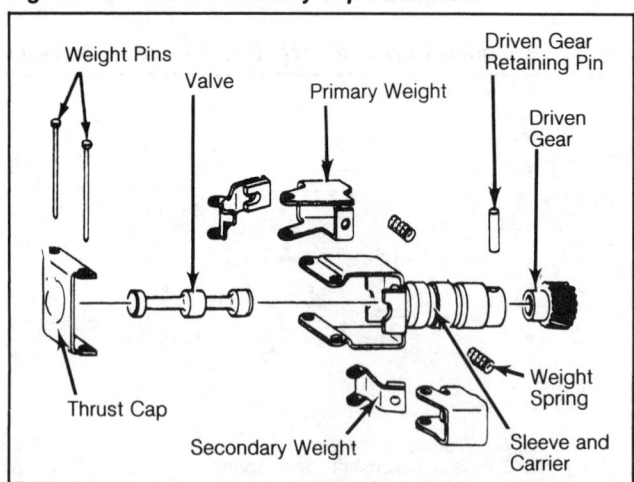

3) To install new gear, support governor on plates installed in exhaust slots. Position new gear on sleeve and press gear into sleeve until seated against shoulder.

4) Locate a new pin hole 90 degrees from existing hole. Center punch new hole, then drill a new hole through sleeve and gear using a standard 1/8" drill. Install new retaining pin and stake in 2 locations. Thoroughly wash governor assembly to remove any chips or shavings.

GENERAL MOTORS TURBO HYDRA-MATIC 700-R4 (Cont.)

Reassembly
Reverse disassembly procedure.

TRANSMISSION CASE
Inspection
1) Inspect case assembly for damage, cracks, porosity or interconnected oil passages. Inspect valve body case pad for flatness or land damage. Air check case passages for restrictions or blockage. Inspect case internal clutch plate lugs for damage or wear.

2) Inspect speedometer, servo and accumulator bores for damage and clearance relative to mating parts. Inspect all bolt holes for damaged threads. Inspect cooler line connectors. Inspect all snap ring grooves for damage. Inspect governor locating pin for proper length. An incorrect length results in a damaged governor gear.

Fig. 13: Front View of Transmission Case

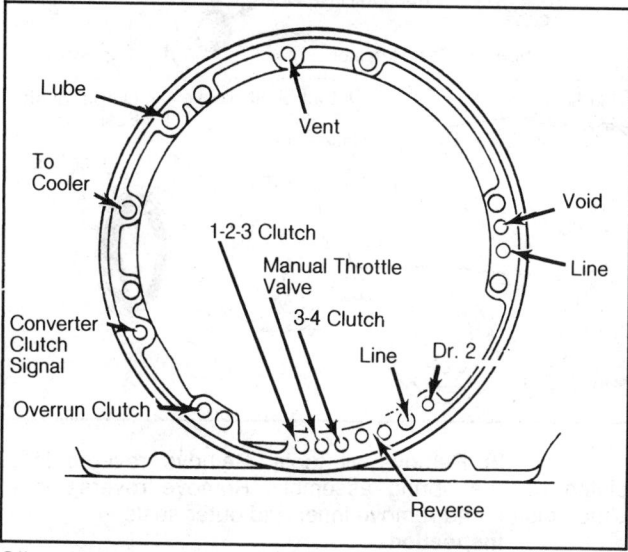

Oil pump-to-case oil passages are shown.

CASE ATTACHING PARTS
Inspection
1) Check 1-2 and 3-4 accumulator parts for porosity or damage to pistons, housing or oil seal rings. Inspect for flatness and condition of accumulator and oil passage plate and gasket.

2) Inspect wiring harness leads and connectors for damage. Inspect "O" ring. Inspect coil and all connections for damage. Inspect speedometer gear and clip for tooth damage or distortion.

REACTION & INPUT GEAR SETS, LOW REVERSE CLUTCH & SUPPORT
Inspection
1) Check reaction and input carriers for pinion gear damage, excessive wear, incorrect number of pinion pin washers and proper staking of pinion pins. Inspect bearings of carrier for heat damage, flatness, and roller condition by rotating top thrust washer.

2) Inspect sun and internal gears and supports for tooth condition and bushing wear. If necessary, remove retaining rings of internal gears. Check all snap rings for damage or distortion. Inspect low reverse clutch plates for damage or burning.

3) Remove seals from low reverse piston and inspect for damage. Reinstall or replace seals as required. Inspect piston for damage or porosity. Check low reverse spring retainer and springs for flatness or distortion. Inspect finish on thrust washers for damage.

THROTTLE LEVER & BRACKET ASSEMBLY
Disassembly
Unhook and remove line boost spring. Remove retaining nut from pin and remove pin, torsion lever spring, line boost lever, throttle lever and bracket.
Inspection
Inspect throttle lever and bracket assembly for sticking, binding or damage. Ensure operation is free and without restriction.
Reassembly
1) Insert a small punch through all parts, leave torsion lever spring unhooked and rearward of top throttle lever to ease reassembly. Install pin through assembly and, at the same time, remove punch.

2) Position short end of torsion spring under bracket and locate in notch. Install retaining nut on end of pin.

Fig. 14: Exploded View of Throttle Lever and Bracket Assembly

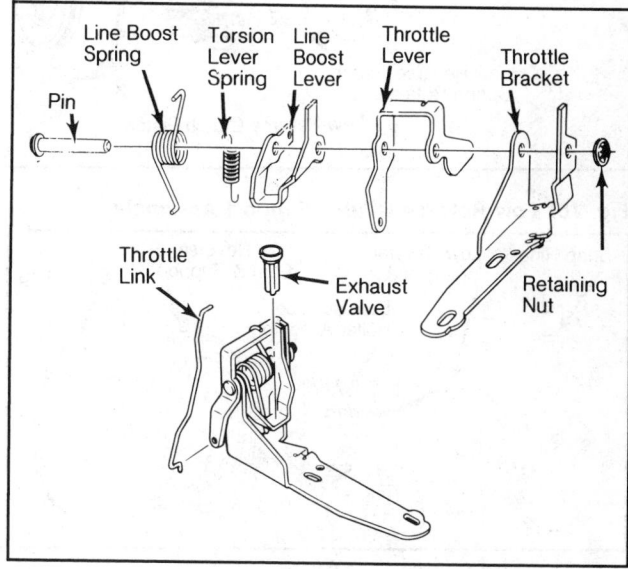

LOW REVERSE SUPPORT ASSEMBLY

Disassembly
With low reverse inner race removed, remove 1 snap ring retaining roller assembly to support. Remove the roller assembly.

Inspection
Check inner and outer races for damage and surface finish. Inspect roller and springs for damage or distortion.

Reassembly
1) Position low reverse support on bench with chamfered side up. Install low reverse roller assembly into support with oil lube hole down (rearward).

GENERAL MOTORS TURBO HYDRA-MATIC 700-R4 (Cont.)

Fig. 15: Exploded View of Input, Reaction and Case Extension Parts

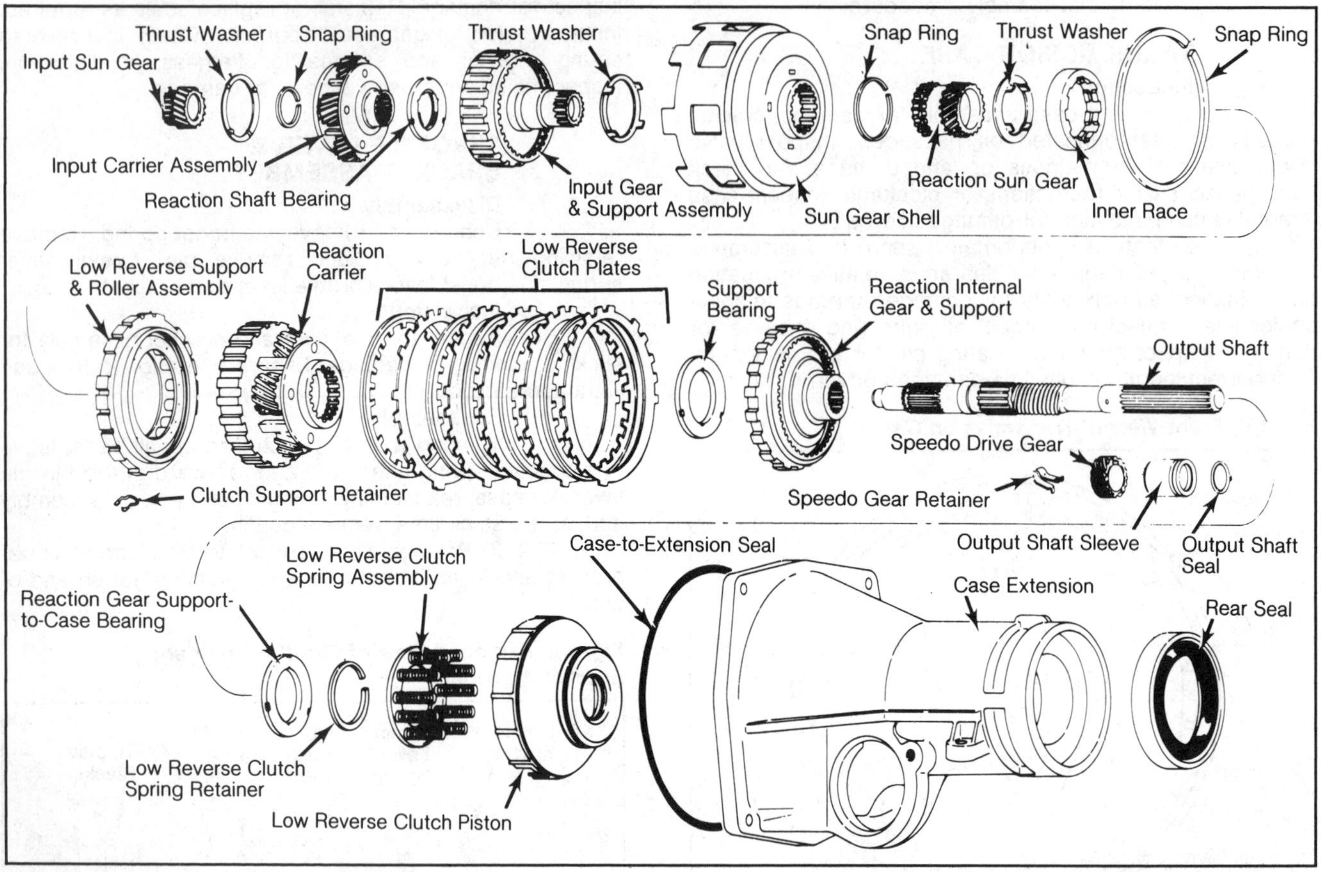

Thrust Washer — Snap Ring — Thrust Washer — Snap Ring — Thrust Washer — Snap Ring

Input Sun Gear

Input Carrier Assembly

Reaction Shaft Bearing

Input Gear & Support Assembly

Sun Gear Shell

Reaction Sun Gear

Inner Race

Low Reverse Support & Roller Assembly — Reaction Carrier — Low Reverse Clutch Plates — Support Bearing — Reaction Internal Gear & Support

Output Shaft

Clutch Support Retainer

Speedo Drive Gear

Speedo Gear Retainer

Output Shaft Sleeve

Output Shaft Seal

Reaction Gear Support-to-Case Bearing

Low Reverse Clutch Spring Assembly

Case-to-Extension Seal

Case Extension

Rear Seal

Low Reverse Clutch Spring Retainer

Low Reverse Clutch Piston

Fig. 16: Low Reverse CLutch Support Assembly

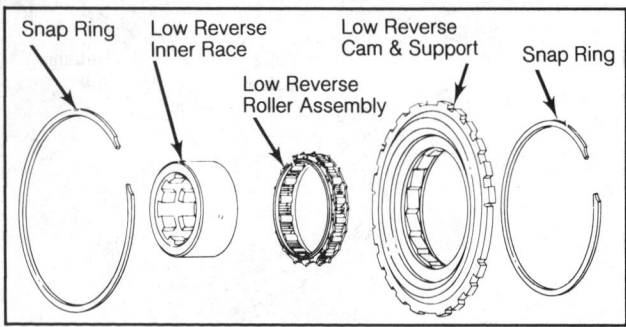

Snap Ring — Low Reverse Inner Race — Low Reverse Roller Assembly — Low Reverse Cam & Support — Snap Ring

CAUTION: Care should be taken to insure roller and springs are not damaged and that rollers do not become dislodged.

2) Install low reverse inner race into roller assembly by rotating clockwise. When installed, the inner race should rotate in the clockwise direction and lock up in the counterclockwise direction.

REVERSE INPUT CLUTCH
Disassembly

1) Remove snap ring from reverse input housing. Remove reverse input clutch backing plate. Remove reverse input steel and composition clutch plates. Using clutch spring compressor (J-23327) compress reverse input spring assembly and remove snap ring.

2) Remove all tools. Remove reverse input clutch release spring assembly. Remove reverse input clutch piston and remove inner and outer seals.

Inspection

1) Inspect reverse input clutch backing plate for damage, distortion, flatness and burred edges on clutch plate face. Inspect reverse plates. Inspect reverse input composition plates. Check release spring retainer for distortion and damage. Check reverse input clutch piston and seals for damage or distortion.

2) Inspect reverse input housing and drum for cracks. Check surface finish on hub and for worn or damaged bushings. Check freeness and condition of ball check. The ball must move freely with applied air pressure.

Reassembly

1) Lube and install inner and outer seals on clutch piston with seal lips facing away from hub. Install piston into reverse input clutch housing with hub upwards, using an .031" (.8 mm) feeler gauge to position seals. Install spring assembly, large opening first, onto clutch piston.

2) Using clutch spring compressor and adapter (J-23327 and J-250l8-A) on spring retainer, compress spring retainer and install retaining snap ring. Remove all tools.

3) Install 1 waved steel reverse plate. No indexing is necessary. Install a composition plate, followed by the balance of plates, alternating composition faced

GENERAL MOTORS TURBO HYDRA-MATIC 700-R4 (Cont.)

Fig. 17: Exploded View of Reverse Input Clutch Assembly

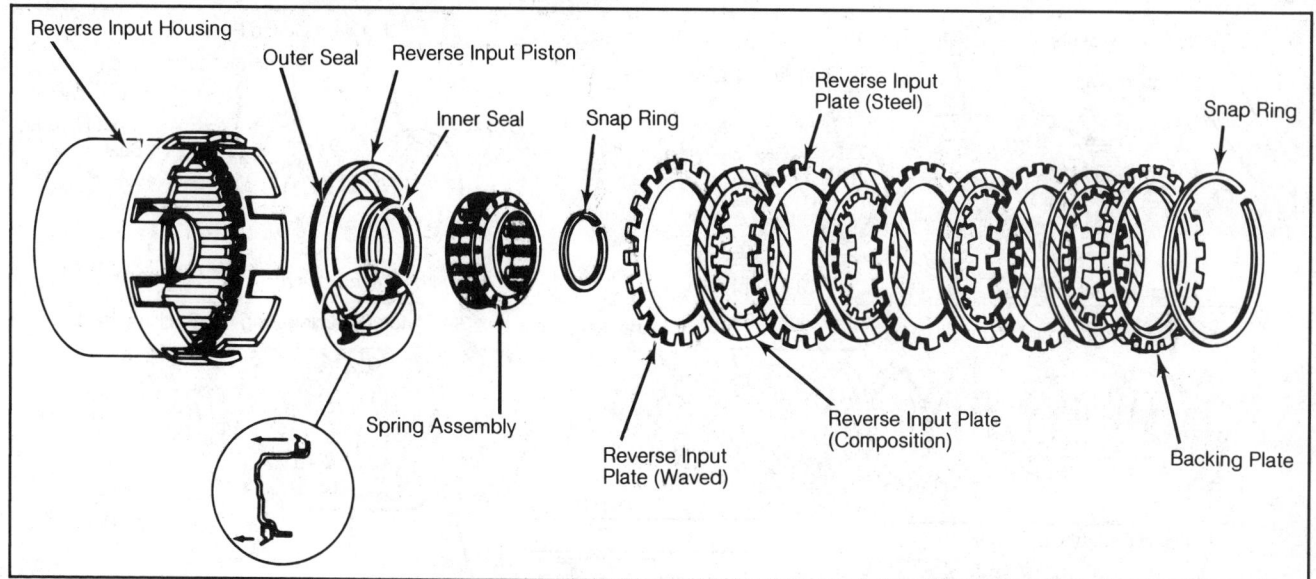

and flat steel. Install reverse input backing plate with chamfered side up. Install backing plate snap ring.

NOTE: The reverse clutch plates are the largest plates with equally spaced tangs.

REVERSE INPUT CLUTCH PLATE USAGE CHART

Application	Flat Steel [1]	Composition [1]
T2,VA,ML,MP,MS, T7,YH,YF,PQ,TC, MB,MC,MJ,VN	2 [2]	3 [2]
All Others	3 [2]	4 [2]

[1] — Plate thickness is .077" (1.97 mm).
[2] — Plus 1 Waved steel plate .079" (2.03 mm) thick installed first.

INPUT CLUTCH & FORWARD CLUTCH CAM ASSEMBLY

Disassembly

1) Position input clutch assembly on bench with turbine shaft located in hole on bench and resting on turbine shaft housing. Remove snap ring retaining the 3-4 clutch backing plate and remove plate. Remove 3-4 clutch plates and the 3-4 apply plate. Remove the retaining apply ring and remove the forward clutch backing plate and backing plate snap ring.

2) Remove forward clutch cam assembly and outer race by pulling up. The complete assembly will consist of the forward clutch roller cam, overrun clutch hub and snap ring, and forward clutch outer race and roller assembly. Remove input sun gear bearing (it can be located on back side of input inner race). Remove output shaft nylon seal.

3) Remove forward clutch plates (steel and composition). Remove apply plate and spacer if used. Remove overrun clutch plates (2 steel and 2 composition). Using clutch spring compressor and adapter (J-23456 and J-25018) compress overrun clutch spring retainer. Remove overrun clutch snap ring and all tools. Remove overrun spring and piston assemblies.

4) Remove inner and outer seals from overrun clutch piston. Remove forward clutch piston assembly. Remove inner and outer seals from forward clutch piston assembly.

NOTE: Apply air pressure to 3-4 feed hole in turbine shaft. It is 3rd hole from shaft end. If unable to remove parts, strike housing on soft surface squarely on open end.

5) Remove forward clutch housing assembly. Remove 3-4 spring assembly. Remove 3-4 apply ring and piston. Remove "O" ring from input housing. Inspect the 4 teflon oil seal rings on turbine shaft for damage or distortion. Remove and replace only if necessary.

6) Remove overrun clutch hub snap ring and overrun hub. Remove forward clutch cam (inner race). Remove roller assembly from forward clutch cam. Be careful not to dislodge any rollers from the roller cage.

Inspection

1) Inspect locating ears on top of forward clutch roller assembly cage for damage or distortion. Inspect rollers for wear or damage. Do not remove rollers from case.

2) Inspect overrun clutch hub for spline damage, excessive wear or damage, and for open oil passages. Inspect forward clutch cam for wear to splines, tangs and roller cam surface. Check forward clutch outer race surface finish.

3) Inspect input clutch housing for spline damage or wear, and for open feed passages. Check rear end of turbine shaft for presence of 3 sealing balls (1 hole is an open feed hole and is not sealed). Inspect the 4 teflon seals on turbine shaft for wear and correct installation. *See Fig. 19.*

4) Inspect converter check ball on front end of turbine shaft for restrictions and free operation. Ball must move with air pressure. If damaged, replace check ball as follows:

- Straighten tangs of retainer and check ball capsule and remove check ball.
- Using a No. 4 screw extractor, remove check valve retainer from shaft by turning and pulling straight out.

GENERAL MOTORS TURBO HYDRA-MATIC 700-R4 (Cont.)

Fig. 18: Exploded View of Input Clutch and Forward Clutch Cam Assembly

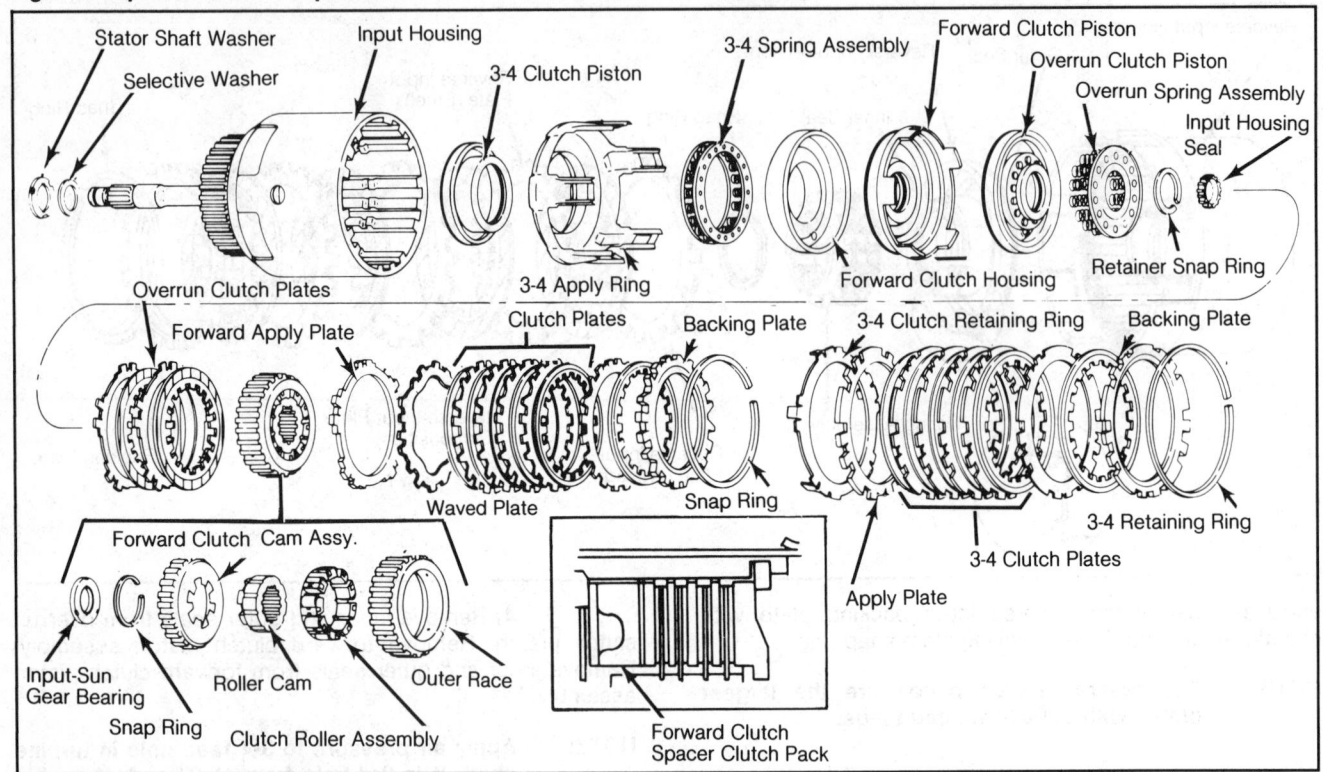

Fig. 19: View of Turbine Shaft Showing Correct Installation of Teflon Oil Seals

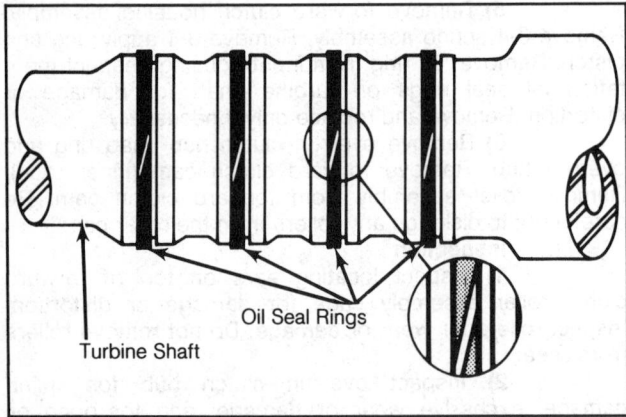

NOTE: **Do not remove turbine shaft teflon oil seals unless damaged.**

• Position new check valve assembly, check valve seat first, into turbine shaft.
• Using a 3/8" (9.5 mm) diameter rod, drive retainer and check valve assembly into shaft until it is 1/8" (3 mm) below top surface of shaft.

5) Check 3-4 check ball in input housing for free operation. Inspect all clutch pistons for wear, damage or porosity. Check piston seals for wear or damage.

6) Inspect all clutch release springs for damage, distortion and spring retainer for flatness and damage. Inspect steel clutch plates for damaged tang ends, high or burned spots, excessive wear, or distortion caused by heat. Inspect composition clutch plates for

damaged tang ends, burning, flaking or excessive wear (thickness).

7) Inspect all snap rings for distortion and damage. Check backing plates for flatness, distortion and sharpness or burrs on inside edge. Inspect clutch apply rings for distortion and damaged apply tangs.

8) Inspect forward clutch housing ball check for proper operation. Inspect housing for distortion or damage. Inspect needle bearings for excessive wear, flatness, damage or flat rollers.

Reassembly

1) Position forward clutch cam with tangs facing upward. Install forward clutch roller assembly over cam, indexing roller cage to engage tangs in ramps of forward clutch cam. When properly seated, the square ears will be flush with inner race.

2) Position the overrun clutch hub assembly or cam and roller assembly and install snap ring. Install assembled hub, cam and roller assembly into the forward clutch outer race by rotating clockwise. When assembled, the forward clutch hub must rotate freely in the clockwise direction and lockup in the counterclockwise direction.

3) If removed, install the 4 teflon oil seal rings on turbine shaft. *See Fig. 19.* Assemble with a long edge and the large "O" ring on inside of housing. If removed, install small "O" ring on end of turbine shaft.

4) Position input clutch housing over bench hole with turbine shaft downward. Install inner and outer seals on 3-4 piston, with lips facing away from hub. Install 3-4 piston in input housing, rotate and gently push downward making certain piston is properly seated. Install inner and outer seals on forward clutch piston with lips facing away from tangs.

5) Lube and install forward clutch piston into forward clutch housing. Install 3-4 spring retainer into 3-4

GENERAL MOTORS TURBO HYDRA-MATIC 700-R4 (Cont.)

clutch apply ring. Install assembled forward clutch housing and piston on spring retainer in 3-4 apply ring. Notches of the forward clutch piston must be indexed with the long apply tangs of the 3-4 apply ring. Install seal protector (J-29883) on input shaft.

6) Hold 3-4 apply ring and assembled parts by the tangs and install into input clutch housing and firmly seat forward clutch piston. Remove tools. Do not let pistons separate. Install overrun clutch seal protector (J-29882) on input housing shaft and install overrun clutch piston with the hub facing upward and remove tool.

7) Overrun piston should be 3/16" below snap ring groove on input housing hub. If not seated properly, install clutch spring compressor (J-23327) and tap until all parts are fully seated. Install overrun clutch spring retainer on overrun clutch piston locating release springs on piston tabs. Use clutch spring compressor press and adapter (J-23456 and J-25018) on the overrun spring assembly and compress spring retainer.

NOTE: Do not over compress springs as distortion to the retainer can occur.

8) With springs compressed, install retaining snap ring and remove all tools. Install splined nylon output shaft seal, with seal lip facing up. On the forward clutch piston in the input housing, install 4 overrun clutch plates. Starting with steel plate and positioning so that the long recessed slot is indexed with a wide notch in housing. Install remaining clutch plates alternating steel and composition.

9) Install input sun gear bearing assembly on input clutch hub on top of nylon seal positioning the outside "L" race in the downward position. Make sure the bearing is centered. Using a screwdriver, align and center inside drive tangs of the 2 overrun clutch plates (composition).

10) Install assembled forward clutch cam assembly and outer race clutch hub, indexing overrun clutch plates. Install forward clutch spacer (thick steel) into input clutch housing, indexing lug on spacer with large slot in input housing.

NOTE: A 5 plate forward clutch will use a single thick apply plate. A 4 plate clutch will use a thick spacer and a thin apply plate, and must be assembled with thin apply plate first and spacer with holes facing thin apply plate.

11) Install "Waved" steel forward clutch plate into input housing, indexing the wide slot with 2 small ears with the wide notch in housing. Install forward clutch plate assembly (composition) on forward clutch hub. Install the remaining forward clutch plates alternating composition and steel. The last plate installed will be composition.

12) Install forward clutch backing plate into input housing, with chamfered side up. Install snap ring into input clutch housing (smaller ring with larger gap). Install 3-4 gear ring retaining plate (flat plate with legs) into clutch housing indexing each apply lug with ends of 3-4 gear apply ring.

13) Install 3-4 gear apply plate (thick steel) into input housing indexing the long wide gear of plate with wide slot in housing. Install 3-4 assembly (composition), then install remaining plates alternating steel and composition indexing the long wide ear of the plate with wide slot in housing. The last plate installed will be composition.

Fig. 20: Exploded View of Model 700-R4 Oil Pump Assembly

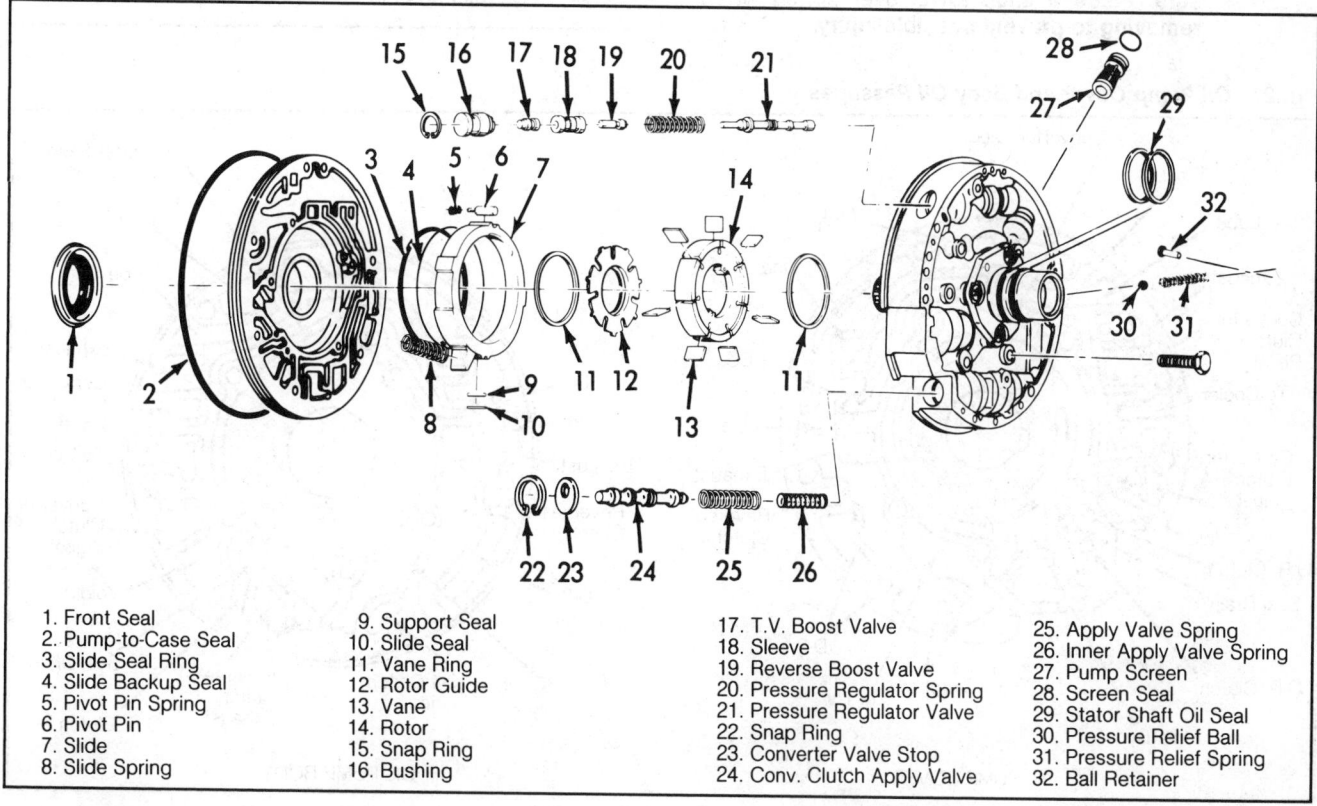

1. Front Seal	9. Support Seal	17. T.V. Boost Valve	25. Apply Valve Spring
2. Pump-to-Case Seal	10. Slide Seal	18. Sleeve	26. Inner Apply Valve Spring
3. Slide Seal Ring	11. Vane Ring	19. Reverse Boost Valve	27. Pump Screen
4. Slide Backup Seal	12. Rotor Guide	20. Pressure Regulator Spring	28. Screen Seal
5. Pivot Pin Spring	13. Vane	21. Pressure Regulator Valve	29. Stator Shaft Oil Seal
6. Pivot Pin	14. Rotor	22. Snap Ring	30. Pressure Relief Ball
7. Slide	15. Snap Ring	23. Converter Valve Stop	31. Pressure Relief Spring
8. Slide Spring	16. Bushing	24. Conv. Clutch Apply Valve	32. Ball Retainer

GENERAL MOTORS TURBO HYDRA-MATIC 700-R4 (Cont.)

14) Install 3-4 gear backing plate with chamfered side up. Install 3-4 retaining ring into input housing assembly. Using feeler gauges, measure end clearance between backing plate and first composition plate. If end clearance is not within specifications, select proper backing plate from chart. Air check all clutches by applying air pressure at feed holes in turbine shaft.

3-4 BACKING PLATE SELECTION CHART

Application	Backing Plate Travel In. (mm)	Backing Plate Diameter/I.D. In. (mm)
TC,MB,MC,MJ,VN, T2,VA,ML,MP,MS, T7,YF,PQ	.055-.109 (1.39-2.78)	.278/1 (7.125) .239/2 (6.125)
All Others	.049-.113 (1.25-2.87)	.200/3 (5.125) .161/4 (4.125)

OIL PUMP ASSEMBLY

Disassembly

1) Remove reverse input clutch drum-to-pump thrust washer, pump-to-case gasket and pump-to-case oil seal ring from pump assembly. Do not remove the 2 teflon oil seal rings from pump hub unless replacement is necessary. Remove attaching bolts and separate pump cover from pump body.

CAUTION: Pump slide spring is under very high pressure. Place a shop towel over spring when removing to prevent possible injury.

2) Using needle-nose pliers, compress pump slide spring and remove from pump by pulling straight out. Remove pump guide rings, pump vanes, pump rotor and rotor guide from pump body pocket. Remove slide from pump pocket. Remove slide seal and support seal from pocket or slide. Remove pivot slide pin and spring. Remove slide seal ring and backup seal from slide pocket.

3) Push in on retainer to compress converter clutch apply valve and spring and remove retaining snap ring from pump cover bore. Slowly release spring tension and remove retainer, apply valve and spring.

CAUTION: Pressure relief spring retaining rivet is under very strong spring pressure. Use care when removing.

CLUTCH PLATE USAGE CHART

Application	Flat Steel	Composition
Overrun Clutch		
All Models	2 [2]	[2] 2
Forward Clutch		
TC,MB,MC,MJ,VN, T2,VA,ML,MP,MS, T7,YH,YF,PQ	3 [3][4]	[2] 4
All Others	4 [3][4]	[2] 5
3-4 Clutch		
TC,MB,MC,MJ,VN, T2,VA,ML,MP,MS, T7,YF,PQ	4 [4]	[2] 5
All Others	5 [4]	w 6

[1] — Plate thickness is .091" (2.31 mm).
[2] — Plate thickness is .079" (2.03 mm).
[3] — Plus 1 waved steel plate .079" (2.03 mm).
[4] — Plate thickness is .077" (1.97 mm).

Fig. 21: Oil Pump Cover and Body Oil Passages

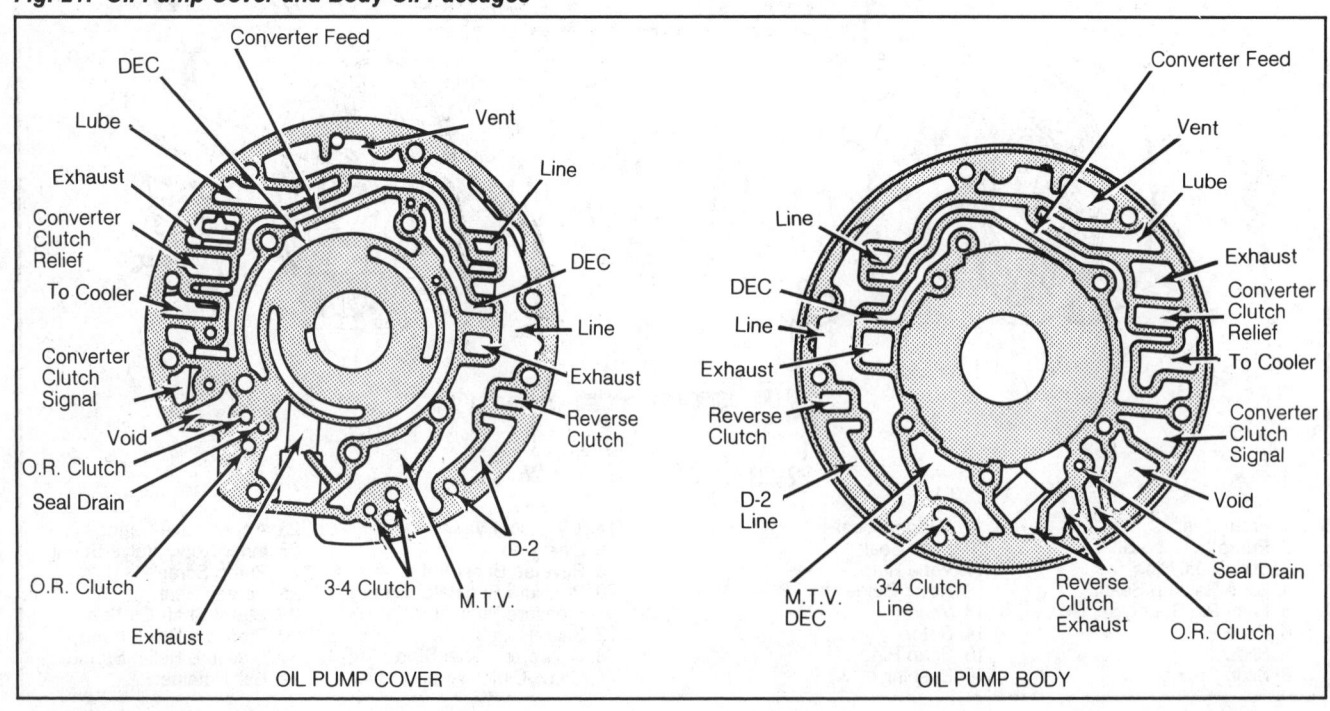

OIL PUMP COVER

OIL PUMP BODY

GENERAL MOTORS TURBO HYDRA-MATIC 700-R4 (Cont.)

4) Using a small punch, remove pressure relief spring retaining rivet. Remove relief spring and ball. If ball is not free, remove by applying air pressure to oil passage located in pump cover. Remove oil screen and "O" ring from pump cover.

5) Position pump with stator shaft down through hole in work bench and secure with a holding bolt. Using a small screwdriver, compress T.V. boost valve bushing and remove snap ring. Remove bushing and valve using a magnet. Using the same procedure, remove reverse boost valve and sleeve and pressure regulator valve and spring.

Inspection
1) Inspect all valves, springs, sleeves and bushings for chips, burrs, distortion and freeness in bores. Check pressure relief ball and spring for damage or distortion. Inspect pump cover screen and "O" ring for wear or damage.

2) Clean pump body and cover and check all bores for obstructions. Inspect mating sides of cover and body for scoring, flatness, porosity or voids between channels. Check channels for dirt, interconnected passages or damage.

3) Inspect rotor and slide for scoring, cracks or damage. Check rotor guide and pump vane rings for excessive wear or damage. Inspect all seals for damage. Inspect front seal for damage or excessive wear and seal retaining spring for proper location.

Reassembly
1) Install "O" ring and flat steel ring into groove on back side of pump slide and retain in place with petroleum jelly. Install small pivot pin and spring into small hole located in pump body pocket.

2) Install slide into pump body, indexing notch in slide with pivot pin hole and with flat oil seal ring facing down into pocket. Install slide seal and support into slide adjacent to rotor.

NOTE: **Position pump slide seal (composition) against outer diameter of pump pocket.**

3) Install a vane ring into pump pocket, centering on stator hole. Install composition rotor guide into deep pocket or rotor, indexing notches. Retain with petroleum jelly. Install rotor and guide into pump pocket with guide positioned downward.

4) Install vanes into rotor, positioning so they are flush with rotor and with the full wear pattern against slide. Install vane guide ring into rotor. Compress pump slide spring and install into pump pocket.

NOTE: **All parts must be flush with pump body face.**

5) Assemble "O" ring on pump screen and install screen into pump cover with seal end last. Install pressure relief ball and spring into cover and install retaining rivet.

6) Position spring on long end of converter clutch apply valve and retain with petroleum jelly. Install apply valve and spring into pump and install retaining snap ring.

7) Position pump cover so that pressure regulator valve bore is in a vertical position. Install regulator valve into bottom of cover bore with large land and orifice hole end installed first. Install pressure regulator valve spring into bore.

8) Install T.V. boost valve into bushing with long land of valve into large hole of bushing and retain with petroleum jelly. Install reverse boost valve into sleeve (small end first). Retain with petroleum jelly.

9) Using a small magnet install reverse and T.V. boost valve assemblies into pump cover bore. Compress T.V. boost valve and install retaining snap ring. Make sure snap ring seats in groove.

10) Place body assembly over hole in work bench with stator shaft downward. Assemble pump cover to body and install attaching bolts finger tight. Align pump body and cover using aligning strap (J-21368), and place a holding bolt or screwdriver through pump-to-case bolt hole and hole in bench. Remove strap and tighten cover-to-body bolts.

11) Position new pump-to-case gasket on pump and retain with petroleum jelly. If removed, install 2 teflon oil seal rings on stator hub. Install new pump-to-case oil seal on cover; do not twist seal and make sure it is properly located. Apply petroleum jelly to seal. Install pump cover-to-case gasket, aligning holes. Retain with petroleum jelly. Install pump-to-drum thrust washer, making sure tangs on washer engage holes in hub.

2-4 SERVO ASSEMBLY
Disassembly
1) Remove 4th apply piston and housing from 2nd apply piston assembly. Remove release spring from apply pin. Compress 2nd servo apply piston assembly and remove snap ring. Separate 2nd apply piston, spring and retainer.

2) Remove retaining "E" ring, washer and spring from apply pin and remove pin. Remove all oil seal rings.

Inspection
Inspect all pistons for porosity or damage. Check all springs and oil seal rings for distortion or damage.

Reassembly
Reverse disassembly procedure making sure all flat edge seals are assembled with flat edge-to-flat edge. Coat seals with petrolatum.

Fig. 22: Exploded View of 2-4 Servo Assembly

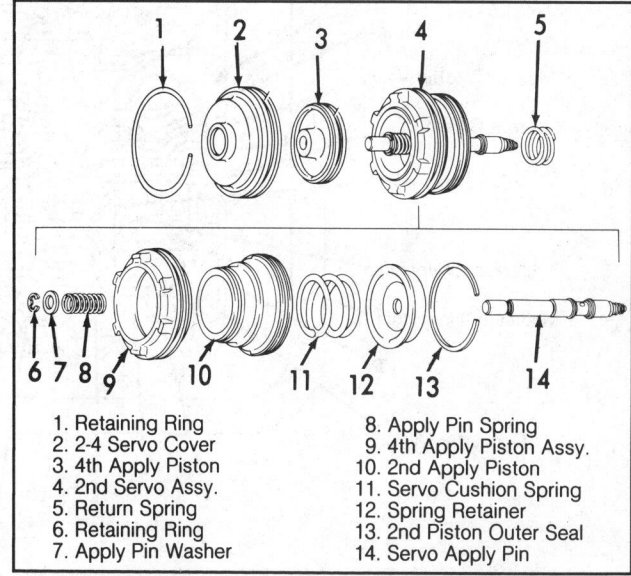

1. Retaining Ring
2. 2-4 Servo Cover
3. 4th Apply Piston
4. 2nd Servo Assy.
5. Return Spring
6. Retaining Ring
7. Apply Pin Washer
8. Apply Pin Spring
9. 4th Apply Piston Assy.
10. 2nd Apply Piston
11. Servo Cushion Spring
12. Spring Retainer
13. 2nd Piston Outer Seal
14. Servo Apply Pin

GENERAL MOTORS TURBO HYDRA-MATIC 700-R4 (Cont.)

TRANSMISSION REASSEMBLY

LOW/REVERSE CLUTCH

1) Place transmission in a vertical position. Oil and install inner, center and outer seals on low/reverse clutch piston. Install piston into transmission case, indexing piston with notch at bottom of case and hub facing down. Make sure piston is fully seated and parking pawl will index into opening in piston wall.

2) Install low/reverse clutch spring retainer assembly into case with flat side of retainer upward. Install clutch spring compressor (J-23327) and compress springs, indexing tool retaining plate so that tool is free to slide over case hub. Install low/reverse clutch snap ring and remove tools.

3) Install reaction internal gear support bearing on case hub so that the longer inside "L" race is positioned downward. Install reaction internal gear and output shaft on bearing assembly in case. When gear is properly seated it will be centered with the long slot in case and parking pawl can be engaged with external teeth of internal gear.

NOTE: If reaction internal gear and output shaft were removed as one unit, install into case at this time, otherwise assemble only the reaction internal gear.

4) Install reaction carrier-to-support thrust bearing on internal gear support so that the longer outside "L" race is positioned downward. Install reaction carrier (with large outside hub) locating the reverse hub upward. Install low/reverse clutch plates, starting with steel and alternating with composition. Make sure clutch plates index with splines of reaction carrier and case, and that steel plates are aligned.

LOW/REVERSE CLUTCH PLATE USAGE CHART

Application	Flat Steel	Composition
T2,VA,ML,MP,MS, VN,T7,YH,YF,PQ, TC,MB,MC,MJ	4 [1]	4 [2]
All Others	5 [1]	5 [2]

[1] — Plate thickness is .069" (1.77 mm).
[2] — Plate thickness is .088" (2.25 mm).

5) Remove low/reverse inner race and install low/reverse support and roller assembly with chamfered side up in case, indexing with case splines. Install low/reverse inner race into roller assembly and rotate until internal splines are engaged. Push down for full engagement. The bottom tangs will be flush with reaction hub when seated. Install low/reverse snap ring and support spring into transmission case.

REACTION & INPUT GEAR SETS

1) If removed, install snap ring on reaction sun gear. Install sun gear into reaction carrier, indexing pinions. Install nylon thrust washer with 4 locating ears on low/reverse clutch inner race. Install reaction sun gear

Fig. 23: View of Transmission Case Showing Oil Passages and Check Ball Locations

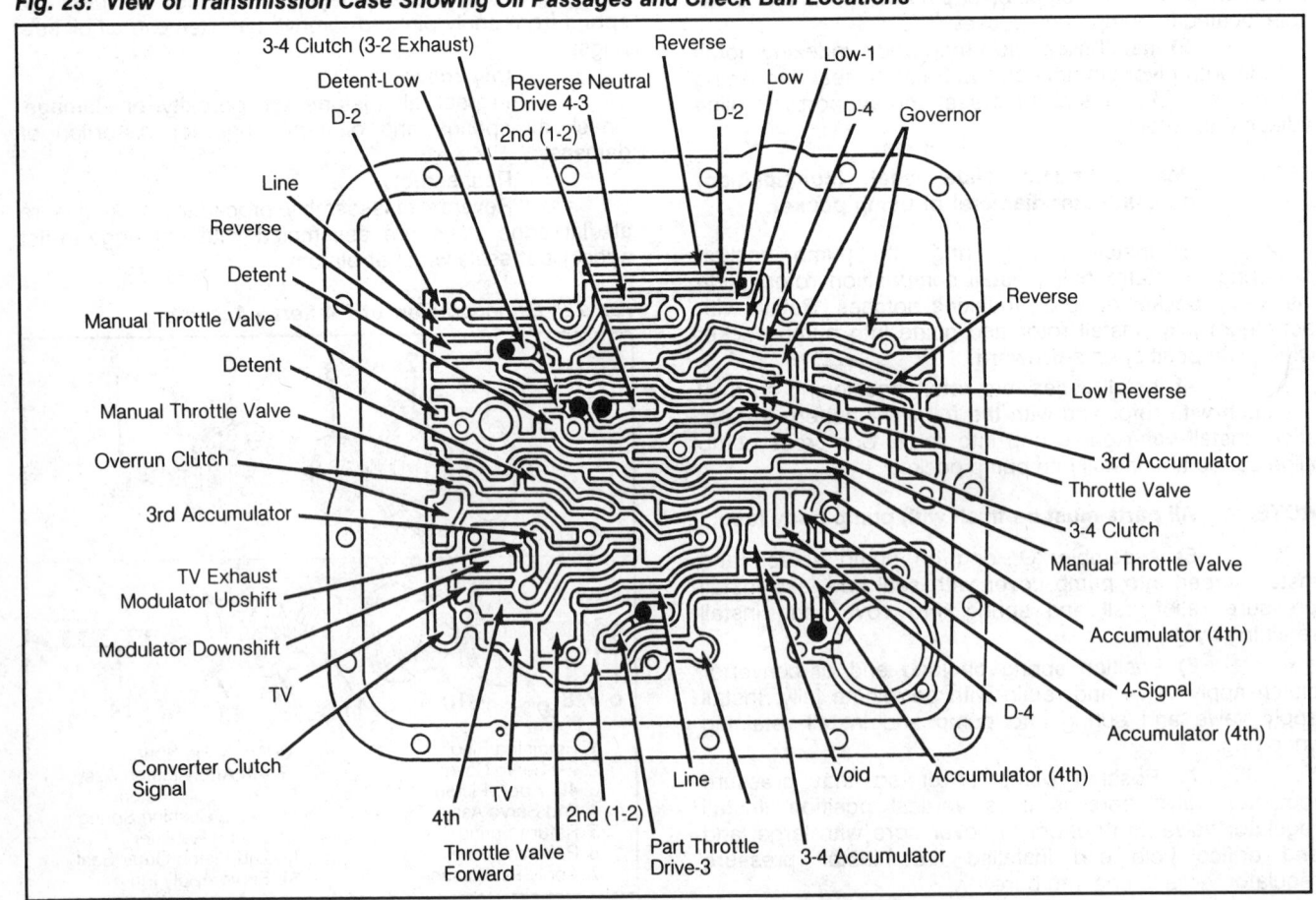

GENERAL MOTORS TURBO HYDRA-MATIC 700-R4 (Cont.)

Fig. 24: Exploded View of Transmission Internal Components

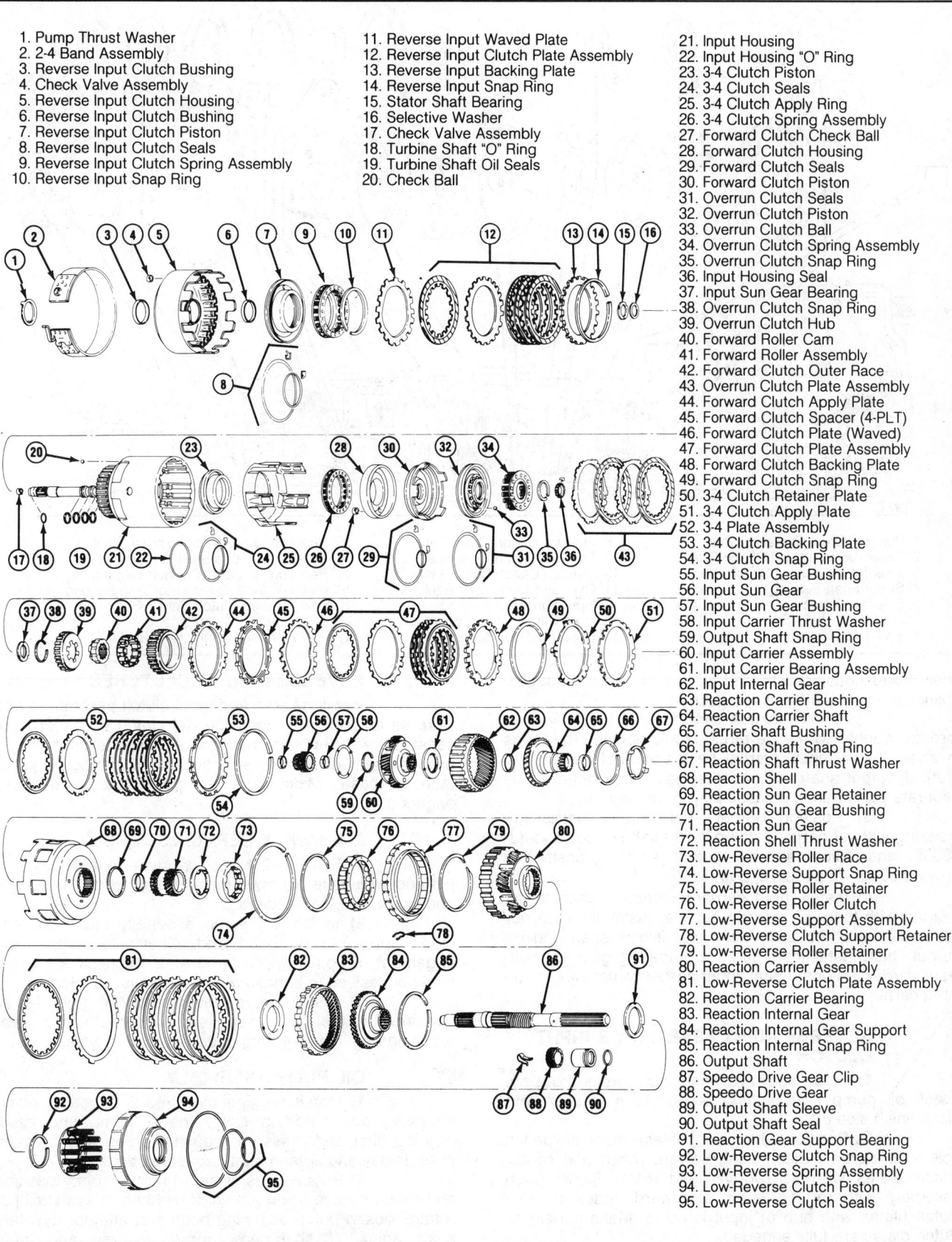

1. Pump Thrust Washer
2. 2-4 Band Assembly
3. Reverse Input Clutch Bushing
4. Check Valve Assembly
5. Reverse Input Clutch Housing
6. Reverse Input Clutch Bushing
7. Reverse Input Clutch Piston
8. Reverse Input Clutch Seals
9. Reverse Input Clutch Spring Assembly
10. Reverse Input Snap Ring
11. Reverse Input Waved Plate
12. Reverse Input Clutch Plate Assembly
13. Reverse Input Backing Plate
14. Reverse Input Snap Ring
15. Stator Shaft Bearing
16. Selective Washer
17. Check Valve Assembly
18. Turbine Shaft "O" Ring
19. Turbine Shaft Oil Seals
20. Check Ball
21. Input Housing
22. Input Housing "O" Ring
23. 3-4 Clutch Piston
24. 3-4 Clutch Seals
25. 3-4 Clutch Apply Ring
26. 3-4 Clutch Spring Assembly
27. Forward Clutch Check Ball
28. Forward Clutch Housing
29. Forward Clutch Seals
30. Forward Clutch Piston
31. Overrun Clutch Seals
32. Overrun Clutch Piston
33. Overrun Clutch Ball
34. Overrun Clutch Spring Assembly
35. Overrun Clutch Snap Ring
36. Input Housing Seal
37. Input Sun Gear Bearing
38. Overrun Clutch Snap Ring
39. Overrun Clutch Hub
40. Forward Roller Cam
41. Forward Roller Assembly
42. Forward Clutch Outer Race
43. Overrun Clutch Plate Assembly
44. Forward Clutch Apply Plate
45. Forward Clutch Spacer (4-PLT)
46. Forward Clutch Plate (Waved)
47. Forward Clutch Plate Assembly
48. Forward Clutch Backing Plate
49. Forward Clutch Snap Ring
50. 3-4 Clutch Retainer Plate
51. 3-4 Clutch Apply Plate
52. 3-4 Plate Assembly
53. 3-4 Clutch Backing Plate
54. 3-4 Clutch Snap Ring
55. Input Sun Gear Bushing
56. Input Sun Gear
57. Input Sun Gear Bushing
58. Input Carrier Thrust Washer
59. Output Shaft Snap Ring
60. Input Carrier Assembly
61. Input Carrier Bearing Assembly
62. Input Internal Gear
63. Reaction Carrier Bushing
64. Reaction Carrier Shaft
65. Carrier Shaft Bushing
66. Reaction Shaft Snap Ring
67. Reaction Shaft Thrust Washer
68. Reaction Shell
69. Reaction Sun Gear Retainer
70. Reaction Sun Gear Bushing
71. Reaction Sun Gear
72. Reaction Shell Thrust Washer
73. Low-Reverse Roller Race
74. Low-Reverse Support Snap Ring
75. Low-Reverse Roller Retainer
76. Low-Reverse Roller Clutch
77. Low-Reverse Support Assembly
78. Low-Reverse Clutch Support Retainer
79. Low-Reverse Roller Retainer
80. Reaction Carrier Assembly
81. Low-Reverse Clutch Plate Assembly
82. Reaction Carrier Bearing
83. Reaction Internal Gear
84. Reaction Internal Gear Support
85. Reaction Internal Snap Ring
86. Output Shaft
87. Speedo Drive Gear Clip
88. Speedo Drive Gear
89. Output Shaft Sleeve
90. Output Shaft Seal
91. Reaction Gear Support Bearing
92. Low-Reverse Clutch Snap Ring
93. Low-Reverse Spring Assembly
94. Low-Reverse Clutch Piston
95. Low-Reverse Clutch Seals

GENERAL MOTORS TURBO HYDRA-MATIC 700-R4 (Cont.)

Fig. 25: *Cutaway View of Transmission Showing Thrust Washer, Bearing and Oil Seal Locations*

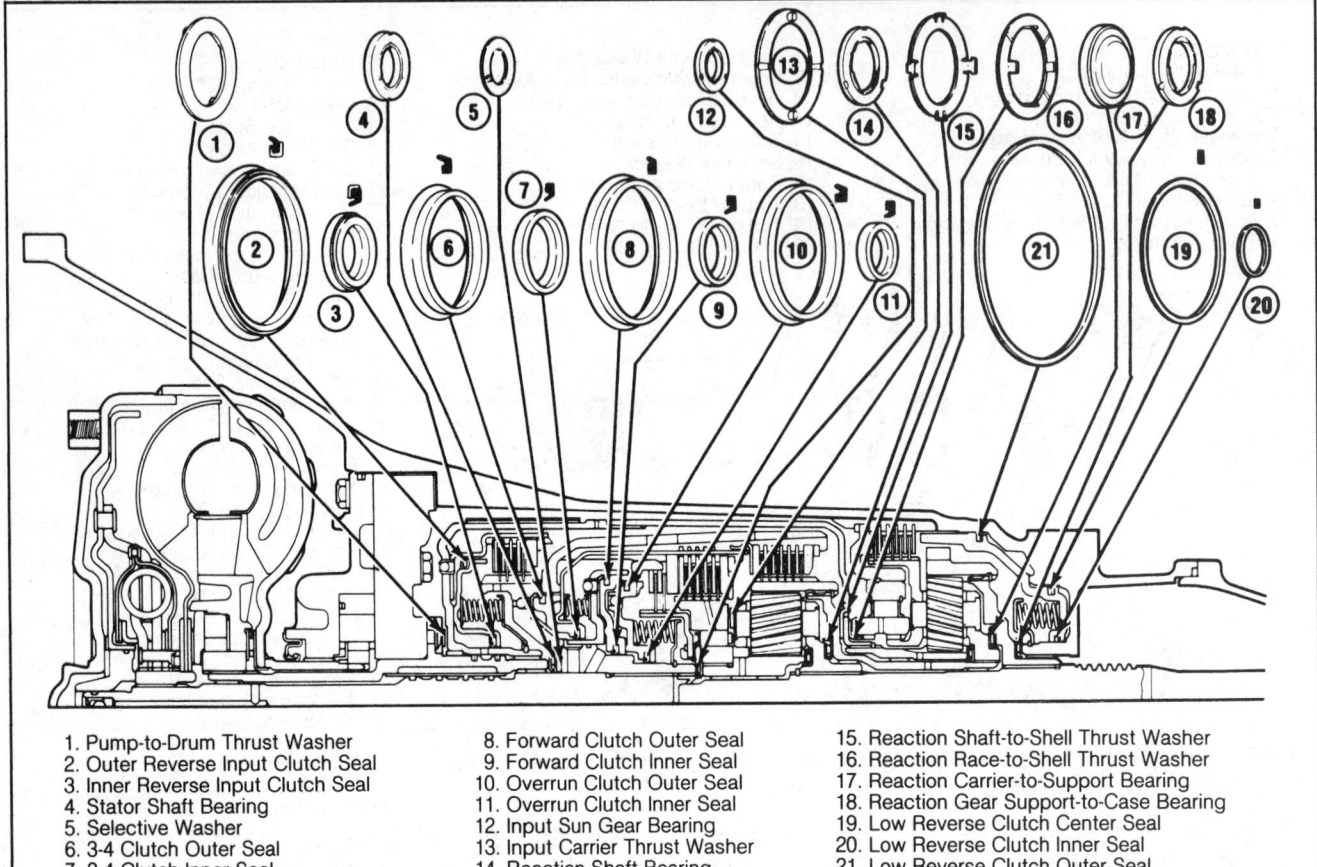

1. Pump-to-Drum Thrust Washer	8. Forward Clutch Outer Seal	15. Reaction Shaft-to-Shell Thrust Washer
2. Outer Reverse Input Clutch Seal	9. Forward Clutch Inner Seal	16. Reaction Race-to-Shell Thrust Washer
3. Inner Reverse Input Clutch Seal	10. Overrun Clutch Outer Seal	17. Reaction Carrier-to-Support Bearing
4. Stator Shaft Bearing	11. Overrun Clutch Inner Seal	18. Reaction Gear Support-to-Case Bearing
5. Selective Washer	12. Input Sun Gear Bearing	19. Low Reverse Clutch Center Seal
6. 3-4 Clutch Outer Seal	13. Input Carrier Thrust Washer	20. Low Reverse Clutch Inner Seal
7. 3-4 Clutch Inner Seal	14. Reaction Shaft Bearing	21. Low Reverse Clutch Outer Seal

shell (large housing with end slots and holes), engaging splines of shell shaft and sun gear.

2) Install reaction shaft-to-shell thrust washer (bronze washer with wide thrust face), indexing the tangs in shell. Install input internal gear and shaft (shaft end first). If output shaft and reaction gear were removed as separate parts during disassembly, go to step **3)**.

3) Position output shaft into transmission, indexing with all parts. Install output shaft support tool (J-29837) and adjust so that output shaft is positioned upward as far as possible. *See Fig. 9.*

4) Install input carrier-to-reaction shaft thrust bearing with long "L" race on outside. Install input carrier assembly, with hub end down. Install new snap ring on output shaft. Install input sun gear, indexing gear end with input carrier pinions. Install input carrier thrust washer on input carrier.

REVERSE INPUT ASSEMBLY & INPUT CLUTCH

1) Install selective washer on turbine housing. Install oil pump hub bearing on selective washer with black finish side up.

2) Position reverse input assembly on bench hole with clutch plates facing upward. Align and center clutch plates with screwdriver and install input clutch assembly with turbine shaft downward. Index reverse clutch plates with hub of input housing. Make certain all clutch plates are fully engaged.

REVERSE & INPUT CLUTCHES

Install reverse and input clutch assemblies into case as an assembly, indexing 3-4 clutch plates of input assembly with input internal gear. Complete assembly is properly seated when reverse housing is just below pump face of case. Make sure all clutch plates are fully engaged.

2-4 BAND & SERVO ASSEMBLY

1) Position 2-4 band in case, indexing anchor pin end with case pin hole. Install band achor pin in case and index with 2-4 band end.

2) Install 2-4 servo assembly into case and index apply pin on band end. Check for proper engagement of apply pin on band end. Recheck 2-4 servo apply pin selection to ensure correct pin is installed.

3) Install servo cover and "O" ring. Install compressor tool and compress cover. Install cover retaining ring, indexing ring ends with slot in case.

OIL PUMP ASSEMBLY

1) Install aligning pins into 2 opposing pump attaching bolt holes in case. Install pump into case, aligning filter and pressure regulator holes with holes in case. Install and tighten pump attaching bolts.

2) Rotate transmission to a horizontal position and rotate turbine or output shaft by hand. If shaft will not rotate, loosen pump attaching bolts and attempt to rotate shaft again. If shaft now turns, reverse and input

GENERAL MOTORS TURBO HYDRA-MATIC 700-R4 (Cont.)

assemblies have not been indexed properly or some other assembly problem has occurred, such as a mispositioned thrust washer. Rotate transmission to a vertical position.

VALVE BODY & WIRING HARNESS

1) Install 1-2 accumulator pin into case. Install accumulator piston and seal over pin with lug end up. Install spring on accumulator piston.

2) Install governor and converter clutch oil screens into case. Install 5 check balls into case pockets. *See Fig. 23.* Install valve body alignment pins, then install spacer plate-to-case gasket (identified with a small "c") on case. Install valve body spacer on case, aligning holes.

3) Install valve body-to-spacer gasket (identified with a "V") on spacer plate. Install 3 exhaust check balls and check valve into valve body pockets. *See Fig. 4.* Retain with petroleum jelly. Install valve body and connect link to inside detent lever. Remove aligning pins and install and tighten valve body-to-case bolts.

4) Attach retaining clip to manual valve link and inside detent lever. Install throttle lever and bracket, and T.V. link, locating slot in bracket with roll pin on valve body top face. Align link through T.V. linkage case bore. Attach assembly with 2 valve body attaching bolts.

5) Install valve body attaching bolt and harness clip. Install parking pawl bracket. Install manual detent spring and roller assembly. Install "O" ring on solenoid. Install assembly into pump, locating attaching wire harness toward transmission. Install wiring harness and connect to all pressure switches.

NOTE: **Each pressure switch is color coded. Match color of switch with same color of wire.**

6) Install "O" ring on outside electrical connector and install into case by compressing inside tang. Locate the tab with the case notch. Attach inside connector terminal to outside connector. Install oil passage cover on transmission with 3 bolts and tighten.

7) Install 3-4 accumulator piston into housing with lug end up. Install 3-4 piston spring into housing on piston. Position 3-4 accumulator plate and gasket on transmission placing gasket on top. Install housing, spring and piston on transmission case and secure with 3 bolts and tighten.

8) Install speedometer gear and retaining clip on output shaft, positioning large notch on speedometer gear rearward. Install output shaft seal in output shaft sleeve and install on output shaft with oil pump seal installer (J-25016).

9) Install oil seal ring on case extension and install on case. Position so speedometer hole is located on same side as governor. Install governor assembly. Apply cup sealant to edge of cover, then install cover. Install "O" ring on filter and install.

10) Position new oil pan gasket on transmission case. Install oil pan and pan attaching bolts. Tighten attaching bolts.

11) Install remaining outside connectors such as driven speedometer gear and adapter, outside manual lever and nut. Remove transmission from holding fixture and install torque converter.

TIGHTENING SPECIFICATIONS

Application	Ft. Lbs. (N.m)
Converter-to-Flywheel	35 (50)
Extension-to-Case	23 (31)
Man. Shaft-to-Detent Lever	23 (31)
Oil Cooler Pipes	28 (38)
Park Bracket-to-Case	31 (41)
Transmission-to-Engine	35 (50)

	INCH Lbs. (N.m)
Accumulator Cover-to-Case	96 (11)
Detent Spring-to-Valve Body	216 (24)
Oil Pan-to-Case	216 (24)
Oil Passage Cover-to-Case	96 (11)
Pressure Plugs	96 (11)
Pump-to-Case	216 (24)
Solenoid Assy.-to-Pump	96 (11)
Valve Body-to-Case	96 (11)

SECTION 3

DOMESTIC MANUAL TRANSMISSIONS

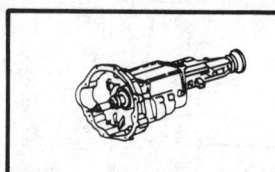

NOTE: ALSO SEE GENERAL INDEX.

Manual Transmissions
AMC/RENAULT ALLIANCE 4 & 5-SPEED

IDENTIFICATION

The 2 manual transaxles can be identified by a tag affixed to the top of the transaxle. Top line of tag identifies transaxle model and build date code. Second line on tag is the transaxle serial number.

Fig. 1: JB 0 & JB 1 Transmission Identification Tag

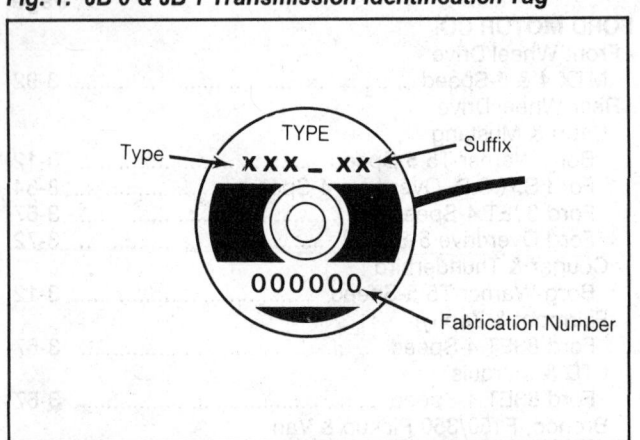

Tag is held in place by 1 of the clutch housing bolts.

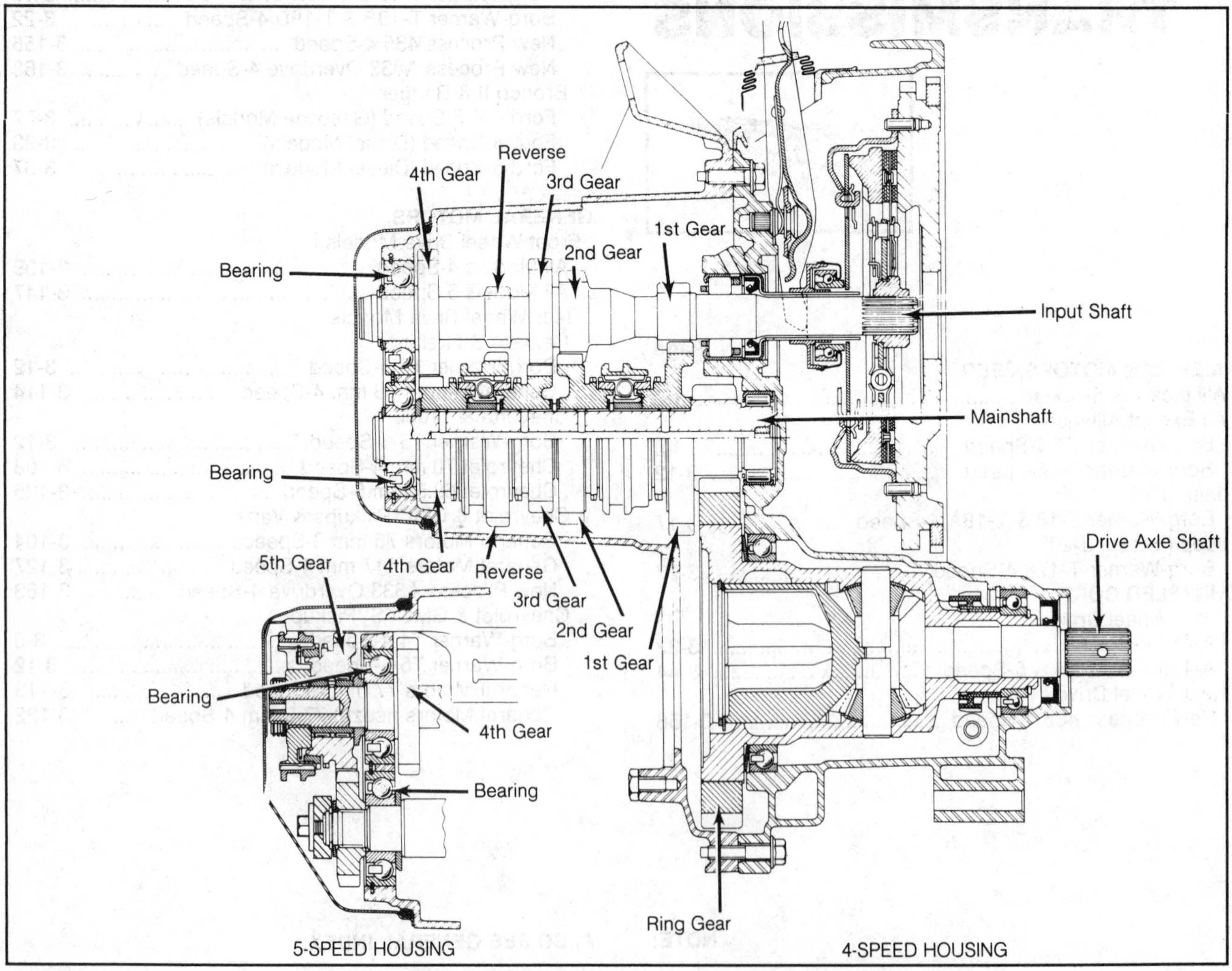

TRANSAXLE IDENTIFICATION CODES

Application	Axle Ratio	Code
JB 0 4-Speed	3.29:1	00
JB 1 5-Speed	3.87:1	00

DESCRIPTION

The manual transaxle combines a 4-speed (JB 0) or 5-speed (JB 1) manual transmission and differential into a single component designed for front drive applications. The transmission and differential are housed in a 2-piece, light weight aluminum alloy housing which is bolted to the back of the engine.

The transaxle is fully synchronized in all forward gears with reverse provided by a separate shaft and gear. All gears, except reverse, are helical cut for quiet operation. Both input and main shafts, are supported in case by roller bearings.

The differential assembly is supported by 2 opposed roller bearings. Side plates are used to hold ends of axle shafts in place. The left side uses a constant velocity joint on the end of the axle. The right side axle shaft has splines to engage with the transaxle.

Fig. 2: Sectional View of Renault 4 & 5-Speed Transaxle

Reverse

4th Gear

3rd Gear

2nd Gear

1st Gear

Bearing

Input Shaft

Mainshaft

Bearing

Drive Axle Shaft

5th Gear

4th Gear

Reverse

3rd Gear

2nd Gear

1st Gear

Bearing

4th Gear

Bearing

Ring Gear

5-SPEED HOUSING

4-SPEED HOUSING

AMC/RENAULT ALLIANCE 4 & 5-SPEED (Cont.)

LUBRICATION & ADJUSTMENTS

See the appropriate article in MANUAL TRANSMISSION SERVICING Section.

SERVICE (IN-VEHICLE)

5TH GEAR

Removal

1) Remove nuts from front and rear mounting pads at chassis end. Place a pan under rear cover and remove cover and gasket.

2) Raise transmission slightly. Insert a block of wood between 5th gear fork and driving gear, and tap out roll pin with a 3/16" pin punch.

3) Remove block of wood. Remove retaining bolt from mainshaft and pull 5th gear off shaft. Remove retaining nut and components from input shaft as an assembly.

Installation

1) Lubricate 5th gear and install it on mainshaft. Install spring washer and circlip using installer tool (B.Vi.948). Install retaining washer and bolt.

2) Assemble input shaft components in reverse order of removal and tighten shaft nut. Install rear cover using a new gasket.

3) Lower transaxle onto mounting pads and tighten nuts at chassis end. Fill transaxle to proper level with lubricant. Start engine and check for leaks.

DRIVE AXLE SHAFTS & CV JOINT

Removal

1) Raise and support vehicle with safety stands. Remove wheel and caliper asssemblies. Support caliper up out of the way. Remove spindle nut using holding tool (Rou. 604-01) attached to lug nuts.

2) On left side, drain oil from transaxle. Remove 3 mounting bolts. Remove boot and drive shaft.

Fig. 3: Drive Shaft Assembly

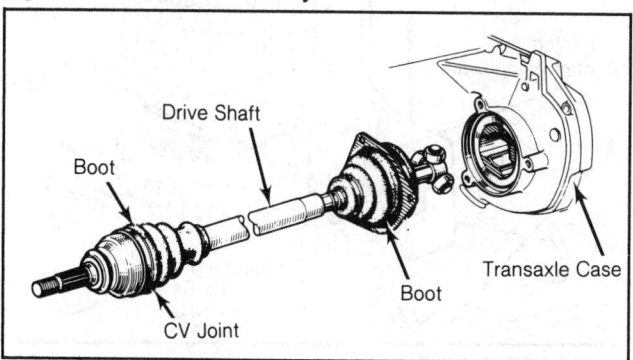

Drive Shaft

Boot

CV Joint

Boot

Transaxle Case

CAUTION: During removal be sure that the 3 rollers on CV joint are not dislodged. Tape CV to prevent the components from falling apart.

3) On right side, remove roll pins using a pin punch. On both sides, remove steering arm ball joint nut and disconnect ball joint assembly using extractor tool (T.AV.476). Remove shock absorber bottom mounting bolts.

4) Tilt stub axle carrier. Remove drive shaft from transaxle at the same time. Install impact tool on hub. Remove drive shaft. Tilt stub axle carrier. Remove drive shaft from its sunwheel at the same time.

Disassembly

1) Remove clip ring from around boot using 2 locally made drilled rods. Install the rods one over each end of clip and grip hard to expand clip and remove.

Fig. 4: Removing Clips From Drive shaft Boots

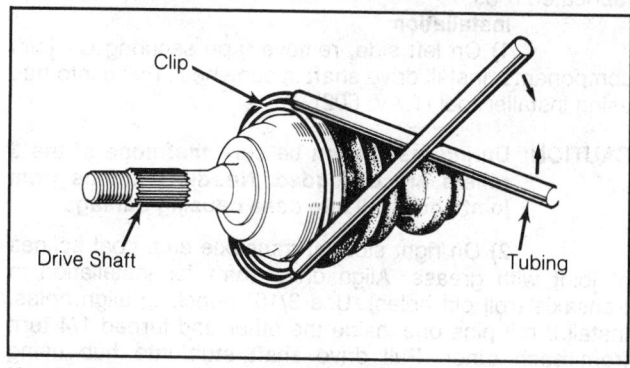

Clip

Drive Shaft

Tubing

Use 2 pieces of tubing to remove clips.

2) Remove as much grease as possible. Remove bell-shaped stub axle from drive shaft by raising starplate arms one by one (DO NOT twist starplate arms).

Fig. 5: Sectional View of Drive Assembly

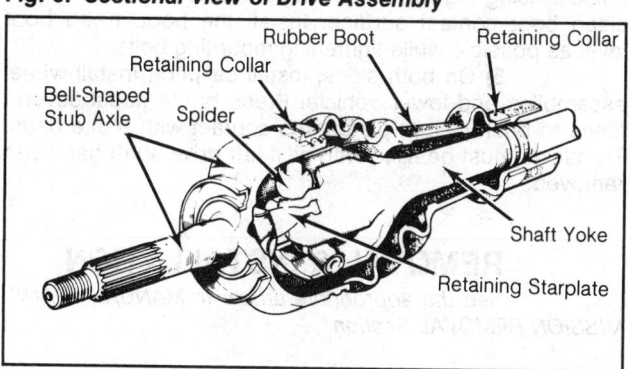

Retaining Collar

Rubber Boot

Retaining Collar

Bell-Shaped Stub Axle

Spider

Shaft Yoke

Retaining Starplate

Reassembly

1) Place and hold drive shaft at a convenient angle in a vise equipped with soft jaws. Install expander (T.AV. 537-02) on end of yoke. Lubricate the whole expander, inside the boots, and the neck in particular.

2) Place a thumb over bottom hole of boot and pour some oil into boot and spread it around inside. Slip boot over end of expander. Wrap a piece of clean rag around one hand and grip boot so that the first fold will stretch when it is slid on.

3) Firmly place expander against vise and, using one hand over the other to obtain a firm grip, pull boot down over expander. Pull boot along expander as far as possible then let it return half-way. Repeat the above 2 or 3 times.

4) Lubricate stems before final positioning. Pull boot firmly and continuously up to circular portion of the tool in one motion. Install spring and thrust ball in spider. Move roller cages toward center.

5) Position retaining starplate so that each arm is centered between each spider trunnion. Insert drive shaft yoke in bell-shaped stub axle. Tilt shaft to fit 1 starplate arm into its slot, then press it in to locate it.

6) The other 2 arms may be installed easily by using a screwdriver with tip ground to fit end of arm. Make

Manual Transmissions

AMC/RENAULT ALLIANCE 4 & 5-SPEED (Cont.)

sure that each starplate arm is located in slot. Check that spider coupling moves freely by hand in all directions.

    7) Distribute grease evenly between boot and bell-shaped stub axle. Position boot lips in grooves in stub axle and drive shaft. Insert a smooth round-ended piece of rod between boot and stub axle to restrict the amount of air inside. Install retaining collars over boot using the 2 fabricated rods.

Installation

    1) On left side, remove tape securing CV joint components. Install drive shaft in sunwheel. Pull it into hub using installer tool (T.AV. 602).

CAUTION: During installation be sure that none of the 3 rollers are dislodged. Needle bearings from joint could fall into case causing damage.

    2) On right side, at transaxle end, coat splines of joint with grease. Align drive shaft for installation in transaxle (roll pin holes). Use 3/16" punch to align holes. Install 2 roll pins one inside the other and turned 1/4 turn from each other. Pull drive shaft stub into hub using installer tool (T.AV. 602).

    3) On both sides, install shock absorber bottom mounting nuts to stub axle carrier, with nuts towards caliper. Install steering arm ball joint and nut.

    4) Tighten nuts and install holding tool to spindle using lug nuts. Tighten stub axle nut. On left side clean boot contact surface. Install the boot. Keep boot level as possible while tightening mounting bolts.

    5) On both sides, install calipers. Install wheel assemblies and lower vehicle. Press brake pedal several times to push caliper piston into contact with brake pads. Transaxle must be filled with oil if left drive shaft has been removed.

REMOVAL & INSTALLATION

    See the appropriate article in MANUAL TRANS-MISSION REMOVAL Section.

DISASSEMBLY

TRANSAXLE

    1) Remove rear cover. On 4-speed models, remove input shaft and mainshaft circlips and washers. On 5-speed models, engage 1st gear with gear selector lever and 5th gear with shift fork.

    2) Remove 5th gear retaining nut. Remove 5th gear roll pin using a 3/16" pin punch. Place a block of wood at the back of shaft for support. Remove shift fork with sliding gear hub and spring from primary shaft.

    3) Remove synchronizer ring, 5th gear, roller bearing, washer, circlip, and 5th retaining bolt. Remove washer and 5th gear from mainshaft. Remove clutch housing bolts. Remove reverse clip.

    4) On 4-speed models, remove threaded limit stop. On 5-speed models, remove 5th gear detent. On all models, remove fork control rod. Insert 2 dummy rods at rear of case to prevent interlocking balls for the 4 froward gears from falling out. See Fig. 6.

    5) On 5-speed models, pull case upwards and remove it with 5th gear fork rod. Retain 5th gear interlocking plunger. On all models, remove roll pin from

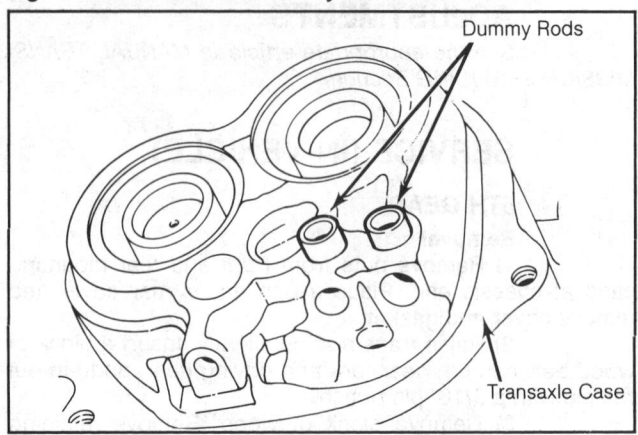

Fig. 6: Placement of 2 Dummy Rods in Transaxle

Rods will keep interlocking balls from falling out.

3rd/4th selector fork using a 3/16" pin punch. Move the 1st/2nd selector rod and reverse rod to neutral position.

    6) Remove 3rd/4th selector rod, fork, and retaining detent. Remove roll pin from 1st/2nd gear rod using a 3/16" pin punch. Reverse shaft must be in neutral. Remove 1st/2nd selector rod. Remove fork and retaining detent from rod. Push interlocking detent toward 3rd/4th selector rod.

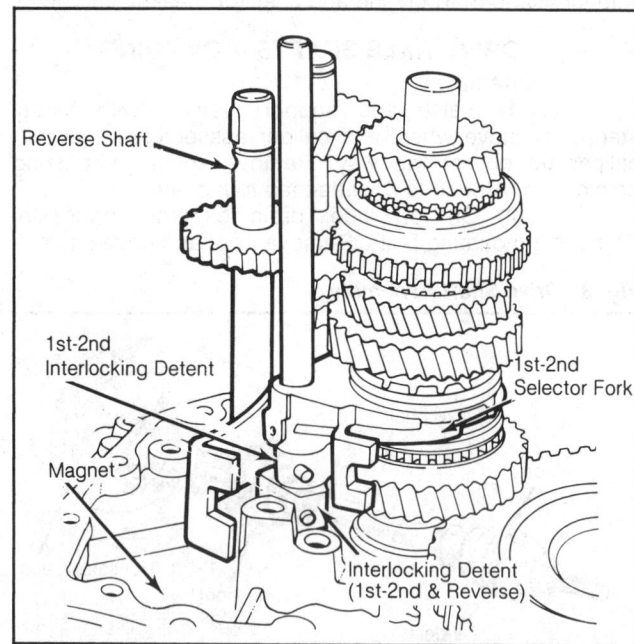

Fig. 7: Removing Input, Main, and Reverse Shafts as an Assembly

    7) Remove input, main, and reverse shafts together. Hold mainshaft vertical with 1st gear at bottom. Remove magnet, clean it and reinstall in case.

INPUT SHAFT

    The input shaft used in both 4 and 5-speed models, cannot be repaired or adjusted. On 5-speed models, the oil passage cannot be disassembled. Clean oil passage for 5th gear.

AMC/RENAULT ALLIANCE 4 & 5-SPEED (Cont.)

Fig. 8: Input Shaft Assembly

Assembly cannot be disassembled.

REVERSE SHAFT

The reverse shaft cannot be repaired or adjusted. Replacement shafts include reverse gear.

Fig. 9: Reverse Shaft Assembly

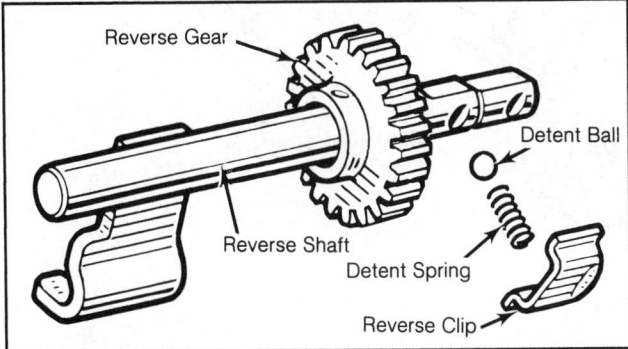

Reverse gear cannot be removed from shaft.

MAINSHAFT

1) Clamp mainshaft in a vise equipped with soft jaws. Remove 4th gear and synchronizer ring. Remove 3rd/4th sliding hub, roller, and roller spring. Remove circlip, grooved ring, and synchronizer ring.

2) Remove 3rd gear, grooved ring, circlip, and grooved ring. Remove 2nd gear, grooved ring, circlip, and synchronizer ring. Remove 1st/2nd gear sliding hub, roller, and roller spring.

3) Remove synchronizer ring and 1st gear. Oil passage in mainshaft can not be disassembled. Clean oil passage.

DIFFERENTIAL

1) Remove "O" ring and tilt oil seal using a pin punch and a small hammer. Remove oil seal using pliers. Do not damage side gear splines. Use an arbor press to move clutch housing and differential and free snap ring.

2) Place a wood block under differential housing before applying press force. Remove snap ring. Remove differential by applying press force against side gear. Remove spacer washer and spring washer.

3) Turn assembly over. Mount differential housing in a vise equipped with soft jaws. Remove snap ring, shim, spider side gear, and pinion shaft. Remove pinion gears, thrust washers, and side gear with tail shaft. Attach each thrust washer to its matching differential pinion gear for reassembly reference.

CLEANING & INSPECTION

1) Wash all parts, except oil seals, in cleaning solvent. Brush or scrape all foreign matter from parts, using care not to damage any part with scraper. Do not clean, wash, or soak transaxle seals in cleaning solvent. Dry all parts with compressed air.

CAUTION: Hold roller bearing assembly to prevent it from rotating when drying it with compressed air.

Fig. 10: Exploded View of Mainshaft Assembly

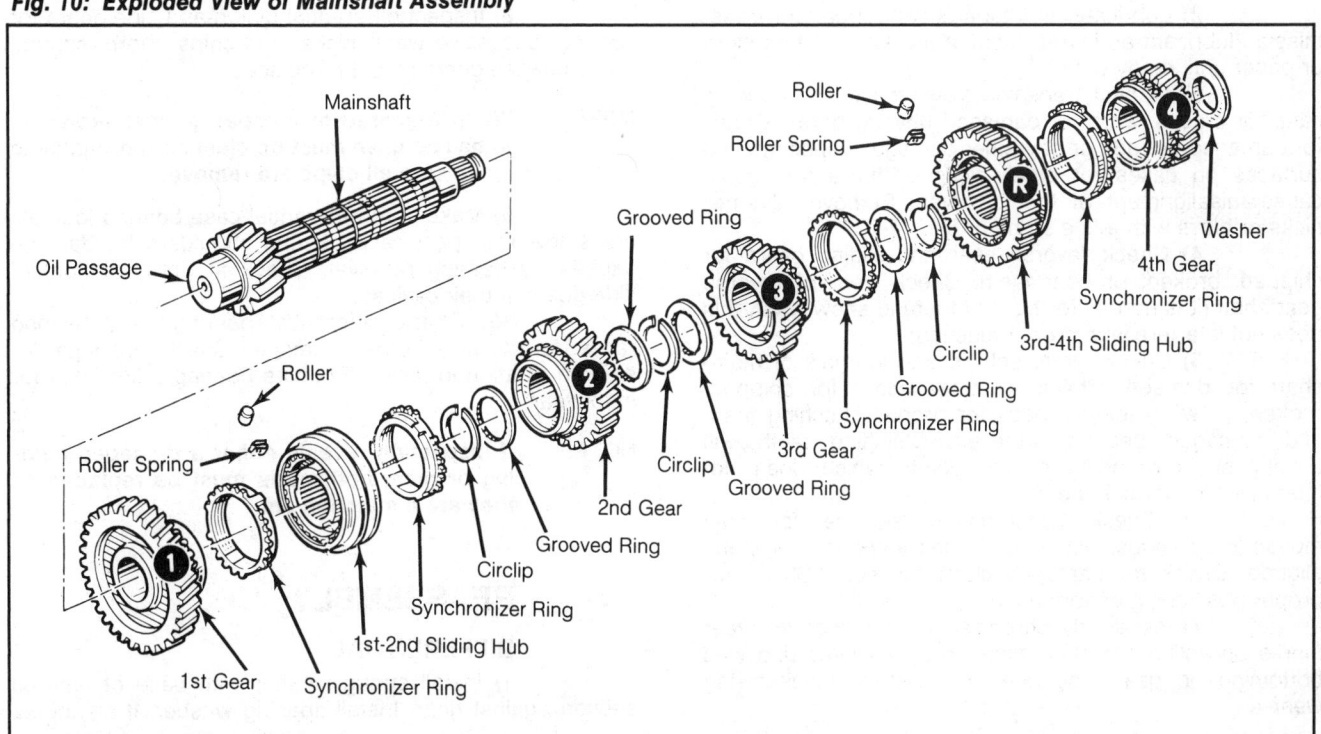

AMC/RENAULT ALLIANCE 4 & 5-SPEED (Cont.)

Fig. 11: Exploded View of Differential Components

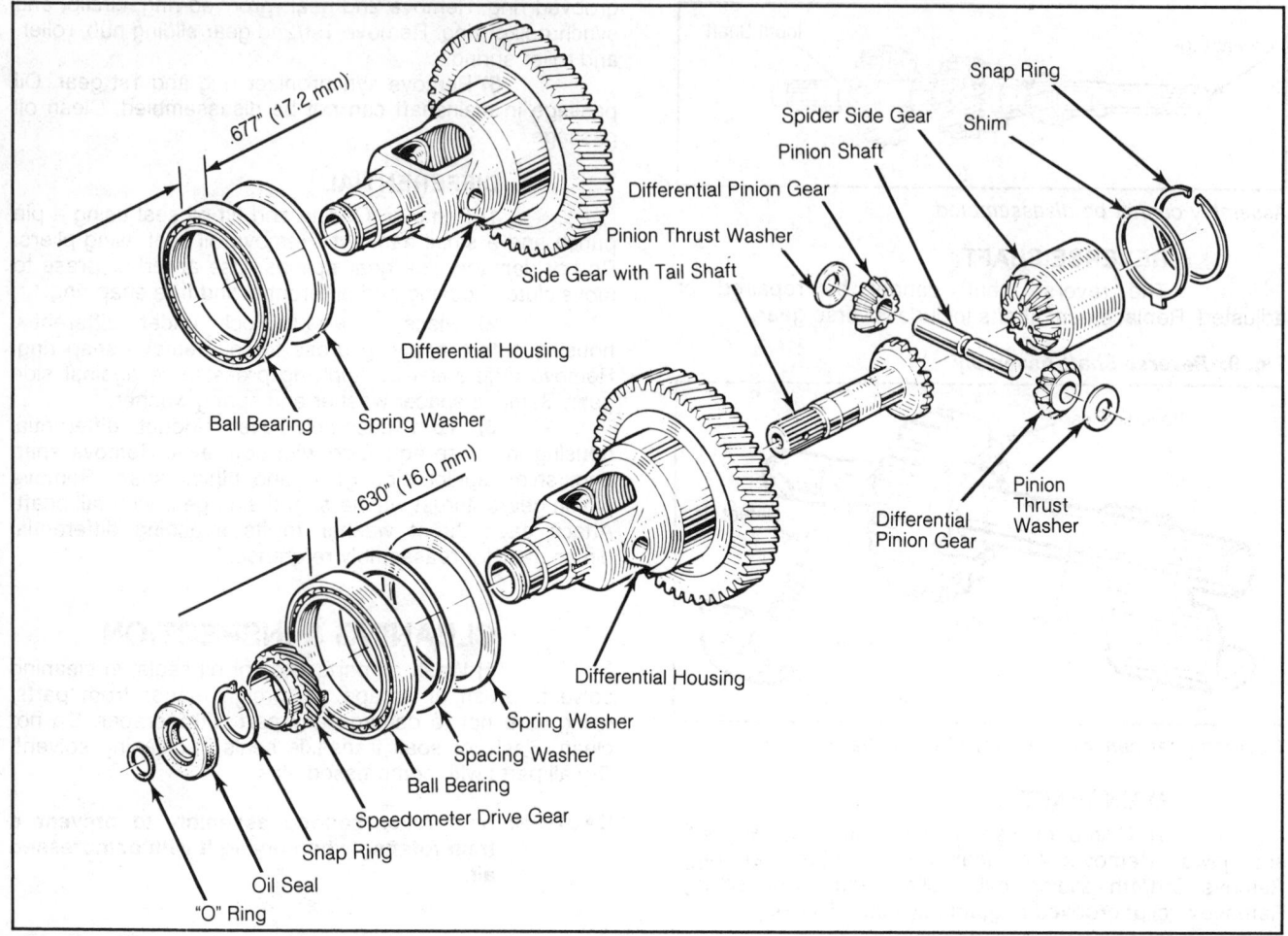

2) Lubricate all bearings with approved transmission lubricant and wrap them in a clean, lint free cloth or paper until ready to use.

3) Inspect transaxle case and clutch housing case for cracks, worn, or damaged bearing bores. Check for damaged threads or any other damage. Inspect mating surfaces on cases for small nicks or burrs that could cause misalignment of the 2 halves. Remove all small nicks or burrs with a fine stone or file.

4) Check reverse gear and sliding gears for chipped, broken, or bent teeth. Check wear of reverse gear shaft (it is normal for front of teeth to show wear, this does not interfere with proper function).

5) Check teeth, splines and journals of mainshaft for damage. Check all other gears for chipped, broken, or worn teeth. Check for eroded clutching teeth and damaged bearing surfaces. Clutching teeth will usually show rounding of the points which does not interfere with normal operation.

6) Check synchronizer sleeves for free movement on hubs. Make sure index marks are properly aligned. Check for damaged clutching teeth. Check for proper positioning of springs.

7) Inspect synchronizer blocker rings for wear marks on spline end back face which indicates ring was bottoming on gear face due to excessive blocker ring wear.

8) Inspect differential pinion and side gears for scoring, excessive wear, nicks, and chips. Worn, scored, and damaged gears must be replaced.

NOTE: **When a scored or chipped gear is replaced, transaxle case must be cleaned thoroughly to make sure all chips are removed.**

9) Make sure differential case bearing journals are smooth. Inspect case bearing shoulders for damage caused by bearing removal. Check fit (free rotation) of side gears in their cavities.

10) Check differential bearings and bearing races for wear or other damage. Check bearings for smooth rotation in races. Examine bearing roller ends for step wear.

NOTE: **If inspection reveals either a damaged bearing or race, both parts must be replaced as they are a matched set.**

REASSEMBLY

DIFFERENTIAL

1) Install spring washer with base of tapered section against gear. Install spacing washer, if equipped,

AMC/RENAULT ALLIANCE 4 & 5-SPEED (Cont.)

and speedometer gear. If a new .677" (17.2 mm) bearing must be installed, discard spacing washer.

2) If original .630" (16 mm) bearing is installed, do not discard spacing washer. Install it with bearing. Install side gear with tail shaft. Install pinion gears with matching thrust washers. Install spider side gear, shim, and snap ring.

MAINSHAFT

1) Install 1st gear and synchronizer ring. Install roller spring, roller, and 1st/2nd gear sliding hub. Install synchronizer ring, circlip, grooved ring, and 2nd gear.

2) Install grooved ring, circlip, grooved ring, and 3rd gear. Install synchronizer ring, grooved ring, and circlip. Install roller spring, roller, and 3rd/4th sliding hub. Install synchronizer ring and 4th gear. *See Fig. 10.*

TRANSAXLE

1) Install magnet in case. Holding mainshaft vertically with 1st gear at bottom, install input, main, and reverse shafts together as an assembly. *See Fig. 7.* Tilt mainshaft to aid installing it in mainshaft bearing in case.

2) Install 1st/2nd/reverse interlocking detent. Install 1st/2nd selector fork with shift rod fingers facing gear. Install 1st/2nd rod in fork and install small plunger.

3) The interlocking ball recesses face shafts. Lift reverse shift rod. Lower 1st/2nd shift rod. Be sure that 1st/2nd/reverse interlocking detent is in recess in reverse shift rod.

4) Be sure that reverse shift rod is locked in place. Install medium sized interlocking shift detent between 1st/2nd and 3rd/4th shift rods. Install 3rd/4th fork with thicker side toward gear.

5) Install 3rd/4th shift rod with interlocking detent recesses facing shift rods. Install fork roll pins using 3/16 pin punch.

NOTE: Roll pin slots must face longitudinal axis of each rod. New roll pins must be used whenever transaxle is disassembled.

6) Apply gasket forming sealer onto joint faces of rear case and clutch case. On 5-speed models, install 5th gear interlocking ball and spring in rear case. Install 5th gear selector fork.

Fig. 12: Using Wire Hook To Lift Reverse Gear

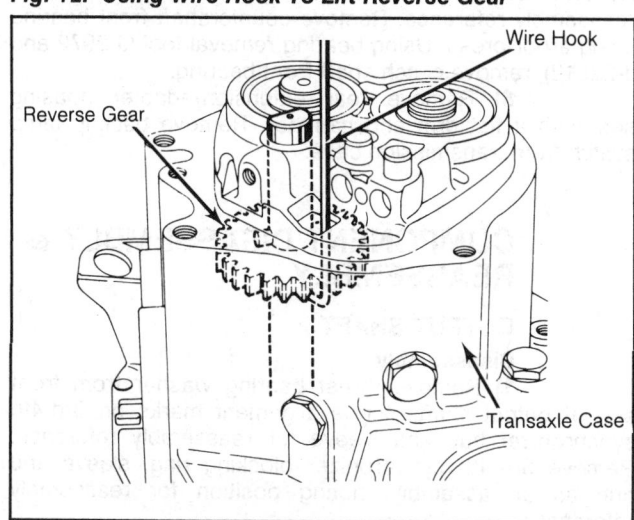

With gear lifted up, install interlocking ball.

7) Pull selector control outward and centralize input shaft, mainshaft, and selector fork shift rods. Install rear case. Remove dummy rods used during disassembly. Tap rear case with soft mallet to help seat input and mainshafts in case bearings.

8) Using a piece of wire in the shape of a hook, lift up reverse shaft and install interlocking ball, spring, and clip. Install 2 case bolts and operate shift mechanism to be sure that transaxle shifts correctly.

9) Install threaded limit stop, or 5th speed detent, and tighten stop. On 4-speed models, install a new mainshaft circlip. Install a new circlip on input shaft. Use installer tool (B.Vi. 902-01) and a hammer.

10) Support shaft on clutch spline side with screw from plate (B.Vi. 902-01). The shaft may also be supported using blocks of wood on bench. Be sure circlip is secure in circlip groove.

11) Install remaining case bolts and tighten all bolts. On 5-speed models, install 5th gear, washer, 5th gear circlip, retainer, and bolt using installer tool (B.Vi. 948). Be sure that 5th gear circlip is located in the groove by looking at slots.

12) Install flange facing bearing, washer, 5th gear bushing, roller bearing, 5th gear, and synchronizer ring. Install 5th gear spring in 5th gear sliding hub and install fork into sliding gear hub. *See Fig. 13.*

Fig. 13: Exploded View of 5th Gear Assembly

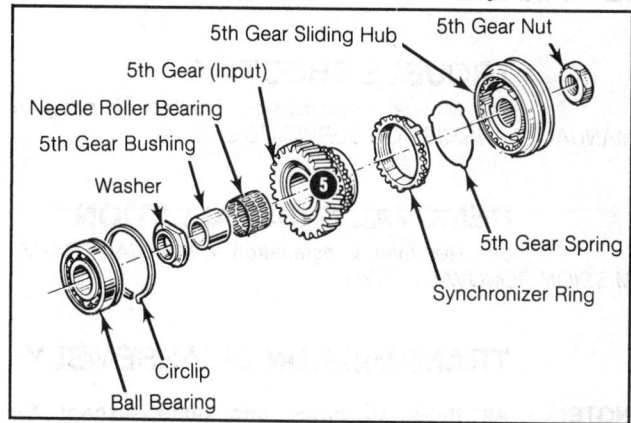

Install components in order shown.

13) Install fork on shaft and install fork roll pin using 3/16" pin punch. Support shaft with a block of wood when installing roll pin. Install input shaft nut. Shift transaxle into 2 gears at once and tighten mainshaft nut.

14) On both models, install rear case "O" ring by rolling it into place with a small screwdriver. Install rear cover. Install and tighten retaining case bolts.

TIGHTENING SPECIFICATIONS

Application	Ft. Lbs. (N.m)
Transaxle Bellows Bolts	18 (25)
Steering Arm Ball Joint Nut	25 (35)
Brake Caliper Bolts	25 (35)
Hub Nut	154 (210)
Switch Bodies	18 (25)
Rear Case Bolts	18 (25)
5th Speed Detent Stop	14 (19)
5th Speed Mainshaft Bolt	18 (25)

Manual Transmissions

BORG-WARNER 4-SPEED MODEL T4

American Motors
  All Models (Except Alliance)
General Motors
  S10/15
Jeep
  4 & 6-Cylinder Models

IDENTIFICATION

Transmission identification tag is attached to transmission shift control housing by one of the mounting bolts.

DESCRIPTION

The model T4 transmission is a constant mesh, fully synchronized unit which provides synchomesh in all 4 forward gears. The forward gears are helical-cut and are in constant mesh. The reverse gears are spur-cut and are not in constant mesh. An interlock system prevents accidental engagement of reverse gears when selecting any of the forward gear ranges.

LUBRICATION

See Lubrication in *MANUAL TRANSMISSION SERVICING* section.

TROUBLE SHOOTING

See *Manual Transmission Trouble Shooting* in *MANUAL TRANSMISSION SERVICING* section.

REMOVAL & INSTALLATION

See *Removal & Installation* in *MANUAL TRANSMISSION REMOVAL* section.

TRANSMISSION DISASSEMBLY

NOTE: **All threaded holes and bolts, except for gearshift lever attaching bolts and fill plug, are metric threaded.**

1) On Spirit and Concord models, remove transmission fill plug and remove lubricant using a siphon. On all other models, remove drain plug bolt. On all models, use punch to remove roll pin attaching offset lever-to-shift rail.

2) Remove extension/adapter housing-to-transmission case bolts and remove housing and offset lever as an assembly. *See Fig. 1.* Remove detent ball and spring from offset lever and remove roll pin from extension/adapter housing or offset lever.

NOTE: **Do not try to remove the offset lever while the extension housing is still bolted in place. Positioning lug prevents moving lever far enough for removal**

3) Remove and retain countershaft rear thrust bearing and bearing race. Remove transmission cover and shift fork assembly attaching bolts and remove cover. Remove "C" clip attaching reverse lever to reverse lever

Fig. 1: *Offset Lever Spring & Ball*

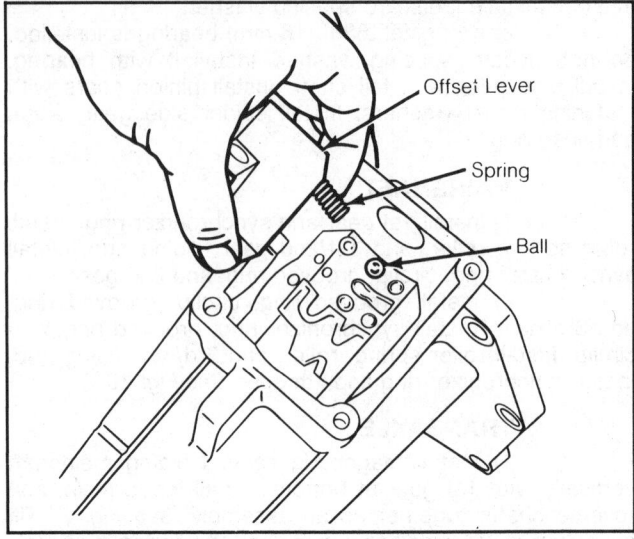

pivot bolt, remove bolt and then remove reverse lever and lever fork as an assembly.

NOTE: **Two of the shift control cover bolts are dowel-type alignment bolts. Note the positions of these bolts for reassembly reference.**

4) Index mark front bearing cap and transmission case with a punch and remove front bearing cap bolts and cap. Remove front bearing race, shims and oil seal from bearing cap. Rotate clutch shaft until flat on gear teeth is facing countershaft and remove shaft.

5) Remove thrust bearing and 15 roller bearings from clutch shaft. Remove output shaft bearing race. If necessary, tap output shaft with rubber hammer to remove bearing race. Tilt output shaft assembly upward and remove from transmission case.

6) Remove coutershaft rear bearing with a brass drift and arbor press. Note position of bearing for reassembly reference. Bearing number should face outward when correctly installed. Move countershaft rearward, tilt upward and remove shaft from case. Note position of washer for reassembly reference.

7) Remove countershaft rear bearing spacer. Remove reverse idler shaft and gear, noting position for reassembly reference. Remove countershaft front bearing using arbor press. Using bearing removal tool (J-2972 and J-22912), remove clutch shaft front bearing.

8) Remove rear extension/adapter housing seal with a flat drift and hammer. Remove backup lamp switch from transmission case.

COMPONENT DISASSEMBLY & REASSEMBLY

OUTPUT SHAFT

Disassembly

1) Remove thrust bearing washer from front end of output shaft. Scribe alignment marks on 3rd-4th synchronizer hub and sleeve for reassembly reference. Remove 3rd-4th synchronizer blocking ring, sleeve and hub as an assembly, noting position for reassembly reference.

BORG-WARNER 4-SPEED MODEL T4 (Cont.)

Fig. 2: Exploded View of Model T4 4-Speed Transmission Assembly

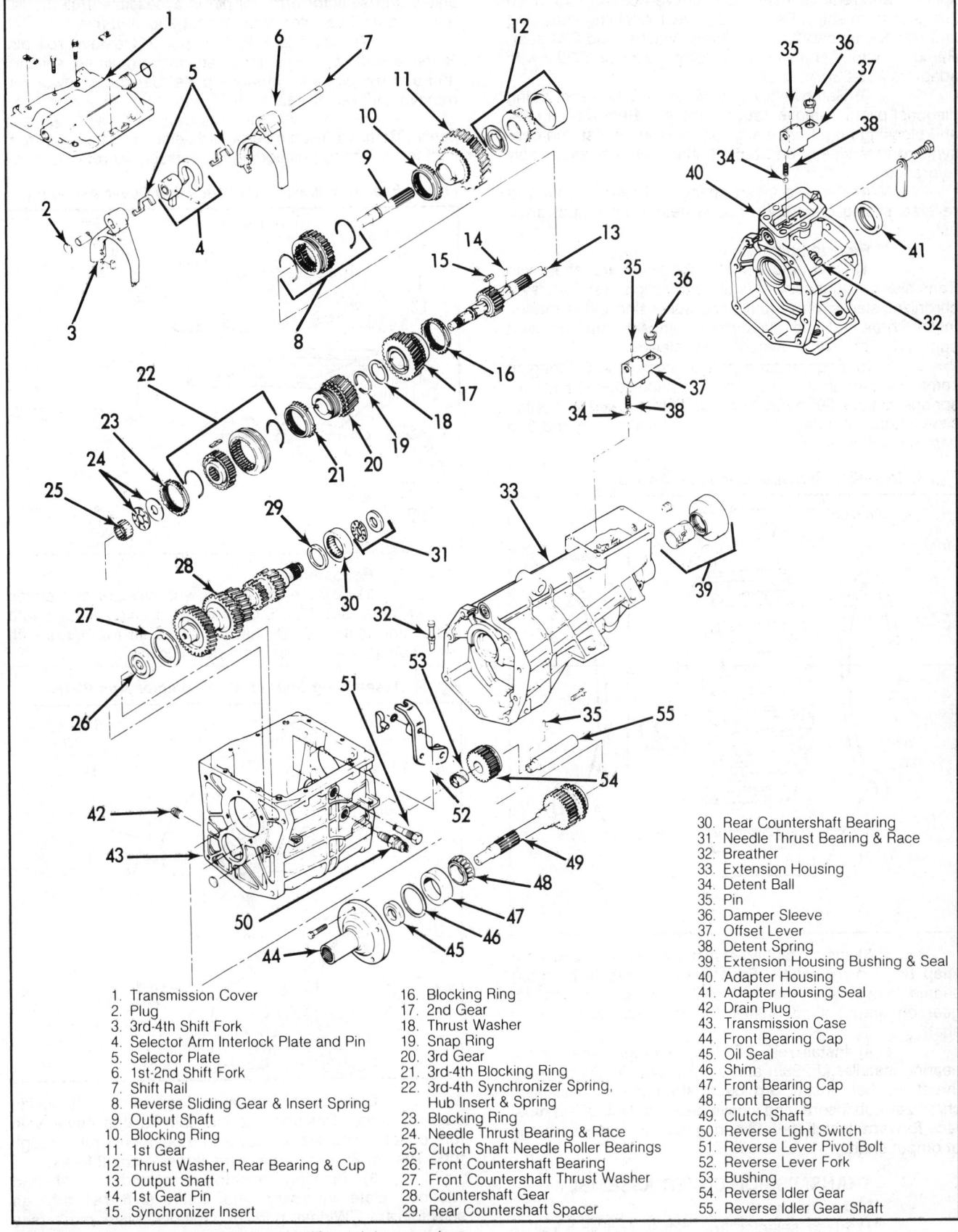

1. Transmission Cover
2. Plug
3. 3rd-4th Shift Fork
4. Selector Arm Interlock Plate and Pin
5. Selector Plate
6. 1st-2nd Shift Fork
7. Shift Rail
8. Reverse Sliding Gear & Insert Spring
9. Output Shaft
10. Blocking Ring
11. 1st Gear
12. Thrust Washer, Rear Bearing & Cup
13. Output Shaft
14. 1st Gear Pin
15. Synchronizer Insert
16. Blocking Ring
17. 2nd Gear
18. Thrust Washer
19. Snap Ring
20. 3rd Gear
21. 3rd-4th Blocking Ring
22. 3rd-4th Synchronizer Spring, Hub Insert & Spring
23. Blocking Ring
24. Needle Thrust Bearing & Race
25. Clutch Shaft Needle Roller Bearings
26. Front Countershaft Bearing
27. Front Countershaft Thrust Washer
28. Countershaft Gear
29. Rear Countershaft Spacer
30. Rear Countershaft Bearing
31. Needle Thrust Bearing & Race
32. Breather
33. Extension Housing
34. Detent Ball
35. Pin
36. Damper Sleeve
37. Offset Lever
38. Detent Spring
39. Extension Housing Bushing & Seal
40. Adapter Housing
41. Adapter Housing Seal
42. Drain Plug
43. Transmission Case
44. Front Bearing Cap
45. Oil Seal
46. Shim
47. Front Bearing Cap
48. Front Bearing
49. Clutch Shaft
50. Reverse Light Switch
51. Reverse Lever Pivot Bolt
52. Reverse Lever Fork
53. Bushing
54. Reverse Idler Gear
55. Reverse Idler Gear Shaft

2WD models use extension housing; 4WD models use adapter.

BORG-WARNER 4-SPEED MODEL T4 (Cont.)

2) Remove 3rd-4th synchronizer, insert springs, and remove inserts and sleeve from hub. Remove 3rd gear from shaft. Remove 2nd gear retaining snap ring and remove tabbed 2nd gear thrust washer and 2nd gear. Remove output shaft bearing using puller (J-29721 with adapters 293-39).

3) Remove 1st gear thrust washer and, using diagonal pliers, remove 1st gear roll pin. Remove 1st gear and blocking ring. Scribe alignment marks on 1st-2nd gear synchronizer sleeve and output shaft hub for reassembly reference.

4) Remove insert spring and inserts from 1st-reverse sliding gear and remove gear from output shaft hub.

Reassembly

1) Coat output shaft gear bores and shaft with transmission lubricant. Install and align 1st-2nd synchronizer sleeve on output shaft hub using index marks. Install three 1st-2nd synchronizer inserts and 2 insert springs in 1st-reverse synchronizer sleeve.

2) Engage tang end of each insert spring in same synchronizer insert but position open ends of springs to face 180° away from each other. *See Fig 3.* Align sleeve hub with index marks. Install blocking ring and 2nd gear on mainshaft.

Fig. 3: Installing Synchronizer Insert Spring

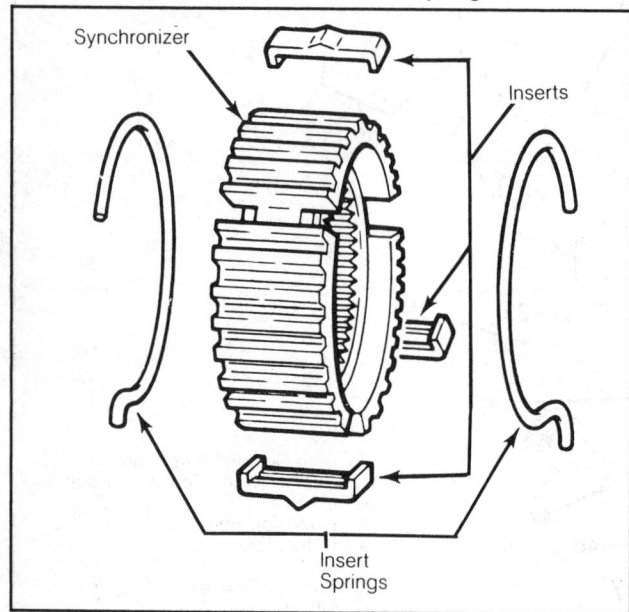

3) Install tabbed thrust washer and 2nd gear snap ring on mainshaft. Ensure washer tab is correctly seated in mainshaft notch. Install blocking ring and 1st gear on output shaft. Install 1st gear roll pin in output shaft.

4) Install rear bearing on output shaft using bearing installer (J-2995) and arbor press. Install 1st gear thrust washer. Install 3rd gear, 3rd and 4th gear synchronizer hub inserts and sleeve on shaft. Hub offset must face forward. Install thrust bearing washer on forward end of output shaft.

TRANSMISSION COVER ASSEMBLY
Disassembly

1) Place selector arm plates and shift rail in centered (neutral) position. Rotate shift rail counterclock-

wise until selector arm disengages from selector arm plates and selector arm roll pin is accessible. Pull the rail rearward until selector contacts 1st-2nd shift fork.

2) Using a 3/16" pin punch, remove roll pin. Remove shift rail, shift forks, selector arm plates, selector arm and roll pin, and interlock plate. Using a screwdriver, remove shift rail oil seal and "O" ring.

3) Remove shift rail plug with hammer and punch. Remove nylon inserts and selector arm plates from shift forks, noting positioning for reassembly reference.

Fig. 4: Exploded View of Transmission Cover Assembly

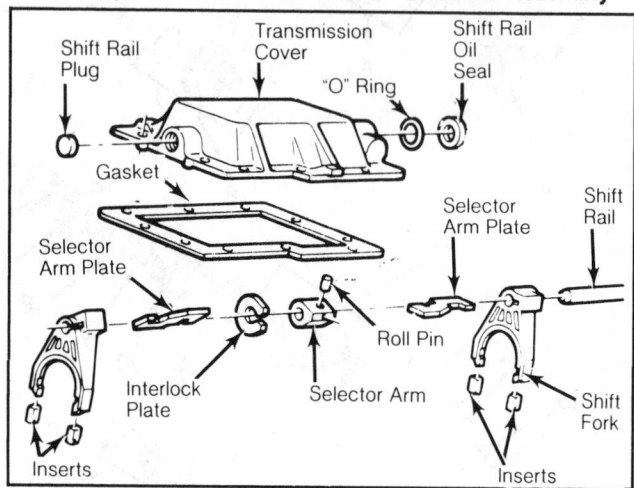

Reassembly

1) Install nylon inserts and selector arm plates in shift forks. *See Fig. 5.* Coat edge of shift rail plug with sealer and install. Coat shift rail and shift rail bores with petroleum jelly and insert shift rail in cover.

Fig. 5: Assembling Shift Forks & Selector Arm Plates

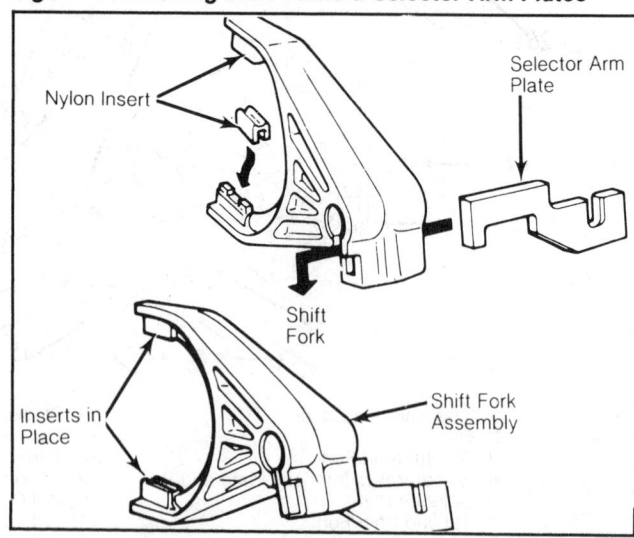

2) Install rail until end of rail is flush with inside edge of cover. Position 1st-2nd shift fork in cover with fork offset facing rear of cover and push shift rail through fork. The 1st-2nd shift fork is the larger of the 2 forks.

3) Position selector arm and "C" shaped interlock plate in cover and insert shift rail through selector arm. Widest part of interlock plate must face away from cover and selector arm roll pin must face downward and toward rear of cover.

BORG-WARNER 4-SPEED MODEL T4 (Cont.)

4) Position 3rd-4th shift fork in cover with fork offset facing rear of cover. The 3rd-4th shift fork selector arm plate must be positioned under 1st-2nd shift fork selector arm plate. Insert shift rail through 3rd-4th shift fork and into front shift rail bore in cover.

5) Rotate shift rail until selector arm plate at forward end of rail faces away from, but is parallel to, cover. Align selector arm and shift rail roll pin holes and install roll pin. Ensure roll pin is flush with selector arm surface. Install "O" ring in groove of shift rail oil seal.

6) Install shift rail oil seal as follows: Install shift rail oil seal protector tool (J-26628) over threaded end of shift rail. Lubricate lip of oil seal with petroleum jelly and slide seal over protector and onto shift rail. Seat seal using oil seal installer tool (J-22628-1).

CLEANING & INSPECTION

1) Wash all parts in solvent and dry with compressed air except for front and rear bearings. Wipe front and rear bearings dry with a clean shop cloth or air dry.

2) Clean needle thrust and roller bearings with solvent in a shallow pan or wipe dry with shop cloth. Inspect transmission case, cover and extension housing.

3) Replace if there are cracks in bores, sides, bosses, or bolt holes. Replace case if there are stripped bolt holes, nicks, burrs, or rough surfaces in shaft bores or on gasket surfaces.

4) Inspect gear train and shift mechanism. Replace any parts exibiting wear, chips, galling, distortion or bending. Check for worn bearings and bores. Check for weak snap rings and stripped offset lever.

TRANSMISSION REASSEMBLY

1) Coat countershaft front bearing outer cage with Loctite 601 (or equivalent). Using arbor press, install countershaft front bearing flush with case.

2) Coat countershaft tabbed thrust washer with petroleum jelly and install so tab engages depression in case. Tip case on end and install countershaft in front bearing bore.

3) Install countershaft rear bearing spacer. Coat countershaft rear bearing with petroleum jelly and install bearing using installer (J-29895) and mallet. Countershaft rear bearing should extend .125" (3.17 mm) beyond case surface.

4) Position reverse idler gear in case with shift lever groove facing rear of case. Install reverse idler shaft from rear of case and install retaining roll pin in shaft. Install assembled output shaft in case.

5) Install front clutch shaft bearing on clutch shaft using bearing installer (J-2995) and arbor press. Coat 15 pilot roller bearings with petroleum jelly and install in clutch shaft. Install thrust bearing and race in clutch shaft.

6) Install 4th gear blocking ring on output shaft. Install rear output shaft bearing race. Install clutch shaft in case and engage shaft in 3rd-4th synchronizer sleeve and blocking ring.

7) Using seal installer (J-26625), install replacement oil seal in front bearing cap. Using seal installer (J-29184), install replacement oil seal in rear adapter housing.

8) Install front bearing race in front bearing cap, but do not install shims. Install front bearing cap. Do not install sealer at this time. Install reverse lever, pivot pin, and retaining "C" clip.

9) Coat countershaft rear bearing race and thrust bearing with petroleum jelly and install in extension/adapter housing. Temporarily install extension/adapter housing. Do not seal housing to case or tighten bolts.

10) Turn transmission case on end. Mount dial indicator on extension/adaptor housing with indicator stylus on end of output shaft. Rotate clutch and output shaft until end play is removed.

11) To completely eliminate output shaft and clutch shaft end play, bearings must be preloaded from .001"-.005" (.03-.13 mm). Read end play dimension on dial indicator.

12) Select shim pack measuring .001-.005" (.03-.13") thicker than end play measurement. Place transmission horizontally on workbench and remove front bearing cap and front bearing race.

13) Add shims to bearing cap to obtain necessary preload and install clutch shaft bearing race in cap. Apply bead of RTV sealant on case mating surface on front bearing cap.

14) Install front bearing cap using index marks. Tighten retaining bolts. Recheck end play. There should be no end play. Remove extension/adaptor housing.

15) Move shift forks on transmission cover and synchronizer rings (inside transmission) to neutral position. Apply a bead of RTV sealant to cover mating surface. Lower cover assembly (slightly off center), onto case while aligning shift forks and synchronizer sleeves.

16) Center cover on case to engage reverse relay lever and install 2 dowel bolts in cover. Install and tighten remaining bolts. The offset lever-to-shift rail pin hole is in a vertical position when steps 15) and 16) are performed correctly.

17) Apply a bead of RTV sealant to extension/adaptor housing-to-transmission case mating surface. Install extension/adaptor housing over output shaft and shift rail to a position where shift rail enters shift cover opening.

18) Install detent spring into offset lever. Place steel ball in neutral guide plate detent. See Fig. 1. Apply pressure on steel ball with detent spring and offset lever.

19) Slide offset lever on shift rail and seal extension/adaptor housing against transmission case. The offset level and shift rail pin holes should be aligned and in a vertical position.

20) Install and tighten adaptor housing retainer bolts. Install roll pin in offset lever and shift rail. Install damper sleeve in offset lever. Coat back-up light switch with RTV sealer and install in case.

TIGHTENING SPECIFICATIONS

Application	Ft. Lbs. (N.m)
Adapter Housing Bolt	11-15 (15-20)
Back-Up Light Switch	12-18 (16-24)
Crossmember Stud Nut	28-32 (38-43)
Extension Housing Bolt	20-32 (27-43)
Transmission Case-to-Transmission Mounting Stud Nuts	24-30 (33-40)
Transmission-to-Clutch Housing Bolt	45-65 (61-88)
Universal Joint Clamp Strap Bolt	12-18 (16-24)

BORG-WARNER 5-SPEED MODEL T5

American Motors
  All Models (Except Alliance)
Ford Motor Co.
  Capri, Cougar, Mustang
  Thunderbird
General Motors
  Camaro, Chevette, Firebird,
  S10/15, T1000
Jeep
  4 & 6-Cylinder Models

IDENTIFICATION

American Motors Passenger Cars — An identification tag is attached to rear of transmission.
  Ford Motor Co. — Identification code is stamped on upper left rear side of extension housing.
  General Motors Passenger Cars — Identification code is stamped on lower right side of transmission case.

  Jeep & S10/15 — An identification tag displaying model part number is attached to right side of adapter housing by an adapter housing-to-transmission case bolt.

DESCRIPTION

The T5 5-speed transmission is a constant mesh, fully synchronized unit which provides synchromesh engagement in all forward gear ranges. The reverse gear is spur-cut and is not in constant mesh. The transmission utilizes an internal-type non-adjustable shift mechanism with a reverse gear lockout. The lockout feature prevents accidental engagement in reverse when selecting any of the forward gears.

LUBRICATION

See Lubrication in MANUAL TRANSMISSION SERVICING section.

TROUBLE SHOOTING

See Manual Transmission Trouble Shooting in MANUAL TRANSMISSION SERVICING section.

REMOVAL & INSTALLATION

See Removal & Installation in MANUAL TRANSMISSION REMOVAL section.

TRANSMISSION DISASSEMBLY

CAUTION: **All threaded holes and bolts, except for gearshift lever attaching bolts and fill plug, have metric threads. If bolts are replaced, use only those of the same size and length as the originals.**

  1) On Concord and Spirit models, remove transmission fill plug and remove lubricant with a siphon pump. On all other models, remove drain bolt on transmission case to drain lubricant.

  2) Using a pin punch and hammer, remove roll pin attaching offset lever to shift rail. Remove extension or adapter housing-to-transmission bolts and remove housing and offset lever as an assembly.

  3) On all except Concord and Spirit models, remove plastic funnel, thrust bearing race and thrust bearing, on end of countershaft or inside adapter housing, from rear of countershaft.

  4) Remove bolts attaching cover and shift fork assembly to transmission and remove cover assembly. Remove roll pin from 5th gear shift fork. Place a wood block under 5th gear shift fork during roll pin removal to prevent damage to 5th gear/reverse shift rail. See Fig. 1.

Fig. 1: Removing 5th Gear Shift Fork Roll Pin

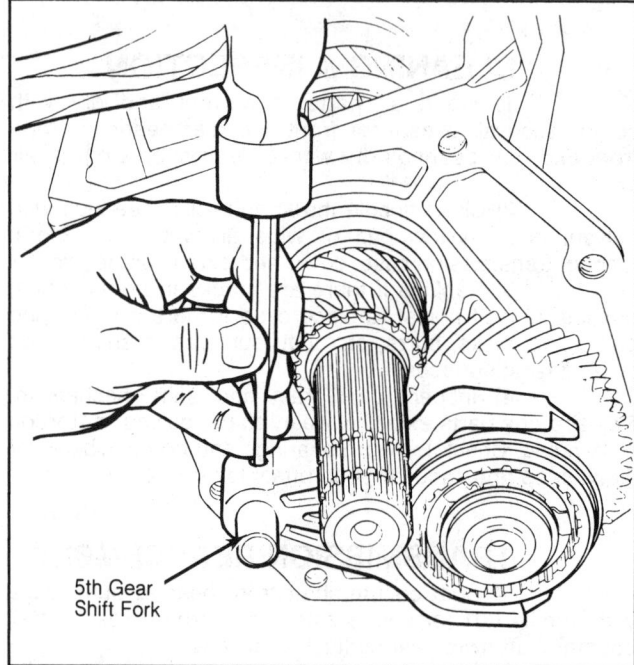

5th Gear
Shift Fork

Place wood block under gear during removal.

  5) Remove 5th gear synchronizer snap ring, shift fork, 5th gear synchronizer sleeve, blocking ring and 5th speed drive gear from rear of countershaft. Remove 5th gear synchronizer insert retainer springs and inserts from sleeve and hub. Mark position of hub and sleeve for assembly reference.

  6) Remove snap ring and 5th speed driven gear from rear of output shaft using puller (J-25215 or equivalent). Mark front bearing cap for assembly reference. Remove front bearing cap bolts and bearing cap. Remove front bearing race, end play shims and oil seal from bearing cap.

  7) Rotate clutch shaft until flat surface on main drive gear faces countershaft, then remove clutch shaft from transmission. Remove clutch shaft needle bearings, thrust bearing and race. Remove output shaft rear bearing race, then tilt output shaft upward and remove through top of transmission case. See Fig. 2.

  8) Unlock overcenter link spring from transmission case. Remove "C" clip that retains reverse lever and fork assembly to reverse lever pivot pin. Rotate 5th/reverse gear shift rail clockwise to disengage rail from reverse lever assembly. Remove shift rail from rear of transmission. See Fig. 3.

BORG-WARNER 5-SPEED MODEL T5 (Cont.)

Fig. 2: Removing & Installing Output Shaft

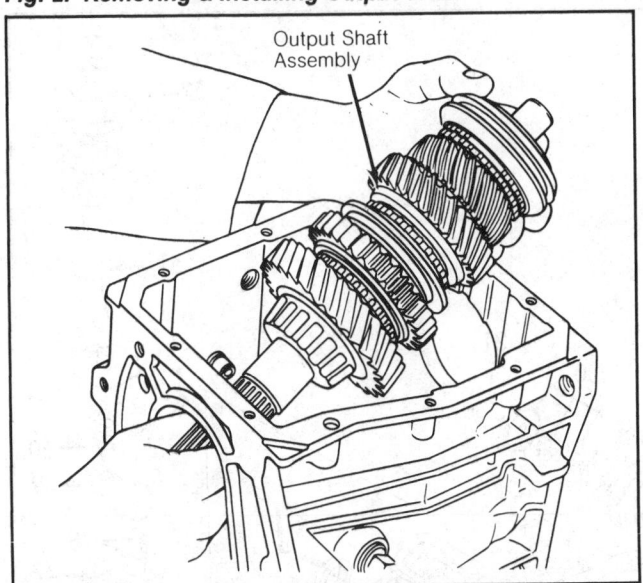

Output Shaft Assembly

Tilt shaft upward and remove through top of case.

9) Remove snap ring and spacer from rear of countershaft. Insert a brass drift through clutch shaft opening in front of transmission case and press countershaft assembly rearward, using arbor press to remove rear countershaft bearing.

Fig. 3: Removing & Installing Reverse Shift Rail

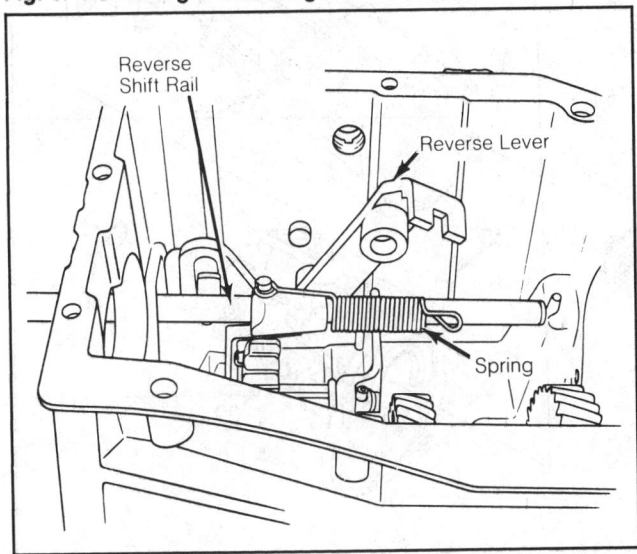

Reverse Shift Rail

Reverse Lever

Spring

10) Slide countershaft assembly rearward, tilt assembly upward and remove from case. Note position of front countershaft thrust washer in case for reassembly reference. Remove countershaft front thrust washer and rear bearing spacer.

11) Remove roll pin from front end of reverse idler shaft, then remove reverse idler shaft and gear from transmission case. Note position of reverse idler gear for reassembly reference.

12) Using an arbor press, remove countershaft front bearing from transmission case. Remove bearing from front of clutch shaft. Using a flat drift and hammer, remove rear extension or adapter housing seal.

COMPONENT DISASSEMBLY & REASSEMBLY

OUTPUT SHAFT
Disassembly

1) Remove thrust bearing washer from front of output shaft. Scribe alignment mark on 3rd-4th synchronizer hub and sleeve for reassembly reference. Remove 3rd-4th gear synchronizer blocking ring, sleeve, hub and 3rd gear as an assembly.

2) Remove snap ring that retains 2nd gear on shaft, then remove tabbed 2nd gear thrust washer and 2nd gear. Using puller (J-22912 or equivalent) and arbor press, remove 5th gear. Slide rear bearing off mainshaft.

3) Remove 1st gear thrust washer, 1st gear roll pin (using diagonal cutters), 1st gear and blocking ring. Scribe alignment marks on 1st-2nd gear synchronizer sleeve and hub for reassembly reference.

4) Remove insert springs and insert from 1st/reverse sliding gear and remove gear from output shaft hub. Do not attempt to remove 1st-2nd/reverse hub from output shaft. Hub and shaft are machined as a matched set.

Reassembly

1) Coat ouput shaft and gear bores with transmission lubricant. Install and align 1st-2nd gear synchronizer sleeve on output shaft hub using reference marks made at disassembly. Install 1st-2nd synchronizer inserts and springs in 1st/reverse synchronizer sleeve.

2) Engage tang end of each insert spring in same synchronizer insert, but position open ends of springs to face 180° from each other. Be sure that reference marks are aligned. *See Fig. 4.*

Fig. 4: Installing Synchronizer Insert Spring

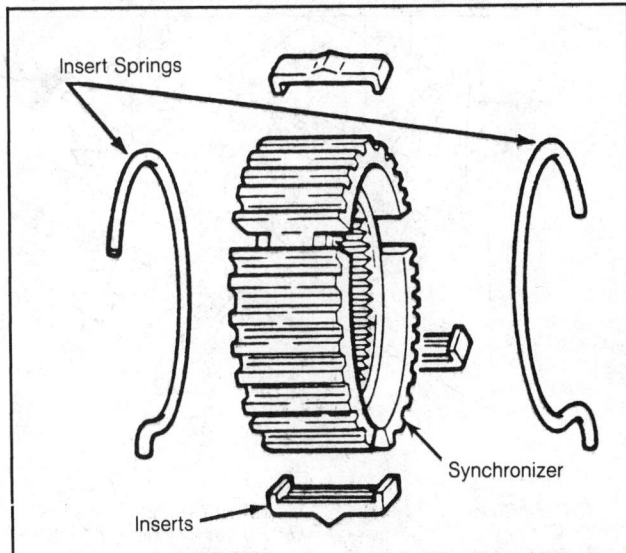

Insert Springs

Synchronizer

Inserts

NOTE: If any output shaft gear is replaced, the countershaft gear must also be replaced to maintain proper gear mesh and avoid noisy operation.

3) Install blocking ring and 2nd gear on output shaft. Install tabbed thrust washer and 2nd gear retaining snap ring on output shaft. Be sure that washer tab is properly seated in output shaft notch.

Manual Transmissions

BORG-WARNER 5-SPEED MODEL T5 (Cont.)

Fig. 5: *Exploded View of Borg-Warner 5-Speed Model T5 Transmission*

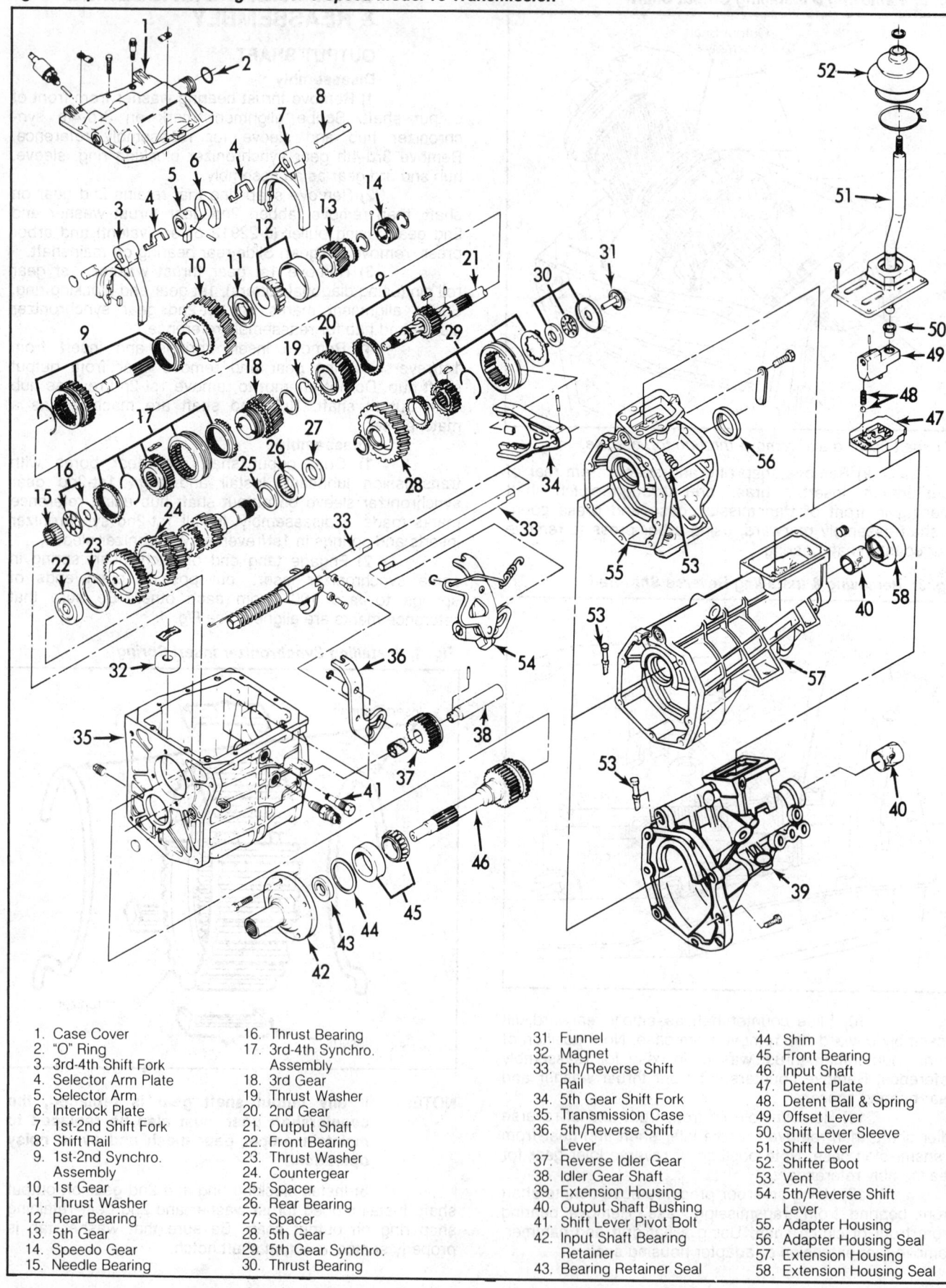

1. Case Cover	16. Thrust Bearing	31. Funnel	44. Shim
2. "O" Ring	17. 3rd-4th Synchro.	32. Magnet	45. Front Bearing
3. 3rd-4th Shift Fork	Assembly	33. 5th/Reverse Shift	46. Input Shaft
4. Selector Arm Plate	18. 3rd Gear	Rail	47. Detent Plate
5. Selector Arm	19. Thrust Washer	34. 5th Gear Shift Fork	48. Detent Ball & Spring
6. Interlock Plate	20. 2nd Gear	35. Transmission Case	49. Offset Lever
7. 1st-2nd Shift Fork	21. Output Shaft	36. 5th/Reverse Shift	50. Shift Lever Sleeve
8. Shift Rail	22. Front Bearing	Lever	51. Shift Lever
9. 1st-2nd Synchro.	23. Thrust Washer	37. Reverse Idler Gear	52. Shifter Boot
Assembly	24. Countergear	38. Idler Gear Shaft	53. Vent
10. 1st Gear	25. Spacer	39. Extension Housing	54. 5th/Reverse Shift
11. Thrust Washer	26. Rear Bearing	40. Output Shaft Bushing	Lever
12. Rear Bearing	27. Spacer	41. Shift Lever Pivot Bolt	55. Adapter Housing
13. 5th Gear	28. 5th Gear	42. Input Shaft Bearing	56. Adapter Housing Seal
14. Speedo Gear	29. 5th Gear Synchro.	Retainer	57. Extension Housing
15. Needle Bearing	30. Thrust Bearing	43. Bearing Retainer Seal	58. Extension Housing Seal

BORG-WARNER 5-SPEED MODEL T5 (Cont.)

4) Install blocking ring, 1st gear, roll pin and thrust washer on output shaft. Slide rear bearing on output shaft. Using installer (J-22912 or equivalent) and arbor press, install 5th gear on output shaft.

5) Install 3rd-4th gear synchronizer hub insert and sleeve on output shaft. Hub offset must face forward. Install thrust bearing washer on forward end of output shaft.

COVER ASSEMBLY
Disassembly

1) Place selector arm plates and shift rail in neutral position. Rotate shift rail counterclockwise until selector arm disengages from selector arm plates and selector arm roll pin is accessible.

2) Pull shift rail rearward until selector arm contacts 1st-2nd shift fork. Using a punch, remove selector arm roll pin. Remove shift rail. *See Fig. 6.*

Fig. 6: Removing Shift Rail Retaining Roll Pin

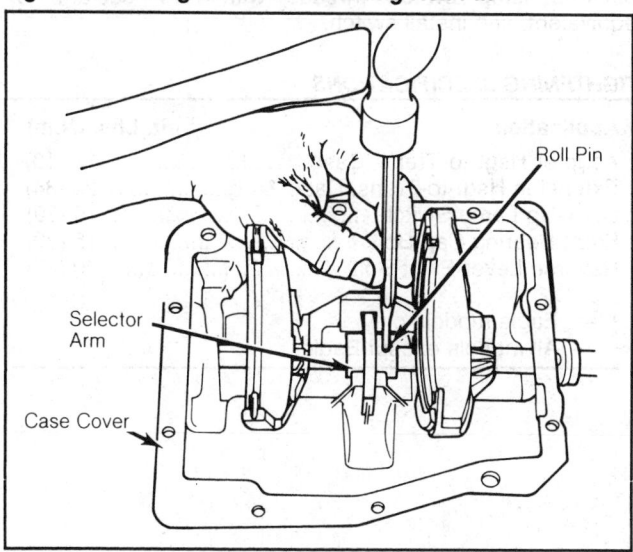

3) Remove shift forks, selector arm plates, selector arm, roll pin and interlock plate. Using a screwdriver, remove shift rail oil seal and "O" ring. Using a hammer and punch, remove shift rail plug.

4) Remove nylon inserts and selector arm plates from shift forks. Note position of inserts and plates for reassembly reference.

Reassembly

1) Install nylon inserts and selector arm plates in shift forks. Apply sealer to edge of shift rail plug and install. Coat shift rail and bore with petroleum jelly and install shift rail in cover with end of rail flush with inside edge of cover.

2) Position 1st-2nd shift fork in cover with fork offset facing rear of cover. Push shift rail through fork. Position selector arm and C-shaped interlock plate in cover and insert shift rail. Widest part of interlock plate must face away from cover, and selector arm roll pin hold must face downward and toward rear of cover.

3) Position 3rd-4th shift fork in cover with fork offset facing rear of cover. Fork selector arm plate must be positioned under 1st-2nd shift fork selector arm plate. Insert shift rail through 3rd-4th shift fork and into shift trail bore in cover. Rotate shift rail until selector arm plate faces away from cover.

4) Align roll pin holes in selector arm and shift rail. Install roll pin. Install "O" ring in groove of shift rail oil seal. Install shift rail oil seal in cover.

CLEANING & INSPECTION

1) Wash all parts in solvent and dry all parts, except bearings, with compressed air. Allow bearings to air dry or wipe dry with a clean shop cloth. Clean needle thrust and roller bearings.

2) Inspect transmission case, cover and extension or adapter housing. Replace if there are cracks in bores, sides, bosses or bolt holes. Replace case if there are stripped bolt holes, nicks, burrs, or rough surfaces in shaft bores or on gasket surfaces.

3) Inspect gear train and shift mechanism. Replace any parts exhibitiing wear, chips, galling, distortion or bending. Check for worn bearings and bores. Check for weak snap rings and stripped offset lever.

TRANSMISSION REASSEMBLY

1) Coat countershaft front bearing outer cage with Loctite 601, or equivalent. Using an arbor press, install countershaft front bearing flush with case. Coat tabbed countershaft thrust washer with petroleum jelly and install with tab engaged with depression in case.

2) Place transmission case on end and install countershaft in front bearing. Install countershaft rear bearing spacer. Coat rear bearing with petroleum jelly and install using bearing installer tool (J-29895 or equivalent).

3) Use sleeve tool to prevent needle bearings from catching on countershaft shoulder. When properly installed, bearing should extend .125" (3.17 mm) beyond surface of case.

4) Place reverse idler gear in case with shift lever groove facing rearward. Install reverse idler shaft from rear of case and install retaining roll pin. Install assembled output shaft in transmission case.

5) Install output shaft rear bearing race in case. Install 4th gear in case and engage 3rd-4th synchronizer sleeve and blocking ring on output shaft. Install front bearing race in front bearing cap without shims.

6) Temporarily install front bearing cap. Install 5th speed/reverse lever, pivot bolt and retaining "C" clip. Coat pivot bolt threads with RTV sealer. Be sure to engage reverse shift fork in reverse idler gear.

7) Install front bearing race in front bearing cap without shims. Temporarily install front bearing cap. Install 5th speed driven gear and retaining snap ring on rear of output shaft. Install 5th speed gear on countershaft.

8) Insert 5th gear/reverse rail through rear of case and install 5th/reverse gear lever. To simplify engagement with lever, rotate rail during installation. Install 5th/reverse gear lever over center spring.

9) Assemble 5th gear synchronizer sleeve, insert springs and insert retainer using marks made at disassembly. Install plastic inserts in notches on each side of 5th gear shift fork. Place 5th gear synchronizer sleeve on 5th gear shift fork and slide onto countershaft and 5th/reverse gear rail.

10) Align roll pin hole in 5th/reverse gear rail and 5th gear shift fork. Place assembled 5th/reverse gear rail and shift fork on block of wood and install retaining

BORG-WARNER 5-SPEED MODEL T5 (Cont.)

roll pin. Install thrust race against 5th gear synchronizer hub and install retaining snap ring.

11) Install needle thrust bearing against thrust race on countershaft. Coat thrust bearing and race with petroleum jelly. Install lipped thrust race over needle thrust bearing and install plastic funnel into hole in end of countershaft gear.

12) Temporarily install extension or adapter housing. Turn transmission case on end and mount dial indicator on extension or adapter housing with indicator stylus on end of output shaft. Rotate clutch and output shaft and zero dial indicator. Pull upward on output shaft and read end play on dial indicator. *See Fig. 7.*

Fig. 7: Measuring Output Shaft End Play

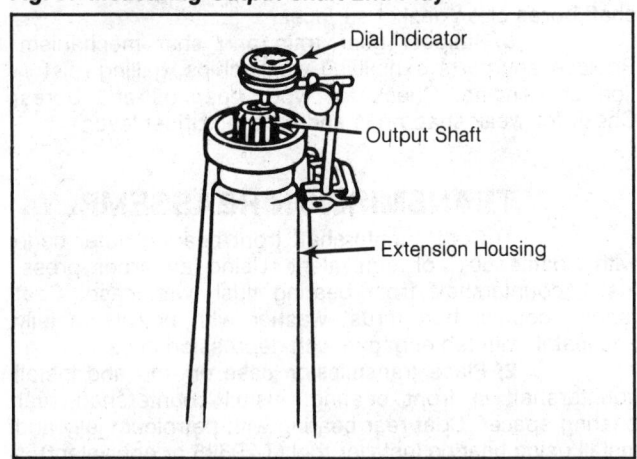

13) Select a shim pack measuring .001-.005" (.03-.13 mm) thicker than end play measured in step **12)**. Horizontally place transmission on bench and remove front bearing cap and race.

14) Add shims to cap and install clutch shaft bearing race in cap. Apply RTV sealant, or equivalent, to front bearing cap and install on transmission case. Tighten bolts. Recheck end play. There should be no end play.

15) Remove extension or adapter housing and install extension or adapter housing seal using a seal

Fig. 8: Offset Lever, Ball & Spring Location

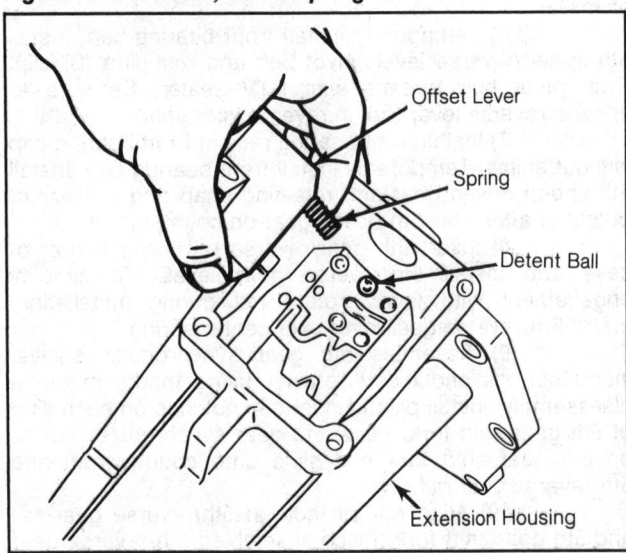

installer. Move transmission shift fork to place transmission in neutral.

16) Apply RTV sealant, or equivalent, to cover. Install cover assembly onto case while aligning shift forks and synchronizer sleeves. Install cover attaching bolts and tighten. Be sure that reverse relay lever is engaged.

17) Apply RTV sealant, or equivalent, to extension or adapter housing and install housing over output shaft and shift rail into position where shift rail just enters shift cover opening.

18) Install detent spring into offset lever and place steel ball in neutral guide plate detent. *See Fig. 8.* Apply pressure to steel ball with detent spring and offset lever.

19) Slide offset lever onto shift rail and seat extension or adapter housing to transmission case. Install and tighten housing attaching bolts. Install roll pin in offset lever and shift rail.

20) Install damper sleeve in offset lever. Coat back-up lamp switch threads with RTV sealant, or equivalent, and install switch.

TIGHTENING SPECIFICATIONS

Application	Ft. Lbs. (N.m)
Adapter Hsg.-to-Trans. Case [1]	13 (18)
Extension Hsg.-to-Trans. Case [2]	25 (34)
Back-Up Lamp Switch	15 (20)
Front Bearing Cap Bolt	15 (20)
Reverse Lever Pivot Bolt	20 (27)

[1] — Eagle models only.
[2] — All models except Eagle.

BORG-WARNER 4-SPEED MODEL T-18 & T-18A

**Ford Bronco, F150/350 & F150/350 4WD
Jeep J-20 Truck Only**

IDENTIFICATION

An identification tag is attached to one of the shift control housing-to-case attaching bolts. Tag shows vehicle and vendor part number.

DESCRIPTION

Transmission is a 4-speed unit, synchronized in 2nd, 3rd, and 4th gears only. First and reverse gears are spur type, while 2nd, 3rd, and 4th gears are constant mesh helical type. The input shaft is supported at the front with a ball bearing. The mainshaft is supported at the front by a pilot bearing in the output shaft and at the rear by a ball bearing. All other gears are supported by needle-type roller bearings.

LUBRICATION

See Lubrication in MANUAL TRANSMISSION SERVICING section.

TROUBLE SHOOTING

See Manual Transmission Trouble Shooting in MANUAL TRANSMISSION SERVICING section.

REMOVAL AND INSTALLATION

See Manual Transmission Removal in this section.

TRANSMISSION DISASSEMBLY

1) Mount transmission in a holding fixture and drain lubricant. Position shift lever in reverse (Jeep), or 2nd gear (Ford), and remove shift control housing. On 2-WD models, lock in 2 gears, then remove "U" joint flange nut, flange, oil seal, speedometer driven gear and bearing assembly. Remove mainshaft bearing retainer or extension housing, speedometer drive gear snap ring, retainer and gear with spacer.

2) On 4-WD models, remove adapter housing. On all models, remove rear bearing spacer and bearing. Using puller, remove input shaft bearing and take off oil baffle or retaining washer.

3) Remove mainshaft assembly from case, using care not to lose 22 needle bearings from input shaft. Remove input shaft assembly from case by pushing rearward and removing from inside case. Remove lock plate retaining bolt from countershaft and reverse gear idler shaft. Remove lock plate.

NOTE: **Input shaft may be removed through front bearing bore on Jeep 6-cylinder models.**

4) Use brass drift to drive countershaft toward rear of case until front end of shaft is approximately even with inside of case. Insert dummy shaft 1" in diameter by 10" long in countershaft bore. Drive countershaft out rear of case, keeping tool in contact with shaft at all times. Remove bearings and washers that may have fallen into case. Remove reverse idler gear shaft and remove gear assembly from case.

NOTE: **On Ford applications, it may be necessary to remove reverse idler shaft and gear prior to removal of countershaft assembly.**

CLEANING & INSPECTION

1) All parts should be thoroughly cleaned in solvent and air dried. If any transmission gear requires replacement, also replace gear with which it meshes. Replace gaskets, oil seals and snap rings.

2) Inspect transmission case for cracks, worn or scored bearing bosses. Examine bearings for cracked races, excessive wear and improper fit in case bores. Inspect gear teeth for cracks or chips. Check countershaft and reverse idler shaft for pitting, wear, scores, nicks, cracks and flat spots. Replace shafts if severely worn or damaged. Replace parts as required.

COMPONENT DISASSEMBLY & REASSEMBLY

MAINSHAFT
Disassembly
1) Scribe alignment marks on mainshaft splines and synchronizer hub for reassembly. Remove pilot bearing spacer from front of mainshaft, if equipped. Remove 3rd-4th synchronizer snap ring from mainshaft.

2) Remove 3rd-4th synchronizer assembly and 3rd gear from mainshaft. Check end play of 2nd gear, it should be .005-.024" (.127-.609 mm). End play is controlled by the thickness of the snap rings. Remove 1st-2nd gear snap ring from mainshaft. Slide 1st-2nd gear synchronizer assembly from mainshaft.

3) Move 2nd gear rearward to gain clearance and remove snap ring. Slide 2nd gear off mainshaft. Punch alignment marks on synchronizer clutch hubs and sleeves for reassembly.

4) Remove insert springs and shift plates from 3rd-4th gear synchronizer assembly. Separate sleeve and hub. Mark position of insert spring and plates for reassembly.

5) Place 1st-2nd gear synchronizer assembly on bench with shift fork groove facing upward. Wrap a towel around sleeve, to avoid losing shift plate lock balls, and separate sleeve and hub. Remove towel and remove lock balls, springs, and shift plates.
Reassembly
1) Use 3rd-4th gear clutch hub as a guide for reassembling 1st-2nd gear synchronizer assembly. Place 3rd-4th gear synchronizer hub on work bench. Position 1st-2nd clutch sleeve over hub with shift groove facing downward.

NOTE: **Coat all parts with petroleum jelly prior to reassembly.**

2) Align marks made during disassembly and position 1st-2nd synchronizer hub in sleeve with lock ball holes facing upward. Insert shift plates in hub slots.

BORG-WARNER 4-SPEED MODEL T-18 & T-18A (Cont.)

Fig. 1: *Exploded View of Warner Model T-18A 4-Speed Transmission (Jeep Model Shown, Ford Model Similar)*

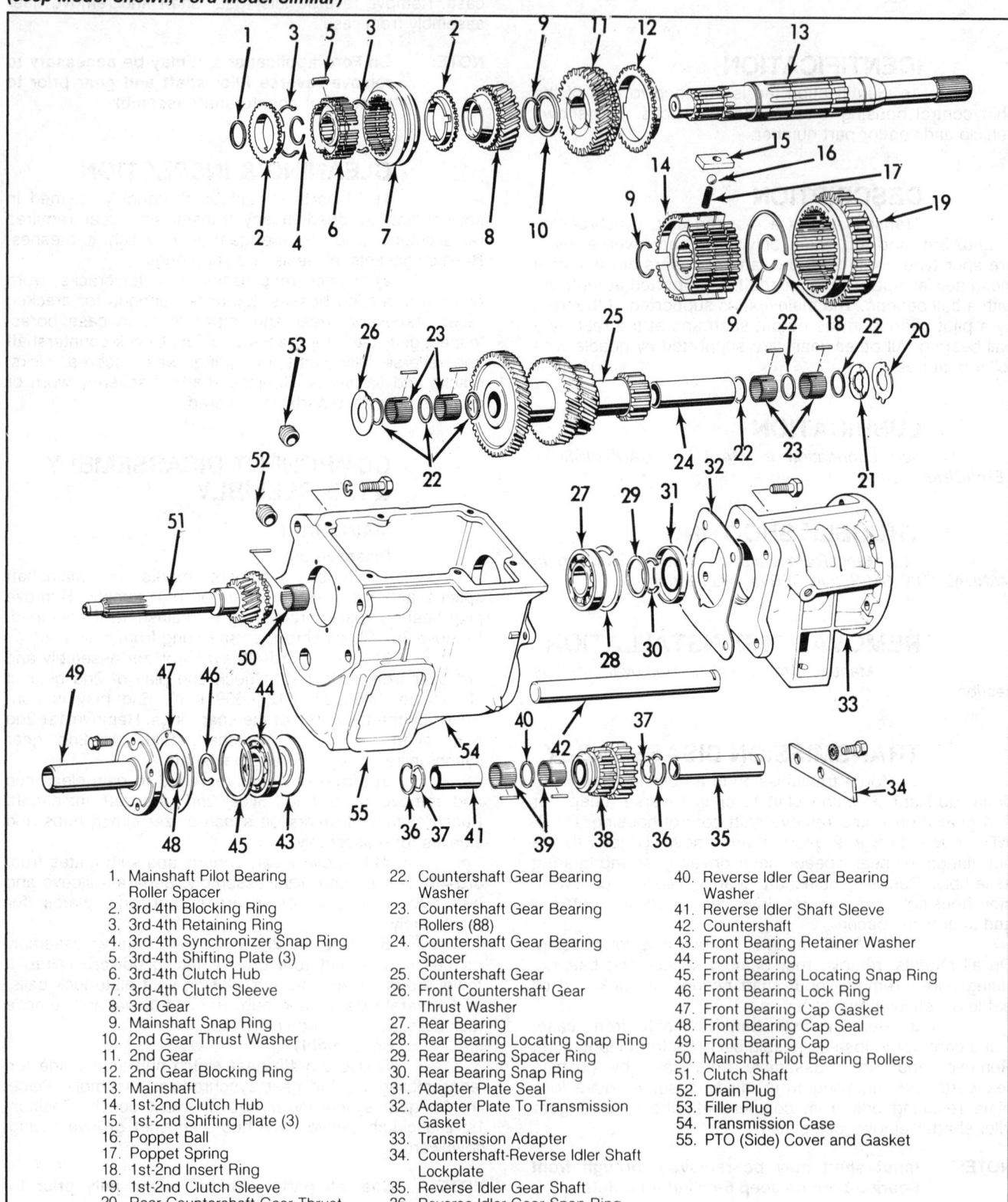

1. Mainshaft Pilot Bearing Roller Spacer
2. 3rd-4th Blocking Ring
3. 3rd-4th Retaining Ring
4. 3rd-4th Synchronizer Snap Ring
5. 3rd-4th Shifting Plate (3)
6. 3rd-4th Clutch Hub
7. 3rd-4th Clutch Sleeve
8. 3rd Gear
9. Mainshaft Snap Ring
10. 2nd Gear Thrust Washer
11. 2nd Gear
12. 2nd Gear Blocking Ring
13. Mainshaft
14. 1st-2nd Clutch Hub
15. 1st-2nd Shifting Plate (3)
16. Poppet Ball
17. Poppet Spring
18. 1st-2nd Insert Ring
19. 1st-2nd Clutch Sleeve
20. Rear Countershaft Gear Thrust Washer (Steel)
21. Rear Countershaft Gear Thrust Washer (Steel-Backed Bronze)
22. Countershaft Gear Bearing Washer
23. Countershaft Gear Bearing Rollers (88)
24. Countershaft Gear Bearing Spacer
25. Countershaft Gear
26. Front Countershaft Gear Thrust Washer
27. Rear Bearing
28. Rear Bearing Locating Snap Ring
29. Rear Bearing Spacer Ring
30. Rear Bearing Snap Ring
31. Adapter Plate Seal
32. Adapter Plate To Transmission Gasket
33. Transmission Adapter
34. Countershaft-Reverse Idler Shaft Lockplate
35. Reverse Idler Gear Shaft
36. Reverse Idler Gear Snap Ring
37. Reverse Idler Gear Thrust Washer
38. Reverse Idler Gear
39. Reverse Idler Gear Bearing Rollers (74)
40. Reverse Idler Gear Bearing Washer
41. Reverse Idler Shaft Sleeve
42. Countershaft
43. Front Bearing Retainer Washer
44. Front Bearing
45. Front Bearing Locating Snap Ring
46. Front Bearing Lock Ring
47. Front Bearing Cap Gasket
48. Front Bearing Cap Seal
49. Front Bearing Cap
50. Mainshaft Pilot Bearing Rollers
51. Clutch Shaft
52. Drain Plug
53. Filler Plug
54. Transmission Case
55. PTO (Side) Cover and Gasket

BORG-WARNER 4-SPEED MODEL T-18 & T-18A (Cont.)

Fig. 2: Assembling 1st-2nd Gear Synchronizer

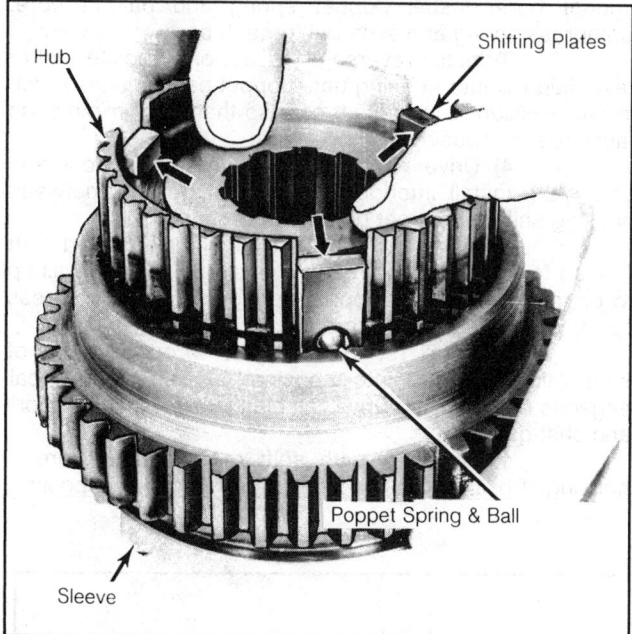

Position ball on poppet spring and compress ball & spring.

3) Install spring through shift plate. Compress spring and lock ball while pressing on shift plate until ball is held in position by synchronizer sleeve.

4) Repeat procedure until all shift plates, springs and lock balls are installed. Press down on hub and pull up on sleeve to complete assembly.

5) Align punch marks on 3rd-4th gear synchronizer clutch hub and synchronizer sleeve made during disassembly. Insert 3 shift plates in hub slots. Install retaining ring so that one end of each ring is held in the same shift plate.

Fig. 3: Assembling 3rd-4th Gear Synchronizer

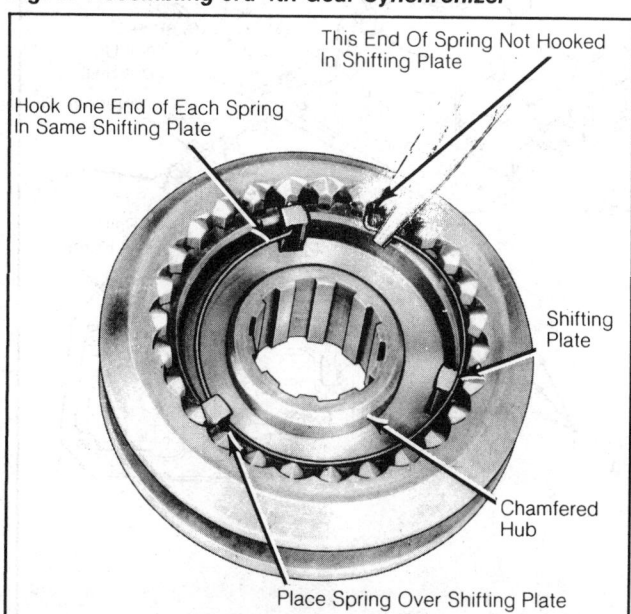

Chamfered side of hub must face front of mainshaft.

6) Slide 2nd gear and thrust washer on front of mainshaft, making sure step bore of thrust washer is toward front. Install snap ring, positioning step bore of thrust washer over snap ring.

7) From rear of mainshaft, install 2nd gear rear snap ring, blocking ring, 1st-2nd gear synchronizer

Fig. 4: Installing 1st-2nd Gear Synchronizer Snap Ring

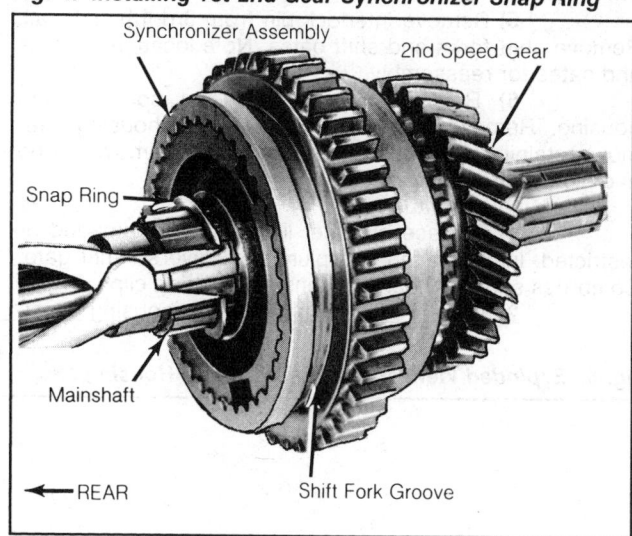

Shift fork groove must face rear of mainshaft.

assembly and snap ring. Make sure 1st-2nd gear synchronizer shift fork groove faces rear of mainshaft.

8) Install 3rd gear, blocking ring, 3rd-4th synchronizer assembly, snap ring, and main drive gear roller bearing thrust washer. Make sure 3rd-4th gear synchronizer chamfered side of hub is facing front of mainshaft.

Fig. 5: Installing 3rd-4th Gear Synchronizer Snap Ring

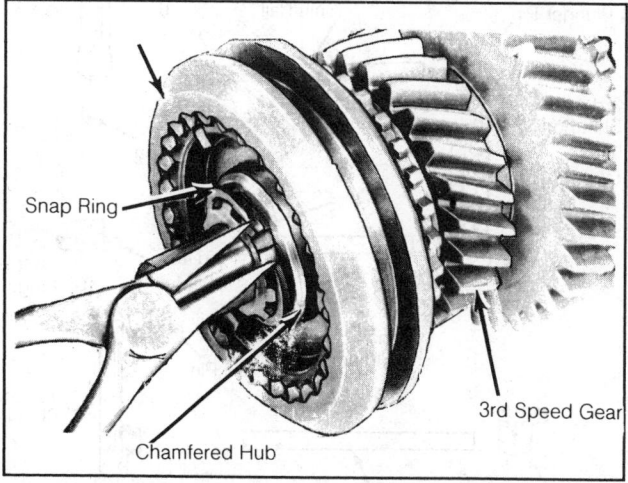

Chamfered side of hub must face mainshaft.

GEAR SHIFT CONTROL HOUSING
Disassembly

1) Unscrew shift lever cap. Remove cap, gasket, if equipped, spring seat, spring and shift lever as an assembly. Remove shift lever locating pins from housing.

Manual Transmissions

BORG-WARNER 4-SPEED MODEL T-18 & T-18A (Cont.)

2) Place housing in a vise with shift forks facing upward. Remove back-up light switch. Using a hammer and a punch, remove shift rail bore plugs.

3) Move shift rails to neutral position. Drive out roll pins securing shift gates to shift rails.

4) Place tape over poppet ball holes to prevent losing balls or springs during disassembly. Drive shift rails out of housing using a hammer and a punch.

5) Remove interlock pin from 3rd-4th shift rail. Remove shift forks and shift gates. Note location of forks and gates for reassembly.

6) Remove poppet balls and springs from housing. Remove interlock plungers from housing. Remove retaining clip from reverse shift gate. Remove spring and plunger from gate.

Reassembly

1) Replace breather in housing if damaged or restricted. Install spring and plunger in reverse shift gate. Compress spring by hand and install retaining clip.

2) Install reverse shift rail into housing. Posi-

tion reverse shift fork on rail. Slide rail up to shift rail poppet bore. Install poppet spring and ball in bore. Compress spring and slide rail through bore.

3) Install reverse shift gate on opposite end of rail. Slide rail into housing until poppet ball engages notch in rail. Position reverse shift gate so that plunger pin boss faces rear of housing.

4) Drive roll pins into reverse shift fork and shift gate. Install interlock plungers in pockets between housing shift rail poppet bores.

5) Install 1st-2nd shift rail. Install 1st-2nd shift fork so fork offset faces rear of housing. Slide shift rail up to poppet bore. Install poppet spring and ball. Compress spring and slide shift rail through bore.

6) Install 1st-2nd shift gate on opposite end of shift rail. Slide rail into housing so that poppet ball engages notch in rail. Drive roll pins into 1st-2nd shift fork and shift gate.

7) Install 3rd-4th shift rail in center bore in housing. Position 3rd-4th shift gate on rail and position

Fig. 6: Exploded View of Gear Shift Control Housing

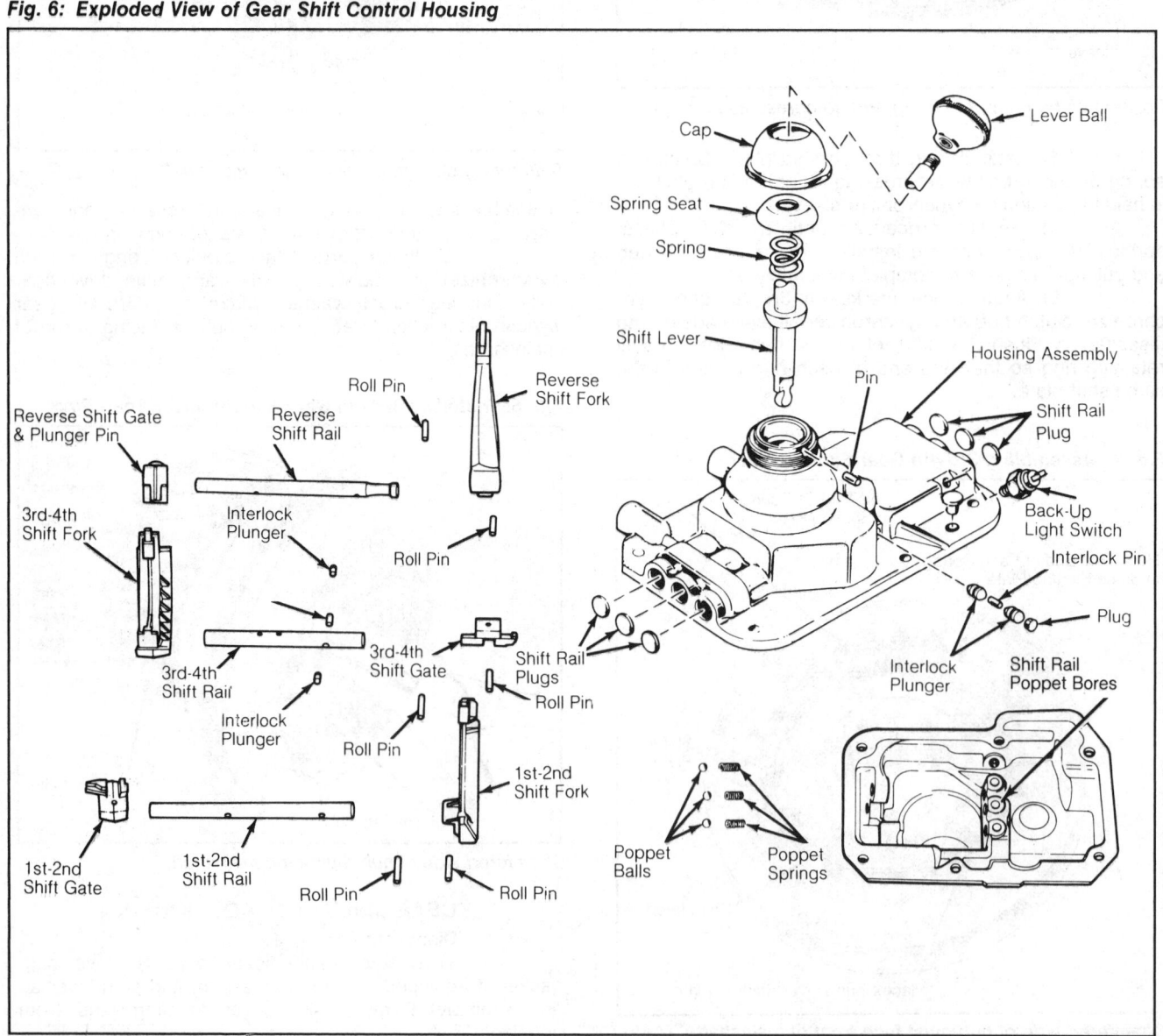

BORG-WARNER 4-SPEED MODEL T-18 & T-18A (Cont.)

gate so that flat tang on gate faces front of housing.

8) Apply petroleum jelly to interlock pin and install pin in 3rd-4th shift rail pin bore. Install 3rd-4th poppet spring and ball in bore. Compress spring and slide shift rail through bore.

9) Position 3rd-4th shift fork on rail. Slide rail into housing until poppet ball engages notch in rail. Drive roll pins into shift fork and shift rail. Install shift rail bore plugs. Be sure 3rd-4th shift gate roll pin is installed so it is flush with bottom of shift gate notch.

COUNTERGEAR & REVERSE IDLER GEAR

Disassembly

Remove arbor tool from countergear. Remove roller bearings, thrust washers and spacer from countergear. Remove snap rings from reverse idler gear. Tap out thrust washer, roller bearings, center spacer and sleeve.

Reassembly

1) Lubricate all components with transmission lubricant. Place snap ring in one end of reverse idler gear. Position idler gear with snap ring down. Insert thrust washer into gear against snap ring.

2) Place sleeve into gear bore and insert 37 roller bearings. Install spacer and 37 more roller bearings. Install second thrust washer and snap ring.

3) Install sleeve and arbor into countergear. Place one spacer ring over arbor against spacer sleeve. Insert 22 roller bearings and slide into place second spacer ring. Insert 22 more roller bearings and third spacer ring. Repeat same operation at opposite end of countergear. Leave arbor installed in gear.

TRANSMISSION REASSEMBLY

NOTE: Lubricate all components with transmission lubricant before assembly.

1) Place both countergear thrust washers in case. Place countergear into position, with arbor still installed. Care must be taken not to move thrust washers or roller bearings out of position.

2) Carefully drive countergear shaft into place while driving arbor shaft out rear of transmission case. Make sure slot in countergear shaft is positioned so that it can be engaged by retaining plate.

3) Check countergear end play. It may be necessary to remove countergear and install thicker or thinner snap rings to obtain correct countergear end play.

4) Place reverse idler gear in position in case, larger gear end must face rear of case. Install reverse idler shaft from rear of case. Make sure shaft is positioned so that slot can be engaged by retaining plate. Install countershaft and reverse idler gear shaft retaining plate.

5) Install the 22 pilot roller bearings in end of input shaft. Use grease to hold bearings in place. Place input shaft in case. Place 4th gear synchronizer blocking ring on input shaft. Install mainshaft in transmission case, taking care not to move pilot bearings out of position.

6) Install input shaft oil baffle. Temporarily install front bearing cap using dummy bearing on transmission input shaft to hold shaft in place while installing mainshaft bearing. Install snap ring on mainshaft bearing

and drive bearing into case until snap ring is seated.

7) Remove dummy bearing tool. Install input shaft bearing washer, with dished side of washer facing mainshaft. Install bearing and snap ring on shaft. Drive bearing into place against input shaft gear. Avoid wedging blocking ring on its mating tapered surface during front bearing installation.

8) Install thickest of 4 available snap rings in input shaft groove. Pull input shaft bearing out of case just far enough to install bearing locating ring. Install bearing retainer with new gasket and tighten bolts to specification.

9) On 4-WD models, install rear oil seal in transfer case adapter. Lip of seal must face toward transfer case. Install adapter plate with new gasket. Use nonhardening sealer on bolts. Install adapter housing and tighten to specification.

10) On 2-WD models, install speedometer drive gear and spacer, if equipped, over mainshaft lock ball. Install snap ring. Install rear bearing retainer or extension housing with new gasket. Tighten bolts to specification.

11) On all models, lock transmission in 2 gears. On 2-WD models, install "U" joint flange, and tighten nut to specification. On 4-WD models, install transfer case drive gear spacer, drive gear, flat washer and lock nut. Tighten nut to specification. Use nonhardening sealer on all case and cover bolts.

12) Move synchronizer sleeves to neutral position. Install power take-off (side) cover and gasket, if removed. Install new shift housing gasket on transmission. Place shift housing into position, making sure that shift forks engage grooves in synchronizing hubs. Install bolts and tighten to specification. Fill transmission to proper level with specified lubricant and shift through all gears to check operation.

TIGHTENING SPECIFICATIONS

Application	Ft. Lbs. (N.m)
Input Shaft Bearing Retainer	10-15 (14-20)
Shift Housing-to-Case	12 (16)
"U" Joint Flange Nut (Ford)	75-110 (102-149)
Transfer Case Gear Nut (Jeep)	150 (203)
Transfer Case Adapter-to-Case (Jeep)	30 (41)
PTO Cover Bolts	
Ford	25-35 (34-47)
Jeep	12 (16)
Mainshaft Rear Retainer Bolts	
3/8"	25-35 (34-47)
1/2"	40-50 (54-67)
Countershaft Rear Retainer	25-35 (34-47)

Manual Transmissions

BORG-WARNER 4-SPEED MODEL T19B & T19D

F250/350 HD (2WD &4WD)

IDENTIFICATION

The manual transmissions have a service identification tag to identify transmissions for servicing. The tag is found attached to right front side of case. Transmission code for the 4-speed transmission is "P". See Fig. 1.

Fig. 1: Transmission Identification Tag

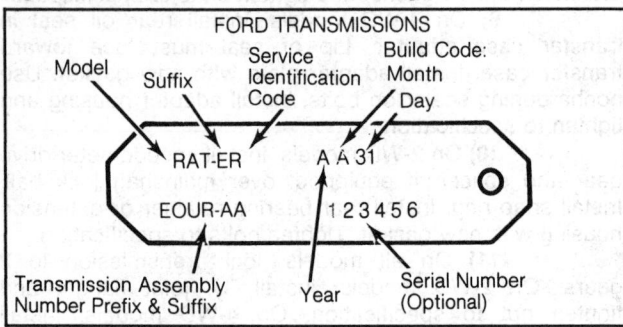

Tag is found at right front side of transmission.

DESCRIPTION

The 4-speed fully synchronized T19B & D transmissions are equipped with a center, floor mounted gear shift lever. The reverse and 1st, 2nd, 3rd, and 4th gears are helical cut for quiet running. The input shaft is supported by a ball bearing. Front end of the output shaft is supported by a pilot bearing installed in the input shaft. The rear end of the output shaft is supported by a ball bearing. The ball bearing and shaft are retained in the case by a snap ring.

LUBRICATION & ADJUSTMENT

See the appropriate article in MANUAL TRANS-MISSION SERVICING Section.

REMOVAL & INSTALLATION

See the appropriate article in MANUAL TRANS-MISSION REMOVAL Section.

SERVICE (IN VEHICLE)

GEAR SHIFT LEVER

NOTE: Remove shift ball only if shift ball, boot, or lever is to be replaced. If either the ball, boot, or lever is not being replaced, remove the ball, boot, and lever as an assembly.

Removal

1) Remove plastic insert from shift ball. Warm ball with heat gun to 140-160°F (60-82°C), knock ball off lever with a block of wood and a hammer, taking care not to damage finish on shift lever.

2) Remove rubber boot and floor pan cover. Shift transmission into 2nd gear, remove lock pin, and shift lever from shift lever housing.

Installation

1) Install shift lever in shifter housing, making sure that slot in lever aligns with tab in housing. Install lock pin. Install rubber boot and floor pan cover.

2) Warm ball with heat gun to 140-180°F (60-82°C) and tap ball on lever with a 7/16" socket and mallet. Install plastic shift pattern insert.

TRANSMISSION DISASSEMBLY

1) Install transmission in bench mounted holding fixture. Remove drain plug and drain lubricant from transmission. Remove bolt retaining gear shift housing to case and remove housing.

2) Lock transmission in two gears and remove U-joint flange and oil seal. Remove speedometer driven gear and bearing assembly. Remove output shaft bearing retainer or extension housing.

3) Remove speedometer drive gear snap ring retainer. Slide drive gear off output shaft. Remove output shaft bearing snap ring from output shaft and snap ring from bearing. Remove bearing spacer.

4) Install remover tube (T75l-7025-B) on output shaft and over bearing. Remove output shaft bearing. Remove input shaft bearing retainer. Remove input shaft bearing snap ring from input shaft and snap ring from bearing.

5) Install remover tube on input shaft and over input shaft bearing. Remove input shaft bearing. Remove input shaft oil baffle. The baffle is installed in an offset position away from bearing.

6) Remove roll pin from reverse shifter arm pivot. Remove pivot from shifter arm and case. Lift shifter arm and shoe assembly out of case by prying with screw driver.

7) Remove input shaft and synchronizer blocking ring. Remove washer and needle bearings. Remove output shaft and gear assemblies from case. Remove input shaft (with flat facing upward) assembly from case. DO NOT lose the 22 pilot bearing rollers from inner end of shaft.

8) Use dummy countershaft (T83T-7111-B) to drive out countershaft (from the front). Keep dummy shaft in contact with countershaft to avoid dropping rollers. The dummy shaft should be 9.379-9.380" (238.23-238.25 mm) long and 1.133-1.135" (28.78-28.83 mm) in diameter.

9) Remove countershaft and cluster gear. Make sure front and rear thrust washers are removed from case. Be careful not to lose any rollers.

10) Remove idler shaft (from front of transmission) using shaft remover (T50T-7140-C) and slide hammer. Remove reverse idler gear, and thrust washers, being careful not to lose any rollers.

CLEANING & INSPECTION

1) Wash all parts in cleaning solvent and dry with compressed air (except bearings). Let bearings air dry in clean shop cloth. Inspect transmission case for cracks, damaged bearing bores, and/or threads.

2) Remove all small nicks or burrs from front and/or rear of case. Check bearings for roughness by slowly turning race by hand.

3) Inspect needle bearing rollers, shafts, and washers for wear and/or damage. Check all other parts

BORG-WARNER 4-SPEED MODEL T19B & T19D (Cont.)

Fig. 2: *Exploded View of Borg-Warner T19B 4-Speed Transmission*

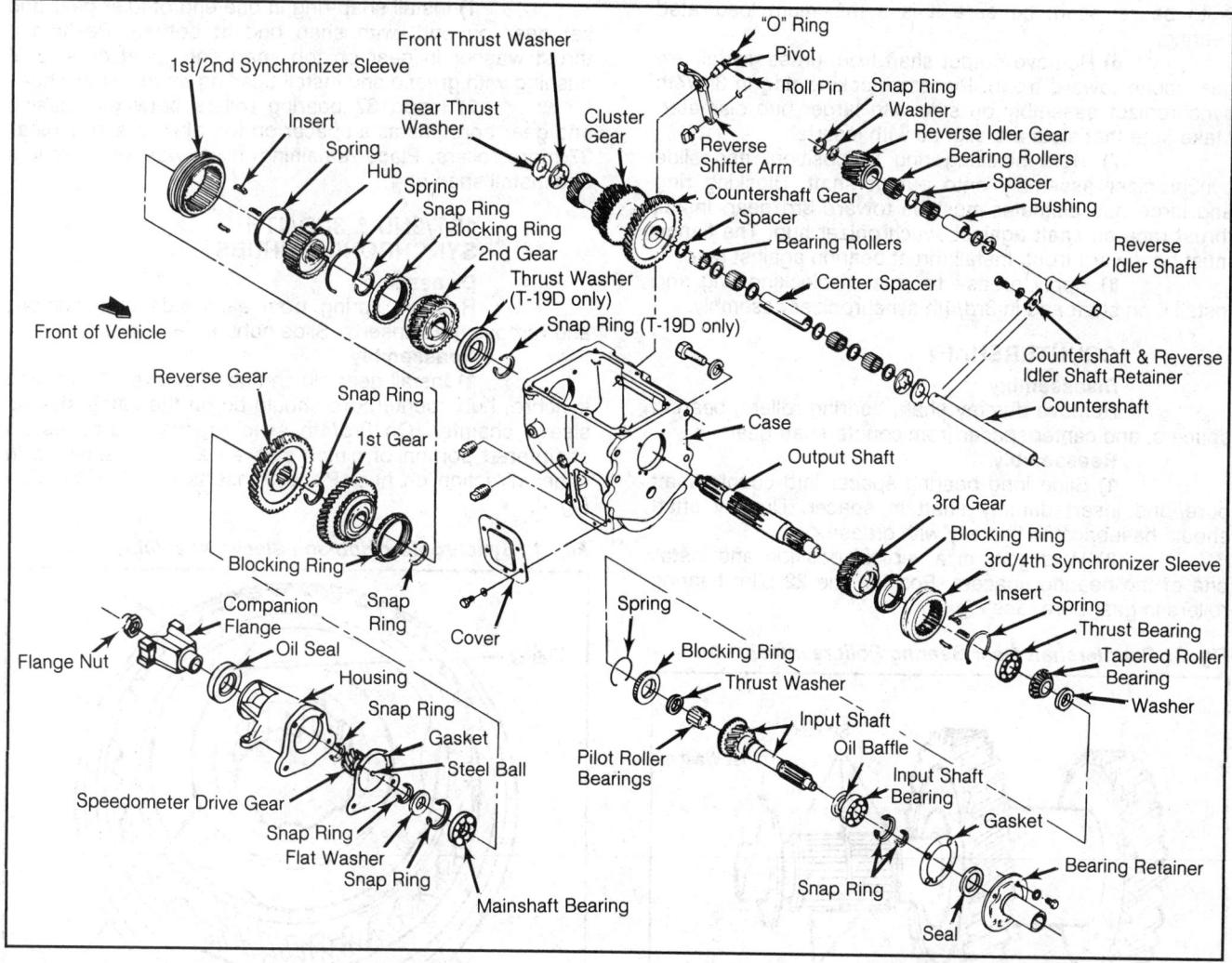

for wear, damage, chipped, and/or broken teeth. Replace parts as necessary.

COMPONENT DISASSEMBLY & REASSEMBLY

INPUT SHAFT

Disassembly

Remove thrust spacer and pilot rollers from gear bore. Using a puller, remove input shaft ball bearing.

Reassembly

Press ball bearing and oil baffle onto input shaft and against gear. Coat bore of gear with grease, and place 17 pilot rollers in bore. Install thrust spacer in bore against rollers. Use grease to hold it in position.

OUTPUT SHAFT

Disassembly

1) Remove snap ring. Slide 3rd/4th synchronizer assembly, blocking ring, and 3rd gear off shaft. Place output shaft in an arbor press and press reverse gear off shaft or pull reverse gear off shaft with puller.

2) Remove 1st gear selective snap ring and slide 1st gear off output shaft. Remove 1st/2nd gear synchronizer snap ring. Slide synchronizer off shaft. Remove snap ring from rear of 2nd gear.

3) Remove blocking ring, sunchronizer gear, thrust washer, and remaining snap ring from output shaft.

Reassembly

1) Install 2nd gear thrust washer and snap ring on output shaft. Hold shaft in a vertical position with front of shaft down, and slide 2nd gear onto shaft (gear cone toward rear). Install selective snap ring of .092-.094" (2.34-2.39 mm) onto output shaft at rear of 2nd gear.

2) Place a blocking ring in 1st/2nd synchronizer assembly next to side of hub with counterbore. Make sure that ring slots are aligned with insert.

3) Hold blocking ring in 1st/2nd synchronizer assembly (with ring slots aligned with inserts) on side with hub counterbore and install assembly on output shaft. The hub counterbore must be toward 2nd gear. Install thickest selective snap ring that can be fit into groove.

4) Install second blocking ring in synchronizer assembly, making sure that ring slots are aligned with inserts. Install 1st gear (coned portion toward 1st/2nd synchronizer assembly) and .101-.103" (2.57-2.61 mm) thick snap ring on shaft.

5) Mount output shaft in a press and press reverse gear (longer hub toward 1st gear) on shaft. Press

BORG-WARNER 4-SPEED MODEL T19B & T19D (Cont.)

rear bearing cone on output shaft. If output shaft bearing is to be replaced, be sure it is a maximum load-rated bearing.

6) Remove output shaft from press. Install 3rd gear (cone toward front). Place a blocking ring in 3rd/4th synchronizer assembly on side with larger hub diameter. Make sure that slots are aligned with inserts.

7) Hold blocking ring in position, and slide synchronizer assembly onto output shaft. Blocking ring and large hub diameter must be toward 3rd gear. Install thrust race on shaft against synchronizer hub. The flange must be toward front. Install thrust bearing against race.

8) Apply grease to face of blocking ring and install it on shaft and in 3rd/4th synchronizer assembly.

COUNTERSHAFT

Disassembly

Remove dummy shaft, bearing rollers, bearing spacers, and center spacer from countershaft gear.

Reassembly

1) Slide long bearing spacer into countershaft bore and insert dummy shaft in spacer. Dummy shaft should be lubricated liberally with grease.

2) Hold gear in a vertical position and install one of the bearing spacers. Position the 22 pilot bearing rollers in gear bore. See Fig. 3.

Fig. 3: Countershaft Gear Bearing Rollers Installation

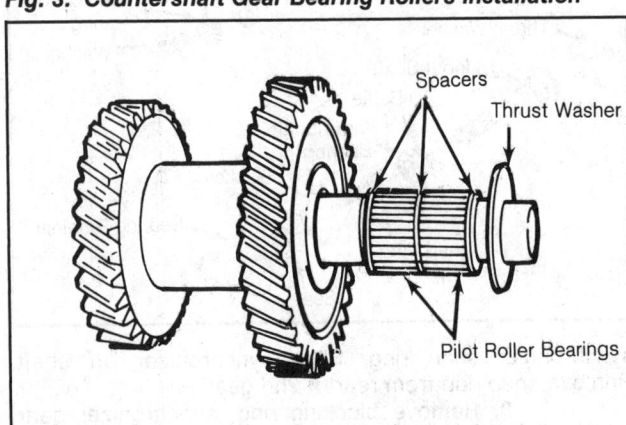

Spacers

Thrust Washer

Pilot Roller Bearings

Install 22 rollers, a spacer, and 22 more rollers.

3) Place a spacer on top of rollers and install 22 pilot bearing rollers and another spacer. Coat face of large thrust washer with grease.

4) Hold a large thrust washer against the end of countershaft gear to prevent rollers from dropping out and turn assembly over. Install rollers, spacers, and thrust washer in the other end of gear.

REVERSE IDLER GEAR

Disassembly

1) Check idler gear roller bearings for roughness by holding bushing to prevent its turning while rotating gear. The gear should then be installed on shaft to check for roughness between shaft and bushing.

2) If gear turns freely and smoothly, disassembly of unit is not necessary. If any roughness is noticed, disassemble unit by removing snap ring from one end of gear.

3) Remove idler gear bearing rollers, thrust washers, bearing spacer, bushing, and remaining snap ring from gear.

Reassembly

1) Install snap ring in one end of idler gear and set gear on end, with snap ring at bottom. Position a thrust washer in gear on top snap ring. Coat outside of bushing with grease and install bushing on top of washer.

2) Insert 37 bearing rollers between bushing and gear bore. Install a spacer on top of rollers and install 37 more rollers. Place remaining thrust washer on rollers and install snap ring.

1ST/2ND & 3RD/4TH SYNCHRONIZER HUBS

Disassembly

Remove spring from each side of assembly, and remove the 3 inserts. Slide hub out of sleeve.

Reassembly

1) Install gear clutch hub in sleeve. On 1st/2nd synchro, hub counterbore should be on the same side as sleeve chamfer. On 3rd/4th synchro, the 2 grooves on chamfered portion of clutch sleeve can be assembled in either direction on hub. Place 3 inserts in hub slots. *See Fig. 4.*

Fig. 4: Synchronizer Hub and Sleeve Assembly

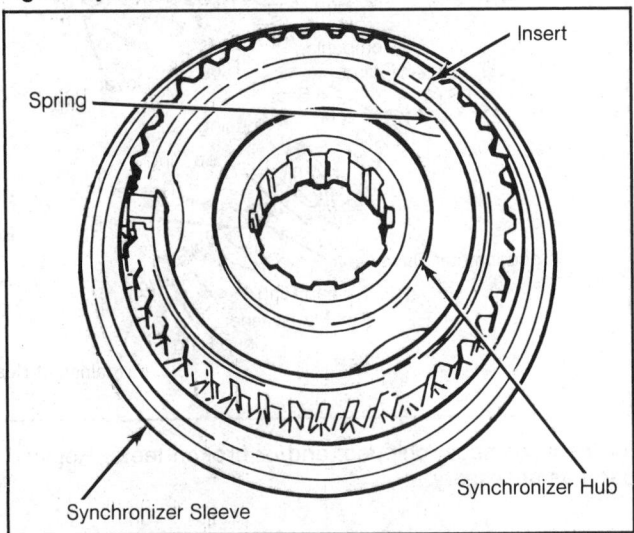

Insert

Spring

Synchronizer Sleeve

Synchronizer Hub

Hub counterbore should be on the side as sleeve chamfer.

2) Hook end of spring under an insert and position spring around hub and under each inserts. Turn assembly over and hook end of second spring over the other end of insert used for hooking first spring.

3) Position spring around hub and under each insert, but on opposite direction of first spring.

GEAR SHIFT HOUSING

Disassembly

1) Remove gear shift lever housing cap and lift lever out of housing. Be sure all shafts are in neutral before disassembly. Remove spring pins from shift forks and shift rail ends. Remove expansion plugs from ends of housing.

2) Tap shift rails out of housing while holding one hand over holes in housing to prevent loss of poppet springs and balls. Remove shift rail ends and forks. Lift the 2 shaft interlock plungers and pin out of housing.

3) To disassemble reverse shift rail end, remove circlip to release plunger and spring. Remove cotter pin, spring, and ball.

Fig. 5: Exploded View of Gear Shift Housing and Shift Rail Locations

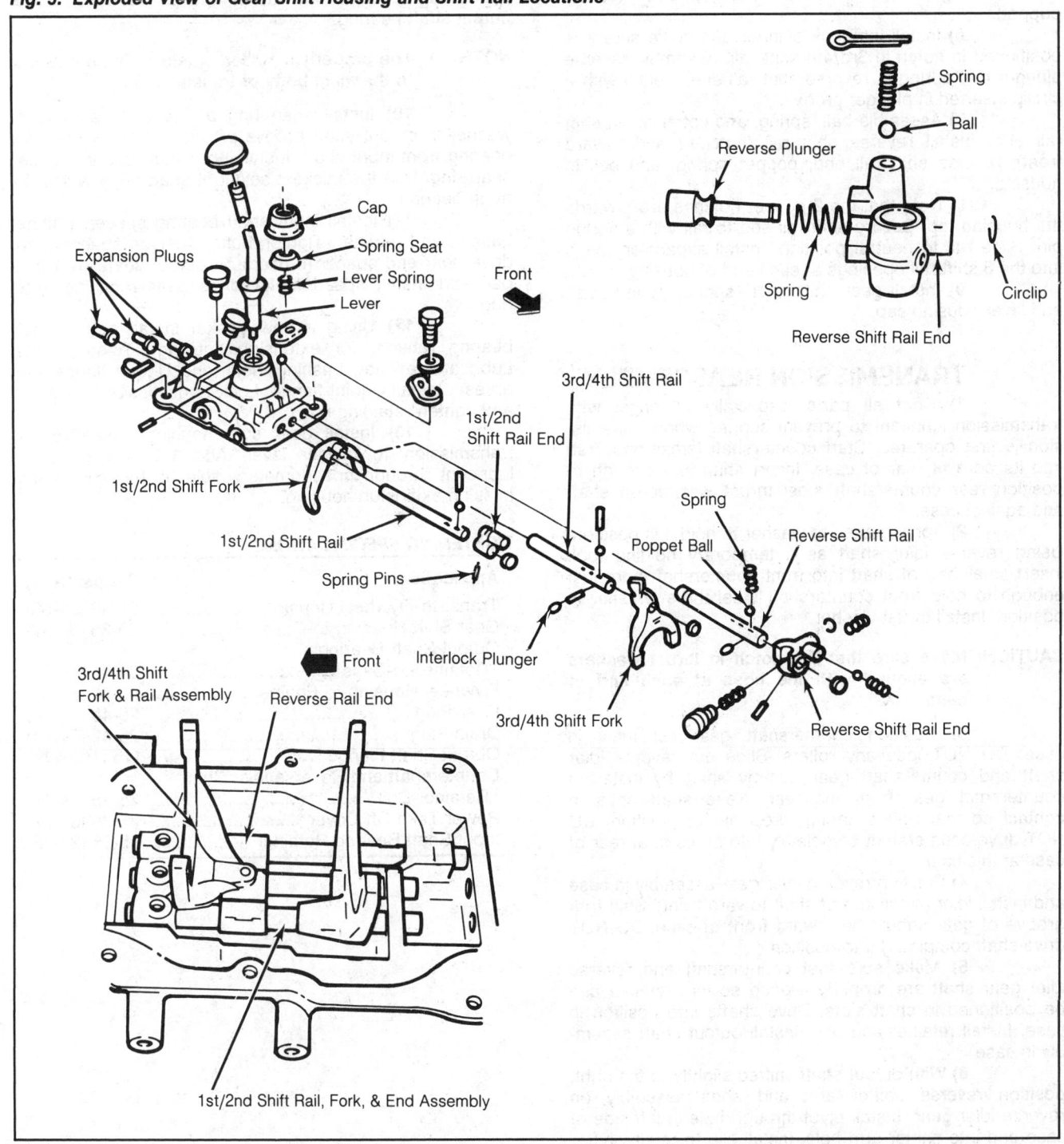

Reassembly

1) Position notched end of 1st/2nd shift rail through rear bore of housing. Slide 1st/2nd shift fork (use outer hole) onto shift rail. DO NOT slide shaft into its bore at front end at this time.

2) The 3 poppet notches should face the top of housing. Slide 1st/2nd shift rail end into rail. Place poppet spring and ball in hole at front of cover. Depress ball and spring, and slide rail into its bore over ball.

3) Drive a spring pin through hole in 1st/2nd shift rail end and into hole in rail. Secure shift fork to rail with spring pin. Slide shift rail to its neutral position (center poppet).

4) Install interlock plunger in housing making sure that end of plunger is in the side notch of 1st/2nd shift rail. Install 3rd/4th shift rail (notched end toward front) in center bore of housing, and assemble shift fork, interlock pin, and poppet spring and ball.

5) Note that 3rd/4th shift rail passes through a second hole in 1st/2nd shift fork and that poppet notches are toward housing top. Secure 3rd/4th shift fork to rail

BORG-WARNER 4-SPEED MODEL T19B & T19D (Cont.)

with a spring pin. Slide rail to neutral position (center poppet).

6) Install interlock plunger and make sure it is positioned in notch in 3rd/4th shift rail. Assemble reverse plunger and spring in reverse shift rail end. Retain with a circlip inserted in plunger groove.

7) Assemble ball, spring, and cotter pin in shift rail end. Install reverse shift rail (notched end toward front), reverse shift rail end, poppet spring, and ball in housing.

8) Note that the 2 poppet notches are towards the housing top. Secure shift rail end to rail with a spring pin. Slide rail to neutral position. Install expansion plugs into the 3 shift rail openings at each end of housing.

9) Install gear shift lever, spring, spring seat, and lever housing cap.

TRANSMISSION REASSEMBLY

1) Coat all parts, especially bearings, with transmission lubricant to prevent scoring when transmission is first operated. Start countershaft (small end first) into its bore at rear of case. Insert shaft just enough to position rear countershaft steel thrust washer on shaft and against case.

2) Apply grease to washer to hold it in position. Using reverse idler shaft as a temporary holding tool, insert small end of shaft into front countershaft bore just enough to hold front countershaft steel thrust washer in position. Install thrust washer.

CAUTION: Make sure that the notch in thrust washers are aligned with the boss at each end of case.

3) Position countershaft gear assembly in case. DO NOT lose any rollers. Slide out reverse idler shaft and countershaft gear dummy shaft by installing countershaft gear from the rear. Keep shaft ends in contact so that rollers cannot drop out of position. DO NOT drive countershaft completely into press fit at rear of case at this time.

4) Position reverse idler gear assembly in case and install idler (small end of shaft toward front). Shift fork groove of gear should be toward front of case. DO NOT drive shaft completely into position.

5) Make sure that countershaft and reverse idler gear shaft are properly aligned so that retainer can be positioned in shaft slots. Drive shafts into position in case. Install retainer and bolt. Install output shaft assembly in case.

6) With output shaft shifted slightly to the right, position reverse shifter arm and shoe assembly on reverse idler gear. Install pivot through hole in left side of case and into shifter arm hole. Install clip to retain shifter arm to pivot. Center output shaft to case bore.

7) Install input shaft through front bore with flats on shaft facing upwards. When past countershaft, turn input shaft so flats are facing downward. Guide input shaft onto output shaft. Install input shaft oil baffle.

8) Install dummy bearing tool (T75L-7025-Q) on transmission input shaft. This tool is necessary to keep input and output shafts in alignment when installing output shaft bearing.

9) Assemble locating snap ring to outer race of output shaft bearing in groove provided. Install output shaft bearing. Install flat washer against rearward face of output shaft bearing.

NOTE: The properly installed washer will be external to the main body of transmission.

10) Install snap ring at rearward surface of washer in output shaft groove provided. Remove dummy bearing from input shaft. Install input shaft bearing. Install snap ring. Use the thickest select fit snap rings which will fit on bearing.

11) Install input shaft bearing spacer, retainer gasket, and retainer. Tighten bolts. Position speedometer drive gear and spacer (if used) on output shaft, over lock ball and install speedometer drive gear retaining snap ring.

12) Using a new gasket install output shaft bearing retainer (or extension housing). Tighten bolts. Lubricate retainer, bushing, seal, and U-joint flange with grease. Install U-joint flange. Lock transmission in 2 gears and tighten retaining nut.

13) Install gear shift housing assembly. Fill transmission to proper level. Add 1/2 pint (1/4L) of lubricant through speedometer cable hole in rear transmission extension housing.

TIGHTENING SPECIFICATIONS

Application	Ft. Lbs. (N.m)
Trans.-to-Flywheel Housing	37-42 (51-56)
Gear Shift Housing-to-Case	25-35 (34-47)
Output Shaft Bearing Retainer-to-Case	34-45 (46-61)
Flywheel Housing-to-Engine	40-50 (55-67)
Filler Plug	25-40 (34-54)
Drain Plug	25-40 (34-54)
Output Shaft Flange Nut	75-115 (102-149)
Countershaft and Reverse Idler Shaft Retainer Bolt	25-35 (34-47)
Power Take Off Cover	25-35 (34-47)
Input Shaft Bearing Retainer	15-25 (21-33)

BORG-WARNER 4-SPEED MODEL T-176

**Jeep, All Models
(Exc. J-20 Trucks)**

IDENTIFICATION

Transmission identification tag showing Jeep part number is attached to transmission shift control housing by one of the mounting bolts.

DESCRIPTION

Transmission is a 4-speed unit, fully synchronized in all forward gears. All forward gears are constant mesh helical cut type and speed changes are accomplished through use of blocker type synchronizer assemblies. Input shaft and mainshaft are supported by ball bearings in front and rear of case. All other gears are supported by needle type roller bearings.

LUBRICATION

See the appropriate article in MANUAL TRANS-MISSION SERVICING Section.

TROUBLE SHOOTING

See Manual Transmission Trouble Shooting in MANUAL TRANSMISSION SERVICING section.

REMOVAL & INSTALLATION

See the appropriate article in MANUAL TRANS-MISSION REMOVAL Section.

TRANSMISSION DISASSEMBLY

NOTE: **The 2 shift control housing bolts are dowel type. Mark location of these bolts on housing for reassembly.**

1) Remove bolts attaching transfer case to transmission, and remove transfer case. Remove shift control housing assembly, if not already removed. Using arbor tool (J-29342), remove countershaft by tapping out rear of case. Let countergear lie at bottom of case.

2) Remove locating ring and retaining snap ring from rear bearing. Remove rear bearing using puller (J-25152). Punch alignment marks in front bearing retainer and case for reassembly. Remove front bearing retainer and gasket. Remove and discard front bearing retainer oil seal.

3) Remove locating ring and retaining snap ring from front bearing. Remove input shaft and front bearing using puller and adapter (J-25152 & J-29344). Remove 3rd-4th blocking ring from input shaft or synchronizer hub. Remove front bearing from input shaft using puller (J-25152). Remove mainshaft pilot bearing rollers from input shaft.

4) Remove mainshaft and geartrain assembly. Move 3rd-4th synchronizer sleeve rearward to 3rd gear position. Lift front end of shaft upward and remove mainshaft assembly from case. Remove countershaft

gear, arbor tool, thrust washers and any needle bearing rollers that may have fallen into case.

5) Tap reverse idler shaft out rear of case. Remove reverse idler gear and thrust washers from case. Remove needle bearings and bearing retainers from gear assembly. Remove sliding gear from idler gear noting position for reassembly.

Fig. 1: Removing Reverse Idler Gear Shaft

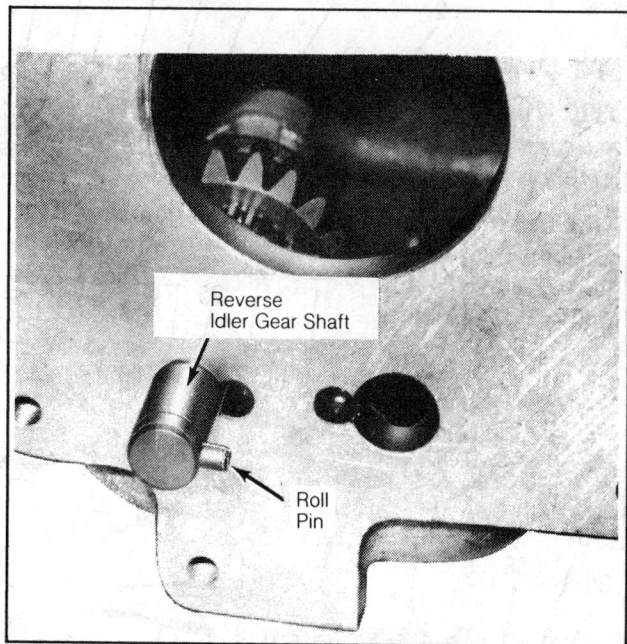

Tap gear out rear of case.

CLEANING & INSPECTION

1) Wash all parts in cleaning solvent. Dry all parts, except bearings, with compressed air. Let bearings air dry in clean shop cloth. Inspect transmission case for cracks, damaged bearing bores or damaged threads. Remove all small nicks or burrs from front or rear of case.

2) Check ball bearings for roughness by slowly turning race by hand. Inspect needle bearing rollers, shafts and washers for wear or damage. Check all other parts for wear, damage, chipped or broken teeth. Replace parts as necessary.

COMPONENT DISASSEMBLY & REASSEMBLY

MAINSHAFT ASSEMBLY

Disassembly

1) Mark sleeves and hubs for reassembly. Remove snap ring from front of mainshaft and slide 3rd-4th synchronizer assembly and 3rd gear from shaft. On 3rd-4th synchronizer, slide hub out of sleeve. Remove insert springs for reassembly.

2) Remove snap ring holding 2nd gear. Remove 2nd gear and blocking ring from shaft. Remove tabbed washer from mainshaft. Remove snap ring retaining 1st-2nd synchronizer hub. Remove hub, reverse gear

Manual Transmissions

BORG-WARNER 4-SPEED MODEL T-176 (Cont.)

Fig. 2: Disassembled View of Warner T-176 4-Speed Manual Transmission

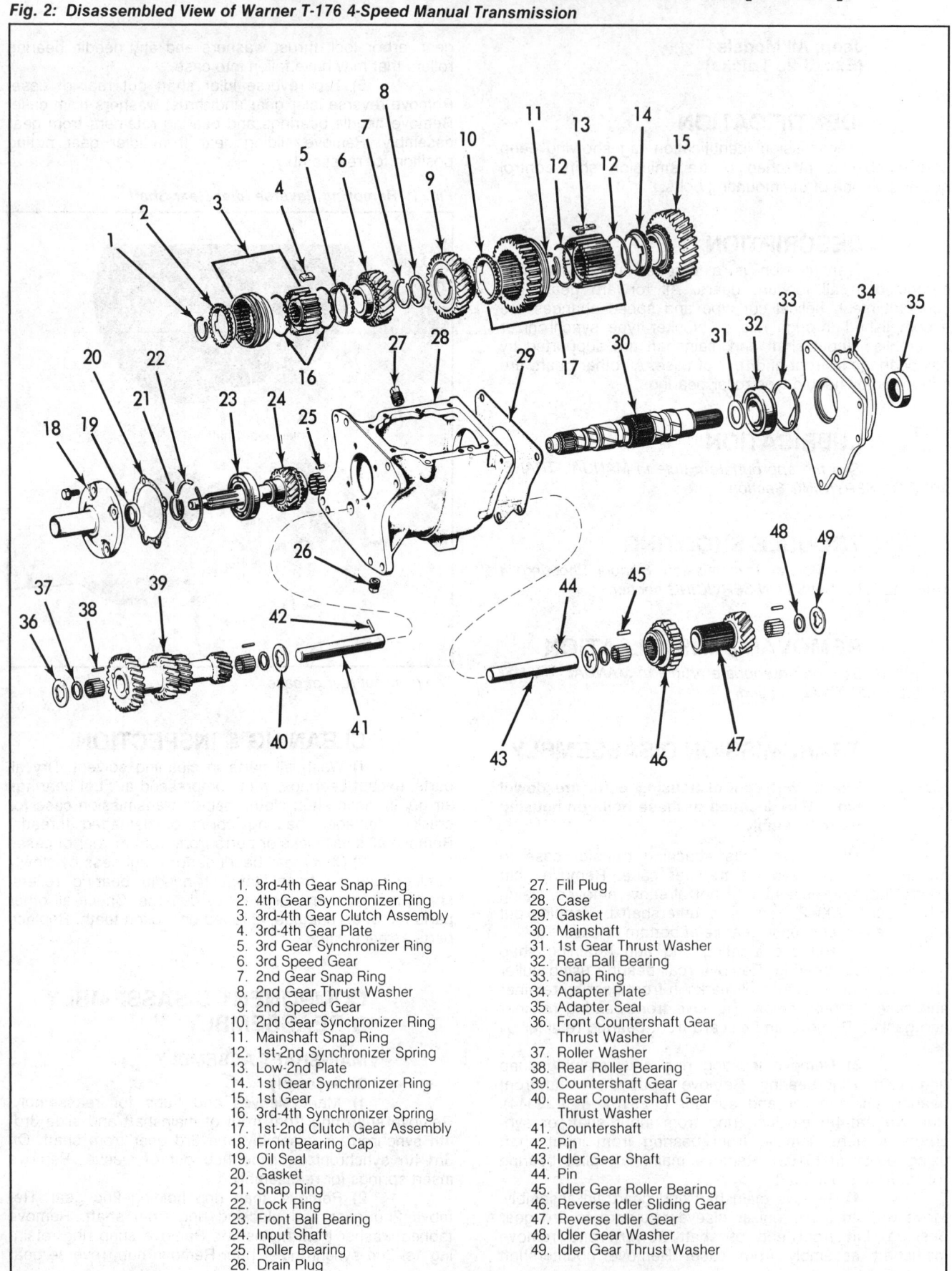

1. 3rd-4th Gear Snap Ring
2. 4th Gear Synchronizer Ring
3. 3rd-4th Gear Clutch Assembly
4. 3rd-4th Gear Plate
5. 3rd Gear Synchronizer Ring
6. 3rd Speed Gear
7. 2nd Gear Snap Ring
8. 2nd Gear Thrust Washer
9. 2nd Speed Gear
10. 2nd Gear Synchronizer Ring
11. Mainshaft Snap Ring
12. 1st-2nd Synchronizer Spring
13. Low-2nd Plate
14. 1st Gear Synchronizer Ring
15. 1st Gear
16. 3rd-4th Synchronizer Spring
17. 1st-2nd Clutch Gear Assembly
18. Front Bearing Cap
19. Oil Seal
20. Gasket
21. Snap Ring
22. Lock Ring
23. Front Ball Bearing
24. Input Shaft
25. Roller Bearing
26. Drain Plug
27. Fill Plug
28. Case
29. Gasket
30. Mainshaft
31. 1st Gear Thrust Washer
32. Rear Ball Bearing
33. Snap Ring
34. Adapter Plate
35. Adapter Seal
36. Front Countershaft Gear Thrust Washer
37. Roller Washer
38. Rear Roller Bearing
39. Countershaft Gear
40. Rear Countershaft Gear Thrust Washer
41. Countershaft
42. Pin
43. Idler Gear Shaft
44. Pin
45. Idler Gear Roller Bearing
46. Reverse Idler Sliding Gear
47. Reverse Idler Gear
48. Idler Gear Washer
49. Idler Gear Thrust Washer

BORG-WARNER 4-SPEED MODEL T-176 (Cont.)

and sleeve as an assembly. Remove insert springs, 3 inserts, sleeve and gear from hub. Remove 1st gear thrust washer from shaft and remove 1st gear and blocking ring.

Reassembly

1) Lubricate mainshaft, synchronizer assemblies and gear bores with transmission lubricant. Align reassembly marks and assemble 1st-2nd synchronizer hub, reverse gear and sleeve. Install gear and sleeve on hub and place assembly on flat surface. Place inserts into hub slots.

Fig. 3: Exploded View of Synchronizer Assembly

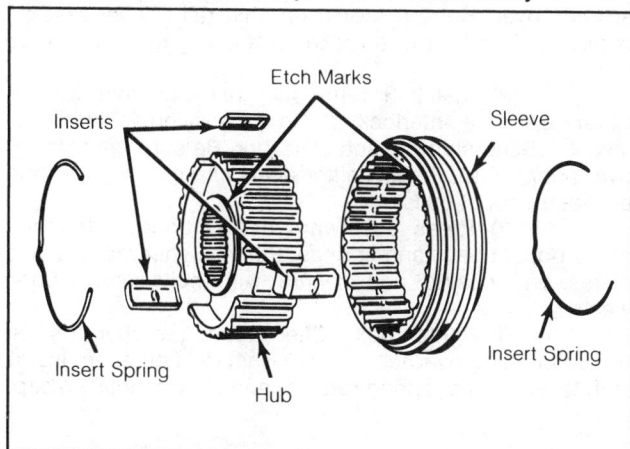

Be sure spring is under lip of each insert.

2) Turn assembly over and install 2nd spring. Place spring so open end is 180° opposite 1st spring. Install 1st-2nd synchronizer assembly, reverse gear, sleeve and new snap ring on mainshaft. Install insert spring, placing loop end of spring in 1 insert. Install spring under lips of remaining inserts.

Fig. 4: Installing Tabbed Thrust Washer in Mainshaft

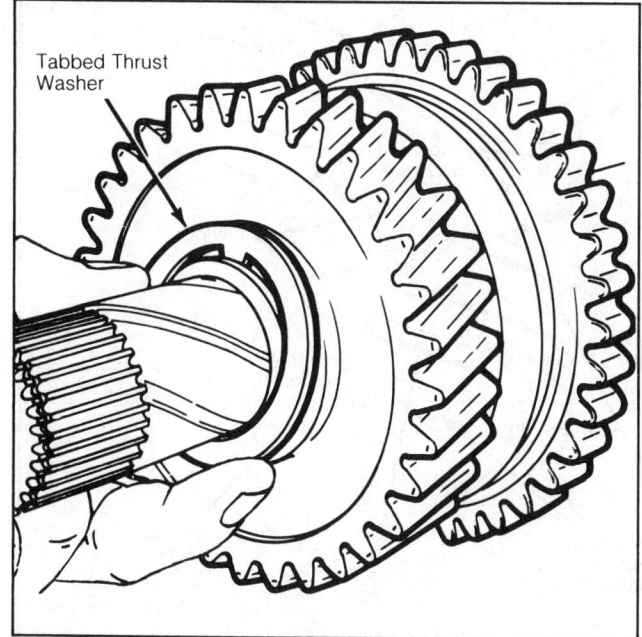

Sharp edge of tab must face outward.

3) Install 1st gear, 1st gear blocking ring, thrust washer and new tabbed thrust washer on mainshaft. Make sure tabbed washer is seated in mainshaft tab bore. Sharp end of thrust washer must face outward. Install 2nd gear, 2nd gear blocking ring and new snap ring on mainshaft. Install 3rd gear and 3rd gear blocking ring on mainshaft.

4) Align etched marks and assemble 3rd-4th synchronizer hub and sleeve. Place assembly on flat surface and place inserts into hub slots. Install insert spring, placing loop end of spring in one insert. Install spring under lips of remaining inserts. Turn assembly over and install remaining spring. Place spring so open end is 180° opposite 1st spring.

5) Install 3rd-4th synchronizer assembly and new snap ring on mainshaft. Measure end play between hub and snap ring with feeler gauge. End play should be .004-.018 (.10-.46 mm). If the end play exceeds .018 (46 mm), replace mainshaft thrust washers and snap rings.

Fig. 5: Measuring Mainshaft End Play

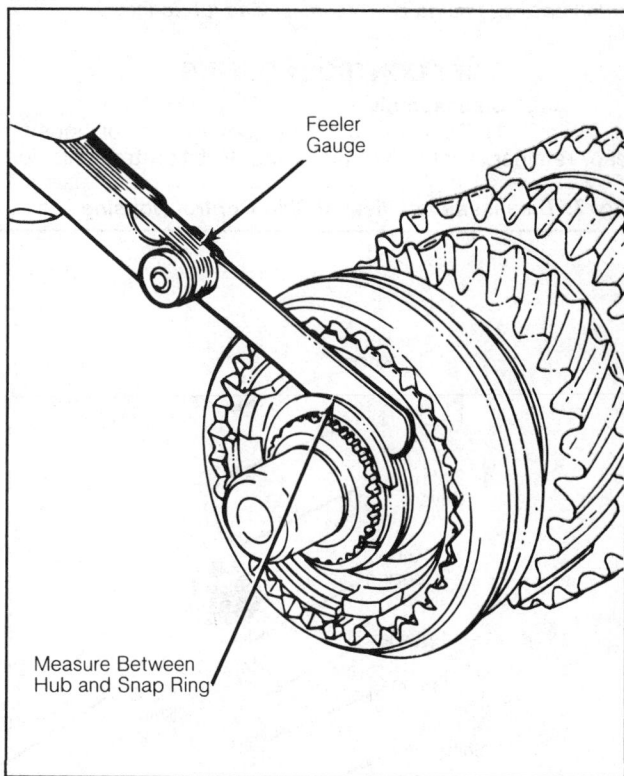

Clearance should be .004-.014" (.10-.46 mm).

INPUT SHAFT

Disassembly

Remove input shaft front bearing using puller and adapter (J-25152 & J-29344). Remove 3rd-4th blocking ring from input shaft. Remove mainshaft pilot bearing rollers from bearing bore. Clean and inspect bearing and input shaft for wear or damage.

Reassembly

Install locating snap ring on front bearing. Install front bearing part way onto input shaft. Using petroleum jelly, install needle rollers (15) into input shaft rear bearing bore.

3-30

Manual Transmissions
BORG-WARNER 4-SPEED MODEL T-176 (Cont.)

Fig. 6: Input Shaft & Bearing Assembly

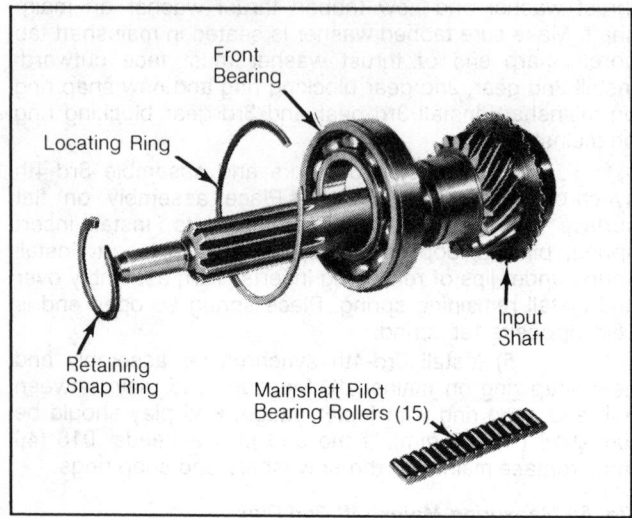

Install bearings using petroleum jelly as lubricant.

SHIFT CONTROL HOUSING
Disassembly
1) Remove shift lever cover, control housing cap, retainer, shift lever and spring. Position transmission case cover in vise so shift forks are facing upward. Use wooden blocks to protect cover.

2) Place shift rails in neutral position and remove shift forks and rails. Note position of components for reassembly. Remove poppet balls and springs. Remove roll pins attaching shift forks to shift rails and remove shift forks.

Reassembly
1) With transmission case cover in vise, lubricate shift rails and rail grooves with petroleum jelly. Install poppet springs and balls (one on each spring). Position reverse gear shift rail and fork on reverse rocker arm in cover. Be sure notch on shift rail is over reverse poppet ball and reverse rocker arm is engaged in reverse fork slot.

2) Install 3rd-4th shift rail and shift fork in cover. Be sure interlock pin is in position in shift rail. Install 1st-2nd shift rail and shift fork. Be sure rail notch is over poppet ball. Install shifter interlock rings in cover and between poppet balls.

3) Press downward evenly on rails to compress poppet balls and springs. Position shift rail retaining plates on housing and secure with bolts and tabbed washers.

4) Tighten bolts. Check tabbed washer position before bending over tabs. Check shift rail operation. Install shift lever, spring, spring retainer and control housing cap.

Fig. 7: Disassembled View of Shift Control Housing

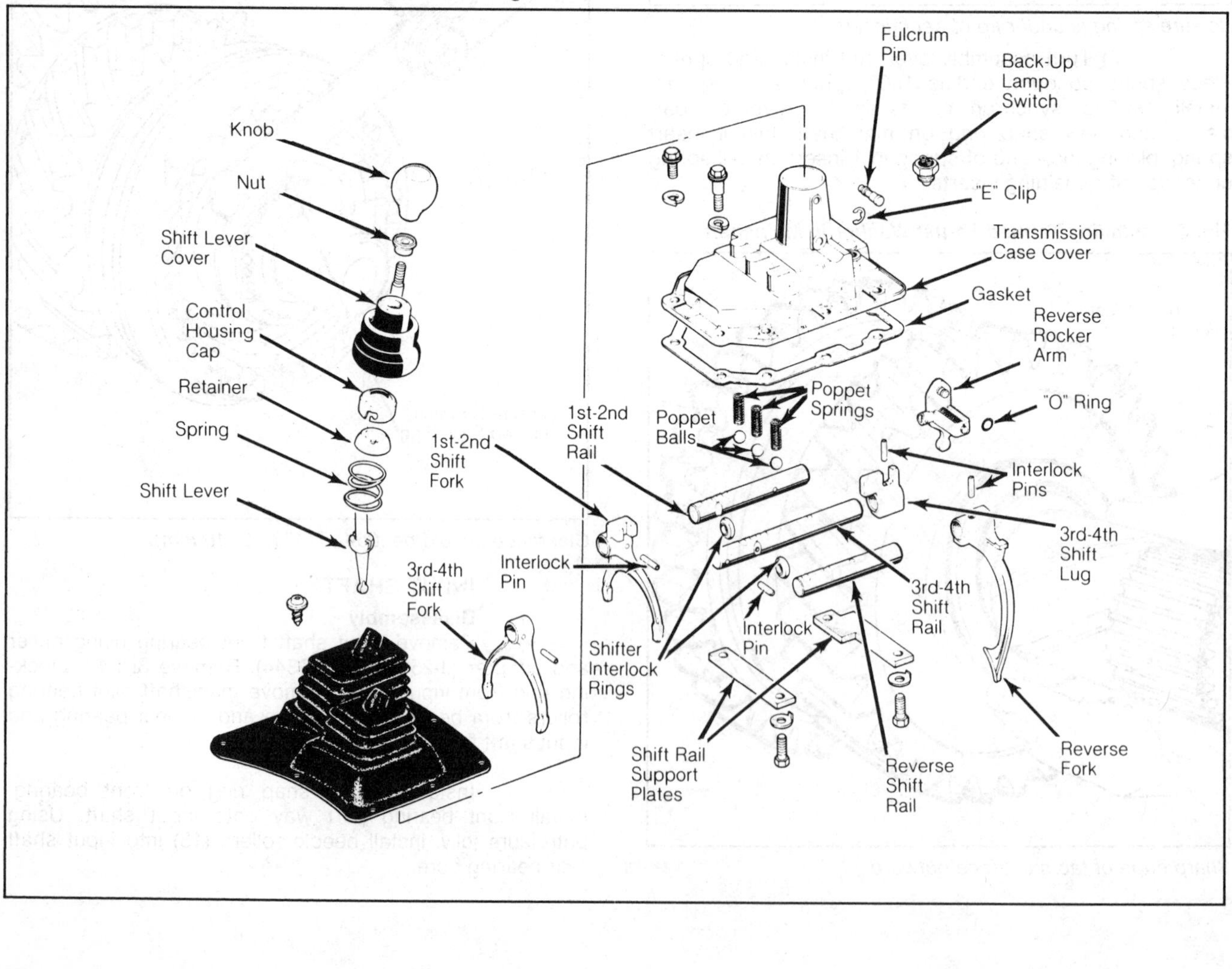

BORG-WARNER 4-SPEED MODEL T-176 (Cont.)

Fig. 8: Assembled View of Shift Control Housing

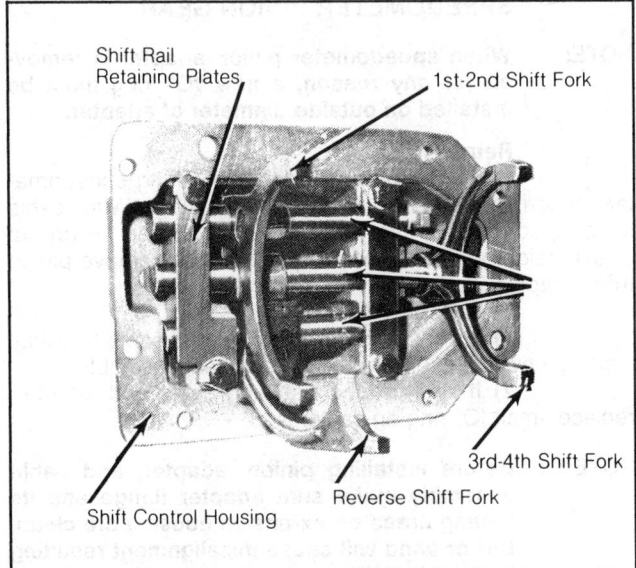

Shift Rail
Retaining Plates

1st-2nd Shift Fork

3rd-4th Shift Fork

Reverse Shift Fork

Shift Control Housing

Shift rail notch must be over reverse poppet ball.

TRANSMISSION REASSEMBLY

1) Lubricate reverse idler gear bore and sliding gear with transmission lubricant. Install sliding gear on reverse idler gear. Install arbor tool (J-29343) in reverse idler gear, and place 22 roller bearings and 1 bearing retainer at each end of gear.

2) Coat reverse idler gear thrust washers with petroleum jelly. Place gear in case with flats of washers facing mainshaft and tabs engaging slots in case. Install reverse idler gear assembly. Align gear bore and install shaft from rear of case. Make sure shaft roll pin is aligned with counterbore in case.

3) Measure reverse idler gear end play by inserting feeler gauge between thrust washer and gear. End play should be .004-.018" (.10-.46 mm). If end play exceeds .018" (.46 mm), replace thrust washer.

4) Coat countershaft gear bore, needle bearings and bearing bores in gear with petroleum jelly. Insert arbor tool (J-29342) in bore and install 22 needle rollers and 1 bearing retainer at each end of gear. Coat countershaft gear thrust washers with petroleum jelly. Place in case with tabs engaging slots in case.

5) Install countershaft gear assembly. Align gear bore, and install shaft from rear, part way into case. Make sure arbor tool enters shaft bore at front of case. Measure countergear end play by inserting feeler gauge between thrust washer and gear. End play should be .004-.018" (.10-.46 mm). If end play exceeds .018" (.46 mm), replace thrust washer.

6) After correct end play is obtained, push arbor tool back into countergear. Remove shaft at rear of case and allow countergear to lie at bottom of case. Leave countergear at bottom of case to provide clearance for installation of mainshaft assembly.

7) Install mainshaft assembly in case. Make sure synchronizers are in neutral position. Coat 3rd-4th blocking ring with transmission lubricant and install on input shaft. Support mainshaft assembly. Install input shaft through front bearing bore in case.

8) Align and seat mainshaft pilot hub in input shaft bore. Tap front bearing and input shaft into case using rawhide mallet, or equivalent. Install front bearing retainer and bolts. Tighten bolts finger tight.

9) Position rear bearing on mainshaft and install into case using installer tool (J-29345). Remove tool and complete installation using rawhide mallet, or equivalent. When bearing is fully seated, install bearing retaining snap ring.

10) Remove front bearing retainer and seat front bearing fully on input shaft. Install bearing retaining snap ring. Apply sealer to front bearing retainer gasket and position on case. Install front bearing retainer oil seal in retainer. Position seal on case aligning notch with oil drain back hole. Install bolts and tighten to specification.

11) Install locating ring on rear bearing and reseat bearing if necessary. Position case on end with input shaft facing downward. Align countershaft gear bores with thrust washers. Install shaft from rear and tap into place being careful not to damage thrust washers.

12) Shift synchronizer sleeves through all gear positions, making sure no binding exists. If input shaft and mainshaft appear to bind in neutral position, check blocking rings for any possibly sticking on tapered portion of gears. Free blocking rings using screwdriver. Place transmission back in neutral position.

13) Install new shift control housing gasket and install housing assembly. Install and tighten bolts to specification making sure 2 dowel type bolts are placed in their correct holes. Install transmission on transfer case.

TIGHTENING SPECIFICATIONS

Application	Ft. Lbs. (N.m)
Back-Up Lamp Switch	15 (20)
Drain/Filler Plugs	15 (20)
Front Bearing Retainer Bolts	13 (18)
Shift Control Housing	13 (18)

Manual Transmissions

CHRYSLER CORP. A-412 MANUAL TRANSAXLE

Dodge Omni, Rampage
Plymouth Horizon, Scamp

IDENTIFICATION

The transaxle part number and build date are stamped into a pad on bottom of clutch housing. The last 8 digits of the vehicle identification number are stamped on rear edge of clutch housing.

DESCRIPTION

The A-412 transaxle combines a fully synchronized 4-speed manual transmission with a 2-pinion differential. The complete assembly is enclosed within a 2-piece magnesium housing, divided into a transmission section and a differential section.

Power flow through the transmission follows a direct pattern, mainshaft to pinion shaft. Both are 1-piece shafts with speed ratios produced directly through the selected gears. Output is from the pinion shaft through the differential to the axle drive flanges.

LUBRICATION & ADJUSTMENT

See the appropriate article in MANUAL TRANSMISSION SERVICING Section.

SERVICE (IN VEHICLE)

SPEEDOMETER PINION GEAR

NOTE: When speedometer pinion adapter is removed for any reason, a new "O" ring must be installed on outside diameter of adapter.

Removal

Remove bolt and washer securing speedometer pinion adapter in extension housing. With cable housing connected, carefully work adapter and pinion out of extension housing. Remove retainer and remove pinion from adapter.

Seal Replacement

1) If transmission oil is found in cable housing, install a new speedometer pinion and seal assembly.

2) If oil is found between cable and adapter, replace small "O" ring on cable.

NOTE: Before installing pinion, adapter, and cable assembly make sure adapter flange and its mating areas on extension housing are clean. Dirt or sand will cause misalignment resulting in speedometer pinion gear damage.

Installation

To install, reverse removal procedures.

Fig. 1: Sectional View of The A-412 Manual Transaxle

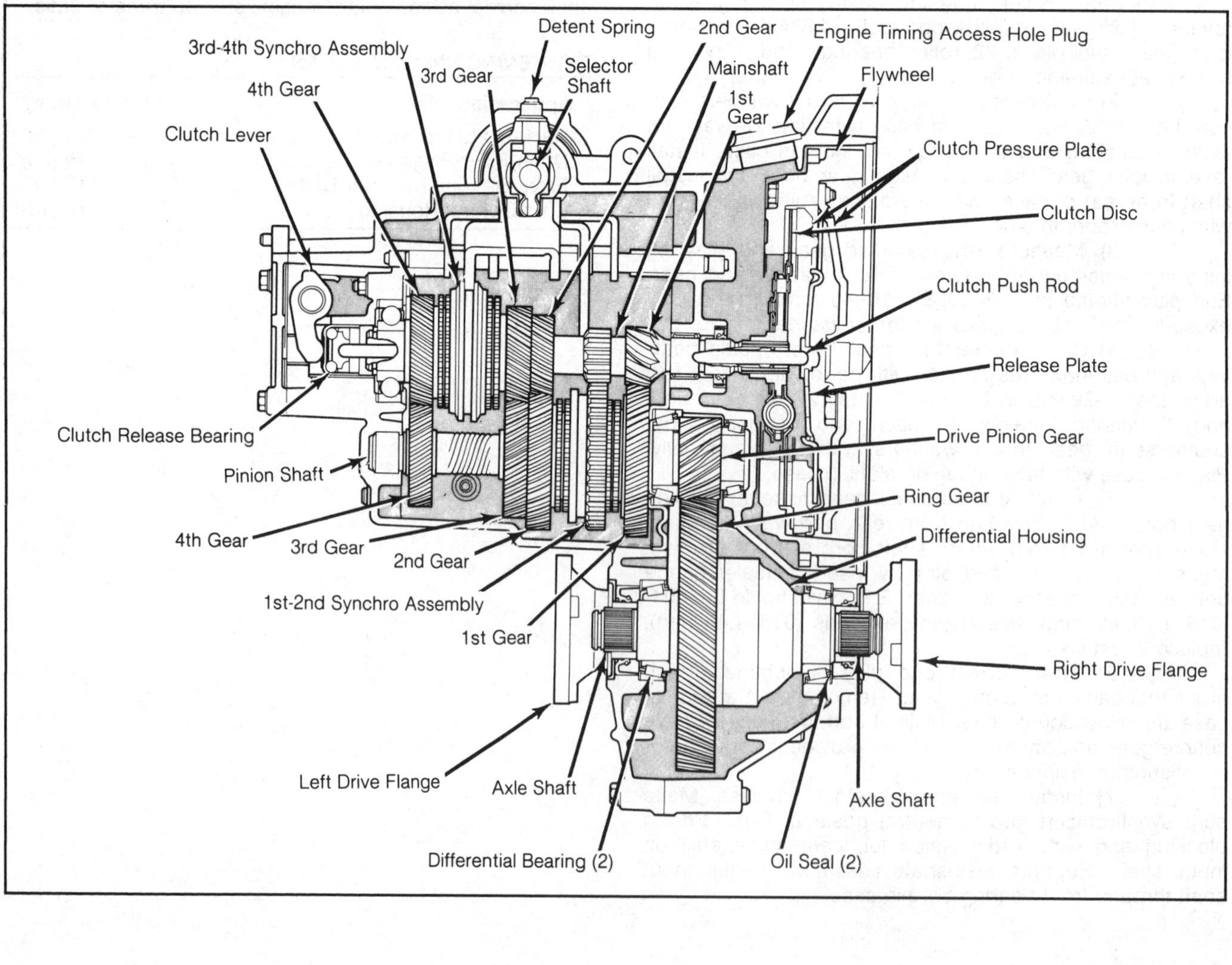

CHRYSLER CORP. A-412 MANUAL TRANSAXLE (Cont.)

Fig. 2: *View of Speedometer Pinion and Adapter*

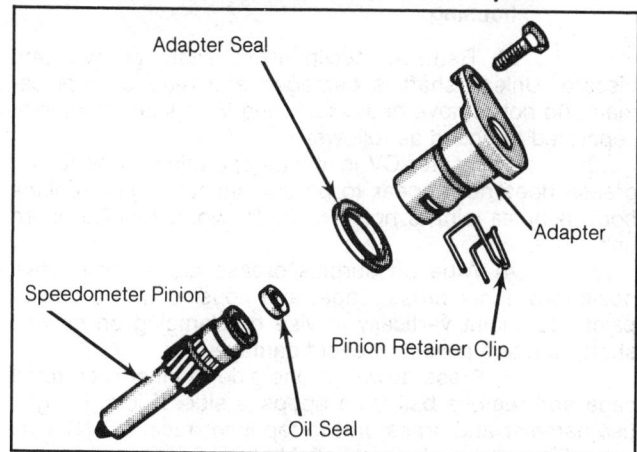

DRIVE AXLE SHAFTS
Removal

1) Remove cotter key and hub nut lock from end of drive axle shaft. Loosen hub and lug nuts. Raise and support front of vehicle. Remove hub nut and wheel assembly.

2) Remove clamp bolt securing ball joint hub to steering knuckle. Separate ball joint from knuckle by prying against knuckle leg and control arm.

3) Separate outer CV joint splined shaft from hub by holding CV joint housing while moving knuckle (hub) assembly away. DO NOT pry on or otherwise damage oil slinger on outer CV joint. Do NOT attempt to remove oil slinger.

4) Support drive shaft assembly at outer CV joint housing. Remove plastic caps from Allen head screws at inner CV joint and Allen head screws retaining inner CV joint to transaxle drive flange.

NOTE: **Pivot inner housing flange surface up and axle shaft down to reduce loss of special lubricant from CV joint. DO NOT pull on shaft.**

INNER CV JOINT
Disassembly

1) With axle shaft assembly removed from vehicle, cut small rubber clamp, and large metal clamp and discard boot.

2) Remove as much grease as possible from inside joint housing and around 3-ball trunnion assembly. On GKN assemblies, remove trunnion assembly from housing. Remove snap ring and drive trunnion off shaft by tapping lightly with a brass punch.

3) On Citroen assemblies, deform retaining ring at each trunnion roller. Remove trunnion assembly from housing, wrap rollers to trunnion with tape. Remove snap ring and drive trunnion off shaft by tapping lightly with a brass punch.

4) Inspect joint housing ball raceway and tripod components for excessive wear and replace if necessary.

Reassembly

1) To install new boot, slide small rubber clamp onto shaft (GKN left side only). Slide small end of boot over shaft.

2) On tubular shafts (right side shaft), position boot lip face in line with mark on the shaft outside

Fig.3: *Exploded View of Drive Axle Shaft Components*

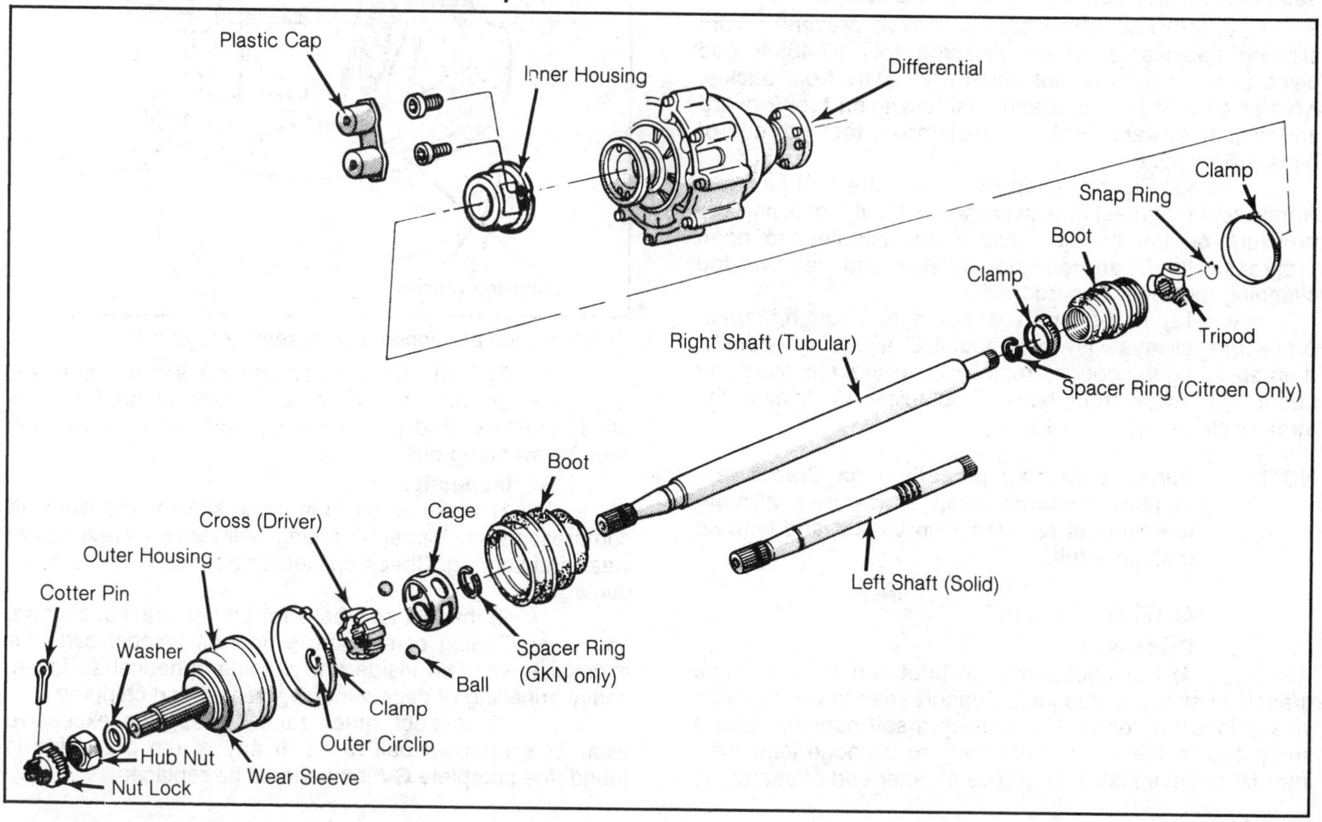

CHRYSLER CORP. A-412 MANUAL TRANSAXLE (Cont.)

diameter. On solid shafts (left side shaft), position small boot end in machined groove provided.

3) Clamp small boot end by placing rubber clamp over boot groove. Reinstall tripod on shaft with non-chamfered face of tripod body facing shaft retainer groove.

4) Assemble snap ring in groove to lock tripod assembly on shaft. Distribute 2 packets of grease (provided in Boot Joint Kit) in boot. Install joint housing over tripod and position large end of boot in groove provided on housing (GKN assemblies only).

5) On GKN assemblies, install metal clamp on boot, making sure that boot is properly located on shaft and housing, and is not twisted. After securing boot to housing, add 2 more packets of grease.

6) Locate clamp tags in slots, making the clamp as tight as possible by hand. Clamp bridge with clamping tool (C-4124) and squeeze to complete tightening. *See Fig. 7.*

NOTE: During this operation, care must be taken not to cut through clamp bridge and/or damage the boot.

7) On Citroen assemblies, add 1 more packet of grease to housing before installing tripod into housing. Slide tripod assembly into housing, reform retaining ring to secure rollers in housing.

8) Position boot over housing. Wrap binding stap around boot twice plus an additional 2 1/2". Pass the strap through buckle and fold it back about 1 1/8" on inside of buckle.

9) Place the strap around boot with eye of buckle toward you. Wrap strap around boot once and pass it through the buckle. Wrap strap around boot a second time, also passing it through the buckle.

10) Fold strap back slightly to prevent it from slipping backwards. Open clamping tool (C-4653) and place strap in narrow slot about 1/2" away from buckle. Hold strap with left hand and push clamping tool forward and slightly upward. Fit hook of clamping tool into eye of buckle. *See Fig. 8.*

11) Tighten strap by closing the tool handles. Rotate tool (handles) downward while slowly releasing the pressure on the handles. Allow tool (handles) to open progressively. Open the tool entirely and remove the clamping tool sideways from strap.

12) If the strap is not tight enough, repeat procedure, always with tool about 1/2" away from buckle. If strap is tight enough, remove tool and cut strap off about 1/8" away from buckle. Complete by folding the strap back neatly.

NOTE: During tightening procedure on Citroen assemblies, ensure strap slides in a straight line without resistance in buckle and without making a fold.

OUTER CV JOINT
Disassembly

1) Cut boot clamp on boot and discard. Wipe grease away to expose joint. Support shaft in a soft-jawed vise, support outer joint, and using a soft hammer, give a sharp tap to the top of joint body to dislodge joint from internal circlip installed in groove at outer end of shaft.

CAUTION: DO NOT attempt to remove wear sleeve from housing.

2) Remove circlip from shaft groove and discard. Unless shaft is damaged and requires replacement, do not remove heavy lock ring from shaft. With joint separated, proceed as follows:

3) If outer CV joint was operating properly and grease does not appear to be contaminated, just replace boot. If outer joint is noisy or badly worn, replace entire unit.

4) Wipe off surplus grease and mark relative position of inner cross, cage, and housing with a dab of paint. Hold joint vertically in vise by clamping on splined shaft, with soft jaws to prevent damage.

5) Press down on one side of inner race to tilt cage and remove ball from opposite side. If joint is tight, use hammer and brass drift to tap inner race. DO NOT hit cage. Repeat this step until all 6 balls are removed.

6) Tilt cage and inner race assembly vertically and position the 2 opposing elongated cage windows in area between ball grooves. *See Fig. 4.* Remove cage and inner race assembly by pulling upward away from housing.

Fig. 4: Removing Cage and Cross Assembly

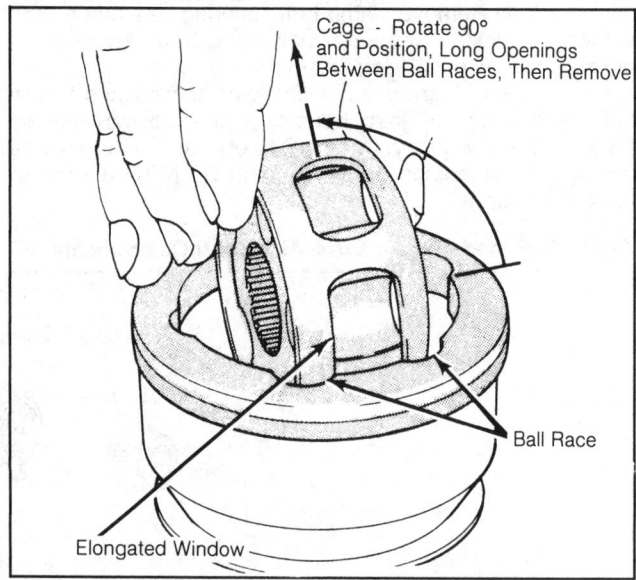

Remove cage and inner race assembly together.

7) Turn inner cross (driver) 90° to cage and align one of race spherical lands with elongated cage window. Raise land into cage window and remove inner race by swinging out.

Inspection

1) Wash all parts in clean solvent and dry with compressed air. Inspect housing ball races for excessive wear and scoring. Check splined shaft and nut threads for damage.

2) Inspect all 6 balls for pitting, cracks, scoring, and wear. Dulling of surface is normal. Inspect cage for excessive wear on inside and outside spherical surfaces, heavy brinelling of cage window, cracks, and chipping.

3) Inspect inner race (cross) for excessive wear or scoring of ball races. If any of the preceding is found, the complete CV joint should be replaced.

CHRYSLER CORP. A-412 MANUAL TRANSAXLE (Cont.)

Fig. 5: Exploded View of Outer CV Joint

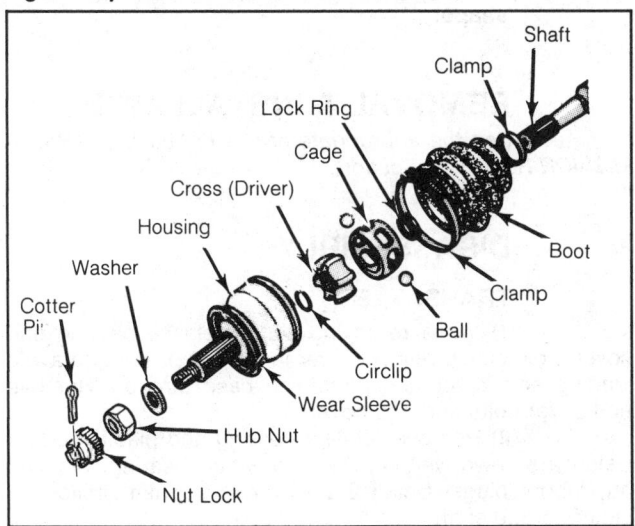

NOTE: Polished areas in races (cross and housing) and on cage spheres are normal and do not indicate need for joint replacement unless they are suspected of causing noise and vibration.

4) If slinger is bent or damaged, carefully pry sleeve from machined ledge of outer CV joint.

Reassembly

1) If wear sleeve was removed, install with installer (C-4698). Lightly oil all components before reassembling outer joint. Align parts according to paint markings made at disassembly.

2) Insert the inner race (cross) lands into an elongated cage window and feed race into cage. Pivot cross 90° to complete cage assembly.

3) Align opposing elongated cage window with housing land and feed race assembly into housing. Pivot cage 90° to complete installation. When properly assembled, curved side of cage windows and the inner cross counterbore should face outwards from joint. *See Fig. 6.*

Fig. 6: Sectional View of Cage and Cross Installation

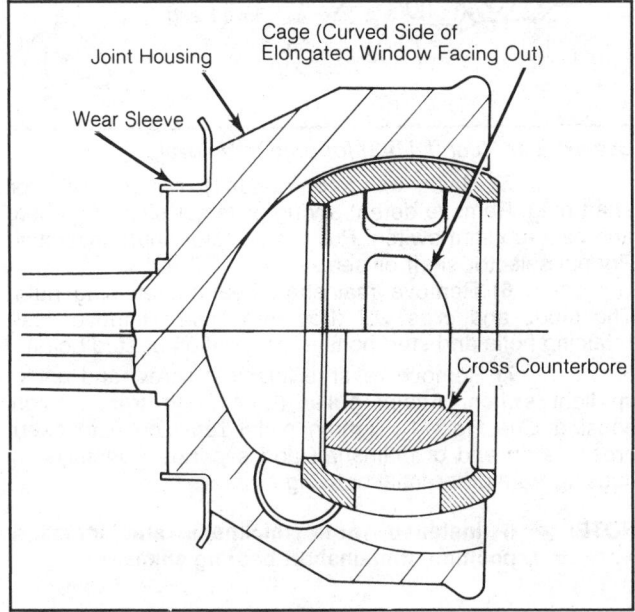

4) Apply lubricant to ball races from packet provided in kit and distribute equally between all sides of ball grooves. One packet is sufficient to lubricate joint.

5) Insert balls into races by tilting cage and inner race assembly. Ensure that lock ring is seated in its groove.

6) To install boot (shaft supported in soft-jawed vise), slip small metal clamp over spacer ring and shaft (GKN assemblies only). Slide small end of boot over spacer ring and shaft, and position in machined groove provided.

NOTE: Citroen assemblies are provided with a vent sleeve, position this vent sleeve under the boot-to-shaft clamp area during boot installation.

7) Insert new circlip in shaft groove, using care not to over expand or twist circlip during assembly. Position outer joint on splined end, engage splines, and tap sharply with soft mallet, allowing small metal clamp to slide along with joint.

8) Remove clamp and check that circlip and spacer ring are properly seated by trying to pull joint from shaft. Locate large end of boot over joint housing, checking that boot is not twisted.

9) On GKN assemblies, install metal clamp on boot, making sure that boot is properly located on shaft and housing and is not twisted.

10) After securing boot to housing, locate clamp tangs in slots, making the clamp as tight as possible by hand. Clamp bridge with clamping tool (C-4124) and squeeze to complete tightening. *See Fig. 7.*

Fig. 7: Clamping Bridge on GKN CV Joint Assemblies

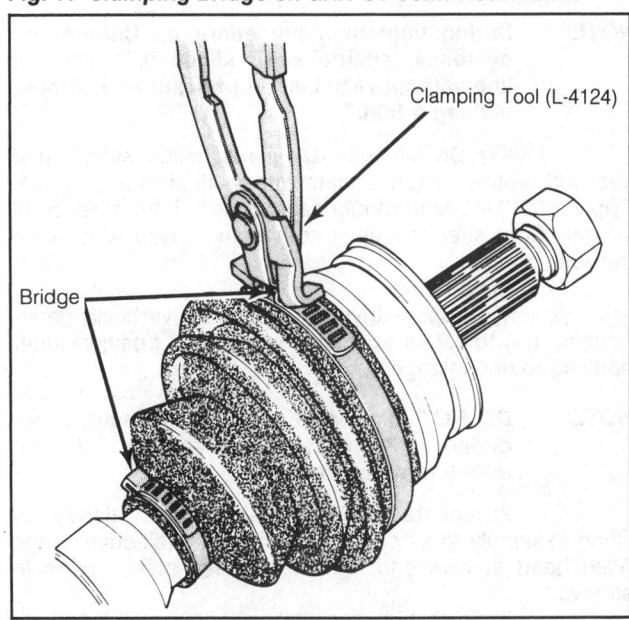

Use clamping tool (C-4124) for proper installation.

11) On Citroen assemblies, position boot over housing. Wrap binding strap around boot twice plus an additional 2 1/2". Pass the strap through buckle and fold it back about 1 1/8" on inside of buckle.

12) Place strap around boot with eye of buckle toward you. Wrap strap around boot once and pass it through the buckle. Wrap the strap around boot a second time, again passing it through the buckle.

CHRYSLER CORP. A-412 MANUAL TRANSAXLE (Cont.)

13) Fold strap back slightly to prevent it from slipping backwards. Open clamping tool (C-4653) and place strap in narrow slot about 1/2" away from buckle.

14) Hold strap with left hand and push clamping tool forward and slightly upward. Fit hook of clamping tool into eye of buckle. *See Fig. 8.*

Fig. 8: Clamping Strap on Citroen CV Joint Assemblies

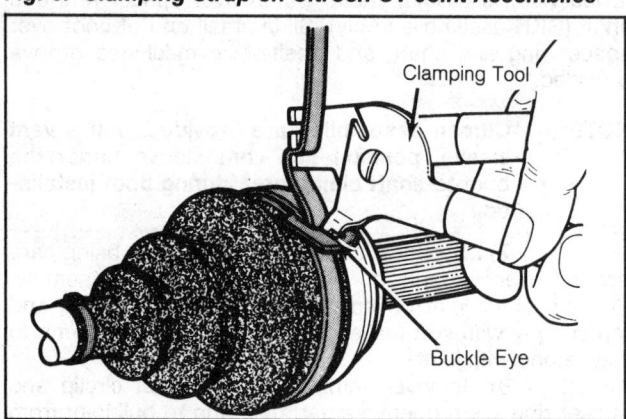

15) Tighten strap by closing the tool handles. Rotate tool handles downward while slowly releasing pressure on handles. Allow tool handles to open progressively. Open tool entirely and remove clamping tool sideways from strap.

16) If strap is not tight enough, repeat procedure, always with tool about 1/2" away from buckle. If strap is tight enough, remove tool and cut strap off about 1/8" away from buckle. Complete by folding the strap back neatly.

NOTE: **During tightening procedure on Citroen assemblies, ensure strap slides in a straight line without resistance in buckle and without making a fold.**

17) On all outer CV joints, clean slinger and seal with solvent and lubricate with multi-purpose grease. Apply a full 1/4" bead of lubricant around circumference of slinger. Coat seal and fill lip-to-housing cavity with multi-purpose grease.

Installation

1) Support drive axle assembly vertically (inner housing up) to retain special lubricant and position inner housing to drive flange.

NOTE: **DO NOT allow axle assembly to hang down during installation. Support outer CV joint during reattachment.**

2) Locate inner housing in drive flange by lifting assembly to a horizontal position. Install drive flange Allen head screws and tighten. Replace plastic caps to screws.

3) Push hub assembly out and install splined outer CV joint shaft into hub. Reinstall steering knuckle assembly on ball joint stud. Install and tighten ball joint clamp bolt.

NOTE: **If after attaching drive axle shaft, inboard boot appears collapsed or deformed, vent inner boot by inserting a round-tipped, small diameter rod between boot and shaft; as**

venting occurs, boot will return to its original shape.

REMOVAL & INSTALLATION

See the appropriate article in MANUAL TRANSMISSION REMOVAL Section.

DISASSEMBLY

TRANSAXLE

1) While removing clutch release bearing end cover, hold clutch release lever in upright position to avoid loading end cover and damaging case threads. Remove end cover bolts and end cover.

2) Remove release bearing and plastic sleeve. Using a screwdriver, remove mainshaft bearing retaining nut rubber plugs. Using 2 screwdrivers, push circlips off clutch torque shaft.

3) While removing torque shaft from case, remove clutch return spring and release lever. Remove clutch release push rod from either end of case. Pry out clutch torque shaft oil seal.

4) Using a screwdriver, remove drive flange dust plug. Remove drive flange snap ring and cone washer. Using drive flange extractor (L-4443), remove drive flange. Pry out drive flange oil seal with remove (L-4445).

Fig. 9: Removing Drive Flange

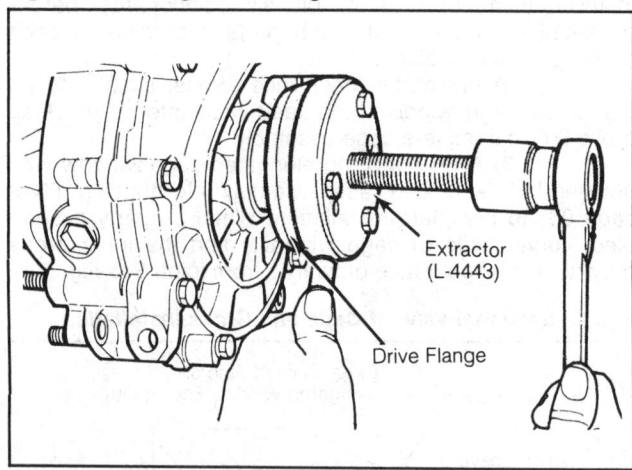

Use extractor tool (L4443) for proper removal.

5) Using extractor (L-4441), remove selector shaft plug. Remove detent spring, selector shaft boot seal and back-up light switch. Pull out selector shaft assembly. Pry out selector shaft oil seal.

6) Remove mainshaft bearing retaining nuts. The studs and clips will drop into case. Remove case retaining bolts and stud bolts (note location of stud bolts).

7) Remove reverse idler set screw and back-up light switch. Attach puller (L-4443) to transmission housing. *See Fig. 11.* Tighten puller ram screw to exert pressure on end of mainshaft and separate transmission housing from differential housing.

NOTE: **If installed, note thickness and installed position of mainshaft bearing shims.**

CHRYSLER CORP. A-412 MANUAL TRANSAXLE (Cont.)

Fig. 10: *Removing Selector Shaft Plug*

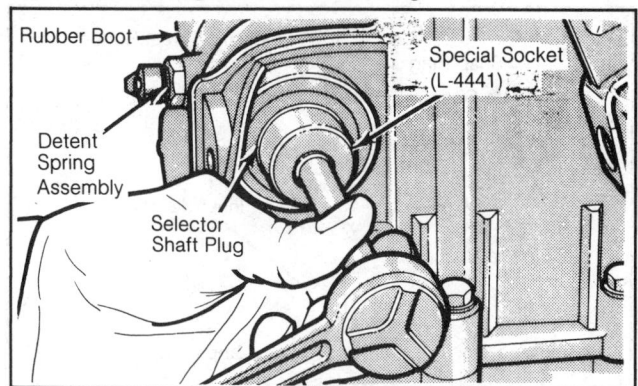

Special socket (L-4441) must be used to remove plug.

8) Loosen retaining bolts and lift off reverse gear shift fork. Remove both retaining bolts and both support brackets. Remove shift rail "E" clips, and lift out shift forks.

Fig. 11: *Separating Transmission Housing from Differential Housing*

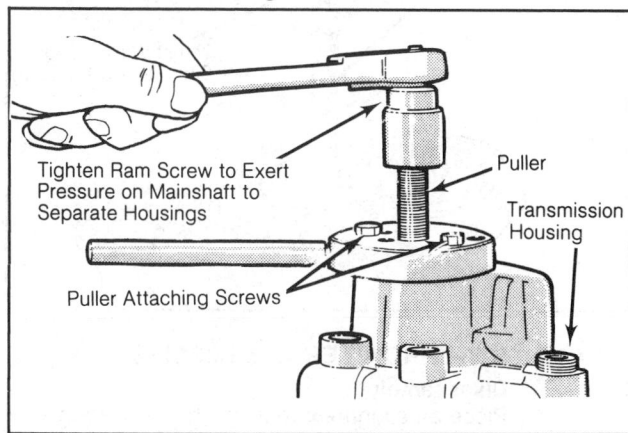

Use puller (L-4443) to remove housing.

9) Remove plastic plug from end of pinion shaft. Remove 4th gear and mainshaft assembly from differential housing as an assembly.

CAUTION: Lift straight up on mainshaft and pinion shaft 4th gear until it clears pinion shaft. Do not scratch mainshaft, needle bearing, or journal.

Fig. 12: *Prying Reverse Idler Shaft from Housing*

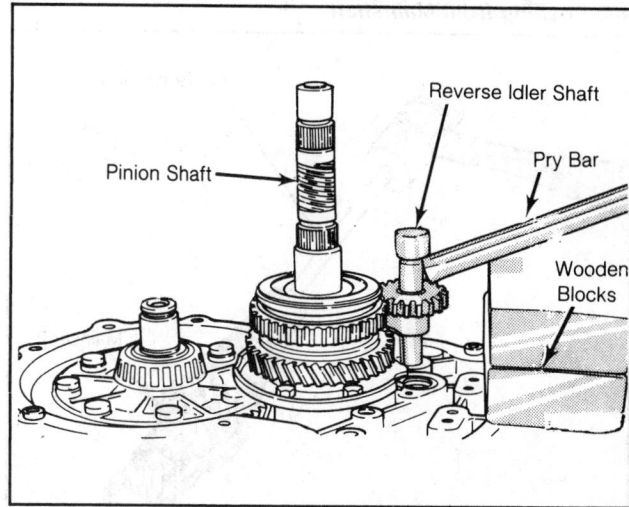

Use pry bar and wooden blocks to prevent damage to case.

10) Remove selective fit snap ring. Slide 3rd gear, 2nd gear, needle bearing, and stop ring from pinion shaft. Pry reverse idler shaft from housing. *See Fig. 12.*

11) Using a puller, pull 2nd gear inner sleeve, 1st-2nd synchronizer assembly, and 1st gear from pinion shaft as an assembly. Lift off 1st gear needle bearing.

12) Remove pinion shaft retainer bolts. Remove retainer, 1st gear thrust washer, and pinion shaft. Lift differential assembly from housing.

COMPONENT DISASSEMBLY & REASSEMBLY

MAINSHAFT

Disassembly

1) Remove mainshaft bearing snap ring. Using a puller, remove bearing and 4th gear as an assembly. Lift off 4th gear needle bearing.

2) Remove snap ring retaining 3rd-4th synchronizer assembly on mainshaft. Pull synchronizer assembly and 3rd gear from shaft. Remove 3rd gear needle bearing.

3) If clutch push rod seal and bushing assembly require replacement, drive it from mainshaft bore using a 3/8" brass rod. *See Fig. 14.*

Fig. 13: *Exploded View of Mainshaft Assembly.*

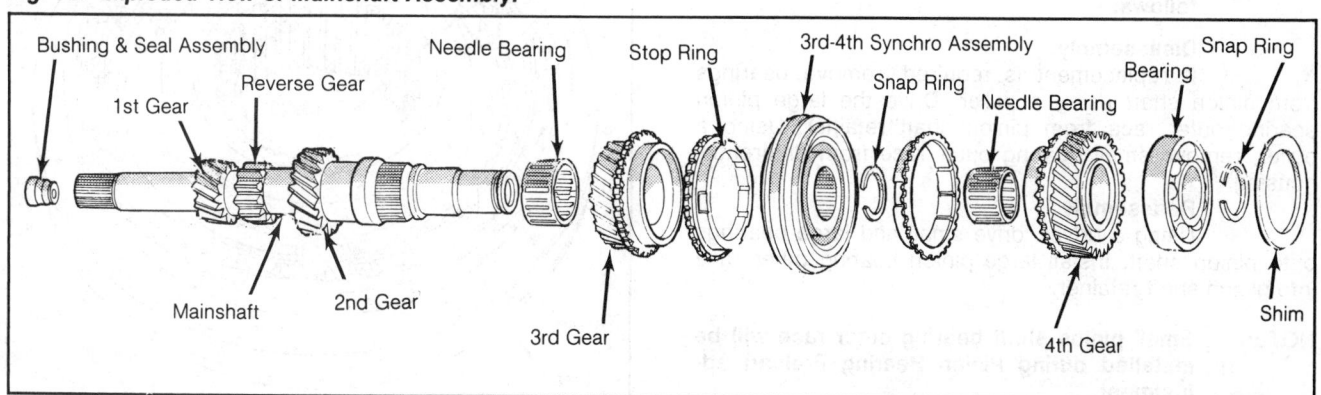

CHRYSLER CORP. A-412 MANUAL TRANSAXLE (Cont.)

Fig. 14: Removing Clutch Push Rod Seal and Bushing from Mainshaft

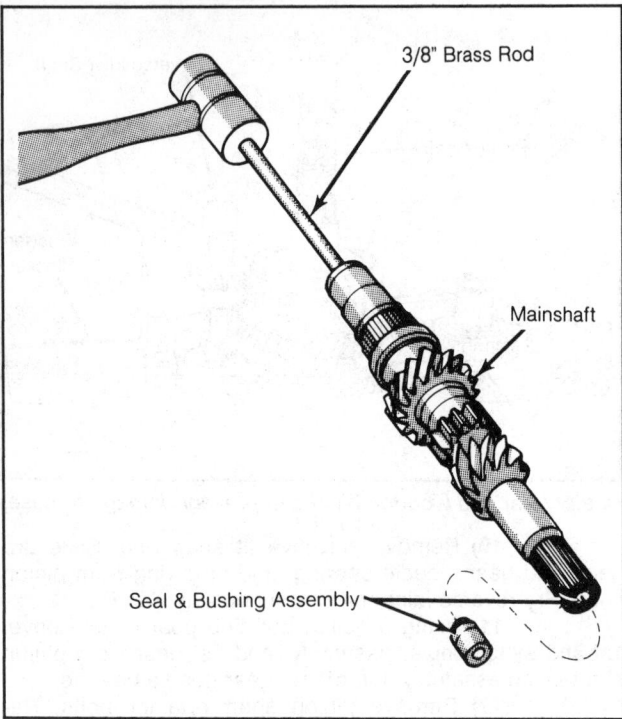

Using 3/8" brass rod drive bushing off end of shaft.

Reassembly

1) If removed, drive clutch push rod seal and bearing assembly into mainshaft using a soft mallet. Drive bushing into shaft until flush.

2) Install 3rd gear needle bearing and 3rd gear onto mainshaft. Install stop ring over 3rd gear. Install 3rd-4th synchronizer assembly onto mainshaft, making sure that synchronizer struts engage in slots of 3rd gear stop ring. Install 3rd-4th synchronizer snap ring. Install 4th gear stop ring.

NOTE: **Final assembly of mainshaft will be done during Transaxle Reassembly.**

PINION SHAFT

NOTE: **Gears and synchronizer assembly were removed during Transaxle Disassembly, and will be installed during Transaxle Reassembly. Pinion bearing and race replacement is as follows:**

Disassembly

If replacement is required, remove bearings from pinion shaft using a puller. Drive the large pinion bearing outer race from pinion shaft retainer. Using a puller, remove small bearing outer race from differential housing.

Reassembly

Using a driver, drive small and large bearings onto pinion shaft. Install large pinion bearing outer race into pinion shaft retainer.

NOTE: **Small pinion shaft bearing outer race will be installed during Pinion Bearing Preload adjustment.**

Fig. 15: Exploded View of Pinion Shaft Assembly

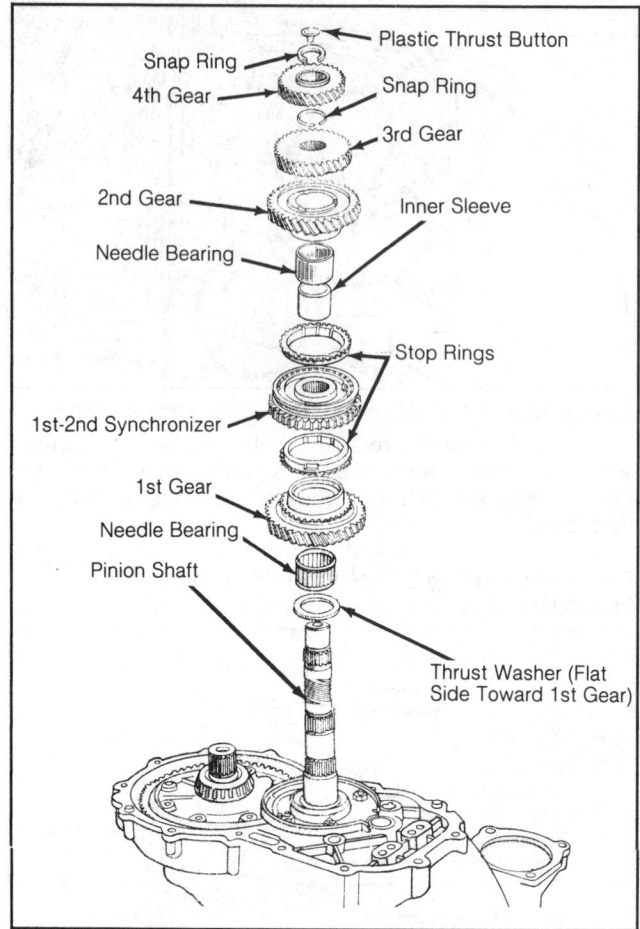

SYNCHRONIZER ASSEMBLIES

Disassembly

Place an alignment mark on hub and sleeve for reassembly reference. Hold sleeve and push hub, struts, and springs from sleeve.

Fig. 16: Assembled View of 3rd-4th Synchronizer

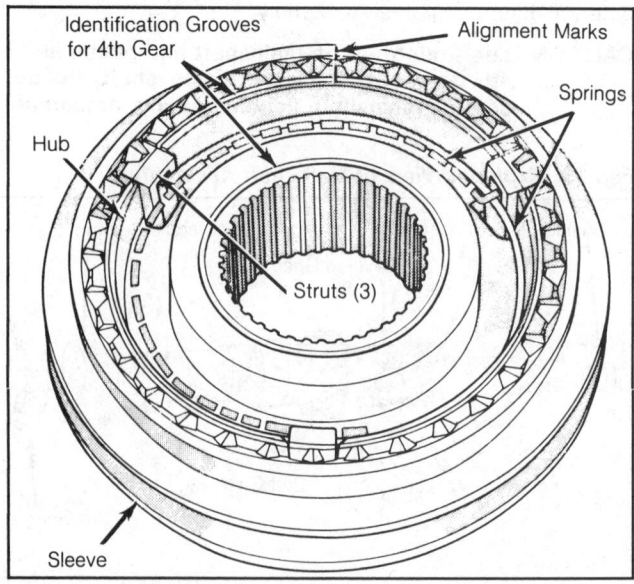

CHRYSLER CORP. A-412 MANUAL TRANSAXLE (Cont.)

NOTE: Synchronizer parts are not interchangeable. Stop ring wear limit is .019" (.048 mm) maximum.

Reassembly
Position struts in slots of synchronizer hub. Slide hub into sleeve and align marks made at disassembly. Install synchronizer springs so that open ends face away from each other.

DIFFERENTIAL ASSEMBLY
Disassembly
1) Ring gear is attached to differential case by rivets. If replacement is necessary, drill out rivet heads with a 15/32" drill bit. Knock rivets out with a drift. Lift ring gear off case.

NOTE: **Ring gear will be reattached with nuts and bolts.**

Fig. 17: Exploded View of Differential Assembly

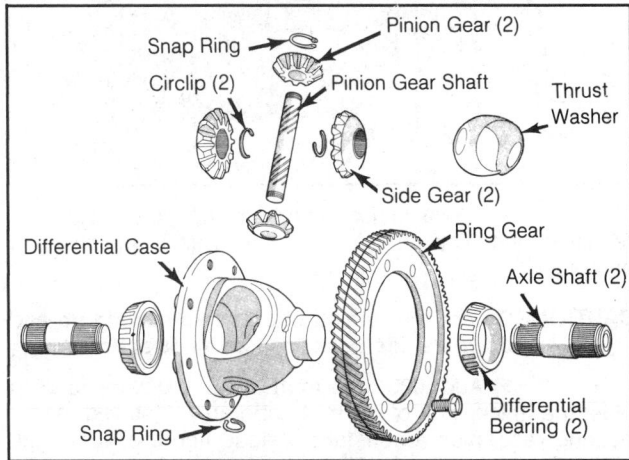

2) Pull out circlips and slide axle shafts from differential case. Roll side gears to case openings and withdraw them from case.

3) Remove snap rings and drive out differential pinion gear shaft with a brass drift. Withdraw pinion gears and the molded 1-piece thrust washer.

4) If replacement is required, remove differential case bearings using a puller. Drive bearing outer races from differential housing and from transmission housing.

Reassembly
1) If removed, drive new differential case bearing onto case.

NOTE: **Differential case bearing outer races will be installed, and preload adjusted, during Transaxle Reassembly and Adjustment.**

2) Assemble thrust washer, gears, and pinion gear shaft into differential case in reverse order of disassembly.

3) Insert axle shafts into differential case. Press axle shafts against pinion gear shaft and press side gears against case. Install thickest possible circlip to retain each axle shaft. *See Fig. 18.*

NOTE: **Snap rings are available in 2 thicknesses: .078" and .090" (1.98 and 2.27 mm). If thicker snap ring jams sideways, install thinner snap ring.**

Fig. 18: Sectional View of Differential

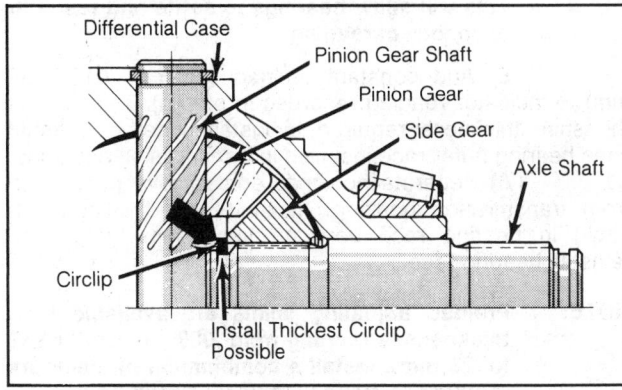

Illustration shows axle shaft circlip installation.

4) If removed, install new ring gear onto differential case. Secure ring gear with replacement bolts, washers, and nuts.

REASSEMBLY & ADJUSTMENT

TRANSAXLE
Differential Bearing Preload
1) If differential case bearings were removed, install outer race of bearing (opposite ring gear) with a .039" (.99 mm) thick shim into differential housing.

2) Install outer race of bearing on ring gear side of differential case into transmission housing WITHOUT a shim.

3) Place differential assembly into position in differential housing. Place transmission housing with gasket onto differential housing. Install and tighten bolts.

4) Attach a dial indicator to transmission housing so indicator plunger contacts axle shaft. *See Fig. 19.* Zero dial indicator. Move differential assembly up and down. Read and record dial indicator reading.

Fig. 19: Using a Dial Indicator to Measure Differential Bearing Preload

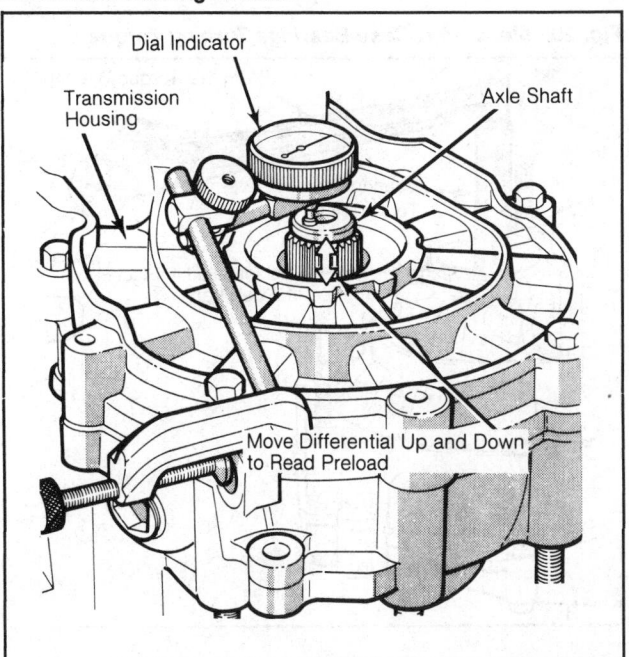

CHRYSLER CORP. A-412 MANUAL TRANSAXLE (Cont.)

NOTE: DO NOT turn differential when measuring. This will allow bearings to settle and result in an incorrect reading.

5) Add constant preload value of .015" (.38 mm) to indicator reading recorded in step 4). This total is the shim thickness required to install under differential case bearing outer race installed in transmission housing.

6) Separate housings and remove outer race from transmission housing. Install required shim (shim pack) in bearing race bore (thickest shim first), then reinstall bearing race.

NOTE: Preload adjusting shims are available in 5 thicknesses ranging from .006" to .031" (.152 to .79 mm). Install a combination of shims as required to make up selected shim pack.

7) Remove right side axle shaft from differential and install Bearing Drag Tool (L-4436) over pinion gear shaft. Lubricate differential bearing with transmission lubricant. Reinstall transmission housing and gasket. Check differential bearing turning torque with an INCH lb. torque wrench. See Fig. 20.

8) If bearing preload is correct, turning torque should be 10-22 INCH lbs. (1-2 N.m) for new bearings or 3 INCH lbs. (.25 N.m) minimum for used bearings. Separate housings and lift out differential assembly. Remove measuring tool and reinstall right axle shaft. Lay parts aside for reassembly at a later time.

Pinion Bearing Preload

1) If not already removed, use a puller and remove pinion shaft small bearing outer race from differential housing bore.

2) Temporarily install a .025" (.64 mm) shim into bearing race bore. Reinstall bearing race. Install pinion shaft into bearing race. Install pinion shaft retainer and tighten retaining bolts to 14 ft. lbs. (19 N.m).

NOTE: For adjustment purposes, original retaining bolts may be used. After adjustment is completed, new pinion shaft retaining bolts must be installed.

Fig. 20: Measuring Case Bearings Turning Torque

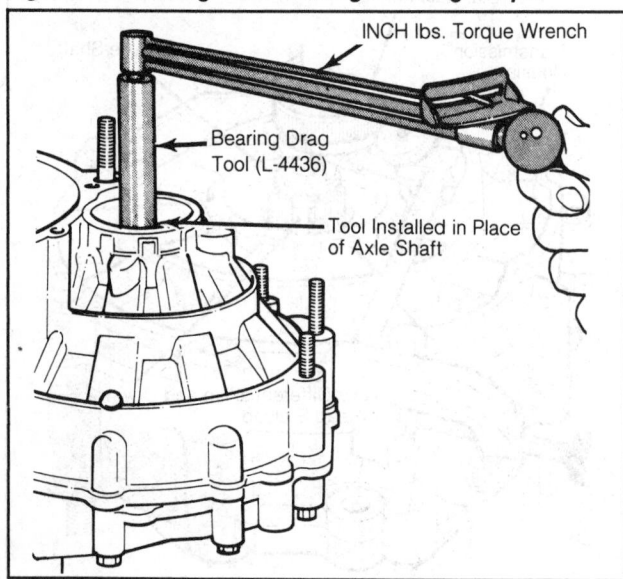

3) Install a dial indicator and support assembly on differential housing so plunger of indicator contacts end of pinion shaft. See Fig. 21. Zero dial indicator.

Fig. 21: Use a Dial Indicator to Measure End Play

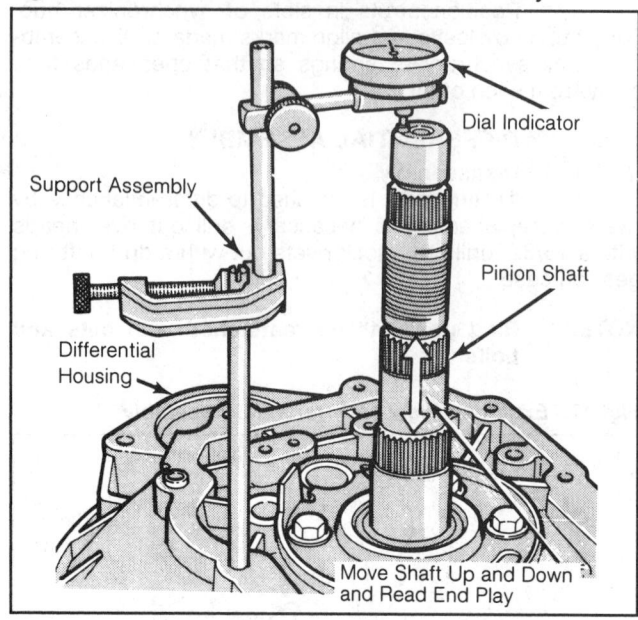

4) Move pinion shaft up and down and read resulting end play on dial indicator. This is pinion shaft end play.

CAUTION: Do not turn pinion shaft when moving up and down as this will cause an incorrect reading.

5) Add .025" (.64 mm) to dial indicator reading plus the thickness of shim temporarily installed under bearing race, plus a constant preload figure of .008" (.20 mm). The resulting sum is the thickness of shim pack to install under small pinion bearing outer race in differential housing.

6) Remove pinion shaft and outer race. Replace .025" (.64 mm) shim with shim pack just determined. Reinstall bearing race, pinion shaft, and shaft retainer.

NOTE: Adjusting shims are available in various thicknesses from .025" to .055" (.64 to 1.40 mm). Install a combination of shims as required to make up selected shim pack.

7) Lubricate pinion shaft bearings with transmission lubricant. Attach adapter (L-4508) to pinion shaft. Check turning torque of pinion shaft bearings with an INCH lb. torque wrench. Turning torque for new bearings should be 4-13 INCH lbs. (.33-1.08 N.m). After checking turning torque, remove tools and pinion shaft.

NOTE: Turning torque of used bearings does not need to be checked.

DIFFERENTIAL & PINION
Installation

1) Place differential housing on a bench. Lubricate differential bearings with gear oil. Install differential assembly into housing.

CHRYSLER CORP. A-412 MANUAL TRANSAXLE (Cont.)

Fig. 22: Checking Pinion Bearing Turning Torque

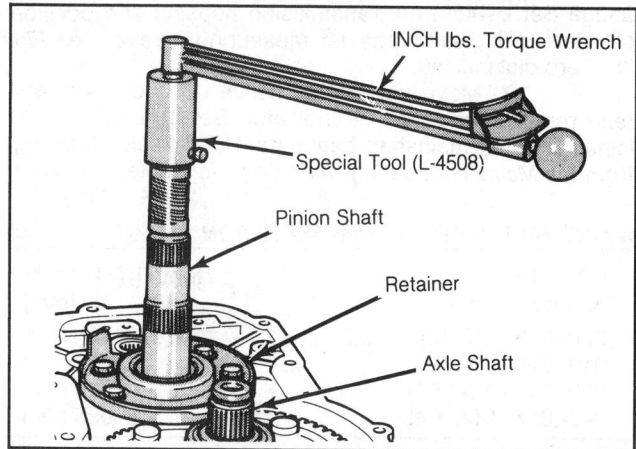

2) Lubricate pinion shaft bearings with gear oil. Install pinion shaft into differential housing. Install 1st gear thrust washer with flat side facing 1st gear. Install pinion shaft retainer. Install NEW pinion shaft retainer bolts and tighten.

PINION SHAFT

1) Install needle bearings and 1st gear onto pinion shaft. Slide 1st gear stop ring onto shaft. Position 1st-2nd synchronizer assembly (shift fork groove up) onto pinion shaft.

2) Ensure slots in stop ring align with struts in 1st-2nd synchronizer assembly. Press 1st-2nd synchronizer assembly onto pinion shaft.

CAUTION: The 1st gear stop ring has 3 missing teeth and is not interchangeable with the other stop rings. If this stop ring is not installed with 1st gear, gear clashing will result.

3) Install second stop ring into 1st-2nd synchronizer assembly. Press 2nd gear inner sleeve onto pinion shaft. Temporarily install reverse idler gear shaft by tapping into case with soft mallet.

4) Install a bolt in reverse idler gear shaft. Center shaft so it is equal distance from each bolt hole in differential housing. Remove bolt without disturbing shaft alignment. *See Fig. 23.*

Fig. 23: Centering Reverse Idler Shaft in Housing

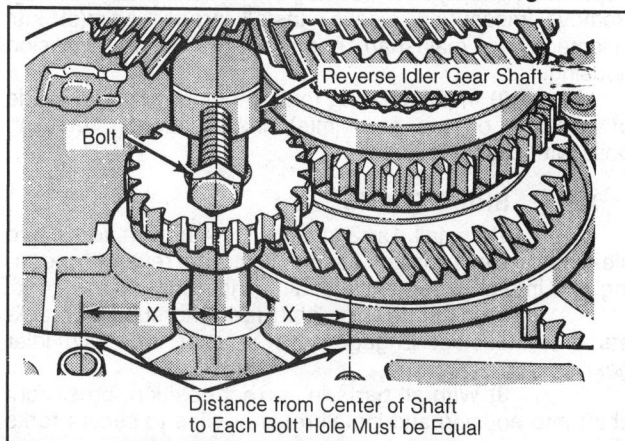

With reverse idler gear temporarily installed.

5) Install 2nd gear needle bearing and 2nd gear. Install 3rd gear onto shaft with thrust collar face down. Install snap ring.

6) Using a feeler gauge, measure clearance between 3rd gear and snap ring to determine 3rd gear end play. End play should be .00-.004" (.00-.10 mm). If end play exceeds .004" (.10 mm), remove and install next thickest snap ring.

NOTE: Pinion shaft 4th gear and snap ring will be installed on shaft after mainshaft is installed.

THIRD GEAR SELECTIVE SNAP RING CHART

Thickness In. (mm) [1]	Color Code
.098 (2.49)	Brown
.102 (2.59)	Black
.106 (2.69)	Silver
.110 (2.79)	Copper
.114 (2.90)	Brass
.118 (3.00)	Blue

[1] — An oil soaked snap ring may tend to discolor so that it will be necessary to measure snap ring for its actual thickness.

MAINSHAFT

1) Install mainshaft into differential housing so that gears mesh with gears of pinion shaft. Install 4th gear needle bearing and 4th gear onto mainshaft.

2) Install pinion shaft 4th gear, snap ring, and plastic plug. Install mainshaft support tool (L-4442) so that adjusting bolt on tool contacts end of mainshaft. *See Fig. 24.*

Fig. 24: Installation of Mainshaft Support Tool

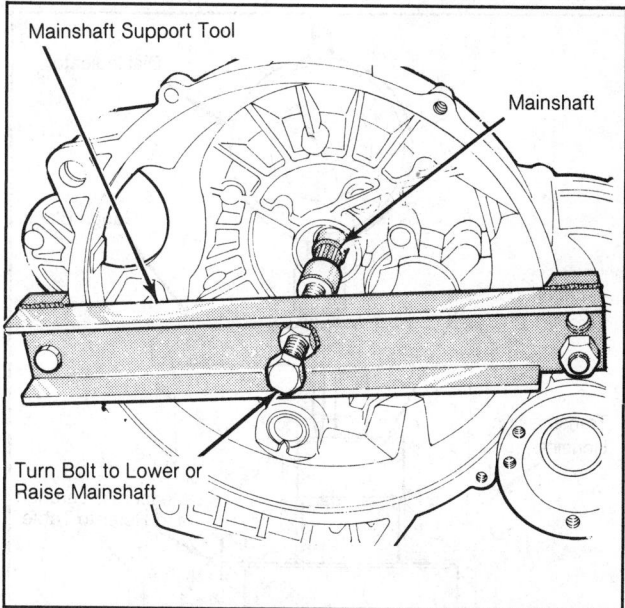

3) Lift mainshaft up or down with adjusting bolt until a clearance of .039" (.99 mm) exists between 2nd gear of pinion shaft and mainshaft 3rd gear. *See Fig. 25.*

4) With mainshaft height correctly set, lock adjusting bolt on support tool. Ensure that clearance between gears has not changed.

CHRYSLER CORP. A-412 MANUAL TRANSAXLE (Cont.)

Fig. 25: Use a Feeler Gauge to Measure Mainshaft Height in Case

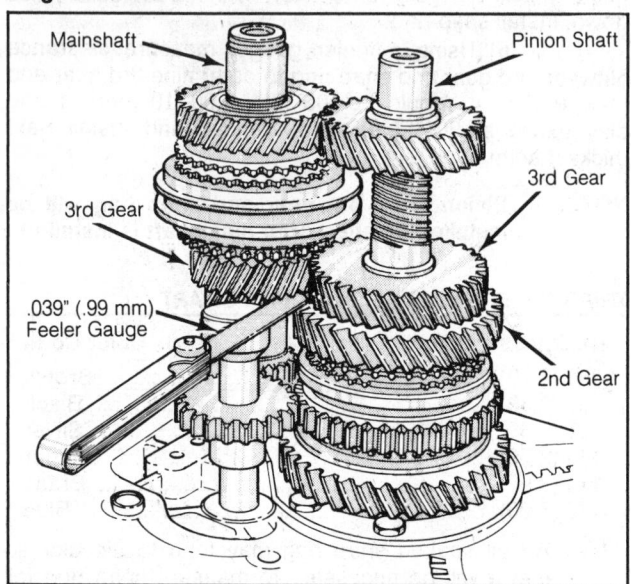

NOTE: If transmission case, clutch housing, or mainshaft has been replaced, the mainshaft bearing shim thickness must be determined using the following procedure:

5) Install measuring sleeve (part of Gauge Set L-4459) onto mainshaft. Install transmission housing (without mainshaft bearing and shim) onto differential housing and retain with bolts tightened to 14 ft. lbs. (19 N.m).

Fig. 26: Installation of Gauge Set (L-4459)

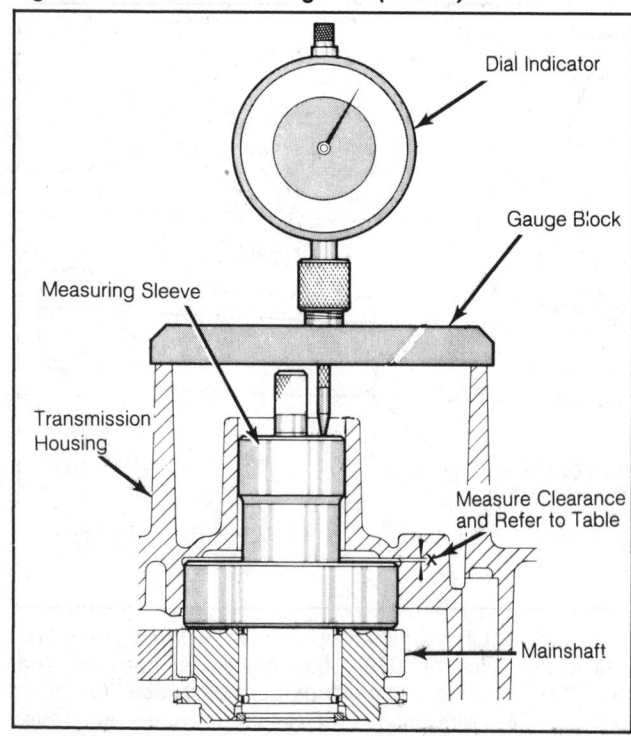

Gauge is used to measure bearing shim thickness.

6) Install dial indicator and gauge block (part of Gauge Set L-4459) on transmission housing and position plunger on indicator against measuring sleeve. See Fig. 26. Zero dial indicator.

7) Move measuring sleeve up and down, and read resulting end play on indicator. Select a shim (to be installed under mainshaft bearing in transmission housing) from the *Mainshaft Bearing Shim Selection* table.

MAINSHAFT BEARING SHIM SELECTION

If Play Is In. (mm)	Install This Shim In. (mm)
.000-.018 (.00-.46)	None
.019-.029 (.47-.75)	.012 (.30)
.030-.041 (.76-1.04)	.024 (.60)
.042-.057 (1.05-1.45)	.035 (.90)

Fig. 27: Location of Mainshaft Bearing and Shim in Transmission Housing

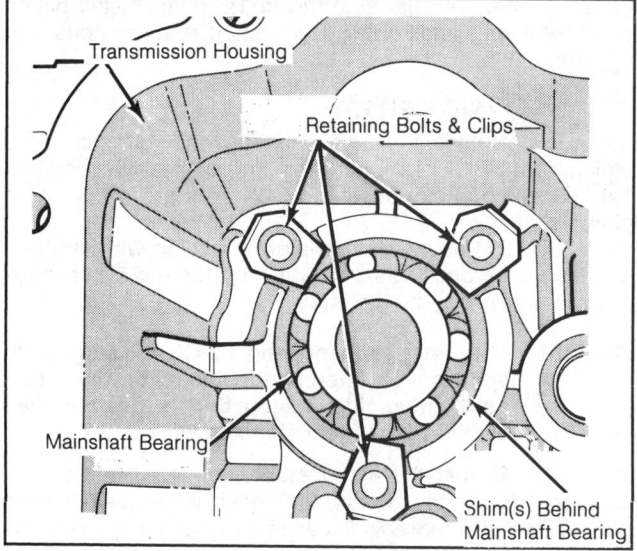

NOTE: Shims are available in thickness of .012" and .024" (.30 and .61 mm). If necessary, combine shims to obtain required thicknesses.

8) Remove gauge block and dial indicator. Separate transmission housing from differential housing. Remove measuring sleeve. Install proper shim(s) just selected into mainshaft bearing bore in transmission housing.

9) Install bearing (hub shoulder towards inside of housing) on top of shim(s). Install bearing retaining bolts with clips and nuts.

SHIFT FORKS

1) Install 1st-2nd and 3rd-4th shift forks into sleeves of synchronizer assemblies, and reverse operating fork into engagement with all 3 shift forks.

2) Install reverse shift fork and support brackets onto housing. Engage reverse shift fork with idler gear.

3) With all parts in correct position, press fork shaft into housing and install retainer clips to secure forks in place.

CHRYSLER CORP. A-412 MANUAL TRANSAXLE (Cont.)

Fig. 28: *Installed Position of Reverse Shift Fork*

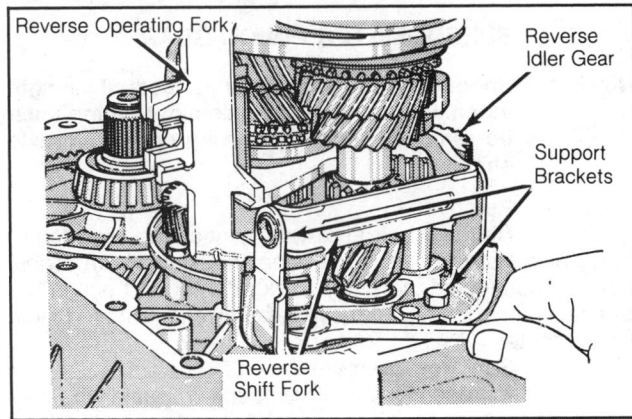

TRANSMISSION HOUSING

1) Install 2 guide pins in dfferential housing bolt holes to align transmission housing with differential housing. Install transmission housing with new gasket onto differential housing, making sure mainshaft is aligned with ball bearing and pinion shaft is aligned with its needle bearing.

2) Using driver (L-4462), drive mainshaft bearing onto mainshaft. Install mainshaft bearing snap ring. Install and tighten case retaining bolts and stud bolts. Install reverse idler set screw.

FINAL DRIVE ASSEMBLY

1) Install new selector shaft oil seal. Install detent spring, selector shaft boot seal and back-up light switch. Ensure transmission is in neutral and install selector shaft assembly. Install selector shaft plug.

CAUTION: Do not force detent spring assembly beyond contact point.

2) Install new drive flange oil seal with installer (L-4446). Lubricate lips of flange oil seal. Install drive flanges with installer (L-4443). Install drive flange cone washer and snap ring. Install drive flange dust plug.

3) Install clutch torque shaft oil seal. Install clutch release push rod from either end of case, with rounded end facing release bearing. Install clutch lever in housing and align splines of lever with splines of operating lever shaft. Slide shaft into lever. Make sure tail of lever engages return spring. *See Fig. 29.*

Fig. 29: *Installing Clutch Lever, Operating Shaft and Return Spring*

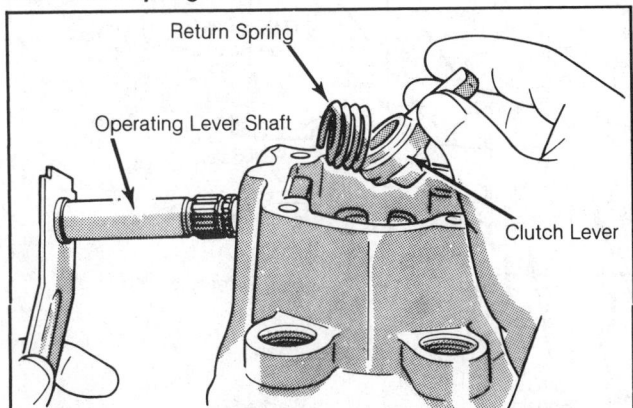

4) Install "E" clips on both sides of lever. Check assembly for free movement. Hold lever down and install release bearing and plastic sleeve. Install end cover and tighten bolts. Install mainshaft bearing retaining nut rubber plugs.

NOTE: While installing clutch release bearing end cover, hold clutch release lever in upright position to avoid loading end cover and damaging case threads.

TIGHTENING SPECIFICATIONS

Application	Ft. Lbs. (N.m)
Ring Gear (Replacement Bolts)	51 (70)
Trans. Hsg.-to-Differ. Hsg.	14 (19)
Housing Retaining Bolts	21 (28)
Selector Shaft Plug	35 (47)
Drain Plug	15 (20)
Fill Plug	15 (20)
Pinion Shaft Retainer Bolts	29 (39)
Reverse Idler Shaft Bolts	15 (20)
	INCH Lbs. (N.m)
Back-Up Lights Switch	144 (16)
Mainshaft Bearing Retaining Bolts	156 (18)
Release Bearing End Cover	105 (12)
Reverse Idler Fork Bracket Bolts	105 (12)

Manual Transmissions

CHRYSLER CORP. A-460 & A-465 MANUAL TRANSAXLE

**Chrysler LeBaron
Dodge Aries, Omni, Rampage, 400
Plymouth Horizon, Scamp**

TRANSAXLE IDENTIFICATION

The transaxle part number, model and build date are stamped on a tag that is attached to an end cover bolt. The last 8 digits of the vehicle identification number are stamped on a raised boss on top of clutch housing.

DESCRIPTION

The A-460 4-speed and A-465 5-speed transaxles contains gear reduction, ratio selection and differential functions all combined into 1 unit. The complete assembly is housed in a one-piece aluminum die casting. The synchronizers feature a "winged strut" design that prevents the struts from popping out of position.

LUBRICATION & ADJUSTMENT

See the appropriate article in MANUAL TRANSMISSION SERVICING Section.

SERVICE (IN-VEHICLE)

SPEEDOMETER PINION GEAR

NOTE: Speedometer pinion gear is located in right extension housing. Speedometer pinion must be removed before removing right drive axle shaft.

Removal

Remove bolt and washer securing speedometer pinion adapter in extension housing. With cable housing connected, carefully work adapter and pinion out of extension housing. Remove retainer and remove pinion from adapter.

Seal Replacement

If transmission oil is found in cable housing, install a new speedometer pinion and seal assembly. If oil is found between cable and adapter, replace small "O" ring on cable.

Installation

Before installing pinion, adapter and cable assembly, make sure adapter flange and its mating areas on extension housing are clean. Dirt or sand will cause misalignment, resulting in speedometer pinion gear damage. Install and tighten bolt.

Fig. 1: Cutaway View of A-460 4-Speed Transaxle

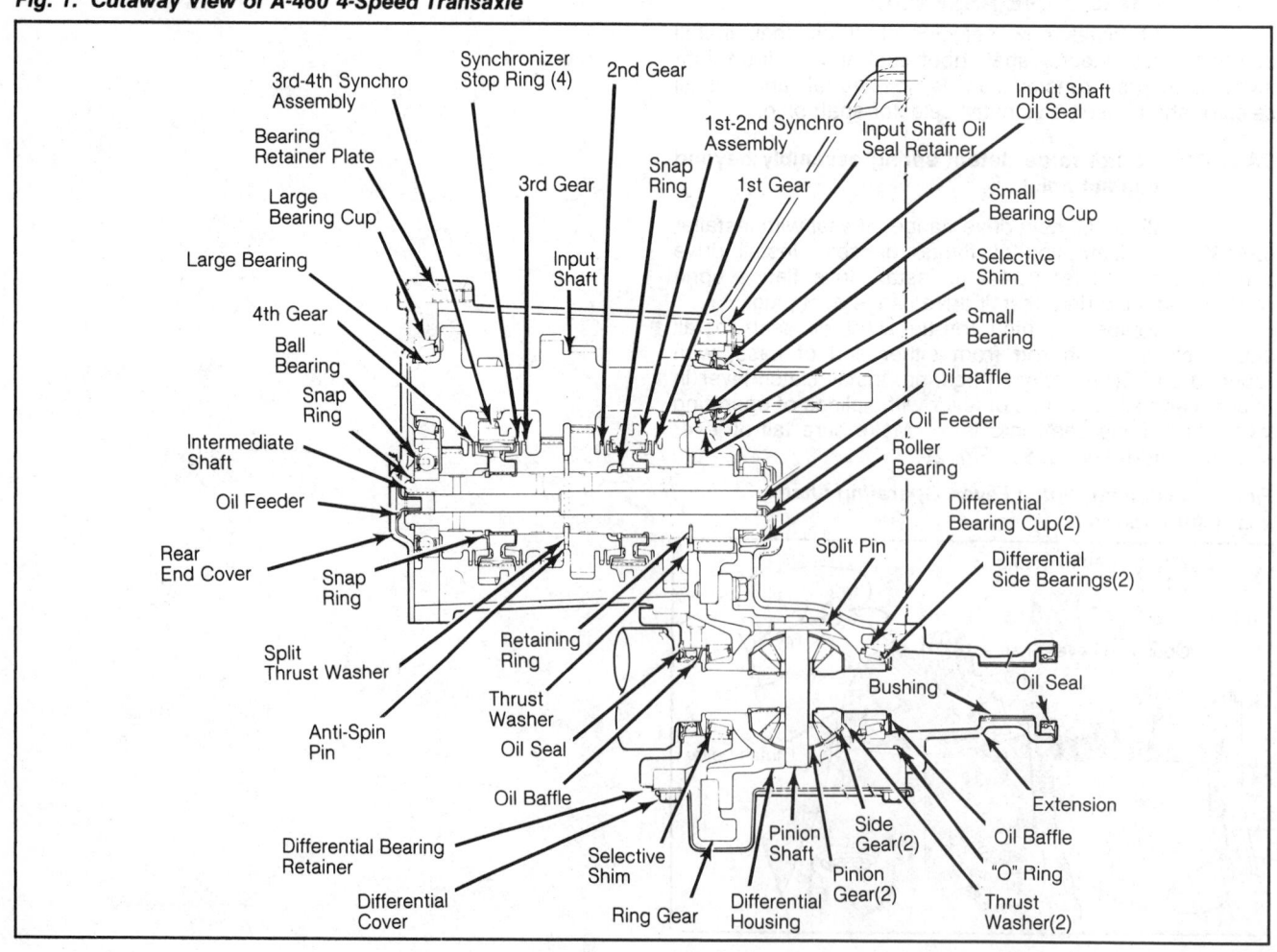

CHRYSLER CORP. A-460 & A-465 MANUAL TRANSAXLE (Cont.)

Fig. 2: Cutaway View of A-465 5-Speed Transaxle

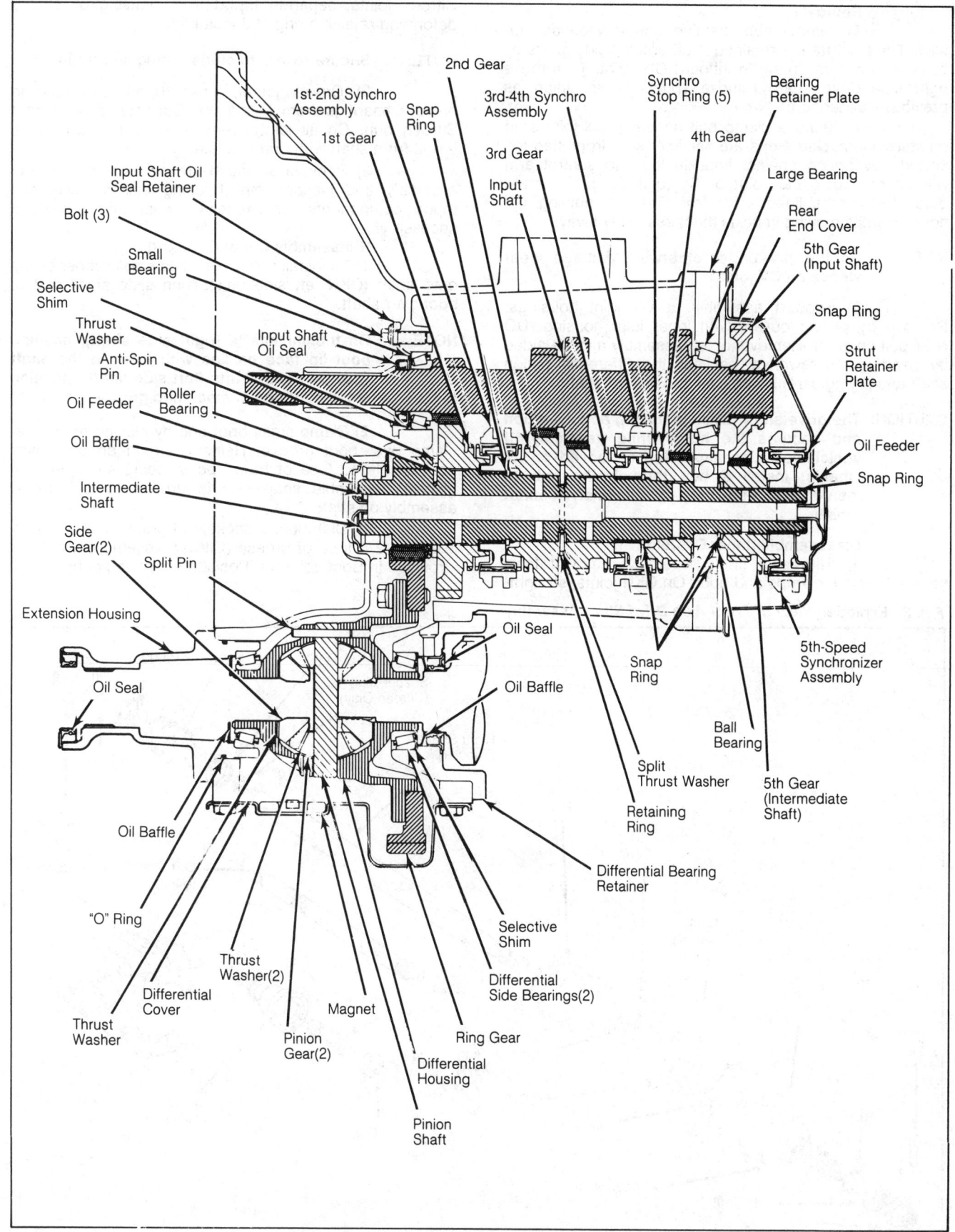

CHRYSLER CORP. A-460 & A-465 MANUAL TRANSAXLE (Cont.)

DRIVE AXLE SHAFTS
Removal

1) Remove hub retaining nuts at wheel assemblies. Drive shafts are retained in differential side gears by constant force of spring in inboard C/V joint. To remove right side drive shaft, remove speedometer pinion as previously described.

2) Remove clamp bolt securing ball joint stud on steering knuckle. Separate ball joint stud from steering knuckle by prying against knuckle leg and control arm without damaging ball joint or CV joint boots. Separate outer CV joint splined shaft from hub by holding CV housing while moving knuckle (hub) assembly away.

NOTE: **Do not pry on or otherwise damage wear sleeve on CV joint.**

3) Support assembly at CV joint housings. Remove by pulling outward on inner joint housing. DO NOT pull on shaft. Removal of left assembly may be aided by inserting a screwdriver between the differential pinion shaft and prying carefully against end face of shaft.

CAUTION: **The drive shaft (when installed) acts as a bolt and secures the hub/bearing assembly. If vehicle is to be supported or moved on its wheels, install a bolt through the hub to insure that hub bearing assembly cannot loosen.**

Disassembly (Inner CV Joint)

1) With axle shaft assembly removed from vehicle, remove clamps and boot. On GKN joints, straight-en tabs to remove shaft and tripod from housing. On Citroen joints, separate tripod from housing by slightly deforming retaining ring at 3 locations.

NOTE: **Secure rollers to studs during separation.**

2) On all joints, wrap tripod with tape to prevent bearings from falling off. Cut retainer ring from Citroen hub. On all joints, remove snap ring and drive tripod from shaft with brass punch.

3) Remove as much grease as possible from assembly and inspect joint housing ball raceway and tripod components for excessive wear and replace if necessary.

Reassembly (Inner CV Joint)

1) To install new boot, slide small rubber clamp onto shaft (GKN left side only), then slide small end of boot over shaft.

NOTE: **On tubular shafts (right side shaft), position boot lip face on line with mark in the shaft O.D. On solid shafts (left side shaft), position small boot end in machined groove provided.**

2) Clamp small boot end by placing the rubber clamp over boot groove. Reinstall tripod on shaft with non-chamfered face of tripod body facing shaft retained groove. Assemble snap ring in groove to lock tripod assembly on shaft.

3) Distribute 2 packets of grease (GKN assemblies) or 2/3 tube of grease (Citroen assemblies) in boot, provided in Boot Joint Kit. Position spring in spring pocket

Fig. 3: Exploded View of Front Axle Drive Shaft Assembly

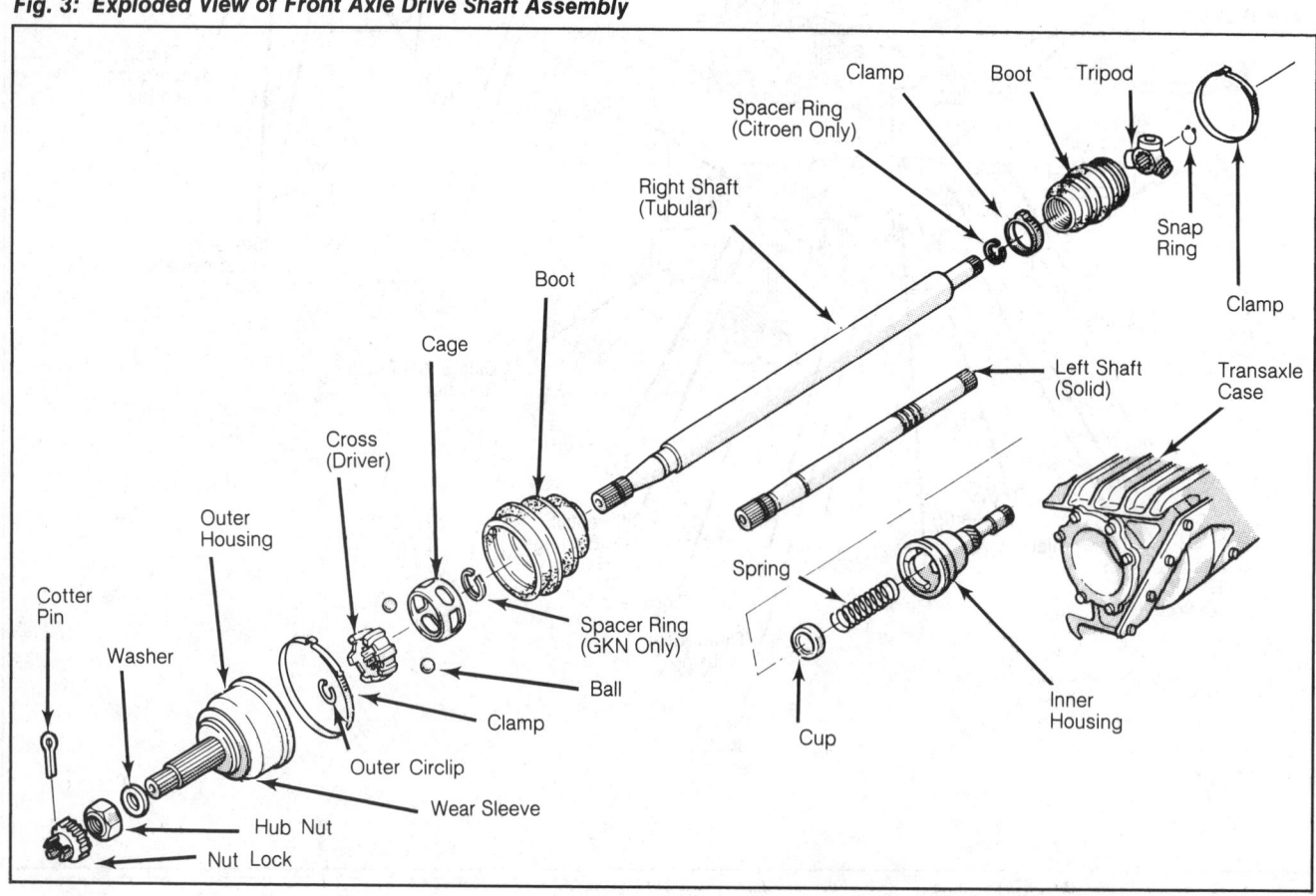

CHRYSLER CORP. A-460 & A-465 MANUAL TRANSAXLE (Cont.)

Fig. 4: Clamping Bridge on GKN CV Joint Assemblies

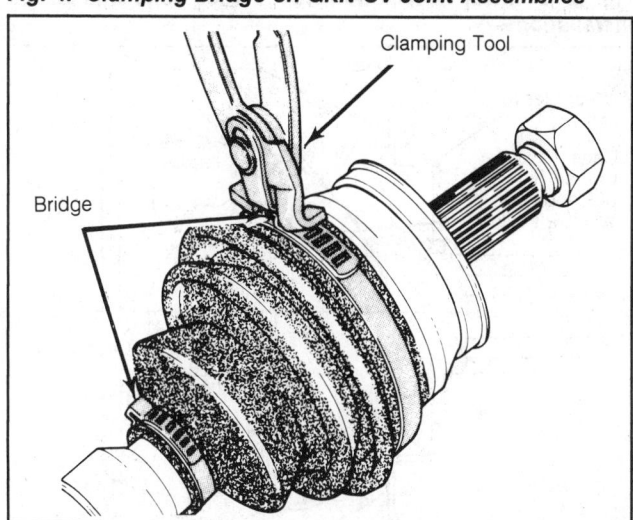

Fig. 5: Tightening Strap on Citroen CV Joint Assemblies

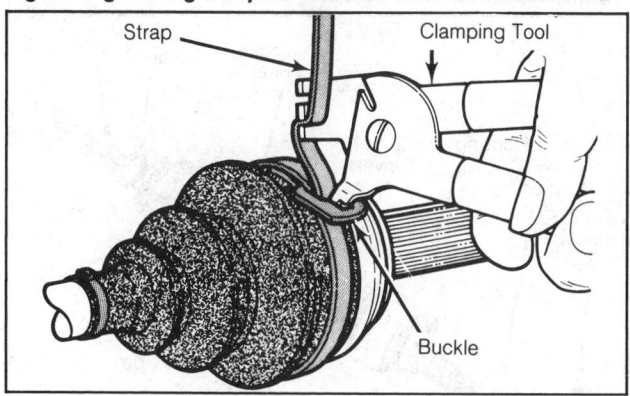

with spring cup attached to free end of spring. Install joint housing over tripod and position large end of boot in groove provided on housing (GKN assemblies only).

4) On GKN assemblies, install metal clamp on boot, making sure that boot is properly located on shaft and housing, and is not twisted. Locate clamp tags in slots, making clamp as tight as possible by hand. Clamp bridge with clamping tool (L-4124) and squeeze to complete tightening. *See Fig.4.*

5) On Citroen assemblies, add 1/3 tube more of grease to housing before installing tripod into housing. Slide tripod assembly into housing, reform retaining ring to secure rollers in housing. Position boot over housing. Wrap binding strap around boot twice, plus an additional 2 1/2".

6) Pass strap through buckle and fold it back about 1 1/8" on inside of buckle. Place strap around boot with eye of buckle toward you. Wrap strap around boot once and pass it through buckle. Wrap strap around boot a second time, also passing it through buckle.

7) Fold strap back slightly to prevent it from slipping backwards. Open clamping tool (C-4653) and place strap in narrow slot about 1/2" away from buckle. Hold strap with left hand and push clamping tool forward and slightly upward, then fit hook of clamping tool into eye of buckle. *See Fig. 5.*

8) Tighten strap by closing tool handles. Rotate tool (handles) downward while sowly releasing pressure on handles. Allow tool (handles) to open progressively. Open tool entirely and remove clamping tool sideways from strap.

9) If strap is not tight enough, repeat procedure, always with tool about 1/2" away from buckle. If strap is tight enough, remove tool and cut strap off about 1/8" away from buckle. Complete by folding the strap back neatly.

Disassembly (Outer CV Joint)

1) Cut boot clamp on boot and discard. Wipe grease away to expose joint. Support shaft in a soft-jawed vise, support outer joint, and using a soft hammer, give a sharp tap to top of joint body to dislodge joint from internal circlip installed in groove at outer end of shaft.

NOTE: DO NOT remove wear sleeve from housing, unless damaged.

2) Remove circlip from shaft groove and discard. Unless shaft is damaged and requires replacement, do not remove heavy lock ring from shaft. With joint separated, proceed as follows:

3) If outer CV joint was operating properly and grease does not appear to be contaminated, just replace boot. If outer joint is noisy or badly worn, replace entire unit.

4) Wipe off surplus grease and mark relative position of inner cross, cage and housing with a dab of paint. Hold joint vertically in vise by clamping on splined shaft, with soft jaws to prevent damage.

5) Press down on one side of inner race to tilt cage and remove ball from opposite side. If joint is tight, use hammer and brass drift to tap inner race. DO NOT HIT CAGE. Repeat this until all 6 balls are removed.

Fig. 6: Removing Cage and Cross Assembly from Outer CV Joint Assembly

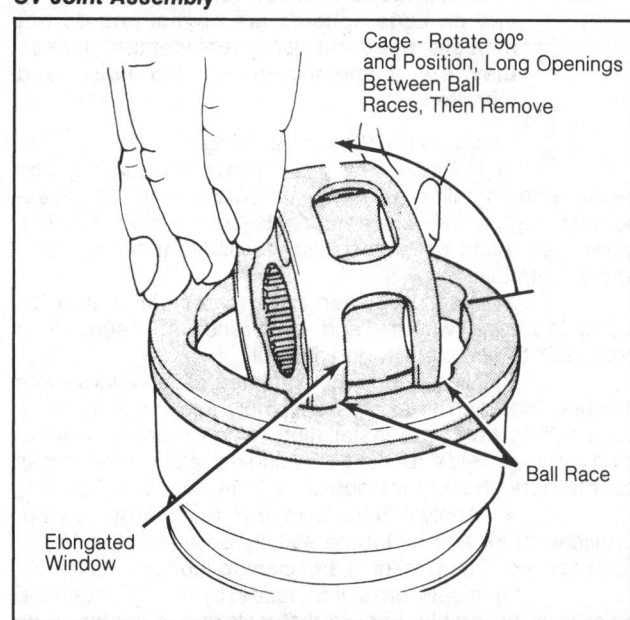

6) Tilt cage and inner race assembly vertically and position 2 opposing elongated cage windows in area between ball grooves. *See Fig. 6.* Remove cage and inner race assembly by pulling upward away from housing.

7) Turn inner cross (driver) 90° to cage and align one spherical land of race with elongated cage window. Raise land into cage window and remove inner race by swinging out.

CHRYSLER CORP. A-460 & A-465 MANUAL TRANSAXLE (Cont.)

Fig. 7: Exploded View of Outer CV Joint

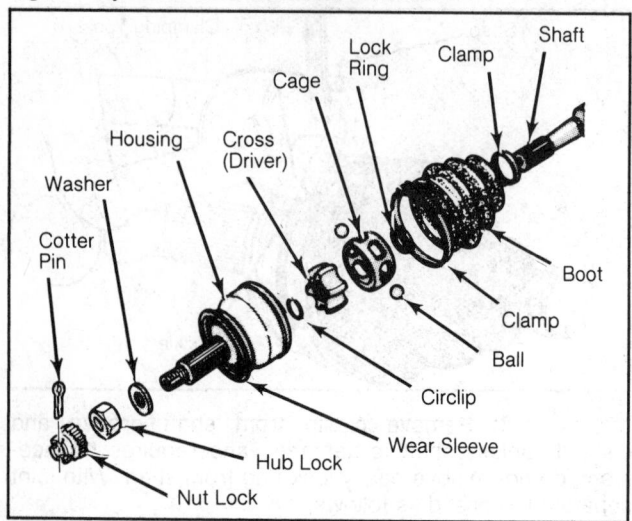

Fig. 8: Cutaway View Showing Correct Cage and Cross Installation

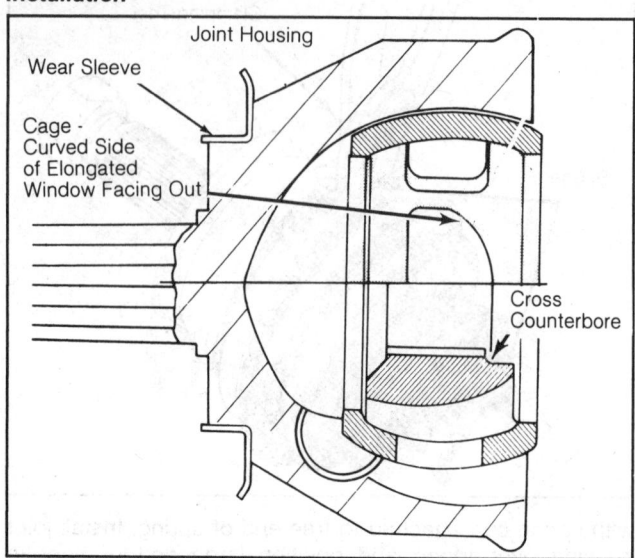

Inspection (Outer CV Joint)

1) Wash all parts in solvent and dry with compressed air. Inspect housing ball races for excessive wear and scoring. Check splined shaft and nut threads for damage.

2) Inspect all 6 balls for pitting, cracks, scoring and wear. Dulling of surface is normal. Inspect cage for excessive wear on inside and outside spherical surfaces, heavy brinelling of cage window, cracks and chipping.

3) Inspect inner race (cross) for excessive wear or scoring of ball races. If any of the preceding is found, the complete CV joint should be replaced.

NOTE: Polished areas in races (cross and housing) and on cage spheres are normal and do not indicate need for joint replacement unless they are suspected of causing noise and vibration.

Reassembly (Outer CV Joint)

1) Position new wear sleeve on housing and install with installer (C-4698), if removed during disassembly. Lightly oil all components before reassembling outer joint. Align parts according to paint markings made at disassembly.

2) Insert 1 inner race (cross) land into an elongated cage window and feed race into cage. Pivot cross 90° to complete cage assembly.

3) Align opposing elongated cage window with housing land and feed race assembly into housing. Pivot cage 90° to complete installation. When properly assembled, curved side of cage windows and inner cross counterbore should face outwards from joint. See Fig. 8.

4) Apply lubricant to ball races from packet provided in kit and distribute equally between all sides of ball grooves. One packet is sufficient to lubricate joint.

5) Insert balls into races by tilting cage and inner race assembly. Ensure that lock ring is seated in its groove.

6) To install boot (shaft supported in soft-jawed vise), slip small metal clamp over lock ring and shaft. Slide small end of boot over lock ring and shaft and position in machined groove provided.

7) Insert new circlip, provided with kit in shaft, using care not to expand or twist clip during installation. Position outer joint on splined end, engage splines and tap

NOTE: Citroen units are provided with a vent sleeve. Position this vent sleeve under boot to shaft clamp area during boot installation.

sharply with a mallet. Check that circlip is properly seated by attempting to pull joint from shaft. Locate large end of boot over joint housing, checking that boot is not twisted.

8) On GKN assemblies, fit metal clamp on boot making sure boot is properly located on shaft and housing without being twisted. Locate clamp tags in slots, making sure clamp is as tight as possible by hand. Clamp bridge with clamping tool and squeeze to complete tightening. See Fig. 4.

NOTE: During this operation, care must be taken not to cut through clamp bridge and/or damage boot.

9) On Citroen assemblies, wrap binding strap around boot twice PLUS an additional 2 1/2". Pass strap through buckle and fold strap back about 1 1/8" on inside of buckle. Place strap around boot with eye of buckle toward you. Wrap the strap around the boot once and pass it through buckle, then wrap it around boot a second time and pass it through buckle.

10) Fold strap back slightly to prevent it from slipping. Install clamping tool by opening tool all the way and placing strap in narrow slot about 1/2" away from buckle. Hold strap with left hand and push tool forward and slightly upward, then fit hook of tool into eye of buckle. Tighten strap by closing handles.

11) Rotate tool (handles) downward while slowly releasing pressure on handles. Allow handles to open progressively, then open tool entirely and remove them from strap. If strap is not tight enough, repeat procedure. When strap is tight, remove tool and cut strap 1/8" away from buckle. See Fig. 5.

NOTE: During any service procedure where knuckle and drive shaft are separated, thoroughly clean the seal and wear sleeve with solvent and lubricate both during reassembly. Apply a 1/4" bead of sealant around circumference

CHRYSLER CORP. A-460 & A-465 MANUAL TRANSAXLE (Cont.)

to seal contact area of wear sleeve. Wet seal lip with lubricant and fill housing cavity with lubricant.

Installation

1) Hold inner joint assembly at housing while aligning and guiding inner joint spline into transaxle. Holding joint housing, spline drive shafts to side gears.

2) Push knuckle (hub) assembly out and install splined outer CV joint shaft in hub. Reinstall knuckle assembly on ball joint stud. Install and tighten clamp bolt. Install speedometer pinion gear.

3) Install and tighten hub retaining nut. Check and fill transaxle fluid level and adjust. Complete installation, by reversing removal procedures.

NOTE: If, after attaching drive axle shaft, the inboard boot appears collapsed or deformed, vent inner body by inserting a round-tipped, small diameter rod between boot and shaft. As venting occurs, boot will return to original shape.

INTERNAL TRANSMISSION PARTS

NOTE: The selector shaft housing, all synchronizers, intermediate shaft speed gears, input shaft, reverse idler gear and shaft, shift forks and pads, shift fork rail and can be serviced in vehicle without removing transaxle from vehicle.

Removal

1) Disconnect negative battery cable. Loosen left engine mount. Remove selector shaft housing bolts, noting 2 pilot bolts, and remove selector shaft housing.

2) Raise vehicle on hoist and remove left wheel and tire assembly. Remove left splash shield. Place drain pan under transaxle and remove transaxle end cover. Remove bearing retainer plate.

NOTE: On A-465 5-speed transaxles, remove 5th speed shifter pin, detent ball and spring (if equipped), fill plug, 5th speed syncronizer, and both 5th speed gears.

3) Remove shift rail. Remove reverse idler shaft and reverse idler gear as an assembly. Rotate both shift forks to the left (toward front of vehicle) and firmly grasp both input shaft and intermediate shaft assemblies. Pull gear set out of transaxle.

NOTE: The differential assembly can only be serviced by removing complete transaxle from vehicle because bearing preload must be reset.

Installation

To install, reverse removal procedure and fill transaxle with transmission fluid to bottom of fill hole in end cover.

REMOVAL & INSTALLATION

See the appropriate article in MANUAL TRANS-MISSION REMOVAL Section.

TRANSAXLE DISASSEMBLY

1) Place transaxle in holding fixture. Remove differential cover bolts and differential cover. Remove 5 differential bearing retainer bolts. Using spanner tool (L-4435), rotate differential bearing retainer to remove retainer. Remove extension housing bolts, then remove extension housing and differential assembly.

NOTE: Remove extension housing and differential as an assembly. DO NOT damage bearing cups.

Fig. 9: Removing Differential Bearing Retainer

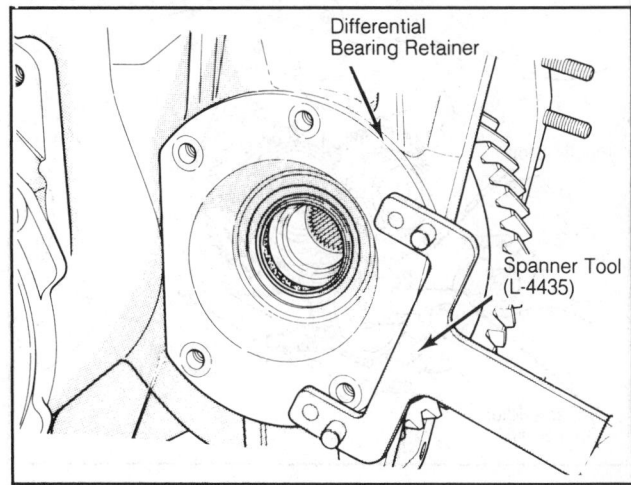

2) Remove selector shaft housing bolts (2 bolts are pilot bolts), then remove housing. Remove rear end cover bolts (12) and nuts (4). Remove 5th gear shifter pin, detent ball and spring (if equipped), on (A-465 transaxle). Using a screwdriver, pry up on cover by placing screwdriver at notch on transaxle assembly and remove end cover.

3) On A-465 transaxle, remove 5th speed synchronizer snap ring, retainer plate and synchronizer assembly from transmission. Remove intermediate shaft 5th speed gear. *See Fig. 10.* Remove input shaft 5th

Fig. 10: Removing 5th Gear Synchronizer Assembly

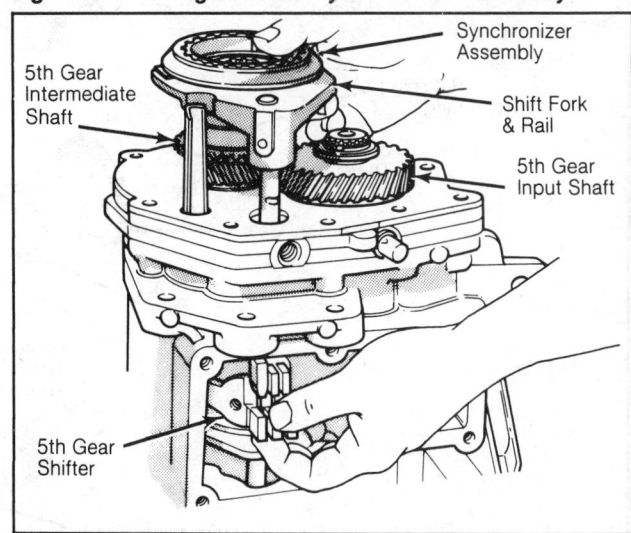

CHRYSLER CORP. A-460 & A-465 MANUAL TRANSAXLE (Cont.)

speed gear snap ring and gear using a pulley puller (C-4333). Remove 2 bearing support plate bolts.

4) Using snap ring pliers, remove intermediate shaft rear bearing snap ring. Using a plastic hammer, tap rear of bearing retainer plate, then remove plate. With retainer plate removed, remove 3rd-4th shift fork rail. Remove reverse idler gear shaft, reverse idler gear and plastic stop as an assembly.

Fig. 11: Removing Reverse Idler Gear Assembly

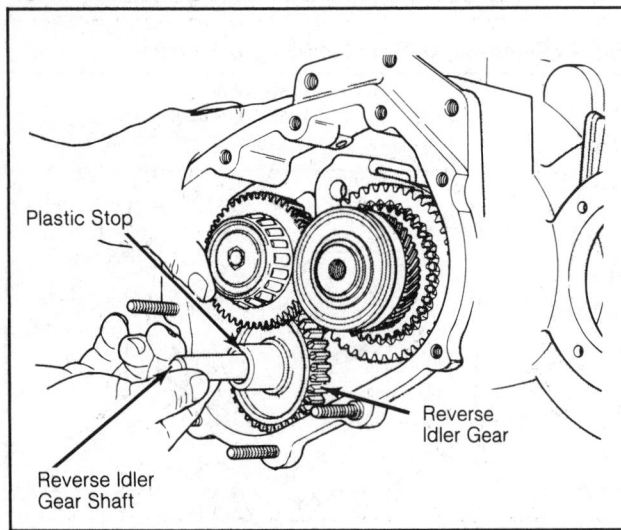

5) Grasp intermediate shaft assembly and input shaft assembly together and remove from transaxle case. Remove shift forks and pads from intermediate shaft assembly.

6) Remove clutch release shaft "E" clip with a screwdriver, then extract clutch release shaft from housing. Separate release shaft by removing "E" clip from release lever and disassembling components. Remove release bearing and fork from clutch housing.

Fig. 12: Removing Input Shaft Seal Retainer

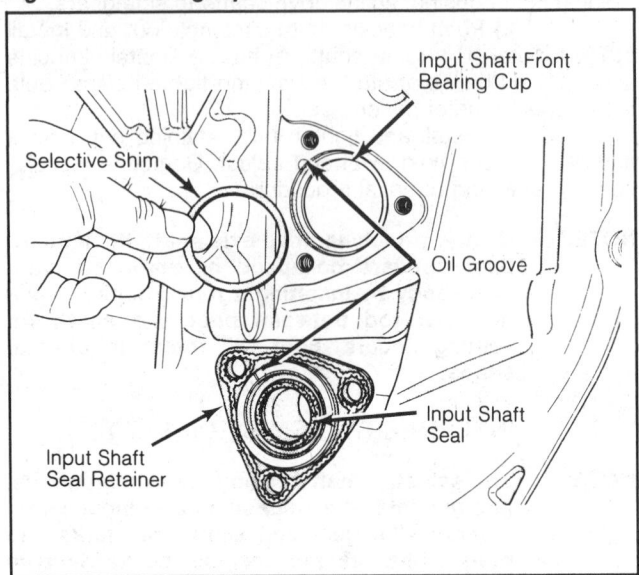

7) Remove input shaft seal retainer bolts, then remove seal retainer and selective shim. Measure shim thickness for transaxle reassembly reference. Remove reverse shift lever "E" clip, then remove flat washer, wave washer and reverse shift lever.

Fig. 13: Disassembled View of Intermediate Shaft Assembly

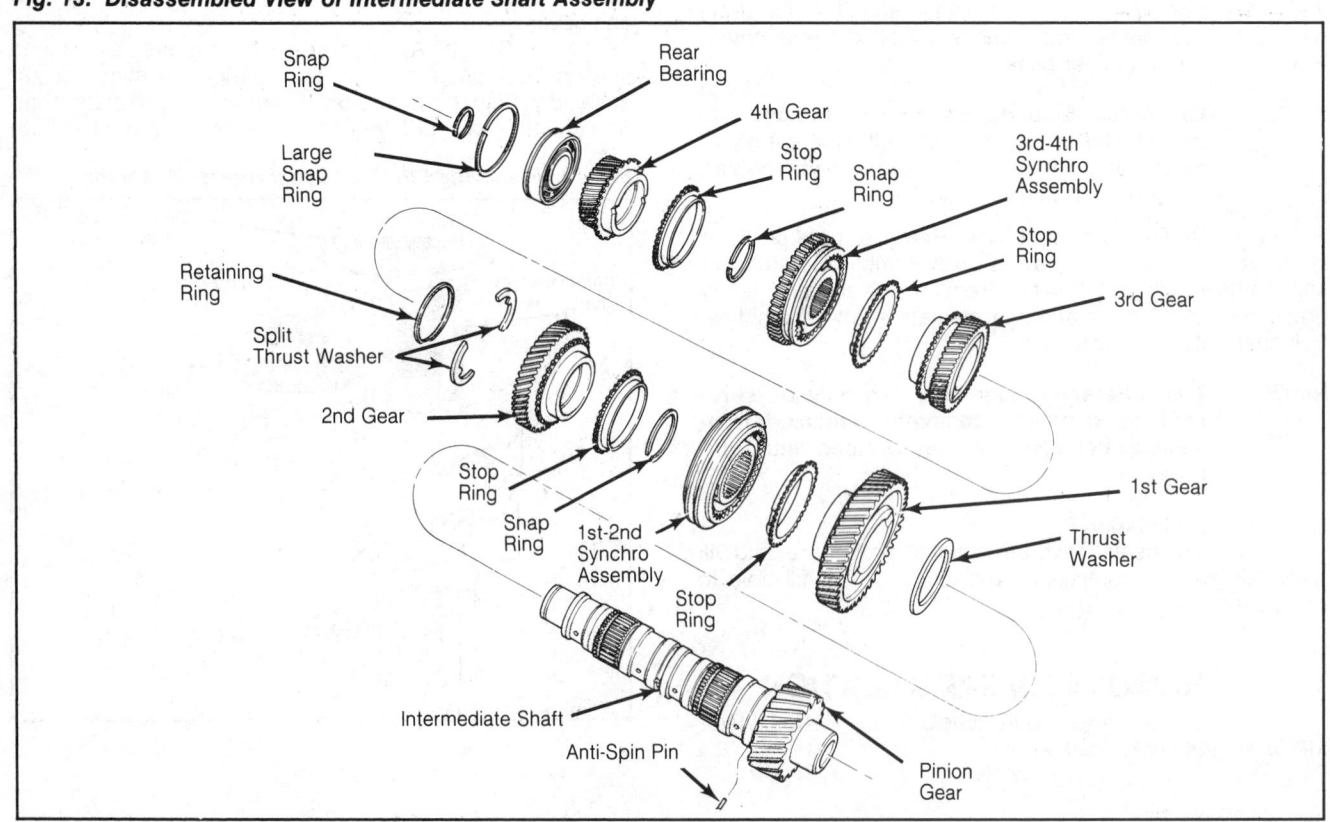

CHRYSLER CORP. A-460 & A-465 MANUAL TRANSAXLE (Cont.)

Fig. 14: Disassembled View of 5th-Speed Assembly

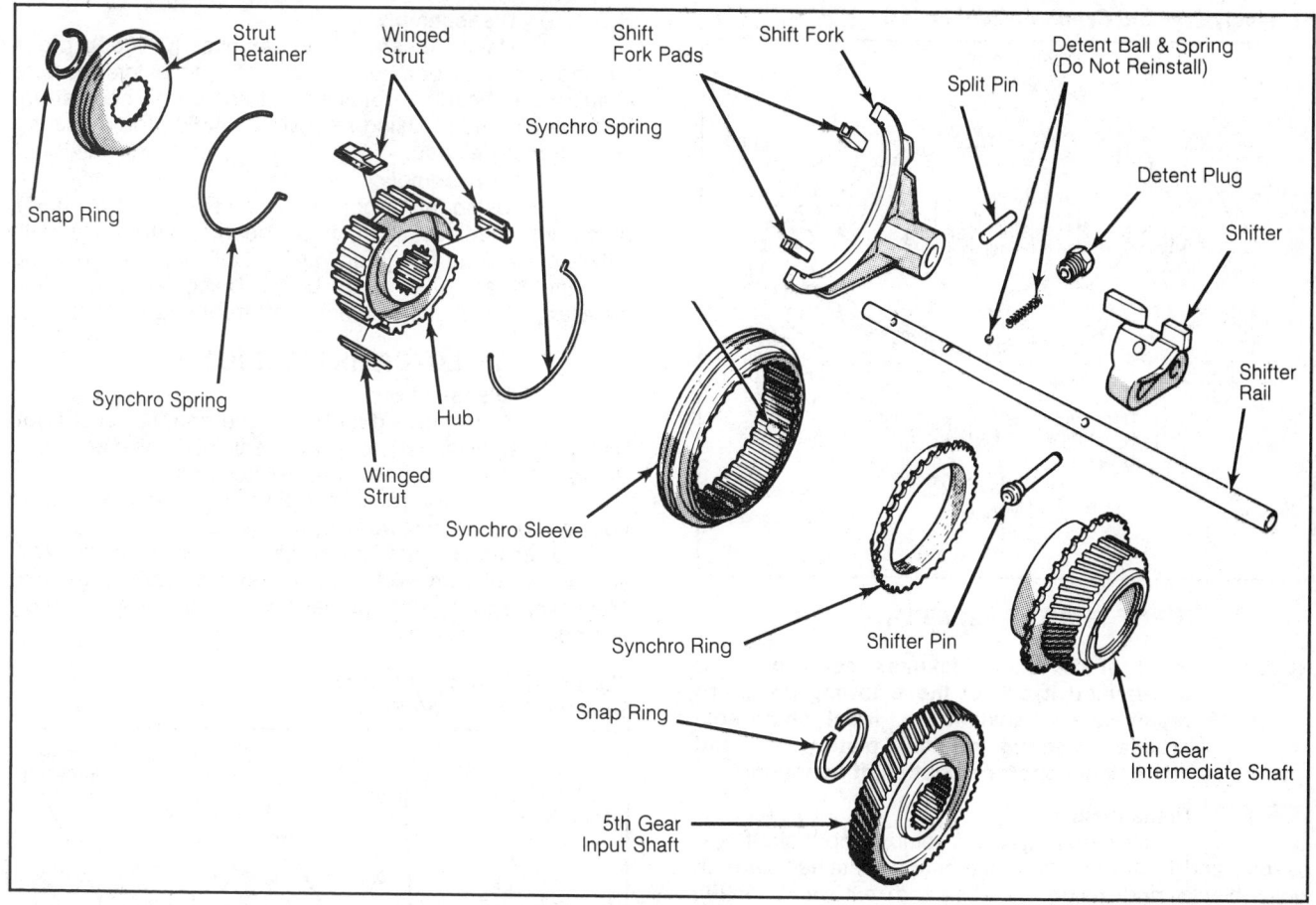

COMPONENT DISASSEMBLY & REASSEMBLY

INTERMEDIATE SHAFT ASSEMBLY

NOTE: The 1st-2nd and 3rd-4th shift forks and synchronizer stop rings are interchangeable. However, if parts are to be reused, reassemble in original position.

Disassembly

1) Remove intermediate shaft rear bearing snap ring. Using a bearing puller, remove rear bearing and 4th gear as an assembly. Remove 3rd-4th synchro hub and snap ring. Using a puller, remove 3rd-4th synchro hub and 3rd gear as an assembly.

2) Remove 2nd gear retaining ring, split thrust washer, 2nd gear and 2nd gear synchro stop ring. Remove 1st-2nd synchro hub snap ring. Remove 1st-2nd synchro assembly, 1st gear stop ring and 1st gear. Remove 1st gear thrust washer and anti-spin pin.

CAUTION: During reassembly of intermediate shaft, make sure all gears turn freely and have a minimum end play of .003" (.076 mm).

Reassembly

1) Install anti-spin pin in shaft recess, install 1st gear thrust washer with chamfered edge toward pinion gear. Install 1st gear, stop ring and 1st-2nd synchro.

NOTE: Relief of 1st-2nd synchronizer assembly faces 2nd gear.

2) Install 1st-2nd synchro snap ring, 2nd gear synchro stop ring and 2nd gear. Install 2nd gear split thrust washer and retaining ring.

3) Using an arbor and sleeve, press 3rd gear and 3rd-4th synchro onto intermediate shaft. Install 3rd-4th synchro onto intermediate shaft. Install 3rd-4th synchro hub snap ring. Using an arbor and installer (C-4672), press on 4th gear and rear bearing. Install rear bearing snap ring.

SYNCHRONIZERS

Disassembly

Place alignment marks on hub and sleeves for reassembly reference. Using care, pry out both synchronizer springs. Separate hubs, sleeve and 3 winged struts, noting their positions. Clean, inspect and replace parts, as necessary.

Reassembly

Align marks made during disassembly, then assemble hub to sleeve. Carefully install spring, prying it back to insert winged struts one at a time. Spring tangs should hold struts in position. Install spring on opposite side of hub, so open end of spring does not align with open end of first spring.

CHRYSLER CORP. A-460 & A-465 MANUAL TRANSAXLE (Cont.)

Fig. 15: *Assembled View of 3rd-4th Synchronizer Assembly (1st-2nd Synchronizer Similar)*

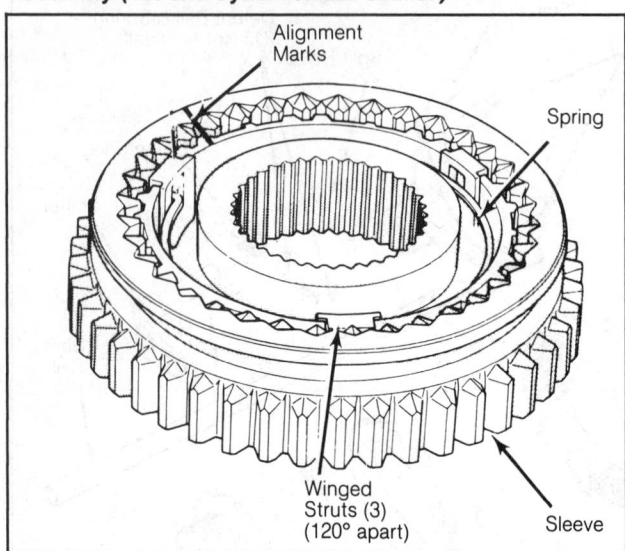

INPUT SHAFT ASSEMBLY

NOTE: Input shaft shim thickness need only be determined if any of the following parts are replaced: Transaxle case, input shaft seal retainer, bearing retainer plate, rear end cover, input shaft or input shaft bearings.

Disassembly

Using a bearing puller, remove input shaft rear bearing and front bearing. Place bearing retainer plate on wood blocks and, using an arbor and remover (L-4520), press out bearing cup.

Reassembly

Using an arbor and installers, press front and rear bearings onto input shaft. Install rear cover to bearing plate as shown in *Fig. 16,* Press bearing cup into plate until cup bottoms on cover.

Fig. 16: *Installing End Cover on Bearing Retainer Plate Before Installing Rear Bearing Cap*

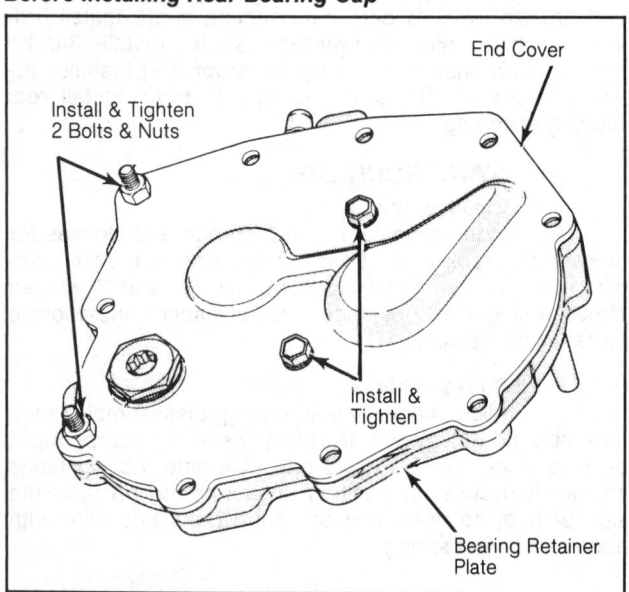

TRANSAXLE CASE
Disassembly

Using an arbor and remover (C-4656), press out input shaft front bearing cup. Remove intermediate shaft front bearing retaining strap bolts and strap. Remove oil feeder. Using remover (C-4660), force bearing out of transaxle case.

Reassembly

Using an arbor press and installer (C-4657), press intermediate shaft front bearing into case with letters on bearing facing upward. Install oil feeder, bearing retaining strap and strap bolts. Using an arbor and installer (C-4655), install input shaft front bearing cup.

SELECTOR SHAFT HOUSING
Disassembly

1) Remove dust boot snap ring and dust boot. Using a screwdriver, pry oil seal off selector shaft. Remove lock pin, back-up lamp switch and gasket.

2) Hold reverse operating lever away from housing. Using a screwdriver, remove 2 "E" clips. Carefully remove selector shaft from shaft housing bore. With selector shaft removed, remove reverse operating lever, crossover spring, flat washer, gearshift block assembly and gearshift selector.

Fig. 17: *Removing "E" Clips from Selector Shaft A-460 Shown*

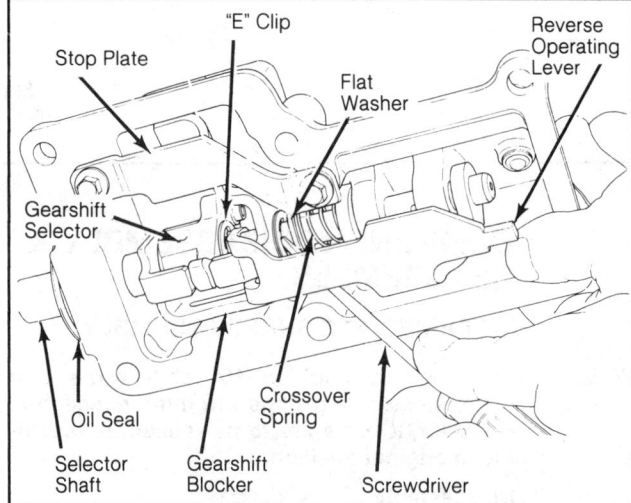

Reassembly

Reverse disassembly procedure and note the following: Install selector shaft oil seal with seal installer (C-4662) and plastic hammer.

DIFFERENTIAL BEARING RETAINER
Disassembly

Using a screwdriver, force oil seal out bottom of retainer without damaging oil baffle. Install bearing cup remover (L-4518) and remove bearing retainer cup. Remove selective shim and oil baffle. Measure and record selective shim thickness.

Reassembly

Using an arbor and installer (L-4520), press oil baffle into bearing retainer. Installer must be inverted to prevent damage to oil baffle. Turn installer over (cone facing down) and install selective shim and bearing

CHRYSLER CORP. A-460 & A-465 MANUAL TRANSAXLE (Cont.)

retainer cup with arbor press. Turn bearing retainer over, invert installer (cone facing up) and press in oil seal.

Fig. 18: Exploded View of Differential Bearing Retainer

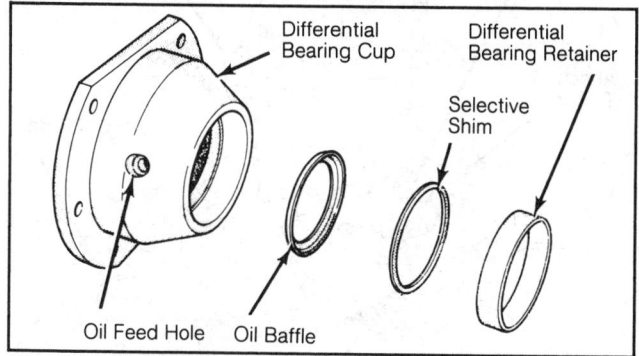

EXTENSION HOUSING

Disassembly

Using a screwdriver, remove extension housing oil seal. Using remover (L-4518), remove bearing cup without damaging oil baffle. Remove oil baffle and "O" ring.

Reassembly

Install "O" ring. Using installer (L-4520) with cone facing up, press oil baffle into housing, then turn installer over and press bearing cup into housing. Install new oil seal in housing using the same installer and a hammer.

DIFFERENTIAL CASE & RING GEAR

NOTE: Differential shim thickness need only be determined if any of the following parts are replaced: Transaxle case, differential bearing retainer, extension housing, differential case or differential bearings.

Fig. 19: Disassembled View of Differential Assembly

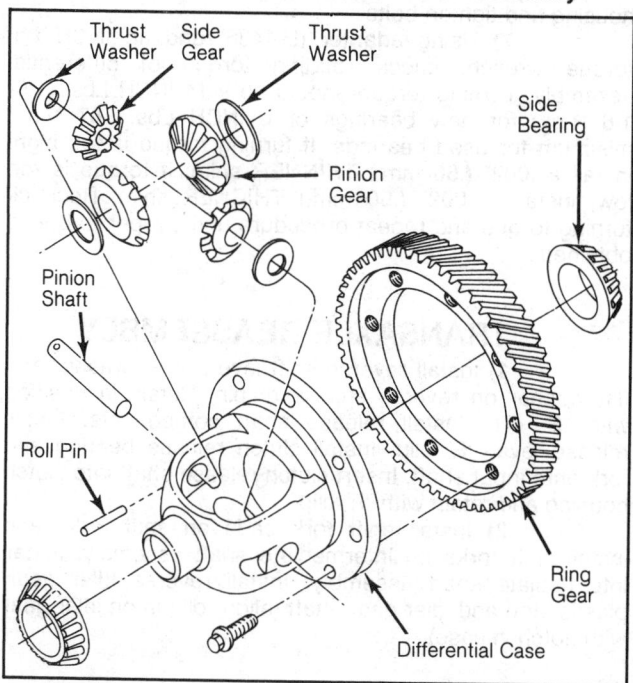

Disassembly

1) Using bearing remover (L-4406-1) and adapters (L-4406-3) remove differential side bearings. Remove 8 ring gear attaching bolts and separate ring gear from differential case.

2) Using a small punch, drive out pinion shaft split pin. Remove pinion shaft. Roll gears around and remove pinion gears, side gears and thrust washers through case opening. Clean and inspect all parts, replace as necessary.

Reassembly

1) Install thrust washers, side gears and pinion gears in differential case. Install pinion shaft and insert split pin.

2) Immerse ring gear in boiling water for 15 minutes, then install on differential case. Install and tighten bolts. Using arbor press and bearing installer (L-4410), install differential side bearings.

TRANSAXLE ADJUSTMENTS

NOTE: All bearing adjustments must be made with no other component interference or gear inter-mesh. Bearing cups and cones should be replaced in pairs if they show signs of pitting or heat distress. Bearings MUST be replaced if removed. Turning torque readings should be obtained while smoothly rotating (break-away reading is not indicative of true turning torque).

INPUT SHAFT BEARING END PLAY

1) Using bearing installer (L-4656) with handle (C-4171), press input shaft front bearing cup slightly forward in case. Then, using installer (L-4655) with handle (C-4171), press bearing cup back into case, from front, to properly position bearing cup before checking input shaft end play.

NOTE: This step is not necessary if installer (L-4655) was used during reassembly of input shaft front bearing and no input shaft selective shim has been installed since pressing cup into case.

2) Select a gauging shim which will give .001-.010" (.025-.25 mm) end play. Gauging shim should be .010" (.25 mm) thinner than original selective shim. Install gauging shim on bearing cup and install input shaft seal retainer. Alternately tighten input shaft seal retainer bolts until input shaft seal retainer is bottomed against case.

NOTE: Input shaft seal retainer is used to draw input shaft front bearing cup the proper distance into case bore during this step.

3) Oil input shaft bearings with transmission fluid and install input shaft in case. Install bearing retainer plate with input shaft rear bearing cup pressed in and end cover installed. Tighten all bolts and nuts to 21 ft. lbs. (28.5 N.m.)

4) Mount a dial indicator on transaxle case with plunger touching end of input shaft. See Fig. 20. Apply moderate pressure, by hand, to input shaft splines. Push input shaft toward rear of case while rotating shaft back and forth several times to seat bearings.

CHRYSLER CORP. A-460 & A-465 MANUAL TRANSAXLE (Cont.)

Fig. 20: *Measuring Input Shaft Bearing End Play*

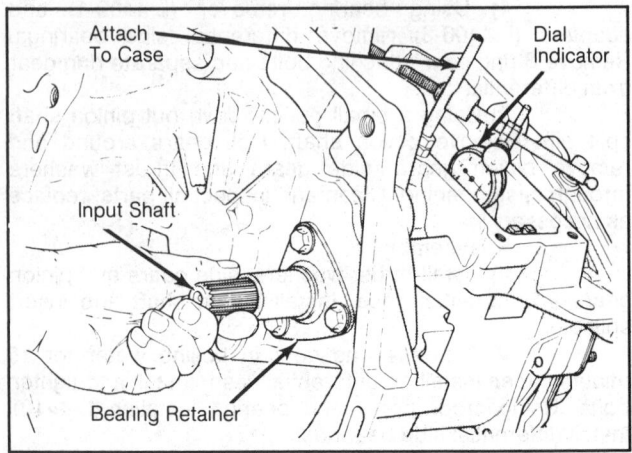

Fig. 21: *Measuring Differential Bearing End Play*

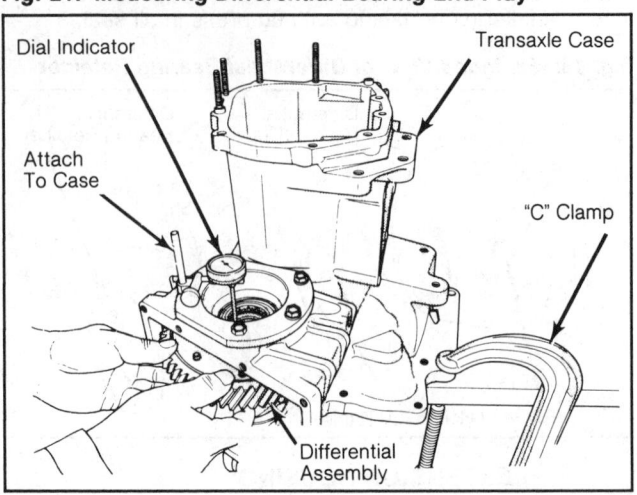

5) Zero dial indicator. Pull input shaft toward front of case while rotating shaft back and forth several times to seat bearings. Record end play.

6) The required shim for proper input shaft end play is to total of gauging shim thickness, plus end play reading recorded in step **5)**, MINUS .002" (.050 mm) constant value. Combine shims (if required) to obtain a shim within .0016" (.040 mm) of the required shim thickness. Shims are available in 30 thicknesses ranging from .024"-.069" (.60-1.75 mm.) Remove dial indicator.

7) Remove input shaft seal retainer and gauging shim. Install required shim(s). Coat input shaft seal retainer with a 1/16" bead of RTV sealant and install and tighten bolts.

NOTE: Do not allow RTV sealant to get in oil slot.

8) Using adapter (L-4508) and an INCH Lb. torque wrench, check input shaft turning torque. Turning torque for new bearings should be 1-5 INCH Lbs. (.11-.56 N.m.), torque for old bearings should be 1 INCH Lb. (.11 N.m.) minimum. If turning torque is too high, install a .0016" (.02 mm) THINNER shim; if torque is too low, install a .0016" (.02 mm.) THICKER shim.

9) If shims require replacement after initial torque reading check, repeat step **1)** to assure that input shaft front bearing cup is properly seated. Repeat step **8)** until proper bearing turning torque is obtained.

DIFFERENTIAL BEARING PRELOAD

1) Remove bearing cup and existing shim from differential bearing retainer. Select a gauging shim which will give .001-.010" (.02-.20 mm) end play. Gauging shim should be .015" (.40 mm.) thinner than original selective shim. Install gauging shim in differential bearing retainer and press in bearing cup.

NOTE: Do not install oil baffle to check differential end play.

2) Oil differential bearings with transmission fluid and install differential assembly in transaxle case. Install extension housing and bearing retainer. Tighten bolts to 21 ft. lbs. (28 N.m.) Mount transaxle case on workbench with "C" clamps (clutch housing facing down). Mount dial indicator with plunger touching case. *See Fig. 21.*

3) Apply a medium pressure to ring gear, by hand, in downward direction while rolling differential assembly back and forth several times to seat bearings. Zero dial indicator. Apply medium pressure, by hand, in upward direction while rotating differential several times to seat bearings. Record end play.

4) The required shim to obtain proper bearing preload is the total of gauging shim thickness, plus end play reading recorded in Step **3)**, PLUS .010" (.25 mm.) constant value. Combine shims (if required) to obtain a shim within .002" (.05 mm.) of the required shim thickness. Shims are available in 29 thicknesses ranging from .020"-.083" (.50-2.10 mm.) Remove dial indicator.

5) Remove differential bearing retainer. Remove bearing cup and gauging shim. Install oil baffle, ensuring not to damage baffle. Install required shim(s). Press bearing cup into differential bearing retainer.

6) Coat bearing retainer with 1/16" bead of RTV sealant and install retainer. Check "O" ring for damage and replace if necessary. Install extension housing and tighten bolts.

7) Using adapter (L-4436) and an INCH Lb. torque wrench, check rotating torque of differential assembly. Turning torque should be 9-14 INCH Lbs. (1.0-1.6 N.m.) for new bearings or 6 INCH Lbs. (.67 N.m.) minimum for used bearings. If turning torque is too high, install a .002" (.50 mm.) THINNER shim; if torque is too low, install a .002" (.50 mm.) THICKER shim. Recheck turning torque and repeat procedure until proper torque is obtained.

TRANSAXLE REASSEMBLY

1) Install reverse shift lever, wave washer and flat washer on reverse shift lever pin. Retain in position with "E" clip. Install release shaft components. Install release lever "E" clip. Install clutch release bearing and fork onto input shaft. Insert clutch release shaft into clutch housing and retain with "E" clip.

2) Install shift fork pads on shift forks and install shift forks on intermediate shaft assembly. Install intermediate shaft assembly. Install reverse idler gear, plastic stop and idler gear shaft (align roll pin on idler gear with notch in case).

CHRYSLER CORP. A-460 & A-465 MANUAL TRANSAXLE (Cont.)

3) Install shift fork rail in case. Apply a 1/8" bead of RTV sealant to bearing retainer plate, then install bearing retainer plate. Install intermediate shaft ball bearing snap ring.

4) Install 5th gear assembly and 5th gear synchronizer assembly to A-465 5-speed transaxle. Apply a 1/8" bead of RTV sealant to end cover, then install end cover. Ensure intermediate shaft oil feeder is in place on end cover.

NOTE: **Manufacturer recommends not to reinstall 5th speed shift shaft ball and spring (if equipped).**

5) Install and tighten end cover bolts and studs. Install detent plug. Coat selector shaft housing with a 1/16" bead of RTV, install selector shaft housing. Apply a 1/8" bead of RTV to differential cover. Install differential cover, catch bracket, cover bolts and nuts.

6) Reverse removal procedure and install transaxle. Fill transaxle with fluid. Shift through gear ranges to test that all parts move freely.

TIGHTENING SPECIFICATIONS

Application	Ft. Lbs. (N.m.)
Anti-Rotational Strut Bracket	17 (23)
Differential Bearing Retainer Bolts	21 (28)
Differential Extension Bolts	21 (28)
Differential Oil Pan Nut & Screw	14 (19)
End Cover-to-Bearing Retainer Bolts	21 (28)
End Cover-to-Case Bolts & Stud Nuts	21 (28)
Axle Shaft (Hub) Nut [1]	180 (245)
Gearshift Hsg.-to-Case	21 (28)
Gearshift Operating Lever Attaching Nut [1]	22 (30)
Impact Bracket-to-Case Stud Nut	21 (28)
Input Shaft Seal Retaining Bolt	21 (28)
Mount-to-Block & Case	70 (95)
Ring Gear Bolts	70 (95)
Steering Knuckle Clamp Bolt	50 (68)
Strut-to-Block & Case Bolts	70 (95)
Transaxle Case-to-Engine Block	70 (95)

	INCH. Lbs. (N.m.)
Intermediate Shaft Bearing Strap Screw	108 (7)
Selector Shaft Housing Lock Pin	108 (7)

[1] — Always replace with new nut.

FORD MOTOR CO. 3-SPEED 3.03

E100, E350, F100, F250

IDENTIFICATION

A service identification tag is located on right front side of transmission case. First line on tag shows transmission model, service identification code and build code year, day and month. Second line of tag shows transmission assembly number prefix and suffix and serial number.

DESCRIPTION

Transmission is a 3-speed, fully synchronized unit. All forward gears are constant mesh helical type. Forward speed changes are accomplished through use of synchronizer sleeves. Synchronizers allow quicker shifts and reduce gear clash.

Reverse gears are spur type and are not synchronized. Transmission uses a system of detents and interlocks within the case, which maintains gear position and prevents selection of more than one speed at a time.

LUBRICATION

See the appropriate article in MANUAL TRANS-MISSION SERVICING Section.

TROUBLE SHOOTING

See Manual Transmission Trouble Shooting in MANUAL TRANSMISSION SERVICING section.

REMOVAL & INSTALLATION

See the appropriate article in MANUAL TRANS-MISSION REMOVAL Section.

DISASSEMBLY

TRANSMISSION

1) With transmission in a sturdy holding fixture, drain transmission lubricant. Remove capscrews attaching cover to case and remove cover and gasket. Remove long spring and detent plug using a magnet.

2) Remove extension housing-to-case bolts and withdraw extension housing retainer and gasket. Remove front bearing retainer-to-case bolts and withdraw front bearing retainer and gasket.

3) Remove filler plug from right side of case. Working through opening, drive roll pin out of case and countershaft using a 1/4" (6.35 mm) punch. Hold countershaft gear with hook, and with dummy shaft, drive countershaft out rear of case. Lower countershaft gear and washers to bottom of case.

4) Remove speedometer drive gear snap ring and slide gear off shaft. Remove gear lock ball from shaft. Remove bearing snap ring from shaft. Using pullers (T75L-7025-B, C, E, G, and J) remove bearing from shaft. Place shift levers in center (neutral) position.

5) Remove set screw that secures 1st-Reverse shift fork to shift rail. Slide shift rail out through rear of

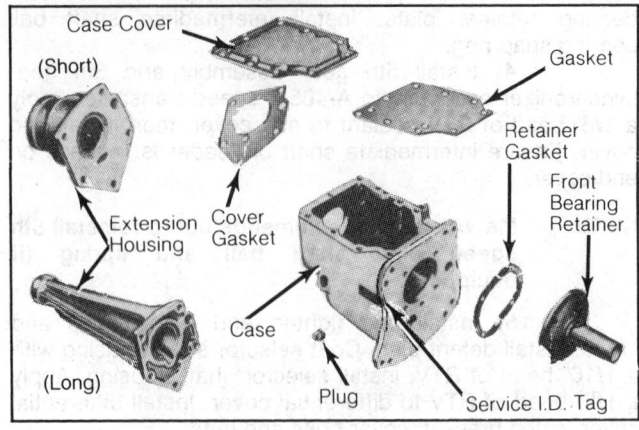

Fig. 1: Exploded View of Transmission Case Assembly

case. Slide 1st-Reverse synchronizer as far forward as possible and rotate shift fork upward and remove.

6) Move 2nd-3rd shift fork to second speed position and remove set screw from fork. Rotate shift rail 90° and lift interlock plug from case with a magnet.

7) Tap on inner end of 2nd-3rd shift rail to remove expansion plug from front of case. Remove shift rail. Remove 2nd-3rd speed shift rail detent plug and spring from detent bore using a magnet.

8) Pull input gear shaft blocking ring, bearing and snap ring from case. Rotate 2nd-3rd shift fork upward and lift from case.

9) Carefully lift output shaft assembly out through top of case. Remove roll pin and reverse idler gear shaft and lift idler gear and 2 thrust washers from case. Lift out countershaft gear, thrust washer and dummy shaft from case.

10) Remove snap ring from front of output shaft and slide 2nd-3rd speed synchronizer and 2nd speed gear off shaft. Remove snap ring and tabbed thrust washer from output shaft and withdraw first gear and blocking ring.

11) Remove next snap ring and using an arbor press, withdraw synchronizer hub assembly from shaft. Do not remove hub by hammering or prying.

Fig. 2: Shift Rails and Shift Forks Installation

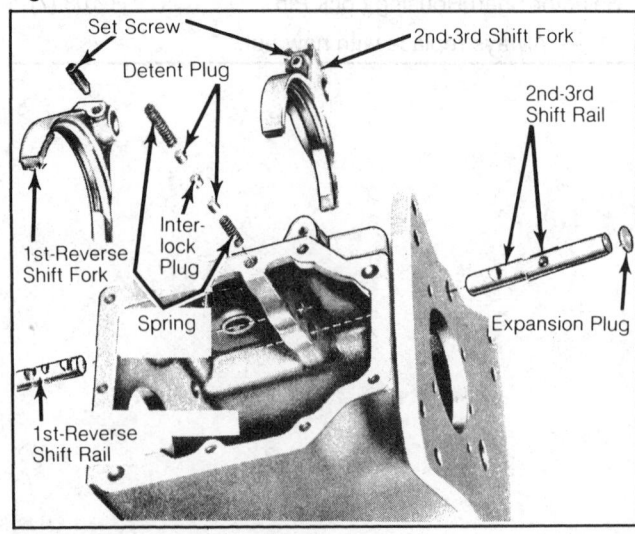

Rotate shift rail 90° to remove.

FORD MOTOR CO. 3-SPEED 3.03 (Cont.)

Fig. 3: Disassembled View of Ford 3.03 3-Speed Manual Transmission

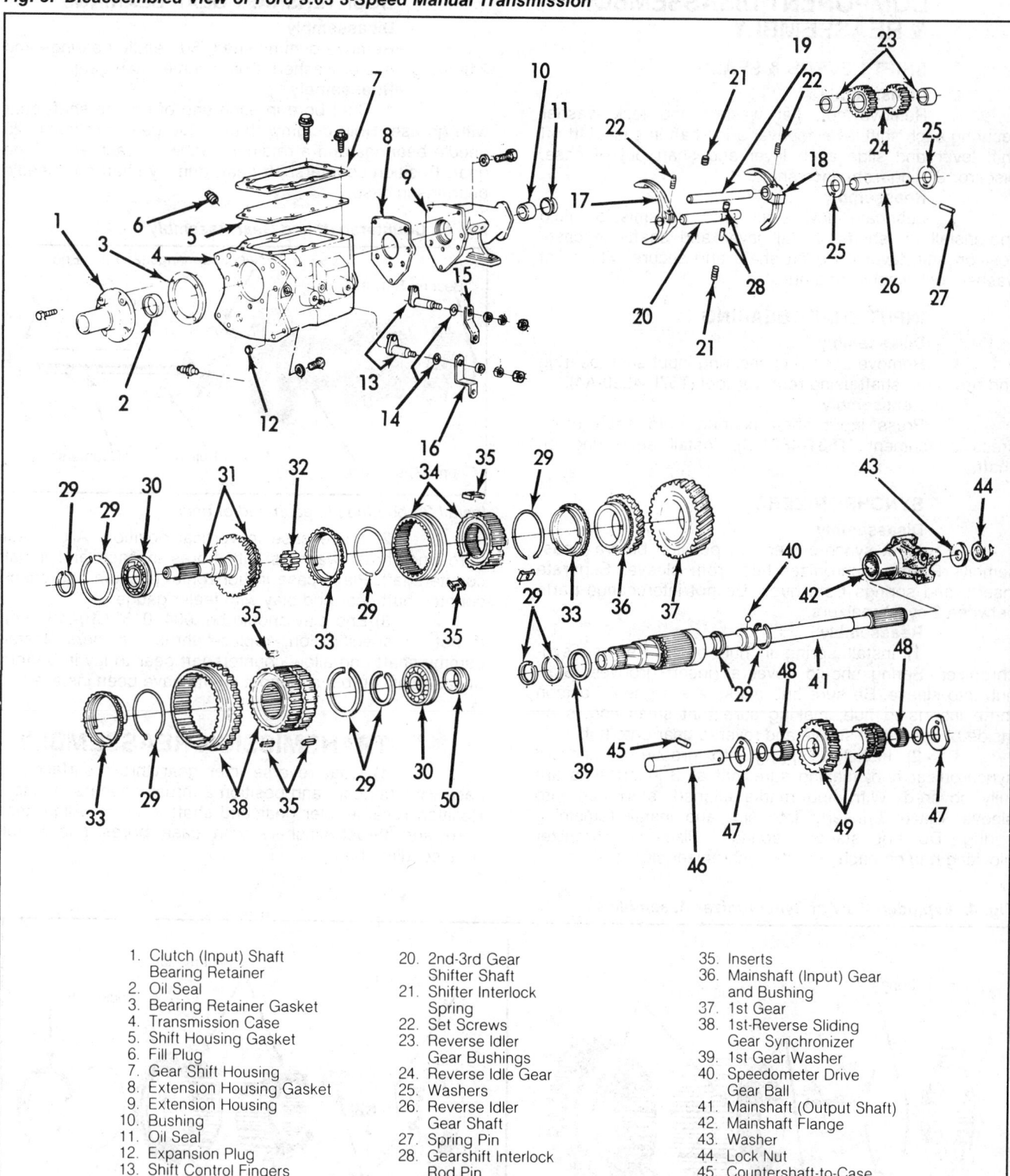

1. Clutch (Input) Shaft
   Bearing Retainer
2. Oil Seal
3. Bearing Retainer Gasket
4. Transmission Case
5. Shift Housing Gasket
6. Fill Plug
7. Gear Shift Housing
8. Extension Housing Gasket
9. Extension Housing
10. Bushing
11. Oil Seal
12. Expansion Plug
13. Shift Control Fingers
14. Seals
15. 1st-Reverse Lever
16. 2nd-3rd Lever
17. Gear Shifter Forks
18. 1st-Reverse Gear
    Shifter Fork
19. 1st-Reverse Gear
    Shifter Shaft

20. 2nd-3rd Gear
    Shifter Shaft
21. Shifter Interlock
    Spring
22. Set Screws
23. Reverse Idler
    Gear Bushings
24. Reverse Idle Gear
25. Washers
26. Reverse Idler
    Gear Shaft
27. Spring Pin
28. Gearshift Interlock
    Rod Pin
29. Snap Rings
30. Ball Bearings
31. Clutch (Input) Shaft
32. Needle Bearings (15)
33. Synchronizing Blocking
    Ring
34. 2nd-3rd Sliding Gear
    Synchronizer

35. Inserts
36. Mainshaft (Input) Gear
    and Bushing
37. 1st Gear
38. 1st-Reverse Sliding
    Gear Synchronizer
39. 1st Gear Washer
40. Speedometer Drive
    Gear Ball
41. Mainshaft (Output Shaft)
42. Mainshaft Flange
43. Washer
44. Lock Nut
45. Countershaft-to-Case
    Pin
46. Countershaft
47. Countershaft Gear
    Thrust Plate
48. Needle Bearings (25)
49. Countershaft Cluster
    Gear
50. Speedometer Drive
    Gear

FORD MOTOR CO. 3-SPEED 3.03 (Cont.)

COMPONENT DISASSEMBLY & REASSEMBLY

SHIFT LEVERS & SEALS

Disassembly

Remove nut, flat washer and lock washer securing each shift lever to lever and shaft in case. Lift off shift lever and slide each lever and shaft out of case. Discard "O" ring from each shaft.

Reassembly

Lubricate new seals with transmission fluid and install on shafts. Install lever and shafts in case, position shift lever on each shaft, and secure with a flat washer, lock washer and nut.

INPUT SHAFT BEARING

Disassembly

Remove snap ring securing input shaft bearing and press out shaft using remover tool (T57L-4220-A4).

Reassembly

Press input shaft bearing onto shaft using press attachment (T53T-4621-B). Install snap ring on shaft.

SYNCHRONIZERS

Disassembly

Mark synchronizer hub position before disassembly. Push synchronizer hub from sleeve. Separate inserts and springs from hubs. Do not interchange parts between 2 synchronizers.

Reassembly

1) Install spring in hub of 1st-Reverse synchronizer. Spring should cover all insert grooves. Start hub into sleeve. Be sure hub marks are aligned. Position three inserts in hub, making sure that small end is on inside of hub. Slide sleeve and reverse gear onto hub.

2) Install 1 spring into groove of 2nd-3rd synchronizer hub, making sure that all 3 insert slots are fully covered. With hub marks aligned, start hub into sleeve. Place 3 inserts into slot and install remaining spring. Do not stagger springs. Place synchronizer blocking ring on each end of synchronizer sleeve.

COUNTERSHAFT GEAR BEARINGS

Disassembly

Remove dummy shaft, 50 needle bearings and 2 bearing retainer washers from countershaft gear.

Reassembly

1) Coat bore in each end of countershaft gear with grease. Hold dummy shaft in the gear and install 25 needle bearings and a retainer washer in each end of the gear. Position countershaft gear, dummy shaft and needle bearings in case.

Fig. 5: Countershaft and Gear Assembly

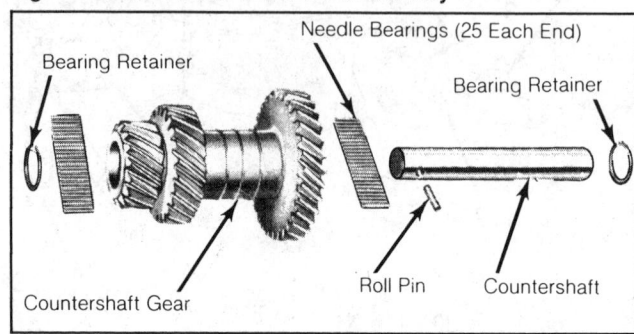

Install 25 bearings in each end of gear.

2) Place case in vertical position. Align gear bore and thrust washers with bores in case and install countershaft. Place case in horizontal position and check countershaft gear end play with feeler gauge.

3) End play should be .004-.018" (.10-.46 mm). If not to specification, replace thrust washers. Install dummy shaft and allow countershaft gear to lay in bottom of case until output and input shafts have been installed.

TRANSMISSION REASSEMBLY

1) Coat reverse idler gear thrust surfaces in case with lubricant and position 2 thrust washers in place. Position reverse idler gear and shaft in place. Align gear bore and thrust washers with case bores and install reverse idler shaft.

Fig. 4: Exploded View of Synchronizer Assemblies

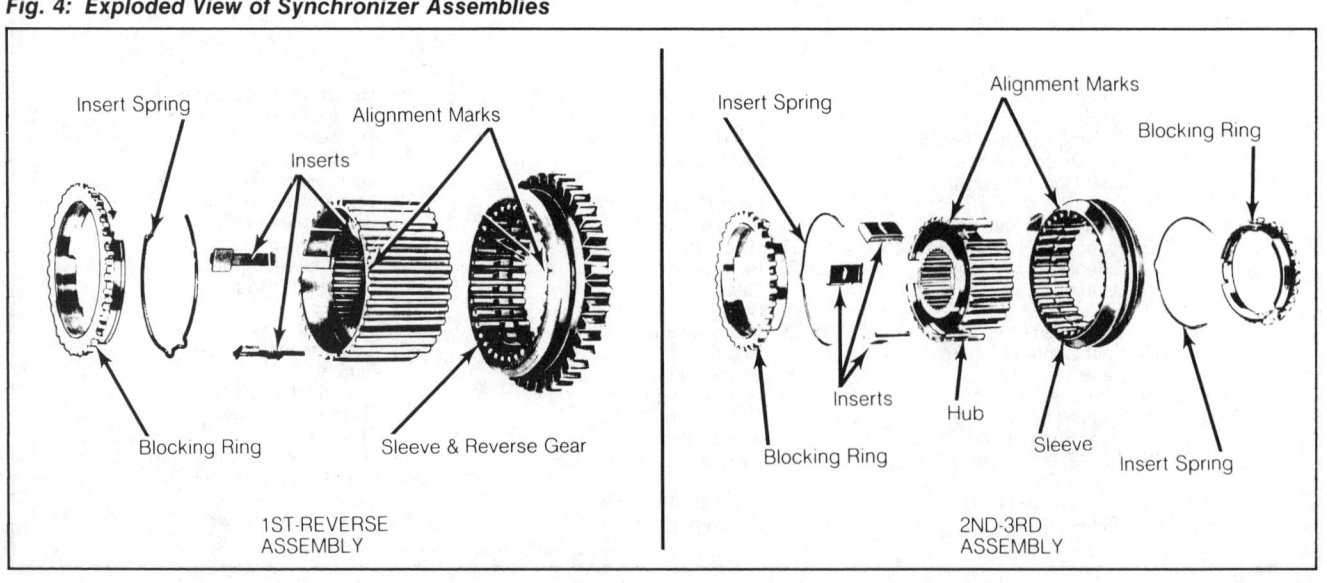

FORD MOTOR CO. 3-SPEED 3.03 (Cont.)

2) Measure reverse idler gear end play with a feeler gauge. End play should be within .004-.018" (.10-.46 mm). If end play is not to specification, replace thrust washers.

3) Lubricate output shaft splines and machined surfaces. Install 1st-Reverse synchronizer hub on shaft with teeth end of gear facing toward rear of shaft. Press on shaft using arbor press, do not attempt to hammer or pry. Secure synchronizer with snap ring, if fitted.

4) Place blocking ring on tapered machined surface of 1st gear and slide 1st gear onto output shaft with blocking ring toward rear of shaft. Rotate gear as necessary to engage 3 notches in blocking ring with synchronzier inserts. Secure 1st gear with thrust washer and snap ring.

5) Slide blocking ring onto tapered machined surface of 2nd gear. Slide 2nd gear, with blocking ring and 2nd-3rd gear synchronizer onto mainshaft. Tapered machined surface of 2nd gear must face toward front of shaft. Make sure notches in blocking ring engage synchronizer inserts and secure with snap ring.

6) Coat bore of input shaft with thin film of grease and install 15 roller bearings. Install input shaft through front of transmission case and install snap ring in bearing groove. Position output shaft assembly in case, and place shift fork on 2nd-3rd synchronizer assembly.

NOTE: Use only a thin film of grease; a thick application will block lubricating holes.

Fig. 6: Reverse Idler Gear and Shaft Assembly

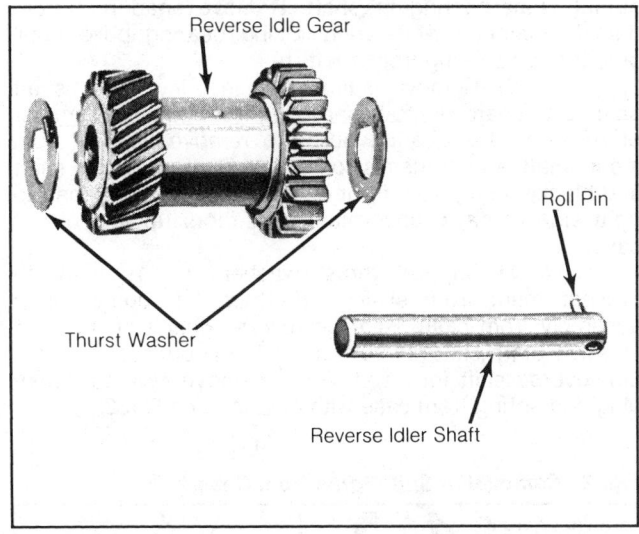

Idler gear end play should be .004-.018" (.10-.46 mm).

7) Place detent spring and plug into case. Position 2nd-3rd synchronizer in 2nd gear position (toward rear of transmission). Align shift fork and install shift rail. Move rail inward until detent plug engages forward notch (2nd gear position).

8) Secure fork to shaft with set screw. Move synchronizer to neutral position, and install interlock plug in case. Move 1st-Reverse synchronizer to 1st speed position and place shift fork in synchronizer groove.

9) Rotate shift fork into position and install shift rail. Move rail inward until center notch (neutral) is aligned with detent bore. Secure fork to rail with set screw. Install a new shift rail expansion plug in front of transmission.

10) Hold input shaft and blocking ring in position. Move output shaft forward to seat pilot in roller bearings of input gear. Tap input gear bearing into place. Hold output shaft to prevent roller bearings from dropping.

11) Install front bearing retainer with new gasket. Make sure oil return slot of retainer is positioned toward bottom of case. Install and tighten retainer-to-case attaching screws.

Fig. 7: Input Shaft and Gear Assembly

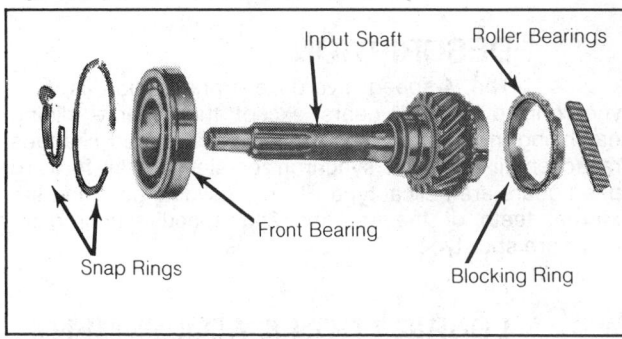

See Fig. 1 for view of front bearing retainer.

12) Install large snap ring on rear bearing and place bearing on output shaft with snap ring toward rear of shaft. Using bearing installer (T75L-7075-B, E, K & P) press bearing into place. Secure bearing to shaft with snap ring.

13) Hold speedometer drive gear lock ball in detent and slide speedometer drive gear into place. Secure gear with snap ring. Place transmission in vertical position. Working with screwdriver through bottom drain hole, align bore of countershaft gear with bore of case.

14) Working from rear of case, push dummy shaft out of countershaft gear with countershaft. Be sure roll pin hole is aligned with hole in case before inserting countershaft. Drive shaft into place and install roll pin.

15) Place output shaft bearing retainer into front of extension housing. Coat new extension housing gasket with sealer and install. Install lock washers on 5 attaching screws and dip threads in sealer.

16) Bolt housing to case and tighten to specification. Place transmission in gear and pour lubricant (ESP-M2C83-C or equivalent) over entire gear train while rotating either input or output shaft.

17) Install remaining detent plug and long spring into case. Coat new cover gasket with sealer. Position gasket and cover on transmission case, and install and tighten attaching screws. Check operation of transmission in all gear positions.

TIGHTENING SPECIFICATIONS

Application	Ft. Lbs. (N.m)
Front Bearing Retainer-to-Case	30-36 (41-48)
Extension Housing-to-Case	42-50 (57-67)
Cover-to-Case	20-25 (28-33)
Outer Shift Lever Nut	18-23 (25-31)
Shift Fork-to-Shift Rail	10-18 (14-24)
Filler Plug	10-20 (14-27)
Transmission-to-Clutch Housing	42-50 (57-67)
Reverse Lamp Switch	8-12 (11-16)

FORD MOTOR CO. 4-SPEED RUG OVERDRIVE

E100, 350

IDENTIFICATION

Transmission may be identified by a tag located on the right side of case at the front. The first line on tag will show transmission model prefix and suffix, service identification code, when required, and build date code. Lower line on tag shows transmission serial number. Additionally, serial number is stamped on top side of transmission flange.

DESCRIPTION

The 4-speed overdrive transmission is fully synchronized with all gears except the reverse sliding gear being in constant mesh. All forward speed changes are accomplished with synchronizer sleeves. All forward speed gears are helical type. Reverse sliding gear and the external teeth of the 1st and 2nd speed synchronizer sleeve are spur type.

LUBRICATION & ADJUSTMENT

See the appropriate article in MANUAL TRANS-MISSION SERVICING Section.

TROUBLE SHOOTING

See the appropriate article in MANUAL TRANS-MISSION TROUBLE SHOOTING Section.

Fig. 1: Exploded View of Shift Rails & Forks

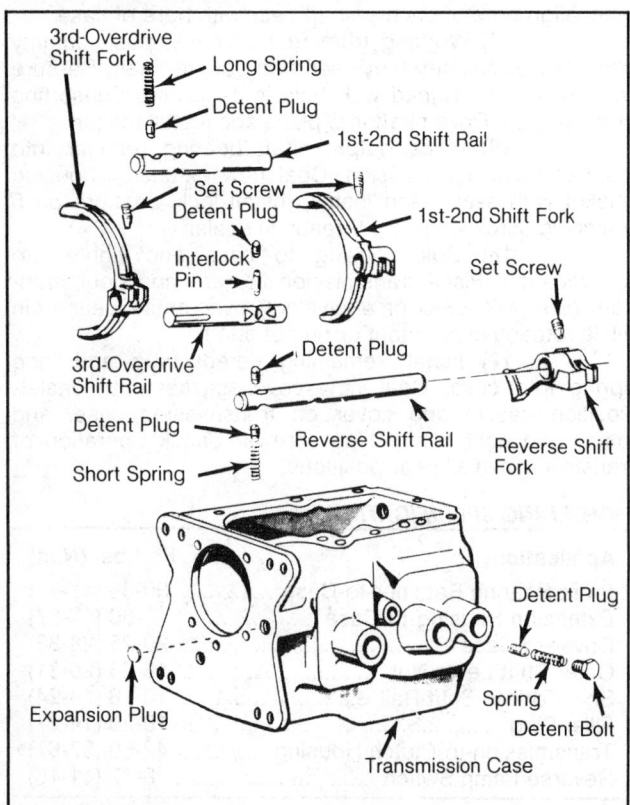

REMOVAL & INSTALLATION

See the appropriate article in MANUAL TRANS-MISSION REMOVAL Section.

TRANSMISSION DISASSEMBLY

1) Mount transmission in a holding fixture. Drain lubricant by removing lower extension housing attaching bolt. Remove cover and gasket from case. Remove long spring which retains detent plug in case and remove detent plug using small magnet.

2) Remove extension housing bolts, washers and gasket, then remove extension housing from case. Remove input shaft bearing retainer screws and slide retainer off input shaft. Support countershaft gear with wire hook. Push countershaft out rear of case. Lower countershaft gear to bottom of case and remove hook.

3) Remove set screw from 1st-2nd shift fork. Slide 1st-2nd shift rail out rear of case. Using magnet, remove interlock detent from between 1st-2nd and 3rd-overdrive shift rails. See Fig. 1. Shift transmission into overdrive position.

4) Remove set screw from 3rd-overdrive shift fork. Remove the side detent bolt, plug and spring. Rotate 3rd-overdrive shift rail 90° clockwise, and tap it out through front of case. Remove interlock plug from top of case with magnet.

5) Remove snap ring securing speedometer drive gear on output shaft. Slide gear off shaft and remove speedometer gear drive ball. Remove snap ring securing output shaft bearing to shaft. Remove snap ring from outside diameter of bearing. Using bearing puller, pull output shaft bearing from shaft.

6) Remove snap ring securing input shaft bearing to shaft. Remove snap ring from outside diameter of bearing. Use bearing puller to remove bearing from input shaft and transmission case. Remove input shaft and blocking ring from front of case. Move output shaft to right side of case, and rotate shift forks up and out of case.

7) Support thrust washer and 1st gear to prevent them from sliding off shaft. Lift output shaft assembly from case. Remove reverse gear shift fork set screw. Rotate shift rail 90° and slide rail out rear of case. Lift reverse shift fork from case. Remove reverse detent plug and spring from case with magnet. See Fig. 2.

Fig. 2: Removal of Shift Forks from Case

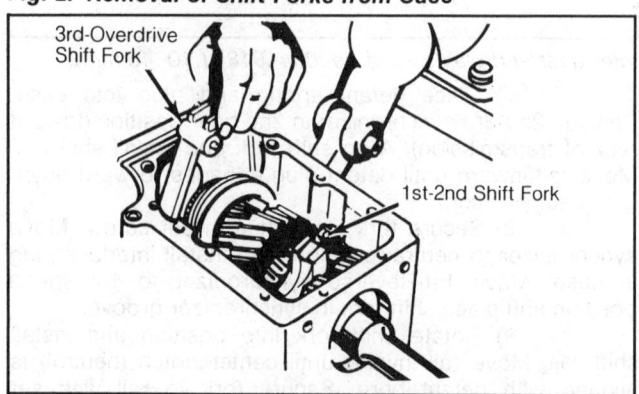

To remove fork, move to right side of case.

FORD MOTOR CO. 4-SPEED RUG OVERDRIVE (Cont.)

8) Remove reverse idler gear shaft from case using dummy shaft. Lift countershaft gear and thrust washers out of case being careful not to drop bearings and dummy shaft from countershaft gear. Lift reverse idler gear and thrust washer from case.

9) Remove snap ring from front of output shaft. Slide 3rd-overdrive synchronizer blocking ring and gear from shaft. Remove next snap ring from output shaft. Slide 2nd gear thrust washer, 2nd gear and blocking ring off shaft. Remove remaining snap ring from output shaft. Remove thrust washer, 1st gear and blocking ring from rear of shaft.

CLEANING & INSPECTION

Wash all parts in cleaning solvent and air dry. Inspect ball and roller bearings for wear or damage. Inspect transmission case for cracks, wear, damaged bearing bores or damaged threads. Remove all small nicks or burrs from front of case. Check all other parts for wear, chipped or broken teeth and/or damage. Replace parts as necessary.

COMPONENT DISASSEMBLY & REASSEMBLY

SHIFT LEVERS AND SEALS

Disassembly

Remove nut, lock washer and flat washer. Lift shift levers off shafts. Slide each lever and shaft from case. Remove and discard "O" ring seal from each lever and shaft.

Reassembly

Lubricate new "O" ring seals with transmission lubricant and install seals on shafts. Install levers and shafts into case. Position shift lever on each shaft and secure with flat washer, lock washer and nut.

SYNCHRONIZER ASSEMBLY

Disassembly

Put alignment marks on hub and sleeve of synchronizer before disassembly. Push hub from each synchronizer sleeve. Separate inserts and insert springs from hubs. Do not mix the parts of 1st-2nd synchronizer with 3rd-overdrive synchronizer.

Reassembly

Install hub in sleeve, making sure alignment marks are properly indexed. Place 3 inserts into place on hub. Install insert springs making sure that irregular surface (hump) is seated in one of the inserts. DO NOT stagger springs. See Fig. 3.

COUNTERSHAFT GEAR BEARINGS

Disassembly

Remove dummy shaft, 2 bearing retainer washers and 21 roller bearings from each end of countershaft gear. See Fig. 4.

Reassembly

Coat bore in each end of gear and install 21 roller bearings and a retainer washer in each end of gear.

REVERSE IDLER GEAR BEARINGS

Disassembly

Slide reverse idler sliding gear off reverse idler

Fig. 3: Exploded View of Synchronizer Assemblies

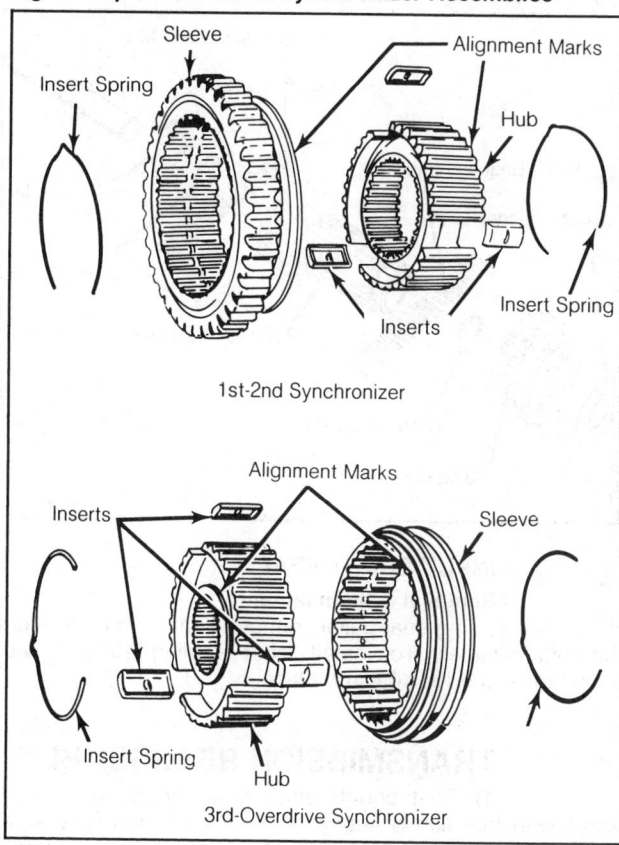

1st-2nd Synchronizer

3rd-Overdrive Synchronizer

gear. Remove dummy shaft, 2 bearing retainer washers and 44 roller bearings from reverse idler gear. See. Fig. 5.

Reassembly

Coat bore in each end of idler gear with grease. Hold dummy shaft in gear and install 22 roller bearings and a retainer washer in each end of gear. Install sliding gear on reverse idler gear making sure shift fork groove faces toward front.

Fig. 4: Exploded View of Countershaft Gear

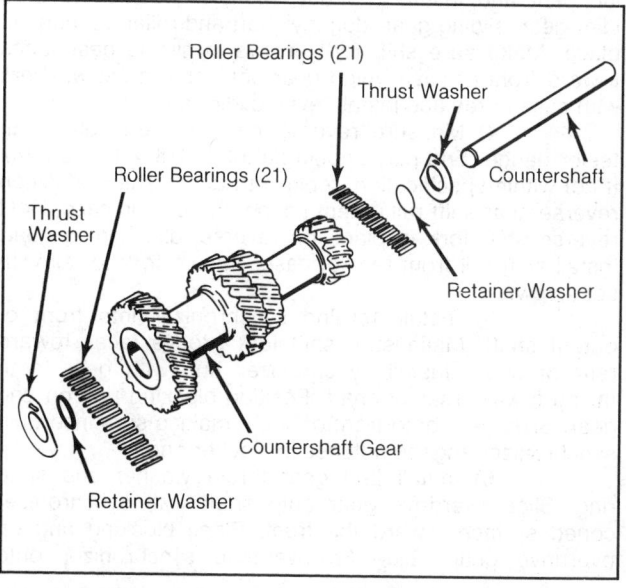

FORD MOTOR CO. 4-SPEED RUG OVERDRIVE (Cont.)

Fig. 5: Exploded View of Reverse Idler Gear Assembly

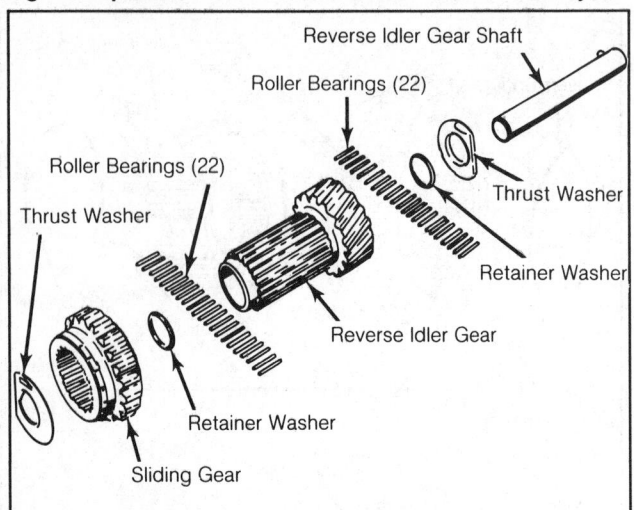

INPUT SHAFT SEAL

Removal & Installation

Using seal puller, remove seal from input shaft bearing retainer. To install, coat sealing surface with lubricant and drive seal into place.

TRANSMISSION REASSEMBLY

1) Coat countershaft gear thrust surfaces in case with thin film of lubricant. Position thrust washer at each end of case. Position countershaft gear, dummy shaft and roller bearings in case. Place case in vertical position. Align gear bore and thrust washers with bores in case and install countershaft.

2) Place case horizontal and check countershaft gear end play with feeler gauge. End play should be .004-.018" (.10-.46 mm). If not within specification, replace thrust washers. With end play correctly set, install dummy shaft in countershaft gear and allow gear to remain at bottom of case.

3) Coat reverse idler gear thrust surfaces with lubricant and install 2 thrust washers. Position reverse idler gear, sliding gear, dummy shaft and roller bearings in place. Make sure shift fork groove in sliding gear faces toward front of case. Align gear bore and thrust washers with case bores and install reverse idler shaft.

4) Measure reverse idler gear end play with feeler gauge. End play should be .004-.018" (.10-.46 mm). If not within specification, replace thrust washers. Position reverse gear shift rail detent spring and plug in case. Hold reverse shift fork in place on reverse idler sliding gear. Install shift rail from rear of case. Secure fork to rail with set screw.

5) Install 1st-2nd synchronizer into front of output shaft. Make sure shift fork groove faces toward rear of shaft. Install synchronizer hub with gear teeth facing toward rear of shaft. Position blocking ring on 2nd gear. Slide gear onto front of shaft, making sure inserts in synchronizer engage notches in blocker ring.

6) Install 2nd gear thrust washer and snap ring. Slide overdrive gear onto shaft with synchronizer coned surface toward the front. Place blocking ring on overdrive gear. Slide 3rd-overdrive synchronizer onto

shaft. Be sure inserts engage notches in blocking ring and thrust surface faces overdrive gear.

7) Install snap ring on front of output shaft. Position blocking ring on 1st gear. Slide 1st gear onto rear of output shaft. Be sure notches of blocking ring engage synchronizer inserts. Install heavy thrust washer on rear of output shaft. Support thrust washer and 1st gear to prevent them from sliding. Carefully lower output shaft assembly into case.

8) Position 1st-2nd shift fork and 3rd-overdrive shift forks on proper gears and rotate them into place. Install spring and detent plug into detent bore. Place reverse shift rail into neutral position. *See Fig. 6.*

Fig. 6: Output Shaft Assembly Installation

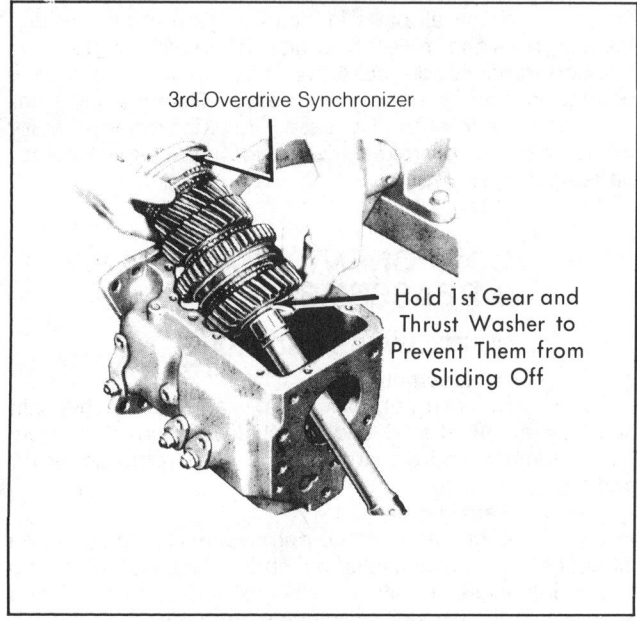

Hold 1st gear and thrust washer to prevent sliding.

9) Coat 3rd-overdrive shift rail interlock pin (tapered ends) with grease and position in shift rail. Align 3rd-overdrive shift fork with shift rail bores and slide rail into place. Be sure 3 detents face toward outside of case. Place front synchronizer into overdrive position and install set screw in 3rd-overdrive shift fork. Move synchronizer to neutral position. Install 3rd-overdrive detent plug, spring and bolt in left side of case. Place detent plug (tapered ends) in detent bore in case.

NOTE: A missing or improperly installed interlock pin could allow the transmission to be shifted into 1st and Reverse gear at the same time.

10) Align 1st-2nd shift fork with case bores and slide shift rail into place, securing shift fork with set screw. Coat input gear bore with thin film of grease. Install 15 roller bearings into bore. Place front blocking ring in 3rd-overdrive synchronizer. Place dummy bearing (T77L-7025-B) on output shaft to support and align shaft assembly in case. *See Fig. 7.*

11) Place input shaft gear into case. Output shaft pilot must enter roller bearings in input gear bore. Position input shaft bearing on input shaft. Slowly and evenly press bearing onto shaft and into case. Install snap rings on bearing and input shaft. Place new gasket on

FORD MOTOR CO. 4-SPEED RUG OVERDRIVE (Cont.)

Fig. 7: Exploded View of Output Shaft Assembly

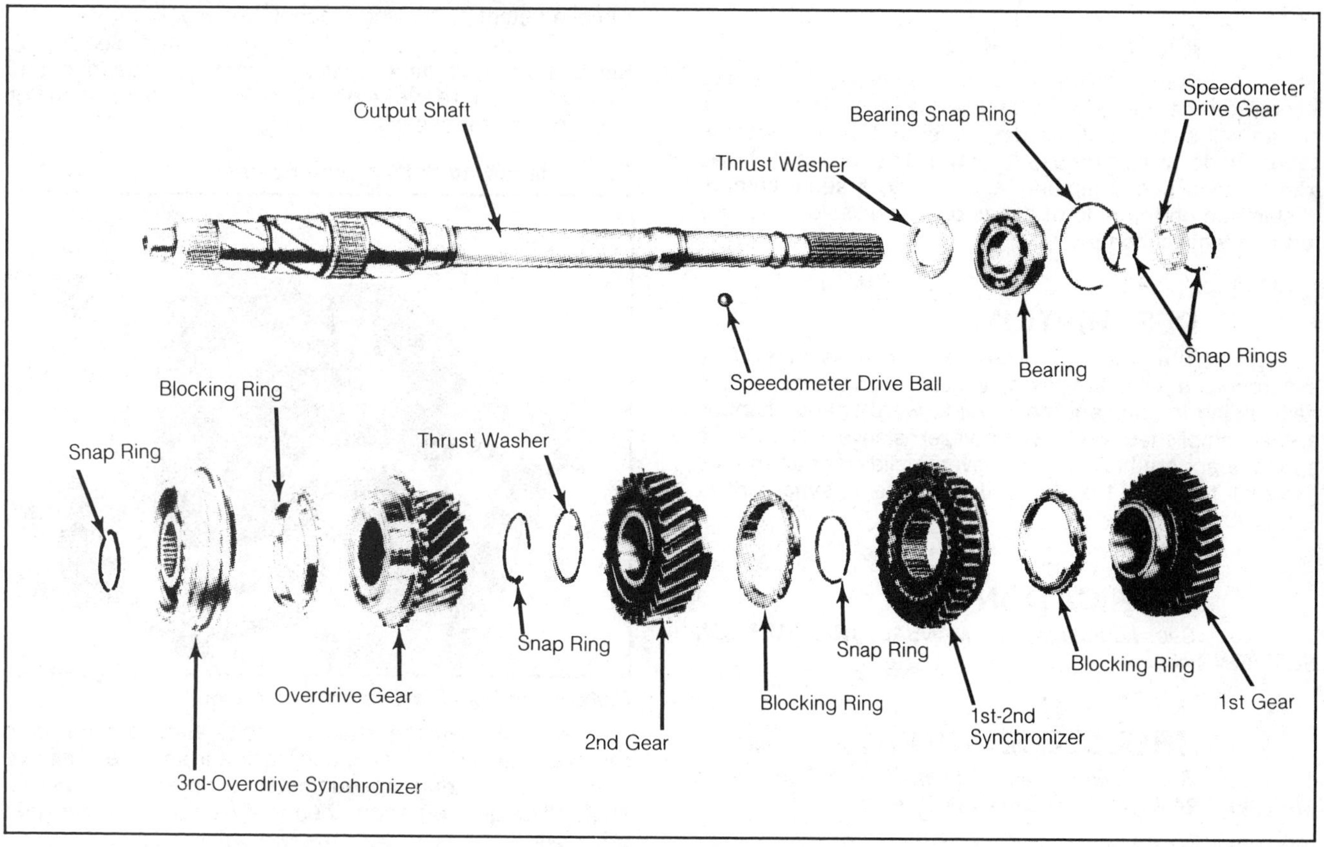

Output Shaft · Bearing Snap Ring · Speedometer Drive Gear · Thrust Washer · Snap Rings · Bearing · Speedometer Drive Ball · Snap Ring · Blocking Ring · Thrust Washer · Overdrive Gear · 3rd-Overdrive Synchronizer · Snap Ring · 2nd Gear · Blocking Ring · Snap Ring · 1st-2nd Synchronizer · Blocking Ring · 1st Gear

NOTE: A thick film of grease could plug lubrication holes and restrict lubrication of bearings.

input shaft bearing retainer. Dip retainer attaching bolts in sealer and install retainer on case. See Fig. 8.

Fig. 8: Exploded View of Input Shaft Assembly

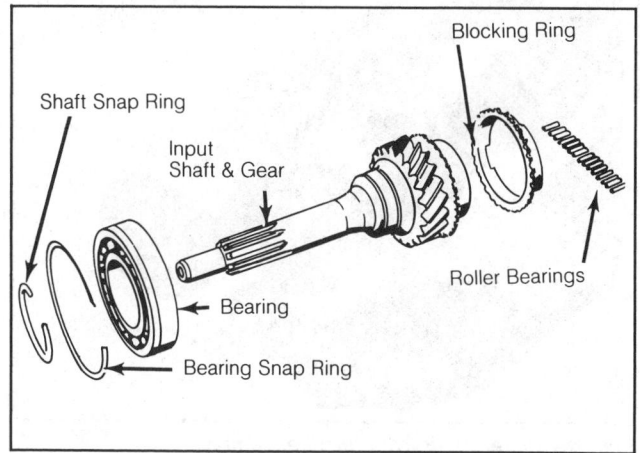

Shaft Snap Ring · Input Shaft & Gear · Blocking Ring · Roller Bearings · Bearing · Bearing Snap Ring

12) Remove dummy bearing from output shaft. Press output shaft bearing onto output shaft and into case. Install snap rings on output shaft and output shaft bearing. Make sure output shaft bearing aligns with bore and countershaft is not in the way of shaft assembly.

13) Position transmission in vertical position. Align countershaft gear bore and thrust washers with bore in case. Install countershaft into case. Pour lubricant over entire gear train while rotating input shaft.

14) Try each shift fork in all positions to ensure proper operation. Install remaining detent plug in case. Install long spring (retained by case) to secure detent plug. Install cover with new gasket. Coat 3rd-overdrive shift rail plug bore with sealant and install new expansion plug.

TIGHTENING SPECIFICATIONS

Application	Ft. Lbs. (N.m)
Input Shaft Bearing Retainer	19-25 (26-33)
Extension Housing Bolts	45-50 (57-67)
Access Cover-to-Case Screw	20-25 (28-33)
Gear Shift Lever Attaching Nuts	18-23 (25-31)
Filler Plug	10-20 (14-27)
Detent Bolt-to-Case	10-15 (14-20)

Manual Transmissions

FORD MOTOR CO. 4-SPEED S.R.O.D. OVERDRIVE

Bronco, Capri, F100/250, Mustang

IDENTIFICATION

Transmission may be identified by a tag located on the right side of case at the front. The first line on tag will show transmission model and service identification code when required. Lower line on tag shows transmission serial number. Additionally, a serial number is stamped on top side of flange on transmission case for further identification.

DESCRIPTION

The 4-speed overdrive transmission is fully synchronized with all gears, except the reverse sliding gear, being in constant mesh. All forward speed changes are accomplished with synchronizer sleeve. All forward speed gears are helical type. Reverse sliding gear and the external teeth of the 1st and 2nd speed synchronizer sleeve are spur type.

LUBRICATION

See Lubrication in MANUAL TRANSMISSION SERVICING section.

TROUBLE SHOOTING

See Manual Transmission Trouble Shooting in MANUAL TRANSMISSION SERVICING section.

REMOVAL & INSTALLATION

See Removal & Installation in MANUAL TRANSMISSION REMOVAL section.

TRANSMISSION DISASSEMBLY

NOTE: The shift control unit is not to be disassembled. The only parts to be removed from it are the shift lever, shift lever knob, back-up lamp switch and retainer.

1) Mount transmission in a holding fixture. Drain lubricant by removing the lower extension housing

Fig. 1: Detent Spring and Plug

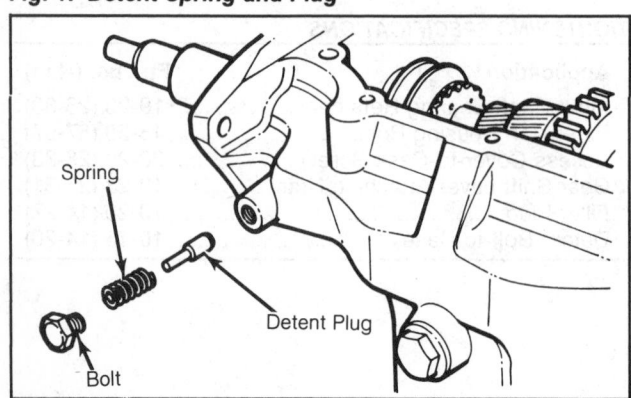

Remove plug using a magnet.

attaching bolt. Remove cover and gasket from case. Remove long spring which retains detent plug in case and remove detent plug using magnet. See Fig. 1.

2) Drive roll pin from shifter shaft. See Fig. 2. Remove back-up lamp switch assembly, snap ring and dust cover from rear of extension housing. Remove shifter shaft from turret assembly. See Fig. 3.

Fig. 2: Removing Shifter Shaft Roll Pin

Remove pin from 3rd-Overdrive shift fork.

3) Remove attaching bolts and washers, then remove extension housing and gasket from case. Remove snap ring securing speedometer drive gear to output shaft. Slide gear off shaft, then remove speedometer gear drive ball.

Fig. 3: Removing Shifter Shaft

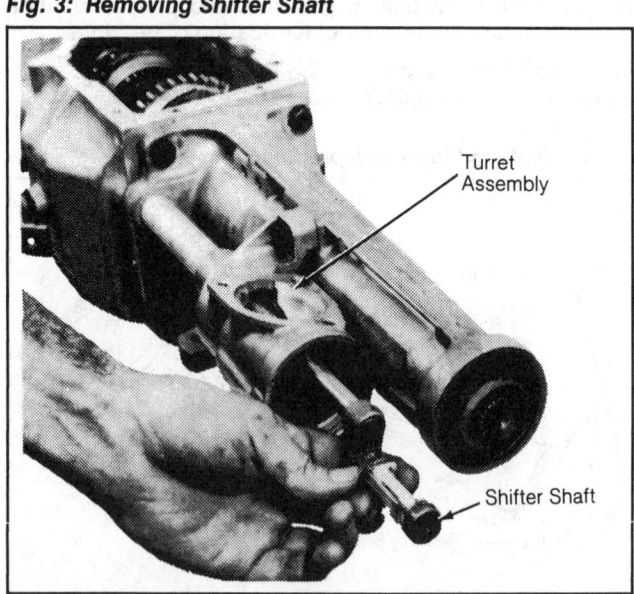

Remove shifter shaft from turret assembly.

4) Remove snap ring securing output shaft bearing to shaft and remove bearing from output shaft (slip fit).

5) From front of case, use a dummy shaft to push countershaft out rear of case. Lower countershaft to bottom of case. Remove input shaft bearing retainer and gasket. Discard gasket.

FORD MOTOR CO. 4-SPEED S.R.O.D. OVERDRIVE (Cont.)

Fig. 4: Exploded View of S.R.O.D. 4-Speed Transmission Assembly

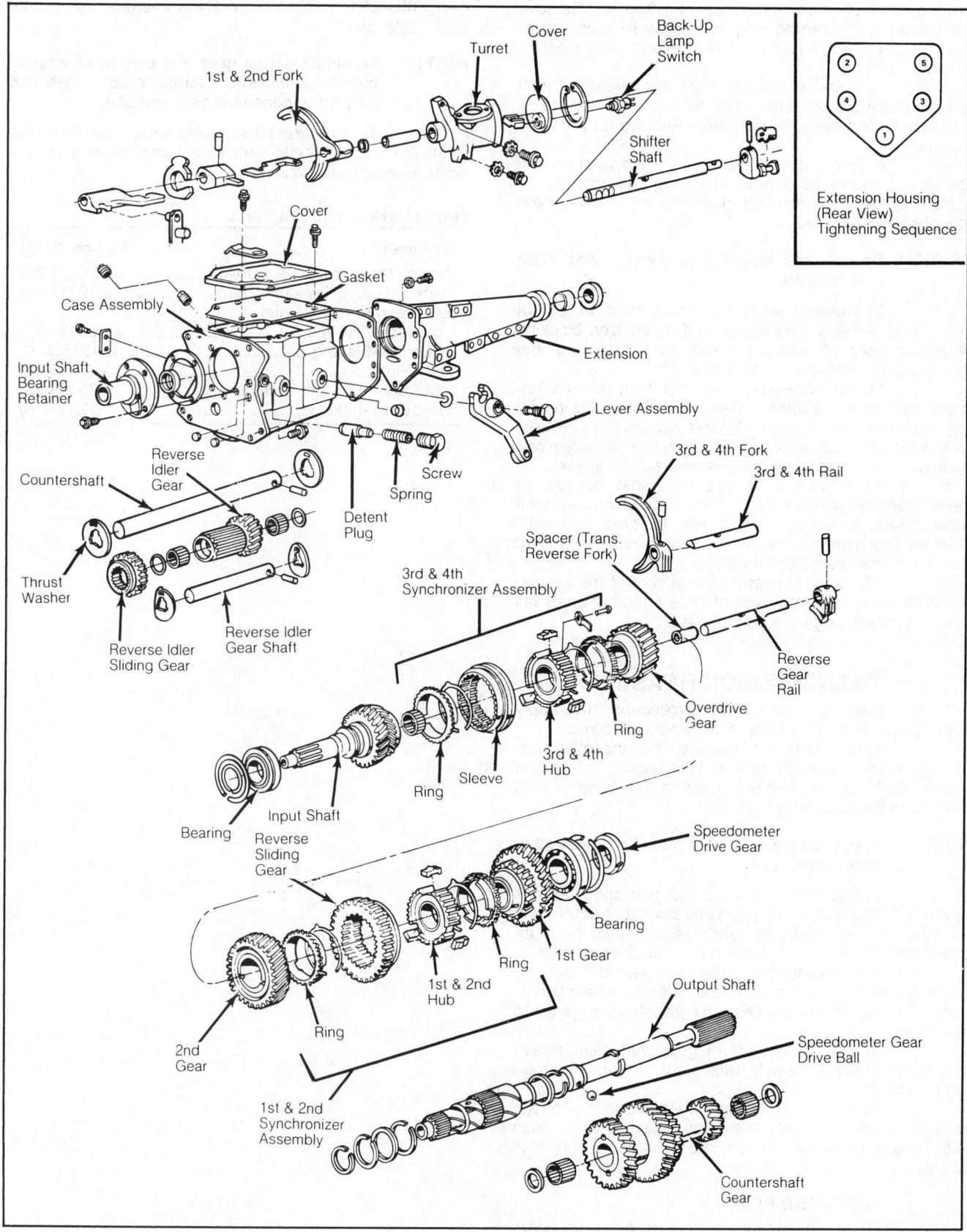

FORD MOTOR CO. 4-SPEED S.R.O.D. OVERDRIVE (Cont.)

6) Remove snap ring securing input shaft bearing to shaft, then remove bearing (slip fit). Remove input shaft and blocking ring from case including roller bearings. Remove overdrive shift pawl and gear selector interlock plate.

7) Remove roll pin from 3rd overdrive shift fork. Remove 3rd overdrive shift rail and expansion plug. Remove the 3rd overdrive shift fork. Remove output shaft assembly.

8) Remove next snap ring, thrust washer, and 2nd gear. Remove 1st gear and blocking ring from rear of shaft. Remove countershaft gear, thrust washers and roller bearings from case.

CAUTION: Do not drop bearings or dummy shaft from countershaft.

9) Remove snap ring from front of output shaft. Slide 3rd gear and overdrive synchronizer, blocking rings and gear off shaft. Remove next snap ring and thrust washer. Remove second gear.

10) Remove next snap ring, then remove 1st-2nd synchronizer assembly. Remove 1st gear and blocking ring from rear of shaft. Remove roll pin from reverse fork, slide reverse shifter rail through rear of case and remove reverse gearshift fork and reverse fork spacer.

11) Drive reverse gear drive shaft out rear of case. Remove reverse idler gear, thrust washers and roller bearings, being careful not to drop bearings. Remove retaining clip, reverse gearshift relay lever and reverse gear selector fork pivot pin.

12) Remove overdrive shift control link assembly; shift shaft seal from rear of case and shift shaft rail hole expansion plug from front of case.

TRANSMISSION REASSEMBLY

Reverse disassembly procedure and apply lubricants prior to completion of assembly as follows:

1) Transmission mainshaft bearing roller, extension housing bushing, reverse idler bearing rollers and countershaft gear bearing rollers are to be lubricated with long life multipurpose type grease.

NOTE: **Extension housing bolts must be tightened in order. See Fig. 4.**

2) Lubricate low gear, 2nd gear and overdrive journal on output shaft with transmission oil or equivalent. All other internal parts of transmission should be lubricated with 1/2 pint (1/4 L) transmission oil or equivalent.

3) Lubricate shifter shaft and gear shift damper bushing with multipurpose grease prior to installation in transmission. Fill transmission to specification prior to operation.

4) Seal both ends of gear shift shaft sleeve and turret cover assembly with sealer to prevent road contamination.

5) Welch plug at front of intermediate and high rail must be seated firmly. Welch plug must sit either flush with case or no more than .06" (1.5 mm) below front face of case.

GEAR END PLAY

Gear end play for 1st, 2nd and overdrive gears must meet following specifications:

1) 1st gear, .005-.024" (.127-.609 mm), 2nd gear, .003-.021" (.076-.533 mm) and overdrive gear .009-.023" (.228-.584 mm).

NOTE: **To obtain actual gear end play in an assembled transmission, subtract output shaft end play from measured gear end play.**

2) Countershaft end play should be .004-.018" (.101-.457 mm). Rebuild with new components if dimensions exceed specifications.

TIGHTENING SPECIFICATIONS

Application	Ft. Lbs. (N.m)
Access Cover-to-Case Screw	20-25 (28-33)
Back-Up Lamp Switch	8-12 (11-16)
Extension Housing Bolts	
Bronco & F100/250	42-50 (54-67)
Capri & Mustang	23-30 (31-41
Filler Plug	10-20 (14-28)
Input Shaft Bearing Retainer	11-25 (15-33)
Turret Assembly	8-12 (11-16)

FORD MOTOR CO. 4-SPEED 83ET

**Capri, Fairmont, Futura
LTD, Marquis, Mustang, Zephyr**

TRANSMISSION IDENTIFICATION

Transmission is manufactured in Germany and may be identified by a tag located under lower left side of extension housing-to-case bolts. The first line on tag shows transmission model prefex and suffix, and the build date code. Lower line on tag shows transmission serial number.

DESCRIPTION

Four speed fully synchronized, except reverse. Forward speed gears are in constant mesh and gear changes are accomplished through forged blocker ring synchronized units.

Engagement of two gears at once is prevented by means of a selector interlock plate pivoted in the transmission case. This plate engages with selector forks which are not in use and holds them positively in the disengaged position.

LUBRICATION & ADJUSTMENT

See the appropriate article in MANUAL TRANSMISSION SERVICING Section.

REMOVAL & INSTALLATION

See the appropriate article in MANUAL TRANSMISSION REMOVAL Section.

TRANSMISSION DISASSEMBLY

1) Remove clutch release bearing and lever. Remove attaching bolts, then separate flywheel housing from transmission case.

2) Remove cover attaching bolts. Remove cover and gasket, then drain lubricant.

3) Remove threaded plug, spring and shift rail detent plunger from upper left front side of transmission case. See Fig. 1.

Fig. 1: Removing Detent Plunger Assembly from Case

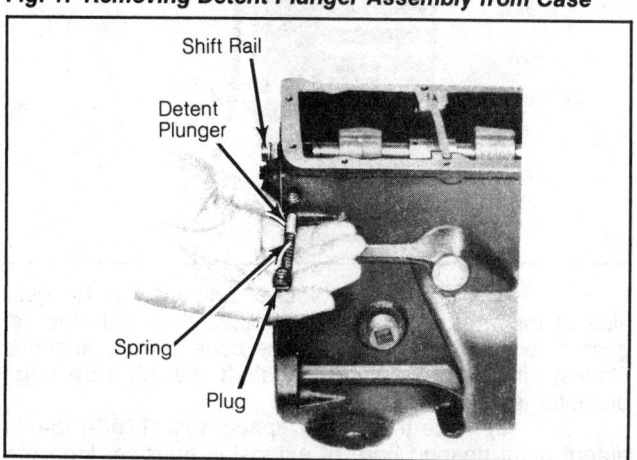

4) Working from inside transmission case, drive access plug from rear of case. See Fig. 2.

Fig. 2: Removing Access Plug from Case

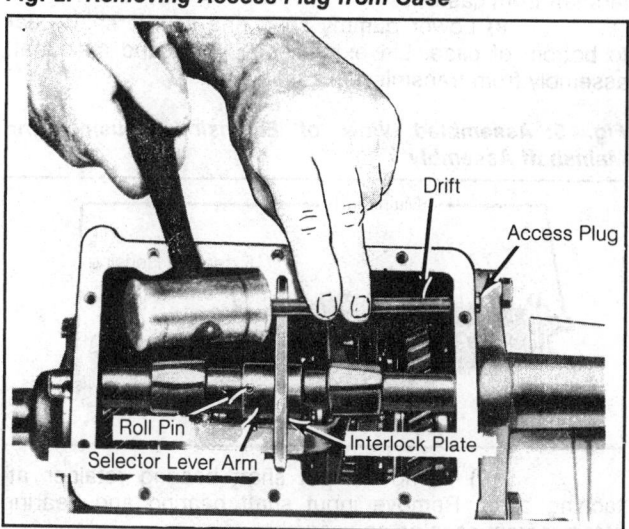

5) Working through access plug hole, drive retaining pin from case and remove interlock plate. See Fig. 3.

Fig. 3: Removing Interlock Retaining Pin

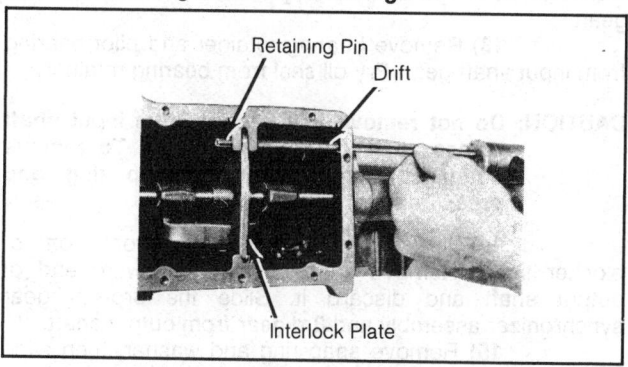

6) Remove roll pin from selector lever arm. Tap front end of shift rail to displace plug at rear of extension housing, then remove shift rail from extension housing and case. Lift selector arm and shift forks from case.

Fig. 4: Removing Shift Rail from Extension Housing

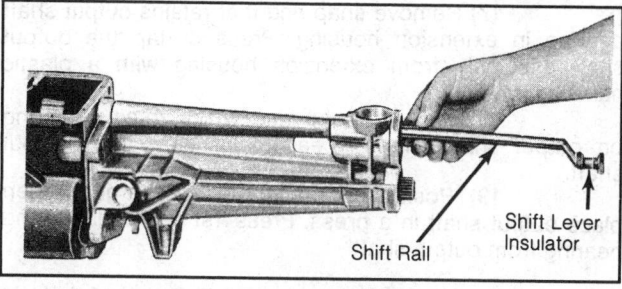

7) Remove extension housing attaching bolts, then tap extension housing with a plastic mallet to loosen it from case. Rotate housing until countershaft is aligned with cutaway in housing flange.

FORD MOTOR CO. 4-SPEED 83ET (Cont.)

8) Using a brass drift, drive countershaft rearward until it just clears front of case. Install a dummy shaft into case and countershaft gear, then drive countershaft from case.

9) Lower dummy shaft and countershaft gear to bottom of case. Lift extension housing and mainshaft assembly from transmission case.

Fig. 5: Assembled View of Extension Housing and Mainshaft Assembly

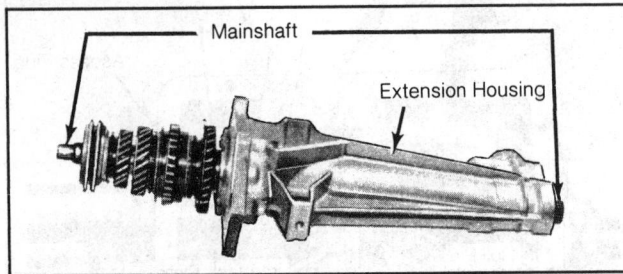

10) Remove input shaft bearing retainer attaching bolts. Remove input shaft bearing and bearing retainer from case as an assembly.

11) Remove reverse idler gear shaft from rear of case. Remove idler gear and spacer from case.

12) Remove countershaft gear and dummy shaft from bottom of case. Separate bearing retainer washers, bearings and dummy shaft from countershaft gear.

13) Remove bearing retainer and pilot bearing from input shaft gear. Pry oil seal from bearing retainer.

CAUTION: Do not remove ball bearing from input shaft unless replacement is required. To remove bearing, remove retaining snap ring and press bearing from shaft.

14) Lift 4th gear blocker ring from front of blocker shaft. Remove snap ring from forward end of output shaft and discard it. Slide the 3rd-4th gear synchronizer assembly and 3rd gear from output shaft.

15) Remove snap ring and washer, then slide 2nd gear and blocker ring off of output shaft.

NOTE: Scratch or etch alignment marks on hub and sleeve of synchronizer before disassembly.

16) Disassemble synchronizer assembly by pulling sleeve off hub and removing the inserts and springs.

17) Remove snap ring that retains output shaft bearing in extension housing. Press or tap the output shaft assembly from extension housing with a plastic hammer.

18) Remove snap ring which retains bearing on output shaft. Press speedometer gear from output shaft.

19) Position a press behind 1st gear, then place output shaft in a press. Press 1st gear, spacer and bearing from output shaft.

CAUTION: The 1st-2nd gear synchronizer and hub is serviced as an assembly with the output shaft. No attempt should be made to separate hub from shaft. The sleeve, springs and inserts may be removed from hub after

scribing alignment marks on hub and sleeve. The only parts that can be serviced are the springs and inserts.

20) If necessary for replacement, drive shift rail bushing from rear of extension housing with a 9/16" socket and extension.

21 Pry shift rail seal from extension housing. Remove remaining shift linkage from case.

CLEANING & INSPECTION

Wash all parts in cleaning solvent and dry with air. Dip bearings in transmission lubricant after they have been dried, then wrap in a clean lint-free cloth until ready for installation.

Inspect transmission case for cracks, wear, damaged bearing bores, or damaged threads. Remove all small nicks or burrs from front of case. Check all other parts for wear, chipped or broken teeth, and damage. Replace parts as necessary.

TRANSMISSION REASSEMBLY

1) Using a 3/4" socket, drive a new shift rail seal into rear of transmission case. If shift rail bushing was removed from extension housing, drive a new one into place with a 9/16" socket and extension.

2) If the 1st-2nd gear synchronizer was disassembled, slide synchronizer sleeve over hub, making sure alignment marks made at disassembly are aligned. Ensure shift fork groove is toward front of shaft.

3) Locate an insert in each of 3 slots cut in hub. Install an insert spring inside synchronizer sleeve beneath inserts. The tab on end of spring must locate in "U" section of insert. Fit other spring on opposite face making sure tab is in same recess and spring is in opposite rotational direction.

Fig. 6: Synchronizer Spring Installation

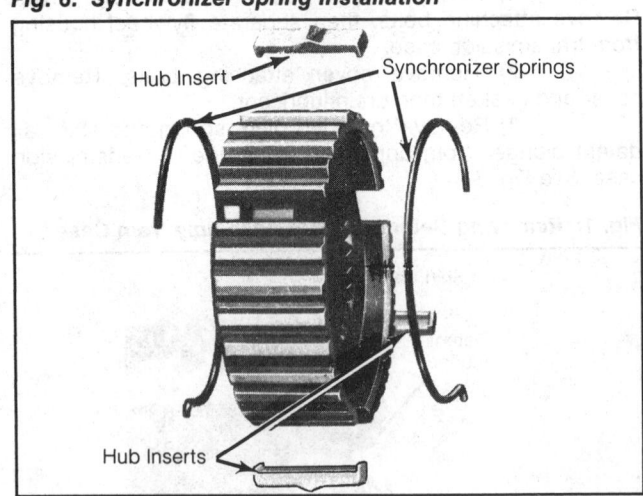

4) Assemble a blocker ring on the 1st gear side of the 1st-2nd gear synchronizer, then slide the 1st gear onto output shaft so that the cone surface engages blocker ring. Install spacer on shaft making sure large diameter is toward rear of shaft.

5) Place the master spacer tool (T70P-7154) in output shaft bearing bore of extension housing. Measure

FORD MOTOR CO. 4-SPEED 83ET (Cont.)

width of output shaft bearing outer race with a micrometer.

6) The difference in thickness between master gauge and bearing outer race will determine the thickness of selective snap ring that will be required to eliminate end play.

7) If bearing race thickness is more than that stamped on master gauge, decrease snap ring thickness. If thickness is less, increase snap ring thickness to remove end play.

OUTPUT SHAFT BEARING-TO-CASE SNAP RING TABLE

Part No. [1]	Identification (Color or Letter)	Thickness In. (mm)
A	Copper	.0679 (1.725)
B	W	.0689 (1.750)
C	V	.0699 (1.775)
D	U	.0709 (1.801)
E	None	.0719 (1.826)
F	Blue	.0728 (1.849)
G	Black	.0738 (1.875)
H	Brown	.0748 (1.899)

[1] - All part numbers are preceded by "D1FZ-7030-".

Fig. 7: Using Special Gauge to Determine End Play Snap Ring Thickness

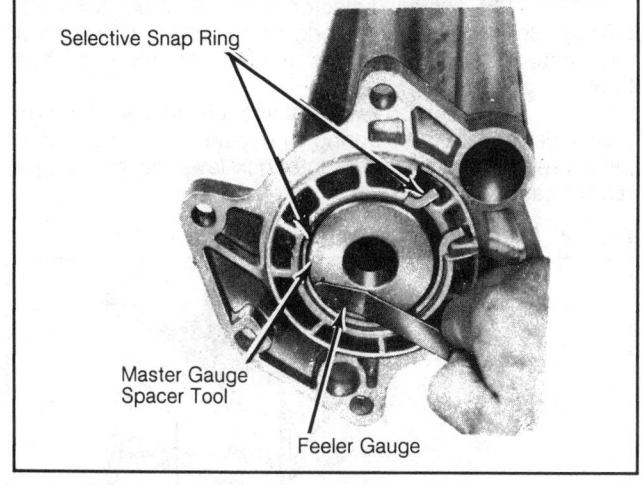

Selective Snap Ring

Master Gauge Spacer Tool

Feeler Gauge

8) Position selected snap ring and output shaft bearing on shaft, then place assembly in a press. Press bearing into place and secure with thickest snap ring that will fit groove in output shaft.

Fig. 9: Cutaway View of Transmission Showing Snap Ring Locations

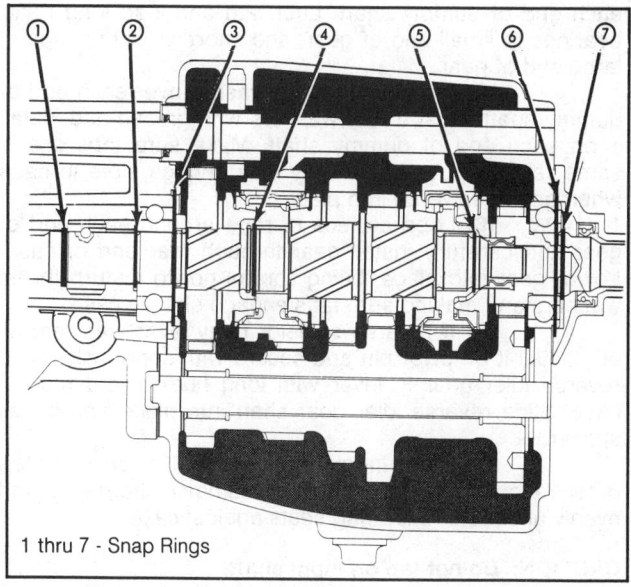

1 thru 7 - Snap Rings

9) Install 2nd gear and blocker ring on output shaft so that dog teeth face rearward, then install washer and snap ring. Install 3rd gear on output shaft so that dog teeth face forward, then install blocker ring on 3rd gear cone.

10) Install 3rd-4th gear synchronizer assembly on output shaft with hub boss (small diameter) facing forward. Retain 3rd-4th gear synchronizer assembly with snap ring. Install 4th gear blocker ring on input shaft gear cone.

11) Press speedometer drive gear onto shaft using support tool (T71P-17271-A) until dowels on tool just contact bearing outer race to properly locate speedometer drive gear on shaft. *See Fig. 10.*

12) Install output shaft in housing. It may be necessary to tap shaft with a plastic hammer while holding the 2 synchronizer sleeves to prevent sleeve separation

Fig. 8: Exploded View of Output Shaft and Speedometer Drive Gear Installation

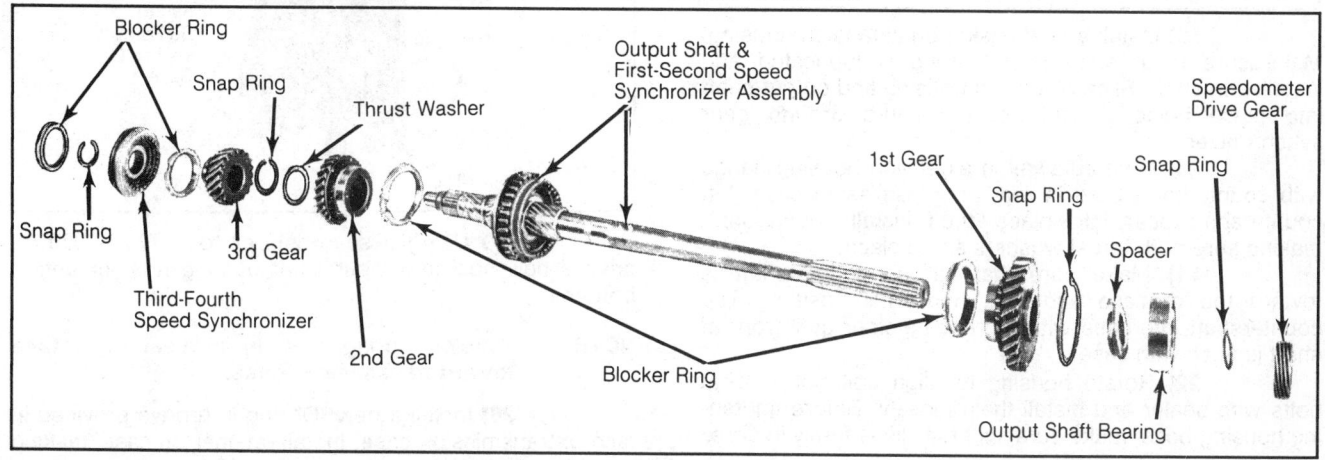

Blocker Ring

Snap Ring

Thrust Washer

Output Shaft & First-Second Speed Synchronizer Assembly

Speedometer Drive Gear

Snap Ring

1st Gear

Snap Ring

Snap Ring

Spacer

3rd Gear

Third-Fourth Speed Synchronizer

2nd Gear

Blocker Ring

Output Shaft Bearing

Manual Transmissions

FORD MOTOR CO. 4-SPEED 83ET (Cont.)

from hubs. Secure it to extension housing with selected snap ring that was previously installed.

13 Press bearing on input shaft, making sure snap ring groove is toward front end of shaft, and retain with thickest snap ring that will fit groove in input shaft.

14) Slide spacer and dummy shaft into countershaft gear, then install a bearing retainer washer at each end of dummy shaft. Lubricate and load long roller bearings in small end of gear, and short roller bearings in large end of gear.

15) Install a retaining washer over each end of dummy shaft. Coat thrust washers with grease and install 1 on each end of dummy shaft. Make sure tabs are in same relative position so they may engage slots in case when gear is lowered into place.

16) Loop a piece of rope around each end of gear and carefully install gear through rear end of case. Lower gear into place, being careful not to disturb thrust washers and making sure tabs engage slots in case.

17) If reverse selector relay lever was removed, install it on pivot pin and secure with spring clip. Hold reverse idler gear in lever with long hub toward rear of case. Slide reverse idler gear shaft into place and install spacer.

18) Install input shaft in case. If necessary, tap outer race of bearing with a soft hammer alternately and evenly until outer snap ring seats against case.

CAUTION: Do not tap on input shaft.

Fig. 10: Exploded View of Mainshaft Assembly

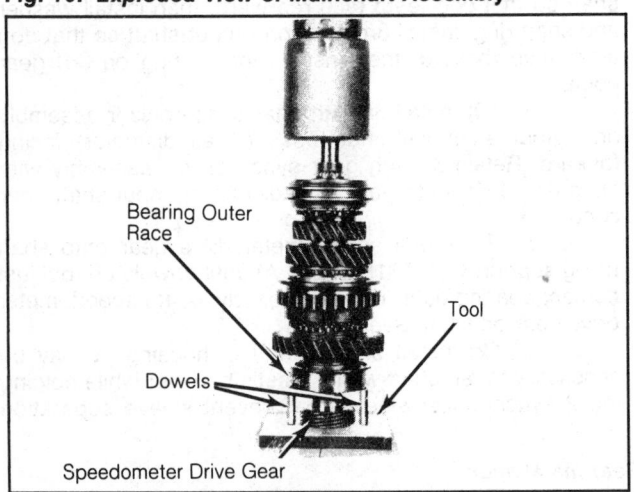

Bearing Outer Race

Tool

Dowels

Speedometer Drive Gear

19) Install a new gasket on extension housing. Make sure input shaft pilot bearing is lubricated and installed in shaft. Slide extension housing and output shaft into place being careful not to disturb 3rd-4th gear synchronizer.

20) Align cutaway in extension housing flange with countershaft bore in rear of transmission case. Lift countershaft gear into place, then install countershaft making sure both thrust washers are in place.

21) Make sure that flat on countershaft is toward top of case and in a horizontal position. Tap countershaft into case with a brass hammer until front of shaft is flush with case.

22) Rotate housing to align bolt holes. Coat bolts with sealer and install them loosely. Before tightening housing bolts, make sure shift rail slides freely in bore.

Fig. 11: Exploded View of Countershaft Gear

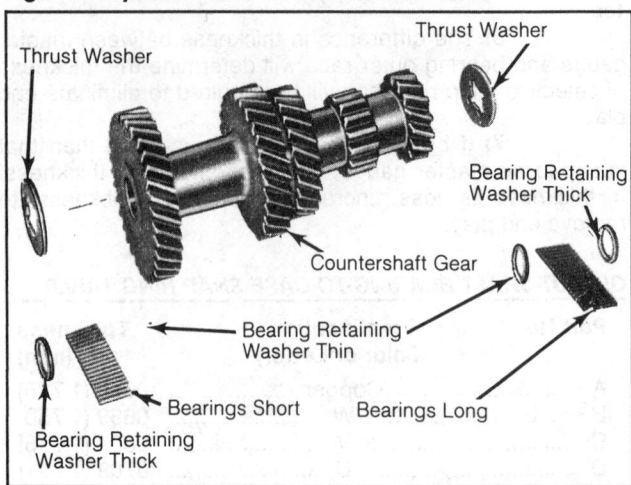

Thrust Washer

Thrust Washer

Bearing Retaining Washer Thick

Countershaft Gear

Bearing Retaining Washer Thin

Bearing Retaining Washer Thick

Bearings Short

Bearings Long

23) If it binds, rotate housing slightly to free rail, then push housing into case. Tighten bolts after making sure housing does not interfere with reverse idler or countershafts.

24) Install shift forks in synchronizer sleeves. Install interlock lever using a new retaining pin. Lubricate shift rail oil seal and slide shift rail through extension housing, transmission case, and 1st-2nd shift fork.

25) Install selector arm on rail, slide rail through 3rd-4th gear shift fork, and then through front of case until the center detent is aligned with detent plunger bore.

26) Install new retaining pin in selector arm. Install detent plunger, spring and plug (apply sealant to plug threads). Install a new interlock lever access plug in rear of case.

Fig. 12: Installing Countershaft into Case

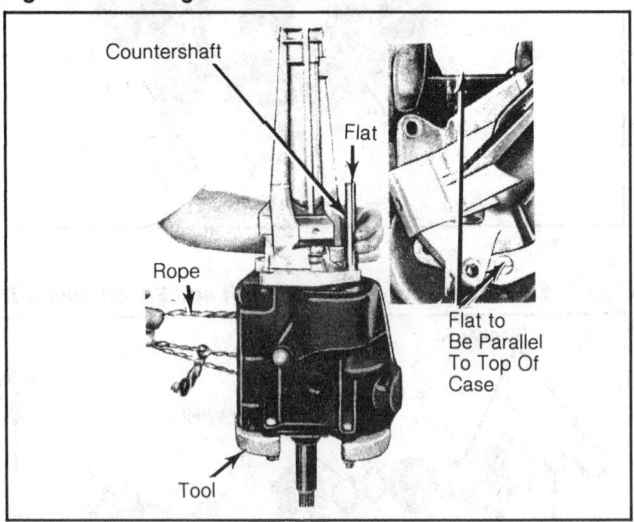

Countershaft

Flat

Rope

Flat to Be Parallel To Top Of Case

Tool

27) Using a seal installer tool (T71P-7050-A), drive a new seal into input shaft bearing retainer until it bottoms.

NOTE: **Tension spring and lip of seal must face toward transmission case.**

28) Install a new "O" ring in groove provided in face of transmission case. Install retainer on case, making

FORD MOTOR CO. 4-SPEED 83ET (Cont.)

sure oil groove in retainer is in line with oil passage in case. Install retainer bolts, using a sealant, but do not tighten at this time.

    29) Install flywheel housing and tighten bolts. Tighten front bearing retainer bolts. Install clutch release arm and bearing. Apply a sealant to extension plug and install it in extension housing behind shift rail.

Fig. 13: Reverse Idler Gear Assembly

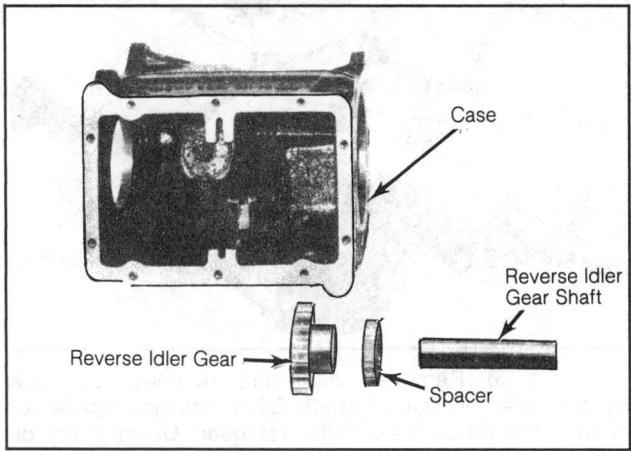

Fig. 14: Exploded View of Input Shaft Assembly

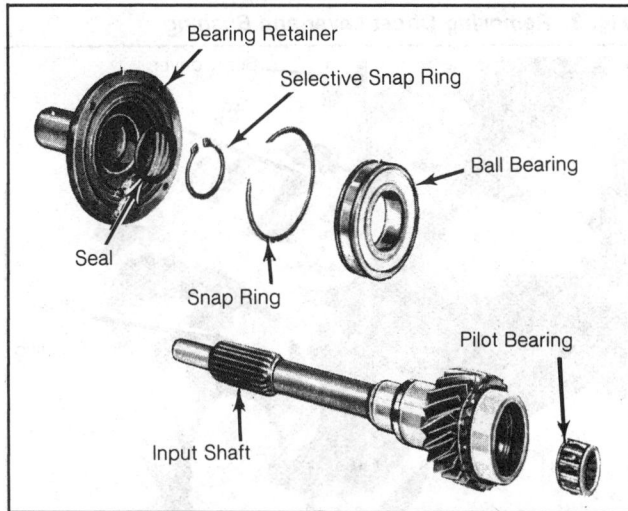

Fig. 15: Installing Interlock Access Plug

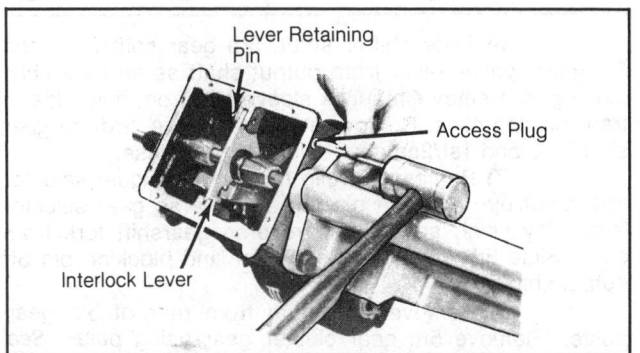

    30) Place a new cover gasket on case, then install cover with vent toward rear. Apply a sealant to

threads of left front cover bolt to seal bolt hole that aligns with detent plunger hole. Install and tighten cover bolts.

Fig. 16: Installing Input Shaft Gear

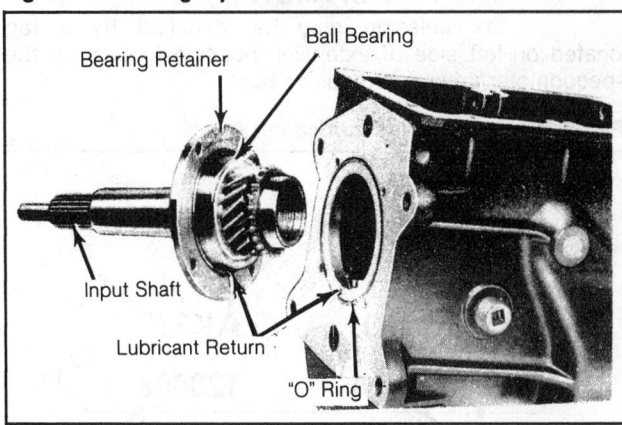

Oil groove in retainer must be in line with oil passage in case.

TIGHTENING SPECIFICATIONS

Application	Ft. Lbs. (N.m)
Detent Plug	12-14 (16-18)
Extension Housing-to-Case Bolt	33-36 (45-48)
Flywheel Housing-to-Engine Block	38-55 (52-75)
Flywheel Housing-to-Transmission Case	35-45 (47-61)
Shift Lever Bolts	17-25 (24-33)
	INCH Lbs. (N.m)
Cover-to-Case Screw	96-120 (11-13)
Input Shaft Bearing Retainer	96-120 (11-13)

Manual Transmission

FORD MOTOR CO. 5-SPEED OVERDRIVE

Capri, Mustang

IDENTIFICATION

Transmission may be identified by a tag located on left side of extension housing forward of the speedometer drive gear housing bore.

Fig. 1: Transmission Identification Tag

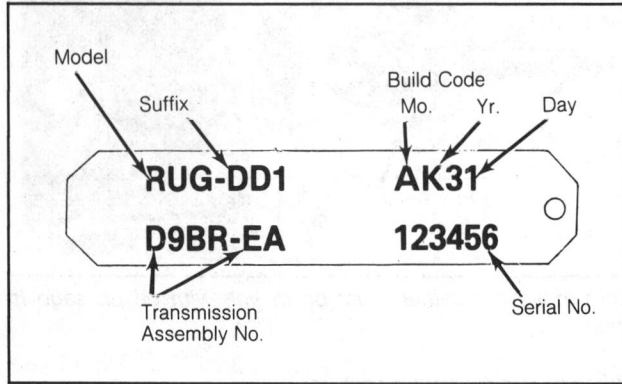

DESCRIPTION

The 5-speed single rail overdrive transmission is basically a 4-speed transmission with a manual overdrive gear assembly located in the extension housing. Transmission is fully synchronized with all 5 forward gears being in constant mesh. All forward gears are helical cut. All forward speed changes are accomplished with synchonizer sleeves, each being activated by its own shift fork. In all, 3 shifter forks slide along transmission's single shifter rail. Only reverse idler spur gear slides along a rail to engage reverse spur gear.

LUBRICATION & ADJUSTMENT

See the appropriate article in MANUAL TRANS-MISSION SERVICING Section.

REMOVAL & INSTALLATION

See the appropriate article in MANUAL TRANS-MISSION REMOVAL Section.

DISASSEMBLY

Transmission

1) Place transmission in holding fixture. Remove 10 cover retaining bolts. Remove cover and gasket, discard gasket. Drain transmission lubricant.

2) Remove shift rail detent plug, spring, and plunger from upper left side of case using a pencil magnet. *See Fig. 2.* Remove access plug from gear of extension housing turret assembly using drift punch and working through shift turret opening.

3) Shift transmission into reverse. Remove shift shaft offset lever roll pin, slide offset lever and bushing off shaft. *See Fig. 3.* Remove 5th gear interlock pilot bolt from front top of extension housing.

4) Remove extension housing retaining bolts, marking position of the 2 pilot bolts for reassembly. Slide

housing and gasket off output shaft. Remove snap ring, speedometer drive gear and drive ball from shaft.

Fig. 2: Removing Detent Plunger

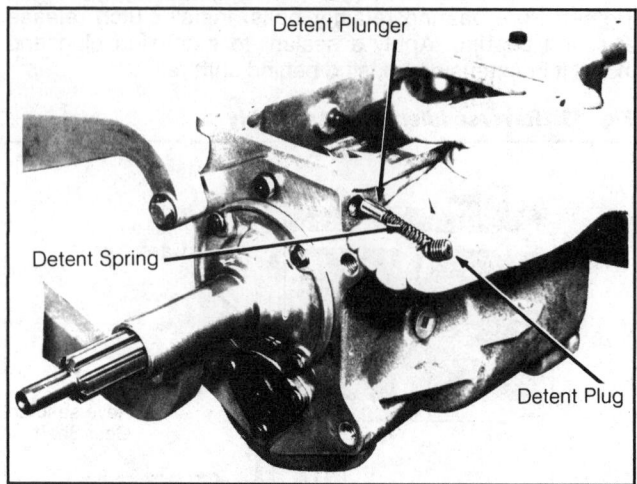

5) Remove snap ring retaining 5th gear synchronizer on output shaft. Slide retaining spacer off shaft. Shift transmission into 1st gear. Using a roll pin punch, remove pin securing 1st, 2nd, 3rd, 4th and Reverse selector pin and remove selector pin.

Fig. 3: Removing Offset Lever and Bushing

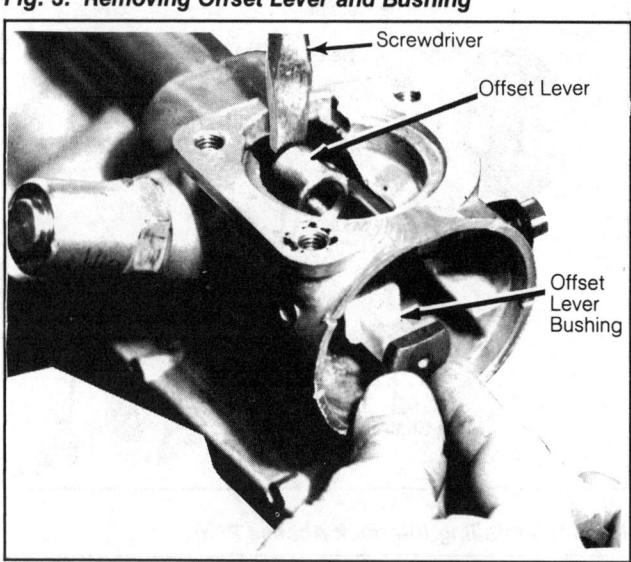

6) Slide shifter shaft, 5th gear shift fork, and 5th gear synchronizer from output shaft as an assembly. *See Fig. 4.* Remove interlock sleeve bolt from right side of transmission case. Remove interlock sleeve, 3rd/4th gear shift fork, and 1st/2nd gear shift fork from case.

7) Remove "C" clip from reverse gear selector fork pivot pin. Remove pin and lift reverse gear selector fork relay lever, spring, and reverse gearshift fork from case. Slide 5th gear maindrive gear and blocking pin off output shaft.

8) Remove snap ring from rear of 5th gear cluster. Remove 5th gear cluster gear using puller. *See Fig. 5.* Remove snap ring from output shaft rear bearing and remove bearing cup from case.

FORD MOTOR CO. 5-SPEED OVERDRIVE (Cont.)

Fig. 4: Removing Shifter Shaft and 5th Gear Synchronizer

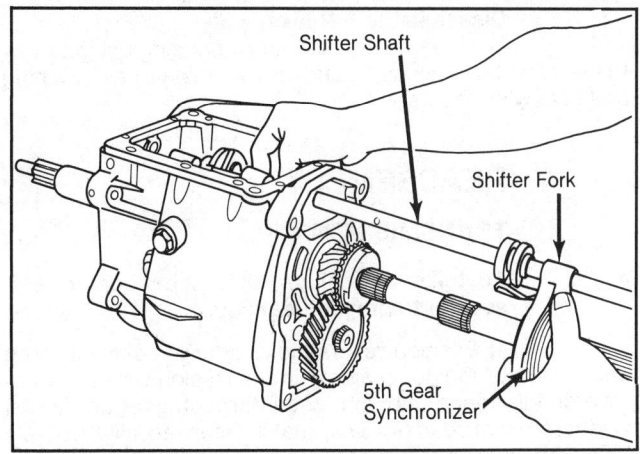

Fig. 5: Removing 5th Gear Cluster Gear

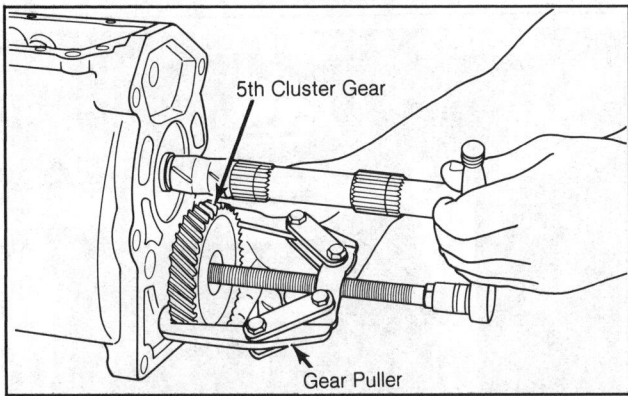

9) Remove bolts retaining input shaft bearing retainer. Remove bearing retainer, shim, "O" ring and oil seal from case. Rotate input shaft to position recess in gear teeth toward countershaft gear to provide clearance for shaft removal.

10) Remove input shaft from case being careful not to lose roller bearings, thrust washers or thrust

Fig. 6: Removing or Installing Output Shaft Assembly

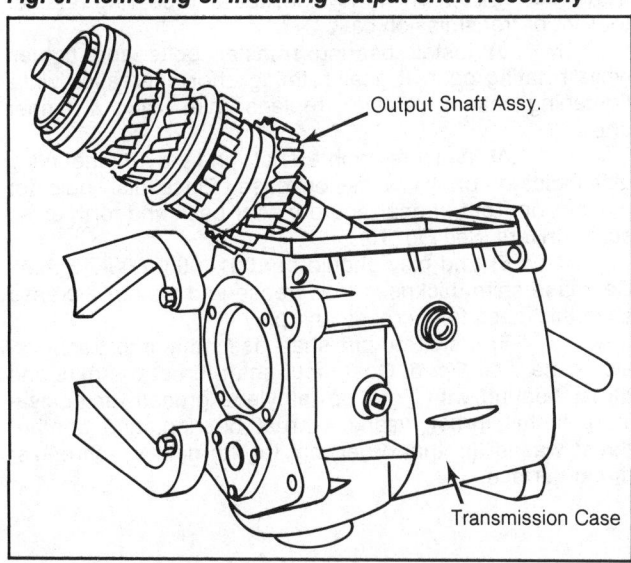

bearing. Remove output shaft assembly through top of case. See Fig. 6.

11) Remove snap ring retaining countershaft gear rear bearing cup from rear of case and remove countershaft gear rear bearing cup. Remove bolts attaching countershaft front bearing retainer to case.

12) Remove front bearing retainer, gasket, shim, and front bearing cup from case. Remove countershaft gear through top of transmission case. Remove roll pin securing reverse idler gear shaft to case. Remove reverse idler gear shaft and gear.

CLEANING & INSPECTION

1) Wash all parts in cleaning solvent and dry with compressed air (except bearings). Let bearings air dry in clean shop cloth. Inspect transmission case for cracks, damaged bearing bores, or threads.

2) Remove all small nicks or burrs from front or rear of case. Check bearings for roughness by slowly turning race by hand.

3) Inspect needle bearing rollers, shafts, and washers for wear or damage. Check all other parts for wear, damage, chipped, or broken teeth. Replace parts as necessary.

COMPONENT DISASSEMBLY & REASSEMBLY

NOTE: **When removing snap rings, be careful not to stretch ring to avoid damage to rings and/or possible personal injury.**

OUTPUT SHAFT
Disassembly

1) Slide 3rd/4th gear synchronizer off output shaft. Remove 3rd gear off front of output shaft. Remove snap ring, 2nd gear thrust washer, 2nd gear, and synchronizer blocking ring from output shaft.

2) Remove snap ring that retains 1st/2nd gear synchronizer and press 1st/2nd gear synchronizer off output shaft. Place output shaft in press and press 1st gear, thrust washer, and output shaft rear bearing from shaft.

NOTE: **DO NOT mix synchronizer parts.**

Reassembly

1) Lubricate output shaft, synchronizer assemblies, and gear bores with transmission lubricant. Position 1st gear, blocking ring, thrust washer, and rear bearing on rear of shaft.

2) Using an arbor press, press rear bearing inner race until bearing is bottomed on spacer and shaft. See Fig. 7. Install new snap ring that will not allow any clearance between bearing inner race and ring groove.

3) Press 1st/2nd gear synchronizer and reverse sliding gear into place, and secure in place with snap ring. Slide 2nd gear and thurst washer into place, and secure with snap ring.

4) Slide 3rd gear and 3rd/4th synchronizer into place, making sure that thrust surface of synchronizer hub is facing toward front of output shaft.

Manual Transmissions

FORD MOTOR CO. 5-SPEED OVERDRIVE (Cont.)

Fig. 7: Installing Output Shaft Rear Bearing

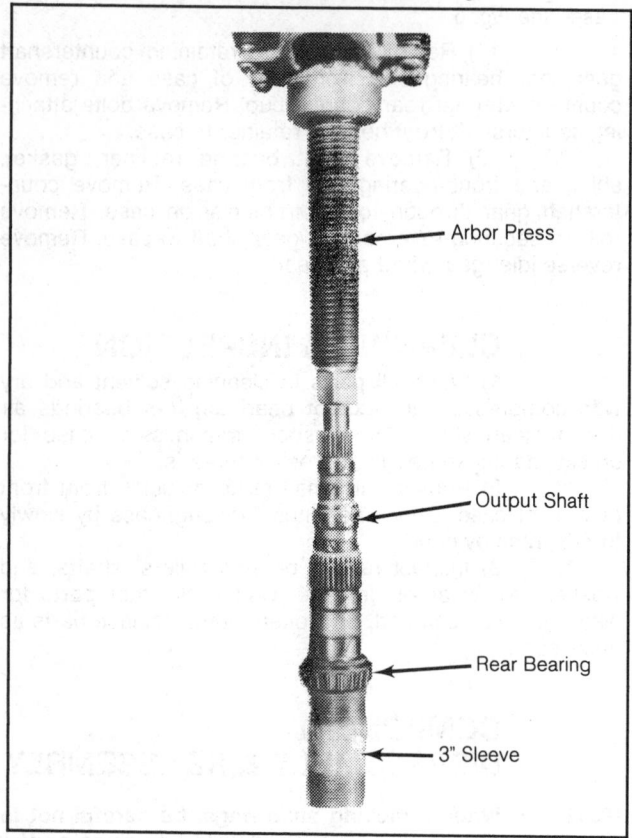

INPUT SHAFT & BEARING RETAINER

Disassembly

Remove the 15 roller bearings from input shaft bearing bore. Position input shaft in arbor press, press input shaft bearing off shaft. Position bearing retainer in vise and carefully remove seal using slide-type puller.

Reassembly

1) Position input shaft bearing on shaft. Using arbor press, press bearing in place by applying pressure to inner race of bearing until race bottoms on shaft.

2) Coat input shaft bearing bore with Lubriplate (or equivalent) and install the 15 roller bearings into shaft bore. Position bearing retainer in vise.

3) Install seal with lip facing toward transmission case. Make sure seal is bottomed in retainer, coat seal lip with Lubriplate (or equivalent).

COUNTERSHAFT GEAR

Disassembly

Position countershaft gear in arbor press and remove rear bearing. Remove gear from press and position in vise with wood blocks, and pry front bearing from shaft.

Reassembly

Position gear in arbor press and press front bearing into place, pressing on bearing inner race until bearing bottoms on gear. Install rear bearing using same procedure.

EXTENSION HOUSING OIL SEAL

Disassembly & Reassembly

Remove seal from rear of housing using driver. Press rear bushing out using driver. Install new bushing and seal with drivers.

REASSEMBLY

TRANSMISSION

NOTE: All bolts and plugs should be coated with sealant to prevent leakage.

1) Position reverse idler gear in case with long end of hub facing rear of transmission case. Install reverse idler gear shaft into case, through gear and thrust washers, from rear of case, making sure to align roll pin hole with slot in shaft. Insert roll pin. See Fig. 8

Fig. 8: Installing Reverse Idler Gear

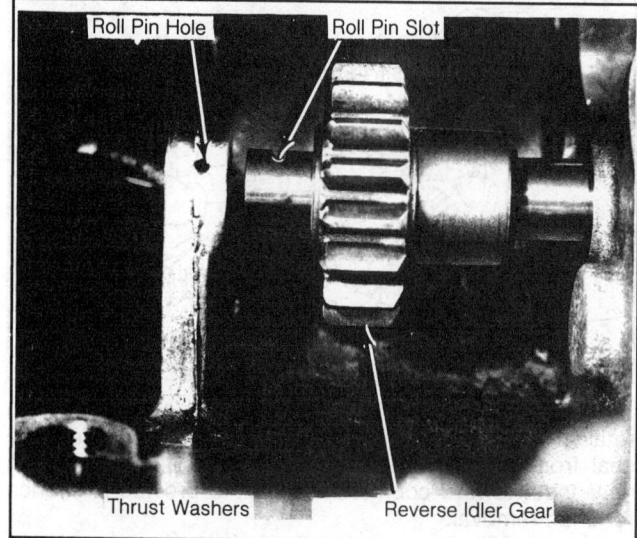

2) Install countershaft and bearing assembly into case. Install rear bearing cup and snap ring. Position front bearing cup, shim, new gasket, and bearing retainer to front of transmission case.

3) Install bearing retainer bolts and tighten while rotating gear. If gear rotating effort increases while tightening bearing retainer, replace shim using a thinner one.

4) Measure countershaft end play by mounting dial indicator on transmission case. Place dial indicator plunger on front of gear and pry gear back and forth using screwdrivers. See Fig. 10.

5) End play should be .001-.005" (.03-.13 mm). Decrease shim thickness to increase end play or increase shim thickness to decrease end play.

6) Install output shaft assembly into transmission case. See Fig. 6. Coat input shaft thrust washers and thrust bearing with Ford polyethylene grease (or equivalent). Install thrust washer, thrust bearing, and another thrust washer (in that order) on 3rd/4th gear synchronizer thrust surface.

FORD MOTOR CO. 5-SPEED OVERDRIVE (Cont.)

Fig. 9: *Exploded View of Ford 5-Speed Single Rail Overdrive Transmission*

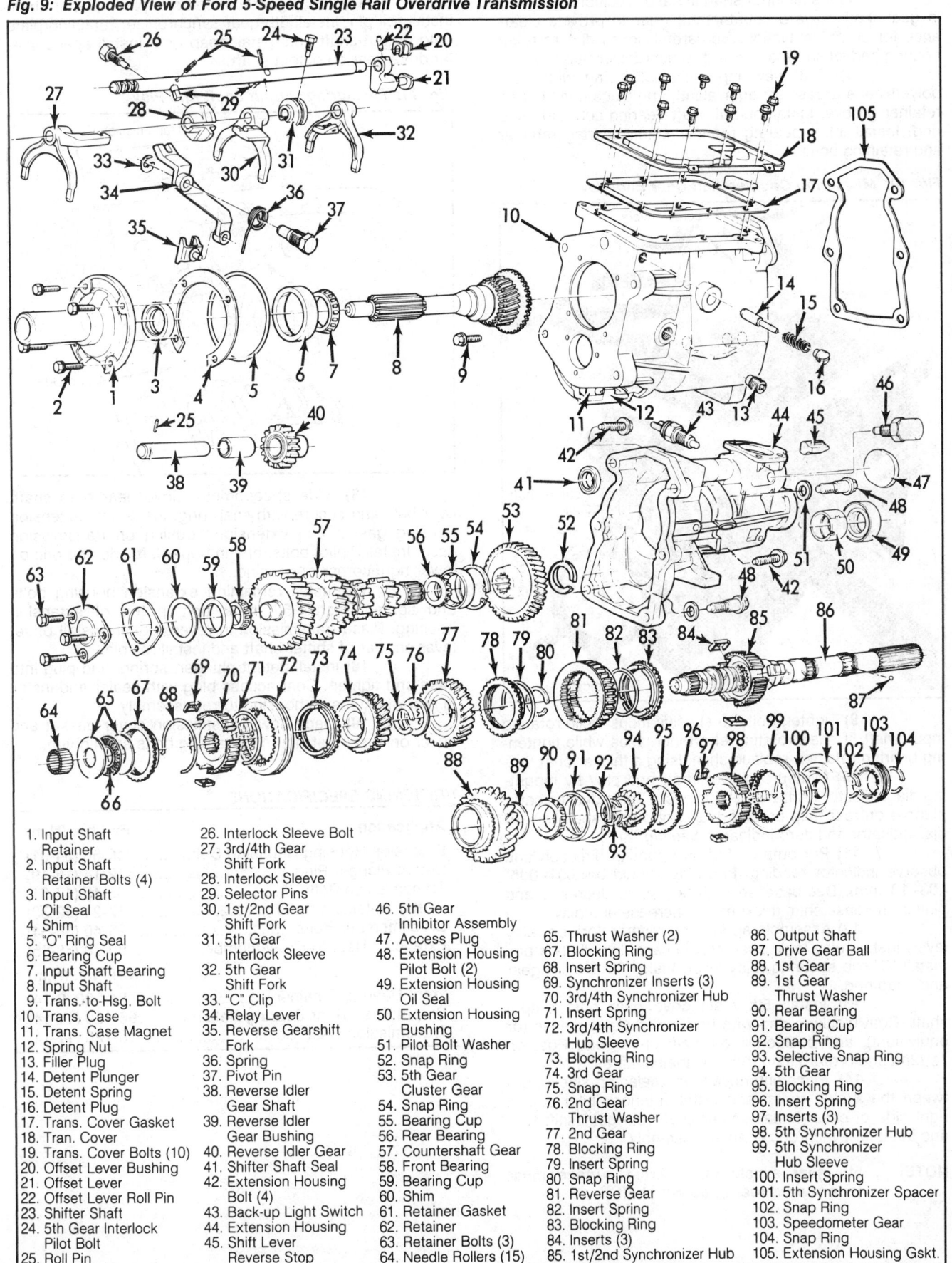

1. Input Shaft
   Retainer
2. Input Shaft
   Retainer Bolts (4)
3. Input Shaft
   Oil Seal
4. Shim
5. "O" Ring Seal
6. Bearing Cup
7. Input Shaft Bearing
8. Input Shaft
9. Trans.-to-Hsg. Bolt
10. Trans. Case
11. Trans. Case Magnet
12. Spring Nut
13. Filler Plug
14. Detent Plunger
15. Detent Spring
16. Detent Plug
17. Trans. Cover Gasket
18. Tran. Cover
19. Trans. Cover Bolts (10)
20. Offset Lever Bushing
21. Offset Lever
22. Offset Lever Roll Pin
23. Shifter Shaft
24. 5th Gear Interlock
    Pilot Bolt
25. Roll Pin

26. Interlock Sleeve Bolt
27. 3rd/4th Gear
    Shift Fork
28. Interlock Sleeve
29. Selector Pins
30. 1st/2nd Gear
    Shift Fork
31. 5th Gear
    Interlock Sleeve
32. 5th Gear
    Shift Fork
33. "C" Clip
34. Relay Lever
35. Reverse Gearshift
    Fork
36. Spring
37. Pivot Pin
38. Reverse Idler
    Gear Shaft
39. Reverse Idler
    Gear Bushing
40. Reverse Idler Gear
41. Shifter Shaft Seal
42. Extension Housing
    Bolt (4)
43. Back-up Light Switch
44. Extension Housing
45. Shift Lever
    Reverse Stop

46. 5th Gear
    Inhibitor Assembly
47. Access Plug
48. Extension Housing
    Pilot Bolt (2)
49. Extension Housing
    Oil Seal
50. Extension Housing
    Bushing
51. Pilot Bolt Washer
52. Snap Ring
53. 5th Gear
    Cluster Gear
54. Snap Ring
55. Bearing Cup
56. Rear Bearing
57. Countershaft Gear
58. Front Bearing
59. Bearing Cup
60. Shim
61. Retainer Gasket
62. Retainer
63. Retainer Bolts (3)
64. Needle Rollers (15)

65. Thrust Washer (2)
67. Blocking Ring
68. Insert Spring
69. Synchronizer Inserts (3)
70. 3rd/4th Synchronizer Hub
71. Insert Spring
72. 3rd/4th Synchronizer
    Hub Sleeve
73. Blocking Ring
74. 3rd Gear
75. Snap Ring
76. 2nd Gear
    Thrust Washer
77. 2nd Gear
78. Blocking Ring
79. Insert Spring
80. Snap Ring
81. Reverse Gear
82. Insert Spring
83. Blocking Ring
84. Inserts (3)
85. 1st/2nd Synchronizer Hub

86. Output Shaft
87. Drive Gear Ball
88. 1st Gear
89. 1st Gear
    Thrust Washer
90. Rear Bearing
91. Bearing Cup
92. Snap Ring
93. Selective Snap Ring
94. 5th Gear
95. Blocking Ring
96. Insert Spring
97. Inserts (3)
98. 5th Synchronizer Hub
99. 5th Synchronizer
    Hub Sleeve
100. Insert Spring
101. 5th Synchronizer Spacer
102. Snap Ring
103. Speedometer Gear
104. Snap Ring
105. Extension Housing Gskt.

Manual Transmissions

FORD MOTOR CO. 5-SPEED OVERDRIVE (Cont.)

7) Install input shaft in case, positioning recess in gear teeth toward countershaft gear to provide clearance for shaft installation. Be careful not to disturb roller bearing and washers on 3rd/4th synchronizer hub.

8) Coat new input shaft "O" ring with Ford polyethylene grease (or equivalent), and place it in bearing retainer groove. Install output shaft bearing cup and snap ring. Install input bearing retainer shim, bearing retainer and retaining bolts.

Fig. 10: *Measuring Countershaft Gear End Play*

9) Tighten bolts to specifications while rotating input shaft. If shaft rotating effort increases while tightening bearing retainer, replace shim using a thicker one.

10) Measure output shaft end play by mounting dial indicator on transmission case. Place dial indicator plunger on rear face on 2nd gear, pry output shaft toward dial indicator and zero indicator. *See Fig. 11.*

11) Pry output shaft in opposite direction and observe indicator reading. End play should be .001-.005" (.03-.13 mm). Decrease shim thickness to decrease end play or increase shim thickness to increase end play.

12) Assemble spring and reverse fork on relay lever. Install relay lever assembly in case. Install pivot pin. Install "C" clip securing relay lever. Install 5th cluster gear and snap ring.

13) Install 5th main drive gear onto output shaft. Coat blocking ring with Ford polythylene grease (or equivalent), and position it on main drive gear. Position 1st/2nd and 3rd/4th shift forks on mainshaft assembly.

14) Place interlock gear selector sleeve between the 2 shift forks, and install interlock pilot bolt in right side of case. Install shifter shaft, 5th gear shift fork and 5th gear synchronizer as an assembly.

NOTE: 5th gear synchronizer thrust surface must face toward rear of output shaft.

15) Install gearshift selector pin in shifter shaft. Install roll pin. Install 5th gear synchronizer retaining plate onto output shaft and install snap ring. Install speedometer drive gear on output shaft.

Fig. 11: *Measuring Output Shaft End Play*

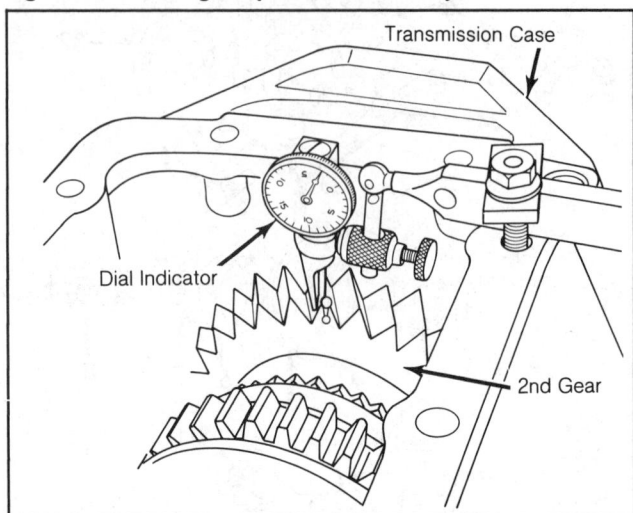

16) Slide speedometer drive gear onto shaft, over ball, and secure with snap ring. Place new extension housing gasket and extension housing on transmission case. Install 2 pilot bolts, one in upper left side and one on lower right corner of housing.

17) Install remaining extension housing bolts and tighten. Install 5th gear bolt in top of extension housing. Place transmission in reverse gear, install offset lever on rear of shifter shaft and install roll pin.

18) Install detent plunger, spring, and plug into case and tighten. Coat access plug with sealer and install in rear of extension housing turret assembly.

19) Place new transmission cover gasket and cover on case. Install all 10 retaining bolts and tighten.

TIGHTENING SPECIFICATIONS

Application	Ft. Lbs. (N.m)
Extension Housing Retaining Bolts	40-60 (54-81)
Detent Plunger Plug	12-14 (16-19)
Transmission Bolts	35-45 (47-61)
Shifter Retaining Bolts	17-24 (22-33)
Crossmember Bolts	28-40 (38-54)
Extension Hsg.-to-Crossmember	50-70 (68-95)

	INCH Lbs. (N.m)
Front Bearing Retainer	84-120 (9-14)
Output Shaft Rear Bearing Retainer	96-120 (11-14)
Transmission Case Cover	96-120 (11-14)

FORD MOTOR CO. 4 & 5-SPEED
BRONCO II & RANGER — GASOLINE

Gasoline Models (Only)

IDENTIFICATION

Bronco II and Ranger 4 and 5-speed manual transmissions have service identification tags located at right front side of case. *See Fig. 1.*

Fig. 1: Transmission Identification Tag

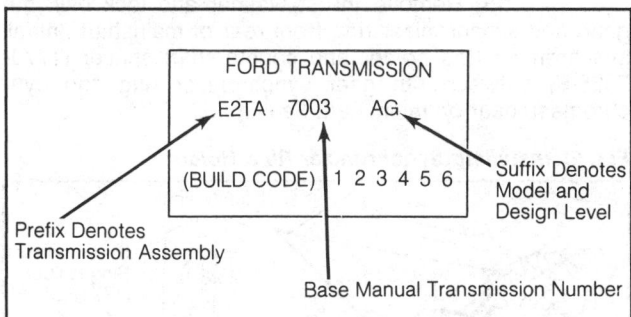

Tag is found at right front side of transmission.

TRANSMISSION IDENTIFICATION CODES

Application	Code
4-Speed	X
5-Speed Overdrive	5

DESCRIPTION

The 4 and 5 speed transmissions are similar. The 5-speed transmission has an additional 5th gear located in the extension housing. On both transmissions, all forward gears are synchronized. The reverse gear is a constant mesh type. All forward gears are helical-cut for quiet running. The reverse gear and reverse idler gear are spur-cut.

The transmission case is of light metal construction with removable clutch and extension housings. The gearshift mechanism is a direct control with a floor shift. The floor shift mechanism is built into the extension housing.

LUBRICATION & ADJUSTMENT

See the appropriate article in MANUAL TRANS-MISSION SERVICING Section.

REMOVAL & INSTALLATION

See the appropriate article in MANUAL TRANS-MISSION REMOVAL Section.

SERVICE (IN VEHICLE)

GEAR SHIFT LEVER

NOTE: Remove shift ball only if shift ball, boot, or lever is to be replaced. If either the ball, boot, or lever is not being replaced, remove the ball, boot, and lever as an assembly.

Removal

1) Remove plastic insert from shift ball. Warm ball with heat gun to 140-160°F (60-82°C). Knock ball off lever with a block of wood and a hammer, taking care not to damage finish on shift lever.

2) Remove rubber boot. Remove bolt retaining shift lever to extension housing.

Installation

1) Lubricate shift lever. Position lever in extension housing. Install bolts and tighten. Install rubber boot and floor pan cover.

2) Warm ball with heat gun to 140-180°F (60-82°C) and tap ball on lever with a 7/16" socket and mallet. Install plastic shift pattern insert.

DISASSEMBLY

TRANSMISSION

1) Remove nuts retaining clutch housing to transmission case. Remove clutch housing gasket. Remove drain plug and drain lubricant. Clean metal filings from magnet of drain plug.

2) Position transmission in holding fixture. Place transmission in neutral. Remove speedometer sleeve and driven gear assembly from extension housing. Remove nuts and bolts retaining extension housing to case.

3) Raise control lever to left and slide towards rear of transmission. Slide extension housing off mainshaft, being careful not to damage oil seal. Pull control lever and rod out front end of extension housing. *See Fig. 2.*

Fig. 2: Removing Control Lever and Rod

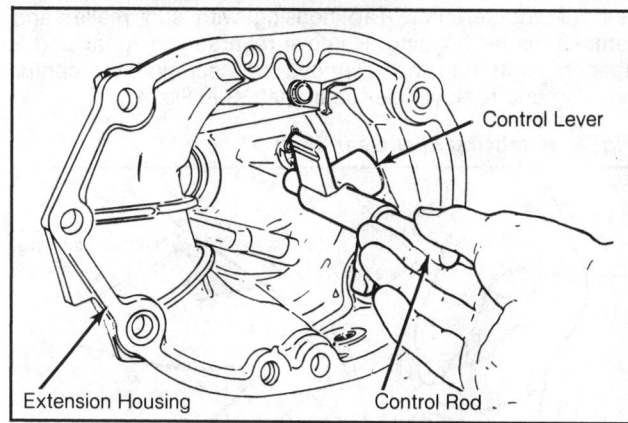

4) Remove anti-spill seal from mainshaft and discard. The seal is not necessary for reassembly. Remove snap ring from mainshaft and remove speedometer drive gear. Remove lock ball.

5) Evenly loosen retaining bolts from case cover and remove cover and gasket. Mark shift rails and fork for reassembly references. Remove roll pins attaching shift rod ends to shift rod. Remove shift rod ends.

6) Gently pry bearing housing away from transmission case, being careful not to damage housing case. Remove snap ring and washer retaining mainshaft rear bearing to mainshaft.

FORD MOTOR CO. 4 & 5-SPEED
BRONCO II & RANGER — GASOLINE (Cont.)

7) Assemble bearing puller ring tool (T77J-7025-J), bearing puller tool (T77J-7025-H), and forcing screw (T75L-7025-J) on remover and replacer tube tool (T75L-7525-B). Slide tool assembly over mainshaft and engage puller jaws behind rear bearing. See Fig. 3.

Fig. 3: Removing Mainshaft Rear Bearing

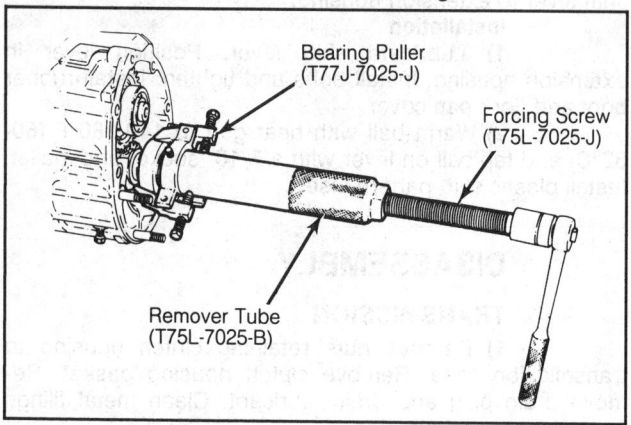

Jaws of puller must be fully behind bearing before removing.

8) Tighten jaws evenly onto bearing with wrench. Turn forcing screw to remove mainshaft rear bearing. Remove snap ring from rear end of countershaft. Assemble bearing puller tool (T77J-7025-J) and forcing screw (T75L-7025-J) onto remover tube (T77J-7025-B).

9) Slide tool assembly over countershaft and engage puller jaws behind countershaft rear bearing. Tighten jaws evenly onto bearing with wrench. Turn forcing screw to remove bearing.

10) Remove counter 5th gear and spacer from rear of countershaft. Tap housing with soft mallet and remove center housing. Remove reverse idler gear and 2 spacers with housing. Remove cap screw from center housing and remove idler gear shaft. See Fig. 4.

Fig. 4: Removing Idler Gear Shaft

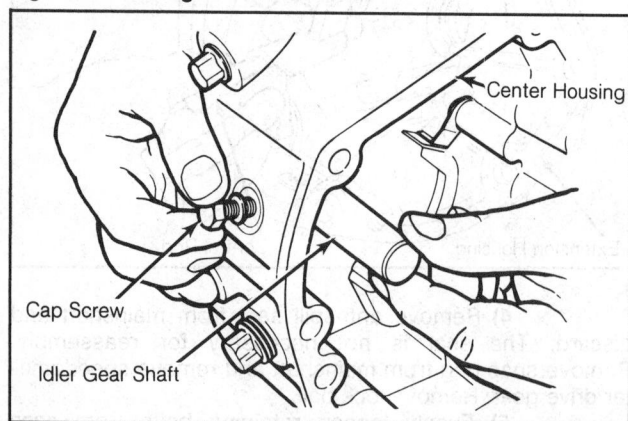

Remove cap screw from side of case and remove shaft.

11) Remove 3 spring cap bolts. The 2 bolts on case upper portion are 17 mm and the bolt on case side is 14 mm. Remove detent springs and balls with a magnet from case.

12) Remove four 10 mm bolts retaining blind covers to case. Remove blind covers and gaskets.

Remove roll pin from 5th/reverse shift fork. Slide 5th/reverse shift fork shaft out of case.

13) Shift transmission into 4th gear. Through hole in side of case drive, out roll pin from 3rd/4th shift fork. Slide 3rd/4th shift fork shaft out of rear of case.

14) Through other hole in side of case, drive out 1st/2nd shift fork. Slide 1st/2nd shift fork shaft assembly out rear of case. Remove interlock pins. Remove snap ring securing 5th gear to mainshaft.

15) Remove thrust washer and lock ball, 5th gear, and synchronizer ring from rear of mainshaft. Install synchronizer ring holder and countershaft spacer (T77J-7025-E) between 4th gear synchronizer ring and synchromesh gear on mainshaft. See Fig. 5.

Fig. 5: Installing Synchronizer Ring Holder

Place holder behind 3rd/4th clutch hub.

16) Shift transmission to 2nd gear to lock mainshaft and prevent assembly from rotating. Straighten staked portion of mainshaft bearing lock nut with staking tool (T77J-7025-F). Using lock nut wrench (T77J-7025-C) remove mainshaft bearing lock nut.

17) Slide reverse gear and clutch hub assembly off mainshaft. Remove counter reverse gear from countershaft. If installed, remove transmission from holding fixture and set on workbench. Remove bolts retaining mainshaft center bearing cover to transmission and remove bearing cover.

18) Remove countershaft center bearing using puller (T77J-7025-H), puller rings (T77J-7025-J), remover tube (T77J-7025-B), and forcing screw (T75L-7025-J) on countershaft. Squarely insert jaws of puller behind center

Fig. 6: Removing Countershaft Center Bearing

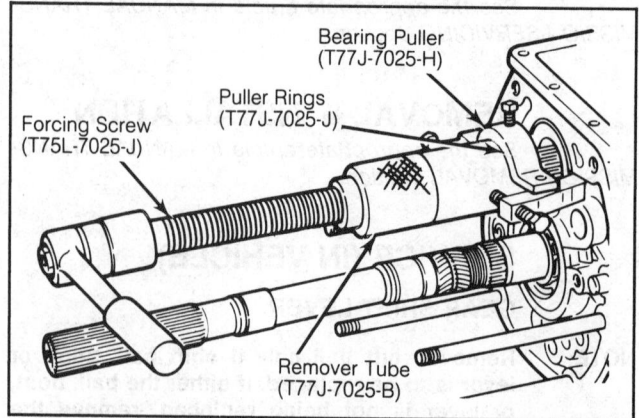

FORD MOTOR CO. 4 & 5-SPEED
BRONCO II & RANGER — GASOLINE (Cont.)

bearing retainer ring in 2 recessed areas of case. Turn forcing screw to remove bearing.

19) Remove mainshaft center bearing, using puller (T77J-7025-H), puller rings (T77J-7025-J), long remover tube (T75L-7025-C), and forcing screw (T75L-7025-J). Squarely insert jaws of puller behind rear mainshaft bearing retainer ring in the 2 recessed areas of case. Turn forcing screw clockwise to remove bearing.

20) Remove shim and spacer from behind mainshaft rear bearing along with bearing. Remove front cover by first removing 4 studs attaching cover to case. Remove studs by installing 2 nuts on stud and drawing stud out of case. Remove the 4 retaining bolts and cover. Save shims found on inside of cover.

21) Remove snap ring from input shaft. Using same pullers and remover tube, remove input shaft bearing. Rotate both shift forks so that main gear train will fall to bottom of case. Remove shift forks. Rotate input shaft so that one of the two flats on input shaft faces upward.

22) Remove snap ring from front of countershaft. Remove synchronizer ring holder (T77J-7025-E) from front of case and insert between first gear on countershaft and rear of case. Install forcing screw (T75L-7025-J), press frame holder (T77J-7025-N), and press frame adapter (T82T-7003-BH) against countershaft assembly. See Fig. 7.

Fig. 7: Pressing Countershaft Rearward

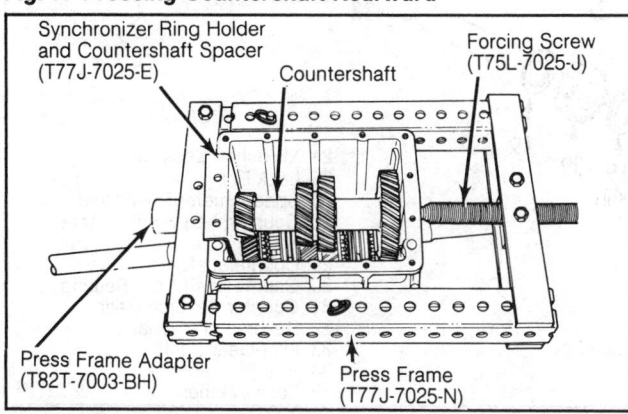

Press countershaft about 3/16".

22) Turn forcing screw clockwise to press countershaft rearward. Press countershaft about 3/16", until it contacts synchronizer ring holder and countershaft spacer.

23) Remove press frame. To remove countershaft front bearing, install puller, puller rings, remover tube, and forcing screw. Squarely insert jaws of puller behind front bearing retainer ring in 2 recessed areas in case.

24) Turn forcing screw clockwise to remove bearing. Remove shim from behind countershaft front bearing. Remove countershaft from case. Remove input shaft from case. Remove synchronizer ring and caged bearing from mainshaft. Remove mainshaft and gear assembly from case.

CLEANING & INSPECTION

1) Wash all parts in cleaning solvent and dry with compressed air (except bearings). Let bearings air

dry in clean shop cloth. Inspect transmission case for cracks, damaged bearing bores, or threads.

2) Remove all small nicks or burrs from front or rear of case. Check bearings for roughness by slowly turning race by hand.

3) Inspect needle bearing rollers, shafts, and washers for wear or damage. Check all other parts for wear, damage, chipped, or broken teeth. Replace parts as necessary.

COMPONENT DISASSEMBLY & REASSEMBLY

COUNTERSHAFT
Disassembly

1) Remove inner race of countershaft center bearing from countershaft in press frame using axle bearing seal plate (T75L-1165-B) and pinion cone remover (D79L-4621-A). See Fig. 8.

Fig. 8: Removing Countershaft Bearing Inner Race

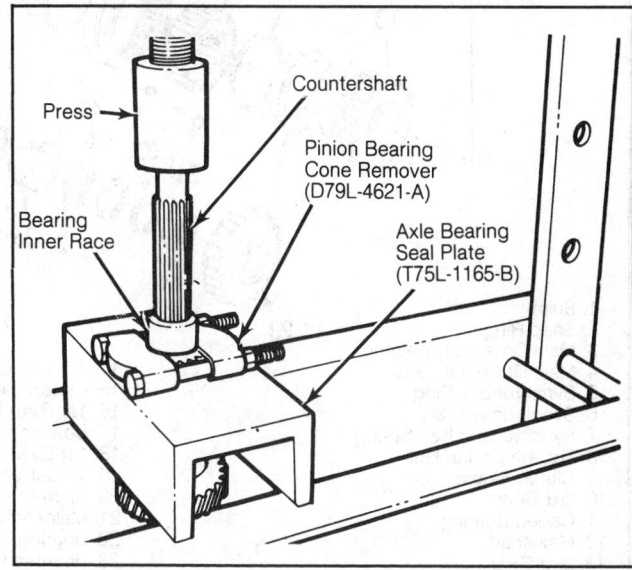

2) Check thrust play by measuring depth of countershaft front bearing bore in case, using a depth micrometer (D80P-4201-A). Measure countershaft front bearing height. The difference between the two measurements indicates the required thickness of the adjusting shims.

3) The standard thrust play is 0.00-.0039" (0.00-0.10 mm). Adjusting shims are available in .0039" (0.10 mm) and .0118" (0.30 mm) sizes.

Reassembly

Press inner race of countershaft rear bearing onto countershaft using center bearing replacer (T77J-7025-K).

MAINSHAFT
Disassembly

1) Remove 1st gear and 1st/2nd synchronizer ring. Remove snap ring retainer from mainshaft. Install bearing remover tool (T71P-4621-B) between 2nd/3rd gear. Press mainshaft out of 3rd gear and 3rd/4th clutch hub sleeve. Press 1st/2nd clutch hub and sleeve assembly, and 1st gear sleeve from mainshaft.

Manual Transmissions

FORD MOTOR CO. 4 & 5-SPEED BRONCO II & RANGER — GASOLINE (Cont.)

Fig. 9: Exploded View of 4 & 5-Speed Transmission Mainshaft

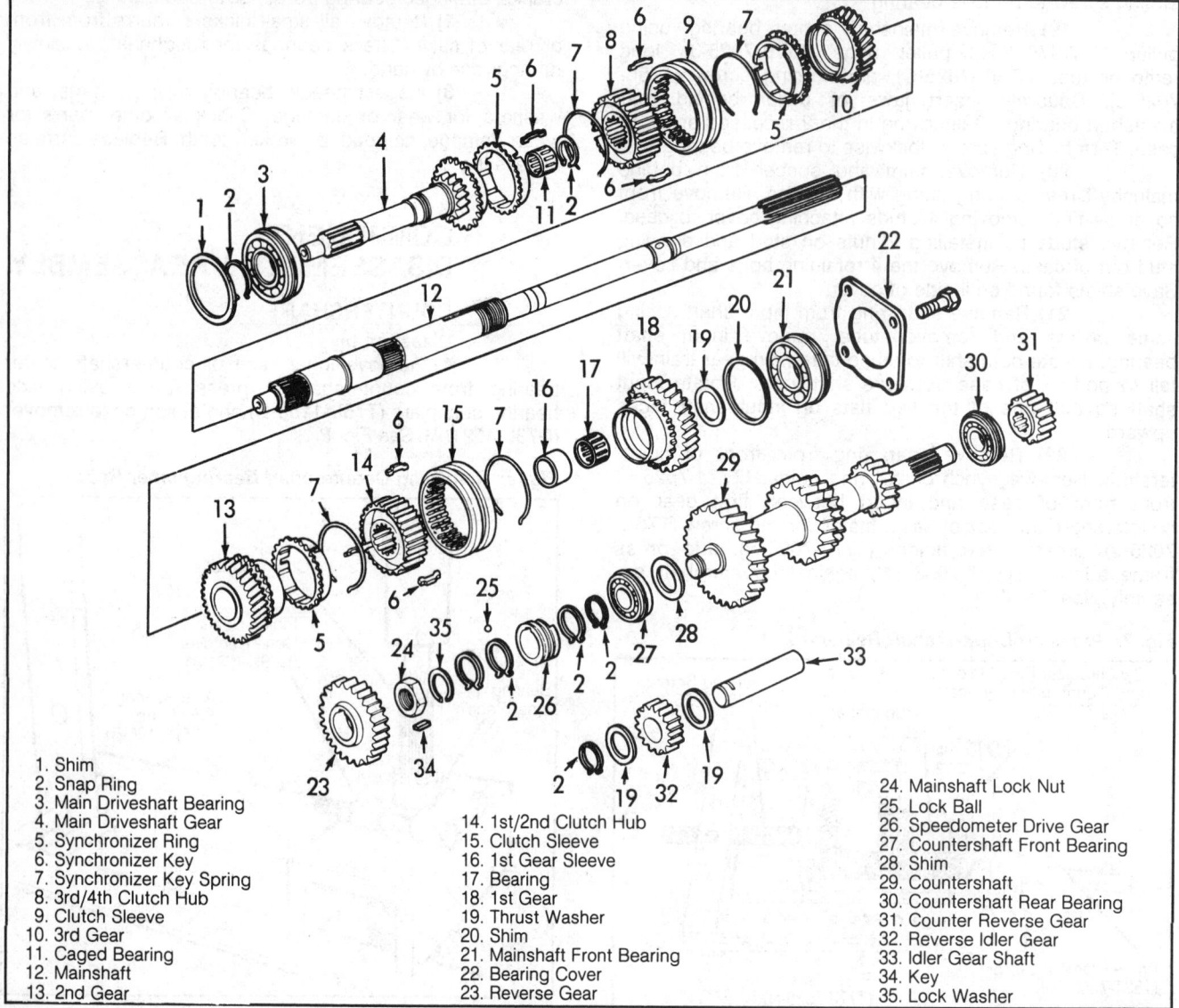

1. Shim
2. Snap Ring
3. Main Driveshaft Bearing
4. Main Driveshaft Gear
5. Synchronizer Ring
6. Synchronizer Key
7. Synchronizer Key Spring
8. 3rd/4th Clutch Hub
9. Clutch Sleeve
10. 3rd Gear
11. Caged Bearing
12. Mainshaft
13. 2nd Gear
14. 1st/2nd Clutch Hub
15. Clutch Sleeve
16. 1st Gear Sleeve
17. Bearing
18. 1st Gear
19. Thrust Washer
20. Shim
21. Mainshaft Front Bearing
22. Bearing Cover
23. Reverse Gear
24. Mainshaft Lock Nut
25. Lock Ball
26. Speedometer Drive Gear
27. Countershaft Front Bearing
28. Shim
29. Countershaft
30. Countershaft Rear Bearing
31. Counter Reverse Gear
32. Reverse Idler Gear
33. Idler Gear Shaft
34. Key
35. Lock Washer

2) Check mainshaft bearing clearance by measuring depth of bearing bore in clutch adapter plate with depth micrometer (D80P-4201-A). Make sure micrometer is on second step of plate. Measure bearing height.

3) The difference between the two measurements indicates the required adjusting shim thickness. Standard clearance is 0.00-.0039" (0.00-1.00 mm). If an adjusting shim is required, select one to bring clearance to within specifications.

Reassembly

1) Assemble 1st/2nd synchromesh mechanism and 3rd/4th sychromesh mechanism by installing clutch hub to clutch hub key slots and install key springs to clutch hub. Place synchronizer ring on 2nd gear and position 2nd gear to mainshaft with synchronizer ring toward rear of shaft.

2) Slide 1st/2nd clutch hub and sleeve assembly to mainshaft with oil grooves of clutch hub toward front of mainshaft. Make sure that 3 synchronizer keys in synchromesh mechanism engage notches in 2nd synchronizer ring.

3) Press into position using press. Insert 1st gear sleeve on mainshaft. Place synchronizer ring on 3rd gear along with caged roller bearing and slide 3rd gear to front of mainshaft with synchronizer ring toward front.

4) Press 3rd/4th clutch hub and sleeve assembly to front of mainshaft. Make sure that 3 synchronizer keys in synchromesh mechanism engage notches in synchronizer ring. Install snap ring to front of mainshaft.

5) Slide needle bearing for 1st gear onto mainshaft. Place synchronizer ring on 1st gear. Slide 1st gear onto onto mainshaft with synchronizer ring facing front of shaft. Rotate 1st gear, as necessary, to engage 3 notches in synchronizer ring with synchronizer keys.

6) Install original thrust washer to mainshaft. Position mainshaft and gear assembly in case. Position 1st/2nd shift fork and 3rd/4th shift fork in groove of clutch hub and sleeve assembly. Position caged bearing in front end of mainshaft.

7) Place synchronizer ring on input shaft (4th gear) and install input shaft to front end of mainshaft. Make sure that the 3 synchronizer keys in 3rd/4th

FORD MOTOR CO. 4 & 5-SPEED
BRONCO II & RANGER — GASOLINE (Cont.)

Fig. 10: *Countershaft Front Bearing Installation*

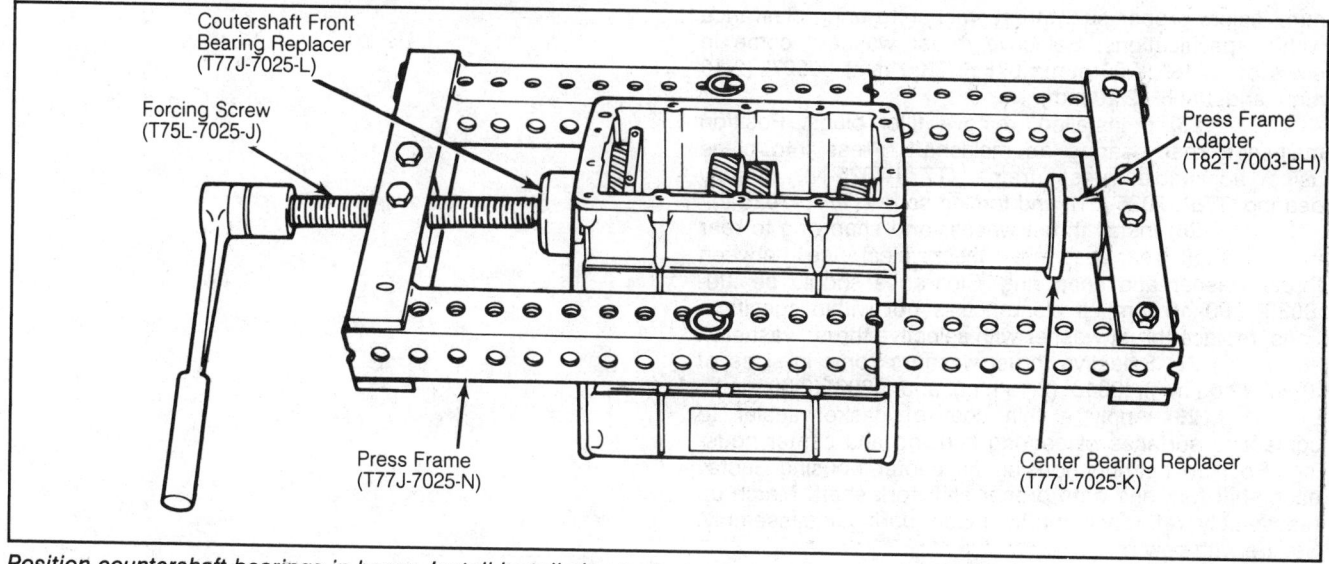

Position countershaft bearings in bores. Install installation tools.

synchromesh mechanism engage notches in synchronizer ring.

8) Press inner race of countershaft rear bearing onto countershaft using center bearing replacer (T77J-7025-K). Position countershaft gear in case, making sure that countershaft gear engages each gear of mainshaft assembly.

9) Install correct shim on mainshaft center bearing. Position input shaft bearing and mainshaft center bearing into proper bearing bores. Be sure synchronizer and shift forks have not been moved out of position.

10) Install synchronizer ring holder tool (T77J-7025-E) between 4th synchronizer ring and synchromesh gear on mainshaft. Install dummy bearing replacer (T75L-7025-Q), input shaft bearing replacer (T82T-7003-DH), replacer tube (T77J-7025-M), and press frame (T77J-7025-N) on case. Turn forcing screw on press frame until both bearings are properly seated.

11) Install input shaft bearing snap ring. Place correct shim in countershaft front bearing bore. Position countershaft front and center bearings in bores. Install press frame, press frame adapter, center and front bearing replacers, and forcing screw on case. *See Fig. 10.*

12) Turn forcing screw until bearing is properly seated. Use center bearing as a pilot. Install snap ring to secure countershaft front bearing. Remove synchronizer ring holder. Install bearing cover to transmission case and tighten retaining bolts.

13) Install reverse idler gear and shaft with a spacer on each side of shaft. Slide counter reverse gear (chamfer side forward) and spacer onto countershaft. Slide thrust washer, reverse gear, caged roller bearings and clutch hub assembly onto mainshaft.

14) Install a new lock nut onto mainshaft (hand tight). Shift into 2nd and reverse to lock rotation of mainshaft. Tighten lock nut using lock nut wrench (T77J-7025-C). Stake lock nut into mainshaft keyway. Place 4th and 3rd clutch sleeve in 3rd gear using synchronizer ring holder and countershaft spacer (T77J-7025-E).

15) Position 5th synchronizer ring on 5th gear. Slide 5th gear onto mainshaft with synchronizer ring toward front of shaft. Rotate 5th gear, as necessary, to engage the 3 notches in synchronizer ring with synchronizer keys in reverse and clutch hub assembly.

16) Install lock ball and thrust washer on rear of 5th gear. Install snap ring on rear of thrust washer. Check clearance between thrust washer and snap ring. If clearance is not within .0039-.0118" (0.10-0.30 mm), select proper size thrust washer to bring clearance within specifications.

17) Slective thrust washers come in sizes of .2362" (6.00 mm), .2441" (6.20 mm), .2520" (6.40 mm), .2559" (6.50 mm), .2598" (6.60 mm), .2638" (6.70 mm), .2677" (6.80 mm), .2756" (7.00 mm), and .2835" (7.20 mm).

18) Slide 1st/2nd shift fork shaft assembly into case. Secure 1st/2nd shift fork to fork shaft with a new roll pin. Insert interlock pin into transmission using lock-out pin replacer tool set (T72J-7280). Shift transmission into 4th gear.

19) Slide 3rd/4th shift fork shaft into case, from rear of case. Secure 3rd/4th shift fork to fork shaft with a new roll pin. Insert interlock pin. Shift synchronizer hub into 5th gear, (if equipped).

20) Position reverse/5th fork on clutch hub and slide reverse/5th fork on clutch hub and slide reverse/5th fork shaft into case (from rear of case). Secure reverse/5th shift fork to fork shaft with new roll pin.

21) Install 2 blind covers and gaskets. Install and tighten retaining bolts on blind covers. Position 3 detent balls and 3 springs into case and install spring cap bolts. Apply a thin coat of gasket sealer to contacting surfaces of center housing and case.

22) Position center housing on case. Align reverse idler gear shaft boss with center housing retaining bolt boss. Install and tighten idler shaft cap screw. Slide counter 5th gear onto countershaft.

23) Position countershaft rear bearing on countershaft. Press into position using adjustable press frame (T77J-7025-N) and forcing screw (T75L-7025-J). Install thrust washer and snap ring onto rear of countershaft rear bearing. Check clearance between thrust washer and snap ring using a feeler gauge.

FORD MOTOR CO. 4 & 5-SPEED
BRONCO II & RANGER — GASOLINE (Cont.)

24) If clearance is not within .00-.0059" (.00-15 mm), select proper size thrust washer to bring clearance within specifications. Selective thrust washers come in sizes of .0748" (1.90 mm), .0787" (2.00 mm), .0827" (2.10 mm), and .0866" (2.20 mm).

25) If installed, remove filler plugs. Position mainshaft rear bearing on mainshaft. Press into place using adjustable press frame (T77J-7025-N), dummy bearing (T75L-7025-Q1), and forcing screw (T75L-7025-J).

26) Install thrust washer and snap ring to rear of mainshaft rear bearing. Check clearance between thrust washer and snap ring. Clearance should be .00-.0039" (.00-.10 mm). If clearance is not within specifications, replace thrust washer with selective thrust washer.

27) Selective thrust washers come in sizes of .0787" (2.00 mm), .0846" (2.15 mm), and .0906" (2.30 mm).

28) Apply a thin coat of gasket sealer to contacting surfaces of bearing housing and center housing. Position bearing housing on center housing. Install each shift fork end onto proper shift fork shaft. Match up reassembly reference marks made during disassembly. Secure with new roll pins.

29) Install lock ball, speedometer drive gear, and snap ring onto mainshaft. If removed, install control lever and rod in extension housing. Apply a thin coat of gasket sealer to contacting surfaces of bearing housing and extension housing.

30) Position extension housing in bearing housing with gearshift control lever end laid down to the left as far as it will go. Tighten retaining bolts and nuts. If removed, insert speedometer driven gear assembly into extension housing and secure it with retaining bolt.

31) Check to ensure gear shift lever operates properly. Install transmission case cover gasket and cover with drain plug towards rear. Install and tighten retaining bolts to cover. Install the correct size shim on second step of front cover.

32) Coat front cover gasket with sealer and install cover to transmission case and tighten 4 bolts and 4 studs. Fill transmission with fluid and install filler plug.

TIGHTENING SPECIFICATIONS

Application	Ft. Lbs. (N.m)
Shift Rail Detent Spring Cap	29-43 (40-58)
Mainshaft Gear Lock Nut	145-203 (197-275)
Clutch Release Lever Pivot	23-34 (32-46)
Drain Plug	29-43 (40-58)
Filler Plug	18-29 (25-39)
Back-Up Lamp Switch	22-29 (30-39)
	INCH Lbs. (N.m)
Interlock Pin Bore Plug	68-132 (11-14)

FORD MOTOR CO. 4-SPEED
BRONCO II & RANGER — DIESEL

Diesel Models (Only)

IDENTIFICATION

The manual transmissions have a service identification tag to identify transmissions for servicing. The tag is found at at right front side of case. Transmission code for the 4-speed transmission is "X". See Fig. 1.

Fig. 1: Transmission Identification Tag

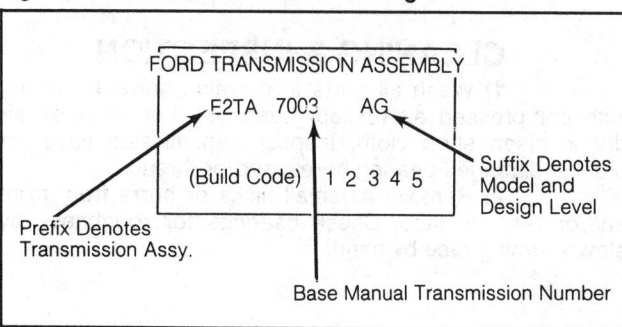

Tag is found at right front side of transmission.

DESCRIPTION

The 4-speed manual transmission is fully synchronized with all gears except reverse gear which is in constant mesh. All forward gears are helical-cut for quiet running operation. The reverse gear and reverse idler gear are spur-cut.

Transmission case is of light metal construction and features an integral clutch housing and gear case. The bearing housing and extension housing are also of a light metal construction. The gear shift mechanism is a direct control with a floor shift. The floor shift mechanism is built into the extension housing.

LUBRICATION & ADJUSTMENT

See the appropriate article in MANUAL TRANSMISSION SERVICING Section.

REMOVAL & INSTALLATION

See the appropriate article in MANUAL TRANSMISSION REMOVAL Section.

SERVICE (IN VEHICLE)

GEAR SHIFT LEVER

NOTE: Remove shift ball only if shift ball, boot, or lever is to be replaced. If either the ball, boot, or lever is not being replaced, remove the ball, boot, and lever as an assembly.

Removal
1) Remove plastic insert from shift ball. Warm ball with heat gun to 140-160°F (60-82°C), knock ball off lever with a block of wood and a hammer, taking care not to damage finish on shift lever.

2) Remove rubber boot. Remove bolt retaining shift lever to extension housing.

Installation
1) Lubricate shift lever. Position lever in extension housing. Install bolts and tighten. Install rubber boot and floor pan cover.

2) Warm ball with heat gun to 140-180°F (60-82°C) and tap ball on lever with a 7/16" socket and mallet. Install plastic shift pattern insert.

TRANSMISSION DISASSEMBLY

1) Install transmission in bench mounted holding fixture. Remove 6 bolts retaining front cover to case. Remove cover, shim, and gasket. Remove front cover oil seal using seal remover (T75P-3504-G). Remove input shaft snap ring.

2) Remove outer snap ring on input shaft bearing. Install bearing collet tool (T75L-7025-E) on input shaft front bearing. Install remover tube (T75L-7025-B), and forcing screw (T75L-7025-J).

3) Slide bearing collet sleeve (T75L-7025-G) over remover tube and bearing collet, and turn forcing screw to remove input shaft bearing. Remove 8 retaining bolts from extension housing to transmission case.

4) Slide extension housing off shaft with control lever end laid down and to the left as far as possible. Remove bolt retaining control lever end to control lever and rod from extension housing.

5) Remove speedometer driven gear assembly from extension housing. Remove back-up lamp switch and neutral safety switch. Remove snap ring that secures speedometer drive gear on mainshaft.

6) Slide drive gear off mainshaft and remove lock ball. Install bearing pusher tool (T83T-7111-A) over countershaft front bearing. Turn forcing screw to force countershaft, together with countershaft front bearing, from transmission housing.

7) Slide bearing holder and gear shaft assembly from transmission housing. Remove 3 spring cap bolts, springs, and shift locking balls. Reverse spring is the shortest spring.

Fig. 2: Removing Shift Lock Balls and Springs

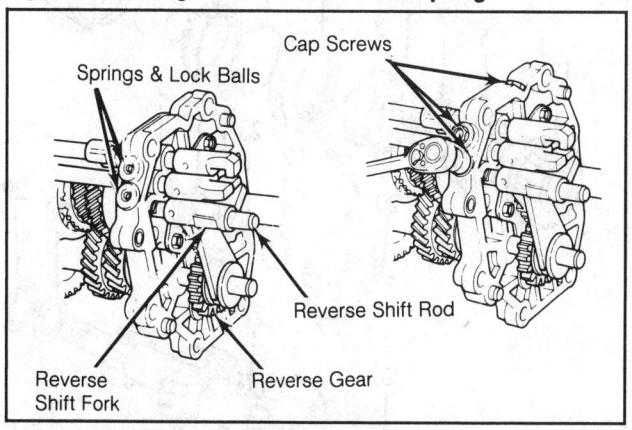

Lower ball will pop out when removed.

8) Remove reverse shift rod and shift fork assembly. Remove reverse gear from bearing housing. Remove roll pins retaining shift forks to rods. Push each

Manual Transmissions

FORD MOTOR CO. 4-SPEED
BRONCO II & RANGER — DIESEL (Cont.)

shift rod rearward through fork and bearing housing. Remove shift rods and forks. Mark shift forks for reassembly reference.

9) Remove lower reverse shift rod locking ball, spring, and interlock pin from bearing housing. Straighten tab of lock washer. Lock transmission synchronizers into any 2 gears and remove mainshaft lock nut using adapter tool (T83T-7025-A) and tool shaft (T77J-7025-C).

10) Remove reverse gear and key from mainshaft. Remove snap ring from rear end of countershaft and slide off counter reverse gear. Remove 5 bearing cover bolts, cover, and reverse idler gear shaft from bearing housing.

11) Carefully separate input shaft and caged needle roller bearing from mainshaft. Remove rear countershaft bearing from bearing housing using remover tube tool (T77J-7025-B). Remove rear mainshaft bearing from bearing housing using remover tool (T77F-4222-A) and remover tube.

12) Remove thrust washer, 1st gear, sleeve, and synchronizer ring from rear of mainshaft. Using snap

ring pliers, remove snap ring from rear of mainshaft. Remove snap ring from front of mainshaft. Using a press and remover tool (T71P-4621-B), remove 3rd/4th clutch hub, sleeve synchronizer ring, and 3rd gear from front of mainshaft.

13) Using a press and remover tool (T71P-4621-B), remove 1st/2nd clutch hub and sleeve assembly synchronizer ring, and 2nd gear from rear of mainshaft. Press front bearing from countershaft using remover tool (T71P-4621-B) and driver.

CLEANING & INSPECTION

1) Wash all parts in cleaning solvent and dry with compressed air (except bearings). Let bearings air dry in clean shop cloth. Inspect transmission case for cracks, damaged bearing bores, and/or threads.

2) Remove all small nicks or burrs from front and/or rear of case. Check bearings for roughness by slowly turning race by hand.

Fig. 3: *Exploded View of Transmission Gear Assemblies*

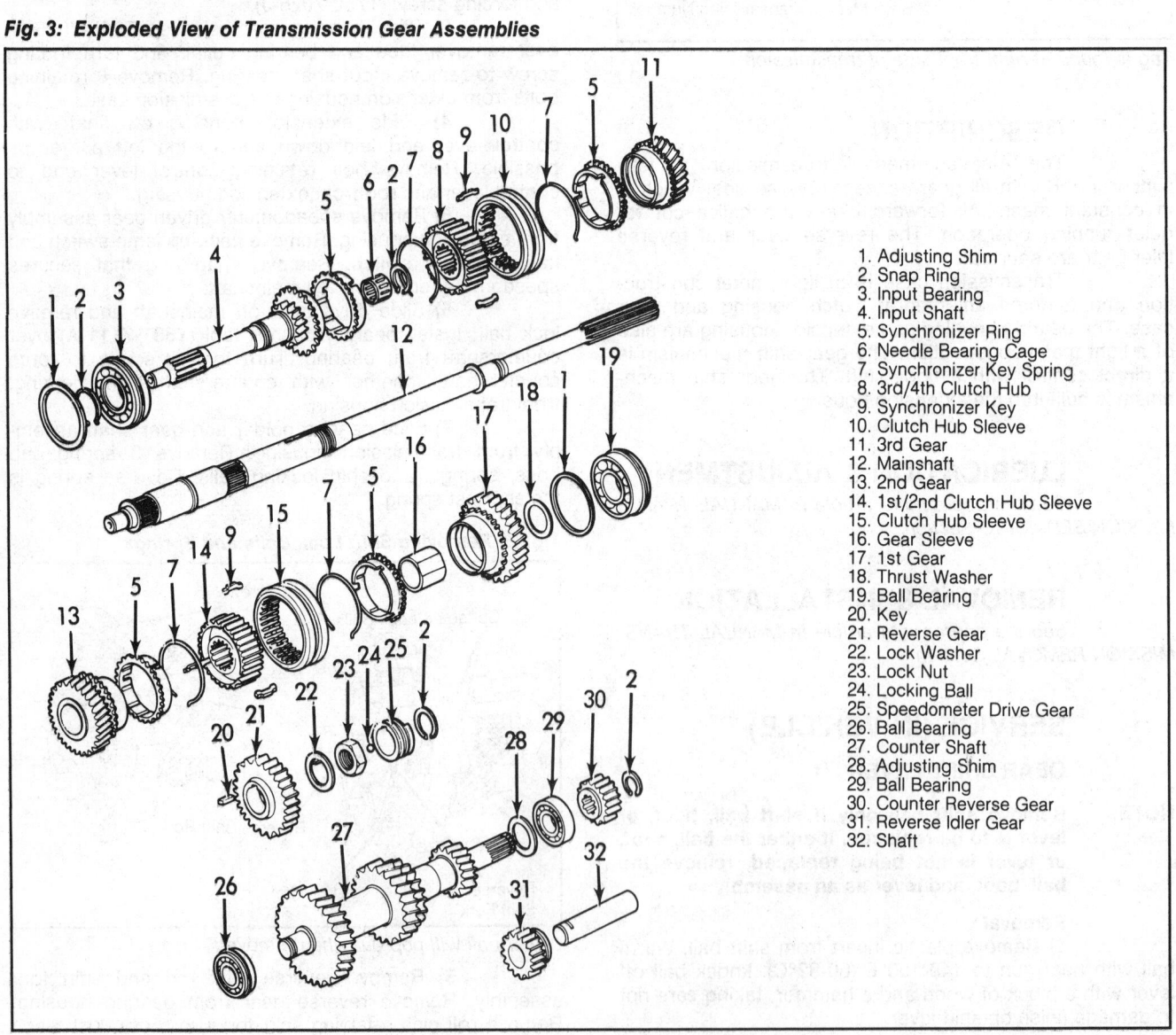

1. Adjusting Shim
2. Snap Ring
3. Input Bearing
4. Input Shaft
5. Synchronizer Ring
6. Needle Bearing Cage
7. Synchronizer Key Spring
8. 3rd/4th Clutch Hub
9. Synchronizer Key
10. Clutch Hub Sleeve
11. 3rd Gear
12. Mainshaft
13. 2nd Gear
14. 1st/2nd Clutch Hub Sleeve
15. Clutch Hub Sleeve
16. Gear Sleeve
17. 1st Gear
18. Thrust Washer
19. Ball Bearing
20. Key
21. Reverse Gear
22. Lock Washer
23. Lock Nut
24. Locking Ball
25. Speedometer Drive Gear
26. Ball Bearing
27. Counter Shaft
28. Adjusting Shim
29. Ball Bearing
30. Counter Reverse Gear
31. Reverse Idler Gear
32. Shaft

FORD MOTOR CO. 4-SPEED
BRONCO II & RANGER — DIESEL (Cont.)

3) Inspect needle bearing rollers, shafts, and washers for wear and/or damage. Check all other parts for wear, damage, chipped, and/or broken teeth. Replace parts as necessary.

TRANSMISSION REASSEMBLY

1) Assemble 3rd/4th and 1st/2nd clutch hub in the same manner. Install clutch hub and synchronizer into sleeve, placing the 3 keys into clutch hub slots and install springs onto hub.

2) When installing key springs, the open end tab of springs should be inserted into hub hole with springs turned in same direction. This will keep spring tension on each key uniform.

3) Install 3rd gear and synchronizer ring onto front section of mainshaft. Install 3rd/4th clutch hub assembly onto mainshaft by using a press. Hold together and slowly press into place. Fit snap ring on mainshaft.

4) Install 2nd gear and synchronizer ring onto mainshaft. Install 1st/2nd clutch hub assembly onto mainshaft by using a press. Install synchronizer ring, 1st gear with sleeve, and thrust washer onto mainshaft.

Fig. 4: Mainshaft Gear Assembly

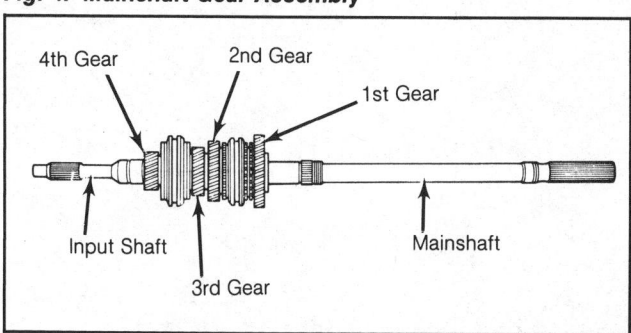

5) Install input shaft and needle roller bearing onto mainshaft. Check countershaft rear bearing clearance. Measure depth of countershaft bearing bore in bearing housing, using a depth micrometer.

6) Measure countershaft bearing height. The difference between the two measurements indicates the required thickness of adjusting shim. The clearance should be less than .0039" (0.10 mm). Adjusting shims come in thicknesses of .0039" (.10 mm) and .0118" (.30 mm).

7) Check mainshaft bearing clearance in same manner as countershaft rear bearing. Clearance should be less than .0039" (.10 mm). Adjusting shims come in thicknesses of .0039" (.10 mm) and .0118" (.30 mm).

8) Position proper shim on countershaft rear bearing and press into bearing housing using installer tool (T77J-7025-B). Position proper shim on mainshaft bearing and press into bearing housing using installer tool (T77J-7025-K).

9) Position front bearing on countershaft and press into place using bearing replacer tool (T71P-7025-A). Mesh countershaft and mainshaft assembly and position the two on bearing housing. Make certain that thrust washer is installed on mainshaft assembly at rear of 1st gear.

10) Hold mainshaft assembly in place and press countershaft assembly into bearing housing using

replacer tool (T71P-7025-A) to hold rear countershaft bearing in housing. *See Fig. 5.*

Fig. 5: Pressing Countershaft Assembly into Housing

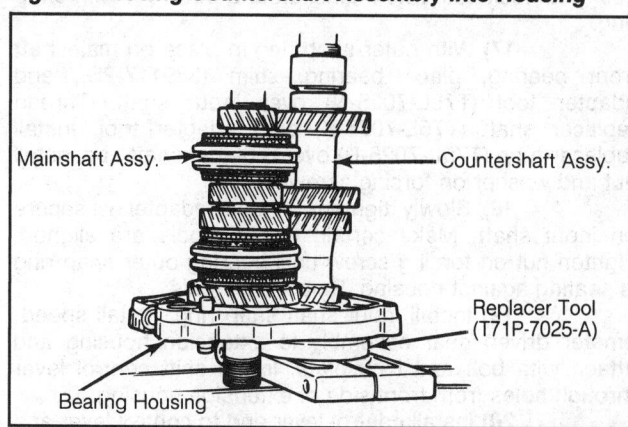

11) Install bearing cover and reverse idler gear shaft to bearing housing. Cover must be seated in groove on idler gear shaft. Install reverse gear with key onto mainshaft. Install lock nut on mainshaft and hand tighten. *See Fig. 6.*

Fig. 6: Installing Reverse Gears and Lock Nut

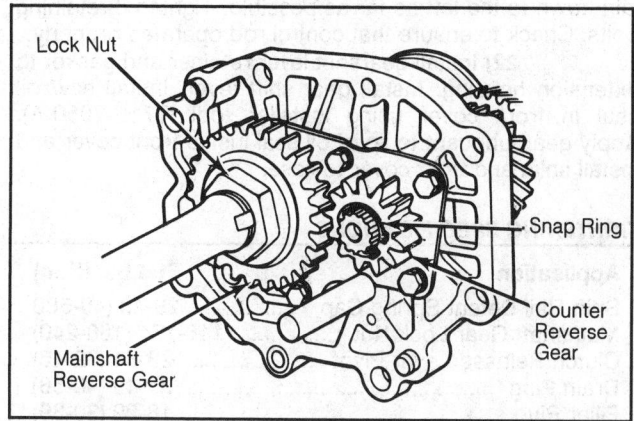

Chamfered side of both gears should face rearward.

12) Install countershaft reverse gear and secure it with snap ring. Lock transmission in any 2 gears. Insert short spring and locking ball into reverse bore of bearing housing. Hold down ball with a punch and install reverse shift rod and shift lever assembly with reverse idler gear at same time.

13) Using dummy shift rails (T72J-7280), install each shift fork rod and interlock pins. Install 1st/2nd shift fork and 3rd/4th shift fork to their respective clutch sleeves. Align roll pin holes of each shift fork and rod. Install new roll pins.

14) Install shift locking balls and springs into their respective positions and install spring cap bolt. Short spring and ball are installed in reverse bore.

15) Apply a thin coat of sealer on both contacting surfaces of bearing housing. Install bearing housing assembly to transmission case. Temporarily attach bearing housing to transmission with 2 top and 2 bottom bolts and tighten extension housing mounting bolts to position countershaft front bearing in bore.

Manual Transmissions

FORD MOTOR CO. 4-SPEED
BRONCO II & RANGER — DIESEL (Cont.)

16) Tighten mainshaft lock nut, using adapter (T77J-7025-A) and tool shaft (T77J-7025-C). Bend tab on lock washer using staking tool. Install speedometer drive gear with lock ball onto mainshaft and secure it with snap ring.

17) With outer snap ring in place on mainshaft front bearing, place bearing, shim (389117-2S), and adapter tool (T75L-7025-N) over input shaft. Thread replacer shaft (T75L-7025-K) onto adapter tool. Install replacer tube (T75L-7025-B) over replacer shaft and install nut and washer on forcing screw.

18) Slowly tighten nut until adapter is secure on input shaft. Make certain that all tools are aligned. Tighten nut on forcing screw until bearing outer snap ring is seating against housing. Remove all tools.

19) Install input shaft snap ring. Install speedometer driven gear assembly to extension housing and attach with bolt and lock plate. Insert shift control lever through holes from front side of extension housing.

20) Install control lever end to control lever and tighten retaining bolt. Install back-up lamp switch and neutral sensing switch to extension housing and tighten. Remove bolts installed previously to temporarily hold bearing housing.

21) Apply a thin coat of sealer on contacting surface of bearing housing and extension housing. Install extension housing to bearing housing with control lever laid down to the left as far as possible. Tighten 8 retaining bolts. Check to ensure that control rod operates properly.

22) Install gearshift lever retainer and gasket to extension housing. Install gear shift lever. Install new oil seal in front cover using installer tool (T71P-7050-A). Apply gear lubricant to lip of oil seal inside front cover and install shim and front cover to case.

TIGHTENING SPECIFICATIONS

Application	Ft. Lbs. (N.m)
Shift Rail Detent Spring Cap	29-43 (40-580
Mainshaft Gear Lock Nut	116-174 (160-240)
Clutch Release Lever Pivot	23-34 (32-46)
Drain Plug	29-43 (40-58)
Filler Plug	18-29 (30-39)
Back-Up Lamp Switch	22-29 (30-39)
Control Lever	
End-to-Control Lever Bolt	20-25 (28-34)

FORD MOTOR CO. 5-SPEED
BRONCO II & RANGER — DIESEL

Diesel Models (Only)

IDENTIFICATION

The manual transmissions have a service identification tag to identify transmissions for servicing. The tag is found at right front side of case. Transmission code for 5-speed transmission is "5". See Fig. 1.

Fig. 1: Transmission Identification Tag

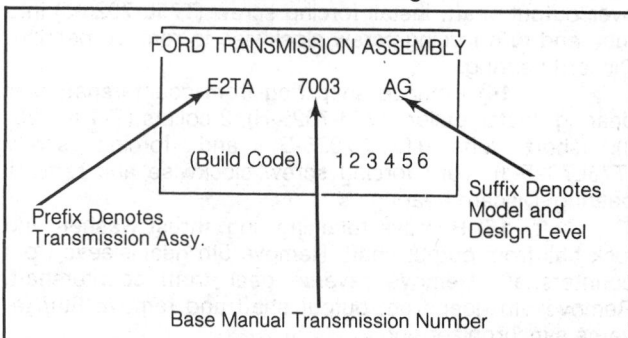

Tag is found at right front side of transmission.

DESCRIPTION

The 5-speed manual overdrive transmission is fully synchronized in all gears, including reverse gear in constant mesh. All forward gears are helical-cut for quiet running operation. The reverse gear and reverse idler gear are spur-cut.

Transmission case is of light metal construction and features an integral clutch housing and gear case. The bearing housing, intermediate housing, and extension housing are also of a light metal construction. The gear shift mechanism is a direct control with a floor shift. Floor shift mechanism is built into extension housing.

LUBRICATION & ADJUSTMENT

See the appropriate article in MANUAL TRANS-MISSION SERVICING Section.

REMOVAL & INSTALLATION

See the appropriate article in MANUAL TRANS-MISSION REMOVAL Section.

SERVICE (IN-VEHICLE)

GEAR SHIFT LEVER

NOTE: **Remove shift ball only if shift ball, boot, or lever is to be replaced. If either the ball, boot, or lever is not being replaced, remove the ball, boot, and lever as an assembly.**

Removal
1) Remove plastic insert from shift ball. Warm ball with heat gun to 140-180°F (60-82°C), knock ball off lever with a block of wood and a hammer, taking care not to damage finish on shift lever.

2) Remove rubber boot. Remove bolt retaining shift lever to extension housing.
Installation
1) Lubricate shift lever. Position lever in extension housing. Install bolts and tighten. Install rubber boot and floor pan cover.
2) Warm ball with heat gun to 140-180°F (60-82°C) and tap ball on lever with a 7/16" socket and mallet. Install plastic shift pattern insert.

TRANSMISSION DISASSEMBLY

1) Install transmission in bench mounted holding fixture. Remove 6 bolts retaining front cover to case. Remove cover, shim, and gasket. Remove front cover oil seal using seal remover (T75P-3504-G). Remove input shaft snap ring.

2) Remove outer snap ring on input shaft bearing. Install bearing collet tool (T75L-7025-E) on input shaft front bearing. Install remover tube (T75L-7025-B) and forcing screw (T75L-7025-J).

3) Slide bearing collet sleeve, (T75L-7025-G) over remover tube and bearing collet. Turn forcing screw to remove input shaft bearing. Remove bolt that attaches control lever end to control rod.

4) Remove control lever end and rod from extension housing. Remove 8 retaining bolts from extension housing-to-intermediate housing and transmission case.

5) Slide extension housing off shaft with control lever end down and to the left as far as possible. Remove speedometer driven gear assembly from extension housing.

6) Remove back-up light switch and neutral safety switch. Remove grommet from end of output shaft. Remove snap ring that secures speedometer drive gear on output shaft. Slide drive gear off output shaft and remove lock ball.

7) Install bearing pusher tool (T83T-7111-A) over countershaft front bearing. Turn forcing screw to force countershaft, together with countershaft front bearing, from transmission housing.

NOTE: **Countershaft front bearing may remain in transmission case. Remove bearing with a driver.**

8) Remove and discard roll pin from 1st/2nd shift fork. Remove circlip from rail. Remove upper cap bolt and with a magnet, remove spring and detent ball from bore. Remove 1st/2nd shift rail and 1st/2nd shift fork. Mark shift fork and rails for reassembly reference.

9) Remove roll pin from 3rd/4th shift fork. Remove circlip from rail. Remove middle cap bolt and with a magnet, remove 3rd/4th shift fork and rail. An interlock pin will drop out of bore when 3rd/4th shift rail is removed.

10) Remove circlip and washer from 5th/Reverse shift rail. Remove bottom cap bolt and with a magnet, remove short length spring and detent ball. Drive roll pin from 5th/Reverse shift lever and remove lever from rail.

11) With a magnet, remove other detent ball and short spring from bottom bore. Gently pry intermediate housing away from bearing housing. Remove gear and bearing assembly out of intermediate housing.

3-88

Manual Transmissions
FORD MOTOR CO. 5-SPEED
BRONCO II & RANGER — DIESEL (Cont.)

Fig. 2: **Shift Lever Lock Ball and Spring Locations**

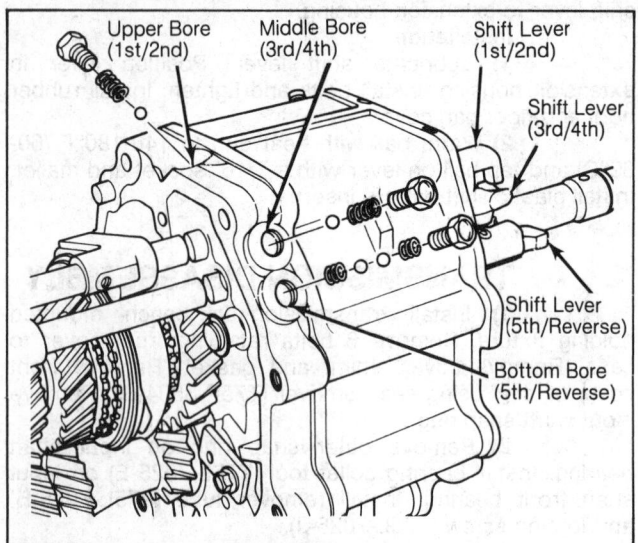

Lower ball will pop out when removed.

Fig. 3: **Output Shaft Rear Bearing Removal**

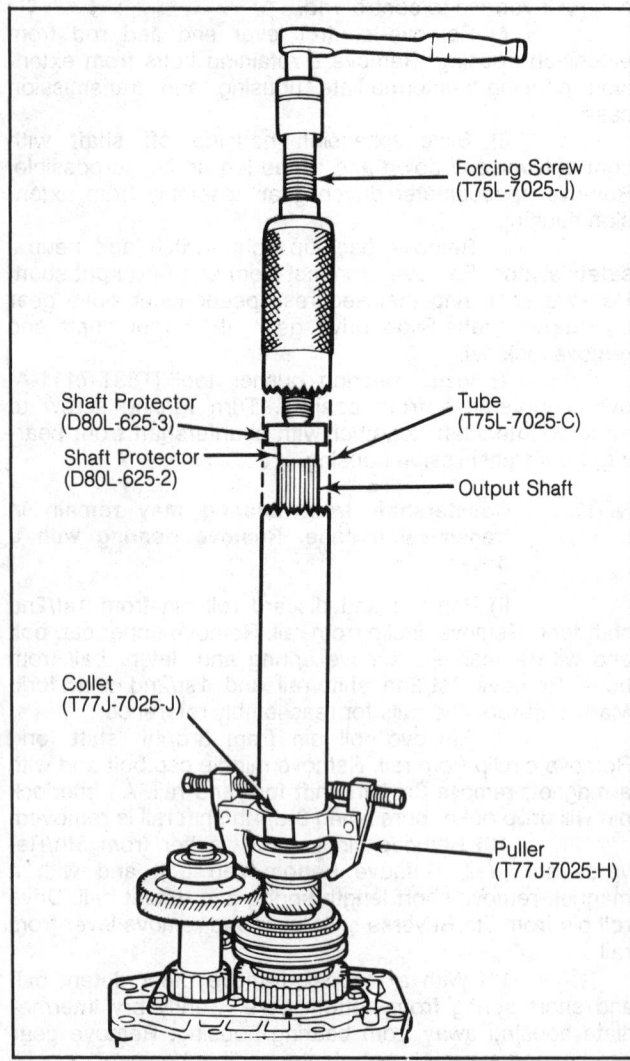

Turn forcing screw clockwise to remove bearing.

12) Install gear train and bearing housing assembly in holding fixture mounted in a vise. An interlock pin will drop out of bore when 5th/Reverse shift rail is removed. Remove retaining ring from output shaft ball bearing. Remove thrust washer. Place shaft protectors (D80L-625-2 & D80L-625-3) on end of output shaft. It may be necessary to hold shaft protectors in place with putty.

13) Install puller (T77J-7025-H), and 2 collets (T77J-7025-J) against bearing so jaws of puller are against rear of bearing. Place long tube (T75L-7025-C) over output shaft. Install forcing screw (T75L-7025-J) into tube and turn forcing screw clockwise to remove bearing. Discard bearing.

14) Remove snap ring from countershaft rear bearing. Install puller (T77J-7025-H), 2 collets (T77J-7025-J), short tube (T77J-7025-B), and forcing screw (T75L7025-J). Turn forcing screw clockwise and remove bearing. Discard bearing.

15) Remove retaining ring, thrust washer, and lock ball from output shaft. Remove 5th gear sleeve from countershaft. Remove reverse gear from countershaft. Remove 5th gear from output shaft and remove 5th/Reverse synchronizer ring.

16) Straighten the peen on lock nut with staking tool. Lock transmission gears in reverse and any forward gear. Install lock nut wrench (T77J-7025-C) on lock nut and remove lock nut and discard. Remove 5th/Reverse synchronizer assembly from output shaft.

17) Pry reverse gear, caged bearing, sleeve, and thrust washer from output shaft. Remove snap ring and remove reverse idler gear from idler shaft. Remove keyed thrust washer from shaft. Remove 5 bolts retaining bearing cover to bearing housing and remove cover.

18) Remove bolt retaining idler shaft to bearing housing. Drive plate and shaft assembly out of housing. With soft mallet, tap rear end of output shaft and countershaft in turn, being careful not to damage shafts. Remove shafts from bearing housing.

19) Remove thrust washer, 1st gear, sleeve, and synchronizer ring from rear of output shaft. Remove snap ring from front output shaft. Using a press and remover tool (T71P-4621-B), remove 3rd/4th hub, sleeve synchronizer ring, and 3rd gear from front of output shaft.

20) Remove 1st/2nd hub and sleeve assembly synchronizer ring, and 2nd gear from rear of output shaft in same manner as 3th/4th hub in step **19)**. Remove front bearing from countershaft using remover tool (D79L-4621-A).

TRANSMISSION REASSEMBLY

1) Assemble 3rd/4th, 1st/2nd, and 5th/Reverse clutch hub in the same manner. Install clutch hub and synchronizer into sleeve, placing the 3 keys into clutch hub slots and install springs onto hub.

2) When installing key springs, the open end tab of springs should be inserted into hub hole with springs turned in same direction. This will keep spring tension on each key uniform. A snap ring has been added to the 5th/Reverse Hub assembly. *See Fig. 5.*

3) Install 3rd gear and synchronizer ring onto front section of output shaft. Install 3rd/4th synchronizer assembly onto output shaft by using a press. Hold

Manual Transmissions

3-89

FORD MOTOR CO. 5-SPEED
BRONCO II & RANGER — DIESEL (Cont.)

Fig. 4: Exploded View of Transmission Gear Assemblies

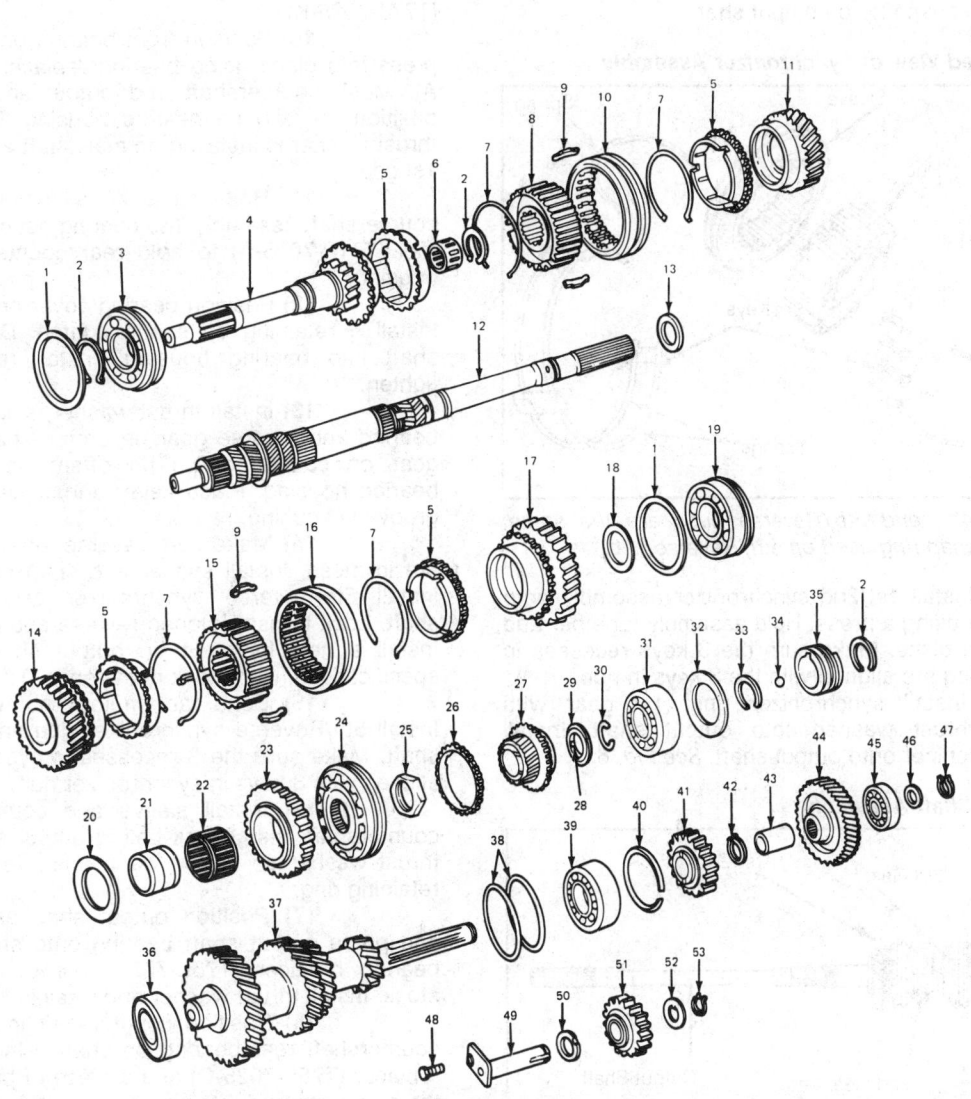

1. Adjusting Shim	19. Ball Bearing (In Housing)	36. Countershaft Front Bearing
2. Snap Ring	20. Thrust Washer	37. Countershaft
3. Input Bearing	21. Sleeve	38. Adjusting Shims
4. Input Shaft and 4th Gear	22. Caged Needle Bearing	39. Ball Bearing (In Housing)
5. Synchronizer Ring	23. Reverse Gear	40. Retaining Ring
6. Caged Needle Bearing	24. 5th/Reverse Synchronizer	41. Countershaft Reverse Gear
7. Synchronizer Key Spring	25. Lock Nut	42. Snap Ring
8. 3rd/4th Hub	26. Synchronizer	43. Sleeve
9. Synchronizer Key	27. 5th Gear	44. Countershaft 5th Gear
10. Hub Sleeve	28. Lock Ball	45. Countershaft Rear Bearing
11. 3rd Gear	29. Thrust Washer	46. Thrust Washer
12. Output Shaft	30. Retaining Ring	47. Snap Ring
13. Grommet	31. Output Bearing	48. Bolt
14. 2nd Gear	32. Thrust Washer	49. Idler Shaft and Retainer
15. 1st/2nd Hub	33. Retaining Ring	50. Keyed Thrust Washer
16. Hub Sleeve	34. Lock Ball	51. Reverse Idler Gear
17. 1st Gear	35. Speedometer Drive Gear	52. Thrust Washer
18. Thrust Washer		53. Snap Ring

Manual Transmissions
FORD MOTOR CO. 5-SPEED
BRONCO II & RANGER — DIESEL (Cont.)

assembly together and slowly press in place. Make sure the 3 recesses in synchronizer ring are aligned with 3 keys in hub. Fit snap ring on output shaft.

Fig. 5: Exploded View of Synchronizer Assembly

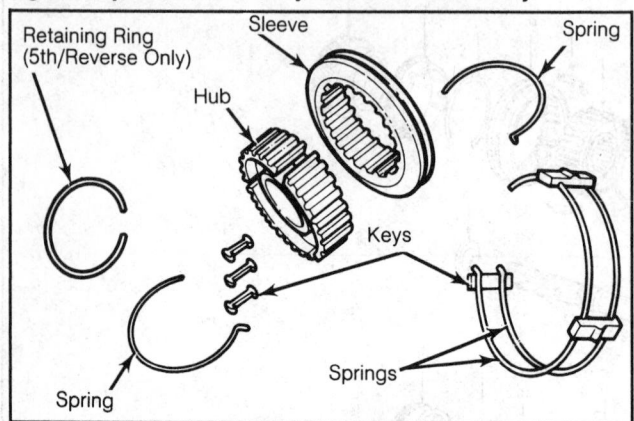

1st/2nd, 3rd/4th, and 5th/Reverse hubs are the same, except for the snap ring used on 5th/Reverse hub.

4) Install 1st/2nd synchronizer assembly onto output shaft by using a press. Hold assembly together and press slowly in place. Make sure the 3 keys recesses in synchronizer ring are aligned with the 3 keys in hub.

5) Install synchronizer ring, 1st gear with sleeve, and thrust washer onto output shaft. Install 1st/2nd synchronizer onto output shaft. See Fig. 6.

Fig. 6: Output Shaft Assembly

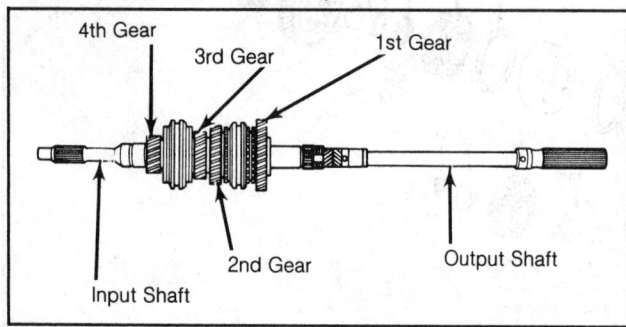

6) Install input shaft and needle roller bearing onto output shaft. Check countershaft rear bearing clearance. Measure depth of countershaft bearing bore in bearing housing, using a depth micrometer.

7) Install retaining ring on bearing and with a depth micrometer measure the distance between inside edge of ring and end of bearing. The difference between the two measurements indicates the required thickness of adjusting shim.

8) The clearance should be less than .0039" (0.10 mm). Adjusting shims come in thicknesses of .0039" (.10 mm) and .0118" (.30 mm). Check output shaft bearing clearance in same manner as countershaft rear bearing. Clearance should be less than .0039" (.10 mm). Adjusting shims come in thicknesses of .0039" (.10 mm) and .0118" (.30 mm).

9) Position proper shim on countershaft rear bearing and press into bearing housing using installer tool

(T77J-7025-B). Position proper shim on output shaft bearing and press into bearing housing using installer tool (T77J-7025-K).

10) Position front bearing on countershaft and press into place using bearing replacer tool (T71P-7025-A). Mesh countershaft and output shaft assembly and position the two on bearing housing. Make certain that thrust washer is installed on mainshaft assembly at rear of 1st gear.

11) Hold mainshaft assembly in place, press countershaft assembly into bearing housing using replacer tool (T71P-7025-A) to hold rear countershaft bearing in housing.

12) Position bearing cover on bearing housing. Install 5 retaining bolts and tighten. Drive reverse idler shaft into bearing housing. Install retaining bolt and tighten.

13) Install thrust washer, sleeve, caged needle bearing and reverse gear on output shaft. Install reverse gear on countershaft. The offset on gear must face bearing housing. Place keyed thrust washer so tab is in groove in housing.

14) Make sure reverse idler gear and reverse are in mesh. Install spacer and snap ring on idler shaft. Install 5th/Reverse synchronizer assembly on output shaft. Lock transmission in reverse and any forward gear. Install a new lock nut on output shaft and tighten to specifications, using lock nut wrench (T77J-7025-C).

15) Bend tab on lock nut with staking tool. Install 5th/Reverse synchronizer ring and gear on output shaft. Make sure the 3 recesses in synchronizer ring are aligned with 3 keys in synchronizer hub.

16) Install sleeve and counter 5th gear on countershaft. Install lock ball in output shaft and position thrust washer so slot in washer is over lock ball. Install retaining ring.

17) Position output shaft assembly in press and press output shaft bearing onto shaft using dummy bearing replacer (T75L-7025-Q) and a piece of press stock. Install thrust washer and retaining ring.

18) Position countershaft in press and press countershaft rear bearing on shaft using dummy bearing replacer (T75L-7025-Q) and a piece of press stock. Install thrust washer and retaining ring.

19) Position all synchronizers in neutral position. Install short spring and detent ball in 5th/Reverse bore (bottom bore). Compress ball and spring with dummy shift rails tools (T72J-7280) and install dummy shift rail in bore.

20) Install 5th/Reverse shift rails in bottom bore and make sure the 3 detent slots in rail face cap bolt and interlock slot in 5th/Reverse rail faces towards 1st/2nd bore. Install interlock pin through top bore so it is positioned in channel between 5th/Reverse rail bore and 3rd/4th rail bore.

21) Install 3rd/4th rail in housing and make sure the 3 detent slots in rail face middle bore. Insert interlock pins in channel, 3rd/4th rail, and 1st/2nd rail bore. Install 1st/2nd shift rail in housing so the 3 detent slots in rail face top bore.

22) Install 1st/2nd shift fork and 3rd/4th shift fork to their respective sleeves. Align roll pin holes of each

FORD MOTOR CO. 5-SPEED
BRONCO II & RANGER — DIESEL (Cont.)

shift fork and rod. Install new roll pins. Install detent balls and springs into their respective bores and install the 3 caps bolts.

23) Install circlips on 1st/2nd and 3rd/4th shift rails. Install circlip and washer on 5th/Reverse shaift rail. Apply a thin coat of sealer to mating surfaces of transmission case and bearing housing. Install transmission case on bearing housing.

24) Apply a thin coat of sealer to mating surfaces of bearing housing and intermediate housing. Install intermediate housing to bearing housing. Position shift lever gates on appropriate shift rails. Install new roll pins.

25) Place lock ball in output shaft and position speedometer drive gear over ball. Install snap ring. Install grommet on end of output shaft. Apply a thin coat of sealer to extension housing and intermediate housing.

26) Slide extension housing over output shaft (the control lever must be moved to the far left) and onto extension housing. Install bolts and tighten.

27) With outer snap ring in place on input shaft front bearing, place bearing, shim, and adapter tool (T75L-7025-N) over input shaft. Thread replacer shaft (T75L-7025-K) onto adapter tool. Install replacer tube (T75L-7025-B) over replacer shaft and install nut and washer on forcing screw.

28) Slowly tighten nut until adapter is securely on input shaft. Make sure tools are aligned. Tighten nut on forcing screw until bearing outer snap ring is seated. Remove installation tools. Install input shaft snap ring.

29) Measure distance between end of installed input shaft bearing in case with depth micrometer. Measure distance between bearing cover gasket and bottom of bearing bore in cover. The difference between the two measurements is the clearance between outer bearing race and front cover.

30) The clearance should be less than .0039" (.10 mm). Clearance can be adjusted by installing an adjusting shim. Shims are available in sizes of .006" (.15 mm) and .012" (.30 mm).

31) Install a new oil seal in front cover using installer tool (T71P-7050-A). Install shim in recess of front cover. Apply gear lubricant to lip of oil seal inside front cover and install front cover to case. Install 6 retaining bolts and tighten.

32) Install control lever end to control lever and tighten attaching bolt. Install back-up lamp switch and neutral safety switch to extension housing and tighten switch. Install gear shift lever retainer and gasket to extension housing. Install 4 bolts and tighten. Install gear shift lever.

TIGHTENING SPECIFICATIONS

Application	Ft. Lbs. (N.m)
Shift Rail Detent Spring Cap	29-43 (40-58)
Output Shaft Lock Nut	94-152 (130-210)
Clutch Release Lever Pivot	23-34 (32-46)
Drain Plug	29-43 (40-58)
Filler Plug	18-29 (30-39)
Back-Up Lamp Switch	20-25 (28-34)
Control Lever	
End-to-Control Lever Bolt	20-25 (28-34)

Manual Transmissions

FORD MOTOR CO. MTX 4 & 5-SPEED MANUAL TRANSAXLE

Escort, EXP, LN7, Lynx, Tiempo, Topaz

IDENTIFICATION

The MTX 4 and 5-speed manual transaxles can be identified by a tag affixed to top of transaxle case. Top line of tag identifies transaxle model, next line identifies transaxle assembly, third line of tag shows the build date code, and bottom line on tags is the transaxle serial number. Transaxle axle ratios are shown in *Transaxle Ratio Table.*

TRANSAXLE RATIO

Model	Axle Ratio
4-Speed	
Standard	3.59:1
Fuel Saver	3.04:1
5-Speed	3.61:1

DESCRIPTION

The MTX transaxle combines a 4 or 5-speed manual transmission and differential into a single component designed for front wheel drive applications. The transmission and differential are housed in a 2-piece, light weight aluminum alloy housing which is bolted to the back of the engine.

The transaxle is fully synchronized in all forward gears with reverse provided by a sliding gear. All gears, except reverse, are helical cut for quiet operation. The 5-speed transaxle has a third shaft which carries the 5th gear. All shafts, the input cluster, main, and 5th gear drive shaft are supported in the case on tapered roller bearings. Preload is maintained on bearings by a shim located behind each bearing race in transaxle housing. The differential assembly is supported by 2 opposed tapered roller bearings and preload is maintained by means of a selective shim.

The inboard constant velocity (CV) joints are positively connected with the differential side gears by means of splines and secured in case with 2 snap rings. The ring gear is riveted to the differential case.

LUBRICATION & ADJUSTMENTS

See the appropriate article in MANUAL TRANS-MISSION SERVICING Section.

Fig. 1: Sectional View of MTX 4-Speed Manual Transaxle Assembly

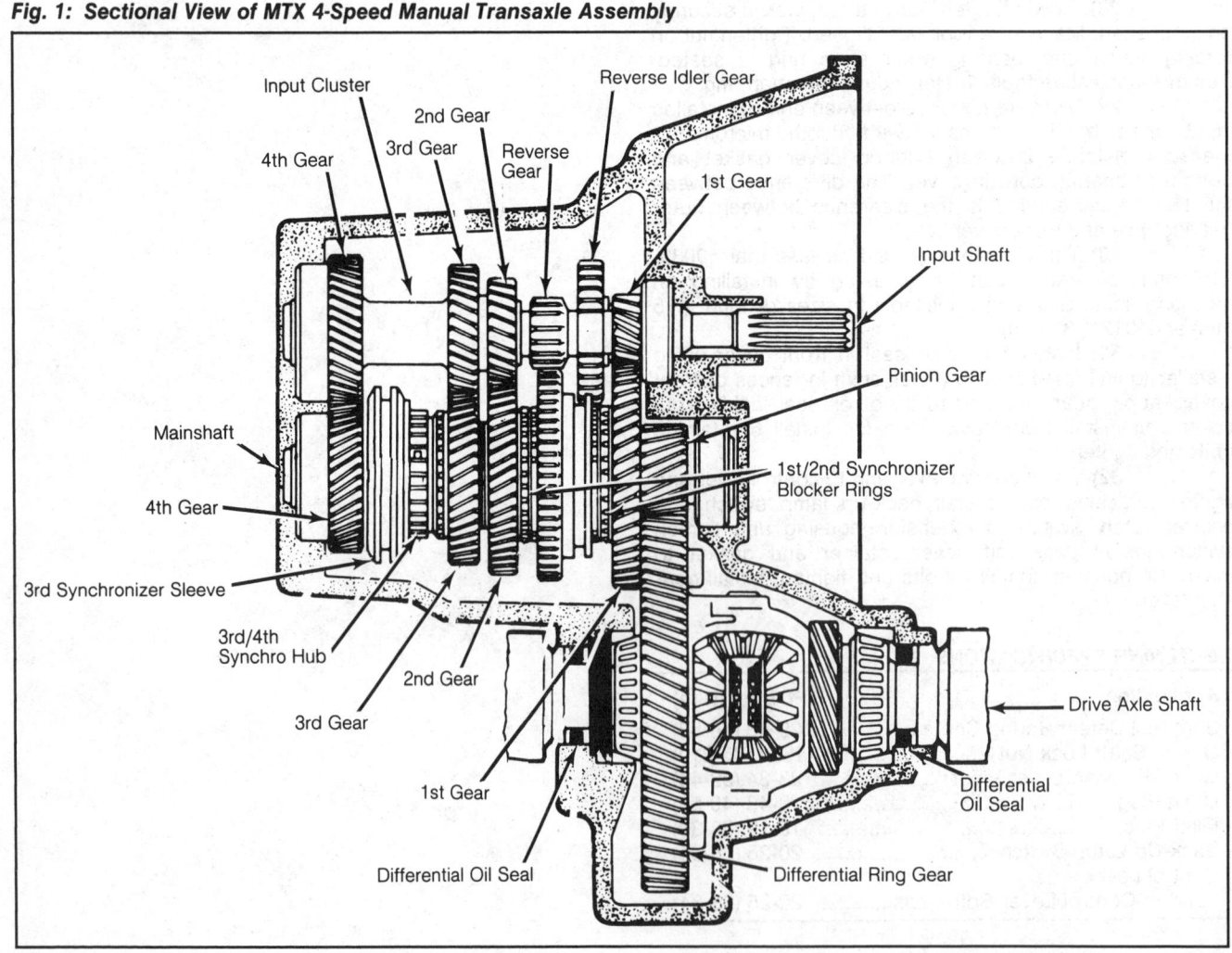

Fig. 2: Sectional View of MTX 5-Speed Manual Transaxle Assembly

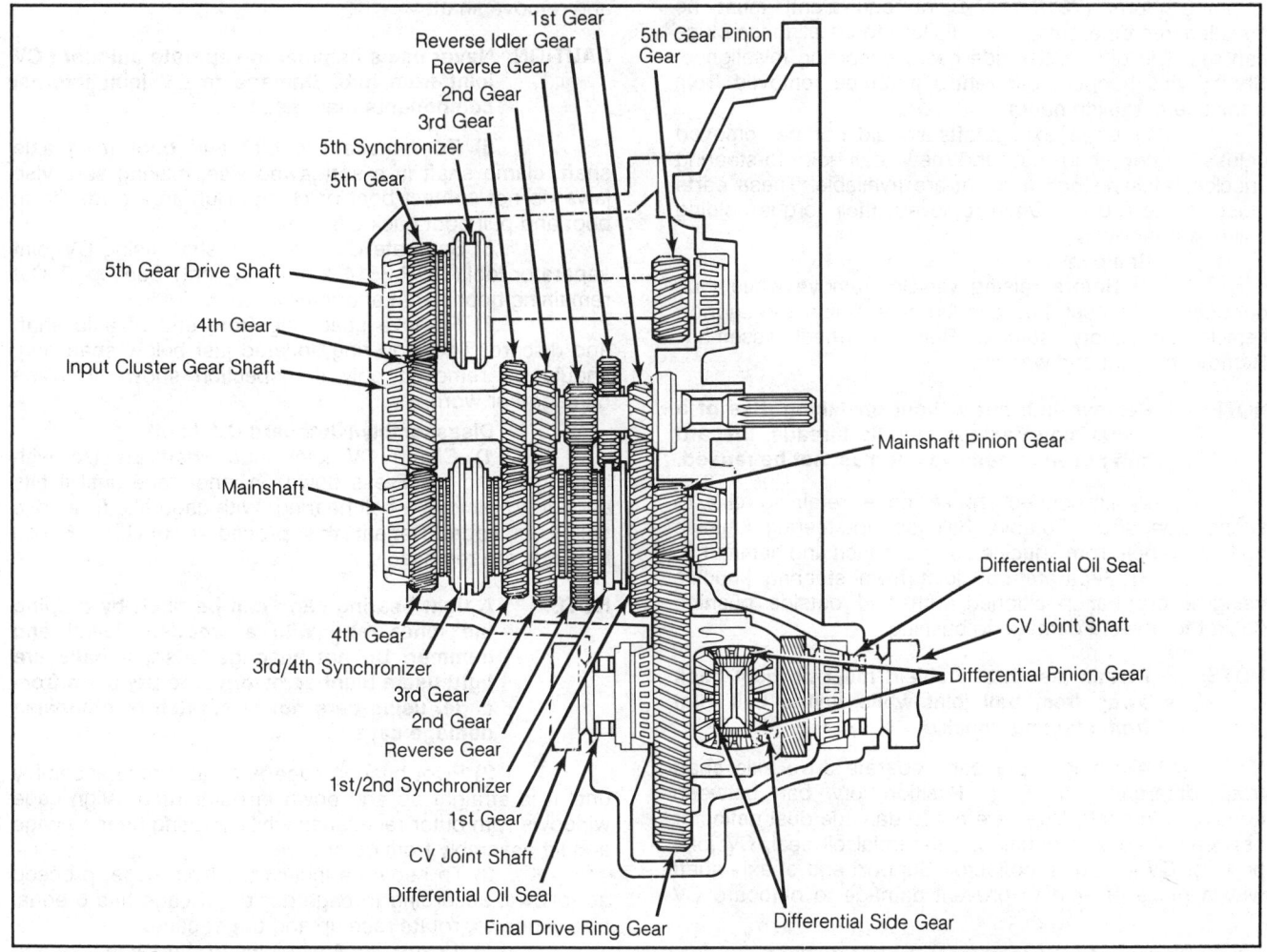

SERVICE (IN-VEHICLE)

BACK-UP LIGHT SWITCH

Removal

Disconnect electrical lead to back-up light switch. Place transaxle in reverse. Remove switch from transaxle case using a 30 mm wrench.

CAUTION: To prevent internal problems, do not shift transaxle until a new switch is installed.

Installation

Reverse removal procedure and wrap switch threads with teflon tape in a clockwise direction.

SPEEDOMETER RETAINER & DRIVEN GEAR

Removal

Clean off top of speedometer driven gear retainer. Remove retainer attaching bolt. Carefully pull up on speedometer cable, pulling retainer and driven gear assembly from case. Remove cable from retainer.

Installation

Lightly grease "O" ring on retainer. Using a 3/16" deep socket, gently tap retainer and gear assembly into case while aligning groove in retainer with screw hole in clutch housing. Install and tighten retaining bolt.

CLUTCH HOUSING EXPANSION PLUG

NOTE: **The 15 mm expansion plug installed on bottom side of clutch housing case should never be removed during normal service. However, if for any reason it becomes necessary to install a new plug, proceed as follows:**

Expansion Plug Replacement

Drive out old plug. Clean plug bore in clutch housing and apply a small bead of sealer (ESP-M4G-214-A) to plug recess in housing. Place expansion plug in its recess and flatten plug with a drift. Stake (in 3 places minimum) clutch housing area surrounding expansion plug to secure it in place.

DRIVE AXLE SHAFTS & CV JOINTS

NOTE: **Prior to removing drive axle shafts, note the following:**

3-94

Manual Transmissions
FORD MOTOR CO.
MTX 4 & 5-SPEED — MANUAL TRANSAXLE (Cont.)

1) When removing both drive axle shafts, shipping plugs (T81P-1177-B or equivalent) must be installed into differential case. Failure to install these plugs can result in differential side gears becoming misaligned. Should this happen, differential must be removed from transaxle to realign gears.

2) Drive axle shafts should not be removed unless a new hub nut and new ball joint-to-steering knuckle retaining bolt and nut are available. These parts must not be reused. Once removed, their torque holding ability is destroyed.

Removal

1) Before raising vehicle, remove wheel hub dust cap and loosen hub and lug nuts. Raise and support vehicle on safety stands. Remove wheel assembly. Remove hub nut and washer.

NOTE: Remove hub nut without unstaking. Use of a chisel may damage spindle threads. Discard hub nut when removed; it must not be reused.

2) Disconnect brake hose retaining clip to suspension strut. Remove ball joint-to-steering knuckle bolt. Drive bolt from knuckle using a punch and hammer.

3) Separate ball joint from steering knuckle using a pry bar positioned with end outside bushing pocket to prevent damage to bushing.

NOTE: Plastic disc brake shield must be bent back away from ball joint while prying ball joint from steering knuckle.

4) Using a pry bar, separate drive axle shaft from differential housing. Position pry bar between housing and shaft. Use care not to damage dust deflector between shaft and housing, differential oil seal, CV joint boot, or CV joint dust deflector. Support end of axle shaft with a piece of wire to prevent damage to outboard CV

Fig. 3: Separating CV Joint from Drive Axle Shaft

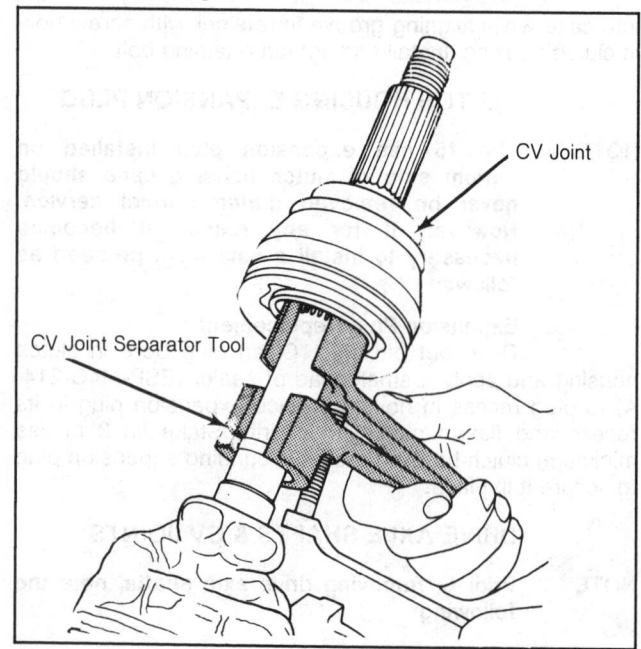

Use CV joint separator (T81P-3514-A) to remove joint.

joint. Using a puller, separate outboard CV joint from hub, and remove shaft.

CAUTION: Never use a hammer to separate outboard CV joint from hub. Damage to CV joint internal components may result.

5) To remove CV joint and boot from axle shaft, clamp shaft in a soft-jawed vise, making sure vise jaws do not contact boot or clamp. Cut large clamp from boot and pull boot back over shaft.

6) Separate CV joint from shaft using CV joint separator tool (T81P-3514-A or equivalent). *See Fig. 3.* Cut remaining boot clamp and remove boot.

7) Remove snap ring from end of axle shaft and discard. The stop ring, located just below snap ring, should be removed only if inspection shows it to be damaged or worn.

Disassembly (Outboard CV Joint)

1) Clamp CV joint stub shaft in vise with bearing facing up. Press down on inner race until it tilts enough to remove a ball bearing. With cage tilted, remove ball from cage. Repeat this procedure until all 6 ball bearings are removed.

NOTE: A tight bearing cage can be tilted by tapping the inner race with a wooden dowel and hammer. Do not hit cage. Also, if balls are tight use a blunt screwdriver to pry them from cage, using care not to scratch or otherwise damage cage.

2) Pivot bearing cage and inner race assembly until it is straight up and down in outer race. Align cage windows with outer race lands while pivoting bearing cage and lift assembly from outer race.

3) To separate inner race from cage, proceed as follows, according to cage design. If cage has 6 equal size windows, rotate race up and out of cage.

4) If cage has 4 windows of the same size and 2 elongated windows, pivot inner race until it is straight up and down in cage. Align one of the inner race lands with one of the elongated windows and position race through window, then rotate race up and out of cage.

Reassembly (Outboard CV Joint)

1) Apply a light coat of grease on inner and outer races. Install inner race into cage. Install race and cage into outer race by installing assembly vertically and pivoting 90° into position.

NOTE: When properly installed, shallow counterbore cut into inner race will be facing up.

2) Align bearing cage and inner race with outer race. Tilt race and cage, and install ball bearing. Repeat procedure to install all ball bearings.

3) After installing bearings, pack CV joint with 1 1/3 packets of specified grease (supplied in service kit). Pack grease into joint by forcing it through splined hole in inner race.

Disassembly (Inboard CV Joint)

1) Remove snap ring from end of CV joint stub shaft. Using side cutters, cut and remove ball bearing retainer.

NOTE: Discard ball bearing retainer when removed. A new retainer is not required for reassembly.

FORD MOTOR CO.
MTX 4 & 5-SPEED — MANUAL TRANSAXLE (Cont.)

Fig. 4: Exploded View of Drive Axle Shaft and CV Joint Assembly

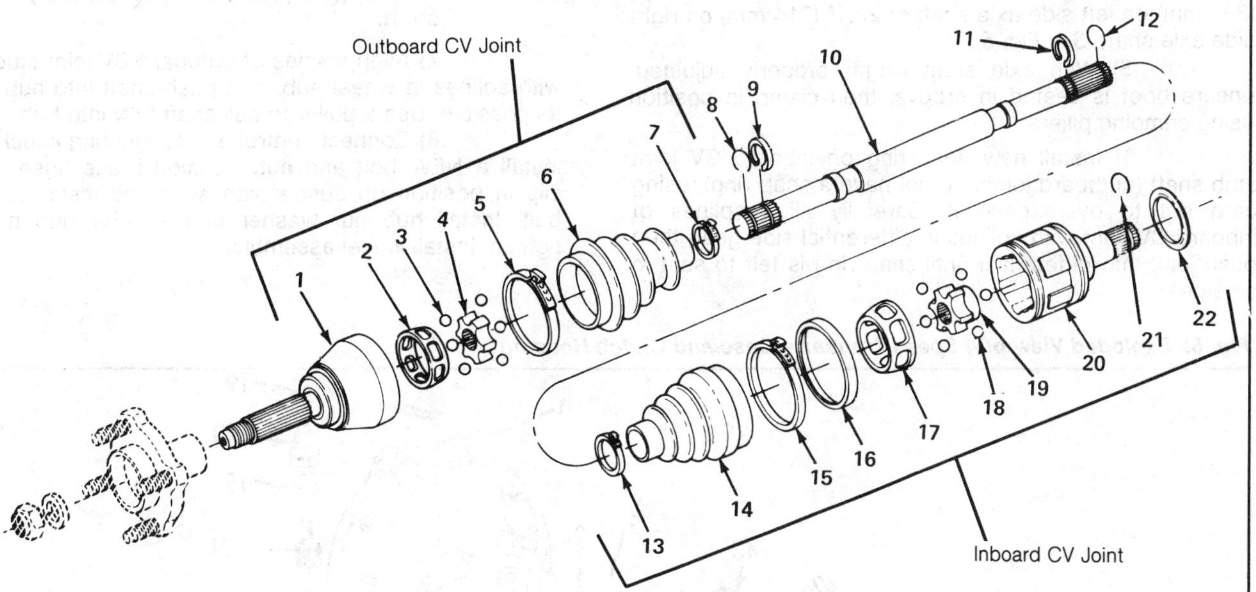

Outboard CV Joint

Inboard CV Joint

1. Outer Bearing Race & Stub	8. Snap Ring	16. Bearing Retainer
2. Bearing Cage	9. Stop Ring	17. Bearing Cage
3. Ball Bearings (6)	10. Drive Axle Shaft	18. Ball Bearings (6)
4. Inner Bearing Race	11. Stop Ring	19. Inner Bearing Race
5. Large Boot Clamp	12. Snap Ring	20. Outer Race & Stub Shaft Assy.
6. Boot	13. Small Boot Clamp	21. Snap Ring
7. Small Boot Clamp	14. Boot	22. Dust Deflector
	15. Large Boot Clamp	

Left side assembly shown, right side is similar.

2) Gently tap CV joint on bench until cage and inner race assembly can be removed by hand. Remove ball bearings by prying from cage with a blunt screwdriver, using care not to scratch or otherwise damage race and cage spheres.

3) Rotate inner race to align lands with cage windows. Lift inner race from bearing cage through wider end of cage.

Reassembly (Inboard CV Joint)

1) Install snap ring on stub shaft, using care not to over-expand it. Install inner race through large end of cage with race hub facing large end of cage. With inner race and cage properly aligned, press ball bearings through cage with hand.

2) Pack outer race with 1 packet of grease (supplied in service kit). Position inner race and bearing assembly in outer race, then push assembly fully into outer race.

NOTE: When properly assembled, inner race hub will face into outer race.

Installation

1) If removed, install a new stop ring into groove on axle drive shaft. Install new snap ring in groove nearest end of shaft, using care not to over-expand it. If removed, install CV joint boot on axle shaft. Make sure boot is seated in groove, then clamp boot in position using crimping pilers.

2) With CV joint boot peeled back, position joint on axle shaft and tap into position using a plastic mallet. When fully seated, snap ring locks in groove cut into CV joint inner race.

3) Before positioning boot over CV joint, pack joint and boot with lubricant supplied in service kit as follows: For outboard CV joint, fill boot with 2/3 packet and pack CV joint with 1 1/3 packets. For inboard CV joint, fill boot with 1 packet and pack CV joint with 1 packet.

4) Remove excess grease from CV joint external surfaces, then position boot over joint. Before installing boot, make sure any air pressure which might

Fig. 5: Drive Axle Shaft Assembled Length

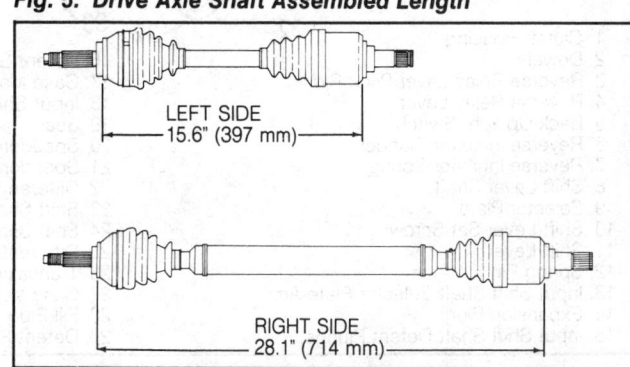

LEFT SIDE
15.6" (397 mm)

RIGHT SIDE
28.1" (714 mm)

Check axle length and that boots are seated in groove.

3-96

Manual Transmissions
FORD MOTOR CO.
MTX 4 & 5-SPEED — MANUAL TRANSAXLE (Cont.)

have built up in boot is relieved. Move CV joint in and out as necessary to adjust length of axle drive shaft to 15.6" (397 mm) on left side axle shaft or 28.1" (714 mm) on right side axle shaft. *See Fig. 5.*

   5) With axle shaft length properly adjusted, ensure boot is seated in groove, then clamp in position using crimping piliers

   6) Install new snap ring on inboard CV joint stub shaft (outboard joints do not have a snap ring), using care not to overexpand it. Carefully align splines of inboard CV joint with splines in differential side gear, then push joint into differential until snap ring is felt to seat in side gear.

NOTE: A soft mallet may be used to aid in seating snap ring. Tap only on outboard CV joint stub shaft.

   7) Align splines of outboard CV joint stub shaft with splines in wheel hub, and push shaft into hub as far as possible. Use a puller to pull shaft fully into hub.

   8) Connect control arm to steering knuckle and install a NEW bolt and nut. Position brake hose routing clip in position on suspension strut and install retaining bolt. Install hub nut washer and a NEW hub nut and tighten. Install wheel assembly.

Fig. 6: *Exploded View of 4-Speed Transaxle Case and Clutch Housing*

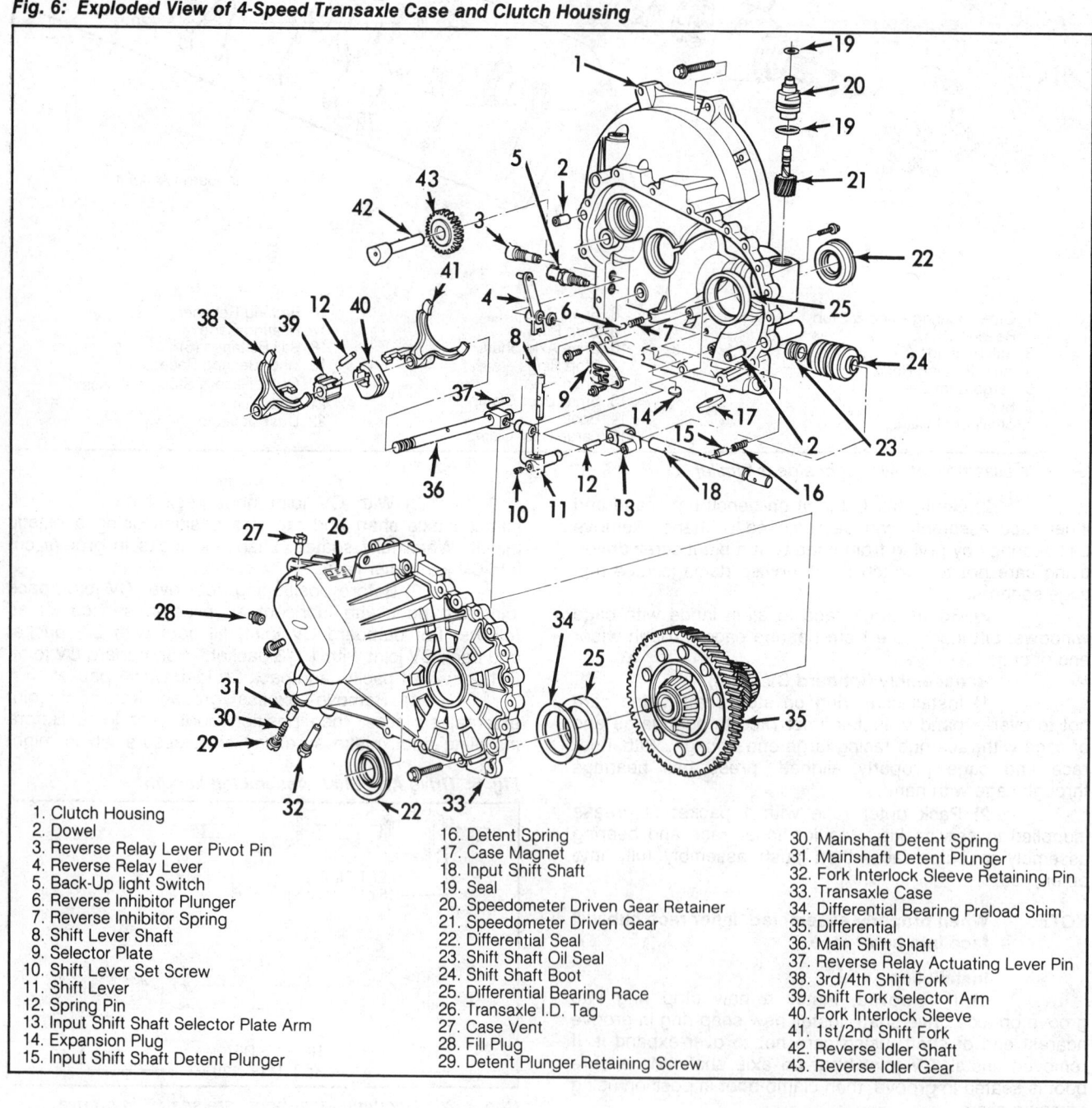

1. Clutch Housing
2. Dowel
3. Reverse Relay Lever Pivot Pin
4. Reverse Relay Lever
5. Back-Up light Switch
6. Reverse Inhibitor Plunger
7. Reverse Inhibitor Spring
8. Shift Lever Shaft
9. Selector Plate
10. Shift Lever Set Screw
11. Shift Lever
12. Spring Pin
13. Input Shift Shaft Selector Plate Arm
14. Expansion Plug
15. Input Shift Shaft Detent Plunger

16. Detent Spring
17. Case Magnet
18. Input Shift Shaft
19. Seal
20. Speedometer Driven Gear Retainer
21. Speedometer Driven Gear
22. Differential Seal
23. Shift Shaft Oil Seal
24. Shift Shaft Boot
25. Differential Bearing Race
26. Transaxle I.D. Tag
27. Case Vent
28. Fill Plug
29. Detent Plunger Retaining Screw

30. Mainshaft Detent Spring
31. Mainshaft Detent Plunger
32. Fork Interlock Sleeve Retaining Pin
33. Transaxle Case
34. Differential Bearing Preload Shim
35. Differential
36. Main Shift Shaft
37. Reverse Relay Actuating Lever Pin
38. 3rd/4th Shift Fork
39. Shift Fork Selector Arm
40. Fork Interlock Sleeve
41. 1st/2nd Shift Fork
42. Reverse Idler Shaft
43. Reverse Idler Gear

Manual Transmissions
FORD MOTOR CO.
MTX 4 & 5-SPEED — MANUAL TRANSAXLE (Cont.)

3-97

Fig. 7: Exploded View of 5-Speed Transaxle Case and Clutch Housing

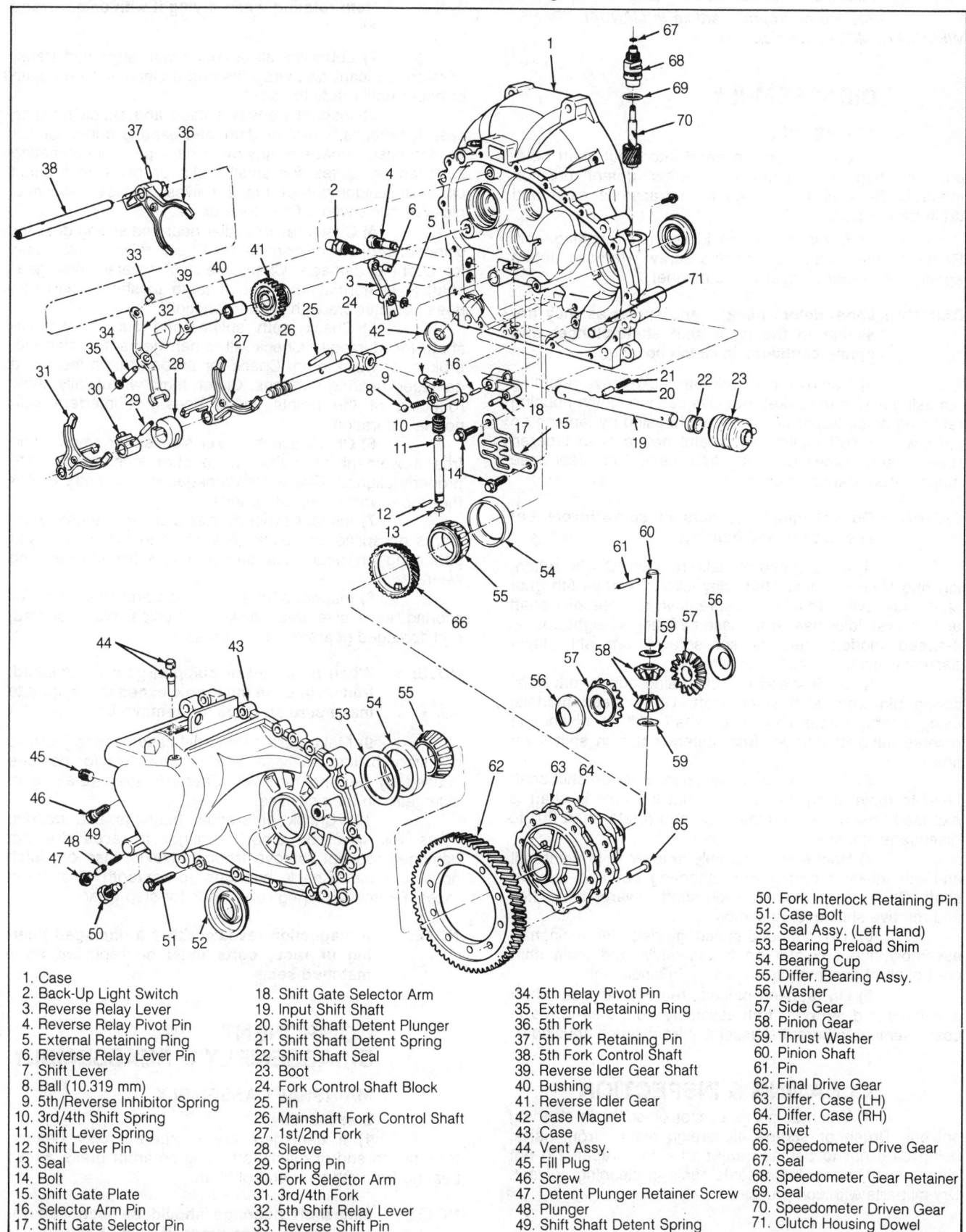

1. Case
2. Back-Up Light Switch
3. Reverse Relay Lever
4. Reverse Relay Pivot Pin
5. External Retaining Ring
6. Reverse Relay Lever Pin
7. Shift Lever
8. Ball (10.319 mm)
9. 5th/Reverse Inhibitor Spring
10. 3rd/4th Shift Spring
11. Shift Lever Spring
12. Shift Lever Pin
13. Seal
14. Bolt
15. Shift Gate Plate
16. Selector Arm Pin
17. Shift Gate Selector Pin

18. Shift Gate Selector Arm
19. Input Shift Shaft
20. Shift Shaft Detent Plunger
21. Shift Shaft Detent Spring
22. Shift Shaft Seal
23. Boot
24. Fork Control Shaft Block
25. Pin
26. Mainshaft Fork Control Shaft
27. 1st/2nd Fork
28. Sleeve
29. Spring Pin
30. Fork Selector Arm
31. 3rd/4th Fork
32. 5th Shift Relay Lever
33. Reverse Shift Pin

34. 5th Relay Pivot Pin
35. External Retaining Ring
36. 5th Fork
37. 5th Fork Retaining Pin
38. 5th Fork Control Shaft
39. Reverse Idler Gear Shaft
40. Bushing
41. Reverse Idler Gear
42. Case Magnet
43. Case
44. Vent Assy.
45. Fill Plug
46. Screw
47. Detent Plunger Retainer Screw
48. Plunger
49. Shift Shaft Detent Spring

50. Fork Interlock Retaining Pin
51. Case Bolt
52. Seal Assy. (Left Hand)
53. Bearing Preload Shim
54. Bearing Cup
55. Differ. Bearing Assy.
56. Washer
57. Side Gear
58. Pinion Gear
59. Thrust Washer
60. Pinion Shaft
61. Pin
62. Final Drive Gear
63. Differ. Case (LH)
64. Differ. Case (RH)
65. Rivet
66. Speedometer Drive Gear
67. Seal
68. Speedometer Gear Retainer
69. Seal
70. Speedometer Driven Gear
71. Clutch Housing Dowel

Manual Transmissions
FORD MOTOR CO.
MTX 4 & 5-SPEED — MANUAL TRANSAXLE (Cont.)

REMOVAL & INSTALLATION

See the appropriate article in MANUAL TRANS-MISSION REMOVAL Section.

DISASSEMBLY

TRANSAXLE

1) Using a drift inserted into input shaft hole, pull or push input shaft into center detent position (neutral). Remove filler plugs from transaxle case and drain transmission fluid.

2) Remove reverse idler shaft retaining bolt. Remove detent plunger retaining screw. Remove detent spring and detent plunger with a magnet.

CAUTION: **Label detent plunger and spring as they are similar to the input shift shaft plunger and spring contained in clutch housing.**

3) Remove shift fork interlock sleeve retaining pin using a 19 mm socket. Remove case-to-clutch housing retaining bolts. Separate case from housing by tapping on case with a soft mallet. Be careful not to drop tapered roller bearing races or shims from case. Withdraw case magnet from transaxle case.

CAUTION: **Do not insert pry bars or screwdrivers between case and housing.**

4) On 5-speed models, remove "C" clip retaining ring from 5th gear shift relay lever. Remove 5th gear shift relay lever. On all models, remove reverse idler shaft and reverse idler gear from case by lifting straight up. On 4-speed models, remove set screw from shift lever assembly using a 4 mm Allen wrench.

5) On 5-speed models, using punch, drive roll spring pin from shift lever shaft. On 4-speed models, using pliers, rotate shift lever shaft 90° to disengage reverse inhibitor plunger from detent notch in shift lever shaft.

6) On 5-speed models, gently pry on shift shaft lever to move it out of case, so that the hole in shaft is exposed. Insert a punch into hole and rotate shaft 90° to disengage inhibitor.

7) Hold a rag over hole in lever to prevent ball and 5th inhibitor spring from shooting out and remove shaft. On 4-speed models, slide shaft toward differential and remove shift lever assembly.

8) On 4 and 5-speed models, lift mainshaft assembly, input cluster shaft assembly, and main shift control shaft assembly from case as a single unit.

9) On 5-speed models, remove 5th gear shaft assembly and 5th gear fork assembly from their bores in case. Remove differential assembly from clutch housing.

CLEANING & INSPECTION

1) Wash all parts, except oil seals, in cleaning solvent. Brush or scrape all foreign matter from parts, using care not to damage any part with scraper. Do not clean, wash, or soak transaxle seals in cleaning solvent. Dry all parts with compressed air.

CAUTION: **Hold roller bearing assembly to prevent it from rotating when drying it with compressed air.**

2) Lubricate all bearings with approved transmission lubricant and wrap them in a clean, lint free cloth or paper until ready to use.

3) Inspect transaxle case and clutch housing case for cracks, worn, or damaged bearing bores. Check for damaged threads or any other damage. Inspect mating surfaces on cases for small nicks or burrs that could cause misalignment of the 2 halves. Remove all small nicks or burrs with a fine stone or file.

4) Check reverse idler gear and sliding gear for chipped, broken, or bent teeth. Check reverse idler gear for bushing damage. Check wear of reverse idler gear shaft (it is normal for front of teeth to show wear; this does not interfere with proper function).

5) Check teeth, splines and journals of mainshaft for damage. Check all other gears for chipped, broken, or worn teeth. Check for eroded clutch teeth and damaged bearing surfaces. Clutch teeth will usually show rounding of the points which does not interfere with normal operation.

6) Check synchronizer sleeves for smooth and free movement on hubs. Make sure index marks are properly aligned. Check for damaged clutch teeth. Check for proper positioning of springs.

7) Inspect synchronizer blocker rings for wear marks on spline end back face which indicates ring was bottoming on gear face due to excessive blocker ring wear.

8) Inspect differential pinion and side gears for scoring, excessive wear, nicks, and chips. Worn, scored, and damaged gears must be replaced.

NOTE: **When a scored or chipped gear is replaced, transaxle case must be cleaned thoroughly to make sure all chips are removed.**

9) Make sure differential case bearing journals are smooth. Inspect case bearing shoulders for damage caused by bearing removal. Check fit (free rotation) of side gears in their cavities.

10) Check differential bearings and bearing races for wear or other damage. If races are not damaged, do not remove from transaxle case or clutch housing case. Check bearings for smooth rotation in races. Examine bearing roller ends for step wear.

NOTE: **If inspection reveals either a damaged bearing or race, parts must be replaced as a matched set.**

COMPONENT DISASSEMBLY & REASSEMBLY

MAINSHAFT ASSEMBLY

Disassembly

1) If damaged, press tapered roller bearing from pinion end of mainshaft using an arbor press. Press bearing from 4th gear end of shaft.

NOTE: **Mainshaft bearings should be identified for reassembly when pressed from shaft.**

Manual Transmissions
FORD MOTOR CO.
MTX 4 & 5-SPEED — MANUAL TRANSAXLE (Cont.)

3-99

Fig. 8: Exploded View of Mainshaft Assembly

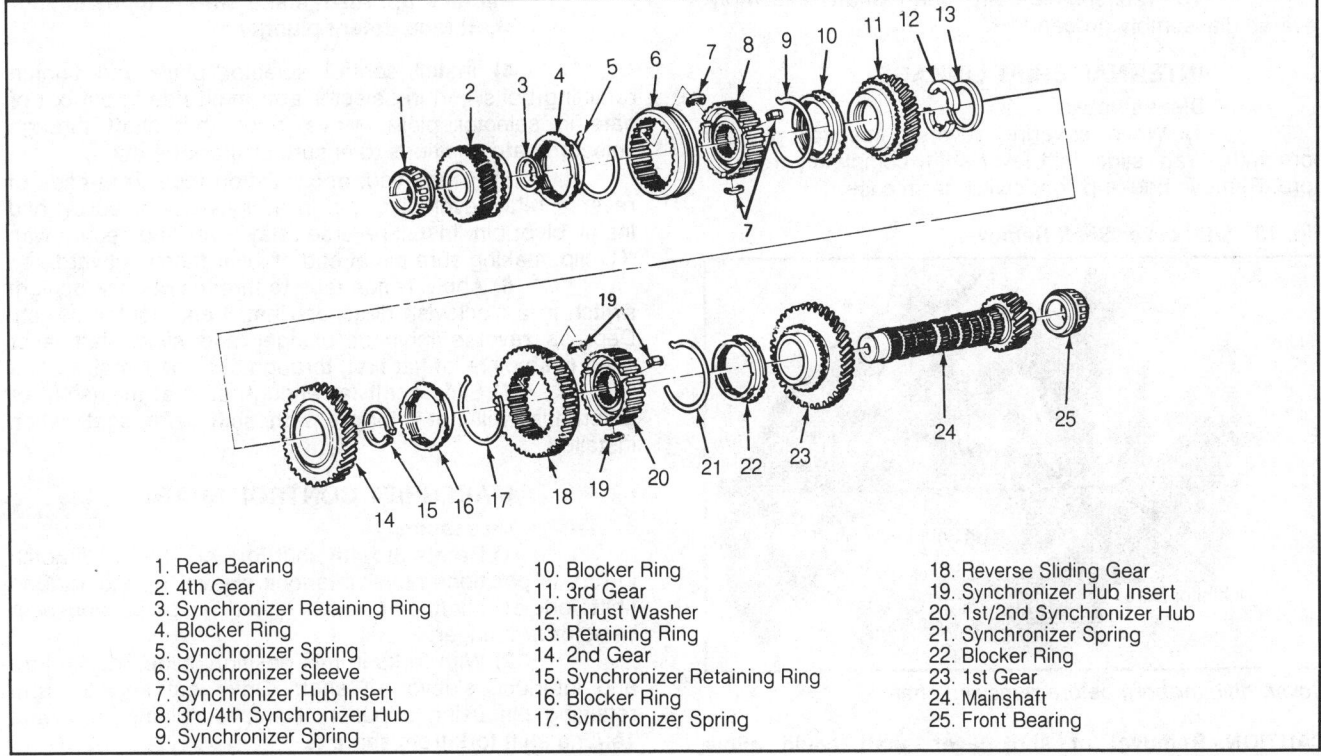

1. Rear Bearing
2. 4th Gear
3. Synchronizer Retaining Ring
4. Blocker Ring
5. Synchronizer Spring
6. Synchronizer Sleeve
7. Synchronizer Hub Insert
8. 3rd/4th Synchronizer Hub
9. Synchronizer Spring
10. Blocker Ring
11. 3rd Gear
12. Thrust Washer
13. Retaining Ring
14. 2nd Gear
15. Synchronizer Retaining Ring
16. Blocker Ring
17. Synchronizer Spring
18. Reverse Sliding Gear
19. Synchronizer Hub Insert
20. 1st/2nd Synchronizer Hub
21. Synchronizer Spring
22. Blocker Ring
23. 1st Gear
24. Mainshaft
25. Front Bearing

2) Slide 4th gear and synchronizer blocker ring from mainshaft. Remove 3rd/4th synchronizer retaining ring. Slide synchronizer assembly, blocker ring, and 3rd gear from shaft.

3) Remove 2nd/3rd thrust washer retaining ring and the 2-piece thrust washer. Remove 2nd gear and blocker ring. Remove retaining ring. Slide 1st/2nd synchronizer assembly, blocker ring, and 1st gear from shaft.

Reassembly

1) Prior to installing components on mainshaft, reassemble synchronizer assemblies and note the following:

2) Align index mark on synchronizer sleeve and hub. Place tab on synchronizer spring into groove of one of the inserts and snap spring into place. Place tab of the other spring into same insert (on opposite side of synchronizer assembly), and rotate spring in the opposite direction and snap into place.

NOTE: **When assembling synchronizer, notice that sleeve and hub have an extremely tight fit and must be held square to prevent jamming. Do not force sleeve onto hub.**

Fig. 9: Exploded View of Synchronizer Assembly

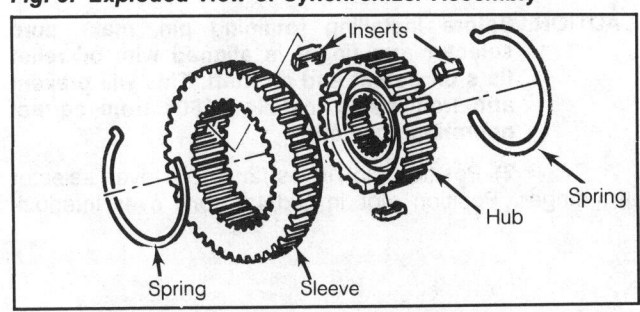

3) To reassemble mainshaft, lightly oil gear bores and other parts with appropriate transmission fluid. Slide blocker ring and 1st gear onto shaft.

4) Slide 1st/2nd synchronizer assembly into place, making sure shift fork groove on reverse sliding gear faces 1st gear. Install synchronizer retaining ring.

NOTE: **When installing synchronizer assembly, align the 3 grooves in 1st gear blocker ring with synchronizer inserts. This allows synchronizer assembly to seat properly in blocker ring.**

5) Install 2nd gear blocker ring and 2nd gear onto shaft. Install thrust washer halves and retaining ring. Slide 3rd gear onto shaft followed by blocker ring and 3rd/4th synchronizer assembly. Install synchronizer retaining ring.

6) Install 4th gear blocker ring and 4th gear onto shaft. Using a 1 1/16" socket, press bearing on 4th gear end of mainshaft. Install bearing on pinion gear end of mainshaft in the same manner. Make sure bearings are seated against shoulder of mainshaft.

NOTE: **Make sure the bearings are placed on proper end of the mainshaft as identified during disassembly procedures.**

5TH GEAR SHAFT ASSEMBLY
Disassembly

1) Remove slip fit bearing from 5th gear end of shaft and label it for reassembly reference. Remove 5th gear and blocking ring. Remove 5th gear synchronizer assembly.

2) Remove the press fit bearing from pinion end of shaft. Use bearing remover/installer tool (D79L-4621-A or equivalent).

3-100

Manual Transmissions
FORD MOTOR CO.
MTX 4 & 5-SPEED — MANUAL TRANSAXLE (Cont.)

Reassembly

To reassemble 5th gear shaft assembly, reverse diassembly procedures.

INTERNAL SHIFT LINKAGE
Disassembly

1) While covering reverse inhibitor plunger bore with a rag, slide shift lever shaft completely from its bore. Remove back-up light switch from case.

Fig. 10: Shift Lever Shaft Removal

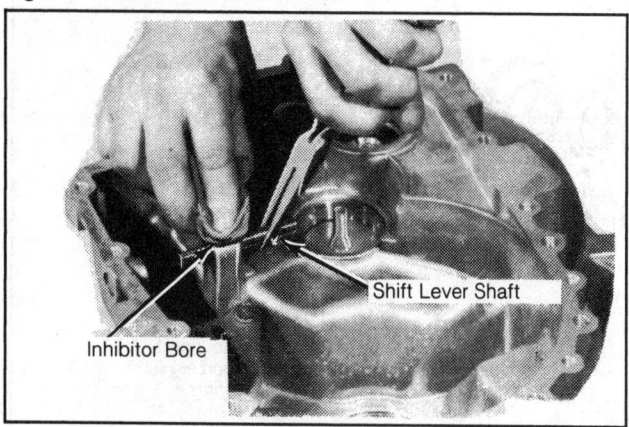

Cover inhibitor bore before removing shaft.

CAUTION: Removal of shift lever shaft could allow reverse inhibitor plunger to spring from its bore in case. Ensure inhibitor bore is covered to prevent possible injury.

2) Using a screwdriver, remove "C" clip and remove reverse relay lever (it is not necessary to remove pivot pin). Remove 2 control selector plate retaining bolts and remove plate from case.

3) Place input shift shaft in center detent position. Drive spring pin through selector plate arm assembly, through shift shaft into recess in clutch housing case. Remove shift shaft boot.

4) Using a drift, rotate input shift shaft 90°. Depress detent plunger from shaft detent notches inside housing and pull shift shaft out. Remove shift shaft selector plate arm assembly and spring pin.

CAUTION: Use care not to damage seal when removing input shift shaft.

5) Using a magnet, remove input shift shaft detent plunger and spring from case, labeling for proper reassembly. Using a slide hammer type puller, remove transmission input shift shaft oil seal.

Reassembly

1) Coat seal lip with grease and install new input shift shaft oil seal in case. Install shift shaft detent spring and plunger in clutch housing case bore.

2) Using a small drift, compress spring and plunger. Slide input shift shaft into its bore and over plunger.

3) Install selector plate arm in working position and slide shaft through selector plate arm. Align hole in arm with hole in shaft and install spring pin. Install input shift shaft boot.

NOTE: When properly installed, pin on selector arm will face up. Also, make sure notches in shift shaft face detent plunger.

4) Install control selector plate and tighten retaining bolts. Pin in selector arm must ride in cut-out of gate in selector plate. Move input shift shaft through selector plate positions to ensure proper operation.

5) If removed, apply Teflon tape to threads of reverse relay lever pivot pin in a clockwise direction and install pivot pin. Install reverse relay lever and secure with "C" clip, making sure pin at end of lever faces outward.

6) Apply Teflon tape to threads of back-up light switch in a clockwise direction. Install and tighten switch. Depress reverse inhibitor plunger and slide shift lever shaft (with oil relief flat first) through case pedestal.

7) Slide shaft far enough so that mainshaft or differential will not interfere with shift lever shaft when installed.

MAIN SHIFT CONTROL SHAFT
Disassembly

1) Rotate 3rd/4th shift fork on shaft until notch in fork is positioned over interlock sleeve. Rotate 1st/2nd shift fork on shaft until notch in fork is positioned over selector arm finger.

2) With forks in this position, slide 3rd/4th fork and interlock sleeve off shaft. Drive out selector arm retaining pin using a punch. Remove selector arm and 1st/2nd shift fork from shaft.

Fig. 11: Assembled View of Main Shift Control Shaft

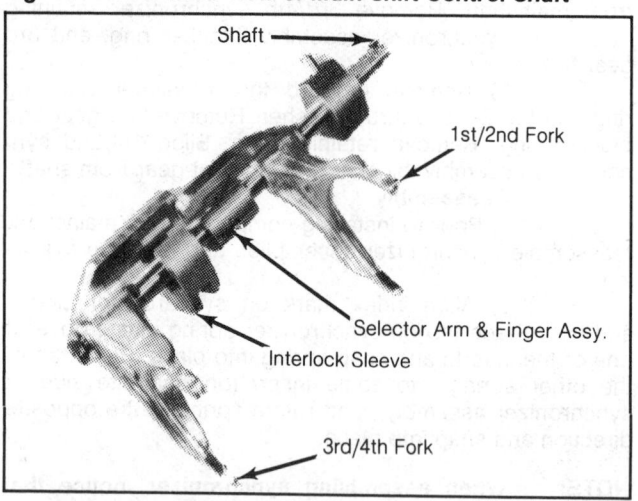

Reassembly

1) Install 1st/2nd shift fork and selector arm on shift shaft. Align hole in selector arm with hole in shaft and install retaining pin.

CAUTION: Before installing retaining pin, make sure selector arm finger is aligned with oil relief flats on detent end of shaft. This will prevent arm from being installed 180° from correct operating position.

2) Position slot in 1st/2nd fork over selector arm finger. Position slot in 3rd/4th fork over interlock

FORD MOTOR CO.
MTX 4 & 5-SPEED — MANUAL TRANSAXLE (Cont.)

sleeve. Slide 3rd/4th fork and sleeve onto shaft. Align interlock sleeve splines with splines on fork selector arm and slide into position.

5TH GEAR SHIFT CONTROL SHAFT
Disassembly

Using a punch, remove roll pin. Slide fork from shaft.

Reassembly

Holding shaft with hole on the left, install 5th gear shift fork so that the protruding spline is pointing toward the long end of the shaft. Install the roll pin.

DIFFERENTIAL ASSEMBLY
Disassembly

1) Using a puller, remove differential side bearings from differential case. Remove speedometer drive gear from case.

2) Remove side gears and thrust washers from differential case by rotating gears toward case windows. Using a punch, drive out differential pinion gear shaft retaining pin. Remove shaft. Withdraw pinion gears and thrust washers from case.

3) If necessary, remove ring gear from differential case as follows: Using a 5/16" drill, drill formed side of attaching rivets, then remove heads of rivets with a chisel. Using a punch, drive remaining rivet shank from case and remove ring gear.

Reassembly

1) To reassemble differential, reverse disassembly procedures and note the following: Lubricate all

Fig. 12: Exploded View of Differential Assembly

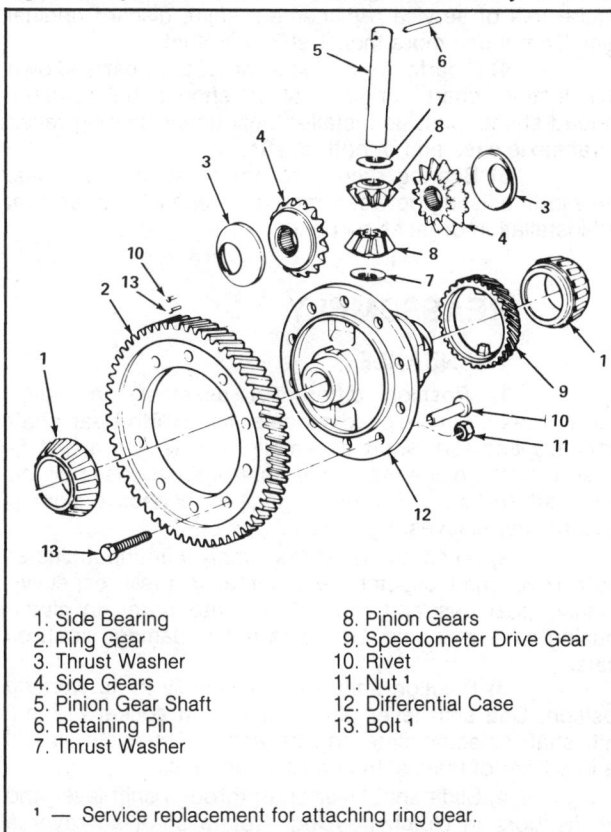

1. Side Bearing	8. Pinion Gears
2. Ring Gear	9. Speedometer Drive Gear
3. Thrust Washer	10. Rivet
4. Side Gears	11. Nut [1]
5. Pinion Gear Shaft	12. Differential Case
6. Retaining Pin	13. Bolt [1]
7. Thrust Washer	

[1] — Service replacement for attaching ring gear.

thrust washers and thrust surfaces on gears and in case with automatic transmission fluid.

2) If removed, press ring gear onto differential case and secure to case with service replacement bolts and nuts. Install bolts with heads on ring gear side of case.

3) Install speedometer gear on case with flat side of gear with chamfer facing ring gear.

NOTE: **Differential side gears must be aligned in case. This alignment must be held while installing differential in transaxle case. Failure to maintain alignment will make it impossible to install axle drive shafts through side gears.**

REASSEMBLY & ADJUSTMENT

DIFFERENTIAL BEARING PRELOAD

1) Differential bearing preload is set at the factory and need not be checked or adjusted unless one of the following components is replaced: transaxle case, differential case, or differential side bearings

2) To check and adjust preload, remove differential seal from transaxle case. Drive differential bearing outer race from case and remove preload adjusting shim located under race.

3) Position differential assembly in clutch housing. Install height gauge spacer (T81P-4451-B) on clutch housing dowel. Position bearing outer race removed from transaxle case on differential bearing. Install shim selector tool (T81P-4451-B) over race. See Fig. 13.

Fig. 13: Positioning Differential Preload Measuring Tools

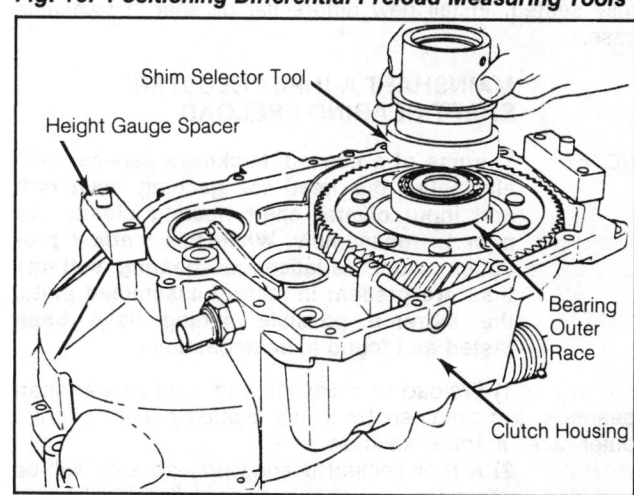

Use 4 retaining bolts supplied with measuring tool.

4) Place transaxle case in position on clutch housing and install the 4 retaining bolts supplied with preload checking tools. Tighten retaining bolts to 17-21 ft. lbs. (23-28 N.m).

5) Place gauge bar (T80L-77003-A) across shim selector tool. Using a feeler gauge, measure clearance between gauge bar and shim selector tool. Obtain measurements from 2 positions around tool and take the average of the reading. See Fig. 14.

3-102

Manual Transmissions
FORD MOTOR CO.
MTX 4 & 5-SPEED — MANUAL TRANSAXLE (Cont.)

Fig. 14: *Measuring Differential Bearing Preload*

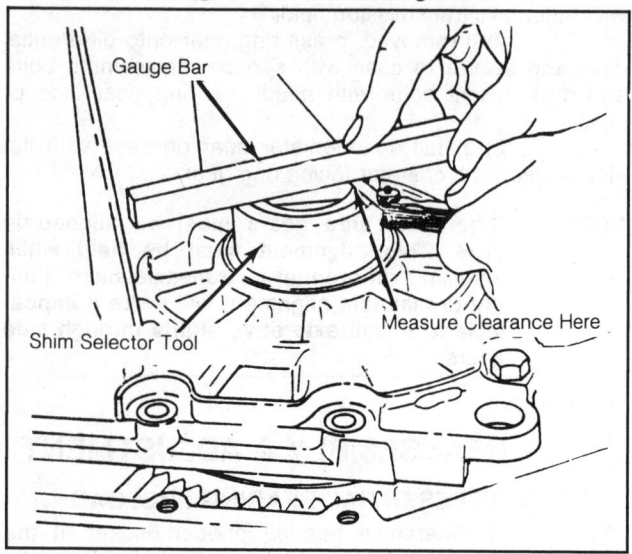

Use feeler gauge to measure bearing preload.

6) The average measurement obtained in preceding step is the thickness of shim needed to obtain specified differential bearing preload. Differential bearing preload shims are available in thicknesses of .012" to .049" (.30 to 1.24 mm) in .002" (.05 mm) increments.

NOTE: If preload adjusting shim required is not available, always use next thickest shim.

7) Separate transaxle case from clutch housing and remove measuring tools. Install selected preload shim in transaxle case. Press outer race into case until fully seated. Install new differential oil seal in transaxle case.

MAINSHAFT & INPUT CLUSTER SHAFT BEARING PRELOAD

NOTE: The use of a nominal thickness service shim eliminates the need for gauging mainshaft and input cluster shaft bearing clearances prior to reassembly. While this method produces wider variations of bearing settings than are present in factory assembled units, the extreme possible setting have been tested and found to be acceptable.

1) Preload of mainshaft and input cluster shaft bearings is maintained by shims located behind bearing outer races in transaxle case.

2) A replacement bearing preload shim will be provided for service and should be installed in place of original shim as outlined in *Preload Shim Selection Chart*.

CAUTION: If bearing outer races are removed from case for any reason, it is very important to keep the race and its matching shim together. It is also important to label bearing races as they are removed from transaxle case or clutch housing. Maintaining proper race-to-shim relationship and proper race labeling will ensure correct bearing preload when transaxle is assembled.

SERVICE SHIM CHART

Parts Replaced	Shims Replaced with Service Shims		
	Input Cluster Shaft	Main Shaft	5th Gear Shaft
1 Input Cluster Bearing	Yes	No	No
2 Input Cluster Bearings	Yes	No	No
1 Input Cluster Bearing	Yes	Yes	Yes
1 Mainshaft Bearing	Yes	Yes	Yes
1 5th Gear Shaft Bearing	Yes	Yes	Yes
2 Input Cluster Bearings	Yes	Yes	Yes
2 Mainshaft Bearings	Yes	Yes	Yes
2 5th Gear Shaft Bearings	Yes	Yes	Yes
1 Mainshaft Bearing	No	Yes	No
2 Mainshaft Bearings	No	Yes	No
1 5th Gear Shaft Bearing	No	No	Yes
2 5th Gear Shaft Bearings	No	No	Yes
Clutch Housing Assembly	Yes	Yes	Yes
Transaxle Case Assembly	Yes	Yes	Yes

3) The following points should be noted when replacing shaft bearing preload shims. When repairs require use of service replacement shim, discard original shim. Do not use more than 1 shim per shaft.

4) If parts are replaced other than parts shown in selection chart, original shim should be re-used. Preload shims must be installed only under bearing races at transaxle case end of both shafts.

5) Bearing races are not pressed into cases. The slip-fit existing between race and case allows removal and installation of races by hand.

REASSEMBLY

TRANSAXLE

1) Position differential assembly in clutch housing case. On 5-speed models, install 5th gear shaft assembly and fork shaft assembly in case. On 4 and 5-speed models, place main shift control shaft assembly on mainshaft so that shift forks engage in respective slots in synchronizer sleeves. See Fig. 15.

2) Mesh mainshaft assembly with input cluster shaft. Hold shaft assemblies together in their respective working positions and lower them into bores in clutch housing case as a unit. Use care not to damage shaft oil seals.

3) Position shift lever assembly in its working position. One shift lever pin should be in socket of input shift shaft selector plate arm assembly. Other pin should be in socket of main shift control shaft block.

4) Slide shift lever shaft through shift lever and into its bore in clutch housing. Rotate shaft so reverse inhibitor notch faces inhibitor plunger.

FORD MOTOR CO.
MTX 4 & 5-SPEED — MANUAL TRANSAXLE (Cont.)

Fig. 15: Assembling Main Shift Control Shaft Assembly to Mainshaft Assembly

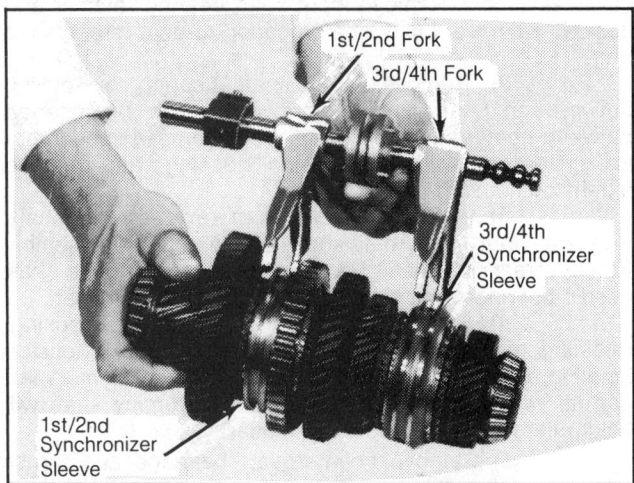

5) On 4-speed models, position shift lever shaft so set screw hole on shaft aligns with hole in shift lever. Install set screw. Before tightening set screw, position shift lever on shaft to make sure set screw is centered in shaft center drilled hole.

6) On 5-speed models, install spring and ball in 5th and reverse inhibitor shaft lever hole. Slide shift lever shaft (notch up) through shift lever. Using a small drift, depress ball and tap the shift shaft into its bore in clutch housing. Rotate shift lever shaft (down) so reverse inhibitor notch faces reverse inhibitor plunger.

7) Before proceeding with transaxle reassembly on 4 and 5-speed models, verify the following: Selector pin should be in neutral gate of control selector plate. Finger of fork selector arm should be partially engaged with 1st/2nd shift fork and 3rd/4th shift fork. *See Fig. 16.*

Fig. 16: Checking Selector Pin Position

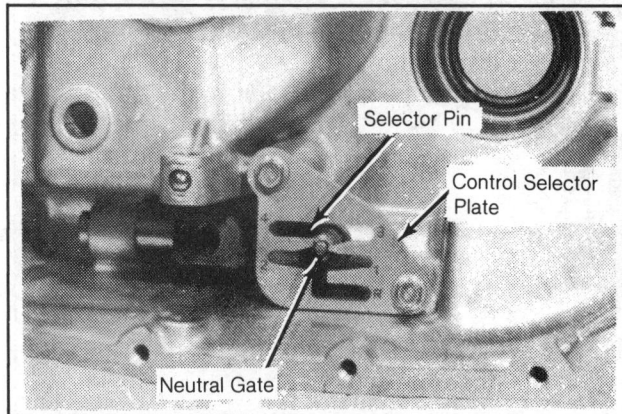

Pin selector should be in neutral gate.

8) Place groove in reverse idler gear in engagement with pin at end of reverse relay lever. Slide shaft through gear and into bore.

9) Align retaining screw hole in reverse idler shaft with hole in case. This allows proper alignment between shaft retaining screw hole in transaxle case, when case is placed over this assembly.

10) Install magnet in pocket of clutch housing case. On 5-speed models, install 5th shift relay lever onto reverse idler shaft. Align it with 5th gear fork interlock and install retaining ring.

11) On 4 and 5-speed models, apply a 1/16" wide bead of sealer (E1FZ-19562-A or equivalent) to clutch housing-to-transaxle case mounting surface.

12) Carefully lower transaxle case over clutch housing case. Gently lower case until shift control shaft, mainshaft, input cluster shaft, and 5th gear shaft (if equipped) align with bores in transaxle case.

13) Gently slide transaxle case over dowels. Case should sit flush on clutch housing, without binding on magnet. Install and tighten transaxle case-to-clutch housing retaining bolts.

14) If necessary, use a drift to align bore in reverse idler shaft with retaining screw hole in transaxle case. Install and tighten reverse idler shaft retaining bolt.

15) Apply Teflon tape to threads of interlock sleeve retaining pin. If necessary, align slot in interlock sleeve with hole in transaxle case using a drift. Install and tighten retaining pin.

16) Apply Teflon tape to threads of detent plunger retaining screw. Install and tighten screw. Place transaxle upright and position drift through hole in input shift shaft. Shift transaxle through all gears to ensure proper installation.

TIGHTENING SPECIFICATIONS

Application	Ft. Lbs. (N.m)
Trans. Case-to-Clutch Hsg.	13-17 (18-23)
Reverse Idler Shaft-to-Case	16-20 (22-27)
Fork Interlock Sleeve Pin	[1] 12-15 (16-20)
Back-Up Light Switch	[1] 14-18 (19-24)
Reverse Relay Lever Pivot Pin	[1] 14-18 (19-24)
Ring Gear-to-Differential Case	55-70 (75-79)
Differential Bearing Retainer-to-Case	15-19 (20-26)
Ball Joint-to-Steering Knuckle	37-44 (50-60)
Stabilizer-to-Control Arm	59-73 (80-99)
Transaxle-to-Engine	28-31 (38-42)

	INCH Lbs. (N.m)
Detent Plunger Retainer Screw	[1] 108-144 (12-16)
Control Selector Plate	72-96 (8-11)
Shift Lever Set Screw	84-120 (10-14)
Filler Plug	108-169 (12-20)

[1] — Coat threads with Teflon tape prior to installation and tightening.

Manual Transmissions

GENERAL MOTORS 3-SPEED — 76 MM

Chevrolet & GMC Trucks

DESCRIPTION

The 76 mm 3-speed transmission is identified by the measured distance (76 mm) between the centerlines of the mainshaft and countergear and by the number of forward gears.

It is a fully-synchronized transmission, providing synchromesh engagement in all forward gears. All gears are helical cut, with the forward gears being in constant mesh.

LUBRICATION & ADJUSTMENT

See the appropriate article in MANUAL TRANS-MISSION SERVICING Section.

TROUBLE SHOOTING

See TROUBLE SHOOTING article.

REMOVAL & INSTALLATION

See the appropriate article in MANUAL TRANS-MISSION REMOVAL Section.

TRANSMISSION DISASSEMBLY

1) Remove side cover attaching bolts and cover assembly. Remove input shaft bearing retainer and gasket. Remove input shaft bearing-to-gear stem snap ring.

2) Remove input shaft bearing by pulling outward on shaft, until a screwdriver can be inserted between bearing snap ring and case. Remove speedometer driven gear from extension housing, and remove extension housing-to-case bolts.

3) Remove "E" clip from reverse idler shaft. Remove input shaft, mainshaft, and extension assembly through rear of case. Remove drive gear, input shaft needle bearings, and synchronizer ring from mainshaft.

4) Expand snap ring in extension housing, retaining mainshaft rear bearing, and remove extension housing. Using a dummy countershaft, drive countershaft and its woodruff key out rear of case. Dummy shaft will hold roller bearings in position in gear.

5) Remove countergear, bearings and thrust washers. Using a long drift, drive the reverse idler shaft and woodruff key out rear of case. Lift out reverse idler gear.

Fig. 1: Cutaway View of General Motors 3-Speed 76 MM Transmission

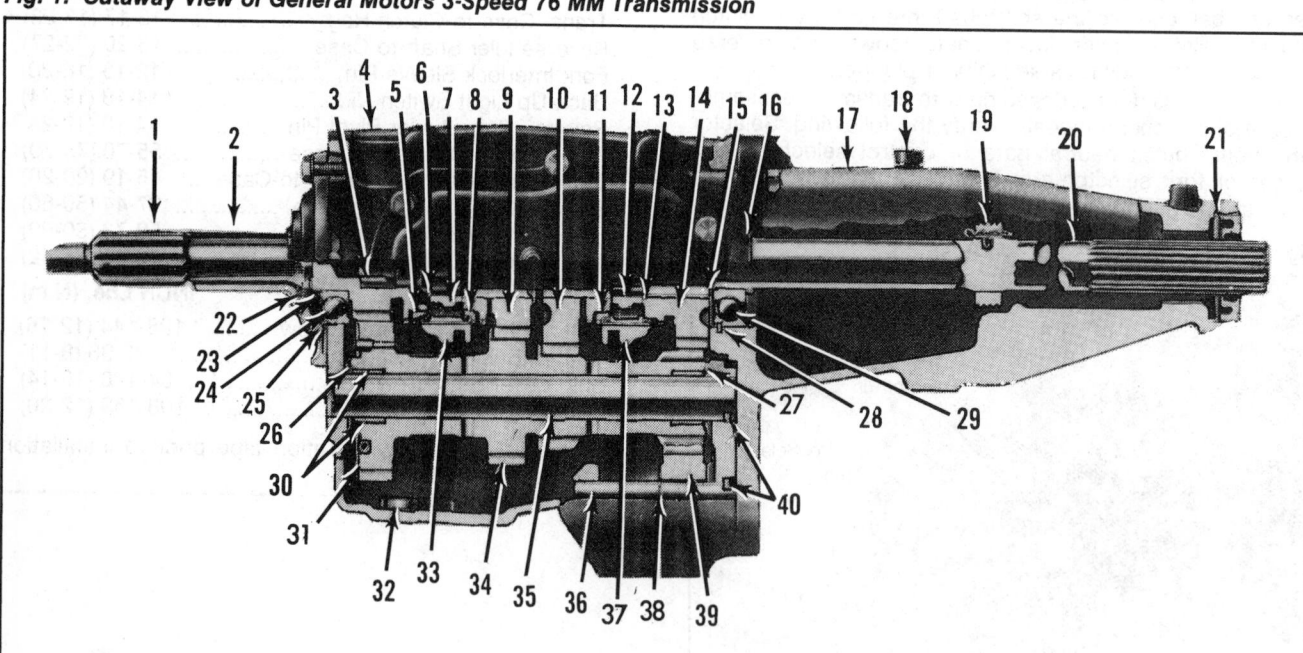

1. Input Shaft
2. Bearing Retainer
3. Pilot Bearings
4. Case
5. 3rd Gear Blocker Ring
6. 2nd-3rd Synchro Snap Ring
7. 2nd-3rd Synchro Hub
8. 2nd Gear Blocker Ring
9. 2nd Gear
10. 1st Gear
11. 1st Gear Blocker Ring
12. 1st Gear Synchro Hub
13. 1st Gear Synchro Snap Ring
14. Reverse Gear
15. Reverse Gear Thrust & Spring Washers
16. Bearing-to-Mainshaft Snap Ring
17. Extension Housing
18. Vent
19. Speedo Drive Gear & Clip
20. Mainshaft
21. Rear Oil Seal
22. Retainer Oil Seal
23. Bearing-to-Gear Snap Ring
24. Input Shaft Bearing
25. Bearing-to-Case Snap Ring
26. Front Thrust Washer
27. Rear Thrust Washer
28. Extension Housing Snap Ring
29. Rear Bearing
30. Countergear Roll Bearings
31. Anti-Lash Plate Assembly
32. Magnet
33. 2nd-3rd Synchro Sleeve
34. Countergear
35. Countershaft
36. Reverse Idler Shaft
37. 1st Gear Synchro Sleeve
38. "E" Ring
39. Reverse Idle Gear
40. Woodruff Key

GENERAL MOTORS 3-SPEED — 76 MM (Cont.)

CLEANING & INSPECTION

1) Wash all components in cleaning solvent and dry with air. Inspect transmission case for cracks, damaged bearing bores, or damaged threads.

2) Remove all small nicks and burrs from front and rear face of case. Check ball bearings for roughness by slowly turning race by hand. Inspect bearing rollers, shafts, and washers for wear or damage.

3) Inspect bushing in reverse gear and reverse idler gear for wear or damage. If worn or damaged, entire gear must be replaced, as bushings are not serviced separately. Check all other components for wear, chipped or broken teeth, and damage. Replace parts as necessary.

Fig. 2: Exploded View of General Motors 3-Speed 76 MM Transmission

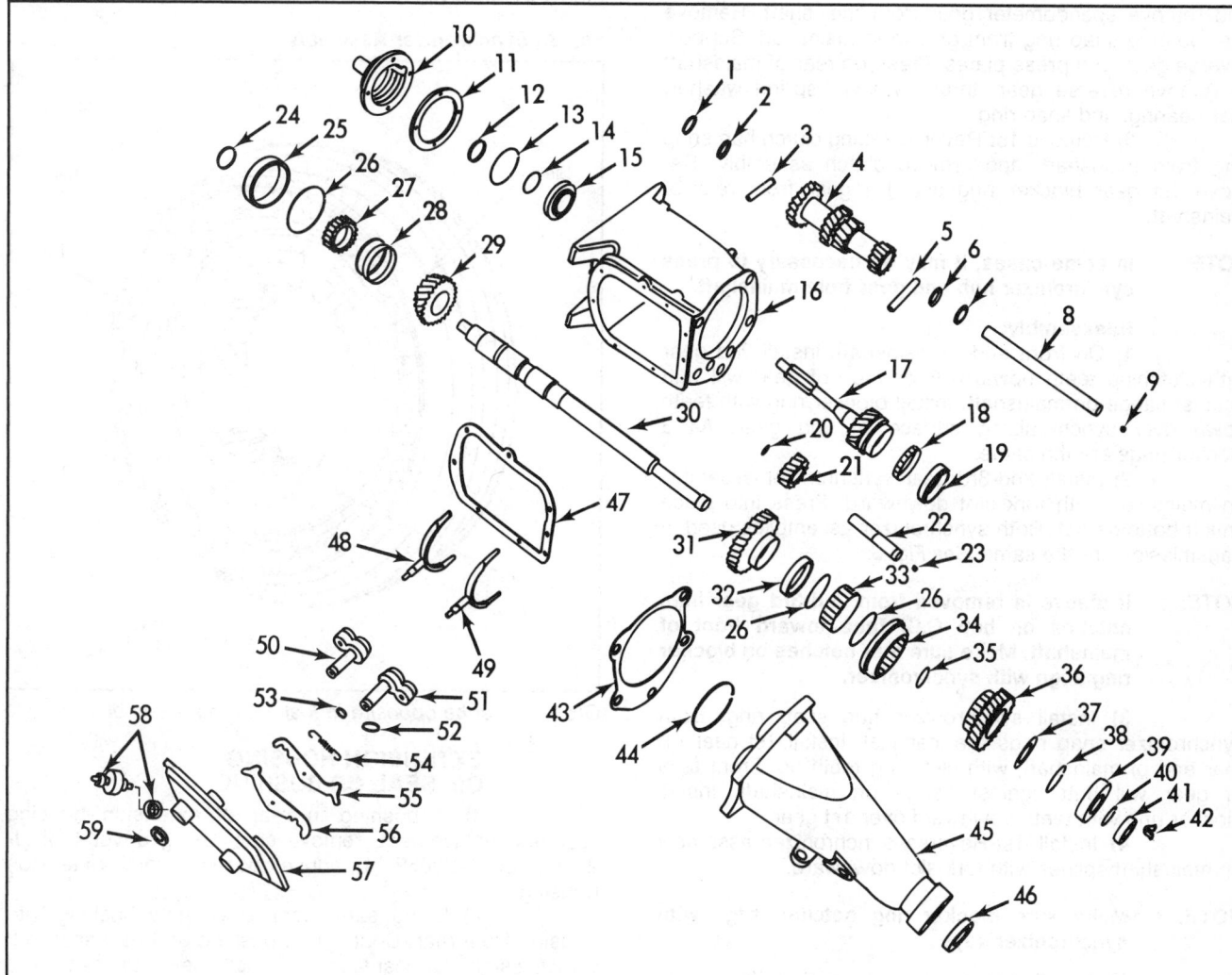

1. Thrust Washer - Front	17. Drive Gear	32. 1st Speed Blocker Ring	47. Gasket
2. Bearing Washer	18. Pilot Bearings	33. 1-2 Synchronizer Hub	48. 2-3 Shift Fork
3. Needle Bearings	19. 3rd Speed Blocker	Assembly	49. 1st and Reverse Shift
4. Countergear	Ring	34. 1-2 Synchronizer Sleeve	Fork
5. Needle Bearings	20. "E" Ring	35. Snap Ring - Hub to Shaft	50. 2-3 Shifter Shaft
6. Bearing Washer	21. Reverse Idler Gear	36. Reverse Gear	Assembly
7. Thrust Washer - Rear	22. Reverse Idler Shaft	37. Thrust Washer	51. 1st and Reverse Shifter
8. Counter Shaft	23. Woodruff Key	38. Spring Washer	Shaft
9. Woodruff Key	24. Snap Ring - Hub	39. Rear Bearing	52. "O" Ring Seal
10. Bearing Retainer	to Shaft	40. Snap Ring - Bearing	53. "E" Ring
11. Gasket	25. 2-3 Synchronizer Sleeve	to Shaft	54. Spring
12. Oil Seal	26. Synchronizer Key Spring	41. Speedometer Drive Gear	55. 2nd and 3rd Detent Cam
13. Snap Ring - Bearing	27. 2-3 Synchronizer Hub	42. Retaining Clip	56. 1st and Reverse Detent
to Case	Assembly	43. Gasket	Cam
14. Snap Ring - Bearing	28. 2nd Speed Blocker Ring	44. Snap Ring - Rear Bearing	57. Side Cover
to Gear	29. 2nd Speed Gear	to Extension	58. TCS Switch and Gasket
15. Drive Gear Bearing	30. Mainshaft	45. Extension	59. Lip Seal
16. Case	31. 1st Speed Gear	46. Oil Seal	

Manual Transmissions

GENERAL MOTORS 3-SPEED — 76 MM (Cont.)

COMPONENT DISASSEMBLY & REASSEMBLY

MAINSHAFT

Disassembly

1) Remove 2nd-3rd gear sliding clutch snap ring from mainshaft. Remove clutch assembly, 2nd gear blocker ring and 2nd gear from front of mainshaft. See Fig. 2.

2) Depress speedometer gear retaining clip, and remove speedometer gear from mainshaft. Remove rear bearing snap ring from groove in mainshaft. Support reverse gear with press plates. Press on rear of mainshaft to remove reverse gear, thrust washer, spring washer, rear bearing, and snap ring.

3) Remove 1st-Reverse sliding clutch hub snap ring from mainshaft, and remove clutch assembly. Remove 1st gear blocker ring and 1st gear from rear of mainshaft.

NOTE: In some cases, it may be necessary to press synchronizer hub and gear from mainshaft.

Reassembly

1) On front end of mainshaft, install 2nd gear with clutching teeth upward. Rear face of gear will butt against flange on mainshaft. Install blocker ring with teeth down over synchronizing surface of 2nd gear. All 3 blocker rings are the same.

2) Install 2nd-3rd gear synchronizer assembly on mainshaft, with fork slot downward. Press into place until it bottoms out. Both synchronizer assemblies used in transmission are the same. See Fig. 3.

NOTE: If sleeve is removed from 2nd-3rd gear hub, notches on hub O.D. face toward front of mainshaft. Make sure that notches on blocker ring align with synchronizer.

3) Install synchronizer hub snap ring. Both synchronizer snap rings are identical. Install 1st gear on rear end of mainshaft, with clutching teeth up. Front face of gear will butt against flange on mainshaft. Install blocker ring with teeth downward over 1st gear.

4) Install 1st-Reverse synchronizer assembly on mainshaft splines, with fork slot downward.

NOTE: Make sure blocker ring notches align with synchronizer keys.

5) Install synchronizer snap ring. Install reverse gear with teeth downward. Install reverse gear thrust washer (steel) and spring washer. Install rear bearing on mainshaft with snap ring slot down. Install bearing snap ring. Install speedometer drive gear and retaining clip.

SYNCHRONIZER CLUTCH ASSEMBLIES

NOTE: The clutch hubs and sliding sleeves are a selected assembly and should be kept together as originally assembled. However, the keys and 2 springs may be replaced if worn or broken.

Disassembly

Mark hub and sleeve, so they can be aligned upon reassembly. Push hub from sliding sleeve, then remove keys and springs.

Reassembly

1) Place 3 keys and 2 springs in position, 1 on each side of hub, so all 3 keys are engaged by both springs. The tanged end of each synchronizer spring should be installed into different key cavities on either side.

2) A groove around outside of synchronizer hub identifies end that must be opposite fork slot in sleeve when assembled. Groove indicates end of hub with greater recess depth. Slide sleeve onto hub, aligning marks before assembly.

Fig. 3: Synchronizer Assembly

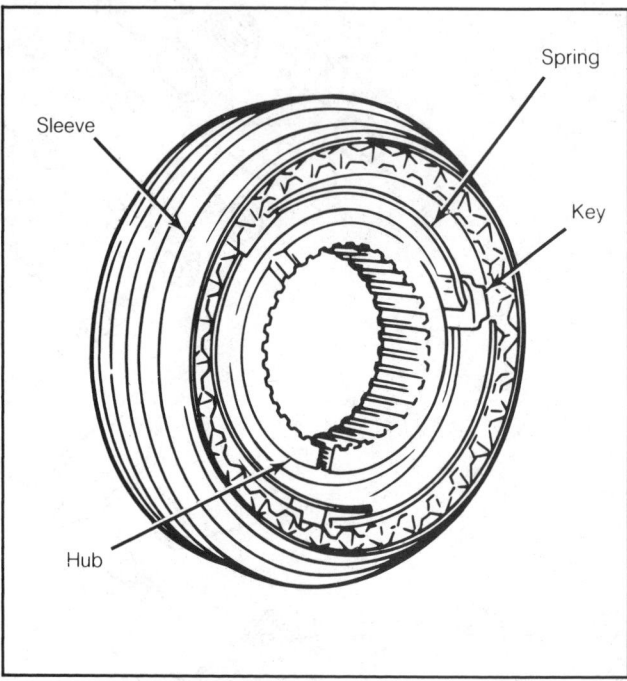

Groove must be opposite fork slot during assembly.

EXTENSION HOUSING OIL SEAL OR BUSHING

1) If bushing in rear of extension housing requires replacement, remove seal. Using driver tool (J-21465 or J-23062-14), drive bushing into extension housing.

2) Using same tool, drive new bushing into housing from rear. Coat I.D. of bushing and new seal with transmission lubricant, and install new oil seal into housing.

INPUT SHAFT RETAINER OIL SEAL

If seal in retainer requires replacement, pry out old seal. Using installer (J-23096), drive new seal into retainer until seal seats in bore. During installation, make sure seal lip faces rear of transmission.

TRANSMISSION CASE COVER

Disassembly

Remove both shift forks from shifter shaft assemblies. Remove detent cam spring, pivot retainer "C" ring, and both detent cams. Inspect and replace damaged parts. Inspect shifter shaft seals, and replace them as necessary.

GENERAL MOTORS 3-SPEED — 76 MM (Cont.)

Reassembly

1) With detent spring tang projecting up over the 2nd-3rd shifter shaft cover opening, install the 1st-Reverse detent cam pivot pin. With detent spring tang projecting up over the 1st-Reverse shifter shaft cover hole, install the 2nd-3rd detent cam onto cam pivot pin.

2) Install detent cam retaining "C" ring to pivot pin, and hook detent spring into detent cam notches. Install both shifter shaft assemblies into cover taking care not to damage seals.

3) Install both shift forks to shifter shaft assemblies. Lift up on detent cam to allow forks to fully seat into position.

TRANSMISSION REASSEMBLY

NOTE: Apply a sealant to all through-bolts used during reassembly.

1) Coat countershaft bore with heavy grease. Insert dummy countershaft into countergear, and install needle roller bearings (27) and thrust washer in each end of gear.

2) Place countergear assembly through rear opening in case along with a tanged thrust washer at each end. Tang should be away from gear. Install countergear shaft and woodruff key from rear of case. Be sure that countershaft picks up both thrust washers and that tangs are aligned in case.

3) Install reverse idler gear and shaft with woodruff key from rear of case. Do not install idler shaft "E" clip at this time. Expand snap ring in extension housing, and install extension housing over rear of mainshaft and onto rear bearing. Seat snap ring in groove.

4) Coat input shaft cavity with heavy grease. Install mainshaft pilot bearings (14) into cavity. Install 3rd gear blocking ring on input shaft with teeth facing input gear.

5) Guide input shaft, bearing and 3rd gear blocking ring assembly over front of mainshaft assembly. *See Fig. 4.* Blocker ring notches should align with keys in 2nd-3rd synchronizer assembly.

6) Install extension housing-to-case gasket. From rear of case, install input shaft, mainshaft and extension housing as an assembly. Install extension housing-to-case bolts.

Fig. 4: Input Shaft Assembly

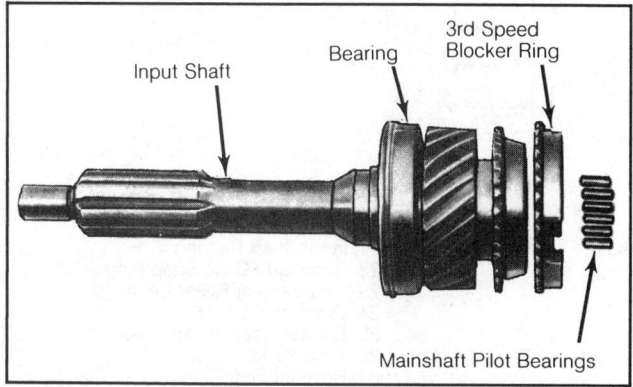

Install shaft from rear of case.

7) Install snap ring on front bearing, and place bearing over input shaft. Slide bearing into bore in case.

Install snap ring on input shaft. Install input shaft bearing retainer and new gasket to case. Bearing retainer oil hole should be on the bottom.

8) Install reverse idler gear "E" clip on shaft. Shift synchronizer sleeves to neutral position and install cover, gasket and fork assembly to case. Make sure forks align with synchronizer sleeve grooves.

9) Install speedometer driven gear in extension housing. Rotate input shaft and shift transmission to check operation.

TIGHTENING SPECIFICATIONS

Application	Ft. Lbs. (N.m)
Input Shaft Retainer-to-Case Bolts	15 (20)
Side Cover-to-Case Bolts	15 (20)
Ext. Housing-to-Case Bolts	45 (61)
Filler Plug	13 (17)
Shift Lever-to-Shifter Shaft Bolts	25 (32)
Case-to-Clutch Housing Bolts	75 (101)

GENERAL MOTORS 4-SPEED — 70 MM

Chevrolet Chevette
Pontiac T1000

TRANSMISSION IDENTIFICATION

Transmission may be identified by a 2-letter code stamped on pad, lower right side of case.

DESCRIPTION

Transmission is a 4-speed unit, synchronized in all forward gears. Reverse gear is not synchronized. Helical gears are used throughout transmission and, with the exception of reverse gears, all transmission gears are in constant mesh. All gears are carried on shafts inside transmission case, except reverse gears, which are mounted on outside of rear case face, inside extension housing. Transmission utilizes single rail shift linkage, supported on one end by extension housing, and on opposite end by clutch housing.

LUBRICATION & ADJUSTMENT

See the appropriate article in MANUAL TRANS-MISSION SERVICING section.

REMOVAL & INSTALLATION

See the appropriate article in MANUAL TRANS-MISSION REMOVAL Section.

TRANSMISSION DISASSEMBLY

1) Place transmission on a bench, clutch housing facing downward. Drive roll pin from shifter arm assembly and shifter shaft, then remove shifter arm. Remove reverse shifter shaft cover, shifter shaft detent cap, spring and ball, and interlock lock pin. Remove bolts attaching extension housing to case and withdraw extension housing.

2) Press down on speedometer gear retainer and slide gear and retainer off mainshaft. Remove shifter shaft snap rings, then using pliers, pull exposed end of

Fig. 1: Cross Sectional View of General Motors 70 MM 4-Speed Transmission Assembly

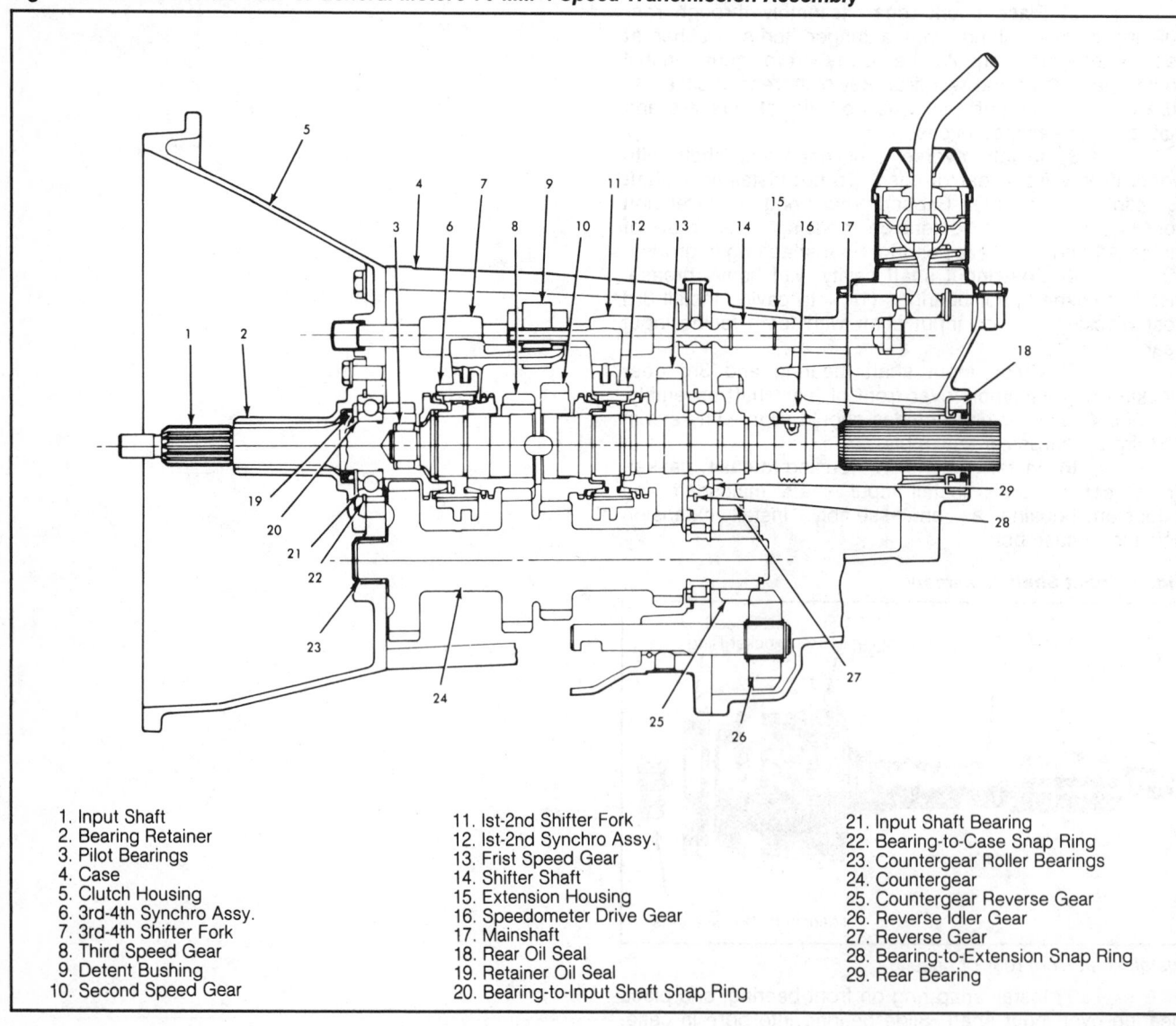

1. Input Shaft
2. Bearing Retainer
3. Pilot Bearings
4. Case
5. Clutch Housing
6. 3rd-4th Synchro Assy.
7. 3rd-4th Shifter Fork
8. Third Speed Gear
9. Detent Bushing
10. Second Speed Gear
11. Ist-2nd Shifter Fork
12. Ist-2nd Synchro Assy.
13. Frist Speed Gear
14. Shifter Shaft
15. Extension Housing
16. Speedometer Drive Gear
17. Mainshaft
18. Rear Oil Seal
19. Retainer Oil Seal
20. Bearing-to-Input Shaft Snap Ring
21. Input Shaft Bearing
22. Bearing-to-Case Snap Ring
23. Countergear Roller Bearings
24. Countergear
25. Countergear Reverse Gear
26. Reverse Idler Gear
27. Reverse Gear
28. Bearing-to-Extension Snap Ring
29. Rear Bearing

GENERAL MOTORS 4-SPEED — 70 MM (Cont.)

Fig. 2: View of Transmission Case Showing Location of Cover, Detent Cap and Interlock Pin

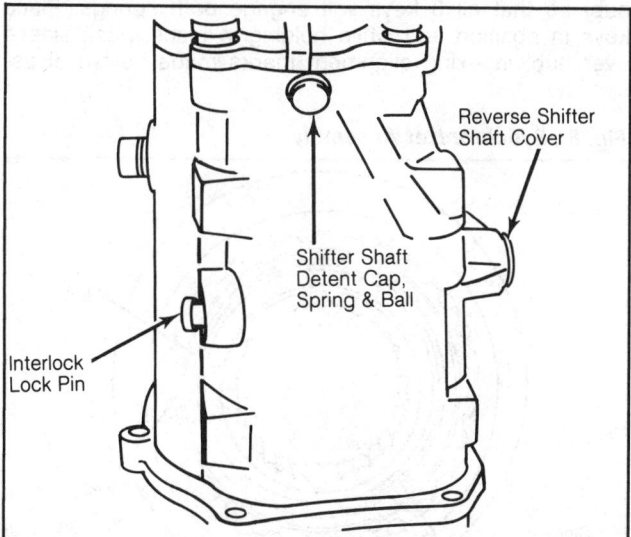

reverse shifter shaft outward to disengage reverse lever from idler shaft. Remove idler shaft with gear attached. Remove snap rings retaining mainshaft reverse gear and countershaft reverse gear, then remove gears.

3) Position transmission on its side and remove input shaft bearing retainer bolts, retainer and gasket. Remove snap ring retaining input shaft bearing to clutch housing, and remove bolts attaching clutch housing to case. Position transmission so it is resting on clutch housing and expand snap ring in mainshaft bearing opening.

4) Remove transmission case by lifting it off the mainshaft. It may be necessary to tap case with a plastic mallet to free it from mainshaft assembly.

NOTE: **Ensure that mainshaft assembly, countergear and shifter shaft assembly remains with clutch housing when case is removed.**

5) Lift mainshaft (with shift forks attached) and countergear from clutch housing as an assembly.

Fig. 3: Removing Reverse Countergear Snap Ring

Use snap ring pliers to remove snap ring.

INSPECTION

1) Wash all parts thoroughly in solvent and blow dry. Check transmission case for cracks. Check front and rear case faces for burrs. Remove burrs with fine mill file. Inspect all bearings for wear or damage, and also check bearing contact surfaces of countergear and reverse idler shaft. Replace parts as necessary.

2) Inspect all gears for excessive wear, chips and cracks. Check reverse idler gear bushing, and if worn or damaged, replace entire gear (bushing is not serviced separately). Inspect both synchronizer assemblies, making sure sleeves slide freely on hubs.

Fig. 4: Removing Bearing-to-Clutch Housing Snap Ring

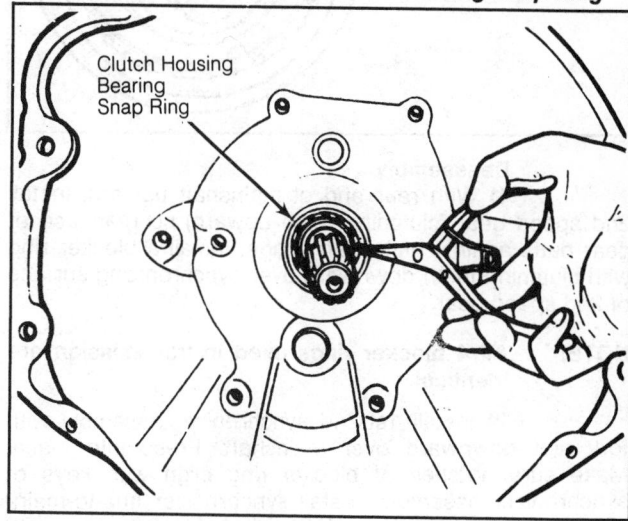

COMPONENT DISASSEMBLY & REASSEMBLY

MAINSHAFT
Disassembly

1) Separate shifter shaft and countergear assemblies from mainshaft, then withdraw input shaft and blocker ring from front of mainshaft.

NOTE: **Input shaft has 15 roller bearings. Catch bearings if they fall out so they may be replaced in correct position during reassembly.**

2) Remove snap ring retaining 3rd-4th synchronizer assembly on mainshaft, then remove synchronizer using a press if required. Remove blocker ring and 3rd speed gear from mainshaft. Using press plates, withdraw ball bearing from rear end of mainshaft.

3) With rear bearing removed, withdraw 1st speed gear and blocking ring from mainshaft. Remove snap ring retaining 1st-2nd synchronizer on mainshaft, then withdraw synchronizer using a press if necessary. Finally, withdraw 2nd speed gear and blocking ring from mainshaft.

NOTE: **Before reassembly of mainshaft, see SYNCHRONIZER CLUTCH ASSEMBLIES.**

GENERAL MOTORS 4-SPEED — 70 MM (Cont.)

Fig. 5: Removing 3rd-4th Synchro Snap Ring

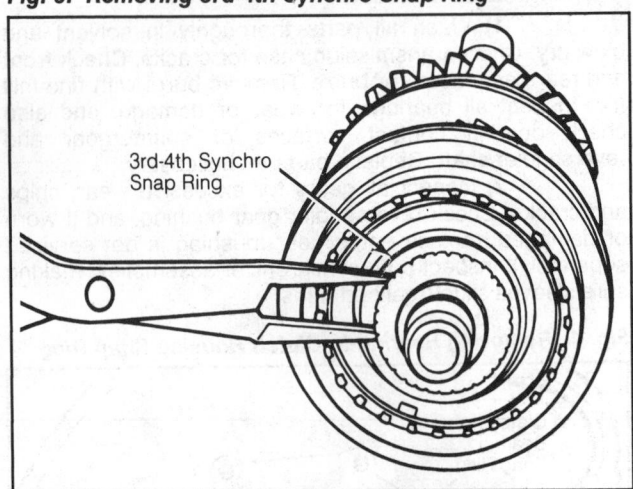

3rd-4th Synchro Snap Ring

Reassembly

1) With rear end of mainshaft upward, install 2nd speed gear (clutching teeth upward) so rear face of gear butts against mainshaft flange. Install a blocker ring with clutching teeth downward over synchronizing surface of 2nd speed gear.

NOTE: All 4 blocker rings used in transmission are identical.

2) Install 1st-2nd synchronizer assembly with fork slot downward over mainshaft. Press into place. Make sure notches of blocker ring align with keys of synchronizer assembly. Install synchronizer hub-to-mainshaft retaining snap ring. Install a blocker ring with notches downward so they align with keys of 1st-2nd synchronizer assembly.

3) Install 1st speed gear over end of mainshaft with clutching teeth downward. Position rear bearing over end of mainshaft with snap ring groove downward. Press into place.

NOTE: Two ball bearings are used in transmission. Rear bearing on mainshaft is not shielded. Input shaft bearing is shielded. Do not switch bearings.

4) Turn mainshaft so front faces upward. Install 3rd speed gear over shaft with clutching teeth upward. Move into place so front face of gear butts against mainshaft flange. Install a blocker ring with clutching teeth downward over synchronizing surface of 3rd speed gear.

5) Install 3rd-4th synchronizer assembly onto shaft with fork slot downward. Install synchronizer mainshaft retaining snap ring. Install blocker ring with notches downward so they align with keys of synchronizer.

SYNCHRONIZER CLUTCH ASSEMBLIES

NOTE: Synchronizer hub and sliding sleeves are select fit and should be kept together as originally assembled. However, keys and springs may be replaced if worn or broken.

Disassembly

If not already marked, mark hub and sleeve for reassembly reference in same position. Then push the hub, springs and keys form sleeve.

Reassembly

Place 2 spring in position (one on each side of hub) so that all 3 keys will engage both springs. Place keys in position and while holding in place, push sleeve over hub, indexing alignment marks made before disassembly.

Fig. 6: Synchronizer Assembly

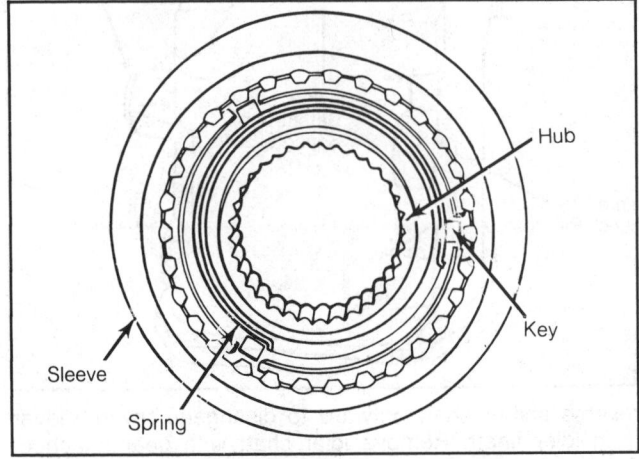

Hub

Key

Sleeve

Spring

Mark relative position of hub to sleeve for reassembly.

EXTENSION HOUSING SEAL & BUSHING
Removal & Installation

Pry rear seal from extension housing using a screwdriver. Using a bushing driver (J-5778), remove bushing from rear of housing. Use same tool to drive new bushing into housing. Coat I.D. of new bushing and seal with transmission lubricant, then install seal into housing using a seal driver (J-21426 or J-5154).

FRONT BEARING RETAINER
Removal & Installation

Pry out old seal using a screwdriver. Install new seal into retainer using a seal driver (J-23096). Lubricate I.D. of new seal with transmission lubricant.

TRANSMISSION REASSEMBLY

1) Using arbor press, install shielded bearing on input shaft with snap ring groove upward. Install snap ring to retain bearing on shaft. Install mainshaft pilot roller bearings into input shaft cavity, using heavy grease to hold them in place. Carefully assemble input shaft to mainshaft assembly.

Fig. 7: Assembling Shift Forks on Shifter Shaft

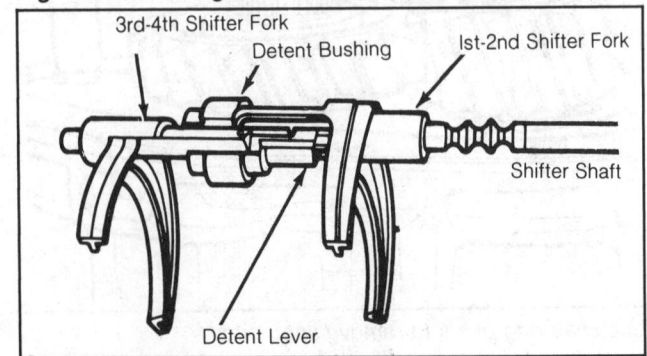

3rd-4th Shifter Fork

Detent Bushing

1st-2nd Shifter Fork

Shifter Shaft

Detent Lever

GENERAL MOTORS 4-SPEED — 70 MM (Cont.)

Fig. 8: Exploded View of General Motors 70 mm 4-Speed Transmission Assembly

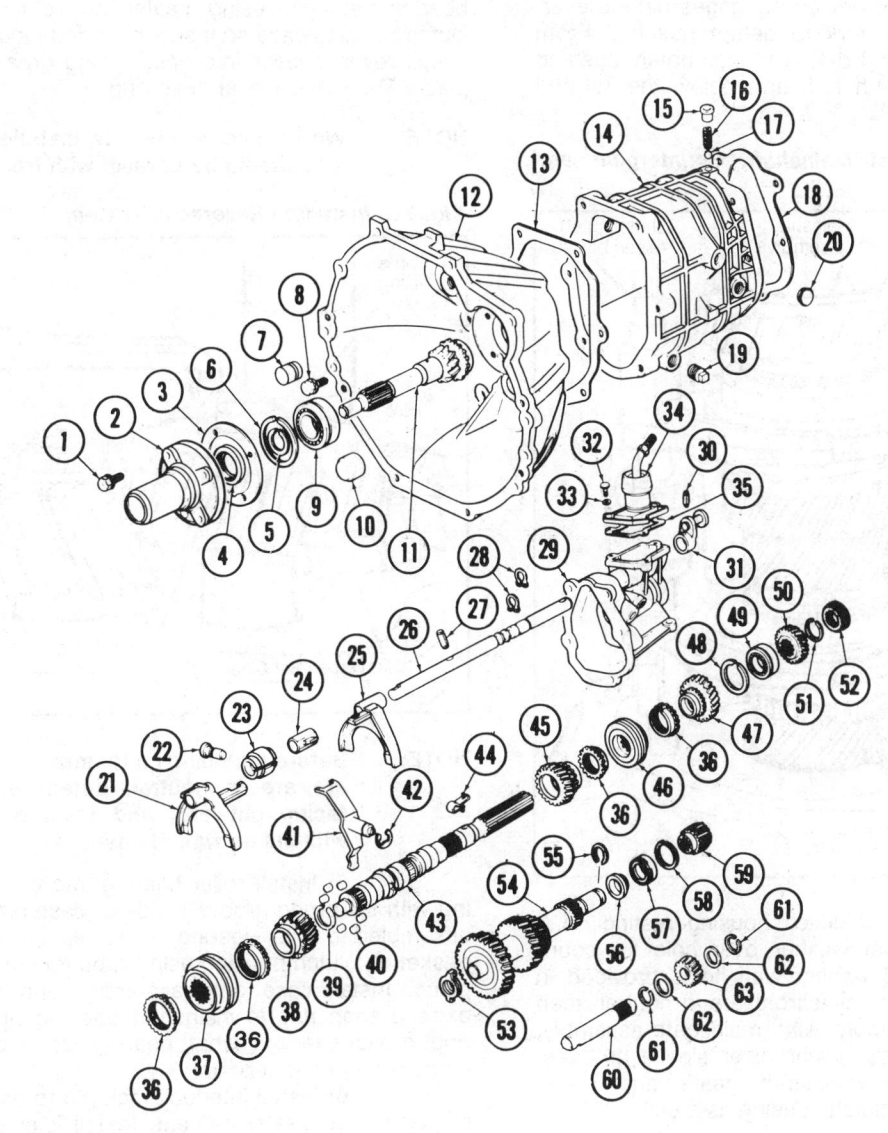

1. Bearing Retainer Bolt	22. Interlock Lock Pin	43. Mainshaft
2. Bearing Retainer	23. Detent Bushing	44. Speedometer Gear Retainer
3. Retainer Gasket	24. Detent Lever	45. Second Speed Gear
4. Retainer Seal	25. Ist-2nd Shift Fork	46. Ist-2nd Synchro Assembly
5. Snap Ring	26. Shifter Shaft	47. First Speed Gear
6. Bearing Outer Snap Ring	27. Detent Lever Pin	48. Bearing Outer Snap Ring
7. Shifter Shaft Stop Plug	28. Shifter Shaft Snap Rings	49. Rear Bearing
8. Clutch Housing-to-Case Bolt	29. Extension Housing	50. Reverse Gear
9. Input Shaft Bearing	30. Shifter Shaft Arm Roll Pin	51. Reverse Gear Snap Ring
10. Countergear Front Needle Bearings	31. Shifter Shaft Arm	52. Speedometer Gear
11. Input Shaft	32. Shift Lever-to-Extension Bolt	53. Countergear Thrust Washer
12. Clutch Housing	33. Washer	54. Countergear
13. Housing-to-Case Gasket	34. Shift Lever Assembly	55. Snap Ring
14. Case	35. Shift Lever Gasket	56. Inner Bearing Race
15. Shifter Shaft Detent Cap	36. Blocker Rings	57. Countergear Bearing
16. Shifter Shaft Detent Spring	37. 3rd-4th Synchro Assembly	58. Bearing Outer Snap Ring
17. Shifter Shaft Detent Ball	38. Third Speed Gear	59. Countergear Reverse Gear
18. Case-to-Extension Gasket	39. Synchro Hub-to-Shaft Snap Ring	60. Idler Gear Shaft
19. Magnet Plug	40. Input Shaft Roller Bearings	61. Idler Gear Thrust Washer
20. Reverse Lever Cap	41. Reverse Lever Assy.	62. Snap Ring
21. 3rd-4th Shift Fork	42. Reverse Lever Snap Ring	63. Reverse Idler Gear

Manual Transmissions

GENERAL MOTORS 4-SPEED — 70 MM (Cont.)

2) Install detent lever to shifter shaft and retain with roll pin. From rear of shifter shaft, slide 1st-2nd shifter fork onto shaft so fork arm engages detent lever. Assemble 3rd-4th shifter fork to detent bushing. From front of shifter shaft, slide 3rd-4th fork and detent bushing onto shaft, locating 3rd-4th fork arm below the 1st-2nd fork arm.

Fig. 9: Installed View of Mainshaft, Countergear and Shifter Shaft

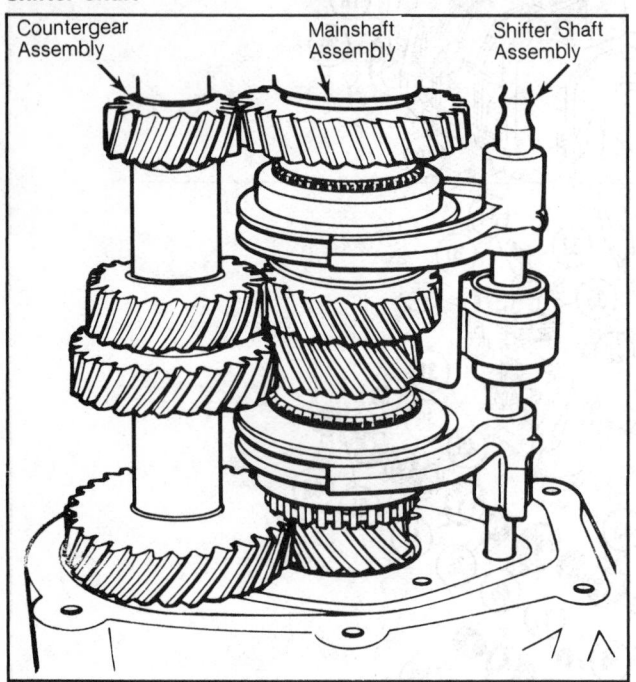

3) With front of clutch housing resting on 2 wood blocks, place thrust washer over hole for countergear, indexing tabs of washer with holes provided in clutch housing. Place both synchronizers in neutral, then mate shifter shaft assembly with mainshaft assembly, indexing shifter forks into synchronizer sleeve grooves. Mesh countergear with mainshaft gears and install complete assembly onto clutch housing as a unit.

Fig. 10: View of Installed Reverse Lever

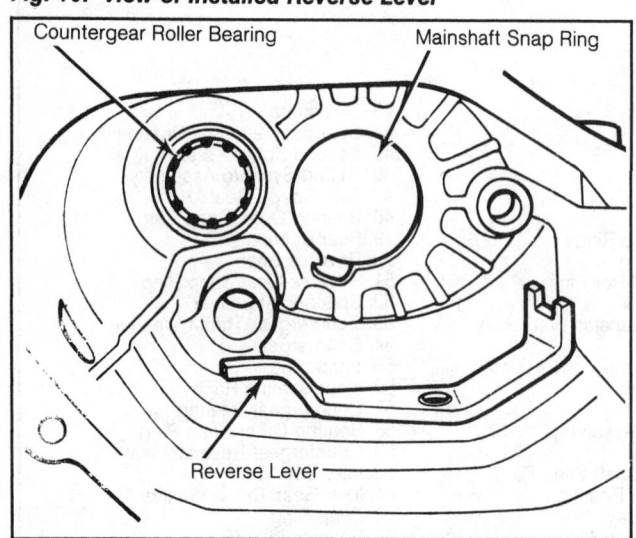

4) Place clutch housing on its side and install snap ring to ball bearing on input shaft. Install gasket and bearing retainer, using sealer on retainer bolts. Turn clutch housing case so it sets on wood blocks. If removed, install reverse lever into case, using grease to hold it in place. Then install lever snap ring.

NOTE: When reverse lever is installed, screwdriver slot should be parallel with front of case.

Fig. 11: Installing Reverse Idler Gear

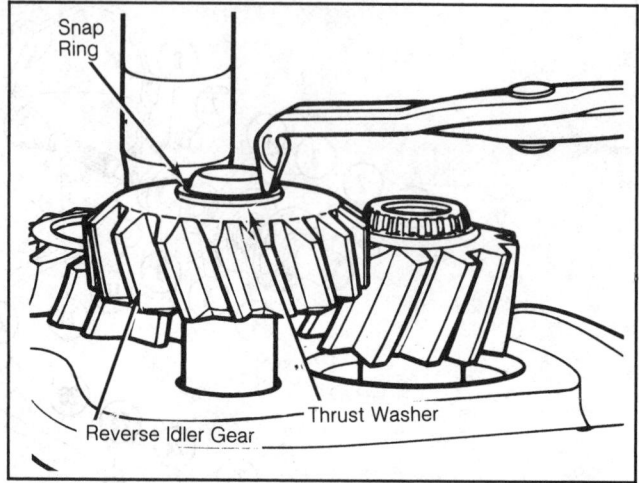

NOTE: Before installing case, make sure synchronizers are in neutral, detent bushing slot is facing outward, and reverse lever is flush with inside wall of case.

5) Install roller bearing into countergear opening with snap ring groove inside of case (snap ring will be assembled to roller bearing). Install case-to-clutch housing gasket on clutch housing using rubber cement to hold it in place. Install case onto assembly, and at same time, expand snap ring in mainshaft opening of case to allow ring to pilot over mainshaft bearing. Use a plastic hammer if necessary to seat parts.

6) Install interlock lock pin to hold shifter shaft in place. Use sealer cement. Install idler shaft so it will

Fig. 12: Installing Shifter Shaft Snap Rings

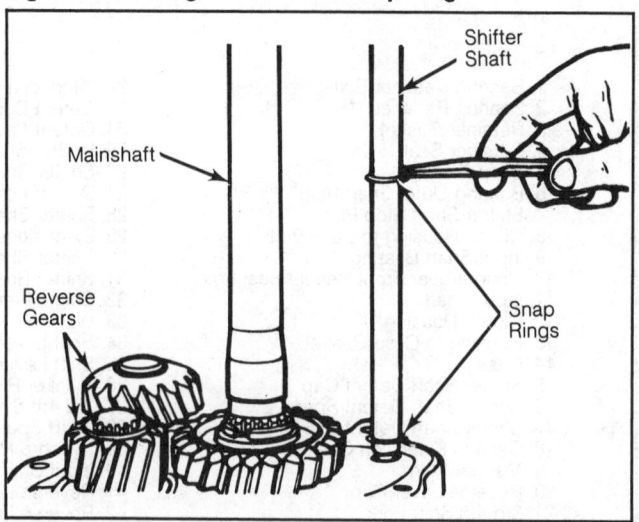

GENERAL MOTORS 4-SPEED — 70 MM (Cont.)

engage with reverse lever inside of case. Install cover over reverse shifter shaft to hold the reverse lever in place. Install the detent ball, spring and cap into case.

7) Position reverse gear over end of mainshaft with chamfer on gear teeth upward, push onto splines of mainshaft, and secure with snap ring. Install the smaller reverse gear onto countershaft with shoulder resting against countergear bearing, then secure snap ring. If removed, install snap ring, thrust washer, and reverse idler gear (chamfer of gear teeth downward) onto idler shaft. Secure parts with thrust washer and snap ring.

8) Install snap rings on shifter shafts. Be sure they are tight in grooves. Position speedometer gear retainer in mainshaft hole. With retainer loop facing forward, slide speedometer gear over mainshaft and into position. Heat gear to 175°F (80°C) with heat lamp or oven prior to installation.

NOTE: Pilot bolts are partially threaded and are installed in upper right corner and lower left corner of case. If pilot bolts are installed in wrong holes, splitting of case may occur.

9) Position extension housing and gasket on case and install 2 pilot bolts. *See Fig. 13.* Install other 3 remaining bolts.

10) Install shifter shaft arm over shifter shaft, and move to a position aligned with drilled hole near end of shaft. Drive roll pin into shifter shaft arm and shaft to retain parts. *See Fig. 14.* Place transmission on its side. Install 2 pilot bolts before installing other 4 attaching bolts to clutch housing and case. *See Fig. 15.*

NOTE: Pilot bolts are partially threaded and are installed in upper right and lower left holes in clutch housing.

Fig. 13: Extension Housing Pilot Bolt Locations

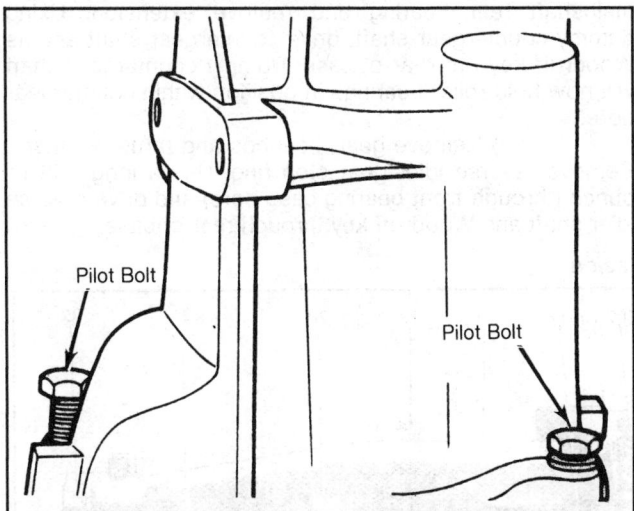

Pilot bolts are located
in top right and bottom left corner.

Fig. 14: Installing Shifter Shaft Arm and Roll Pin

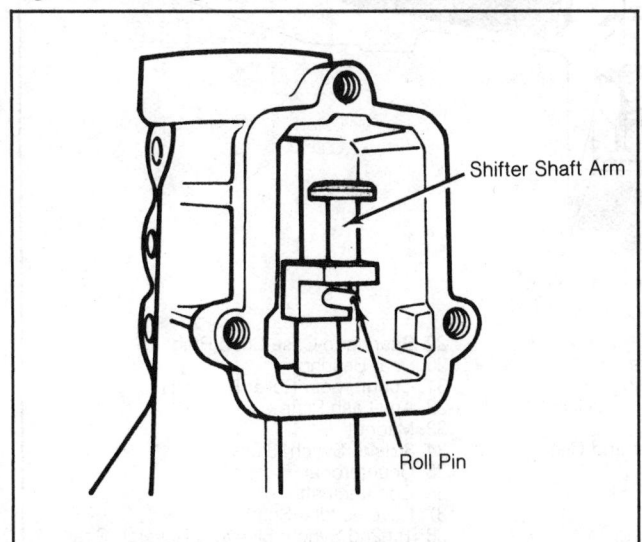

Fig. 15: Location of Pilot Bolts in Clutch Housing

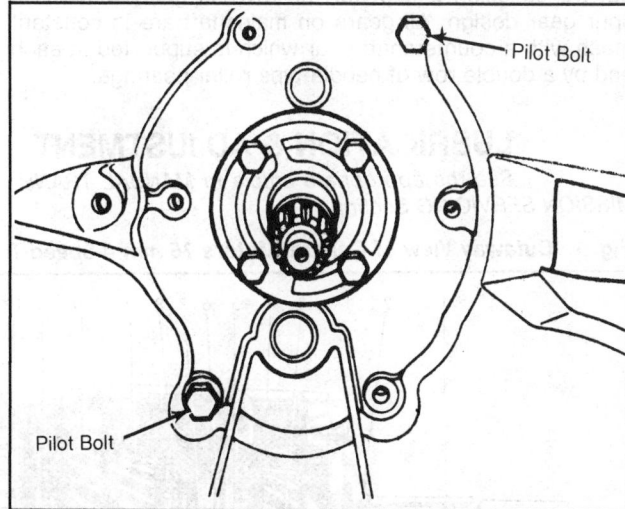

Pilot bolts are located
in top right and bottom left corner.

TIGHTENING SPECIFICATIONS

Application	Ft. Lbs. (N.m.)
Clutch Housing-to-Engine	25 (34)
Clutch Cover-to-Flywheel	18 (24)
Crossmember-to-Transmission	
Center Nut	33 (45)
End Nut	21 (28)
Crossmember-to-Frame	40 (54)
Extension Housing-to-Case	26 (35)
Clutch Housing-to-Case	26 (35)
Rear Support-to-Transmission	32 (43)
Clutch Fork Ball Stud Lock Nut	24 (33)
Back-up Lamp Switch	25 (34)
	INCH Lbs. (N.m.)
Shift Lever Retaining Bolts	35 (4)

Manual Transmissions

GENERAL MOTORS 4-SPEED — 76 MM

Camaro, Firebird

TRANSMISSION IDENTIFICATION

Transmission model may be identified by 2 letters, approximately one inch high, painted on right side of transmission case. To further identify transmission, a derivative of the Vehicle Identification Number is stamped on a machined pad located on upper right side of case. The 76 mm transmission may be identified by the case cover, which contains 3 shifter levers.

DESCRIPTION

Transmission is a 4-speed unit, synchronized in all forward gears through use of two synchronizer clutch assemblies. Helical gears are incorporated throughout transmission except for the reverse gear, which is a spur gear design. All gears on mainshaft are in constant mesh with a countershaft gear which is supported at each end by a double row of needle-type roller bearings.

LUBRICATION & ADJUSTMENT

See the appropriate article in MANUAL TRANS-MISSION SERVICING Section.

REMOVAL & INSTALLATION

See the appropriate article in MANUAL TRANS-MISSION REMOVAL Section.

TRANSMISSION DISASSEMBLY

1) Place transmission shifter levers in neutral position and remove side cover assembly. Remove front bearing retainer and gasket. Remove front bearing-to-shaft snap ring, then remove bearing by pulling outward on drive gear until a screwdriver can be inserted between case and large snap ring on bearing. Bearing is a slip fit in case and on shaft.

2) Remove extension housing-to-case bolts, then withdraw drive gear, mainshaft and extension housing as an assembly through rear case opening. Remove drive gear and bearings from mainshaft.

3) Expand snap ring in extension which retains mainshaft rear bearing and remove extension. Using dummy countergear shaft, drive countergear shaft and its Woodruff key out rear of case. Dummy countergear shaft will now hold roller bearings in position within countergear bore.

4) Remove gear, bearings and thrust washers. Remove reverse idler gear stop ring. Use a long drift or punch (through front bearing case bore) and drive reverse idler shaft and Woodruff key through rear of case.

Fig. 1: Cutaway View of General Motors 76 mm 4-Speed Transmission

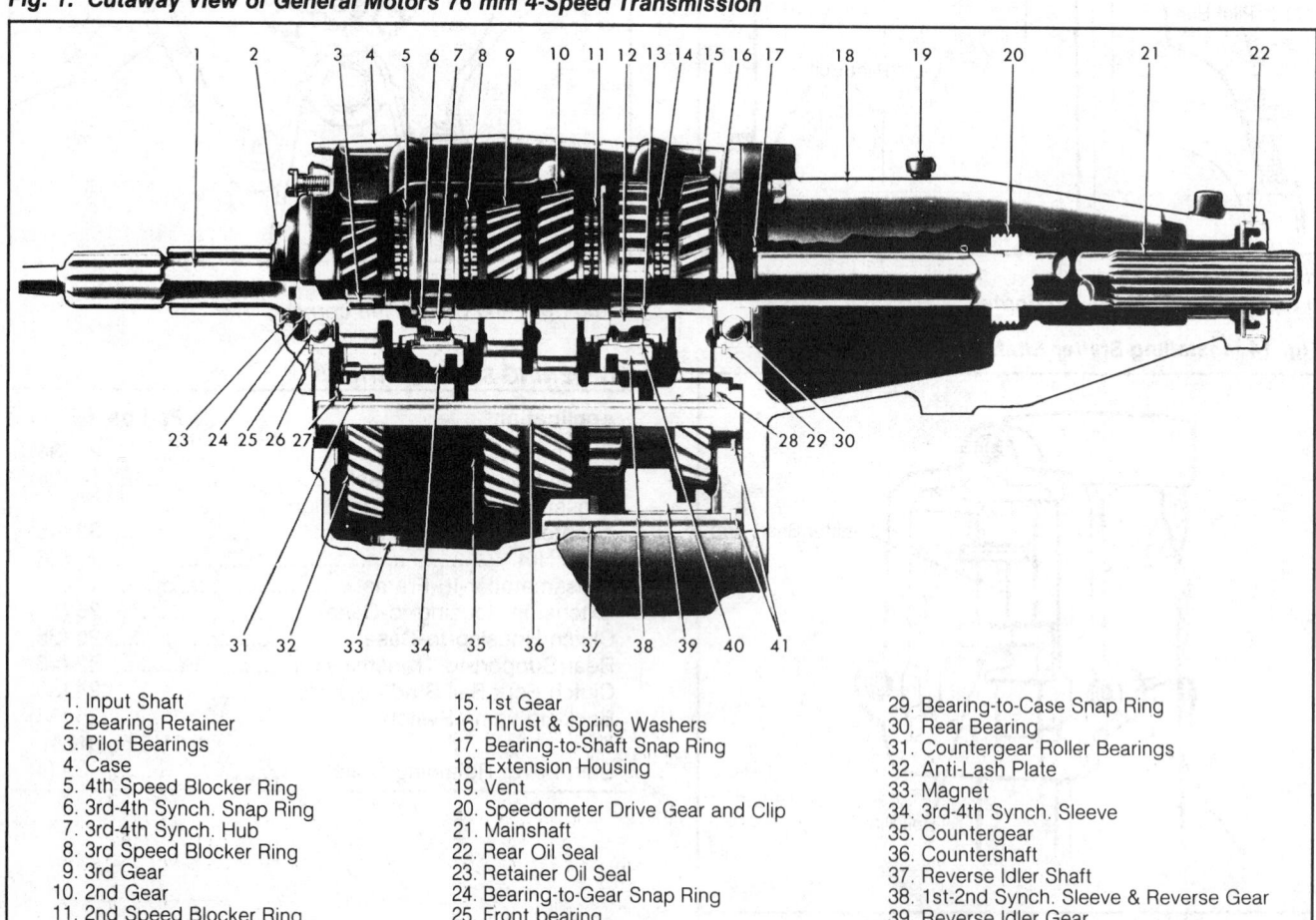

1. Input Shaft	15. 1st Gear	29. Bearing-to-Case Snap Ring
2. Bearing Retainer	16. Thrust & Spring Washers	30. Rear Bearing
3. Pilot Bearings	17. Bearing-to-Shaft Snap Ring	31. Countergear Roller Bearings
4. Case	18. Extension Housing	32. Anti-Lash Plate
5. 4th Speed Blocker Ring	19. Vent	33. Magnet
6. 3rd-4th Synch. Snap Ring	20. Speedometer Drive Gear and Clip	34. 3rd-4th Synch. Sleeve
7. 3rd-4th Synch. Hub	21. Mainshaft	35. Countergear
8. 3rd Speed Blocker Ring	22. Rear Oil Seal	36. Countershaft
9. 3rd Gear	23. Retainer Oil Seal	37. Reverse Idler Shaft
10. 2nd Gear	24. Bearing-to-Gear Snap Ring	38. 1st-2nd Synch. Sleeve & Reverse Gear
11. 2nd Speed Blocker Ring	25. Front bearing	39. Reverse Idler Gear
12. 1st-2nd Synch. Hub	26. Bearing-to-Gear Snap Ring	40. Synchro. Clutch Key
13. 1st-2nd Synch. Snap Ring	27. Front Thrust Washer	41. Woodruff Key
14. 1st Speed Blocker Ring	28. Rear Thrust Washer	

GENERAL MOTORS 4-SPEED — 76 MM (Cont.)

INSPECTION

1) Wash all parts in cleaning solvent and dry with air. Inspect transmission case for cracks, damaged bearing bores, or damaged threads. Remove all small nicks or burrs from front or rear face of case. Check ball bearings for roughness by slowly turning race by hand.

2) Inspect bearing rollers, shafts and washers for wear or damage. Inspect bushing(s) in reverse idler gear. If worn or damaged, replace gear (bushing(s) not serviced separately). Check all other parts for wear, chipped or broken teeth and other damage. Replace parts as necessary.

COMPONENT DISASSEMBLY & REASSEMBLY

MAINSHAFT ASSEMBLY
Disassembly

1) Remove 3rd-4th synchronizer hub snap ring from mainshaft and remove synchronizer assembly, blocking ring and 3rd gear from mainshaft. Depress speedometer drive gear retaining clip and slide gear from shaft.

2) Remove rear bearing snap ring from mainshaft groove, then support 1st gear on press plates and press on rear of mainshaft to remove 1st gear, thrust washer, spring washer, and rear bearing.

3) Remove 1st-2nd synchronizer hub snap ring from mainshaft and remove synchronizer assembly, blocking ring, and 2nd gear.

Reassembly

1) With front end of mainshaft upward, install the 3rd speed gear (clutch teeth upward) and butt rear face of gear on flange of mainshaft. Install a blocking ring (clutch teeth downward) over synchronizing surface of 3rd gear.

2) Install the 3rd-4th synchronizer assembly on mainshaft with fork slot downward; push assembly onto splines until it bottoms on flange. Install synchronizer hub-to-mainshaft snap ring.

NOTE: All 4 blocker rings are identical. Make sure that notches on blocker ring align with keys on synchronizer assembly.

3) On rear end of mainshaft, install the second speed gear with clutching teeth upward (front face of gear will butt against flange on mainshaft). Install a blocker ring with clutching teeth downward over synchronizing surface of second speed gear.

4) Install the 1st-2nd synchronizer assembly with fork slot downward. Install synchronizer hub to mainshaft snap ring. Install a blocker ring with notches downward so they align with keys of 1st-2nd synchronizer assembly.

5) Install first gear with clutching teeth downward. Install first gear thrust washer (steel). Install ring slot downward. Press onto mainshaft. Install rear bearing-to-mainshaft snap ring. Install retaining clip and speedometer drive gear.

SYNCHRONIZER CLUTCH ASSEMBLIES
Disassembly

Mark hub and sleeve so they can be matched during reassembly. Push hub from sliding sleeve, then remove keys and springs.

NOTE: Clutch hubs and sleeves are a select fit assembly, and as such, should not be interchanged. The 2 keys and 3 springs may be replaced, however, if worn or broken.

Reassembly

Place the 3 keys and 2 springs in position on the hub, making sure that all 3 keys are engaged by both springs. The tanged end of each spring should be installed into different keys on either side of hub. Using alignment marks made at disassembly, reinstall hub onto sleeve.

NOTE: A groove around outside of synchronizer hub identifies end that must be opposite fork slot in sleeve when assembled on 3rd-4th synchronizer. On 1st-2nd synchronizer the synchronizer groove is on the same end as fork slot. This groove indicates end of hub with greater recess depth.

Fig. 2: Exploded View of Drive Gear and Mainshaft Assembly

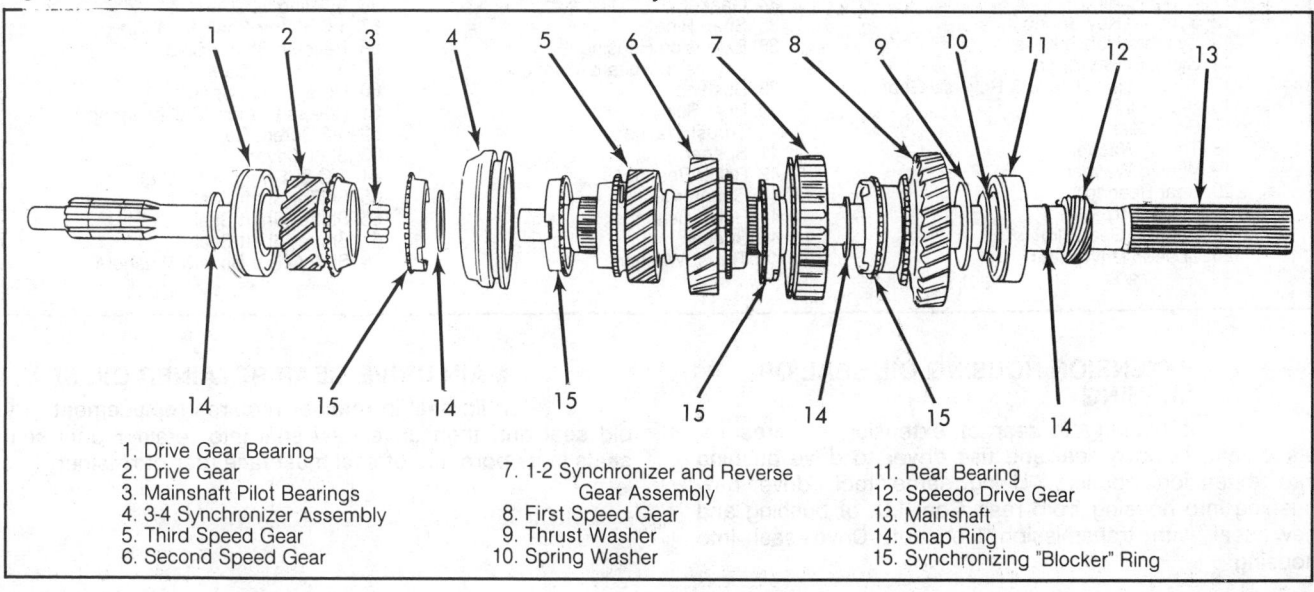

1. Drive Gear Bearing
2. Drive Gear
3. Mainshaft Pilot Bearings
4. 3-4 Synchronizer Assembly
5. Third Speed Gear
6. Second Speed Gear
7. 1-2 Synchronizer and Reverse Gear Assembly
8. First Speed Gear
9. Thrust Washer
10. Spring Washer
11. Rear Bearing
12. Speedo Drive Gear
13. Mainshaft
14. Snap Ring
15. Synchronizing "Blocker" Ring

Fig. 3: *Exploded View of General Motors 76 mm 4-Speed Transmission*

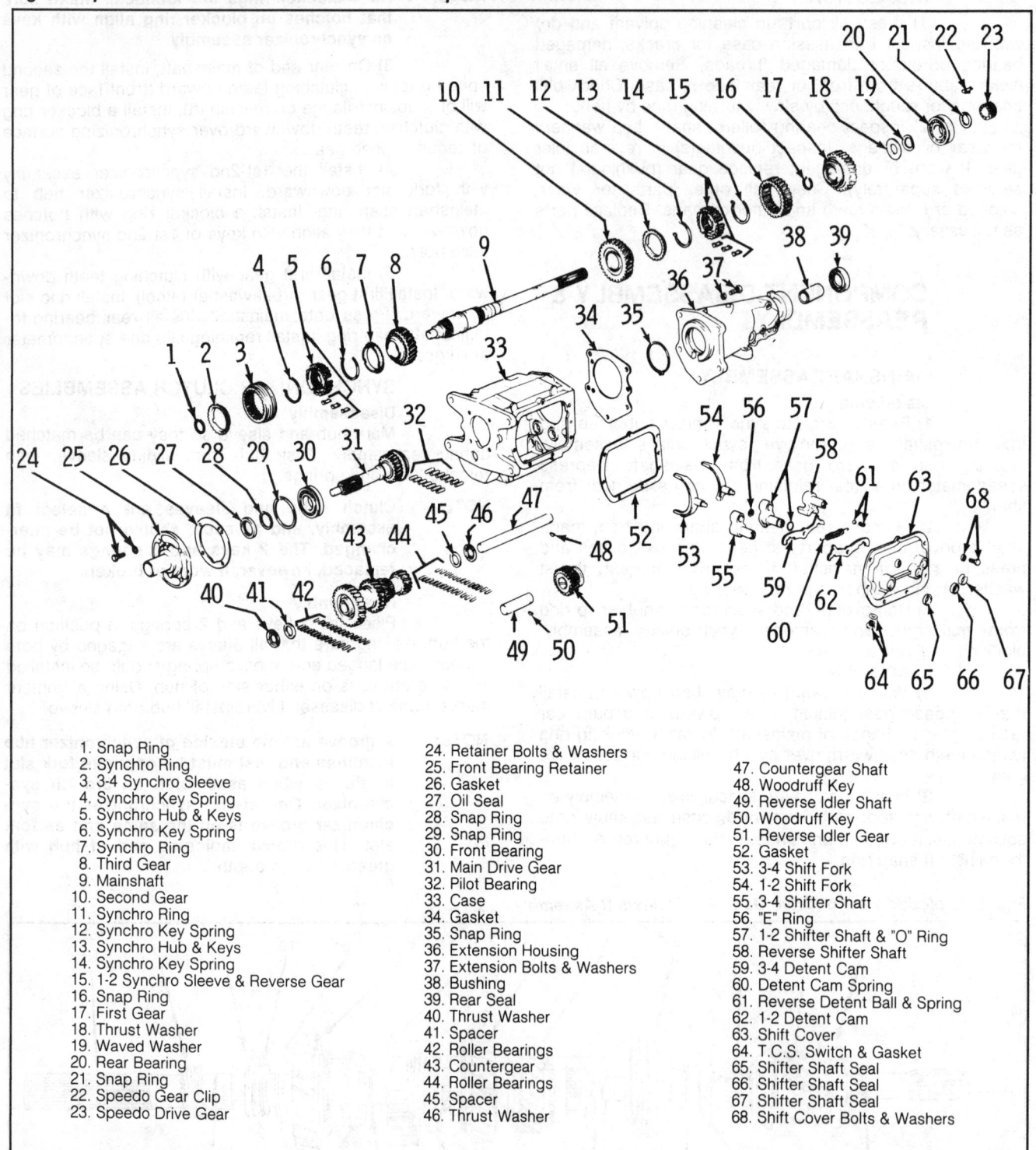

1. Snap Ring	24. Retainer Bolts & Washers	47. Countergear Shaft
2. Synchro Ring	25. Front Bearing Retainer	48. Woodruff Key
3. 3-4 Synchro Sleeve	26. Gasket	49. Reverse Idler Shaft
4. Synchro Key Spring	27. Oil Seal	50. Woodruff Key
5. Synchro Hub & Keys	28. Snap Ring	51. Reverse Idler Gear
6. Synchro Key Spring	29. Snap Ring	52. Gasket
7. Synchro Ring	30. Front Bearing	53. 3-4 Shift Fork
8. Third Gear	31. Main Drive Gear	54. 1-2 Shift Fork
9. Mainshaft	32. Pilot Bearing	55. 3-4 Shifter Shaft
10. Second Gear	33. Case	56. "E" Ring
11. Synchro Ring	34. Gasket	57. 1-2 Shifter Shaft & "O" Ring
12. Synchro Key Spring	35. Snap Ring	58. Reverse Shifter Shaft
13. Synchro Hub & Keys	36. Extension Housing	59. 3-4 Detent Cam
14. Synchro Key Spring	37. Extension Bolts & Washers	60. Detent Cam Spring
15. 1-2 Synchro Sleeve & Reverse Gear	38. Bushing	61. Reverse Detent Ball & Spring
16. Snap Ring	39. Rear Seal	62. 1-2 Detent Cam
17. First Gear	40. Thrust Washer	63. Shift Cover
18. Thrust Washer	41. Spacer	64. T.C.S. Switch & Gasket
19. Waved Washer	42. Roller Bearings	65. Shifter Shaft Seal
20. Rear Bearing	43. Countergear	66. Shifter Shaft Seal
21. Snap Ring	44. Roller Bearings	67. Shifter Shaft Seal
22. Speedo Gear Clip	45. Spacer	68. Shift Cover Bolts & Washers
23. Speedo Drive Gear	46. Thrust Washer	

EXTENSION HOUSING OIL SEAL OR BUSHING

If bushing in rear of extension requires replacement, remove seal and use driver to drive bushing into extension housing. Using same tool, drive new bushing into housing from rear. Coat I.D. of bushing and new seal with transmission lubricant. Drive seal into housing.

MAIN DRIVE GEAR RETAINER OIL SEAL

If lip seal in retainer requires replacement, pry old seal out, then drive new seal into retainer until seal seats in its bore. Lip of seal must face rear of retainer.

GENERAL MOTORS 4-SPEED — 76 MM (Cont.)

Fig. 4: Countergear Bearing Installation

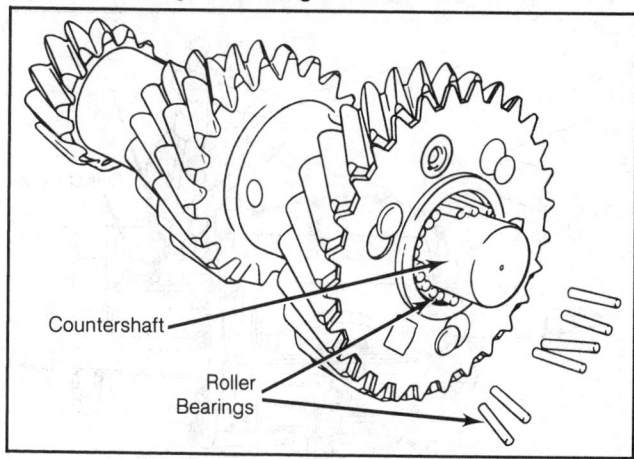

TRANSMISSION CASE COVER

Removal

Place transmission shift lever in neutral position. Raise vehicle on hoist. Remove shift levers from shifter shafts. Remove cover assembly and allow lubricant to drain.

Disassembly

1) Remove shift levers. Remove both shift forks from shifter shaft assemblies. Remove shifter shaft assemblies. Remove reverse shifter shaft. Pry out lip seal from cover and "O" ring seal on 1st-2nd and reverse shafts.

2) Remove detent ball and detent spring. Remove detent cam spring and pivot retainer "C" ring. Mark to identify for reassembly, then remove both detent cams. Inspect and replace damaged parts. Inspect shifter shaft seals and replace, if necessary.

Fig. 5: Assembled View of Transmission Side Cover

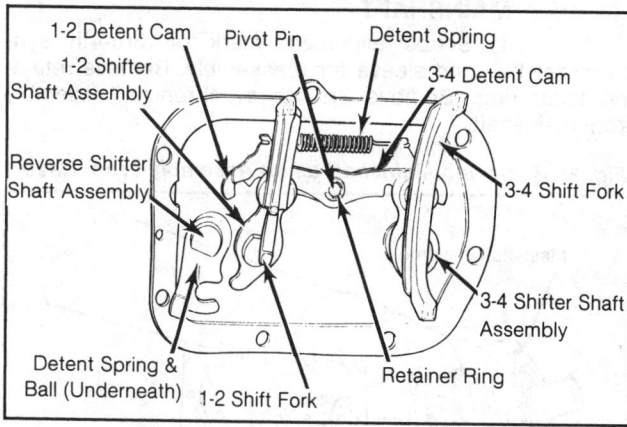

Reassembly

1) With detent spring tang projecting up over 3rd-4th shifter shaft cover opening, install the 1st-2nd detent cam onto detent cam pivot pin.

CAUTION: Take care not to damage seals when installing shifter shafts.

2) With detent spring tang projecting up over the 1st-2nd shifter shaft cover hole, install the 3rd-4th detent cam. Install detent cam retaining "C" ring to pivot pin, and hook spring into detent cam notches.

3) Install 1st-2nd and 3rd-4th shifter shaft assemblies into cover. Install both shift forks to shifter shaft assemblies, lifting up on detent cam to allow forks to fully seat into position.

4) Install reverse detent ball and spring to cover, then install reverse shifter shaft assembly to cover. If equipped, install T.C.S. switch.

Installation

To install, reverse removal procedure.

TRANSMISSION REASSEMBLY

1) Install a dummy countergear shaft into countergear. Install 27 roller bearings and a bearing thrust washer at each end of countergear. Use grease to retain parts.

2) Place countergear assembly through rear opening along with a tanged thrust washer (tang away from gear) at each end. Install countergear shaft and Woodruff key through rear of case, pushing dummy countergear shaft out through front of case. Install reverse idle gear, shaft and Woodruff key from rear of case.

NOTE: **Be sure countergear shaft engages both thrust washers and that thrust washers are aligned with notches in case.**

3) Expand snap ring in extension housing and assemble housing over rear of mainshaft and onto rear bearing. Seat snap ring in rear bearing groove. Install 14 roller bearings in main drive gear (retain with heavy grease).

4) Install fourth speed blocker ring onto drive gear clutching surface with its clutching teeth toward gear. Pilot the drive gear, pilot bearings and fourth speed blocker ring assembly over front of mainshaft assembly. Do not assemble bearing to gear at this time.

CAUTION: Be sure notches in blocker ring align with keys in the 3rd-4th synchronizer assembly.

5) Install extension-to-case gasket at rear of case (retain with grease). From rear of case, assemble clutch gear, mainshaft and extension to case as an assembly, then install extension to case bolts, using seal cement on bottom bolt only.

6) Install front bearing outer snap ring to bearing and install bearing over stem of drive gear and into front case bore. Install snap ring to drive gear stem. Install drive bearing retainer and gasket to case.

CAUTION: Retainer oil return hole should be at bottom.

7) Shift synchronizer sleeves to neutral positions and install cover, gasket and fork assembly to case. Be sure forks align with their synchronizer sleeve grooves. Tighten all bolts to specifications. Rotate drive gear and shift transmission to check free rotation of all gears.

TIGHTENING SPECIFICATIONS

Application	Ft. Lbs. (N.m)
Front Bearing Retainer-to-Case	15 (20)
Side Cover-to-Case	15 (20)
Extension Housing-to-Case	45 (60)
Transmission-to-Clutch Housing	55 (75)

Manual Transmissions

GENERAL MOTORS 4-SPEED — 77 MM

Chevrolet & GMC; "S" Series

IDENTIFICATION

Transmission can be identified by a 2 letter code, stamped on a machined pad, on right side of case. Clutch housing and gearbox are 2 separate pieces.

DESCRIPTION

The 4-speed 77 mm transmission is a fully synchronized unit with blocker ring synchronizers and a sliding mesh reverse gear. It has an aluminum transmission case that houses the various gears and bearings and an extension housing. The gearshift lever assembly is floor mounted and is located on top of the extension housing. The shift mechanism does not require adjustment and can be serviced independently of the transmission.

LUBRICATION & INSTALLATION

See the appropriate article in MANUAL TRANSMISSION SERVICING Section.

REMOVAL & INSTALLATION

SHIFT LEVER

Removal

Remove screws from transmission shift lever boot retainer. Slide boot up lever. Remove shift lever retaining bolts at transmission and remove lever.

Installation

To install, reverse removal procedures.

TRANSMISSION

See the appropriate article in MANUAL TRANSMISSION REMOVAL Section.

DISASSEMBLY

TRANSMISSION

1) Remove drain plug and drain lubricant from transmission. Thoroughly clean exterior of transmission assembly. Using a hammer and punch, remove roll pin that attaches offset lever to shift rail. See Fig. 1.

2) Remove extension housing retaining bolts. Separate extension housing from transmission case. Remove housing and offset lever as an assembly.

3) Remove detent ball and spring from offset lever. Remove roll pin from extension housing or offset lever. Remove shift cover retaining bolts. Using a screwdriver, pry shift cover loose. Remove cover from case.

4) Remove clip that retains reverse lever to pivot bolt. Remove pivot bolt. Remove reverse lever and fork as an assembly.

5) Using a hammer and punch, mark position of front bearing cap to transmission case. Remove front bearing cap bolts and remove bearing cap.

6) Remove small retaining and large locating snap rings from front drive gear bearing. Install bearing

Fig. 1: Removing Roll Pin From Offset Lever

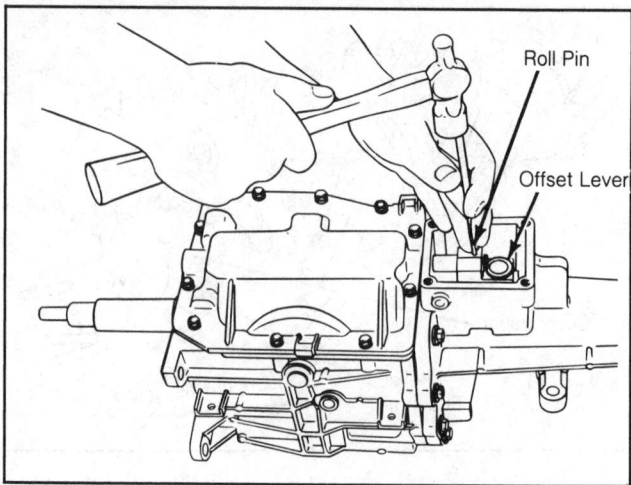

Use correct size punch and tap lightly with hammer.

puller (J-22912-01) on front bearing, and puller (J-8433-1) with 2 bolts on end of drive gear. Remove and discard bearing.

7) Remove retaining and locating snap rings from rear bearing and mainshaft. Install puller on bearing. Remove bearing from mainshaft and discard bearing.

8) Remove drive gear from mainshaft and transmission case. Remove mainshaft from transmission case by tipping mainshaft down at rear and lifting shaft out through shift cover opening.

9) Using a hammer and punch, remove roll pin retaining reverse idler gear shaft in transmission case. Remove idler gear and shaft from case. Remove countershaft from rear of case using loading tool (J-26624).

10) Remove countershaft gear and loading tool as an assembly from case along with thrust washers.

MAINSHAFT

1) Scribe alignment mark on 3rd-4th synchronizer hub and sleeve for reassembly. Remove retaining snap ring. Remove 3rd-4th synchronizer assembly from mainshaft.

Fig. 2: Removing Mainshaft as an Assembly From Case

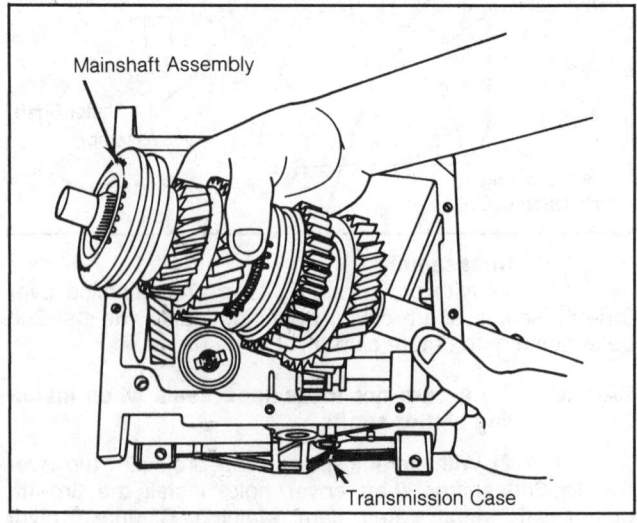

Be careful not to nick gear teeth when removing.

GENERAL MOTORS 4-SPEED — 77 MM (Cont.)

Fig. 3: Exploded View of 77 MM 4-Speed Transmission

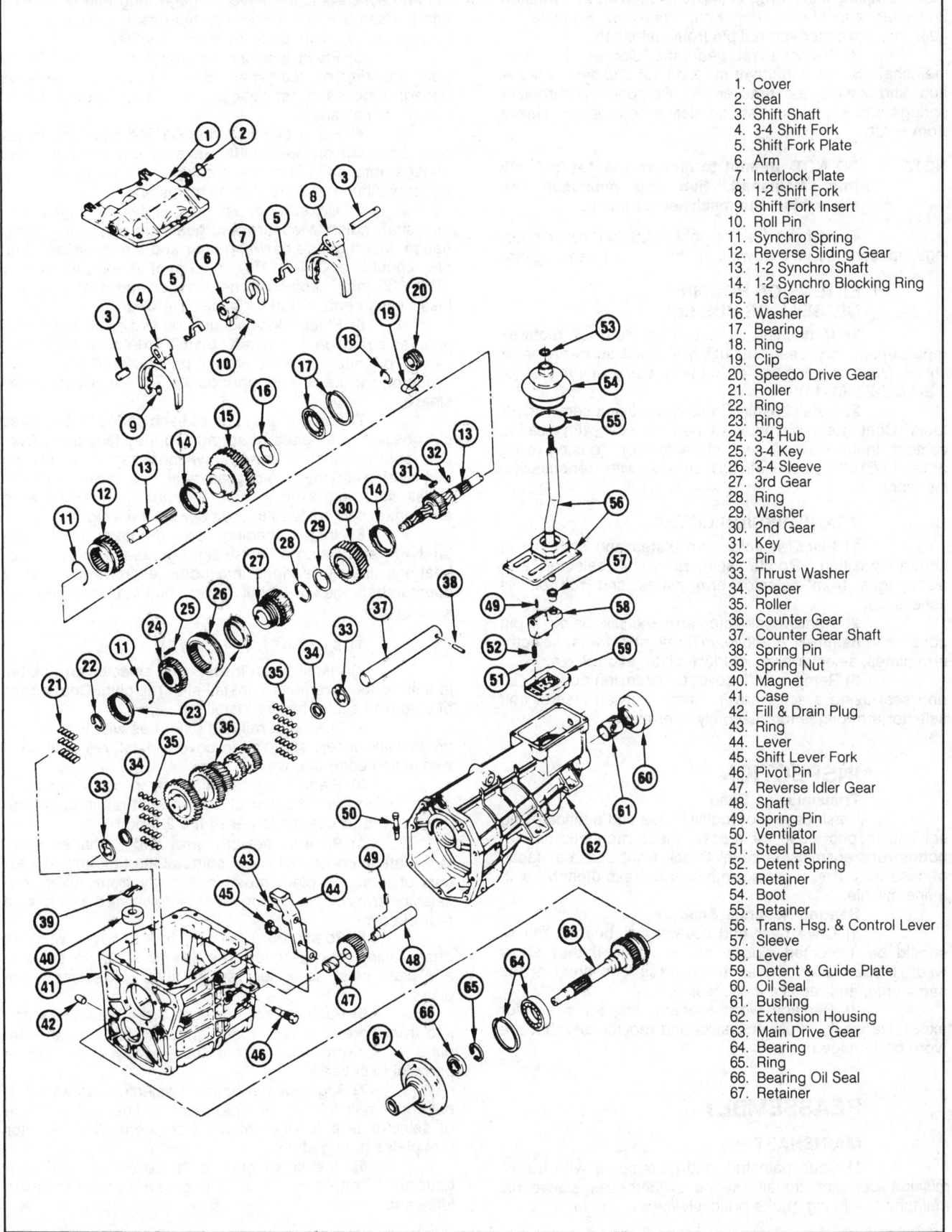

1. Cover
2. Seal
3. Shift Shaft
4. 3-4 Shift Fork
5. Shift Fork Plate
6. Arm
7. Interlock Plate
8. 1-2 Shift Fork
9. Shift Fork Insert
10. Roll Pin
11. Synchro Spring
12. Reverse Sliding Gear
13. 1-2 Synchro Shaft
14. 1-2 Synchro Blocking Ring
15. 1st Gear
16. Washer
17. Bearing
18. Ring
19. Clip
20. Speedo Drive Gear
21. Roller
22. Ring
23. Ring
24. 3-4 Hub
25. 3-4 Key
26. 3-4 Sleeve
27. 3rd Gear
28. Ring
29. Washer
30. 2nd Gear
31. Key
32. Pin
33. Thrust Washer
34. Spacer
35. Roller
36. Counter Gear
37. Counter Gear Shaft
38. Spring Pin
39. Spring Nut
40. Magnet
41. Case
42. Fill & Drain Plug
43. Ring
44. Lever
45. Shift Lever Fork
46. Pivot Pin
47. Reverse Idler Gear
48. Shaft
49. Spring Pin
50. Ventilator
51. Steel Ball
52. Detent Spring
53. Retainer
54. Boot
55. Retainer
56. Trans. Hsg. & Control Lever
57. Sleeve
58. Lever
59. Detent & Guide Plate
60. Oil Seal
61. Bushing
62. Extension Housing
63. Main Drive Gear
64. Bearing
65. Ring
66. Bearing Oil Seal
67. Retainer

GENERAL MOTORS 4-SPEED — 77 MM (Cont.)

2) Slide 3rd gear off mainshaft. Remove 2nd gear retaining snap ring. Remove tabbed thrust washer, 2nd gear, and blocker ring from mainshaft. Remove 1st gear thrust washer and roll pin from mainshaft.

3) Remove 1st gear and blocker ring from mainshaft. Scribe alignment mark on 1st-2nd synchronizer hub and sleeve for reassembly. Remove synchronizer springs and keys from 1st-2nd sleeve and remove sleeve from shaft.

NOTE: **DO NOT attempt to remove the 1st-2nd hub from mainshaft. Hub and mainshaft are assembled and machined as a unit.**

4) Remove loading tool (J-26624), roller bearings, spacers, and thrust washers from countershaft gear.

EXTENSION HOUSING OIL SEAL OR BUSHING

1) If bushing in extension housing requires replacement, pry seal out, using a small screwdriver or chisel. Drive bushing out of housing, using driver tool (J-8092 & J-23062-14).

2) Install bushing in housing, using same driver tools. Coat outer diameter of new oil seal with sealing cement. Install new oil seal into extension housing using driver (J-21426). Lubricate I.D. of seal with transmission lubricant.

TRANSMISSION COVER

1) Place selector arm plates and shift rail in neutral position. Rotate shift rail until selector arm disengages from selector arm plates and roll pin is accessible.

2) Remove selector arm roll pin using a pin punch and hammer. Remove shift rail, shift forks, selector arm plates, selector arm, interlock plate, and roll pin.

3) Remove shift cover to extension housing "O" ring seal using a screwdriver. Remove nylon inserts and selector arm plates for assembly references.

INSPECTION

Transmission Case
Wash case thoroughly inside and outside using solvent. Inspect case for cracks. Clean magnetic disc at bottom of transmission case. Check front and rear faces of case for burrs. If burrs are present, dress them off with a fine mill file.

Bearing Rollers & Spacers
1) Drive gear and countergear bearing rollers should be inspected closely and replaced if they show wear. Inspect countergear and reverse idler shaft at the same time, and replace if necessary.

2) Replace worn spacers. Inspect gears for excessive wear, chips, or cracks and replace any that are worn or damaged.

REASSEMBLY

MAINSHAFT

1) Coat mainshaft and gear bores with transmission lubricant. Install 1st-2nd synchronizer sleeve on mainshaft, aligning marks preiously made.

2) Install synchronizer keys and springs into 1st-2nd synchronizer sleeve. Engage tang end of springs into the same synchronizer key but position open ends of springs so they face away from one another.

3) Place blocking ring on 1st gear and install gear and ring on mainshaft. Be sure synchronizer keys engage notches in 1st gear blocking ring. Install 1st gear roll pin in mainshaft.

4) Place blocking ring on 2nd gear and install gear and ring on mainshaft. Be sure snychronizer keys engage notches in 2nd gear blocking ring. Install 2nd gear thrust washer and snap ring on mainshaft.

5) Be sure thrust washer tab is engaged in mainshaft notch. Measure 2nd gear end play using feeler gauge. Insert gauge between gear and thrust washer. End play should be .004-.014" (.10-.35 mm). If end play is over .014" (.35 mm), replace thrust washer and snap ring and insert synchronizer hub for excessive wear.

6) Place blocking ring on 3rd gear and install gear and ring on mainshaft. Install 3rd-4th synchronizer sleeve on hub, aligning marks previously made. Install synchronizer keys and springs in 3rd-4th synchronizer sleeve.

7) Engage tang end of each spring in same key but position open ends of springs so they face away from one another. Install 3rd-4th synchronizer assembly on mainshaft with machined groove in hub facing forward. Install snap ring on mainshaft. Be sure synchronizer keys are engaged in notches in 3rd gear blocker ring.

8) Install loading tool (J-26624) into countershaft gear. Using a light weight grease, lubricate roller bearings. Install bearings into bores at front and rear of countershaft gear. Install roller bearing retainers on loading tool.

TRANSMISSION COVER

1) Install nylon inserts and selector arm plates in shift forks. If removed, install shift rail plug. Coat edges of plug with sealer before installing.

2) Coat shift rail and rail bores with light weight grease and insert shift rail in cover. Install rail until flush with inside edge of cover.

3) Place 1st-2nd shift fork in cover with fork offset facing rear of cover and push shift rail through fork (the 1st-2nd fork is the larger of the 2 forks).

4) Position selector arm and C-shaped interlock plate in cover and insert shift rail through arm. Widest part of interlock plate must face away from cover, and selector arm roll pin hole must face downward and toward rear of cover.

5) Position 3rd-4th shift fork in cover with fork offset facing rear of cover. The 3rd-4th shift fork selector arm plate must be under 1st-2nd shift fork selector arm plate.

6) Push shift rail through 3rd-4th shift fork and into front bore in cover. Rotate shift rail until selector arm plate at forward end of rail faces away from, but is parrallel to cover.

7) Align roll pin holes in selector arm and shift rail and install roll pin. Roll pin must be flush with surface of selector arm to prevent pin from contacting selector arm plates during shifts.

8) Install a new shift cover to extension housing "O" ring seal. Coat "O" ring seal with transmission lubricant.

GENERAL MOTORS 4-SPEED — 77 MM (Cont.)

TRANSMISSION

1) Coat countershaft gear thrust washers with grease and position washer in case. Position countershaft gear in case and install countershaft from rear of case.

2) Be sure that thrust washers stay in place during installation of countershaft and gear. Position reverse idler gear in case with shift lever groove facing rear of case and install reverse idler shaft from rear of case.

3) Install roll pin in shaft and center pin in shaft. Install mainshaft assembly into case. DO NOT disturb position of synchronizer assemblies during installation.

4) Install 4th gear blocking ring in 3rd-4th synchronizer sleeve. Be sure synchronizer keys engage in notches in blocker ring. Install drive gear into case and engage with mainshaft.

5) Position mainshaft 1st gear against rear of case. Using a new bearing, start front bearing onto drive gear. Align bearing with bearing bore in case and drive bearing onto drive gear and into case.

6) Install front bearing retaining and locating snap rings. Apply a 1/8" bead of RTV sealant on case mating surface of front bearing cap. Install bearing cap aligning marks previously made.

7) Apply non-hardening sealer on retaining bolts and install bolts. Tighten to specifications. Install 1st gear thrust washer with oil groove facing 1st gear on mainshaft, aligning slot in washer with 1st gear roll pin.

8) Using a new bearing, position rear bearing on mainshaft. Align bearing with bearing bore in case and drive bearing into case. Install locating and retaining snap rings on rear bearing.

9) Install speedometer gear and retaining clip on mainshaft. Apply non-hardening sealer to threads of reverse lever pivot bolt and start bolt into case. Engage reverse lever fork in reverse idler gear and reverse lever on pivot bolt. Tighten bolt to specifications and install retaining clip.

10) Rotate drive gear and mainshaft gears. If blocker rings tend to stick on gears, release rings by gently prying them off cones. Apply a 1/8" bead of RTV sealant, on transmission cover mating surface.

11) Place reverse lever in neutral, and position cover on case. Install 2 dowel type bolts first to align cover on case. Install remaining cover bolts and torque to specifications.

NOTE: The offset lever to shift rail roll pin hole must be in the vertical position after cover installation.

12) Apply a 1/8" bead of RTV sealant, on the extension housing to transmission case mating surface. Place extension housing over mainshaft to a position where shift rail is in shift cover opening.

13) Install detent spring in offset lever. Place ball in neutral guide plate detent position. Apply pressure on the offset lever, slide offset lever onto shift rail and seat extension housing to transmission case.

14) Install retaining bolts, align hole in offset lever and shift rail, and install roll pin. Fill transmission to its proper level with lubricant.

TIGHTENING SPECIFICATIONS

Application	Ft. Lbs. (N.m)
Transmission-to-Engine	55 (75)
Extension Housing-to-Case	25 (30)
Shift Cover-to-Case	10 (13)
Front Bearing Retainer-to-Case	15 (20)
Reverse Pivot Bolt-to-Case	20 (27)
Fill Plug-to-Case	20 (27)
Crossmember-to-Frame	25 (30)
Mount-to-Transmission	35 (50)
Mount-to-Crossmember	25 (30)

Manual Transmissions

GENERAL MOTORS (ISUZU) 77.5 MM 4-SPEED

Chevrolet & GMC "S" Trucks

IDENTIFICATION

Transmission identification tag showing model part number, is attached on driver's side to a transmission extension housing bolt. Transmission can also be identified by the measured distance (3.05", 77.5 mm) between centerlines of the mainshaft and the countergear.

DESCRIPTION

The 4-speed 77.5 mm transmission is a floor shifted, fully synchronized unit with blocker ring synchronizers and a sliding mesh type reverse gear. Unit consists of a case with integral clutch housing, center support and an extension housing that holds the various gears and bearings.

LUBRICATION & ADJUSTMENT

See the appropriate article in MANUAL TRANS-MISSION SERVICING Section.

TROUBLE SHOOTING

See Manual Transmission Trouble Shooting in MANUAL TRANSMISSION SERVICING section.

SERVICE (IN VEHICLE)

SHIFT CONTROL LEVER

Removal
Remove screws from transmission shift lever boot retainer. Slide boot up lever. Remove lever attaching bolts at transmission and remove lever.
Installation
To install shift control lever, reverse the removal procedure.

EXTENSION HOUSING OIL SEAL

Removal
Raise vehicle. Disconnect propeller shaft. Using a screwdriver, pry oil seal from extension housing.
Installation
Install new oil seal in extension housing using seal installer tool (J-33035). Connect propeller shaft. Check transmission fluid level and add fluid as necessary. Lower vehicle.

REMOVAL & INSTALLATION

See the appropriate article in MANUAL TRANS-MISSION REMOVAL Section.

TRANSMISSION DISASSEMBLY

1) Disconnect retaining springs from bearing side. Remove bearing, boot and clutch fork. Remove drain plug and drain lubricant from transmission. Remove bearing retainer bolts, retainer and gasket. Remove ball stud, if necessary.

2) Remove speedometer driven gear and back-up light switch. Remove 4 shift cover bolts, cover and gasket. Remove rear extension bolts, rear extension and gasket. Remove speedometer drive gear from mainshaft.

3) Using a punch, remove pin from reverse shift block while supporting end of shaft with bar or wood block. Remove reverse block retaining bolts. Remove reverse shifter shaft, shift block, shift fork and reverse gear as an assembly. See Fig. 1. Remove retaining rings from drive gear shaft bearing outer race and countershaft front bearing outer race.

Fig. 1: Removing Reverse Shifter Assembly

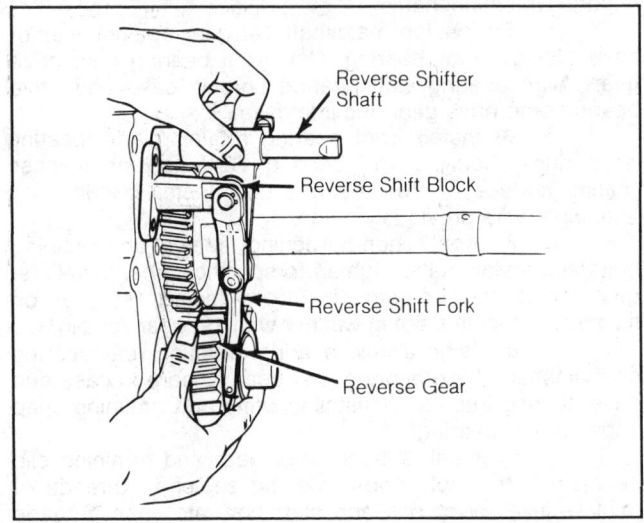

Remove shifter shaft, block, fork and gear as an assembly.

4) Remove support assembly from transmission case. Drive pins from 1st-2nd and 3rd-4th shift forks using a punch. See Fig. 2. Support ends of shafts during removal. Loosen retaining bolts and remove plate, gasket and springs.

Fig. 2: Removing Pin From Shifter Shafts

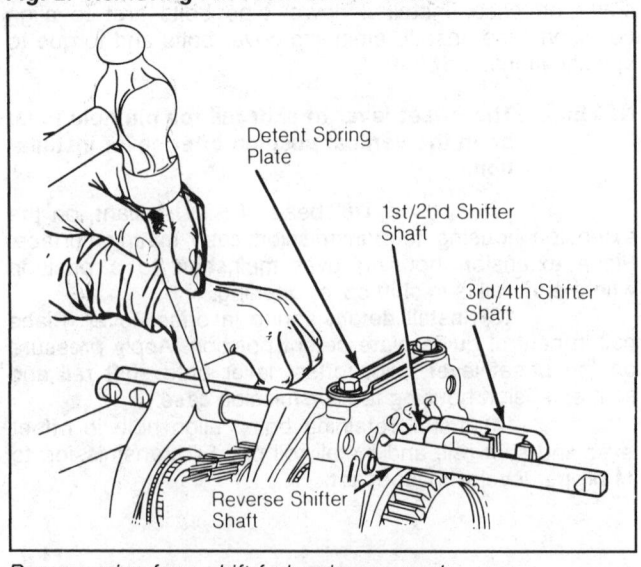

Remove pins from shift fork using a punch.

GENERAL MOTORS (ISUZU) 77.5 MM 4-SPEED (Cont.)

Fig. 3: Exploded View of General Motors (Isuzu) 77.5 MM 4-Speed Transmission

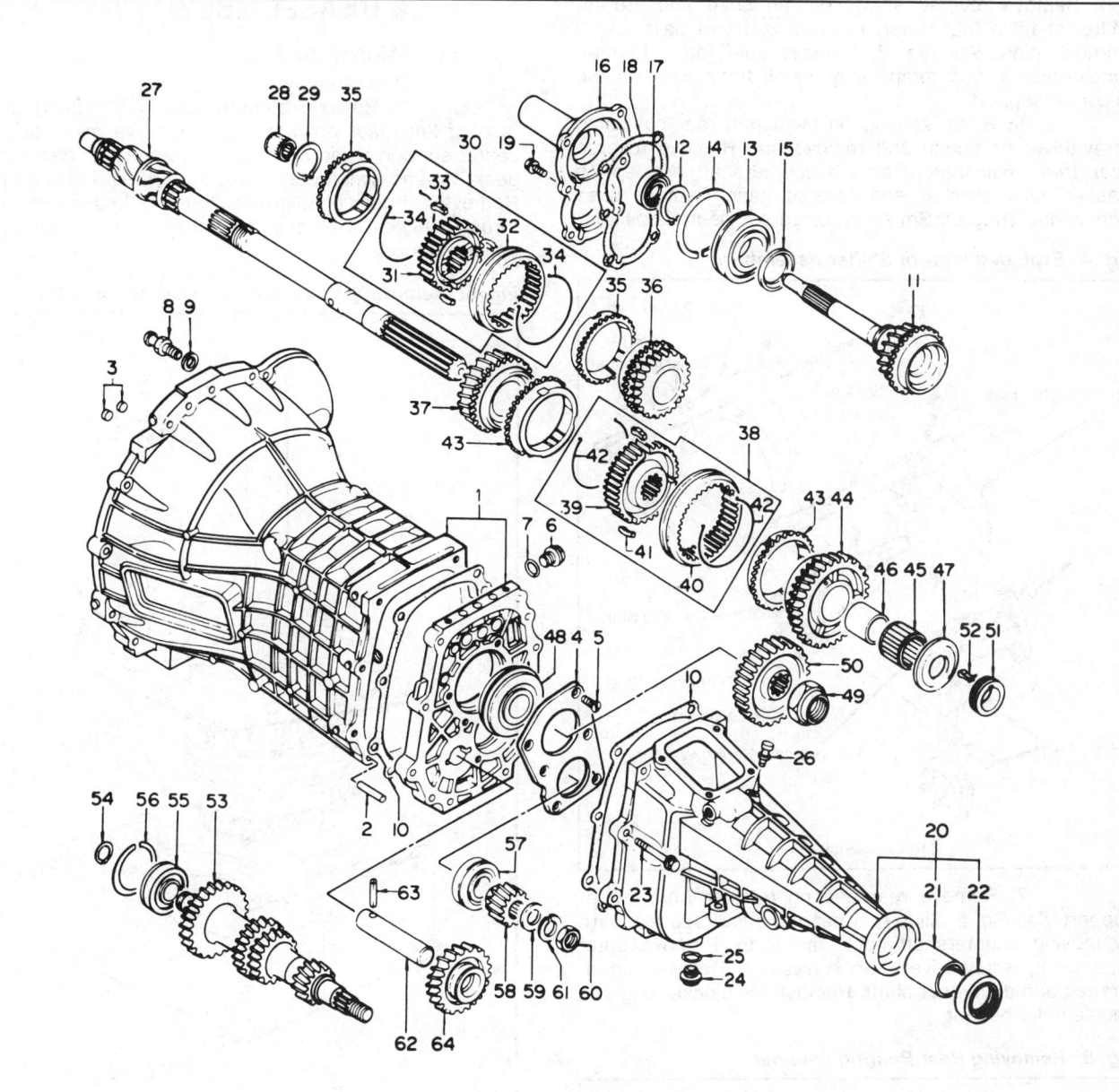

1. Transmission Case and Center Support	17. Oil Seal	33. Insert	49. Nut
2. Dowel	18. Gasket	34. Spring	50. Reverse Gear
3. Plug	19. Bolt and Spring Washer	35. Blocker Ring	51. Speedometer Drive Gear
4. Rear Bearing Retainer	20. Extension Housing	36. 3rd Gear	52. Clip
5. Screw	21. Bushing	37. 2nd Gear	53. Counter Shaft
6. Oil Filler Plug	22. Rear Oil Seal	38. 1st/2nd Synchronizer	54. Retaining Ring
7. Gasket	23. Bolt, Plain Washer and Spring Washer	39. Clutch Hub	55. Bearing
8. Ball Stud	24. Oil Drain Plug	40. Sleeve	56. Retaining Ring
9. Washer	25. Gasket	41. Insert	57. Bearing
10. Gasket	26. Ventilator	42. Spring	58. Reverse Gear
11. Drive Gear Shaft	27. Mainshaft	43. Blocker Ring	59. Plain Washer
12. Retaining Ring	28. Needle Roller Bearing	44. 1st Gear	60. Nut
13. Bearing	29. Retaining Ring	45. Needle Roller Bearing	61. Spring Washer
14. Retaining Ring	30. 3rd/4th Synchronizer	46. Bearing Collar	62. Reverse Idler Shaft
15. Spacer	31. Clutch Hub	47. Thrust Washer	63. Spring Pin
16. Front Bearing Retainer	32. Sleeve	48. Bearing	64. Reverse Idler Gear

Manual Transmissions

GENERAL MOTORS (ISUZU) 77.5 MM 4-SPEED (Cont.)

5) Position 3 shifter shafts into neutral position. Remove reverse shaft, 1st-2nd shaft and 3rd-4th shifter shaft in that order. Remove 3 detent balls and 2 interlock pins. *See Fig. 7.* Remove shift forks. Engage synchronizers, and temporarily install transmission case to center support.

6) Raise staking on mainshaft rear nut using screwdriver or punch and remove nut. Remove reverse gear from mainshaft. Remove countershaft nut, spring washer, plain washer and reverse gear. Remove case from center support. Set synchronizers in neutral position.

Fig. 4: *Exploded View of Shifter Assemblies*

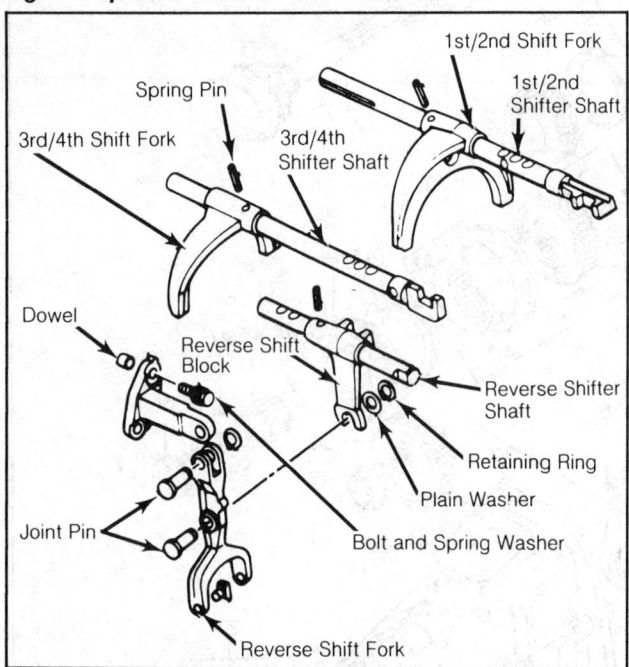

7) Remove rear bearing retainer from center support. *See Fig. 5.* Slide rear bearing outer race rearward by moving countershaft back and forth. Remove outer race using screwdrivers or equivalent. Remove countershaft and drive gear shaft. Remove 4th blocker ring and needle roller bearing.

Fig. 5: *Removing Rear Bearing Retainer*

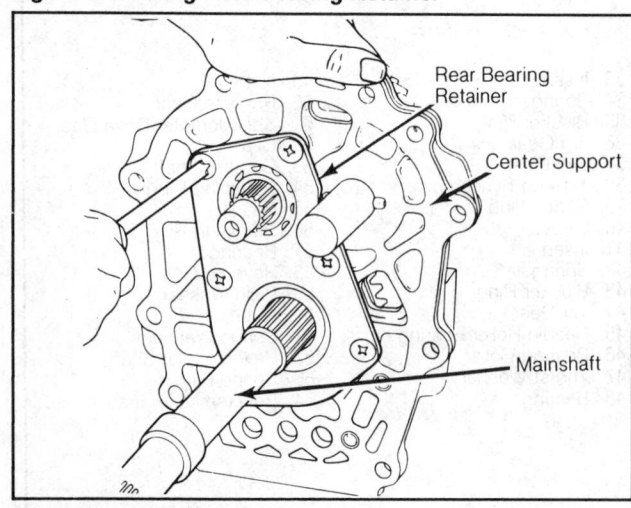

Remove retainer from center support.

COMPONENT DISASSEMBLY & REASSEMBLY

MAINSHAFT
Disassembly

1) Position support tool (J-22912-01) at rear face of 2nd gear on mainshaft. Remove mainshaft from center support using arbor press. *See Fig. 6.* Remove 2nd gear, 1st-2nd synchronizer and 1st and 2nd blocker rings. Remove 1st gear needle roller bearing, bearing collar and thrust washer. Remove mainshaft rear bearing from center support.

Fig. 6: *Removing Mainshaft From Center Support*

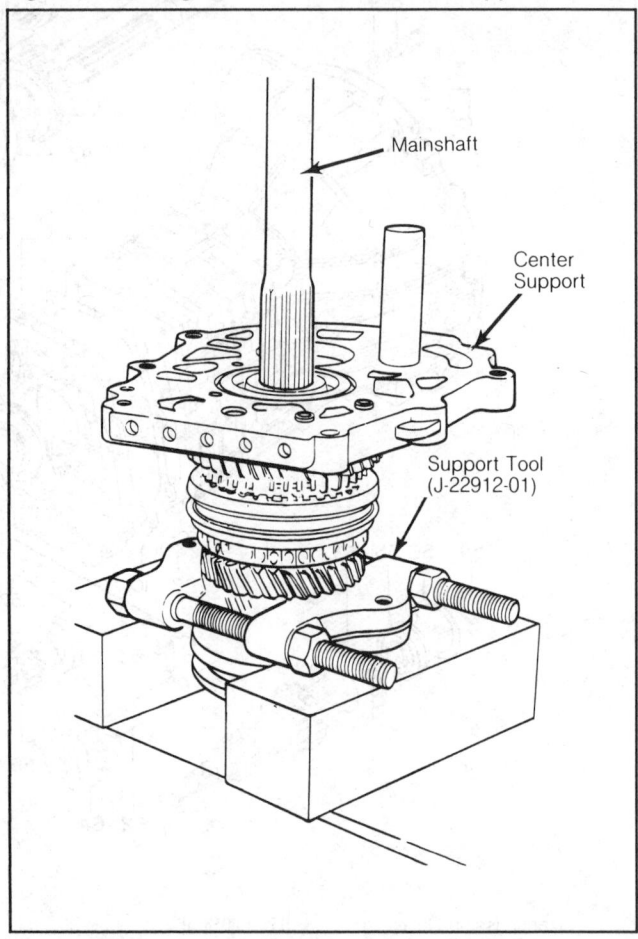

Use arbor press to remove mainshaft from support.

2) Remove snap ring from front of mainshaft. Set rear face of 3rd gear in blocks and remove mainshaft using arbor press. Remove 3rd gear, 3rd blocker ring and 3rd-4th synchronizer.

Reassembly

1) Install 3rd gear and 3rd gear blocker ring to front of mainshaft. Install 3rd-4th synchronizer assembly to mainshaft using arbor press. Install retaining ring to front of mainshaft. Install 2nd gear and 2nd gear blocker ring to rear of mainshaft.

2) Install 1st-2nd synchronizer assembly to mainshaft using arbor press. Install 1st gear bearing collar to mainshaft using installer (J-33036) and arbor press. Install 1st blocker ring, needle roller bearing and 1st gear. Install thrust washer with oil grooves turned toward gear.

GENERAL MOTORS (ISUZU) 77.5 MM 4-SPEED (Cont.)

3) If reverse idler shaft has been removed, reinstall shaft into center support with press. Be sure spring pin is fitted to shaft.

CLEANING & INSPECTION

1) Wash parts in solvent and dry all parts, except front and rear bearings, with compressed air. Wipe front and rear bearings with a clean cloth or air dry. Do not allow bearings to spin. Turn them slowly by hand. Spinning may damage race and balls. Lubricate bearings with light oil and check for roughness by slowly turning race by hand.

2) Inspect transmission case, cover and extension housing. Replace if there are cracks in bores, sides, bosses or bolt holes. Replace case if there are stripped bolt holes, nicks burrs, or rough surfaces in shaft bores or on gasket surfaces. Inspect gear train and shift mechanism.

3) Replace any parts exhibiting wear, chips, galling, distortion or bending. Check for worn bearings and bores. Check for weak snap rings and stripped offset lever. Synchronizer hubs and sliding sleeves are a selected assembly. Keep together as originally assembled. Keys and springs may be replaced if worn or broken.

TRANSMISSION REASSEMBLY

1) Fit snap ring to mainshaft rear bearing. Install bearing into center support with snap ring side turned rearward. Using arbor press, install mainshaft into bearing which has been fitted to center support. Install 4th blocker ring, needle roller bearing and drive gear shaft.

2) Install countershaft to center support. Install rear bearing outer race to countershaft from rear side of center support. Install bearing retainer to center support. Clean threaded hole in center support and apply coat of Loctite 242, or equivalent. Install screws and tighten to specification.

3) Engage synchronizers in lock and temporarily set center support into transmission case. Install

Fig. 7: Installing Interlock Pins

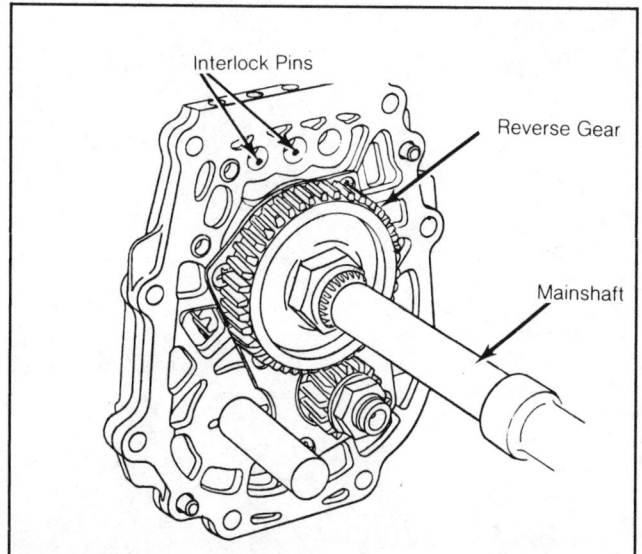

Install greased pins to center support.

reverse gear, washer and spring washer to rear end of countershaft. Tighten nut. Install reverse gear so teeth with rounded edges are turned rearward.

4) Install reverse gear to mainshaft with rounded teeth turned rearward. Tighten nut to specification. Stake nut to mainshaft. Remove case from center support. Grease 2 interlock pins and install to center support. See Fig. 7. Install shift fork to synchronizers.

5) Install 3rd-4th shifter shaft to center support and shift fork. Bring shaft into neutral position. Install 1st-2nd shifter shaft and reverse shifter shaft to center support. Drive spring pin into 1st-2nd and 3rd-4th shift forks. Support shaft end when installing spring pin.

6) Install 3 detent balls and springs into holes in center support. See Fig. 8. The spring for reverse is shorter in length than others. Install gasket and plate. Tighten bolts to specification. Install gasket to transmission case. Install center support by aligning it with dowels on case.

Fig. 8: Installing Detent Balls and Springs

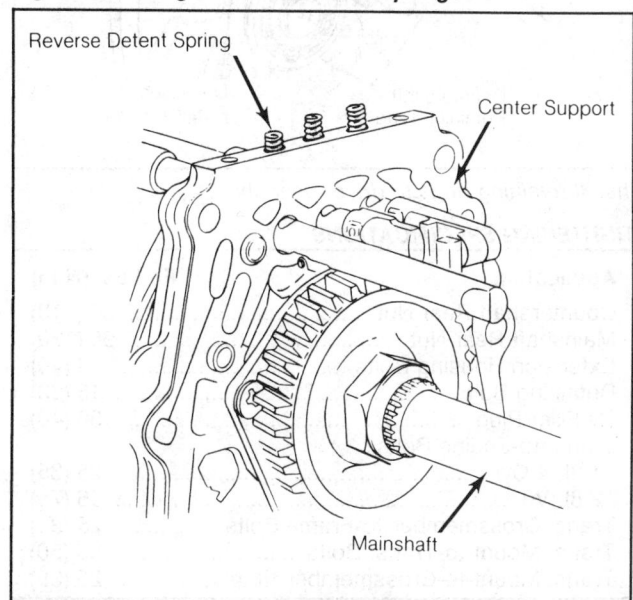

Install 3 balls and springs into center support holes.

7) Install retaining rings to drive gear shaft and countershaft bearing outer races. See Fig. 9. Assemble reverse shift block, reverse block and reverse shift fork using pins and snap rings. Install shift block assembly to reverse shift fork. Insert shift fork into groove in reverse idler gear. Install gear to idler shaft. Install reverse shift block to shifter shaft.

8) Tighten the reverse block retaining bolts. Secure reverse shift block to shifter shaft by installing spring pin using hammer and punch. Insert end of clip into hole in mainshaft and install speedometer drive gear. Install gasket to center support. Install extension housing to support by aligning it with dowels. Tighten bolts.

9) Install back-up light switch. Install gasket to upper face of extension housing. Install shifter cover. Install speedometer driven gear. Install ball stud, if removed. Install gasket to transmission case. Apply Permatex 2, or equivalent, to thread of bolts. Install and tighten to specification. Install bearing, boot and clutch fork. Install gearshift lever to shifter cover and check that shifting is smooth.

GENERAL MOTORS (ISUZU) 77.5 MM 4-SPEED (Cont.)

10) Install transmission assembly to vehicle and install gearshift lever assembly. Fill transmission with lubricant.

Fig. 9: *Installing Drive Gear Retaining Rings*

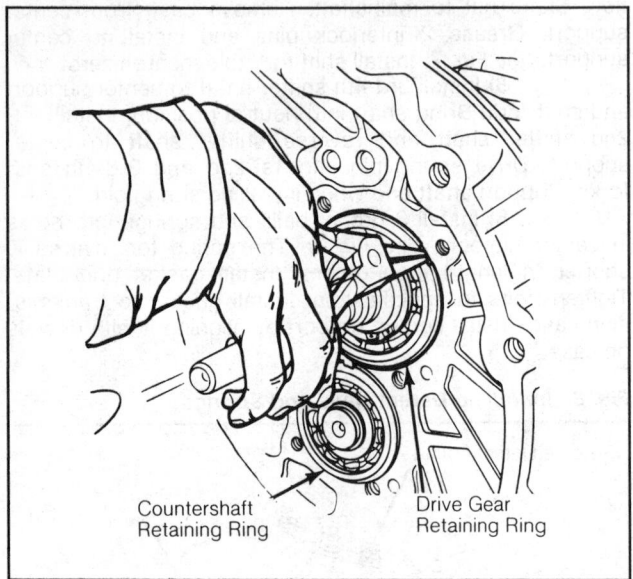

Countershaft
Retaining Ring

Drive Gear
Retaining Ring

Install retaining rings to drive gear shaft.

TIGHTENING SPECIFICATIONS

Application	Ft. Lbs. (N.m)
Countershaft Rear Nut	80 (110)
Mainshaft Rear Nut	95 (130)
Extension Housing Bolts	30 (40)
Retaining Bolts	15 (20)
Oil Filler Plug	30 (40)
Trans.-to-Engine Bolts	
1.9L 4-Cyl.	25 (35)
2.8L V6	55 (75)
Trans. Crossmember-to-Frame Bolts	25 (35)
Trans. Mount-to-Trans. Bolts	35 (50)
Trans. Mount-to-Crossmember Nuts	25 (35)

GENERAL MOTORS 4-SPEED — 117 MM

Chevrolet & GMC Trucks

IDENTIFICATION

Transmission can be identified by a 2 letter code, stamped on a machined pad, on right side of case. Clutch housing and gearbox are 2 separate pieces.

DESCRIPTION

The 117 MM 4-speed transmission is identified by the measured distance (117 mm) between the centerlines of the mainshaft and countergear and by the number of forward gears. The 1st gear is a constant mesh type that engages with the 2nd gear synchronizer sleeve. The 2nd, 3rd, and 4th gears are synchronized.

LUBRICATION & ADJUSTMENT

See the appropriate article in MANUAL TRANSMISSION SERVICING Section.

TROUBLE SHOOTING

See the appropriate article in MANUAL TRANSMISSION TROUBLE SHOOTING Section.

SERVICE (IN VEHICLE)

SHIFT LEVER

Removal

1) On 4WD models, remove transfer case shift lever boot retaining screws and retainer from compartment floor.

2) On all models, remove transmission shift lever boot retaining screws. Slide boot and retainer up on shift lever and remove shift lever.

Installation

1) Install transmission shift lever. Slide boot and retainer down shift lever and install attaching screws.

2) On 4WD models, install transfer case shift lever boot, retainer and attaching screws.

EXTENSION HOUSING OIL SEAL

Removal

1) Raise vehicle and support with safety stands. Drain lubricant from transmission. Disconnect propeller shaft and tie out of the way. Disconnect speedometer cable and remove speedometer driven gear.

2) Using flange/yoke holding tool, remove output yoke/companion flange nut. Pull output yoke and companion nut off mainshaft. Support transmission while removing mounting bolts and bearing retainer bolts.

3) Remove bearing retainer and gasket. Discard gasket. Remove oil seal and discard seal.

Installation

1) Clean gasket surfaces. Coat outer diameter of new oil seal with sealing cement. Install oil seal using drive tool (J-22834-2). Install retaining bolts and tighten.

2) Install output yoke on mainshaft. Using a flange/yoke holding tool, install retaining nut. Tighten nut to specifications. Install speedometer driven gear, and connect speedometer cable.

3) Connect propeller shaft to transmission. Fill transmission with lubricant and lower vehicle.

REMOVAL & INSTALLATION

COVER & SHIFT FORK ASSEMBLY

Removal

1) Mount transmission in holding fixture and remove cover bolts. Move reverse shifter fork so reverse idler gear is partially engaged before removing cover.

2) Forks must be set so rear edge of slot in reverse fork is in line with front edge of slot in forward forks as viewed through tower opening.

3) If necessary, insert 2 bolts in cover flange threaded holes and turn evenly to raise cover dowel pins from case.

Fig. 1: Shifter Shaft Positions

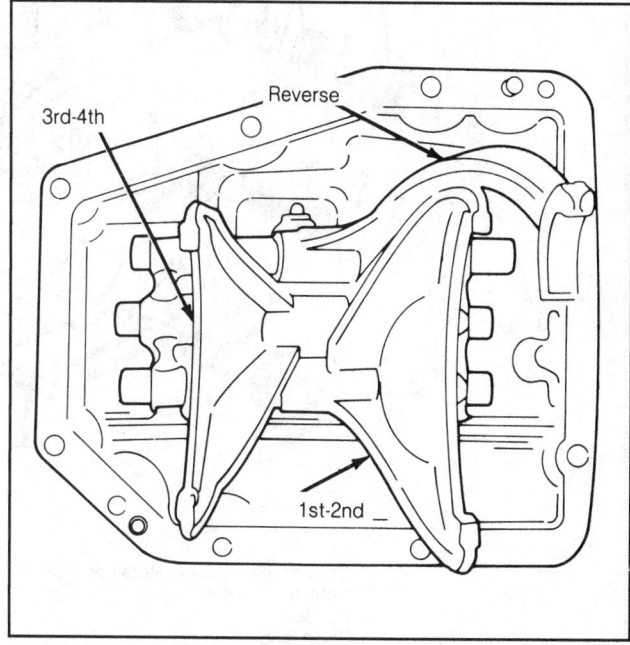

Shafts must be in neutral position for removal.

Installation

1) Move transmission gears to neutral except reverse idler gear which should be engaged about 3/8". Install cover with new gasket.

2) Shift forks must slide into their proper positions on clutch sleeves and reverse idler gear. Forks must be positioned as in removal. Install cover bolts and tighten.

DRIVE GEAR OIL SEAL

Removal

Remove retainer and oil seal assembly. Pry oil seal from retainer and replace with new seal.

Installation

Install new seal with installer (J-22833). Insert seal in retainer so lip of seal is toward flange of installer tool. Install retainer with a new gasket and tighten bolts.

TRANSMISSION

See the appropriate article in MANUAL TRANSMISSION REMOVAL Section.

Manual Transmissions

GENERAL MOTORS 4-SPEED — 117 MM (Cont.)

Fig. 2: *Exploded View of General Motors 117 MM Manual Transmission*

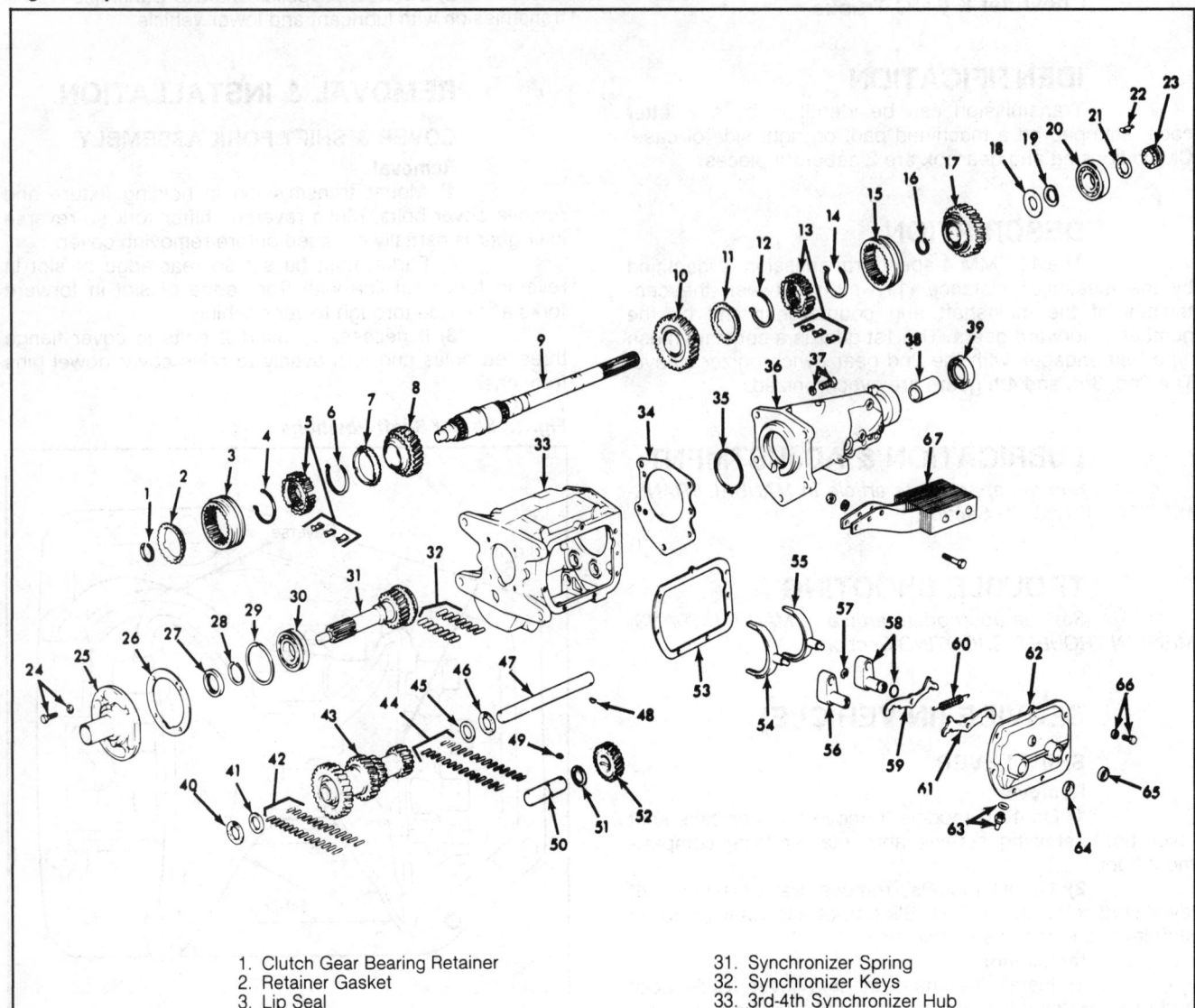

1. Clutch Gear Bearing Retainer	31. Synchronizer Spring
2. Retainer Gasket	32. Synchronizer Keys
3. Lip Seal	33. 3rd-4th Synchronizer Hub
4. Snap Ring	34. Synchronizer Spring
5. Drive Pinion Bearing	35. 3rd-4th Gear Blocker Ring
6. Oil Slinger	36. 3rd-4th Gear Synchronizer Sleeve
7. Drive Pinion & Pilot	37. Snap Ring
8. Power Take-Off Cover Gasket	38. Snap Ring
9. Power Take-Off Cover	39. Thrust Washer
10. Retaining Screws	40. Pinion Countergear
11. 1st-2nd Gear Blocker Ring	and Spacer
12. Synchronizer Spring	41. Snap Ring
13. 1st-2nd Gear Synchronizer Hub	42. Snap Ring
14. Synchronizer Keys	43. 3rd Gear Countergear
15. Synchronizer Spring	44. Countergear Shaft
16. Reverse Driven Gear	45. Countergear Rear Bearing
17. 1st Gear Bushing	46. Snap Ring
18. 1st Gear	47. Bearing Outer Snap Ring
19. Thrust Washer	48. Rear Retainer Gasket
20. Rear Main Bearing	49. Rear Retainer
21. Bearing Snap Ring	50. Retainer Bolts
22. Speedometer Gear	51. Retainer Lip Seal
23. Rear Mainshaft Lock Nut	52. Reverse Idler Shaft
24. 2nd Gear Bushing (On Shaft)	53. Drain Plug
25. Mainshaft	54. Reverse Idler Gear
26. 2nd Gear	55. Case
27. 3rd Gear Bushing	56. Fill Plug
28. Thrust Washer	57. Countergear Front Bearing
29. 3rd Gear	58. Gasket
30. 3rd Gear Blocker Ring	59. Front Cover

GENERAL MOTORS 4-SPEED — 117 MM (Cont.)

DISASSEMBLY

TRANSMISSION

1) Mount transmission in holding fixture and remove cap screws retaining transmission cover assembly to case. If required, insert two 5/16" x 18 bolts in cover flange threaded holes and turn evenly to raise cover dowel pin from case.

2) Move reverse shifter fork so that reverse idler gear is partially engaged before attempting to remove cover. Forks must be positioned so rear edge of slot in reverse fork is in line with front edge of slot in forward forks as viewed throught tower opening.

3) Place transmission in 2 gears at once to lock gears. Remove universal joint flange and brake drum assembly. On 4WD models, use main bearing lock nut remover/installer (J-23070) to remove mainshaft rear lock nut. *See Fig. 3.*

Fig. 3: Removing 4WD Mainshaft Rear Bearing Lock Nut

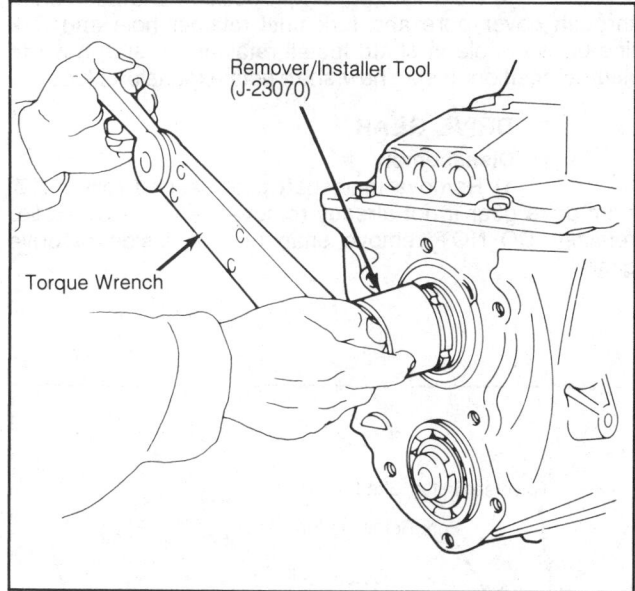

To remove lock nut, use remover/installer tool (J-23070).

4) On all models, remove parking brake and brake flange plate assembly. Remove rear bearing retainer and gasket. Slide speedometer drive gear off mainshaft.

5) Remove drive gear bearing retainers and gasket. Remove countergear front bearing cap and gasket. Pry countergear front bearing out, by inserting a two-pronged puller (J-28509) through cast slots in case.

6) Remove countergear rear bearing snap ring from shaft and bearing. Using bearing puller, remove countergear rear bearings. Let countergear assembly rest on bottom of case.

7) Remove drive gear bearing outer race to case retaining ring. Remove drive gear and bearing by tapping gently on bottom side of drive gear shaft and prying directly opposite against case and bearing snap ring groove at the same time.

8) Remove 4th gear synchronizer ring. Index cut out section of drive gear in down position with countergear to obtain clearance for removing clutch gear. Remove rear mainshaft bearing retainer ring and using bearing remover, remove bearing from case.

Fig. 4: Removal of Rear Countergear Bearing

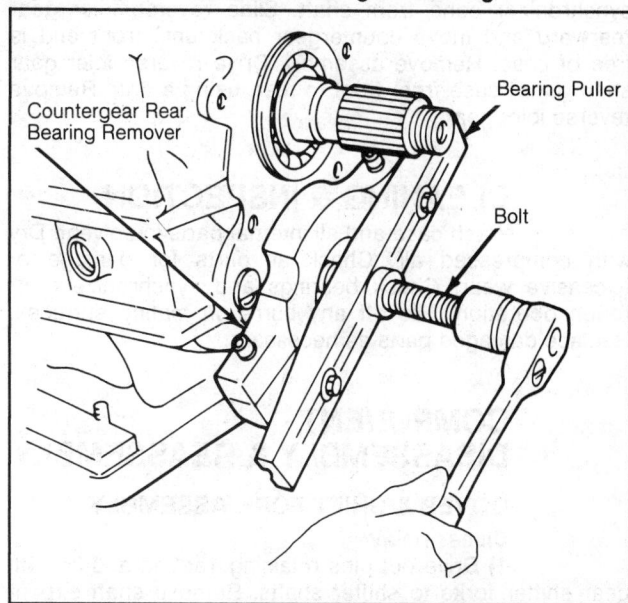

Let countergear rest on case for mainshaft removal.

9) Slide 1st gear thrust washer off mainshaft. Raise rear of mainshaft assembly and push rearward in case bore, swing front end and lift from case. Remove synchronizer cone from shaft.

10) Slide reverse idler gear rearward and move countergear rearward until front end is free of case, then lift to remove from case. Remove reverse idler gear, drive reverse idler gear shaft out of case from front to rear using a driver. Remove reverse idler gear from case.

MAINSHAFT, COUNTERGEAR & REVERSE IDLER GEAR

1) Remove mainshaft rear bearing snap ring. Using bearing pullers (J-22832 and J-8433-1), remove bearing from case. *See Fig. 5.* Slide 1st gear thrust washer off mainshaft. Raise rear of mainshaft and move rearward.

Fig. 5: Rear Mainshaft Bearing Removal

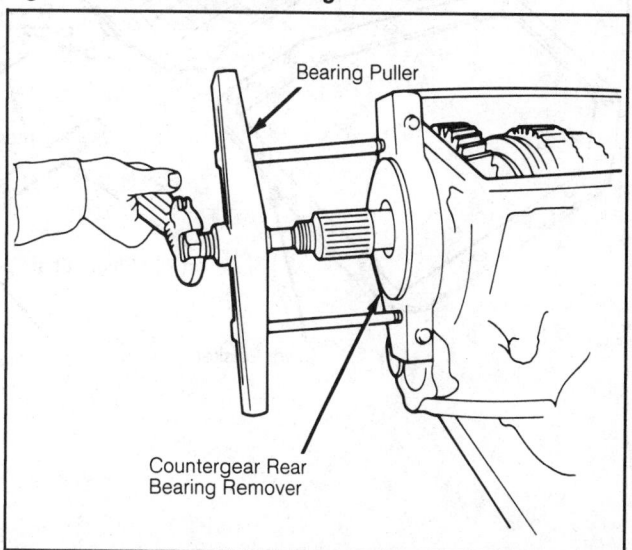

To remove shaft, lift up and out of case.

Manual Transmissions

GENERAL MOTORS 4-SPEED — 117 MM (Cont.)

2) Lift shaft front up and out of case. Remove synchronizer cone from shaft. Slide reverse idler gear rearward and move countergear back until front end is free of case. Remove assembly. Drive reverse idler gear shaft out of case from front to rear, using a drift. Remove reverse idler gear.

CLEANING & INSPECTION

Wash case and all internal parts in solvent. Dry with compressed air. Check all parts for damage or excessive wear. Check bearings and synchronizers for rough operation. File off any burrs on mating surfaces. Replace damaged parts as necessary.

COMPONENT DISASSEMBLY & REASSEMBLY

COVER & SHIFT FORK ASSEMBLY
Disassembly

1) Drive out pins retaining 1st-2nd and 3rd-4th gear shifter forks to shifter shafts. Remove shaft expansion plugs. Note that pin retaining 3rd-4th gear shifter must be removed before removing shifter head pin. With shifter shafts in neutral position, drive shafts out of cover to remove shifter forks.

2) Ensure that detent balls, springs, and interlock pins are not lost as shifter shafts are removed. Drive out pin holding reverse shifter head and drive out shaft. Ensure that detent balls are not lost as they are under spring tension in rear rail boss holes.

Reassembly

1) Install shifter shafts in correct order. See *Fig. 6.* Install reverse shaft, 3rd-4th shaft, and 1st-2nd shaft. Place fork detent ball springs and balls in hole positions in cover. Start shafts into cover, depressing yoke detent balls with a small punch, and push shaft on over balls.

2) Starting with reverse shifter shaft, hold fork in position and push shaft through yoke. Install split pin in fork and shaft, position fork in neutral position.

3) Hold 3rd-4th fork in position and push shaft through yoke, but not through front support bore. Place 2 interlock balls between reverse and 3rd-4th shifter shafts in cross bore of front support boss. Install interlock pin in 3rd-4th shaft hole and grease to hold in place.

4) Push 3rd-4th shaft through fork and cover bore, keeping both balls and pin in fork and shaft. Position fork in neutral position. Place 2 interlock balls between 1st-2nd shaft and 3rd-4th shaft in cross bore of front support boss.

5) Hold 1st-2nd fork in position and push shaft through cover bore and fork until retainer hole and fork line up with hole in shaft. Install retainer pin and move to neutral position. Install new shaft hole expansion plugs.

DRIVE GEAR
Disassembly

1) Remove mainshaft pilot bearing rollers (17) from drive gear if not already removed, and remove roller retainer. DO NOT remove snap ring on inside of drive gear.

Fig. 6: Exploded View of Cover and Shift Assembly

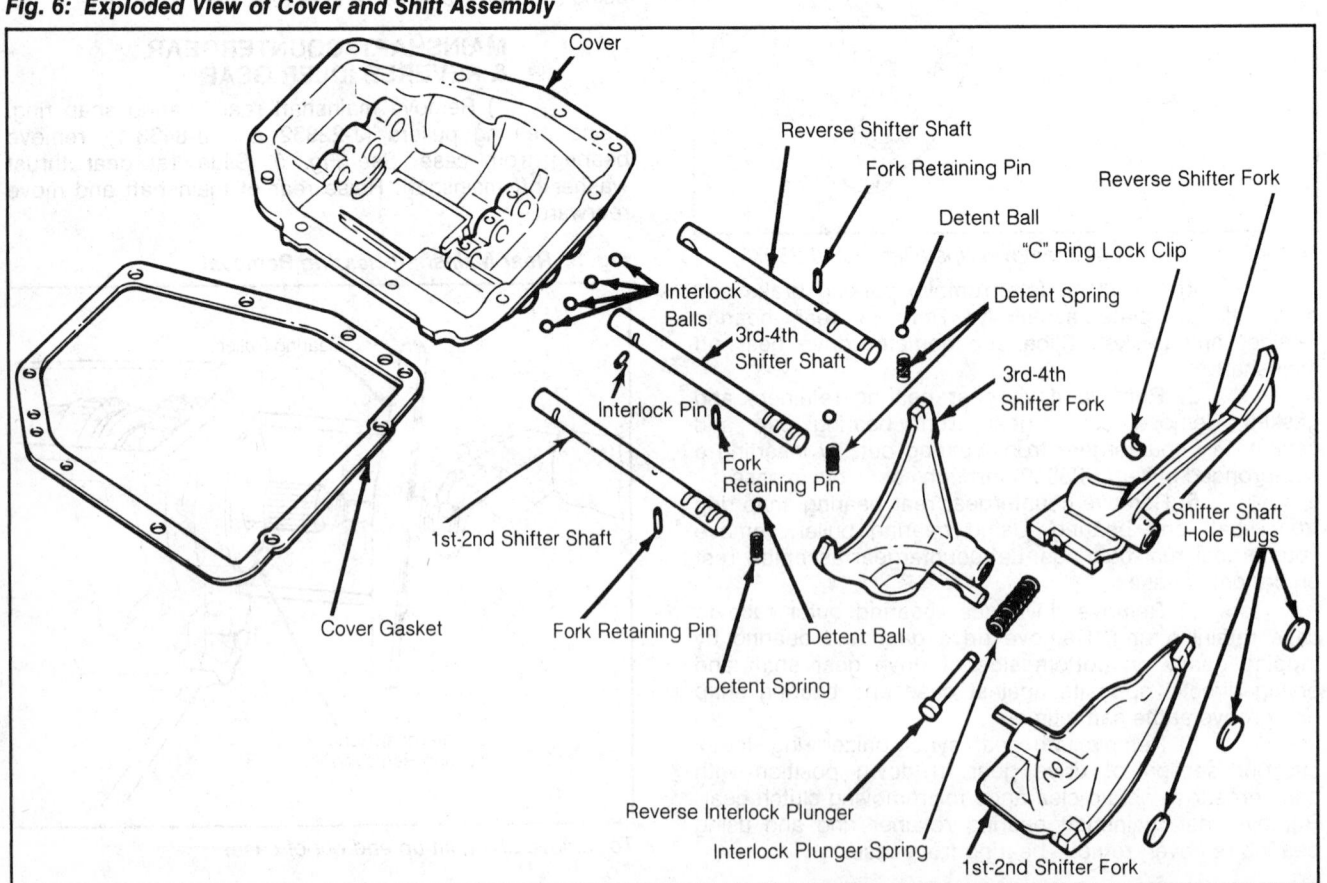

GENERAL MOTORS 4-SPEED — 117 MM (Cont.)

2) Remove snap ring securing bearing on stem of drive gear. To remove bearing, position bearing support tool under bearing and using an arbor press, press gear and shaft out of bearing.

Reassembly

1) Press bearing and new oil slinger onto drive gear shaft. Slinger should be flush with bearing shoulder on drive gear. Install snap ring on shaft to secure bearing. Install bearing retainer ring in groove on outside diameter of bearing.

Fig. 7: Installing Drive Gear Bearing

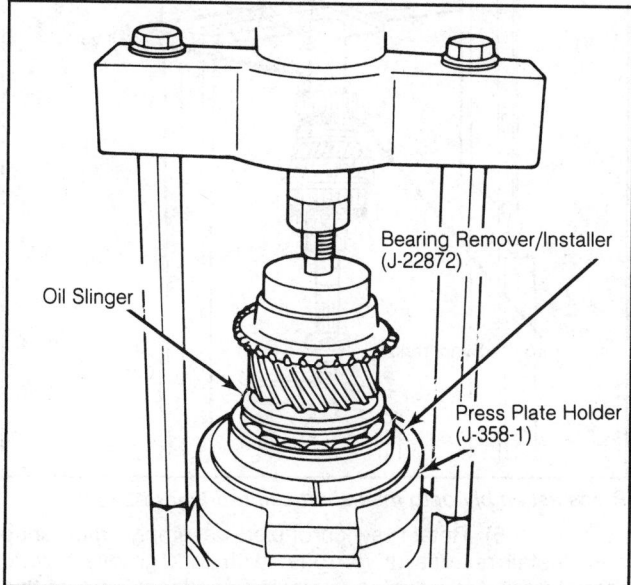

Bearings must turn freely after installation.

2) Ensure bearing turns freely after installed on shaft. Install snap ring in mainshaft pilot bearing bore, if previously removed. Apply grease to bearing surface and install 17 roller bearings and 1 bearing retainer. Bearing retainer holds bearings in position and is pushed forward into recess by mainshaft pilot during final assembly.

MAINSHAFT

Disassembly

1) Remove 1st gear and thrust washer. Remove snap ring in front of 3rd-4th synchronizer assembly. Withdraw reverse driven gear. Press behind 2nd gear to remove 3rd-4th synchronizer, 3rd gear, and 2nd gear with 3rd gear bushing and thrust washer.

2) Remove 2nd gear synchronizer ring. Support 2nd gear synchronizer hub on front face and press mainshaft through, removing 1st gear bushing and 2nd gear synchronizer hub. Split 2nd gear bushing with a chisel and remove bushing from shaft.

Reassembly

1) Bushing for 1st, 2nd, and 3rd gears are sintered iron and care should be taken when installing to prevent damaged. Lubricate all bushings with oil before installing gears. Press 2nd gear onto mainshaft until it bottoms on shoulder.

2) Press 1st-2nd synchronizer hub onto mainshaft until it bottoms on shoulder with annulus toward rear

Fig. 8: Mainshaft Disassembly

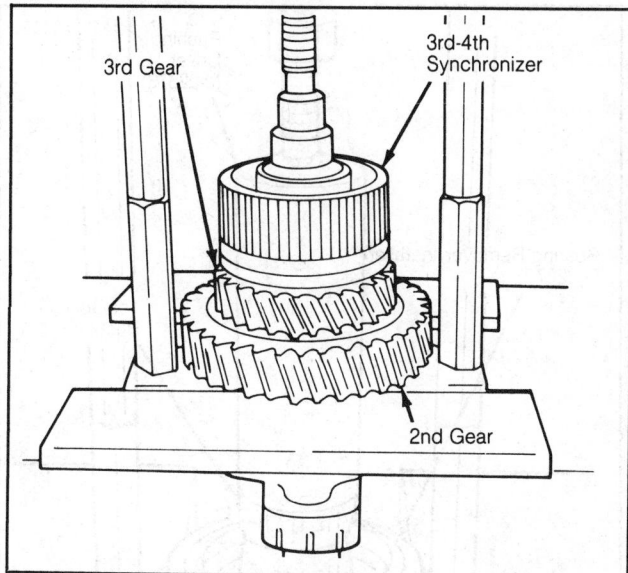

The 3rd gear should be a running fit on mainshaft.

of shaft. Install 1st-2nd synchronizer keys and springs, if removed. Using arbor press and driver (J-22873), press 1st gear bushing on mainshaft until it bottoms against hub.

Fig. 9: Installing 2nd Gear Bushing

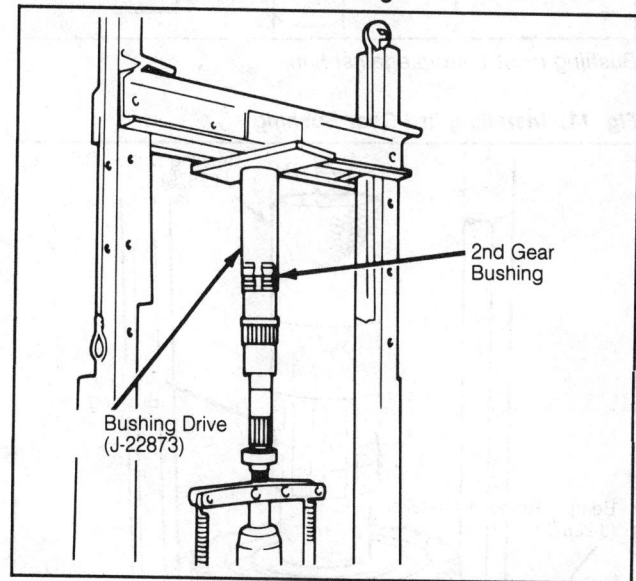

Bushing should bottom on mainshaft shoulder.

3) Install synchronizer blocker ring and 2nd gear on mainshaft, against synchronzier hub. Index synchronizer key slots with keys in hub. Install 3rd gear thrust washer on mainshaft with tang in slot on shaft and against 2nd gear bushing. Press 3rd gear bushing on mainshaft using arbor press and driver (J-22875), until it bottoms thrust washer. See Fig. 11.

Fig. 10: Installing 1st Gear Bushing

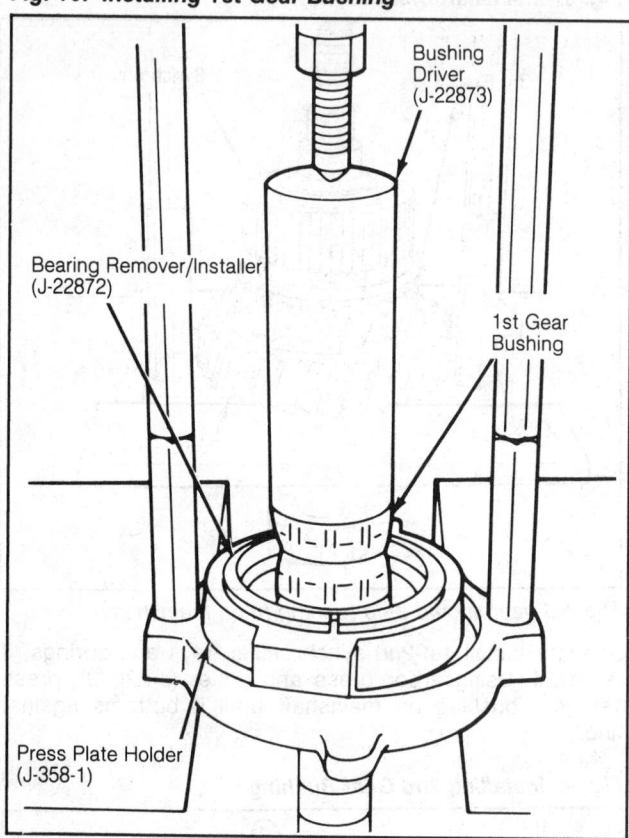

Bushing must bottom against hub.

Fig. 11: Installing 3rd Gear Bushing

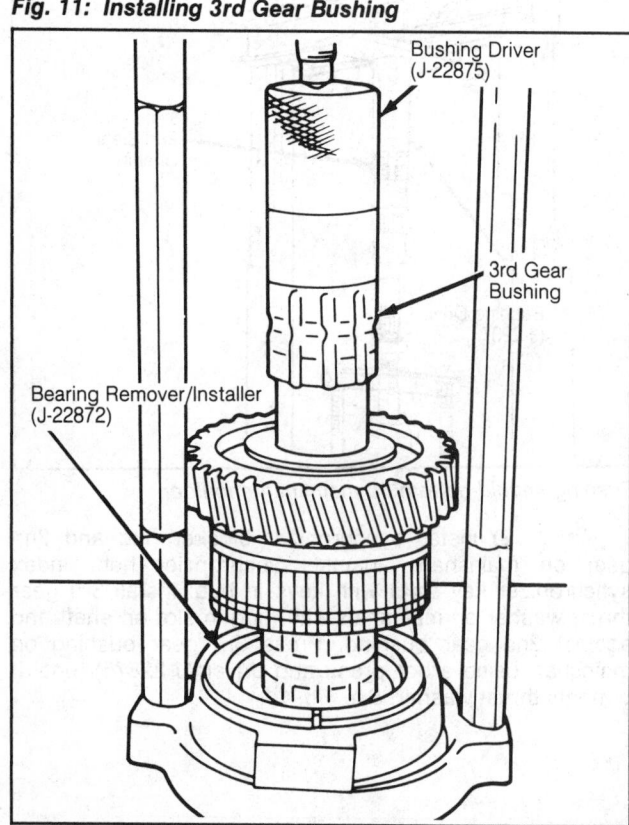

Bushing must bottom on thrust washer.

4) Install 3rd gear and 3rd synchronizer blocker ring on mainshaft, against 3rd gear thrust washer. Index synchronizer ring key slots with keys. Using arbor press and driver (J-22875), press 3rd-4th synchronizer hub assembly onto mainshaft and against 3rd gear with thrust washer facing toward 3rd gear.

Fig. 12: Installing 3rd-4th Synchronizer

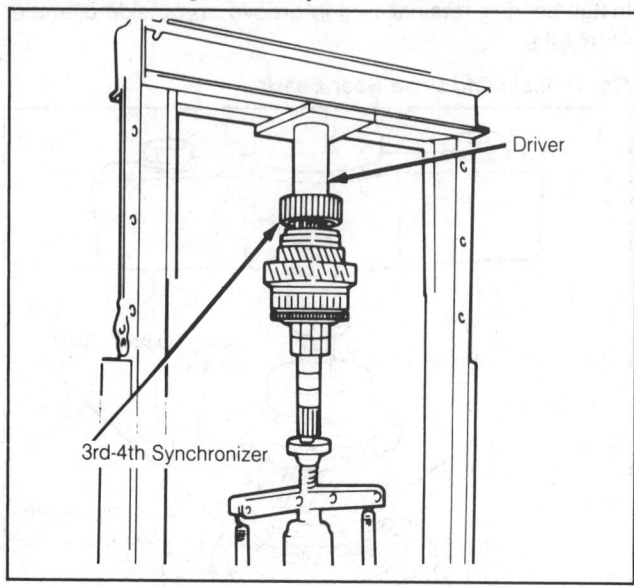

Press assembly onto mainshaft using driver (J-22875).

5) Retain synchronizer assembly with snap ring. Install reverse driven gear with fork groove toward rear. Install 1st gear on mainshaft and against 1st-2nd synchronizer hub. Install 1st gear thrust washer.

Disassembly

1) Remove front countergear shaft snap ring and thrust washer. Discard snap ring. Install press plates (J-22832) on countershaft with open side to spacer. *See Fig. 13.*

Fig. 13: Removal of Countergear

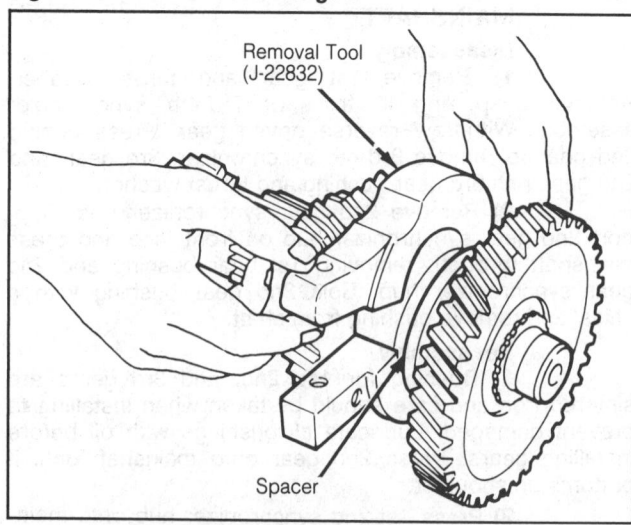

Insert remover (J-22832) with open side to spacer.

2) Support assembly in an arbor press and press countershaft out of clutch countergear assembly. Countergear is a slip fit and pressing may not be required.

GENERAL MOTORS 4-SPEED — 117 MM (Cont.)

3) Remove clutch countergear rear retaining ring and discard. Remove and discard 3rd gear countergear retaining ring. Position assembly on an arbor press and press shaft from 3rd speed gear.

Reassembly

1) Position 3rd gear countergear on shaft with machined surface toward front of shaft. Press gear on shaft with arbor press using a minimum force of 1500 lbs. (680 kg). If gear can be installed with less than 1500 lbs. (680 kg), replace gear.

2) Install spacer and press front gear on countershaft. Using snap ring pliers, install snap ring. Install new countergear rear snap ring using sleeve tools (J-22830 & J-22873) and snap ring pliers as follows: Install inner sleeve over shaft and place snap ring over tool.

Fig. 14: Installing Countergear Snap Ring

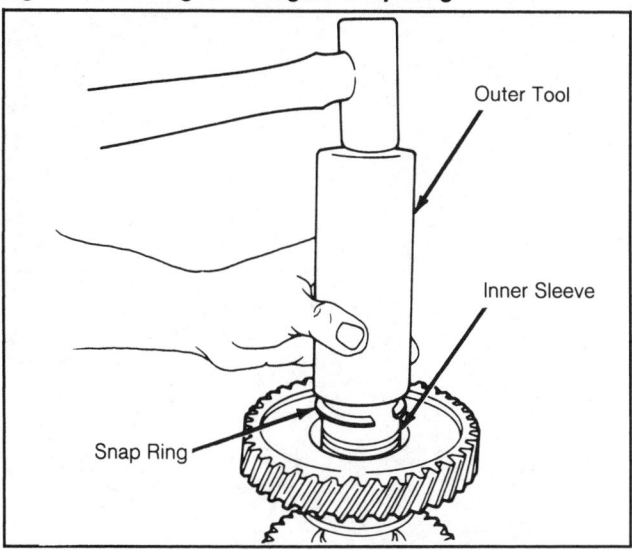

3) Push outer tool down on snap ring until it engages groove on shaft. Using snap ring pliers, carefully expand ring until it just slides onto splines. Push ring down until it engages groove on shaft. Do not over-stress snap ring.

Fig. 15: Installing Countergear

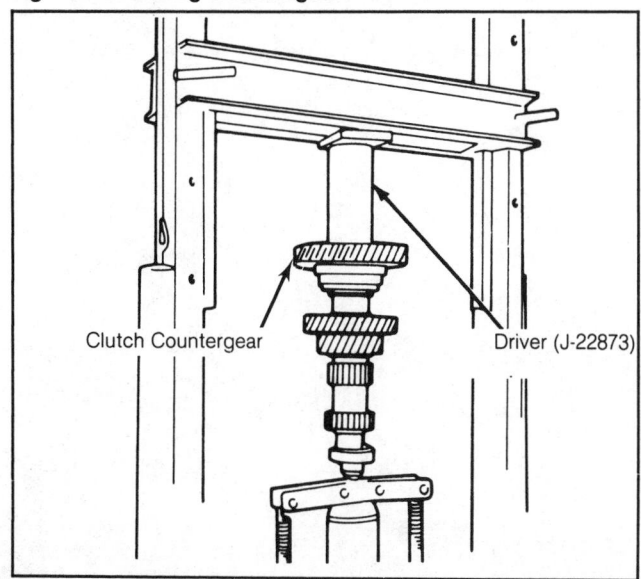

Press countergear onto shaft against snap ring.

4) Position clutch countergear and spacer on shaft using driver (J-22873). Install countergear thrust washer and retaining ring. Position clutch countergear and spacer on shaft using driver (J-22873). Install countergear thrust washer and retaining ring.

REASSEMBLY

TRANSMISSION

1) Lower countergear into case until it rests on bottom of case. Place reverse idler gear in transmission case with gear teeth toward front.

2) Install idler gear shaft from rear to front, being careful to have slot in end of shaft facing down. Shaft slot face must be at least flush with case.

3) Install mainshaft assembly into case with rear of shaft protruding out rear bearing hole in case. Position installer tool (J-22874) in clutch gear case opening and engage front mainshaft. Rotate case onto front end. *See Fig. 16.*

Fig. 16: Installing Mainshaft Rear Bearing

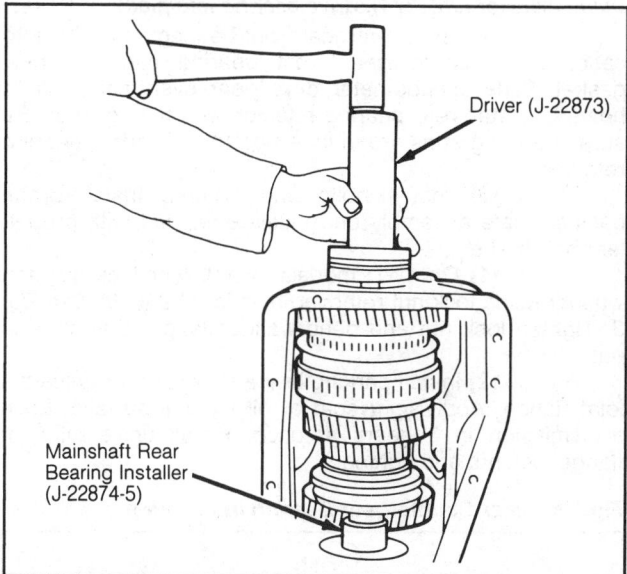

Drive bearing onto mainshaft and into case.

4) Install 1st gear thrust washer on shaft, if not previously installed. Install snap ring on bearing outside diameter and position rear mainshaft bearing on shaft.

5) Using driver tool (J-22874-1), drive bearing on shaft and into case. Rotate case and remove tool. Install synchronizer cone on pilot end of mainshaft and slide rearward to clutch hub.

6) Make sure the 3 cut out sections of 4th gear synchronizer cone align with 3 clutch keys in clutch assembly. Install snap ring on drive gear bearing outside diameter.

7) Index cut out portion of drive gear teeth to obtain clearance over countershaft drive gear teeth. Start clutch gear, then tap bearing outer race with mallet.

8) Install drive gear bearing retainer using a new gasket, install and tighten bolts. Install snap ring on countergear rear bearing outside diameter position, bearing on countergear, and using driver tool (J-22874-1), drive bearing into place. Rotate case, install snap ring on countershaft at rear bearing and remove tool.

GENERAL MOTORS 4-SPEED — 117 MM (Cont.)

Fig. 17: Rear Countergear Bearing Installation

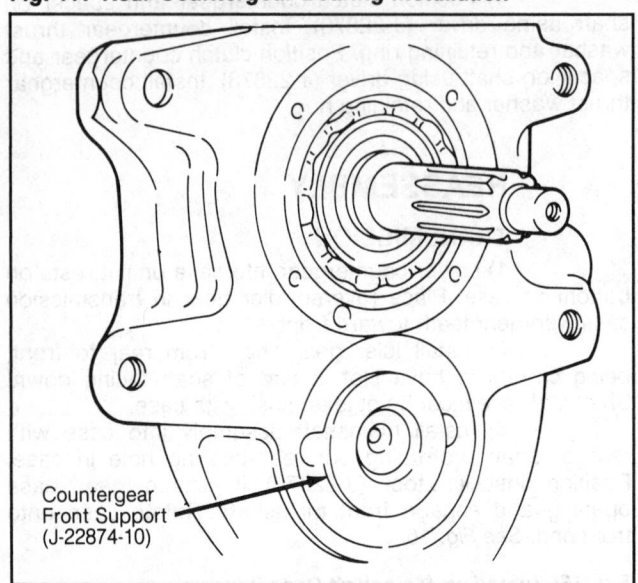

Countergear
Front Support
(J-22874-10)

Using installer (J-22874), drive bearing into place.

9) Tap countergear front bearing assembly into case. Install countergear front bearing cap and new gasket. Slide speedometer drive gear over mainshaft to bearing. Install rear bearing retainer with new gasket. Be sure snap ring ends are in lube slot and cut out in bearing retainer.

10) Install bolts and tighten. Install brake backing plate assembly on models equipped with propeller shaft brake.

11) On 4WD models, install rear lock nut and washer using lock nut remover/installer (J-23070). *See Fig. 3.* Tighten lock nut and bend washer tangs to fit slots in nut.

12) Install parking brake drum and/or universal joint flange. Apply light coat of oil to seal surface. Lock transmission in 2 gears at once. Install universal joint flange lock nut and tighten.

Fig. 18: Rear Countergear Bearing Installation

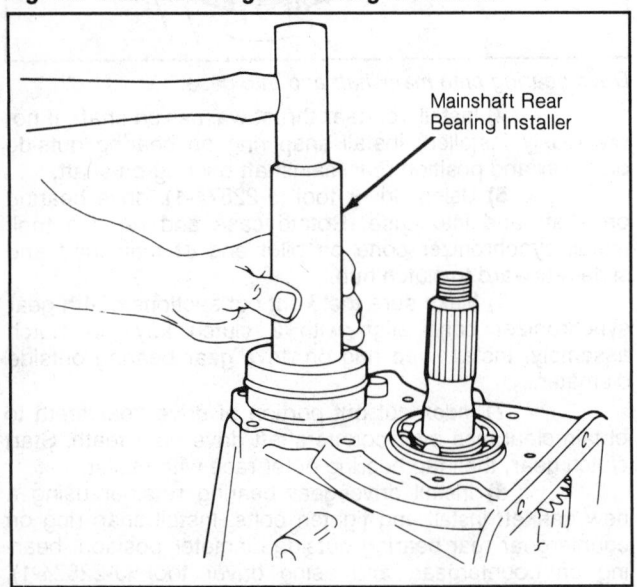

Mainshaft Rear
Bearing Installer

Using installer (J-22874-1) drive bearing into place.

TIGHTENING SPECIFICATIONS

Application	Ft. Lbs. (N.m)
Drive Gear Bearing	
Retainer-to-Case Bolts	25 (32)
Cover-to-Case Bolts	20 (27)
Clutch Gear Bearing-to-Case	25 (32)
Extension and Retainer-to-Case Bolts	
Upper	20 (27)
Lower	30 (40)
Drain & Filler Plug	30 (40)
Shift Lever-to-Shifter Shaft Nut	20 (27)
Crossmember-to-Frame Nuts	55 (75)
Crossmember-to-Mount Bolts	40 (55)

GENERAL MOTORS 5-SPEED — 69.5 MM

Chevrolet Chevette (Diesel)

IDENTIFICATION

Transmission can be identified by a 2 letter code, stamped on a machined pad, on right side of case. Clutch housing and gearbox are a single piece casting.

DESCRIPTION

The transmission is a 5-speed fully synchronized unit with blocker ring synchronizers and a constant mesh reverse gear. First through 4th gears are housed within the case. Reverse and 5th gears are contained in the extension housing.

The input-output shaft and the countershaft are supported by 3 ball bearings. The bearings are located in the front wall of the case, the center support and the extension housing. All gear teeth are helical cut.

LUBRICATION & ADJUSTMENT

See the appropriate article in MANUAL TRANSMISSION SERVICING Section.

REMOVAL & INSTALLATION

TRANSMISSION

See the appropriate article in MANUAL TRANSMISSION REMOVAL Section.

Fig. 1: Cutaway View of General Motors 69.5 mm 5-Speed Transmission

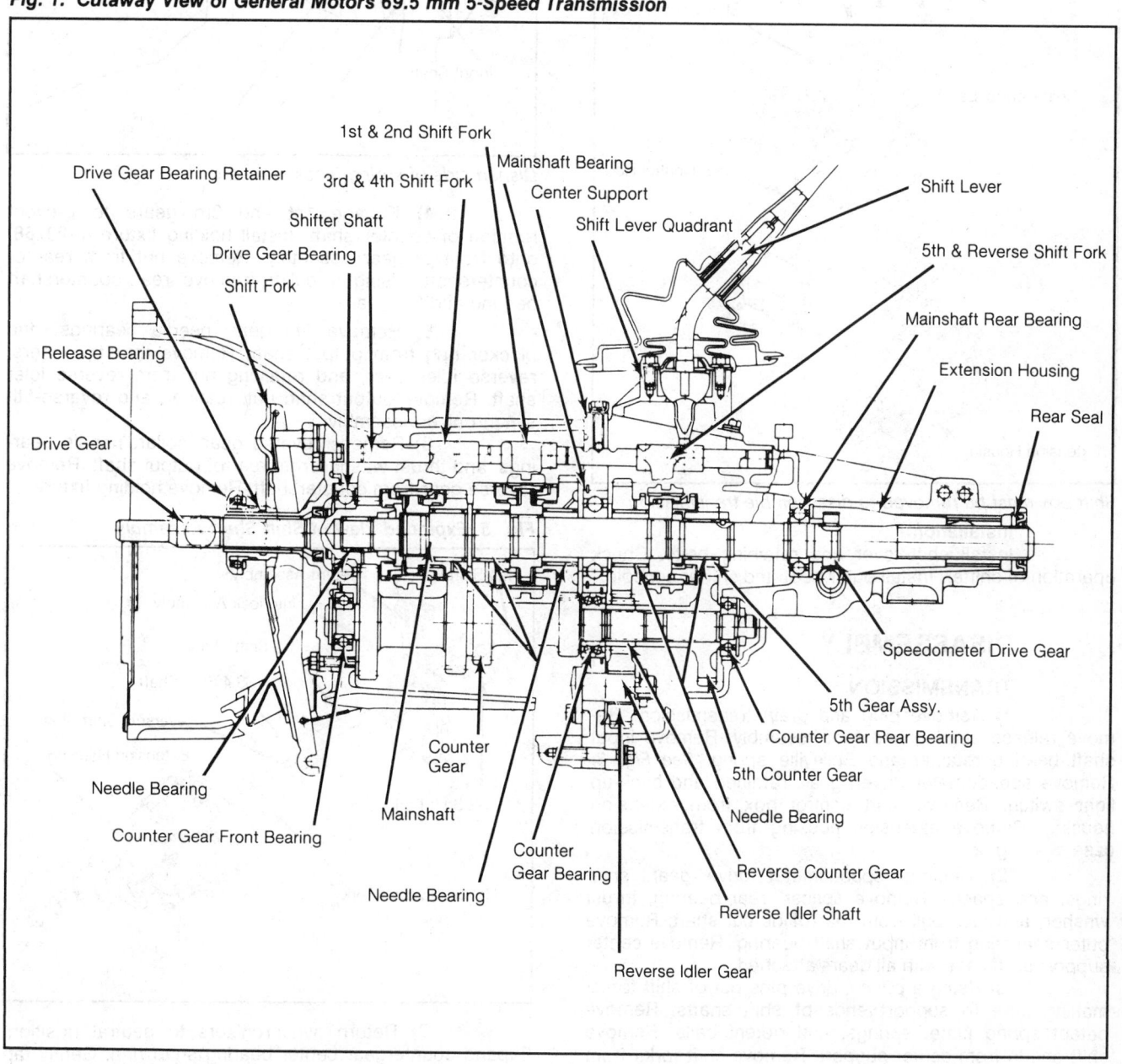

Manual Transmissions

GENERAL MOTORS 5-SPEED — 69.5 MM (Cont.)

SHIFT LEVER

Removal

Removal shifter console. Remove inner and outer shift boots. Remove retaining bolts and shift lever. *See Fig. 2.*

Fig. 2: Exploded View of Shifter

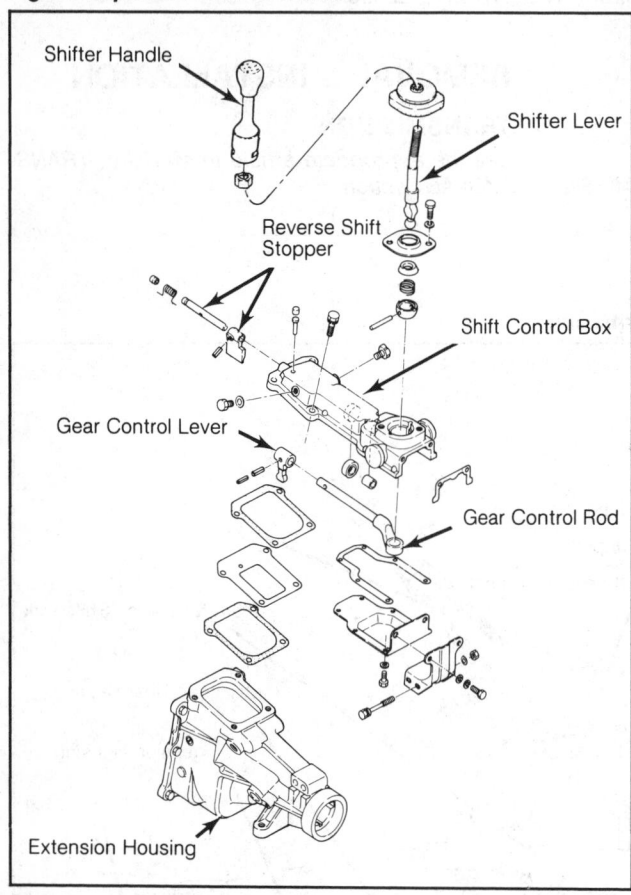

Shift box must be removed to disassemble transmission.

Installation

Install shift lever and retaining bolts. Check operation of shifter. Install outer boot and shifter console.

DISASSEMBLY

TRANSMISSION

1) Remove plug and drain transmission. Remove release bearing and fork assembly. Remove input shaft bearing retainer and Belleville spring. *See Fig. 3.* Remove speedometer driven gear, retainer, and back-up light switch. Remove shift control box from extension housing. Remove extension housing from transmission case. *See Fig. 2.*

2) Remove speedometer drive gear, snap rings, and spacer. Remove spacer, rear bearing, thrust washer, and lock ball from rear of output shaft. Remove outer snap ring from input shaft bearing. Remove center support from case with all gears attached.

3) Using a punch, drive pins out of shift forks, making sure to support ends of shift shafts. Remove detent spring plate, springs, and detent balls. Remove shift shafts from center support. Remove shift forks from synchronizer sleeves. Remove interlock pins. *See Fig. 5.*

Fig. 3: Input Bearing Retainer Assembly

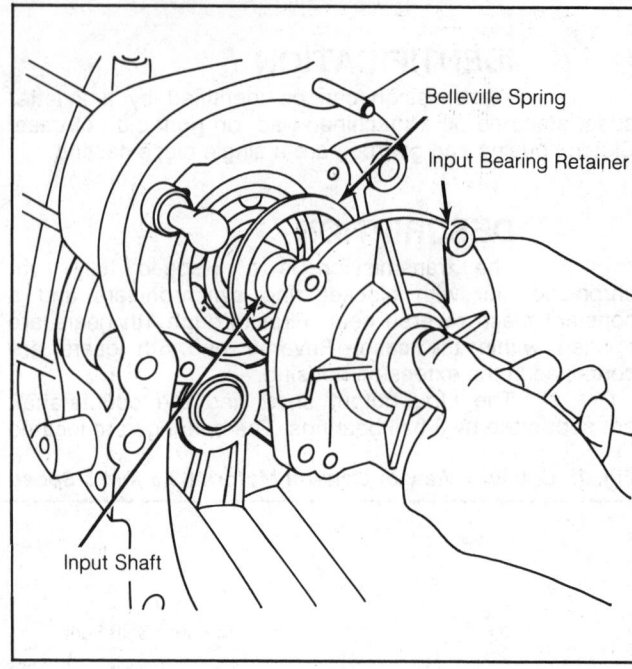

Dished side of spring faces rearward.

4) Engage 1st and 3rd gears to prevent rotation of counter shaft. Install holding fixture (J-29768) onto front of gear assembly. Remove nut from rear of countershaft. Using a puller, remove rear countershaft bearing and 5th gear.

5) Remove 5th gear, needle bearings, and blocker ring from output shaft. Remove thrust washers, reverse idler gear, and retaining nut from reverse idler shaft. Remove output shaft nut, retainer, and reverse-5th synchronizer assembly.

6) Remove reverse gear, collar, needle bearings, and thrust washer from rear of output shaft. Remove reverse gear from countershaft. Remove holding fixture.

Fig. 5 Exploded View of Shift Shaft Assembly

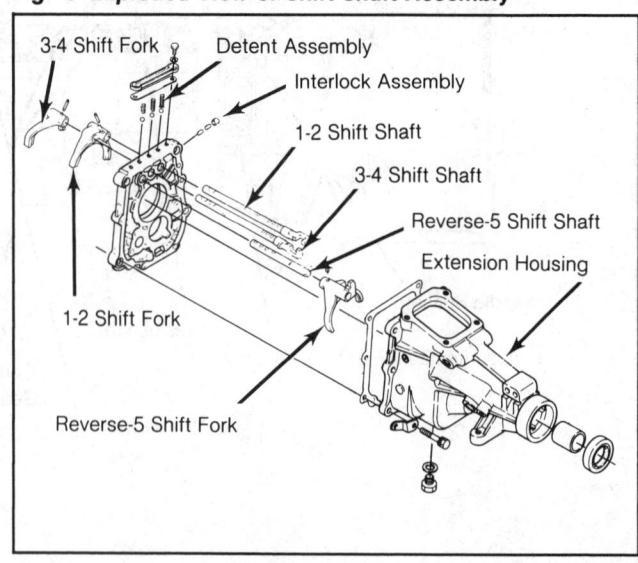

7) Return synchronizers to neutral position. Expand countergear center bearing snap ring. Gently tap on front of center support to remove countershaft.

GENERAL MOTORS 5-SPEED — 69.5 MM (Cont.)

Fig. 4: *Exploded View of 69.5 mm 5-Speed Transmission*

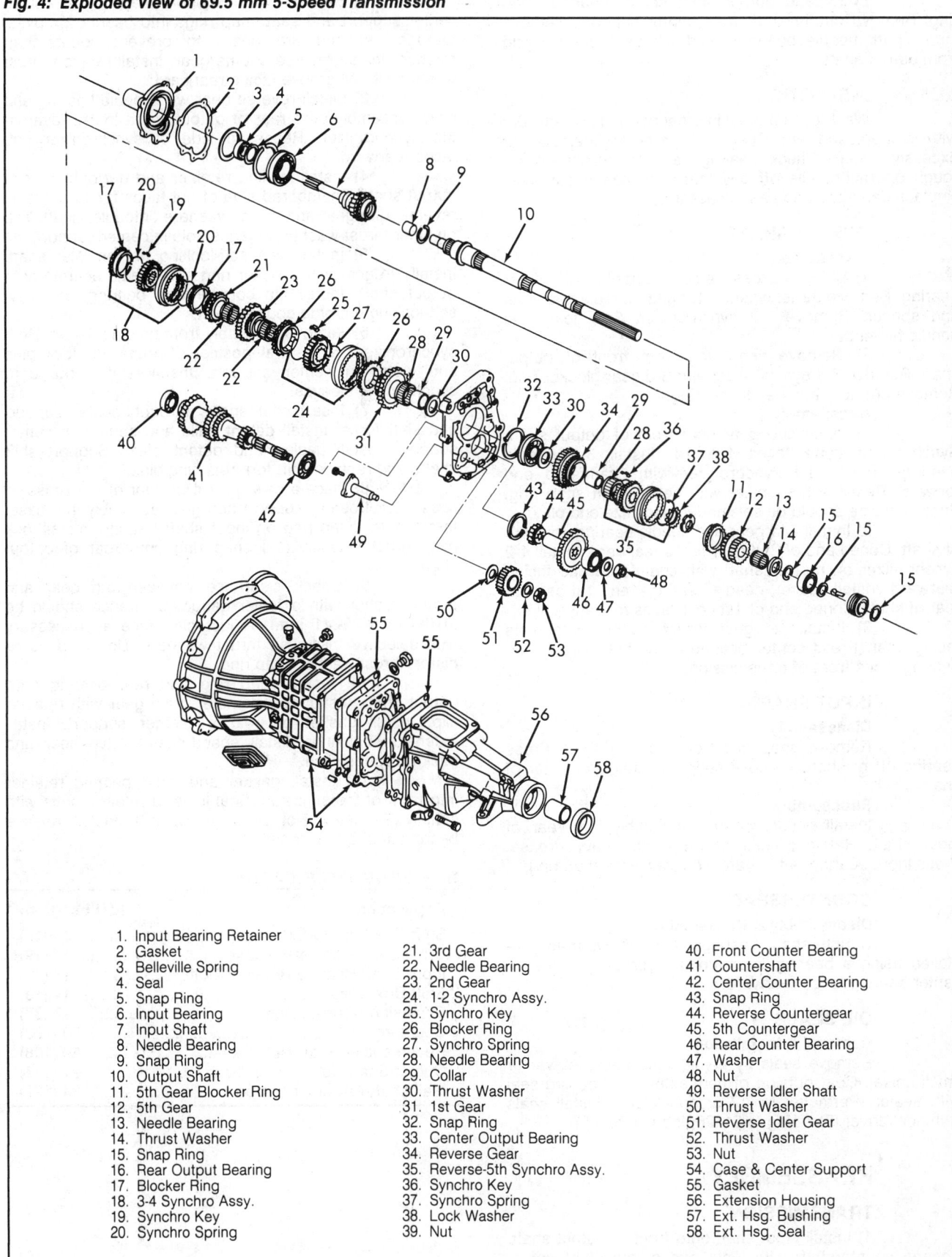

1. Input Bearing Retainer
2. Gasket
3. Belleville Spring
4. Seal
5. Snap Ring
6. Input Bearing
7. Input Shaft
8. Needle Bearing
9. Snap Ring
10. Output Shaft
11. 5th Gear Blocker Ring
12. 5th Gear
13. Needle Bearing
14. Thrust Washer
15. Snap Ring
16. Rear Output Bearing
17. Blocker Ring
18. 3-4 Synchro Assy.
19. Synchro Key
20. Synchro Spring

21. 3rd Gear
22. Needle Bearing
23. 2nd Gear
24. 1-2 Synchro Assy.
25. Synchro Key
26. Blocker Ring
27. Synchro Spring
28. Needle Bearing
29. Collar
30. Thrust Washer
31. 1st Gear
32. Snap Ring
33. Center Output Bearing
34. Reverse Gear
35. Reverse-5th Synchro Assy.
36. Synchro Key
37. Synchro Spring
38. Lock Washer
39. Nut

40. Front Counter Bearing
41. Countershaft
42. Center Counter Bearing
43. Snap Ring
44. Reverse Countergear
45. 5th Countergear
46. Rear Counter Bearing
47. Washer
48. Nut
49. Reverse Idler Shaft
50. Thrust Washer
51. Reverse Idler Gear
52. Thrust Washer
53. Nut
54. Case & Center Support
55. Gasket
56. Extension Housing
57. Ext. Hsg. Bushing
58. Ext. Hsg. Seal

Manual Transmissions

GENERAL MOTORS 5-SPEED — 69.5 MM (Cont.)

8) Expand output shaft center bearing snap ring. Remove output shaft from center support. Remove input shaft, needle bearings, and 4th gear blocker ring from output shaft.

INSPECTION

Wash case and all internal parts in solvent. Dry with compressed air. Check all parts for damage or excessive wear. Check bearings and synchronizers for rough operation. File off any burrs on mating surfaces. Replace damaged parts as necessary.

OUTPUT SHAFT

Disassembly

1) Using a press, remove output shaft center bearing. Remove thrust washer, 1st gear, needle bearings, and spacer. Remove 1-2 synchronizer, 2nd gear, and needle bearings.

2) Remove snap ring from front of output shaft. Remove 3-4 synchronizer and 3rd gear blocker ring. Remove 3rd gear and needle bearings.

Reassembly

1) Install 3rd gear onto front of output shaft. Synchronizer cone faces forward. Install 3rd needle bearings. Install 3-4 synchronizer with chamfered end forward. Retain synchronizer with selective fit snap ring. Snap ring size should be selected to minimize end play.

2) Install 2nd gear and needle bearings on rear of shaft. Coned end of 2nd gear faces rearward. Install 1-2 synchronizer on rear of shaft with chamfered end facing rearward. Install spacer, needle bearing, and 1st gear on rear of shaft. Coned end of 1st gear faces forward.

3) Install 1st gear thrust washer with slots facing gear. Press center bearing onto shaft. Groove on bearing faces front of transmission.

INPUT SHAFT

Disassembly

Remove snap ring from front of shaft. Press bearing off of shaft. Remove needle bearing from rear of shaft.

Reassembly

Install needle bearing assembly into rear of input shaft. Retain needle bearing with heavy grease. Press input bearing onto shaft and retain with snap ring.

COUNTERSHAFT

Disassembly & Reassembly

Countershaft bearings are removed and installed using a bearing separator and press. Groove on center bearing faces rearward.

OIL SEALS

Removal & Installation

Remove seals by prying with a screwdriver or small chisel. Coat outside of new extension housing seal with sealer (Permatex No. 2 or equivalent). Install seals with seal driver (Ext. Hsg. J-21426; Input J-26540).

REASSEMBLY

TRANSMISSION

1) Install input shaft onto front of output shaft. Engage countershaft with input and output shaft gears. Install gear assembly into holding fixture (J-29768). Install center support onto gear assembly.

2) Expand center support snap rings. Position center support and seat snap rings into bearing grooves. Engage 1st and 3rd gears to prevent countershaft rotation. Install reverse countergear. Install reverse thrust washer with oil groove facing rearward.

3) Install reverse gear with needle bearing and collar assembly onto rear of output shaft. Install reverse-5th synchronizer. Recessed side of synchronizer hub faces rearward.

4) Install locking retainer and nut onto rear of output shaft. Chambered side of nut faces forward. Install reverse idler gear and thrust washers onto idler shaft. Tab on inner thrust washer engages hole in center support.

5) Install new self-locking nut on idler shaft. Install 5th gear with blocker ring and needle bearing onto output shaft. Install 5th countergear, bearing, and new self-locking nut onto countershaft.

6) Remove assembly from holding fixture. Shift synchronizers to neutral position. Grease interlock pins and install in center support. Install shift forks onto synchronizer sleeves.

7) Insert shift shafts through center support and shift forks. Install detent balls and springs in center support. Install gasket and detent plate. Support shift shafts and replace shift fork retaining pins.

8) Place a new gasket on rear of transmission case. Install center support and gear assembly into case. Install outer snap ring on input shaft bearing. Install lock ball, thrust washer, and snap ring onto rear of output shaft.

9) Check clearance between 5th gear and thrust washer with a feeler gauge. Clearance should be .010-.016" (.25-.41 mm). Adjust clearance as necessary with selective thickness thrust washers. Do not bend or distort thrust washer snap ring.

10) Install snap ring and rear bearing onto output shaft. Install speedometer drive gear with retainer clip. Install gasket on rear of center support. Install extension housing. Install speedometer drive gear and back-up light switch.

11) Install gasket and input bearing retainer into front of transmission. Seal lower 3 retainer bolts with sealer (Permatex No. 2 or equivalent). Install release bearing and fork assembly.

TIGHTENING SPECIFICATIONS

Application	Ft. Lbs. (N.m)
Shift Quadrant-to-Extension Housing	14 (19)
Drive Gear Retainer-to-Case	14 (19)
Input Shaft Bearing Retainer Bolts	14 (19)
Shift Box Bolts	14 (19)
Extension Housing Bolts	27 (37)
Countergear Nut	80 (108)
Reverse Idler Shaft Nut	80 (108)
Output Shaft Nut	94 (127)
Mainshaft-to-Center Support	94 (127)

GENERAL MOTORS 4-SPEED MANUAL TRANSAXLE

Buick
   Century
   Skyhawk
Chevrolet
   Cavalier
   Celebrity
   Citation

Oldsmobile
   Cutlass Ciera
   Firenza
   Omega
Pontiac
   Phoenix
   2000
   6000

IDENTIFICATION

Transaxle may be identified by code stamped on a machined pad on forward side of transaxle case (clutch housing) next to middle transaxle-to-engine retaining bolt.

NOTE: **For the purpose of this article, Celebrity, Century, Cutlass Ciera and 6000 will be referred to as "A" Body models. Cavalier, Firenza, Skyhawk and 2000 will be referred to as "J" Body models. Citation, Omega, Phoenix and Skylark will be referred to as "X" Body models.**

DESCRIPTION

Final drive and 4-speed transmission are mounted in a common 2-piece aluminum case. Transmission is fully synchronized in all forward gears. Forward gears are helically cut and in constant mesh. Reverse gears are spur cut and are engaged by sliding reverse idler gear. Fourth gear is indirect (overdrive).

The input gear, output gear and differential assembly are all supported by preloaded tapered roller bearings. Final output gear with its integral shaft, turns ring gear and differential assembly, drive axles and front wheel assemblies. *See Fig. 1.*

Gears are shifted by 2 cable assemblies, the trans-selector and trans-shifter cables.

SERVICE (IN VEHICLE)

TRANSAXLE MOUNTS

To check mounts, raise vehicle on hoist. Push up and pull down on transaxle case, observing mounts as you do. If rubber separates from metal plate or mount, or if case moves up but not down, replace mount.

Fig. 1: Cutaway View of General Motors 4-Speed Manual Transaxle

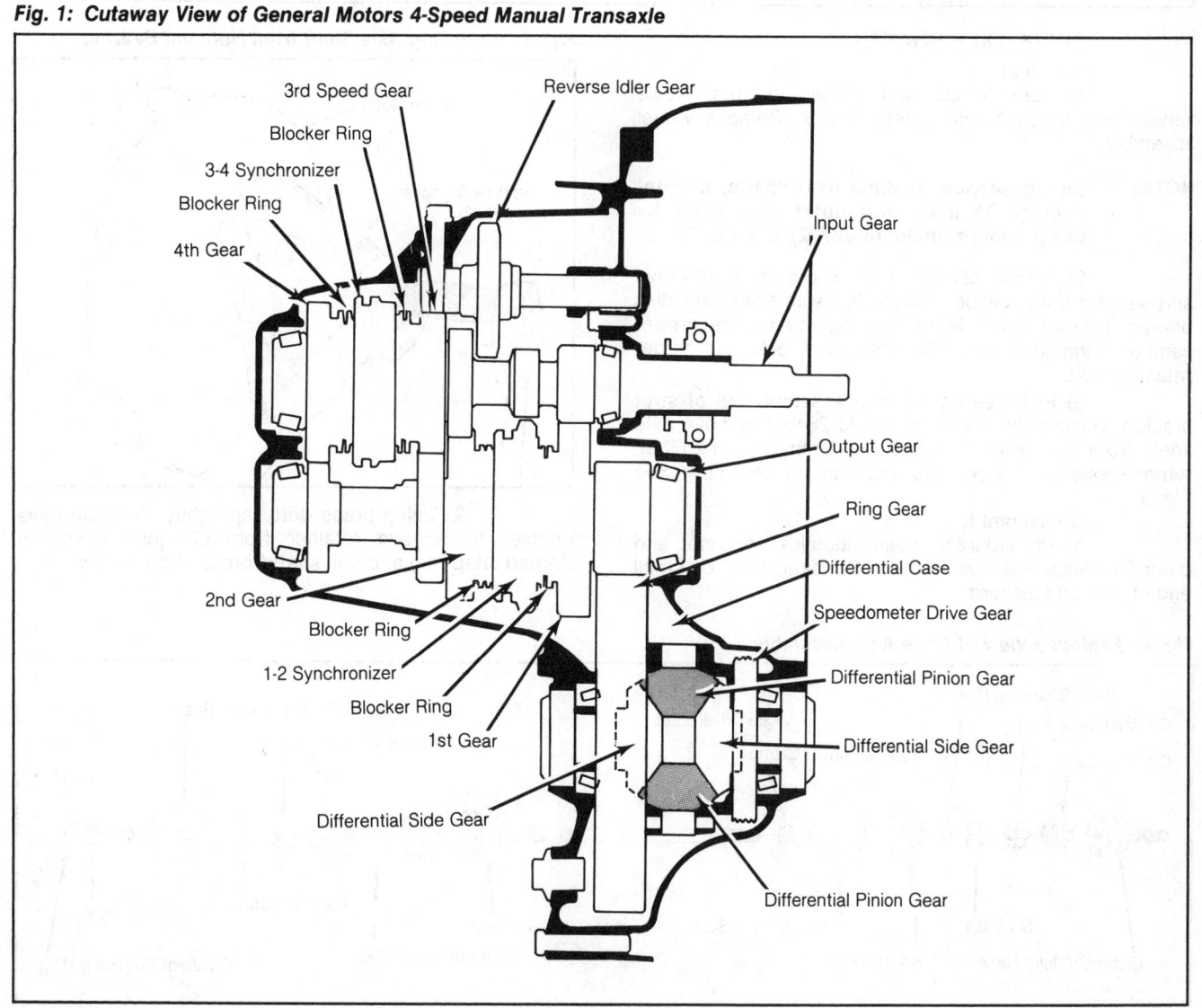

Manual Transmissions

GENERAL MOTORS 4-SPEED MANUAL TRANSAXLE (Cont.)

Fig. 2: Removing Drive Axles from Transaxles

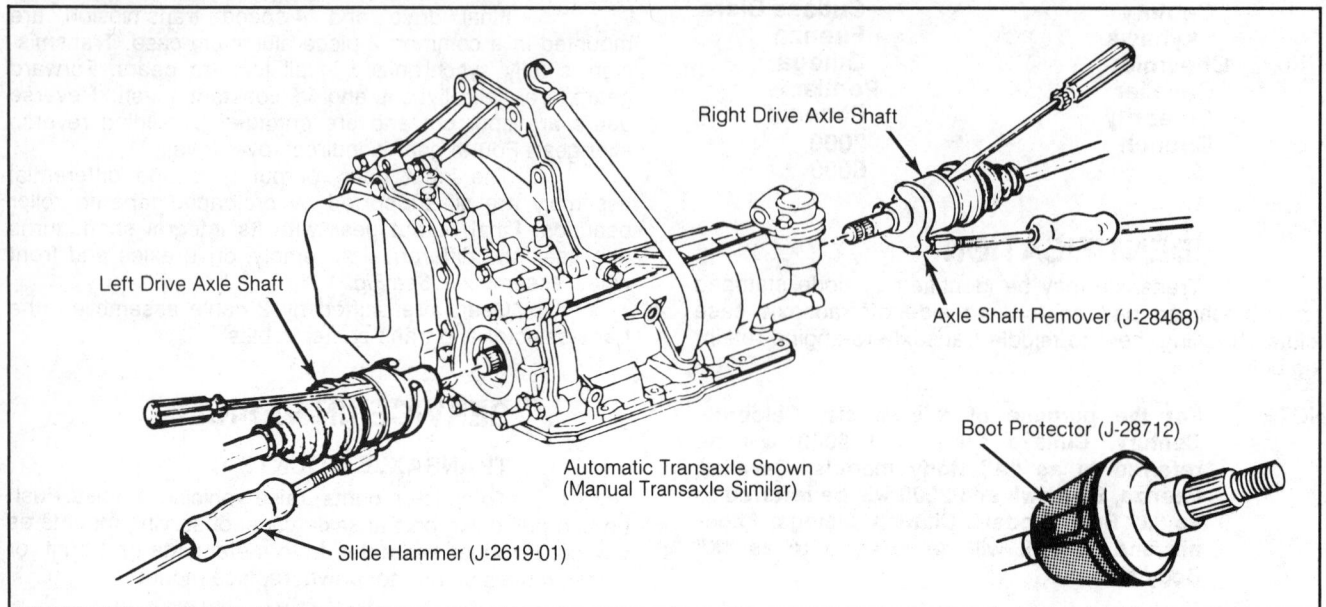

DRIVE AXLE SHAFTS

Removal

1) Loosen hub and wheel lug nuts. Raise vehicle and support with safety stands. Remove wheel assembly.

NOTE: **During service of drive axle shafts, prevent damage to inner and outer joint seals by using boot protector (J-28712). See Fig. 2.**

2) Disconnect brake line clip at strut. Remove and support brake caliper. On models with solid rotor disc brakes, remove rotor. Mark cam bolt to ensure proper camber alignment later. Remove cam bolt and upper retaining bolt.

3) Pull steering knuckle assembly out of strut bracket. Using axle shaft remover (J-28468), remove axle shaft from transaxle. Using spindle remover (J-28733), remove axle shaft from hub and bearing assembly. *See Fig. 3.*

Disassembly

1) Procedure is nearly identical for inner and outer CV joints. *See Figs. 4 and 5.* Cut seal clamp on small end of seal and discard.

Fig. 3: Removing Axle Shaft from Hub and Bearing

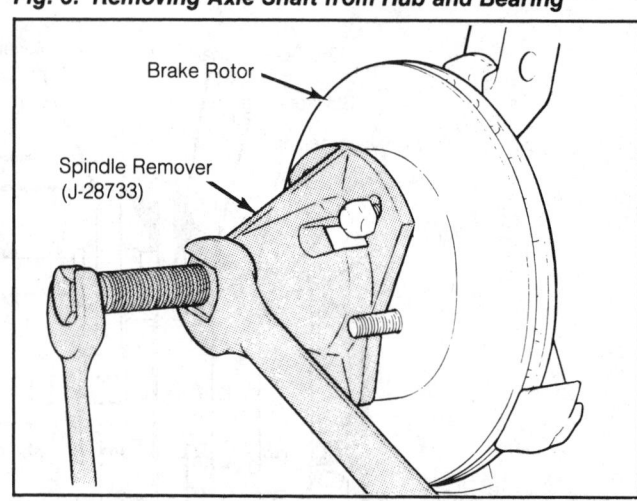

2) Using brass drift, tap lightly all around seal retainer to remove retainer from CV joint assembly. Spread snap ring and pull shaft from joint assembly.

Fig. 4: Exploded View of Drive Axle Assembly

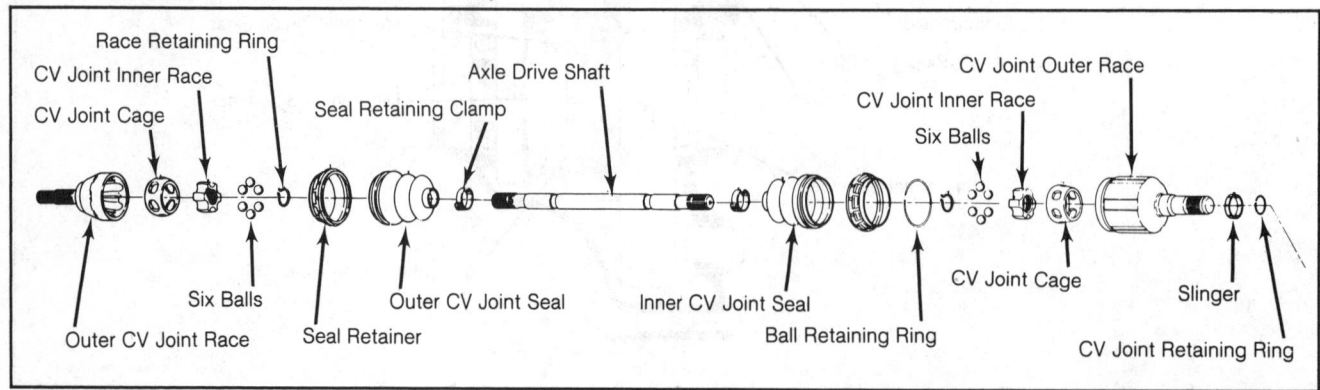

GENERAL MOTORS 4-SPEED MANUAL TRANSAXLE (Cont.)

Fig. 5: Disassembly of Drive Axle and CV Joints

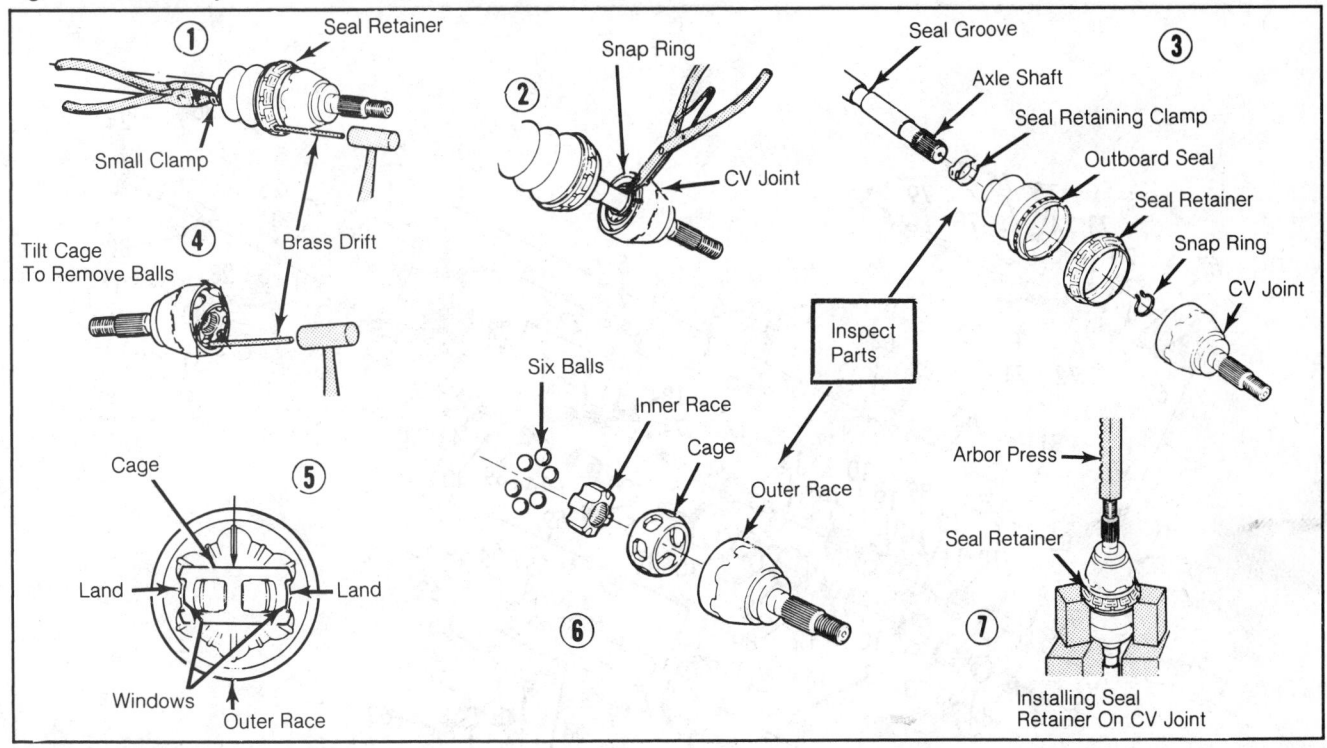

Outer joint illustrated, inner joint is similar.

3) For outer CV joint, use brass drift to tap lightly on bearing cage until it tilts enough to remove one ball bearing. Rotate cage while tapping until all 6 balls are removed from cage.

NOTE: On inner CV joint, remove ball retaining ring and balls will come out when cage and inner race are removed from outer race.

4) On outer joints, pivot cage, and inner race until 90° to normal installed position (cage windows will align with lands of outer race). *See Fig. 5.*

5) Lift cage and inner race out of outer race. Rotate inner race and lift upward out of cage.

Cleaning & Inspection

1) Wash all parts in solvent and dry with compressed air. Inspect outer ball races for excessive wear and scoring. Inspect splined stub shaft for wear and cracks.

2) Inspect all 6 ball bearings for pitting, cracking, or scoring. Dulling of surface is normal. Inspect cage for excessive wear on inside and outside spherical surfaces. Look for heavy brinelling of cage window and for cracks or chips.

3) Inspect inner race for excessive wear or scoring. If any of the above damage is found, replace entire CV joint assembly. Polished areas in races and on cage spheres are normal and do not require joint replacement.

Reassembly

1) Apply a light coat of grease on ball grooves of inner and outer races. Install inner race into cage using a rotating action opposite of removal. Inner race snap ring should face axle side.

2) On inner CV joints, be sure ball bearing retaining ring is installed on inner race side facing small end of cage. Align windows of cage with outer race lands, and pivot cage with inner race into tilted position (opposite of removal).

3) Install ball bearings one at a time into outer CV joint as cage is rotated and tilted. On inner CV joint, insert ball bearings through cage windows. After all 6 balls have been installed into cage of outer CV joint, pivot cage and inner race assembly into installed position.

4) Slide new seal clamp for small end of seal, seal, and seal retainer onto axle shaft. Coat inside lip (large diameter end) of seal with grease. Slide seal retainer onto end of seal.

5) Spread ears of bearing race snap ring, and slide CV joint onto axle shaft until snap ring seats in groove. Pack joint with approximately 1/2 the grease provided in seal kit. Apply remaining grease inside seal. Slide seal toward joint until small end of seal is in groove of axle shaft.

6) Position small clamp over small end of seal and into groove and tighten. Place assembly vertically into an arbor press, with CV joint up so seal retainer is supported. *See Fig. 5.* Press CV joint downward onto retainer. Make sure seal stays in retainer during reassembly.

Installation

1) Position drive axle loosely into steering knuckle and transaxle. Install steering knuckle into strut bracket and tighten strut bracket bolts finger tight only. Install brake caliper and tighten.

NOTE: If drive axle is being replaced, replacement of knuckle seal is recommended.

2) Install drive axle through steering knuckle. Install hub nut and tighten. When shaft begins to turn, use

Manual Transmissions

GENERAL MOTORS 4-SPEED MANUAL TRANSAXLE (Cont.)

Fig. 6: Exploded View of General Motors 4-Speed Manual Transaxle

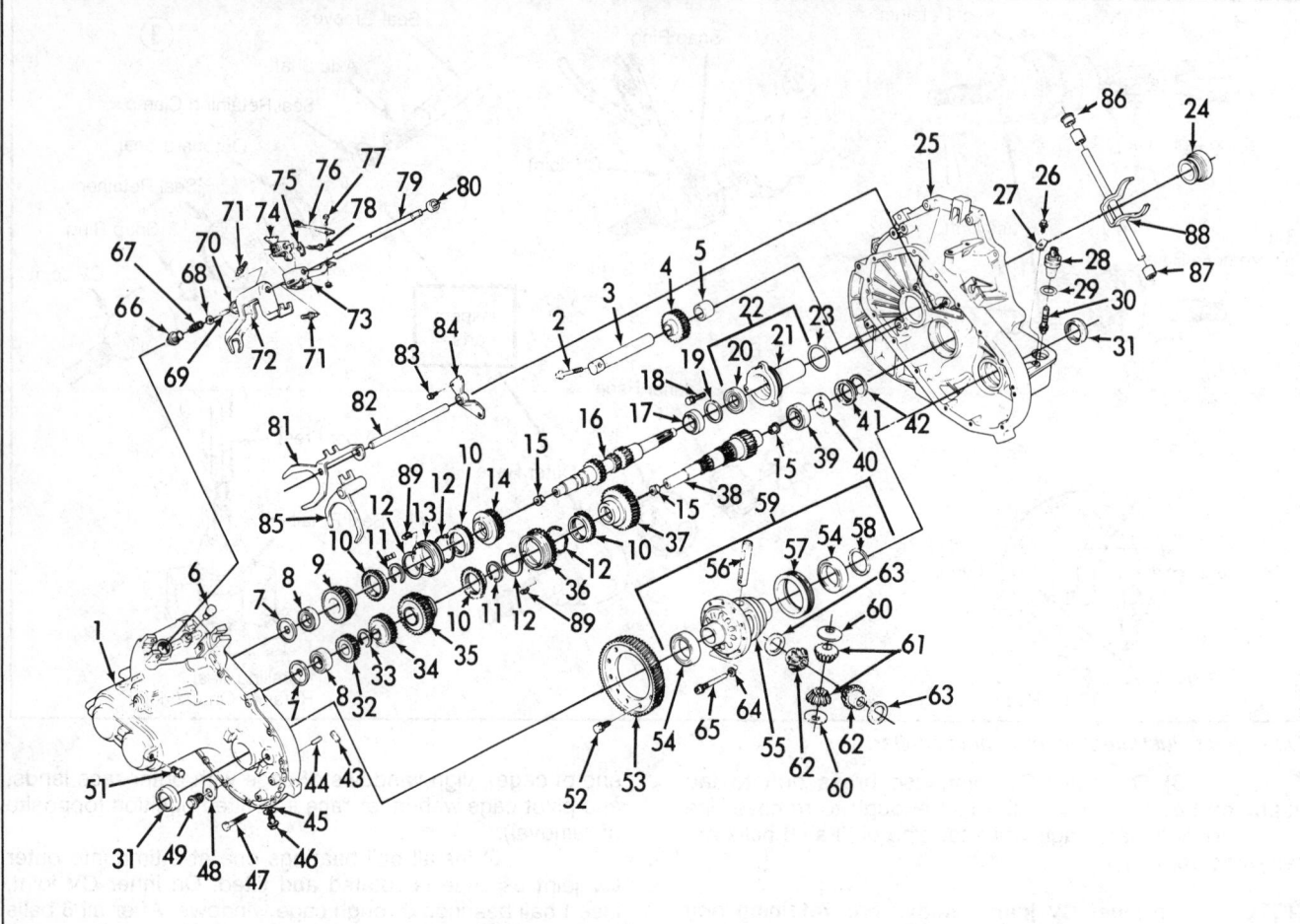

1. Transaxle Case	31. Axle Shaft Seal	60. Pinion Thrust Washer
2. Reverse Idler Screw	32. 4th Speed Output Gear	61. Differential Pinion Gear
3. Reverse Idler Shaft	33. 3rd Speed Output Gear Retaining Ring	62. Differential Side Gear
4. Reverse Idler Gear	34. 3rd Speed Output Gear	63. Side Gear Thrust Washer
5. Reverse Idler Shaft Spacer	35. 2nd Speed Output Gear	64. Lock Washer
6. Vent Assembly	36. Synchronizer Assembly	65. Pinion Shaft Screw
7. Oil Shield	37. 1st Gear Output	66. Reverse Inhibitor Spring Seat
8. Bearing Assembly	38. Output Gear	67. Reverse Inhibitor Spring
9. 4th Gear Input	39. Output Bearing Assembly	68. Reverse Inhibitor Spring Washer
10. Synchronizer Blocking Ring	40. Output Gear Bearing Adjustment Shim	69. Pin
11. Synchronizer Retaining Ring	41. Output Bearing Oil Shield	70. Shift Shaft Shim
12. Synchronizer Key Retaining Ring	42. Output Gear Bearing Oil Shield Retainer	71. Reverse Lever Locating Stud
13. Synchronizer Assembly	43. Magnet	72. Reverse Shift Lever
14. 3rd Gear Input	44. Pin	73. Shift Interlock
15. Oil Shield Sleeve	45. Drain Screw Washer	74. Detent Lever Assembly
16. Input Cluster Gear	46. Drain Screw	75. Lock Detent Lever Washer
17. Input Bearing Assembly	47. Bolt	76. Detent Spring
18. Screw	48. Fill Plug Washer	77. Bolt
19. Input Gear Bearing Adjustment Shim	49. Fill Plug	78. Bolt
20. Input Gear Seal Assembly	50. Nut	79. Shift Shaft
21. Input Gear Retainer	51. Plug	80. Shift Shaft Seal Assembly
22. Input Gear Bearing Retainer Assembly	52. Bolt	81. 3rd-4th Shift Fork
23. Input Gear Bearing Retainer Seal	53. Differential Ring Gear	82. Shift Fork Shaft
24. Clutch Release Bearing Assembly	54. Differential Bearing	83. Screw
25. Clutch & Differential Housing	55. Differential Case	84. Oil Guide
26. Screw	56. Differential Pinion Shaft	85. 1st-2nd Shift Fork
27. Speedometer Gear Retainer	57. Speedometer Drive Gear	86. Clutch Fork Shaft Seal
28. Speedometer Driven Gear Sleeve	58. Differential Bearing Adjustment Shim	87. Clutch Fork Shaft Bearing
29. Speedometer Gear Sleeve Seal	59. Differential Assembly	88. Clutch Fork Shaft
30. Speedometer Driven Gear		89. Synchronizer Keys

GENERAL MOTORS 4-SPEED MANUAL TRANSAXLE (Cont.)

holding tool to prevent hub from turning. Replace rotor if removed.

NOTE: **Axle shaft is an interference fit in steering knuckle and should seat properly when tightened to 70 ft. lbs. (95 N.m).**

3) Apply upward load to hub assembly by lowering vehicle onto safety stand. Align cam bolt with alignment marks made earlier. Tighten, and then tighten strut bracket.

4) Position screwdriver in groove provided on inner retainer. See Fig. 2. Complete axle shaft installation by tapping screwdriver until shaft seats.

5) Connect brake line clip to strut bracket, and install wheel assembly. Lower vehicle and tighten lug nuts and hub.

REMOVAL & INSTALLATION

See the appropriate article in MANUAL TRANSMISSION REMOVAL Section.

DISASSEMBLY

TRANSAXLE

1) Place transaxle assembly into work stand (J-28408) to prevent assembly from falling over. Remove 15 bolts retaining clutch cover.

2) Using soft mallet, tap clutch cover from case. See Fig. 7. Remove ring gear and differential assembly.

3) Position shifter shaft in neutral position, so shifter moves easily and is not engaged in any drive gear. Remove bolt from shifter shaft. Remove shaft and shift forks from synchronizer forks.

4) Remove reverse shift fork by disengaging it from guide pin and interlock bracket. Remove gear, shaft, and spacer assembly.

5) Remove detent shift lever and interlock assembly. Leave shift forks engaged with synchronizers. Grasp input and output shafts and lift them from transaxle

Fig. 7: Transaxle with Clutch Cover Removed

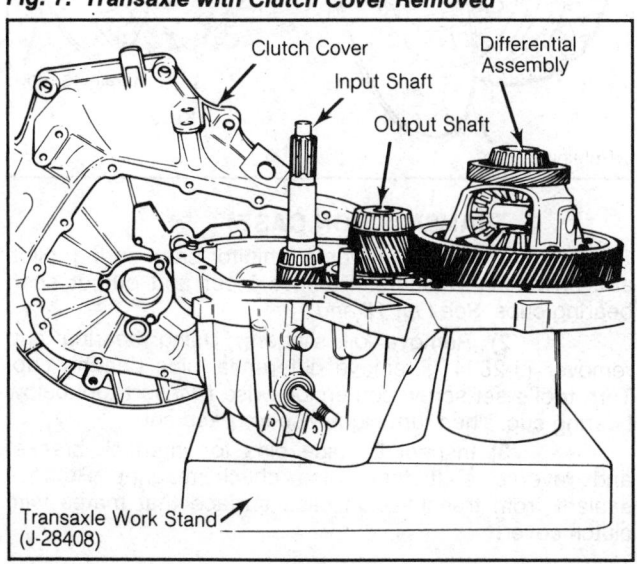

Clutch Cover
Input Shaft
Output Shaft
Differential Assembly
Transaxle Work Stand
(J-28408)

Fig. 8: Input and Output Shafts With Shift Forks

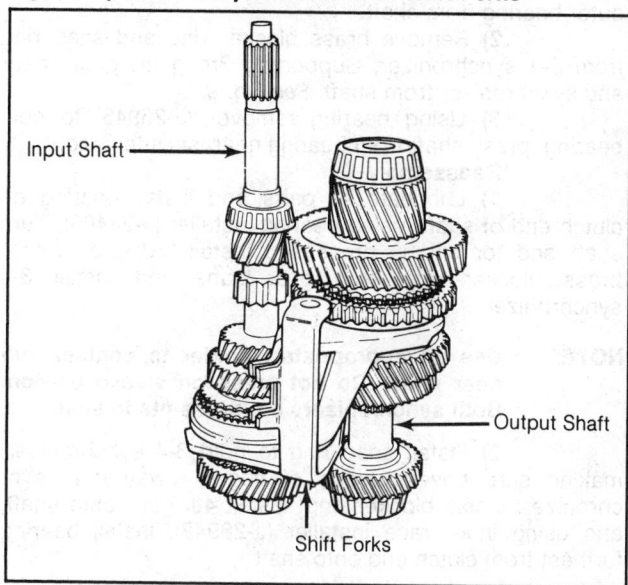

Input Shaft
Output Shaft
Shift Forks

case as an assembly. See Fig. 8. After noting shift fork positions for reassembly reference, remove shift forks.

COMPONENT DISASSEMBLY & REASSEMBLY

INPUT SHAFT

Disassembly

1) Pressing on end of shaft furthest from clutch in normal installed position, and supporting 4th gear

Fig. 9: Components of Input Shaft

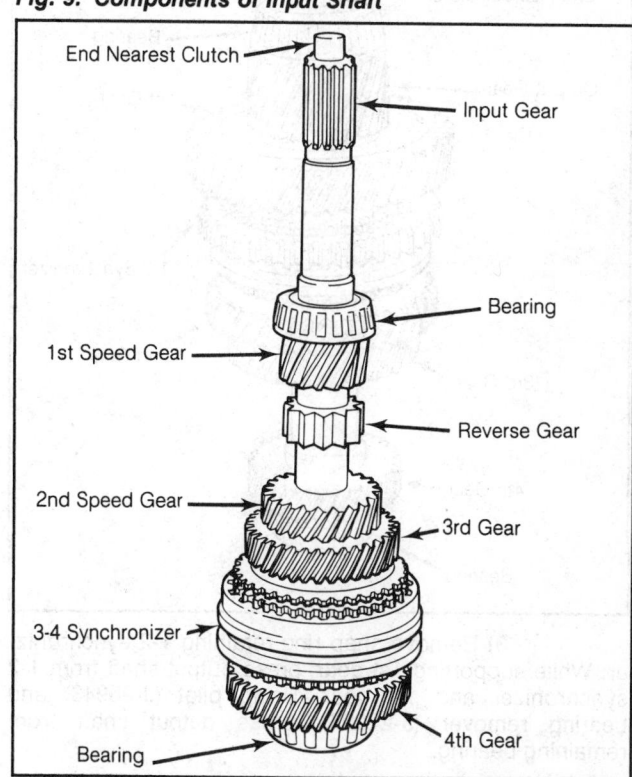

End Nearest Clutch
Input Gear
Bearing
1st Speed Gear
Reverse Gear
2nd Speed Gear
3rd Gear
3-4 Synchronizer
4th Gear
Bearing

GENERAL MOTORS 4-SPEED MANUAL TRANSAXLE (Cont.)

with bearing remover (J-22912-01), remove 4th gear and outer bearing from shaft.

2) Remove brass blocker ring and snap ring from 3-4 synchronizer. Supporting 3rd gear, press gear and synchronizer from shaft. *See Fig. 9.*

3) Using bearing remover (J-26946) to hold bearing, press shaft from bearing nearest clutch end.

Reassembly

1) Lubricate all parts and install bearing on clutch end of shaft, using bearing installer (J-28406). Turn shaft end for end in press and install 3rd gear. Install brass blocker ring onto gear cone and install 3-4 synchronizer.

NOTE: **Use an appropriate cylinder to contact hub near shaft. Do not press on sleeve portion. Both synchronizers are press fits to shaft.**

2) Install snap ring to hold 3-4 synchronizer, making sure beveled edge of ring is away from synchronizer. Install blocker ring. Install 4th gear onto shaft, and using inner race installer (J-26942), install bearing furthest from clutch end onto shaft

OUTPUT SHAFT

Disassembly

1) Place support under 4th gear and install pilot (J-26943) on end of shaft. Press output shaft from 4th gear and bearing. *See Fig. 10.*

2) Remove snap ring retaining 3rd gear. Slide 1-2 synchronizer assembly into 1st gear position, so press plates support 2nd gear. Press 2nd gear and 3rd gear from output shaft and remove brass blocker ring.

Fig. 10: Components of Output Shaft

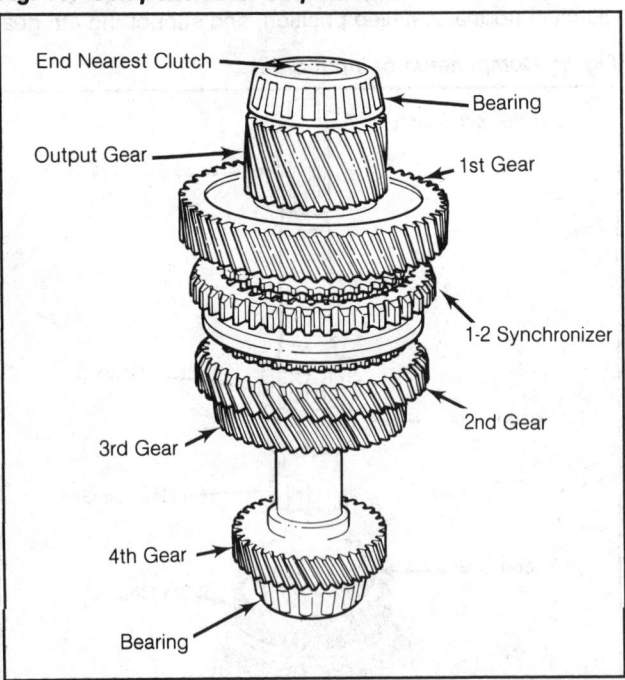

End Nearest Clutch
Bearing
Output Gear
1st Gear
1-2 Synchronizer
2nd Gear
3rd Gear
4th Gear
Bearing

3) Remove snap ring retaining 1-2 synchronizer. While supporting 1st gear, press output shaft from 1-2 synchronizer and 1st gear. Using pilot (J-26943) and bearing remover (J-22227), press output shaft from remaining bearing.

Reassembly

1) Using pilot (J-6133A), install bearing on end of output shaft that is normally closest to clutch. Turn shaft end for end and install 1st gear, brass blocker ring and 1-2 synchronizer. Using an appropriate cylinder, press on hub near shaft. Do not press on sleeve.

2) Install snap ring for 1-2 synchronizer and place brass blocker ring into position. Place 2nd gear on shaft. Press 3rd gear onto shaft with hub toward 4th gear. Use a cylinder that contacts 3rd gear near shaft.

3) Install snap ring for 3rd gear. Press 4th gear onto output shaft with hub toward 3rd gear. Use inner race installer (J-26942) to install remaining bearing on end of shaft furthest from clutch.

SYNCHRONIZERS

Disassembly

Using care, pry out both synchronizer retaining rings. Separate hub, sleeve, and 3 keys, noting their position. *See Fig. 11.* Scribe hub to sleeve location and separate. Clean, inspect, and replace parts, as necessary.

Reassembly

1) Assemble hub to sleeve with lip of hub away from shift fork groove in sleeve. Align scribe marks. Carefully install retaining ring, prying it back to insert keys one at a time.

2) Flats on retaining ring should hold keys in place. Install retaining ring on opposite side of hub, so open end of ring does not align with open end of first ring.

Fig. 11: Components of Synchronizer Assemblies

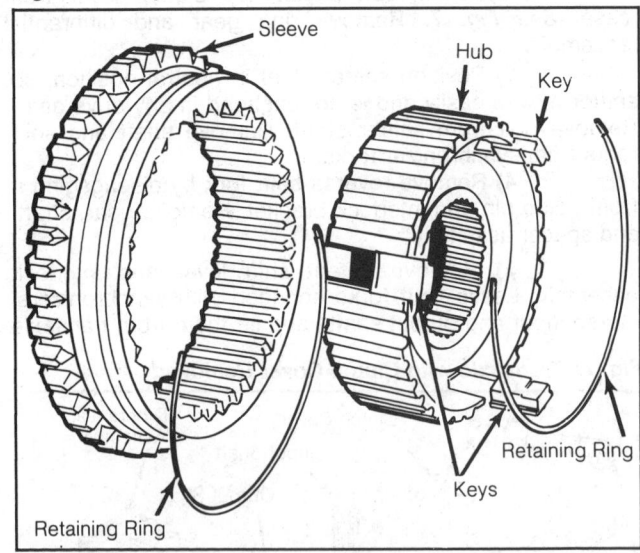

Sleeve
Hub
Key
Retaining Ring
Keys
Retaining Ring

TRANSMISSION CASE

1) Remove reverse inhibitor seat, spring, pilot, and shimming washers. Remove input and output shaft bearing cups. *See Fig. 12 and 13.*

2) Remove oil slingers. Using bearing cup remover (J-26941), remove differential side bearing cup. Turn tool's set screw couterclockwise to insert tool below bearing cup. Then turn clockwise to grasp cut.

3) Inspect 2 guide pins for interlock bracket and reverse shift fork. Also check magnet. Remove sealant from transmission case surface that mates with clutch cover.

GENERAL MOTORS 4-SPEED MANUAL TRANSAXLE (Cont.)

Fig. 12: Removing Reverse Inhibitor Assembly

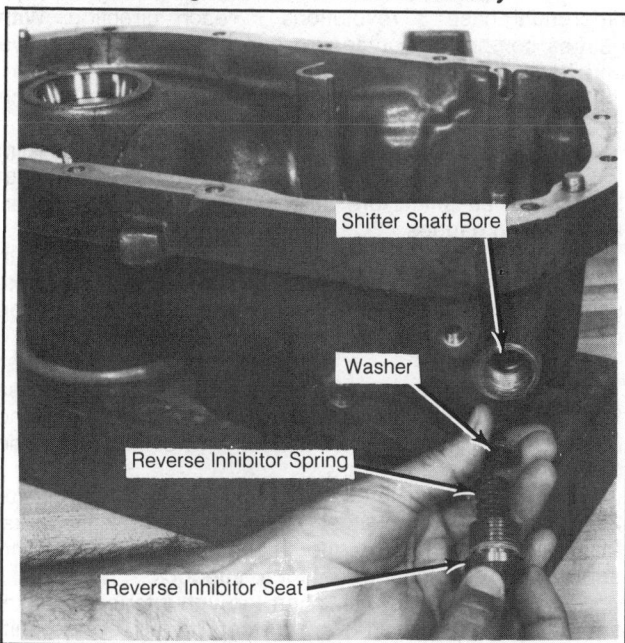

Fig. 13: Removing Bearing Cups

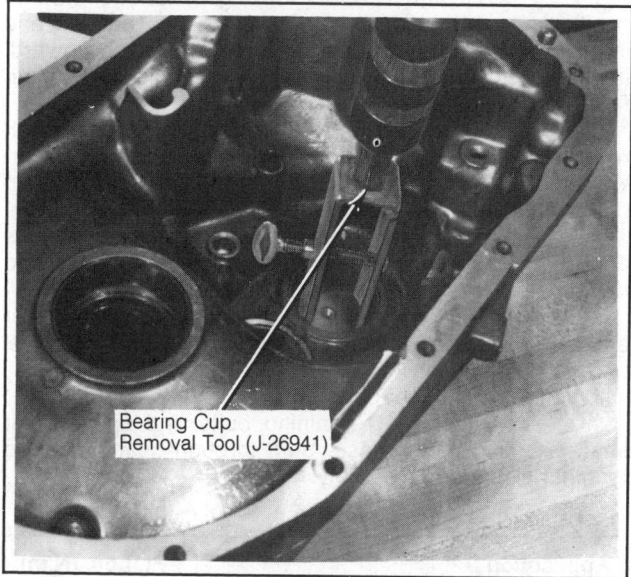

Use bearing cup remover (J-26941). When installing cups, use bearing cup installer (J-26938).

4) Take care not to gouge mating surfaces, as leaks could result. Clean all parts. Replace parts, as necessary, after careful inspection.

CLUTCH COVER

Disassembly

1) Using bearing cup remover (J-26941), remove differential side bearing cup and shim from cover. Remove input and output shaft bearing cups with same tool. Remove oil shield, shim, and retainer from under output shaft bearing cup.

2) Remove input gear bearing retainer (release bearing sleeve). Tap carefully, if necessary, to remove.

Remove external oil ring and internal oil seal from sleeve. Remove plastic oil scoop.

3) If replacement of clutch fork shaft or bushing is necessary, use bushing remover/installer (J-28412) for both removal and installation. Always replace seal after installing clutch fork shaft or bushing. *See Fig. 14.*

Fig. 14: Replacing Clutch Fork Shaft and Bushings

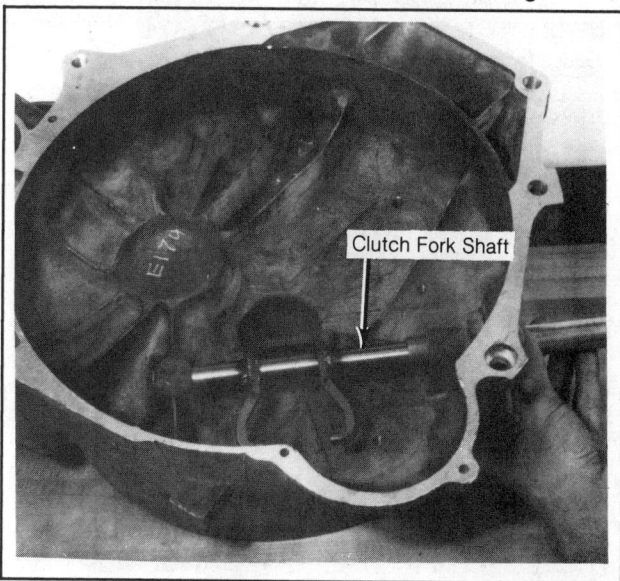

4) Remove sealant from cover mating surfaces, using care not to damage surfaces. Clean and inspect all parts, replacing those that are damaged.

Reassembly

Install plastic oil scoop, replace external square cut oil ring on sleeves. Install input bearing retainer (release bearing sleeve). Using bearing cup installer (J-26936), install internal oil seal. Reverse remainder of disassembly procedures.

DIFFERENTIAL CASE & RING GEAR

Disassembly

1) Separate ring gear from differential case. Remove pinion shaft lock bolt and pinion shaft. Roll gears and thrust washers out through opening in case.

2) If differential side bearings are to be replaced, use puller (J-22888 and J-22888-20). Use cone installer (J-22919) when installing bearings. Clean and inspect all parts. Replace parts, where necessary.

Reassembly

Install gears and thrust washers into case. Install pinion shaft and lock bolt. Attach ring gear to differential case.

REASSEMBLY

TRANSAXLE

Shim Selection

NOTE: **Shims may be selected for proper preload as soon as input and output shaft assemblies and differential assembly are reassembled and ready for installation in transaxle case.**

GENERAL MOTORS 4-SPEED MANUAL TRANSAXLE (Cont.)

1) Place transaxle case into holding fixture (J-28408). *See Fig. 7.* Install 3 bearing races into case, and install input, output and differential assemblies in position. Install remaining 3 bearing races onto their respective bearings.

Fig. 15: Installing Gauges Over Shaft Bearings

2) Install gauges over each bearing (J-26935-2 for input shaft; J-26935-4 for output shaft; and J-26935-3 for differential shaft). *See Fig. 16.* Be sure bearing races fit smoothly in bores of gauges.

3) Install metal oil shield retainer into bore on top of output shaft gauge (J-26935-4). Carefully assemble clutch cover over gauges and onto transaxle case, using 7 spacers evenly around case mating surfaces.

4) Install bolts supplied and tighten bolts alternately to gradually draw clutch cover to transaxle case. Tighten bolts to 10 ft. lbs. (14 N.m) to compress gauge sleeves.

Fig. 16: Measuring Gap to Determine Preload Shim Requirements

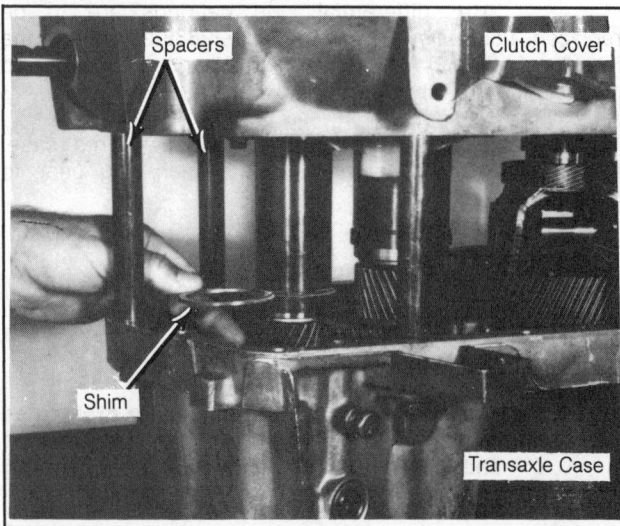

Rotate case 3 times in each direction.

5) Rotate each gauge to seat bearings. Rotate differential case 3 revolutions in each direction. With gauges compressed, measure gap between outer sleeve and base pad of each shaft. This will provide the shim thickness required for proper bearing preloading at each shaft. *See Fig. 16.*

6) Use one size smaller than the largest shim that can be placed into the gap and drawn through without binding. When shims are selected, remove clutch cover, spacers and gauges.

7) Install shims into their respective bores in clutch cover. Add metal shield, and install bearing cups, using cup installer (J-26936 on input shaft; J-23423-A on output shaft; and J-26938 on differential bearing cup).

Case

1) Position input and output shaft assemblies together on bench. Install 2 shift forks. Grasp shafts and forks as an assembly, and carefully lower into transaxle case. Do not damage gears.

2) Place interlock bracket onto guide pin (J-28411). Be sure bracket engages fingers on shift forks. Place detent shift lever into interlock. Using a straight-edge, check alignment of detent to interlock.

3) Install shifter shaft through interlock bracket and detent shift lever, but no further. Install reverse shift fork onto guide pin. Be sure reverse shift fork engages interlock bracket.

4) Install reverse idler gear and shaft into position. Be sure long end of shaft points upward and large champfered ends of gear tooth are facing upward. Install spacer onto shaft. Flat on reverse idler shaft must face input gear shaft.

5) Complete installation of shifter shaft through reverse shift fork until it pilots into inhibitor spring spacer. With shaft in neutral position, install bolt and lock through detent shift lever. Bend tab of lock over bolt head.

6) Install fork shaft through synchronizer forks and into bore in case. Carefully install ring gear and differential case assembly. Install magnet.

7) Apply a thin bead of sealant to clutch cover and carefully install cover onto transaxle case. Use dowel pins to guide cover into position. Tap clutch cover lightly with soft mallet to seat parts securely.

8) Install 15 retaining bolts and tighten idler shaft retaining bolt in case. Shift through gear ranges to test that all parts move freely.

TIGHTENING SPECIFICATIONS

Application	Ft. Lbs. (N.m)
Case-to-Clutch Cover	
Shim Selection	10 (14)
Final Assembly	16 (22)
Engine-to-Transaxle	55 (75)
Stabilizer Bar Bushing Retainer	
Crossmember	40 (54)
Control Arm	35 (47)
Suspension	
Cam Bolt	140 (190)
Upper Bolt	140 (190)
Brake Caliper	30 (41)
Drive Axle-to-Steering Knuckle	70 (95)
Hub Nut	225 (305)
Cradle	
Sidemember-to-Crossmember	34-47 (46-64)
Body Mount	66 (90)
Engine Support Bolts	50 (68)

GENERAL MOTORS 5-SPEED MANUAL TRANSAXLE

**Buick Skyhawk, Cadillac Cimarron,
Chevrolet Cavalier, Oldsmobile Firenza,
Pontiac 2000**

IDENTIFICATION

Transaxle may be identified by code stamped on a machined pad on forward side of transaxle case (clutch housing) next to middle transaxle-to-engine retaining bolt.

DESCRIPTION

Final drive and 5-speed transmission are mounted in a common 2-piece aluminum case. Transmission is fully synchronized in all forward gears. Forward gears are helically cut and in constant mesh. Reverse gears are spur cut and are engaged by sliding reverse idler gear.

The input gear, output gear and differential assembly are all supported by preloaded tapered roller bearings. Final output gear with its integral shaft, turns ring gear and differential assembly, drive axles, and front wheel assemblies. *See Fig. 1.*

Gears are shifted by 2 cable assemblies, the trans-selector and trans-shifter cables.

SERVICE (IN VEHICLE)

TRANSAXLE MOUNTS

To check mounts, raise vehicle on hoist. Push up and pull down on transaxle case. If rubber separates from metal plate or mount, or if case moves up but not down, replace mount.

DRIVE AXLE SHAFTS
Removal

1) Loosen hub and wheel lug nuts. Raise vehicle and support with safety stands. Remove wheel assembly.

NOTE: During service of drive axle shafts, prevent damage to inner and outer joint seals by using boot protector (J-28712). See Fig. 2.

2) Disconnect brake line clip at strut. Remove and support brake caliper. On models with solid rotor disc brakes, remove rotor. Mark cam bolt to ensure proper camber alignment later. Remove cam bolt and upper retaining bolt.

Fig. 1: Sectional View of General Motors 5-Speed Manual Transaxle

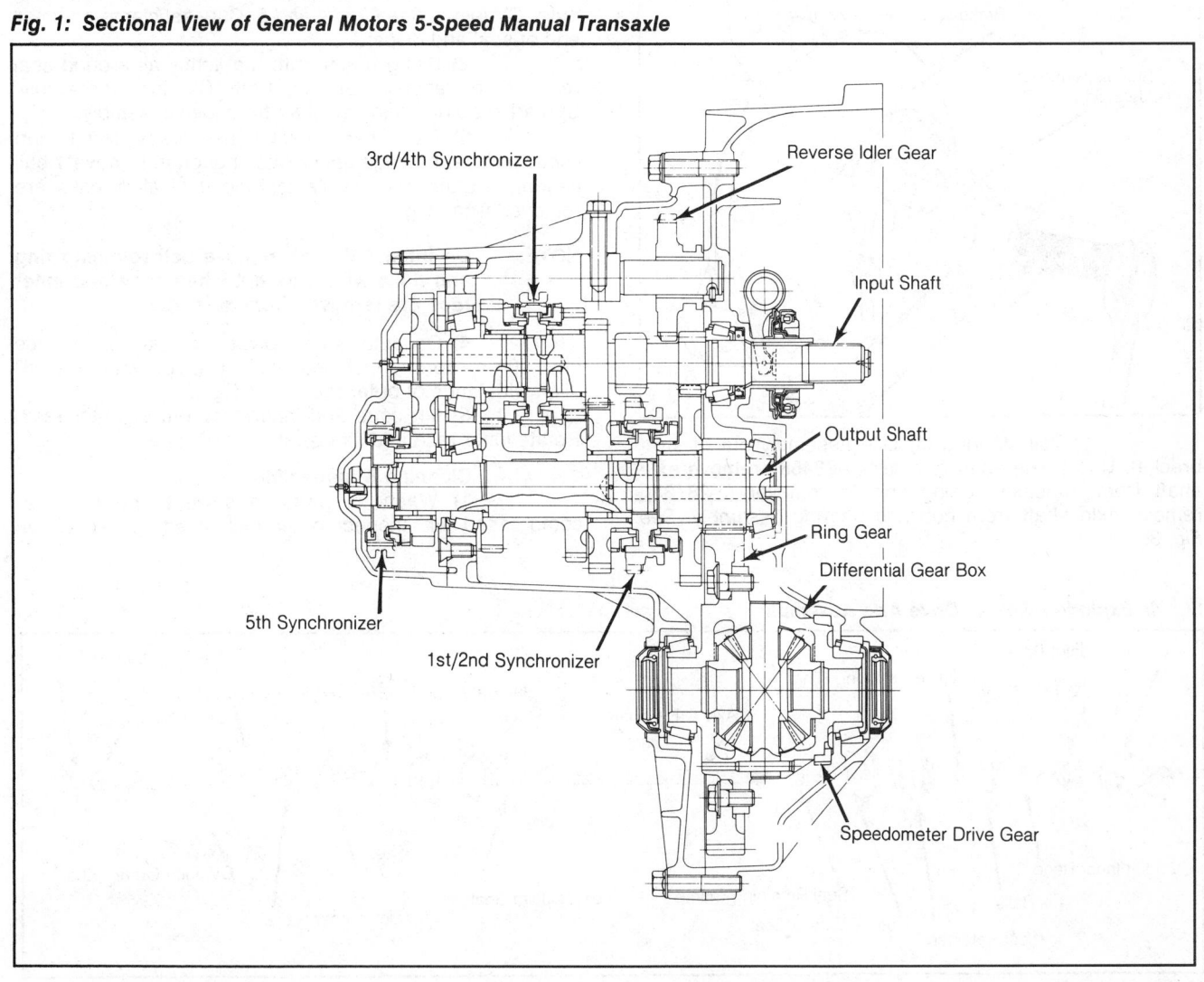

GENERAL MOTORS 5-SPEED MANUAL TRANSAXLE (Cont.)

Fig. 2: Removing Drive Axles from Transaxles

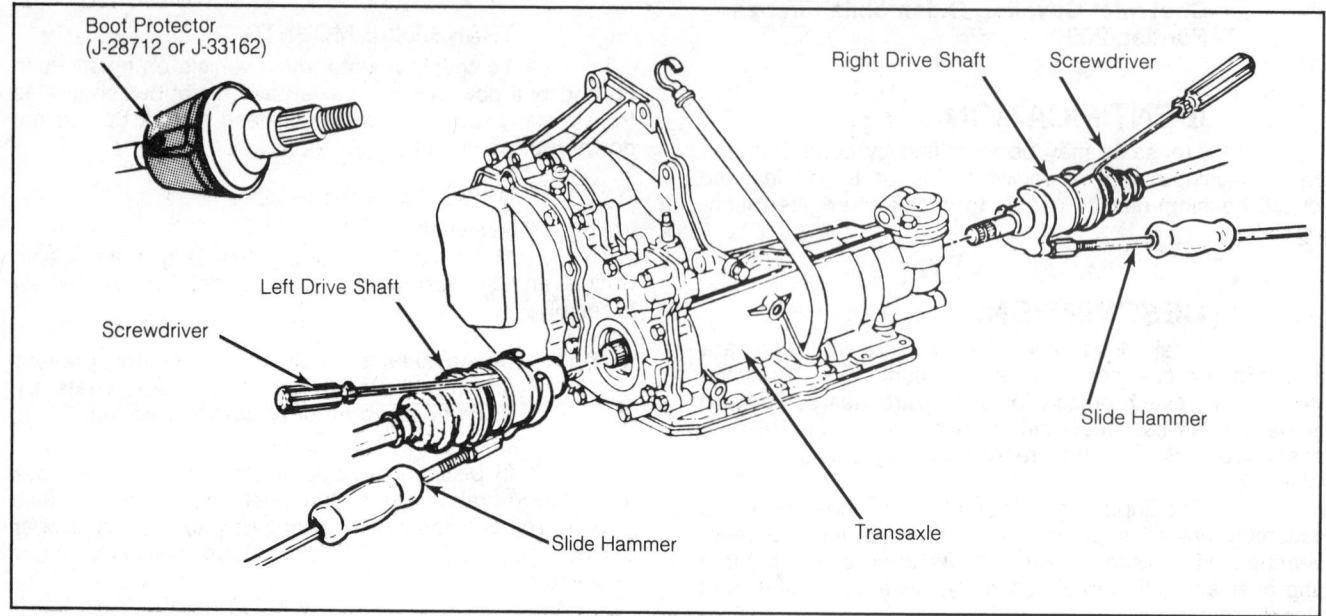

Fig. 3: Removing Axle Shaft from Hub and Bearing

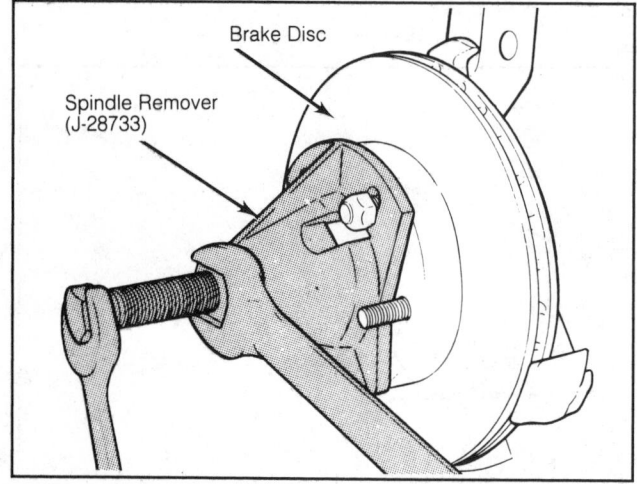

3) Pull steering knuckle assembly out of strut bracket. Using axle shaft remover (J-28468), remove axle shaft from transaxle. Using spindle remover (J-28733), remove axle shaft from hub and bearing assembly. See Fig. 3.

Disassembly

1) Procedure is nearly identical for inner and outer CV joints. See Figs. 4 and 5. Cut seal clamp on small end of seal and discard.

2) Using brass drift, tap lightly all around seal retainer to remove retainer from CV joint assembly. Spread snap ring and pull shaft from joint assembly.

3) For outer CV joint, use brass drift to tap lightly on bearing cage until it tilts enough to remove 1 ball bearing. Rotate cage while tapping until all 6 balls are removed from cage.

NOTE: **On inner CV joint, remove ball retaining ring and balls will come out when cage and inner race are removed from outer race.**

4) On outer joints, pivot cage, and inner race until 90° to normal installed position (cage windows will align with lands of outer race). See Fig. 5.

5) Lift cage and inner race out of outer race. Rotate inner race and lift upward out of cage.

Cleaning & Inspection

1) Wash all parts in solvent and dry with compressed air. Inspect outer ball races for excessive

Fig. 4: Exploded View of Drive Axle Assembly

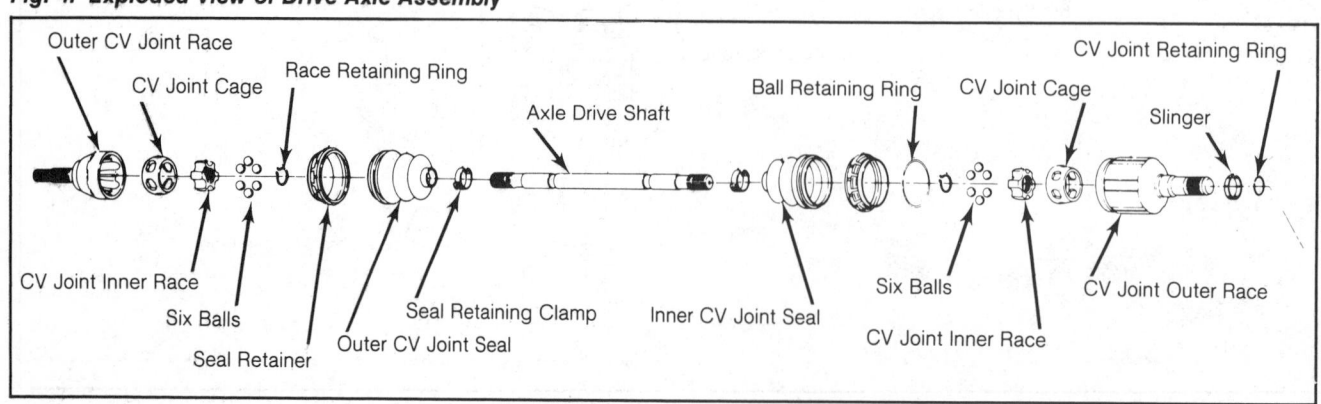

GENERAL MOTORS 5-SPEED MANUAL TRANSAXLE (Cont.)

Fig. 5: Disassembly of Drive Axle and CV Joints

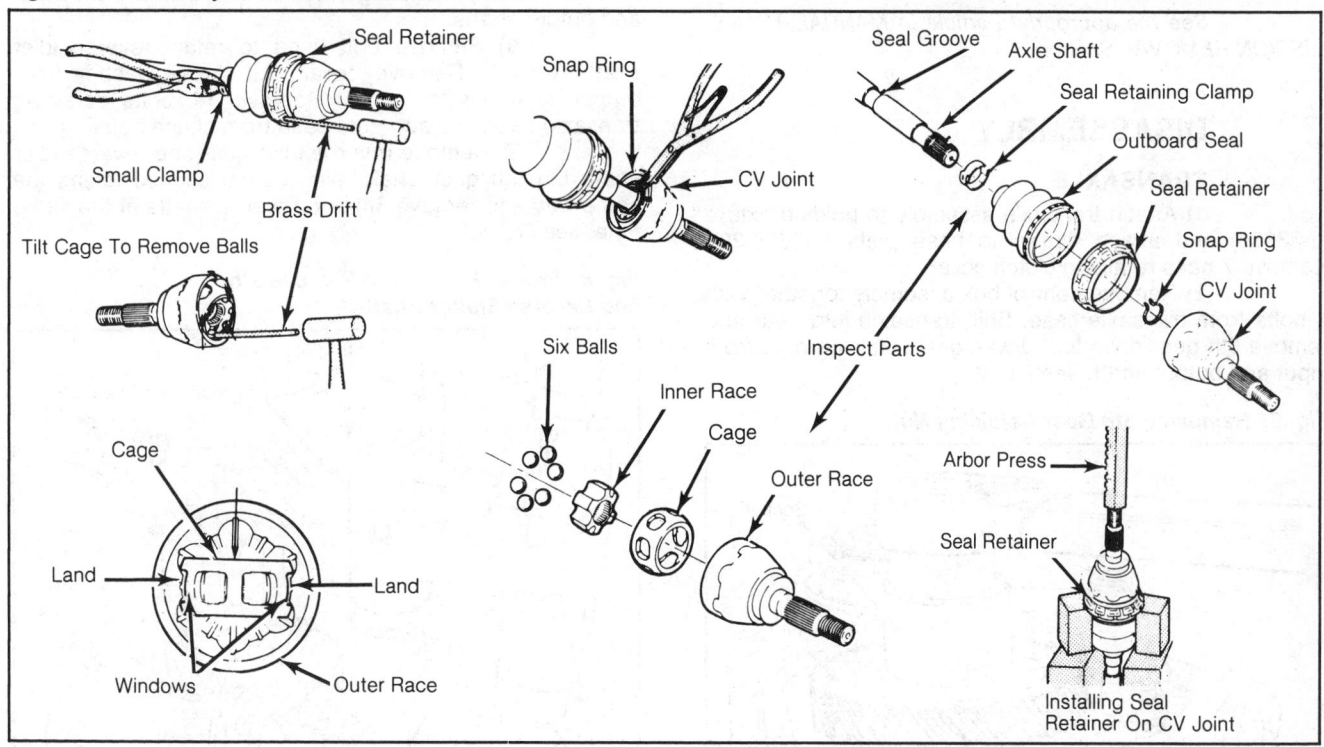

Outer joint illustrated, inner joint is similar.

wear and scoring. Inspect splined stub shaft for wear and cracks.

2) Inspect all 6 ball bearings for pitting, cracking, or scoring. Dulling of surface is normal. Inspect cage for excessive wear on inside and outside spherical surfaces. Look for heavy brinelling of cage window and for cracks or chips.

3) Inspect inner race for excessive wear or scoring. If any of the above damage is found, replace entire CV joint assembly. Polished areas in races and on cage spheres are normal and do not require joint replacement.

Reassembly

1) Apply a light coat of grease on ball grooves of inner and outer races. Install inner race into cage using a rotating action opposite of removal. Inner race snap ring should face axle side.

2) On inner CV joints, be sure ball bearing retaining ring is installed on inner race side facing small end of cage. Align windows of cage with outer race lands, and pivot cage with inner race into tilted position (opposite of removal).

3) Install ball bearings one at a time into outer CV joint as cage is rotated and tilted. On inner CV joint, insert ball bearings through cage windows. After all 6 balls have been installed into cage of outer CV joint, pivot cage and inner race assembly into installed position.

4) Slide new seal clamp for small end of seal, seal, and seal retainer onto axle shaft. Coat inside lip (large diameter end) of seal with grease. Slide seal retainer onto end of seal.

5) Spread ears of bearing race snap ring, and slide CV joint onto axle shaft until snap ring seats in groove. Pack joint with approximately 1/2 the grease provided in seal kit. Apply remaining grease inside seal.

Slide seal toward joint until small end of seal is in groove of axle shaft.

6) Position small clamp over small end of seal and into groove and tighten. Place assembly vertically into an arbor press, with CV joint up so seal retainer is supported. See Fig. 5. Press CV joint downward onto retainer. Make sure seal stays in retainer during reassembly.

Installation

1) Position drive axle loosely into steering knuckle and transaxle. Install steering knuckle into strut bracket and tighten strut bracket bolts finger tight only. Install brake caliper and tighten.

NOTE: **If drive axle is being replaced, replacement of knuckle seal is recommended.**

2) Install drive axle through steering knuckle. Install hub nut and tighten. When shaft begins to turn, use holding tool to prevent hub from turning. Replace rotor if removed.

NOTE: **Axle shaft is an interference fit in steering knuckle and should seat properly when tightened to 70 ft. lbs. (95 N.m).**

3) Apply upward load to hub assembly by lowering vehicle onto safety stand. Align cam bolt with alignment marks made earlier. Tighten, and then tighten strut bracket.

4) Position screwdriver in groove provided on inner retainer. See Fig. 2. Complete axle shaft installation by tapping screwdriver until shaft seats.

5) Connect brake line clip to strut bracket, and install wheel assembly. Lower vehicle and tighten lug nuts and hub.

GENERAL MOTORS 5-SPEED MANUAL TRANSAXLE (Cont.)

REMOVAL & INSTALLATION

See the appropriate article in MANUAL TRANS-MISSION REMOVAL Section.

DISASSEMBLY

TRANSAXLE

1) Attach transaxle assembly to holding fixture (J-33366) and attach fixture to base plate (J-3389-20). Remove 7 bolts retaining clutch cover.

2) Remove control box assembly together with 4 bolts from transaxle case. Shift transaxle into gear and remove 5th gear drive and driven gear retaining nuts from input and output shaft. *See Fig. 6.*

Fig. 6: *Removing 5th Gear Retaining Nut*

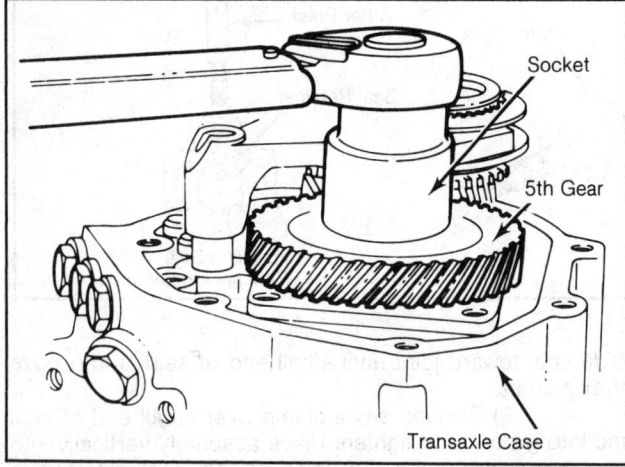

Socket

5th Gear

Transaxle Case

3) Remove detent spring retaining bolts for 1st/2nd, 3rd/4th, reverse, and 5th gear, and remove detent springs and balls. *See Fig. 7.*

Fig. 7: *Removing Detent Springs and Balls From Case*

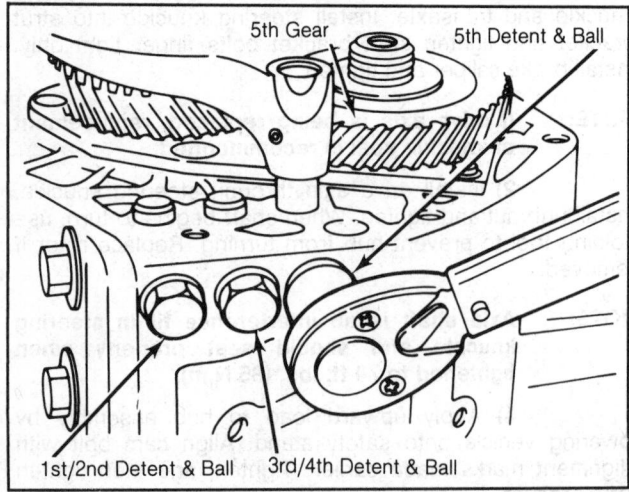

5th Gear

5th Detent & Ball

1st/2nd Detent & Ball

3rd/4th Detent & Ball

Reverse is located on opposite side of case.

4) Place 5th gear synchronizer in neutral and remove roll pin at 5th gear shift fork. Remove 5th gear synchronizer hub, sleeve roller bearing, and gear with shift fork as an assembly from output shaft.

5) Remove 5th gear from input shaft. Remove 7 screws using removal tool (J-25359-6) from bearing retainer. Remove bearing retainer and shims from input and output shafts.

6) Remove bolt used to retain reverse idler shaft at case. Remove collar and thrust washer from output shaft using puller. Remove 14 bolts retaining transaxle case and separate case from clutch housing.

7) Remove reverse idler gear and reverse idler shaft. Lift 5th gear shaft. With detent aligned facing the same way and remove 5th and reverse shafts at the same time. *See Fig. 8.*

Fig. 8: *Proper Position to Remove 5th and Reverse Shifter Shafts*

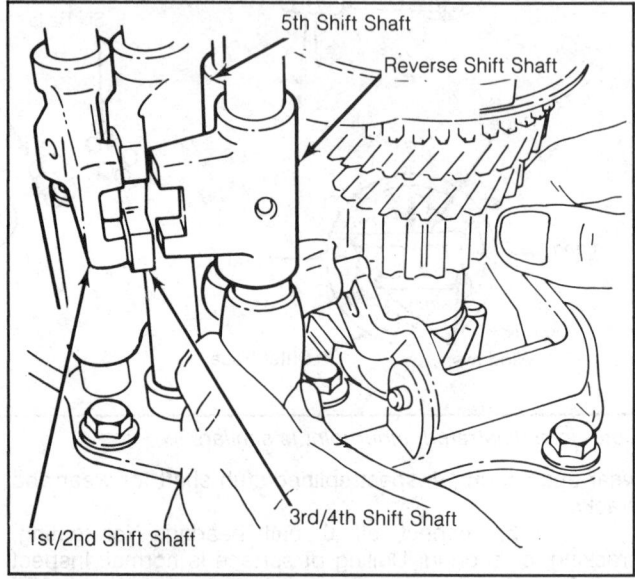

5th Shift Shaft

Reverse Shift Shaft

3rd/4th Shift Shaft

1st/2nd Shift Shaft

Remove shafts together at the same time.

8) Remove roll pin from 1st/2nd shift fork, slide 1st/2nd shaft upward to clear housing and remove fork and shaft from case. Remove roll pin and reverse shift lever.

9) Remove input and output shafts with 3rd/4th shift fork and shaft as an assembly. Remove differential case assembly. Remove reverse shift bracket together with 4 bolts, and take out 3 inter lock pins.

10) Remove rear bearing outer races from transaxle case. Drive input and output shaft races out with driver tools. Remove outer races for input shaft front bearing, output shaft front and differential side bearings.

11) Remove input shaft seals from housing. Remove clutch shaft seal only when replacement is required. Drive out bushing toward inside of case. Remove fork assembly only when replacing clutch fork assembly.

COMPONENT DISASSEMBLY

INPUT SHAFT

Remove front bearing using gear remover and press. Remove rear bearing 4th gear, 3rd/4th synchronizer assembly and 3th gear all together, using gear remover and press.

OUTPUT SHAFT

1) Remove front bearings using bearing removal tool (J-22227-A), driver (J-33369), and arbor press.

GENERAL MOTORS 5-SPEED MANUAL TRANSAXLE (Cont.)

Fig. 9: Exploded View 5-Speed Manual Transaxle Gear Assemblies

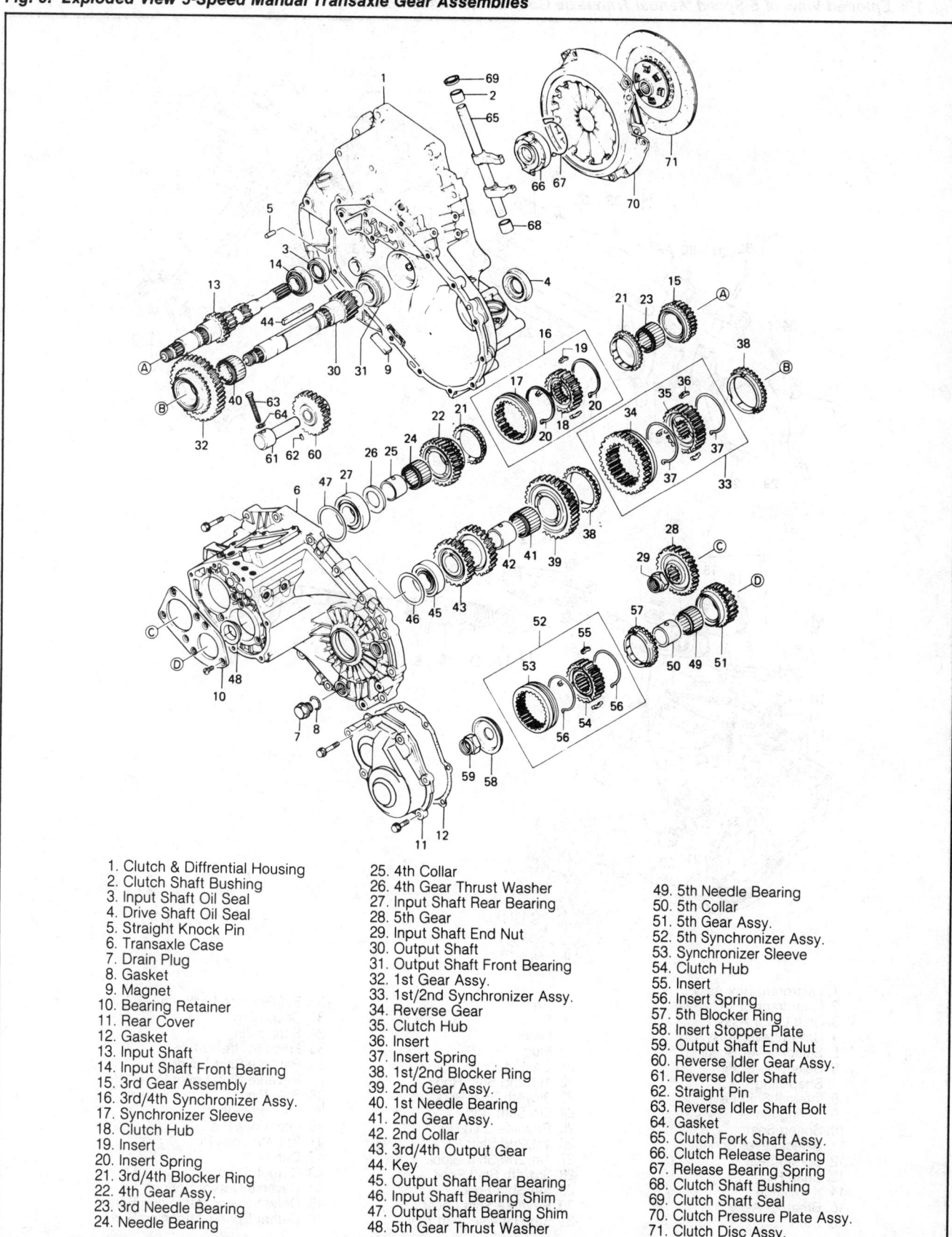

1. Clutch & Diffrential Housing
2. Clutch Shaft Bushing
3. Input Shaft Oil Seal
4. Drive Shaft Oil Seal
5. Straight Knock Pin
6. Transaxle Case
7. Drain Plug
8. Gasket
9. Magnet
10. Bearing Retainer
11. Rear Cover
12. Gasket
13. Input Shaft
14. Input Shaft Front Bearing
15. 3rd Gear Assembly
16. 3rd/4th Synchronizer Assy.
17. Synchronizer Sleeve
18. Clutch Hub
19. Insert
20. Insert Spring
21. 3rd/4th Blocker Ring
22. 4th Gear Assy.
23. 3rd Needle Bearing
24. Needle Bearing

25. 4th Collar
26. 4th Gear Thrust Washer
27. Input Shaft Rear Bearing
28. 5th Gear
29. Input Shaft End Nut
30. Output Shaft
31. Output Shaft Front Bearing
32. 1st Gear Assy.
33. 1st/2nd Synchronizer Assy.
34. Reverse Gear
35. Clutch Hub
36. Insert
37. Insert Spring
38. 1st/2nd Blocker Ring
39. 2nd Gear Assy.
40. 1st Needle Bearing
41. 2nd Gear Assy.
42. 2nd Collar
43. 3rd/4th Output Gear
44. Key
45. Output Shaft Rear Bearing
46. Input Shaft Bearing Shim
47. Output Shaft Bearing Shim
48. 5th Gear Thrust Washer

49. 5th Needle Bearing
50. 5th Collar
51. 5th Gear Assy.
52. 5th Synchronizer Assy.
53. Synchronizer Sleeve
54. Clutch Hub
55. Insert
56. Insert Spring
57. 5th Blocker Ring
58. Insert Stopper Plate
59. Output Shaft End Nut
60. Reverse Idler Gear Assy.
61. Reverse Idler Shaft
62. Straight Pin
63. Reverse Idler Shaft Bolt
64. Gasket
65. Clutch Fork Shaft Assy.
66. Clutch Release Bearing
67. Release Bearing Spring
68. Clutch Shaft Bushing
69. Clutch Shaft Seal
70. Clutch Pressure Plate Assy.
71. Clutch Disc Assy.

Manual Transmissions

GENERAL MOTORS 5-SPEED MANUAL TRANSAXLE (Cont.)

Fig. 10: Eploded View of 5-Speed Manual Transaxle Gear Shifter Assemblies

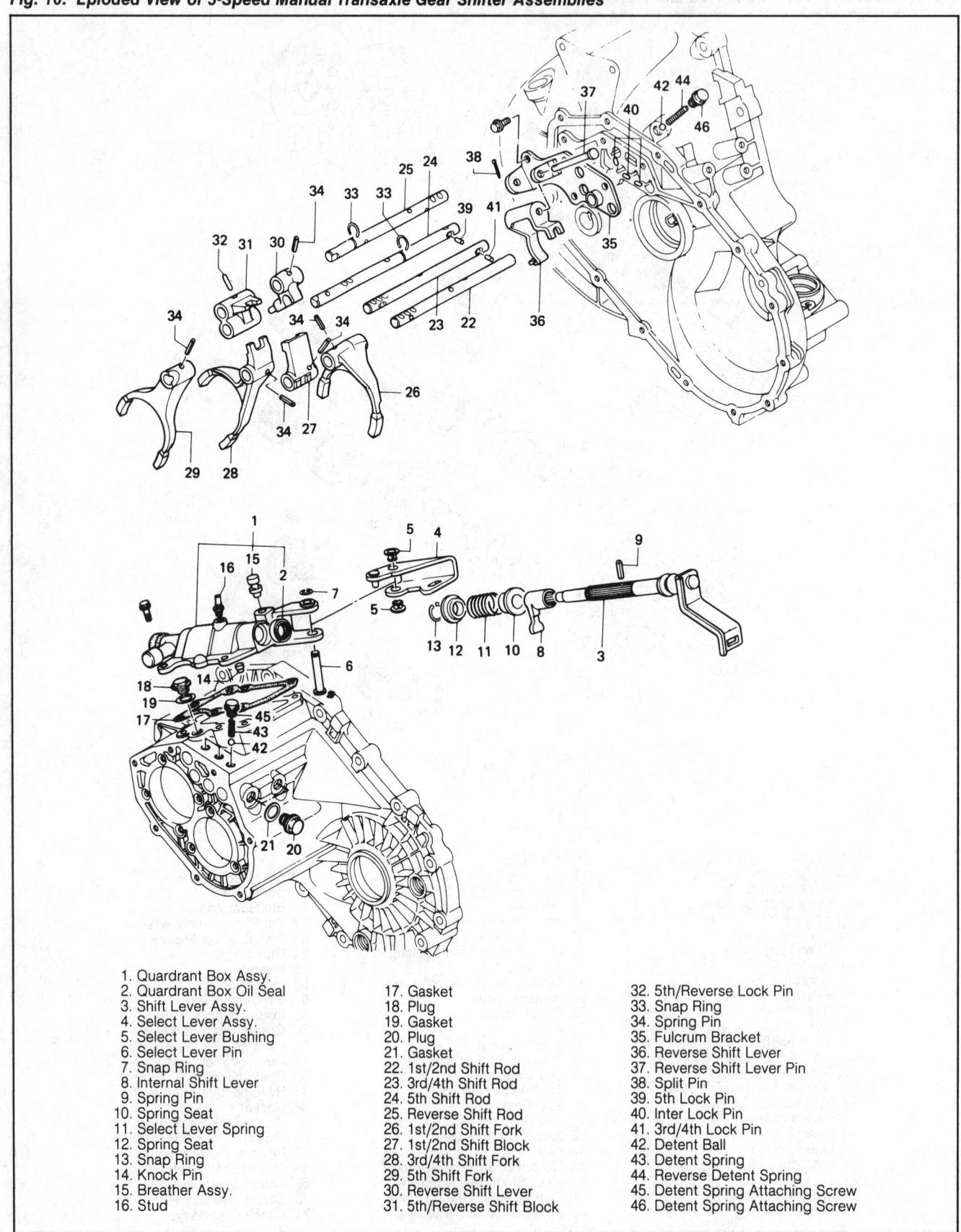

1. Quardrant Box Assy.
2. Quardrant Box Oil Seal
3. Shift Lever Assy.
4. Select Lever Assy.
5. Select Lever Bushing
6. Select Lever Pin
7. Snap Ring
8. Internal Shift Lever
9. Spring Pin
10. Spring Seat
11. Select Lever Spring
12. Spring Seat
13. Snap Ring
14. Knock Pin
15. Breather Assy.
16. Stud

17. Gasket
18. Plug
19. Gasket
20. Plug
21. Gasket
22. 1st/2nd Shift Rod
23. 3rd/4th Shift Rod
24. 5th Shift Rod
25. Reverse Shift Rod
26. 1st/2nd Shift Fork
27. 1st/2nd Shift Block
28. 3rd/4th Shift Fork
29. 5th Shift Fork
30. Reverse Shift Lever
31. 5th/Reverse Shift Block

32. 5th/Reverse Lock Pin
33. Snap Ring
34. Spring Pin
35. Fulcrum Bracket
36. Reverse Shift Lever
37. Reverse Shift Lever Pin
38. Split Pin
39. 5th Lock Pin
40. Inter Lock Pin
41. 3rd/4th Lock Pin
42. Detent Ball
43. Detent Spring
44. Reverse Detent Spring
45. Detent Spring Attaching Screw
46. Detent Spring Attaching Screw

GENERAL MOTORS 5-SPEED MANUAL TRANSAXLE (Cont.)

Remove rear bearing and 3rd/4th gear together using bearing removal tool (J-22912-01) and a press.

2) Remove key, 2nd gear, needle bearing, and blocker ring. Remove collar, reverse gear assembly, and 1st gear all together by using arbor press.

DIFFERENTIAL

1) Remove side bearings using bearing puller. Remove 10 bolts from ring gear and remove gear. Remove speedometer drive gear and discard.

2) Drive out lockpin, and pull out cross pin. Remove pinion gears and thrust washers. Remove side gears and thrust washers.

SYNCHRONIZERS

Using care, pry out both synchronizer retaining rings. Separate hub, sleeve, and 3 keys, noting their position. *See Fig. 11.* Scribe hub to sleeve location and separate. Clean, inspect, and replace parts, as necessary.

Fig. 11: Components of Synchronizer Assemblies

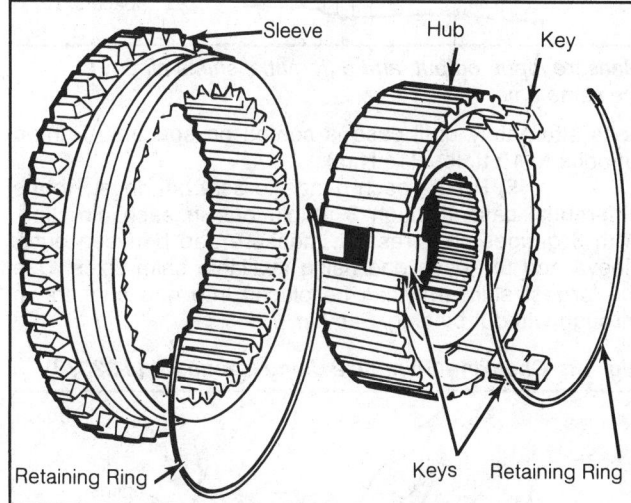

CLEANING & INSPECTION

1) Wash all parts, except oil seals, in cleaning solvent. Brush or scrape all foreign matter from parts, using care not to damage any part with scraper. Do not clean, wash, or soak transaxle seals in cleaning solvent. Dry all parts with compressed air.

CAUTION: **Hold roller bearing assembly to prevent it from rotating when drying it with compressed air.**

2) Lubricate all bearings with approved transmission lubricant and wrap them in a clean, lint free cloth, or paper until ready to use.

3) Inspect transaxle case and clutch housing case for cracks, worn, or damaged bearing bores. Check for damaged threads or any other damage. Inspect mating surfaces on cases for small nicks or burrs that could cause misalignment of the 2 halves. Remove all small nicks or burrs with a fine stone or file.

4) Check reverse idler gear and sliding gear for chipped, broken, or bent teeth. Check reverse idler gear for bushing damage. Check wear of reverse idler gear shaft (it is normal for front of teeth to show wear, this does not interfere with proper function).

5) Check reverse idler gear and sliding gear for chipped, broken, or bent teeth. Check reverse idler gear for bushing damage. Check wear of reverse idler gear shaft (it is normal for front of teeth to show wear, this does not interfere with proper function).

6) Check teeth, splines, and journals of mainshaft for damage. Check all other gears for chipped, broken, or worn teeth. Check for eroded clutching teeth and damaged bearing surfaces. Clutching teeth will usually show rounding of the points which does not interfere with normal operation.

7) Check synchronizer sleeves for free movement on hubs. Make sure index marks are properly aligned. Check for damaged clutching teeth. Check for proper positioning of springs.

8) Inspect synchronizer blocker rings for wear marks on spline end back face which indicates ring was bottoming on gear face due to excessive blocker ring wear.

9) Inspect differential pinion and side gears for scoring, excessive wear, nicks, and chips. Worn, scored, and damaged gears must be replaced.

NOTE: **When a scored or chipped gear is replaced, transaxle case must be cleaned thoroughly to make sure all chips are removed.**

10) Make sure differential case bearing journals are smooth. Inspect case bearing shoulders for damage caused by bearing removal. Check fit (free rotation) of side gears in their cavities.

11) Check differential bearings and bearing races for wear or other damage. If races are not damaged, do not remove from transaxle case or clutch housing case. Check bearings for smooth rotation in races. Examine bearing roller ends for step wear.

NOTE: **If inspection reveals either a damaged bearing or race, both parts must be replaced as they are a matched set.**

COMPONENT REASSEMBLY

SYNCHRONIZERS

1) Assemble hub to sleeve with lip of hub away from shift fork groove in sleeve. Align scribe marks. Carefully install retaining ring, prying it back to insert keys one at a time.

2) Flats on retaining ring should hold keys in place. Install retaining ring on opposite side of hub, so open end of ring does not align with open end of first ring.

DIFFERENTIAL

1) Install 2 side gears on differential case together with thrust washers. Position 2 thrust washers and pinion gears opposite each other, and install them in thier positions by turning side gear.

2) Insert cross pin, and make sure backlash is within rated range of .0012-.0031" (.03-.08 mm). Install lock pin and stake it. Heat speedometer drive gear to about 176°F (80°C), and install it on differential.

3) Apply oil to threads of bolts, cross pin, differential gears, thrust portion, side gear shaft portion, side gear spline portion before installation. Install ring gear on differential case. Install 10 ring gear bolts and tighten.

GENERAL MOTORS 5-SPEED MANUAL TRANSAXLE (Cont.)

OUTPUT SHAFT

1) Install needle bearing, 1st gear, and blocker ring. Match inserts of sleeve and hub assembly with grooves of blocker ring. Press sleeve and hub assembly together with collar (oil collar before and after installation) using driver (J-33374) and press.

2) Install blocker ring needle bearing and 2nd gear, and install key on key groove. Apply oil to 3th/4th gear interior, match key with key groove, and fit key together with rear bearing. Using driver (J-33374) and press, press bearing on shaft. Press front bearing on shaft using driver (J-33368) and press.

INPUT SHAFT

1) Install needle bearing, 3th gear, and block ring onto shaft. Match inserts of 3rd/4th sleeve and hub assembly with grooves of blocker ring. Press on sleeve, hub assembly and collar. Apply oil to collar and hub before and after installation. Use driver (J-33374) and press.

2) Install blocker ring and needle bearing. Install 4th gear and thrust washer. Install thrust washer with recessed area facing 4th gear. Install front and rear bearings using driver (J-33374) and press.

REASSEMBLY

TRANSAXLE

1) Place transaxle case in holding fixture. Using seal installer (J-26540), drive input shaft seal into case. Install front outer bearing races for input shaft, output shaft, and differential into clutch housing.

2) Using installer tools drive input race into housing. Using driver, press output race into housing. Using driver, press differential race into housing. Apply grease to 3 interlock pins, and install them on clutch housing.

3) Install reverse shift bracket on clutch. Use 3rd/4th shaft rod to align bracket to housing. Make sure rod operates smoothly after installation. Install differential assembly first, then install input and output shaft with 3rd/4th shift fork and shaft together as an assembly into clutch housing.

4) The 3rd/4th shift shaft is installed into raised collar of reverse shift lever bracket. Install 1st/2nd shift fork onto synchronizer sleeve and insert shifter shaft into plate.

5) Align hole in fork with shaft and install roll pin. Install reverse lever on shift bracket. Install reverse and 5th gear shifter shaft and at the same time, engage reverse shaft with reverse shift lever. Install reverse idler shaft together with gear into clutch housing. Make sure reverse lever is engaged in collar of gear.

6) Measure and determine shim size using the 7 spacers and shim selector gauges (J-33373). Position outer bearing races on input, output, and differential bearings. Position shim selection gauges on bearing races. See Fig. 12.

7) The 3 gauges are identified: *Input, Output, and Differential.* Install bearing and shims retainer on ends of shafts. Tighten bolts to 11-16 ft. lbs. (15-22 N.m).

8) Place 7 spacers (provided with gauges), evenly around perimeter of clutch housing. *See Fig. 12.* Carefully position transaxle case over gauges and on spacers. Install 7 bolts provided with gauge kit and tighten

Fig. 12: Shim Gauges Sets Used to Measure Shims

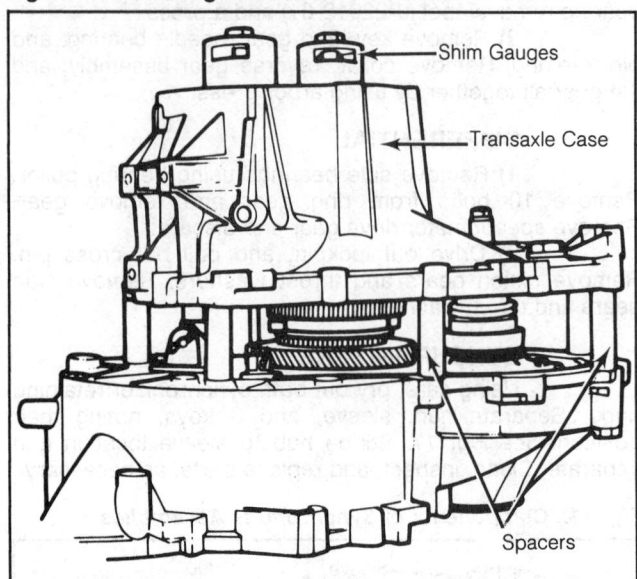

Measure input, output, and differential shims all at the same time.

bolts alternately until case is seated on spacers. Tighten kit bolts to 10 ft. lbs. (14 N.m).

9) Rotate each gauge to seat bearings. Rotate differential case through 3 revolutions in each direction. With 3 gauges compressed, measure gap between outer sleeve and the base pad using available shim sizes. Use the largest shim that can be placed into gap and drawn through without binding. *See Fig. 13.*

Fig. 13: Checking Shim Size Using Gauge Kit (J-33373)

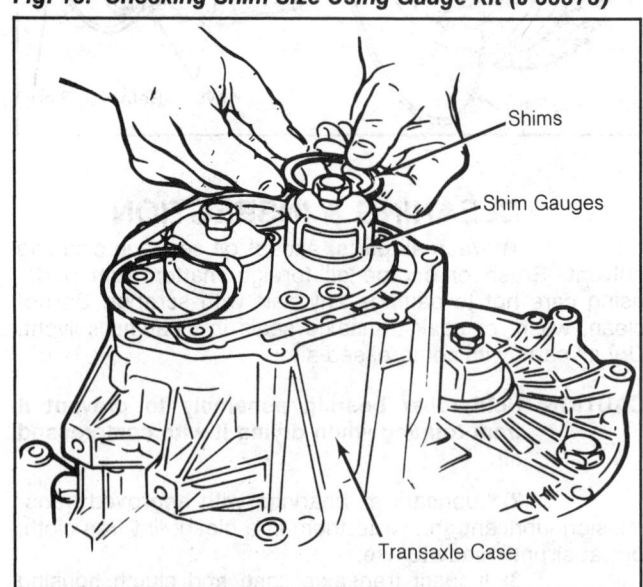

Use largest shim without binding in gauge.

10) Preload shims for input shaft are available in thicknesses of .0457" to .0961" (1.16 to 2.44 mm) in .003" (.07 mm) increments. Preload shims for output shaft are available in thicknesses of .0394" to .0961" (1.00 to 2.44 mm) in .003" (.07 mm) increments. Preload shims for differential are available in thicknesses of .0394" to .0898" (1.00 to 2.02 mm) in .003" (.07 mm) increments.

GENERAL MOTORS 5-SPEED MANUAL TRANSAXLE (Cont.)

11) When each of the 3 shims have been selected, remove transaxle case, the 7 spacers, and 3 gauges. Position shims selected for input shaft, output shaft, and differential into bearing race bores in transaxle-case. Install rear input shaft bearing race.

12) Press bearing until seated in its bore. Install rear output shaft bearing race. Press bearing until seated in its bore. Install rear differential case bearing race. Press bearing until seated in its bore.

13) Apply a 1/8" bead of sealant to the mating surfaces of clutch housing and transaxle case. Be sure magnet is installed in transaxle case. Install transaxle case on clutch housing.

14) Install reverse idle shaft bolt into transaxle case. Install 14 case bolts and tighten in diagonal sequence. Install drive axle seals. Install thrust washer and collar to output shaft.

15) Install 5th gear to input shaft. Install needle bearing, 5th gear, blocker ring, hub/sleeve assembly with shift fork in its groove and back plate on output shaft.

16) Align shift fork on shifter shaft and install roll pin. Install detent balls and detent springs for reverse, 1st/2nd, 3rd/4th, and 5th gears. Install retaining bolts and tighten. Stake nuts after reaching final torque.

17) Install gasket and control box assembly on transaxle case, and tighten 4 bolts. Make sure transaxle shifts properly before installing rear cover. Install gasket and rear cover with 7 bolts, and tighten bolts.

18) Install clutch fork assembly if it has been removed. Lubricate and install bushing into upper hole using bushing installer (J-28412). Install oil seal. Install the clutch release bearing.

TIGHTENING SPECIFICATIONS

Application	Ft. Lbs. (N.m)
Ring Gear Bolts	73-79 (98-107)
Transaxle-to-Clutch Hsg. Bolts.	22-33 (30-45)
Reverse Idler Shaft Bolt	22-33 (30-45)
Detent Spring Retaining Bolts	15-21 (21-29)
Input/Output Shaft Nuts	87-101 (118-137)
Control Box-to-Case Bolts	11-16 (15-22)
Rear Cover Bolts	11-16 (15-22)

Manual Transmissions

NEW PROCESS 435

Chrysler Corp., Ford Bronco, F100/350, F350 4WD

DESCRIPTION

The New Process 435 4-speed transmission uses a direct-mounted shift lever and cover. The 1st and reverse gears are spur type. The 2nd, 3rd, and 4th gears are helical, constant mesh type and are synchronized for easier shifting.

The input shaft is supported at front by tapered roller bearings. End play is controlled by gasket thickness between the case and bearing retainer. The front of the mainshaft is supported by a pilot roller bearing in the input shaft. The rear of the mainshaft is supported by a ball bearing.

The countershaft gear is a solid, 1-piece unit, supported by caged roller bearings at each end. A roller-type thrust bearing and race are provided at rear of countershaft gear, with a thrust washer at front of gear.

Reverse idler gear uses roller bearings in Ford models and bronze bushings in Chrysler Corp. models. The 3rd-4th speed synchronizer is mounted at front of mainshaft, 2nd speed synchronizer and 1st speed sliding gear at rear of mainshaft.

LUBRICATION & ADJUSTMENT

See the appropriate article in MANUAL TRANS-MISSION SERVICING Section.

TROUBLE SHOOTING

See Manual Transmission Trouble Shooting in MANUAL TRANSMISSION SERVICING Section.

REMOVAL & INSTALLATION

See the appropriate article in MANUAL TRANS-MISSION REMOVAL Section.

TRANSMISSION DISASSEMBLY

SHIFT CONTROL COVER

1) Mount transmission assembly in holding fixture and remove drain and filler plugs. Place gearshift lever in Neutral position. Remove shift control cover screws.

2) Remove cover by lifting while rotating slightly counterclockwise to provide clearance for shift forks. Remove and discard gasket. See Fig. 7.

INPUT SHAFT & MAINSHAFT

1) Lock transmission in 2 gears. Remove mainshaft flange nut and mainshaft flange, if equipped. Remove extension housing and slide speedometer drive gear off mainshaft.

2) Measure and record synchronizer outer stop ring and 3rd gear end play for reference during reassembly. See Fig. 14.

3) Remove input shaft bearing retainer. Rotate gear to align space in input shaft gear clutch teeth with countershaft drive gear teeth.

4) Remove input shaft assembly and tapered roller bearing. Remove snap ring, washer, and pilot roller bearing from recess in rear of input shaft. See Fig. 1.

Fig. 1: Input Shaft Assembly

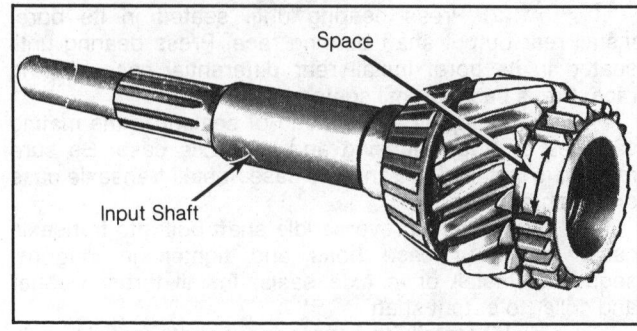

Align space in input gear clutch teeth with countershaft gear teeth.

5) Place brass drift in front center of mainshaft and drive mainshaft to rear. Remove rear bearing with puller. Move mainshaft to rear and tilt front of mainshaft upward.

6) Remove roller type thrust bearing. Remove synchronizer and stop rings separately. Remove mainshaft assembly. See Figs. 2 and 3.

Fig. 2: Removing Rear Mainshaft Bearing

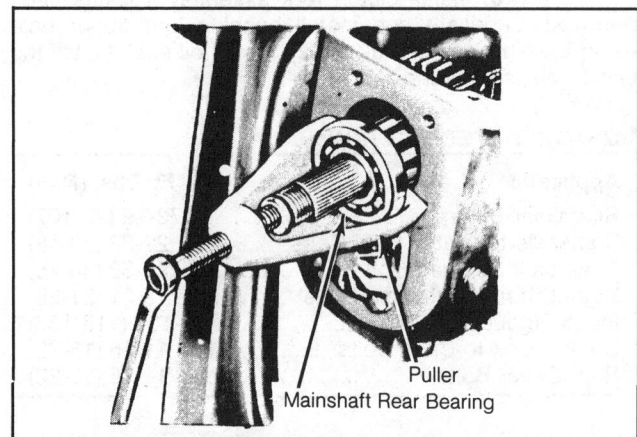

Attach puller to rear bearing and remove bearing.

Fig. 3: Removal of Mainshaft from Case

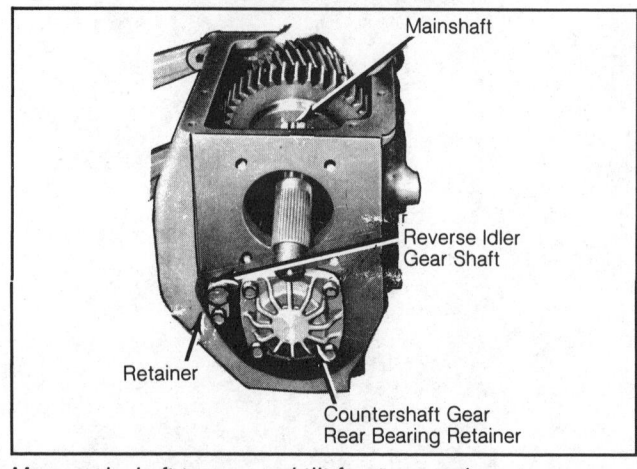

Move mainshaft to rear and tilt front upward.

NEW PROCESS 435 (Cont.)

Fig. 4: Exploded View of New Process 435 4-Speed Transmission

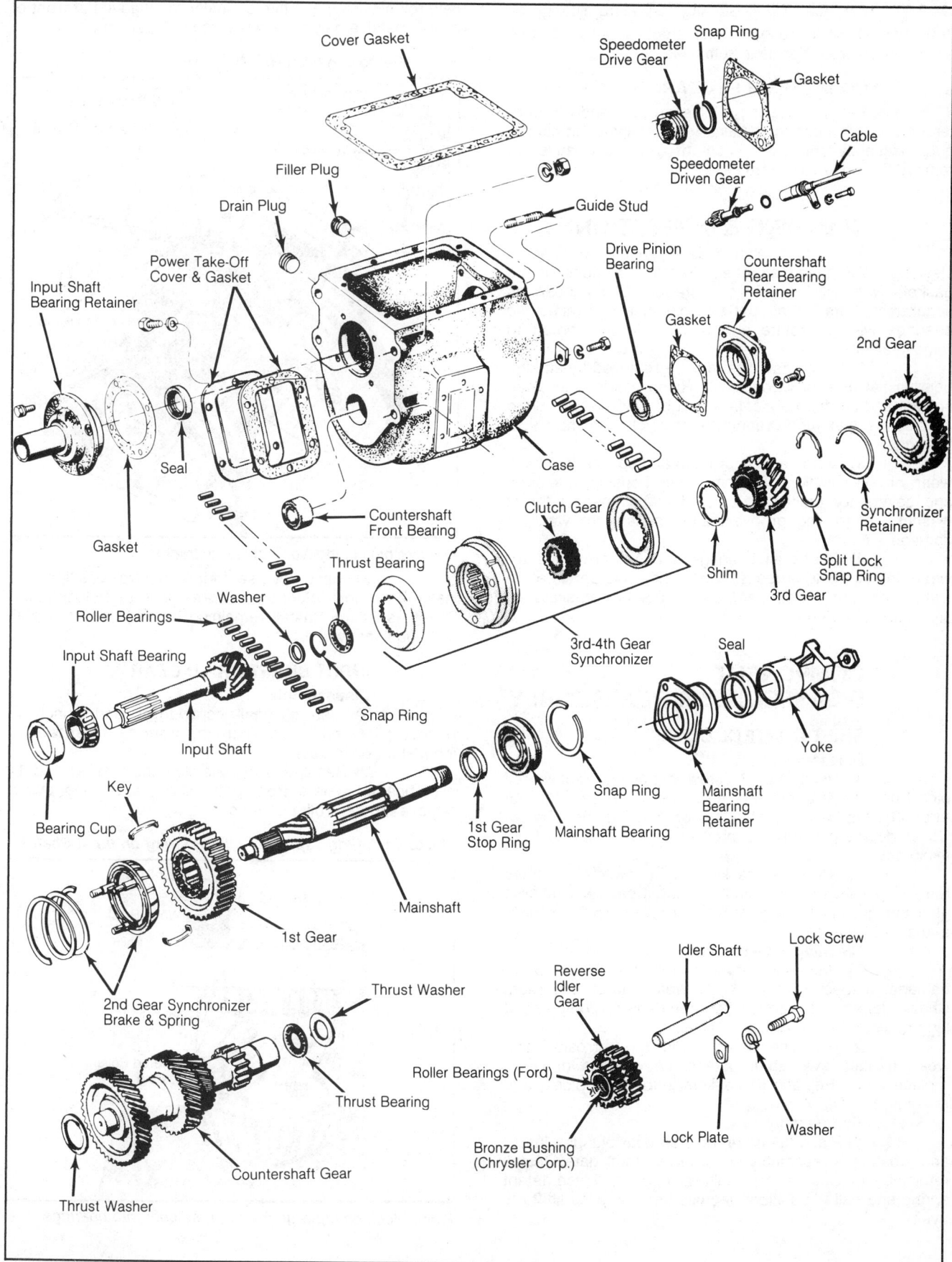

NEW PROCESS 435 (Cont.)

REVERSE IDLER GEAR

Remove lock screw and lock plate. Use brass drift, held at angle, to drive idler shaft to rear. Remove shaft. Lift reverse idler gear from case.

COUNTERSHAFT GEAR

Remove bearing retainer at rear end of countershaft. Roller bearing remains with retainer. Tilt cluster gear assembly and work it out of case. Use driver to remove front bearings from case.

CLEANING & INSPECTION

1) All parts should be thoroughly washed in cleaning solvent and air dried. Remove portions of old gaskets with stiff brush or scraper. Clean bearings separately from other parts. Hold bearing races so bearings will not rotate and brush with soft brush to remove all dirt.

2) Loose particles may be removed by striking bearing flat against wood block. Rinse bearings in clean solvent and air dry. Lubricate with light grade oil and wrap in clean paper until ready to reinstall. Do not spin bearings.

3) Examine all gear teeth and splines for chips, wear, breaks, or nicks. Examine case, housing, retainers, and covers for cracks or other damage. Inspect thrust washers, snap ring grooves, and spacers for wear or damage.

4) Check all bearings and synchronizers for wear, damage, and proper fit. Coat all moving parts before installation with lubricant and always use new gaskets, oil seals, and snap rings.

COMPONENT DISASSEMBLY & REASSEMBLY

SHIFT CONTROL COVER

Disassembly

1) Using No. 2 screw extractor, remove roll pins from 1st-2nd shift fork and gate. Push shift rail out through front to force plug out of housing. *See Fig. 5.* Cover detent ball hole to prevent ball and spring from flying out.

2) Remove back-up light switch. Remove remaining shift rails in same manner. Compress reverse gear plunger and remove retaining clip. Withdraw plunger and spring from gate.

Cleaning & Inspection

1) Examine housing for cracks or other damage. Inspect shift forks for wear and/or distortion. Check detent ball springs for free length, compressed length, distortion, or collapsed coils.

2) Examine detent balls for corrosion and wear. If shift lever shaft detents show signs of wear, replace them. Replace all gaskets, expansion plugs, and roll pins. *See Fig. 7.*

Reassembly

1) Place spring on reverse gear plunger, install and compress assembly in reverse shift gate. Install retaining clip. Start reverse shift rail in cover. Place detent spring and ball in position, depress ball and slide shift rail over it.

2) Install gate and shift fork on shaft and install new roll pins. Apply a film of sealer to plug seat at front of cover. Install a new plug in reverse shift rail bore.

Fig. 5: Removing Shift Rail Roll Pins

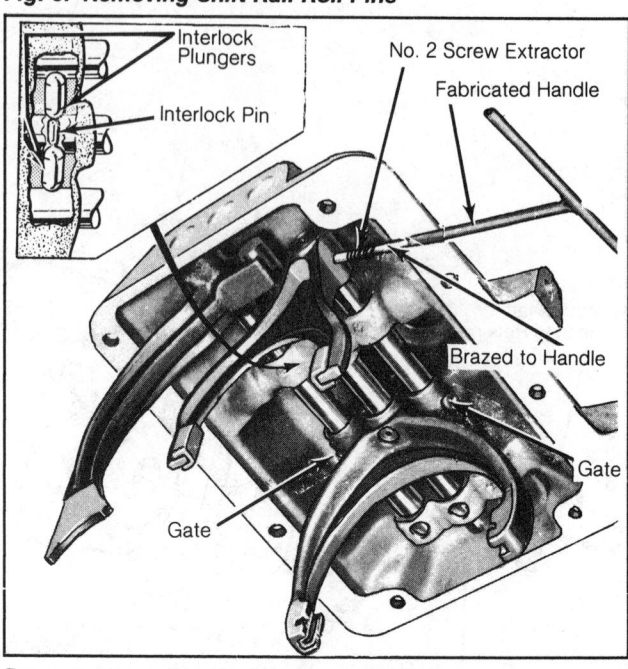

Remove pins using No. 2 screw extractor.

3) Place reverse fork in neutral position and install 2 interlock plungers in bores. Insert interlock pin in 3rd-4th shift rail. Install remaining bores in cover. Install back-up light switch.

INPUT SHAFT DRIVE GEAR

Disassembly

1) Use a small screwdriver and punch to remove pilot bearing retainer ring from cavity at rear of input shaft drive gear.

2) Remove pilot roller bearing washer and 14 pilot bearing rollers from gear. Using a bearing puller, remove tapered roller bearing.

Fig. 6: Installing Tapered Roller Bearing on Input Shaft

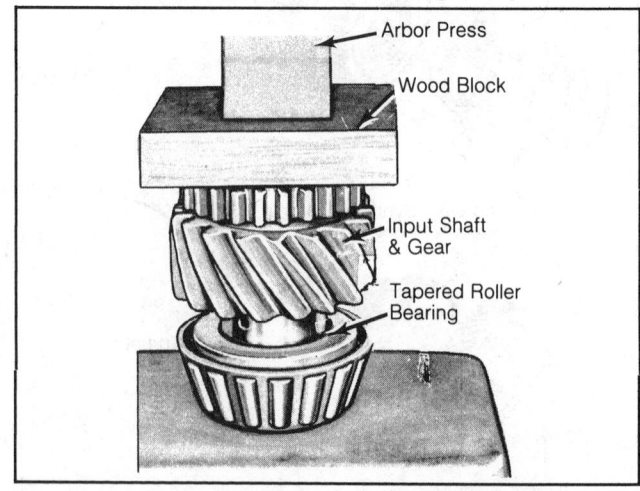

Place block on input gear and press gear into bearings.

NEW PROCESS 435 (Cont.)

Reassembly

Press bearing cone and roller assembly onto input shaft. *See Fig. 6.* Lubricate 14 pilot bearing rollers with light grease and insert them into cavity at rear of input shaft. Position roller bearing washer over pilot bearing rollers, and install retaining ring in groove of gear.

MAINSHAFT

Disassembly

Remove clutch gear snap ring. Withdraw clutch gear, synchronizer outer stop ring-to-3rd gear shim(s), and 3rd gear. Remove special split lock ring with 2 screwdrivers, and withdraw 2nd gear and synchronizer assembly. Remove 1st-reverse sliding gear from shaft.

Reassembly

1) Place mainshaft assembly in a soft-jawed vise with rear end up. Install 1st-reverse gear making sure 2 spline springs are in place inside gear as it is installed on shaft.

2) Move mainshaft in vise so that forward end is up. Install synchronizer spring and brake on 2nd gear.

Secure brake with snap ring, making sure snap ring tangs are away from gear.

3) Slide 2nd gear assembly onto mainshaft making sure synchronizer brake is toward rear. Secure gear to shaft with split lock snap rings, then install 3rd gear.

NOTE: **Synchronizer clutching gear must be installed with BOTH oil slots facing 3rd gear. Oil slots must NOT face thrust bearing.**

4) Install correct shim(s) between 3rd gear and 3rd-4th synchronizer stop ring. Refer to end play measurement obtained during disassembly to bring end play within specification. Exact determination of end play will be made after mainshaft and main drive gear are installed in case.

REVERSE IDLER GEAR

Gear is serviced by replacement only. Replacement gear is equipped with roller bearings rather than a bushing as on original gear.

Fig. 7: *Exploded View of Shift Control Cover Assembly*

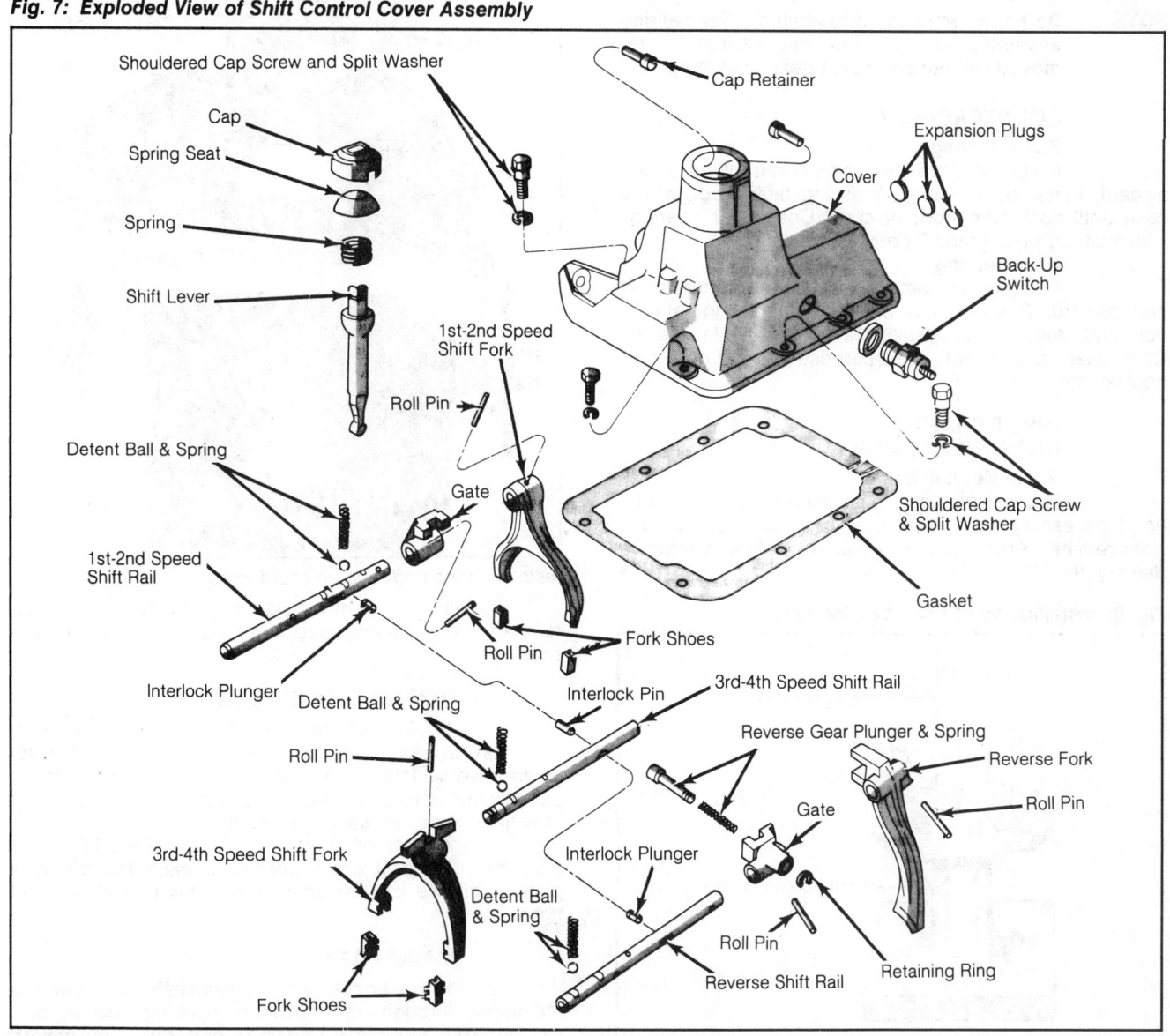

Manual Transmissions

NEW PROCESS 435 (Cont.)

Fig. 8: Installing Synchronizer End Play Shims

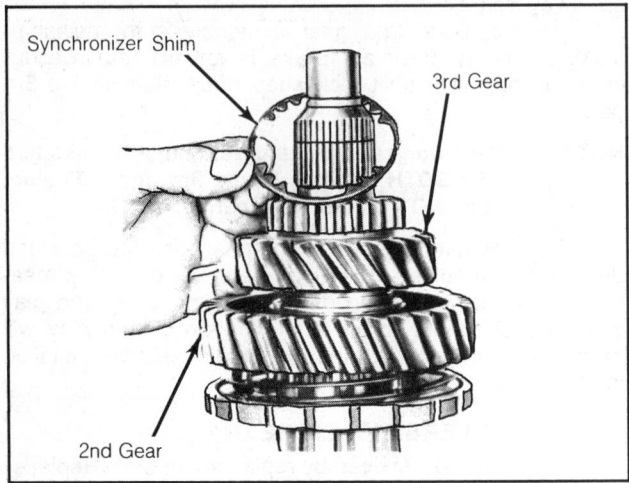

NOTE: **Do not attempt to disassemble roller bearing assembly. Bearing lock ring cannot be removed without damaging gear or bearing.**

COUNTERSHAFT
Front Bearing
Press or drive old bearing out of case and discard. Install new bearing, pressing bearing cage into case until flush with front of case. Coat roller bearings with multi-purpose grade 2 grease or equivalent.
Rear Bearing
Using puller, remove rear bearing from retainer and discard. Position new bearing squarely in retainer bore and press into place until bearing bottoms in retainer. Coat roller bearings with multi-purpose grade 2 grease or equivalent.

INPUT SHAFT
BEARING RETAINER
Roller Bearing Race
Bearing race cup is installed in bearing retainer. If necessary to replace, use puller and remove cup from retainer. Press new race cup squarely into retainer. See Fig. 9.

Fig. 9: Installing Input Shaft Bearing Race

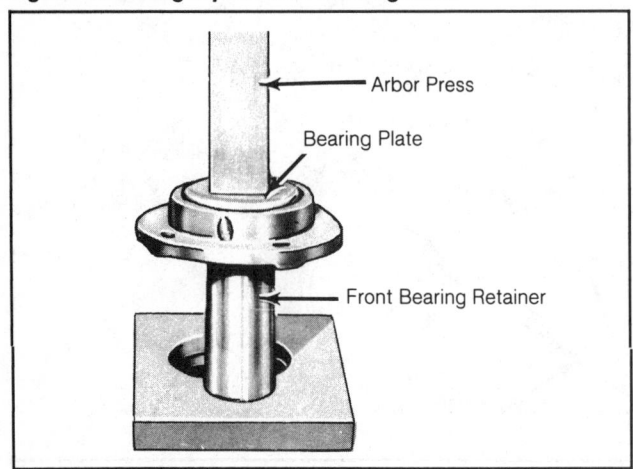

Press new race directly into retainer.

Oil Seal Replacement
Pry old oil seal out of retainer, and press new seal into place using a sleeve. Lip of oil seal should point toward gasket surface of retainer.

TRANSMISSION REASSEMBLY

COUNTERSHAFT GEAR
1) Position transmission case on work bench with front of case down. Coat front thrust washer with grease and position it in case over countershaft front bearing.

2) Position countershaft gear in case, making sure front thrust washer is not disturbed. Install countershaft gear rear thrust bearing and race on pilot diameter of countershaft. Install new gasket, rear bearing retainer and bolts and tighten to specification. See Fig. 10.

Fig. 10: Installing Rear Countershaft Bearing

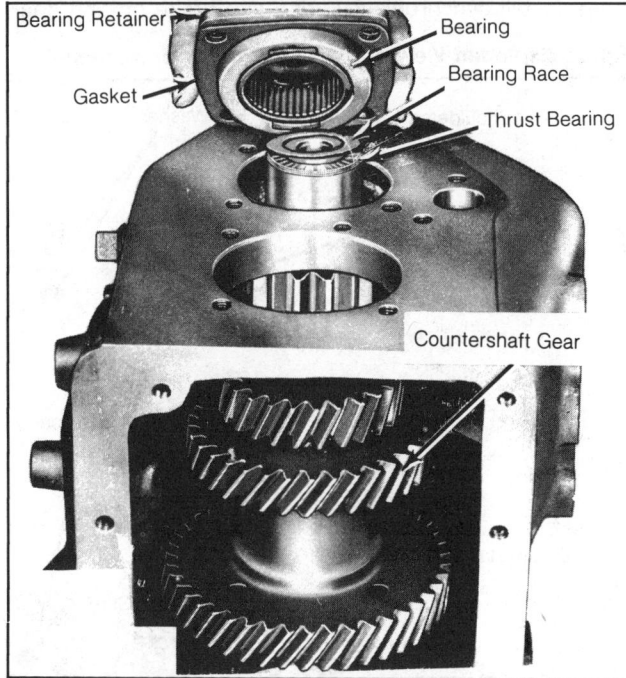

Install bearing and race on countergear.

3) Using new gasket, install gasket, countershaft rear bearing retainer and countershaft rear bearing.

REVERSE IDLER GEAR
1) Position reverse idler gear assembly in transmission case with large gear toward rear of case. Insert reverse idler gear shaft, with slot in shaft down, partially into bore of case and idler gear. Coat outer end of idler gear shaft with sealing cement.
2) Coat lock screw with sealer. Drive idler gear shaft into idler gear and transmission case. Position lock plate in groove of idler shaft and install lock screw and tighten.

MAINSHAFT
1) Lower rear end of mainshaft into case and maneuver through rear bearing opening. Make sure synchronizer and shims remain in position on mainshaft. Install roller thrust bearing. See Fig. 11.

NEW PROCESS 435 (Cont.)

Fig. 11: Installing Rear Mainshaft Bearing

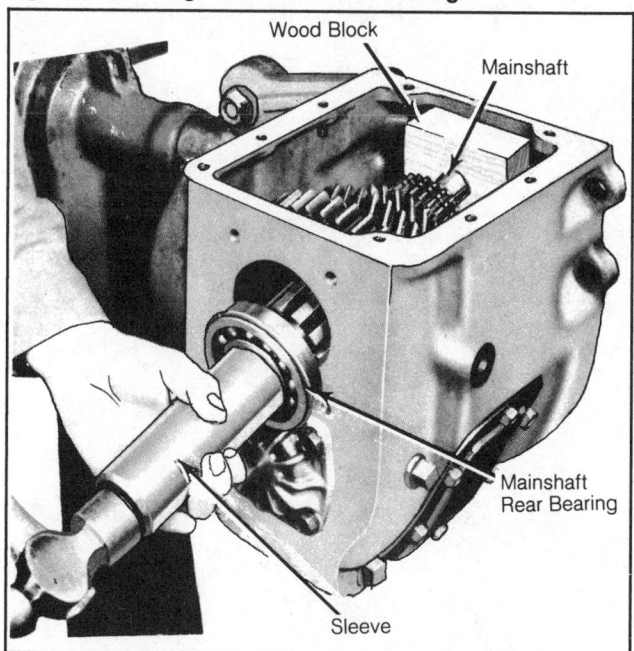

Place wood block between front of mainshaft and case.

2) Place a block of wood between front end of mainshaft and front of case. Install 1st gear stop ring and rear bearing onto mainshaft, drive into case until bearing snap ring is flush with case.

INPUT SHAFT DRIVE GEAR

1) Position input shaft drive clutch gear with missing teeth facing downward to permit for passage over countershaft gear. Guide input shaft and gear assembly into transmission case and over front end of mainshaft. Be sure 3rd-4th speed synchronizer stop ring engages teeth of drive gear.

Fig. 12: Measuring Bearing Retainer Clearance

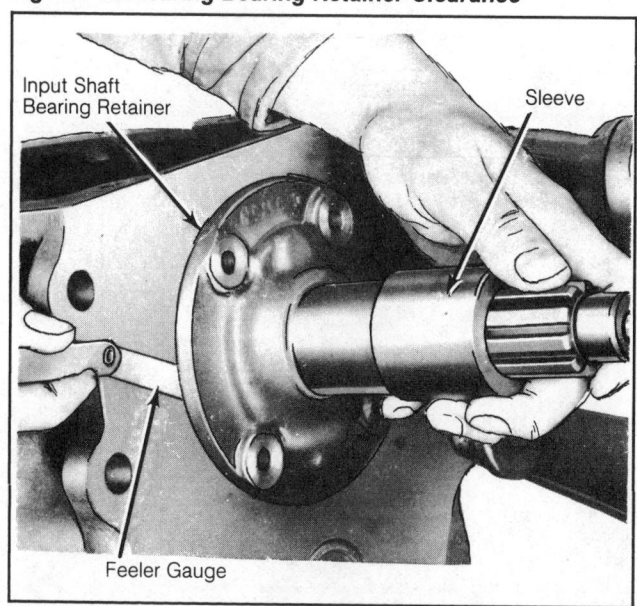

Measure clearance between retainer and case.

2) Position input shaft bearing retainer (without gasket) against transmission case. While holding bearing retainer in place with input shaft, measure clearance between retainer and face of case with a feeler gauge. *See Fig. 12.*

3) Remove bearing retainer, then reinstall with gasket shim pack .010-.015" (.254-.381 mm) thicker than measured clearance between retainer and case.

4) Using a dial indicator to measure input shaft and gear end play, bring end play within specification. *See Fig. 13.* End play of input shaft and gear is necessary to allow for normal heat expansion of parts during operation.

Fig. 13: Measuring Input Shaft Drive Gear End Play

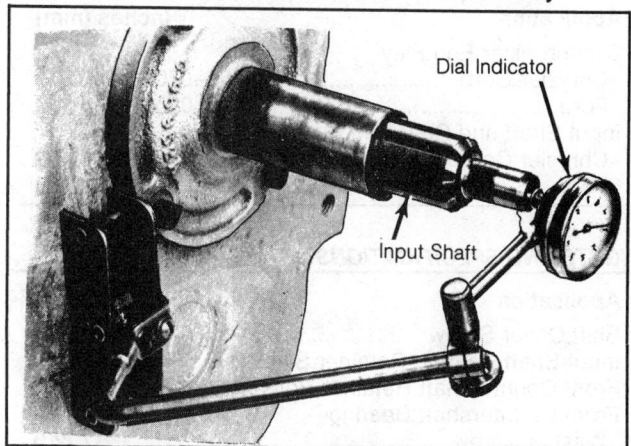

See TRANSMISSION SPECIFICATIONS table for correct specifications.

5) Check synchronizer end play after all mainshaft components are in position and properly tightened. Two equal size feeler gauges are used to measure synchronizer end play.

6) Keep gauges as close as possible to both sides of mainshaft. Disassemble mainshaft and add or subtract shims to bring end play within specification. *See Fig. 14.*

Fig. 14: Measuring Synchronizer End Play

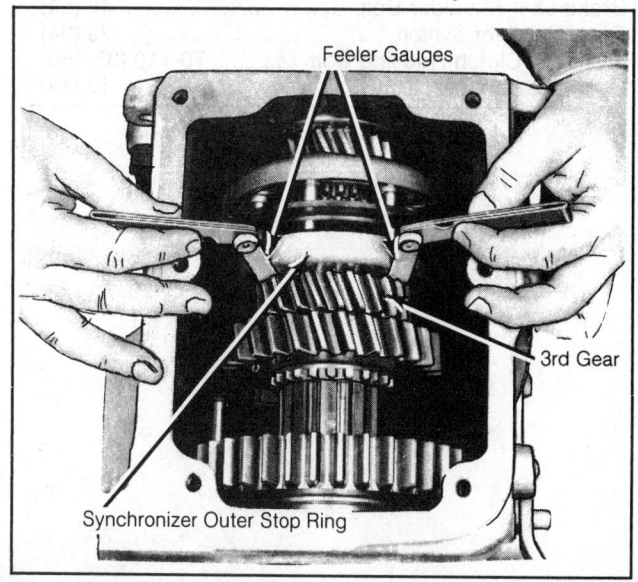

Measure play between synchronizer stop ring and 3rd gear.

NEW PROCESS 435 (Cont.)

SHIFT CONTROL COVER

1) Make sure all internal parts of transmission are well lubricated before installing shift control cover. Coat gasket surface on top of transmission case with gasket cement and position new gasket on top of case.

2) Place all transmission gears in neutral position. Position all shift rails in shift control cover in neutral position. Lower cover with new gasket into place, carefully engaging shift forks and lugs into proper gears. Attach cover to case with 8 screws and washers and tighten.

TRANSMISSION SPECIFICATIONS

Application	Inches (mm)
Synchronizer End Play	
Chrysler Corp.	.050-.070 (1.27-1.77)
Ford	.070-.095 (1.77-2.41)
Input Shaft and Gear End Play	
Chrysler Corp.	.007-.017 (.177-.432)
Ford	.007-.014 (.177-.355)

TIGHTENING SPECIFICATIONS

Application	Ft. Lbs. (N.m)
Shift Cover Screw	30 (41)
Input Shaft Bearing Retainer Screw	20 (27)
Front Countershaft Retainer Bolt	20 (27)
Front Countershaft Bearing Washer Screw	17 (23)
Output Flange Nut	
Chrysler Corp.	125 (169)
Ford	75-110 (102-150)
Mainshaft Rear Retainer Bolt	
Chrysler Corp.	20 (27)
Ford	35-45 (48-61)
Rear Countershaft Retainer Bolt	20 (27)
PTO Cover Bolt	
Chrysler Corp.	10 (14)
Ford	12-18 (16-24)
Drain & Filler Plugs	35 (48)
Reverse Idler Shaft Lock Bolt	30 (41)
Brake Link Shoulder Bolt	40 (54)
Back-Up Light Switch	25 (34)
Trans.-to-Clutch Housing Bolt	70-110 (95-150)
Case Breather	10 (14)

NEW PROCESS A833 OVERDRIVE

Chrysler Corp., General Motors

IDENTIFICATION

Transmission may be identified by a number stamped on a machined pad on right side of case. First two letters of code identify manufacturing plant, next three numbers designate transmission type (833), next four numbers indicate manufacturing date, and last four numbers are the production sequence series.

DESCRIPTION

Transmission is a 4-speed unit providing clash-free shifting in all forward gears due to the use of 2 synchronizer assemblies. The drive pinion (input shaft) is supported by a ball bearing in the front of transmission case and an oilite bushing pressed in rear of crankshaft.

The front end of the mainshaft is supported by roller bearings in the end of the drive pinion and by a ball bearing in the front of the extension housing.

The rear end of the mainshaft is supported by the sliding yoke of the propeller shaft, which is supported by a bushing in extension housing. The countershaft gear is supported by a double row of needle-type roller bearings at each end.

Gear thrust is taken up by means of thrust washers located between ends of gear and case. The reverse idler gear is supported in case by a bronze bushing which is pressed into gear.

LUBRICATION & ADJUSTMENT

See the appropriate article in MANUAL TRANSMISSION SERVICING Section..

TROUBLE SHOOTING

See Manual Transmission Trouble Shooting in MANUAL TRANSMISSION SERVICING section.

REMOVAL & INSTALLATION

See the appropriate article in MANUAL TRANSMISSION SERVICING Section.

SERVICE (IN-VEHICLE)

SPEEDOMETER PINION GEAR

Removal

Remove bolt and retainer securing pinion adapter to extension housing. With cable housing connected, work adapter and pinion out of extension housing.

Seal Replacement

1) If transmission fluid is found in cable housing, replace seal in adapter. Start new seal and retainer ring in adapter, then push them into adapter with installer (C-4004) until tool bottoms.

2) Be sure adapter flange and mating area on extension housing are clean and lubricated. Dirt or sand will cause misalignment and pinion gear damage.

Installation

1) Note number of gear teeth and install speedometer pinion gear into adapter. Rotate pinion gear

Fig. 1: Exploded View of Speedometer Pinion and Adapter Assembly

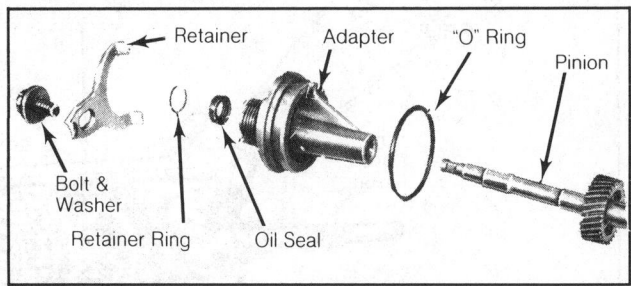

Fig. 2: Installing Speedometer Pinion Seal

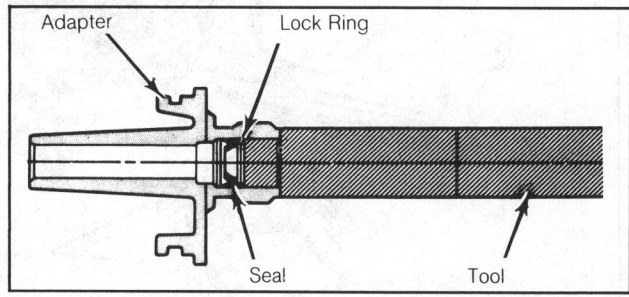

Push seal and retainer ring into adapter until it bottoms.

and adapter assembly so that number of teeth on adapter, corresponding to number of teeth on gear, is in the 6 o'clock position as assembly is installed.

2) Install retainer and bolt, with retainer tangs in adapter positioning slots. Tap adapter firmly into extension housing and tighten retaining bolt to specification.

Fig. 3: Installed View of Speedometer Pinion and Adapter

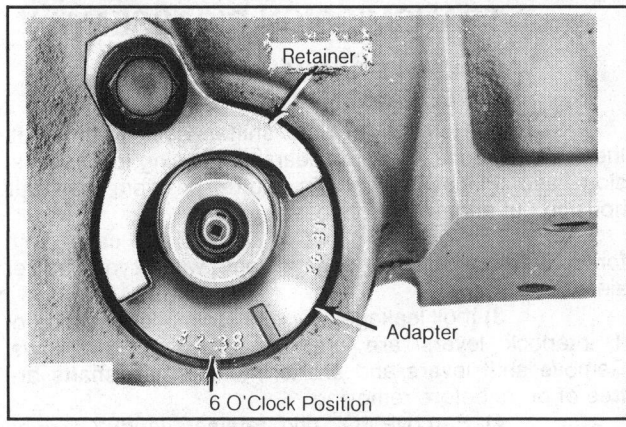

Secure pinion adapter in extension housing.

EXTENSION HOUSING YOKE SEAL

Removal

Mark rear universal joint for reassembly and remove propeller shaft. Remove oil seal from housing using seal remover (C-3985).

Installation

Position new seal in opening of extension housing and drive into housing with seal installer (C-3972). Install propeller shaft, aligning marks made at removal.

Manual Transmissions
NEW PROCESS A833 OVERDRIVE (Cont.)

Fig. 4: Cutaway View of A833 Overdrive Transmission

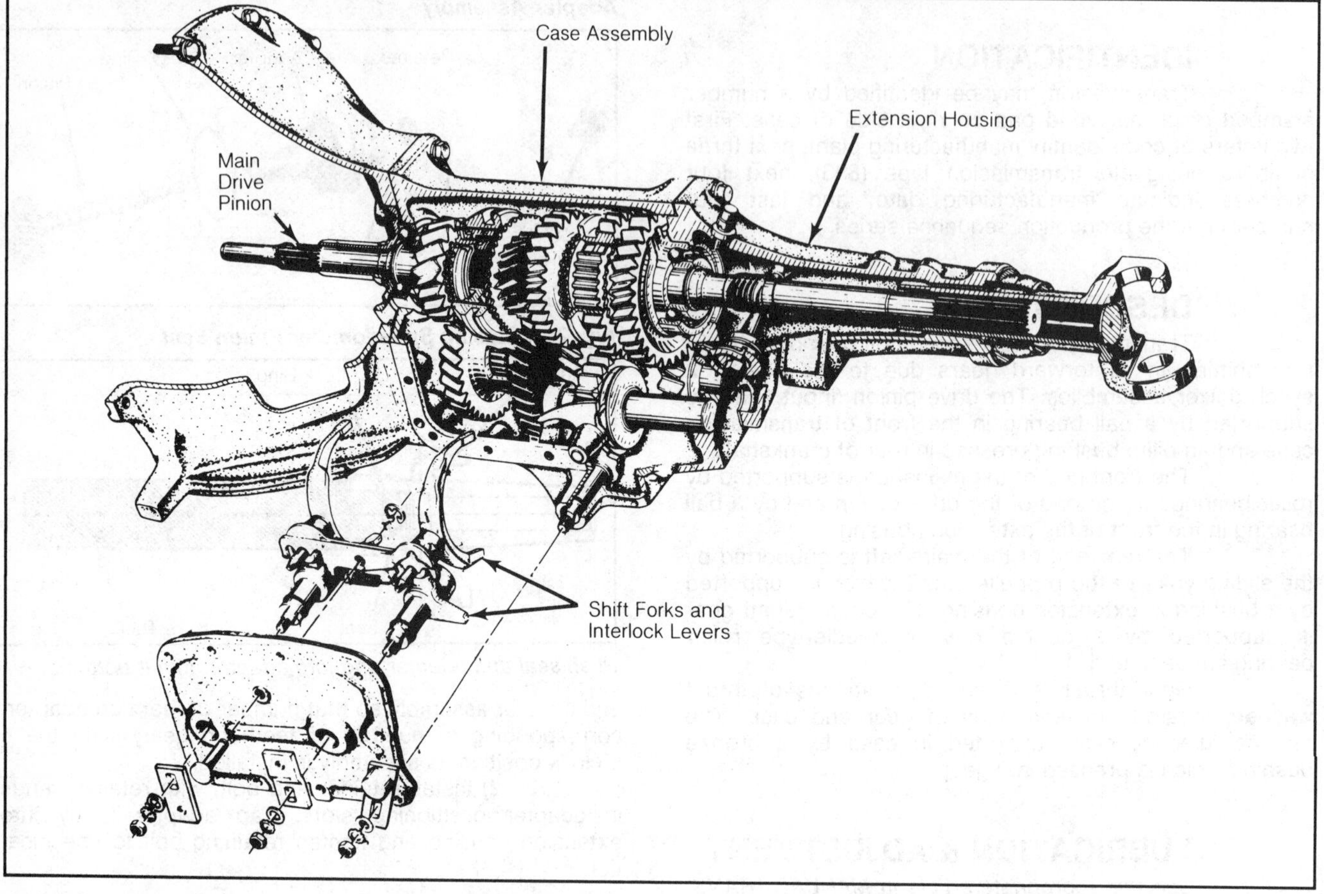

Case Assembly

Extension Housing

Main Drive Pinion

Shift Forks and Interlock Levers

TRANSMISSION DISASSEMBLY

GEARSHIFT HOUSING & MECHANISM

1) Remove reverse shifter lever from shaft, then remove bolts attaching gearshift housing to transmission case. Place all levers in neutral position, then pull housing out and away from case.

2) Work forks out of sleeves and case. Shift forks may remain in engagement with synchronizer sleeves.

3) If oil leakage is visible around lever shafts or if interlock levers are cracked, proceed as follows: Remove shift levers and shafts, making sure shafts are free of burrs before removing.

4) Remove "O" ring retainers and "O" rings from housing. Remove "E" ring from interlock lever pivot pin and remove interlock levers and spring from housing. Remove reverse detent spring and ball from bore in side of case.

EXTENSION HOUSING, MAINSHAFT & DRIVE PINION

1) Remove speedometer pinion and adapter from extension housing. Remove bolts attaching extension housing to transmission case. Rotate extension housing on output shaft to expose rear of countershaft.

2) Install 1 extension housing bolt to hold extension housing in inverted position. With centerpunch or drill, make hole in countershaft expansion plug at front of case.

3) Working through hole, drive countershaft forward and remove Woodruff key. Push countershaft forward until expansion plug is driven out of case.

Fig. 5: Exploded View of Gearshift Housing and Mechanism

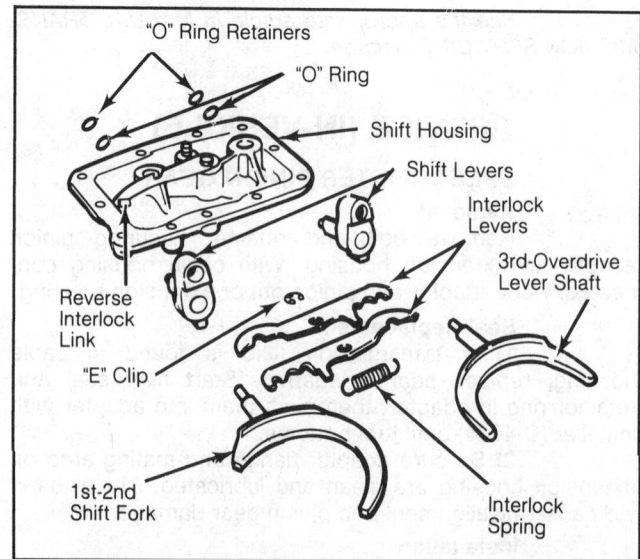

"O" Ring Retainers

"O" Ring

Shift Housing

Shift Levers

Interlock Levers

3rd-Overdrive Lever Shaft

Reverse Interlock Link

"E" Clip

1st-2nd Shift Fork

Interlock Spring

NEW PROCESS A833 OVERDRIVE (Cont.)

Fig. 6: Exploded View of A833 Overdrive Transmission

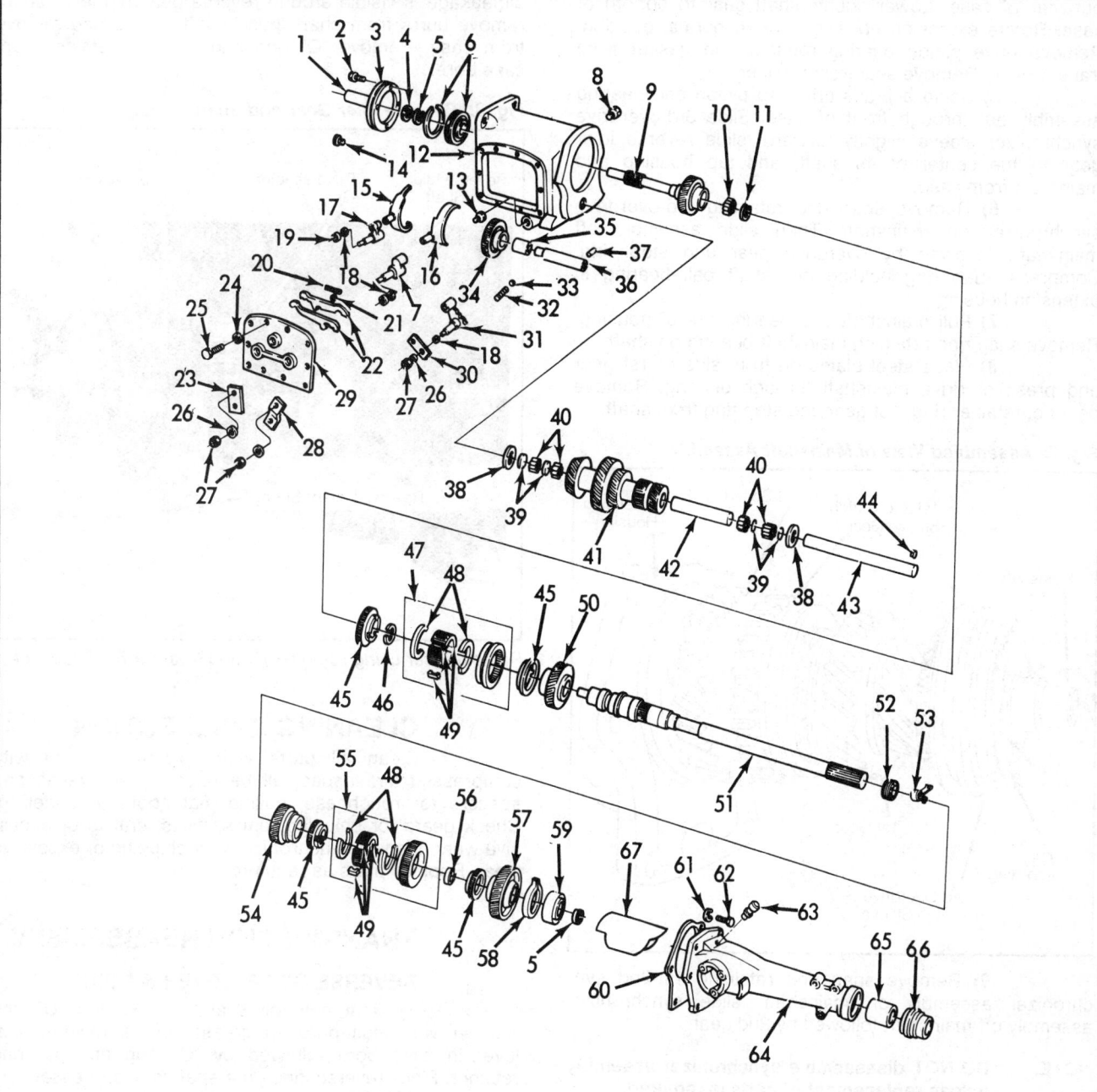

1. Bearing Retainer	18. Oil Seal (2)	34. Reverse Idler Gear
2. Bolt	19. Seal Retainer	35. Idler Gear Bushing
3. Gasket	20. Detent Spring	36. Reverse Idler Shaft
4. Bearing Retainer Oil Seal	21. "E" Ring	37. Woodruff Key
5. Snap Ring	22. Interlock Lever (2)	38. Thrust Washers
6. Pinion Bearing & Snap Ring	23. 3rd-Overdrive Operating Lever	39. Needle Spacer Rings (2)
7. 1st-2nd Lever	24. Lock Washer	40. Needle Rollers
8. Filler Plug	25. Cover Bolt	41. Countershaft Gear
9. Main Drive Pinion	26. Washer	42. Bearing Spacer
10. Needle Bearing Rollers	27. Nut	43. Countershaft
11. Snap Ring	28. 1st-2nd Operating Lever	44. Woodruff Key
12. Gasket	29. Gearshift Control Housing	45. Stop Ring
13. Drain Plug	30. Reverse Operating Lever	46. Snap Ring
14. Expansion Plug	31. Reverse Lever	47. 3rd-Overdrive Gear Synchronizer Assembly
15. 3rd-Overdrive Shift Fork	32. Detent Ball Spring	48. Shift Strut Spring
16. 1st-2nd Shift Fork	33. Reverse Detent Ball	49. Shift Struts
17. 3rd-Overdrive Lever		50. Overdrive Gear

51. Mainshaft
52. Speedometer Drive Gear
53. Clip
54. 2nd Gear
55. 1st-2nd Synchronizer Assembly
56. Snap Ring
57. 1st Gear
58. Stop Ring
59. Rear Bearing
60. Extension Gasket
61. Lock Washer
62. Screw
63. Extension Ventilator (General Motors Only)
64. Transmission Extension
65. Mainshaft Yoke Bushing
66. Extension Oil Seal
67. Baffle (Chrysler Corp.)

Manual Transmissions

NEW PROCESS A833 OVERDRIVE (Cont.)

4) Using arbor tool (C-3938), push countershaft out rear of case. Lower countershaft gear to bottom of case. Rotate extension housing back to normal position. Remove drive pinion bearing retainer and gasket from transmission. Remove seal from retainer.

5) Using a brass drift, tap pinion and bearing assembly out through front of case. Slide 3rd-overdrive synchronizer sleeve slightly forward, slide reverse idler gear to the center of its shaft, and tap housing and mainshaft from case.

6) Remove snap ring retaining 3rd-overdrive synchronizer on mainshaft. Then slide assembly off mainshaft, followed by overdrive gear and stop ring. Compress snap ring holding mainshaft ball bearing in extension housing.

7) Pull mainshaft and bearing out of housing. Remove snap ring retaining mainshaft bearing on shaft.

8) Place steel plates on front side of 1st gear and press or drive mainshaft through bearing. Remove bearing, retainer ring, 1st gear and stop ring from shaft.

Fig. 7: _Assembled View of Mainshaft Assembly_

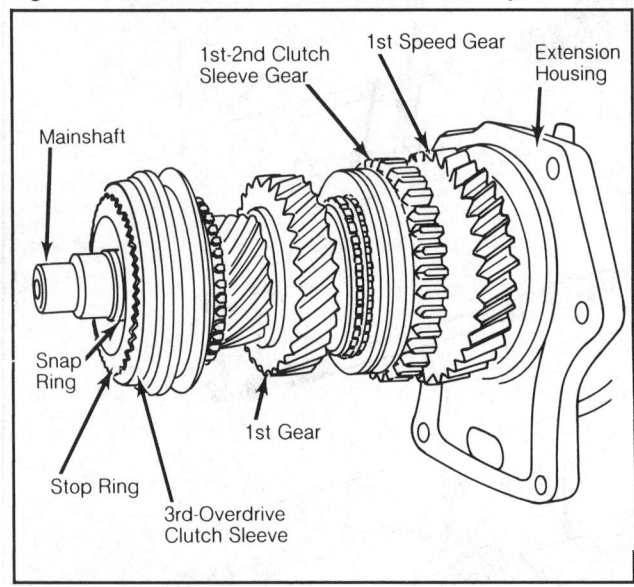

9) Remove snap ring retaining 1st-2nd synchronizer assembly on mainshaft, slide synchronizer assembly off mainshaft followed by 2nd gear.

NOTE: DO NOT disassemble synchronizer assembly unless replacement of parts is required.

DRIVE PINION & COUNTERSHAFT GEAR

1) Remove pinion bearing inner snap ring and remove ball bearing from drive pinion. Remove snap ring and 16 bearing rollers from cavity in drive pinion.

2) Remove countershaft gear from bottom of case and withdraw arbor, 76 needle roller bearings, thrust washers and spacers from center of countershaft gear.

REVERSE GEAR, LEVER & FORK

1) Remove reverse idler gear shaft using remover (C-3638) and a 7/16" socket. Place tool in case with socket against end of shaft and tool against case. Press shaft out of case. Remove Woodruff key from shaft.

2) Remove back-up light switch and gasket. If oil leakage is visible around reverse gearshift lever shaft, remove burrs from shaft, push shaft inward and remove from case. Remove "O" ring and "O" ring retainer from case bore.

Fig. 8: _Reverse Idler Gear and Shaft_

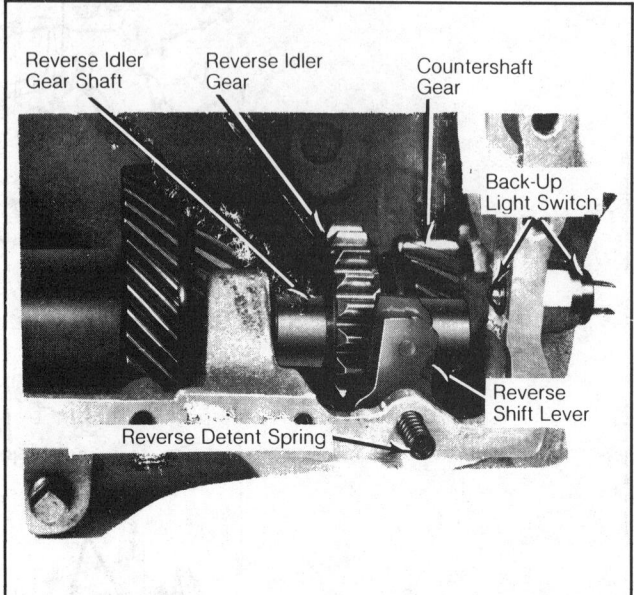

Remove gear using remover (C-3638) and a 7/16" socket.

CLEANING & INSPECTION

Clean all parts with solvent and dry with compressed air. Inspect all bearings, rollers, races and spacers for roughness, galling, flat spots or brinelling. Check gears for chipping, burrs, nicks, cracks or excessive wear. Inspect synchronizers for chipping or excessive wear. Replace parts as required.

TRANSMISSION REASSEMBLY

REVERSE GEAR, LEVER & FORK

1) Coat new oil seal "O" ring and "O" ring retainer with multi-purpose grease. Install reverse shift lever in case bore followed by "O" ring and "O" ring retainer. Place reverse idler gear shaft in end of case.

2) Press in shaft far enough to position reverse idler gear on shaft with fork slot toward rear and engage slot with reverse shift fork. Press shaft further into case and install Woodruff key.

3) Press shaft flush with end of case and install back-up light switch and gasket. Tighten to specification.

COUNTERSHAFT GEAR & DRIVE PINION

1) Coat inner bore of countershaft gear with light film of grease and install and center roller bearing spacer. Insert arbor tool and center it in gear.

2) Coat needle bearings with grease. At each end of gear, install 19 rollers followed by a spacer ring and 19 more roller bearings and 1 spacer ring.

NEW PROCESS A833 OVERDRIVE (Cont.)

3) Coat thrust washers with grease and install over arbor with tang side toward case boss. Install countershaft gear in bottom of case, making sure thrust washers stay in position.

Fig. 9: *Assembled View of Drive Pinion*

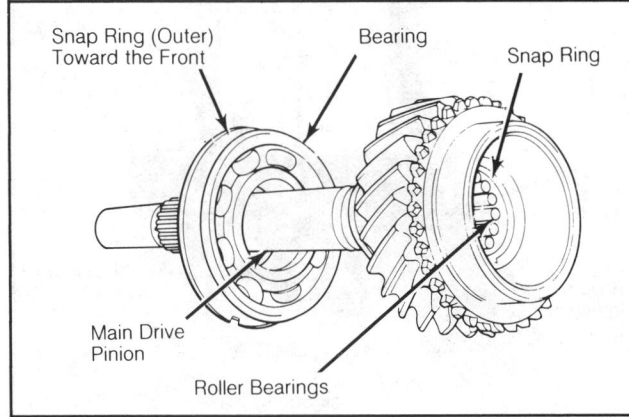

Snap Ring (Outer) Toward the Front

Bearing

Snap Ring

Main Drive Pinion

Roller Bearings

Select inner snap ring to give minimum end play.

4) Press main drive bearing on pinion shaft, with outer snap ring groove toward front, and seat bearing fully against shoulder of gear. Select and install a new inner snap ring on shaft to retain bearing and give minimum end play. Be sure snap ring is fully seated.

5) Place pinion shaft in a soft-jawed vise and install 16 bearing rollers in cavity of shaft. Coat rollers with grease and install retaining snap ring. Using seal installer (C-3789), install new oil seal in retainer bore.

EXTENSION HOUSING BUSHING REPLACEMENT

Remove extension housing yoke seal. Drive bushing out of housing using remover (C-3974). Slide a new bushing on installing end of tool. Align hole in bushing with oil slot in housing, then drive bushing into place. Drive a new oil seal into housing using seal installer (C-3972).

MAINSHAFT

CAUTION: Synchronizers are serviced as an assembly. Except for stop rings, synchronizer parts should not be interchanged. If synchronizers are disassembled, and parts are in good condition, reassemble as follows:

1) Place a stop ring flat on bench followed by clutch gear and sleeve. Drop struts in their slots and snap in a strut spring, placing tang inside one strut. Turn assembly over on stop ring. Install second strut spring tang in a different strut.

2) Slide 2nd gear over mainshaft and against shoulder, with sychronizer cone toward rear. Slide 1st-2nd synchronizer assembly, including stop ring with lugs indexed in hub slots, over mainshaft, down against 2nd gear cone and secure with a new snap ring.

3) Slide next stop ring over shaft and index lugs into clutch hub slots. Slide 1st gear over mainshaft into position against clutch sleeve gear. Install mainshaft bearing retaining ring, and mainshaft rear bearing.

4) Using arbor and driving tool, drive or press bearing into position. Install new snap ring on shaft to

secure bearing. Snap ring is a select fit for minimum end play.

5) Install partially assembled mainshaft into extension housing far enough to engage bearing retaining ring in slot in extension housing. Compress ring with pliers so that mainshaft ball bearing can bottom against extension housing. Release ring and seat it all around its groove in housing.

6) Slide overdrive gear over mainshaft with synchronizer cone toward front, and follow with stop ring. Install 3rd-overdrive synchronizer assembly on mainshaft with shift fork slot toward rear.

7) Make sure to index stop ring with shift struts. Install retaining ring. Grease and install front stop ring on synchronizer, indexing ring lugs with shift struts.

Fig. 10: *Exploded View of 1st-2nd Synchronizer Assembly*

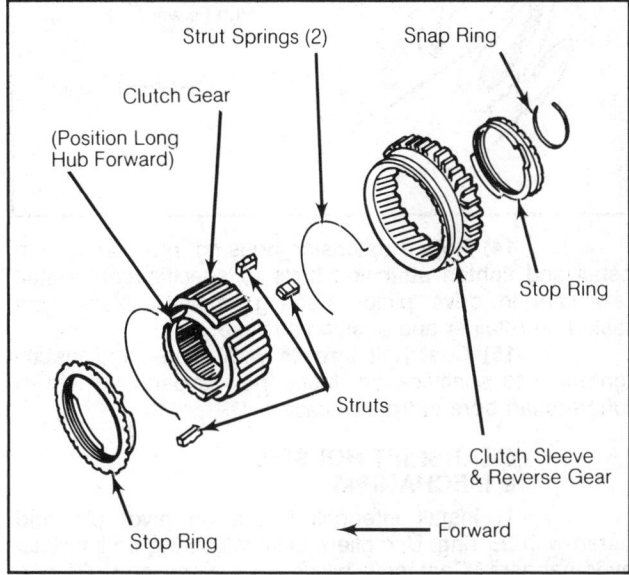

Strut Springs (2)

Snap Ring

Clutch Gear

(Position Long Hub Forward)

Stop Ring

Struts

Clutch Sleeve & Reverse Gear

Stop Ring

Forward

8) Coat a new extension housing-to-case gasket with grease and install on extension housing. Slide reverse idler gear to center of its shaft and move 3rd-overdrive synchronizer sleeve as far forward as possible.

9) Insert mainshaft assembly into case, tilting it as required to clear idler and cluster gears. Place 3rd-overdrive synchronizer in neutral position. Rotate extension housing on output shaft to expose rear of countershaft.

10) Install 1 extension housing bolt to hold extension housing in inverted position. Install snap ring in drive pinion bearing groove and install drive pinion into case indexing it with mainshaft.

11) Snap ring should bottom on case. If not, internal parts are not in correct position. Turn transmission upside down while holding countershaft gear assembly to prevent damaging it.

12) Lower countershaft gear assembly into position, with teeth meshed with drive pinion gear. Make sure thrust washers remain in position and tangs are aligned with slots in case.

13) Install countershaft into bore from rear of case and push forward until installed approximately halfway. Install Woodruff key, then push shaft forward until end is flush with rear of case and arbor tool is removed.

NEW PROCESS A833 OVERDRIVE (Cont.)

Fig. 11: *Exploded View of 3rd-Overdrive Synchronizer Assembly*

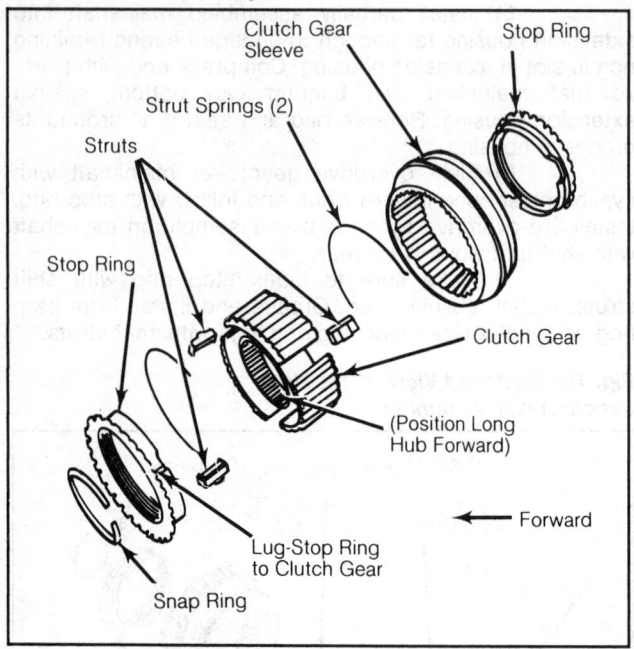

Fig. 12: *Assembled View of Gearshift Mechanism*

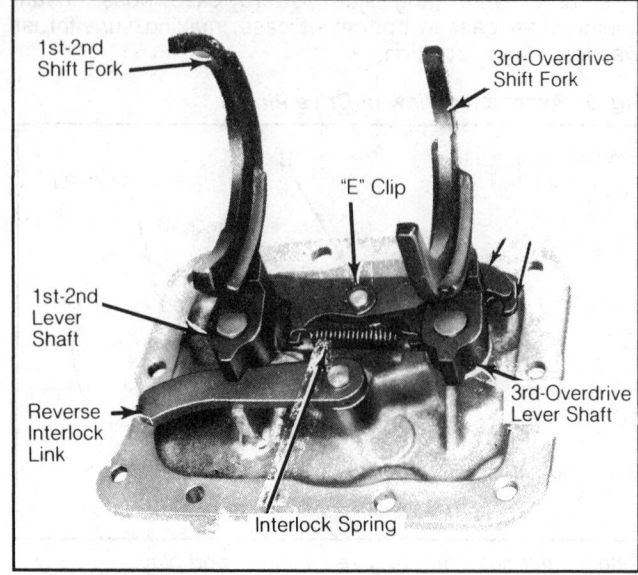

After assembly, check transmission in all gears.

14) Rotate extension housing into place, then install and tighten attaching bolts to specification. Install new seal in drive pinion bearing retainer, place new gasket on retainer and position on case.

15) Coat bolt threads with sealer and install, tightening to specification. Install new expansion plug in countershaft bore at front of case.

GEARSHIFT HOUSING & MECHANISM

1) Install interlock levers on pivot pin and fasten with "E" ring. Use pliers to install spring on interlock lever hangers. Coat new oil seal "O" rings and "O" ring retainers with multi-purpose grease.

2) Install each shift lever shaft into its proper bore, followed by an "O" ring and "O" ring retainer. Install operating levers and retaining nuts and tighten to specification.

3) Rotate each shaft fork bore to neutral (straight up), and install 3rd-overdrive shift fork in its bore and under both interlock levers. Position both synchronizer sleeves in neutral. Place 1st-2nd shift fork in groove of 1st-2nd synchronizer sleeve.

4) Slide reverse idler gear to neutral. Lay transmission on its right-hand side, coat gearshift housing gasket with grease and position on case. Install reverse detent ball and spring into its bore in side of case.

5) As shift housing is lowered into place, guide 3rd-overdrive shift fork into 3rd-overdrive synchronizer groove. Position shaft of synchronizer 1st-2nd shift fork into bore of 1st-2nd shift lever. Hold reverse interlock link against 1st-2nd shift lever to provide clearance as shift cover is lowered into position.

6) Using screwdriver, raise interlock lever against spring tension to allow 1st-2nd shift fork shaft to slip under levers. Install housing bolts finger tight, shift transmission through all gears to insure proper operation.

7) The reverse shift lever and 1st-2nd shift lever have cam surfaces which mate in reverse position to lock 1st-2nd shift lever, fork and synchronizer in neutral. Grease reverse shaft and install operating lever and retaining nut and tighten to specification.

NOTE: Eight of the shift housing bolts are shoulder bolts, 1 has a longer shoulder and acts as a dowel at center of rear flange. Two bolts installed at lower rear of cover are standard.

8) Install speedometer drive pinion gear and adapter making sure correct range number, corresponding to number of teeth on pinion gear, is in 6 o'clock position.

TRANSMISSION SPECIFICATIONS

Application	In. (mm)
Countershaft-to-Case Bore Diameter	.005-.006 (.127-.152)
Clutch Housing Bore Run-Out	.008 (.203)
Clutch Housing Face Squareness	.006 Max. (.152)
Countershaft Gear End Play	.015-.029 (.381-.736)

TIGHTENING SPECIFICATIONS

Application	Ft. Lbs. (N.m)
Back-up Light Switch	15 (20)
Drain Plug	15 (20)
Extension Hsg.-to-Case Bolts	50 (68)
Gearshift Mount-to-Ext. Hsg. Bolts	12 (16)
Gearshift Mount-to-Plate Bolts	24 (32)
Input Bearing Retainer Bolts	30 (41)
Shift Lever Nuts	18 (24)
Transmission-to-Clutch Hsg. Bolts	50 (68)
	INCH Lbs. (N.m)
Speedometer Pinion Adapter Bolt	96 (11)

SECTION 4

DOMESTIC TRANSFER CASES

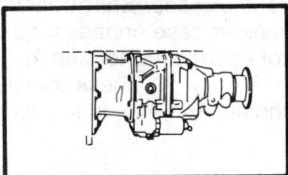

NOTE: **ALSO SEE GENERAL INDEX.**

Transfer Cases

AMERICAN MOTORS MODEL 129

Eagle

DESCRIPTION

Eagle models are equipped with model 129 full-time 4-wheel drive transfer case. This unit provides fully differentiated 4-wheel drive under all operating conditions. The model 129 is a single range unit. Selection of 4-wheel drive is automatic and does not require any external linkage to achieve 4-wheel operation.

Differentiated operation occurs through a coupling connected to an open differential. Torque is distributed to the front and rear propeller shafts through 2 drive sprockets and drive chain. Case assembly is cast aluminum. Case consists of front and rear halves and a rear retainer.

Eagles may be equipped with optional Select Drive system. Select Drive consists of a dash mounted switch, vacuum actuated shift lever in transfer case and vacuum actuated front axle disconnect.

Select Drive provides drive train selection appropriate for road conditions. Selection of "2WD" mode activates transfer case shift lever to provide torque to rear propeller shaft only. Selection of "4WD" mode activates transfer case shift lever to provide torque to both front and rear propeller shafts. *See Fig. 1.*

LUBRICATION

SERVICE INTERVAL

Check transfer case fluid level at first 5 month or 5,000 mile interval; then, every 7 1/2 months or 7,500 miles. Change fluid every 12 1/2 months or 12,500 miles.

FLUID TYPE

Use Dexron II automatic transmission fluid or equivalent.

CAPACITY

Capacity is 6 pints (2.8L) or up to bottom edge of fill plug hole.

TROUBLE SHOOTING

LUBRICANT LEAKS PAST YOKE OR OUT OF VENT

Overfilled condition or vent could be closed or restricted. Yoke seal could be worn or damaged.

NOISY OPERATION

Incorrect or insufficient lubrication. Incorrect tire pressure. Mismatched or unequal tire sizes and type.

SEVERE LOW SPEED SHUDDER

Low viscous silicone fluid level.

WILL NOT ENGAGE 2WD

1) Raise vehicle so that all 4 wheels are free to rotate. Start engine. Disconnect mode selector vacuum harness at steel tube connection. Check for vacuum at Red hose that attaches to canister. If vacuum exists, go to step 3). If no vacuum, go to step 2).

2) Check intake manifold vacuum supply fitting, vacuum hose and storage tank. If damaged, repair or replace components as necessary. If vacuum leak still exists, repair vacuum line between canister and steel tube. If vacuum exists at Red hose, proceed with system check.

3) Stop engine. Connect vacuum pump to steel tube that connects to Green hose in vacuum harness. Apply 20 in. Hg and rotate propeller shaft to engage transfer case. Shift transmission into park or first gear. If transfer case engages, go to step 6). If transfer case does not engage, go to step 4).

4) Check transfer case shift motor. Motor stem should be extended. If stem is not extended, check

Fig. 1: Eagle Select Drive Transfer Case

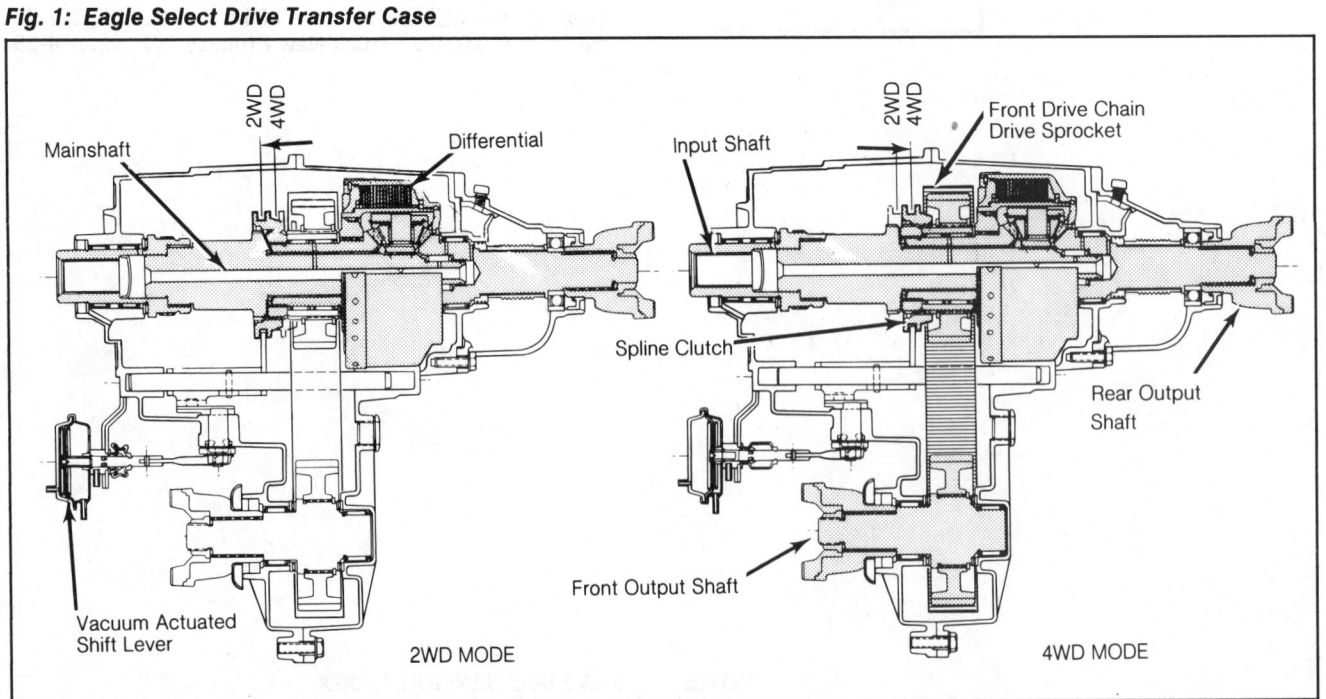

AMERICAN MOTORS MODEL 129 (Cont.)

vacuum tubes for leaks and damage. Repair as necessary. If transfer case shift motor is still inoperative, check shift motor function. If shift motor is defective, replace motor. If shift motor is operative go to step 5).

5) If transfer case will not engage in 2WD, check transfer case shift linkage and repair as necessary. If linkage is okay and transfer case will not shift into 2WD, repair case. If transfer case now engages in 2WD, check axle for 2WD mode engagement (disconnected). If front axle is not in 2WD mode, check axle shift motor and replace as necessary.

6) If front axle shift motor is okay, check the shift mode selector switch and vacuum harness. Repair as necessary. If front axle shift motor will not disengage, check vacuum lines and repair as necessary.

7) If vacuum lines are okay and axle will not disengage, remove axle housing cover and shift motor. Inspect shift fork, collar and axle components. Repair as necessary.

WILL NOT ENGAGE 4WD

1) Raise vehicle so that all 4 wheels are free to rotate. Start engine. Disconnect mode selector vacuum harness at steel tube connection. Check for vacuum at Red hose that attaches to canister. If vacuum exists, go to step 3). If no vacuum, go to step 2).

2) Check intake manifold vacuum supply fitting, vacuum hose and storage tank. If damaged, repair or replace components as necessary. If vacuum leak still exists, repair vacuum line between canister and steel tube. If vacuum exists at Red hose, proceed with system check.

3) Stop engine. Connect vacuum pump to steel tube that connects to Yellow hose in vacuum harness. Apply 20 in. Hg and rotate right front wheel to engage axle. If front axle is engaged, go to step 6). If front axle is not engaged proceed with system check.

4) Check front axle shift motor for operation. If shift motor is okay, check vacuum lines and tubes for leaks or damage. Repair as necessary. If axle shift motor is inoperative, replace motor and recheck for axle engagement.

5) If axle will not engage, remove axle housing cover and shift motor. Inspect shift fork, collar, and axle components. Repair as necessary.

6) Check that motor stem is retracted in transfer case shift motor. If transfer case motor stem is retracted, check transfer case shift linkage and repair as necessary. If transfer case shift motor is inoperative, stem is not retracted, check vacuum hoses and repair as necessary.

7) If transfer case motor is still inoperative, test motor operation with vacuum pump. If vacuum motor is defective, replace motor and retest. If transfer case motor is okay and transfer case does not engage in 4WD, check axle shift linkage and repair as necessary. If linkage is okay, repair transfer case as necessary.

VACUUM SHIFT MOTOR TEST

1) Disconnect vacuum harness from shift motor. Connect vacuum pump to front port and apply 15 in. Hg to motor. On transfer case, rotate propeller shaft to engage transfer case in 4WD mode. On front axle, rotate right wheel to fully disengage axle.

2) Shift motor should maintain vacuum applied for at least 30 seconds. If motor does not maintain vacuum, replace motor. If motor does hold vacuum, go to step 3).

3) Disconnect vacuum pump from the front port of the vacuum motor. Connect pump to the rear port of the motor and plug the connecting port. Apply 15 in. Hg to motor. Vacuum should be maintained for 30 seconds. If vacuum is not maintained, replace motor. If motor maintains vacuum, go to step 4).

4) Remove plug from connecting port and check for vacuum at this port. If vacuum is not present, rotate propeller shaft on transfer case or right wheel on front axle, to ensure full engagement of shift motor.

5) If no vacuum exists at connecting port, pull back boot on stem and measure distance that stem has extended. Stem should extend a distance of 5/8" (16 mm) as measured from the edge of shift motor housing to "E" ring on stem. If stem does not extend the specified distance or if stem extends the specified distance but no vacuum is present at the connecting port, replace motor.

SERVICE (IN VEHICLE)

NOTE: **The following procedure outlines replacement of front and rear yokes, yoke seals, rear retainer, rear bearing and speedometer gear.**

REMOVAL

1) Raise and support vehicle. Remove skid plate. Remove transfer case drain plug and drain lubricant. Mark propeller shaft and transfer case yoke for installation reference.

2) Disconnect propeller shaft and secure to underside of vehicle. Remove speedometer cable and adapter from rear retainer. Remove and discard speedometer adapter seal.

3) Support engine with support stand (under converter housing if equipped). Remove rear crossmember bolts. Using a jack, lower transmission/transfer case assembly to gain access to rear retainer bolts. Mark rear retainer and case for installation reference.

4) Remove rear yoke nut and seal washer. Remove rear yoke. Remove rear retainer bolts and tap off rear retainer with plastic mallet. DO NOT pry retainer from case.

5) Remove differential shim(s) and speedometer gear from rear output shaft. Remove bearing snap ring (if equipped), bearing and rear yoke seal from retainer.

INSTALLATION

1) Install rear output bearing in rear retainer with shielded side facing case interior. Install bearing snap ring (if equipped), then, install yoke seal.

2) Coat rear retainer mating surface with sealant, align marks made during removal and install rear retainer. Tighten retainer bolts. Install yoke, new seal washer and nut. Torque nut to specifications.

3) Install transfer case drain plug and fill transfer case. Raise transmission/transfer case and rear crossmember. Install and tighten crossmember attaching bolts.

4) Remove engine support and jack. Connect propeller shaft after aligning marks made during removal. Install new seal on speedometer adapter. Install adapter and speedometer cable in rear retainer. Install skid plate and lower vehicle.

AMERICAN MOTORS MODEL 129 (Cont.)

REMOVAL & INSTALLATION

TRANSFER CASE

Removal (Automatic Transmission)

1) Raise and support vehicle. Support engine and transmission with transmission jack or support stand. Disconnect catalytic converter support bracket at adapter housing. Remove skid plate, stiffening brace (if equipped), speedometer cable and adapter. Remove and discard adapter seal.

2) Mark propeller shafts and transfer case yokes for installation reference. Disconnect propeller shafts at yokes and secure to underside of vehicle. Disconnect gearshift and throttle linkage at transmission. Remove rear crossmember and transfer case-to-adapter housing nuts. Lower and remove transfer case from vehicle.

Installation

To install transfer case, reverse removal procedure. Always replace speedometer adapter seal.

Removal (Manual Transmission)

1) Working inside vehicle, place transmission in neutral and remove gearshift lever bezel-to-floorpan (console) retaining screws. Slide bezel and boot up on gearshift lever and remove lever-to-mounting cover bolts. Remove lever. Remove mounting cover-to-transmission adapter housing bolts and remove cover.

2) Working inside transmission adapter housing, remove transfer case mounting stud nut. Raise and support vehicle. Remove skid plate and stiffening brace (if equipped). Mark position of speedometer adapter, then remove adapter retainer, adapter and speedometer cable. Plug adapter opening to prevent fluid leak.

3) Mark propeller shafts and transfer case yokes for installation reference. Disconnect propeller shafts at yokes and secure to underside of vehicle. Support transfer case with transmission jack. Remove transfer case mounting stud nuts. Lower and remove from vehicle.

Installation

To install transfer case, reverse removal procedure. Always replace speedometer adapter seal.

OVERHAUL

TRANSFER CASE

Disassembly

1) Drain lubricant from transfer case. Remove front and rear yoke nuts. Remove and discard seal washers. Remove yokes. Mount transfer case on wooden blocks ("V" notch blocks to clear front case mounting studs). Mark rear retainer and rear case for reassembly reference, then remove retainer bolts. Using 2 screwdrivers inserted in retainer and case slots, pry retainer loose.

2) Remove retainer, differential shim(s) and speedometer drive gear. Using 2 screwdrivers inserted in slots at each end of rear case, loosen case halves. Remove rear case.

CAUTION: Do not attempt to wedge case halves apart. Case mating surfaces may be damaged.

Fig. 2: Speedometer Gear and Differential Shim

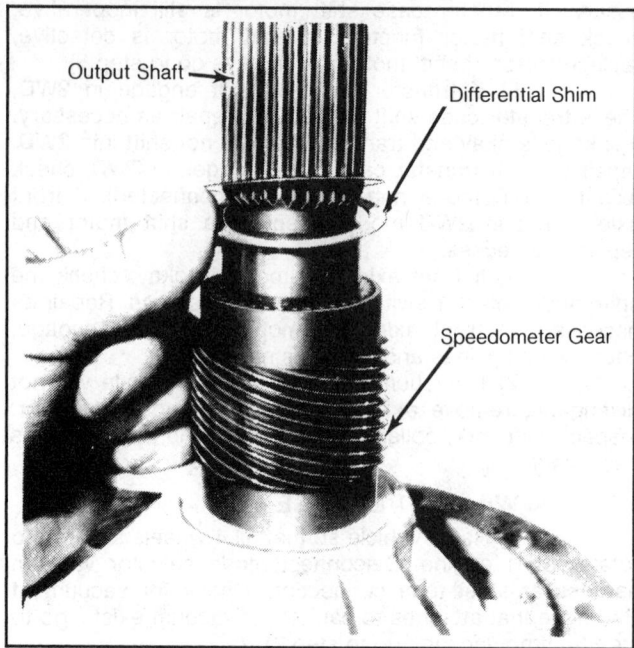

Output Shaft

Differential Shim

Speedometer Gear

3) Remove thrust bearing and races from front output shaft. Note position of bearing and races for reassembly reference. Remove oil pump from rear output shaft. Note position of pump for reassembly reference (recessed side faces case interior). Remove rear output shaft from viscous coupling.

4) Remove 15 mainshaft pilot bearing rollers from shaft or coupling. Remove mainshaft "O" ring from end of shaft. Remove viscous coupling from mainshaft and side gear.

5) Lift front shaft, sprocket and chain upward as an assembly. Tilt front shaft toward mainshaft, slide chain off drive sprocket and remove assembly. Remove front output shaft front thrust bearing assembly from front case or shaft, if bearing and races remained on shaft during removal. Remove drive chain from front output shaft and sprocket.

6) Remove driven sprocket snap ring from front output shaft. Mark sprocket and shaft for reassembly reference, then remove sprocket. Remove mainshaft, side gear, clutch gear, drive sprocket and spline gear as an assembly. Place assembly aside on clean surface.

7) Remove range fork, rail and clutch sleeve as an assembly. Mark sleeve and fork for reassembly reference, then remove sleeve from fork. Drive roll pin out of fork and rail. Remove rail from fork. Remove mainshaft thrust washer from input gear. Remove input gear, input thrust bearing and race. Remove detent bolt, spring and plunger. Remove range sector shaft retaining nut and washer.

8) Remove range sector. Tap sector shaft with plastic mallet to remove shaft from case bore. Remove range sector shaft "O" ring seal and seal retainer from case bore. Remove rear output bearing and rear yoke seal from rear retainer. Note position of bearing for reassembly reference (bearing is shielded on one side). Remove input gear. Pry front yoke seals out of front case.

AMERICAN MOTORS MODEL 129 (Cont.)

Cleaning

Clean all parts in cleaning solvent. Be sure all old lubricant or foreign material is removed from surfaces of every part. Apply compressed air to blow dry parts.

Inspection

1) Inspect all gear teeth for signs of excessive wear or damage and check all gear splines for burrs, nicks, wear or damage. Remove minor nicks or scratches using an oilstone. Replace any part exhibiting excessive wear or damage.

NOTE: **Front output shaft thrust bearing race surfaces are heat treated, causing brown or blue discoloration. Do not replace front output shaft because of this discoloration.**

2) Inspect case halves and rear retainer for cracks, porosity, damaged mating surfaces, stripped bolt threads or distortion.

3) Inspect the condition of all bearings. Also check the condition of all bearing bores. Replace any part that exhibits signs of wear or damage.

CAUTION: **All bearings used in transfer case halves must be correctly positioned to avoid blocking bearing oil feed holes. After replacing bearing, check that feed hole is not covered by bearing.**

MAINSHAFT

Disassembly

1) Grasp drive sprocket and lift sprocket, clutch gear and side gear upward and off mainshaft.

Fig. 3: Removing Drive Sprocket, Clutch Gear, Side Gear and Sprocket Carrier from Mainshaft

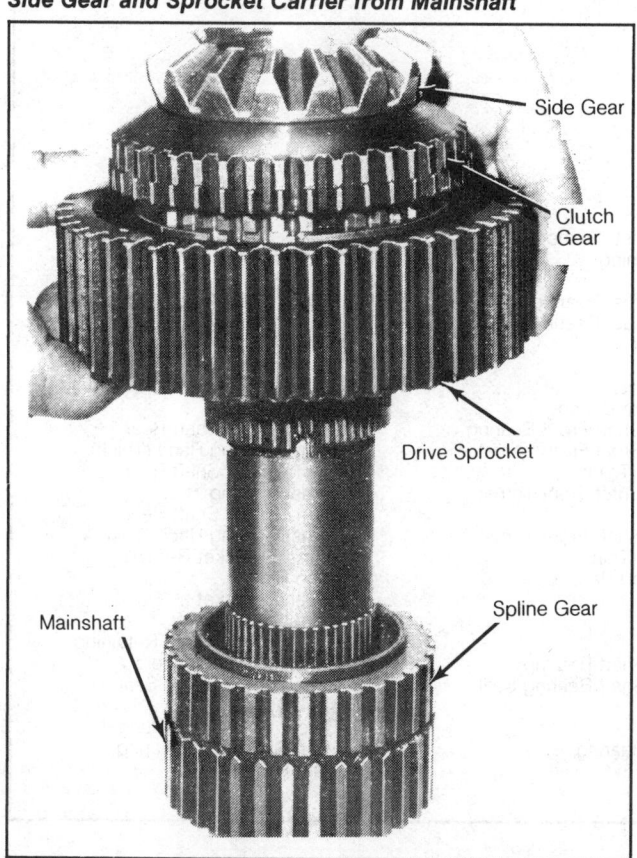

Remove mainshaft needle bearings (82) and bearing spacers (3) from mainshaft. Note spacer position for reassembly reference. *See Fig. 3.*

2) Remove spline gear and thrust washer from mainshaft. Remove side gear, clutch gear and clutch gear thrust washer from sprocket carrier and sprocket. Remove clutch gear and thrust washer from side gear.

3) Remove 1 sprocket carrier snap ring and remove drive sprocket from carrier. Mark sprocket and carrier for reassembly reference. Remove 3 bearing spacers and all sprocket carrier needle bearings from carrier. A total of 120 needle bearings are used.

NOTE: **The sprocket carrier and mainshaft needle bearings are different sizes. Take care to avoid intermixing them.**

Reassembly

1) Install thrust washer, new "O" ring, needle bearings and bearing spacers on mainshaft. Coat shaft bearing surfaces and all needle bearings with petroleum

Fig. 4: Installation of Mainshaft Needle Bearing and Spacers

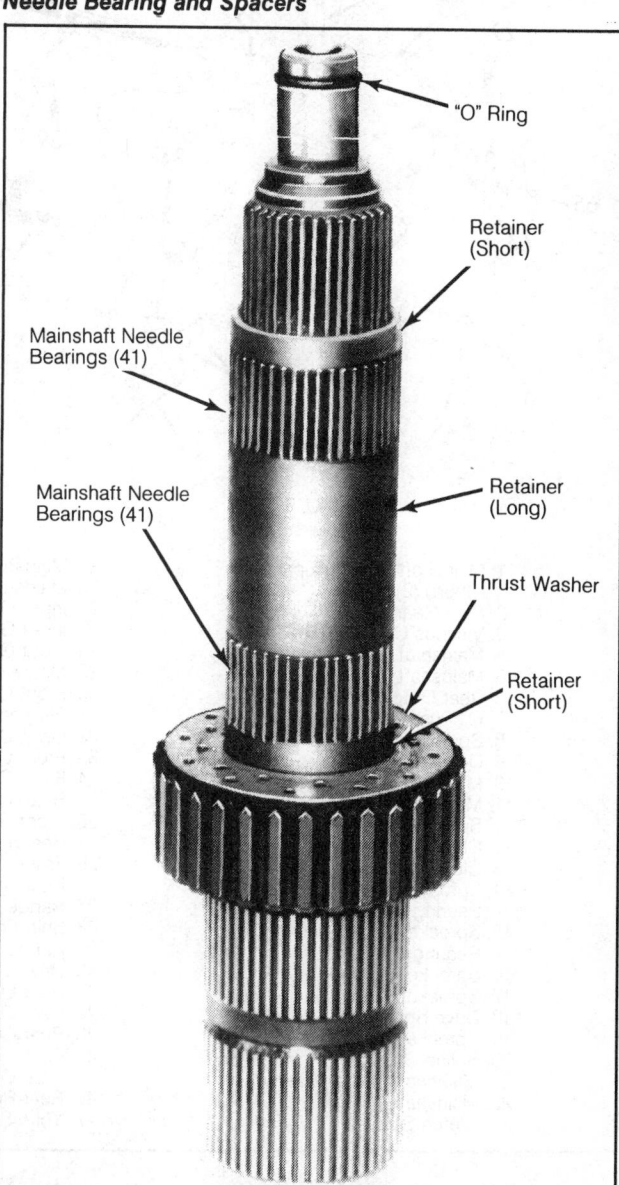

Transfer Cases

AMERICAN MOTORS MODEL 129 (Cont.)

Fig. 5: American Motors Model 129 Transfer Case

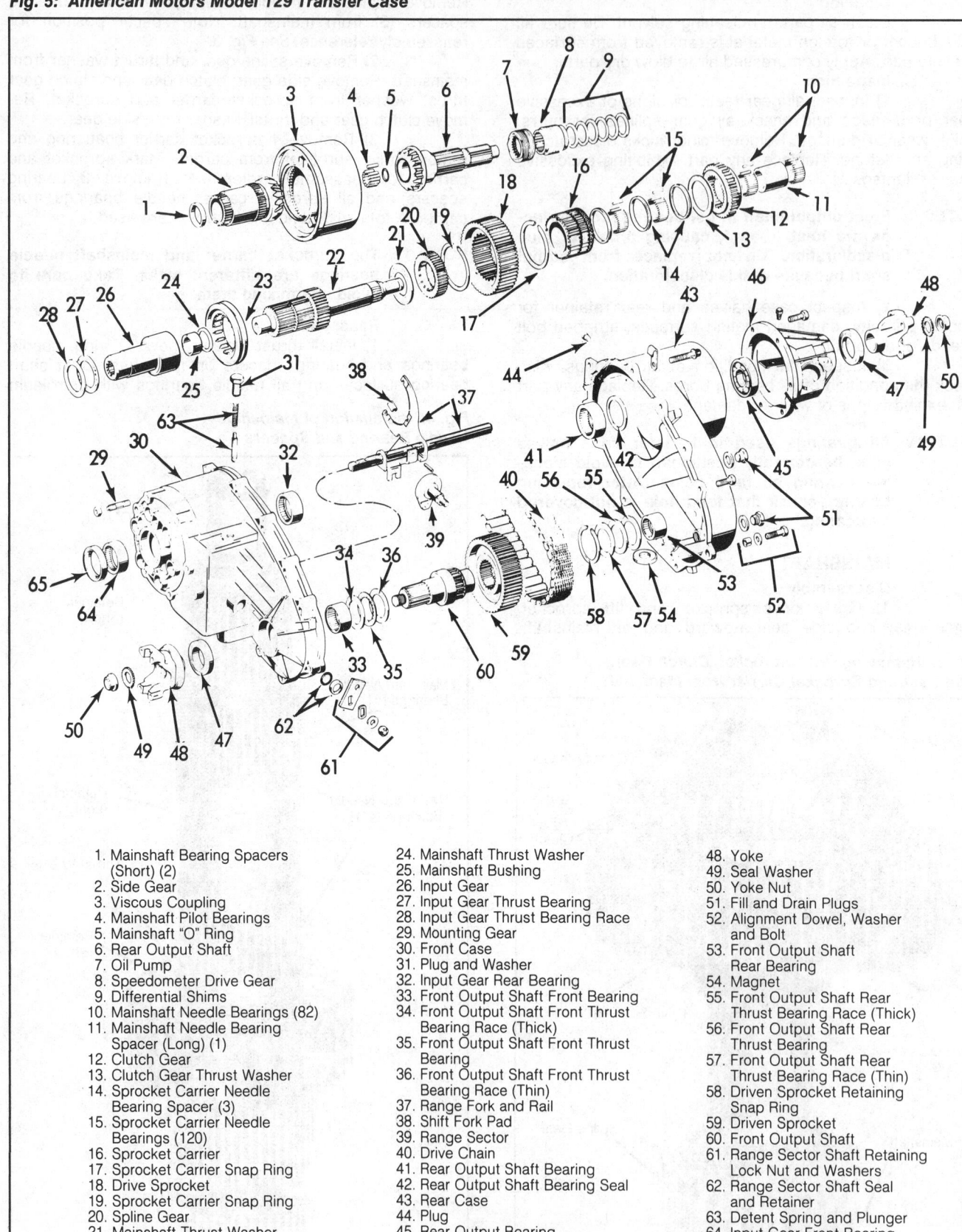

1. Mainshaft Bearing Spacers (Short) (2)
2. Side Gear
3. Viscous Coupling
4. Mainshaft Pilot Bearings
5. Mainshaft "O" Ring
6. Rear Output Shaft
7. Oil Pump
8. Speedometer Drive Gear
9. Differential Shims
10. Mainshaft Needle Bearings (82)
11. Mainshaft Needle Bearing Spacer (Long) (1)
12. Clutch Gear
13. Clutch Gear Thrust Washer
14. Sprocket Carrier Needle Bearing Spacer (3)
15. Sprocket Carrier Needle Bearings (120)
16. Sprocket Carrier
17. Sprocket Carrier Snap Ring
18. Drive Sprocket
19. Sprocket Carrier Snap Ring
20. Spline Gear
21. Mainshaft Thrust Washer
22. Mainshaft
23. Clutch Sleeve

24. Mainshaft Thrust Washer
25. Mainshaft Bushing
26. Input Gear
27. Input Gear Thrust Bearing
28. Input Gear Thrust Bearing Race
29. Mounting Gear
30. Front Case
31. Plug and Washer
32. Input Gear Rear Bearing
33. Front Output Shaft Front Bearing
34. Front Output Shaft Front Thrust Bearing Race (Thick)
35. Front Output Shaft Front Thrust Bearing
36. Front Output Shaft Front Thrust Bearing Race (Thin)
37. Range Fork and Rail
38. Shift Fork Pad
39. Range Sector
40. Drive Chain
41. Rear Output Shaft Bearing
42. Rear Output Shaft Bearing Seal
43. Rear Case
44. Plug
45. Rear Output Bearing
46. Rear Retainer
47. Yoke Seal

48. Yoke
49. Seal Washer
50. Yoke Nut
51. Fill and Drain Plugs
52. Alignment Dowel, Washer and Bolt
53. Front Output Shaft Rear Bearing
54. Magnet
55. Front Output Shaft Rear Thrust Bearing Race (Thick)
56. Front Output Shaft Rear Thrust Bearing
57. Front Output Shaft Rear Thrust Bearing Race (Thin)
58. Driven Sprocket Retaining Snap Ring
59. Driven Sprocket
60. Front Output Shaft
61. Range Sector Shaft Retaining Lock Nut and Washers
62. Range Sector Shaft Seal and Retainer
63. Detent Spring and Plunger
64. Input Gear Front Bearing
65. Input Gear Seal

AMERICAN MOTORS MODEL 129 (Cont.)

jelly. Install short bearing spacer on shaft and install first 41 needle bearings.

    2) Install long bearing spacer, remaining 41 needle bearings and remaining short spacer. Be careful to avoid displacing bearings as spacers are installed. Use additional petroleum jelly to hold bearings in place if necessary. Install spline gear on mainshaft. Take care to avoid displacing bearings while installing spline gear.

    3) Install sprocket carrier in drive sprocket and install sprocket carrier snap rings. Be sure to align carrier and sprocket according to reference marks made during disassembly. *See Fig. 6.*

NOTE: **The sprocket carrier teeth are tapered on one side and the drive sprocket has a deep recess on one side. Be sure to assemble these components so the carrier tapered teeth and sprocket recess are on the same side.**

Fig. 6: Installing Drive Sprocket on Sprocket Carrier

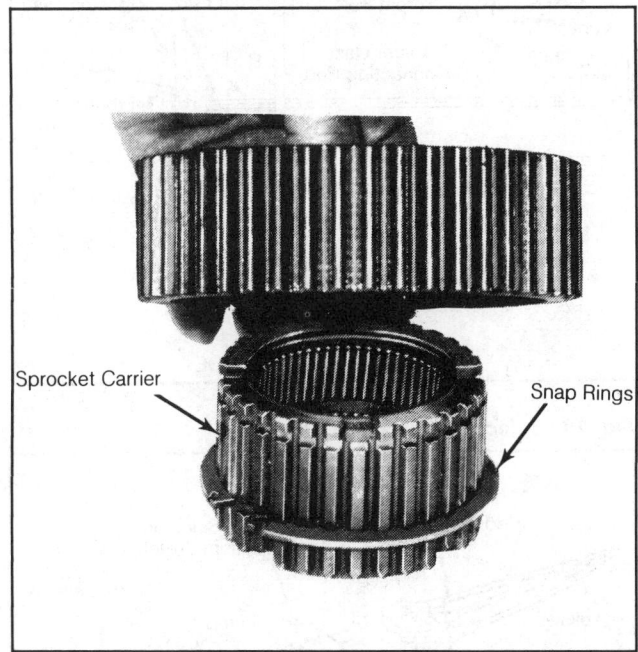

    4) Install sprocket carrier bearings and spacers. Coat carrier bore and all 120 carrier needle bearings with petroleum jelly. Install center spacer. Install 60 bearings in each end of carrier and install 2 remaining spacers (1 at each end of carrier). Use additional petroleum jelly to hold bearings in place if necessary.

    5) Install assembled sprocket carrier and drive sprocket on mainshaft. Do not displace mainshaft bearings during installation. Install clutch gear thrust washer in mainshaft. Position washer on sprocket carrier. *See Fig. 7.*

    6) Install clutch gear on side gear. Be sure tapered edge of clutch gear faces side gear teeth. Install assembled side gear and clutch gear on mainshaft. Be sure gear is fully seated in sprocket carrier. Take care to avoid displacing any carrier or mainshaft needle bearings.

NOTE: **Clutch gear should be flush with coupling and gear teeth should not be visible.**

Fig. 7: Installing Clutch Gear Thrust Washer

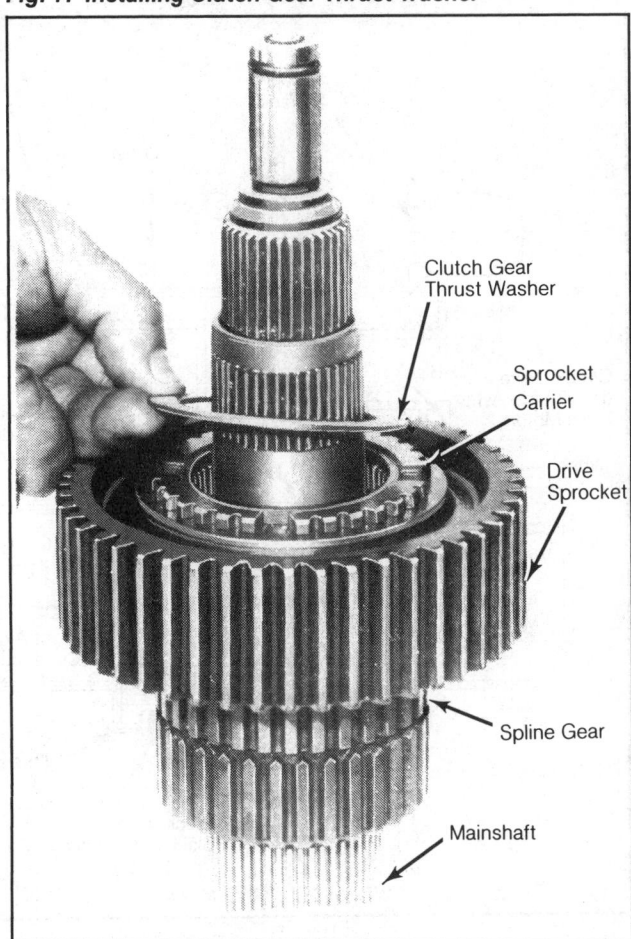

TRANSFER CASE
Reassembly

NOTE: **Before reassembling transfer case, verify viscous coupling operation. See Coupling Torque Bias Check in Adjustment section of this article.**

    1) Install new range sector shaft "O" ring and retainer in case shaft bore. Install range sector, washers and lock nut on sector shaft. Tighten lock nut.

    2) Install thrust bearing and race on input gear and install gear in front case. Install mainshaft thrust washer in input gear. Assemble range fork, rail and clutch sleeve. Install assembly in case. Be sure rail is fully seated in case bore.

NOTE: **The rail bore in the front case must be absolutely dry and free of oil. A small amount of oil in the bore will prevent the rail from seating completely and also prevent rear case installation.**

    3) Install mainshaft and gear assembly in case. Be sure mainshaft is fully seated in input gear. Install driven sprocket on front output shaft and install sprocket

Transfer Cases

AMERICAN MOTORS MODEL 129 (Cont.)

Fig. 8: Select Drive System Vacuum Diagram

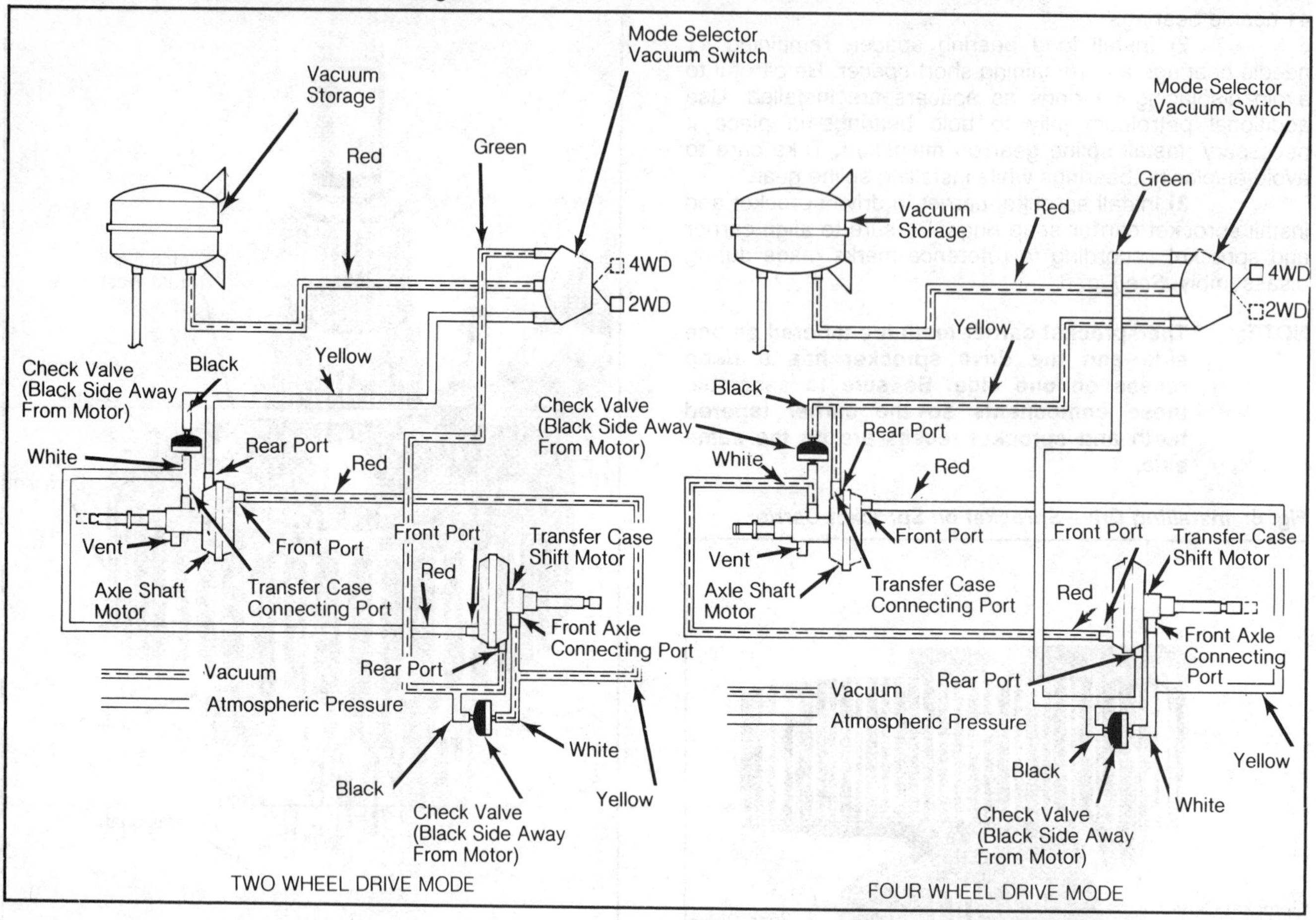

TWO WHEEL DRIVE MODE   FOUR WHEEL DRIVE MODE

Fig. 9: Typical Select Drive Vacuum Shift Motor

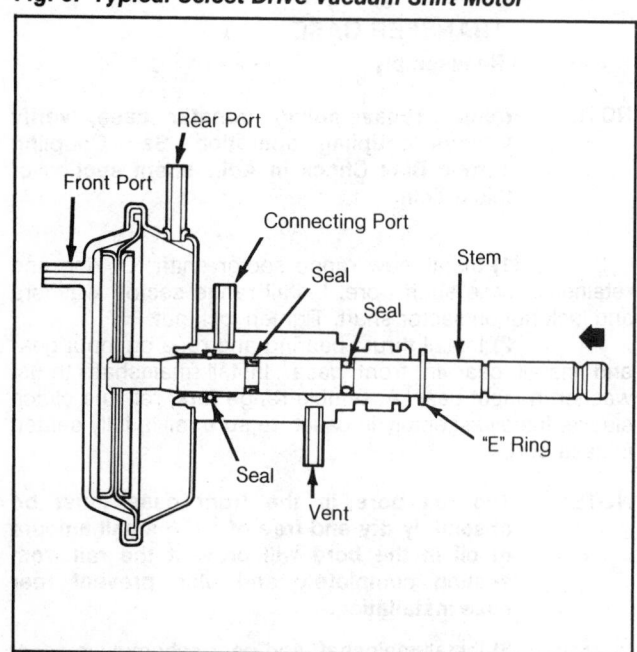

Connecting port is supplied with air when stem is extended. Stem is shown in retracted position.

Fig. 10: Select Drive Switch Assembly

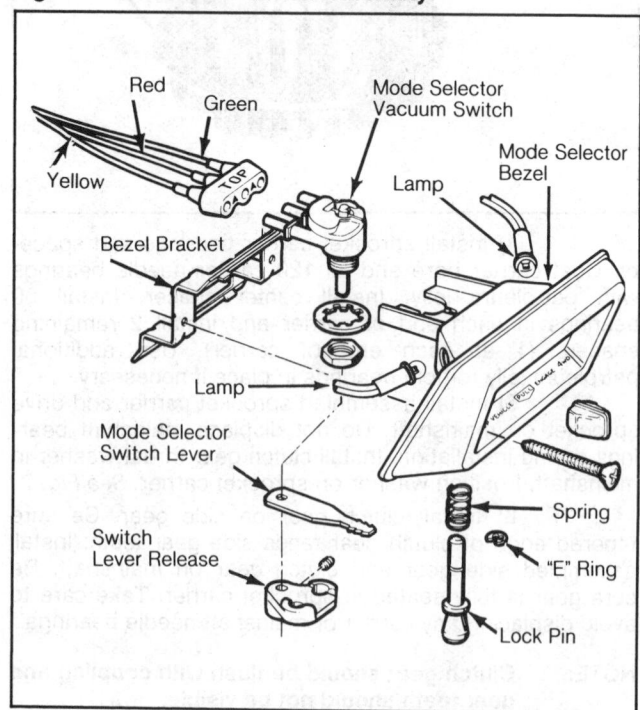

AMERICAN MOTORS MODEL 129 (Cont.)

retaining snap ring. Install according to reference marks made during disassembly. Install front output shaft thrust bearing assembly in front case.

4) Install thick race in case, then install bearing and thin race. Install drive chain, front output shaft and driven sprocket. Raise and tilt driven sprocket and chain and install opposite end of chain on drive sprocket. Align front output shaft with shaft bore in front case and install shaft in case. Be sure front shaft thrust bearing assembly is fully seated in case.

5) Install front output shaft rear thrust bearing assembly on front output shaft. Install thin race first, then install bearing and thick race. Install viscous coupling on side gear and clutch gear. Coupling must be fully seated on clutch gear.

6) Coat mainshaft pilot bearing surface and all 15 pilot roller bearings with petroleum jelly and install bearings on shaft. Install rear output shaft on mainshaft and into viscous coupling. Tap shaft with mallet to seat it if necessary. Install oil pump on rear output shaft. Install new rear output bearing oil seal in rear case. Apply bead of sealer to mating surface of rear case, install rear case on front case.

7) Install and tighten rear case-to-front case bolts. Flat washers are used on bolts at case ends where alignment dowels are located. Install speedometer drive gear and differential shim(s) on rear output shaft.

8) Align rear retainer on rear case and install retainer. Install retainer bolts and tighten securely; DO NOT tighten to specified torque. Install front and rear output shaft yokes and original yoke nuts. Tighten yoke nuts finger tight.

NOTE: If rear case will not seat properly in the front case, check for the following: Oil in the range fork rail bore, front output shaft rear thrust bearing assembly is not aligned with the rear case, mainshaft is not completely seated, rear case not aligned with oil pump.

ADJUSTMENTS

NOTE: Coupling Torque Bias Check must be performed during reassembly of transfer case.

COUPLING TORQUE BIAS CHECK

1) Install clutch gear on side gear. Install assembled clutch gear and side gear in viscous coupling. Mount assembled viscous coupling and gears in vise which has wood blocks installed to prevent gear damage. Firmly clamp assembly on side gear.

2) Check engagement of clutch gear in viscous coupling. Clutch gear must be fully engaged in coupling. If necessary, reposition wood blocks so they support gear in coupling. Install rear output shaft and install yoke retaining nut. Install torque wrench on yoke nut.

3) Rotate output shaft and measure torque required to rotate shaft in coupling. Rotating torque should be 25 ft. lbs. MINIMUM. If rotating torque is less than specified, replace coupling. If torque is at or above specification, coupling is operating properly.

DIFFERENTIAL END PLAY

1) Mount dial indicator on rear retainer and position indicator stylus so it contacts rear yoke nut.

2) Rotate front output shaft 10 to 12 revolutions and zero dial indicator. Rotate front shaft 1 more revolution and note dial indicator reading. End play should be .002-.010" (.05-.25 mm). If end play is incorrect, remove retainer and add or subtract shims as necessary to correct end play.

3) After checking end play, remove front and rear yokes. Discard original yoke nuts, remove rear retainer and apply sealer to retainer mating surfaces. Reinstall retainer and tighten bolts.

4) Install front and rear yokes, new yoke nut and seal. Tighten nut. Install detent ball and spring. Apply sealer to detent bolt and install and tighten bolt. Install drain plug and fill transfer case with lubricant.

TIGHTENING SPECIFICATIONS

Application	Ft. Lbs. (N.m)
Detent Retainer Bolt	20-25 (27-34)
Front and Rear Yoke Nuts	90-130 (122-176)
Rear Case-to-Front Case Bolts	20-25 (27-34)
Rear Retainer Bolts	20-25 (27-34)
Sector Shaft Lock Nut	15-20 (20-27)
Skid Plate Bolts	25-35 (34-47)
Indicator Switch	15-20 (20-27)
Operating Lever Lock Nut	15-20 (20-27)
Drain and Fill Plugs	15-20 (20-27)

Transfer Cases

BORG-WARNER 1345

Ford

DESCRIPTION

Transfer case is a 2-piece, part-time unit using planetary gearing, a chain drive, and an aluminum case. The unit is lubricated by a positive-displacement oil pump that channels oil flow through drilled holes in rear output shaft. Pump turns with the rear output shaft, permitting towing of the vehicle for extended distances without disconnecting rear propeller shaft.

LUBRICATION

SERVICE INTERVALS

Check fluid level whenever malfunction is suspected or when fluid leakage or contamination is observed. Also check after operation in water.

FLUID TYPE

Use fluid labeled Dexron II Automatic Transmission Fluid.

CAPACITY

Capacity is 6.5 pts. (3.1L).

ADJUSTMENTS

Adjust shift linkage so that all positions may be selected without interference or binding. Inspect all swivels, rods and mountings for wear or damage. Replace as necessary.

REMOVAL & INSTALLATION

TRANSFER CASE

Removal

1) Raise vehicle. Remove drain plug and drain fluid from transfer case. Replace plug. Disconnect 4WD indicator switch connector at transfer case. If equipped, remove skid plate.

2) Disconnect front and rear propeller shafts from transfer case output shaft yokes, and wire out of way. Do not allow shafts to hang free as damage to universal joints may result.

3) Disconnect speedometer driven gear from rear bearing retainer. Remove retaining clips and shift rod from transfer case control and transfer case shift levers. Disconnect vent hose from case.

4) Remove heat shield. Support transfer case with transmission jack, remove transfer case-to-transmission adapter bolts and slide transfer case off of transmission output shaft (towards rear). Lower transfer case out of vehicle and remove gasket from between transfer case and adapter.

Installation

Reverse removal procedures to install transfer case. Fill case with 6.5 pints (3.1 liters) of Dexron II type automatic transmission fluid.

DISASSEMBLY

TRANSFER CASE

1) Remove transfer case from vehicle and drain fluid. Remove both output shaft yoke nuts and washers. Remove output yokes from transfer case. Remove 4-WD indicator switch. Separate cover from case by removing attaching bolts. Pry case and cover apart by inserting a screwdriver in pry bosses.

2) Remove magnetic chip collector from bottom case half. Slide shift collar hub off rear output shaft. Compress shift fork spring, and remove upper and lower spring retainers from shaft. See Fig. 1.

3) Remove 4-WD lockup fork and lockup shift collar from case as an assembly. Take care not to lose nylon wear pads on fork. Remove snap ring and thrust washer from front output shaft. Grip chain and sprockets, and lift straight up to remove drive sprocket, driven sprocket, and chain from ouput shafts.

Fig. 1: Removing Spring Retainers

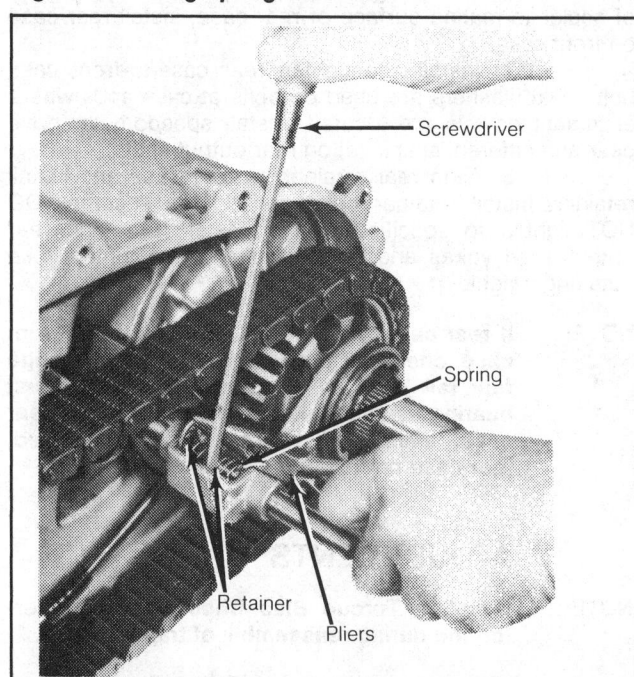

Use a screwdriver and a needle-nose pliers.

4) Remove thrust washer from rear output shaft. Remove front output shaft from case. Remove oil pump attaching bolts and remove oil pump rear cover, pickup tube, pump body and filter, 2 pump pins, pump spring and oil pump front cover from rear output shaft. Disconnect oil pickup tube from the front of pump body.

5) Remove bearing retainer snap ring from inside case. Lift out rear output shaft, while tapping on bearing retainer with a plastic hammer. Lift rear output-shaft and bearing retainer from case, noting that 2 dowel pins will fall into case.

6) Remove rear output shaft from bearing retainer. If necessary, press needle bearing assembly from bearing retainer. Remove "C" clip holding shift cam to

BORG-WARNER 1345 (Cont.)

Fig. 2: Exploded View of Borg-Warner 1345 Transfer Case

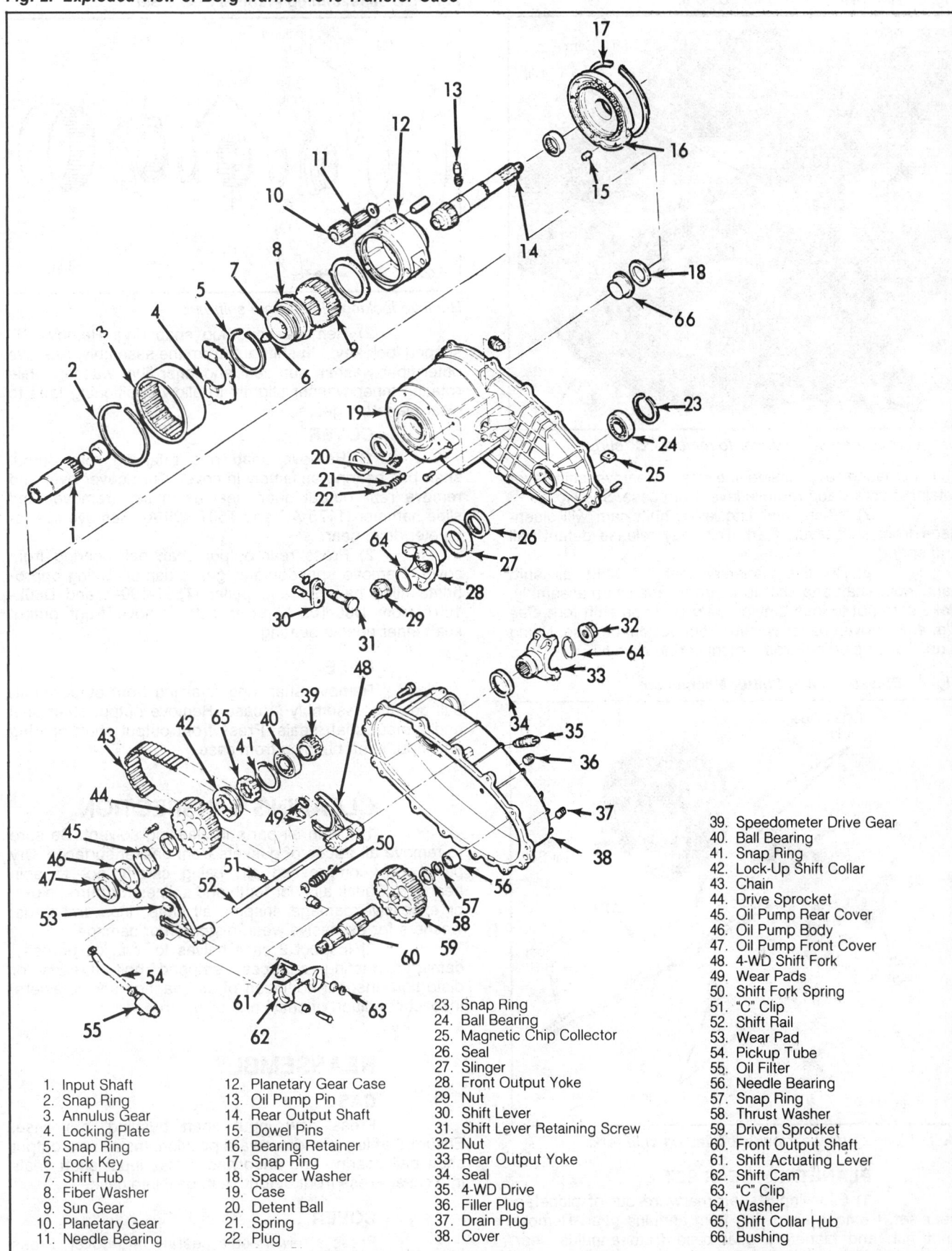

39. Speedometer Drive Gear
40. Ball Bearing
41. Snap Ring
42. Lock-Up Shift Collar
43. Chain
44. Drive Sprocket
45. Oil Pump Rear Cover
46. Oil Pump Body
47. Oil Pump Front Cover
48. 4-WD Shift Fork
49. Wear Pads
50. Shift Fork Spring
51. "C" Clip
52. Shift Rail
53. Wear Pad
54. Pickup Tube
55. Oil Filter
56. Needle Bearing
57. Snap Ring
58. Thrust Washer
59. Driven Sprocket
60. Front Output Shaft
61. Shift Actuating Lever
62. Shift Cam
63. "C" Clip
64. Washer
65. Shift Collar Hub
66. Bushing

23. Snap Ring
24. Ball Bearing
25. Magnetic Chip Collector
26. Seal
27. Slinger
28. Front Output Yoke
29. Nut
30. Shift Lever
31. Shift Lever Retaining Screw
32. Nut
33. Rear Output Yoke
34. Seal
35. 4-WD Drive
36. Filler Plug
37. Drain Plug
38. Cover

1. Input Shaft
2. Snap Ring
3. Annulus Gear
4. Locking Plate
5. Snap Ring
6. Lock Key
7. Shift Hub
8. Fiber Washer
9. Sun Gear
10. Planetary Gear
11. Needle Bearing
12. Planetary Gear Case
13. Oil Pump Pin
14. Rear Output Shaft
15. Dowel Pins
16. Bearing Retainer
17. Snap Ring
18. Spacer Washer
19. Case
20. Detent Ball
21. Spring
22. Plug

Transfer Cases

BORG-WARNER 1345 (Cont.)

Fig. 3: Removing Shift Cam "C" Clip

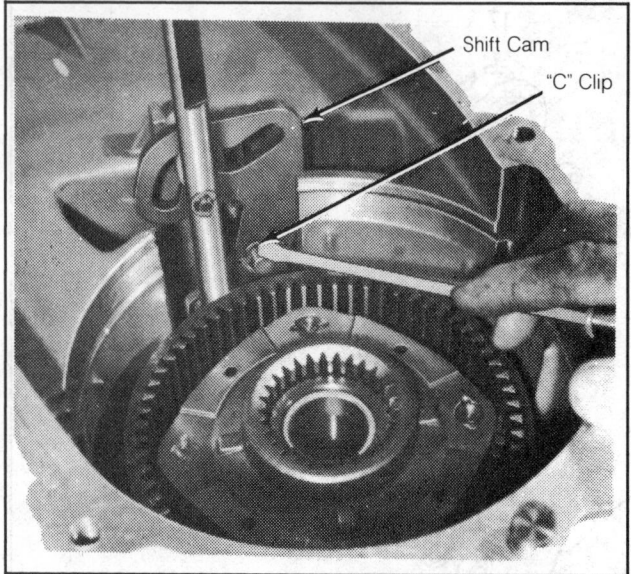

Use a flat-bladed screwdriver to remove "C" clip.

shift actuating lever inside the case. Remove shift lever retaining screw and remove lever from case. *See Fig. 3.*

7) When removing lever, shift cam will disengage from shift lever shaft. This may release detent ball and spring.

8) Remove planetary gear set, shift rail, shift cam, input shaft and shift forks from case as an assembly. Take care not to lose 2 nylon wear pads on shift fork. *See Fig. 4.* Remove spacer washer from bottom of case. Using a drift, drive plug out from detent spring bore.

Fig. 4: Disassembling Shifter Mechanism

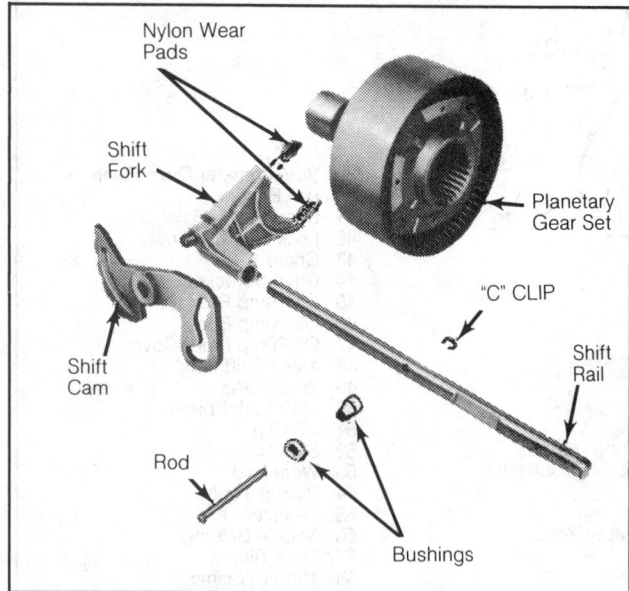

Do not lose nylon wear pads located on shift forks.

PLANETARY GEAR SET

1) Slide input shaft rearward out of planetary gear set. Remove snap ring from annulus gear. Remove shift hub and planetary gear case from annulus gear. Remove locking plates from hub. *See Fig. 5.*

Fig. 5: Disassembling Planetary Gear Set

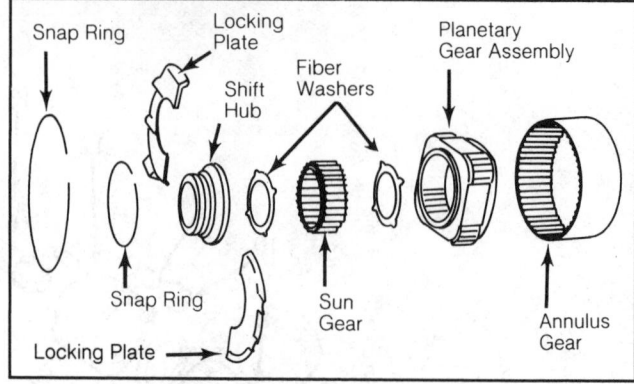

Remove locking plates from shift hub.

2) Remove shift hub snap ring. Remove "T" shaped lock key. Lift shift hub from the assembly. Remove outer fiber washer, sun gear and inner fiber washer, while rotating inner washer slightly to allow positioning tabs to clear planetary gears.

COVER

1) Remove snap ring retaining rear output shaft ball bearing assembly in cover. Turn cover over and remove rear output shaft seal using seal remover and slide hammer (1175-AC and T50T-100-A). Remove speedometer drive gear.

2) Press rear output shaft ball bearing from cover. Remove speedometer gear adapter. Using appropriate slide hammer and puller (T50T-100-A and D80L-100T from D80-100-A puller set), remove front output shaft inner needle bearing.

CASE

Remove snap ring retaining front output shaft ball bearing assembly in case. Remove output shaft seal and 2 input shaft seals. Press front output shaft bearing and input shaft bushing from case.

CLEANING & INSPECTION

1) Clean all parts in cleaning solvent. Be sure to remove all traces of gaskets from gasket surfaces. Dry parts with compressed air, being careful not to spin bearings. Check all gear teeth and splines for burrs, nicks, or excessive damage. Inspect all snap rings and thrust washers for excessive wear, distortion or damage.

2) Inspect 2 case halves for cracks, porosity, damaged mating surfaces, stripped bolt threads or distortion. Inspect condition of all bearings and retainers. Inspect condition of chain and oil pump.

REASSEMBLY

CASE

Press new input shaft bushing into case. Ensure that lug is in downward position. Install new output shaft ball bearing and snap ring. Press input shaft seals into case. Press front output shaft seal into case.

COVER

Press a new needle bearing into cover. Press a new ball bearing into cover and install snap ring. Turn

BORG-WARNER 1345 (Cont.)

cover over and install speedometer drive gear. Install new output shaft seal. Install speedometer gear adapter.

PLANETARY GEAR ASSEMBLY

1) Place a new inner fiber washer into the planetary gear housing. Install sun gear. Coat new outer fiber washer with petroleum jelly, and install on hub. *See Fig. 5.* Place hub in planetary gear cage, and install "T" shaped lock key and snap ring.

2) Install locking plates on shift hub, with dished side toward planetary gear set. Lower planetary assembly into annulus gear. Be sure tabs on locking plate engage annulus gear teeth. Install snap ring.

TRANSFER CASE

1) Lubricate all parts with Dexron II Automatic Transmission Fluid. Assemble the planetary gear set, shift rail, shift cam, input shaft, and shift fork together as an assembly. *See Fig. 6.* Ensure that the boss on the shift cam is installed toward the case. *See Fig. 7.* Install spacer washer on input shaft.

Fig. 6: Installing Planetary Gear Set and Shifter Mechanism

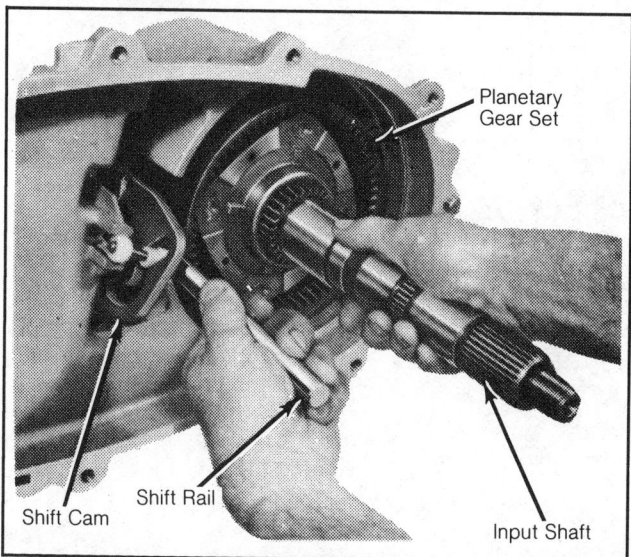

Install components as an assembly.

2) Place rear output shaft in planetary gear set, making sure shift cam engages shift fork actuating pin. Lay case on its side. Insert rear output shaft and planetary gear set into case. Be sure spacer washer remains on input shaft.

3) Install shift rail into hole in case. Install outer roller bushing into guide in case. Remove rear output shaft, and position shift fork in neutral. Place shift control lever shaft through cam, and install clip ring.

4) Ensure shift control lever is pointed downward and is parallel to front face of the case. Check shift fork and planetary gear engagement. Unit should operate freely without binding. Press new needle bearing into bearing retainer (if removed).

5) Insert output shaft through bearing retainer from the bottom side outward. Insert rear output shaft pilot into the input shaft rear bushing. Align dowel holes, and lower bearing into position. Install dowel pins. Install bearing retainer snap ring.

Fig. 7: Installing and Engaging Shift Cam

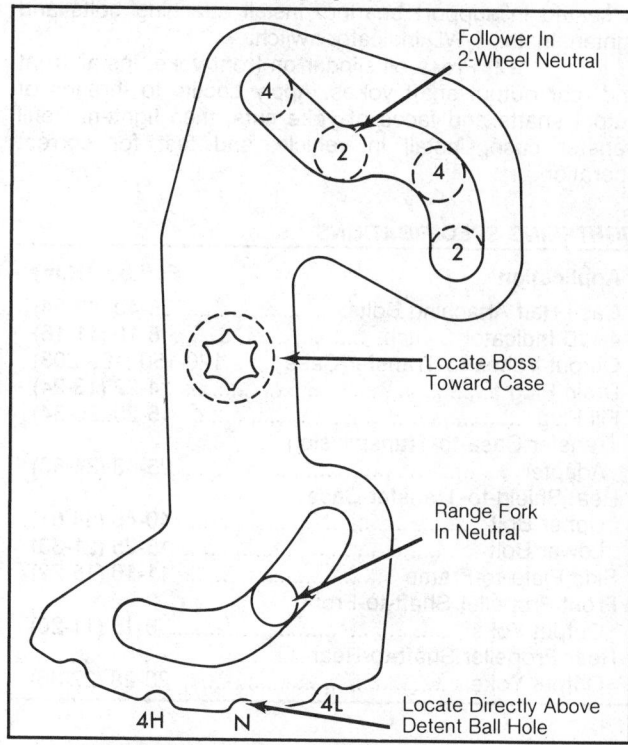

Install shift cam with boss toward case.

6) Insert detent ball and spring in detent bore in case half. Coat seal plug with RTV sealant. Drive plug into case until plug lip is 1/32" (.79 mm) below surface of case. Stake the plug to case in 2 places. Install the oil pump front cover over the output shaft with flanged side down. The marking "TOP" must face the top of the transfer case as it is positioned for installation in the vehicle.

7) Install the oil pump spring and 2 pump pins, with flat side outward in the hole in output shaft. Install oil pump body, pickup tube and filter, and push in pins. Place oil pump rear cover onto output shaft, with flanged side outward. Prime oil pump with Dexron II Automatic Transmission Fluid.

8) The marking "TOP" must face the top of the transfer case (as it is positioned for installation in the vehicle.) Apply Loctite to oil pump bolts, install to pump cover, and tighten. Install thrust washer to rear output shaft near oil pump. Install chain on drive and driven sprockets, if previously removed.

9) Lower chain and sprockets into position in case. The driven sprocket should be installed over front output shaft and the drive sprocket should be installed to rear output shaft. Install washer and snap ring behind driven sprocket. Engage 4-WD shift fork on shift collar. Slide shift fork over shift shaft. Install shift collar over rear output shaft.

10) Ensure nylon wear pads are installed on shift fork tips, and necked down portion of shift collar is facing rearward. Push 4-WD shift spring down and install upper spring retainer. Push spring upward and install lower spring retainer. Install shift collar hub on rear output shaft.

11) Apply RTV sealant to the case mounting surface. Lower the cover over rear output shaft. Align shift

BORG-WARNER 1345 (Cont.)

rail with blind hole in cover. Ensure the front output shaft is seated in support bearing. Install attaching bolts and tighten. Install 4-WD indicator switch.

12) Press oil slinger on front yoke. Install front and rear output shaft yokes. Apply Loctite to threads of output shafts and faces of yoke nuts, then tighten. Refill transfer case, install in vehicle, and test for correct operation.

TIGHTENING SPECIFICATIONS

Application	Ft. Lbs. (N.m)
Case Half Attaching Bolts	35-40 (48-54)
4-WD Indicator Switch	8-12 (11-16)
Output Yokes-to-Transfer Case	120-150 (163-203)
Drain Plug	14-22 (13-24)
Fill Plug	15-25 (20-34)
Transfer Case-to-Transmission Adapter	25-43 (34-58)
Heat Shield-to-Transfer Case	
Upper Bolt	40-45 (54-61)
Lower Bolt	15-25 (21-33)
Skid Plate-to-Frame	11-16 (15-22)
Front Propeller Shaft-to-Front Output Yoke	8-15 (11-20)
Rear Propeller Shaft-to-Rear Output Yoke	20-28 (27-38)

BORG-WARNER 1350

Bronco II, Ranger

DESCRIPTION

The Borg-Warner 1350 is a chain driven, aluminum case, part time 4WD unit. It provides 4 driving modes. This unit offers 2WD and 4WD high ranges, 4WD low range and neutral. The 1350 has a 3 piece aluminum case, an internal oil pump driven off the rear output shaft and an angular front output shaft with a cardan joint. Floor mounted shift levers select the driving ranges, high and low, and the driving modes, 2WD and 4WD. The oil pump is driven by the rear output shaft. This allows the vehicle to be towed for long distances without disconnecting the drive shafts.

LUBRICATION

SERVICE INTERVALS

Check and refill transfer case when malfunction is suspected, fluid leakage or contamination is observed or after axle is submerged in water.

FLUID TYPE

Use automatic transmission fluid labeled Dexron II or equivalent.

CAPACITY

Refill capacity is 3 pts. (1.4L).

REMOVAL & INSTALLATION

TRANSFER CASE

Removal

1) Raise vehicle on hoist, remove skid plate and drain transfer case lubricant. Disconnect the 4WD indicator switch wire at the transfer case.

2) Disconnect the front drive shaft from the axle input yoke. Loosen the clamp retaining the front drive shaft boot to the transfer case. Pull the drive shaft and front boot assembly out of the transfer case front output shaft. Disconnect the rear drive shaft from the transfer case output yoke. Disconnect the speedometer driven gear from the case rear cover.

Fig. 1: Exploded View of Borg-Warner 1350 Transfer Case

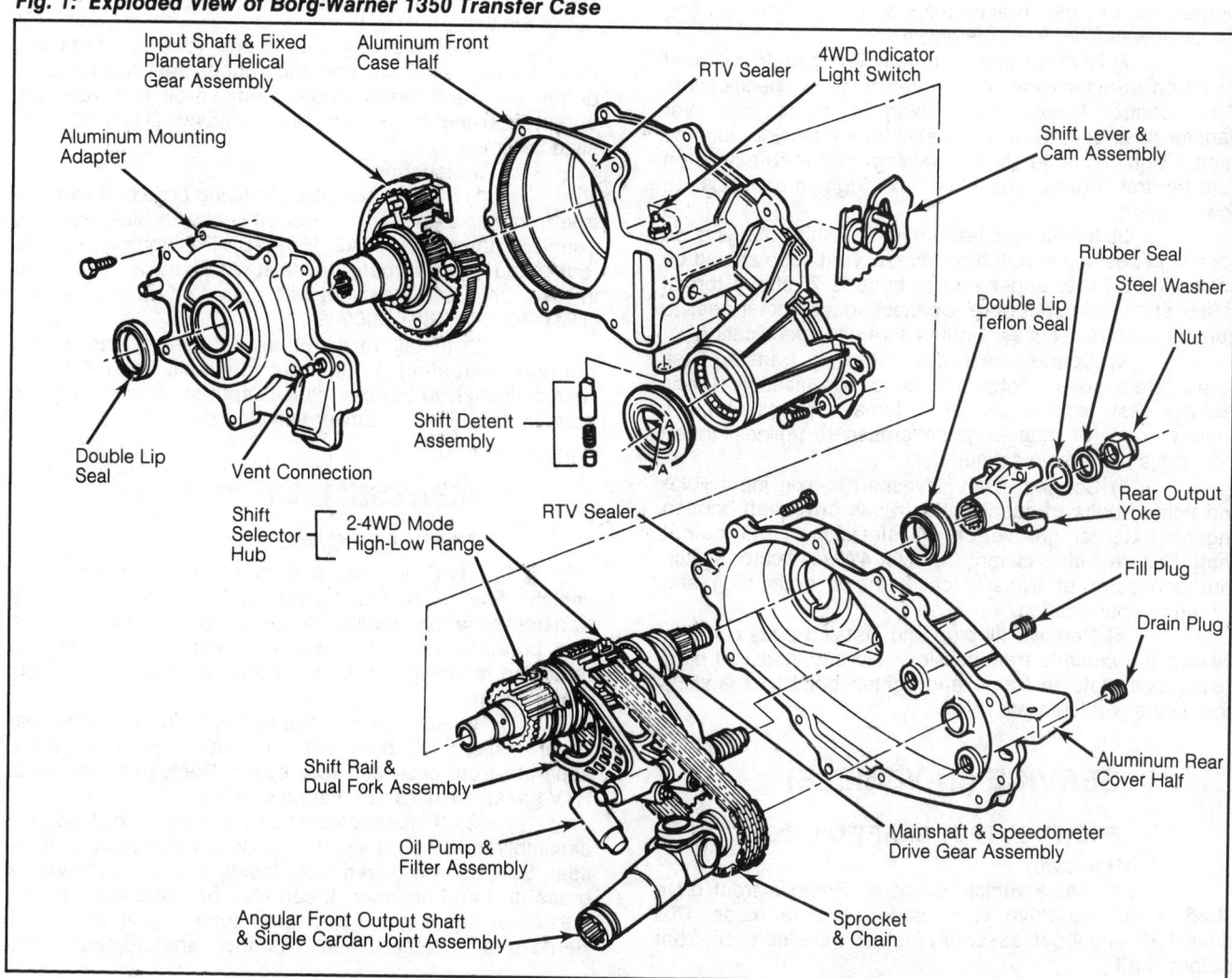

Transfer Cases

BORG-WARNER 1350 (Cont.)

3) Disconnect the vent hose from the control lever. Loosen or remove the large bolt and the small bolt retaining the shifter to the extension housing. Pull on the control lever until the bushing slides off the transfer case shift lever pin. If necessary, unscrew the shift lever from the control lever. Remove the heat shield from the transfer case.

CAUTION: Catalytic converters generate an extreme amount of heat. The catalytic converter is located beside the heat shield. Be careful when working near the converter.

4) Support the transfer case with a transmission jack. Remove the bolts retaining the transfer case to the transmission and the extension housing. Slide the transfer case rearward off the transmission and lower the case from the vehicle. Clean gasket from the mating surface between transmission and case.

Installation

1) Use new gasket between transmission and transfer case. Raise transfer case with jack and position it so splines on transfer case input shaft align with transmission output shaft. Slide case forward onto transmission output shaft and dowel pin. Install bolts that retain case-to-transmission and tighten to specification. Tighten bolts evenly in alternating sequence from locating pin as viewed from front of vehicle.

2) Remove jack from transfer case. Install heat shield on transfer case and tighten bolts to specification. Move control lever until bushing is in position over transfer case shift lever pin. Install both attaching bolts by hand. Tighten large bolt retaining shifter-to-extension housing first. Tighten small bolt next. Tighten both bolts to specification.

3) Install vent assembly so White marking on hose is in position in notch on shifter. Vent hose should be positioned so that upper end of hose is 2" above top of shifter and inside shift boot. Connect speedometer gear to transfer case rear cover. Tighten screw to specification.

4) Connect rear drive shaft to transfer case output shaft yoke. Tighten bolts to specification. Clean transfer case front output shaft female splines. Apply a small amount of multi-purpose grease to splines. Insert front drive shaft male spline.

5) Connect front driveshaft-to-axle input yoke and tighten bolts to specification. Push driveshaft boot to engage external groove on transfer case front output shaft. Secure with a clamp. Connect 4WD indicator switch wire connector at transfer case. Install drain plug and tighten to specification.

6) Remove fill plug and install 3 pints (1.4L) of Dexron II automatic transmission fluid and install fill plug. Install skid plate to frame and tighten bolts to specification. Lower vehicle from hoist.

SERVICE (IN-VEHICLE)

FRONT OUTPUT SHAFT OIL SEAL
Removal

1) Raise vehicle on hoist. Remove front drive shaft from axle drive shaft boot-to-transfer case. Pull driveshaft and boot assembly out of transfer case front output shaft.

2) Place a drain pan under transfer case, remove drain plug and drain fluid from case. Remove oil seal from front output housing bore with seal remover (1175-AC) and slide hammer.

Installation

1) Make sure output housing bore and face are free from nicks and burrs. Coat oil seal with a small amount of multi-purpose grease. Position oil seal into rear output housing bore. Make sure oil seal is not cocked in bore. Drive seal into bore with output shaft seal installer (T83T-7065-B, T80T-4000-W).

2) Clean transfer case front output female spline and apply small amount of multi-purpose grease. Insert front driveshaft male spline. Connect front driveshaft to axle input yoke. Tighten bolts to specification.

3) Push driveshaft boot to engage external groove on transfer case front output shaft and secure with clamp. Install drain plug and tighten to specification. Refill transfer case with Dexron II automatic transmission fluid to bottom of filler hole. Install filler plug and tighten to specification. Lower vehicle from hoist.

REAR OUTPUT SHAFT OIL SEAL
Removal

1) Raise vehicle on hoist. Remove rear drive-shaft from transfer case output shaft yoke. Wire driveshaft out of the way.

2) Remove output shaft yoke by removing retaining nut, steel washer and rubber seal from rear of output shaft and remove yoke. Remove oil seal from rear output housing bore with seal remover (1175-AC) and slide hammer.

Installation

1) Make sure output housing bore and face are free from nicks and burrs. Coat oil seal with Multi-Purpose Long-Life Lubricant (C1AZ-19590-B). Position oil seal into rear output housing bore. Make sure oil seal is not cocked in bore. Drive seal into bore with output shaft seal installer (T83T-7065-B, T80T-4000-W).

2) Install yoke, rubber seal, steel washer and nut on output shaft. Tighten nut to specification. Connect rear driveshaft to transfer case output shaft yoke. Tighten bolts to specification. Lower vehicle from hoist.

DISASSEMBLY

TRANSFER CASE

1) Drain transfer case and remove from vehicle. *See REMOVAL & INSTALLATION section.* Mount transfer case on bench. Remove 4WD indicator switch and breather vent. Remove rear output shaft yoke by removing retaining nut, steel washer and rubber seal from output shaft.

2) Remove all bolts retaining front case to rear cover. Insert a 1/2" breaker bar between 3 pry bosses and separate front case and rear cover. Remove all traces of RTV gasket sealer from mating surfaces.

3) If speedometer drive gear or ball bearing assembly is to be replaced, first drive out output shaft oil seal. Seal can be driven from inside of rear cover with a brass drift and hammer. It can also be removed from the outside by bending and pulling on curved-up lip of oil seal. Remove and discard seal. Remove speedometer drive

BORG-WARNER 1350 (Cont.)

gear assembly. Note that round end of speedometer gear clip faces inside of rear cover.

4) Remove internal snap ring that retains rear output shaft ball bearing in bore. From outside of the case, drive out ball bearing with output shaft bearing replacer (T83T-7025-B, T80T-4000-W). If required, remove front output shaft caged needle bearing from rear cover using puller collet (D80L-100-S) and slide hammer. Remove the 2-4WD shift fork from the boss in rear cover.

5) Remove shift collar hub from output shaft. Remove 2-4WD lock-up assembly and 2-4WD shift fork together as an assembly. Remove 2-4WD lock-up assembly from 2-4WD fork. See Fig. 2. If required, remove external clip and roller bushing assembly from 2-4WD shift fork.

Fig. 2: Removing Shift Collar Hub & Drive Chain

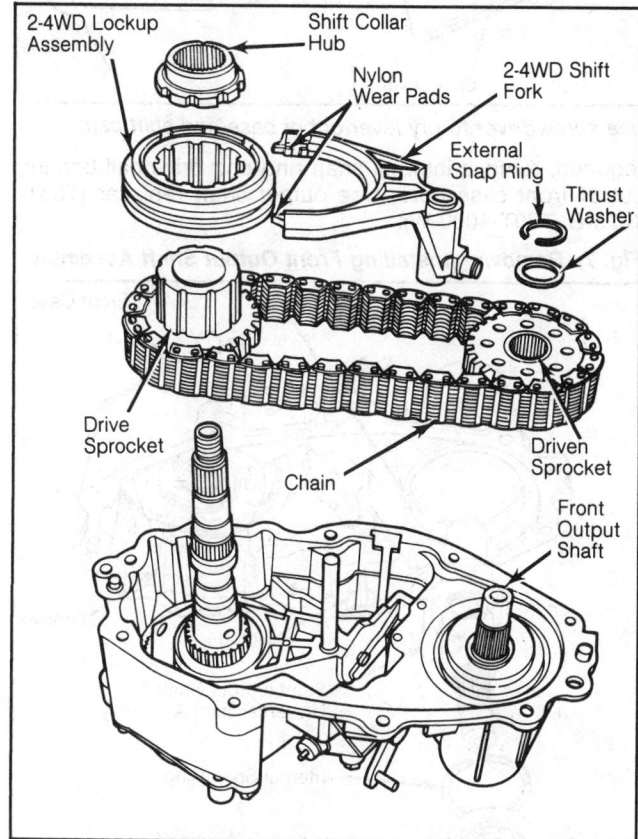

Remove 2-4WD lockup assembly and shift fork as an assembly.

6) If disassembly of 2-4WD lock-up assembly is necessary, remove internal snap ring and pull lock-up hub and spring from lock-up collar. Remove external snap ring and thrust washer that retains driven sprocket to front output shaft. Remove chain, driven sprocket and drive sprocket as an assembly. Remove collector magnet from notch in front case bottom.

7) If disassembly of oil pump is necessary, remove bolts from pump body. Note position and markings of front cover, body, pins, rear cover and pump retainer as removed. Pull out shift rail.

8) Slip high-low range shift fork out of inside track of shift cam. If required, remove external clip and roller bushing assembly (bushing, shaft and external clip) from high-low range shift fork. Remove high-low shift hub from planetary gearset in front case. See Fig. 3.

Fig. 3: High-Low Range Shift Assembly & Output Shaft

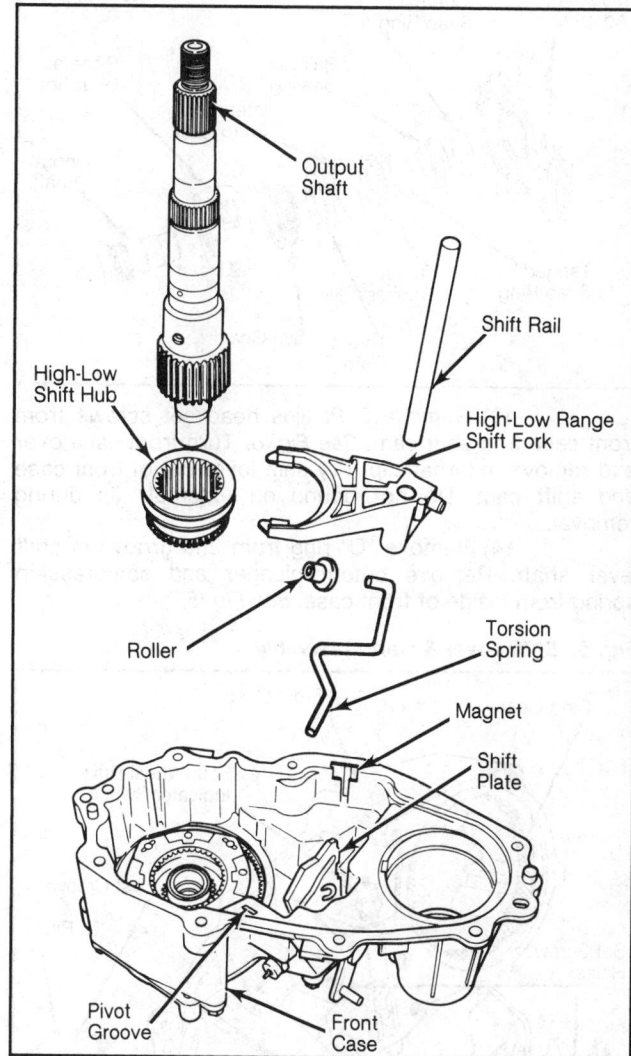

Remove roller bushing, shaft and clip as an assembly.

9) Push and pull out anchor end of torsion spring from locking post in front case half. Remove torsion spring and roller out of shift cam (if so equipped). Turn case over and remove 6 bolts retaining mounting adapter to front case. Remove mounting adapter, input shaft and planetary gearset as an assembly.

10) If required, remove ring gear from front case using a press. Note relationship of serrations to chamfered pilot diameter during removal. Expand tangs of large snap ring in mounting adapter and pry under planetary gearset with screwdrivers. Separate input shaft and planetary gearset from mounting adapter.

11) If required, remove oil seal from mounting adapter with seal remover (1175-AC) and slide hammer. Remove internal snap ring from planetary carrier and separate planetary gear set from input shaft assembly. Remove external snap ring from input shaft. See Fig. 4.

12) Place input shaft assembly in a press and remove ball bearing from input shaft with a bearing splitter. Remove thrust washer, thrust plate and sun gear off input shaft. Move shift lever by hand until shift cam is in 4WD high position. Mark a line on outside of front case using side of shift lever and a grease pencil. See Fig. 5.

Transfer Cases

BORG-WARNER 1350 (Cont.)

Fig. 4: Exploded View of Planetary Gear Set

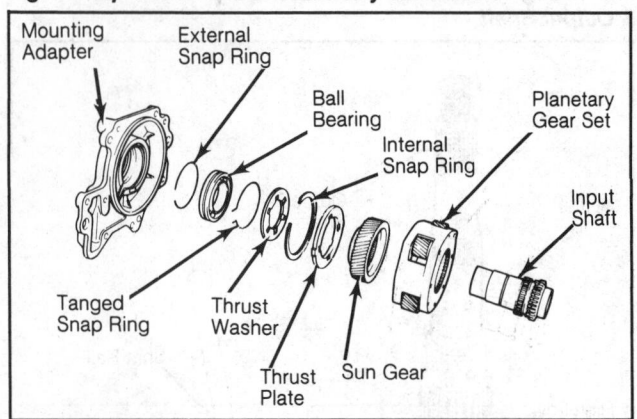

13) Remove 2 Phillips head set screws from front case and shift cam. *See Fig. 6.* Turn front case over and remove external clip. Pry shift lever out of front case and shift cam. Do not pound on external clip during removal.

14) Remove "O" ring from 2nd groove in shift lever shaft. Remove detent plunger and compression spring from inside of front case. *See Fig. 5.*

Fig. 5: Shift Lever & Cam Assembly

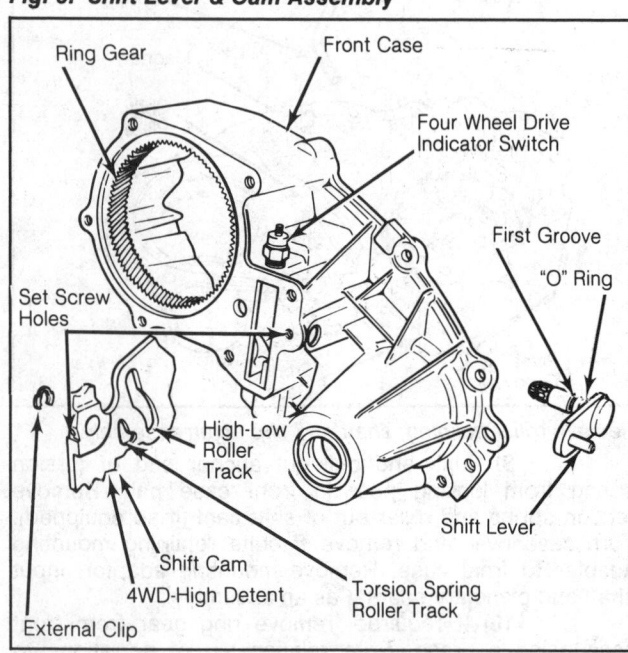

Mark case with cam in 4WD high detent position.

15) Remove internal snap ring and ball bearing retainer from front case by tapping on face of front output shaft and universal joint assembly using a plastic hammer. Remove internal snap ring and drive ball bearing out of bearing retainer using output shaft bearing replacer (T83T-7025-B, T80T-4000-W). *See Fig. 7.*

NOTE: The clip on bearing retainer is required to prevent bearing retainer from rotating. Do not discard clip.

16) Remove front output shaft and universal joint assembly from front case. If required, remove oil seal with seal remover (1175-AC) and slide hammer. If

Fig. 6: Removing Shift Cam & Lever

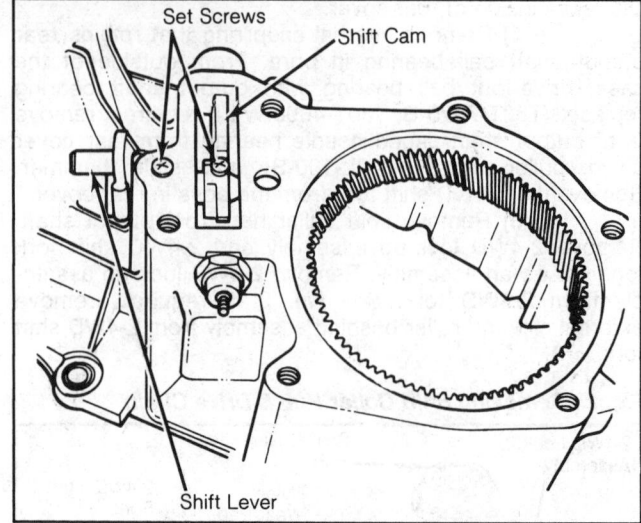

Use screwdriver to pry lever out of case and shift cam.

required, remove internal snap ring and drive ball bearing out of front case bore. Use output shaft replacer (T83T-7025-B, T80T-4000-W).

Fig. 7: Removing/Installing Front Output Shaft Assembly

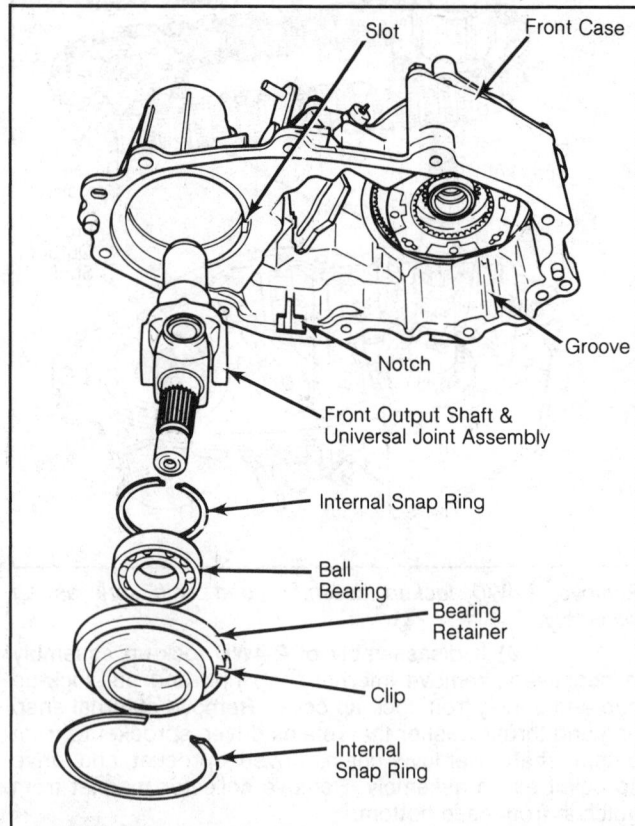

Do not discard clip.

17) If required, place front output shaft and universal joint assembly in a vise. Use copper or wood vise jaws to prevent damage to assembly. Remove internal snap rings that retain bearings in shaft. Position universal joint tool (T74P-4635-C) over shaft ears and press bearing out. If bearing cannot be pressed all the

BORG-WARNER 1350 (Cont.)

way out, remove with a pair of vise grips or channel lock pliers.

18) Reposition universal joint tool on spider to remove opposite bearing. Repeat procedure in step 17) until all bearings are removed.

REASSEMBLY

TRANSFER CASE

NOTE: **Before reassembly, lubricate all parts with Dexron II automatic transmission fluid or equivalent.**

1) Support front output shaft in a vise equipped with copper or wood jaws. If removed, start a new bearing into end of a shaft ear. Position spider into bearing and press bearing below snap ring groove using universal joint press. Remove tool and install a new internal snap ring in groove.

2) Start new bearing into opposite end of shaft ear. Using bearing installer, press bearing until opposite bearing contacts snap ring. Remove tool and install new internal snap ring in groove. Reposition front output shaft assembly and install other 2 bearings in same manner.

3) Check universal joint for freedom of movement and binding. If universal joint shows any sign of binding, tap ears of both shafts sharply to relieve bind. Do not install front output shaft assembly if universal joint shows any sign of binding.

4) If removed, drive the ball bearing into the front output case bore using output shaft bearing replacer (T83T-7025-B, T80T-4000-W). Drive the ball bearing in straight, making sure it is not cocked in the bore. Install the internal snap ring that retains the ball bearing in the front case. If removed, install the front output oil seal in front case bore. Use output shaft seal installer (T80T-4000-W, T83T-7065-W).

5) If removed, install ring gear in front case. Align serrations on outside diameter of ring gear to serrations previously cut in front case bore. Using a press, start piloted chamferred end of ring gear first and press in until it is fully seated. Make sure ring gear is not cocked in bore.

6) If removed, install ball bearing in bearing retainer bore. Drive bearing into retainer using output shaft bearing replacer (T83T-7025-B, T80T-4000-W). Make sure ball bearing is not cocked in bore. Install internal snap ring that retains ball bearing to retainer. Install front output shaft and universal joint assembly through front case seal.

7) Position ball bearing and retainer assembly over front output shaft and install in front case bore. Make sure clip on bearing retainer aligns with slot in front case. Tap bearing retainer into place with a plastic hammer. Install internal snap ring that retains ball bearing and retainer assembly to front case. See Fig. 7.

8) Install compression spring and detent plunger into bore from inside of front case. Install a new "O" ring in second groove of shift lever shaft. See Fig. 5. Coat shaft and "O" ring with a small amount of multi-purpose grease. Use a rubber band to fill the first groove so as not to cut "O" ring. Discard rubber band.

9) Position shift cam inside front case with 4WD high position over detent plunger. Holding shift cam by hand, push shift lever shaft into front case to engage shift cam aligning side of shift lever shaft with mark previously scribed on case. Install external clip on end of shift lever shaft.

10) Install 2 Phillips head screws in front case and in the shift cam. Tighten screws to specification. Make sure set screw in front case is in first groove of shift lever shaft and not bottomed out against shaft itself. Shift lever should be able to move freely to all detent positions.

11) Slide sun gear, thrust plate and thrust washer over input shaft. Press ball bearing over input shaft. Install external snap ring to input shaft. Install planetary gear set to sun gear and install input shaft assembly. Install internal snap ring to planetary gear.

NOTE: **The sun gear recessed face and ball bearing snap ring groove should be toward rear of transfer case. The stepped face of thrust washer should face toward the ball bearing.**

12) Drive oil seal into bore of mounting adapter with input shaft seal installer (T83T-7065-A, T80T-4000-W). Place tanged snap ring in mounting adapter groove. Position input shaft and planetary gearset in mounting adapter and push inward until planetary assembly and input shaft assembly are seated in adapter. When properly seated, tanged snap ring will snap into place.

13) Check installation of snap ring by holding mounting adapter by hand and tapping face of input shaft against a wooden block to ensure that snap ring is engaged. Apply RTV sealer to mating surface of front case and mounting adapter. Position adapter on case and install retaining screws. Tighten screws to specification.

14) Position roller on 90° bent tang of torsion spring. The larger diameter end of spring must be installed first. Install roller into torsion spring roller track of shift cam. See Fig. 5. Locate center of spring in pivot groove in front case at the same time. Push anchor end of torsion spring behind locking post adjacent to ring gear face.

15) Position high-low shift hub into planetary gearset. Slip high-low shift fork bushing into high-low roller track of shift cam and groove of high-low shift hub. See Fig. 5. Install shift rail through high-low fork and make sure shift rail is seated in bore in front case. See Fig. 3.

NOTE: **Make sure nylon wear pads are installed on shift fork and dot on pad is installed in fork hole.**

16) Place oil pump cover with word TOP facing front of case. Install 2 pump pins (flats facing upward) with spring between pins and place assembly in oil pump bore in output shaft. Place oil pump body and pick up tube assembly over shaft. Make sure pins are riding against inside of pump body.

17) Place oil pump rear cover with words TOP REAR facing rear of front case. The word TOP on front cover and rear cover should be on the same side. Install pump retainer, 4 bolts and rotate output shaft while tighening bolts to prevent pump from binding. Tighten bolts to specification. Output shaft must turn freely within oil pump. If binding occurs, loosen 4 bolts and retighten.

18) Install output shaft and oil pump assembly in input shaft. Make sure external splines of output shaft engage internal splines of high-low shift hub. Make sure oil pump retainer and oil filter leg are in groove and notch

Transfer Cases

BORG-WARNER 1350 (Cont.)

of front case. Install collector magnet in notch in front case.

19) Install chain, drive sprocket and driven sprocket as an assembly over shafts. Install thrust washer on front output shaft and external snap ring over thrust washer to retain driven sprocket.

20) If disassembled, assemble 2-4WD lock-up assembly. Install spring in lock-up collar. Place lock-up hub over spring and engage lock-up hub in notches in lock-up collar. Retain lock-up hub to lock-up collar with an internal snap ring. *See Fig. 8.* Install 2-4WD shift fork to 2-4WD lock-up assembly.

Fig. 8: Exploded View 2-4WD Lock-up Assembly

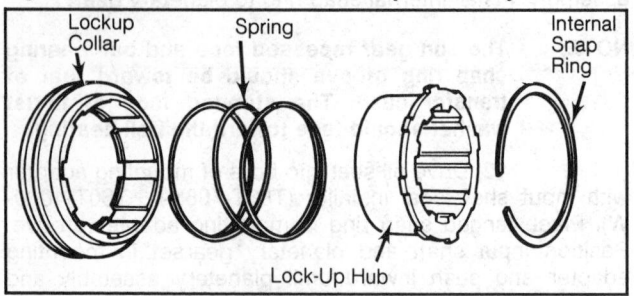

NOTE: If removed, make sure nylon wear pads are installed on fork and dot on pad is installed in hole in fork.

21) Install 2-4WD lock-up collar and hub assembly over output shaft and onto shift rail. *See Fig. 2.* If removed, install shaft, bushing and external clip to 2-4WD lock-up fork. Install shift collar hub to output shaft. If removed, drive caged needle bearing into rear cover bore with needle bearing replacer (T80T-4000-W, T83T-7127-A).

22) If removed, install ball bearing in rear cover bore. Drive bearing into rear cover bore with output shaft bearing replacer (T83T-7025-B, T80-4000-W). Make sure ball bearing is not cocked in bore. Install internal snap ring that retains ball bearing to rear cover.

23) Install speedometer drive gear assembly into rear cover bore with round end of speedometer gear clip facing toward inside of rear cover. Drive oil seal into rear cover bore with output shaft seal installer (T83T-7065-B, T80T-4000-W). Install 2-4WD shift fork spring on inside boss of rear cover.

24) Prior to assembly of rear cover to front case half, transfer case shift lever assembly should be shifted into 4WD high detent position to assure positioning of shift rail to rear cover. Coat mating surface of front case with a bead of RTV sealer. Position rear cover on front case. Make sure that 2-4WD shift fork spring engages shift rail and does not fall off rear cover boss. Install bolts and tighten to specification.

NOTE: If rear cover assembly does not seat properly, move rear cover up and down slightly to permit end of shift rail to enter shift rail hole in rear cover boss.

25) Install rear yoke on output shaft. Install rubber seal, washer and nut. Tighten nut to specification. Install 4WD indicator switch and breather plug. Install drain plug and fill transfer case with 3 pints (1.4L) of Dexron II. Install filler plug and reinstall transfer case in vehicle.

TIGHTENING SPECIFICATIONS

Application	Ft. Lbs. (N.m)
Breather Vent	6-14 (8-19)
Case to Cover Bolts	23-30 (31-41)
Drain & Fill Plug	14-22 (19-30)
4WD Indicator Switch	25-35 (34-47)
Front & Rear Driveshaft Bolts	12-15 (16-20)
Shift Control Bolts (Large)	70-90 (95-122)
Shift Control Bolts (Small)	31-42 (42-57)
Skid Plate-to-Frame Bolt	22-30 (30-41)
Transfer Case-to-Transmission	25-35 (34-47)
Shift Control Lever & Heat Shield	27-37 (37-50)
Yoke Nut	120-150 (163-203)

	INCH Lbs. (N.m)
Oil Pump Bolts	36-40 (4-4.5)
Shift Shaft & Shift Cam Set Screw	60-84 (6.8-9.5)
Speedometer Screw	20-25 (2.3-2.8)

NEW PROCESS MODEL 205

Chevrolet, Chrysler Corp., GMC

DESCRIPTION

Transfer case provides two gears, high for highway driving and low for off the road or heavy operation. With the transfer case, direct drive is available in both 2-wheel drive and 4-wheel drive.

Sliding clutch gears are used in controlling the various selections of gear combinations. The transfer case contains constant-mesh helical cut gears with shafts mounted in ball and roller bearings. When driving in a 4-wheel mode, hubs on the front wheels must be turned to the "Locked" position.

LUBRICATION

SERVICE INTERVALS

Chrysler Corp.

Check fluid level and fill as necessary. Drain and refill transfer case every 37,500 miles.

General Motors

Check fluid level and fill as necessary every 4 months or 6,000 miles.

FLUID TYPE

Chrysler Corp.

NOTE: **Either multipurpose gear oils meeting API specification GL-5 or engine oils labeled for API Service "SF" may be used in this transfer case.**

If multipurpose gear oil is used and the minimum anticipated air temperature is:
- Above 90°F (32°C), use SAE 140.
- Below 90°F (32°C) but above -10°F (-23°C), use SAE 90.
- Below -10°F (-23°C), use SAE 80.

If engine oil is used and the air temperature is:
- Above 32°F (0°C), use SAE 50.
- Below 32°F (0°C), use SAE 30.

General Motors

Use fluid of the type labeled Dexron II Automatic Transmission Fluid.

CAPACITY

Chrysler Corp.

Capacity is 4.5 pints (2.1L).

General Motors

Capacity is 5.1 pints (2.4L).

ADJUSTMENTS

SHIFT LINKAGE

Adjust shift linkage so that all positions may be selected without interference or binding.

REMOVAL & INSTALLATION

TRANSFER CASE

Removal

1) Raise vehicle, remove plug and drain transfer case. Disconnect speedometer cable. Remove skid plate, crossmember and strut rods, if equipped. Disconnect input and output shafts and secure out of way.

2) Disconnect shift lever rod from shift rail link. Support transfer case and remove bolts attaching case to transmission adapter. Move transfer case to rear until input shaft clears adapter and remove from vehicle.

Installation

To install, reverse removal procedure. Ensure that all attaching bolts are tight and fill transfer case with recommended lubricant.

DISASSEMBLY

REAR OUTPUT SHAFT & YOKE ASSEMBLY

1) Loosen rear output shaft yoke nut. Remove rear output shaft housing bolts and remove housing and retainer from case. Remove retaining nut and yoke from shaft. Then remove shaft assembly from housing. Remove snap ring and discard.

2) Remove thrust washer and washer pin. Remove tanged bronze washer. Remove gear and gear needle bearings (32 per row). Remove spacer and 2nd row of needle bearings. Remove tanged bronze thrust washer from shaft.

3) Remove pilot rollers from shaft (15 rollers). Remove pilot roller retainer ring and washer and discard retainer ring. Remove oil seal retainer, ball bearing, speedometer gear and spacer. Discard all gaskets. Press out bearing and remove oil seal.

FRONT OUTPUT SHAFT ASSEMBLY

1) Remove lock nut, washer and yoke. Remove front bearing retainer attaching bolts and retainer. Remove front output shaft rear bearing retainer attaching bolts.

2) Using a soft-faced hammer, tap on output shaft and remove shaft, gear assembly and rear bearing retainer from case. *See Fig. 1.* Remove the sliding clutch from output high gear and remove washer and bearing remaining in case.

3) Remove snap ring and gear retaining ring from the shaft. Discard retaining ring. Remove thrust

Fig. 1: Removing Front Output Shaft Assembly

Using a soft-faced hammer, tap shaft of transfer case.

Transfer Cases

NEW PROCESS MODEL 205 (Cont.)

Fig 2: *New Process Model 205 Transfer Case*

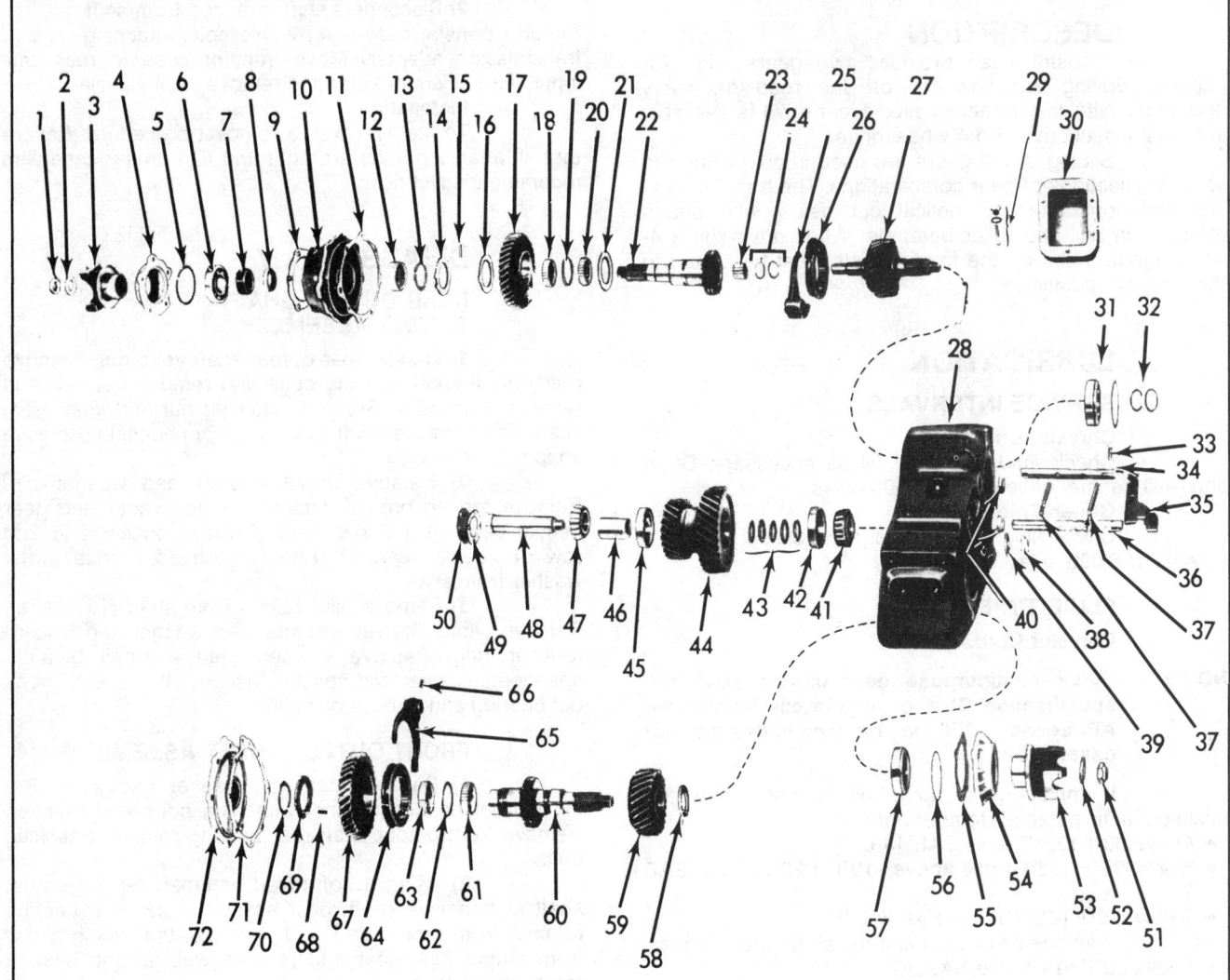

1. Rear Output Shaft Lock Nut	25. Shift Fork	49. Cover Gasket
2. Washer	26. Sliding Clutch	50. Rear Cover
3. Rear Output Shaft Yoke	27. Imput Shaft	51. Front Output Shaft Lock Nut
4. Bearing Retainer & Seal	28. Transfer Case	52. Washer
5. Snap Ring	29. Poppet Plug, Spring & Ball	53. Yoke
6. Bearing	30. P.T.O. Gasket & Cover	54. Bearing Retainer & Seat
7. Speedometer Gear	31. Imput Shaft Bearing & Snap Ring	55. Gasket
8. Spacer	32. Snap Ring & Rubber "O" Ring (General Motors Only)	56. Snap Ring
9. Gasket	33. Shift Link Clevis Pin	57. Front Bearing
10. Rear Output Shaft Housing	34. Range Shift Rail	58. Thrust Washer
11. Gasket	35. Shift Rail Connector Link	59. Front Wheel High Gear
12. Bearing	36. Front Wheel Drive Shift Rail	60. Front Output Shaft
13. Snap Ring	37. Interlock Pins	61. Needle Bearing
14. Thrust Washer	38. Rear Idler Lock Nut	62. Spacer
15. Thrust Washer Lock Pin	39. Washer	63. Needle Bearing
16. Thrust Washer (Tanged)	40. Shift Rail Seals	64. Sliding Clutch Gear
17. Low Speed Gear	41. Idler Shaft Bearing	65. Shift Fork
18. Needle Bearings	42. Bearing Cup	66. Roll Pin
19. Spacer	43. Shims	67. Front Output Low Gear
20. Needle Bearings	44. Idler Gear	68. Thrust Washer Lock Pin
21. Tanged Thrust Washer	45. Bearing Cup	69. Thrust Washer
22. Rear Output Shaft	46. Spacer	70. Snap Ring
23. Needle Bearings	47. Idler Shaft Bearing	71. Rear Cover Gasket
24. Washer & Retainer	48. Idler Shaft	72. Rear Cover & Bearing

NEW PROCESS MODEL 205 (Cont.)

washer and pin from shaft. Remove gear, needle bearings (32 per row) and spacer.

4) If necessary to replace front output shaft rear bearing, support cover and press bearing from cover. Position new bearing to outside face of cover and using a pipe or piece of wood, press bearing into cover until flush with opening. Use a new retainer when replacing bearing.

SHIFT RAIL & FORK ASSEMBLIES

1) Remove the 2 poppet nuts and springs on top of case. Using a magnet, remove the poppet balls. Drive cup plugs into case using a ¼" (6.35 mm) punch. Position both shift rails in neutral position. Using a long, narrow punch, drive shift fork pins into case.

2) Remove clevis pins and shift rail link. Remove shift rails, upper range rail, then lower (4-WD) rail. Remove shift forks and sliding clutch from case. Remove front output high gear, washer and bearing from case.

3) Remove shift rail cup plugs and pins from case. Remove snap ring in front of bearing. Using a soft-faced hammer, tap shaft out rear of case. Tap bearing out front of case. Tip case on PTO and remove 2 interlock pins from inside.

IDLER GEAR

Remove idler gear shaft nut. Remove idler shaft rear cover. Remove idler gear shaft using a soft-faced hammer and tool J-23429. Tilt case at 45° angle and roll idler gear to front output shaft hole and remove from case. Remove 2 bearing cups from idler gear.

CLEANING & INSPECTION

1) Clean all parts in suitable solvent, and blow parts dry with compressed air. Direct air across bearings, ensuring that they do not spin. Remove all traces of gaskets from surfaces where used.

2) Examine all individual roller bearing surfaces for wear or evidence of chipping or cracks. Replace bearings as necessary. Bearings are non-adjustable, and if worn or damaged, they must be replaced.

3) Inspect teeth of all gears for excessive wear or damage. Replace any gear where these conditions exist.

4) Carefully examine splines and shaft for scoring or evidence of wear. Sliding clutch gears must move freely on splines. Parts should be replaced if spline or shaft is scored or heavily worn.

REASSEMBLY

IDLER GEAR

1) Using a press or arbor, install 2 bearing cups in idler gear. Assemble 2 bearing cones, spacer, shims and idler gear on dummy shaft with bore up. Check end play; limits are .000-.002" (.00-.05 mm). *See Fig 3.* Install idler gear assembly with dummy shaft into case. Install through front output bore, large end first.

2) Install idler shaft from large bore side, and drive through using soft-faced hammer. Install washer and new lock nut. Check for end play and free rotation. Tighten lock nut to specification. Install idler shaft cover and gasket. Torque bolts to specification.

Fig. 3: Checking Idler Gear End Play

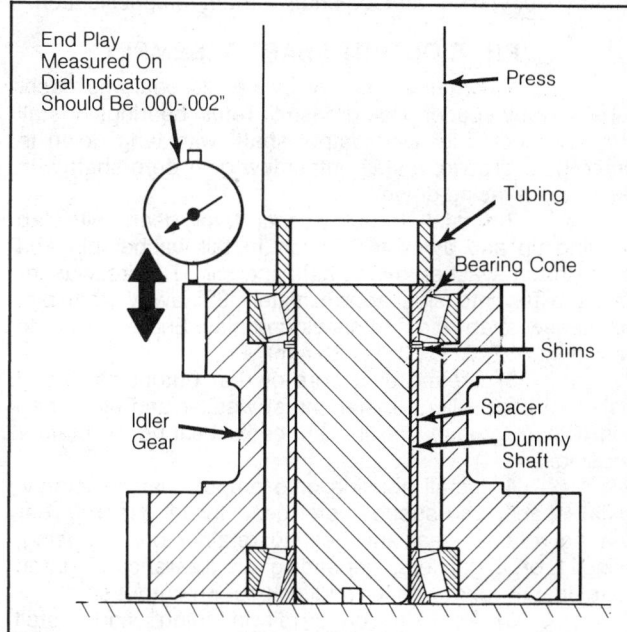

Install idler gear with dummy shaft, large end first.

SHIFT RAIL & FORK ASSEMBLIES

1) Press 2 rail seals into case. Seals should be installed with metal lip outward. Install interlock pins through large bore or PTO opening. Start front output drive shift rail into case from back, with slotted end first and poppet notches up.

2) Install shift fork, with long end inward, into rail. Push rail through to neutral position. Install input shaft bearing and shaft into case. Start range rail into case from front, with poppet notches up.

3) Install sliding clutch onto fork, placing over input shaft in case. Position to receive range rail, and push rail through to neutral position. Install new lock pins through holes at top of case and drive into forks. Tip case on PTO opening when installing range rail lock pin.

FRONT OUTPUT SHAFT & GEAR ASSEMBLY

1) Install 2 rows of 32 needle bearings, separated by spacer, in front low output gear. Retain with a sufficient amount of grease. Place front output shaft in a soft-jawed vise, with yoke end down. Install front low gear over shaft with clutch gear facing down.

2) Install thrust washer pin, thrust washer and new snap ring. Position snap ring so opening is opposite the pin. Position front wheel high gear and washer in case. Install sliding clutch in fork. Then put shift fork and rail in front wheel drive position with clutch teeth meshed with teeth of front wheel high gear.

3) Line up washer, high gear and sliding clutch with bearing bore. Insert front output shaft and low gear assembly through high gear assembly. Install new seal in bearing retainer, using tool J-22836. Install front output bearing and retainer in case.

4) Clean and grease rollers in front output rear bearing retainer. Install onto case using 1 gasket. Dip

NEW PROCESS MODEL 205 (Cont.)

bolts into sealant. Install bolts and tighten. Install front ouput yoke, washer and lock nut. Tighten to specification.

REAR OUTPUT SHAFT ASSEMBLY

1) Install 2 rows of 32 needle bearings each, separated by spacer. Use grease to retain bearings. Install thrust washer onto rear output shaft, with tang down in clutch gear groove. Install output low gear onto shaft with clutch teeth facing down.

2) Install thrust washer over gear, with tab pointing up and away from gear. Install washer pin and large thrust washer over shaft and pin. Rotate washer until tab fits into slot, approximately 90° away from pin. Install new snap ring and check end play. End play should be within .002-.027" (.051-.686 mm).

3) Grease pilot bore of rear output shaft and install 15 pilot rollers. Install thrust washer and new snap ring. Clean, grease and install needle bearing in retainer housing.

4) Install housing onto output shaft assembly. Install spacer and speedometer gear. Install bearing, rear bearing retainer seal and bearing retainer onto housing, using 1 or 2 gaskets, depending on clearance. Tighten bolts. Install yoke, washer and lock nut on output shaft.

5) Position range rail in "High" and install output shaft and retainer assembly on transfer case. Tighten bolts. Install PTO cover and gasket. Install and seal cup plugs at rail pin holes. Install drain and filler plugs. Install shift rail cross link, clevis pins and lock pins.

Fig. 4: Rear Output Spacer and Speedometer Gear

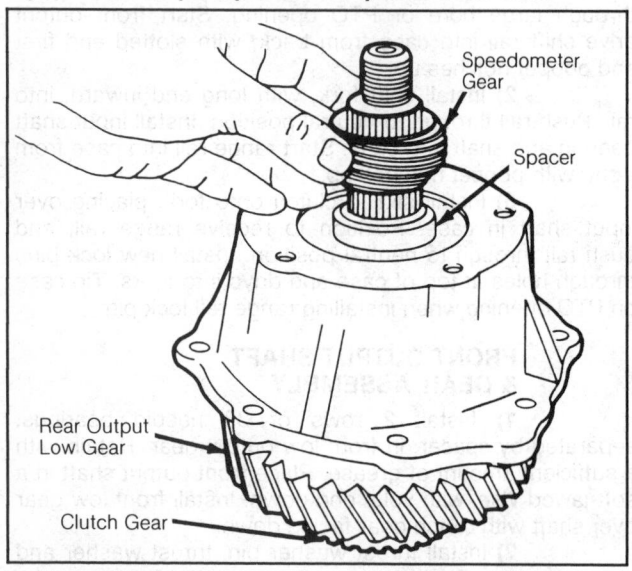

Speedometer Gear

Spacer

Rear Output Low Gear

Clutch Gear

Install housing onto output shaft assembly

TIGHTENING SPECIFICATION

Application	Ft. Lbs. (N.m)
Yoke Lock Nuts	150 (202)
Idler Shaft Lock Nut	150 (202)
Imput & Output Bearing	
Retainer Bolts	30 (40)
Transfer Case-to-Adapter Bolts	45 (61)
Idler Shaft Cover Bolts	20 (27)
Drain & Fill Plugs	30 (40)
PTO Cover Bolts	15 (20)

Transfer Cases

NEW PROCESS 207

Chevrolet & GMC "S" Truck

DESCRIPTION

The 207 transfer case is an aluminum case, chain drive, 4-position unit. It is a part time 4WD unit that provides 2WD and 4WD high ranges, 4WD low range and neutral. High ranges are a 1:1 gear ratio and low range is a 2.61:1 gear ratio. Torque input in both 4WD ranges is undifferentiated. Range positions on the transfer case are selected by a floor mounted shift lever.

The 207 transfer case has a 2 piece aluminum case containing front and rear output shafts, 2 drive sprockets, a shift mechanism and a planetary gear assembly. The drive sprockets are connected and operated by a drive chain. The planetary gear assembly consists of a 3-pinion carrier and an annulus gear. It provides the 4WD low range when needed.

The drive range positions are indicated by 4 lamps in the console panel. These lamps are controlled by an indicator switch at the shift lever.

LUBRICATION

SERVICE INTERVALS

Check fluid and refill as necessary every 12 months or 7500 miles.

FLUID TYPE

Use automatic transmission fluid labeled Dexron II or equivalent.

CAPACITY

Refill capacity is 5 quarts (4.9L).

REMOVAL & INSTALLATION

TRANSFER CASE

Removal

1) Shift transfer case into 4WD high range and disconnect battery negative cable. Raise vehicle, remove skid plate and drain lubricant from transfer case.

2) Mark front and rear output shaft yokes and front and rear propeller shafts for reassembly reference. Remove propeller shafts taking care not to let their weight hang on universal joints. Disconnect speedometer cable and vacuum harness at transfer case. Remove shift lever from case.

3) Remove catalytic converter hanger bolts at converter. Raise transmission and transfer case and remove mount attaching bolts. Remove mount and catalytic converter hanger and lower transmission and transfer case. Support transfer case and remove transfer case attaching bolts.

4) On vehicles equipped with automatic transmissions, it will be necessary to remove the shift lever bracket mounting bolts from the transfer case. This will allow for removal of the upper left transfer case attaching bolt. Separate transfer case from transmission and remove case from vehicle.

Installation

1) Clean all old gasket material from transmission and transfer case mating surfaces. Position new gasket on transfer case with orientation tab at the upper left bolt hole. *See Fig. 1.* Install transfer case, aligning splines of input shaft with transmission. Slide transfer case forward until seated against transmission.

Fig. 1: Assembling Transfer Case to Transmission

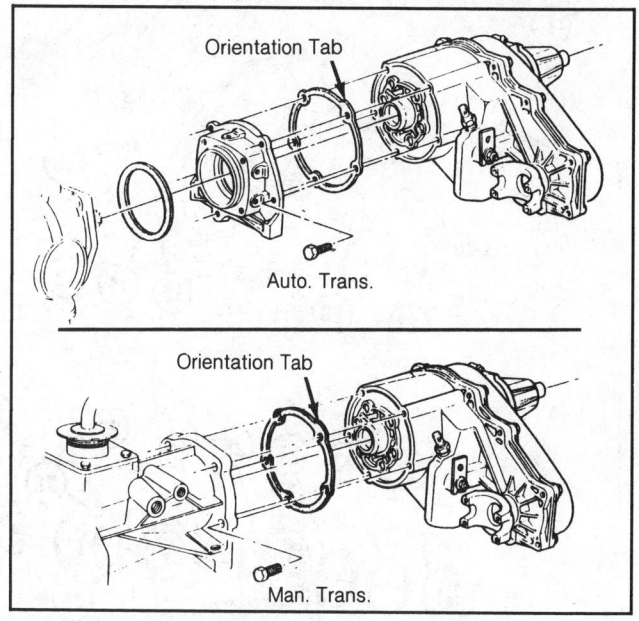

Note position of orientation tab.

2) Install transfer case attaching bolts and torque to specification. On vehicles equipped with automatic transmission, reinstall shift lever. Raise transmission and transfer case, install mount and hanger bracket, install bolts and torque to specification.

3) Install catalytic converter hanger bolts at converter and torque to specification. Attach shift lever, connect speedometer and vacuum harness at transfer case. Using reference marks, made during removal, reinstall front and rear propeller shafts

4) Fill transfer case with amount and type of lubricant specified. *See LUBRICATION section.* Install skid plate and lower vehicle. Connect negative battery cable. Road test vehicle.

DISASSEMBLY

TRANSFER CASE

1) Drain transfer case and remove from vehicle. Remove drain and fill plugs and front yoke, discard seal washer and yoke nut. Turn transfer case on end and position transfer case on wood blocks. Shift transfer case to 4WD low.

2) Remove extension housing bolts and, using a hammer, tap the shoulder on the housing to break sealer loose. Remove the snap ring for the rear bearing from the mainshaft and discard snap ring. Remove the rear retainer attaching bolts and, using a hammer, tap the shoulder on retainer to break sealer loose.

3) Remove the rear retainer and the pump housing from the transfer case. Remove the pump seal from the pump housing and discard seal. Remove the speedometer drive gear and the pump gear from the mainshaft.

Transfer Cases

NEW PROCESS 207 (Cont.)

Fig. 2: Exploded View of New Process 207 Transfer Case

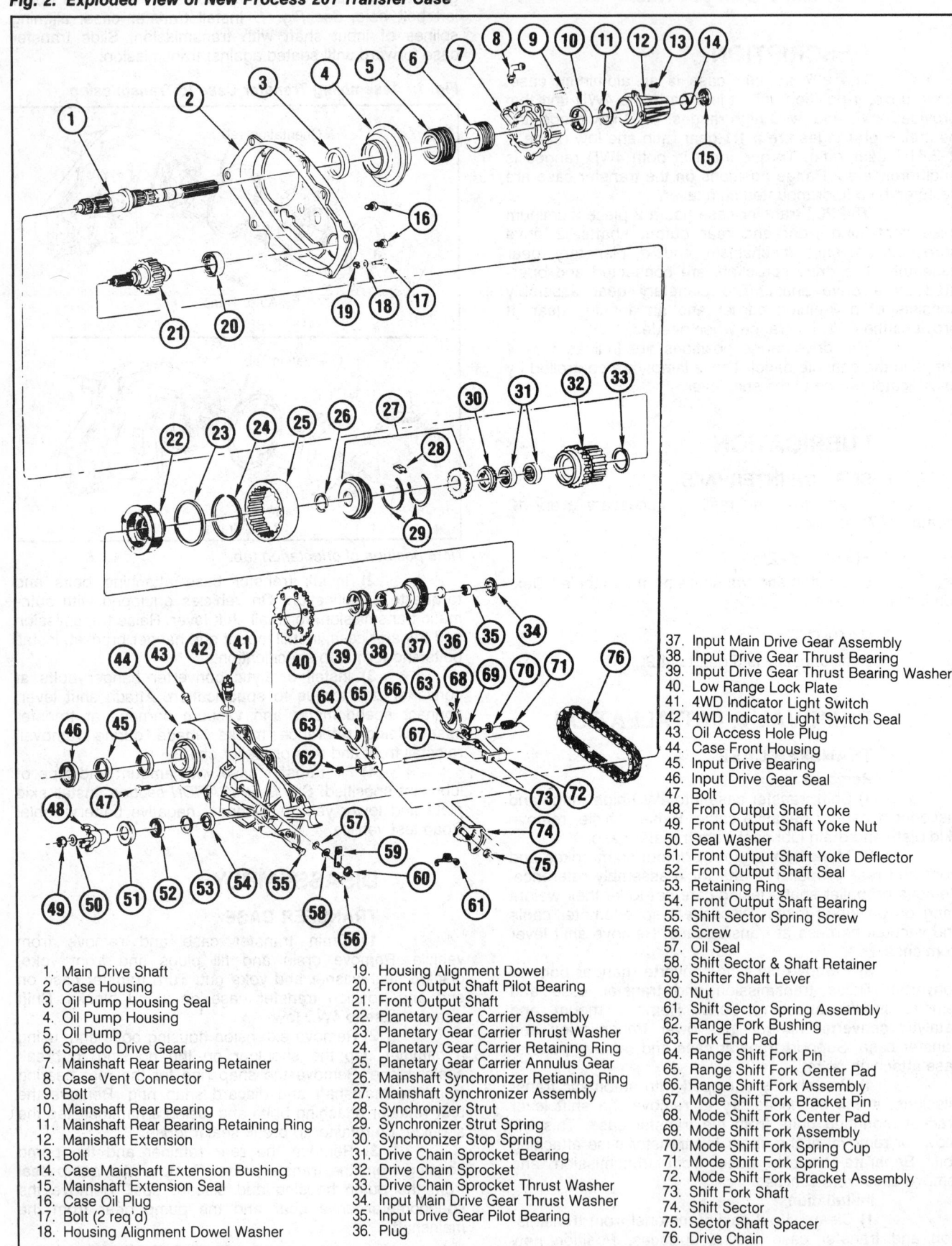

37. Input Main Drive Gear Assembly
38. Input Drive Gear Thrust Bearing
39. Input Drive Gear Thrust Bearing Washer
40. Low Range Lock Plate
41. 4WD Indicator Light Switch
42. 4WD Indicator Light Switch Seal
43. Oil Access Hole Plug
44. Case Front Housing
45. Input Drive Bearing
46. Input Drive Gear Seal
47. Bolt
48. Front Output Shaft Yoke
49. Front Output Shaft Yoke Nut
50. Seal Washer
51. Front Output Shaft Yoke Deflector
52. Front Output Shaft Seal
53. Retaining Ring
54. Front Output Shaft Bearing
55. Shift Sector Spring Screw
56. Screw
57. Oil Seal
58. Shift Sector & Shaft Retainer
59. Shifter Shaft Lever
60. Nut
61. Shift Sector Spring Assembly
62. Range Fork Bushing
63. Fork End Pad
64. Range Shift Fork Pin
65. Range Shift Fork Center Pad
66. Range Shift Fork Assembly
67. Mode Shift Fork Bracket Pin
68. Mode Shift Fork Center Pad
69. Mode Shift Fork Assembly
70. Mode Shift Fork Spring Cup
71. Mode Shift Fork Spring
72. Mode Shift Fork Bracket Assembly
73. Shift Fork Shaft
74. Shift Sector
75. Sector Shaft Spacer
76. Drive Chain

1. Main Drive Shaft
2. Case Housing
3. Oil Pump Housing Seal
4. Oil Pump Housing
5. Oil Pump
6. Speedo Drive Gear
7. Mainshaft Rear Bearing Retainer
8. Case Vent Connector
9. Bolt
10. Mainshaft Rear Bearing
11. Mainshaft Rear Bearing Retaining Ring
12. Manishaft Extension
13. Bolt
14. Case Mainshaft Extension Bushing
15. Mainshaft Extension Seal
16. Case Oil Plug
17. Bolt (2 req'd)
18. Housing Alignment Dowel Washer

19. Housing Alignment Dowel
20. Front Output Shaft Pilot Bearing
21. Front Output Shaft
22. Planetary Gear Carrier Assembly
23. Planetary Gear Carrier Thrust Washer
24. Planetary Gear Carrier Retaining Ring
25. Planetary Gear Carrier Annulus Gear
26. Mainshaft Synchronizer Retaining Ring
27. Mainshaft Synchronizer Assembly
28. Synchronizer Strut
29. Synchronizer Strut Spring
30. Synchronizer Stop Spring
31. Drive Chain Sprocket Bearing
32. Drive Chain Sprocket
33. Drive Chain Sprocket Thrust Washer
34. Input Main Drive Gear Thrust Washer
35. Input Drive Gear Pilot Bearing
36. Plug

NEW PROCESS 207 (Cont.)

4) Remove the bolts attaching the rear case to the front case and remove the rear case. To separate the case, insert screwdrivers into the slots cast in the case ends and pry upward. Do not attempt to wedge the case halves apart at any point on the mating surface. Remove the front output shaft and drive chain as an assembly. It may be necessary to raise the mainshaft slightly for the output shaft to clear the case. See Fig. 3.

Fig. 3: Installing/Removing Front Output Shaft and Drive Chain

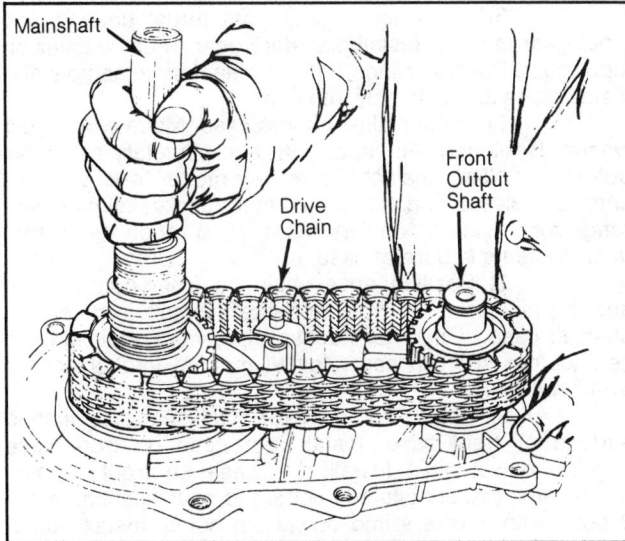

Install/remove chain and shaft as an assembly.

5) Pull up on the mode fork rail until rail clears range fork. Rotate mode fork and rail and remove from transfer case. Pull up on the mainshaft until it separates from the planetary assembly. Remove the mainshaft assembly from the transfer case. See Fig. 4.

Fig. 4: Installing/Removing Mainshaft Assembly

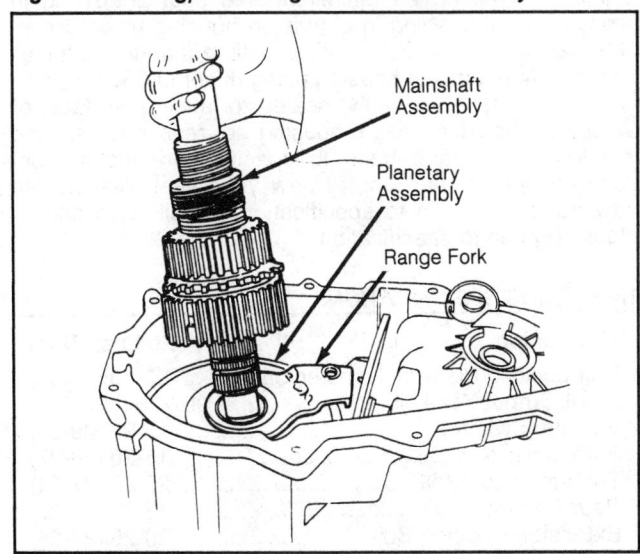

6) Remove the planetary assembly with the range fork. Remove the planetary thrust washer, input gear thrust bearing and front thrust washer from the transfer case. Remove the shift sector detent spring and retaining bolt.

7) Remove the shift sector, shaft, and spacer from the transfer case. Remove the locking plate retaining bolts and lock plate from the transfer case. Remove the input gear pilot bearing using puller (J-29369-1) and slide hammer. Remove front output shaft seal, input shaft seal and rear extension seal using a screwdriver or a brass drift.

8) Using a driver and adapter, (J-33841 and J-8092), press the 2 caged roller bearings for the front output shaft from the transfer case. Using a puller or slide hammer, remove the rear bearing for the front output shaft. Using a hammer and a drift, remove the rear mainshaft bearing from the rear retainer.

9) Using a screwdriver, remove the snap ring retaining the front output shaft bearing. Using a hammer and drift, remove the bearing from the case. Remove the bushing from the extension housing using a driver and adapter (J-8092 and J-33839). Press bushing from extension housing.

MAINSHAFT

1) Remove the speedometer gear. Using a screwdriver, pry off the pump gear from the mainshaft. Remove the snap ring retaining the synchronizer hub from the mainshaft.

2) Using a brass hammer, tap the synchronizer hub from the mainshaft. See Fig. 5. Remove the drive sprocket. Using a driver and adapter, (J-33826 J-8092), press two caged roller bearings from the drive sprocket.

Fig. 5: Mainshaft Assembly

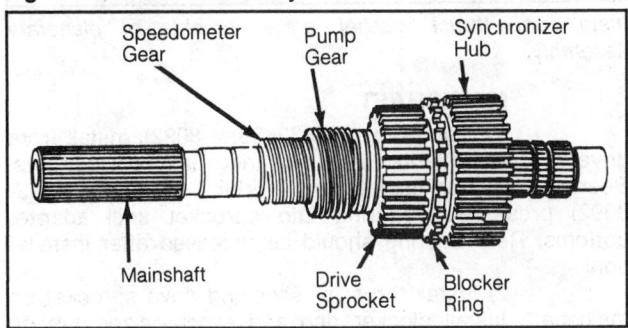

Use brass hammer to remove synchronizer hub.

3) Remove synchronizer keys and retaining rings from the synchronizer hub. Clean and inspect all parts. Replace any part if it shows evidence of excessive wear, distortion or damage.

PLANETARY GEAR

1) Remove snap ring retaining the planetary gear in the annulus gear. Remove outer thrust ring and discard. Remove planetary assembly from annulus gear.

2) Remove inner thrust ring from the planetary assembly and discard. Clean and inspect all parts if they show evidence of excessive wear, distortion or damage.

CLEANING & INSPECTION

1) Clean all parts in cleaning solvent. Be sure to remove all traces of gaskets from gasket surfaces. Dry parts with compressed air, being careful not to spin bearings. Check all gear teeth and splines for burrs, nicks, or excessive damage. Inspect all snap rings and thrust washers for excessive wear, distortion or damage.

NEW PROCESS 207 (Cont.)

2) Inspect 2 case halves for cracks, porosity, damaged mating surfaces, stripped bolt threads or distortion. Inspect condition of all bearings and retainers. Inspect condition of chain and oil pump.

ASSEMBLY

PLANETARY GEAR

Install the inner thrust ring on planetary assembly. Install the planetary assembly into the annulus gear. Install the outer thrust ring and then the snap ring. *See Fig. 6.*

Fig. 6: Installing Thrust Washers in Planetary Assembly

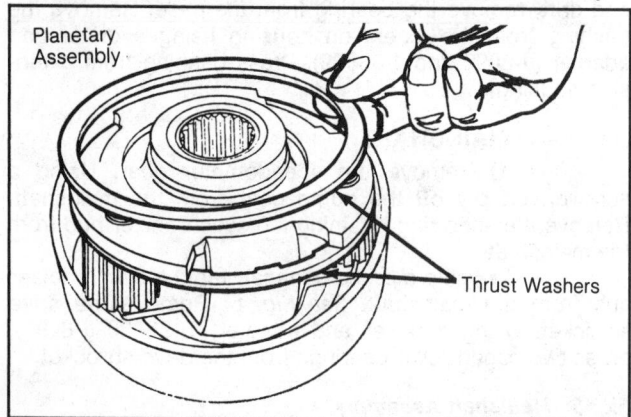

Install one thrust washer on each side of planetary assembly.

MAINSHAFT

1) Using driver, (J-33828, J-8092), install front drive sprocket bearing. Press bearing until tool bottoms. Bearing should be flush to front surface. Reverse tool, (J-8092) press rear bearing into sprocket until adapter bottoms. Rear bearing should be recessed after installation.

2) Install thrust washer and drive sprocket on mainshaft. Install blocker ring and synchronizer hub on mainshaft. Seat hub on mainshaft, install new snap ring to retain it.

3) Install pump gear on mainshaft. Tap gear with hammer to seat it on mainshaft. Install speedometer gear on mainshaft.

TRANSFER CASE

CAUTION: All bearings used in transfer case must be correctly positioned to avoid covering bearing oil feed holes. After installation of bearings, check bearing position to be sure feed hole is not blocked by bearing.

1) Install lock plate in transfer case. Coat case and lock plate surfaces around bolt holes with RTV sealer. Position lock plate to case and align bolt holes in lock plate with case. Install attaching bolts and tighten to specification.

2) Install roller bearings for input shaft into case using driver, (J-33830, J-8092). Press bearings until tool bottoms. Using driver (J-33832, J-8092), install front output shaft rear bearing. Press bearing until tool bottoms.

3) Install front output shaft front bearing using driver (J-33832, J-8092). Press bearing until tool bottoms. Install snap ring that retains front output shaft bearing in case. Install front output and input shaft seals using driver.

4) Install spacer on shift sector shaft and install sector in case. Install shift lever and retaining nut. Torque nut to specification. Install shift sector detent spring and retaining bolt. Using driver (J-33829, J-8092), install pilot bearing into input gear. Press bearing until tool bottoms.

5) Install input gear front thrust bearing and input gear in case. Install planetary gear thrust washer on input gear. Position range fork on planetary assembly and install planetary assembly into case.

6) Install mainshaft into case. Make sure thrust washer is aligned with input gear and planetary assembly before installing mainshaft. Install mode fork on synchronizer sleeve and rotate until mode fork is aligned with range fork. Slide mode fork rail down through range fork until rail seats in bore of case.

7) Position drive chain on front output shaft and install chain on drive sprocket. Install front output shaft in case. It may be necessary to raise mainshaft to seat output shaft in case. Install magnet into pocket of transfer case.

8) Apply 1/8" bead of RTV sealer to mating surface of front case. Install rear case on front case aligning dowel pins. Install rear case on front aligning dowel pins. Install bolts and tighten to specification. Install 2 bolts with washers into dowel pin holes. Install output bearing into rear retainer using driver (J-33833, J-8092). Press bearing until seated in bore.

9) Install pump seal using installer. Apply petroleum jelly to pump housing tabs and install housing in rear retainer. Apply RTV sealer to mating surface of rear retainer. Align retainer to case and install retaining bolts. Torque bolts to specification.

10) Using new snap ring, install snap ring on mainshaft. Pull up on mainshaft and seat snap ring in groove. Install bushing in extension housing using driver (J-33826, J-8092). Press bushing until tool bottoms. Install new seal in extension housing using driver (J-33843).

11) Apply RTV sealer to mating surface of extension housing. Align housing to rear retainer and install bolts. Torque bolts to specification. Install front yoke on output shaft. Install new yoke seal washer with new nut and tighten to specification. Install drain and fill plugs. Tighten to specification.

TIGHTENING SPECIFICATIONS

Application	Ft. Lbs. (N.m)
Bolt Locking Plate-to-Transfer Case	20-30 (27-40)
Front Output Yoke Nut	90-130 (122-176)
Vacuum Switch	15-25 (20-34)
Shift Lever Nut	15-20 (20-27)
Transfer Case Bolt	20-25 (27-34)
Rear Retainer Bolt	15-20 (20-27)
Extension Housing Bolt	20-25 (27-34)
Drain/Fill Plug	30-40 (40-54)
Adapter to Transfer Case Bolt	19-29 (26-40)
Shift Bracket Bolt	47-62 (65-85)
Shift Lever Pivot Bolt	88-103 (120-140)
Shift Lever Adjusting Bolt	25-35 (34-48)

NEW PROCESS MODEL 208

Chevrolet, Chrysler Corp., Ford, GMC, Jeep

DESCRIPTION

The Model 208 is a part-time 4-wheel drive unit having an integral 4-wheel low range. This model is a 4-position unit, providing 2 gear ratios in 4-wheel drive (high and low), a 2-wheel drive high and neutral.

A chain drive is used with front and rear output shafts mounted in ball and roller bearings. Two drive sprockets and a planetary gear assembly, consisting of a 4-pinion carrier and annulus gear are housed in a 2-piece aluminum case. All models have manual locking front drive hubs as standard equipment and 4-wheel drive indicator lamps. These lamps inform the driver of the operating mode of the vehicle.

LUBRICATION

SERVICE INTERVALS

Check fluid level. Case should be filled to edge of fill plug opening. Add fluid as necessary every 4 months or 6,000 miles. Drain and refill transfer case every 36,000 miles.

FLUID TYPE

All Models
Use Dexron II, Series D Automatic Transmission Fluid or equivalent.

CAPACITY

Chrysler Corp. & Jeep
Capacity is 6 pints (2.8L).
Ford
Capacity is 7 pints (3.3L).
General Motors
Capacity is 10 pints (4.8L).

ADJUSTMENTS

Adjust shift linkage so that all positions may be selected without interference or binding. Inspect all swivels, rods and mountings for wear or damage. Replace as necessary.

REMOVAL & INSTALLATION

TRANSFER CASE

Removal (Chrysler Corp. & Jeep)
1) Raise vehicle and drain transfer case. Mark transfer case front and rear output shaft yokes and propeller shafts for installation alignment reference. Disconnect speedometer cable and indicator switch wires. Disconnect shift lever link from operating lever.
2) Place transmission jack under transfer case and remove crossmember. Disconnect front and rear propeller shafts at yokes, and secure to frame with wire.
3) If necessary, disconnect parking brake cable guide from pivot on right frame rail, and remove bolts attaching exhaust pipe support bracket-to-transfer case. Remove transfer case-to-transmission bolts. Move

assembly rearward until free of output shaft, and remove from vehicle.
4) Remove all gasket material from rear of transmission adapter housing.
Removal (Ford)
1) Raise vehicle and drain transfer case. Disconnect indicator switch wire, speedometer driven gear and nut retaining transmission shift lever assembly to transfer case. Remove skid plate from frame, if equipped. Remove heat shield from transfer case.

CAUTION: Catalytic converter is located beside heat shield. Be careful of extremely high temperatures generated by converter.

2) Place transmission jack under transfer case. Disconnect front and rear driveshafts at yokes. Remove transfer case-to-transmission adapter bolts. Remove gasket between transfer case and adapter. Lower and remove transfer case from vehicle.
Removal (General Motors)
1) Place transfer case selector lever in "4H" position. Raise vehicle and drain transfer case. Remove cotter pin from shift lever swivel. Mark transfer case front and rear output shaft yokes and propeller shafts for installation alignment reference.
2) Disconnect speedometer cable and indicator switch wires. If necessary, disconnect parking brake cable guide from pivot on right frame rail. On automatic transmission models, remove engine strut rod from transfer case.
3) Place transmission jack under transfer case. Remove transfer case-to-transmission adapter bolts. Move assembly rearward until free of output shaft and remove from vehicle.
4) Remove all gasket material from rear of transmission adapter housing.
Installation (All Models)
Install new transmission-to-transfer case gasket and align transfer case to transmission. Rotate transfer case output shaft until transmission output shaft engages transfer case input shaft. Move transfer case until case seats flush against transmission. Install transfer case attaching bolts and complete installation by reversing removal procedure.

DISASSEMBLY

TRANSFER CASE

1) Remove fill and drain plugs. Remove front and rear yokes. Discard yoke seal washers and nuts. Place transfer case on end and position front case on wood blocks. It may be necessary to cut notches in wooden block to clear mounting studs in front case.
2) Remove lock mode indicator switch and washer. Remove detent bolt, spring and ball. Mark rear retainer and case for assembly alignment reference. Remove rear retainer attaching bolts, retainer and pump housing as an assembly. See Fig. 1. Use mallet to remove retainer from case, DO NOT pry retainer.
3) Remove pump housing from retainer and pump seal from housing. Discard pump seal. Remove speedometer drive gear from mainshaft. Remove oil pump from mainshaft. Mark position of pump for reassembly.

Transfer Cases

NEW PROCESS MODEL 208 (Cont.)

Side of oil pump facing case interior is recessed. Remove rear case-to-front attaching bolts and remove rear case.

Fig. 1: Rear Retainer Case Removal & Installation

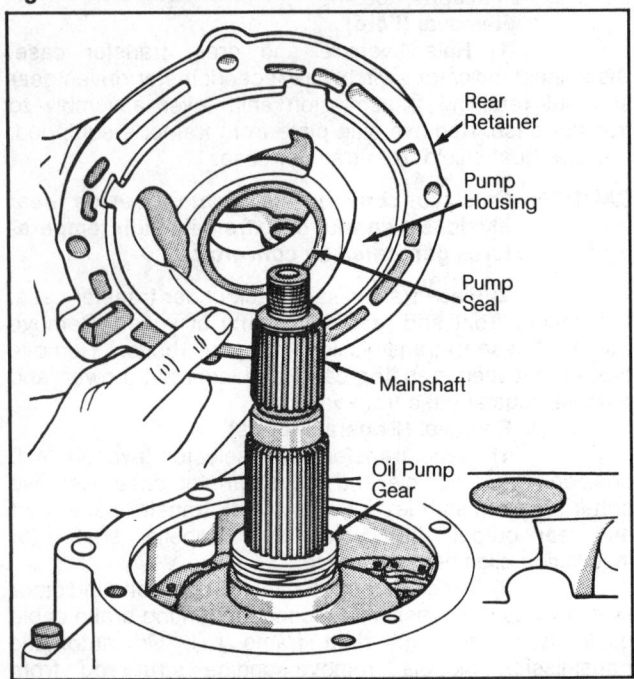

Tap retainer from case using plastic mallet.

NOTE: To remove rear case, insert screwdrivers into slots in case ends and gently pry upward. DO NOT pry case halves apart at any point on mating surface.

4) Remove front output shaft rear thrust bearing assembly, marking position of bearing and races for reassembly. Remove driven sprocket retaining snap ring, drive sprocket retaining snap ring, thrust washer and spacer washer, if equipped.

5) Remove sprockets and drive chain as assembly. Lift evenly on both sprockets to remove. *See Fig. 2.* Remove front output shaft and thrust bearing assembly. Remove sprocket carrier stop ring and clutch spring. Remove sliding clutch, mode fork, mode fork spring and bracket as an assembly.

6) Remove shift rail. Remove sprocket carrier, needle bearing upper retainer, thrust washer and mainshaft needle bearings as an assembly. Remove mainshaft. Remove annulus gear retaining ring and thrust washer.

7) Remove annulus gear and range fork as an assembly. Turn fork counterclockwise to disengage fork lug from range sector, and lift assembly out of case. Remove planetary thrust washer, and remove planetary assembly.

8) Remove mainshaft thrust bearing from input gear, and remove gear by lifting straight up and out of case. Remove input gear thrust bearing and race, marking position of bearing and race for reassembly.

9) Remove range sector operating lever nut and washer. Remove lever, sector shaft seal and seal retainer. Remove range sector. Inspect lock plate. If lock plate is loose, worn or cracked, remove and replace.

10) Remove output shaft seals from front and rear case seal bores.

Fig. 2: Sprocket & Chain Removal & Installation

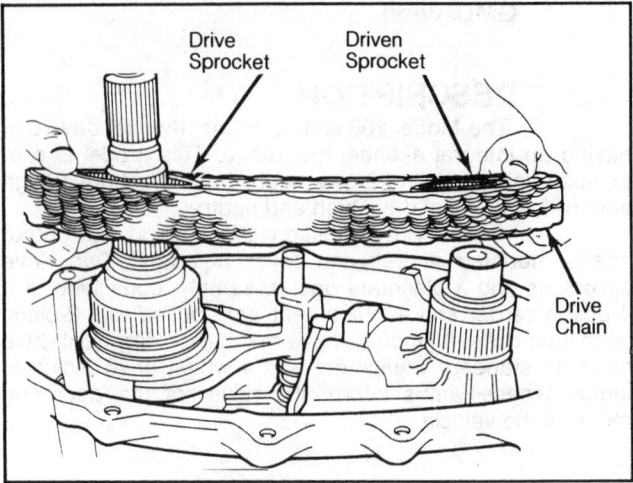

Remove sprocket and chain as assembly.

CLEANING & INSPECTION

1) Wash all parts in cleaning solvent. Be sure to remove all traces of gasket from surfaces where used. Apply compressed air to each oil feed port and channel in each case half to remove any obstruction or residue.

2) Check all gear teeth and splines for burrs, nicks, excessive wear or damage. Inspect all snap rings and thrust washers for excessive wear, distortion or damage.

3) Inspect both case halves for cracks, porosity, damaged mating surfaces, stripped bolt threads or distortion. Check lock plate teeth and hub for cracks, chips or excessive wear.

4) Inspect condition of all bearings in both case halves and input gear. Check condition of bearing bores in both case halves and in input gear, rear output shaft, side gear and rear retainer. Replace bearings as required.

REASSEMBLY

TRANSFER CASE

NOTE: During assembly, lubricate all components with Dexron II type oil or petroleum jelly where indicated only. Do not use any other type of lubricants.

1) Install input gear race and thrust bearing in front case. Install input gear and mainshaft thrust bearing in input gear.

2) Install range sector shaft seal and seal retainer. Install range sector. Install operating lever on range sector shaft. Install and tighten shaft washer and locknut.

3) Install planetary assembly over input gear making sure planetary is fully seated and meshed with gear. Install planetary thrust washer on planetary hub.

4) Install inserts in range fork, if removed. Engage range fork in annulus gear. Install annulus gear over planetary assembly. Install annulus gear thrust washer and retaining snap ring. Align shift rail bores in case and range fork. Install shift rail.

NEW PROCESS MODEL 208 (Cont.)

Fig. 3: New Process Model 208 Transfer Case

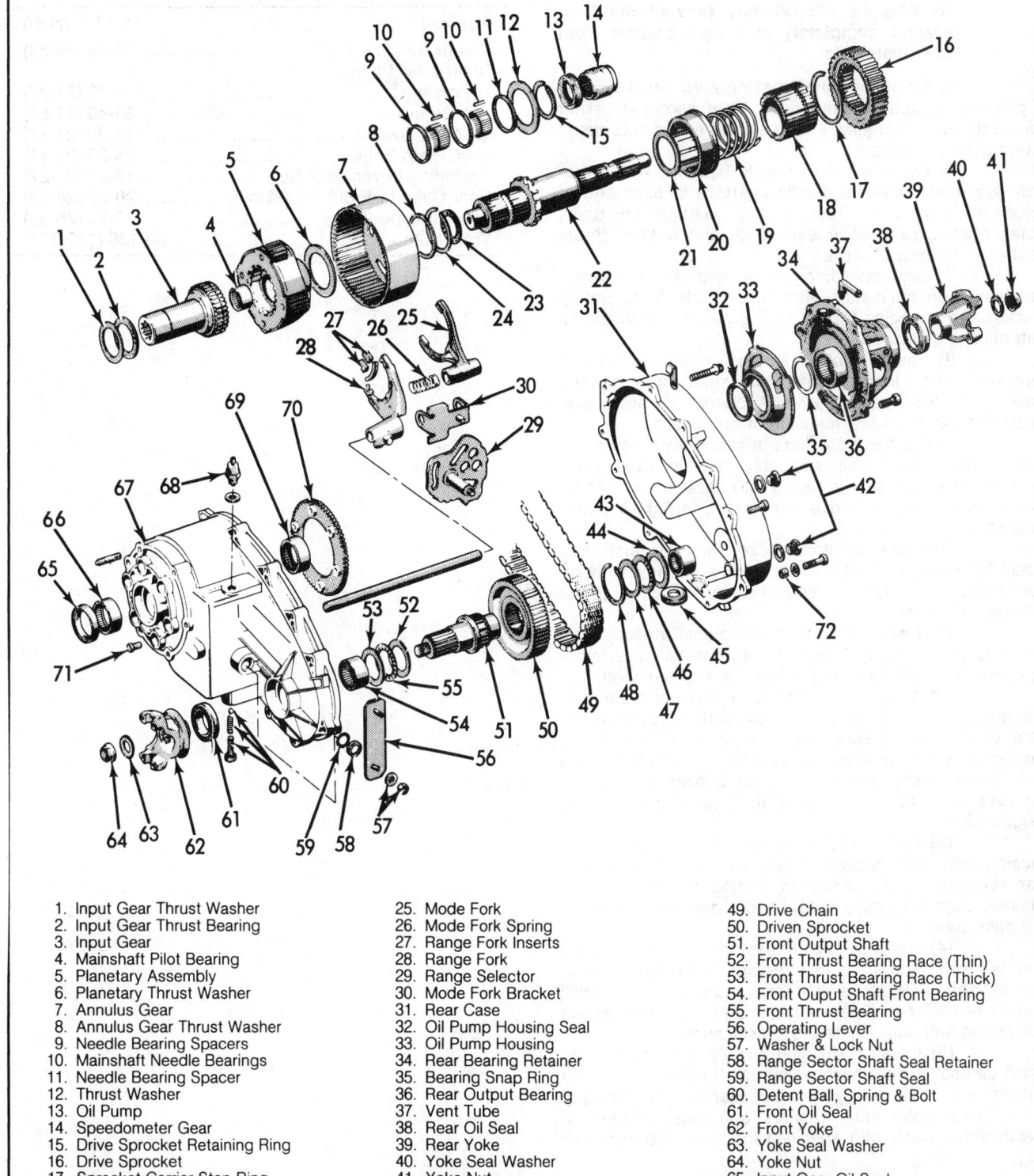

1. Input Gear Thrust Washer
2. Input Gear Thrust Bearing
3. Input Gear
4. Mainshaft Pilot Bearing
5. Planetary Assembly
6. Planetary Thrust Washer
7. Annulus Gear
8. Annulus Gear Thrust Washer
9. Needle Bearing Spacers
10. Mainshaft Needle Bearings
11. Needle Bearing Spacer
12. Thrust Washer
13. Oil Pump
14. Speedometer Gear
15. Drive Sprocket Retaining Ring
16. Drive Sprocket
17. Sprocket Carrier Stop Ring
18. Sprocket Carrier
19. Clutch Spring
20. Sliding Clutch
21. Thrust Washer
22. Mainshaft
23. Mainshaft Thrust Bearing
24. Annulus Gear Retaining Ring

25. Mode Fork
26. Mode Fork Spring
27. Range Fork Inserts
28. Range Fork
29. Range Selector
30. Mode Fork Bracket
31. Rear Case
32. Oil Pump Housing Seal
33. Oil Pump Housing
34. Rear Bearing Retainer
35. Bearing Snap Ring
36. Rear Output Bearing
37. Vent Tube
38. Rear Oil Seal
39. Rear Yoke
40. Yoke Seal Washer
41. Yoke Nut
42. Drain & Fill Plugs
43. Front Output Shaft Rear Bearing
44. Rear Thrust Bearing Race (Thick)
45. Case Magnet
46. Rear Thrust Bearing
47. Rear Thrust Bearing Race (Thin)
48. Driven Sprocket Retaining Ring

49. Drive Chain
50. Driven Sprocket
51. Front Output Shaft
52. Front Thrust Bearing Race (Thin)
53. Front Thrust Bearing Race (Thick)
54. Front Ouput Shaft Front Bearing
55. Front Thrust Bearing
56. Operating Lever
57. Washer & Lock Nut
58. Range Sector Shaft Seal Retainer
59. Range Sector Shaft Seal
60. Detent Ball, Spring & Bolt
61. Front Oil Seal
62. Front Yoke
63. Yoke Seal Washer
64. Yoke Nut
65. Input Gear Oil Seal
66. Input Gear Front Bearing
67. Front Case
68. Lock Mode Switch & Washer
69. Input Gear Rear Bearing
70. Lock Plate
71. Lock Plate Bolts
72. Case Alignment Dowels

Exploded view of transfer case assembly.

Transfer Cases

NEW PROCESS MODEL 208 (Cont.)

NOTE: Be sure shift rail bore is completely dry and contains no oil. Oil may prevent rail from seating completely and also prevent front case installation.

5) Install mainshaft making sure thrust bearing is properly seated in input gear. Coat sprocket carrier bore with petroleum jelly, and position bearing retainer at center of carrier bore.

6) Coat mainshaft needle bearings with petroleum jelly and install 60 needle bearings in each end of sprocket carrier bore. Total of 120 bearings are used. Install bearing retainer in each end, and postion thrust washer on bottom of carrier.

7) Align assembled carrier and needle bearings and install on mainshaft. Assemble mode fork, spring, bracket and engaging fork in sliding clutch and install on shift rail and mainshaft.

8) Install clutch spring and stop ring in sprocket carrier. Install front output shaft thrust bearing assembly in front case. Correct sequence is: thick race, thrust bearing, thin race. Install front output shaft.

9) Position sprockets in chain, align sprockets with shafts and install assembly making sure drive sprocket recessed side is facing into case. Install spacer and thrust washer on drive sprocket. *See Fig. 3.* Install snap ring.

10) Install driven sprocket retaining snap ring. Install front output shaft rear thrust bearing assembly on front ouput shaft. Correct sequence is: thin race, thrust bearing, thick race.

11) Install oil pump on mainshaft making sure recessed side of pump faces into case. Install speedometer drive gear. Install magnet in front case, if removed.

12) Apply Loctite 515, or equivalent sealant, to 1 side of case and mate surfaces. Install rear case on front case, making sure front output shaft rear thrust bearing assembly is seated in rear case. Align bolt holes and dowels. Install flat washers on 2 bolts installed at opposite ends of case. Install all bolts and tighten to specification.

13) Install seal in pump housing. Coat pump housing tabs with petroleum jelly and install housing in rear retainer. Apply sealer to mating surface of rear retainer, align with case index marks and install retainer and bolts. *See Fig. 1.*

14) Install oil seal in rear retainer bore, coating seal lip with petroleum jelly before installation. Install washer and indicator switch and tighten. Apply small amount of sealer to detent retainer bolt and install detent ball, spring and bolt. Tighten to specification.

15) Install drain plug and gasket and tighten. Install oil seal in front case output shaft bore. Install front and rear yokes. Be sure yoke with collar is on front output shaft. Install yoke seal washers and nuts. Tighten to specification. Refill with specified lubricant and install fill plug.

TIGHTENING SPECIFICATIONS

Application	Ft. Lbs. (N.m)
Detent Retainer Bolt	20-25 (28-33)
Drain & Fill Plugs	
Chrysler	15-20 (21-27)
All Others	30-40 (41-54)
Indicator Switch	15-20 (21-27)
Lock Plate Bolts	25-35 (24-41)
Operating Lever Lock Nut	15-20 (21-27)
Rear Case-to-Front Case Bolts	20-25 (28-33)
Rear Retainer Bolts	20-25 (28-33)
Yoke Nuts	90-130 (123-176)

SELEC-TRAC MODEL 229

Jeep

DESCRIPTION

The Selec-Trac Model 229 transfer case is a full-time 4-wheel drive unit that provides for 2-wheel operation. Selec-Trac is only available with automatic transmission and includes: Model 44 front axle with 2WD disconnect, a vacuum control system, Model 229 transfer case, and a 2/4WD mode selector on the instrument panel. This unit provides 4 driving ranges: 4WD high, 4WD low, 2WD high and Neutral.

The vacuum control system consists of 2 vacuum shift motors, a vacuum storage tank, lines and hoses, check valves and a 2/4WD mode selector. *See Fig. 1.* This system will allow for low range operation only after 4WD mode has been selected. The design of the vacuum motors allows for sequential engagement of the vacuum controlled components. *See Fig. 2.* When shifting into 4WD, the axle is shifted first. When shifting into 2WD, the transfer case is shifted first.

LUBRICATION

SERVICE INTERVALS

Check fluid every 5 months or 5000 miles. Replace as necessary. Drain and refill transfer case every 30 months or 30,000 miles.

FLUID TYPE

Use only Jeep Automatic Transmission fluid or equivalent labeled Dexron II.

CAPACITY

Capacity is 6 pints (2.8L).

Fig. 1: Drive Mode Selector on Instrument Panel

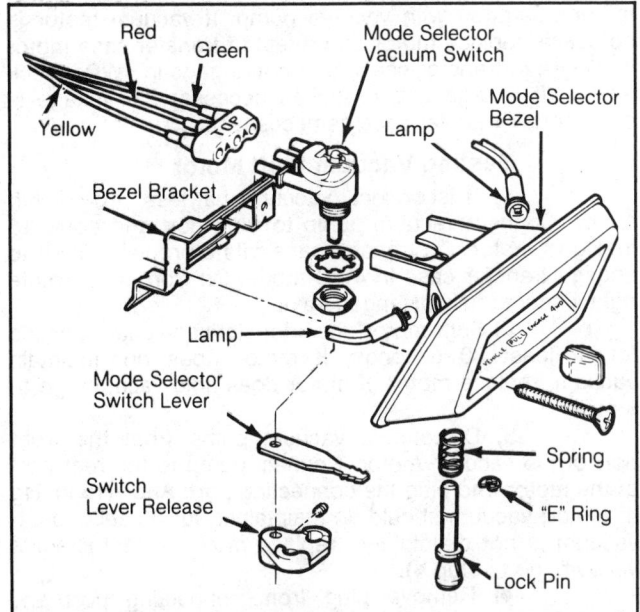

LO range can only be selected when operating in 4WD mode.

Fig. 2: Vacuum Shift Motor

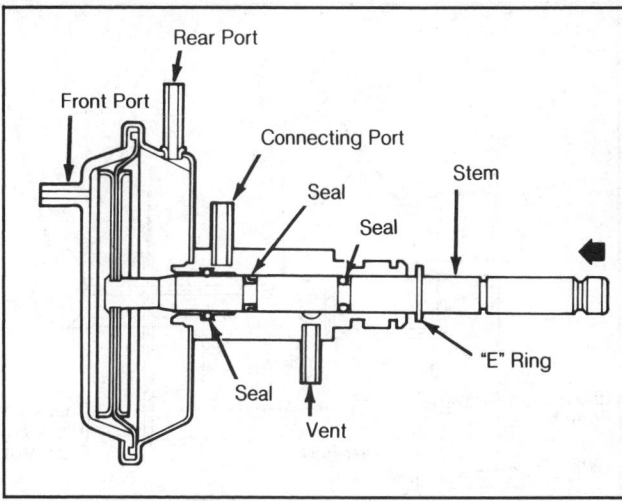

Vacuum at connecting port only when stem is fully extended.

TROUBLE SHOOTING

Will Not Engage in 2WD

1) Raise vehicle so that all 4 wheels are free to rotate. Start engine. Disconnect mode selector vacuum harness at steel tube connection. Check for vacuum at Red hose that attaches to canister. If vacuum exists, go to step 3). If no vacuum, go to step 2).

2) Check intake manifold vacuum supply fitting, vacuum hose and storage tank. If damaged, repair or replace components as necessary. If vacuum leak still exists, repair vacuum line between canister and steel tube. If vacuum exists at Red hose, proceed with system check.

3) Stop engine. Connect vacuum pump to steel tube that connects to Green hose in vacuum harness. Apply 20 in. Hg and rotate propeller shaft to engage transfer case. Shift transmission into park or first gear. If transfer case engages, go to step 6). If transfer case does not engage, go to step 4).

4) Check transfer case shift motor. Motor stem should be extended. If stem is not extended, check vacuum tubes for leaks and damage. Repair as necessary. If transfer case shift motor is still inoperative, check shift motor function. If shift motor is defective, replace motor. If shift motor is operative go to step 5).

5) If transfer case will not engage in 2WD, check transfer case shift linkage and repair as necessary. If linkage is okay and transfer case will not shift into 2WD, repair case. If transfer case now engages in 2WD, check axle for 2WD mode engagement (disconnected). If front axle is not in 2WD mode, check axle shift motor and replace as necessary.

6) If front axle shift motor is okay, check the shift mode selector switch and vacuum harness. Repair as necessary. If front axle shift motor will not disengage, check vacuum lines and repair as necessary.

7) If vacuum lines are okay and axle will not disengage, remove axle housing cover and shift motor. Inspect shift fork, collar and axle components. Repair as necessary.

Transfer Cases

SELEC-TRAC MODEL 229 (Cont.)

Fig. 3: Selec-Trac System Vacuum Diagram

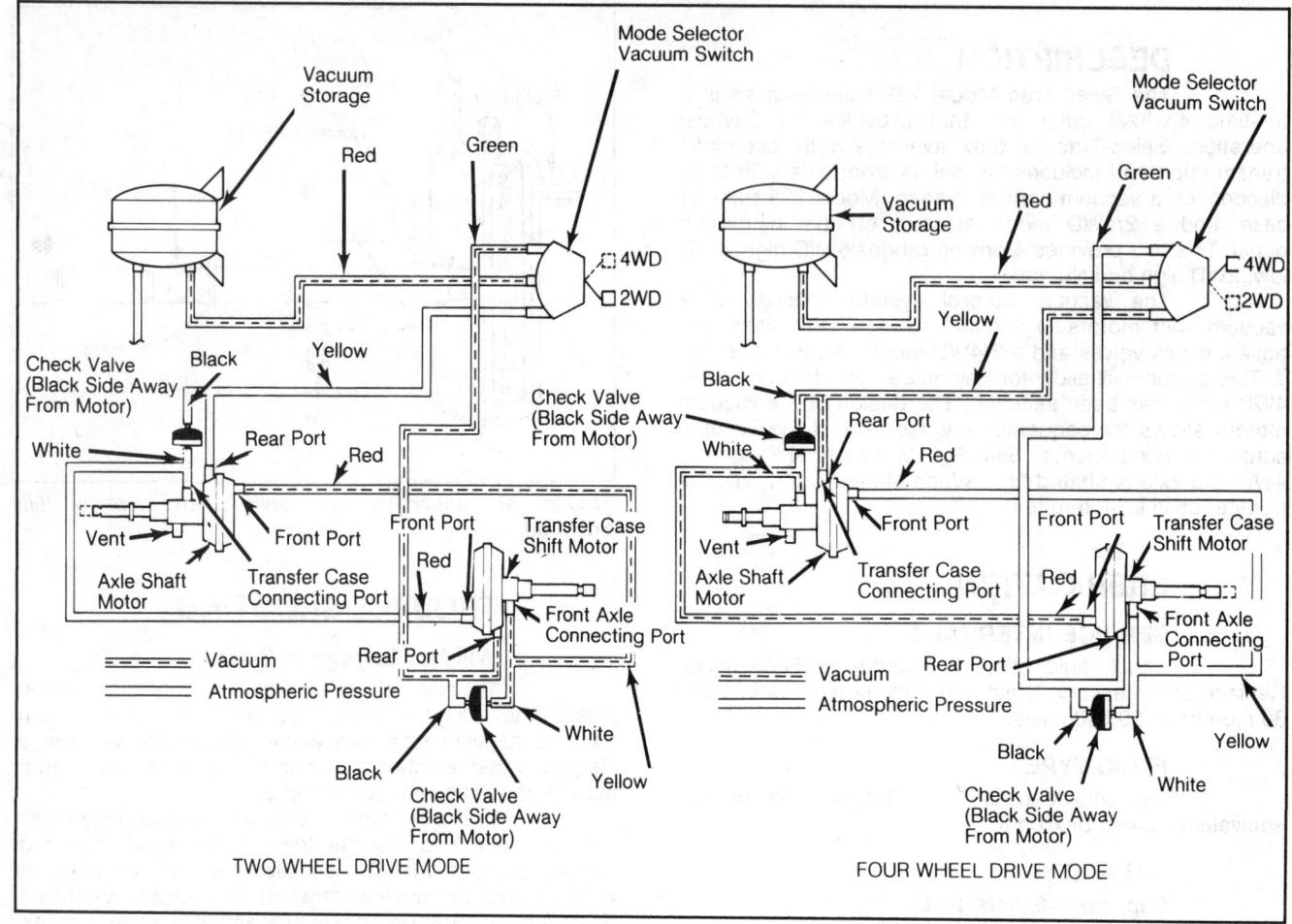

TWO WHEEL DRIVE MODE

FOUR WHEEL DRIVE MODE

Will Not Engage in 4WD

1) Raise vehicle so that all 4 wheels are free to rotate. Start engine. Disconnect mode selector vacuum harness at steel tube connection. Check for vacuum at Red hose that attaches to canister. If vacuum exists, go to step **3)**. If no vacuum, go to step **2)**.

2) Check intake manifold vacuum supply fitting, vacuum hose and storage tank. If damaged, repair or replace components as necessary. If vacuum leak still exists, repair vacuum line between canister and steel tube. If vacuum exists at Red hose, proceed with system check.

3) Stop engine. Connect vacuum pump to steel tube that connects to Yellow hose in vacuum harness. Apply 20 in. Hg and rotate right front wheel to engage axle. If front axle is engaged, go to step **6)**. If front axle is not engaged proceed with system check.

4) Check front axle shift motor for operation. If shift motor is okay, check vacuum lines and tubes for leaks or damage. Repair as necessary. If axle shift motor is inoperative, replace motor and recheck for axle engagement.

5) If axle will not engage, remove axle housing cover and shift motor. Inspect shift fork, collar, and axle components. Repair as necessary.

6) Check that transfer case shift motor stem is retracted. If so, check transfer case shift linkage and repair as necessary. If not, check vacuum hoses and repair as necessary.

7) If transfer case motor is still inoperative, test motor operation with vacuum pump. If vacuum motor is defective, replace motor and retest. If transfer case motor is okay and transfer case does not engage in 4WD, check axle shift linkage and repair as necessary. If linkage is okay, repair transfer case as necessary.

Testing Vacuum Shift Motor

1) Disconnect vacuum harness from shift motor. Connect vacuum pump to front port and apply 15 in. Hg to motor. On transfer case rotate propeller shaft to engage transfer case in 4WD mode. On front axle, rotate right wheel to fully disengage axle.

2) Shift motor should maintain vacuum applied for at least 30 seconds. If motor does not maintain vacuum, replace motor. If motor does hold vacuum, go to step **3)**.

3) Disconnect vacuum pump from the front port of the vacuum motor. Connect pump to the rear port of the motor and plug the connecting port. Apply 15 in. Hg to motor; vacuum should be maintained for 30 seconds. If vacuum is not maintained, replace motor. If motor holds vacuum, go to step **4)**.

4) Remove plug from connecting port and check for vacuum at this port. If vacuum is not present, rotate propeller shaft on transfer case or right wheel on front axle, to ensure full engagement of shift motor.

5) If no vacuum exists at connecting port, pull back boot on stem and measure distance that stem has

SELEC-TRAC MODEL 229 (Cont.)

extended. Stem should extend a distance of 5/8" (15.9 mm) as measured from the edge of shift motor housing to "E" ring on stem. If stem does not extend the specified distance or if stem extends the specified distance but no vacuum is present at the connecting port, replace motor.

REMOVAL & INSTALLATION

TRANSFER CASE

Removal

1) Raise vehicle and drain transfer case lubricant. Disconnect speedometer cable, indicator switch and transfer case shift lever link at operating lever. Disconnect parking brake cable guide from pivot located on right frame rail, if necessary.

2) Place support stand under transmission and remove rear crossmember. Mark the output shaft yokes for reassembly reference. Mark the yokes and the propeller shafts.

3) Disconnect front and rear propeller shafts, support them in vehicle with wire. Do not allow shafts to hang on universal joint as damage to joint may result. Disconnect shift motor vacuum lines and transfer case shift linkage.

4) Remove bolts attaching exhaust pipe support bracket-to-transfer case, if necessary. Remove transfer case-to-transmission bolts. Move transfer case assembly rearward until it is free of transmission output shaft and lower assembly out of vehicle. Remove all gasket material from transmission housing and transfer case.

Installation

1) Align and install transfer case assembly on transmission. Be sure transfer case input gear splines are aligned with transmission output shaft. Align splines by rotating transfer case rear output shaft yoke, if necessary.

NOTE: Do not install any transfer case-to-transmission bolts until transfer case is fully seated on transmission.

2) Install transfer case attaching bolts and tighten to specified torque. Attach exhaust pipe support to transfer case, if removed. Align and connect propeller shafts. Connect parking brake cable guide to pivot bracket on frame rail, if removed.

3) Connect speedometer cable and indicator switch wires. Connect transfer case shift lever link to operating lever. Install rear crossmember and remove transmission support stand. Fill transfer case with automatic transmission fluid labeled Dexron II or equivalent.

4) Connect shift motor vacuum hoses and transfer case shift linkage. Lower vehicle.

DISASSEMBLY

TRANSFER CASE

1) Remove drain and fill plugs, front and rear yoke nuts and seal washers. Discard washers. Mark front and rear yokes and drive shafts for assembly alignment reference. Remove front and rear yokes, using puller if necessary.

2) Mount transfer case on wood blocks. Cut V-notches in blocks to clear front case mounting studs.

Mark rear retainer and rear case for assembly reference. Remove rear retainer bolts and retainer. Use 2 screw drivers to pry retainer off case. Position screwdrivers in slots in retainer and case to pry retainer loose.

3) Remove differential shims and speedometer gear from rear output shaft. Remove bolts attaching rear case to front case. Remove rear case from front case by prying with screwdriver. See Fig. 4.

Fig. 4: Separating Rear and Front Cases

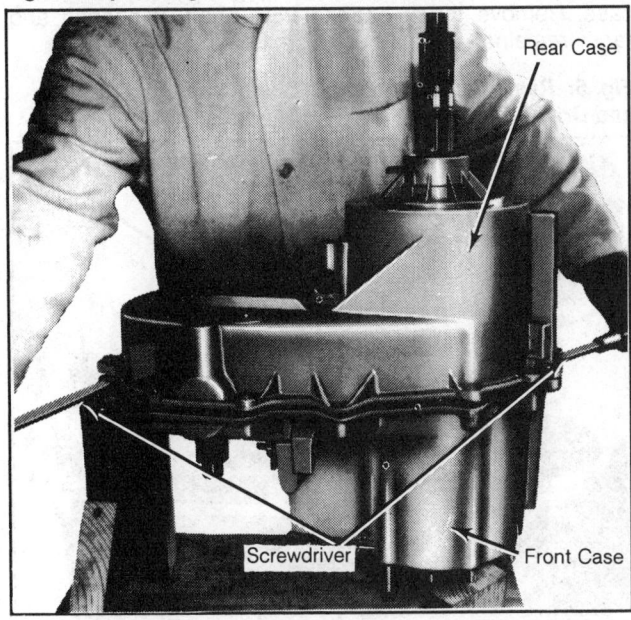

Make sure case is not damaged when separated.

CAUTION: Insert screwdrivers in the slots at each end of the rear case to loosen it. Do not attempt to wedge the case halves apart. The case mating surfaces will be damaged.

4) Remove thrust bearing and races from front output shaft. Note position of bearing and races for assembly reference. See Fig. 5. Remove oil pump from rear output shaft. Note that the recessed side of the pump faces case interior. Remove rear output shaft from the viscous coupling.

Fig. 5: Thrust Bearing and Races on Front Output Shaft,

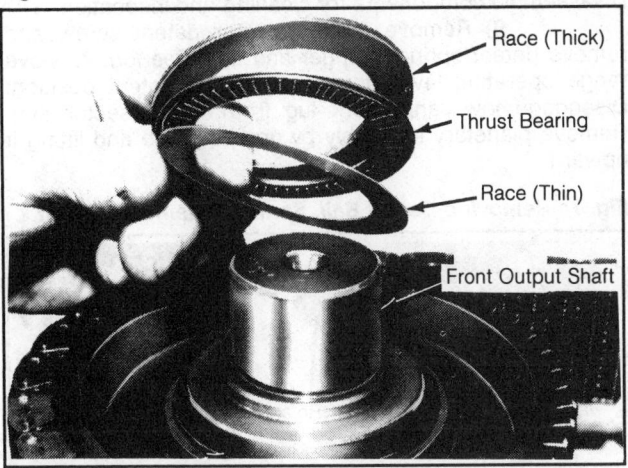

Note position of races when removing.

SELEC-TRAC MODEL 229 (Cont.)

5) Remove 15 mainshaft pilot bearing rollers from shaft or coupling if rollers dropped off during removal of rear output shaft. Remove mainshaft "O" ring from end of shaft. Remove viscous coupling from mainshaft and side gear.

6) Remove front output shaft, driven sprocket and drive chain assembly. Lift front shaft, sprocket and chain upward. *See Fig. 6.* Tilt front shaft toward mainshaft. Slide chain off sprocket and remove assembly. Remove front output shaft front thrust bearing assembly from front case. Remove thrust bearing from shaft, if bearing and races remained on shaft during removal.

Fig. 6: *Removing Front Output Shaft, Chain and Driven Sprocket*

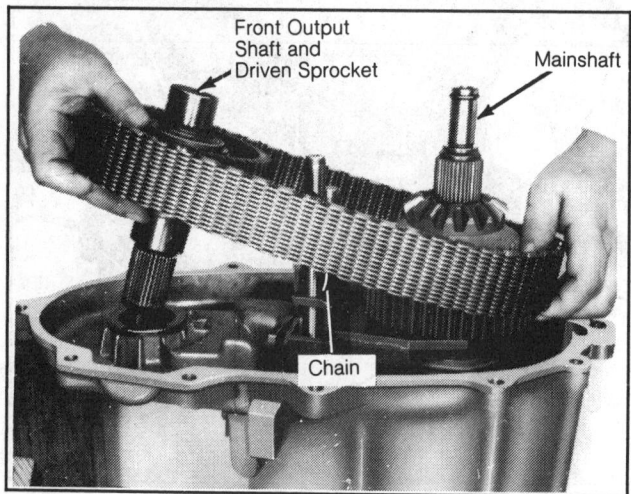

Slide chain off sprocket and remove assembly.

7) Remove drive chain from front output shaft and sprocket. Remove snap ring that retains driven sprocket on front output shaft. Mark sprocket and shaft for assembly reference and remove sprocket from shaft. Remove mainshaft, side gear, clutch gear drive sprocket and spline gear as assembly. Set aside until front case disassembly is completed.

8) Remove mode fork, shift rail and clutch sleeve as an assembly. Mark sleeve and fork for assembly reference and remove sleeve from fork. Remove locking fork, clutch sleeve, fork brackets and fork springs as assembly. Note position of components for reassembly. Disassemble components for cleaning and inspection.

9) Remove range selector detent screw and remove detent spring, plunger and ball. *See Fig. 7.* Move range operating lever downward to last detent position. Disengage low range fork lug from range sector slot. Remove planetary assembly by grasping hub and lifting it upward.

Fig. 7: *Removing Detent Ball, Spring, Retainer and Bolt*

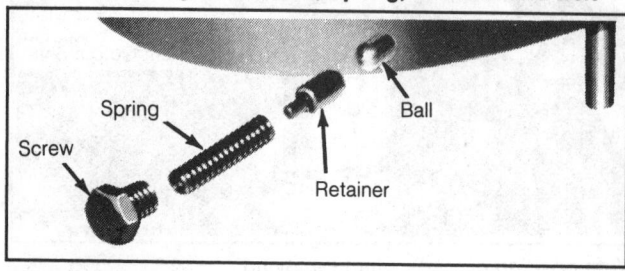

Note order for reassembly.

10) Remove mainshaft thrust bearing from input gear. Remove input gear and remove input gear thrust bearing and race. Remove range sector and operating lever attaching nut and lock washer and remove lever. Remove range sector and shaft from front case. Remove range sector "O" ring and retainer.

11) Remove rear output bearing and rear yoke seal from rear retainer. The bearing is shielded on one side. Note bearing position for reassembly. Remove input gear and front yoke seals from front case. Use screwdriver to pry seals out of case.

MAINSHAFT & GEARS

1) Grasp drive sprocket and lift sprocket clutch gear and side gear upward and off mainshaft. *See Fig. 8.* Remove mainshaft needle bearings and 2 bearing spacers from mainshaft. A total of 82 bearings are used. Note spacer position for reassembly.

Fig. 8: *Removing Mainshaft and Gear Assembly*

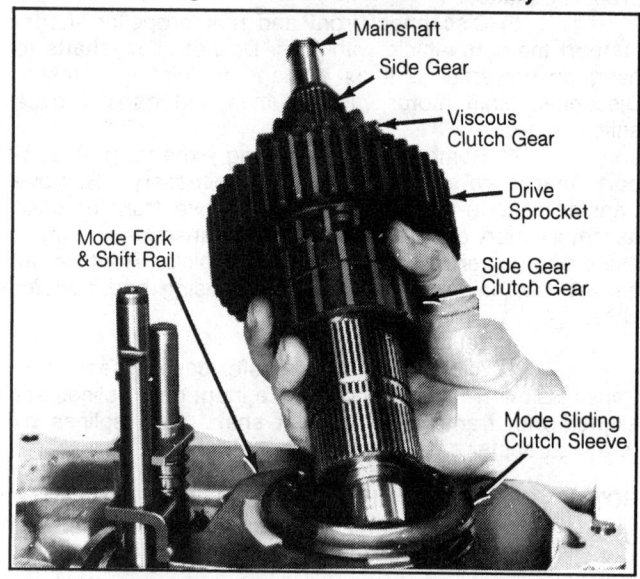

Note order for reassembly.

2) Remove spline gear and thrust washer from mainshaft. Remove side gear, clutch gear and clutch gear thrust washer from sprocket carrier and sprocket. Remove clutch gear and thrust washer from side gear.

3) Remove one sprocket carrier snap ring and remove drive sprocket from carrier. Mark for assembly references. Remove 3 bearing spacers and all sprocket carrier needle bearings from carrier. A total of 120 needle bearings are used.

SUB-ASSEMBLY OVERHAUL

BEARING/BUSHING REPLACEMENT

CAUTION: All bearings used in the transfer case must be correctly positioned to avoid blocking the bearing oil feed holes. After replacing any bearing, check the bearing position to be sure the feed hole is not covered by the bearing.

SELEC-TRAC MODEL 229 (Cont.)

Rear Output Shaft Bearing

1) Remove bearing using slide hammer and bearing remover (J-26941). Remove rear output lip seal using a small screwdriver.

2) Install new lip seal. Install new bearing using driver J-29166. After bearing installation, check that bearing does not cover oil feed hole.

Front Output Shaft Front Bearing

Drive front output shaft front bearing out of case using driver (J-29168). Install bearing using same tool, check that bearing does not cover oil passage.

Front Output Shaft Rear Bearing

1) Support front case so that it will not be damaged. Using slide hammer and puller (J-26941), remove front output shaft rear bearing.

2) Install new bearing using driver (J-29163). Remove installer tool and check that bearing does not block oil passage.

Input Gear Front/Rear Bearing

1) Remove both bearings simultaneously using driver (J-29169). Install new bearings one at a time, rear bearing first. Use same tool for installation.

2) Remove bearing installer and check that bearing does not block oil passage. Check that bearings are flush with case. Install new oil seal using seal installer (J-29162).

Mainshaft Pilot Bushing

1) After carefully supporting input gear to prevent damage, remove bushing using slide hammer and remover tool (J-29369-1).

2) Install new bushing using driver (J-29174). Check that bushing is clear of oil passage.

Rear Output Bearing & Rear Yoke Seal

1) Remove bearing using brass drift and hammer. Remove seal from retainer using brass drift and hammer.

2) Install new bearing using driver (J-7818). Install bearing so that shielded side is facing the case interior after installation. Install seal in retainer using driver (J-29162).

CLEANING & INSPECTION

Cleaning

Clean all parts in cleaning solvent. Be sure all old lubricant or foreign material is removed from surfaces of every part. Apply compressed air to blow dry parts.

Inspection

1) Inspect all gear teeth for signs of excessive wear or damage and check all gear splines for burrs, nicks, wear or damage. Remove minor nicks or scratches using an oilstone. Replace any part exhibiting excessive wear or damage.

NOTE: **Front output shaft thrust bearing race surfaces are heat treated, causing brown or blue discoloration. Do not replace front output shaft because of this discoloration.**

2) Inspect case halves and rear retainer for cracks, porosity, damaged mating surfaces, stripped bolt threads or distortion.

3) Inspect the condition of all bearings. Also check the condition of all bearing bores. Replace any part that exhibits signs of wear or damage.

4) Inspect the viscous coupling and differential drive pinions. If the pinions or carrier are damaged or worn excessively, replace the coupling as an assembly only. If the coupling is cracked, leaking or damaged, replace the coupling as an assembly only.

ASSEMBLY

TRANSFER CASE

NOTE: **During assembly, prelubricate all transfer case internal components with Jeep Dexron II automatic transmission fluid or petroleum jelly where indicated. Do not use chassis lubricant or other "heavy" grease.**

1) Install new input gear and rear output shaft bearing oil seals. Seat seals flush with edge of seal bore or in groove in case. Coat seal lips with petroleum jelly after installation. Install input gear thrust bearing race in case counterbore.

2) Install input gear thrust bearing on input gear and install gear and bearing in case. *See Fig. 9.* Install mainshaft thrust bearing in bearing recess in input gear. Install planetary assembly on input gear. Be sure planetary pinion teeth mesh fully with input gear. Install planetary thrust washer on planetary hub. *See Fig. 10.*

Fig. 9: Installing Input Gear and Thrust Bearing in Centerbore

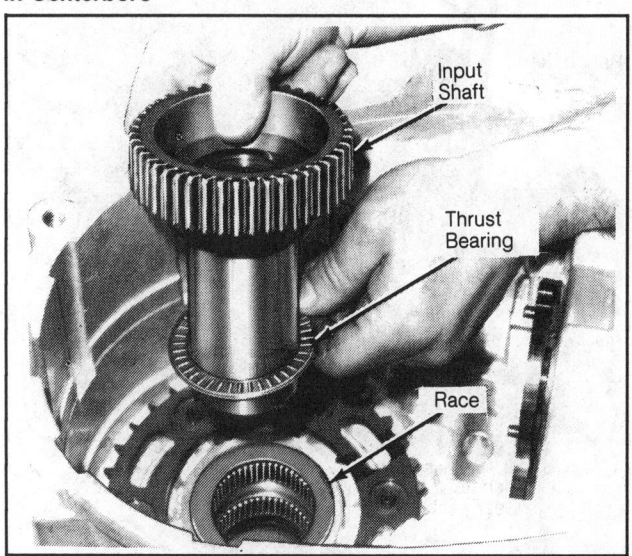

Install gear and bearing as an assembly.

3) Install new sector shaft "O" ring and install retainer in shaft bore in case. Install "O" ring on mode sector shaft and install mode sector through range sector. Install range sector in front case. Install operating lever and snap ring on range sector shaft.

4) Install lever attaching washer and lock nut on mode sector shaft. Tighten lock nut to specified torque. Assemble annulus gear, range fork, and rail. *See Fig. 11.* Install assembled fork on and over planetary assembly. Be sure annulus gear is fully meshed with planetary pinions. Install annulus thrust washer and annulus retaining ring on annulus gear hub.

Transfer Cases

SELEC-TRAC MODEL 229 (Cont.)

Fig. 10: Installing Planetary Gear Assembly

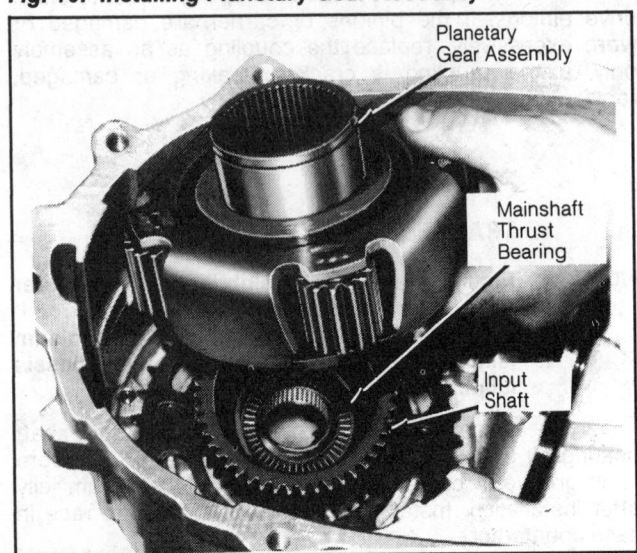

Be sure planetary pinion teeth mesh fully with input gear.

Fig. 11: Installing Annulus Gear Assembly, Range Rail and Fork

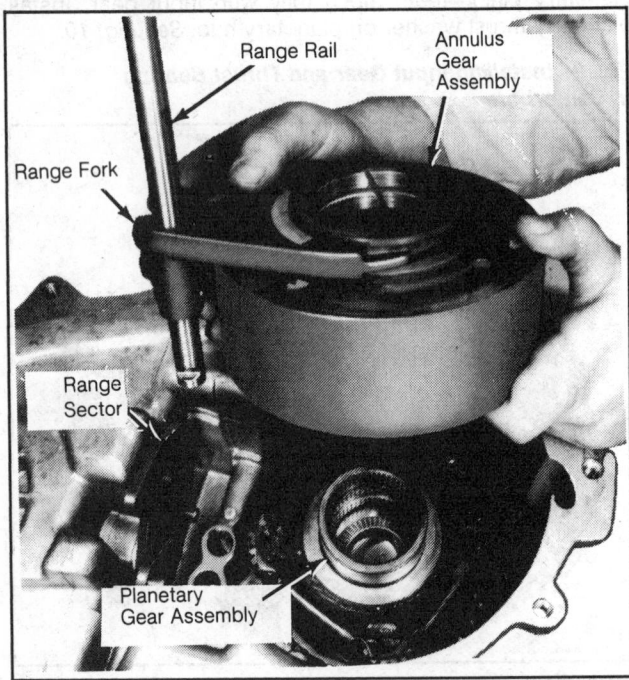

Be sure annulus gear is fully meshed with planetary pinions.

5) Install detent spring plunger ball and retainer screw in front case detent bore. *See Fig. 7.* Torque bolt to specifications. Assemble and install locking fork, fork brackets, fork springs and clutch sleeve. Be sure lug on fork is seated in range sector detent slot.

6) Install range fork lug in range sector detent notch. Move range sector to high range position. Assemble and install mode fork, shift rail and mode clutch sleeve. Install thrust washer and new "O" ring on mainshaft.

7) Install needle bearings and bearing spacers on mainshaft. *See Fig. 12.* Coat shaft bearing surface and all needle bearings with petroleum jelly. Install first 41 needle bearings. Install long bearing spacer, remaining 41 needle bearings and remaining short spacer. Be careful to avoid displacing bearings as spacers are installed. Use additional petroleum jelly to hold bearings in place if necessary.

Fig. 12: Installing Needle Bearings and Spacers on Mainshaft

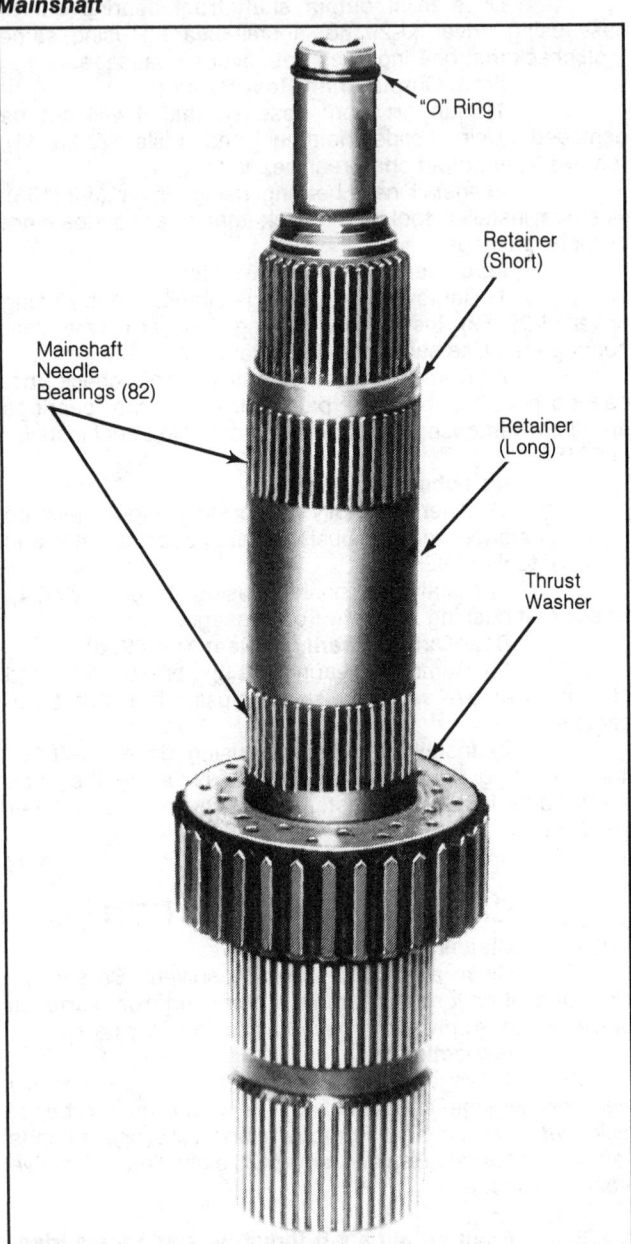

Use new "O" ring.

8) Install spline gear on mainshaft. Take care to avoid displacing bearings while installing gear. Install sprocket carrier in drive sprocket and install sprocket carrier snap rings. Be sure to align carrier and sprocket according to reference marks made during disassembly. Be sure that the tapered teeth on the drive sprocket carrier and the recess on the sprocket are on the same side.

SELEC-TRAC MODEL 229 (Cont.)

9) Install sprocket carrier bearings and spacers. Coat carrier bore and all 120 carrier needle bearings with petroleum jelly. Install center spacer. Install 60 bearings in each end of carrier and install remaining 2 spacers, one at each side of carrier. Use additional petroleum jelly to hold bearings in place if necessary.

10) Install assembled sprocket carrier and drive sprocket on mainshaft. Do not displace mainshaft bearings during installation. Be sure recessed side of drive sprocket is facing downward. Install clutch gear thrust washer in mainshaft. Position washer on sprocket carrier.

11) Install clutch gear on side gear. *See Fig. 13.* Be sure tapered edge of clutch gear faces side gear teeth. Install assembled side gear and clutch gear on mainshaft. Be sure side gear is fully seated in sprocket carrier. Take care to avoid displacing any of the carrier or mainshaft needle bearings.

Fig. 13: Installing Side Gear on Clutch Gear

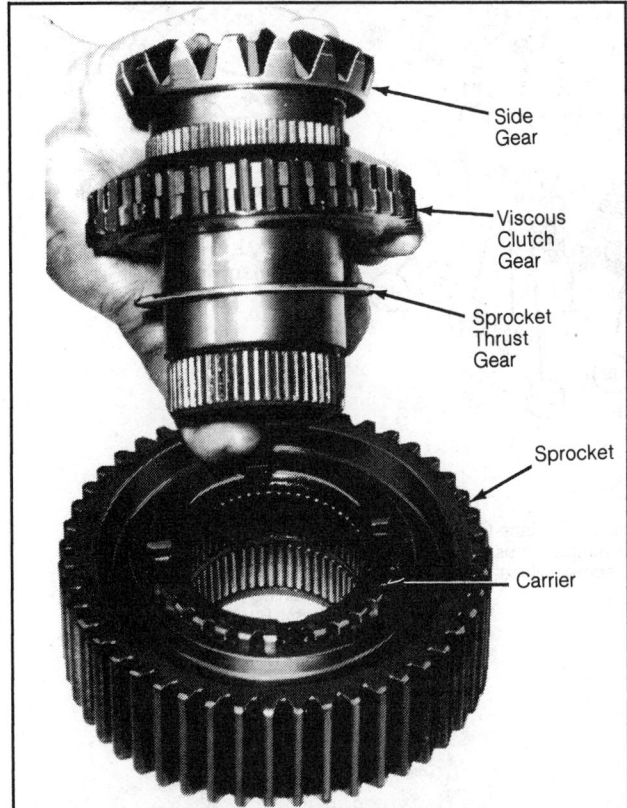

Note position of thrust washer.

12) Install mainshaft and gear assembly in case. Be sure mainshaft is fully seated in input gear. Install driven sprocket on front output shaft and install sprocket retaining snap ring. Be sure sprocket is installed according to reference marks made during disassembly.

13) Install front output shaft front thrust bearing assembly in front case. Install thick race in case, then install bearing and thin race. *See Fig. 5.* Install drive chain, front output shaft and driven sprocket. Install chain on driven sprocket. Raise and tilt driven sprocket and chain and install opposite end of chain on drive sprocket. *See Fig. 6.*

14) Align front output shaft with shaft bore in front case and install shaft in case. Be sure front shaft

thrust bearing assembly is seated in case. Install front output shaft rear thrust bearing assembly on front output shaft. Install thin race first; then install bearing and thick race. *See Fig. 5.*

15) Install viscous coupling on side gear and clutch gear. Be sure coupling is fully seated on clutch gear. Clutch gear should be flush with coupling and gear teeth should be visible. *See Coupling Torque Bias Check.* Coat mainshaft pilot bearing surface and all 15 pilot roller bearings with petroleum jelly and install bearings on shaft. Use additional petroleum jelly to hold bearings in place if necessary.

16) Install rear output shaft on mainshaft and into viscous coupling. Be sure shaft is completely seated in coupling. Tap shaft with plastic mallet or brass punch to seat it if necessary. Do not displace pilot bearings during shaft installation. Install oil pump on rear output shaft. Install new rear output shaft bearing oil seal in rear case.

17) Apply suitable sealer to mating surface of rear case. Install magnet in case, if removed. Install rear case on front case. Be sure alignment dowels are aligned with bolt holes in rear and seat rear case on front case.

NOTE: If the rear case will not seat completely in the front case, check for the following: oil in the range fork rail bore, front output shaft rear thrust bearing assembly is not aligned with the rear case, mainshaft is not completely seated, rear case not aligned with oil pump.

18) Install rear case-to-front bolts and torque to specifications. Be sure that flat washers are used on bolts at case ends where alignment dowels are located. Install speedometer drive gear and differential shims on rear output shaft. Align rear retainer on rear case and

Fig. 14: Checking Differential End Play

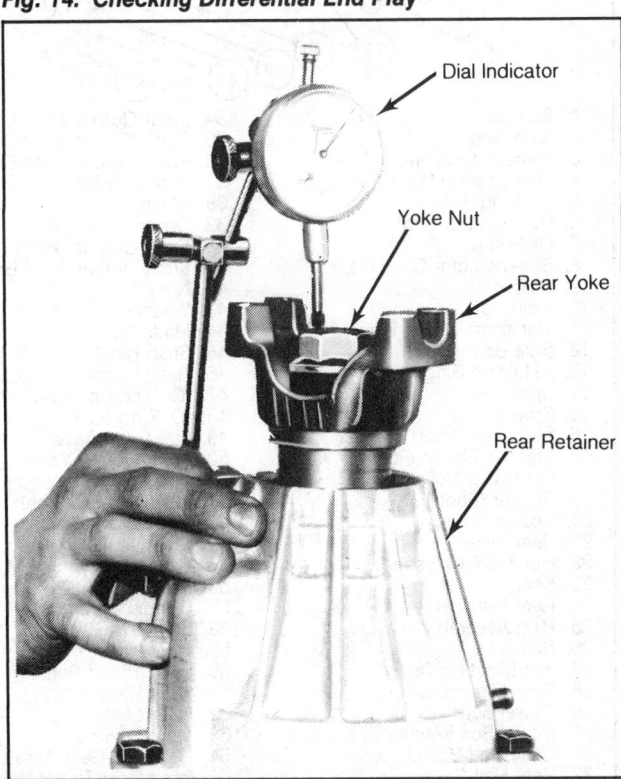

Indicator reading should be .002"-.010" (.05-.25 mm).

Transfer Cases

SELEC-TRAC MODEL 229 (Cont.)

Fig. 15: *Exploded View of Transfer Case Model 229*

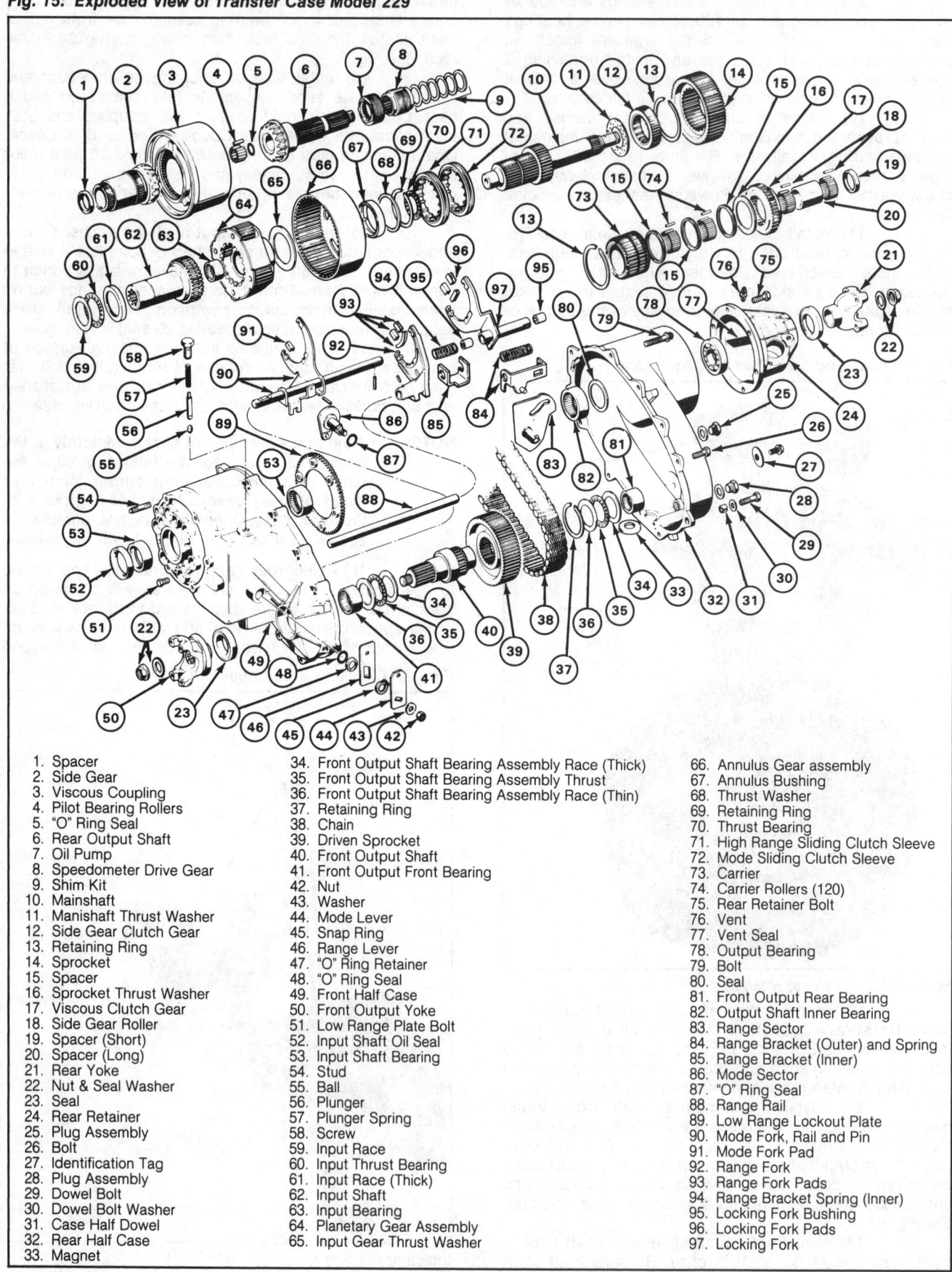

1. Spacer	34. Front Output Shaft Bearing Assembly Race (Thick)	66. Annulus Gear assembly
2. Side Gear	35. Front Output Shaft Bearing Assembly Thrust	67. Annulus Bushing
3. Viscous Coupling	36. Front Output Shaft Bearing Assembly Race (Thin)	68. Thrust Washer
4. Pilot Bearing Rollers	37. Retaining Ring	69. Retaining Ring
5. "O" Ring Seal	38. Chain	70. Thrust Bearing
6. Rear Output Shaft	39. Driven Sprocket	71. High Range Sliding Clutch Sleeve
7. Oil Pump	40. Front Output Shaft	72. Mode Sliding Clutch Sleeve
8. Speedometer Drive Gear	41. Front Output Front Bearing	73. Carrier
9. Shim Kit	42. Nut	74. Carrier Rollers (120)
10. Mainshaft	43. Washer	75. Rear Retainer Bolt
11. Manishaft Thrust Washer	44. Mode Lever	76. Vent
12. Side Gear Clutch Gear	45. Snap Ring	77. Vent Seal
13. Retaining Ring	46. Range Lever	78. Output Bearing
14. Sprocket	47. "O" Ring Retainer	79. Bolt
15. Spacer	48. "O" Ring Seal	80. Seal
16. Sprocket Thrust Washer	49. Front Half Case	81. Front Output Rear Bearing
17. Viscous Clutch Gear	50. Front Output Yoke	82. Output Shaft Inner Bearing
18. Side Gear Roller	51. Low Range Plate Bolt	83. Range Sector
19. Spacer (Short)	52. Input Shaft Oil Seal	84. Range Bracket (Outer) and Spring
20. Spacer (Long)	53. Input Shaft Bearing	85. Range Bracket (Inner)
21. Rear Yoke	54. Stud	86. Mode Sector
22. Nut & Seal Washer	55. Ball	87. "O" Ring Seal
23. Seal	56. Plunger	88. Range Rail
24. Rear Retainer	57. Plunger Spring	89. Low Range Lockout Plate
25. Plug Assembly	58. Screw	90. Mode Fork, Rail and Pin
26. Bolt	59. Input Race	91. Mode Fork Pad
27. Identification Tag	60. Input Thrust Bearing	92. Range Fork
28. Plug Assembly	61. Input Race (Thick)	93. Range Fork Pads
29. Dowel Bolt	62. Input Shaft	94. Range Bracket Spring (Inner)
30. Dowel Bolt Washer	63. Input Bearing	95. Locking Fork Bushing
31. Case Half Dowel	64. Planetary Gear Assembly	96. Locking Fork Pads
32. Rear Half Case	65. Input Gear Thrust Washer	97. Locking Fork
33. Magnet		

SELEC-TRAC MODEL 229 (Cont.)

install retainer. Install retainer bolts securely but not to specified torque.

19) Install front and rear output shaft yokes with original yoke nuts. Tighten nuts finger tight only. Check differential end play with dial indicator. Mount dial indicator on rear retainer and position stylus so it contacts rear yoke nut. *See Fig. 14.*

20) Rotate front output shaft 10 to 12 revolutions and zero dial indicator. Rotate front shaft one more revolution and note dial indicator reading. Dial indicator should read .002"-.010" (.05-.25 mm). If end play is correct go to step 21). If end play is incorrect, remove retainer, add or subtract differential shims as necessary to correct end play and recheck end play.

21) After checking or adjusting end play, remove front and rear yokes. Discard original yoke nuts. Remove rear retainer and apply a suitable sealer to retainer mating surface and bolts. Install retainer and torque bolts to specification. Install front and rear yokes using new yoke seal washers and yoke nuts. Torque yoke nuts to specification

22) Install detent ball, spring and bolt if not installed previously. Use sealer on bolt and torque bolt to specification. Install drain plug and washer and fill case with specified amount of Dexron II. Install filler plug and washer and torque to specification.

ADJUSTMENTS

NOTE: **Coupling Torque Bias Check must be performed during reassembly of transfer case.**

COUPLING TORQUE BIAS CHECK
In Vehicle
1) Shift into 4 HI range and place vehicle on a level surface. Stop engine. Place transmission shift lever in neutral and transfer case shift lever in 4 HI.

2) Raise one front wheel off floor and remove hubcap. Assemble socket and torque wrench and install on any lug nut on the wheel just raised.

3) Rotate wheel using torque wrench and measure torque required to rotate wheel. If coupling is operating properly, MINIMUM torque required is 45 ft. lbs. (34 N.m). If coupling is below minimum torque, perform torque bias test on bench.

On Bench
1) Bench test is performed with transfer case disassembled. Install clutch gear on side gear. Install assembled clutch gear and side gear in viscous coupling. Mount assembled viscous coupling and gears in vise which has wood blocks installed to prevent gear damage. Firmly clamp assembly on side gear.

2) Check engagement of clutch gear in viscous coupling. Clutch gear must be fully engaged in coupling. If necessary, reposition wood blocks so they support gear in coupling. Install rear output shaft and install yoke retaining nut. Install torque wrench on yoke nut. *See Fig. 16.*

3) Rotate output shaft and measure torque required to rotate shaft in coupling. Rotating torque should be 25 ft. lbs. (34 N.m) MINIMUM. If rotating torque is less than specified, replace coupling. If torque is at or above specification, coupling is operating properly.

Fig. 16: Testing Torque Bias on Bench

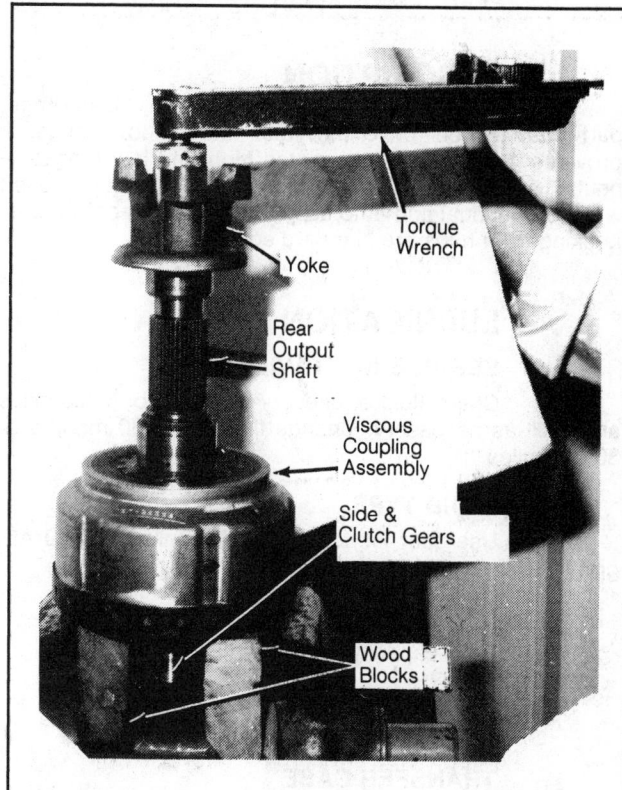

Bench test is required for reassembly.

TIGHTENING SPECIFICATIONS

Application	Ft. Lbs. (N.m)
Detent Retainer Bolt	23 (31)
Drain & Fill Plugs	18 (24)
Front & Rear Yoke Nuts	120 (163)
Operating Lever Lock Nut	18 (24)
Rear Case-to-Front Case Bolts	23 (31)
Rear Retainer Bolts	23 (31)

Transfer Cases

SPICER (DANA) MODEL 300

Jeep

DESCRIPTION

The Model 300 is a 4-position, dual range, part-time 4-wheel drive unit with integral low range. It provides 4-wheel undifferentiated high and low ranges, a neutral position and 2-wheel high range. The 300 is used with both manual and automatic transmission applications. Locking front hubs are standard equipment.

LUBRICATION

SERVICE INTERVALS

Check fluid level every 5 months or 5,000 miles and refill as necessary. Change fluid every 30 months or 30,000 miles.

FLUID TYPE

Use gear lubricant of SAE quality 85W-90 API grade GL-5.

CAPACITY

Refill capacity is 4.0 pints (1.9L).

REMOVAL & INSTALLATION

TRANSFER CASE

Removal

1) Remove shift lever knob, trim ring and boot from transfer case shift lever. Remove floor covering, if equipped, and remove transmission access cover. Raise vehicle and drain transfer case. Support transmission and remove rear crossmember.

2) Mark front and rear yokes and driveshafts for reassembly. Disconnect driveshaft flanges at transfer case. Disconnect speedometer cable at transfer case. Disconnect parking brake cable at equalizer.

3) Disconnect exhaust pipe support bracket at transfer case, if equipped. Remove transfer case-to-transmission attaching bolts and remove case and gasket.

Installation

1) Install transmission-to-transfer case gasket on transmission. Shift transfer case to "4L" position. Rotate transfer case output shaft until transmission ouput shaft engages transfer case input shaft. Move case forward until case seats against transmission.

NOTE: **DO NOT install transfer case attaching bolts until case is completely seated against transmission.**

2) Install attaching bolts and tighten. Install drain plug and refill case. Connect speedometer driven gear to case. Connect shift levers and control links to shift rods.

3) Align reassembly marks and install driveshafts to flanges at transfer case. Install the rear crossmember and remove transmission support. Install parking brake cable at equalizer and connect exhaust pipe support bracket at transfer case, if equipped.

4) Lower vehicle and install transmission access cover and floor covering, if equipped. Install shift lever boot, trim ring, levers and shift knob.

DISASSEMBLY

TRANSFER CASE

1) Remove shift lever assembly. Remove bottom cover, using a putty knife to break the seal. Remove front and rear yokes and discard lock nuts using yoke remover (J-8614-01).

2) Remove screws attaching input shaft support to case. Remove support, rear output shaft gear and input shaft as assembly using a putty knife to break the seal. *See Fig. 1.*

Fig. 1: Rear Output Shaft Gear & Input Assembly

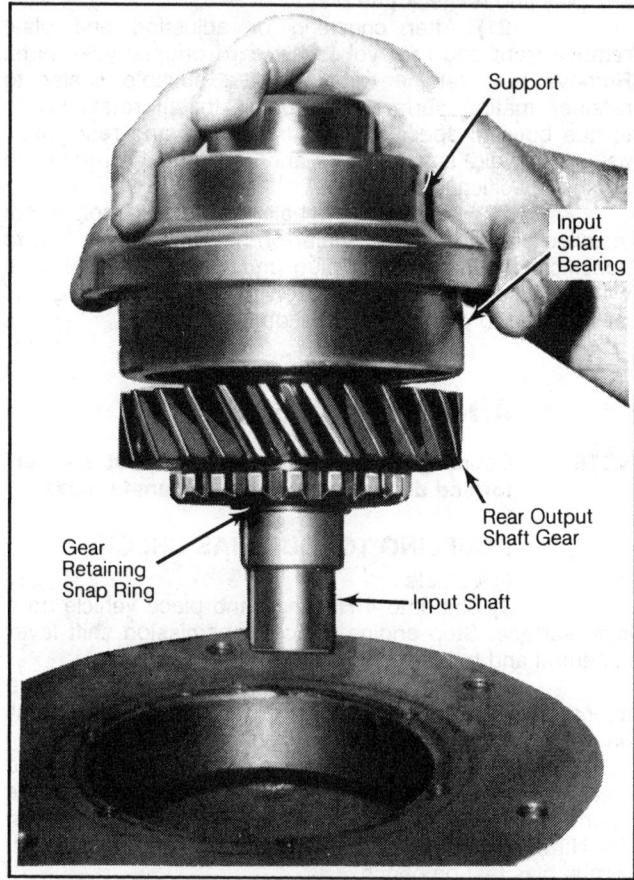

Support

Input Shaft Bearing

Rear Output Shaft Gear

Input Shaft

Gear Retaining Snap Ring

Loosen support using a putty knife.

3) Remove rear output shaft clutch sleeve from case. Remove and discard snap ring holding rear output shaft gear on input shaft. Remove gear. Remove and discard input shaft bearing snap ring.

4) Remove input shaft and bearing from support using a plastic mallet to tap end. Remove bearing and shims from input shaft using arbor press. Remove and discard seal from input shaft support. Remove intermediate shaft lockplate bolt and lockplate.

5) Tap intermediate shaft out of case using a brass punch and plastic mallet. Remove and discard intermediate shaft seal. Remove thrust washers and intermediate gear assembly making note of location of tabs on thrust washers for reassembly.

6) Remove 48 needle bearings and 3 bearing spacers from intermediate gear. Remove rear bearing cap bolts. Remove rear bearing cap using a putty knife to break the seal and a plastic mallet to tap output shaft.

SPICER (DANA) MODEL 300 (Cont.)

Remove end play shims and speedometer drive gear from rear output shaft.

7) Remove and discard rear output shaft oil seal. Remove bearings and races from rear bearing cap. Remove setscrews retaining front and rear output shaft shift forks from shift rods.

8) Using a punch inserted in pin holes in rods, rotate rods to remove them from case, taking care not to lose poppet balls and springs. Remove shift forks from case.

9) Remove bolts attaching front bearing cap-to-case. Remove front cap using a putty knife to break the seal. Remove front output shaft from front cap. Remove and discard shift rod oil seals from front cap.

10) Remove bearing race from front cap using bearing remover (J-29168). Remove cover plate and shims from case. Keep shims together for reassembly. Move front output shaft toward front of case and remove rear bearing race from case.

11) Remove rear output shaft front bearing. Position case on wood blocks to allow for rear output shaft removal clearance. Seat clutch gear on case interior surface and tap shaft out of bearing using a rawhide mallet.

12) Remove rear output shaft front bearing, thrust washer, clutch gear and output shaft from case. Using arbor press and press tool, remove front output shaft rear bearing. Remove case from arbor press and remove front output shaft, clutch gear and sleeve and shaft rear bearing from case.

13) Remove front output shaft using arbor press and press tool (J-22912-01). Support rear output shaft in a vise and using bearing remover (J-29369-1), remove input shaft rear needle bearing from shaft. Use 3/8" drive, 7/16" socket and extension to tap shift rod thimbles out of case.

CLEANING & INSPECTION

1) Clean all parts in suitable cleaning solvent and dry with compressed air. Be sure to remove all traces of gasket from surfaces where used.

NOTE: **DO NOT dry any bearings with compressed air. Use clean shop towels only.**

2) Inspect all individual bearing surfaces for wear, chipping or cracking. Inspect teeth of all gears for excessive wear or damage. Replace as necessary.

3) Replace any shaft that has damaged splines, threads or bearing surfaces. Check shift rods and rod bores for wear or damage. Replace as necessary.

- Wash all parts throughly in cleaning solvent and dry with compressed air. Make sure all oil feed ports and channels in case halves are free of obstructions and/or cleaning residue.
- Inspect all gear teeth and gear splines for burrs, nicks, wear and/or damage. Remove minor burrs and nicks using suitable oilstone. Replace any excessively worn and/or damaged parts.
- Inspect all snap rings and thrust washers for excessive wear and/or damage. Inspect case halves for cracks, porosity, damaged mating surfaces, stripped bolt threads and/or distortion. Replace any excessively worn and/or damaged parts.

- Inspect bearing bores in both case halves, input gear, rear output shaft, side gear and rear retainer. Replace any excessively worn and/or damaged parts. Inspect viscous coupling for fluid leakage and pinion gears for wear and/or damage. If coupling is leaking or pinion gears are worn or damaged in any way, replace viscous coupling as an assembly.

REASSEMBLY

TRANSFER CASE

1) Apply Loctite 220 sealant or equivalent to shift rod thimbles and install parts. Install front output shaft gear on front output shaft making sure gear clutch teeth face shaft gear teeth. See Fig. 2.

2) Install front bearing on front output shaft using arbor press and press tool. Make sure bearing is seated against gear.

Fig. 2: Front Output Shaft Rear Bearing Installation

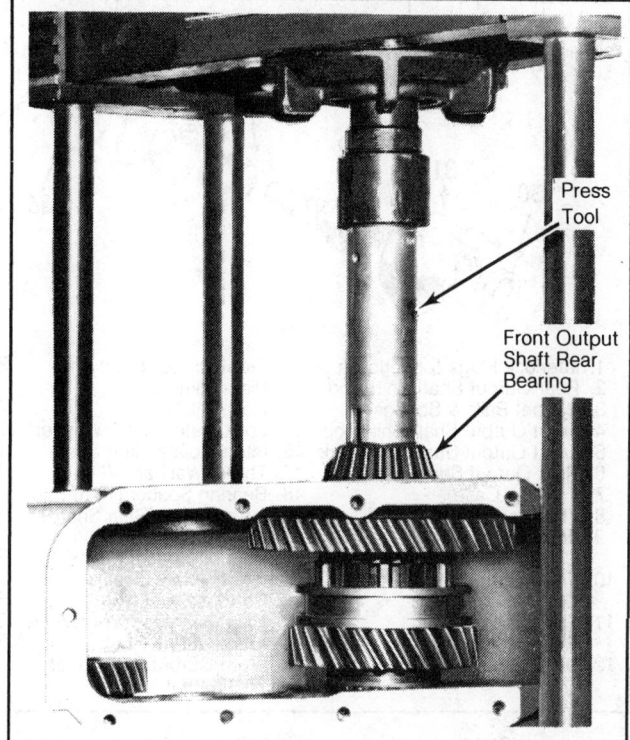

Be sure bearing is seated against gear.

3) Install front output shaft in case and install clutch sleeve and gear on shaft. Install front output shaft rear bearing using arbor press and press tool. Install input shaft rear needle bearing in rear output shaft using bearing installer (J-29179).

4) Position rear output shaft clutch gear in case and insert rear output shaft into gear. Install thrust washer and front bearing on rear output shaft. Install shims and bearing on input shaft. Use arbor press and press tool to reinstall parts.

5) Install new oil seal in input shaft support using seal installer (J-29184). Install input shaft, bearing and snap ring in support. Install rear output shaft gear and snap ring on input gear.

Transfer Cases

SPICER (DANA) MODEL 300 (Cont.)

Fig. 3: Exploded View of Model 300 Transfer Case

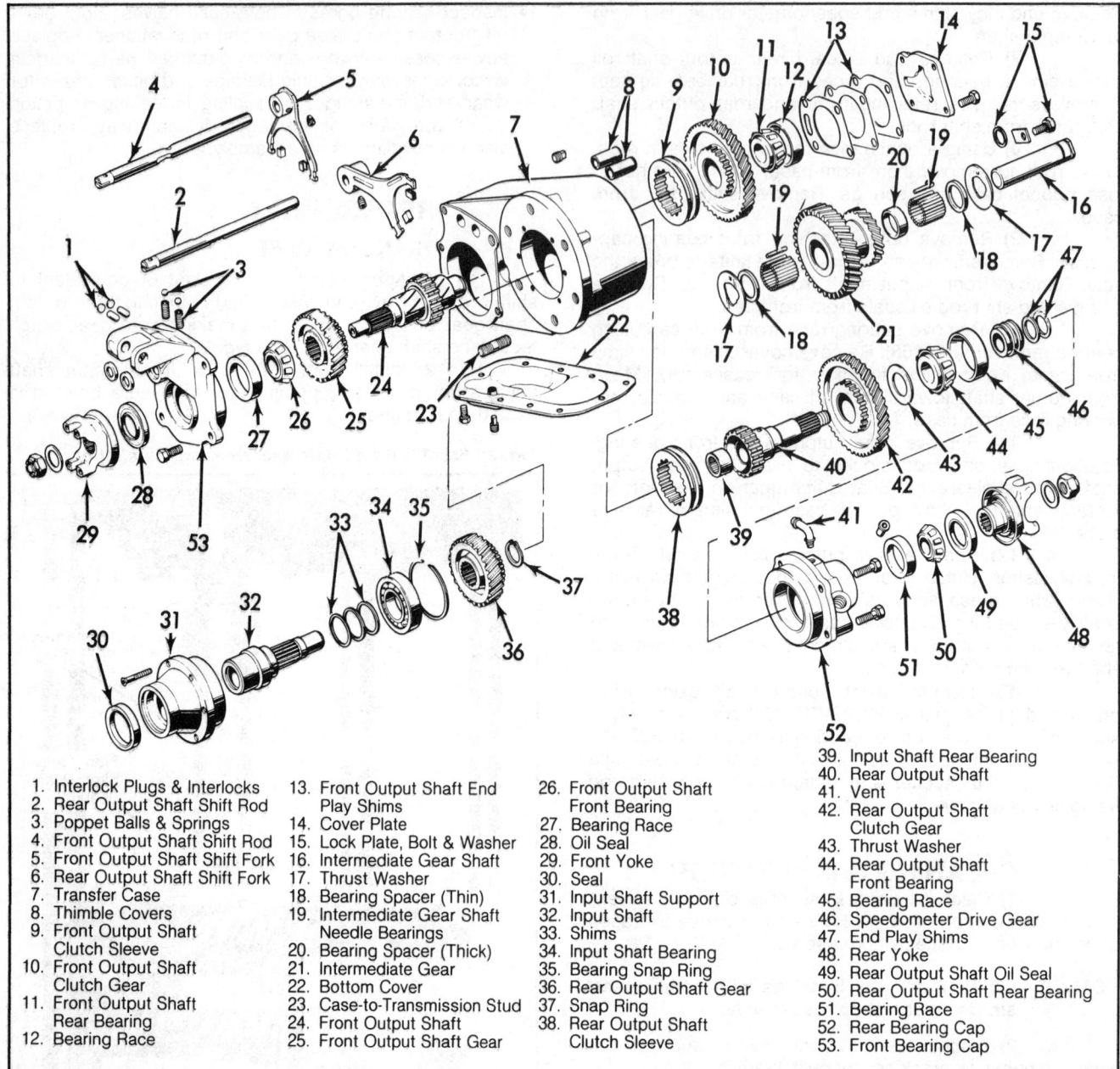

1. Interlock Plugs & Interlocks
2. Rear Output Shaft Shift Rod
3. Poppet Balls & Springs
4. Front Output Shaft Shift Rod
5. Front Output Shaft Shift Fork
6. Rear Output Shaft Shift Fork
7. Transfer Case
8. Thimble Covers
9. Front Output Shaft Clutch Sleeve
10. Front Output Shaft Clutch Gear
11. Front Output Shaft Rear Bearing
12. Bearing Race
13. Front Output Shaft End Play Shims
14. Cover Plate
15. Lock Plate, Bolt & Washer
16. Intermediate Gear Shaft
17. Thrust Washer
18. Bearing Spacer (Thin)
19. Intermediate Gear Shaft Needle Bearings
20. Bearing Spacer (Thick)
21. Intermediate Gear
22. Bottom Cover
23. Case-to-Transmission Stud
24. Front Output Shaft
25. Front Output Shaft Gear
26. Front Output Shaft Front Bearing
27. Bearing Race
28. Oil Seal
29. Front Yoke
30. Seal
31. Input Shaft Support
32. Input Shaft
33. Shims
34. Input Shaft Bearing
35. Bearing Snap Ring
36. Rear Output Shaft Gear
37. Snap Ring
38. Rear Output Shaft Clutch Sleeve
39. Input Shaft Rear Bearing
40. Rear Output Shaft
41. Vent
42. Rear Output Shaft Clutch Gear
43. Thrust Washer
44. Rear Output Shaft Front Bearing
45. Bearing Race
46. Speedometer Drive Gear
47. End Play Shims
48. Rear Yoke
49. Rear Output Shaft Oil Seal
50. Rear Output Shaft Rear Bearing
51. Bearing Race
52. Rear Bearing Cap
53. Front Bearing Cap

6) Measure clearance between input gear and gear retaining snap ring using feeler gauge. If clearance exceeds .003" (.076 mm), disassemble input shaft and add shims between input shaft and shaft bearing until proper measurement is attained. Install clutch sleeve on rear output shaft.

7) Apply Loctite 515 sealant, or equivalent to mating surface of input shaft support. Install assembled support, shaft and gear in case. Using 2 support bolts to align support on case, tap support into position with a plastic mallet.

8) Install and tighten support socket head screws. Install rear bearing cap front bearing race using bearing installer (J-9276-3). Install rear bearing cap rear bearing race using press tool (J-29182).

9) Position rear output shaft rear bearing in rear bearing cap. Install rear output shaft yoke oil seal using installer (J-25160). Install speedometer gear and end play shims on rear output shaft. Install rear bearing cap.

10) Apply Loctite 515 sealant, or equivalent to mating surface of rear bearing cap. Align bolt holes with 2 cap bolts and tap rear bearing cap into position using a plastic mallet. Tighten cap bolts.

11) Install rear output shaft yoke. Tighten nut using installer (J-8614-01) to hold yoke while tightening nut.

12) Clamp dial indicator (J-8001) onto bearing cap. Position indicator stylus so it contacts end of shaft. *See Fig. 4.* Pry rear output shaft back and forth to check end play. End play should be .001-.005" (.025-.127 mm). If end play is not correct, remove or add shims between speedometer drive gear and output shaft rear bearing.

13) Install front output shaft rear bearing race. Install front output shaft end, shims and cover plate. Apply

SPICER (DANA) MODEL 300 (Cont.)

Loctite 220 sealant, or equivalent to cover plate bolt threads and install bolts. Install front output shaft front bearing race using driver handle and installer (J-8092 and J-29181).

14) Install front output shaft yoke oil seal using seal installer (J-25160). Install shift rod oil seals using punch (J-25167). Install front bearing cap. Apply Loctite 515 sealant, or equivalent to mating surface of front bearing cap. Using 2 bolts to align cap-to-case bolt holes, tap front bearing cap into position and install on case.

15) Install and tighten bearing cap bolts to specification. Seat rear bearing cup against cover plate by tapping end of front output shaft with plastic mallet.

16) Mount dial indicator on front bearing cap and postion indicator stylus against end of output shaft. Pry front output shaft back and forth to check end play. End play should be .001-.005" (.025-.129 mm). If end play is not correct, remove or add shims between cover plate and case. If shims are added, reseat rear bearing cup before checking end play again.

17) Install front output shaft yoke. Install new lock nut. Use installer (J-8614-01) to hold yoke while tightening nut. Insert front and rear output shaft shift forks into case. Install front output shaft shift rod poppet ball and spring in front bearing cap. Compress poppet ball and spring. Install front output shaft shift rod part way in case. Insert shift rod through shift fork.

18) Align setscrew hole in shift fork and rod and tighten. Compress and install remaining poppet ball and spring in front bearing cap. Install rear output shaft shift rail part way in case through shift fork and align set screw hole on fork and rod. Install and tighten set screws.

Fig. 4: Checking Rear Output Shaft End Play

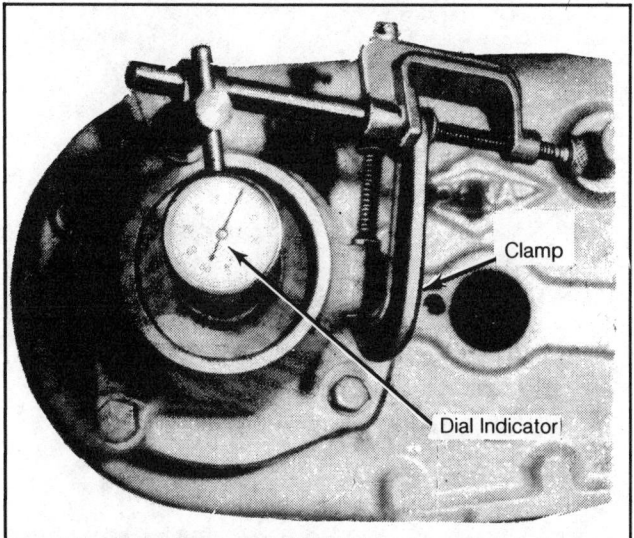

End play should be .001-.005" (.025-.129 mm).

19) Insert holding tool (J-25142) in intermediate gear and install needle bearings and spacers in gear. Install intermediate gear thrust washers in case. Make sure washer tangs align with grooves in case. Install new "O" ring on intermediate shaft.

20) Position intermediate gear in case. Install intermediate shaft in case bore. Using plastic mallet, tap intermediate shaft into gear until shaft forces holding tool (J-25142) out of case and shaft is in place.

21) Install intermediate shaft lockplate and bolt. Apply Loctite 515 sealant, or equivalent to mating surface of bottom cover. Use new gasket, install bottom cover and tighten.

TIGHTENING SPECIFICATIONS

Application	Ft. Lbs. (N.m)
Bottom Cover Bolts	15 (20)
Cover Plate Bolts	35 (47)
Front/Rear Bearing Cap Bolts	35 (47)
Front/Rear Yoke Lock Nuts	120 (163)
Input Shaft Support Screws	10 (14)
Lock Plate Bolts	23 (31)
Shift Fork Set Screws	14 (19)

METRIC CONVERSIONS

Metric conversions are making life more difficult for the mechanic. In addition to doubling the number of tools required, metric-dimensioned nuts and bolts are used alongside English components in many new vehicles. The mechanic has to decide which tool to use, slowing down the job. The tool problem can be solved by trial and error, but some metric conversions aren't so simple.

Converting temperature, lengths or volumes requires a calculator and conversion charts, or else a very nimble mind. Conversion charts are only part of the answer though, becuase they don't help you "think" metric, or "vizualize" what you are converting. The following examples are intended to help you "see" metric sizes:

LENGTH

Meters are the standard unit of length in the metric system.The smaller units are 10ths (decimeter), 100ths (centimeter), and 1000ths (millimeter) of a meter. These common examples might help you to visualize the metric units:

* A meter is slightly longer than a yard (about 40 inches).
* An aspirin tablet is about one centimeter across (.4 inches).
* A millimeter is about the thickness of a dime.

VOLUME

Cubic meters and centimeters are used to measure volume, just as we normally think of cubic feet and inches. Liquid volume measurements include the liter and milliliter, like the English quarts or ounces.

* One teaspoon is about 5 cubic centimeters.
* A liter is about one quart.
* A liter is about 61 cubic inches.

WEIGHT

The metric weight system is based on the gram, with the most common unit being the kilogram (1000 grams). Our comparable units are ounces and pounds:

* A kilogram is about 2.2 pounds.
* An ounce is about 28 grams.

TORQUE

Torque is somewhat complicated. The term describes the amount of effort exerted to turn something. A chosen unit of weight or force is applied to a lever of standard length. The resulting leverage is called torque. In our standard system, we use the weight of one pound applied to a lever a foot long—resulting in the unit called a foot-pound. A smaller unit is the inch-pound (the lever is one inch long). Metric units include the meter kilogram (lever one meter long with a kilogram of weight applied) and the Newton-meter(lever one meter long with force of one Newton applied). Some conversions are:

* A meter kilogram is about 7.2 foot pounds.
* A Newton-meter is about 1.4 foot pounds.
* A centimeter kilogram (cmkg) is equal to .9 inch pounds.

PRESSURE

Pressure is another complicated measurement. Pressure is described as a force or weight applied to a given area. Our common unit is pounds per square inch. Metric units can be expressed in several ways. One is the kilogram per square centimeter (kg/cm²). Another unit of pressure is the Pascal (force of one Newton on an area of one square meter), which equals about 4 ounces on a square yard. Since this is a very small amount of pressure, we usually see the kiloPascal, or kPa (1000 Pascals). Another common automotive term for pressure is the bar (used by German manufacturers), which equals 10 Pascals. Thoroughly confused? Try the examples below:

* Atmospheric pressure at sea level is about 14.7 psi.
* Atmospheric pressure at sea level is about 1 bar.
* Atmospheric pressure at sea level is about 1 kg/cm².
* One pound per square inch is about 7 kPa.

Mitchell Manuals also offers audio visual presentations for mechanic training and microfiche products. For details on ordering, please contact:

MITCHELL MANUALS, INC.
P.O. Box 26260
San Diego, CA 92126

Notes

Notes

Notes

Notes

Notes

Notes

Notes

Notes

Latest Changes & Corrections

FOR 1983 & EARLIER MODELS

TRANSMISSION SERVICING

CHRYSLER CORP.

1 1983 CHRYSLER CORP. FRONT WHEEL DRIVE VEHICLES WITH MANUAL TRANSAXLE (EXC. 1.7L ENGINE AND A-412 TRANSAXLE) : TRANSAXLE FLUID BREAKDOWN — Some subject vehicles operated at sustained high speeds during hot weather, above 90°F (32°C), may develop excessive transaxle fluid breakdown. The transaxle fluid should be changed and the magnet, attached to the inside of the differential cover, cleaned every 15,000 miles, as follows:

1) Remove differential cover on the side of the differential and allow the transmission fluid to drain. Using a clean, dry cloth, clean magnet and inside surface of the differential cover.

2) Use RTV sealant to form a gasket when replacing the differential cover. Refill transaxle to specified level with specified fluid.

2 1981-83 CHRYSLER CORP. DIPLOMAT, LEBARON, NEW YORKER AND FIFTH AVENUE: SPEEDOMETER CABLE NOISE — Some 1981-83 Diplomat, LeBaron, New Yorker and New Yorker 5th Avenue with Rear Wheel Drive may exhibit a grinding or ticking noise in the speedometer area. This noise may be caused by interference between the cable housing connector and the dash panel opening.

1) Disconnect the battery ground cable. Remove the speedometer cluster. The printed circuit board may also need to be removed for drilling clearance.

2) Release the spring clip and push the speedometer cable housing back into the instrument panel housing far enough to prevent damage to the cable during drilling or grinding. Cover the cable housing.

3) Using a 1/8" drill bit, enlarge the hole in the instrument panel to about 1" in diameter. This will prevent the speedometer cable and instrument panel from amplifying speedometer cable noise.

4) Reinstall the instrument cluster. Reconnect the battery and road test for proper speedometer operation.

AUTOMATIC TRANSMISSIONS

CHRYSLER CORP.

1 1981-83 CHRYSLER CORP. FRONT WHEEL DRIVE VEHICLES WITH AUTOMATIC TRANSAXLE: DELAYED 1-2 UPSHIFT AFTER OPERATING VEHICLE IN REVERSE — Some 1981-83 Chrysler Corp. FWD vehicles with automatic transaxle may exhibit a delayed 1st-2nd gear upshift after operating in reverse, especially when the transaxle is cold. The 1st-2nd gear upshift may not occur when the vehicle has traveled as much as 1/4 of a mile and/or when shift speed may be 10-12 MPH above normal shift speed range. This delay in shift may be due to the throttle valve.

It is a normal condition for the shifts to be slightly delayed during very cold ambient temperatures due to transmission fluid viscosity or cold engine performance. Do not repair this condition if the shifts are only slightly delayed.

1) Remove the transaxle oil pan and allow the oil to drain. Remove the valve body.

2) Remove the throttle valve from the valve body. Check the lands for proper size on the valve. If the lands on the valve are short, replace the valve. See illustration.

3) Reinstall the valve body and tighten the screws. Reinstall the transaxle oil pan and add fluid to bring the transaxle to the proper fill level.

4) Road test the vehicle to ensure proper transaxle operation.

Chrysler Corp. FWD Throttle Valve Land Sizes

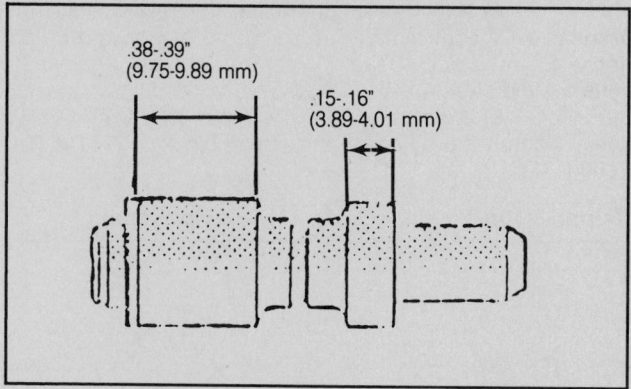

2 1978-82 CHRYSLER CORP. REAR WHEEL DRIVE VEHICLES WITH AUTOMATIC TRANSMISSION AND LOCK-UP TORQUE CONVERTER: SHUDDER DURING LOCK-UP ENGAGEMENT — Some subject vehicles may develop a shudder during lock-up engagement of the torque converter. This condition may happen on high mileage vehicles or after repair of the transmission valve body. The shudder may be caused by throttle pressure bracket tab wear or distortion of the bracket due to improper assembly.

1) Remove transmission oil pan. Remove valve body. Remove spring retainer and adjusting screw bracket. Check throttle pressure bracket for being distorted or worn by measuring across the switch valve spring tab with a straight edge.

2) Ensure that tab is flush with, or extends up to .040" (1 mm) above, the straight edge. If tab is below straight edge or shows indications of wear, replace bracket and switch valve spring.

3) Install new switch valve spring. Install new bracket on springs. While holding springs compressed, install the screw that goes into the side of the valve body. Leave screw 1 turn loose.

4) Install 2 remaining screws that secure the bracket. Leave these screws 1 turn loose. Tighten first screw, then tighten remaining 2 screws to 35 INCH lbs. (4 N.m). Set line and throttle pressure to specifications. Road test vehicle to verify repairs.

FORD MOTOR CO.

3 1984 FORD MOTOR CO. TEMPO AND TOPAZ WITH 2.3L HIGH SWIRL COMBUSTION ENGINE (HSC) AND AUTOMATIC TRANSAXLE: RPM INCREASE OR DECREASE — Some 1984 Tempo and Topaz models with 2.3L High Swirl Combustion (HSC) engine and

FOR 1983 & EARLIER MODELS (Cont.)

automatic transaxle may exhibit an increase or decrease of more than 100 RPM. This condition could be caused by the throttle valve linkage. The linkage should be checked and readjusted if necessary.

1) Run the engine until it reaches normal operating temperature. Be sure all accessories are in the "Off" position.

2) Ensure that the hot engine curb idle speed is to specification. Loosen the bolt on the sliding trunnion block on the TV control rod assembly at least one turn.

3) Remove any corrosion from the control rod and free-up the trunnion block so that it slides freely on the control rod.

4) With the engine idling in "Park", rotate the transaxle TV control lever up using one finger and a light force to ensure that the TV control lever is against its internal idle stop.

5) Without relaxing the force on the TV control lever, tighten the bolt on the trunnion block to 7-11 ft. lbs. (10-15 N.m.)

Tempo & Topaz Throttle Valve Linkage Adjustment

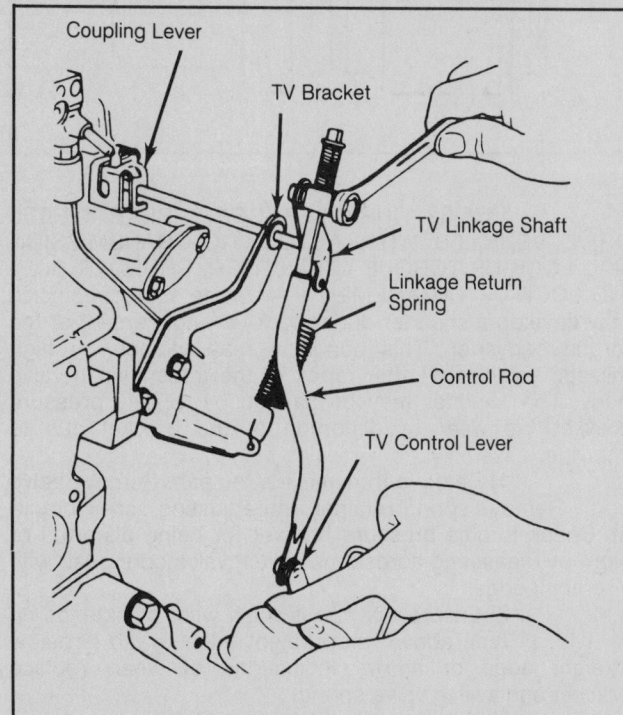

Coupling Lever
TV Bracket
TV Linkage Shaft
Linkage Return Spring
Control Rod
TV Control Lever

▷4▷ 1983 FORD MOTOR CO. CONTINENTAL, COUGAR, CROWN VICTORIA, GRAND MARQUIS, LTD, MARK VI, MARQUIS, THUNDERBIRD, TOWN CAR, E100/250 AND F100/250 PICKUPS WITH AUTOMATIC OVERDRIVE TRANSMISSION: HARSH DOWNSHIFT — Some 1983 Continental, Cougar, Crown Victoria, Grand Marquis, LTD, Mark VI, Marquis, Thunderbird, Town Car, E100/250 & F100/250 models with automatic overdrive transmission may exhibit harsh downshifts. This condition may be caused by the torsion return spring binding on the throttle shaft and preventing the TV linkage from completely returning to idle position, thus resulting in harsh downshifts. A carburetor service kit (E3PZ-9590-A) is now available to correct this condition. Diagnosis and repair is as follows:

DIAGNOSIS

1) Place the transmission in "N" or "P". Start engine and warm to normal operating temperature. Remove the air cleaner.

2) With the engine running, apply foot brake and place transmission in a forward gear. Accelerate to 1/2 throttle, then slowly return to idle.

3) While still idling in a forward gear, have another technician check that the TV linkage at the carburetor returned all the way to idle by looking for a gap between the TV lever adjusting screw and the throttle lever pad.

4) Turn engine off. If a gap occurred, determine if it was caused by interference with the TV rod or binding of the grommets.

5) If no interference or binding of the grommets exists, lack of return of the TV linkage is due to insuffcient return force from the torsion spring at the carburetor.

REPAIR

1) Disconnect the transmission TV rod at the carburetor lever. Install the drill guide fixture, furnished in kit, over the TV lever ball stud.

2) Using a greased #17 (.170") drill bit with drill guide in position, drill through the lever as shown. Use care as the drill breaks through.

3) Deburr both sides of the hole and press in the bushing, furnished with large diameter flange outboard in the kit. Unhook the torsional spring where it loops around the TV lever.

4) Cut the loop or hook area of the spring with sidecutters to prevent possible interference at wide open throttle. Install a new return spring, attaching it through the bushing and to the hole in the throttle solenoid positioner bracket.

5) Check freedom of movement of the lever and reinstall the transmission TV rod. Recheck the returnability of the TV lever per steps 2) and 3) of the diagnosis procedure. Check and, if necessary, reset curb idle speed.

Ford Automatic Overdrive Location
For Drilling Hole in Throttle Valve Lever

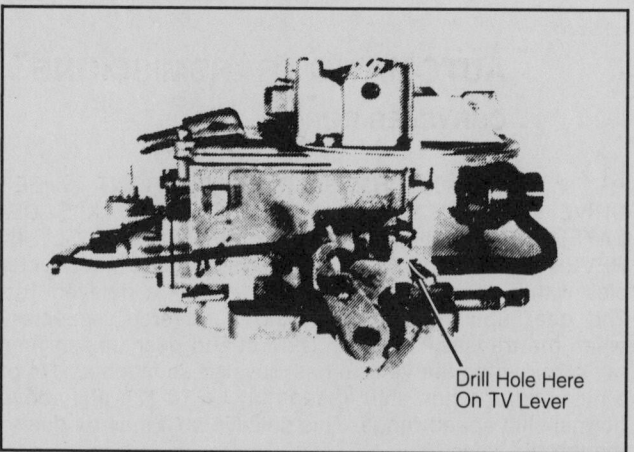

Drill Hole Here
On TV Lever

▷5▷ 1981-83 FORD "E" & "F" TRUCKS WITH AUTOMATIC TRANSMISSION AND 1-PIECE DRIVE-SHAFT: DRIVE SHAFT CLUNK — Some 1981-83 Ford

FOR 1983 & EARLIER MODELS (Cont.)

"E" and "F" Truck models with automatic transmission and 1-piece drive shaft may develop a "clunk/grunt" noise at start-up and stop driving modes. This condition may be caused by the slip yoke binding up. A new design slip yoke (E1TZ-4841-B for C4, C5, and AOT, E1TZ-4841-C for C6 except E250/350 and D5UZ-4841-A for C6 E250/350) is now available to correct this condition. Install slip yoke as follows:

1) Raise vehicle. Mark the drive shaft in relation to the companion flange for reassembly reference. Remove the drive shaft assembly.

2) Inspect the extension housing seal and replace as required. Remove and discard the slip yoke from the drive shaft.

3) Install replacement slip yoke on the drive shaft. Using multi-purpose long life lubricant (ESA-M1C75-B), grease entire slip yoke.

4) Reinstall the drive shaft and tighten U-bolts to 8-15 ft. lbs. (11-20 N.m). Warm vehicle to normal operating temperature and road test.

6 1982 FORD LIGHT DUTY TRUCKS WITH C6 AUTOMATIC TRANSMISSION: DELAYED OR NO UP-SHIFT/DOWNSHIFT — A condition of delayed, or no upshift/downshift may be experienced on 1982 Ford Light Trucks with C6 automatic transmissions built between 10-1-81 and 2-28-82. This may be caused by the forward and reverse planet assembly bearing spacer and thrust washers being deteriorated. Transmissions which may be affected can be determined from the build date code on the metal tag attached to the imtermediate servo cover.

This condition is characterized by fine scoring of the pump gear cavities and/or the converter impeller hub. In addition, excessive magnetic metallic contamination in the main control, oil pan and oil filter screen may be noticed.

When servicing a transmission with this condition, remove the transmission oil pan to inspect for excessive magnetic contamination. If such contamination is present in the oil pan or oil pickup screen, remove the transmission and replace the forward and reverse planet assemblies.

Replace any other components as required. Replacement of the forward and reverse planet assemblies is required because deterioration of the spacer and thrust washer is not readily apparent by visual inspection.

GENERAL MOTORS

7 1982 GENERAL MOTORS FRONT WHEEL DRIVE CAVALIER, CELEBRITY, CENTURY, CIMARRON, CITATION, CUTLASS CIERA, FIRENZA, OMEGA, PHOENIX, SKYHAWK, SKYLARK, J2000 AND 6000 WITH THM 125C AUTOMATIC TRANSAXLE: TRANSAXLE OIL FOAMING — Some 1982 Cavalier, Celebrity, Century, Cimarron, Citation, Cutlass Ciera, Firenza, Omega, Phoenix, Skyhawk, Skylark, J2000, and 6000 models with THM 125C automatic transaxle may exhibit some oil foaming which is most noticeable while checking transmission oil levels. When the oil foaming condition exists, the oil level indications on the dipstick will be inaccurate. A new design manual valve (8643316) and auxiliary valve body (8643326) are now available to correct this condition.

1) Remove the transaxle valve body cover. Disconnect the electrical wires from the plastic electrical connector on the side of the case cover and remove the electrical connector.

2) Slide the manual rod retaining clip off of the manual valve and slide the manual valve through the electrical connector hole in the side of the case.

3) Replace the existing manual valve with new design valve. Replace the electrical wire connector and reconnect the wires.

4) Reconnect the manual rod retaining clip to the manual valve. Remove the auxiliary valve body and replace it with new design valve body.

5) Using RTV sealant, seal the valve body cover and replace it. If oil foaming condition still exists, replace the case cover.

8 1982 CADILLAC DEVILLE, ELDORADO, FLEETWOOD AND SEVILLE WITH 4.1L V6 ENGINE: SHIFT BUSYNESS WITH CRUISE CONTROL — Some 1982 DeVille, Eldorado, Fleetwood and Seville models with 4.1L V6 engine may experience shift "busyness" with cruise control engaged. Shift "busyness" refers to cycling of the transmission between 4th and 3rd gears and is most noticeable while driving up inclines. A new service package (8634987 for DeVille and Fleetwood or 8635944 for Eldorado and Seville) is now available to correct this condition. Install appropriate service package into the control valve assembly using instructions provided in the package.

9 1983 CADILLAC ELDORADO AND SEVILLE WITH AUTOMATIC TRANSMISSION: SLIPPING OR NO DRIVE — Some 1983 Eldorado and Seville models may experience a slipping or no drive condition in forward gears only. This condition may be caused by a missing or loose solid cup plug in the input shaft of the forward clutch assembly.

1) Check forward clutch assembly for signs of burning. Inspect the housing end of the input shaft, which is part of the forward clutch assembly, as shown.

2) Check if solid cup plug is loose or missing from the feed passage. If solid cup plug is missing, it could possibly be in the open end of the output shaft. Tap the end of the output shaft to remove it.

3) Using a 5/16" punch and applying Loctite 290 to the plug, install new cup plug (8628145) into the larger of the 2 holes until it is .039" (1.0 mm) below the surface.

Cadillac Cup Plug Location

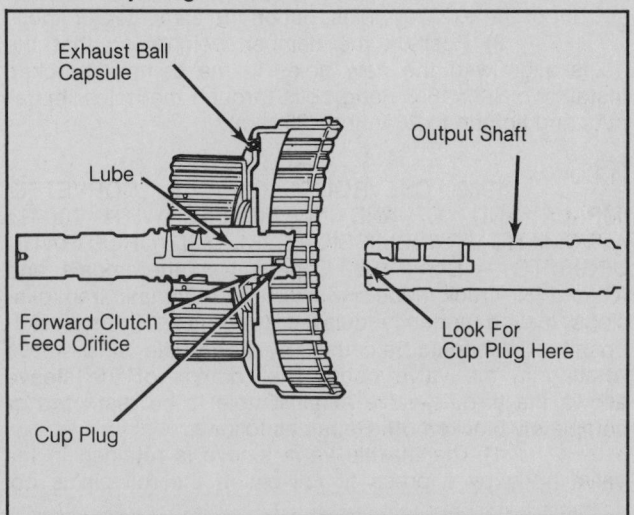

10▷ 1983 CADILLAC DEVILLE & FLEETWOOD WITH 4.1L ENGINE AND THM 200-4R AUTOMATIC TRANSMISSION: TRANSMISSION OIL LEAKS — Some early production 1983 DeVille and Fleetwood models with 4.1L engine and THM 200-4R transmission may exhibit signs of a transmission oil leak at the front edge of the transmission oil pan. This condition may be caused by interference between the back edge of the flywheel cover and the front edge of the transmission oil pan flange.

Beginning with production number 173549, a new design flywheel cover (1627822) is available to eliminate the interference condition.

Remove approximately 1/16-1/8" from the length of the edge of the flywheel cover with a file or grinder. Before resealing the transmission oil pan with RTV (do not use a gasket), be sure the oil pan flange is not deformed.

Cadillac Flywheel Cover Modification

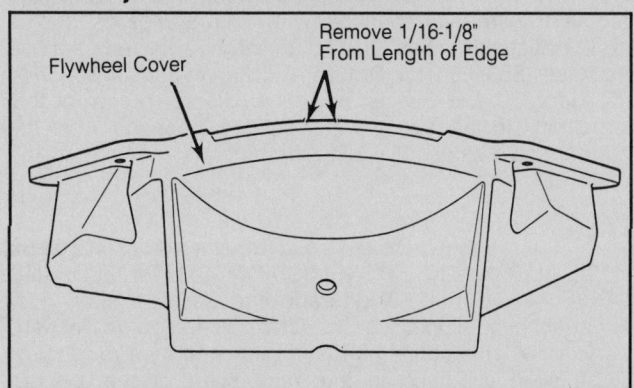

11▷ 1982 CHEVROLET CAMARO WITH 2.5L ENGINE AND AUTOMATIC TRANSMISSION: MOANING NOISE AND VIBRATION — Some 1982 Camaro models with 2.5L engines and automatic transmissions may develop a "moaning" noise and vibration when engine speed is 3600-4800 RPM. This can be caused by an improperly positioned transmission damper assembly. Repair as follows:

1) Remove the transmission damper weights from the bracket by grinding or chiseling off the rivet heads and driving the rivets out.

2) Drill two 3/8" holes in the damper bracket 2" in front of the existing holes, but on the same center line.

3) Position the damper weights so that the holes align with the new holes in the damper bracket. Install two 3/8"x16 3" long bolts through the holes. Install nuts and tighten to 26 ft. lbs. (35 N.m).

12▷ 1982 CHEVROLET CAPRICE, CORVETTE, IMPALA AND "C" AND "K" TRUCKS WITH 700-R4 AUTOMATIC TRANSMISSION: DELAYED OR ERRATIC UPSHIFTS — Some 1982 Caprice, Corvette, Impala, and "C" and "K" Truck models with 700-R4 automatic transmissions may experience delayed or erractic transmission upshifts. This could be caused by the throttle valve sleeve rotating in the valve body. The rotation of the sleeve allows the throttle valve exhaust hole to be restricted or completely blocked off. Repair as follows:

1) The throttle valve sleeve is retained in the valve body by a press fit roll pin. If the roll pin is not

completely seated in the slot of the sleeve, the sleeve may rotate.

2) This can be corrected by properly positioning the throttle valve sleeve and tapping the roll pin in deeper to provide better retention of the throttle valve sleeve.

13▷ 1982-83 OLDSMOBILE TORONADO WITH 325-4L AUTOMATIC TRANSMISSION: TRANSMISSION OIL PAN LEAKS - Some 1982-83 Toronado models with 325-4L automatic transmissions may exhibit a transmission oil pan leak. This leak may be caused by an interference between the accumulator housing and the transmission oil pan.

Beginning in late March, 1983 all 325-4L transmissions were produced using a new accumulator housing to correct the interference condition.

If interference exists between the accumulator housing and oil pan, remove the accumulator housing and grind or file a portion of the casting boss. Be careful not to damage the cup plug. Remove as little material from the accumulator housing as possible while still eliminating the interference condition.

Toronado 325-4L Transmission Accumulator Housing Interference

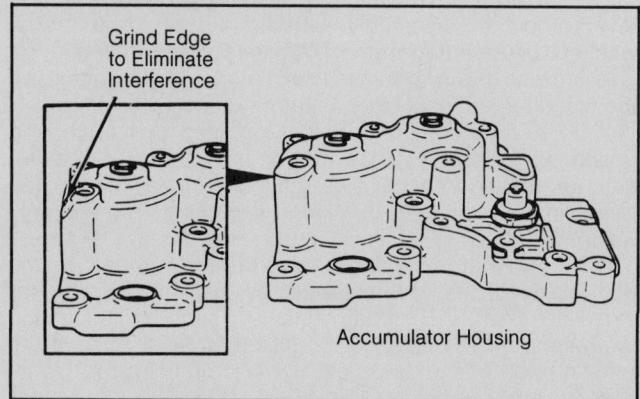

14▷ 1983 OLDSMOBILE CUTLASS CIERA AND OMEGA AND PONTIAC 6000 WITH 2.5L 4-CYLINDER OR 2.8L V6 ENGINE: KNOCKING NOISE FROM ENGINE COMPARTMENT — Some 1983 Cutlass Ciera, Omega and Pontiac 6000 models with 2.5L 4-cylinder or 2.8L V6 engine may exhibit a knocking noise from under the hood. This condition could be caused by loose torque converter-to-flywheel bolts.

Loose torque converter bolts sound much like a bearing knock and will give several raps on quick acceleration (engine running free). With the transaxle in gear, the noise may or may not appear at idle depending on the idle smoothness.

Check torque converter-to-flywheel bolts before attempting to repair any bearing-type knock noise.

15▷ 1983 PONTIAC BONNEVILLE, FIREBIRD, GRAND PRIX, PARISIENNE & T1000 WITH THM 200C OR 200-4R AUTOMATIC TRANSMISSION: WHINE NOISE IN 1ST, 2ND & REVERSE - Some 1983 THM 200C and 200-4R transmissions may experience a noise condition that sounds like a high pitched whine. This noise condition

FOR 1983 & EARLIER MODELS (Cont.)

may be coming from the front internal gear assembly and should not be confused with a torque converter bearing noise or a pump cavitation noise.

In diagnosing this condition, if the noise is noticeable in drive with the brake applied and the engine at approximately 1500 RPM, the cause could be a torque converter bearing noise or an oil pump cavitation noise. If the whine noise is noticeable when driving the car in 1st, 2nd or reverse only, the cause could be the front internal gear.

When servicing any 1983 THM 200C or 200-4R transmission for this whine noise condition and the cause has been diagnosed to be the front internal gear, replace it with a new gear (8630909).

[16] ALL PONTIAC MODELS WITH THM 700-R4 AUTOMATIC TRANSMISSION: LACK OF TRANSMISSION LUBRICANT — When overhauling a THM 700-R4 transmission that shows signs of high oil temperature, such as burned transmission fluid or parts that have turned a blue color, be sure to check the lubrication passages.

Do not confuse a wear pattern with lack of lubrication. A worn thrust washer or any part which shows a localized heat pattern is not generally caused by lack of lubrication. If the part is completely blue, this is an indication of insufficient lubrication.

On the THM 700-R4 transmission, the converter clutch must be functioning when the vehicle is driven in 4th gear or above normal oil temperatures will result. The higher oil temperatures may cause wear of the transmission parts. Above normal transmission oil temperatures can result in deterioration of the oil's lubricating quality. Check oil as follows:

1) Flush the oil cooler and cooler lines.

2) Air check the lubrication passages in the case and the oil pump cover.

3) Air check the lubrication passage in the input housing. Check the input housing-to-output shaft lip seal for wear or damage. Replace as necessary.

4) Flush and air check the lubrication passages in the output shaft.

Pontiac Oil Pump Cover Lubrication Channels

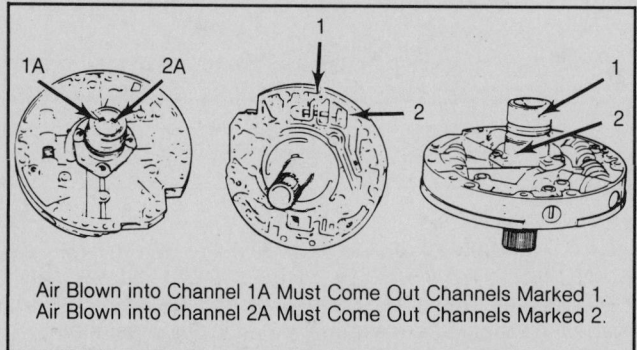

Air Blown into Channel 1A Must Come Out Channels Marked 1.
Air Blown into Channel 2A Must Come Out Channels Marked 2.

MANUAL TRANSMISSIONS

AMERICAN MOTORS

[1] 1980-81 AMERICAN MOTORS AMX, CONCORD, EAGLE, PACER AND SPIRIT WITH SR4 MANUAL TRANSMISSION: JUMPS OUT OF GEAR — Some 1980-81 AMC vehicles with SR4 4-speed manual transmissions

may experience a gear jump-out condition. This may be caused by a damaged or bent reverse gear selector pivot pin.

When servicing 1980-81 SR4 4-speed transmissions for a gear jump-out or damaged gear condition, always replace the reverse gear selector pivot. This pin, which is threaded into the transmission case and serves as the reverse lever pivot, should be replaced to ensure proper shifting.

CHRYSLER CORP.

[2] 1976-83 CHRYSLER CORP. TRUCKS, VANS AND WAGONS WITH A833 4-SPEED OVERDRIVE MANUAL TRANSMISSION: NEUTRAL GEAR RATTLE — Some 1976-83 Chrysler Corp. Trucks, Vans and Wagons with A833 4-speed overdrive manual transmission may exhibit a rattling noise from the transmission area with the clutch pedal out, transmission in neutral and engine idling. If neutral gear rattle occurs during any other condition that lowers the engine idle speed below the normal idle speed, the noise is considered normal and no attempts should be made to repair it. Neutral gear rattle is not detrimental to vehicle components or operation.

1) The engine and transmission should be at their normal operating temperatures. With the engine idling, transmission in neutral, and the clutch pedal out, listen for gear rattle.

2) Raise the engine idle speed slightly to see if the noise disappears. If it does, then attach a tachometer to the engine and check the curb idle speed.

3) Adjust the idle speed to the recommended idle speed. As little as 50 RPM can make a big difference in the gear rattle sound, but never adjust the idle speed above the recommended RPM range.

FORD MOTOR CO.

[3] 1983 FORD MOTOR CO. CAPRI, AND MUSTANG WITH 5.0L ENGINE AND 1983 THUNDERBIRD WITH 2.3L TURBO ENGINE AND MANUAL TRANSMISSION: GEAR SHIFT KNOB COMES OFF SHIFT LEVER — On some 1983 Capri and Mustang models with 5.0L engine and Thunderbird models with 2.3L turbo engine, the gear shift knob may pull off.

To service this condition, replace the shift lever extension and the snap-on shift knob with a threaded shift lever extension (E3ZZ-7210-C). and a threaded shift knob (E3ZZ-7213-B).

Vehicles built after March 30, 1983, are equipped with a new design threaded type shift knob to prevent pull off during shifting.

[4] 1983 CAPRI AND MUSTANG WITH 5-SPEED (M50D) MANUAL TRANSMISSION: HIGH SHIFT EFFORTS — Some early production 1983 Capri and Mustang models may have a high shift effort in the first few thousand miles. The addition of 2 ounces of friction modifier (C8AZ-19B546-A) will reduce the effort.

1) Raise vehicle on a hoist. Remove transmission drain plug and remove about 1 pint of fluid.

2) Add 2 ounces of friction modifier to transmission. Top off fluid with manual transmission fluid to bottom of fill hole.

3) Install fill plug and tighten. Clean off transmission.

5️⃣ 1983 CAPRI AND MUSTANG WITH 5.0L ENGINE AND THUNDERBIRD WITH 2.3L EFI TURBO-CHARGED ENGINE: CLICKING OR RATTLE IN SECOND GEAR UNDER LOAD — This condition may be caused by the fifth/reverse gearshift lever return spring not being secured at both ends. The following procedure should be used to connect the return spring.

1) Remove transmission from vehicle. Mount transmission in a holding fixture. Remove drain plug on lower right side of transmission case.

2) Using a 13 mm socket, position the shift lever in neutral position and remove turret cover attaching bolts. Break turret cover-to-extension housing seal by prying carefully between housing and cover. Remove turret cover.

3) Using a 3/16" pin punch and hammer, remove roll pin attaching offset lever to shifter shaft.

NOTE: Do not try to remove offset lever while extension housing is bolted in place. A lug on bottom of offset lever meshes with detent plate preventing rearward movement of offset lever.

4) Remove extension housing attaching bolts. Break extension housing-to-case seal. Remove housing and offset lever as an assembly by sliding rearward away from case.

5) Remove offset lever, roll pin, detent spring and detent ball from extension housing detent plate. Remove cover attaching bolts. Break cover-to-case seal.

6) Remove cover by lifting slightly and sliding toward filler plug side of transmission. When shift mechanism clears groove in 5th/reverse shift lever, continue lifting cover.

7) Using needle nose pliers, remove "C" clip attaching 5th/reverse lever to lever pivot pin. Remove shift lever pivot pin. DO NOT remove 5th/reverse shift lever. Using needle nose pliers, connect lever return spring.

8) Apply pipe sealant to pivot pin threads and install pin. Make sure reverse shift fork pin and 5th gear shift rail pin are engaged with shift lever. Install "C" clip on lever pivot pin.

9) Apply bead of silicone sealer to shift cover assembly and install. Position cover and lower into position until shift forks engage synchronizers. Continue lowering and move into position to engage 5th/reverse shift lever.

NOTE: Make sure synchronizers and shift forks in cover are in neutral position.

10) Install shift cover attaching bolts and tighten. Apply bead of silicone sealer to extension housing mating surface. Coat detent spring with petroleum jelly and install in offset lever. Lubricate detent plate and install detent ball in neutral position on plate.

11) Position offset lever in extension housing with spring over detent ball. Slide lever and extension housing into position. Press downward on offset lever to compress detent spring and push lever and housing into position. Install extension housing attaching bolts and tighten.

12) Using a 3/16" pin punch, align the hole in shifter shaft with hole in offset lever and install roll pin. Install damper sleeve in offset lever. Check output shaft gear end play. Apply bead of silicone sealer to turret cover.

13) Install turret cover on extension housing and tighten attaching bolts. Install drain plug. Add transmission lubricant. Install transmission.

GENERAL MOTORS

6️⃣ 1983 CADILLAC CIMARRON WITH 5-SPEED MANUAL TRANSAXLE: LOSS OF SHIFTER CABLE RETAINER CLIP — Some 1983 Cimarron models with 5-speed manual transaxle may experience loss of the retainer clip that secures the shifter cable to the mounting bracket. Loss of the clip could occur during a hard 1st to 2nd or 3rd to 4th upshift and result in the transaxle remaining in the last selected gear range.

Beginning with VIN 403069, new design retainer clips (14034650) have been installed during production. These new design clips are also available to service vehicles manufacturered with the old style retainer clip.

A new design cable mounting bracket (14051054) is available and has been installed on vehicles beginning with VIN 403223. The old style mounting bracket may be too thick and could have the center reinforcement rib mispositioned so that the cable retaining clip could bottom out on the rib and not fully seat onto the shifter cable.

Cadillac Cimarron Transaxle Shifter Cable & Assembly

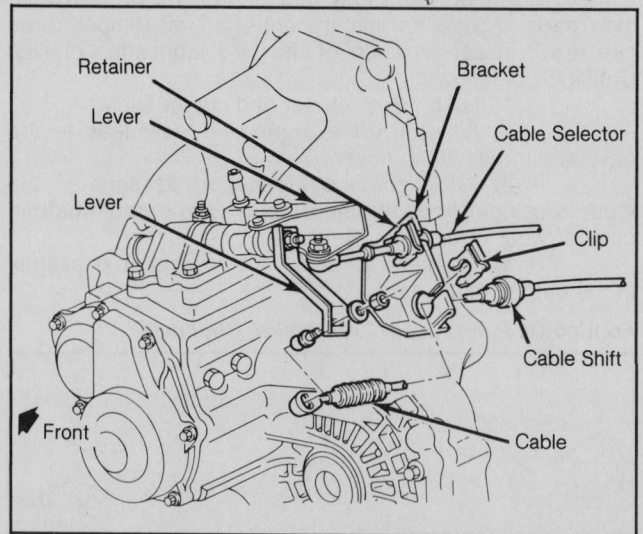

7️⃣ 1983 CADILLAC CIMARRON WITH 5-SPEED MANUAL TRANSAXLE: DIFFICULT GEAR SELECTION — Some 1983 Cimarron models with 5-speed manual transaxle may experience difficulty in selecting 1st and 2nd gear ranges. Gear clash into 2nd and/or 3rd gear with moderate shift speed may also occur after an overnight soak with ambient temperatures near or below 40°F (4°C).

These conditions may be caused by too tight of a bearing preload shim. Beginning with vehicle number 409801, a change was made to reduce the input shaft bearing shim thickness by .004" (.08 mm). The transaxles with the thinner shim can be identified by a dab of Green paint on the left side of the rear cover.

FOR 1983 & EARLIER MODELS (Cont.)

To correct the shifting difficulty or gear clash, it will be necessary to remove the transaxle and replace the shims.

Cadillac Cimarron 5-Speed Manual Transaxle

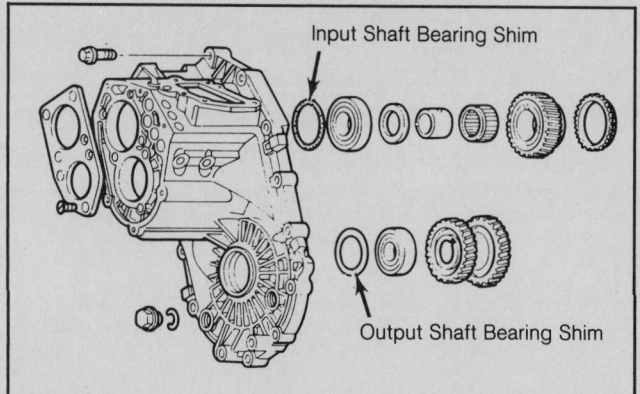

Input Shaft Bearing Shim

Output Shaft Bearing Shim

8▷ 1983 PONTIAC FIREBIRD WITH 2.5L 4-CYLINDER ENGINE AND MANUAL TRANSMISSION: REVERSE SHUDDER — Some 1983 Firebird models with 2.5L 4-cylinder engine and manual transmission may exhibit a shudder condition while releasing the clutch in reverse gear.

Install spacers (10031852) in locations shown in illustration. Remove washer (if equipped) under square spacer. Position spacer square to mount.

Installing Spacers To Correct Reverse Shudder Condition on 1983 Firebird

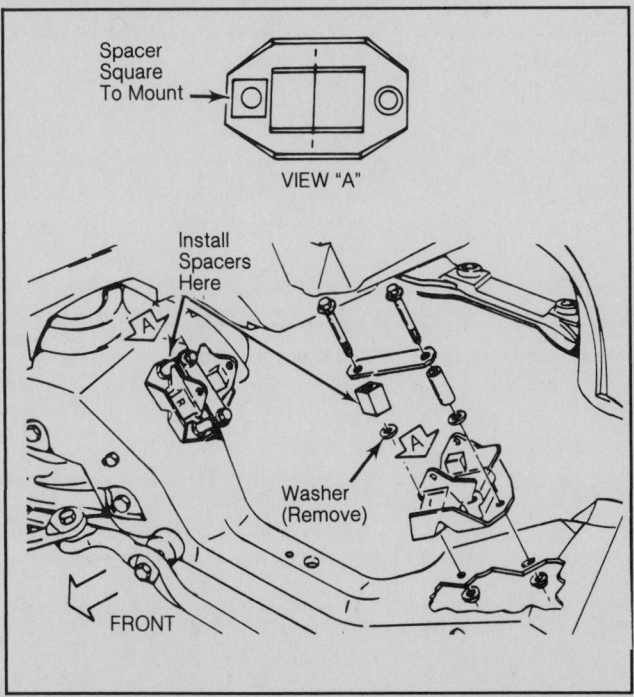

Spacer Square To Mount

VIEW "A"

Install Spacers Here

Washer (Remove)

FRONT

9▷ 1982 CHEVROLET CAMARO WITH 2.5L ENGINE AND MANUAL TRANSMISSION: 4000 RPM BOOMING — Some 1982 Camaro models with 2.5L engine and manual transmission may exhibit a throttle sensitive engine "boom"/vibration which is heard and felt at approximately 4000 RPM. This condition may be improved by removing the transmission damper. When the damper is removed, a spacer (10018110) must be installed between the torque arm bracket and the transmission.

10▷ 1982 OLDSMOBILE FIRENZA WITH FOUR SPEED MANUAL TRANSAXLE: NOISE IN SECOND GEAR — A metallic tapping or ticking noise may occur during second gear operation. This can occur during a left turn or at a straight ahead heavy acceleration. Movement may also be felt in the shifter lever. The noise is created by interference between the reverse idler gear and output 1st and 2nd gear synchronizer assemblies and can be caused by one of the following conditions:

1) A misadjusted shift cable or shift mechanism that causes an overshift condition in second gear.

2) A reverse shift lever with an incorrect profile, or spread forks that cause the reverse idler gear to be positioned toward the synchronizer assembly.

3) An interlock assembly that is mispositioned or mismachined, causing the reverse lever to move the idler gear toward the synchronizer assembly.

After necessary repairs have been performed, bench test the transaxle using the following procedure to assure the interference is eliminated: Place transaxle in second gear. Lift idler gear to remove excess slack. Rotate input shaft clockwise and listen for noise that would indicate an interference still exists.

TRANSFER CASES

FORD MOTOR CO.

1▷ 1982-83 FORD BRONCO AND F150/250 WITH FOUR WHEEL DRIVE: TRANSFER CASE RANGE FORK AND ANNULUS GEAR HUB — Models built after January, 1982, with New Process 208 transfer cases have a new range fork and annulus gear hub assembly design.

The annulus gear hub and web assembly can be damaged when the transfer case is operated with low lubricant levels or with a rough surface finish fork or thrust washer. This will result in transfer case shifting difficulties. The damaged nylon hub will appear to be melted or severely scored and must be replaced.

The range fork and thrust washer must also be replaced since surface finish damage or sharp edges created during prior condition can cause accelerated wear of the new hub and web assembly. The transfer case should be refilled with 7 pints of new automatic transmission fluid lube and checked for any leaks. With vehicle in normal operating position, the fluid level must be up to the fill plug opening.

JEEP

2▷ 1980 JEEP CHEROKEE, "J" TRUCK AND WAGONEER WITH AUTOMATIC TRANSMISSION: TRANSFER CASE SHIFT LEVER RATTLE — Some 1980 Jeep Cherokee, Truck and Wagoneer vehicles with automatic transmissions may develop a transfer case shift lever rattle. The rattle occurs at the point where the transfer case shift lever is connected to the upper shift rod. Repair as follows:

1) Raise vehicle on hoist. Remove shift lever-to-shift rod retainer and disconnect lever from rod. Install 1 flat washer (943961) on shift rod.

2) Install shift lever on shift rod. Install spring washer (815535) and remaining flat washer on shift rod. Install cotter pin (4004295). Lower vehicle. Check transfer case shift lever operation.

▷③ **1980-82 JEEP MODELS WITH NEW PROCESS 208 TRANSFER CASE: INTERMITTENT CLUNK NOISE IN 4WD** — Some 1980-82 Jeep models with New Process 208 transfer cases may develop a "clunk" noise that occurs in 4-wheel drive high or low range and primarily when driving on pavement. The noise occurs every 1/4-1/2 mile and is a result of increasing front-to-rear wheel torque bias that causes the sliding clutch to rapidly disengage then reengage with the sprocket carrier. A clutch and carrier kit is now available to correct this condition.

1) Remove transfer case from vehicle. Disassemble case but do not remove planetary assembly, input gear, range sector or lock plate.

2) Discard original sprocket carrier, sliding clutch, clutch spring and mode fork.

3) Clean and inspect remaining transfer case components that were removed. Pay particular attention to the annulus gear. Replace the fork if inserts exhibit wear and the annulus gear if fork groove surface is rough or worn.

4) Install replacement parts from kit and reassemble the transfer case. Do not fill case with lubricant at this time.

5) Install transfer case in vehicle. Refill transfer case with 6 pints of Dexron II ATF or equivalent.

1982 IMPORT GENERAL INDEX

The first step in using these pages is to locate the listed components that you require information on. Go down the list under the specific component heading to the model or transmission type of the vehicle you are working on. On the right-hand side of the column is the number of the article you require.

1982 Import General Index

Cont.

1982 Import General Index

Cont.

1982 Import General Index

F

FINAL DRIVE
See Automatic or Manual Transaxle

1982 Import General Index

Cont.

1982 Import General Index

SECTION 5

IMPORT GENERAL SERVICING

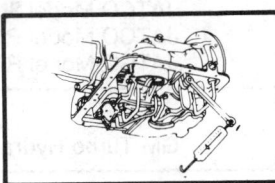

NOTE: ALSO SEE GENERAL INDEX.

Transmission Application
AUTOMATIC TRANSMISSIONS

MANUFACTURER & MODEL	[1] TRANSMISSION MODEL
AUDI 4000 & 5000	Model 087/089 Transaxle
BMW 320i, 528e, 633CSi & 733i	Model ZF 3 HP-22
CHRYSLER CORP. IMPORTS Arrow Pickup & Ram-50 Pickup Challenger & Sapporo Champ & Colt	Torqueflite MA-904A Torqueflite MA-904 Mitsubishi KM170 Transaxle
COURIER Pickup	JATCO Model 3N71B
DATSUN/NISSAN Maxima, 200SX & 210 Pickup & 280ZX Sentra 310	JATCO Model L3N71B JATCO Model 3N71B JATCO Model RL3F01A Transaxle JATCO Model RN3F01A Transaxle
FIAT Spider 2000	GM Turbo Hydra-Matic 180 — Fiat
HONDA Accord, Civic & Prelude	Honda Automatic Transaxle
ISUZU I-Mark P'UP	Aisin-Warner Model 55 GM Turbo Hydra-Matic 200
JAGUAR XJS XJ6	GM Turbo Hydra-Matic 400 — Jaguar Borg-Warner Model 65
MAZDA GLC (Exc. Wagon) GLC Wagon & 626 RX7	Mazda F3A Transaxle JATCO Model L3N71B JATCO Model 3N71B
MERCEDES-BENZ 240D 300 & 380 Series	MB Type W 4 B 025 4-Speed MB Type W 4 A 040 4-Speed
PEUGEOT 504, 505 & 604 Turbo Diesel	Model ZF 3 HP-22
PORSCHE 924 & 944 928	Model 087 Transaxle Model A22.01 Transaxle
RENAULT Fuego & 18i	Renault Automatic Transaxle
SAAB 900, 900S & 900 Turbo	Borg-Warner Model 37 Transaxle

[1] — Unless otherwise specified, all models use 3 forward gears.

BMW

IDENTIFICATION

TRANSMISSION CODES

Application	Code
All Models	ZF 3HP 22

LUBRICATION

SERVICE INTERVALS

Check fluid level at least at every oil change. Drain and refill transmission every 30,000 miles.

FLUID LEVEL

Transmission must be at normal operating temperature with vehicle on a level surface, engine at idle and gear selector in "Park". Fluid level should be between the "MAX" and "MIN" marks on the dipstick. Distance between marks represents .42 qts. (.40L).

FLUID TYPE

Automatic Transmission Fluid (ATF)
Dexron or Dexron II

FLUID CAPACITY

Dry Fill 6.4 qts. (6.0L)
Refill 2.1 qts. (2.0L)

DRAINING & REFILLING

1) With transmission at normal operating temperature, remove drain plug and allow fluid to drain. Remove oil pan bolts and tap on pan to break seal loose.

2) Remove oil screen and clean or replace as necessary. Clean oil pan. Reinstall filter screen and oil pan. Fill transmission with new transmission fluid of the correct type.

ADJUSTMENT

SHIFT LINKAGE

1) Check tightness of bearing bracket before adjusting. Disconnect selector rod from lever at adjustment pin.

Fig. 1: BMW Shift Linkage Adjustment

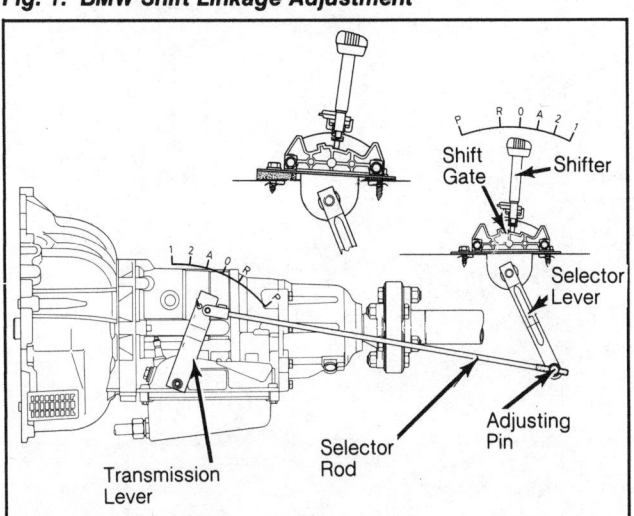

2) Move transmission shifter lever to "O" (Neutral) position. Press shifter against shift gate stop.

3) Alter length of selector rod with adjusting pin until adjusting pin aligns with hole in selector lever.

4) Shorten selector rod by 1 turn of adjusting pin. Attach selector rod, adjusting pin and selector lever together.

THROTTLE CABLE & KICKDOWN STOP

320i

1) With accelerator cable properly adjusted and transmission in Neutral, turn adjusting screw until throttle cable clearance is .010-.030" (.25-.75 mm).

2) Depress accelerator to kickdown stop. Clearance should now be 1.71-2.20" (43.5-51.5 mm). If not, adjust kickdown stop screw. *See Fig. 2.*

Fig. 2: Throttle Cable Adjustment on 320i Models

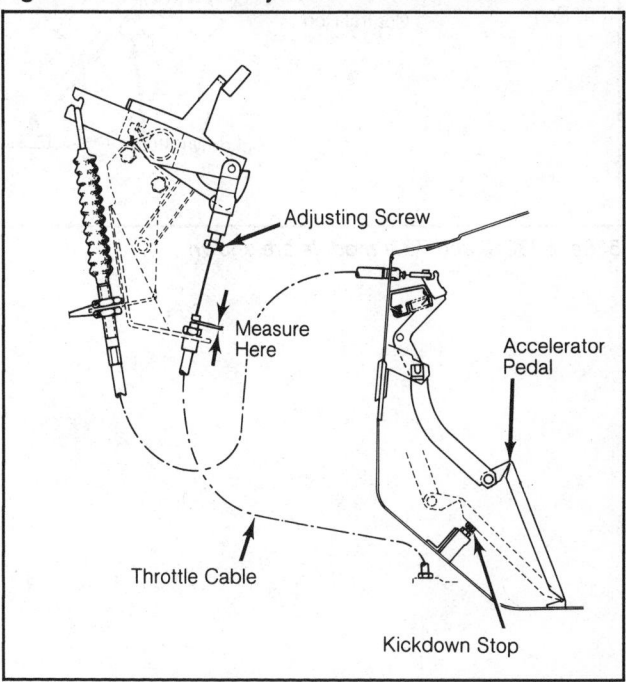

528e, 633CSi & 733i

1) Adjust accelerator pull rod length to 16.93" (430 mm). With throttle at idle, adjust cable housing nuts to give .010-.030" (.25-.75 mm) clearance between seal and cable housing end. Loosen kickdown stop nut and screw stop in as far as it will go.

2) Depress accelerator pedal until transmission pressure point is felt. Loosen stop until it just touches pedal. Tighten lock nut. Press accelerator pedal full down and adjust control rod so that clearance from seal to cable end is 1.7-2.0" (43-52 mm).

NEUTRAL SAFETY SWITCH

Neutral safety switch is connected with selector lever and a relay. If not operating properly, check relay and selector adjustment.

Automatic Transmission Servicing

BMW (Cont.)

Fig. 3: Throttle Cable and Kickdown Stop Adjustment

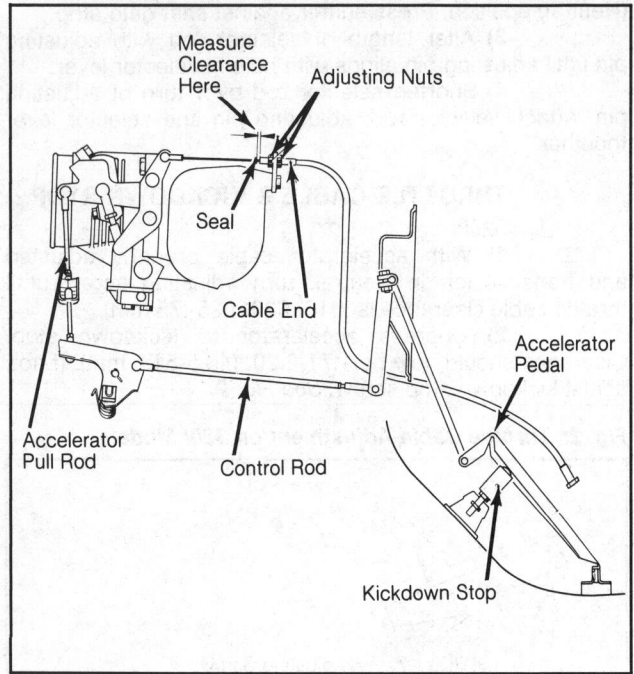

528e, 633CSi and 733i models are shown.

CHRYSLER CORP. IMPORTS

IDENTIFICATION

TRANSMISSION CODES

Application	Transmission (Code)
Champ & Colt	Mitsubishi (KM170)
All Others	Torqueflite (MA904A)

LUBRICATION

SERVICE INTERVALS

Torqueflite

Under normal usage, band adjustment and fluid and filter change are not required. Under severe usage, adjust bands and change fluid and filter every 30,-000 miles. Fluid level should be checked every 6 months.

Mitsubishi

Under normal conditions, change fluid and filter and adjust bands every 30,000 miles. With more than 50% operation in heavy city traffic at temperatures over 90°F (32°C), service more frequently.

FLUID LEVEL

Torqueflite and Mitsubishi

1) With vehicle parked on level area, fluid at normal operating temperature, parking brake engaged and engine idling, select each gear momentarily.

2) Place selector in "N" (Neutral) position and clean area around dipstick tube. Check fluid level between lower and upper marks, but never over upper mark. Add or drain fluid as necessary.

CAUTION: If severe darkening of the fluid and a strong odor is noted, fluid and filter should be changed and bands adjusted.

FLUID TYPE

Automatic Transmission Fluid (ATF)
Dexron II

FLUID CAPACITY

Torqueflite 7.2 qts. (6.8L)
Mitsubishi 6.0 qts. (5.7L)

DRAINING & REFILLING

Torqueflite

1) Carefully remove oil pan and drain fluid. Install new filter on bottom of valve body. Clean oil pan, replace gasket and install oil pan. Pour 4 quarts of specified fluid through filler tube. Start engine and allow to idle for 2 minutes.

2) Shift transmission into each position, ending in "N" position. Check fluid level with engine running at idle and add sufficent fluid to bring level to "ADD 1 PINT" mark. Recheck fluid level after transmission is at normal operating temperature. *See Fluid Level in this article.*

Mitsubishi

1) Remove drain plugs from both differential and pan and drain fluid. If replacing filter, remove bolts and lower oil pan. Install new filter on bottom of valve body. Replace pan gasket and install pan.

2) Tighten differential plug to 22-25 ft. lbs (30-34 N.m) and pan plug to 18-21 ft. lbs. (24-28 N.m). Ensure

that dipstick hole area is clean and pour in approximately 4 quarts of specified fluid.

3) Run engine for 2 minutes at idle. Shift transmission to each position, ending in "N" position. Add sufficient fluid to reach lower mark. After reaching normal operating temperature, fluid should be between upper and lower marks of "HOT" range.

Fig. 1: Mitsubishi Drain Plug Locations

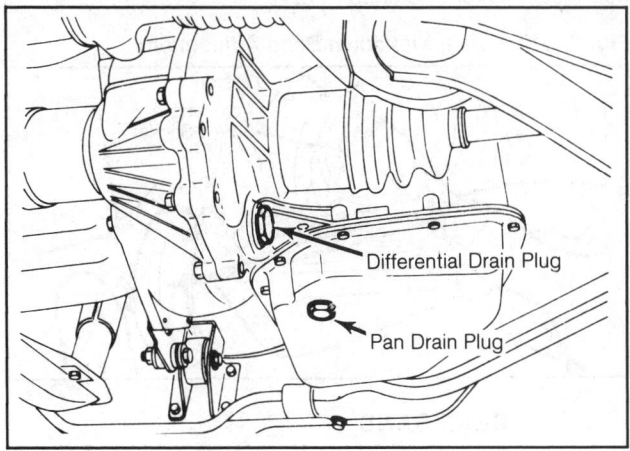

ADJUSTMENT

FRONT (KICKDOWN) BAND

Torqueflite

1) Front (kickdown) band adjuster screw is located on left side of transmission case. To adjust band, loosen and back off lock nut about 5 turns. Check that adjuster screw turns freely.

2) Using wrench (C-3380-A) with adapter (C-3705), tighten band adjuster screw to 47-50 INCH lbs. (5.3-5.7 N.m).

3) If adapter (C-3705) is not used, tighten adjuster screw to 72 INCH lbs. (8 N.m), which is the true torque. Back off adjusting screw 3 turns, hold adjuster screw and tighten lock nut.

Fig. 2: Torqueflite Front Band Adjusting Screw Location

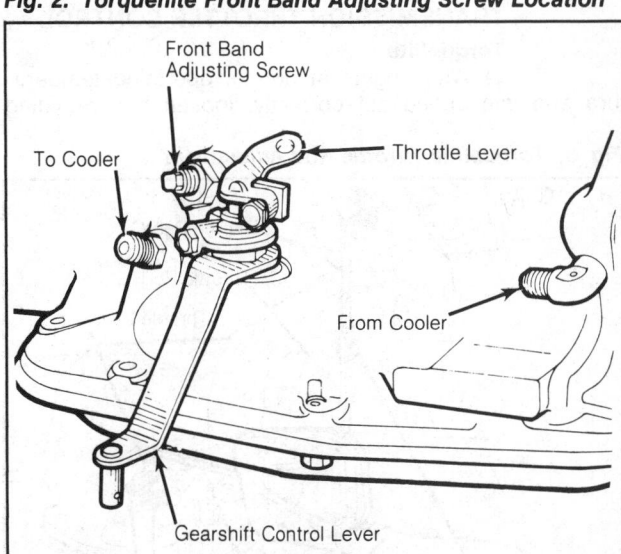

Mitsubishi

1) Clean all dirt from kickdown servo cover and remove snap ring. Remove cover and loosen lock nut. Hold servo piston from turning and tighten adjusting screw to 84 INCH lbs. (10 N.m) and back it off.

2) Repeat this twice to seat kickdown band against drum. Tighten adjusting screw to 42 INCH lbs. (5 N.m) and back off 3 1/2 turns. Hold screw and tighten lock nut. Install cover and snap ring.

Fig. 3: Mitsubishi Kickdown Band Adjustment

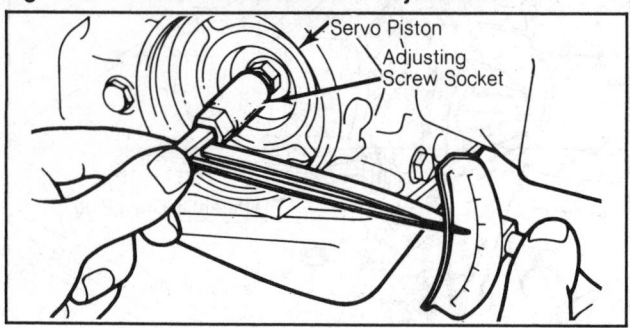

REAR BAND
Torqueflite

1) Remove oil pan. Loosen lock nut and Allen head adjusting screw at servo end of lever and tighten screw to 42 INCH lbs. (4.5 N.m) of torque.

2) Back off screw 7 turns. Hold adjusting screw and tighten lock nut. Reinstall oil pan.

Fig. 4: Torqueflite Rear Band Adjusting Screw Location

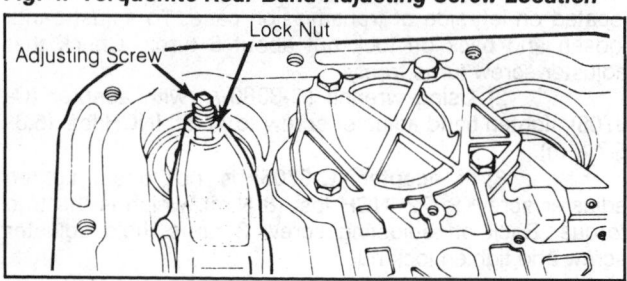

TRANSMISSION THROTTLE CONTROL
Torqueflite

1) With engine at normal operating temperature and idle speed set correctly, loosen bolt retaining

Fig. 5: Torqueflite Throttle Rod Adjustment

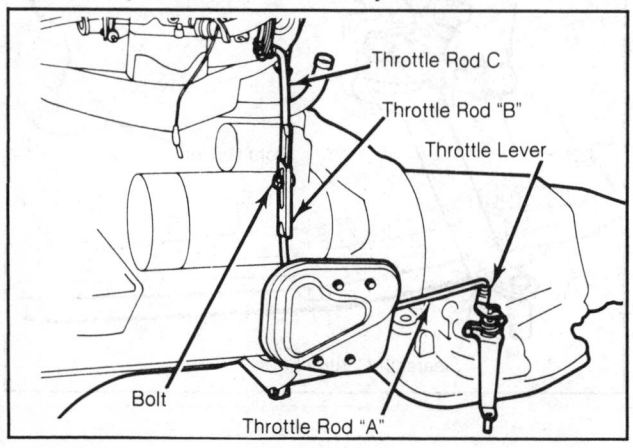

throttle rod "C" to "B". Lightly push throttle rod "A" or the transmission throttle lever and rod toward idle stop and set rods to idle position.

2) Tighten bolt retaining rod "B" to "C". Open throttle to wide open position. Make sure that transmission lever moves from idle to wide open position (total movement 45° to 54°). Some play should still exist in throttle lever stroke at wide open throttle.

Mitsubishi

1) Open throttle to wide open position and loosen lower cable bracket mounting bolt. Move bracket until distance between nipple and top of cover "A" on throttle cable is 2.019-2.059" (51.3-52.3 mm).

2) With throttle lever still in wide open position, pull cable upward to ensure freedom of cable movement.

Fig. 6: Mitsubishi Throttle Cable Adjustment

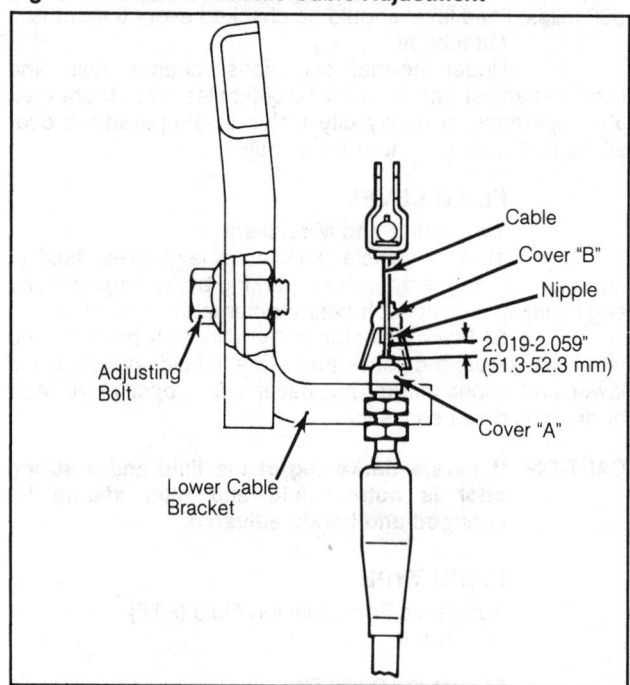

SHIFT LINKAGE
Torqueflite

1) Remove shift handle by loosening set screw and pulling off handle. Place selector lever in "N" and turn adjusting cam in top of lever until surface "A" of cam is flush with end of selector lever "B". *See Fig. 7.*

Fig. 7: Adjusting Selector Rod Cam On Torqueflite Transmission

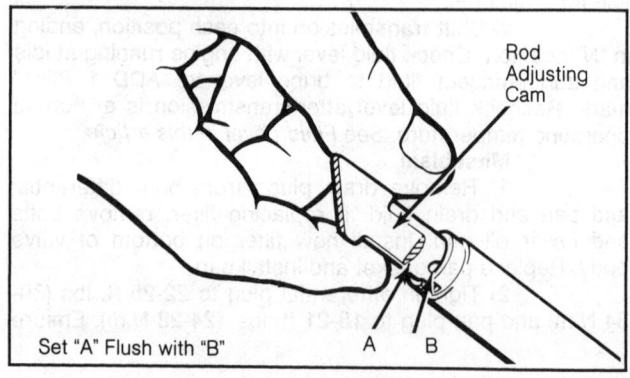

CHRYSLER CORP. IMPORTS (Cont.)

2) Loosen lock nut at connection of rod and arm at transmission. Place transmission lever arm in neutral. Place selector lever in neutral and tighten lock nut to adjust control rod length.

Mitsubishi
1) Place selector in "N" position. Loosen set screw retaining handle to lever. Depress selector knob and turn handle to give .008-.035" (.2-.9 mm) clearance between selector lever end pin and detent plate. *See Fig. 8.*

Fig. 8: Adjusting Selector Lever On Mitsubishi Transmission

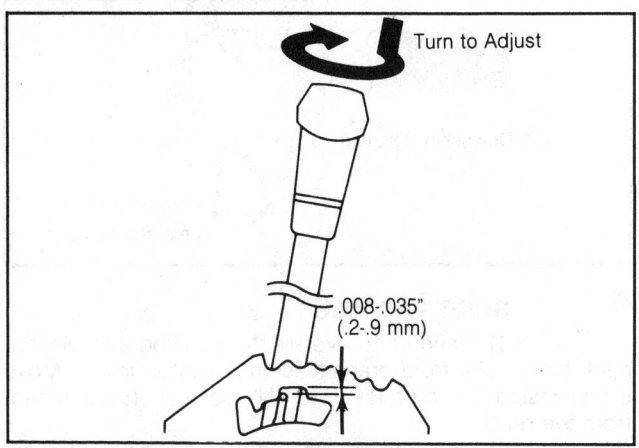

2) When knob is on driver's side, tighten set screw. With selector lever and neutral safety switch in "N" position, turn adjusting nuts at cable end until slack is removed from control cable.

NEUTRAL SAFETY SWITCH
Torqueflite
1) Switch is located under shift lever console and is operated by shift lever. In addition to the neutral safety switch function, switch also operates back-up lights and seat belt warning system.
2) To adjust switch, place selector lever in "N" position and slide switch back and forth to measure contact range of "N" position.
3) Place switch in center of contact range and adjust so that there is .06" (1.5 mm) side clearance between selector lever and switch. Tighten attaching screws.

Fig. 9: Adjusting Torqueflite Neutral Safety Switch

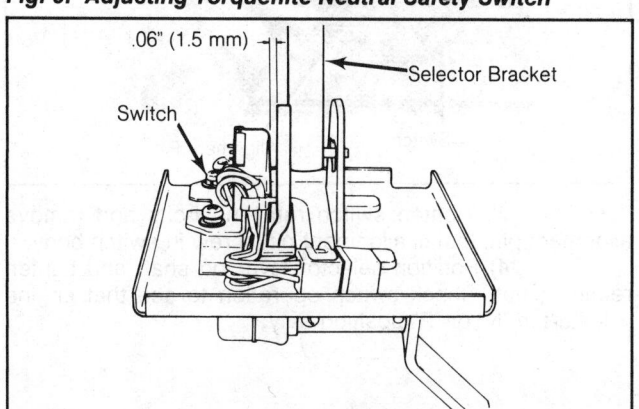

Mitsubishi
Place transmission control lever in neutral and loosen switch retaining bolts. Turn inhibitor switch body so that aligning hole end of lever overlaps switch body flange and tighten bolts. *See Fig. 10.*

Fig. 10: Adjusting Neutral Safety Switch On Mitsubishi Transmission

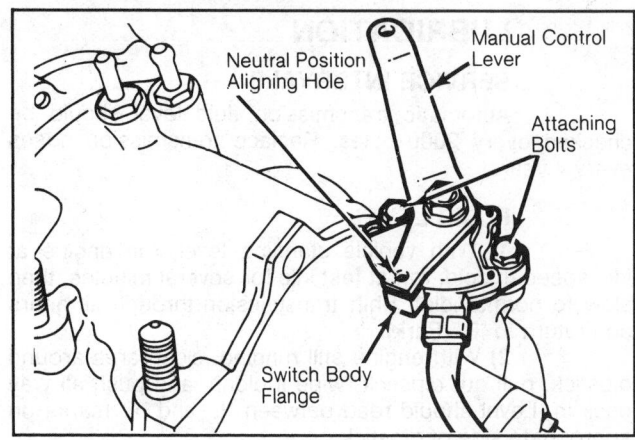

COURIER

IDENTIFICATION

TRANSMISSION CODES

Application	Transmission (Code)
Courier	Jatco (3N71B)

LUBRICATION

SERVICE INTERVALS

Automatic transmission fluid level should be checked every 2000 miles. Replace transmission hoses every 4 years.

FLUID LEVEL

1) With vehicle standing level, run engine at idle speed (if cold, run at fast idle for several minutes, then slow to normal idle). Shift transmission through all gears and return to "P" (Park).

2) With engine still running, clean area around dipstick, pull out dipstick, wipe it clean, and push all way back in. Level should read between "L" and "F" marks on appropriate side of dipstick.

FLUID TYPE

Automatic Transmission Fluid (ATF) type "F".

FLUID CAPACITY

6.7 qts. (6.3L)

DRAINING & REFILLING

1) Loosen oil pan bolts and allow ATF to drain. Remove oil pan and filter screen and thoroughly clean them. Using a new oil pan gasket, install filter screen and oil pan.

2) Add 3 qts. (2.8L) of fluid to transmission through filler tube. Run engine at idle speed for about 2 minutes, then run engine at fast idle (1200 RPM) until it reaches normal operating temperature.

3) Shift selector through all ranges, ending in "N" or "P" position. Check fluid level and add as required.

CAUTION: **Do not race engine while warming up. Do not overfill transmission.**

ADJUSTMENT

BAND

1) Remove servo cover bolts on right front of transmission and remove servo cover. Loosen lock nut and tighten adjusting screw to 9-11 ft. lbs. (12-15 N.m).

Fig. 1: Showing Band Adjusting Screw

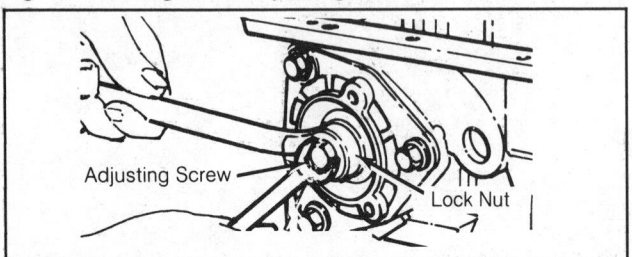

Adjusting Screw   Lock Nut

2) Back off the adjusting screw 2 turns. Holding the adjusting screw, tighten lock nut to 22-29 ft. lbs. (30-39 N.m). Replace servo cover.

KICKDOWN SWITCH

With ignition switch on, adjust switch to engage when accelerator pedal is between 7/8-15/16" (22-24 mm) of full pedal travel. Downshift solenoid will click when switch engages.

Fig. 2: Schematic of Kickdown Switch

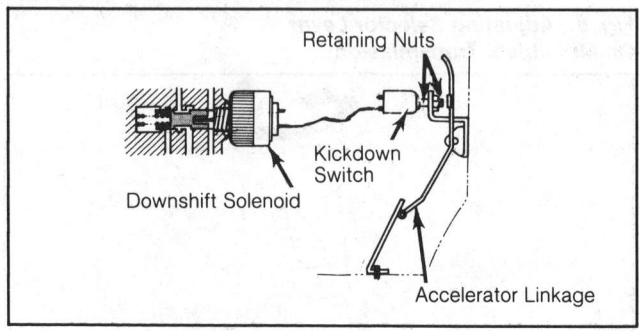

Retaining Nuts
Kickdown Switch
Downshift Solenoid
Accelerator Linkage

SHIFT LINKAGE

1) Place shift lever in "N" position and disconnect clevis pin from transmission selector lever. Move transmission selector lever to "N" position (third detent from the rear).

2) Adjust control rod so that clevis pin engages selector lever. Check that transmission correctly engages all selector positions.

NEUTRAL SAFETY SWITCH

1) Place transmission selector lever in "N" position (third detent from rear). Remove lever retaining nut. Loosen switch retaining bolts. Remove screw from alignment pin hole at bottom of switch.

2) Rotate switch and insert a .079" (2.0 mm) pin through alignment pin hole and hole of internal rotor.

Fig. 3: Making Neutral Safety Switch Adjustment

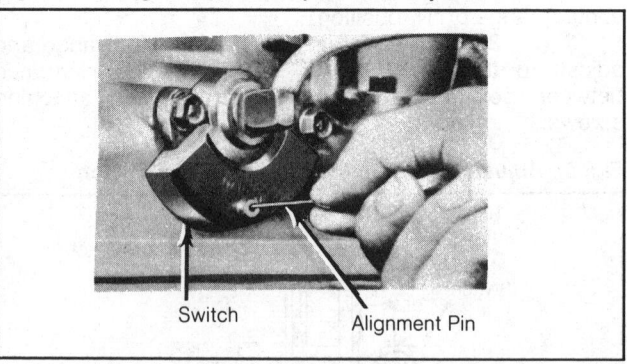

Switch   Alignment Pin

3) Tighten switch retaining bolts and remove alignment pin. Install alignment pin screw in switch body.

4) Position selector lever on shaft and tighten retaining nut. Check switch operation to see that engine will start in "N" or "P" position only.

DATSUN/NISSAN

**200SX, 210, 280ZX, 310,
Maxima, Pickup, Sentra, Stanza**

IDENTIFICATION

TRANSMISSION CODES

Application	Code
RWD Transmission	Jatco (3N71B)
FWD Transaxle	RL3F01A

LUBRICATION

SERVICE INTERVAL
Inspect fluid level every 15,000 miles.

FLUID LEVEL
1) Check fluid with engine and transmission at normal operating temperatures (this is reached after several minutes of driving).

2) With vehicle standing level and at idle, shift transmission through all positions and return to "P" (Park). Clean area around dipstick. Remove dip stick wipe clean, insert and withdraw.

3) Level should be between "H" and "L" marks. If not, add as necessary. Normal fluid should be clear with a Pink color and should not have a strong odor.

4) If fluid has a strong, burned odor or is dark in color, overheating and internal wear may be indicated. If milky in appearance, moisture from cooling system or road may have entered the system

5) Foamy or excessively bubbled fluid indicates overfilling and aeration.

FLUID TYPE
Automatic Transmission Fluid (ATF)
  Dexron

FLUID CAPACITY
RWD Transmission 5.9 qts. (5.5L)
FWD Transaxle 6.4 qts. (6.0L)

DRAINING & REFILLING
1) Loosen oil pan bolts and allow ATF to drain. Remove oil pan and clean pan and screen thoroughly. Install pan using a new gasket.

2) Add approximately 3 quarts of fluid through filler tube. Run engine at idle speed for about 2 minutes, then at fast idle (1200 RPM) for several more minutes, until normal operating temperatures are reached.

3) Shift transmission through all gears and return to "P" (Park). Check fluid level and add to obtain appropriate level.

ADJUSTMENT

BRAKE BAND
RWD Transmission
Loosen piston stem lock nut and tighten piston stem (adjusting screw) to 108-132 INCH lbs. (12-15 N.m). Back off piston stem 2 turns and tighten lock nut to 168 INCH lbs. (20 N.m).

FWD Transaxle
Loosen lock nut. Tighten anchor end pin to 36-48 INCH lbs. (4-6 N.m). Back off anchor end pin 2 1/2 turns. Tighten lock nut (while holding anchor pin) to 12-16 ft. lbs. (16-22 N.m).

SHIFT LINKAGE
RWD Transmission
1) Starting in "P" position, shift through all positions to "1" position. If detents cannot be felt or pointer is improperly aligned, linkage must be adjusted.

2) Place shift lever in "D" position and loosen lock nuts on rod. Turn lock nuts until pointer aligns properly and all detents can be felt. Tighten lock nuts and recheck positions, ensuring that full detent is felt in "P" position.

3) If unable to adjust, grommets at ends of rod may be worn or damaged and require replacement.

FWD Transaxle
1) Place control lever at "P" position. Connect control cable end to manual lever in transaxle unit, and tighten control cable retaining bolts. Move control lever from "P" to "1".

2) Make sure that control lever can move smoothly and without any sliding noise. Place control lever at "P". Make sure that control lever locks at "P". Back off lock nut at control cable and loosen adjusting. Connect control cable to trunnion.

3) Tighten adjusting nut and then lock nut. Move control lever from "P" to "1" again. Make sure that control lever can move smoothly and without sliding noise. Apply grease to spring washer.

KICKDOWN SWITCH
RWD Transmission
Kickdown switch is located at top of accelerator pedal post. A "click" should be heard just before accelerator bottoms out when depressed. If not, loosen lock nut on switch and adjust. Do not allow switch to close too soon, or downshift will occur at part throttle.

NEUTRAL SAFETY SWITCH
RWD Transmission
1) Switch operates back-up lights and prevents starting except in "P" or "N". To adjust, ensure that transmission is in "N" with lever at transmission in vertical position.

2) Remove alignment hole screw at bottom of switch and loosen retaining bolts. Move switch until alignment pin can be inserted in rotor. Tighten retaining bolts and replace alignment hole screw.

Fig. 1: Adjusting Neutral Safety Switch

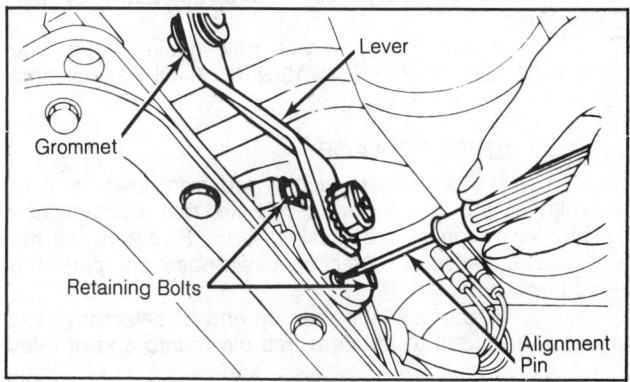

Automatic Transmission Servicing

FIAT SPIDER 2000 & 2000 TURBO

IDENTIFICATION

TRANSMISSION CODES

Application	Transmission (Code)
Spider 2000 & Turbo	GM THM 180 (4427284)

LUBRICATION

SERVICE INTERVALS

Check automatic transmission fluid level every 3000 miles. Change fluid every 30,000 miles or 2 years.

FLUID LEVEL

With engine running at normal operating temperature, place transmission in "N" or "P" position. Clean area around dipstick, remove, wipe clean, insert to fully-seated position. Remove and note level. Fluid should be between "MIN" and "MAX". Add fluid if necessary.

FLUID TYPE

Automatic Transmission Fluid (ATF)
  Dexron or Dexron II

FLUID CAPACITY

Dry Fill 6 qts. (5.7L)
Refill 3 qts. (2.8L)

DRAINING & REFILLING

1) Remove drain plug and allow fluid to drain. Remove oil pan and filter. Discard gasket. Clean pan and screen thoroughly and dry with compressed air.

2) Install screen, position new gasket and install oil pan. Replace drain plug. Add approximately 2/3 of refill capacity. Start engine and bring to normal operating temperature.

3) Complete fluid level check as described and add necessary amount, constantly checking fluid level to avoid overfilling.

ADJUSTMENT

BRAKE BAND

1) Drain transmission oil. Remove pan and gasket. Remove servo brake cover. Loosen adjusting screw lock nut. Tighten adjusting screw to 40 INCH lbs. (4.5 N.m.). Back adjusting screw off exactly 5 turns.

2) Hold screw in this position and tighten lock nut to 144-180 INCH lbs. (16-20 N.m.). Install servo cover, new gasket, and tighten cover bolts to 204-228 INCH lbs. (23-26 N.m.).

3) Install oil pan with new gasket, tightening bolts to 84-108 INCH lbs. (10-12 N.m.). Refill transmission fluid.

SHIFT LINKAGE

1) Disconnect selector rod from lower end of relay lever and pull selector rod so that transmission selector lever (on side of casing) is in "P" detent (all the way back). Selector lever in passenger compartment should also be set in "P".

2) Use adjusting nut on end of selector rod to adjust as required to obtain a free pin fit into end of relay

lever. Pull lower gear selector handle up and move gear selector through all 6 positions.

3) A definite click should be felt in each position. Set selector (with lower handle still pulled up) into position "1". Release lower handle. The stop tooth should engage into the selector gate causing selector lever to be shifted from position.

4) Repeat this check in all other gear positions. Make any necessary adjustments on selector rod as previously described.

Fig. 1: Spider Shift Linkage Adjustment

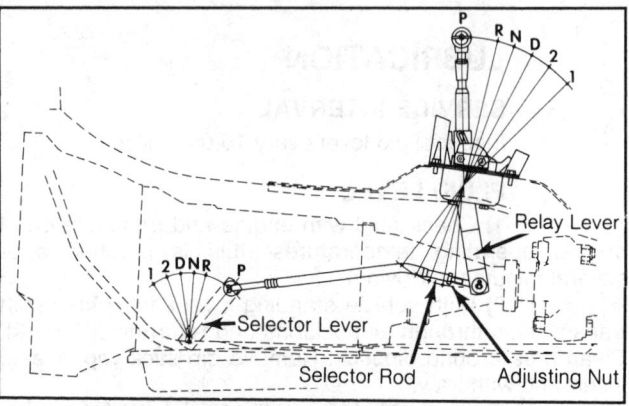

Indicator plate may also be shifted to align proper gear positions once all adjustments have been properly set.

THROTTLE LINKAGE

1) Disconnect telescoping link from control lever. Push accelerator pedal down until ball end on kickdown cable is just touching cable pin.

2) Push pedal to stop and check that kickdown cable has extended .28-.35" (7.0-9.0 mm). If not, make correction with adjusting nuts on cable housing.

3) Push pedal to stop. Hold control lever in full throttle position and extend telescoping link .32-.39" (8.0-10.0 mm). Check that telescoping link can be connected to control lever when extended. If not, loosen nuts on both ends of link an even amount.

Fig. 2: Components for Adjusting Throttle Linkage

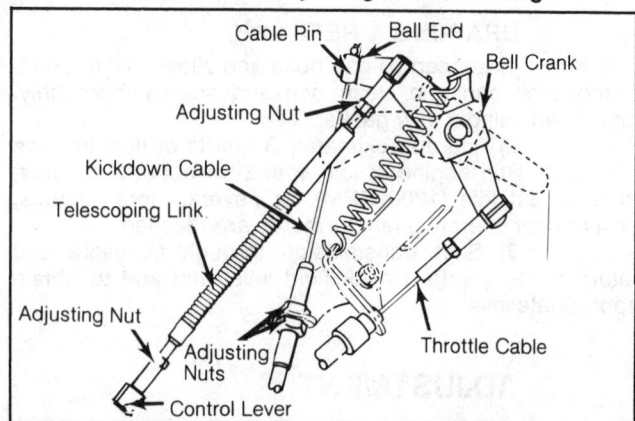

4) Release accelerator pedal until ball end is just touching cable pin. Move control lever to full throttle position.

5) Check that telescoping link can be connected to control lever without extending. Adjust nuts on link as required. Also note that kickdown valve moves properly when accelerator pedal is fully depressed.

HONDA ACCORD, CIVIC & PRELUDE

IDENTIFICATION

TRANSMISSION CODES

Application	Transmission (Code)
All Models	Honda Automatic Transaxle (AK)

LUBRICATION

SERVICE INTERVALS

Check fluid level at every oil change. Transmission fluid should be changed at 15,000 miles, then every 30,000. No filter service or band adjustment is required.

FLUID LEVEL

1) With vehicle on level floor and at normal operating temperature, stop engine. Clean area around dipstick and unscrew dipstick. Remove dipstick and wipe clean, then insert into hole but do not screw down.

2) Remove dipstick and check level. Fluid should be between upper and lower marks. Add as necessary.

FLUID TYPE

Automatic Transmission Fluid (ATF)
Dexron

FLUID CAPACITY

Dry Fill 5.2 qts (4.9L)
Refill 2.6 qts. (2.5L)

DRAINING & REFILLING

1) Ensure that operating temperature is up to normal and remove transmission drain plug. Use new gasket and replace drain plug when fluid is drained.

2) Fill with about 2 quarts of fluid through dipstick hole and check level. Add fluid to bring to upper mark on dipstick.

NOTE: **Refill capacity will always be slightly less than specified capacity due to fluid remaining in recesses of housing and converter.**

ADJUSTMENT

SHIFT CONTROL CABLE

1) Ensure that reverse gear engages. Remove center console. Place shift lever in "R" position. Remove lock clip and control cable pin. Check that hole in cable end is aligned with holes in selector lever arm.

2) If not, loosen lock nuts on control cable and adjust as required. Tighten lock nuts and install pin with lock clip. If pin does not go in easily, further adjustment is required. Check gear operation. *See Fig. 1.*

Fig. 1: Shift Control Cable Alignment

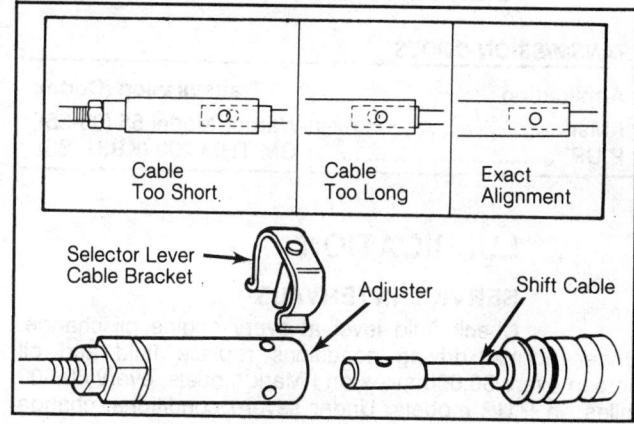

THROTTLE CONTROL CABLE & BRACKET

1) Ensure that engine is warmed up to normal operating temperature and cable securing clamps are in position. Disconnect control cable from lever and lay end on top of shock absorber tower.

2) Using throttle gauge (07974-6890300), adjust cable control bracket so that distance between bracket and lever is 3.29" (83.5 mm). Depress accelerator until there is no slack in carburetor throttle cable.

3) Adjust distance between control cable end and nut "A" to 3.37" (85.5 mm). Install cable and tighten lock nut "B", ensuring that lock nut "A" does not turn. *See Fig. 2.*

Fig. 2: Throttle Cable & Bracket Adjustment

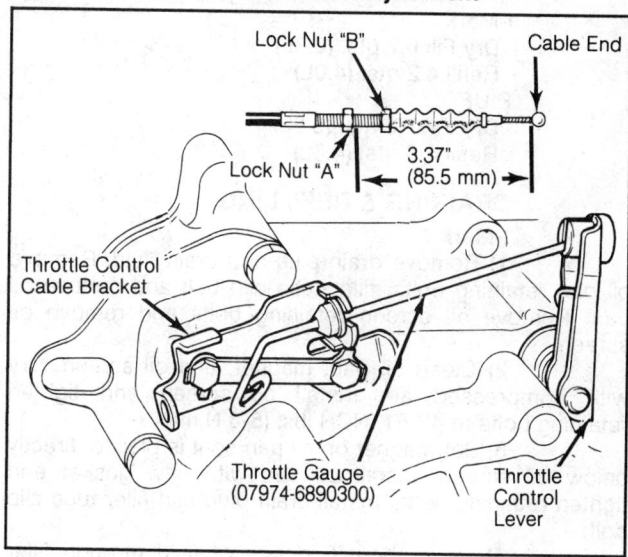

Automatic Transmission Servicing

ISUZU I-MARK & P'UP

IDENTIFICATION

TRANSMISSION CODES

Application	Transmission (Code)
I-Mark	Aisin-Warner Model 55 (03-55)
P'UP	GM THM 200 (KB31, 36)

LUBRICATION

SERVICE INTERVALS

Check fluid level at every engine oil change. Under normal driving conditions replace fluid and oil screen every 30,000 miles on I-Mark models, every 60,000 miles on P'UP models. Under severe conditions, change oil and screen at 15,000 mile intervals.

FLUID LEVEL

1) Place vehicle on level floor. Warm engine to normal operating temperature. Apply parking brake and place shift lever in "P" position. With engine idling, pull out dipstick, wipe clean and reinstall.

2) Remove dipstick and check level reading. Fluid level should be between the 2 dimples indicating "Hot" range. If not, add sufficient fluid to bring fluid to proper level.

FLUID TYPE

Automatic Transmission Fluid (ATF) Dexron II

FLUID CAPACITY

I-Mark
Dry Fill 6.7 qts. (6.3L)
Refill 4.2 qts. (4.0L)
P'UP
Dry Fill 7.0 qts. (6.6L)
Refill 4.5 qts. (4.3L)

DRAINING & REFILLING

I-Mark

1) Remove drain plug and drain fluid. Remove oil pan retaining bolts, filler tube clip bolt and remove oil pan. Remove oil screen retaining bolts and remove oil screen.

2) Clean oil pan, magnet, and oil screen. Dry with compressed air. Install oil screen and tighten retaining bolts to 43-51 INCH lbs. (5-6 N.m).

3) Set magnet on oil pan so it is placed directly below oil screen. Install oil pan with new gasket and tighten retaining bolts. Install drain plug and filler tube clip bolt.

4) Pour about 2 quarts of fluid through filler tube. Place selector lever in "P" and start engine. Shift through all gears, ending in "P" position.

5) Remove dipstick and check fluid level. Add fluid as necessary to bring level to correct mark on dipstick.

P'UP

1) Raise vehicle and place jack under transmission damper. Remove oil pan retaining bolts from front and side of pan. Loosen rear bolts 4 turns and pry pan loose, allowing fluid to drain.

2) Remove remaining bolts and remove oil pan. Clean pan and dry with compressed air. Remove 2 oil screen-to-valve body retaining bolts and remove screen. Clean screen and dry with compressed air.

3) Install new gasket on screen and install retaining bolts. Tighten to 72-120 INCH lbs. (21-35 N.m). Install oil pan with new gasket and tighten retaining bolts.

4) Lower vehicle and add about 3 quarts of fluid through filler tube. Place selector lever in "P", apply parking brake and start engine. Allow to idle.

5) Move selector lever through all gears, ending in "P". Check fluid level. Add fluid as required to bring fluid to correct mark on dipstick.

ADJUSTMENTS

THROTTLE VALVE CABLE

I-Mark (Gasoline Engine)

1) Loosen throttle valve cable adjusting nuts. Ensure that carburetor throttle adjusting screw is in contact with stopper for normal idling.

2) Adjust setting of outer cable, using adjusting nuts, so that distance between upper face of rubber boot on outer cable and cable stopper on inner cable is less than .04" (1 mm). Tighten adjusting nuts. See Fig. 1.

Fig. 1: I-Mark Gasoline Throttle Valve Cable Adjustment

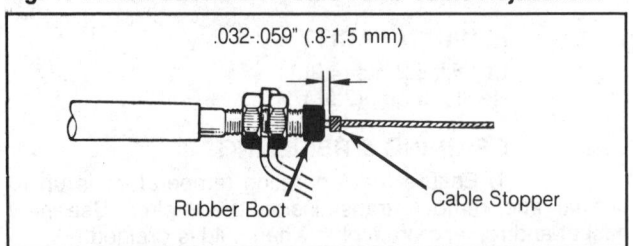

.032-.059" (.8-1.5 mm)

Rubber Boot

Cable Stopper

3) Check that stroke of inner cable from normal idling position to maximum speed position is 1.30-1.36" (32.9-33.9 mm).

I-Mark (Diesel Engine)

1) Loosen throttle valve cable adjusting nuts. With accelerator pedal fully depressed, ensure that injection pump lever is in contact with maximum speed adjust screw.

2) Hold lever in this position. Adjust setting of outer cable, using adjusting nuts, so that distance between end of rubber boot on outer cable and cable stopper on inner cable is less than .04" (1 mm). See Fig. 2.

Fig. 2: I-Mark Diesel Throttle Valve Cable Adjustment

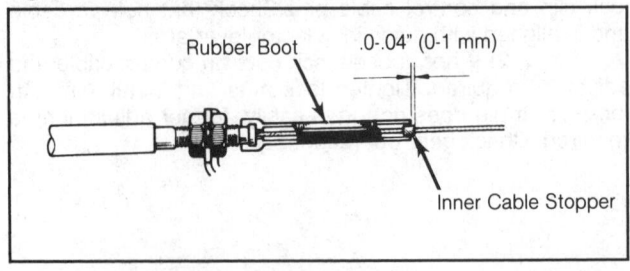

Rubber Boot

.0-.04" (0-1 mm)

Inner Cable Stopper

3) Tighten adjusting nuts. Check that stroke of inner cable from normal idling position to maximum speed position is 1.30-1.36" (32.9-33.9 mm).

ISUZU I-MARK & P'UP (Cont.)

P'UP (Gasoline Engine)

1) Check that carburetor lever and throttle valve control cable are normal and free from distortion. Loosen cable adjusting nuts at base of carburetor.

2) Bring carburetor lever to wide open position and adjust setting of inner cable by turning adjustment nut (lower nut) on the outer cable by hand, so that the inner cable has a play of about .04" (1 mm).

3) Tighten lock nut (upper nut). Check that stroke of inner cable from wide open position to closed position is 1.37-1.41" (34.8-35.8 mm). *See Fig. 3.*

Fig. 3: P'UP Gasoline Throttle Valve Cable Adjustment

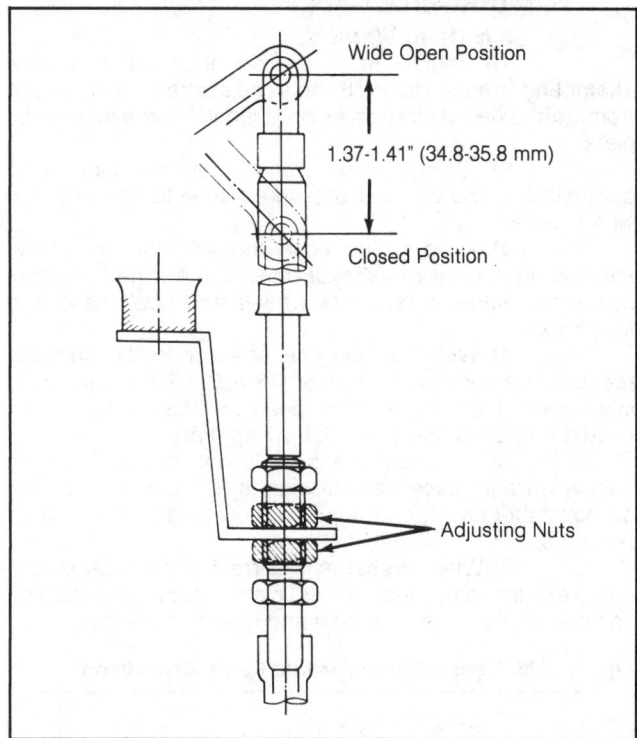

NOTE: Throttle valve cable adjustment for P'UP models with diesel engine was not available from manufacturer.

SHIFT LINKAGE

I-Mark

1) Loosen shift control rod adjusting nuts on transmission. Turn manual shaft fully clockwise as viewed from right side of transmission. Turn back to 3rd stop and set shaft in "N" position.

2) With transmission in "N", check that manual shift lever is in vertical position. Hold manual shaft in position and place shift lever in "N".

3) To remove play, tighten adjusting nuts with control shaft lever pushed rearward together with shift control lever. Road test vehicle to ensure that shift lever moves properly and transmission operates smoothly.

P'UP

1) Loosen control rod lock nuts on transmission. Turn manual shaft on transmission counterclockwise, as viewed from left side as far as it will go. Back off 3 stops to "N" position.

2) Hold shaft in this position and place shift lever in "N" position. Holding levers in this position, push shift control lever rearward to remove all play. Tighten lock nuts. Check for proper movement of shift control lever.

NEUTRAL SAFETY SWITCH

Loosen switch retaining screws (near base of selector lever). Place selector lever in "N". Bring the center of the switch moving piece into alignment with the line scribed on the steel case of the switch. Tighten retaining screws. Ensure that vehicle will only start in "P" or "N" position.

JAGUAR

IDENTIFICATION

TRANSMISSION CODES

Application	Transmission (Code)
XJ6	Borg-Warner Type 65
XJS	GM THM 400

LUBRICATION

SERVICE INTERVALS

Check fluid level every 3000 miles. Change fluid and filter at 24,000 mile intervals.

FLUID LEVEL

1) With vehicle resting on level floor, engine running, and transmission at normal operating temperatures. Apply hand brake and position gear selector in all ranges and return to "P" position.

2) Withdraw and wipe off dipstick, check fluid level. If necessary, add fluid to reach "MAX" level on "HOT" side of dipstick. After adding, repeat checking procedure to make sure overfilling has not occurred.

FLUID TYPE

XJ6 Automatic Transmission Fluid (ATF)
 Type "F"
XJS Automatic Transmission Fluid (ATF)
 Dexron II

FLUID CAPACITY

XJ6 Dry Fill 7.5 qts. (7.0L)
XJS Dry Fill 9.6 qts. (9.1L)

DRAINING & REFILLING

1) Place drain pan under transmission and disconnect oil cooler lines. Detach dipstick/filler tube and remove pan. Remove and discard filter and gasket.

2) Ensure that oil pan is clean and install filter and pan, using new gaskets. Replace dipstick/filler tube and add approximately 2 quarts. Proceed as in Fluid Level.

NOTE: Since converter is not drained, fluid required will be less than specified in Fluid Capacity.

ADJUSTMENT

FRONT BAND

XJ6 (Borg-Warner)

1) Remove nut retaining selector lever to selector shaft and remove lever. Push left seat fully to rear and lift carpet from left footwell.

2) Remove console side casing. Remove transmission access plate. Loosen lock nut retaining band adjuster screw and loosen adjuster 2 or 3 turns.

3) Tighten adjuster to 60 INCH lbs. (7 N.m). Back off screw 3/4 turn. Tighten lock nut while holding adjuster and replace covers and carpet.

NOTE: No front band adjustment on XJS (GM THM 400) transmission.

REAR BAND

XJ6 (Borg-Warner)

1) Loosen lock nut and rear band adjusting screw 2 or 3 turns, ensuring that adjusting screw rotates freely in case.

2) Tighten adjusting screw to 60 INCH lbs. (7 N.m). Back off 3/4 turn. Tighten lock nut while holding adjusting screw.

NOTE: No rear band adjustment on XJS (GM THM 400) transmission.

THROTTLE CABLE

XJ6 (Borg-Warner)

1) Engine must be correctly tuned before attempting transmission throttle adjustment. Lift carpet from left side of transmission tunnel. Remove access plate.

2) Using Allen wrench, remove plug from transmission and connect pressure gauge to transmission with adapter.

3) Feed gauge hose through hole in tunnel, keeping hose clear of exhaust pipe. Run engine to normal operating temperature. Block wheels and apply hand and foot brake.

4) With transmission selector in "D" position, pressure gauge should read 60-75 psi (4.2-5.3 kg/cm²) at idle speed. Increase engine speed to 1200 RPM. Gauge should now read 85-95 psi (5.9-6.7 kg/cm²).

5) If correct pressure is not obtained, switch engine off and place transmission in "N". Loosen lock nut on downshift cable, and adjust nut on outer cable to alter pressure.

6) When pressure is correct, tighten cable lock nut, reinstall plug and cover plate using new sealing compound. Replace carpeting and road test vehicle.

Fig. 1: XJ6 Transmission Throttle Cable Adjustment

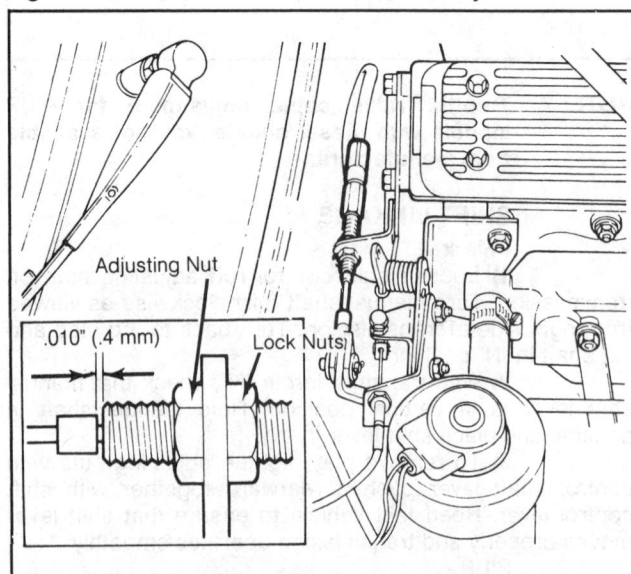

Ferrule crimped on inner cable should be .010" (.4 mm) from threaded portion of outer cable.

NOTE: Increasing length of cable increases pressure. Decreasing length decreases pressure.

JAGUAR (Cont.)

DETENT DOWNSHIFT SWITCH

XJS (GM THM 400)

1) With ignition on, check that power is available at input terminal (Green wire). With one lead of test light grounded, connect other lead to output terminal (Grn/Wht wire).

2) Fully depress accelerator and depress switch arm. If light still does not operate, replace switch. If switch is OK, loosen switch screws. Move switch towards cable until at full throttle opening, light operates. Tighten switch screws and recheck.

Fig. 2: XJS Detent Downshift Switch Adjustment

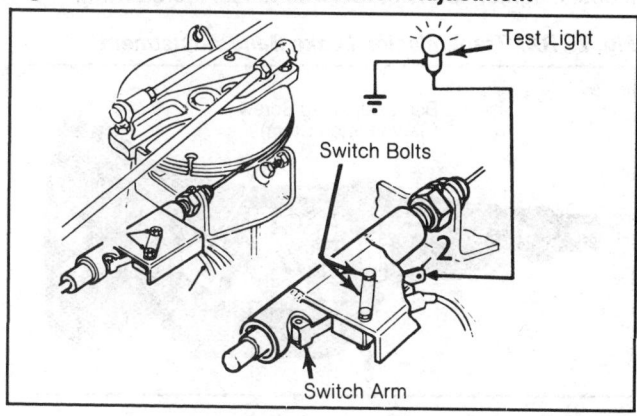

SHIFT LINKAGE

1) Remove console and place selector lever in position "1" on XJ6 models, and in "N" position on XJS models. Unscrew shift knob and remove indicator plate.

2) Remove cotter pin and washer retaining cable to bracket on lever. Ensure transmission lever is in "1" position on XJ6 and in "N" position on XJS models.

3) Adjust front and rear lock nuts until cable can be connected without selector or transmission lever being disturbed. Tighten lock nuts and secure cable with new cotter pin. Reinstall selector plate and shift knob.

Fig. 3: Jaguar Shift Linkage

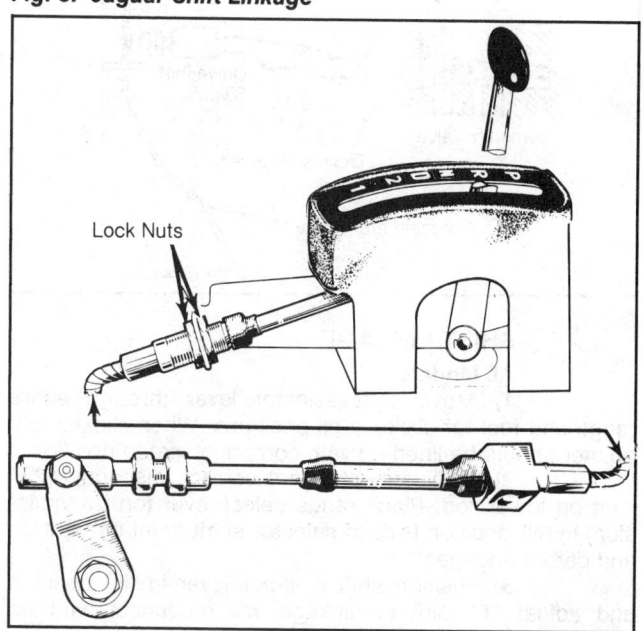

NEUTRAL SAFETY SWITCH

1) Remove selector indicator and position electric window switch panel away from console. Move control panel to gain access to cigar lighter wiring and door lock switch wiring. Disconnect these wires after noting positions for reassembly.

2) Remove control panel. Disconnect feed wire to switch and connect powered test light to terminal. Place selector lever in "N" position and loosen lock nuts which secure the switch. Adjust switch until test light operates.

3) Tighten switch lock nuts and check that light remains on with lever in "P", and goes off with lever in any driving positions. Remove test light, reconnect feed wire, and reinstall all removed parts.

Fig. 4: Neutral Safety Switch Adjustment

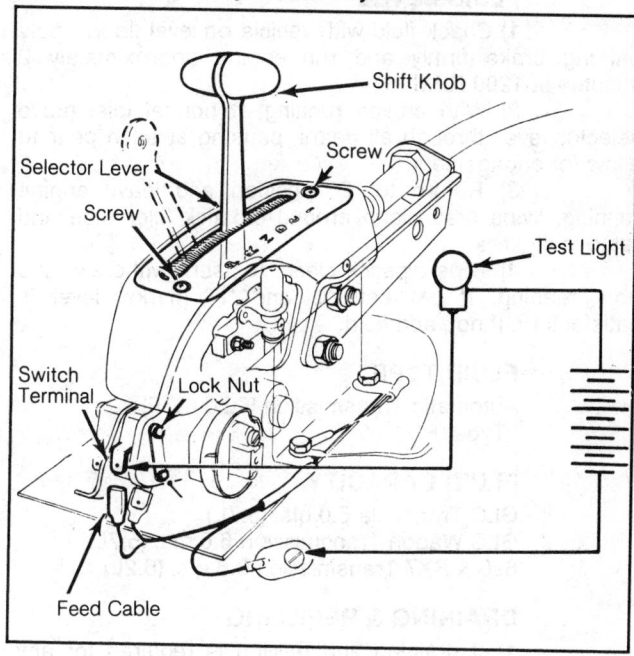

Automatic Transmission Servicing

MAZDA

IDENTIFICATION

TRANSMISSION CODES

Application	Codes
GLC	F3A
626, GLC Wagon, RX7	3N71B

LUBRICATION

SERVICE INTERVALS

Inspect automatic transmission fluid level every 7500 miles or 7 1/2 months.

FLUID LEVEL

1) Check fluid with vehicle on level floor. Apply parking brake firmly and run engine approximately 2 minutes at 1200 RPM.

2) With engine running at normal idle, move selector lever through all gears, pausing at each gear to allow for engagement.

3) Return to "P" position and leave engine running. Wipe area clean around dipstick filler tube and remove dipstick.

4) Wipe dipstick clean, reinsert, withdraw, and note reading. If between "L" and "F" marks, level is satisfactory. If not, add fluid.

FLUID TYPE

Automatic Transmission Fluid (ATF)
  Type "F"

FLUID CAPACITY

GLC Transaxle 6.0 qts. (5.7L)
GLC Wagon Transmission 6.0 qts. (5.7L)
626 & RX7 Transmission 6.6 qts. (6.2L)

DRAINING & REFILLING

1) If draining and refilling is required for any operation, remove pan bolts and allow fluid to drain. Remove pan and gasket, (discard gasket).

2) Clean pan thoroughly and reinstall new gasket, tightening pan bolts to 36-60 INCH lbs. (4-9 N.m). Add fluid, make sure not to overfill.

Fig. 1: GLC Wagon and 626 Transmission Brake Band Adjustment

ADJUSTMENT

BRAKE BAND
All Models

1) Oil pan must be removed on GLC Wagon & 626 to adjust brake band. Loosen servo piston stem lock nut and back off a few turns.

2) Using a torque wrench, tighten servo piston stem to 108-132 INCH lbs. (12-15 N.m), then back off piston stem exactly 2 turns.

3) Hold piston stem in this position and tighten lock nut to 132-348 INCH lbs. (15-39 N.m), on GLC (FWD) models, tighten lock nut to 41-59 ft. lbs. (56-80 N.m).

Fig. 2: RX7 Transmission Brake Band Adjustment

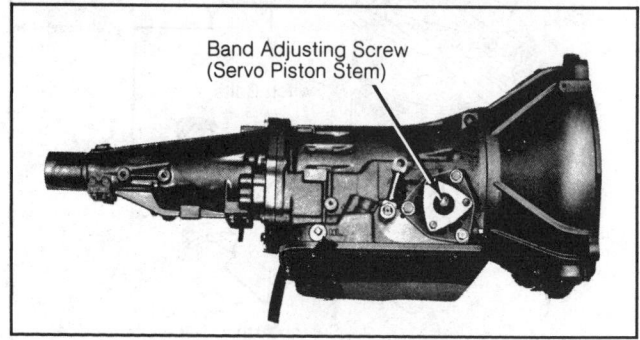

KICKDOWN SWITCH & DOWNSHIFT SOLENOID
All Models

1) Depress accelerator pedal to limit. Near wide-open throttle, click should be heard from solenoid. Switch must operate at or after 7/8 of pedal travel.

2) If not, loosen switch retaining nut and adjust switch to engage when pedal is at 7/8 of its full travel, tighten retaining nut and check solenoid.

Fig. 3: Kickdown Switch and Downshift Solenoid

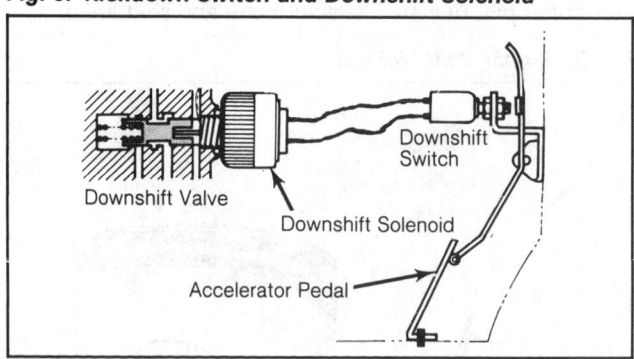

SHIFT LINKAGE
All Models

1) Move shift selector lever through entire range and feel for clicks in all positions. When click is felt, pointer should be lined up with correct indicated position.

2) If adjustment is not correct, disconnect "T" joint on lower rod. Place range select lever (on transmission) in "N" position (slot of selector shaft point straight up and detent engages).

3) Position shift selector lever in "N" position and adjust "T" joint so linkage will reconnect with no looseness. Recheck setting in all ranges.

MAZDA (Cont.)

Fig. 4: Transmission Shift Linkage

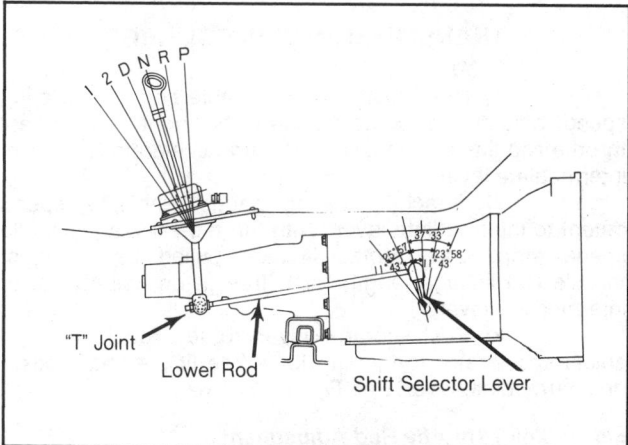

NEUTRAL SAFETY SWITCH

GLC Wagon & RX7

1) After checking and adjusting shift linkage, place the transmission lever in the "N" position. Remove transmission manual lever retaining nut.

2) Loosen inhibitor switch retaining bolts. Remove screw from alignment pin hole at bottom of switch.

3) Rotate switch and insert a .078" (2.0 mm) diameter alignment pin through the alignment hole and into hole of internal rotor. Tighten switch retaining bolts and remove alignment pin.

4) Reinstall alignment pin hole screw. Reinstall transmission manual lever and check operation of switch. The engine should only start in "N" or "P" position.

Fig. 5: Adjusting Neutral Safety Switch On GLC Wagon & RX7 Transmissions

626

1) Shift the selector lever to "N" position and loosen switch retaining screws. Insure that selector lever is in the "N" position, adjust if necessary.

2) Move switch so that the identification marks on the switch body and sliding plate are aligned. Tighten switch retaining screws.

3) Check operation of switch in the "N" and "P" position to insure proper operation. The engine should only start when the selector lever is in "N" or "P" position.

Fig. 6: Adjusting Neutral Safety Switch On 626

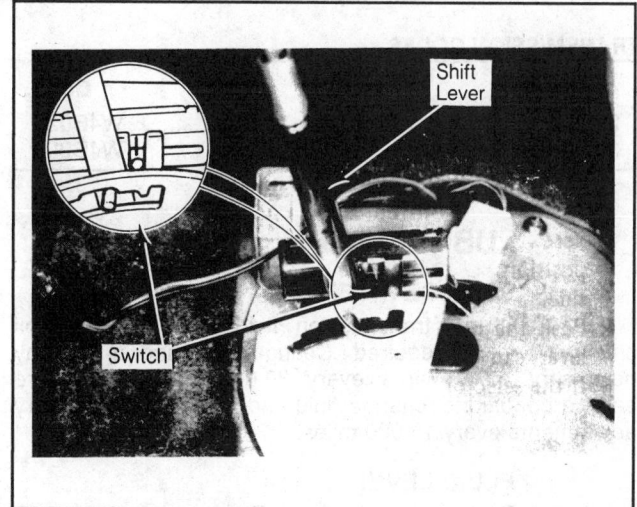

Automatic Transmission Servicing

MERCEDES-BENZ

IDENTIFICATION

TRANSMISSION CODES

Application	Code
240D	W4B025
300 & 380 Series	W4B025

LUBRICATION

SERVICE INTERVALS

Check transmission fluid level at every oil change. Add as required. Change fluid and make any necessary adjustments every 30,000 miles. In severe service conditions, change fluid and make any necessary adjustments every 15,000 miles.

FLUID LEVEL

Transmission at Room Temperature

1) Fluid level can be determined more accurately in a cold transmission with temperature between 68-86°F (20-30°C). With vehicle on a level surface, apply parking brake and place selector lever in "P" position.

2) With engine at normal idle, check fluid. Fluid must be 1.18" (30 mm) below minimum marking. Add (or remove) fluid as necessary to reach this level. Do not overfill.

Transmission at Operating Temperature

1) With vehicle on a level floor and transmission in "P" position, idle engine for at least 2 minutes to make sure torque converter is filled.

2) At this time, fluid level should be between upper and lower marks on the dipstick. Add (or remove) fluid as necessary to reach this level. Do not overfill.

3) Difference between the 2 marks represents approximately 0.6 pint. After adding fluid, shift gear selector through all ranges and recheck fluid.

FLUID TYPE

Automatic Transmission Fluid (ATF)
Dexron

FLUID CAPACITY

240D
  Refill 5 qts. (4.8L)
  Dry Fill 6.4 qts. (6.1L)
300 & 380 Series
  Refill 6.5 qts. (6.2L)
  Dry Fill 7.7 qts. (7.3L)

DRAINING & REFILLING

1) Remove filler tube and allow fluid to drain. Rotate engine until drain plug in torque converter is accessible through hole in bottom of torque converter housing. When all fluid has drained, remove pan and oil filter screen.

2) Install new screen and gasket. Install pan. Replace plug in torque converter. Attach filler tube to oil pan and add fluid.

3) When majority of fluid is added, start engine, idle for about 2 minutes, place selector in each gear and return to "P" position. Check fluid level and adjust as necessary. Do not overfill.

ADJUSTMENT

TRANSMISSION THROTTLE ROD
240D

1) Turn rotary knob of cable control for idling speed adjustment completely to the right. Disconnect throttle rod linkage, throttle rod, and accelerator rod from intermediate lever.

2) Attach adjusting gauge with idle speed detent to intermediate lever. With throttle valve against idle speed stop, and throttle linkage pulled back, adjust throttle rod linkage length for a free fit on ball socket of intermediate lever.

3) Push control lever to idle position, then adjust accelerator rod length for a free fit over ball socket on intermediate lever. See Fig. 1.

Fig. 1: 240D Throttle Rod Adjustment

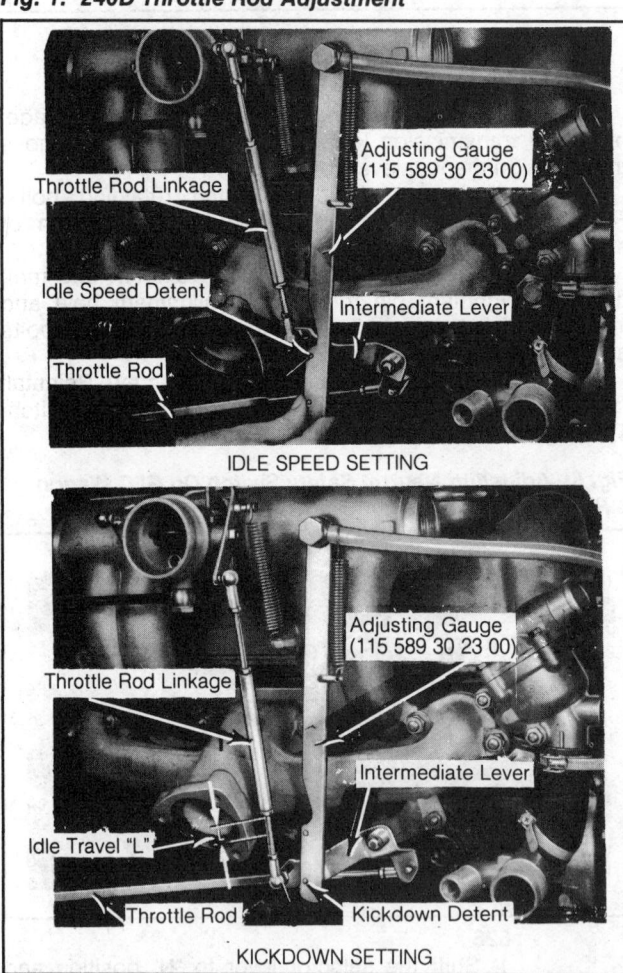

IDLE SPEED SETTING

KICKDOWN SETTING

4) Remove adjusting gauge idle detent from intermediate lever. Press accelerator pedal to kickdown position, adjusting gauge full-throttle detent should fit freely into intermediate lever.

5) If not, adjust length of accelerator rod for a free fit. With adjustments made, check that travel "L" of throttle rod linkage from full throttle position to kickdown position is approximately .236" (6 mm). If not, adjust ball socket in oblong hole of intermediate lever. When adjustments are correct, remove adjusting gauge.

MERCEDES-BENZ (Cont.)

300 & 380 Series

1) During adjustment, accelerator must be in full-throttle position. Disconnect control pressure rod. In the full throttle position (kickdown position), the control lever must rest against full-throttle stop.

2) If not, control shaft has to be adjusted by loosening screw on bellcrank. Pull control pressure rod forward to full-throttle position and adjust length on ball socket so that rod can be reconnected without tension.

Fig. 2: Throttle Rod Adjustment

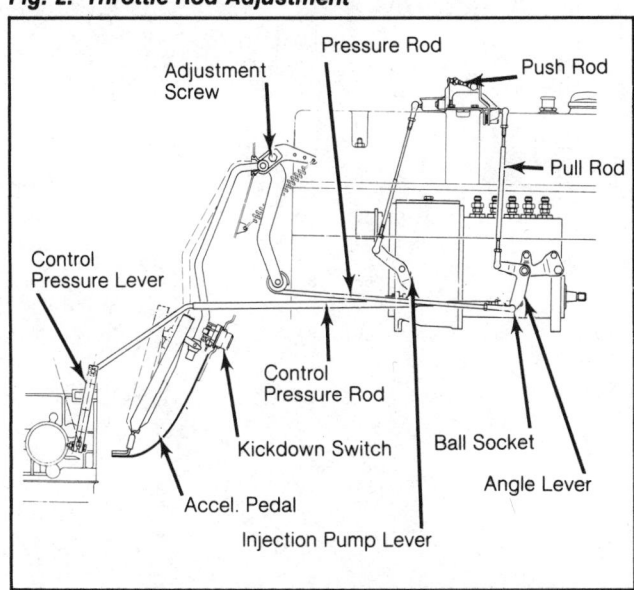

NEUTRAL SAFETY SWITCH

1) Place control lever in "N" position and disconnect shift rod from selector lever. Loosen adjusting screw and insert pin through selector lever into locating hole in shift housing.

2) Tighten adjusting screw and connect shift rod to selector lever. Check that engine starts only in "N" and "P" positions. *See Fig. 4.*

NOTE: If shift rod does not fit freely in selector lever see Shift Linkage Adjustment in this article.

Fig. 3: Neutral Safety Switch Adjustment

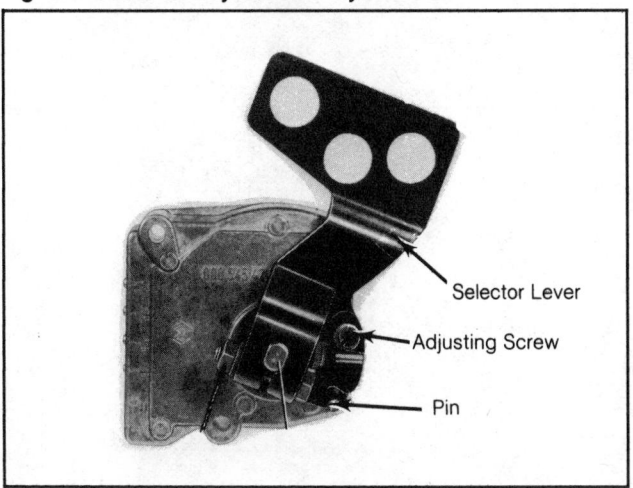

SHIFT LINKAGE
Floor Shift

1) Disconnect shift rod from selector lever. Place selector lever and control lever in "N" position. Make sure there is approximately .04" (1 mm) clearance between control lever and the "N" position stop on console.

2) Adjust shift rod length for a free fit in selector lever. Tighten lock nut.

PEUGEOT

IDENTIFICATION

TRANSMISSION CODES

Application	Transmission (Code)
All Models	ZF 3HP 22

LUBRICATION

SERVICE INTERVALS

Check transmission level at every oil change. Drain and refill transmission every 30,000 miles or 2 years, whichever comes first. If operated under severe driving conditions, change fluid every 15,000 miles.

FLUID LEVEL

1) Park vehicle on level floor with engine at normal operating temperature. Apply parking brake. Move selector lever through all positions, ending in "P".

2) Remove dipstick and wipe with a clean lint free cloth. Reinstall dipstick and check fluid level. "MAX" mark is maximum hot level. "MIN" mark is minimum cold level. "MIDDLE" mark is minimum hot level or maximum cold level.

FLUID TYPE

Automatic Transmission Fluid (ATF)
 Dexron B or D

FLUID CAPACITY

Refill 1.7 qts. (1.6L)
Dry Fill 5.4 qts. (5.2L)

DRAINING & REFILLING

1) With engine at normal operating temperature, remove drain plug from transmission oil pan, allow all fluid to drain and reinstall drain plug. Add approximate amount of fluid as indicated in *Fluid Capacity*.

2) Start engine and let idle. Move shift selector lever through all positions. Recheck fluid level and add as needed. DO NOT overfill.

ADJUSTMENT

KICKDOWN CABLE

With throttle control drum in normal hot idle position, adjust cable housing to give maximum clearance of .020" (.5 mm) between end of cable housing and clip on cable.

SHIFT LINKAGE

Disconnect selector rod at transmission lever. Place transmission lever in "N" position. Place gear selector lever in "N" and adjust rod length to fit both levers without tension.

NEUTRAL SAFETY SWITCH

Engine should start in "N" or "P" only. To adjust, install or remove shims at base of switch until proper operation is achieved.

PORSCHE

IDENTIFICATION

TRANSMISSION CODES

Application	Code
924 & 944	087
928	A22

LUBRICATION

SERVICE INTERVALS

Check fluid level every 15,000 miles. Change fluid every 30,000 miles.

FLUID LEVEL

1) With vehicle on level floor, run engine until normal operating temperatures are reached. Shift selector lever to "N" position.

2) The fluid level is checked visually through the transparent reservoir, located at the rear end of the transmission. Oil level must be between the 2 marks. Do not overfill.

FLUID TYPE

Automatic Transmission Fluid (ATF)
DEXRON

FLUID CAPACITY

Dry Fill 6.3 qts. (6.0L)
 Oil cooler requires .9 qts. (.8L)
Refill 3.0 qts. (2.8L)

ADJUSTMENT

SELECTOR LEVER
924 & 944

1) Move selector lever to "P" position. Loosen nut on clamping sleeve for selector lever cable. Move operating lever on transmission to "P" position (against stop). See Fig. 1.

Fig. 1: 924 & 944 Selector Lever Adjusting Point

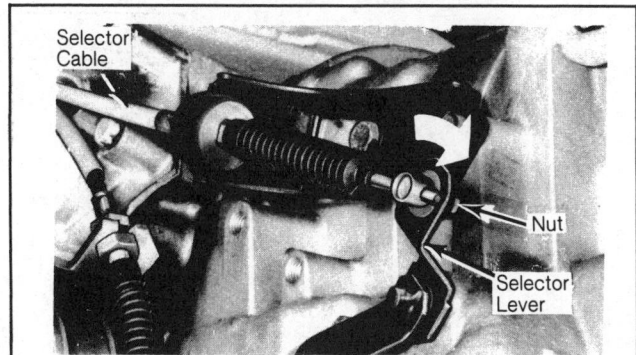

2) Tighten nut on clamping sleeve. Move selector through all positions with engine running. Engagement should be felt after 5 seconds.
928
1) Place selector lever in "N" position. Detach cable from operating lever on transmission. Place selector lever (on transmission) in "N" position.

2) Adjust cable so that socket attaches to operating lever without tension and reattach cable to lever. See Fig. 2.

Fig. 2: 928 Selector Lever Adjusting Point

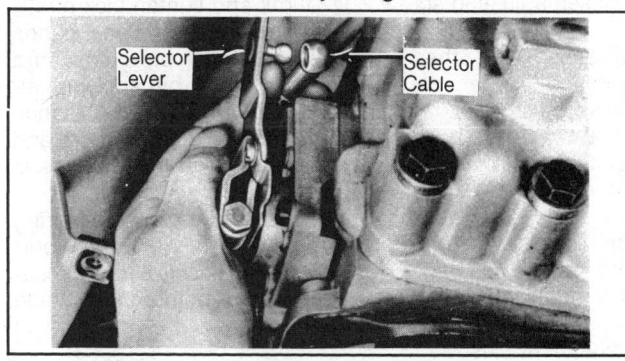

NEUTRAL SAFETY SWITCH
924 & 944

Starter should operate only in "P" or "N" positions. If starter operates in any other position, remove selector lever gate and loosen retaining bolts on safety switch. Adjust switch as necessary.
928

Move selector lever to "N" position. Loosen adjusting screw, insert .157" (4 mm) pin through drive dog into hole in case. Tighten adjusting screw and remove locating pin. Check to see that engine starts in "N" or "P" positions only.

THROTTLE PRESSURE CABLE
924 & 944

1) Screw in cable sleeve retaining nut on transmission bracket and tighten. Push roller holder in slot forward as far as possible and tighten bolts.

2) Completely loosen short cable at firewall and long cable at roller holder. Turn roller so that operating lever is forward.

3) Hold roller in this position and mount throttle valve push rod without tension. Place cable around roller and adjust long cable sleeve until cable locator just rests in opening without tension.
928

Detach cable at transmission lever. Adjust lever with adjusting bolt "A" after loosening bolt "B" so that cable can be attached without tension or free play. See Fig. 3.

Fig. 3: 928 Throttle Cable Pressure Adjustment

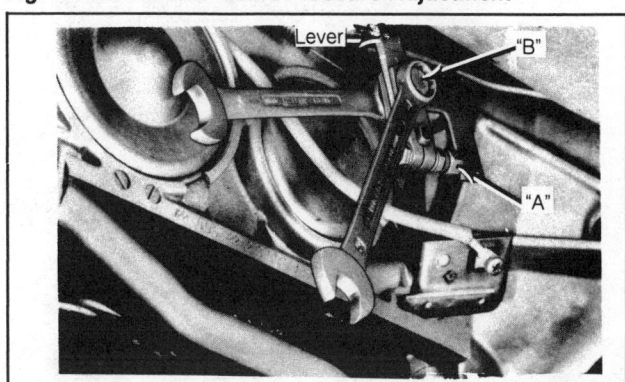

Automatic Transmission Servicing
PORSCHE (Cont.)

BRAKE BANDS

1) On all models. loosen lock nut, tighten adjusting screw to 84 INCH lbs. (10 N.m). Back off adjusting screw and retighten to 48 INCH lbs. (5 N.m). Loosen adjusting screw 2 1/2 turns and tighten lock nut.

2) On 928 models, there are 2 additional bands to adjust and they are adjusted with pins. Measure distance of free play for piston No. 2 by applying air pressure to No. 2 release port. *See Fig. 4.* Check distance at "B", then apply air pressure to No. 2 apply port and recheck distance "B". The difference of both distances is the free play.

3) Brake band No. 1 is checked by measuring the distance at "A". Apply air pressure to No. 1 apply port and recheck distance "A". The difference of both measurements is the free play. Free play of both bands should be .118-.157" (3-4 mm). Adjustments are made with adjustment pins.

Fig. 4: 928 Brake Band Measurement

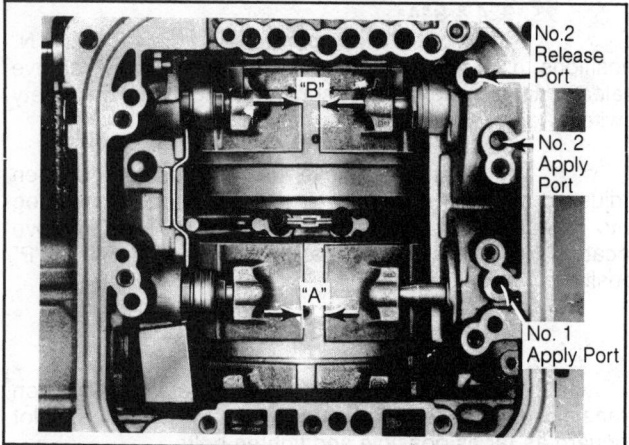

RENAULT

IDENTIFICATION

TRANSMISSION CODES

Application	Codes
Fuego & 18i	4139

LUBRICATION

SERVICE INTERVALS

Check fluid every 6000 miles. Change fluid at first 1000 miles and every 24,000 miles thereafter.

FLUID LEVEL

1) With vehicle on level floor, place selector lever in "P" position. Apply parking brake and start engine. Allow engine to idle, and remove dipstick. Wipe clean, replace and remove again.

2) With engine at normal operating temperature, fluid level should be between "Mini Hot" and "Maxi Hot" marks. With fluid level at ambient temperatures, level should be between "Mini Cold" marks.

3) If level is not to specifications, add fluid to bring level to correct mark, do not overfill.

FLUID TYPE

Automatic Transmission Fluid (ATF)
Dexron II

FLUID CAPACITY

Dry Fill 5.2 qts. (5.0L)
Refill 2.7 qts. (2.5L)

ADJUSTMENTS

KICKDOWN SWITCH

Make sure that the accelerator cable has sufficient play to allow a 1/16" (1.58 mm) movement in the stop sleeve when accelerator pedal is completely depressed. Make sure that cover is in position to prevent tarnishing of contacts. See Fig. 1.

Fig. 1: Adjusting Kickdown Switch

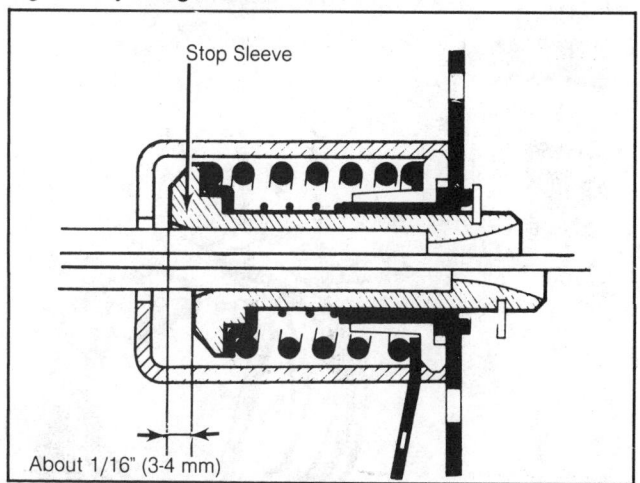

Adjust kickdown switch before adjusting other components.

ACCELERATOR CABLE

Depress accelerator fully to wide open throttle. Adjust accelerator cable to obtain .080" (2 mm) compression of spring in the cable stop. See Fig. 2.

Fig. 2: Adjusting Accelerator Cable

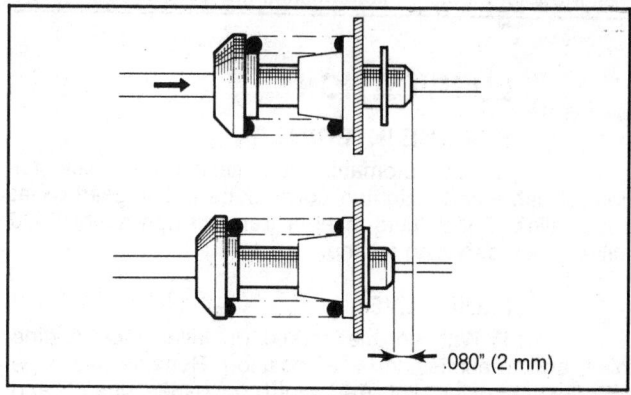

Make sure kickdown switch is functioning correctly.

GOVERNOR CABLE

Adjust cable adjusters on both governor and throttle sides to mid way. Adjust cable stop to obtain a clearance of .008-.028" (.20-.70 mm). See Fig. 3.

Fig. 3: Adjusting Governor Cable.

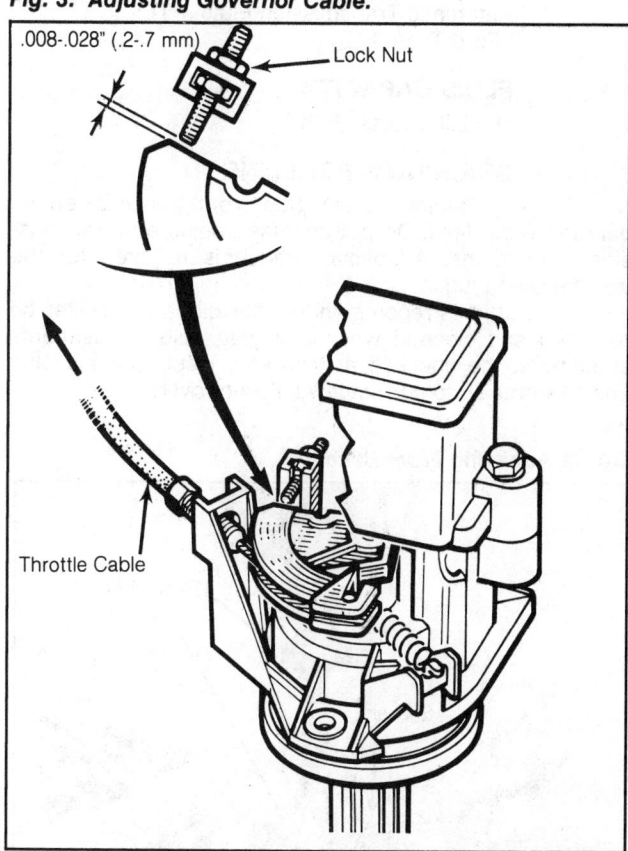

All other components must be operating properly before adjusting governor.

SAAB

IDENTIFICATION

TRANSMISSION CODES

Application	Transmission (Code)
All Models	Borg-Warner (37)

LUBRICATION

SERVICE INTERVALS

Adjust automatic transmission gear selector control cable and retighten cover bolts under gearbox at 1000 miles. Check fluid level in transmission every 7500 miles, when servicing engine.

FLUID LEVEL

1) With vehicle parked on level floor, engine idling and transmission in "P" position. Remove and wipe off dipstick using lint free cloth or paper. Insert and remove dipstick.

2) Fluid level should be between the maximum and minimum marks on the dipstick. Be sure to read hot or cold markings on dipstick, depending on transmission oil temperature. Do not overfill.

FLUID TYPE

Automatic Transmission Fluid (ATF)
  Ford Type "F"

FLUID CAPACITY

Dry Fill 8.5 qts. (8.0L)

DRAINING & REFILLING

1) Remove drain plug from transmission oil pan and drain fluid. Do not confuse engine and transmission drain plugs. A special wrench is required for the transmission plug.

2) It is recommended that oil pan and filter be removed and cleaned when changing fluid. Adjustments should also be checked at this time. Replace drain plug and fill with ATF to correct level. Do not overfill.

Fig. 1: Adjusting Front Band

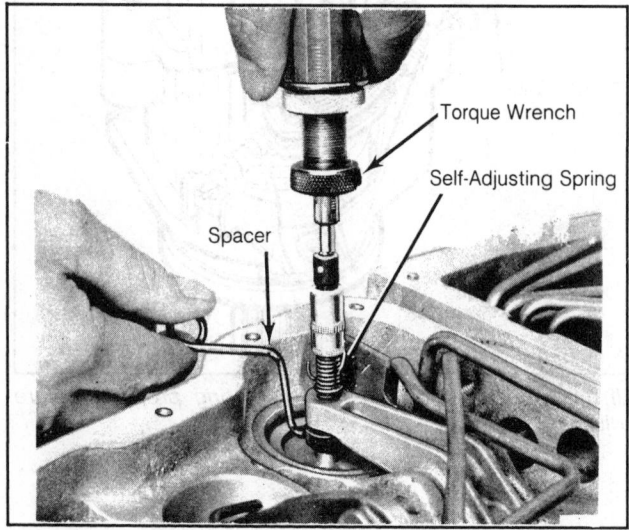

Pan must be removed to adjust front band.

ADJUSTMENT

FRONT BAND

1) Drain fluid and remove pan. Place a 1/4" (6.35 mm) thick spacer tool (8790073) between adjusting screw and boss on servo piston.

2) Tighten adjusting screw to 10 INCH lbs. (14 N.m). Check that gap between self-adjusting spring and lever is 1.5-2.0 screw threads. *See Fig. 1.*

REAR BAND

Rear band adjusting screw is located outside transmission housing on left side. To adjust band, loosen lock nut a few turns and tighten adjusting screw to 108-120 INCH lbs. (12-14 N.m). Back screw off 3/4 turn and hold in position while tightening lock nut.

Fig. 2: Adjusting Rear Band

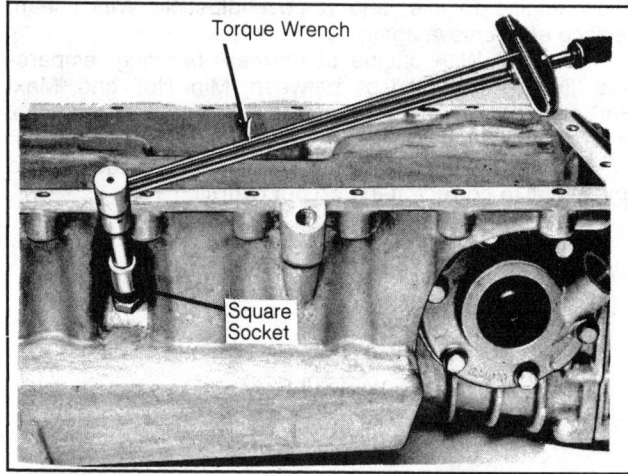

Adjustment is made on left side of transmission.

TRANSMISSION THROTTLE CABLE

1) Connect tachometer to engine and pressure gauge to transmission. Apply parking brake, start engine and ensure that idle speed is to specification. Move transmission selector to "D" position.

Fig. 3: Pressure Gauge Connecting Point for Throttle Pressure Test

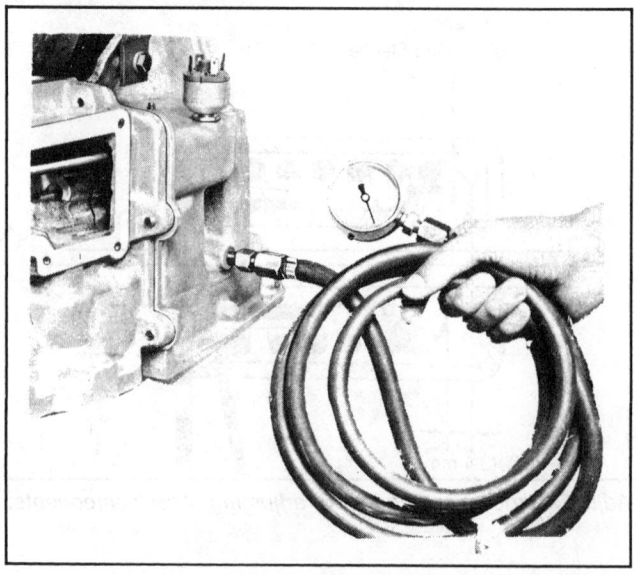

SAAB (Cont.)

2) Pressure should read 50-70 psi (3.5-4.9 kg/cm²). Increase engine speed 500 RPM above idle. Pressure should increase 10-20 psi (.7-1.4 kg/cm²). If pressure is too low, adjust throttle cable outward. If pressure rise is too high, adjust cable inward.

Fig. 4: Throttle Cable Adjustment Point

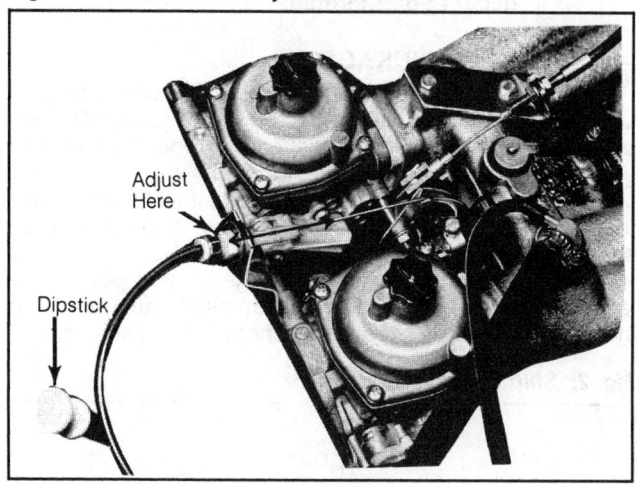

SHIFT LINKAGE

1) To check linkage adjustment, depress pawl button and move lever slightly back and forth until a click can be heard and you feel the selector valve lock in the neutral position.

2) Release pawl button and selector lever should now be in "N" position. To adjust, loosen cable attachment at lever with Allen wrench and extension while selector valve is locked in neutral. Move lever to position pawl in notch on selector segment and tighten cable set screw.

Fig. 5: Shift Selector Segment with "N" Detent

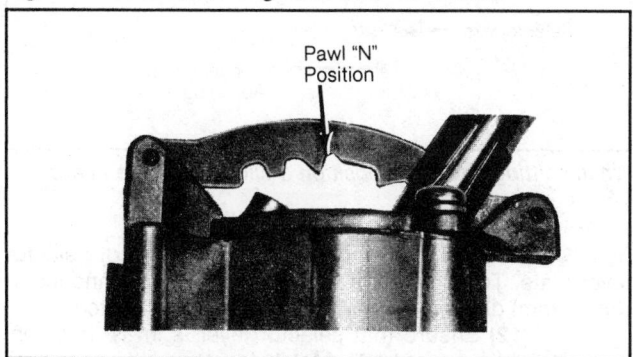

NEUTRAL SAFETY SWITCH

1) Disconnect wires from switch. With transmission in "D" position, loosen switch and connect self-powered test light to neutral safety switch terminals.

2) Test light should operate. Screw switch in until light goes out and mark position. Move test light probes to back-up switch (wide) terminals and light should go out.

3) Screw in switch and count turns until light goes on, then unscrew half way between these positions and tighten switch lock nut. Do not overtighten lock nut or switch may be damaged.

Fig. 6: Neutral Safety Switch Testing Points

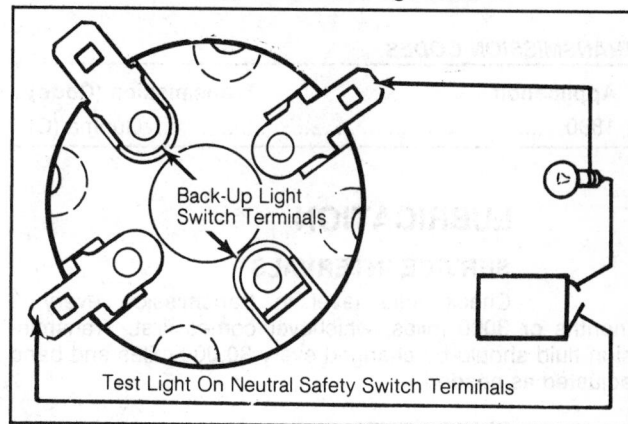

SUBARU

IDENTIFICATION

TRANSMISSION CODES

Application	Transmission (Code)
1800	Gunma (C)

LUBRICATION

SERVICE INTERVALS

Check fluid level in transmission every 3 months or 3000 miles, whichever comes first. Transmission fluid should be changed every 30,000 miles and band adjusted as needed.

FLUID LEVEL

1) Normal operating temperature for fluid is 122-176°F (50-80°C) and is reached after driving for 10 minutes or idling for 25 minutes. With vehicle parked on level floor and at normal operating temperature.

2) Set transmission selector lever in "P" position with engine idling. Remove dipstick and clean with lint-free cloth.

3) Insert and remove dipstick, note fluid level and add through dipstick hole to bring to full mark. When filling transmission, do not overfill.

FLUID TYPE

Automatic Transmission Fluid (ATF) Dexron

FLUID CAPACITY

5.9-6.3 qts. (5.6-6.0L)

DRAINING & REFILLING

Remove drain plug and drain fluid. Replace drain plug and fill transmission with about 4 quarts of ATF. Start engine and check fluid level with engine idling. Add fluid as necessary, do not overfill.

ADJUSTMENT

REAR BAND

Loosen lock nut on band adjusting screw and tighten screw to 78 INCH lbs. (9 N.m). Loosen screw 2 turns and hold in position while tightening lock nut.

Fig. 1: Rear Band Adjustment

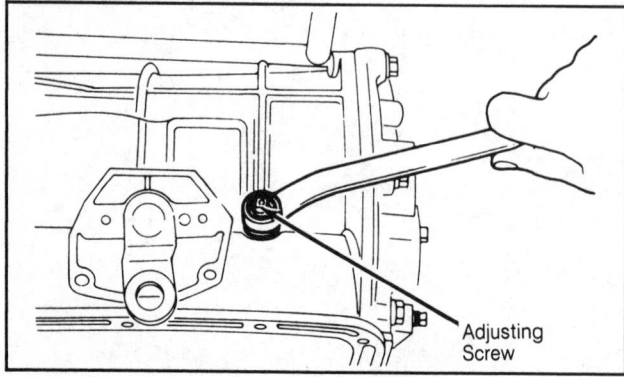

Adjustment is made at left side of transaxle.

KICKDOWN SWITCH

Switch on ignition and depress accelerator fully. A "click" should be heard just as accelerator bottoms out. Adjust switch inward or outward for proper operation.

NOTE: **If switch operates too soon, downshift will occur at part throttle.**

SHIFT LINKAGE

1) Move selector lever from "P" to "1" position. Lever should set into each position with a "click". At each position, check that selector dial gives proper indication of gear position.

2) If linkage is out of adjustment, make sure that selector lever does not move below "1" position, then shift to "D" position.

3) Adjust length of linkage so that position of lever corresponds with detent of manual valve and that indicator is correctly lined up. Recheck in all positions.

Fig. 2: Shift Linkage Adjustment

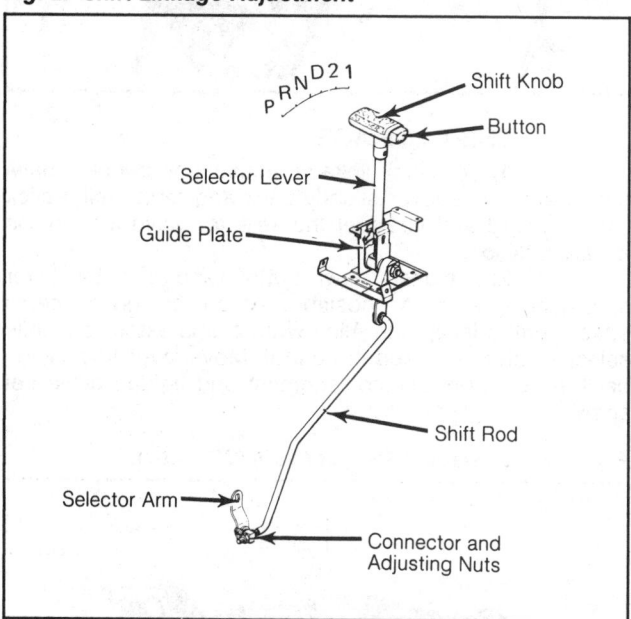

When shifting into each position a click should be heard.

NEUTRAL SAFETY SWITCH

1) Switch is mounted on right side of selector lever plate. To adjust, remove switch from plate and insert .08" (2 mm) diameter pin in alignment hole on switch.

2) Ensure that selector lever is in "N" position, pushed lightly toward "P". Match locator to bracket hole and moving plate pin to arm hole. Tighten retaining bolts in position and remove alignment pin.

Fig. 3: Neutral Safety Switch Adjustment

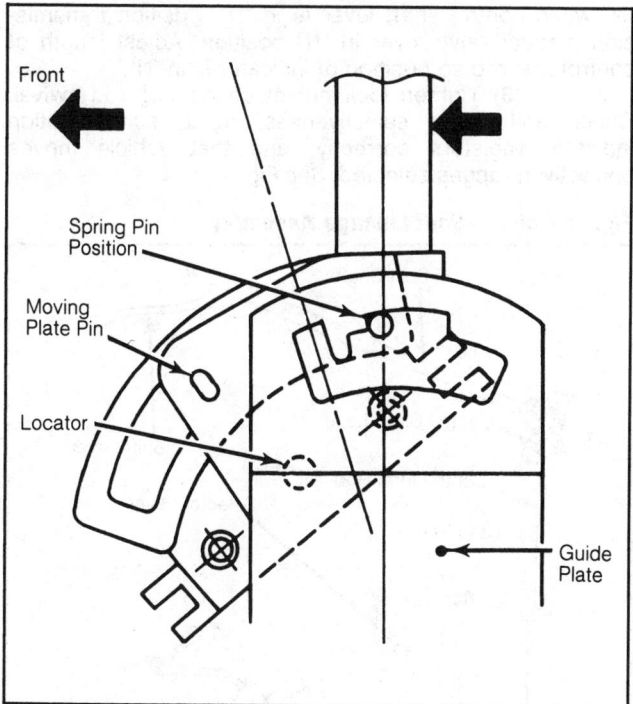

Front

Spring Pin
Position

Moving
Plate Pin

Locator

Guide
Plate

Insert a .08" (2 mm) diameter pin to align hole in switch.

Automatic Transmission Servicing

TOYOTA

IDENTIFICATION

TRANSMISSION CODES

Application	Code
Celica & Corona	A40D
Corolla	A40 & A40D
Cressida & 2WD Pickup	A43D
Supra	A43DL
Tercel (FWD)	A55

LUBRICATION

SERVICE INTERVALS

Check transmission fluid every 15,000 miles. In severe conditions, fluid should be changed every 15,000 miles.

FLUID LEVEL

Check transmission fluid level with engine idling. Shift each gear from "P" through "L" and back to "P". Fluid level should be within cold or hot ranges marked on dipstick. Do not overfill.

FLUID TYPE

Automatic Transmission Fluid (ATF)
 Type "F"

FLUID CAPACITY

Celica, Corolla, Corona
 Dry Fill 6.7 qts. (6.3L)
 Refill 2.5 qts. (2.4L)
Cressida, 2WD Pickup, Supra
 Dry Fill 6.9 qts. (6.5L)
 Refill 2.5 qts. (2.4L)
Tercel
 Dry Fill 4.8 qts. (4.5L)
 Refill 2.5 qts. (2.4L)

DRAINING & REFILLING

1) Remove drain plug and drain fluid. Remove oil pan retaining bolts. Remove oil pan and filter screens. Clean filter screens and dry with compressed air.

2) Install screens, oil pan and a new pan gasket. Tighten oil pan bolts to 48-72 INCH lbs. (5-8 N.m) on Tercel or 36-48 INCH lbs. (4-5 N.m) on all other models. Repeat tightening several times until torque remains constant, taking care not to over tighten bolts.

3) Replace drain plug and fill transmission with approximately 2 quarts of ATF fluid. Start engine and select all gears. Check fluid level and add additional fluid as necessary. Do not overfill.

ADJUSTMENTS

SHIFT LINKAGE
Column Shift Models

1) Inspect bushing between control shaft and manual valve lever for damage or deterioration. Loosen nut on connecting rod swivel and move shift lever to verify that position indicator shows ranges corresponding to shift lever ranges.

2) Check that position indicator is indicating "N" when control shaft lever is in "N". Position transmission manual valve lever in "N" position. Adjust length of control first rod so position of indicator is in "N".

3) Tighten lock nut at connecting rod swivel. Check shift lever selectiveness, make sure position indicator registers correctly, and that vehicle moves correctly in ranges selected. See Fig. 1.

Fig. 1: Column Shift Linkage Assembly

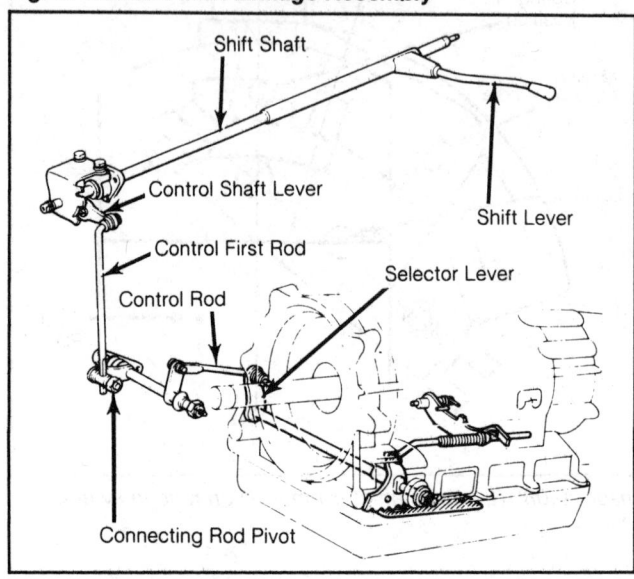

Floor Shift Models

Place transmission shift lever in "N" position and adjust shift rod until shift lever indicates "N" position correctly. Tighten lock nuts and check that all ranges are correctly engaged.

Fig. 2: Floor Shift Linkage Assembly

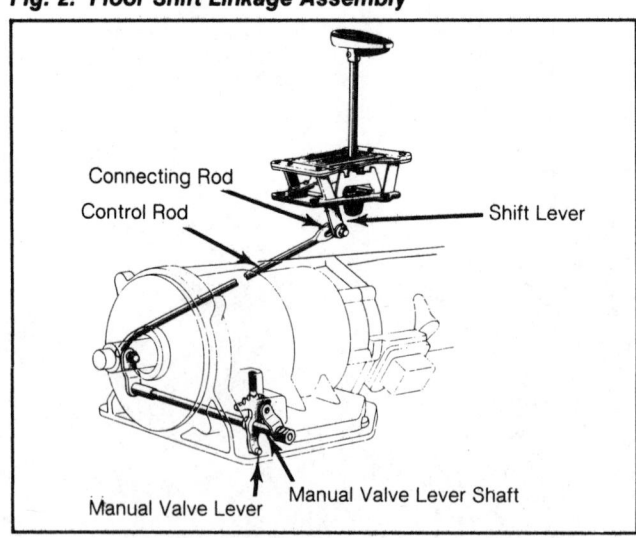

THROTTLE CABLE
Bellows Type (All Models Except Tercel)

1) Remove air cleaner. Check throttle cable bracket and linkage for looseness or bending. Pull back rubber boot from outer cable. Open throttle valve wide-open.

TOYOTA (Cont.)

2) Adjust cable housing so distance between end of housing and stopper collar is 2.05" (52 mm). Tighten lock nut and secure rubber boot.

Straight Boot Type (Tercel)

Remove air cleaner. Check throttle cable bracket and linkage for looseness or bending. Open throttle valve wide-open. Adjust cable housing so distance between rubber boot end and inner cable stopper is .04" (1 mm). Tighten lock nut.

Fig. 3: Adjusting Throttle Cable

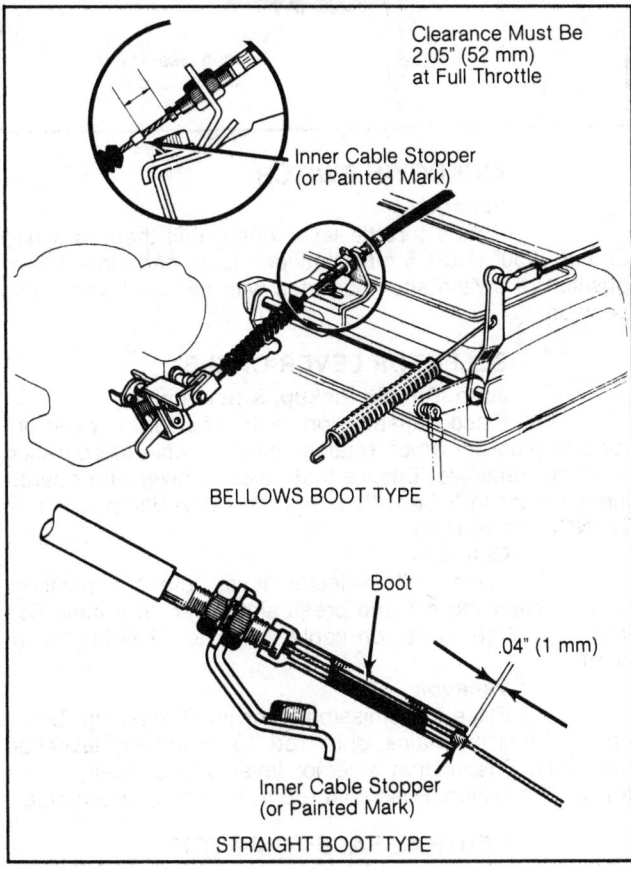

Clearance Must Be 2.05" (52 mm) at Full Throttle

Inner Cable Stopper (or Painted Mark)

BELLOWS BOOT TYPE

Boot

.04" (1 mm)

Inner Cable Stopper (or Painted Mark)

STRAIGHT BOOT TYPE

Illustration applies to all models except Tercel.

THROTTLE LINK
TERCEL

1) Remove air cleaner. Check throttle cable bracket and linkage for looseness or bending. Open throttle valve wide open.

2) Adjust linkage by turning turnbuckle until throttle valve lever indicator lines up with mark on transmission case. Tighten lock nut.

Fig. 4: Throttle Link Adjustment

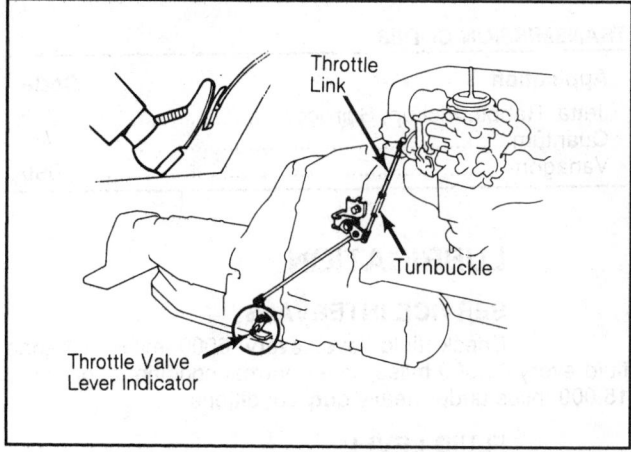

Throttle Link

Turnbuckle

Throttle Valve Lever Indicator

NEUTRAL SAFETY SWITCH

Loosen adjusting bolt. Position shift lever in "N" position. Align switch shaft groove to neutral basic line. Tighten adjusting bolt.

Fig. 5: Neutral Safety Switch

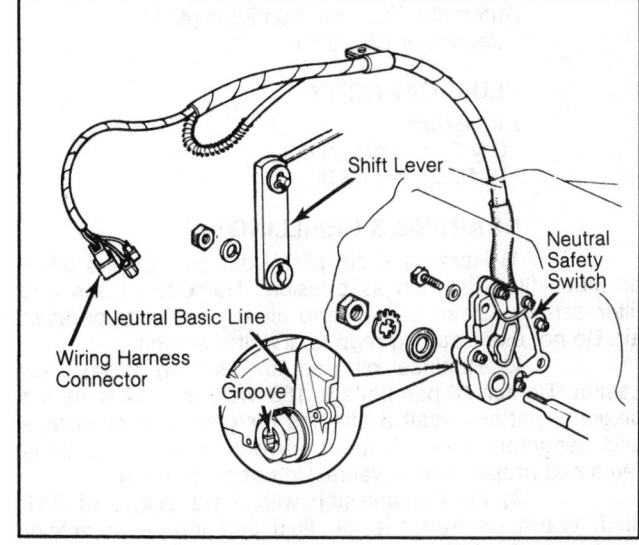

Shift Lever

Neutral Safety Switch

Neutral Basic Line

Wiring Harness Connector

Groove

Automatic Transmission Servicing

VOLKSWAGEN

IDENTIFICATION

TRANSMISSION CODES

Appication	Code
Jetta, Rabbit, Pickup, Scirocco	010
Quantum	089
Vanagon	090

LUBRICATION

SERVICE INTERVALS

Check fluid level every 6000 miles. Change fluid every 30,000 miles under normal conditions, or every 15,000 miles under heavy duty conditions.

FLUID LEVEL

With transmission warm and engine idling in neutral, check that ATF fluid is between marks on dipstick. The ring shaped handle should be in a vertical position when checking level. Only 1 pint (.5L) of fluid is required to raise fluid level from lower to upper mark on dipstick.

FLUID TYPE

Automatic Transmission Fluid (ATF)
 Dexron or Dexron II

FLUID CAPACITY

All Models
 Dry Fill 6.4 qts. (6.0L)
 Refill 3.2 qts. (3.0L)

DRAINING & REFILLING

1) Remove drain plug from oil pan and allow as much fluid to drain as possible. Remove oil pan and filter screen. Clean screen and air dry with compressed air. Do not use cleaning rags to dry filter screen.

2) Replace oil pan and screen using new gasket. Tighten oil pan bolts to 168 INCH lbs. (19 N.m) in a diagonal pattern. Wait 5 minutes for gasket to compress and retighten bolts. Repeat several times until bolts remain at proper torque value. Do not over tighten.

3) Fill transmission with 2 1/2 quarts of ATF fluid. Warm up transmission fluid and top-up to proper level, as in Fluid Level.

ADJUSTMENT

BRAKE BAND

Adjust brake band with transmission in a horizontal position. Tighten 2nd gear brake band adjusting screw to 84 INCH lbs. (10 N.m). Loosen adjusting screw, then tighten again to 48 INCH lbs. (5 N.m). Back off screw 2 1/2 turns, and tighten lock nut to 168 INCH lbs. (19 N.m).

Fig. 1: Brake Band Adjusting Location

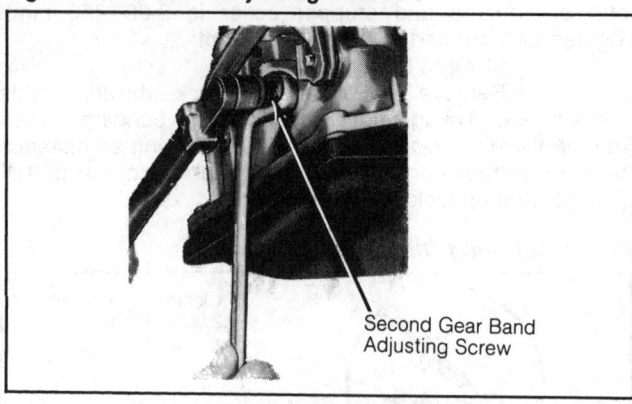

Second Gear Band
Adjusting Screw

KICKDOWN SWITCH

Vanagon
 Rotate throttle lever open until there is a gap of .040-.060" (1.0-1.5 mm) between lever and stop. Adjust position of switch so it operates with throttle lever in this position.

SELECTOR LEVER CABLE

Jetta, Rabbit, Pickup, & Scirocco
 Place transmission in "P" position. Loosen nut for clamping pin which retains selector cable to operating lever on transaxle. Ensure that selector lever and operating lever are in "P" position. Tighten cable clamping nut to 72 INCH lbs. (8 N.m).

Quantum
 Place shift selector lever into "P" position. Loosen clamping nut and press shift lever on tranmission into park. Tighten nut on cable clamp to 72 INCH lbs. (8 N.m).

Vanagon
 Place transmission lever in "P" position. Loosen bolt which retains shift rod to operating lever on transaxle. Ensure that selector lever and operating lever are in "P" position. Push shift rod to rear and tighten bolt.

NEUTRAL SAFETY SWITCH

Neutral safety switch is located in shift console. Remove console cover and adjust switch so that it makes contact only in "P" and "N" positions.

VOLVO

IDENTIFICATION

TRANSMISSION CODES

Application	Code
All Models	Borg-Warner Model 55

LUBRICATION

SERVICE INTERVAL

Under normal use it is not necessary to change the transmission fluid. Tranmission fluid should be checked every 7500 miles or twice a year. For vehicles in heavy duty service, transmission fluid should be changed every 25,000 miles.

FLUID LEVEL

1) Position vehicle on level floor. Apply parking brake and shift selector lever into "P" position. Start engine and let idle. Shift selector lever through all gears pausing 4-5 seconds for engagement at each position.

2) Return selector lever to "P". Wait 2 minutes, then remove dipstick. Wipe dipstick off with lint free cloth and reinsert. Withdraw dipstick and check reading. Level must be between "MIN" and "MAX" marks. If not, add (or remove) fluid to obtain correct level.

FLUID TYPE

Automatic Transmission Fluid (ATF)
  Type "F" or "G"

FLUID CAPACITY

Borg-Warner Model 55 7.1qts. (6.8L)

ADJUSTMENT

THROTTLE & KICKDOWN CABLES

1) Transmission cable should be stretched in idle position. Distance between clip and sheath should be .010-.040" (.25-1.0 mm). *See Fig. 1.*

Fig. 1: Checking Throttle Controls

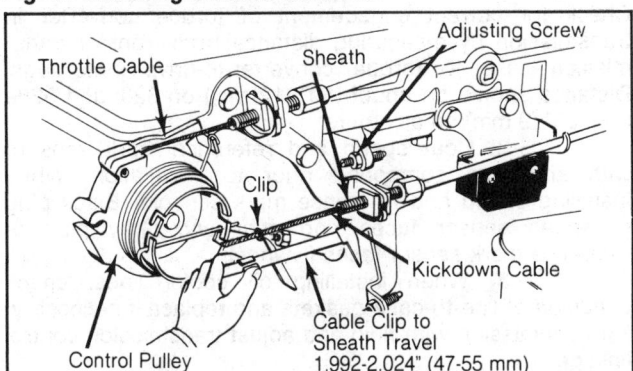

2) Pull transmission cable out by hand approximately .39-.59" (10-15 mm), and release. A distinct "click" should be heard from transmission, indicating cable moves freely and throttle cam returns to initial position.

3) Depress accelerator pedal completely. The transmission cable should travel 1.992-2.024" (47-55 mm), from idle position to full throttle position. *See Fig. 1.*

GEAR SELECTOR

1) Press on gear selector and check that clearance from "D" to stop is approximately the same as from "2" to stop. If clearance is incorrect, control rod needs adjustment.

2) Adjustment is made by turning clevis in or out on control rod. Maximum visible thread length permitted is 1.1" (28 mm).

3) Increasing rod length reduces position "D" clearance. Decreasing rod length increases position "D" clearance. Shift to position "1" then to position "P" for recheck. *See Fig. 2.*

Fig. 2: Gear Selector Adjustment

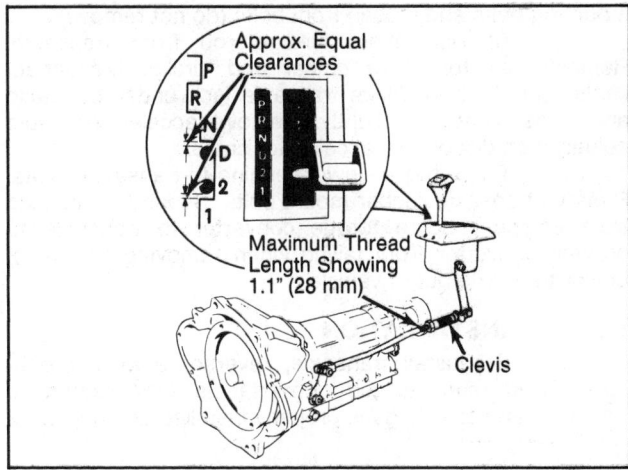

NEUTRAL SAFETY SWITCH

1) Switch is located at and directly controlled by the gear shift control lever. Place selector lever in "P" position. Adjust neutral safety switch to set "P" mark at center of switch lever.

2) Place selector lever in "N" position. Confirm "N" mark is at center of switch lever. Move selector lever from "P" to "1" and back again.

3) Check that control pin does not slide out of switch lever. *See Fig. 3.* Check that engine only starts in "P" and "N", and that the back-up lights illuminate in position "R" only.

Fig. 3: Adjusting Neutral Safety Switch

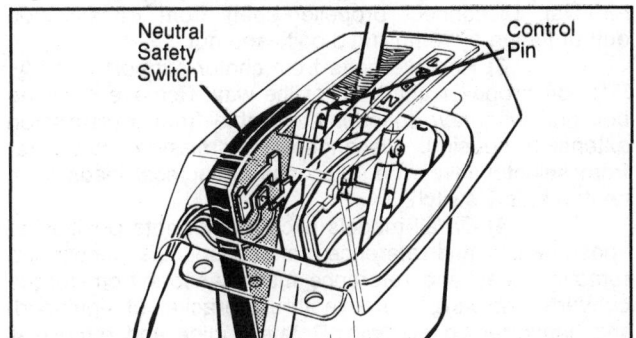

Automatic Transmission Removal

AUDI

AUDI COUPE & 4000

REMOVAL

1) Disconnect battery ground cable. Disconnect accelerator linkage rod. Disconnect speedometer cable. Remove upper engine-to-transaxle bolts.

2) Support engine from above. Disconnect automatic transaxle cooler lines. Disconnect exhaust pipe from manifold. Disconnect exhaust pipe bracket at transaxle.

3) Unbolt exhaust pipe from catalytic converter. Remove axle shaft guard plate, then disconnect axle shafts from transaxle flanges. Wire axle shafts back out of the way. Remove starter. Remove the 3 bolts securing torque converter to drive plate.

4) On 089 transaxle, mark left ball joint position on control arm. Remove bolts attaching ball joints to control arm. On all models, remove subframe rear mounting bolts and loosen front bolts (do not remove).

5) Disconnect linkage rod from transaxle. Remove selector cable holder and circlip. Disconnect cable and "O" ring. Place transaxle jack under transaxle and raise transaxle slightly. Remove accelerator cable holder, then disconnect accelerator cable.

6) Remove lower engine-to-transaxle bolts. Remove transaxle rubber mount bolts. Separate transaxle from engine. Secure torque converter to transaxle to prevent converter from falling when removing transaxle. Lower transaxle out of vehicle.

INSTALLATION

To install transaxle, reverse removal procedure. Make sure torque converter is fully seated to transaxle and all linkage is properly installed and adjusted.

5000

REMOVAL

1) Disconnect battery ground cable. Disconnect hoses from transaxle cooler. Disconnect accelerator linkage and speedometer cable. Support engine from above. Remove upper engine-to-transaxle bolts. Remove guard plate from subframe and remove exhaust pipe.

2) Remove right guard plate at right axle drive shaft and remove drive shaft bolts. Remove starter, selector lever cable holder and selector lever cable at transaxle lever.

3) Disconnect lower accelerator linkage rod and accelerator cable from transaxle lever. Remove right side guard plate from subframe. Remove torque converter-to-drive plate bolts.

4) Support transaxle with jack and raise slightly. Remove lower engine-to-transaxle bolts and rear subframe bolts. Position drive shafts to rear of vehicle. Separate transaxle from engine, secure torque converter in place and lower transaxle from vehicle.

INSTALLATION

To install, reverse removal procedure. When attaching torque converter to drive plate use new bolts and lock washers. After transaxle installation, check and adjust accelerator cable and throttle linkage (if necessary).

BMW

ALL MODELS

REMOVAL

1) Disconnect battery ground cable. Detach transmission throttle cable from accelerator cross shaft and bracket. Remove oil filler tube from transmission and plug hole in transmission. Remove all transmission-to-engine bolts that can be removed from above.

2) Drain transmission fluid. Detach exhaust system bracket from transmission extension housing. Disconnect exhaust pipe from exhaust manifold. Turn steering wheel to full left lock to provide clearance for removal. Disconnect propeller shaft from transmission output flange by removing 3 bolts and nut.

3) Remove bolts from center support to body. Position propeller shaft out of the way. Remove retaining bolt and withdraw speedometer cable from transmission extension housing. Disconnect transmission shift lever from selector lever rod. Disconnect electrical leads from neutral safety switch.

4) On all models except 320i, note position of speed sensor and reference mark sensor. Disconnect and remove speed and reference mark sensors from torque converter housing. Remove thrust bracket (if equipped) and converter cover plate. Rotate engine and remove 4 converter-to-drive plate bolts.

5) Disconnect oil cooler lines from transmission. Position a jack under transmission and disconnect crossmember. Remove remaining transmission-to-engine attaching bolts and remove transmission.

INSTALLATION

1) To install, reverse removal procedure. Check for correct engagement of torque converter in transmission by measuring distance from front of transmission case to torque converter-to-drive plate lugs. Distance should be about .50" (12 mm) on 320i and 528e and .35" (9 mm) on all others.

2) Coat speed and reference mark sensors with anti-seize compound prior to installation. When installing speed and reference mark sensors, Black plug of speed sensor faces ring gear and Gray plug of reference mark sensor faces flywheel.

3) When installing oil cooler lines, check condition of line-to-case gaskets and replace if necessary. Fill transmission with fluid and adjust transmission control linkage.

CHRYSLER CORP. IMPORTS

ALL RWD MODELS

REMOVAL

NOTE: **Transmission and converter must be removed as an assembly to prevent damage to drive plate, pump bushing, and oil seal. Do not allow weight of transmission to rest on drive plate at any time during removal or installation.**

1) Disconnect battery ground cable. Remove oil cooler lines at transmission. Remove starter motor and cooler line bracket. Loosen pan to drain transmission.

2) Mark converter and drive plate for reassembly reference. Using socket wrench on crankshaft vibration damper bolt, rotate engine clockwise to position converter attaching bolts for removal. Remove bolts and propeller shaft.

3) Disconnect electrical leads. Disconnect gearshift rod and torque shaft assembly, throttle rod lever from left side of transmission, and linkage bellcrank (if so equipped) from transmission.

4) Remove oil filler tube and speedometer cable. Support rear of engine with engine support fixture. With a transmission support on a service jack, support transmission. Raise transmission slightly to relieve load on supports.

5) Remove bolts securing transmission mount to crossmember and crossmember to frame, then remove crossmember. Remove all converter housing bolts, then carefully work transmission and converter assembly rearward off engine block dowels and disengage converter hub from end of crankshaft.

6) Attach a small "C" clamp to edge of converter housing to hold converter in place during transmission removal. Lower transmission and remove from under vehicle. To remove converter assembly, remove "C" clamp from edge of converter housing and carefully slide assembly from transmission.

INSTALLATION

1) To install, reverse removal procedures. To install converter, rotate pump rotors with special tool (C3756) until 2 small holes in handle are vertical. Carefully slide converter over input shaft and reaction shaft. Make sure converter hub slots are also vertical and fully engage pump inner rotor lugs.

2) Test for full engagement by placing straight edge on face of converter housing. Surface of converter front cover lug should be at least 1/2" from rear of straightedge when converter is pushed all the way into transmission. Attach a small "C" clamp to converter housing to hold converter in place during transmission installation.

3) Inspect converter drive plate for distortion or cracks and replace if necessary. Coat converter hub hole in crankshaft with multi-purpose grease. When drive plate replacement has been necessary, make sure both transmission dowel pins are in engine block and they are protruding far enough to hold transmission in alignment.

4) Place transmission and converter assembly on a jack and position under vehicle for installation. Raise or tilt as necessary to align transmission to engine. Rotate converter so that mark on converter (made during removal) will align with mark on drive plate.

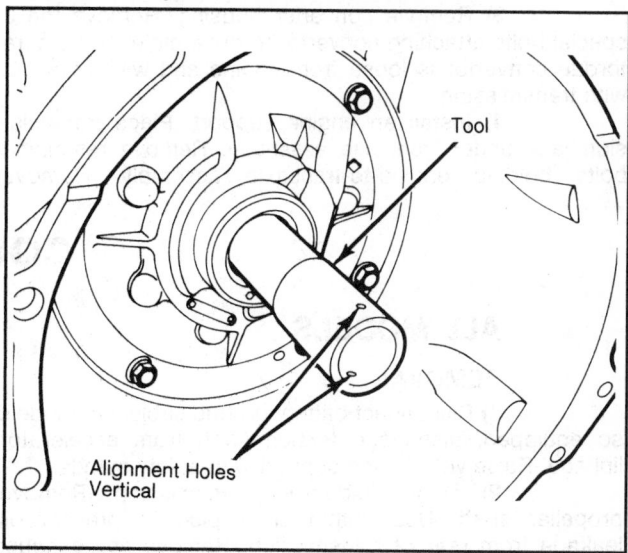

Fig. 1: Using Special Tool to Align Pump Rotors for Torque Converter Installation

Tool

Alignment Holes Vertical

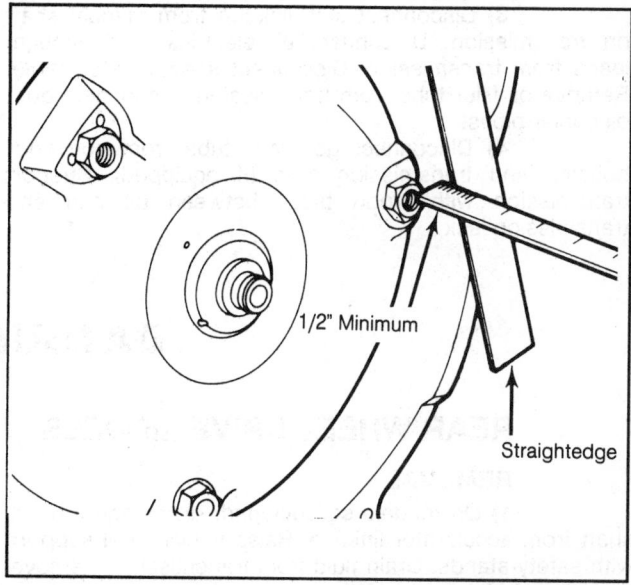

Fig. 2: Measuring for Full Converter Engagement

1/2" Minimum

Straightedge

5) Carefully work transmission assembly forward over engine block dowels with converter hub entering crankshaft opening. After transmission is in position on engine, install and tighten all bolts. Adjust shift and throttle linkage, then refill transmission with DEXRON type automatic transmission fluid.

CHAMP & COLT

REMOVAL

1) Disconnect battery ground cable. Disconnect throttle cable at carburetor and manual control cable at transaxle. Remove inhibitor switch connector, cooler hoses and the 4 top engine-to-transaxle mounting bolts.

2) Raise vehicle and remove front wheels. Remove under cover and drain transaxle fluid. Remove strut and stabilizer bars from lower control arm. Remove

CHRYSLER CORP. IMPORTS. (Cont.)

both drive shafts from transaxle case. Remove starter and disconnect speedometer cable from transaxle.

    3) Remove converter housing. Remove the 3 special bolts attaching convertor to drive plate. Make sure torque convertor is loose from engine and will come out with transmission

    4) Install an engine support. Place transmission jack under transaxle assembly. Remove remaining bolts holding engine-to-transaxle assembly. Remove

transaxle mounting bolts. Lower transaxle assembly (with torque convertor) out of vehicle.

INSTALLATION

    To install transaxle assembly, reverse removal procedure noting the following: Install torque converter to transaxle, not to engine. Make sure transaxle is filled wih fluid and all cables are properly connected and adjusted.

COURIER

ALL MODELS

REMOVAL

    1) Disconnect battery ground cable. On models so equipped, disengage torsion shaft from accelerator linkage. Raise vehicle and support with safety stands.

    2) Drain fluid from transmission. Remove propeller shaft. Use output shaft plug to prevent oil leakage from rear of transmission. Remove any exhaust mounts attached to transmission. Disconnect exhaust pipe from manifold.

    3) Disconnect shift linkage from manual shaft on transmission. Disconnect all electrical and vacuum leads from transmission. Disconnect speedometer cable. Remove oil filler tube from transmission. Disconnect both oil cooler pipes.

    4) Disconnect governor tube from converter housing and transmission case (if equipped). Support transmission with wood block between oil pan and transmission jack.

    5) Remove converter inspection plate. Mark converter and flywheel for realignment reference during installation. Remove torque converter-to-flywheel attaching bolts.

    6) Remove rear mount and crossmember mounting bolts. Remove starter (lower transmission as needed to gain access to starter bolts). Remove transmission-to-engine bolts and slowly lower transmission out of vehicle.

INSTALLATION

    1) To install, reverse removal procedure. When installing torque converter, be sure that notch in converter lines up with notch in oil pump.

    2) When bolting converter to flywheel, be sure to align mark made during removal to ensure proper alignment. After transmission is installed, turn crankshaft several times to be sure that transmission rotates freely without binding.

DATSUN/NISSAN

REAR WHEEL DRIVE MODELS

REMOVAL

    1) On models so equipped, disengage torsion shaft from accelerator linkage. Raise vehicle and support with safety stands. Drain fluid from transmission. Remove propeller shaft.

    2) Use output shaft plug to prevent oil leakage from rear of transmission. Remove any exhaust mounts attached to transmission. Disconnect exhaust pipe from manifold. Disconnect shift linkage from manual shaft on transmission.

    3) Disconnect all electrical and vacuum leads from transmission. Disconnect speedometer cable. Remove oil filler tube from transmission, then disconnect both oil cooler pipes.

    4) Disconnect governor tube from converter housing and transmission case (if equipped). Support transmission with wood block between oil pan and transmission jack. On Datsun 200SX and 810 models, remove gussets from front of transmission.

    5) On all models, remove converter inspection plate. Mark converter and flywheel for realignment reference during installation. Remove torque convrter-to-flywheel attaching bolts.

    6) Remove rear mount and crossmember mounting bolts. Remove starter (lower transmission as

needed to gain access to starter bolts). Remove transmission-to-engine bolts and slowly lower transmission out of vehicle.

INSTALLATION

    1) Reverse removal procedure to install transmission, noting the following: Check flywheel runout with dial indicator before installing transmission. Runout must not exceed .02" (.5 mm).

    2) When installing torque converter, be sure that notch in converter lines up with notch in oil pump. Measure distance from front of converter housing to flywheel bolt mounting surface on converter. If distance is less than amount shown in *Torque Converter Installed Depth* table, converter or other components are incorrectly assembled.

TORQUE CONVERTER INSTALLED DEPTH

Application	Converter Depth In. (mm)
200SX & 810	1.38 (35.0)
210	1.02 (25.9)
280ZX & Pickup	.85 (21.5)

    3) When bolting converter to flywheel, be sure to align mark made during removal to ensure proper

DATSUN/NISSAN (Cont.)

alignment. After transmission is installed, rotate crankshaft several times to be sure that transmission rotates freely without binding.

310

REMOVAL

NOTE: **Engine and transaxle must be removed as an assembly.**

1) Mark hood hinge locations and remove hood. Disconnect battery cables and remove battery and support. Remove air cleaner and plug carburetor with rags to prevent entry of dirt and foreign matter. Drain coolant and remove radiator with cooling fan. Remove power steering pump (if equipped).

2) Remove A/C compressor and idler pulley (if equipped), without discharging system and strap compressor to engine. Disconnect exhaust pipe from exhaust manifold and loosen exhaust pipe mounting bolt. Disconnect control linkage, speedometer cable and throttle cable.

3) Remove all fuel, vacuum and air hoses between engine and vehicle body. Disconnect all cables, wires and harness connectors. Remove wheel and tire. Pry cotter pin out of hub. Loosen, do not remove, wheel hub nut from axle shaft while preventing hub from turning. Disconnect lower ball joint from transverse link.

4) Drain gear oil from transaxle case. Disconnect side rod ball stud at steering knuckle arm. Remove axle shaft from transaxle. Do not damage oil seal during axle shaft removal. Insert a bar or equivalent tool into each side of differential case to prevent dropping of side gears.

5) Disconnect brake tube. Remove steering knuckle bolts from strut and separate knuckle from strut. Remove axle shaft, hub, knuckle and caliper as an assembly. Remove and discard axle shaft snap ring. Attach engine lifting slings. Disconnect engine mounting bolts. Lift engine up and away from vehicle. Separate engine and transaxle.

INSTALLATION

To install, reverse removal procedure. Make sure all components are properly secured and all lines, hoses and cables are properly routed.

SENTRA

REMOVAL

1) Disconnect battery ground cable. Raise and support vehicle. Remove wheels and tires. Drain transaxle fluid. Remove left fender protector. Remove brake caliper and pry cotter pin out of hub. Loosen, do not remove, wheel hub nut from axle shaft while preventing hub from turning.

2) Remove tie rod end from steering knuckle. Remove lower ball joint and discard nut. Remove axle shaft from transaxle and discard axle shaft snap ring. Do not damage oil seal during axle shaft removal. Insert a bar or equivalent tool into each side of differential case to prevent dropping of side gear.

3) Remove knuckle attaching bolts and remove hub, knuckle and axle shaft as an assembly. Disconnect speedometer cable, throttle cable and control linkage. Remove fluid dipstick and tube assembly. Place transmission jack under engine and transaxle assembly. DO NOT place jack under oil pan drain plug.

4) Disconnect oil cooler lines. Remove inspection plate from torque converter. Rotate crankshaft and remove torque converter-to-drive plate bolts. Mark position of torque converter in relation to housing for installation reference. Remove engine mount bolts. Remove starter motor.

5) Remove transaxle-to-engine bolts. Gradually move jack to rear until transaxle can be removed. Carefully remove transaxle from vehicle by taking out through left wheel housing.

INSTALLATION

1) To install, reverse removal procedure. Measure drive plate runout with a dial indicator before installing torque converter. Runout should not exceed .020" (.5 mm). After installing torque converter to transaxle, ensure distance from converter housing surface to converter face ring is more than .83" (21 mm).

2) Apply sealant to torque converter bolts prior to installation. Align reference marks made during removal when installing converter. After converter is installed, rotate crankshaft several times and make sure transaxle rotates freely without binding.

FIAT

SPIDER 2000

REMOVAL

1) Raise vehicle, remove oil pan drain plug and drain transmission fluid. Lower vehicle. Remove dipstick and tube. Disconnect battery ground cable. Raise and support vehicle.

2) Remove starter. Disconnect speedometer cable at transmission. Remove 2 exhaust pipe bracket retaining bolts and remove bracket. Disconnect vacuum line to modulator. Remove vacuum line clip from transmission.

3) Remove cooling lines clamp and disconnect cooling lines from transmission. Remove bracket for kickdown cable and disconnect kickdown cable from

kickdown valve. Bolt for kickdown cable bracket is located above the modulator valve at rear of transmission.

4) Remove nut holding shift lever to transmission control rod, then disconnect lever. Remove propeller shaft. Support transmission with jack, then remove transmission support bolts.

5) Remove flywheel cover, then turn flywheel to gain access to bolts (3) holding flywheel to converter and remove bolts. Remove 4 transmission-to-engine mounting bolts and tip rear of transmission down to prevent converter from falling out. Slide transmission back and remove from vehicle.

Automatic Transmission Removal

FIAT (Cont.)

Fig. 1: Measuring Torque Converter Installed Clearance

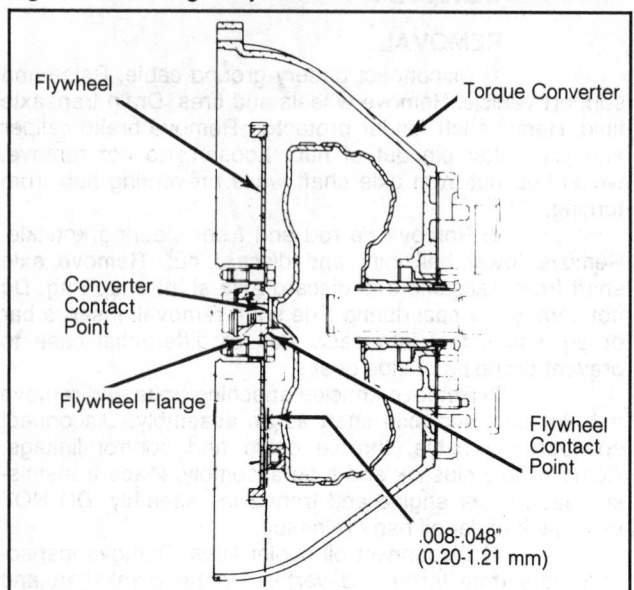

Flywheel

Torque Converter

Converter Contact Point

Flywheel Flange

Flywheel Contact Point

.008-.048"
(0.20-1.21 mm)

INSTALLATION

To install, reverse removal procedure. After attaching transmission to engine, push converter against flywheel flange and check that gap between boss and attachment point is .008-.048" (.20-1.21 mm). If clearance is not correct, replace flywheel.

HONDA

ALL MODELS

REMOVAL

1) Disconnect battery ground cable and ground strap at transmission. Release steering lock and place selector lever in "N". Disconnect battery cable from starter and wires from starter solenoid. Disconnect wire from water temperature sender and wire from ignition timing thermosensor.

2) Disconnect cooler hoses and wire them up out of way, making sure they won't drain. Remove starter mounting bolt, on transmission side, and top transmission mounting bolt. Raise and support front of vehicle. Remove wheels. Remove fender well shield from right front wheel well on Accord models only.

3) On all models, drain transmission and reinstall plug. Remove throttle control cable from transmission. Remove speedometer cable from transmission. Do not remove speedometer cable holder or speedometer gear may fall into transmission housing.

4) On Accord models only, remove starter side mounting bolt and remove 2 upper transmission mounting bolts. Place a jack under transmission and attach an engine support to engine. Remove crossbeam. Disconnect radius rods, then disconnect axle shafts from transmission.

5) Remove remaining starter bolt and remove starter. Remove transmission damper bracket, located in front of torque converter cover plate, then remove cover plate. Remove center console and shift indicator. Place selector lever in "R" and remove shift cable from shift lever. Loosen nuts and pull shift cable out of transmission housing.

6) Remove torque converter-to-drive plate bolts. Remove 3 engine-to-transmission mounting bolts and lower transmission mounting bolt. Pull transmission rearwards, then lower transmission out of vehicle.

7) On Civic and Prelude models only, remove splash shields, stabilizer bar nuts, mounting brackets and then remove stabilizer bar. Remove axle shafts from transmission. Remove engine torque rods and brackets. Remove engine side starter mounting bolt, then remove starter.

8) Attach engine support to engine and place a jack under transmission. Remove nuts from front and rear engine mounts. Remove crossbeam bolts and crossbeam. Remove torque converter cover plate and center damper bracket.

9) Remove center console and shift indicator. Place selector lever in "R" and remove shift cable from selector lever. Loosen "U" bolt nuts and pull shift cable out of transmission housing. Remove torque converter-to-drive plate bolts. Remove remaining transmission mounting bolts and pull transmission rearward. Lower transmission out of vehicle.

INSTALLATION

1) To install, reverse removal procedures. Be sure ignition is off when connecting ground cable to battery and transmission.

2) With installation complete and transmission filled with oil, start engine and shift through all gear ranges. Check shift cable adjustment. Road test vehicle. With engine at operating temperature, check fluid level.

ISUZU

I-MARK

REMOVAL

1) Disconnect negative battery cable. Disconnect throttle valve control cable from engine. Remove transmission oil dipstick and tube. Raise vehicle on hoist and drain transmission.

2) Remove starter attaching hardware. Remove starter by moving it toward front of vehicle. Remove propeller shaft. Disconnect shift control rod from shifter lever. Disconnect speedometer cable from transmission. Remove exhaust pipe bracket.

3) Remove transmission oil cooler lines from transmission and position aside to avoid damage. Remove under cover on front of engine. Remove converter housing cover. Remove 6 bolts attaching converter to drive plate. Access to bolts is obtained by rotating crankshaft pulley.

4) Remove bolt from center part of rear mounting frame bracket. Raise engine and transmission assembly. Support rear of engine with a jack. Remove 4 nuts (gas engine) or 4 bolts (diesel engine) attaching rear mounting frame bracket to frame. Remove bracket.

5) Lower transmission and engine slightly. Remove transmission-to-engine bolts. Remove transmission from vehicle by moving it toward rear of vehicle.

INSTALLATION

Reverse removal procedure and note the following: Tighten all nuts and bolts evenly. After installation, fill transmission with fluid. Adjust throttle linkage and shift control linkage.

P'UP

REMOVAL

1) Disconnect negative battery cable. Detach throttle valve cable from bracket on carburetor. Remove

air cleaner and transmission dipstick. Remove dipstick tube upper mounting bolt.

2) Raise and support vehicle. Remove dust cover from lower side of converter housing. Remove starter mounting bolts, then move starter assembly forward.

3) Mark propeller shaft for reassembly reference and remove. Disconnect speedometer cable, and oil cooler lines from transmission. Disconnect shift control linkage.

4) Support transmission with jack and remove rear transmission support bolt and mount. Remove exhaust pipe bracket.

NOTE: **Mark converter and flywheel for reassembly to same position.**

5) Remove torque converter bolts under pan. Lower transmission until jack barely supports it and remove transmission-to-engine attaching bolts. Raise transmission to normal position. Support engine with jack. Slide transmission away from engine and lower out of vehicle.

NOTE: **Use converter holding tool to prevent converter from sliding out of transmission during removal.**

INSTALLATION

1) Reverse removal procedure and note the following: Before installing drive plate-to-converter bolts, make sure welded brackets on converter are flush with drive plate. Check that converter rotates freely by hand in this position.

2) Hand start all 3 bolts and finger tighten before final tightening to ensure correct converter alignment. After installation, adjust shift linkage and downshift cable. Fill transmission with fluid.

JAGUAR

XJS

Information not available from manufacturer.

XJ6

REMOVAL

1) Disconnect battery cable. Remove transmission dipstick from tube and bolts securing tube to manifold. Remove upper fan shroud and disconnect the kickdown cable from throttle bellcrank.

2) Raise vehicle on hoist. Remove transmission fill tube, exhaust intermediate pipe and heat shields. Secure transmission jack-to-transmission, and raise enough to support weight of transmission. Remove rear transmission support plate. Remove mount-to-transmission securing bolts and remove mount.

3) Remove drive shaft from vehicle as a unit. Lower transmission jack to position required to remove

transmission, but do not remove transission at this time. Remove rubber pad from top of transmission.

4) Position engine support (MS 53A) and attach to rear lifting eye on engine. Turn adjusting nut to support weight of engine. Take care not to damage water heater valve.

5) From transmission unit selector lever, remove nut to release ball peg on inner selector cable. Remove set screw and spring washer securing outer selector cable clamp. Disconnect speedometer cable from transmission.

6) Remove dipstick tube and cover on front of converter housing. Remove 4 bolts retaining torque converter to drive plate. Disconnect oil cooler lines from transmission case and plug lines.

JAGUAR (Cont.)

7) Remove all converter housing-to-engine bolts. Move starter out of way. Separate and lower transmission from engine.

INSTALLATION

Secure transmission to jack, fit torque convert- er to transmission and reverse removal procedure to complete installation.

LUV

ALL MODELS

REMOVAL

1) Disconnect negative battery cable and detach throttle valve cable from bracket on carburetor. Remove air cleaner and transmission dipstick. Remove dipstick tube upper mounting bolt.

2) Raise and support vehicle. Remove dust cover from lower side of converter housing. Remove starter mounting bolts, then move starter assembly forward.

3) Mark propeller shaft for reassembly reference and remove. Disconnect speedometer cable and oil cooler lines from transmission. Disconnect shift control linkage.

4) Support transmission with jack and remove rear transmission support bolt and mount. Remove exhaust pipe bracket.

NOTE: **Mark converter and flywheel for reassembly to same position.**

5) Remove torque converter bolts under pan. Lower transmission until jack barely supports it and remove transmission-to-engine attaching bolts. Raise transmission to normal position. Support engine with jack. Slide transmission rearward from engine and lower away from vehicle.

NOTE: **Use converter holding tool to prevent converter from sliding out of transmission during removal.**

INSTALLATION

1) Reverse removal procedure and note the following: Before installing drive plate-to-converter bolts, make sure welded brackets on converter are flush with drive plate. Make sure that converter rotates freely by hand in this position.

2) Hand start all 3 bolts and finger tighten before final tightening to ensure correct converter alignment. After installation, adjust shift linkage and downshift cable. Fill transmission with fluid.

MAZDA

ALL RWD MODELS

REMOVAL

1) Disconnect negative battery cable. On RX-7, remove air cleaner, converter housing upper and side covers, and top bolts attaching transmission to engine. On models so equipped, disengage torsion shaft from accelerator linkage. Raise vehicle and support with safety stands.

2) Drain fluid from transmission. Remove propeller shaft. Use output shaft plug to prevent oil leakage from rear of transmission. Remove any exhaust mounts attached to transmission. Disconnect exhaust pipe from manifold. Disconnect shift linkage from manual shaft on transmission.

3) Disconnect all electrical and vacuum leads from transmission. Disconnect speedometer cable. Remove oil filler tube from transmission, then disconnect both oil cooler pipes.

4) Disconnect governor tube from converter housing and transmission case (if equipped). Support transmission with wood block between oil pan and transmission jack.

5) Remove converter inspection plate. Mark converter and flywheel for realignment reference during installation. Remove torque converter-to-flywheel attaching bolts.

6) Remove rear mount and crossmember mounting bolts. Remove starter (lower transmission as needed to gain access to starter bolts). Remove transmission-to-engine bolts and slowly lower transmission out of vehicle.

INSTALLATION

Reverse removal procedure to install transmission, noting the following: When installing torque converter, be sure that notch in converter lines up with notch in oil pump. When bolting converter to flywheel, be sure to align mark made during removal to ensure proper alignment. After transmission is installed, rotate crankshaft several times to be sure that transmission rotates freely without binding.

GLC (FWD)

REMOVAL

1) Drain all fluid from tranxaxle assembly (oil pan must be removed to completely drain transaxle as drain plug alone will not drain all fluid). Disconnect negative cable from battery. Disconnect speedometer cable, inhibitor switch connector, neutral switch connector and kickdown solenoid connector.

MAZDA (Cont.)

2) Remove vacuum diaphragm line. Raise front end of vehicle and support. Remove wheels, disconnect lower control arm ball joints and pull driveshafts out of transaxle. Use care when removing driveshafts to avoid stressing outer constant velocity joint to its limit, as this will damage the joint. Remove engine undercover.

3) Attach engine support to engine hanger and support engine. Remove shift linkage from transaxle assembly. Remove crossmember. Disconnect oil hose from oil pipe and plug ends of hose and pipe. Remove rear transmission mount. Remove starter, end cover and torque converter-to-drive plate retaining bolts.

4) Support transaxle with jack and remove transaxle-to-engine retaining bolts. Lower transaxle assembly out of vehicle. Use care when removing transaxle so that torque converter does not fall out.

INSTALLATION
Reverse removal procedure to install.

MERCEDES-BENZ

240D

REMOVAL

1) Disconnect negative battery terminal and raise vehicle on a hoist. Disconnect fluid filler tube from oil pan and remove torque converter drain plug to drain fluid from transmission assembly. Disconnect fluid cooler lines from transmission case, then remove clips attaching lines to transmission and engine.

2) Loosen bolts attaching center support bearing to body tunnel, but do not remove at this time. Loosen clamping nut on front propeller shaft section, then remove mounting bracket for front exhaust pipe. Remove two bolts attaching transmission mount to rear crossmember, remove crossmember, then disconnect mount from transmission.

3) Disconnect selector rod from range selector lever on transmission and place lever in park position. Disconnect speedometer driven gear and cable, kickdown switch wire, control pressure lever, and leads to neutral safety switch.

4) Disconnect front propeller shaft from transmission flange, leaving adapter plate attached to propeller shaft. Slide propeller shaft towards rear as far as possible and position out of the way. Disconnect vacuum line from vacuum modulator unit, and remove clamp retaining vacuum line to transmission.

5) Remove access plate from front of converter housing, then remove bolts attaching torque converter to drive plate. Position jack under transmission assembly. Remove transmission-to-engine attaching bolts. Move transmission rearward until torque converter hub clears drive plate and lower assembly from vehicle. Withdraw torque converter from transmission.

INSTALLATION
Reverse removal procedure and note the following: When installing torque converter in transmission, lubricate torque converter tangs, turbine and stator shaft splines with molykote paste. When properly installed, distance between front face of transmission and converter mounting lugs should be more than .16" (4 mm). After installation, adjust transmission control linkage and fill transmission with fluid.

300 & 380 SERIES

REMOVAL

1) Disconnect negative battery cable. Remove transmission oil filler pipe clamp from cylinder head. Force off ball socket on control wire linkage pivot. Pull out wire lock and loosen control wire. Compress tabs on plastic clip and pull retainer control wire from bracket.

2) Raise vehicle on hoist. Remove cross yoke center body support. Remove oil pan drain plug and drain oil from transmission. Remove drain plug from torque converter and drain. Reinstall drain plugs. Remove torque converter cover plates. Remove 6 bolts that secure torque converter-to-drive plate.

3) Place a block of wood between engine oil pan and front crossmember. Disconnect exhaust pipes at coupler at rear of transmission and remove exhaust pipes. Remove rear crossmember and rear transmission mount as an assembly. Remove cable strap and unscrew kickdown solenoid valve cable. Remove impulse transmitter retaining screws and remove transmitter.

4) Remove bolts attaching transmission companion flange to propeller shaft 3-arm flange. Remove exhaust shielding plate. Loosen propeller shaft clamping nut and slide propeller shaft as far rearward as possible. Turn starter lock-out switch plug retainer ring in upward direction. Carefully remove plug with 2 screwdrivers.

5) Disconnect shift control rod from range selector lever. Unscrew holder and remove vacuum line from vacuum control unit. Disconnect oil cooler lines from transmission. Remove oil filler tube retainer bolt and push tube upward to remove.

6) Remove all engine-to-transmission attaching bolts except for 2 bottom bolts. Slightly raise transmission with transmission jack. Remove 2 bottom engine-to-transmission bolts. Push transmission and jack toward rear of vehicle as far as possible. Remove transmission from vehicle. Place transmission in vertical position. Install converter handles (065) and lift converter from transmission.

INSTALLATION
Reverse removal procedures and note the following: When installing torque converter to transmission, coat converter tangs, turbine and stator shaft with assembly lubricant. Be sure that converter is fully seated in transmission before installing in vehicle.

PEUGEOT

ALL MODELS

REMOVAL

1) Open hood as far as possible without forcing and support open with block placed under safety hook. Disconnect negative battery cable. Remove air duct between metering unit and butterfly housing. Remove 2 bolts from control pressure regulator.

2) Remove upper and lower radiator mounts and fan shroud. Place a piece of cardboard between radiator and fan to protect radiator from damage during transmission removal. Disconnect kickdown control cable at throttle linkage.

3) Remove exhaust-to-manifold nuts. Disconnect all exhaust system hangers. Remove heat shield from above muffler. Remove front seat stiffener located above muffler.

4) Remove vibration damper from propeller shaft tube. Remove extension housing bracket bolts. Disconnect differential from its mount. Mark position of lower steering column flange coupling and remove bolts.

5) On models with power steering, remove front crossmember-to-front mount bolts and replace with 2" (50 mm) bolts. Remove remaining crossmember bolts. Lower crossmember about 2" (50 mm) by unscrewing 2 bolts in crossmember. On all other models, remove steering box mounting bolts and lower steering gear without disconnecting links.

6) On all models, drain transmission fluid. Disconnect and plug cooler lines at transmission. Remove starter motor bolts. Disconnect filler tube from transmission. Remove torque converter cover plate and sensor from bellhousing. DO NOT alter sensor adjustment.

7) Remove torque converter-to-flywheel bolts. Using a retainer, secure torque converter in housing so it will not fall out during transmission removal. Place jack under transmission and remove 4 propeller shaft-to-transmission bolts.

8) Separate transmission from tube about .8" (20 mm) and install retaining plate (8.0403SZ) between the 2 units. Install 2 bolts to hold plate in place.

9) Pull differential and propeller shaft assembly to the rear of vehicle and allow front of tube to rest on rear crossmember. Disconnect gear shift linkage, speedometer and electrical connections from transmission. Lower and tilt transmission as far as possible.

10) Install engine lift equipment to front of engine. Lift engine far enough to gain access to upper transmission-to-engine bolts. Remove bolts and remove transmission from vehicle.

INSTALLATION

Reverse removal procedure to install, noting the following: Apply grease to torque converter pilot bushing. Adjust shift and throttle linkage as needed. Fill transmission with fluid and check for leaks.

PORSCHE

924 & 944

REMOVAL

1) Remove heat shield and rear muffler bracket. Detach axle shafts at transaxle. Suspend axle shafts in horizontal position to prevent damage to dust covers. Remove transaxle oil filter shield.

2) Detach selector and transaxle lever cables. Remove converter bolts through hole in torque converter housing. Support transaxle with jack and remove transaxle-to-engine bolts and transaxle mounts. Slide transaxle toward rear of vehicle and remove.

INSTALLATION

Reverse removal procedures to install, noting the following: Ensure pump shaft and torque converter are fully seated in transaxle or damage to internal components may result during installation.

928

REMOVAL

1) Disconnect and remove battery. Remove self-locking nuts from spring struts in trunk. Disconnect multiple plug in spare wheel well and pull toward rear. Disconnect parking brake cable and lock. Remove rear wheels and splash shield. Drain torque converter and transmission oil sump. Remove oil filler tube. Disconnect transmission oil cooler lines.

2) Remove lower body brace. Disconnect exhaust pipe from catalytic converter. Remove exhaust pipe heat shields. Remove battery box. Remove rubber cap from inspection hole in front converter housing and turn crankshaft to position coupling so that socket head screw can be removed. Disconnect brake calipers and suspend with wire. Disconnect axle shafts and swing out of the way. Remove rear reinforcement plate. Disconnect stabilizer bar from lower control arm.

3) Support transaxle with tool (9164) and remove 2 bolts from transaxle mounts. Remove 2 bolts holding rear axle crossmember to frame. Mark position of eccentric bolts and remove bolts. Mark position of rear axle crossmember for reinstallation. Place jack under transaxle crossmember and remove mounting bolts from crossmember.

4) Lower rear axle carefully and take care that spring struts, crossmember and bearing brackets do not tilt. Mount special tool 9163 on adjustable floor jack. Lift transaxle and remove special tool 9164. Lower transaxle slightly and remove selector lever. Disconnect modulator vacuum line. Remove 6 bolts from central tube. Pull transaxle out of coupling splines and lower carefully.

NOTE: **Transaxle has to be lowered as far as possible to gain access to all tube bolts.**

INSTALLATION

To install, reverse removal procedure and check rear end alignment.

RENAULT

FUEGO & 18i

REMOVAL

1) Raise and support vehicle. Disconnect battery. Drain transmission fluid. Disconnect vacuum capsule hose from intake manifold. Disconnect transaxle wiring connectors and remove support. Insert spacer tool (T. Av. 509-01) between lower shock mounting base and lower control arm pivot shaft on each side.

Fig. 1: Location of Spacer Tool in Front Suspension

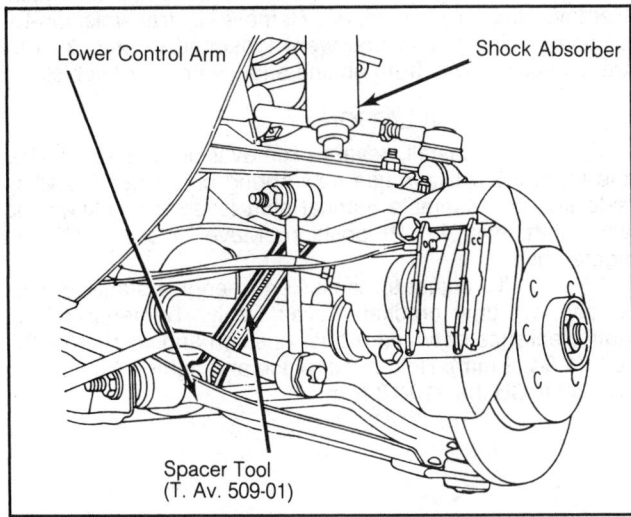

Lower Control Arm
Shock Absorber
Spacer Tool
(T. Av. 509-01)

Install tool between lower shock mount and lower control are pivot shaft.

2) Remove drive shaft retaining roll pins with drift. Separate tie rod end ball joints and upper control arm ball joints from steering knuckle using puller. Tilt axle carriers away from transaxle to separate drive shafts from side gears.

3) With shift lever in neutral position, disconnect shift rod at entry to transaxle and at the shift lever. Remove dipstick and inspection plate. Remove torque converter retaining bolts (3). Remove exhaust pipe bracket nut at transaxle.

4) Position transmission jack (Desvil 701 ST) under rear of transaxle and raise until assembly is supported on the 4 studs. Remove transaxle mounts. Lower assembly enough to remove speedometer and governor cables. Remove engine-to-transaxle retaining bolts. Lower transaxle from vehicle. Attach torque converter retaining strap (B. Vi. 465 Ref. D) to hold torque converter in place in case.

INSTALLATION

1) Reverse removal procedures to install, noting the following: Lightly lubricate axle shaft splined ends before installing. Tilt stub axle carrier as needed to line up roll pin holes. If equipped with TDC sensor, make sure it is adjusted correctly when installed.

2) If a new TDC sensor is used, install into position until pegs (3) on sensor contact flywheel. Tighten retaining screw. If reusing an old sensor, install until it contacts flywheel, mark position with a fine line on sensor body, and back sensor out about .04" (1 mm). Tighten retaining screw.

3) Adjust selector lever and governor cable. Check computer and governor connections and make sure ground wire is connected.

SAAB

ALL MODELS

REMOVAL

NOTE: **Engine and transaxle must be removed as an assembly.**

1) Disconnect positive battery terminal from battery. Drain radiator. Disconnect windshield washer hose from hood. Remove hood.

2) Disconnect all engine or transaxle electrical connections as needed for engine removal. Remove air cleaner, preheater hose and crankcase ventilation hose.

3) Disconnect fuel line and plug. Disconnect choke, throttle cable, hose to expansion tank and brake servo vacuum hose. Remove clamps from drivers side inner universal joint.

4) Place special tool 83 93 209 between the upper control arm underside and frame (insert tool from engine compartment side). Raise and support vehicle.

5) Remove lower control arm-to-ball joint bolts. Pull control arm assembly from control arm and support with jack stand.

6) Remove gear selector cable screw at transmission. Pull cable out of transmission and slide back spring loaded sleeve, then disconnect from control lever.

Disconnect speedometer cable from transmission. Remove rear engine mounting bolts.

7) Loosen front engine mounting nut so mount can be lifted from bracket. Attach engine lifting device on 2 engine lifting lugs and raise engine slightly. Move engine assembly side to side to free universal joints. Lift assembly from vehicle and place on engine stand.

8) To separate transaxle from engine, drain engine oil and remove inspection cover. Remove starter. Disconnect throttle cable. Remove engine-to-transaxle bolts. Remove converter-to-flex plate bolts (4). Turn flex plate until plate angles are horizontal and lift engine off of transaxle.

INSTALLATION

To install, reverse removal procedure and note the following: Mating surfaces of transaxle and engine must be thoroughly clean. Use gasket sealer on new gasket when assembling transaxle and engine. Apply sealer to bolts indicated in *Fig. 1* of Saab Manual Transaxle Removal procedure.

Pack inner universal joints with grease, adjust shift cable if necessary and check cooling system for leaks.

Automatic Transmission Removal

SUBARU

1800

REMOVAL

1) Remove spare tire from engine compartment. Disconnect negative battery cable. Remove spare tire mount. Disconnect transmission diaphragm vacuum hose. Disconnect speedometer cable from transmission and unfasten clip on cable.

2) Disconnect back-up light switch connector from transmission, ground cable from body and starter harness. Remove torque converter-to-drive plate retaining bolts (4) through hole in torque converter housing (timing hole). Be careful that bolts do not fall into housing. Disconnect transmission fluid lines from transmission and drain transmission fluid.

3) Remove starter (cable still attached) and set aside. Remove upper transmission-to-engine retaining bolts and loosen lower nuts. Loosen retaining nut on transmission-to-engine stabilizer rod (transmission side of bracket) not more than .4" (10 mm). Tighten nut on opposite side by an equal amount. Tilt engine back slightly.

4) Disconnect oxygen sensor harness and unclamp. Raise front of vehicle and remove exhaust pipe assembly. Use care not to damage oxygen sensor during exhaust removal. Drain transmission fluid and disconnect oil supply pipe. With shift lever in "P" position, mark location of connector nut on manual lever. Separate manual lever from linkage rod.

5) Remove suspension stabilizer bar and transverse link-to-front crossmember retaining bolts (both sides). Lower transverse links. Drive out left and right axle shaft retaining spring pins. Push wheels toward outside of vehicle to separate axle shafts from transmission drive shafts.

6) Remove transmission mount-to-crossmember attaching nut and support transmission on a jack. Remove the crossmember. Remove 2 transmission-to-engine retaining nuts that were loosened in step 3). Pull transmission away from engine and lower out of vehicle.

INSTALLATION

To install, reverse removal procedures noting the following: Always use new spring pins when installing axle shafts. Assemble manual shift lever and linkage rod with shift lever in "P" position. Move lever to "N" and tighten nut.

To adjust transmission-to-engine stabilizer rod, loosen nut until bracket moves freely. Tighten rear nut until clearance between rubber cushion and washer is .07-.09" (1.8-2.2 mm). Hold nut in place and tighten front nut to 84-156 INCH lbs. (10-18 N.m).

TOYOTA

TERCEL

REMOVAL

1) Disconnect battery ground cable and neutral safety switch. Partially drain radiator, then disconnect upper radiator hose at engine. Remove air cleaner. Disconnect throttle linkage, transmission cooler pipes and clamps. Disconnect cooler pipes from transmission.

2) Remove transmission-to-engine top bolts. Remove drive axle assemblies. Raise and support vehicle. Disconnect exhaust pipe from manifold. Remove 2 right side stiffener plate bolts. Disconnect shift control link bolt and speedometer cable (from transmission).

3) Remove engine under cover. Remove torque converter cover and torque converter-to-drive plate bolts. Hold crankshaft from turning when removing bolts. Disconnect oil cooler outlet pipe.

4) Place transmission jack under transmission and remove remaining transmission to-engine bolts. Disconnect rear bond cable. Remove rear transmission support. Pull transmission to the rear to separate torque converter from drive plate. Lower transmission out of vehicle.

INSTALLATION

1) Before installing transmission, apply grease to torque converter shaft and crankshaft pilot hole. Install guide pin (SST 09350-12010) in outside converter mounting hole. Align guide pin with 1 of the drive plate holes.

2) Be careful not to tilt transaxle forward or torque converter will slide out. Install transaxle to engine so that tip of converter goes into crankshaft hole. Remove guide pin. Temporarily insert 2 bolts about 3/8" (10 mm) and tighten evenly a little at a time.

3) Install 4 transaxle-to-engine bolts and install exhaust pipe bracket and throttle link bracket on the right side of the transaxle case. Install rear transaxle support member and tighten to 26-36 ft. lbs. (35-48 N.m). Remove temporarily installed bolts from torque converter and install 6 bolts finger tight.

4) Turn crankshaft to gain access. Tighten bolts evenly to 11-15 ft. lbs. (15-20 N.m). Install torque converter cover and connect bond cable. Connect cooler outlet pipe and tighten to 15-21 ft. lbs. (20-28 N.m). Install engine under cover. Install 2 right side stiffener plate bolts. Install exhaust pipe. Connect speedometer and rear bond cable.

5) Align shift lever and control link at neutral position. Connect control link. Lower vehicle. Install both drive shafts. Connect oil cooler inlet pipe. Install cooler pipe clamp. Connect throttle linkage. Connect all wiring connectors. To complete installation, reverse removal procedure.

6) Check and adjust wheel alignment, throttle link rod and selector lever if necessary. Fill transmission with automatic transmission fluid Type F. Fill differential with 1 quart of SAE 80W-90 gear oil.

TOYOTA (Cont.)

ALL RWD MODELS

REMOVAL

NOTE: Specific removal and installation procedures for Corona and Cressida not available from manufacturer.

1) Disconnect negative battery cable. Remove air cleaner. On Celica, Corolla and Supra, drain coolant. Disconnect upper radiator hose. On all models, disconnect transmission throttle cable. Remove upper starter mounting nut.

2) Raise vehicle and drain transmission. Check outside of transmission case for oil leaks or cracks which may necessitate repair while unit is out of vehicle. Disconnect wiring connectors to neutral start switch and back-up light.

3) Remove starter. Remove propeller shaft and plug opening. Disconnect exhaust pipe clamp from transmission housing. Disconnect speedometer cable. Disconnect manual shift linkage at the rear connection. Disconnect oil cooler lines.

4) On all except Pickup, remove stiffener plates from transmission housing. On Pickup models, remove oil filler tube. On all models, jack up transmission slightly to take weight off rear crossmember. Remove rear support member, removing rubber exhaust hanger and ground strap if equipped.

5) Remove engine undercover to gain access to crankshaft pulley. On Pickup, insert a wood block between engine oil pan and crossmember. Lower transmission on wood piece. On all models, pry out rubber plugs from service holes for torque converter.

6) Turn crankshaft as necessary to gain access to torque converter bolts and remove bolts. Install guide pin or cut off bolt in a torque converter bolt hole. Remove transmission housing mounting bolts. Pry on end of guide pin to start transmission movment to rear of vehicle.

7) Move transmission toward rear of vehicle, being careful not to catch throttle cable or neutral start switch cable. Keep oil pan positioned down. Place pan under converter housing and remove converter, pulling straight off and allowing fluid to drain into pan. If not already removed, remove filter tube and rear transmission support with ground strap.

INSTALLATION

1) Measure drive plate runout with dial indicator. If runout exceeds .079" (.20 mm), or if ring gear is damaged, replace drive plate. If installing new drive plate, note positioning of spacers and tighten with new bolts.

2) Measure torque converter sleeve runout. If runout exceeds .012" (.30 mm), try to correct by repositioning converter. If runout cannot be corrected in this manner, torque converter must be replaced. Be sure to mark position of converter to ensure correct installation.

3) On all except Pickup, install filler tube. On all models, apply grease to center hub of torque converter and pilot hole in drive plate. Install torque converter in transmission. Refill with fresh ATF. Check torque converter installation.

4) For Pickup, distance from center of hub to front surface of transmission housing should be .79" (20 mm). For Celica and Corolla, distance should be 1.02" (26 mm). Install guide pin in torque converter. Install transmission assembly. Align guide pin with a drive plate hole.

NOTE: Center distances for other models not available from manufacturer.

5) Align upper starter stud with hole on engine plate. Align 2 sleeves on block with converter housing. Tighten transmission housing mounting bolts. Install and tighten torque converter bolts.

6) To complete installation, reverse removal procedure. Fill transmission with automatic transmission fluid. Road test vehicle for proper operation of all functions.

VOLKSWAGEN

JETTA, PICKUP, RABBIT & SCIROCCO

REMOVAL

1) Disconnect battery ground strap and starter cable at battery. Disconnect speedometer cable from transmission. Remove 2 upper engine-to-transmission attaching bolts. Loosen left side transmission mount. Install support fixture (10-222).

2) Remove rear transmission mounting bolts (5). Mark axle drive shafts for reassembly reference, and disconnect from final drive flanges. Remove starter bolts and position starter out of the way.

3) Remove transmission protection plate and converter cover plate, then remove drive plate-to-torque converter bolts. Place selector lever in "P" position and disconnect selector cable from transmission lever. Remove cable bracket from transmission, then disconnect accelerator and pedal cables from bracket.

4) Support transmission with fixture (US 4470) attached to engine hoist. Detach side carrier and mount left side engine/transmission mount. Detach side carrier and mount

from transmission. Remove front mount. Remove lower transmission-to-engine bolt. Remove remaining transmission-to-engine bolts. Lift transmission slightly and, taking care not to allow converter to drop, lower transmission from vehicle.

INSTALLATION

Reverse removal procedure and note the following: Be sure that torque converter is fully seated on one-way clutch support. Adjust selector lever cable.

To check converter installation, lay a straight edge across converter housing and measure distance from straight edge to center converter hub. If distance is less than 1.2" (30 mm), converter is not fully engaged.

QUANTUM

REMOVAL

1) Disconnect negative battery cable. Disconnect accelerator linkage rod. Disconnect speedometer cable then remove upper engine-to-transaxle bolts.

VOLKSWAGEN (Cont.)

2) Support engine from above. Disconnect automatic transaxle cooler lines. Disconnect exhaust pipe from manifold, exhaust pipe bracket at transaxle and unbolt exhaust pipe from catalytic converter.

3) Remove axle shaft guard plate, then disconnect axle shafts from transaxle flanges. Wire axle shafts back out-of-way. Remove starter. Remove 3 bolts securing torque converter-to-drive plate.

4) On 089 transaxle, mark left ball joint position on control arm. Remove ball joint-to-control arm bolts. On all models, remove sub-frame rear mounting bolts and loosen front (do not remove).

5) Disconnect linkage rod from transaxle. Remove selector cable holder and circlip, then disconnect cable and "O" ring.

6) Place transaxle jack under transaxle and raise slightly. Remove accelerator cable holder, then disconnect accelerator cable. Remove lower engine-to-transaxle bolts. Remove transaxle rubber mount bolts. Separate transaxle from engine. Lower transaxle out of vehicle.

CAUTION: Secure torque converter to transaxle to prevent converter from falling out when removing transaxle.

INSTALLATION

To install transaxle, reverse removal procedures. Make sure torque converter is fully seated in transaxle and all linkage is properly installed and adjusted.

VANAGON

REMOVAL

1) Disconnect battery ground and remove fan housing grill. Remove torque converter bolts. To gain access to bolts, rotate engine until each bolt is visible in hole at top of transmission housing.

NOTE: When turning crankshaft, use "T" handle and adapter 3052. This adapter has a pin that must engage recess on cooling fan hub.

2) Disconnect both drive shafts from transmission. Disconnect wires from starter, remove starter. Loosen bracket for automatic transmission filler tube. Disconnect accelerator linkage, accelerator cable and selector lever cable from operating lever.

3) Install engine support and disconnect engine ground wire. Support transmission with jack. Remove mounting bracket bolts, then disconnect rear transmission mount from body. Remove lower engine-to-transmission bolts and lower transmission out of vehicle.

NOTE: When lowering transmission from vehicle, torque converter must be secured to transmission so it will not slide off transmission.

INSTALLATION

To install transaxle assembly, reverse removal procedures. Make sure torque converter is fully seated on one-way clutch support or damage to oil pump could occur when assembly is bolted to engine.

VOLVO

ALL MODELS

REMOVAL

1) Remove air cleaner. Disconnect throttle cable at pulley and cable sheath at bracket. Remove 2 upper transmission-to-engine bolts. Remove transmission oil dipstick.

2) Raise and support vehicle. Disconnect oil filler pipe from oil pan and drain transmission fluid. Remove vehicle splash guard.

3) Disconnect muffler from hanger. Disconnect propeller shaft from transmission rear drive flange. Remove exhaust pipe clamps from bracket. Remove transmission support member attaching bolts. Pull support member back, twist and lift out. Remove rear transmission mount and exhaust pipe bracket.

4) Disconnect speedometer cable from transmission. Disconnect oil cooler lines from transmission and oil cooler, then remove from vehicle. Disconnect gear shift control rod from transmission.

5) Remove torque converter cover plate. Remove starter motor attaching bolts and starter motor cover. Remove 4 torque converter-to-drive plate attaching bolts.

6) Support transmission with transmission jack. Remove 2 lower transmission-to-engine attaching bolts. Using a screwdriver, separate torque converter from drive plate. Lower transmission from vehicle.

INSTALLATION

Reverse removal procedure and note the following: Tighten all nuts and bolts evenly. After installation, fill transmission with fluid. Adjust throttle linkage and shift control linkage.

MANUAL TRANSMISSIONS

MANUFACTURER & MODEL	[1] TRANSMISSION MODEL
AUDI 4000, Coupe & Quattro 5000	4 & 5-Speed Transaxle 5-Speed Transaxle
BMW 320i, 528e, 633CSi & 733i	BMW 5-Speed
CHRYSLER CORP. IMPORTS Arrow Pickup & Ram-50 Pickup Arrow Pickup, Ram-50 Pickup, Challenger & Sapporo Champ & Colt	Model KM 130 Model KM 132 5-Speed & KM 145 (4WD) Model KM 160 & KM 165 Transaxle
COURIER Pickup	4 & 5-Speed

DATSUN/NISSAN
Maxima, Pickup, 200SX & 280ZX
Pickup
Sentra, Stanza & 310
Sentra, Stanza & 310
210
  1.2L Engine
  1.5L Engine
210
	Model FS5W71B 5-Speed
	Model F4W71B
	Model F4W F60A
	Model F5W F60A 5-Speed
	
	Model F4W56A
	Model F4W60L
	Model FS5W 60A 5-Speed

FIAT Spider 2000 X1/9	5-Speed 5-Speed Transaxle
HONDA Accord, Civic & Prelude	Honda 4 & 5-Speed Transaxle
ISUZU I-Mark & 2WD P'UP 4WD P'UP I'Mark & P'UP	4-Speed 4-Speed with Integral Transfer Case 5-Speed

LUV
Pickup
  2WD
  4WD
Pickup
	
	4-Speed
	4-Speed with Integral Transfer Case
	5-Speed

MAZDA GLC Wagon, Pickup, RX7 & 626 GLC (FWD)	Mazda 4 & 5-Speed Mazda 4 & 5-Speed Transaxle
MERCEDES-BENZ 240D	MB Type GL 68/20A
PEUGEOT All Models	Peugeot 4 & 5-Speed
PORSCHE 911SC 924 & 944 928 924 Turbo	Model 915/63 5-Speed Transaxle Model 016 K 5-Speed Transaxle Model G28.05 5-Speed Transaxle Model 016 Y 5-Speed Transaxle

[1] — Unless otherwise specified, all models use 4 forward gears.

Transmission Application
MANUAL TRANSMISSIONS (Cont.)

MANUFACTURER & MODEL	[1] TRANSMISSION MODEL
RENAULT	
Fuego & 18i	Renault 4 & 5-Speed Transaxle
Le Car	Renault 4-Speed Transaxle
SAAB	
900	Saab 4 & 5-Speed
SUBARU	
1600 & 1800	Subaru 4 & 5-Speed Transaxle
TOYOTA	
Celica	Model W58 5-Speed
Corolla	Model T40 & T41; Model T50 5-Speed
Corona	Model W55 5-Speed
Land Cruiser	Model H42
Pickup (2WD)	Model L48; Model W50 5-Speed
Pickup (4WD)	Model L45; Model L52 5-Speed
Starlet	Model K51 5-Speed
Tercel	Model Z41 & Z42 Transaxle
Tercel	Model Z51 5-Speed Transaxle
VOLKSWAGEN	
Jetta, Pickup, Rabbit & Scirocco	4 & 5-Speed Transaxle
Quantum	5-Speed Transaxle
Vanagon	Type 091 Transaxle
VOLVO	
All Models	Model M45; Model M46 with Overdrive

[1] — Unless otherwise specified, all models use 4 forward gears.

AUDI

4000, 5000

LUBRICATION

SERVICE INTERVALS

Inspect transmission lubricant level when vehicle is serviced. Oil does not have to be changed.

FLUID LEVEL

Check lubricant level at fill hole. Lubricant should be slightly below bottom of fill hole.

FLUID TYPE

Hypoid SAE 80 or SAE 80W/90.

FLUID CAPACITY

4000
   4-speed (014/1) 1.8 qts. (1.7L).
   5-speed (013) 2.2 qts. (2.0L).
   5-speed (093) 2.5 qts. (2.4L).
5000
   5-speed (016) 2.9 qts. (2.7L).

ADJUSTMENT

GEAR LEVER

Audi 4000

1) Place gear shift lever in Neutral. Loosen shift rod clamp nut. Check that shift finger slides freely on shift rod. Remove shift lever knob and rubber shift boot.

2) Align holes of gear shift lever housing and shift lever bearing housing. Install adjustment tool (3057), with locating pin toward front. Push shift lever into 5th/Rev cutout of tool.

3) Tighten lower screw on tool, move shift lever and slide to right stop. Tighten upper screw on tool. Push shift lever into left cutout of tool (3rd/4th) and align shift rod and finger. Tighten clamp nut and remove tool.

4) Push shift lever into 1st gear and press to left stop. Shift lever should spring back .2-.4" (5-10 mm). If not, move shift lever housing sideways until correct deflection is reached. Check engagement of gears.

Audi 5000

1) Position lever in Neutral in line with 1st-2nd gear. Loosen stop plate retaining bolts and align holes in stop plate with bearing support. Tighten bolts.

2) Loosen clamp between front and rear shift rods. Shift rods should move freely on splines. With front shift rod in Neutral, install adjustment tool (3048).

3) Ensure that locating pins fit into holes of stop plate. Tighten shift rod clamp and remove tool. Shift through all gears to see that they engage easily. Readjust stop plate, if necessary.

BMW

320i, 528e, 633CSi, 733i

LUBRICATION

SERVICE INTERVALS

Inspect transmission lubricant level when vehicle is serviced. Change transmission oil at first 600 miles, then at 30,000 miles and at 30,000 mile intervals thereafter.

FLUID LEVEL

Check lubricant at fill hole. Lubricant should be to bottom of fill plug hole.

FLUID TYPE

Hypoid SAE 80W.

FLUID CAPACITY

320i 1.6 qts. (1.5L).
528e, 633CSi, 733i 1.1 qts. (1.0L).

ADJUSTMENT

LINKAGE

All models use floor-mount shift with no external linkage. No adjustment is provided.

CHRYSLER CORP. IMPORTS

Arrow Pickup, Challenger, Champ, Colt, Ram-50 Pickup, Sapporo

LUBRICATION

SERVICE INTERVALS

Check the fluid level every 6 months, or every 15,000 miles.

FLUID LEVEL

Check lubricant level at fill hole. Lubricant should be within 1/4" of bottom fill hole.

FLUID TYPE

Hypoid SAE 80W (API GL-4)

Manual Transmission Servicing

CHRYSLER CORP. IMPORTS (Cont.)

FLUID CAPACITY

Arrow & Ram-50 Pickup
  2.0L engine 2.2 qts. (2.1L)
  2.6L engine 2.4 qts. (2.3L)
Colt & Champ 2.4 qts. (2.3L)
Challenger & Sapporo 2.4 qts. (2.3L)

ADJUSTMENT

LINKAGE

4-Speed Transaxle

No linkage adjustment is required.

4 & 5-Speed Transmissions

Shifter is integral with transmission housing and has no external linkage. No adjustment is required.

COURIER

LUBRICATION

SERVICE INTERVALS

Change fluid after first 7500 miles. Then check fluid every 7 1/2 months and change every 24 months or 22,500 miles.

FLUID LEVEL

Lubricant level should be even with bottom of oil fill hole.

FLUID TYPE

Hypoid SAE 90 with E.P.

FLUID CAPACITY

4-speed 1.5 qts. (1.4L).
5-speed 1.7 qts. (1.6L).

ADJUSTMENT

LINKAGE

The floor shifter attaches directly into the transmission housing; therfore, no adjustment is provided.

DATSUN/NISSAN

**200SX, 210, 280ZX, 310,
Maxima, Pickup, Sentra, Stanza**

LUBRICATION

SERVICE INTERVALS

Check oil level every 15,000 miles.

FLUID LEVEL

Lubricant level should be to bottom of fill hole.

FLUID TYPE

Hypoid SAE 80W (API GL-4)

FLUID CAPACITY

200SX 2.0 qts. (1.9L)
210
  4-speed (A12A) 1.3 qts. (1.2L)
  4-speed (A15) 1.4 qts. (1.3L)
  5-speed 1.3 qts. (1.2L)
280ZX & Maxima 5-speed 2.0 qts. (1.9L)
310 4 & 5-speed 2.5 qts. (2.3L)
Pickup
  4-speed 1.8 qts. (1.7L)
  5-speed 2.0 qts. (1.9L)
Sentra
  4-speed 2.4 qts. (2.3L)
  5-speed 2.9 qts. (2.7L)
Stanza 2.9 qts. (2.7L)

ADJUSTMENT

LINKAGE

All models except 310 have a floor shift which has no external linkage and requires no adjustment.

Fig. 1: 4-Speed Transmission Control Linkage

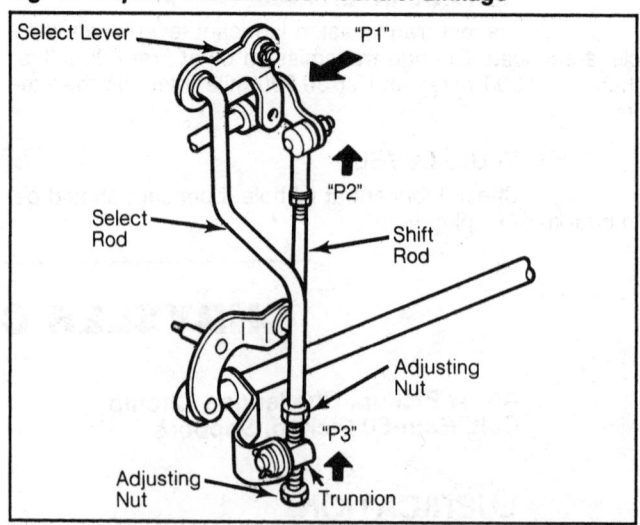

310

1) Loosen adjusting nut on each end of control rod lever. Set shift lever in Neutral. Push shift lever in

DATSUN/NISSAN (Cont.)

direction "P1", pull it back .31" (8 mm) on 4-speed models, and .45" (11 mm) on 5-speed models.

    2) With select lever held in this position, move shift lever in direction "P2". This is 3rd gear on 4-speed models, and 2nd gear on 5-speed models.

Fig. 2: Positioning Shift Lever

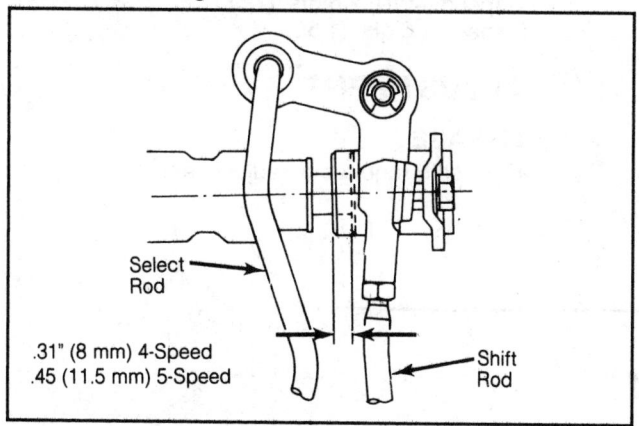

    3) Push control rod select lever in direction "P3", and turn adjusting nut until it touches trunnion. Turn

adjusting nut 1/4 turn further, and lock select lever with adjusting nut on either side of lever.

Fig. 3: 5-Speed Transmission Control Linkage

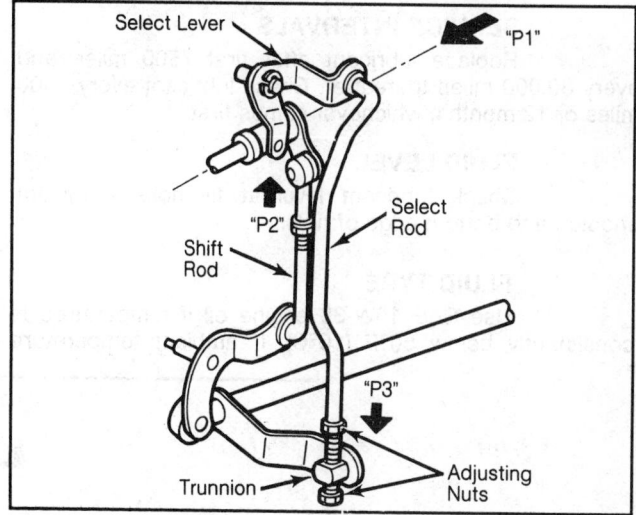

FIAT

Spider 2000, 2000 Turbo, X 1/9

LUBRICATION

SERVICE INTERVALS
Check lubricant level every 12,500 miles and change every 30,000 miles.

FLUID LEVEL
Check lubricant level at transmission fill hole. Lubricant should be up to bottom of opening.

FLUID TYPE
Spider 2000
Hypoid SAE 80W/90 (with E.P.)

X 1/9
Hypoid SAE 90W (with no E.P.)

FLUID CAPACITY
Spider 2000 1.7 qts. (1.6L)
X 1/9 3.5 qts. (3.3L)

ADJUSTMENT

LINKAGE
All models have a floor shift which has no external linkage and requires no linkage adjustment.

HONDA

Accord, Civic, Prelude

LUBRICATION

SERVICE INTERVALS
Change lubricant every 30,000 miles.

FLUID LEVEL
Check lubricant level at transmission fill hole. Lubricant should be up to bottom of the opening.

FLUID TYPE
SAE 10W-40 engine oil rated SE.

FLUID CAPACITY
Accord 2.5 qts. (2.4L)
Civic 2.6 qts. (2.5L)
Prelude 2.5 qts. (2.4L)

ADJUSTMENT

LINKAGE
No external adjustments required.

Manual Transmission Servicing

ISUZU

I-Mark, P'UP

LUBRICATION

SERVICE INTERVALS
Replace lubricant after first 7500 miles and every 30,000 miles thereafter. Check lubricant every 7500 miles or 12 months, whichever comes first.

FLUID LEVEL
Check lubricant level at fill hole. Lubricant should be to bottom edge of hole.

FLUID TYPE
Use SAE 10W-30 engine oil if temperature is consistantly below 50°F (10°C). If ambient temperature varies, but falls within the 0-90°F (-18°-32°C) range, use 30W engine oil. Finally, if temperatures are consistently above 50°F (10°C), 40W engine oil should be used.

FLUID CAPACITY
4-speed (2WD) 1.4 qts. (1.3L)
4-speed (4WD) 2.6 qts. (2.5L)
5-speed 1.6 qts. (1.5L)

ADJUSTMENT

LINKAGE
Floor shift requires no adjustment.

LUV

LUBRICATION

SERVICE INTERVALS
Replace lubricant after first 7500 miles, then every 30,000 miles. Check level every 6 months or 7500 miles (whichever comes first).

FLUID LEVEL
Check lubricant level at fill hole. Lubricant should be to bottom edge of hole.

FLUID TYPE
Use SAE 10W-30 engine oil if ambient temperature is consistantly below 50°F (10°C). If normal temperatures vary within the 0°-90°F (-18°-32°C) range, use 30W engine oil. If temperatures are consistently above 50°F (10°C), 40W engine oil should be used.

FLUID CAPACITY
4-speed (2WD) 1.3 qts. (1.2L)
4-speed (4WD) 2.6 qts. (2.5L)
5-speed 1.6 qts. (1.5L)

ADJUSTMENT

LINKAGE
Shift linkage is integral with transmission housing and requires no external adjustment.

MAZDA

B2000 & B2200 Pickups, GLC, RX7, 626

LUBRICATION

SERVICE INTERVALS
Replace lubricant at first 7500 miles, then every 30,000 miles. Check lubricant level every 7500 miles.

FLUID LEVEL
GLC FWD
Remove speedometer cable and driven gear from transaxle case. Wipe driven gear clean and reinsert. Pull it out again. Lubricant level should between the "L" and "F" marks on driven gear.
All Other Models
Check lubricant level at fill hole. Lubricant should be up to bottom of fill hole.

FLUID TYPE
Hypoid SAE 80W or 90W (API GL-4 or GL-5)

FLUID CAPACITY
4-speed 1.3 qts. (1.2L)
4-speed W/Transfer Case 2.6 qts. (2.6L)
5-speed 1.6 qts. (1.5L)

ADJUSTMENT

LINKAGE
Shift linkage is integral with transmission housing and requires no external adjustment.

MERCEDES-BENZ

240D

LUBRICATION

SERVICE INTERVALS

Transmission fluid has to be changed at first 800-1000 and 5000 miles of operation. Thereafter check and replenish fluid every 15,500 miles.

FLUID LEVEL

Check lubricant level at fill hole. Lubricant should be up to bottom of fill hole.

FLUID CAPACITY

4-speed 1.4 qts. (1.3L)

ADJUSTMENT

1) Disconnect shift rods at shift lever. Align 3 intermediate levers at bottom of shift bracket by inserting a centering pin. *See Fig. 1.*

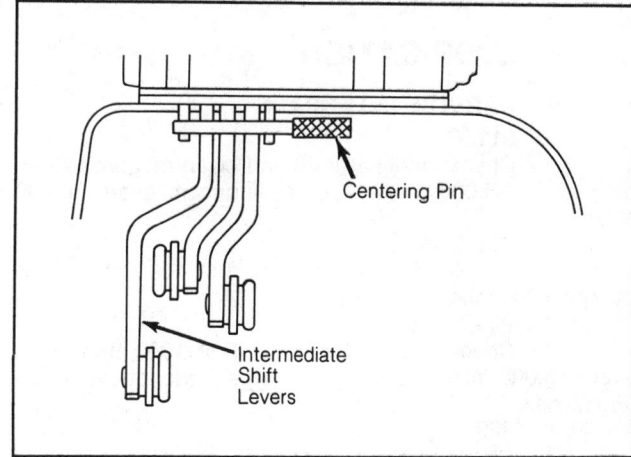

Fig. 1: View Showing Shift Lever Adjustment

2) Place transmission in neutral. Adjust shift rods so they will fit into their respective holes in intermediate levers without tension. Install lock pins, remove centering pin and check for proper operation.

PEUGEOT

504, 505, 604

LUBRICATION

SERVICE INTERVALS

504 & 505 Diesel
Check transmission oil level every 3000 miles. Replace every 18,500 miles.

505 Gasoline
Check transmission oil level every 5000 miles. Replace every 20,000 miles.

604
Change oil at first 1500 miles and every 12,500 miles thereafter. Check level every 4500 miles.

FLUID LEVEL

Transmission oil fill plug is located on side of transmission. Lubricant should be at bottom edge of hole.

FLUID TYPE

SAE 10W/40 engine oil (API grade CC)

FLUID CAPACITY

504 & 505 Diesel
  4-speed 2.0 qts. (1.9L)
  5-speed 1.7 qts. (1.8L)
604 5-speed 2.0 qts. (1.9L)

ADJUSTMENT

LINKAGE

Adjustment is accomplished by setting the 2 control levers to proper dimensions. *See Fig. 1.*

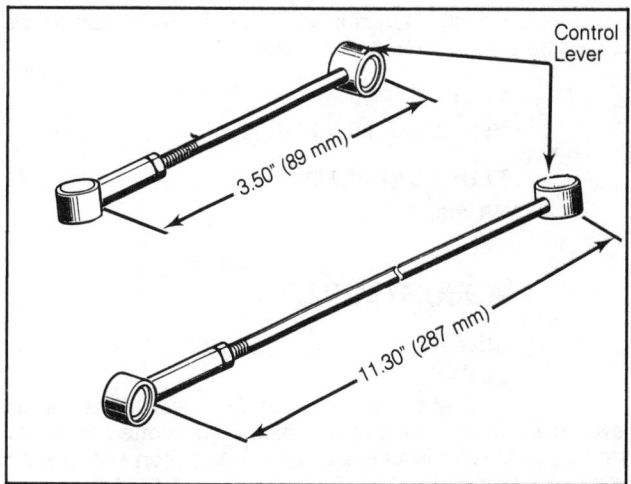

Fig 1: Shift Lever Adjustment

PORSCHE

911SC, 924, 924 Turbo, 928, 944

LUBRICATION

SERVICE INTERVALS

911SC

Check lubricant level and clean magnetic drain plug every 15,000 miles. Replace lubricant every 30,000 miles.

924 & 944

Check lubricant level at first 1000 miles and every 15,000 miles thereafter.

924 Turbo

Check lubricant level at first 1000 miles and every 15,000 miles thereafter. Change lubricant every 60,-000 miles.

928

Check lubricant level and clean magnetic drain plug at first 1000 miles. Check lubricant level every 15,000 miles and replace every 30,000 miles.

FLUID LEVEL

911SC Hypoid SAE 90W (API GL-5)
924, 924 Turbo, & 944
 Hypoid SAE 80 (API GL-4)
928 Hypoid SAE 75W-90 (API GL-5)

FLUID CAPACITY

911SC 3.2 qts. (3.0L)
924, 924 Turbo, & 944 2.7 qts. (2.6L)
928 4 qts. (3.8L)

ADJUSTMENT

LINKAGE

No adjustment required.

RENAULT

18i, Fuego, Fuego Turbo, Le Car

LUBRICATION

SERVICE INTERVALS

Change lubricant after first 1,000 miles, and at 12,000 mile intervals thereafter.

FLUID LEVEL

Check lubricant level at fill hole. Lubricant should be even with bottom of hole.

FLUID TYPE

Hypoid SAE 80 (API GL-5)

FLUID CAPACITY

2.1 qts. (2.0L)

ADJUSTMENT

LINKAGE

Le Car

1) Place shift lever in 3rd gear. Press shift lever toward 1st-2nd gear position. Use slotted holes in stop plate to visually check clearance between end of shift lever and stop plate. Clearance should be 1/8" (3 mm).

2) Adjustments are made by placing washers between the stop plate and floor panel. The tolerance of the reverse stop should be 3/16-9/32" (5-7 mm) when the end of the shift lever is resting against stop plate.

Fig 1: Setting Le Car Shift Lever Dimension

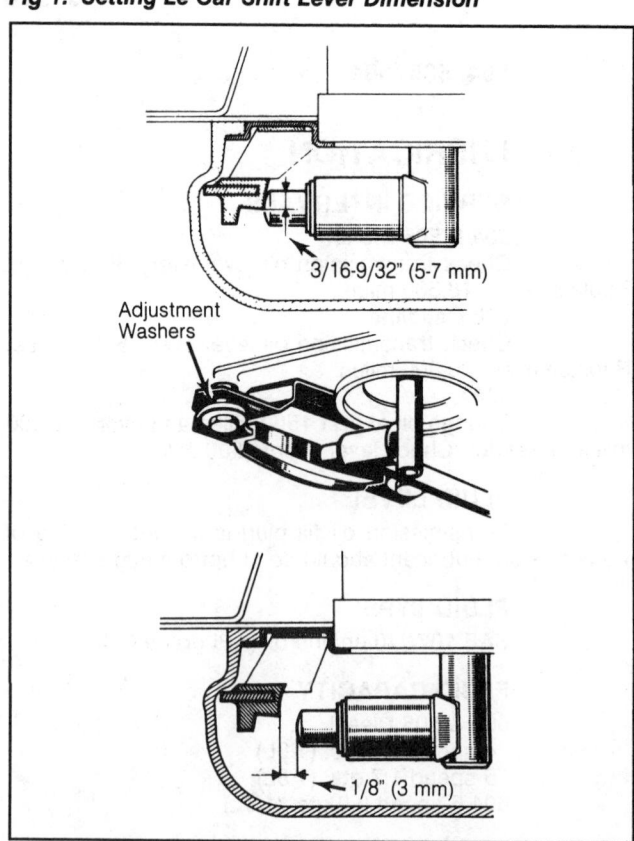

RENAULT (Cont.)

Fig. 2: 18i, Fuego, & Fuego Turbo Shift Lever Adjustment

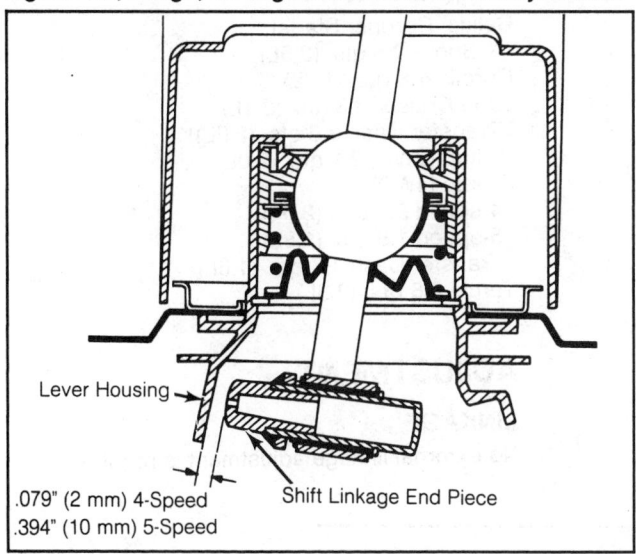

Lever Housing

.079" (2 mm) 4-Speed
.394" (10 mm) 5-Speed

Shift Linkage End Piece

18i, Fuego & Fuego Turbo

1) Place shift lever in Neutral position. Loosen lock nut on yoke so shift linkage turns freely. Put transmission lever at transmission case exit, against 3rd-4th gear line.

2) Place a .079" (2 mm) shim (4-Speed) or a .394" (10 mm) shim (5-Speed) between the end piece of the shift linkage and the surface of the housing. Tighten yoke nut. Make sure that clearance between end piece and lever housing is the same as the shim.

SAAB

900, 900 Turbo

LUBRICATION

SERVICE INTERVALS

Change transmission lubricant and clean magnetic drain plug at first 1000 miles. Check and adjust fluid level every 7500 miles. Check every 5000 miles on 900 Turbo.

FLUID LEVEL

Check fluid level with dipstick located in engine compartment. Fluid level should be between "Min" and "Max" marks on dipstick.

FLUID TYPE

SAE 10W/30 or 10W/40 engine oil

FLUID CAPACITY

4-speed 2.6 qts. (2.5L)
5-speed 3.2 qts. (3.0L)

ADJUSTMENT

LINKAGE

1) Select reverse gear. Loosen clamp on the gear shift rod joint so that the gear shift rod can be moved in the joint.

2) Lock gear lever in reverse by inserting a 6 mm Allen wrench into the apertures in the gear lever housing and gear shift rod. The apertures are accessible once the gear lever console cover has been loosened and removed rearward.

3) Check that reverse gear is fully engaged. Tighten clamp on gear shift rod joint. Torque to 12-16 ft. lbs. (16-22 N.m).

SUBARU

1600, 1800

LUBRICATION

SERVICE INTERVALS

Replace lubricant at first 1000 miles and every 30,000 miles thereafter. Check lubricant level every 15,000 miles.

FLUID LEVEL

Check lubricant level at dipstick located in engine compartment. Transmission and differential (transaxle) are lubricated through a common oil supply.

FLUID TYPE

SAE (API GL-5) engine oil
SAE 90W above 30°F (0°C)
SAE 85W from -30°F (-34°C)

FLUID CAPACITY

4 & 5-speed 2WD 2.9 qts. (2.7L)
4WD 3.2 qts. (3.0L)

ADJUSTMENT

LINKAGE

All models use shift linkage which does not require external adjustment.

Manual Transmission Servicing

TOYOTA

Celica, Corolla, Corona, Land Cruiser, Pickup, Starlet, Supra, Tercel

LUBRICATION

SERVICE INTERVALS
Check lubricant level every 15,000 miles. No fluid change is required.

FLUID LEVEL
Check lubricant level at fill hole. Lubricant should be to bottom of hole.

FLUID TYPE
Land Cruiser
  SAE 90W (API GL-4 or GL-5)
All Others
  SAE 80 (API GL-4 or GL-5)
  SAE 75W/90 (API GL-4 or GL-5)

FLUID CAPACITY
Celica, Corona, Starlet,
  & Supra 2.6 qts. (2.5L)
Corolla 1.8 qts. (1.7L)
Land Cruiser 3.3 qts. (3.1L)
  Transfer Case 2.6 qts. (2.5L)
Pickup (2WD) 2.1 qts. (2.0L)
Pickup (4WD)
  4-speed 2.1 qts. (2.0L)
  5-speed 1.9 qts. (1.8L)
  Transfer Case 1.7 qts. (1.6L)
Tercel 3.5 qts. (3.3L)

ADJUSTMENT

LINKAGE
No external linkage adjustment is required.

VOLKSWAGEN

Jetta, Pickup, Quantum, Rabbit, Scirocco, Vanagon

LUBRICATION

SERVICE INTERVALS
No oil changes are required. Check oil every 15,000 miles.

FLUID LEVEL
Check oil level through fill plug hole in side of transmission. Oil level should be to bottom of hole.

FLUID TYPE
Hypoid SAE 80W or 80W/90 (API GL-4)

FLUID CAPACITY
Jetta, Quantum, Rabbit, & Scirocco
  2.1 qts. (2.0L)
Rabbit Pickup
  4-speed 1.6 qts. (1.5L)
  5-speed 2.1 qts. (2.0L)
Vanagon 3.7 qts. (3.5L)

ADJUSTMENT

LINKAGE
Jetta, Pickup, Quantum, Rabbit & Scirocco
1) Loosen bolts holding lever housing. Pull boot off of housing. Loosen shift rod clamp bolt so selector lever moves freely on shift rod. Adjust shift finger in center of lock out plate so that an equal distance is obtained on both sides of the shift finger. See Fig. 1.
2) Adjust shift rod end so that a distance of 3/4" (20 mm) for 4-speed models, or 9/32" (15 mm) for 5-speed models, exists between shift finger and stop plate. See Fig. 2. Tighten shift rod clamp. Shift through gears and check for proper engagement.

Fig. 1: Correct Position of Shift Finger

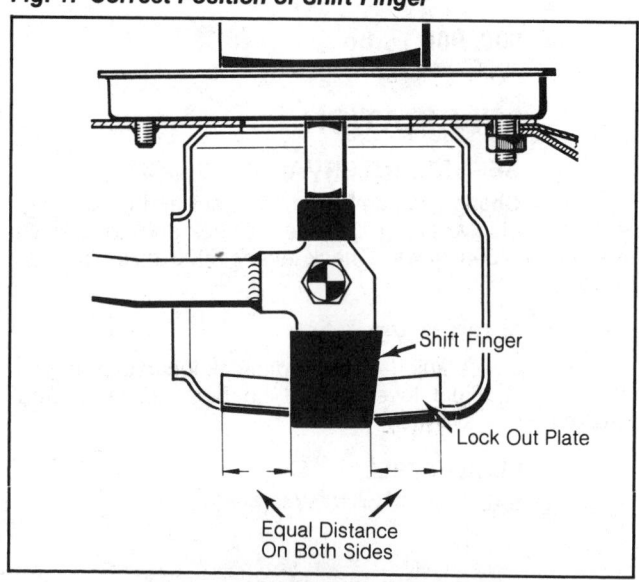

Fig. 2: Adjusting Shift Finger Distance

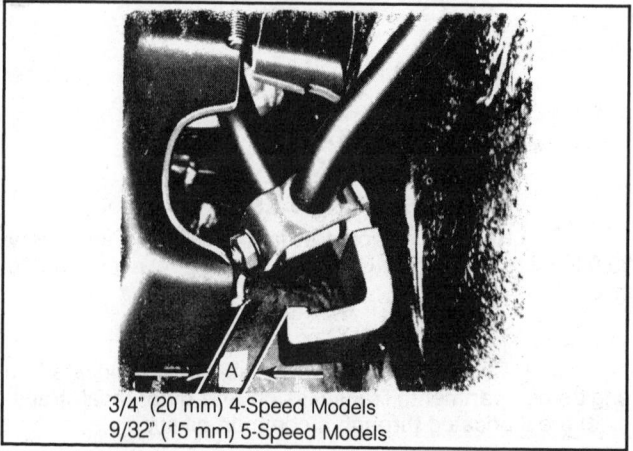

3/4" (20 mm) 4-Speed Models
9/32" (15 mm) 5-Speed Models

VOLKSWAGEN (Cont.)

Vanagon

1) Place shift lever in Neutral position. Align holes of upper lever bearing plate with holes in lower lever bearing plate.

2) Loosen shift rod clamp so selector lever moves freely on shift rod. Remove spare tire. Move shift finger of front shift rod to center of rubber stop in housing.

3) Adjust shift rod end so that a distance of 3/4" (20 mm) exists between shift rod end and stop plate. Check for proper operation.

GEAR SHIFT LEVER

Jetta, Pickup, Quantum, Rabbit & Scirocco

Move the lever bearing assembly on its elongated bolt holes until the round holes indicated in *Fig. 3* are perfectly aligned with the corresponding round holes in lever plate and housing.

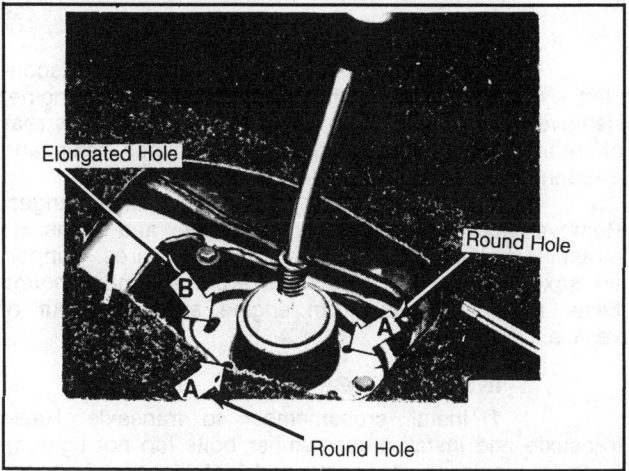

Fig. 3: Adjusting Shift Lever All Models (Except Vanagon)

Elongated Hole
Round Hole
Round Hole

VOLVO

DL, GL, GLE, GLT, GLT Turbo

LUBRICATION

SERVICE INTERVALS

Replace transmission oil at first 600-1200 miles. Check every 7500 miles.

FLUID LEVEL

Check lubricant level at fill hole. Oil should be up to bottom of fill hole. When adding oil, allow sufficient time for oil to flow into overdrive unit.

FLUID TYPE

F or G Automatic Transmission Fluid (FLM)

FLUID CAPACITY

2.4 qts. (2.3L) (With overdrive M46)

ADJUSTMENT

No external linkage adjustment is required.

Manual Transmission Removal

AUDI

4000 4-SPEED

REMOVAL

1) Disconnect battery ground strap. Disconnect exhaust pipe from transaxle bracket and engine. Remove square bolt and press shifter coupling from rear of transmission shifting shaft. Unhook clutch cable and disconnect speedometer cable.

2) Disconnect CV joints at inner drive flanges. Remove starter, front mounting plate and transaxle mounting bolts. Disconnect back-up light wires. Support transaxle on floor jack and remove crossmember mount. Lever transaxle away from engine and lower out of vehicle.

INSTALLATION

1) Install crossmember to transaxle. Raise transaxle and install crossmember bolts (do not tighten). Slide transaxle up to engine and install mounting bolts. Install front mounting plate and starter. Install CV joint Allen screws and tighten. Tighten crossmember mounting bolts.

NOTE: **Always use longer hex head bolt when replacing shift rod coupling instead of original square head bolt. Secure with safety wire.**

2) Install shift rod coupling bolt and install lock wire. Connect exhaust pipe allowing 3/8" (10 mm) between pipe and floor pan. Reconnect back-up light wires and battery ground strap.

4000 5-SPEED

REMOVAL

1) Disconnect battery ground strap. Disconnect exhaust pipe from transaxle bracket and engine. Remove square bolt and press shifter coupling from rear of transaxle shifting shaft. Unhook clutch cable and disconnect speedometer. On models equipped with a 5-cylinder engine, support front of engine when transaxle is removed.

2) Disconnect CV joints at inner drive flanges. Support axle shafts from vehicle with wire. Remove starter, front mounting plate and transaxle mounting bolts. Disconnect back-up light switch connector. Support transaxle on floor jack and remove crossmember mount. Remove transaxle from engine and lower from vehicle.

INSTALLATION

1) Install crossmember to transaxle. Raise transaxle up to vehicle and install crossmember bolts finger tight. Slide transaxle up to engine and install mounting bolts. Install front mounting plate and starter. Install inner CV joint mounting bolts into CV joint and drive flange. Tighten crossmember mounting bolts.

NOTE: **Always use longer hex head bolt when replacing shift rod coupling instead of original square head bolt. Secure with safety wire.**

2) Install shift rod coupling bolt and lock with safety wire. Connect exhaust pipe, allowing 3/8" (10 mm) clearance between pipe and floor. Reconnect all wires, cables and linkages that were removed during removal procedure.

5000

REMOVAL

1) Remove air cleaner (diesel only). Disconnect battery ground cable. Remove windshield washer reservoir. Remove upper engine-to-transaxle bolts. Disconnect speedometer cable.

2) Remove right side guard plate. Disconnect drive axle shafts from drive flanges and support on top of subframe. Disconnect wire from back-up light switch. Disconnect shift linkage from transaxle case.

3) Remove lower engine-to-transaxle bolts, starter and guard plate from subframe. Lift transaxle slightly and remove transaxle supports. Remove rear subframe mounting bolts. Remove right transaxle bracket, then remove transaxle from below.

INSTALLATION

Reverse removal procedure and note the following: Lubricate mainshaft splines lightly with grease. Make sure transaxle seats on engine dowels. Adjust shift linkage as necessary.

BMW

ALL MODELS

REMOVAL

1) Push up shift lever boot and foam ring, then remove circlip from shift lever ball socket. Remove exhaust bracket from transmission and exhaust pipe from manifold. Remove upper clutch housing bolts.

2) Remove propeller shaft from transmission (coupling or flexible disc remains with shaft). Remove propeller shaft center support bearing, pull shaft downward and away from centering pin.

3) Remove shift lever bearing pin and push shift lever upward. Remove clutch linkage and slave cylinder as required. Loosen angle support and remove transmission front cover plate.

4) Support engine using a block between engine and front axle subframe. Remove speedometer shaft and electrical connections. Loosen crossmember and turn steering to full right lock position.

5) On 320i models, remove remaining bolts securing transmission to engine and frame; remove transmission. On all other models, remove transmission-to-clutch housing bolts and separate transmission from clutch housing.

INSTALLATION

Reverse removal procedure and note the following: Use new lock nuts on propeller shaft; tighten nuts on propeller shaft only, never bolts; use shims under shift lever circlip to remove play in shift lever; preload center bearing .079" (2 mm); adjust clutch pedal free play.

CHRYSLER CORP. IMPORTS

ALL FWD MODELS

REMOVAL

1) Disconnect battery negative cable. Remove the following parts from transaxle: Clutch cable, speedometer cable, back-up light switch harness, starter, and 4 top engine-to-transaxle mounting bolts.

2) Raise vehicle and remove wheels. Remove shift rod and extension. Drain transaxle fluid. Remove drive shafts. Disconnect gear selector cable. Remove engine rear cover.

3) Connect engine to hoist and remove remaining transaxle-to-engine bolts. Remove transaxle mount insulator bolt. Lower and remove transaxle.

INSTALLATION

To install, reverse removal procedure and note the following: The coupling bolt at each end of front roll rod should be temporarily tightened at installation. After the transaxle has been installed, tighten bolts to specifications.

ALL RWD MODELS – 4-SPEED

REMOVAL

1) In engine compartment, disconnect negative battery cable. Remove air cleaner and starter. Remove 2 upper transmission mounting bolts.

2) Inside vehicle, take out console box (if equipped) and carpet. Remove dust cover retainer plate at base of shift lever. Lift up dust cover and remove attaching bolts at lower part of extension housing and remove gearshift lever.

NOTE: **Make sure gearshift lever is in 2nd speed position before removing.**

3) With vehicle raised and supported, drain transmission. Remove bolts from rear of propeller shaft and draw shaft out of transmission.

4) Disconnect speedometer and back-up light switch harness at transmission side. Disconnect front exhaust pipe. From clutch control lever, disconnect clutch cable.

5) Support rear of engine with jack, place transmission jack under transmission and remove rear supports and crossmember.

6) Remove clutch housing inspection cover and bolts attaching clutch housing to engine block. Pulling rearward and downward, remove transmission from vehicle.

INSTALLATION

1) To install, reverse removal procedure and note the following: When installing control lever assembly, place shift lever in 2nd gear position so that nylon bushing hole is vertical.

CAUTION: During this operation, use care that dirt does not enter through opening.

2) When installing clutch housing inspection cover, make sure that it is not bent. When installing shift lever dust boot, make sure cover is tightly installed to prevent noise entry into vehicle. After installing transmission, refill with SAE 80 gear oil.

ARROW & RAM-50 (2WD) 5-SPEED

REMOVAL

1) In engine compartment, disconnect negative battery cable. Remove air cleaner and starter. Remove 2 upper transmission mounting bolts.

2) Inside vehicle, take out console box (if equipped), and carpet. Remove dust cover retainer plate at base of shift lever. Lift up dust cover and remove attaching bolts at lower part of extension housing and remove gearshift lever.

NOTE: **Make sure gearshift lever is in 2nd speed position before removing.**

3) With vehicle raised and supported, drain transmission. Remove bolts from rear of propeller shaft and draw shaft out of transmission.

4) Disconnect speedometer and back-up light switch harness at transmission side. Disconnect front exhaust pipe. From clutch control lever, disconnect clutch cable.

5) Support rear of engine with jack, place transmission jack under transmission and remove rear supports and crossmember.

6) Remove clutch housing inspection cover and bolts attaching clutch housing to engine block. Pulling rearward and downward, remove transmission from vehicle.

INSTALLATION

1) To install, reverse removal procedure and note the following: When installing control lever assembly, place shift lever in 2nd gear position so that nylon bushing hole is vertical.

CAUTION: During this operation, use care that dirt does not enter through opening.

2) When installing clutch housing inspection cover, make sure that it is not bent. When installing shift lever dust boot, make sure cover is tightly installed to prevent noise entry into vehicle. After installing transmission, refill with SAE 80 gear oil.

CHALLENGER & SAPPORO 5-SPEED

REMOVAL

1) In engine compartment, disconnect negative battery cable. Remove air cleaner. Insert a rag between rocker cover and firewall. Place gearshift lever in any position except "R".

2) With vehicle raised and supported, remove starter. Disconnect clutch cable from clutch control lever and remove it from transmission case. Remove clutch housing cover.

3) Disconnect speedometer and back-up light switch harness at transmission side. Remove bolts from rear of propeller shaft and draw shaft out of transmission.

4) Support rear of engine with jack, place transmission jack under transmission and remove rear supports and crossmember. Remove control housing and remaining transmission mounting bolts. Remove transmission.

Manual Transmission Removal

CHRYSLER CORP. IMPORTS (Cont.)

INSTALLATION
To install, reverse removal procedure.

RAM-50 (4WD)
REMOVAL

1) Inside vehicle, take out console box (if equipped), and carpet. Remove dust cover retainer plate at base of shift lever. Lift up dust cover and remove attaching bolts at lower part of extension housing and remove gearshift lever. Shift levers should be in neutral position (transmission) and "4H" position (transfer case).

2) Raise and support vehicle. Remove drain plugs and drain transission and transfer case fluid. Remove front and rear propeller shafts.

3) Disconnect speedometer cable, back-up light switch wiring and 4WD indicator light switch harness from transmission. Disconnect front exhaust pipe. Disconnect clutch cable from clutch control lever.

4) Support rear of engine with safety stand. Support transmission with transmission jack. Disconnect plate and remove transfer case mounting bracket. Remove second crossmember.

5) Remove clutch housing cover, then remove remaining transmission mounting bolts. Pull transmission assembly back and lower out of vehicle.

INSTALLATION
Reverse removal procedure to install, noting the following: Shift lever assembly must be installed with transmission lever in neutral position and transfer case lever in "4H" position.

COURIER

4-SPEED
REMOVAL

1) With gearshift lever in neutral, lift up large shift lever boot. Remove 4 screws securing shift lever tower to extension housing. Remove shift lever, tower, gasket and both shift lever boots. Cover shift tower opening in extension housing with a clean cloth to prevent foreign matter from entering transmission.

2) Raise vehicle and position on safety stands. Disconnect drive shaft at rear axle flange. Remove center support bearing nuts and washers. Pull drive shaft rearward out of transmission and remove from vehicle.

3) Install a seal installer (T72J-7095) in end of transmission to prevent oil leakage. Disconnect exhaust pipe bracket at transmission and at clutch housing. Disconnect exhaust pipe at manifold and muffler. Remove pipe and catalytic converter.

4) Disconnect clutch lever return spring. Remove clutch slave cylinder without disconnecting hydraulic line and position out of way. Disconnect speedometer cable, back-up light wires and starter motor wires. Remove starter.

5) Place a jack under engine, protecting oil pan with a wood block. Place a transmission jack under transmission. Remove bolts securing clutch housing to engine.

6) Remove bolts securing crossmember to transmission and frame and remove crossmember. Lower engine jack and work clutch housing off dowels. Slide transmission rearward and lower to remove.

INSTALLATION
Make sure all mating surfaces are clean and free of burrs. To install transmission, reverse removal procedure. Adjust clutch release lever free play. Check transmission lubricant level and refill as necessary.

5-SPEED
REMOVAL

1) Remove console box, if equipped. Remove boot retaining screws and bolts attaching retainer cover.

Place gearshift lever in neutral position and pull gearshift lever, shim and bushing straight up from gearshift lever retainer.

2) Cover shift tower opening in extension housing to avoid dropping dirt into transmission.

3) Disconnect the negative battery cable. Raise vehicle. Disconnect drive shaft at rear axle drive flange. Remove drive shaft center bearing support attaching nuts and washers.

4) Pull drive shaft to rear and disconnect from transmission. Install a plug in extension housing to prevent leakage of lubricant.

5) Remove bolt and nut attaching exhaust pipe hanger to clutch housing. Disconnect exhaust pipe at exhaust manifold and muffler. Remove exhaust pipe and catalyst assembly.

6) Remove clutch release cylinder and secure it to side. Remove speedometer cable from extension housing. Disconnect starter motor and back-up light switch wires.

7) Place jack under engine, protecting oil pan with wood block. Remove starter motor. Place transmission jack under transmission. Remove bolts and washers attaching transmission-to-engine rear plate.

8) Remove nuts and bolts attaching transmission mount-to-crossmember. Remove nuts attaching crossmember-to-frame side rails. Remove crossmember.

9) Lower engine jack. Work clutch housing off locating dowels. Slide transmission to rear until input shaft spline clears clutch disc. Remove transmission from vehicle.

INSTALLATION

1) To install, reverse removal procedure and note the following: Position gearshift lever, shim and bushing straight above gearshift lever retainer. Make sure no dirt falls into transmission while installing gearshift lever.

2) Tighten all attaching nuts and bolts. Check transmission fluid level and fill with specified fluid if necessary. Adjust clutch release lever free play as required.

DATSUN/NISSAN

ALL RWD MODELS

REMOVAL

1) Disconnect negative battery cable. Remove console (if equipped) and shift lever boot. Place transmission in neutral. Remove snap ring or nut from control lever pin. Remove control lever pin and control lever.

2) Raise vehicle and remove exhaust pipe. Disconnect wiring at back-up light switch, high gear switch, neutral switch (if equipped) and overdrive switch (210 5-speed). Disconnect speedometer cable.

3) On 4WD pickups, disconnect wires from 4WD indicator switch. Disconnect propeller shaft between transmission and transfer case. Remove front differential carrier crossmember. Disconnect propeller shaft between transfer case and front differential carrier.

4) On all other models, disconnect propeller shaft from transmission. On all models, remove clutch cylinder from transmission case. Support engine and transmission. Remove rear transmission mounting bolts and crossmember bolts. Remove starter. Remove transmission-to-engine mounting bolts.

5) Slide transmission to rear away from engine. Remove transmission from vehicle. Use care when removing transmission to avoid striking any adjacent parts or main drive shaft.

INSTALLATION

Reverse removal procedures to install transmission, noting the following:
- Clean mating surfaces of engine rear plate and transmission case. Apply a light coat of grease to splined parts of clutch disc, input shaft and moving surfaces of control lever and striking rod.
- Lubricate oil seal lip and bushing of extension housing before installing propeller shaft.
- Fill transmission with gear oil to level of filler hole.

SENTRA & STANZA

REMOVAL

NOTE: **If equipped with air conditioning, disconnect compressor without removing lines and lay on top of engine.**

1) Remove battery and battery holding plate. Remove radiator reservoir tank. Remove drive shafts from transaxle without damaging oil seals. Insert a shaft into each side of differential to prevent side gears from falling into differential case.

2) Remove wheel well protector. Separate shifter control rod and support rod from transaxle. Remove exhaust pipe securing nuts and bolts. Remove engine gusset bolts and transmission protector. Remove clutch control cable from withdrawl lever.

3) Disconnect speedometer cable. Disconnect wires from reverse and neutral switches. Support engine with a jack and a block of wood placed under the oil pan. Support the transaxle with a jack.

4) Remove starter motor. Remove engine mount securing bolts. Remove bolts securing transaxle to engine. Separate transaxle from engine and remove transaxle from under vehicle.

INSTALLATION

To install, reverse removal procedure and note the following: Clean mating surface between engine and clutch housing. Apply grease to splines on input shaft and clutch disc. Remove filler plug and fill transaxle with recommended amount and type of gear lube.

310

REMOVAL

NOTE: **If equipped with air conditioning, disconnect compressor without removing lines and lay on top of engine.**

1) Transmission is removed from above vehicle. Remove hood. Remove battery and drain gear oil. Remove axle shafts from transaxle without damaging shaft seal. Insert a shaft into each side of differential to prevent side gears from falling into differential case.

2) Remove distributor, air induction tube, EGR tube and exhaust manifold cover. Remove heater hose clamp. Remove clutch control cable from withdrawl lever. Disconnect speedometer cable. Disconnect wires from reverse and neutral switches.

3) Separate shifter control and support rods from transmission. Support engine with a jack and a wooden block under the oil pan. Support the transaxle with a jack. Remove engine gusset bolts. Remove engine right-side (5-speed only) and rear side mounting brackets.

4) Support transaxle by attaching a hoist to clutch control cable bracket. Remove bolts securing transaxle to engine. Separate transaxle from engine and lift transaxle from vehicle making sure not to strike input shaft or engine compartment components.

INSTALLATION

To install, reverse removal procedure and note the following: Clean mating surface between engine and clutch housing. Apply grease to splines on input shaft and clutch disc. Remove filler plug and fill transaxle with recommended amount and type of gear lube.

FIAT

SPIDER 2000

REMOVAL

1) Disconnect negative battery cable. Unscrew gearshift knob. Unsnap rear of console cover and lift up, along with boot, over gearshift lever. Unclip plastic retainer at bottom of gearshift lever assembly. Separate top half of lever from bottom half.

2) Disconnect electrical connector to reverse switch. Remove top cover. Remove screws at front of console. Remove coin holder at rear of console to remove rear screw. Lift console up slightly, and carefully pull back about 3" to obtain clearance for gearshift lever when transmission is lowered.

3) Raise vehicle on hoist. Remove plug and drain transmission. Remove clutch lever return spring.

FIAT (Cont.)

Disconnect clutch cable from clutch lever. Withdraw cable through clutch housing.

NOTE: **It may be necessary to loosen emergency brake cable adjustment in order to raise brake handle high enough for console to be moved to rear.**

4) Unscrew speedometer connector from transmission. Remove 3 bolts holding starter to clutch housing. Position starter out of the way. Remove 4 bolts and remove flywheel cover.

5) Install compressor on flexible coupling. Remove nuts and bolts holding coupling to transmission flange. Remove bolts holding crossmember for pillow block and bolts holding protection bracket for front shaft. Remove nuts holding rear shaft yoke to differential flange. Remove drive shaft.

6) Place transmission jack under transmission. Remove 4 nuts and remove transmission mount. Remove 4 bolts holding transmission to engine. Separate transmission from engine and move it to the rear. Tilt transmission and lower from vehicle.

INSTALLATION

Reverse removal procedure to install, noting the following: Fill transmission with lubricant and adjust clutch pedal free play as needed.

X1/9

REMOVAL

1) Remove air cleaner and duct. Disconnect positive battery cable. Loosen 2 bolts securing clutch slave cylinder and open bleed valve to allow push rod to retract. Disconnect return spring from clutch shaft. Disconnect push rod and move slave cylinder out of way.

2) Install support on engine and remove nuts and bolts securing transaxle to engine which are accessible from engine compartment. Raise vehicle and remove rear wheels. Remove 3 lower shields on left side.

3) Mark position of gearshift flexible link in relation to shift tube and remove bolts securing link to tube. Loosen bolt at transaxle end of link and swing link out of way. Disconnect all wiring to transaxle. Remove starter motor. Disconnect ground strap and remove exhaust pipe.

4) Remove CV joint-to-hub nuts. Remove bolts and nuts securing suspension control arm to supports. Pull hub off CV joints and tie differential output shafts to transaxle to prevent their falling out.

5) Remove flywheel cover and engine supporting crosspiece. Remove remaining nuts and bolts securing transaxle to engine. Using support fixture (A.70575) installed on hydraulic jack, lower and remove transaxle from vehicle.

INSTALLATION

To install, reverse removal procedure. Tighten suspension bolts with weight of vehicle on wheels.

HONDA

ACCORD

REMOVAL

1) Disconnect ground cable from battery and transaxle. Release steering lock and place shift selector lever in neutral. Disconnect the following electrical leads: Positive battery cable at starter, starter solenoid and back-up light switch.

2) Disconnect clutch cable at release arm. Remove starter mounting bolt from transaxle and upper transaxle mounting bolts. Raise and support vehicle, drain transaxle and remove front wheels.

3) Support transaxle with jack. Remove speedometer drive holder retaining bolt and pull assembly out of transaxle. Disconnect torque rod from clutch housing. Remove shift rod clevis bolt.

4) Disconnect and remove tie-rod ball joints. Remove lower arm ball joint pinch bolts and free arms by tapping downward with soft (brass) hammer. Turn steering knuckle to outward-most position, pry CV joint out about 1/2" and pull axle shaft out of transaxle housing. Repeat on other side.

5) Remove right-side radius rod. Remove torque arm brackets from clutch housing. Remove damper bracket from center beam. Remove clutch housing bolts at both transaxle mounting brackets. Remove clutch cover.

6) Remove remaining starter mounting bolt and remove starter. Remove front transaxle mounting bolt. Pull transaxle back until it clears dowel pins and lower assembly out of vehicle.

INSTALLATION

Reverse removal procedures to install transaxle, noting the following: Clean and lightly grease release bearing sliding surface. Always use new spring clips when installing axle shafts.

CIVIC & PRELUDE

REMOVAL

1) Disconnect ground cable from battery and transaxle. Release steering lock and place gear shift in neutral position. Disconnect the following electrical leads: Starter motor, starter solenoid, temperature sending unit, ignition timing thermosensor, back-up light switch and coil wires from distributor (Prelude).

2) Remove speedometer cable and clip without disassembling speedometer gear holder. On Civic models, remove clutch cable at release arm. On Prelude, remove clutch slave cylinder with hydraulic line attached. On all models, remove transaxle-side starter mounting bolt and top transaxle mounting bolt. On Civic, remove forward bolt for rear torque arm bracket.

3) On all models, raise and support vehicle on hoist. Drain transaxle fluid and remove wheels. Remove engine shields, if equipped. Remove stabilizer bar and brackets. Disconnect tie rod ends and lower ball joints from suspension arms. Remove CV joints from transaxle and remove axle shafts.

HONDA (Cont.)

4) Disconnect shift lever torque rod from clutch housing. On Civic models, slide pin retainer back and drive out spring with punch. Disconnect shift rod. On Prelude, remove bolt from shift rod. Raise engine slightly and remove engine torque rods and brackets. Remove engine damper bracket and engine damper (Prelude) from center beam. Remove transaxle and rear engine mount and bracket.

5) Place 1" x 2" x 4" wooden board between engine oil pan and center beam. Lower engine until it rests on beam. Remove engine-side starter mounting bolt and starter. Place transmission jack under transaxle and remove remaining transaxle mounting bolts. Raise transaxle just enough to remove weight from engine and pull assembly away from engine until mainshaft clears clutch pressure plate. Lower transaxle out of vehicle.

INSTALLATION

To install, reverse removal procedure and note the following: When connecting axle shafts to transaxle, ensure they are fully seated in transaxle case. After installation, refill transaxle with fluid and adjust shift linkage as needed.

ISUZU & LUV

I-MARK

REMOVAL

1) Disconnect negative battery cable. From inside vehicle, remove shift lever assembly. Loosen clutch cable adjusting nuts at left side of engine compartment. Disconnect upper starter mounting nut and starter wiring.

2) Raise and support vehicle. Disconnect speedometer cable and clutch cable. Remove propeller shaft. Remove lower starter mounting bolt, and remove starter. Disconnect exhaust pipe from manifold. Remove exhaust pipe bracket.

3) Remove flywheel inspection cover. Remove rear support mounting bolt. Support transmission under case and remove rear support. Lower transmission about 4" from normal position and remove any wires connected to transmission. Remove transmission-to-engine bolts. Remove transmission by sliding straight back and lowering from vehicle.

INSTALLATION

Reverse removal procedure and note the following: Lubricate input shaft splines and release bearing support with a light coat of grease. Adjust clutch. Refill transmission with lubricant.

LUV & P'UP 4-SPEED (2WD)

REMOVAL

1) Disconnect negative battery terminal. Slide gearshift boot up on lever and remove lever attaching bolts, then withdraw lever. Remove starter attaching bolts and place starter out of way.

2) Raise vehicle on hoist. Disconnect exhaust pipe hanger at transmission, speedometer cable at extension housing, battery ground cable at transmission and propeller shaft from rear axle. Remove propeller shaft and either drain transmission fluid or install plug in extension housing to prevent fluid loss.

3) Remove return spring from clutch fork. Remove bolts attaching flywheel cover and remove frame bracket-to-transmission rear mount bolts. Raise engine and transmission as required and remove crossmember-to-frame bracket bolts. Remove rear mounting from extension housing.

4) Lower engine and transmission assembly and support rear of engine with support stand. Disconnect electrical connectors at back-up light and "coasting richer solenoid" (Federal models) switches. Remove transmission-to-engine attaching bolts. Pull transmission straight back until disengaged from clutch, tip front of transmission down and remove transmission from vehicle.

INSTALLATION

Reverse removal procedure and note the following: Adjust clutch cable and clutch pedal height if required. Refill transmission to correct fluid level.

LUV & P'UP 5-SPEED (2WD)

REMOVAL

1) Disconnect negative battery cable. Remove gearshift lever boot, lever attaching bolts and lever. Remove starter attaching bolts and remove starter. Raise vehicle on hoist and remove exhaust hanger at transmission.

2) Place pan under rear extension to catch oil. Disconnect speedometer cable, ground cable and propeller shaft. Remove propeller shaft. Remove flywheel stone guard and clutch fork return spring.

3) Remove 2 frame bracket-to-transmission rear mounting bolts and nuts. Raise engine and transmission and remove 4 crossmember-to-frame bracket attaching bolts. Remove rear mounting nuts from transmission rear extension.

4) Lower engine and transmission and support rear of engine. Disconnect "coasting richer solenoid" switch and back-up light switch. Remove transmission-to-engine attaching bolts. Pull transmission back until disengaged from clutch. Remove transmission.

INSTALLATION

Reverse removal procedure and note the following: Lubricate input shaft splines and release bearing support with a light coat of grease. Adjust clutch. Refill transmission with lubricant.

LUV & P'UP 4-SPEED WITH INTEGRAL TRANSFER CASE (4WD)

REMOVAL

1) Disconnect battery negative terminal. Slide gearshift boot up on lever and remove lever attaching bolts. Disconnect transfer gear shift lever return spring. Remove both gear shift levers.

Manual Transmission Removal

ISUZU & LUV (Cont.)

2) Remove starter attaching bolts and lay starter out of way. Raise vehicle on hoist. Disconnect exhaust pipe from manifold and at hanger on transmission. Disconnect speedometer cable at transfer case, ground cable at transmission and propeller shaft from rear axle. Disconnect front propeller shaft and remove both shafts from vehicle.

3) Disconnect clutch fork return spring, then remove clutch cable from hooked portion of fork. Pull cable forward through stiffener bracket. Remove the lower 2 bolts attaching transmission rear mount to frame.

4) Raise engine and transmission just enough so the 4 crossmember-to-frame bolts can be removed. Remove the 2 transfer case rear mounting bolts, then remove bolts attaching transfer side case to transfer case and remove transfer side case.

NOTE: Be sure not to lose shift rod detent spring and ball from transfer side case.

5) Remove stud bolt from transfer case then lower engine and transmission, supporting rear of engine. Disconnect electrical connectors at back-up light and "coasting richer solenoid" (Federal models) switches. Remove 4 bolts holding shift cover to transfer case and remove cover and gasket.

6) Remove all bolts attaching transmission to engine then remove transmission with transfer case. To ease removal, turn transfer case side of transmission downward, slide transmission backward until clear of clutch, then tilt front of transmission down and slide forward and out of vehicle.

INSTALLATION

To install, reverse removal procedure while noting the following: Install transmission with transmission shift lever in neutral and transfer case shift lever in "4H" position. Fill transmission with lubricant and adjust clutch fork and pedal height as needed.

MAZDA

GLC

REMOVAL

1) Disconnect negative battery cable, speedometer cable and any wires or connectors that may be connected to transaxle. Remove 2 clutch cable brackets and disconnect clutch cable from release lever. Remove water pipe bracket and harness clips.

2) Raise and support vehicle. Drain fluid from transaxle. Remove wheels and any shields or guards that may interfere with transmission removal. Remove ball joint from lower control arm. Disconnect drive shaft from differential by pulling outward on knuckle.

3) Support drive shaft out of the way. Support rear of engine with a support beam. Separate shift control rod and extension bar from transaxle.

4) Remove transaxle support crossmember and separate transaxle mount. Remove starter. Support transaxle with a jack. Remove transaxle-to-engine bolts. Lower transaxle out of vehicle.

INSTALLATION

Reverse removal procedure and note the following: Refill transaxle with lubricant. Check operation of shifter and clutch linkages and adjust as necessary.

ALL RWD MODELS

REMOVAL

1) Disconnect negative battery cable. Place gearshift lever in neutral position, and remove gearshift knob. Remove console box (if equipped) and gearshift lever. B2000 gearshift lever components include a wave washer, shim and bushing.

2) On RX7, remove air cleaner and upper transmission-to-engine bolts. On all models, raise and support vehicle and drain transmission. Disconnect and remove propeller shaft. Disconnect and/or remove under cover, exhaust components and emission control components as required.

3) On GLC, disconnect clutch cable from release lever. On all other models, remove clutch slave cylinder and place out of the way without removing hydraulic line. On all models, disconnect and remove starter, speedometer cable, back-up light wires and other electrical connections.

4) Place jack under rear of engine, protecting oil pan with wooden block. Position transmission jack under transmission and remove transmission-to-engine mounting bolts. If equipped, remove transmission-to-crossmember bolts, crossmember-to-frame bolts and crossmember. Slide transmission back until input shaft is cleared. Remove from vehicle.

INSTALLATION

To install, reverse removal procedure, ensuring that splines in input shaft align with those in clutch disc.

MERCEDES-BENZ

240D

REMOVAL

1) Disconnect negative battery cable and regulating shaft near valve cover. Support transmission with transmission jack. Remove bolts attaching rear transmission mount to transmission. Remove rear crossmember bolts and remove crossmember.

2) Remove exhaust mounting bracket from transmission and exhaust pipe. Note position of the washers and rubber insulators on the bracket.

3) Loosen large clamping nut on driveshaft. Loosen but do not remove bolts for driveshaft intermediate bearing. Remove bolts attaching driveshaft to transmission in such a manner that companion flange

MERCEDES-BENZ (Cont.)

remains on driveshaft. Push driveshaft to rear as far as possible.

   4) Remove speedometer drive from transmission and disconnect speedometer cable from frame. Remove bracket holding line for clutch slave cylinder. Remove cylinder and set aside cylinder and line as an assembly.

   5) After pushing off clip locks, remove shift rods from intermediate levers on shift bracket. Note position of disc springs. Remove starter bolts.

NOTE: **With shift rods disconnected, do not move shift lever into reverse gear. Damage to reverse light switch may result.**

   6) Remove all bolts attaching transmission to engine. Remove transmission from vehicle by moving straight back until clutch assembly is cleared.

NOTE: **Do not tilt transmission down until input shaft is clear of clutch assembly. Damage to clutch may result.**

INSTALLATION

   Installation of transmission is the reverse of removal procedure. Lightly grease input shaft of transmission before installation. Put transmission in gear and rotate output shaft back and forth until input shaft engages clutch splines.

PEUGEOT

ALL MODELS

REMOVAL

   1) Open hood as far as possible and support with wooden blocks under safety hooks. Disconnect battery cable and fan shroud. Remove header pipe bolts and disconnect oxygen sensor (if equipped). Remove heat shield and air injection hose.

   2) Remove front seat track floor brace. Remove rear tailpipe brackets. Remove rear axle mounts. Mark position of strap on steering column flange and remove bolts.

   3) On each side of crossmember, remove bolt and install bolt 2" longer than original. Remove 2 remaining bolts. Lower crossmember by backing off new bolts about 2 inches.

   4) Place transmission jack under transmission and remove propeller shaft tube bolts. Separate propeller shaft from transmission by 13/16" (20 mm). Insert

transmission shaft retaining plate (80403 SZ) to clear transmission output shaft.

   5) Remove front mount for gear selector rod. Remove shifting link rod, selector link rod and back-up light switch. Remove speedometer cable. Remove bolts from inspection plates on clutch housing. Remove plates.

   6) Remove slave cylinder circlip and flexible hose bracket. With engine suspended from hoist and hooks, lower hoist to tilt the transmission as far as possible. Remove starter. Remove clutch housing bolts and lower transmission.

INSTALLATION

   To install, reverse removal procedures and note the following: Lubricate input shaft splines and clutch release bearing guide with grease (Molykote or equivalent). Prior to fully engaging transmission into place, engage the slave cylinder into its housing. Refill transmission to proper level. Adjust linkage as needed.

PORSCHE

911

REMOVAL

   1) Transaxle and engine must be removed as a unit. After removal, assemblies may be separated. Vehicle must be raised and supported with safety stands to remove assembly from below vehicle.

   2) Disconnect battery ground cable. Remove engine block vent hose and plug hose. On A/C equipped vehicles, detach compressor at console but leave hoses connected.

NOTE: **Air conditioning system is under pressure. DO NOT unhook hoses unless system is discharged first.**

   3) Remove relay plate cover and disconnect engine wires at relay plate, adapter plug, relay, socket and ignition control unit. Remove fuel hoses at filter and return line. Disconnect accelerator linkage.

   4) Remove rear center tunnel cover in passenger compartment. Remove rubber boot in tunnel by pulling forward over selector rod. Loosen shift rod coupling and pull coupling off of transmission inner shift rod.

   5) Disconnect speedometer sensor wires in tunnel. Remove rubber plug with wire plug. Drain crankcase and plug hoses on engine and oil tank. Remove heater hoses at exchangers. Remove rear stabilizer.

   6) Disconnect ground strap at body and battery wires at starter. Disconnect accelerator linkage at pedal and clutch cable from transmission.

CAUTION: **Be careful when jacking assembly upward not to damage secondary air injection pipes.**

   7) Place a jack under engine/transmission assembly and apply a little upward pressure to relieve tension on motor mounts. Remove transmission and engine mount bolts. Lower engine/transmission assembly out of vehicle.

CAUTION: **Do not move vehicle unless drive shafts are suspended horizontally, to prevent damage to dust covers.**

INSTALLATION

   To install, reverse removal procedure and note the following: Do not clamp heater hoses. Slide them onto exchangers just before engine/transmission assembly is in final installation position.

924 (Except Turbo) & 944

TRANSAXLE

Removal

1) Detach exhaust pipe from catalytic converter and loosen exhaust system brackets at central tube. Remove muffler clamp from transaxle end plate and remove entire converter and muffler assembly.

2) Push shift linkage dust boot back and remove lock wire from shift linkage connecting bolt. Remove connecting bolt. From inside vehicle, fold back dust boot and inner cover on shift lever. Remove clamp from shift lever knob, then remove knob.

3) Remove circlip holding selector rod to shift lever. Pull shift rod and spring washer from shift lever pin. Turn shift lever 180° and tilt out to right. Press down on rubber seal between central tube and tunnel. Slide selector rod forward in tunnel about 12" to clear linkage at rear.

4) Remove plug from rear of central tube housing. Push shift rod protective tube back far enough so shift rod tube is outside central tube housing. Remove inspection plugs (1 located at bottom of central tube housing; the other on upper left side of transmission case). Remove propeller shaft-to-mainshaft coupling screws through inspection holes. Slide coupling back toward transmission case.

5) Detach axle shafts from transaxle and suspend from vehicle in horizontal position. Disconnect wires from back-up light switch. Place a jack with transmission adapter (US 618 and 618/1) under transmission and raise slightly to release pressure from transmission suspension.

6) Remove transmission-to-central tube housing flange bolts. Remove transaxle mount bolts. Lower transaxle assembly and central tube until central tube rests on rear axle cross tube. Remove transaxle out rear.

Installation

1) To install, reverse removal procedure and note the following: Before installing transaxle, check propeller shaft protrusion at rear flange. Shaft should extend .49-.53" (12.5-13.5 mm) beyond flange lips. Make small corrections by tapping on end of shaft with soft-faced hammer.

2) After installation, adjust shift linkage as follows: Place transmission in neutral and install intermediate shift lever with a 5° rearward offset from center of shaft. Ensure shift lever is in neutral, then move shift lever base to adjust shift lever to an 85° angle from rear of central tube.

3) With shift lever in neutral, transverse selector shaft will be held in 3rd/4th gear (middle shift pattern) by spring pressure. With shift linkage connected and adjusted properly, shift lever will not lean to either side. If shift lever leans to either side, adjust at intermediate shift lever.

CENTRAL TUBE

Removal

1) With transaxle assembly removed from vehicle, disconnect negative battery strap. Suspend engine from front eyelet with support fixture (VW10-222) and hold tight in installation position.

2) Support tube at front tunnel reinforcing brace with locally made block. Detach central tube from clutch housing. Remove rear reinforcement strut, then loosen rear axle mountings and lower torsion bar tube. Pull selector rod rearward. Remove central tube by lowering and pulling out to rear.

Inspection

Check for free rotation of central tube bearings by turning propeller shaft by hand. Shaft must turn easily without binding. If bearings or shaft are damaged, central tube with shaft and bearings must be replaced.

NOTE: **Shaft must turn easily without noise or flat spots. If bearings or shaft are damaged the entire assembly must be replaced. Separate component replacement is not possible at this time.**

Installation

To install, reverse removal procedure and check propeller shaft protrusion. Check and adjust shift linkage.

924 TURBO

TRANSAXLE

Removal

1) Loosen screw clamping selector rod to transmission linkage at rear of tunnel.

2) Lift shift lever dust cover and remove circlip holding selector rod to shift lever. Remove selector rod from shift lever pin.

3) Turn shift lever 180° and tilt out to right. Press down on rubber seal between central tube and tunnel. Slide selector rod forward in tunnel to clear linkage at rear.

4) Detach exhaust pipe at primary muffler and loosen exhaust holding brackets at central tube. Remove exhaust mounting bolts from transmission end plate and remove entire muffler assembly.

5) Disconnect back-up light switch wires and remove switch from transmission to prevent damage. Take wires out of clip on transmission.

6) Disconnect axle shafts from transaxle and suspend horizontally from vehicle to prevent damage to boots. Remove socket head bolt at rear propeller shaft coupling through inspection hole in rear clutch housing.

7) Place a jack (with support, US 618/1, attached) under transaxle and raise slightly. Remove transaxle bolts, then remove transaxle mounts.

8) Remove clutch housing-to-central tube bolts. Lower transaxle with central tube so that tube rests on rear axle cross tube. Move transaxle out to rear.

NOTE: **Do not raise too high. Left rear brake line is located above selector rod.**

Installation

To install, reverse removal procedure and note the following: Propeller shaft extends .75-.79" (19-20 mm) beyond rear flange surface. Improper position may cause clutch drag due to improper engagement of spline and clutch disc. Tighten all connecting bolts.

PORSCHE (Cont.)

TRANSAXLE CENTRAL TUBE

Removal

1) Transaxle must out of vehicle. Disconnect battery ground strap. Suspend engine from front eyelet with fixture (VW10-222) and hold tight in installation position.

2) Support tube at front tunnel reinforcing brace with locally made block. Detach central tube from front clutch housing and slide back about 4".

3) Remove rear reinforcement strut, then loosen rear axle mountings and lower torsion bar tube. Pull selector rod rearward. Remove central tube by lowering and pulling out to the rear.

Inspection

Propeller shaft must extend .75-.79" (19-20 mm) beyond face of clutch housing flange in order to properly engage clutch disc splines. Correct shaft position by tapping on end with soft-faced hammer. Check for free rotation of shaft.

NOTE: **Shaft must turn easily without noise or flat spots. If bearings or shaft are damaged the entire assembly must be replaced. Separate component replacement is not possible at this time.**

Installation

Reverse removal procedure to install.

928

TRANSAXLE ASSEMBLY

Removal

1) Remove battery from case. Loosen rear wheels and position transmission in 5th gear. Loosen screw clamping selector rod to transmission linkage at rear of tunnel.

2) Open inspection cover (rubber cap) in transmission. Turn 1 wheel and hold opposite wheel to position coupling bolt between drive and input shafts for removal. Remove bolt.

3) Position shift lever in neutral. Remove rear wheels and detach brake calipers and suspend them to relieve hoses of any tension. Disconnect axle shafts from transaxle and suspend horizontally from car to prevent damage to boots.

Fig. 1: Location of Input Shaft Coupling Bolt and Shift Rod Coupling Set Screw

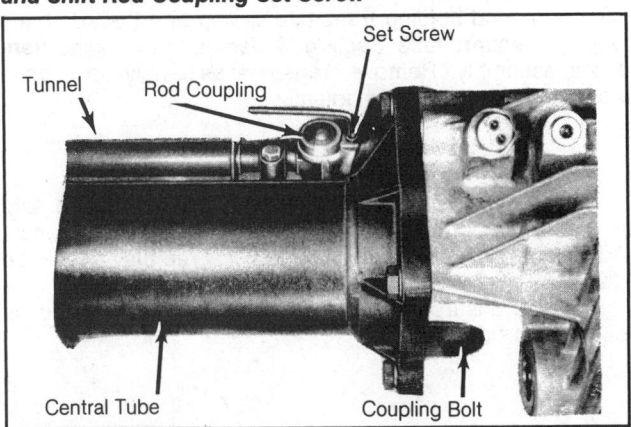

4) Push dust cover back and remove set screw from shift rod coupling. Detach shift rod and slide rod forward in tunnel to clear linkage at rear. Disconnect back-up light wires and speedometer pulse transmitter wires from transmission. Remove switch and pulse transmitter.

5) Detach exhaust assembly and remove entire assembly after the catalytic converter. This requires removal of 4 bolts between converter and intermediate muffler, 2 bolts on front rubber mount, 1 bolt on rear rubber mount and 2 bolts on holder for main muffler. Remove battery box.

6) Remove 2 transmission mounting bolts on rear axle crossmember and 2 bolts between rear axle crossmember and frame. Place transmission jack beneath rear axle crossmember and mark position of crossmember. Remove remaining 4 bolts on crossmember. Tilt rear axle carefully and support in tilted position taking weight off the lower control arm link pins.

7) Mount transmission support bracket to transmission with fixtures (9148 and 9149). *See Fig. 2.* Remove 6 bolts between central tube and transmission. Pull transmission back to one side and lower from vehicle.

Fig. 2: Installing Transmission Support Brackets

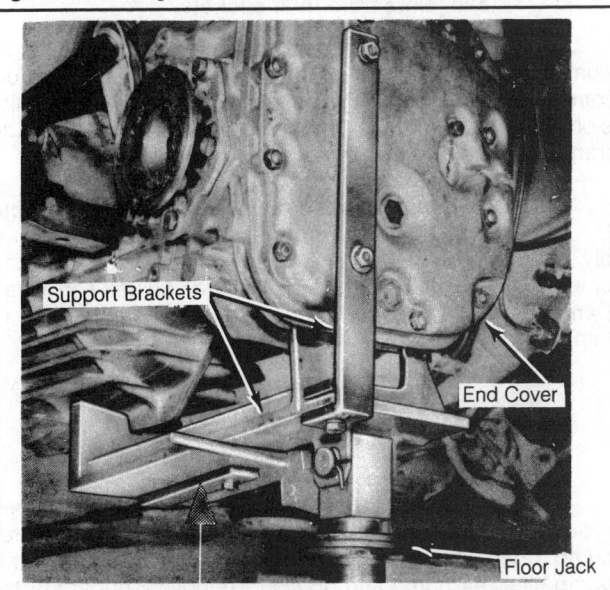

Installation

To install, reverse removal procedure noting that propeller shaft extends .50-.53" (12.5-13.5 mm) beyond rear flange surface. Improper position may cause clutch drag due to improper engagement of spline and clutch disc. Tighten all nuts and bolts to specifications.

TRANSAXLE CENTRAL TUBE

Removal

1) With transaxle removed from vehicle, disconnect negative battery cable. Suspend engine from front eyelet with fixture (VW 10-222) and hold tightly in installation position.

2) Support tube at front tunnel reinforcing brace with a front block. Detach central tube from front clutch housing and slide back about 4".

3) Remove rear cross traverse in tunnel, then loosen rear axle mountings and lower torsion bar tube.

Manual Transmission Removal

PORSCHE (Cont.)

Pull selector rod out to the rear. Remove central tube by lowering and pulling out to the rear.

Inspection

Propeller shaft must extend .50-.53" (12.5-13.5 mm) beyond face of clutch housing flange in order to properly engage clutch disc splines. Correct shaft position by tapping end with soft faced hammer. Check free rotation of shaft turning by hand.

NOTE: Shaft must turn easily without noise or flat spots. If bearings or shaft are damaged, entire assembly must be replaced. Separate component replacement is not possible as individual parts are not available.

Installation

To install, reverse removal procedure.

RENAULT

18i & FUEGO

REMOVAL

1) Disconnect battery ground cable and starter wiring harness. Remove starter attaching bolts and starter. Disconnect clutch cable at release lever.

2) Remove axle shafts from transaxle as previously described, but do not disconnect outer end from hub unless outer CV joint service is required. Disconnect speedometer cable, shift linkage and any wires that are connected to transaxle.

NOTE: DO NOT remove any of the gear shift linkage ball joints from their sockets.

3) Remove clutch cover and any shields or guards that may interfere with transaxle removal. Support transaxle with a transmission jack and remove transmission mounts. Remove engine-to-transaxle bolts. Slide transaxle rearward and remove from vehicle.

Installation

To install, reverse removal procedure and note the following: Lightly coat input shaft splines with assembly lube prior to reinstalling transaxle. Adjust and check operation of shifter and clutch linkage. Adjust Top Dead Center sensor as needed. End of sensor should be .04" (1 mm) from flywheel face.

LE CAR

REMOVAL

1) Disconnect battery cables and transaxle ground wire. Detach speedometer cable. Remove water pump drive belt. Remove camshaft pulley. Remove air pump filter, air pump and bracket. Remove 2 upper starter mounting bolts.

2) Remove clutch housing mounting bolts located on engine. Remove lower left nut of clutch housing. Remove brake calipers without disconnecting brake hoses. Disconnect steering arms at steering rack end. Disconnect upper ball joints from front suspension.

3) Remove drive shafts from side gears by tilting stub axle carriers downward. Remove 2 mounting bolts from supporting bracket on transaxle. Disconnect clutch cable at lever. Using a screwdriver, push against sleeve retainer to free from supporting bracket.

4) Remove tubular crossmember top bolt and tilt crossmember in direction of arrow in *Fig. 1*. Remove bottom bolt and tap crossmember toward rear of vehicle to remove. Support front of transaxle with jack. Remove mounting pad and bracket.

5) Remove starter and lay aside. Remove side reinforcement mounting bolts and clutch cover. Fabricate a square tube to specifications shown in *Fig. 2*.

Fig. 1: Removing Tubular Crossmember

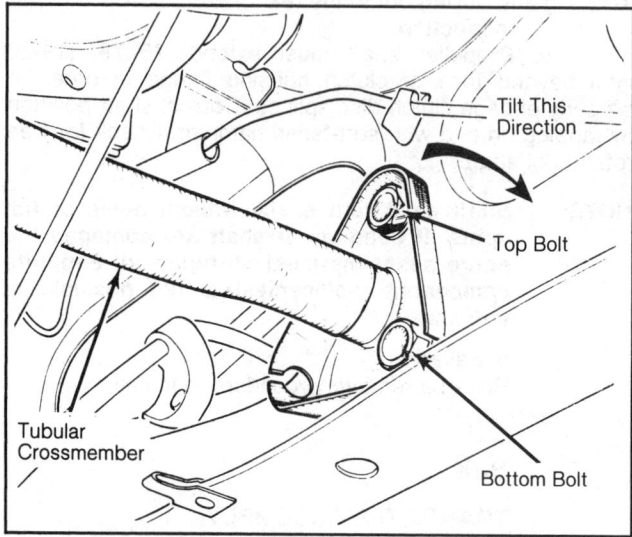

Tap crossmember toward rear of vehicle to remove.

Fig. 2: Specifications of Square Tube Tool

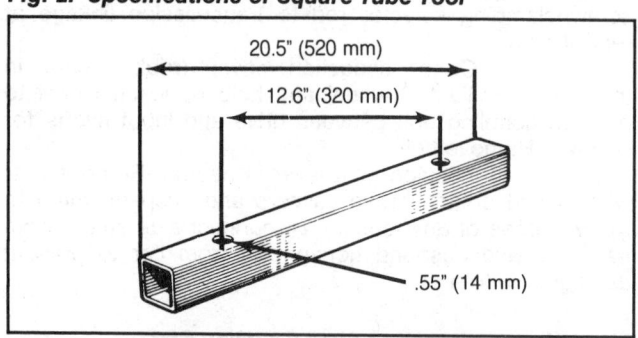

6) Position spring compressor tool (Sus. 21) with hook end holding transaxle casing and threaded end bolted to square tube. *See Fig. 3.* Jack and tilt engine/transaxle assembly. Remove transaxle assembly so it does not catch on clutch mechanism.

INSTALLATION

To install, reverse removal procedure and note the following: Lightly coat clutch shaft splines with grease. Adjust free play at end of clutch lever. Free play should be .125-.157" (3.2-4.0 mm).

Ensure drive shaft end is fully seated in differential side gears.

RENAULT (Cont.)

Fig. 3: Spring Compressor and Square Tube Installation

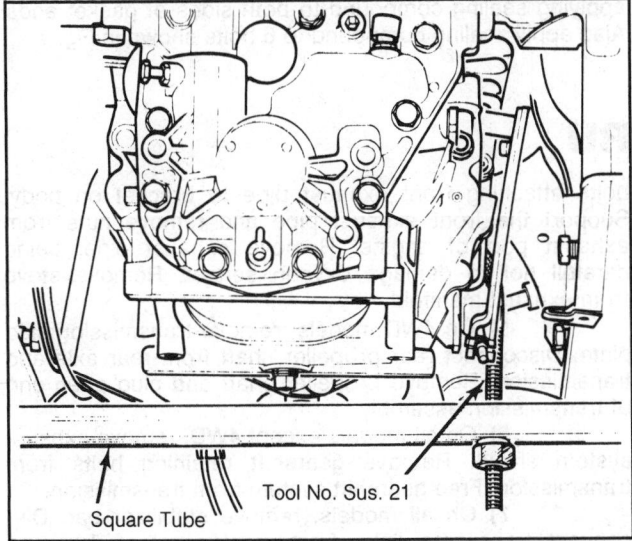

Square Tube

Tool No. Sus. 21

Install tools before final transaxle removal.

SAAB

ALL MODELS

REMOVAL

1) Remove hood, then disconnect battery cables and lift out battery. Drain coolant from radiator and engine. Disconnect power brake unit vacuum hose from intake manifold. Remove rubber bellows between air flow sensor and intake manifold. Disconnect and plug fuel line. Disconnect air flow sensor electrical leads. Remove air cleaner and mixture control unit.

2) Remove air intake, preheater hose, crankcase ventilation hose and intake hose. Disconnect cable from oil pressure sender. On California models, disconnect all EGR system hoses. If equipped with power steering, disconnect and plug hoses at steering pump.

3) Disconnect and remove ignition coil. Disconnect the following electrical connections: Temperature sending unit, radiator fan, thermostat contact, oil pressure sender, headlights and starter leads. Disconnect and plug all fuel injection lines (if equipped). Disconnect choke and throttle cables. Disconnect all water hoses. Disconnect hose to expansion tank.

4) Remove grill and hood locking cable. Remove radiator/headlight assembly. Disconnect hose from clutch slave/cylinder and plug hose and hole in cylinder. Disconnect exhaust pipe from manifold and ground cable from transaxle. Remove bellows clamp and bellows from inner CV joints.

5) Place spacer (8393209) between upper control arm underside and body to unload suspension when vehicle is raised. Insert spacer from engine compartment side. Raise and support front of vehicle.

6) Remove lower end piece from control arm. Pull out steering knuckle assembly and support end piece against control arm outer end. Place shifter in neutral. Remove nut and knock out taper pin in gear shift rod joint.

NOTE: Gear shift rod joints are made of steel or plastic. DO NOT knock out taper pin from plastic joints.

7) Remove rear engine mounting bolts. Loosen nut on front engine mounting so mounting can be lifted from bracket. Slightly raise engine and move engine/transaxle unit to each side to free CV joints. Lift engine/transaxle unit from vehicle.

8) To separate transaxle from engine, drain engine oil. Remove clutch cover, starter and clutch shaft. Remove 3 clutch slave cylinder retaining screws. Remove engine-to-transaxle attaching bolts and carefully lift engine off transaxle unit.

Fig. 1: Installing New Transmission Housing Gasket

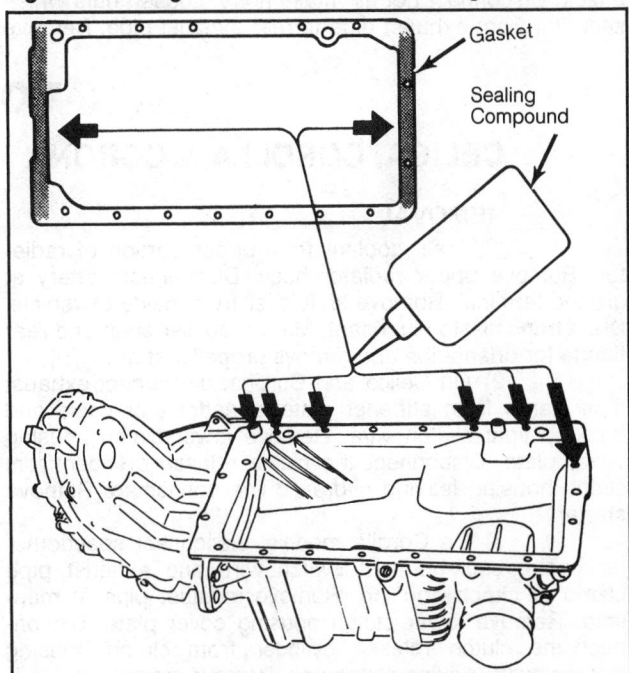

Gasket

Sealing Compound

Apply sealing compound on ends of gasket and in bolt holes indicated.

Manual Transmission Removal

SAAB (Cont.)

INSTALLATION

To install, reverse removal procedure. Be sure CV joints are packed with grease prior to installation. Apply sealing compound to 3 clutch slave cylinder retaining bolts. Use new gasket on transmission housing, applying sealing compound to both sides of gasket ends. Also apply sealing compound to 6 bolts shown in *Fig. 1*.

SUBARU

ALL MODELS

REMOVAL

1) Disconnect battery cables. Remove spare tire and air cleaner. Remove clutch cable return spring and clutch cable. Disconnect clip from speedometer cable and remove cable from transaxle housing. Disconnect back-up light switch, ground strap from vehicle body and starter harness. DO NOT remove battery cable from starter.

2) Remove starter with battery cable attached. Remove upper engine-to-transmission mounting bolts. Loosen lower mounting bolts. Loosen transmission side stabilizer bar .39" (10 mm) and tighten engine side stabilizer bar the same amount. Slightly tilt engine backward to facilitate transaxle removal.

NOTE: **DO NOT tighten engine side stabilizer bar more than .39" (10 mm).**

3) On 4WD vehicles, remove hand brake tray cover and brake cover. Remove the rod cover. Set the drive selector lever at 4WD position. Remove the nut connecting gear shift and drive selector rods. Remove 2 nuts securing drive selector rod and drive selector to plate. Remove gearshift lever boot installing screws. Remove nut connecting gearshift lever with operating lever. Pull up on gearshift lever and remove lever and boot.

4) On all models, disconnect the oxygen sensor harness and unclamp it. Raise front of vehicle with a jack. Disconnect hot air intake hose. Loosen nuts which securing front exhaust pipe to rear exhaust pipe. Remove bolts attaching front exhaust pipe to bracket on body. Support the front exhaust pipe and remove nuts from exhaust port of engine. Remove exhaust pipe, being carefull not to damage oxygen sensor. Remove stove from exhaust manifold.

5) On 4WD models, remove transmission skid plate. Disconnect rear propeller shaft from rear axle and transmission. Remove propeller shaft and plug open end of transmission assembly.

6) On all models except 4WD, remove exhaust system shield. Remove gearshift retaining bolts from transmission. Free gearshift system from transmission.

7) On all models, remove stabilizer bar. Disconnect transverse links from front crossmember and lower transverse links. Drive out retaining pin which secures inner axle shaft to drive axle. Push wheel assembly toward outside of vehicle and separate axle shaft from drive axle. Remove clamp on left side of parking brake cable to facilitate removal of rear crossmember.

8) Remove left and right transmission mounts. Support transaxle assembly with a jack. Remove crossmember. Remove 2 nuts securing engine to transaxle. Move transaxle assembly rearward to clear mainshaft, then lower transaxle from vehicle.

INSTALLATION

To install, reverse removal procedure being sure to replace all locking nuts and spring pins. Tighten nut connecting control arm to crossmember only when vehicle has been lowered to floor.

TOYOTA

CELICA, COROLLA & CORONA

REMOVAL

1) Drain coolant from upper portion of radiator. Remove upper radiator hose. Disconnect battery at ground terminal. Remove shift lever from inside of vehicle. Drain transmission lubricant. Mark propeller shaft and rear flange for orientation and remove propeller shaft.

2) On Celica and Corona, disconnect exhaust pipe clamp from stiffener plate, speedometer cable and back-up light switch wire. Remove lower clutch housing cover plate. Disconnect the clutch release cylinder from clutch housing leaving hydraulic line connected. Remove starter.

3) On Corolla models, disconnect speedometer cable, back-up light switch wire and exhaust pipe clamp at clutch housing. Remove exhaust pipe at manifold. Remove lower clutch housing cover plate. Disconnect the clutch release cylinder from clutch housing leaving hydraulic line connected. Remove starter.

4) On all models, support transmission and remove rear support member. Remove remaining bolts attaching clutch housing to engine. Move transmission rearward and lower from vehicle, clear of clutch assembly.

INSTALLATION

Lightly grease friction surfaces and reverse removal procedure. Ensure that propeller shaft and rear flange marks are aligned. Refill transmission lubricant.

LAND CRUISER

REMOVAL

1) Disconnect battery cable. Raise and support vehicle. Drain gear oil from transmission and transfer cases. Remove transmission skid plate. Disconnect the following from transmission/transfer case assembly: Propeller shafts, speedometer cable, and parking brake cable.

2) From inside vehicle, remove scuff plate, side panel trim, heater duct and carpets. Remove shift lever knobs, dust boots and transmission shift lever.

3) Disconnect electrical wiring and vacuum hoses (if necessary) from transmission/transfer case

TOYOTA (Cont.)

assembly. Remove attaching bolts, then remove transmission/transfer case assembly from vehicle.

4) To separate transfer case from transmission, move transfer case lever to "4L" position. Remove back-up light switch from transmission case. Remove stake marks from transmission output shaft nut, then hold power take-off companion flange stationary and remove output shaft nut.

NOTE: **When removing transmission output shaft nut, have front drive engaged.**

5) Remove 5 transfer case-to-transmission case attaching bolts. Using a puller, separate transfer case from transmission case, holding power take-off gear to prevent it from dropping out of case.

INSTALLATION

1) To install, reverse removal procedure and note the following: After transfer case is attached to transmission case, stake transmission output shaft nut in place.

2) With transmission/transfer case assembly installed in vehicle, fill transmission case and transfer case with gear oil and adjust shift linkage.

PICKUP

REMOVAL

1) Disconnect negative battery cable. Remove floor mat and shifter boot(s). Remove shift lever(s) and retainer from inside vehicle. Remove upper starter mounting nut.

2) Raise and support vehicle. Drain transmission (and transfer case on 4WD models). Remove clutch slave cylinder (with hydraulic line connected) and position out of way. Remove starter. Mark propeller shaft and transmission yoke for reassembly reference and remove shaft.

3) Disconnect speedometer cable. Disconnect back-up light switch wire. Disconnect exhaust pipe clamp from transmission housing. Remove 4 mounting bolts from extension housing.

4) On 2WD models, raise transmission slightly by raising engine with jack and wooden block under engine. Remove the 4 bracket bolts from support member and remove rear mounting with bracket.

5) On 4WD models, jack up transmission enough to remove the weight from the rear support. Remove 8 bolts, and remove support member. On all models, remove remaining transmission housing bolts. Place a safety support with a wooden block under engine and lower jack until engine is resting on support.

6) Draw out transmission and transfer case assembly, down and toward the rear. Remove engine rear mounting. Remove transfer case from transmission.

INSTALLATION

To install, reverse removal procedure. Apply a small amount of multi-purpose grease to end of input shaft, shaft splines, release bearing and diaphragm spring contact surfaces before installation. Refill transmission and transfer case with lubricant after installation.

STARLET

REMOVAL

1) Remove shift boot and snap ring. Remove shift lever from transmission. Disconnect negative battery terminal. Remove water hose from thermostat housing.

2) Remove air cleaner. Disconnect accelerator pump lever. Disconnect wiring harness connector. Wrap steering rack boot with a towel.

3) Remove exhaust muffler clamp. Remove clutch and speedometer cables. Disconnect propeller shaft and plug extension housing with extension housing plug (09325-12010).

4) Remove starter motor and engine rear support. Remove engine-to-transmission bolts. Remove rear transmission support member and remove transmission.

INSTALLATION

To install, reverse removal procedures, ensuring that splines on input shaft align with those in clutch disc.

TERCEL

REMOVAL

NOTE: **Transmission assembly may be removed without removing differential assembly. Procedure given here covers removal of complete transaxle assembly.**

1) Drain coolant from upper radiator tank. Disconnect negative battery cable, air cleaner inlet duct and upper radiator hose (from engine). Disconnect clutch cable. Remove starter motor. Remove 4 upper clutch housing-to-engine bolts. Raise and support vehicle. Remove axle drive shafts as previously outlined. Remove 3 drain plugs and drain transaxle fluid.

2) Disconnect exhaust pipe at manifold and remove exhaust system. Remove transaxle stiffener plate on right side. Disconnect gear shift rod at housing rod yoke, then disconnect and remove shift lever housing rod retaining bolt. Disconnect and remove back-up light wiring connector. Disconnect speedometer cable at transaxle housing. Support transaxle on jack.

3) Remove 5 lower transaxle/clutch housing-to-engine mounting bolts. Disconnect ground wire. Remove engine rear support member and lower transaxle assembly out from under vehicle. Place a 1.2" (30 mm) block of wood between crossmember and oil pan to support engine for installation of transaxle assembly.

INSTALLATION

To install transaxle assembly, reverse removal procedure and note the following: Install all drain plugs (3) and fill transaxle assembly with gear oil (SAE 90 GL-5 or SAE 80W-90).

Manual Transmission Removal
VOLKSWAGEN

QUANTUM
REMOVAL

1) Disconnect battery ground strap. Disconnect exhaust pipe from transaxle bracket and engine. Remove square bolt and press shifter coupling from rear of transaxle shifting shaft. Unhook clutch cable and disconnect speedometer.

2) Disconnect CV joints at inner drive flanges. Support axle shafts from vehicle with wire. Remove starter, front mounting plate and transaxle mounting bolts. Disconnect back-up light switch connector. Support transaxle on floor jack and remove crossmember mount. Remove transaxle from engine and lower from vehicle.

INSTALLATION

1) Install crossmember to transaxle. Raise transaxle up to vehicle and install crossmember bolts finger tight. Slide transaxle up to engine and install mounting bolts. Install front mounting plate and starter. Install inner CV joint mounting bolts into CV joint and drive flange. Tighten crossmember mounting bolts.

2) Install shift rod coupling bolt and lock with safety wire. Connect exhaust pipe, allowing 3/8" (10 mm) clearance between pipe and floor. Reconnect all wires, cables and linkages that were removed during removal procedure.

NOTE: Always use longer hex head bolt when replacing shift rod coupling instead of original square head bolt. Secure with safety wire.

JETTA, RABBIT, PICKUP & SCIROCCO
REMOVAL

1) Disconnect negative battery cable. Install engine support bar. Remove 3 transmission mount bolts located on left side of vehicle near battery. Disconnect speedometer cable from case and plug opening. Remove upper transaxle-to-engine bolts, electrical connection at back-up light switch and clutch cable. Remove shift linkage parts from relay lever on transaxle and rod lever.

2) Disconnect ground strap from transaxle. Remove starter and 2 engine-to-transaxle bolts on either side of starter opening. Remove exhaust pipe bracket from bottom of transaxle. Place floor jack with adapter under transaxle and raise until transaxle is supported. Remove rear transaxle mount and bracket.

3) Disconnect both axle drive shafts from drive flanges and wire up out of the way. Remove bolts attaching cover plates to transaxle. Remove small cover plate, then remove remaining transaxle-to-engine bolts and nuts. Lower transaxle and remove from under vehicle.

INSTALLATION

Reverse removal procedure to install. Fill with lubricant and adjust shift linkage.

VANAGON
REMOVAL

1) Disconnect negative battery cable. Remove upper right transmission-to-engine bolt. Disconnect clutch hydraulic line from transmission case, then remove clutch slave cylinder from bracket and suspend out of way with wire.

NOTE: Do not disconnect hydraulic line from slave cylinder.

2) Remove upper left, then lower left transmission-to-engine bolts. Remove the bolts from left axle shaft, remove axle shaft from transmission and suspend with wire. Disconnect starter cables. Remove the bolts from right axle shaft, remove axle shaft from transmission and suspend with wire.

3) Remove lower right transmission-to-engine nut. Support engine. Disconnect back-up light wires, shift linkage and ground strap from transmission. Remove front transmission support-to-body bolts and support transmission. Separate transmission from engine and remove transmission.

INSTALLATION

To install transmission, reverse removal procedures and note the following: Clean and lubricate splines with grease. Make sure air deflector plates are positioned correctly. Make sure engine compartment seals are not damaged or missing.

VOLVO

4-SPEED
REMOVAL

1) Disconnect battery ground cable. From under vehicle, disconnect gearshift lever from rod by removing lock bolt and pressing out pivot pin.

2) Working inside vehicle, lift shift lever boot and remove left side of center console. Disconnect back-up light and overdrive connectors (if equipped) and remove reverse detent plate. Remove lock ring and lift out gearshift lever. Remove plastic bushing and rubber ring.

3) From under vehicle, remove crossmember at rear of transmission and disconnect clutch fork return spring and release cable. Disconnect speedometer cable and unbolt propeller shaft from drive flange. Remove exhaust pipe attachment to clutch housing and unhook rubber supports for front muffler.

4) Remove starter from engine and take out all except 2 bottom bolts holding clutch housing to engine. Attach transmission jack and support transmission. Remove 2 bottom bolts and pull transmission to rear, turning slightly to clear tunnel while separating from vehicle.

INSTALLATION

To install, reverse removal procedure.

DRIVE AXLE GEAR TOOTH PATTERNS

INSPECTION

Wipe lubricant from internal parts. Rotate gears and inspect for wear or damage. Mount a dial indicator to housing and check backlash at several points around ring gear. Backlash must be within specifications at all points. If no defects are found, check gear tooth contact patterns.

GEAR TOOTH CONTACT PATTERN

NOTE: **Drive pattern should be well centered on ring gear teeth. Coast pattern should be centered but may be slightly toward toe of ring gear teeth.**

1) Paint ring gear teeth with gear marking compound. Apply some form of load to differential case to resist rotation. Rotate pinion gear until ring gear has made 1 full revolution.

2) Turn pinion gear in opposite direction to complete 1 full revolution of ring gear. Examine ring gear teeth for contact pattern. Correct as necessary by moving appropriate shims.

ADJUSTMENTS

GEAR BACKLASH & PINION SHIM CHANGES

NOTE: **Change in tooth pattern is directly related to change in shim and/or backlash adjustment.**

1) With no change in backlash, moving pinion further from ring gear moves drive pattern toward heel and top of tooth, and moves coast pattern toward toe and top of tooth.

2) With no change in backlash, moving pinion closer to ring gear moves drive pattern toward toe and bottom of tooth, and moves coast pattern toward heel and bottom of tooth.

3) With no change in pinion shim thickness, an increase in backlash moves ring gear further from pinion. Drive pattern moves toward heel and top of tooth, and coast pattern moves toward heel and top of tooth.

4) With no change in pinion shim thickness, a decrease in backlash moves ring gear closer to pinion gear. Drive pattern moves toward toe and bottom of tooth, and coast pattern moves toward toe and bottom of tooth.

Fig. 1: Drive Axle Gear Tooth Patterns Showing Necessary Corrections

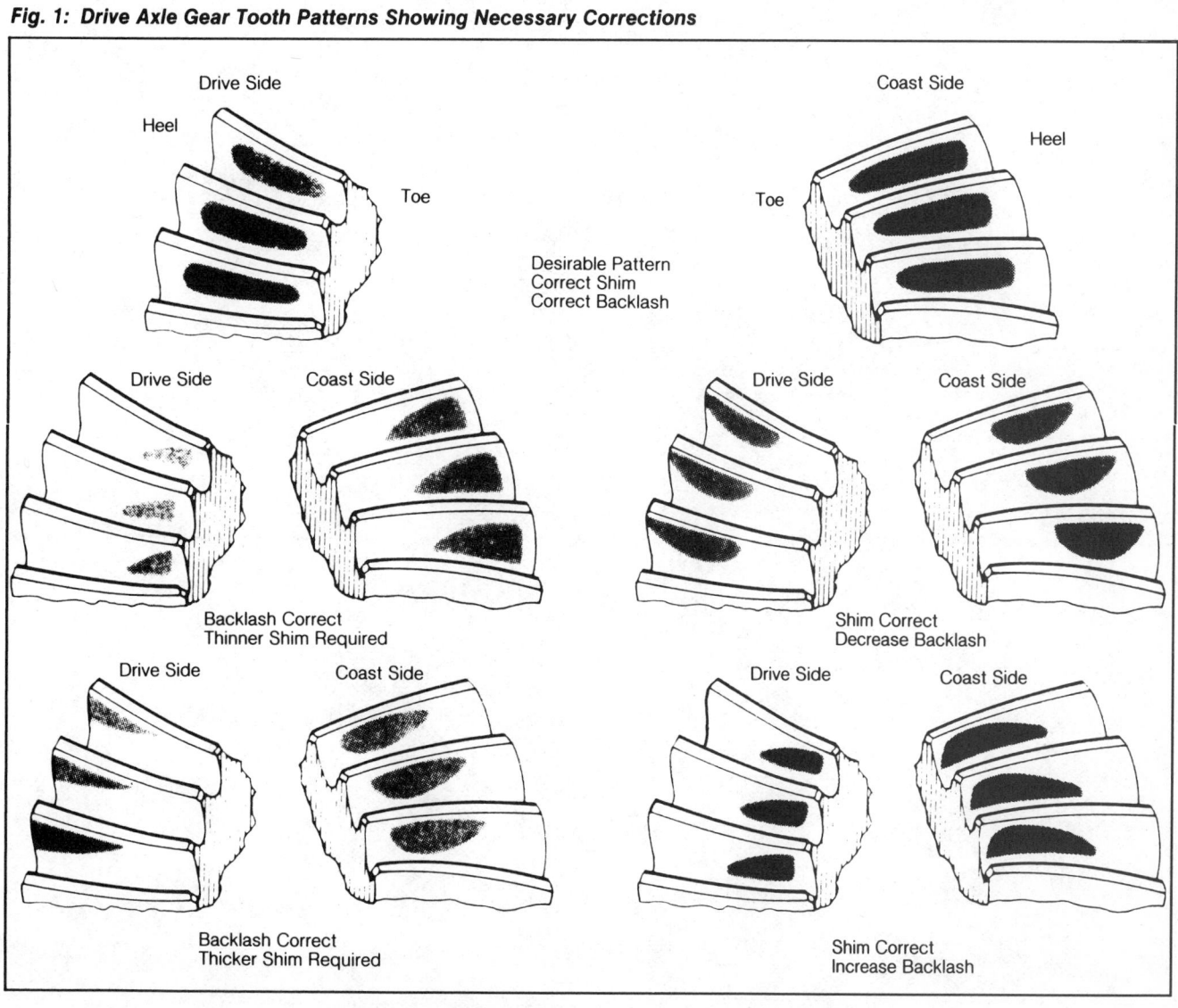

SECTION 6

IMPORT AUTOMATIC TRANSMISSIONS

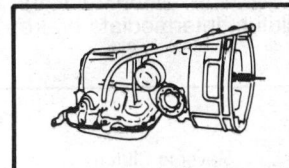

NOTE: ALSO SEE GENERAL INDEX.

Automatic Transmissions

AISIN-WARNER 55, 70, 71 & BORG-WARNER 55

ISUZU I-Mark; VOLVO DL, GL, GLE, GLT, GLT Turbo, Diesel

TRANSMISSION IDENTIFICATION

Transmissions may be identified by a plate attached to left side of transmission case. Plate shows vendor (Aisin-Warner or Borg-Warner), the transmission model number, and transmission serial number.

DESCRIPTION

Transmissions are fully automatic 3-speed units consisting basically of a 3-element torque converter, a compound planetary gear set, 2 multiple-disc clutches, 2 one-way roller clutches, and 3 multiple-disc brakes. A hydraulic system, pressurized by a gear type pump, provides the working pressure required to operate the automatic controls.

Aisin-Warner 70 and 71 transmissions are equipped with an overdrive in combination with 3rd gear. The overdrive is normally engaged, but can be manually disengaged by depressing a button on shift lever. Disengagement of overdrive will illuminate an "OD OFF" warning lamp on instrument panel. A relay automatically returns transmission to engage overdrive mode when transmission downshifts or ignition is turned off.

Aisin-Warner 70 and 71 transmissions have oversize oil pans and are 3" (78 mm) longer than Aisin-Warner and Borg-Warner 55 transmissions. Aisin-Warner 55 transmissions use 1 big spring for front and rear clutches and Borg-Warner 55 transmissions use 16 and 18 small coil springs, respectively. Valve bodies also vary.

LUBRICATION & ADJUSTMENT

See the appropriate article in AUTOMATIC TRANSMISSION SERVICING Section.

TROUBLE SHOOTING

NOTE: **Almost any transmission problem will show up in one or more of the following tests: Check for proper fluid level, gear selector adjustment, throttle cable adjustment, line pressure, stall speed, or governor pressure. These tests show the condition of the most important transmission components and should be checked to arrive at a proper diagnosis of the reported complaint.**

NO MOVEMENT IN "D" OR SLIPS IN "D"

Manual linkage out of adjustment. Faulty rear clutch, intermediate brake, 1-way clutch for planetary gear

Fig. 1: Aisin-Warner 55 Transmission Hydraulic Circuit Diagram

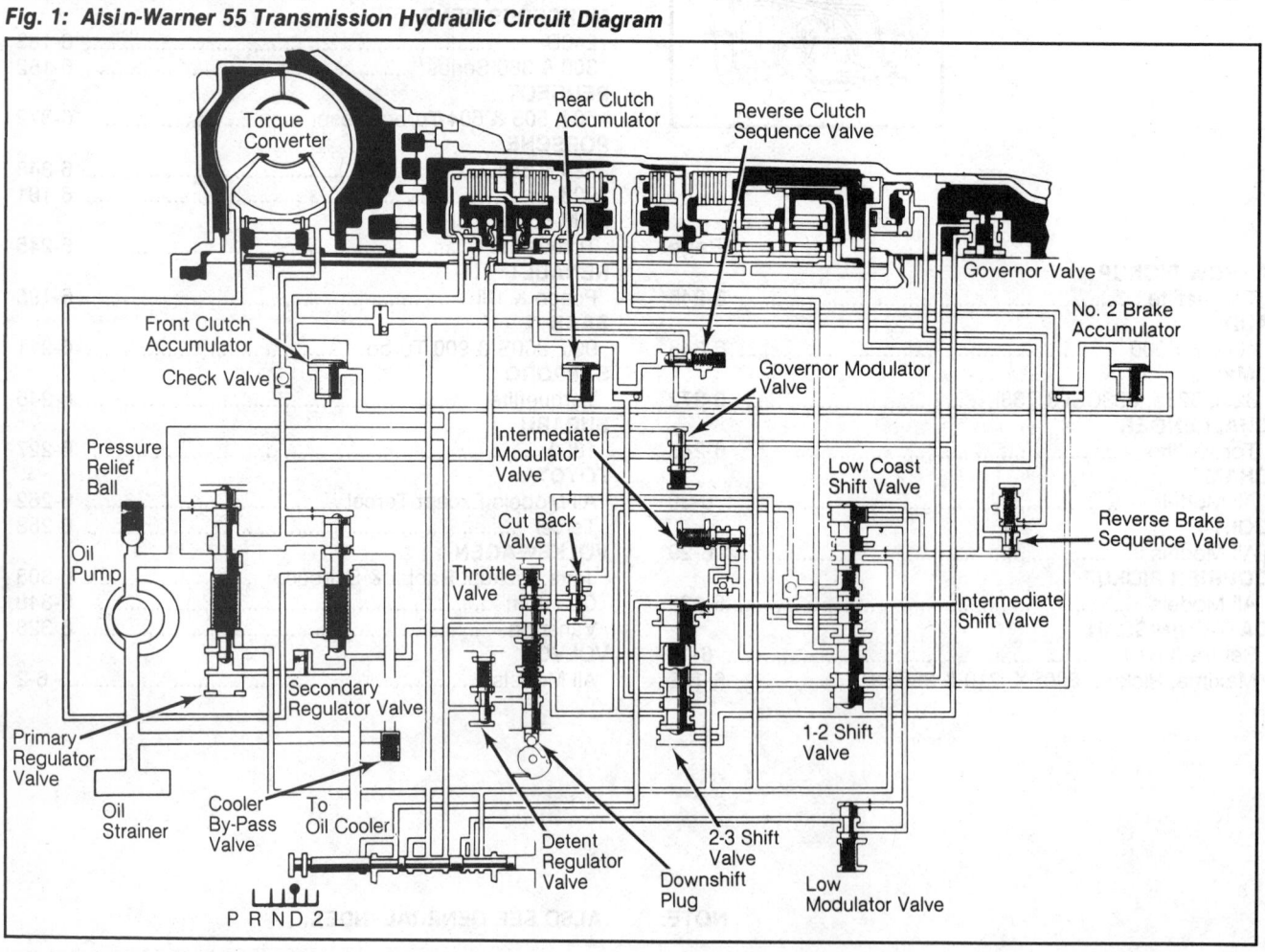

AISIN-WARNER 55, 70, 71 & BORG-WARNER 55 (Cont.)

set, front clutch, secondary regulator valve or valve body assembly.

NO MOVEMENT IN "R" OR SLIPS IN "R"

Manual linkage out of adjustment. Faulty rear clutch, intermediate brake, oil pump, or valve body assembly.

NO MOVEMENT IN ANY RANGE

Manual linkage out of adjustment. Parking pawl jammed or defective. Faulty torque converter, valve body assembly, or oil pump. Multiple unit damage. Shaft and or spline damage.

HARSH SHIFT FROM "N" TO "D" OR "R"

Manual linkage out of adjustment. Accumulator pistons for front or rear clutch seized or leaking. Defective valve bodies or accumulator pistons.

HARSH "1-2" OR "2-1" SHIFT

Second speed brake accumulator piston seized or leaking. Intermediate coast shift valve seized.

HARSH "2-3" OR "3-2" SHIFT

Rear clutch accumulator piston seized or leaking. Defective governor valve body assembly. Check intermediate coast modulator valve.

SLIP ON "1-2" UPSHIFT

Intermediate coast shift valve seized, thereby not engaging No. 1 brake. Defective No. 1 brake. Defective No. 2 brake. Center support 1-way clutch defective.

SLIP ON "2-3" UPSHIFT

Defective rear clutch or its oil circuit. Faulty valve body assembly (2-3 shift valve, etc.).

NO ENGINE BRAKING IN "1"

Defective No. 3 brake. Low coast modulator valve seized or low coast valve frozen in top position.

NO ENGINE BRAKING IN "2"

No. 1 brake or its oil circuit defective. Intermediate coast modulator valve seized.

NO "2-1" SHIFT IN "1"

Defective No. 3 brake. Low coast modulator valve or low coast shift valve seized.

VEHICLE STARTS OUT IN "2" OR "3"

Governor pressure inaccurate (should be 0 with vehicle stationary). Defective valve body assembly, 1-2 throttle valve, 2-3 shift valve, primary throttle valve or primary regulator valve.

TRANSMISSION NOISE

Growling On Acceleration

Low fluid level, clogged oil filter or worn oil pump. Defective torque converter.

Gear Noise

Torque converter-to-drive plate bolts loose. Faulty coupling of 1-way clutches. Faulty planetary gear sets. Worn thrust needle bearings or bushings.

Whining or Humming Noise

Defective torque converter (noise may disappear in "N"). Defective oil pump (noise varies with engine speed).

TESTING

ROAD TEST

1) Before road testing, ensure that fluid level and condition, and control linkage adjustments have been checked and corrected as necessary. During test, transmission should upshift and downshift at speed shown in *Shift Speed* chart.

2) All shifts may vary somewhat due to production tolerances or tire size. The important factor is the quality of the shifts. All shifts should be smooth,

CLUTCH AND BAND APPLICATION CHART (ELEMENTS IN USE)

Selector Lever Position	Front Clutch	Rear Clutch	Overdrive Clutch (70 & 71 Only)	No. 1 Brake	No. 2 Brake	No. 3 Brake	Overdrive Brake (70 & 71 Only)
D — DRIVE							
First	X		X				
Second	X		X	X [1]	X		
Third	X	X	X		X		
Overdrive (70 & 71 Only)	X	X			X		X
2 — SECOND							
First	X		X				
Second	X		X	X	X		
1 — LOW	X		X			X	
R — REVERSE		X	X			X	
P — PARK						X [2]	X [2]
N — NEUTRAL			X				

[1] — Except 70 & 71 transmissions.
[2] — Engine running.

Automatic Transmissions

AISIN-WARNER 55, 70, 71 & BORG-WARNER 55 (Cont.)

responsive, and with no slippage or engine speed runaway.

3) Slippage or engine runaway in any gear usually indicates clutch or brake problems. The slipping unit in a particular gear can usually be identified by noting transmission operation in other selector positions and comparing which internal units are applied in those positions. *See Clutch and Brake Application* chart.

4) This process of elimination can be used to detect any unit which slips, and to confirm proper operation of good units; however, the actual cause of the malfunction usually cannot be easily decided.

5) Almost any condition can be caused by leaking hydraulic circuits or sticking valves. Therefore, unless an obvious condition exists, do not disassemble transmission until hydraulic pressure tests have been made.

STALL SPEED TEST

Stall Test Precautions

Before making a stall speed test, ensure that line pressure is correct. If line pressure is too low when

SHIFT SPEED SPECIFICATIONS [1]

Application	MPH
DL, GL, GLT [2]	
1-2 Upshift	38
2-3 Upshift	64
3-4 Upshift (3/4 throttle)	68
4-3 Downshift (Coasting)	24
3-2 Downshift	60
2-1 Downshift	30
GLE [3]	
1-2 Upshift	35-44
2-3 Upshift	62-71
3-2 Downshift	56 (Min.)
3-1 Downshift	22-35
GLT Turbo [4]	
1-2 Upshift	39
2-3 Upshift	65
3-4 Upshift (3/4 throttle)	69
4-3 Downshift (Coasting)	24
3-2 Downshift	62
2-1 Downshift	31
Diesel [3]	
1-2 Upshift	35
2-3 Upshift	64
3-2 Downshift	59 (Min.)
3-1 Downshift	30
I-Mark [5]	
Gas Engine	
1-2 Upshift	36-43
2-3 Upshift	67-73
3-2 Downshift	60-67
3-1 or 2-1 Downshift	22-29
Diesel Engine	
1-2 Upshift	29-35
2-3 Upshift	53-58
3-2 Downshift	49-55
3-1 or 2-1 Downshift	20-25

[1] — At full throttle (kick-down) unless otherwise noted.
[2] — Aisin-Warner 70.
[3] — Borg-Warner 55.
[4] — Aisin-Warner 71.
[5] — Aisin-Warner 55.

performing a stall test, transmission can be damaged. Also, during stall test, do not hold throttle open for more than 5 seconds at a time.

Stall Test Procedure

1) Road test vehicle and warm transmission to normal operating temperature. Connect tachometer to engine. Position tachometer so that it can be read from driver's seat.

2) Set parking and service brakes. Start engine and place selector lever in "D". Depress accelerator pedal completely and note maximum RPM obtained. RPM should be approximately as shown in *Stall Speed* chart.

3) Place selector lever in "N" and allow engine to idle to cool off transmission. Then, place selector lever in "R" and repeat stall test. Stall RPM should be approximately as shown in *Stall Speed* chart.

STALL SPEED SPECIFICATIONS

Application	Stall Speed (RPM)
DL, GL & GLT	1800
GLE	2150-2400
GLT Turbo	2220
Diesel	2200
I-Mark	
Gas Engine	1700-2000
Diesel Engine	1900-2200

Stall Test Results

1) If stall test RPM is about 600 RPM lower than specifications, torque converter 1-way clutch is slipping and torque converter should be replaced. If stall RPM is about 300 RPM lower than specifications, engine performance may be unsatisfactory.

2) If stall test RPM is about 300 RPM above specifications in "R", rear clutch or No. 3 brake is slipping. If RPM is about 300 RPM above specifications in "D", front clutch is slipping. If stall speed is about 300 RPM above specifications, and no clutch or brake is slipping, fluid level is incorrect or valve body oil strainer is clogged.

Fig. 2: Transmission Case Pressure Test Port Locations

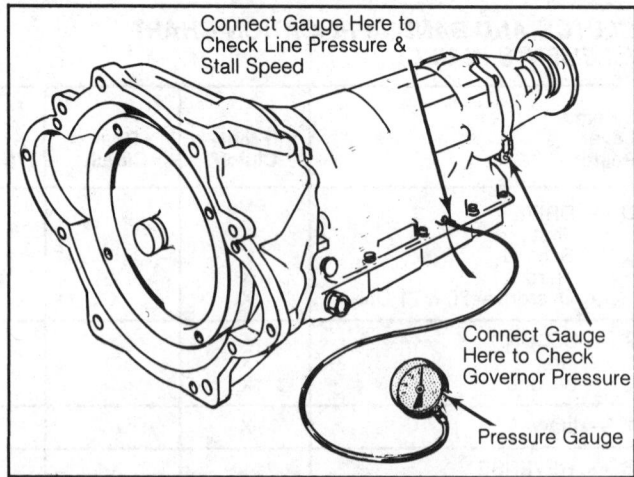

Test port locations apply to all transmissions.

LINE PRESSURE TEST

1) Road test vehicle to bring transmission to normal operating temperature. Connect a pressure gauge to front plug on transmission. *See Fig. 2.* Place gauge so

AISIN-WARNER 55, 70, 71 & BORG-WARNER 55 (Cont.)

that it is visible from driver's seat. Connect tachometer to engine.

2) Start engine and if necessary, adjust idle speed to 900 RPM (1000 RPM on I-Mark). Depress brake pedal and place selector lever in "D". Note line pressure reading on gauge. Pressure should be approximately as shown in *Line Pressure* chart.

3) Repeat line pressure test with selector lever in "R". Pressure should be approximately as shown in *Line Pressure* chart.

LINE PRESSURE SPECIFICATIONS

Application	psi (kg/cm²)
Aisin-Warner 55	
In "D"	57-64 (4.0-4.5)
In "R"	82-97 (5.8-6.8)
Aisin-Warner 70 & 71	
In "D"	65-77 (4.6-5.4)
In "R"	108-117 (7.6-8.2)
Borg-Warner 55	
In "D"	75-90 (5.3-6.3)
In "R"	104-129 (7.3-9.1)

LINE PRESSURE TEST RESULTS

Pressure Too High

If pressure is too high, check throttle cable adjustment. If cable is correctly adjusted and pressure is still high, primary regulator valve or throttle valve may be seized.

Pressure Too Low

If line pressure is too low, check for seizing of primary regulator valve or throttle valve in valve body. If valves are not seized, check pressure relief valve and oil pump assembly for damage. A defective oil pump assembly will usually make noise.

GOVERNOR PRESSURE SPECIFICATIONS

Vehicle Speed	psi (kg/cm²)
DL, GL, GLT, GLT Turbo	
21 MPH	15-24 (1.1-1.7)
35 MPH	24-33 (1.7-2.3)
66 MPH	54-71 (3.8-5.0)
GLE	
20 MPH	14-18 (1.0-1.3)
35 MPH	21-27 (1.5-1.9)
68 MPH	51-65 (3.6-4.6)
Diesel	
19 MPH	17-20 (1.2-1.4)
37 MPH	27-32 (1.9-2.2)
69 MPH	61-68 (4.3-4.8)
I-Mark	
Gas Engine	
19 MPH	13-21 (0.9-1.5)
39 MPH	23-33 (1.6-2.3)
68 MPH	58-75 (4.1-5.3)
Diesel Engine	
18 MPH	14-23 (1.0-1.6)
37 MPH	33-43 (2.3-3.0)
64 MPH	64-81 (4.5-5.7)

GOVERNOR PRESSURE TEST

NOTE: Governor pressure is a "modified" line pressure. Therefore, governor pressure will be incorrect if line pressure is incorrect. Line pressure must be correct before checking governor pressure.

Testing Procedures

Road test vehicle to warm transmission to normal operating temperature. Connect pressure gauge to rear pressure port on transmission case. *See Fig. 2.* Position gauge so it is visible from driver's seat. Test drive vehicle in "D" and note pressure readings. Pressures should be about as shown in *Governor Pressure* chart.

SERVICE (IN-VEHICLE)

NOTE: The following units can be removed from transmission without removing transmission from vehicle: Oil Pan, Valve Body Assembly, Accumulator Pistons, Parking Pawl, Rear Extension Housing and Oil Seal, Speedometer Driven Gear, Overdrive Solenoid (70 & 71 only) and Governor Body. See procedures given in Transmission Disassembly and Transmission Reassembly.

REMOVAL & INSTALLATION

See the appropriate article in AUTOMATIC TRANSMISSION REMOVAL Section.

TORQUE CONVERTER

NOTE: Torque converter is a sealed unit and cannot be disassembled for service. Replace if found defective.

NOTE: If torque converter is replaced, oil cooler and lines must be cleaned.

TRANSMISSION DISASSEMBLY

NOTE: Specific disassembly and reassembly procedures for Aisin-Warner 70 and 71 transmissions not available at time of publication.

1) Clean outside of transmission thoroughly before disassembly to prevent dirt or foreign material from entering transmission. Pull torque converter from transmission. Place transmission in a holding fixture.

2) Remove converter housing-to-transmission case bolts. Separate converter housing from case. Remove speedometer driven gear assembly retaining bolt. Using a screwdriver, pry speedometer driven gear assembly from case.

3) Hold output shaft drive flange stationary and remove flange bolt. Using a puller, pull drive flange from output shaft. Remove extension housing-to-case bolts. Lift off extension housing.

4) If equipped, remove speedometer drive gear snap ring and slide gear and spacer ring (if equipped) from output shaft. If equipped, remove 2nd snap ring. Remove governor retaining clip and pull governor assembly off shaft.

5) Invert transmission case so oil pan is facing up. Remove oil pan and gasket. Remove attaching bolts

AISIN-WARNER 55, 70, 71 & BORG-WARNER 55 (Cont.)

Fig. 3: Valve Body Schematics for Aisin-Warner 71 and Borg-Warner 55 Transmissions
(Aisin-Warner 70 Similar to Aisin-Warner 71 & Aisin-Warner 55 Similar to Borg-Warner 55)

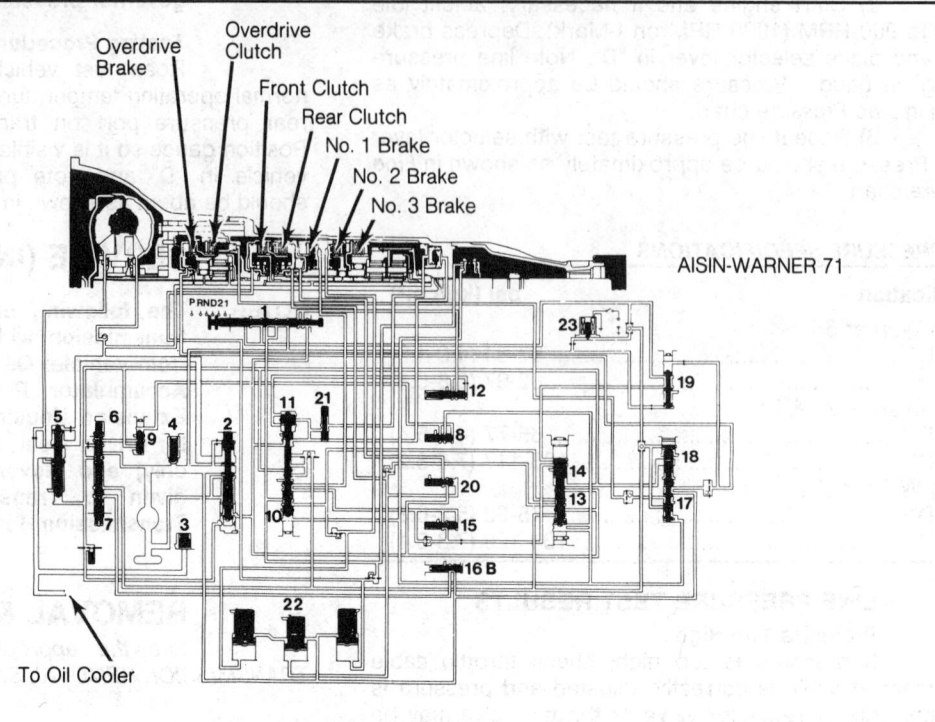

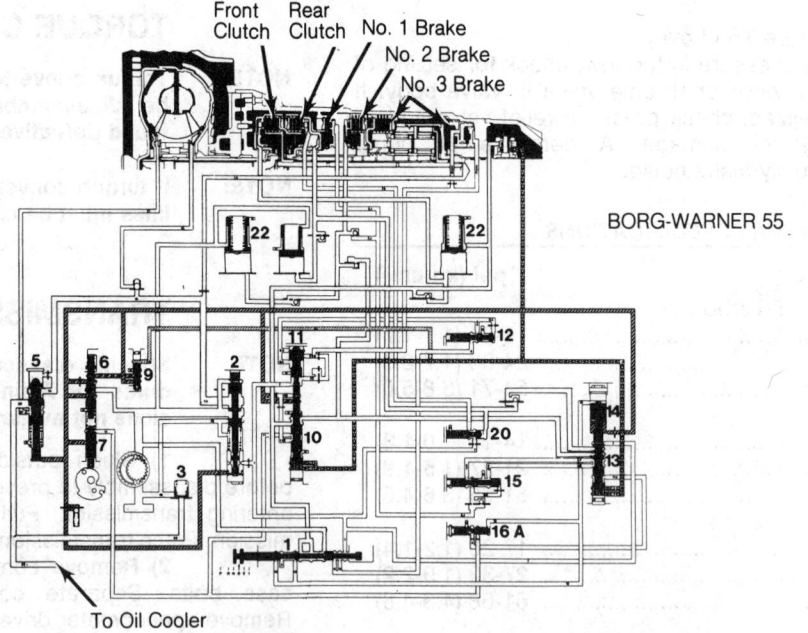

1. Manual Valve	9. Cutback Valve	18. High Coast Shift Valve
2. Primary Regulator Valve	10. 1-2 Shift Valve	(Aisin-Warner 71 Only)
3. By-Pass Valve	11. Low Coast Shift Valve	19. "D-2" Manual
4. Pressure Relief Valve	12. Low Coast Modulator Valve	Downshift Valve
(Aisin-Warner 71 Only)	13. 2-3 Shift Valve	20. Rear Clutch Control Valve
5. Secondary Regulator Valve	14. Intermediate Coast Shift Valve	21. No. 3 Brake Control Valve
6. Throttle Valve	15. Intermediate Coast Modulator Valve	(Aisin-Warner 71 Only)
7. Kickdown Valve	16. Detent Regulator Valve *	22. Accumulator Pistons
8. Governor Modulator Valve	17. 3-4 Shift Valve	23. Overdrive Solenoid Valve
(Aisin-Warner 71 Only)	(Aisin-Warner 71 Only)	(Aisin-Warner 71 Only)

* Detent regulator valve is located between kickdown valve trand 2-3 shift valve on Borg-Warner 55.
It is located AHEAD of kickdown valve on Aisin-Warner 71.

AISIN-WARNER 55, 70, 71 & BORG-WARNER 55 (Cont.)

and lift oil strainer and particle magnet from transmission case. Remove valve body-to-case bolts. Carefully lift valve body and disconnect throttle cable from valve body cam. Lift valve body assembly from case.

Fig. 4: Accumulator Pistons and Springs Removal

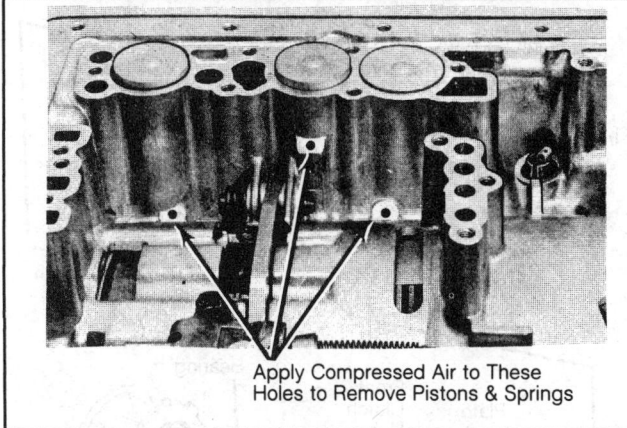

Apply Compressed Air to These
Holes to Remove Pistons & Springs

Spring sizes vary; note position for reassembly.

    6) Apply low pressure compressed air to holes under accumulator pistons to force pistons from case bores. *See Fig. 4.* Remove pistons and springs. Invert transmission case so oil pump faces up. Remove oil pump attaching bolts. Using a puller, remove oil pump assembly from case.

    7) Hold input shaft with hand and pull front clutch assembly from case. Remove bearing and race from clutch. Remove rear clutch bearing and race. Pull rear clutch assembly from case. Remove center support bolts. *See Fig. 5.* Lift center support assembly from case.

Fig. 5: Location of Center Support Attaching Bolts

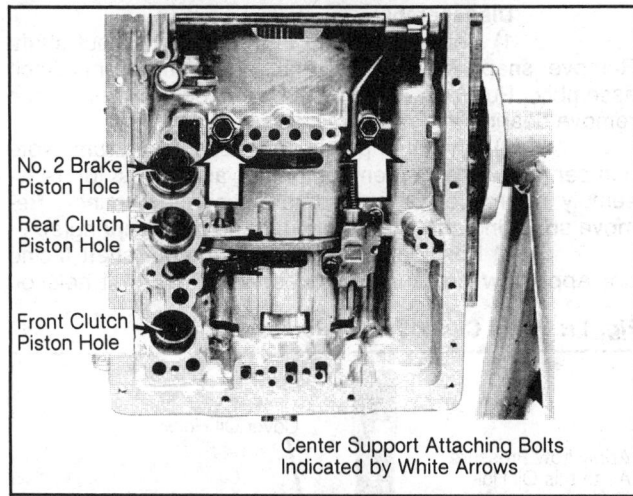

No. 2 Brake
Piston Hole

Rear Clutch
Piston Hole

Front Clutch
Piston Hole

Center Support Attaching Bolts
Indicated by White Arrows

Note positions for reassembly reference.

    8) Remove No. 3 brake snap ring from groove in case. Lift No. 3 brake disc pack and planetary gear assembly from case as a unit. Remove brake apply tube, thrust bearing and races from transmission case.

    9) Turn transmission so rear face of case is up. Remove governor oil duct cover screws and cover from case. Note position for reassembly reference, then remove oil cooler line nipples from case. Remove governor and line pressure plugs.

    10) Turn transmission so oil pan attaching surface is up. Remove parking pawl rod plate bolts. Remove plate and rod. Using a drift, drive detent lever lock pin out of lever and shaft. Pull shaft out of lever and case. Lift up parking pawl, press out shaft and spring, then lift parking pawl from case.

Fig. 6: Detent Lever Retaining Pin Removal

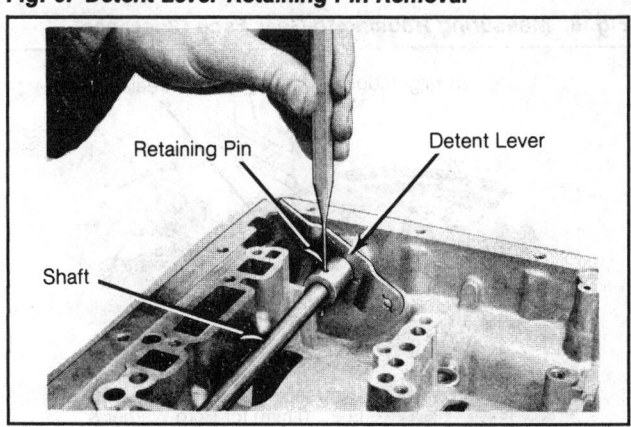

Retaining Pin

Detent Lever

Shaft

COMPONENT DISASSEMBLY & REASSEMBLY

OIL PUMP ASSEMBLY

Disassembly

    Remove oil seal rings from pump cover. Remove cover bolts and separate cover from pump housing. Remove large "O" ring from housing. Mark pump drive and driven gears for reassembly in same position. DO NOT punch marks. Remove gears from pump housing. Pry oil seal from housing.

Fig. 7: Exploded View of Oil Pump Assembly

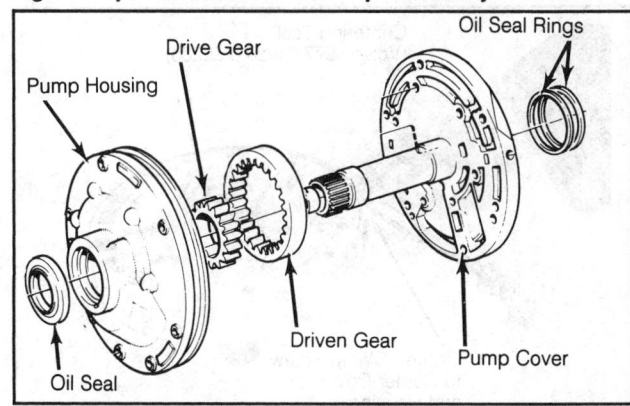

Drive Gear

Oil Seal Rings

Pump Housing

Oil Seal

Driven Gear

Pump Cover

Mark gears for reassembly reference.

Inspection

    Clean all parts thoroughly and dry with compressed air. Inspect all parts for wear, cracks, or scoring. If pump housing, cover, drive gear or driven gear requires replacement, complete oil pump assembly must be replaced as a matched set.

Reassembly

    1) Install drive and driven gear into housing, aligning marks made at reassembly. Using a feeler gauge, measure clearance between pump driven gear and pump

AISIN-WARNER 55, 70, 71 & BORG-WARNER 55 (Cont.)

housing. Clearance should be .003-.012" (.07-.30 mm) for Borg-Warner and .003-.006" (.07-.15 mm) for all others. If not, replace oil pump assembly.

2) Check clearance between driven gear and crescent. Clearance should be .004-.020" (.11-.50 mm) for Borg-Warner and .004-.006" (.11-.14 mm) for all others. If not, replace oil pump.

Fig. 8: *Measuring Housing-to-Gear Face Clearance*

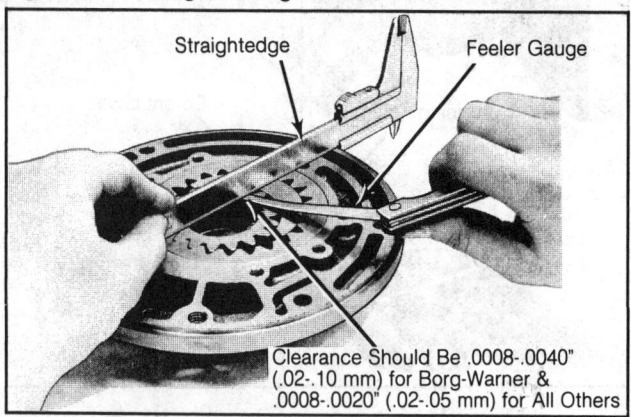

Use straightedge and feeler gauge.

3) Using a straightedge and feeler gauge, check pump housing face-to-gear face clearance. Clearance should be .0008-.0040" (.02-.10 mm) for Borg-Warner and .0008-.0020" (.02-.05 mm) for all others. If not, replace oil pump assembly.

4) Lubricate all parts with type F ATF. Press new oil seal into pump housing. Assemble pump cover to housing, then install bolts finger tight. Fit centering tool (Volvo 5077 or Isuzu J-25280) around housing and cover. Tighten centering tool clamp screw to align housing and cover. *See Fig. 9.*

Fig. 9: *Aligning Oil Pump Housing and Cover*

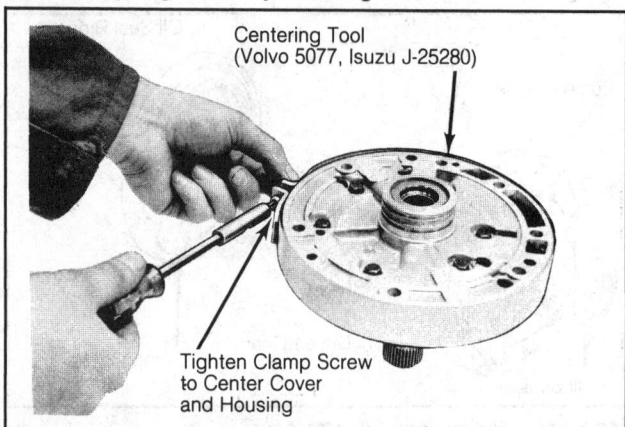

Bolts must be installed in cover finger tight.

5) Tighten bolts and remove centering tool. Lubricate large "O" ring with ATF and install in groove on pump housing. Lubricate oil seal rings with petroleum jelly and install on pump cover.

FRONT CLUTCH ASSEMBLY

NOTE: The front clutch assembly used in the Borg-Warner 55 transmission uses 16 small return springs while the Aisin-Warner 55 transmission uses 1 big return spring.

Fig. 10: *Exploded View of Front Clutch Assembly*

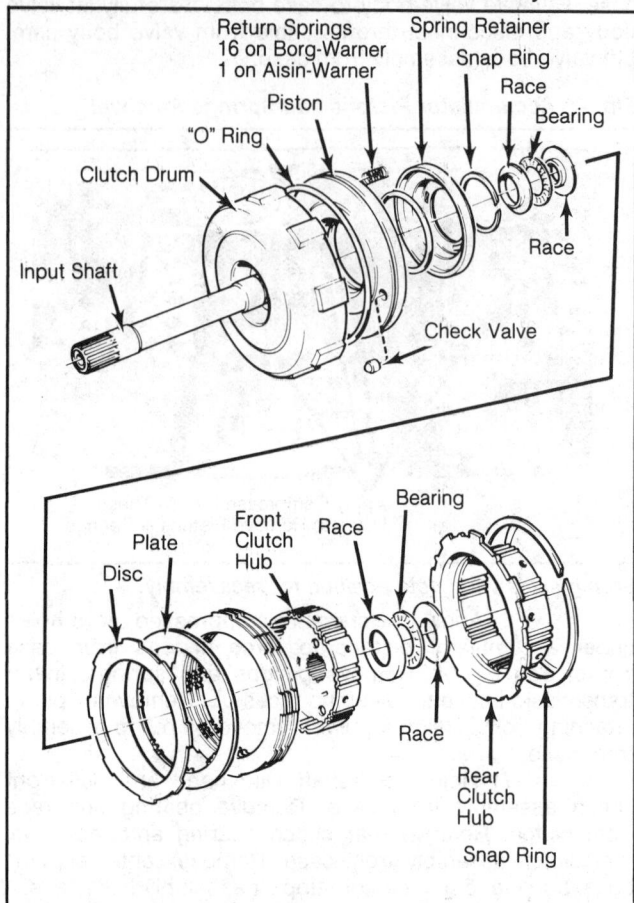

Borg-Warner uses 16 springs; all others use 1 big spring.

Disassembly

1) Remove bearing and race from input shaft. Remove snap ring and lift rear clutch hub from clutch assembly. Pull rear clutch hub from clutch drum, then remove bearing and races.

2) Lift clutch plates and discs from drum. Note number and arrangement of plates and discs for reassembly reference. Compress return spring retainer. Remove snap ring and lift out retainer and return spring(s).

3) Position clutch drum with input shaft facing up. Apply low pressure compressed air to 1 oil hole on

Fig. 11: *Front Clutch Piston Removal*

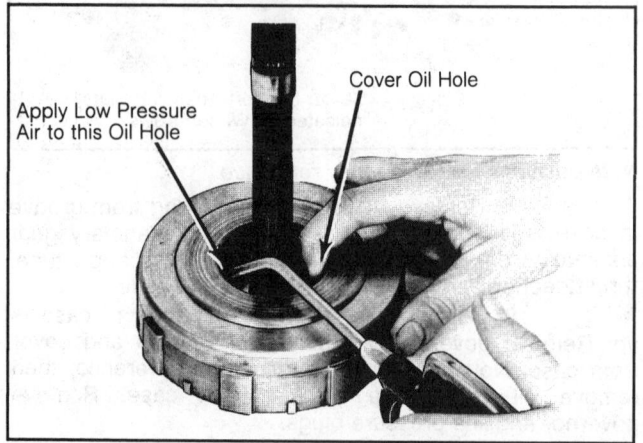

Use low pressure compressed air to remove piston.

AISIN-WARNER 55, 70, 71 & BORG-WARNER 55 (Cont.)

inside of drum. Cover other hole with finger and force piston from drum. *See Fig. 11.* Remove and discard "O" rings from clutch piston.

Inspection

1) Clean all parts (except plates and discs) with clean solvent and dry with compressed air. Inspect clutch plates and discs to ensure they are flat, not burned, cracked or deformed.

2) Minimum thickness of discs is .08" (2.1 mm). Inspect all other parts for wear or damage. Check clutch piston to ensure that check ball is not stuck. Replace any defective part.

Reassembly

1) Coat all friction surfaces with type F ATF. Install new "O" rings on clutch piston. Install piston into clutch drum with check valve toward input shaft end. Install return spring(s) and retainer.

2) Using a compressor tool, compress return spring retainer and install snap ring. Remove compressor tool. Install clutch plates and discs into clutch drum. Alternate plates and discs until the number and position of plates and discs are installed as they were removed.

3) Install bearing and races onto top of return spring retainer. Install front clutch hub and ensure hub meshes with clutch discs. Install rear clutch hub and snap ring.

4) Check operation of piston by applying low pressure compressed air to 1 oil hole while covering the other. When air is applied on Borg-Warner transmissions, a "plop" should be heard as piston is applied. Install bearing and race on input shaft.

5) On all other transmissions, install dial indicator so tip is resting on rear clutch hub lip. Apply compressed air and read dial indicator. Piston stroke should be .060-.092" (1.5-2.3 mm).

6) If stroke exceeds specification, clutch pack is excessively worn. If stroke does not meet specification, clutch components have been incorrectly installed or too much ATF was applied to clutch plates and discs. Remove dial indicator and install bearing and race on input shaft.

REAR CLUTCH ASSEMBLY

NOTE: The rear clutch assembly used in the Borg-Warner 55 transmission uses 18 small return springs while the Aisin-Warner 55 transmission uses 1 big return spring.

Fig. 12: Exploded View of Rear Clutch Assembly

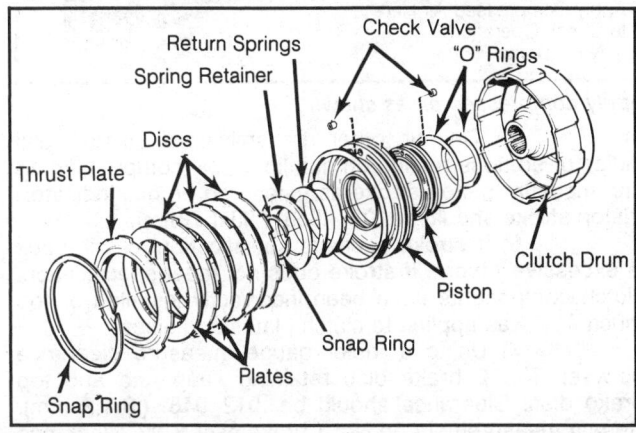

Borg-Warner uses 18 springs; all others use 1 spring.

Disassembly

1) Using a screwdriver, remove clutch disc pack snap ring. Lift out backing plate, clutch discs and plates. Note number and arrangement of discs and plates for reassembly reference.

2) Using a compressor tool, compress return spring retainer. Remove snap ring. Remove compressor tool. Lift retainer and clutch return spring(s) from drum.

3) Apply low pressure compressed air to 1 oil hole in clutch drum while covering the other oil hole. *See Fig. 13.* Force piston from drum. Remove "O" rings from piston.

Fig. 13: Rear Clutch Piston Removal from Drum

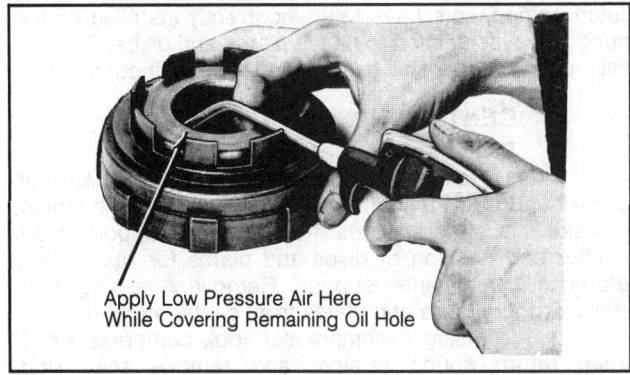

Apply Low Pressure Air Here While Covering Remaining Oil Hole

Use low pressure compressed air to remove piston.

Inspection

Clean all parts (except plates and discs) in clean solvent and dry with compressed air. Inspect clutch discs for signs of burning and wear. Check thickness of clutch discs. Minimum thickness is .08" (2.1 mm). Inspect all other parts for wear or damage. Shake piston to ensure that check ball is free. Replace any defective part.

Reassembly

1) Lubricate all friction surfaces with type F ATF. Lubricate and install new "O" rings on clutch piston. Install piston into drum. Install return spring(s) on piston and install retainer over spring(s). Compress spring retainer and install snap ring.

2) On Borg-Warner transmissions, check operation of piston by applying compressed air to 1 oil hole while blocking the other. When air is applied, a "plop" should be heard as piston is activated.

Fig. 14: Measuring Rear Clutch Clearance

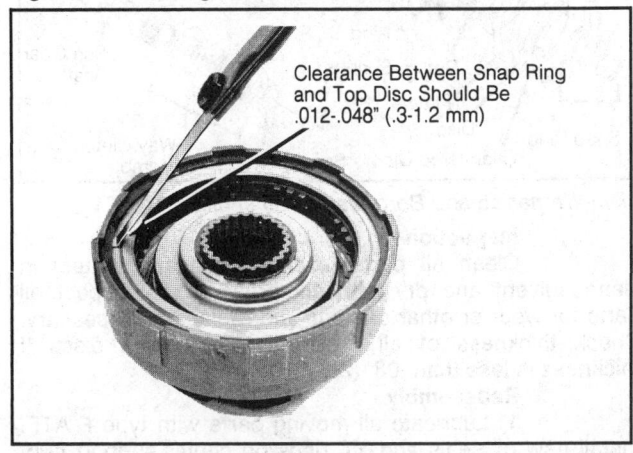

Clearance Between Snap Ring and Top Disc Should Be .012-.048" (.3-1.2 mm)

Measure between snap ring and top disc.

AISIN-WARNER 55, 70, 71 & BORG-WARNER 55 (Cont.)

3) On all transmissions, install clutch plates and discs into clutch drum. Alternate plates and discs until the number and position of plates and discs are installed as they were removed. Install backing plate with bevelled side facing discs and plates. Install clutch pack snap ring.

4) Using a feeler gauge, measure clearance between retaining snap ring and top clutch disc. Clearance should be .012-.048" (.3-1.2 mm). See Fig. 14.

5) On all transmissions (except Borg-Warner), install dial indicator so tip is resting on hub lip. Apply compressed air and read dial indicator. Piston stroke should be .037-.068" (.93-1.7 mm).

6) If stroke exceeds specification, clutch pack is excessively worn. If stroke does not meet specification, clutch components have been incorrectly installed or too much ATF was applied to clutch plates and discs. Remove dial indicator and install bearing and race on input shaft.

CENTER SUPPORT ASSEMBLY
Disassembly

1) Remove snap ring from sun gear shaft. Pull center support from shaft. Remove snap ring, then lift No. 1 brake discs and plates from center support. Note number and position of discs and plates for reassembly reference. Invert center support. Remove snap ring, then lift No. 2 brake discs and plates from center support.

2) Using a compressor tool, compress No. 2 brake return spring retainer and remove snap ring. Remove tool and lift return springs and retainer from center support. Repeat procedure on No. 1 brake.

3) Using compressed air, force No. 2 brake piston and No. 1 brake piston from center support. Slide 1-way clutch hub from sun gear shaft. Remove 3 oil seal rings from center support hub and 2 oil seal rings from sun gear shaft. Remove "O" rings from brake pistons.

Fig. 15: Exploded View of Center Support Assembly

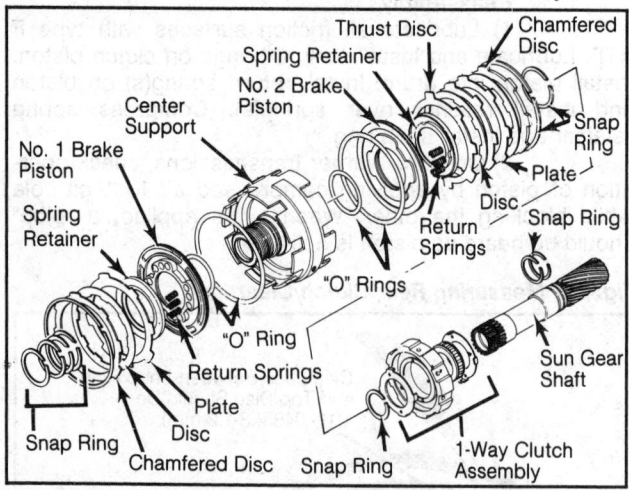

Aisin-Warner 55 and Borg-Warner 55 similar.

Inspection

Clean all parts (except discs and plates) in clean solvent and dry with compressed air. Inspect all parts for wear or other damage and replace as necessary. Check thickness of all brake discs. Replace discs if thickness is less than .08" (2.1 mm).

Reassembly

1) Lubricate all moving parts with type F ATF. Install new oil seals and "O" rings on center support hub, sun gear shaft and brake piston.

2) Lubricate "O" rings and install No. 2 brake piston into center support, using care not to damage "O" rings. Install 12 return springs into position on piston, then place retainer onto return springs. Compress return springs and install snap ring. Repeat procedure for No. 1 brake piston.

3) Install No. 1 brake disc and plate into center support in the same position as removed. Install chamfered disc with chamfered side facing discs. Install No. 1 brake snap ring into center support so that snap ring opening is between openings on center support. Repeat procedure for brake No. 2. See Fig. 16.

Fig. 16: Installation of Brake Disc Retaining Snap Ring

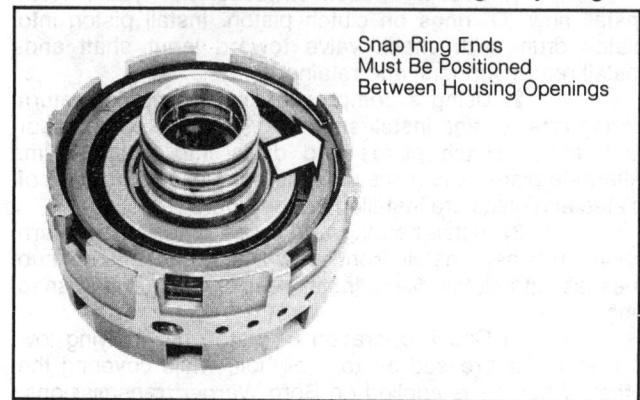

Snap Ring Ends Must Be Positioned Between Housing Openings

Note position of snap ring openings.

4) On Borg-Warner transmissions, check operation of No. 1 brake piston by applying compressed air to oil hole. When air is applied, a distinct clicking should be heard as piston is activated. See Fig. 17. Repeat for brake No. 2.

Fig. 17: Checking Brake Piston Operation

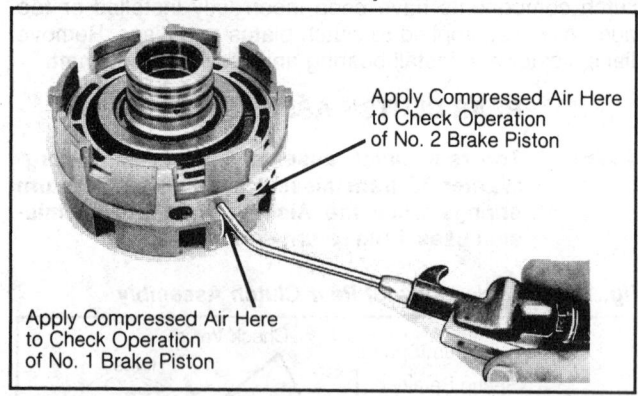

Apply Compressed Air Here to Check Operation of No. 2 Brake Piston

Apply Compressed Air Here to Check Operation of No. 1 Brake Piston

Apply compressed air as shown.

5) On all other transmissions, install dial indicator so tip is resting on hub lip. Apply compressed air and measure piston stroke as measured on dial indicator. Piston stroke should be .037-.068" (.93-1.7 mm).

6) If stroke exceeds specification, clutch pack is excessively worn. If stroke does not meet specification, clutch components have been incorrectly installed or too much ATF was applied to clutch plates and discs.

7) Using a feeler gauge, measure clearance between No. 2 brake disc retaining snap ring and top brake disc. Clearance should be .012-.048" (.3-1.2 mm). Repeat measurement on No. 1 brake assembly. Clearance should be the same as No. 2 brake clearance.

AISIN-WARNER 55, 70, 71 & BORG-WARNER 55 (Cont.)

Fig. 18: Measuring Brake Disc Clearance

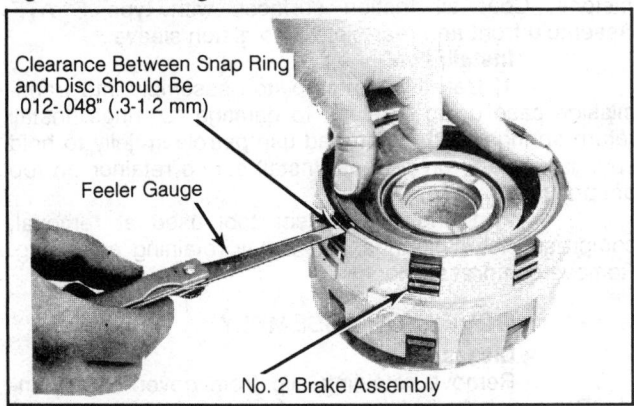

Measure between snap ring and top brake disc.

8) Install 1-way clutch on sun gear shaft. Check that 1-way clutch is not loose or stiff when installed on shaft; if so, clutch should be replaced. Align splines of 1-way clutch with brake disc splines, then install 1-way clutch and sun gear shaft into center support. Install oil seal rings on sun gear shaft, ensuring that seal ring ends are correctly hooked.

PLANETARY GEAR ASSEMBLY
Disassembly

1) Separate front planetary gear set and No. 3 brake discs from output shaft assembly. Invert shaft assembly so that assembly is resting on output shaft. Compress snap ring and lift front planetary ring gear from assembly. Pull intermediate shaft and rear planetary gear set from output shaft housing. Remove bearing and race from output shaft housing.

2) Remove plastic and steel thrust washers from intermediate shaft. Pull rear planetary gear set from rear ring gear, then remove bearing and race. Remove snap ring and slide rear ring gear from intermediate shaft. Slide rear bearing race from shaft.

3) Remove oil seal rings from output shaft. Remove steel thrust plate from front planetary gear set. Lift No. 3 brake discs and plates from around planetary gear set. Remove 1-way clutch inner hub from planetary gear set. Remove snap ring from 1-way clutch. Remove both bearing cages, 1-way clutch and plastic ring from gear set.

Fig. 19: Exploded View of Planetary Gear Set

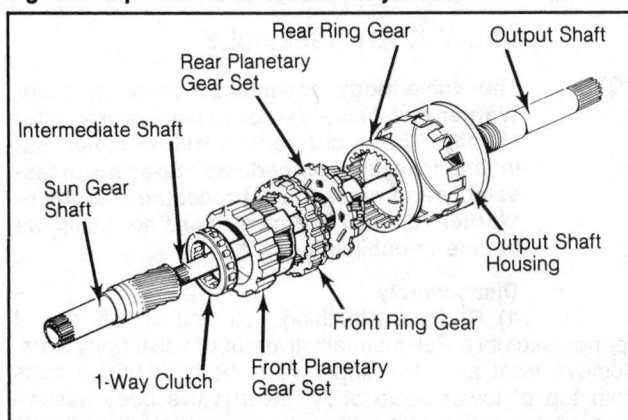

Note component position during disassembly.

Inspection

Clean all parts (except discs and plates) with clean solvent and dry with compressed air. Inspect all parts for wear, cracks, or other damage and replace as necessary. Check thickness of each brake disc. Replace discs if thickness is less than .08" (2.1 mm).

Reassembly

1) Lubricate all moving parts with type F ATF. Install plastic ring and lower bearing cage into front planetary gear set. Install 1-way clutch into gear set with arrow on side of clutch pointing down. Install 1-way clutch upper bearing cage on top of clutch and retain with snap ring.

2) Install 1-way clutch and front planetary gear set into front ring gear. With 1-way clutch installed in front ring gear, front planetary gear set should rotate freely in a counterclockwise direction only without sticking. Assemble No. 3 brake discs to front planetary gear set.

3) Install new oil seal rings on output shaft and ensure that ring ends are properly hooked. Position rear race on intermediate shaft. Slide rear ring gear onto shaft. Secure with snap ring. Position bearing and front race in rear ring gear. Install rear planetary gear set into ring gear.

4) Position thrust bearing and race in output shaft housing. Assemble intermediate shaft to output shaft. Install front ring gear into output shaft housing and secure with snap ring. Front ring gear retaining snap ring must be installed in housing with ring ends in recess of housing. See Fig. 20.

Fig. 20: Front Ring Gear Snap Ring Installation

Snap ring ends must fit in housing recess.

5) Place plastic thrust washer into front ring gear so that it rests on top of rear planetary gear set. Place steel thrust washer on front planetary gear set and retain with petroleum jelly. Assemble front gear set to output shaft housing.

NO. 3 BRAKE PISTON
Removal

1) To remove No. 3 brake piston from Volvo transmission case, attach compressor tool (Volvo 5073) to case. See Fig. 21. Alternately tighten tool bolts until snap ring on piston return spring retainer is free of tension. Isuzu uses an internal compressor tool (Isuzu J-25048). Using a screwdriver, pry off snap ring. Remove compressor tool.

AISIN-WARNER 55, 70, 71 & BORG-WARNER 55 (Cont.)

Fig. 21: Volvo Compressor Tool Installation

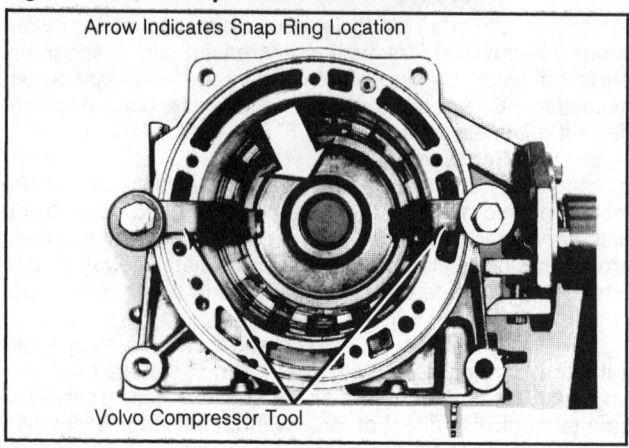

Arrow Indicates Snap Ring Location

Volvo Compressor Tool

Isuzu uses an internal compressor tool.

2) Lift return spring retainer and 16 return springs from transmission case. Turn transmission so front side is facing down. Apply compressed air to oil hole. *See Fig. 22.* Force piston from its seat in case and lift piston out of case.

Fig. 22: No. 3 Brake Piston Removal

Apply Low Pressure Air
to Hole to Force Piston from Case

Use compressed air to force out piston.

Disassembly & Reassembly
Pull front and rear pistons from piston sleeve. Remove "O" rings from pistons. Clean and inspect all

Fig. 23: Exploded View of No. 3 Brake Piston

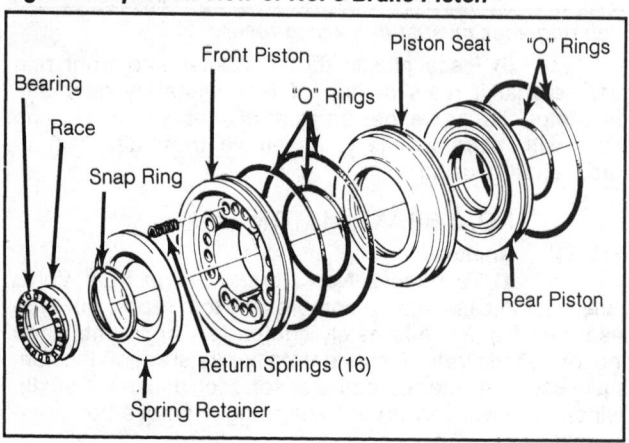

Bearing
Race
Snap Ring
Front Piston
"O" Rings
Piston Seat
"O" Rings
Rear Piston
Return Springs (16)
Spring Retainer

parts and replace as necessary. Install new "O" rings on pistons. Coat all friction surfaces with type F ATF. Assemble front and rear pistons to piston sleeve.

Installation
1) Carefully install piston assembly into transmission case using care not to damage "O" rings. Install return springs onto piston and use petroleum jelly to hold springs in place on pistons. Install spring retainer on top of springs.

2) Using compressor tool used at removal, compress piston springs and install retaining snap ring. Remove compressor tool.

GOVERNOR ASSEMBLY
Disassembly
Remove retaining clip from governor assembly. Remove "E" clip from end of governor shaft. Remove shaft along with governor valve, spring and weight.

Fig. 24: Disassembled View of Governor Assembly

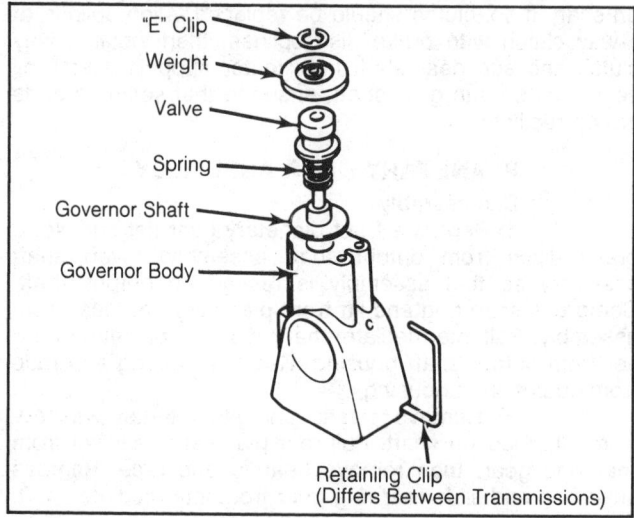

"E" Clip
Weight
Valve
Spring
Governor Shaft
Governor Body

Retaining Clip
(Differs Between Transmissions)

Retaining clip is different on Borg-Warner models.

Inspection
Clean all parts with solvent and dry with compressed air. Inspect all parts for wear or damage.
Reassembly
Lubricate all parts with type F ATF. Install spring and valve on shaft. Install shaft into governor body. Place weight on shaft. Install "E" clip to retain parts. Install retaining clip on governor housing.

VALVE BODY ASSEMBLY

NOTE: The valve body assemblies used on Borg-Warner and Aisin-Warner transmissions differ slightly. These differences will be called out in the following procedures. Specific disassembly and reassembly procedures for Aisin-Warner 70 and 71 transmissions not available at time of publication.

Disassembly
1) Remove attaching bolt and lift off detent spring assembly. Pull manual valve out of valve body bore. Remove front and rear upper valve body attaching bolts from top of lower valve body. Invert valve body assemblies and remove retaining bolts from bottom of lower valve body.

AISIN-WARNER 55, 70, 71 & BORG-WARNER 55 (Cont.)

2) Carefully lift lower body off both upper bodies without losing check balls, if equipped. Place lower body aside with gasket up. To disassemble front upper valve body, place valve body on a work bench with cored face up. Remove check ball and throttle valve retaining plate. Using a screwdriver, push out cutback valve retainer. Remove cutback valve and spring.

NOTE: **The Aisin-Warner 55 valve body is not equipped with a cutback valve spring.**

3) Remove throttle cam bolt, throttle cam, spring and spacer sleeve from front upper valve body. Pull out throttle valve, kickdown valve, spring and spacers, noting number of spacers removed with throttle valve. Equal amount of spacers must be installed for proper throttle valve adjustment.

4) Remove 1 secondary regulator valve cover plate bolt. Loosen other bolt while keeping tension on plate. Carefully remove plate without allowing spring to pop out of cavity. Remove regulator valve.

5) To disassemble rear upper valve body, place body on a work bench with cored face up. On Borg-Warner transmissions, remove 2 check balls from valve body passages, if equipped. On Aisin-Warner transmissions, remove 4 check balls (3 rubber and 1 steel).

6) On both models, push in intermediate coast shift valve and remove retainer. Slide coast valve and spring for 2-3 shift valve out of valve body. Remove 2-3 shift valve retainer and shift valve. Using a small screwdriver, push out detent regulator valve retainer. Remove valve and spring.

7) Remove remaining cover plate from rear upper valve body. Remove the following valves and springs from valve body bores, keeping valve and springs together for identification: Low coast modulator valve, governor modulator valve (if equipped), reverse clutch sequence valve, and intermediate coast modulator valve.

8) To disassemble lower valve body, lift off spacer plate and gaskets. Remove cooler by-pass valve and spring. On Borg-Warner transmissions, remove 4

Fig. 25: Exploded View of Aisin-Warner and Borg-Warner Valve Body Assemblies

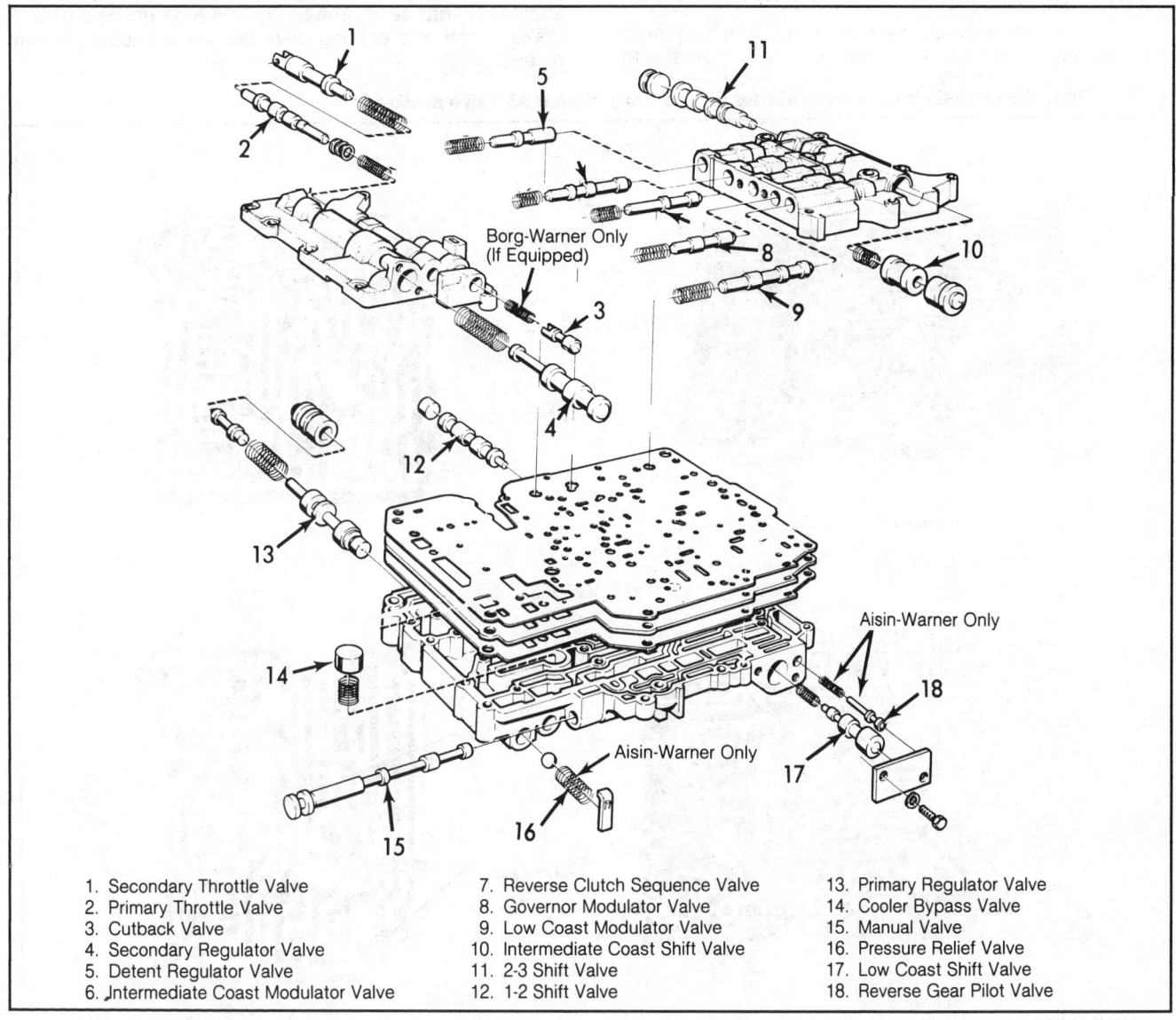

Borg-Warner Only (If Equipped)

Aisin-Warner Only

Aisin-Warner Only

1. Secondary Throttle Valve
2. Primary Throttle Valve
3. Cutback Valve
4. Secondary Regulator Valve
5. Detent Regulator Valve
6. Intermediate Coast Modulator Valve
7. Reverse Clutch Sequence Valve
8. Governor Modulator Valve
9. Low Coast Modulator Valve
10. Intermediate Coast Shift Valve
11. 2-3 Shift Valve
12. 1-2 Shift Valve
13. Primary Regulator Valve
14. Cooler Bypass Valve
15. Manual Valve
16. Pressure Relief Valve
17. Low Coast Shift Valve
18. Reverse Gear Pilot Valve

AISIN-WARNER 55, 70, 71 & BORG-WARNER 55 (Cont.)

check balls from valve body passages (if equipped). On Aisin-Warner transmissions, remove 2 check balls from valve body passages.

9) On all transmissions, push in 1-2 shift valve and allow retainer to drop out of valve body. Remove 1-2 shift valve. Remove cover plate. Slide low coast shift valve and reverse gear pilot valve and spring from valve body.

NOTE: The Borg-Warner transmission valve body is not equipped with a reverse gear pilot valve.

10) If equipped, remove pressure relief ball retainer. Lift out relief ball and spring. Remove primary regulator valve train retainer. Slide valve train and spring out of valve body.

Inspection

1) Thoroughly clean all parts in clean solvent, then use compressed air to dry parts. Blow out all channels and passages in valve bodies.

2) Check spacer plate to ensure all holes are open. Check all valves and valve bores for wear and damage. After cleaning and lubricating valves with ATF, they must slide freely in their bores.

Reassembly

1) Reverse disassembly procedure and note the following: Lubricate all valves and valve bores with type F ATF before reassembly. Ensure that all check balls are installed in correct valve body passages. *See Fig. 26.*

2) When installing throttle valve in front upper valve body, install the same number of spacers that were removed. This ensures correct throttle valve adjustment.

TRANSMISSION REASSEMBLY

1) Install new "O" rings on oil cooler line nipples. Install nipples in transmission case so they point in same direction as when removed. Install new "O" rings on line pressure and governor pressure plugs. Install plugs in case.

2) Install governor oil ducts cover on transmission case using a new gasket. Install throttle cable in case. Assemble parking pawl, spring and shaft in case. Install detent lever and shaft. Drive detent lever retaining pin through lever and into shaft. Fit parking pawl rod to pawl and detent lever. Install parking pawl cam plate.

3) Invert transmission case so case opening is up. Install rearmost bearing and race. Install No. 3 brake apply tube into case. Lower lugs on tube go inside No. 3 brake piston and parking pawl pin fits in middle of drum recess.

Fig. 26: *Check Ball Installation in Aisin-Warner 55 and Borg-Warner 55 Valve Bodies*

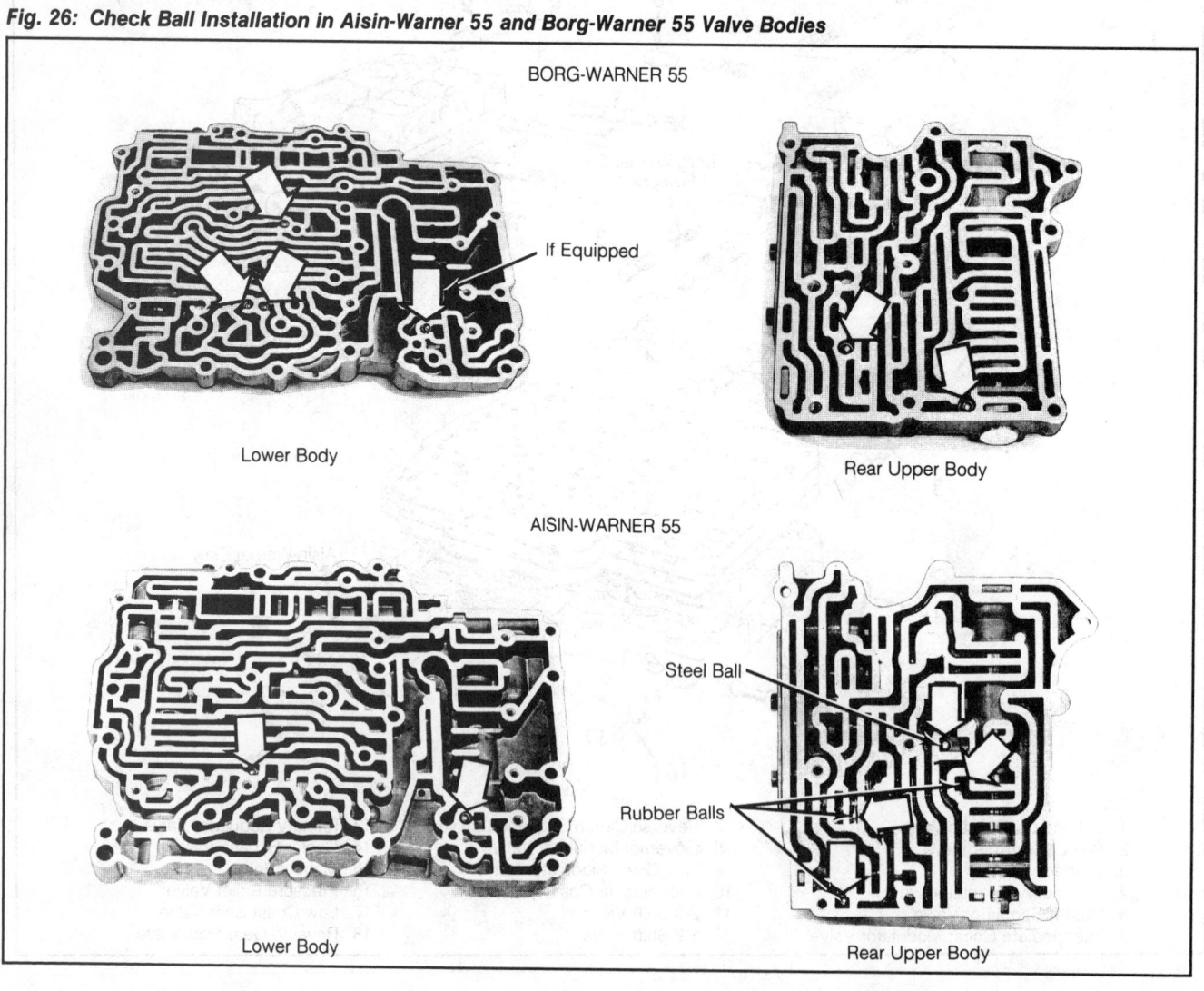

AISIN-WARNER 55, 70, 71 & BORG-WARNER 55 (Cont.)

4) Install planetary gear and No. 3 brake disc assembly into transmission case with recess in reaction plate facing oil pan. Install planetary assembly retaining snap ring in groove of case. Snap ring ends must be between splines. *See Fig. 27.*

Fig. 27: *Installation of Planetary Assembly Snap Ring*

Snap Ring Ends
Must Be Between
Disc Splines
(White Arrow)

Note position of snap ring ends.

5) Check operation of No. 3 brake piston by applying low pressure compressed air to oil holes. *See Fig. 28.* When air is applied, an audible "plop" should be heard.

6) Hold sun gear shaft and lower center support assembly into transmission case until it mates with planetary gear assembly. Install center support bolts into case by hand to avoid thread damage. DO NOT tighten bolts at this time.

7) Align discs on center support and install rear clutch assembly into transmission case. If rear clutch is properly assembled, clutch splines and sun gear shaft splines should mesh. Position bearings and races on rear clutch hub. Align discs and assemble front clutch to rear clutch. Install bearing and race on input shaft.

8) Position oil pump in case, then install and tighten attaching bolts. Tighten center support bolts in 4 steps, starting with bolt next to accumulator piston bores.

Fig. 28: *Checking No. 3 Brake Piston Operation*

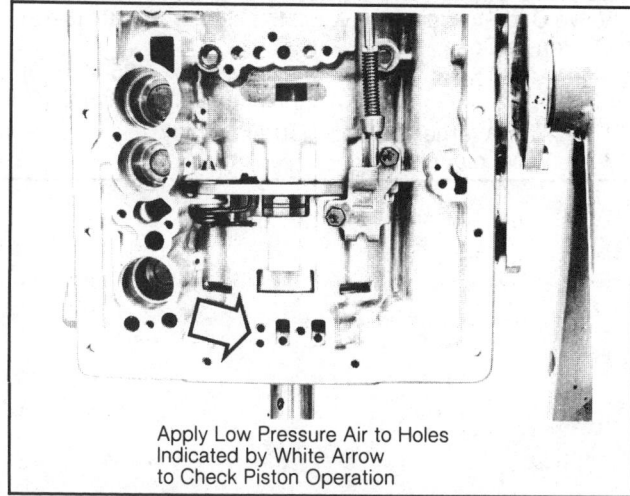

Apply Low Pressure Air to Holes
Indicated by White Arrow
to Check Piston Operation

Apply low pressure compressed air to oil hole.

Tighten bolts alternately and evenly, without damaging "O" rings.

9) Check operation of brake and clutch pistons by applying low pressure compressed air to respective oil hole. *See Fig. 29.* When air is applied to each oil hole, a distinct "plop" should be heard.

Fig. 29: *Checking Clutch and Brake Piston Operation*

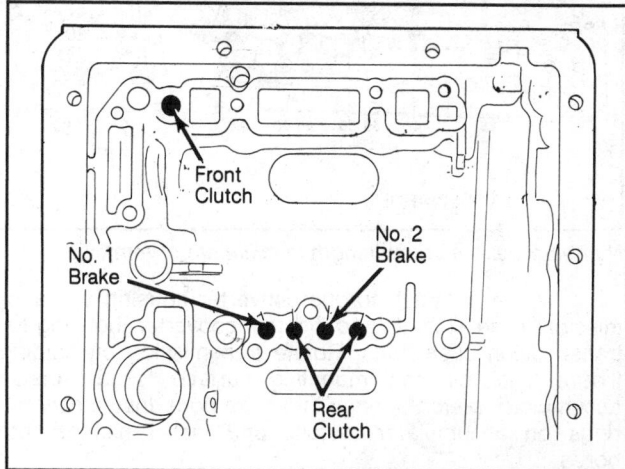

Front
Clutch

No. 1
Brake

No. 2
Brake

Rear
Clutch

Apply low pressure compressed air to each hole.

10) Mount a dial indicator on transmission case with indicator tip touching end of input shaft. *See Fig. 30.* Zero dial indicator. Move input shaft up and down and note maximum dial indicator reading. This reading is input shaft end play. End play should be .009-.020" (.22-.53 mm) for Borg-Warner 55 and .012-.035" (.30-.90 mm) for all others. Input shaft should rotate without binding.

Fig. 30: *Measuring Input Shaft End Play*

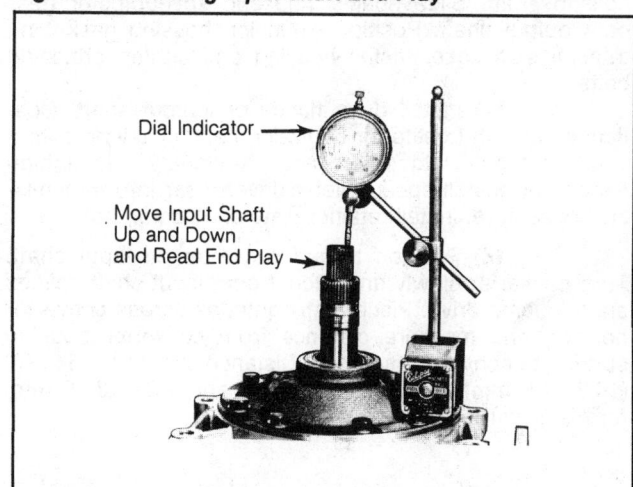

Dial Indicator

Move Input Shaft
Up and Down
and Read End Play

Make sure tip of dial indicator rests on input shaft.

NOTE: On Aisin-Warner 70 and 71 transmissions, No. 2 brake spring is longer than front clutch spring. On Aisin-Warner and Borg-Warner 55 transmissions, front clutch spring is larger than No. 2 brake spring. Short spring is installed in center bore on all transmissions. Install small piston in center bore on all transmissions. The 2 large pistons are different sizes and cannot be incorrectly installed.

Automatic Transmissions

AISIN-WARNER 55, 70, 71 & BORG-WARNER 55 (Cont.)

Fig. 31: Valve Body Attaching Bolt Identification and Location

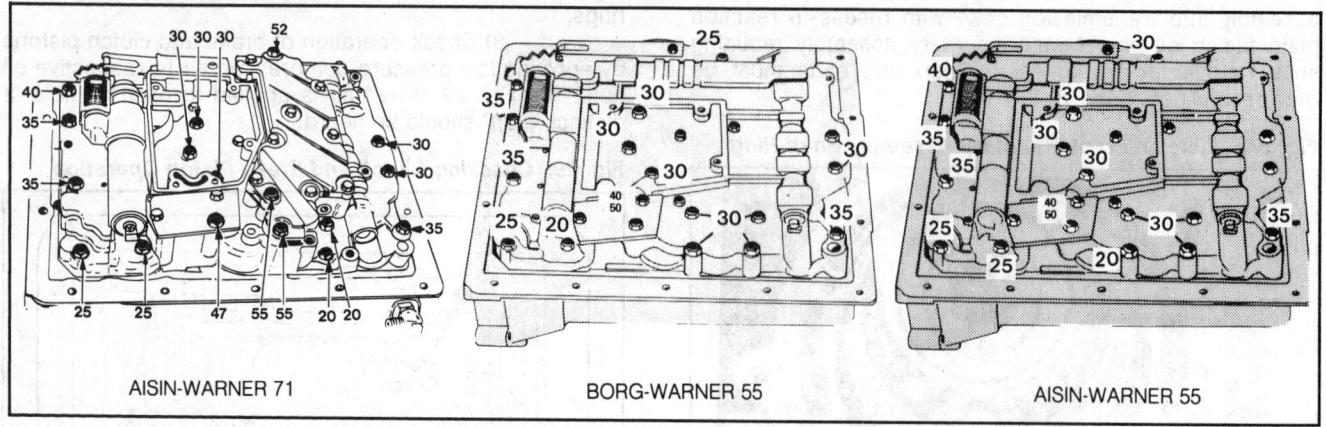

AISIN-WARNER 71   BORG-WARNER 55   AISIN-WARNER 55

Numbers denote screw length in millimeters (mm).

11) Attach torque converter housing to transmission case. Install and tighten converter housing-to-transmission case bolts. Rotate transmission on holding fixture until oil pan mounting surface is up. Install accumulator piston springs into case bore. Install new "O" rings on accumulator pistons and install pistons into bores.

12) Connect throttle cable to throttle cam on valve body. Place valve body assembly in position with selector cam pin fitted in manual valve recess. Install and tighten valve body attaching bolts. *See Fig. 31.* Install strainer on valve body and tighten attaching bolts. Install particle magnet, oil pan gasket and oil pan. Install and tighten attaching bolts.

13) Align governor retaining clip with hole in output shaft. Slide governor onto shaft and engage clip in hole in shaft. Slide spacer ring and speedometer gear onto output shaft. Position extension housing gasket on transmission case. Install housing and tighten attaching bolts.

14) Install drive flange on output shaft. Coat flange nut with Loctite (or equivalent) and install on output shaft threads. Hold drive flange stationary and tighten flange nut. Install speedometer driven gear into transmission case bore. Install retainer plate and tighten bolt.

15) Position torque converter on input shaft. Turn converter slowly and slide it onto input shaft splines and oil pump drive. Place a straightedge across converter housing and measure distance from converter housing surface to converter face ring. Distance should be .64-.77" (16.2-19.6 mm) for Borg-Warner 55 and 1.24" (31.5 mm) for Aisin-Warner 55 transmissions.

TIGHTENING SPECIFICATIONS [1]

Application	Ft. Lbs. (N.m)
Converter Hsg.-to-Engine	
Isuzu	29 (39)
Volvo	
Gas Engine	30-37 (41-50)
Diesel Engine	13-20 (18-27)
Converter Hsg.-to-Transmission Case	
M10 Bolts	19-29 (26-39)
M12 Bolts	35-43 (47-58)
Converter-to-Drive Plate	
Isuzu	14 (19)
Volvo	
Gas Engine	30-37 (41-50)
Diesel Engine	13-20 (18-27)
Oil Pump-to-Transmission Case	
Isuzu	13-18 (18-28)
Volvo	16-21 (22-29)
Center Support Bolts	
Step 1	5 (7)
Step 2	10 (14)
Step 3	15 (20)
Final Step	18-21 (24-28)
Extension Hsg.-to-Case	19-29 (26-39)
Drive Flange Nut	[2] 30-37 (41-50)
	INCH Lbs. (N.m)
Oil Pump Cover-to-Oil Pump	53 (6)
Lower-to-Upper Valve Bodies	43-52 (5-6)
Valve Body-to-Case	70-104 (8-12)
Oil Pan-to-Case	
Isuzu	35-43 (4-5)
Volvo	53-89 (6-10)

[1] — Aisin-Warner & Borg-Warner 55 only.
[2] — Volvo models only.

BORG-WARNER MODEL 66

Jaguar XJ6

DESCRIPTION

Transmission is a fully automatic 3-speed unit consisting basically of a 3 element torque converter and a compound planetary gear set. Two multiple-disc clutches, one roller clutch, and two brake bands provide friction elements required to obtain desired function of planetary gear set. A hydraulic control system, pressurized by a gear-type oil pump, provides working pressure required to operate automatic controls. Transmission kickdown is actuated by cable, attached to accelerator assembly and a cam internal in case.

LUBRICATION & ADJUSTMENT

See the appropriate article in AUTOMATIC TRANSMISSION SERVICING Section.

TROUBLE SHOOTING

ROUGH INITIAL ENGAGEMENT

Engine idle speed too high. Throttle cable out of adjustment. Valve body assembly faulty, valves sticking or worn.

NO ENGAGEMENT

In Any Position

Incorrect fluid level. Manual linkage out of adjustment. Throttle cable out of adjustment. Input shaft broken. Primary regulator valve sticking. Front pump worn.

In Forward Gears

Governor valve stuck or damaged. Output shaft seal rings or governor pressure tube seals worn or faulty. Also check front clutch, stator support shaft bearing, and front seal rings on sun gear shaft.

In First Gear in "D"

One-way clutch faulty or installed backwards.

In Second Gear

Front band faulty or out of adjustment. Front servo piston or seals worn or damaged. Oil pipes loose, damaged, or missing. Foreign matter or damage in valve body.

In Third Gear

Foreign matter in valve body or governor. Check rear clutch feed pipes, rear clutch, and piston rings in hub of intermediate shaft.

No Overrun Braking in "1"

Rear band out of adjustment or worn. Rear servo seals or feed pipes damaged or missing.

SLIPPING OR LATE SHIFTS

Throttle cable out of adjustment. Main pressure not within specifications (check oil pump and seals on pump tubes). Governor faulty. Valve body faulty. Check output shaft oil seal rings and governor tubes for wear or damage. Check front and rear bands and servos for wear or damage.

Fig. 1: Cross-Sectional View of Borg-Warner Model 65 Automatic Transmission

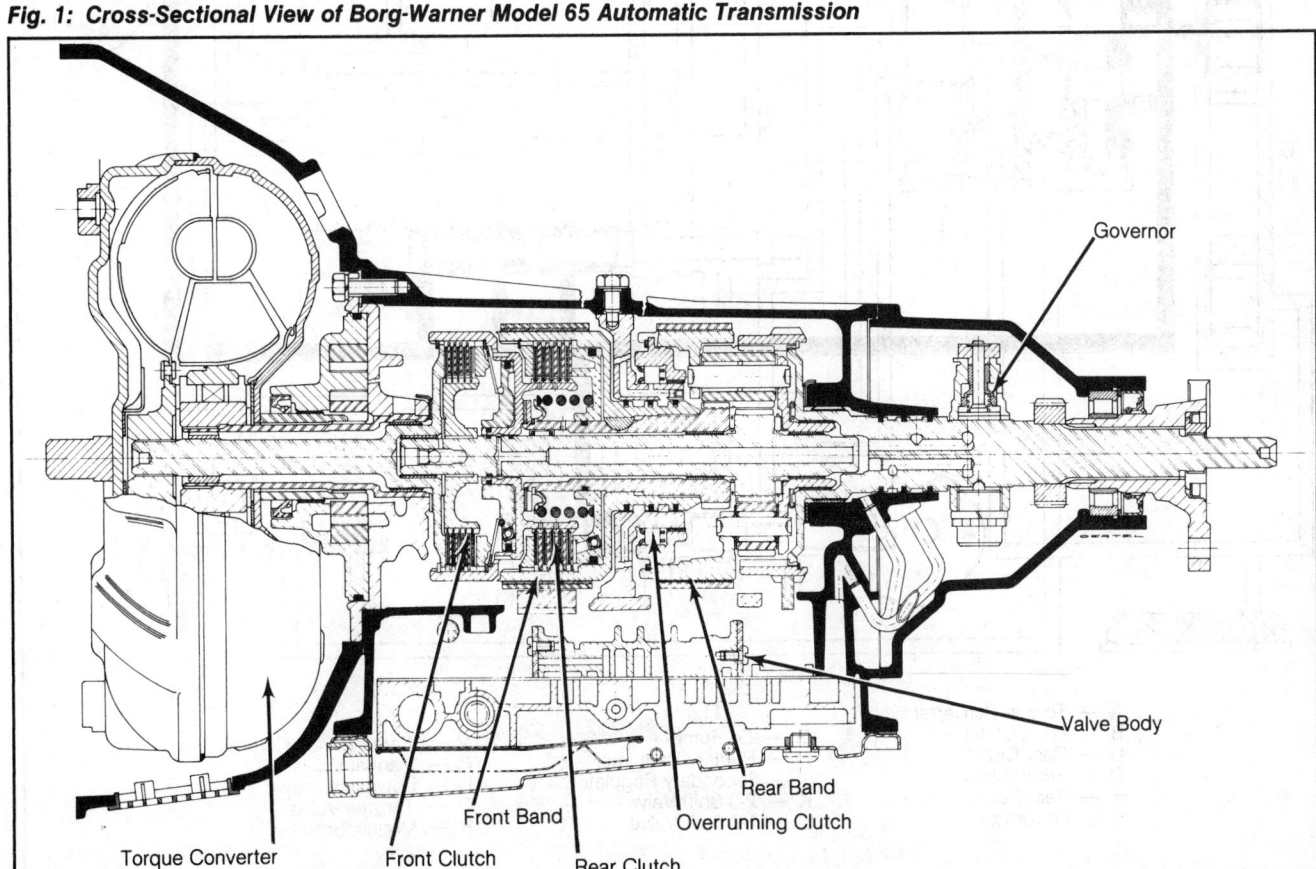

Governor

Valve Body

Rear Band

Overrunning Clutch

Torque Converter

Front Band

Front Clutch

Rear Clutch

Automatic Transmissions
BORG-WARNER MODEL 66 (Cont.)

Fig. 2: *Borg-Warner Model 65 Automatic Transmission Hydraulic Circuits Diagram*

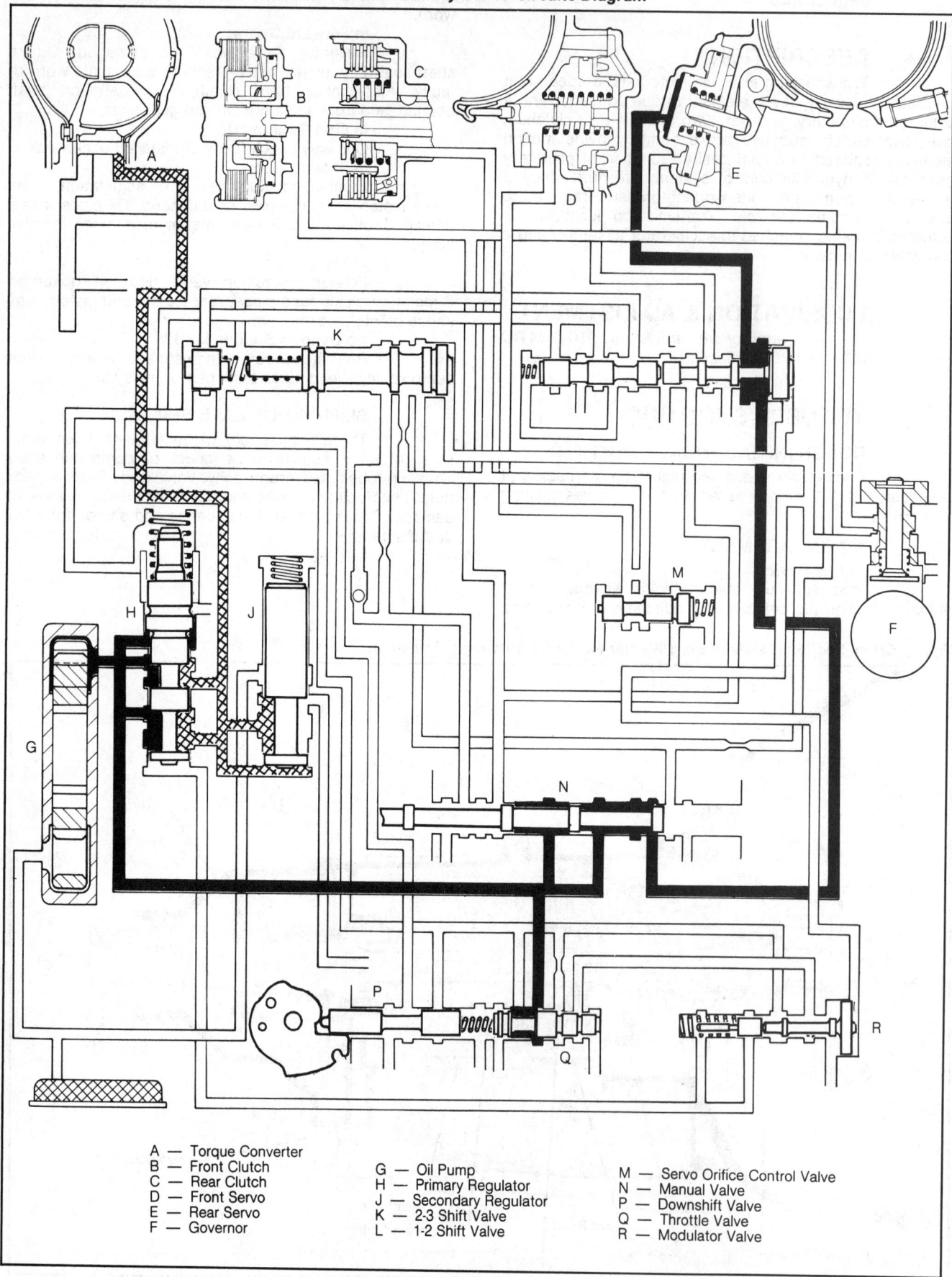

A — Torque Converter		
B — Front Clutch	G — Oil Pump	M — Servo Orifice Control Valve
C — Rear Clutch	H — Primary Regulator	N — Manual Valve
D — Front Servo	J — Secondary Regulator	P — Downshift Valve
E — Rear Servo	K — 2-3 Shift Valve	Q — Throttle Valve
F — Governor	L — 1-2 Shift Valve	R — Modulator Valve

BORG-WARNER MODEL 66 (Cont.)

TRANSMISSION NOISE

Whine In and Out of Second Gear
Front band out of adjustment. Front servo parts worn or damaged. Oil pipes loose. Front band worn or damaged. Valve body faulty.

Whine In and Out of Third Gear
Rear clutch, feed pipe, or seals worn or damaged. Valve body faulty.

Whining Noise with Engine Running
Oil pump gears worn or damaged. Bushing worn in torque converter.

Irregular Noise (All Except Third Gear)
Planetary gear set defective.

TESTING

ROAD TEST
Drive vehicle on the road, allowing transmission to shift through all ranges. Note transmission performance under varying load conditions: Light throttle, full throttle, and kickdown. Transmission should operate smoothly but firmly, with no apparent slipping or engine speed flare-up. Compare transmission shift points with figures given in *Shift Speeds* chart.

SHIFT SPEED SPECIFICATIONS

Shift Condition	MPH
Part Throttle	
1-2 Upshift	8-12
2-3 Upshift	13-18
Full Throttle	
1-2 Upshift	41-51
2-3 Upshift	73-81
Full Throttle Kickdown	
3-2 Downshift	63-73
3-1 Downshift	25-35
Part Throttle Kickdown	
3-2 Downshift	32-42
Closed Throttle Kickdown	
2-1 Downshift	5-10

NOTE: Shift speeds may vary slightly due to production tolerances, rear axle ratio, or tire size.

OIL PRESSURE TEST

NOTE: Before making pressure test, be certain that fluid level and condition, and control linkage adjustments have been checked and corrected as necessary. Connect a tachometer to engine and a pressure gauge to main pressure take-off point on rear of transmission. *See Fig. 3.*

1) Apply service and parking brake, place transmission selector lever in "D" position, and with engine at idle (750 RPM), check main pressure. Main pressure should be 60-75 psi (4.2-5.3 kg/cm²).

2) Next, increase engine speed to 1200 RPM. Again check pressure gauge. Pressure should be 85-95 psi (5.9-6.7 kg/cm²).

3) If pressures are not within specified limits, first check adjustment of transmission throttle cable. *See*

Fig. 3: Hydraulic Pressure Test Hook-Up

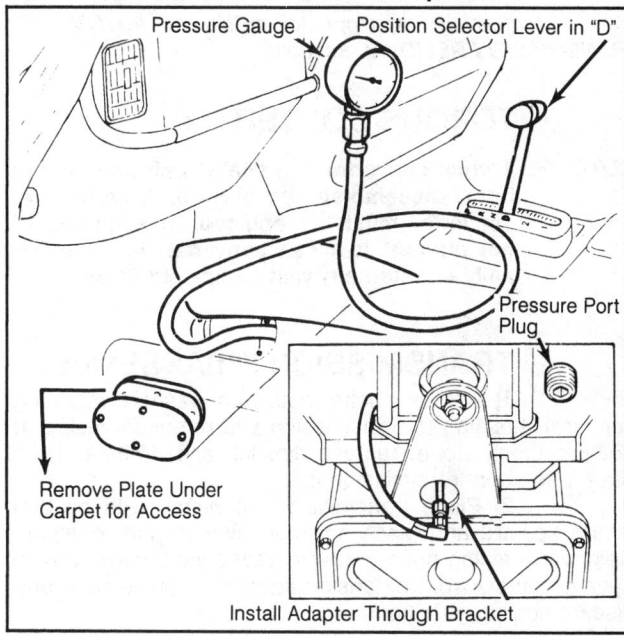

CLUTCH AND BAND APPLICATION CHART (ELEMENTS IN USE)

Selector Lever Position	Front Clutch	Rear Clutch	Front Band	Rear Band	One-Way Clutch
D — DRIVE					
First Gear	X				X
Second Gear	X		X		
Third Gear	X	X			
2 — INTERMEDIATE					
Second Gear	X		X		
1 — LOW	X			X	
R — REVERSE		X		X	

NEUTRAL OR PARK — All clutches, brakes, and bands released and/or ineffective.

BORG-WARNER MODEL 66 (Cont.)

the appropriate article in AUTOMATIC TRANSMISSION SERVICING Section.

STALL TEST

1) With engine and transmission at normal operating temperature, tachometer installed, and parking and service brakes applied, place transmission selector lever in "D". Press accelerator pedal to the floor and read maximum engine speed obtained.

CAUTION: To prevent damage to transmission by overheating, DO NOT perform stall test for more than 10 seconds at a time.

2) Stall speed should be 1950-2100 RPM. If stall speed is considerably less than specified, check for insufficient engine output or one-way clutch slippage in torque converter. If stall speed is higher then specified, clutch or band slippage is indicated.

REMOVAL & INSTALLATION

See the appropriate article in AUTOMATIC TRANSMISSION REMOVAL Section.

TORQUE CONVERTER

NOTE: **Torque converter is a sealed unit and cannot be disassembled for service. If defective, converter must be replaced. In addition, do not attempt to clean converter, either internally or externally with flammable fluids.**

TRANSMISSION DISASSEMBLY

1) Remove bolts, nuts and washers retaining converter housing to transmission and remove housing. If not previously done, remove dipstick and breather from case, and drain transmission fluid.

2) Place transmission on bench with oil pan facing upward and place selector lever in park position. Remove retaining bolts and withdraw speedometer driven gear assembly from extension housing, then remove and discard sealing "O" ring.

3) Remove bolt or nut securing flange to output shaft and withdraw flange using a puller if necessary. Remove bolts and nuts securing extension housing to case, then withdraw housing and discard gasket.

4) If necessary, remove and discard oil seal from extension housing. Slide speedometer drive gear off output shaft. Remove oil pan-to-case bolts and washers, remove oil pan, and discard gasket.

5) Note installed positions of oil tubes for reassembly reference, and using a screwdriver, pry out 5 oil tubes connected to valve body. DO NOT attempt to remove the oil tube partially covered by valve body.

6) Disconnect throttle cable from throttle cam, remove valve body-to-case bolts, and withdraw valve body (take care not to lose manual valve). Remove 2 remaining oil tubes from valve body area of case. Remove bolts retaining oil pump tube plate and withdraw plate and tubes.

7) Scratch alignment marks on oil pump housing and transmission case, remove pump-to-case

Fig. 4: Removal of Valve Body Assembly and Related Components

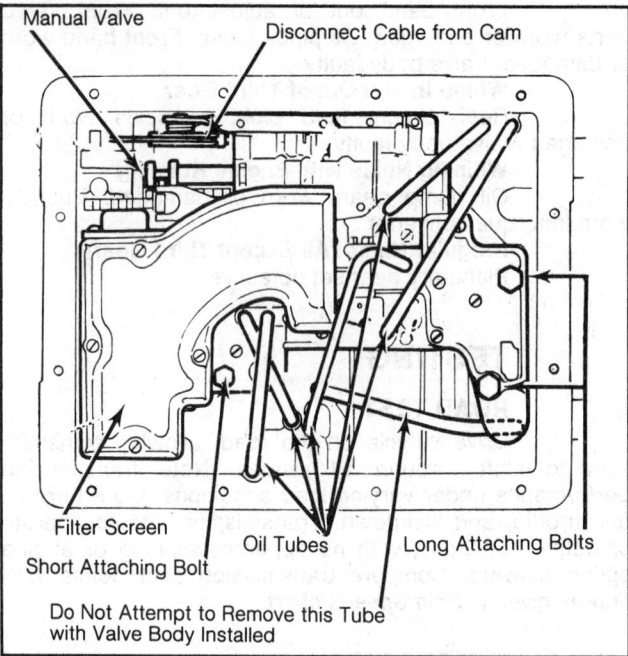

Manual Valve
Disconnect Cable from Cam
Filter Screen
Oil Tubes
Long Attaching Bolts
Short Attaching Bolt
Do Not Attempt to Remove this Tube with Valve Body Installed

bolts, and withdraw oil pump. Remove and discard pump-to-case gasket and pump-to-front clutch thrust washer.

8) At rear end of transmission, remove plug and spring washer retaining governor to output shaft, note installed position of governor, and remove from shaft. Using a screwdriver, carefully pry oil tubes from case and governor support.

9) Loosen both band adjusting screw lock nuts, remove adjusting screws from case then withdraw both band struts. Withdraw front clutch and input shaft

Fig. 5: Removal of Governor and Oil Tubes

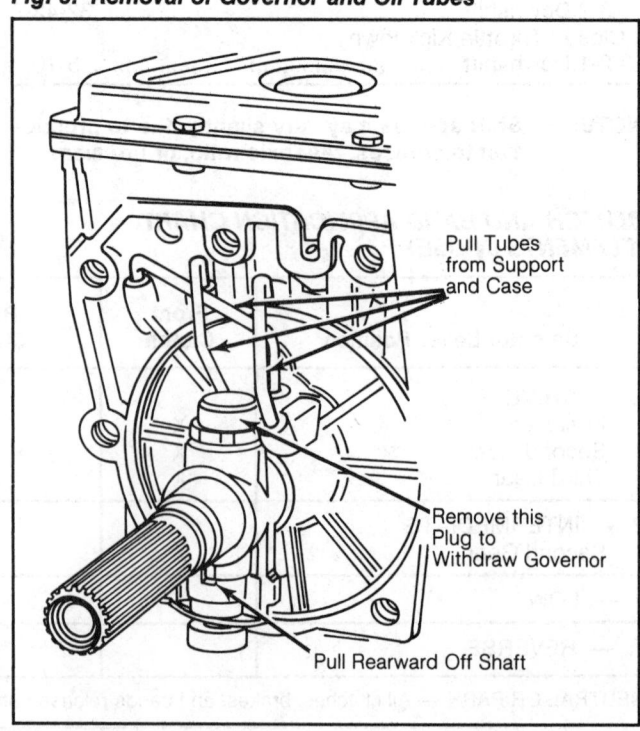

Pull Tubes from Support and Case
Remove this Plug to Withdraw Governor
Pull Rearward Off Shaft

BORG-WARNER MODEL 66 (Cont.)

assembly from case, remove bronze and steel thrust washers, then withdraw rear clutch assembly.

10) Compress ends of front band together and remove from case. Withdraw forward sun gear shaft from case, along with small needle thrust bearing from front end of shaft and large needle thrust bearing and race from rear end of shaft.

Fig. 6: Disassembled View of Transmission Gear Train Components

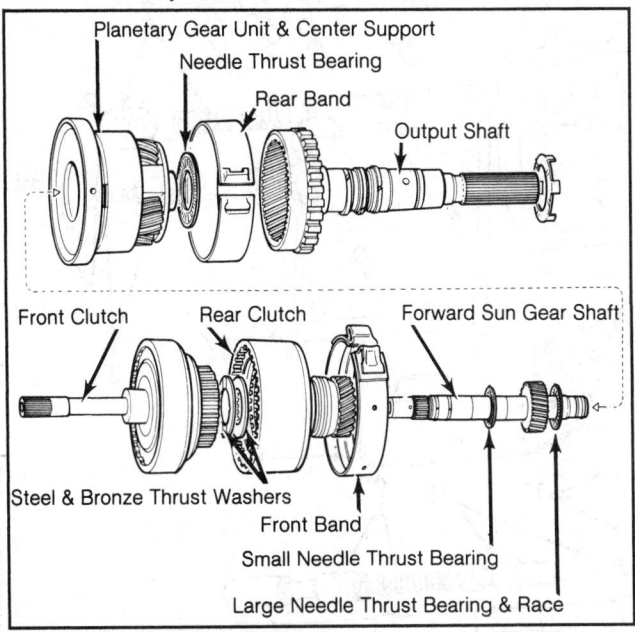

Planetary Gear Unit & Center Support
Needle Thrust Bearing
Rear Band
Output Shaft

Front Clutch
Rear Clutch
Forward Sun Gear Shaft
Steel & Bronze Thrust Washers
Front Band
Small Needle Thrust Bearing
Large Needle Thrust Bearing & Race

11) Remove bolts securing center support in case, push forward on output shaft to break support loose, then withdraw center support and planetary assembly from case. Remove planetary-to-output shaft needle thrust bearing, then separate support and planetary.

12) Move output shaft back into original position, compress ends of rear band together, and remove band from case. Remove output shaft assembly from case along with output shaft-to-case thrust washer.

13) Remove bolts securing front servo cover to case, remove cover, and withdraw servo piston, rod and spring. Scribe alignment marks on rear servo cover and transmission case, remove bolts attaching servo cover, then remove rear servo cover, piston, rod and spring from case.

14) Remove retaining bolts from plate covering parking pawl, withdraw pivot pin, and remove rear servo operating lever.

NOTE: If any valve body component is damaged or worn, entire valve body assembly must be replaced; parts are not serviced separately.

Fig. 7: Removing Rear Servo Operating Lever

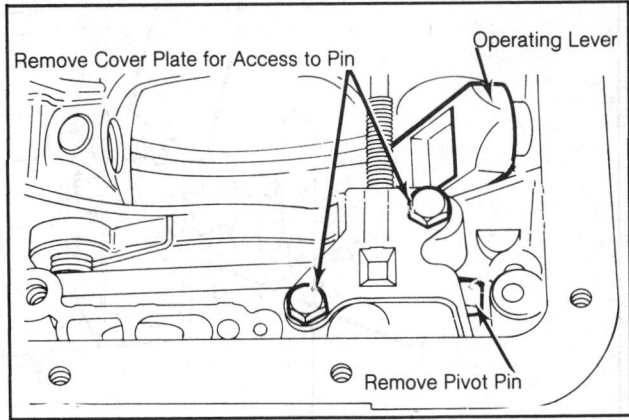

Remove Cover Plate for Access to Pin
Operating Lever
Remove Pivot Pin

Reassembly

Reverse disassembly procedure and note the following: Coat all components with transmission fluid before installing into bodies. Make sure check ball and spring are installed in correct main body passage. See Fig. 8. Always use a new strainer filter gasket when assembling.

CAUTION: Do not overtighten valve body attaching bolts and screws.

PLANETARY CARRIER & ONE-WAY CLUTCH

Inspection

Check planetary gear teeth for chipping or scoring (light scoring is acceptable). Make sure all gears rotate freely by hand, and that end play of gears is not excessive. Inspect bushing in hub of planetary carrier for wear. If any part of carrier is worn or damaged, complete carrier must be replaced. Withdraw one-way clutch roller assembly from carrier and inspect for worn or broken rollers and damage to outer race. If any one-way clutch component is damaged, replace roller and outer race assembly.

NOTE: When installing roller assembly into outer race (in carrier), make sure lip of roller cage faces outward.

JAGUAR VALVE BODY SPRING IDENTIFICATION CHART

Valve Spring	Length In. (mm)	Diameter In. (mm)	Number Of Coils	Color
Secondary Regulator Valve	2.59 (65.8)	.480-.490 (12.3-12.4)	23	Blue
Primary Regulator Valve	2.94 (74.6)	.604-.610 (15.3-15.5)	14	Blue
Servo Orifice Control Valve	1.00 (25.5)	.198-.208 (5.0-5.3)	17	Yellow
2-3 Shift Valve	1.59 (40.4)	.275-.285 (6.9-7.2)	22.5	Yellow
1-2 Shift Valve	1.09 (27.7)	.230-.240 (5.8-6.1)	13	Natural
Throttle Return Valve	0.80 (20.5)	.136-.146 (3.4-3.7)	28	Yellow
Modulator Valve	1.07 (27.1)	.150-.160 (3.8-4.1)	19	Natural
Throttle Valve	1.18 (29.9)	.230-.240 (5.8-6.1)	18	Green
Dump Ball Valve	0.70 (17.7)	.210-.230 (5.3-5.8)	16	Natural/White

Automatic Transmissions

BORG-WARNER MODEL 66 (Cont.)

Fig. 8: Exploded View of Valve Body Assembly

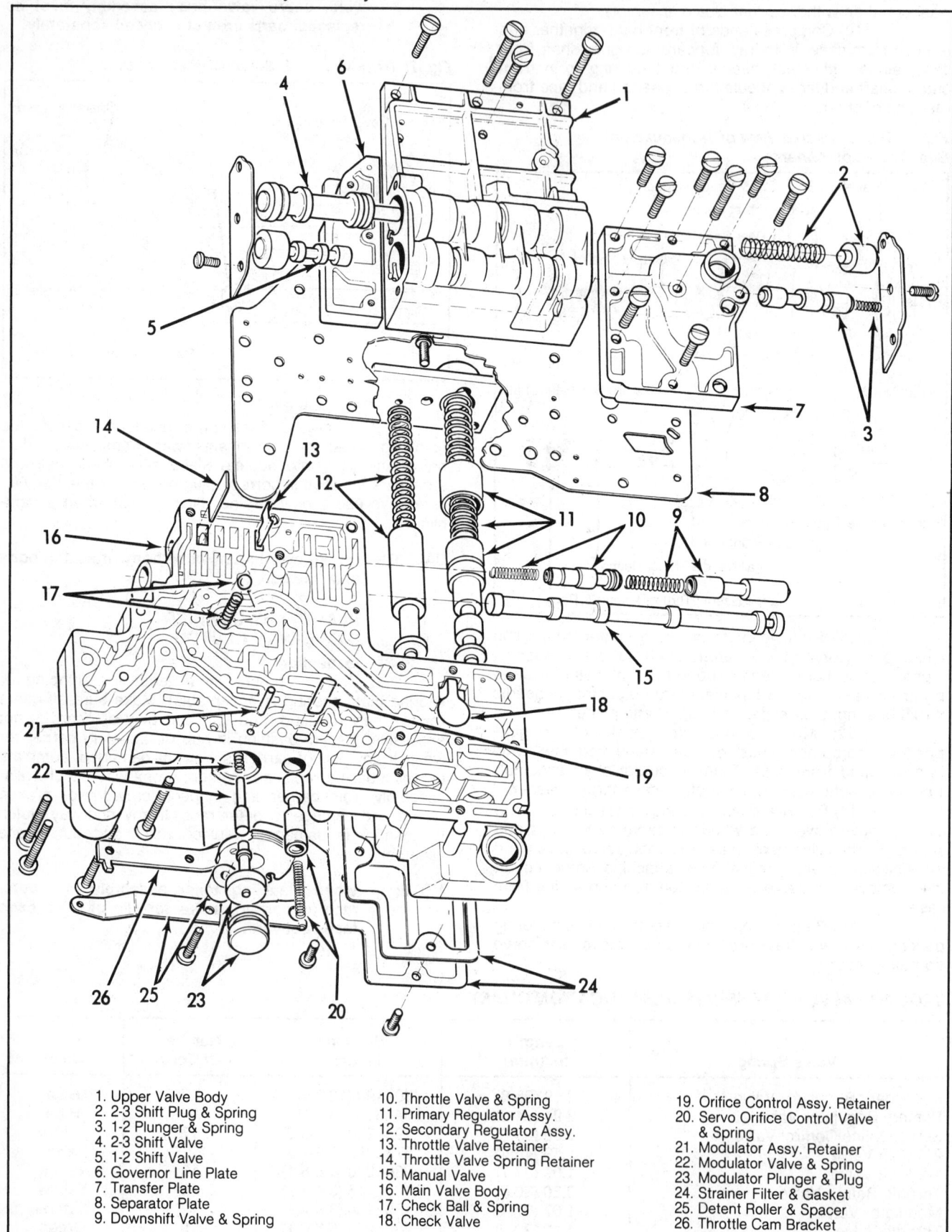

1. Upper Valve Body
2. 2-3 Shift Plug & Spring
3. 1-2 Plunger & Spring
4. 2-3 Shift Valve
5. 1-2 Shift Valve
6. Governor Line Plate
7. Transfer Plate
8. Separator Plate
9. Downshift Valve & Spring

10. Throttle Valve & Spring
11. Primary Regulator Assy.
12. Secondary Regulator Assy.
13. Throttle Valve Retainer
14. Throttle Valve Spring Retainer
15. Manual Valve
16. Main Valve Body
17. Check Ball & Traping
18. Check Valve

19. Orifice Control Assy. Retainer
20. Servo Orifice Control Valve
    & Spring
21. Modulator Assy. Retainer
22. Modulator Valve & Spring
23. Modulator Plunger & Plug
24. Strainer Filter & Gasket
25. Detent Roller & Spacer
26. Throttle Cam Bracket

BORG-WARNER MODEL 66 (Cont.)

COMPONENT DISASSEMBLY & REASSEMBLY

VALVE BODY ASSEMBLY

Disassembly

1) Remove manual valve from body. Remove screws retaining filter screen (and adapter if equipped) to body and remove filter screen. Remove 6 upper valve body retaining screws from lower valve body, invert valve body, and remove 4 screws retaining upper body and cam mounting arm. Remove cam mounting arm, withdraw downshift valve and spring, then separate upper body from assembly.

2) Remove screws securing end plates to upper body and remove plates. Remove 1-2 shift valve, plunger and spring, and 2-3 shift valve, plunger and spring. Remove retaining screws and lift transfer plate off main valve body.

3) Loosen, but do not remove, governor pressure plate retaining screws. Hold separator plate in contact with main valve body, remove governor pressure plate retaining screws, and remove plate. Carefully remove separator plate from main body, noting position of ball valve and spring.

4) From main valve body, remove following parts: Retainer, spring, and servo orifice control valve; retaining pin, plug, spring, and modulator valve; 2 retainers, spring, and throttle valve. Remove retaining screw and detent roller and spring assembly.

5) Remove screws securing regulator valve retaining plate to main valve body, slowly release pressure on plate, then withdraw plate, spring, sleeve and primary regulator valve, and spring and secondary regulator valve.

Inspection

Clean all parts in solvent and air dry. Check all valves, plugs, and sleeves for wear, burrs, and scoring. Make sure all valves and plugs move freely in valve body bores. Also check all valve springs for distortion or collapsed coils.

FORWARD SUN GEAR SHAFT

Inspection

Check oil passages in shaft for obstructions; clear out with compressed air only. Inspect splines, seal ring grooves, and gear teeth for damage (minor damage may be removed with a fine abrasive). Check large and small needle thrust bearings for damage and replace as necessary.

REAR CLUTCH

Disassembly

Remove clutch pack retaining snap ring, then withdraw pressure plate, 5 steel clutch plates, and 5 line discs. Using a compressor tool, compress piston return spring, remove snap ring, then withdraw tool, spring retainer, and piston return spring. Remove clutch piston by applying air pressure to fluid supply passage in clutch hub. Remove inner seal from clutch drum and outer seal from piston.

Inspection

Check clutch drum for scoring or wear and all fluid passages for obstructions. Clear passages with compressed air only. Inspect piston for damage and free operation of check ball. Check all lined discs for wear and distortion; all lined discs must be flat. Check steel clutch plates for scoring or burrs; replace any plates found

damaged. Also check steel plates for coning; plates must be coned at least .010" (.25 mm). Inspect needle roller bearing in clutch hub for wear. If bearing is worn or damaged, replace complete clutch housing.

Fig. 9: Disassembled View of Planetary Carrier and One-Way Clutch Assembly

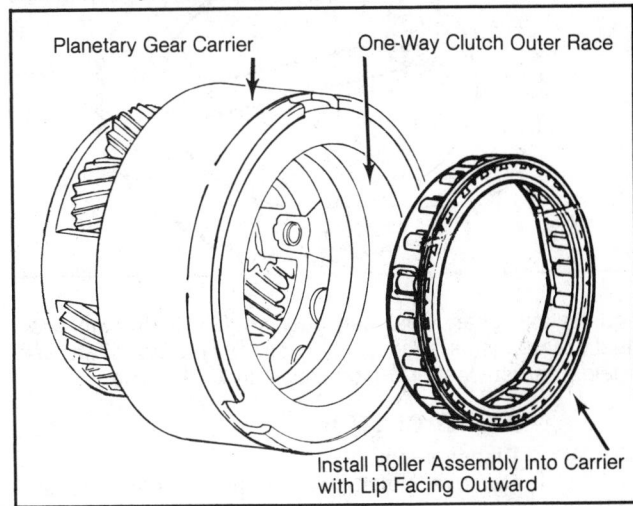

Planetary Gear Carrier

One-Way Clutch Outer Race

Install Roller Assembly Into Carrier with Lip Facing Outward

Fig. 10: Exploded View of Rear Clutch Assembly

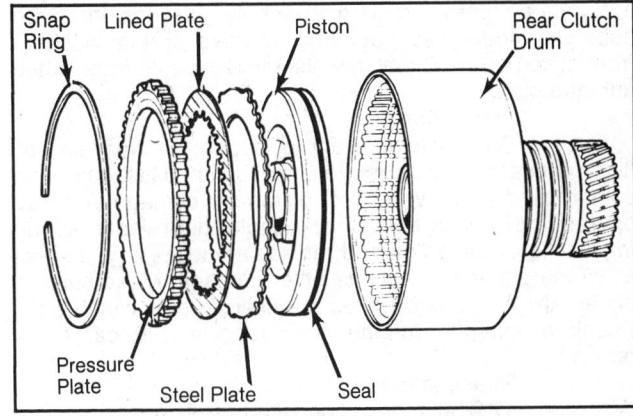

Snap Ring

Lined Plate

Piston

Rear Clutch Drum

Pressure Plate

Steel Plate

Seal

Reassembly

1) Coat new piston seals with petrolatum and install onto piston and clutch hub. Position a piston installing tool into clutch drum, coat piston with transmission fluid, and install into bottom of drum. Position piston return spring and retainer on top of piston, compress assembly, and install retaining snap ring.

NOTE: If new lined discs are used, soak in transmission fluid before installation.

2) Install clutch pack into drum, starting with steel plate and alternating lined discs and steel plates until correct number are installed (5 steel and 5 lined). Make sure all steel plate cones are facing in same direction. Install pressure plate into clutch drum (flat side downward) and install clutch pack retaining snap ring.

3) Install new sealing rings onto clutch drum hub and lock ends (if used). Install new seal rings onto forward sun gear shaft, then position shaft in a holding fixture with long end of shaft upward. Coat small needle thrust bearing with petrolatum and install over shaft and

Fig. 11: Checking Rear Clutch Steel Plate Coning

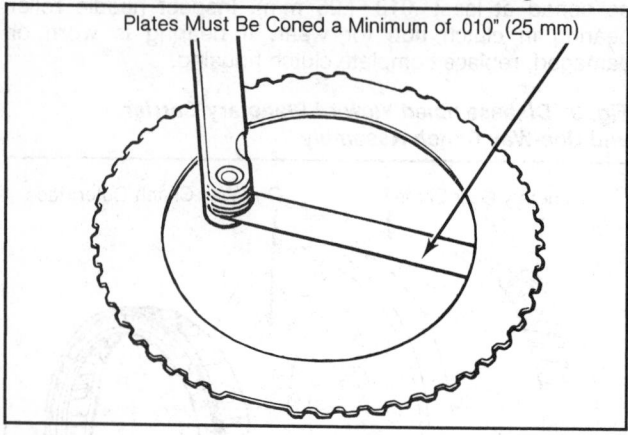

Plates Must Be Coned a Minimum of .010" (25 mm)

against sun gear. Coat sun gear shaft with transmission fluid, then install rear clutch assembly onto shaft and against thrust washer. Place assembly to the side.

FRONT CLUTCH

Disassembly

Remove clutch pack retaining snap ring and withdraw turbine shaft, thrust washer, clutch hub, and clutch pack from drum. Remove large retaining snap ring and diaphragm return spring. Remove clutch piston by applying air pressure to fluid supply passage in clutch hub. On models so equipped, remove spring washers from clutch drum. On all models, remove seals from clutch hub and piston.

Inspection

Check clutch drum for scoring or wear and all fluid passages for obstructions. Clear passages with compressed air only. Inspect piston for damage and free operation of check ball. Check diaphragm release spring for cracks or distortion and replace as necessary. Inspect all clutch plates for wear or other damage. Make sure all plates are flat; coned plates are used in rear clutch only. Check bushing in turbine shaft for wear; if damaged, replace.

Reassembly

1) Coat a new seal with petrolatum and install onto clutch piston. On models with an "O" ring type seal

on clutch hub, coat seal with petrolatum and install. On all other models, install spring washers into bottom of piston and follow with inner seal.

NOTE: Open end of seal should face out of piston.

2) Position a piston installing tool into clutch drum, coat all parts with transmission fluid, and install piston into drum. Install diaphragm spring into drum with cone facing upward, then install retaining snap ring.

3) With rear clutch and sun gear shaft assembly again positioned on bench, install steel backing washer and bronze thrust washer over sun gear shaft and against rear clutch. Make sure seal ring gaps on sun gear shaft are staggered, and that rear clutch lined disc splines are aligned, then install forward clutch drum and piston assembly into rear clutch.

NOTE: Make sure all parts are fully mated.

4) Install pressure plate into front clutch drum and against diaphragm spring snap ring. Follow with clutch pack, starting with a lined plate and alternating steel and lined plates until all plates are installed.

5) Align inner splines of lined plates and install clutch hub, making sure it fully engages all plates. Position a new thrust washer into recess of hub. Install turbine shaft and snap ring, making sure ring is correctly seated in groove of clutch drum.

CAUTION: With all parts assembled, do not allow front and rear clutches to separate as damage to seal rings on sun gear shaft may occur.

OIL PUMP

Disassembly

1) Remove bolts and screw retaining pump housing to cover, then separate cover and housing. Mark mating surfaces of pump drive and driven gears with a die marker for reassembly reference.

CAUTION: Do not punch or scribe marks in gears.

2) Remove "O" ring seal from outer diameter of pump housing, and converter lip seal from front of pump housing.

Fig. 12: Exploded View of Front Clutch Assembly

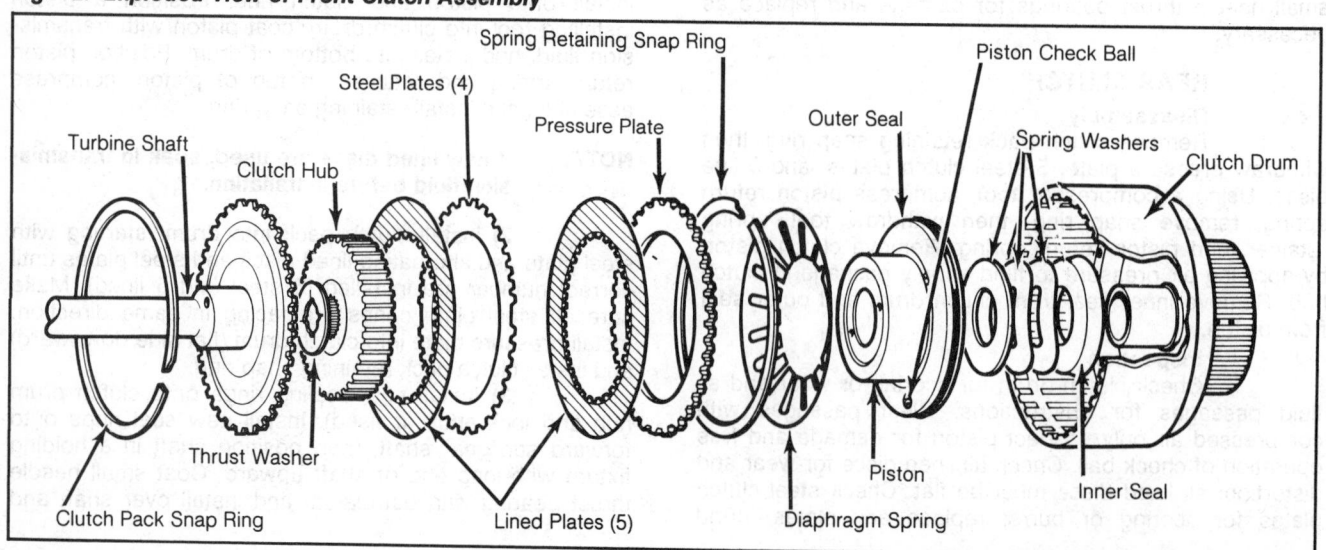

Turbine Shaft

Clutch Hub

Steel Plates (4)

Spring Retaining Snap Ring

Pressure Plate

Outer Seal

Piston Check Ball

Spring Washers

Clutch Drum

Thrust Washer

Clutch Pack Snap Ring

Lined Plates (5)

Diaphragm Spring

Piston

Inner Seal

BORG-WARNER MODEL 66 (Cont.)

Inspection

Check surfaces of housing and cover, gears, splines, and bushings for scoring, wear or other damage. If any part shows evidence of wear, entire assembly must be replaced; parts are not serviced separately.

Fig. 13: Exploded View of Oil Pump Assembly

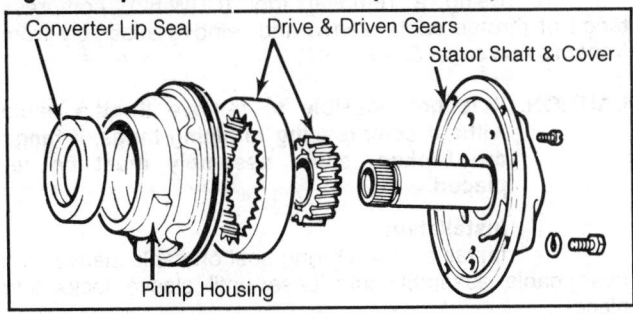

Reassembly

Soak new converter lip seal and housing "O" ring seal in transmission fluid and install into pump housing. Install drive and driven gears into housing, aligning marks made at disassembly. Install cover into housing, align bolt and screw holes, then install and tighten attaching bolts and screw. Rotate pump gears to check for freedom of movement.

FRONT & REAR SERVOS

Disassembly

Remove spring from servo piston, then withdraw piston from servo body. Remove seals from piston and body. Clean all parts in solvent. Blow dry with compressed air, clearing out all lubrication passages.

Fig. 14: Exploded View of Front Servo Assembly

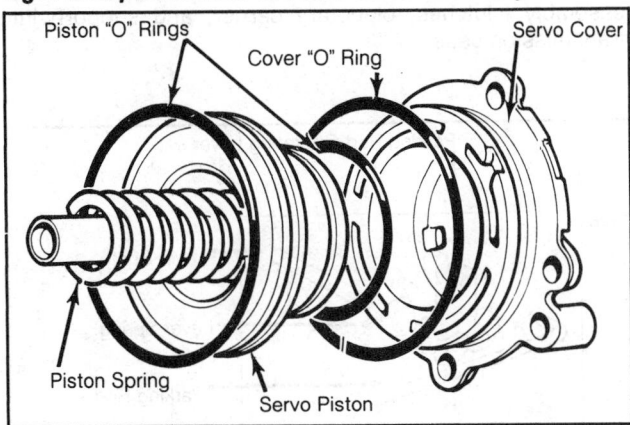

Reassembly

Coat new seals with petrolatum and install onto piston and servo body. Position spring on servo piston, then place assembly to the side.

GOVERNOR

Disassembly

Depress governor shaft to expose snap ring, remove snap ring and weight from outside of assembly, withdraw governor shaft, spring, and valve from inside governor body. Wash all parts in solvent and air dry. Check all parts for wear or damage, and spring especially for distortion. If any part of governor is found to be damaged, entire governor assembly must be replaced.

Fig. 15: Exploded View of Rear Servo Assembly

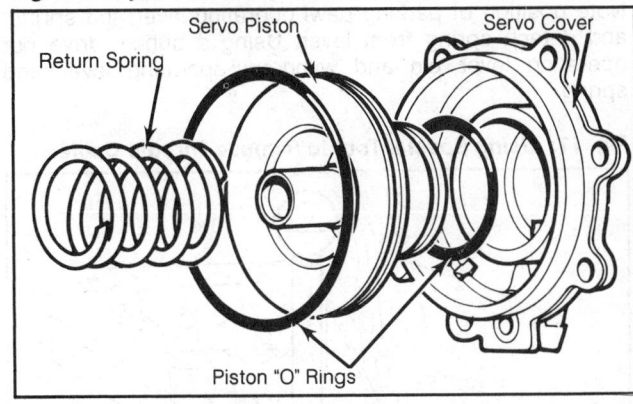

Reassembly

Lubricate all parts with transmission fluid. Install governor valve, spring, and shaft into body, position weight on shaft, then install snap ring. Check all parts for freedom of movement. If governor shaft shows signs of sticking, governor assembly must be replaced.

Fig. 16: Exploded View of Governor Assembly

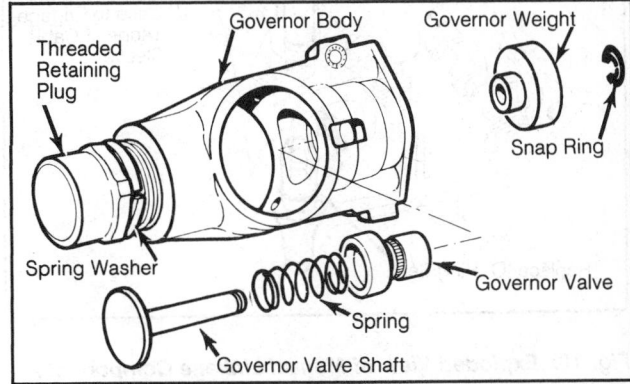

OUTPUT SHAFT & RING GEAR

Disassembly

Remove seal rings from groove in output shaft. Remove large retaining snap ring and withdraw output shaft from ring gear.

Inspection

Check all passages in output shaft for obstructions and clear using compressed air only. Inspect splines, seal ring grooves, and gear teeth of shaft and ring gear for burrs, scoring, or other damage (minor damage may be removed with a fine abrasive). If any part is worn or damaged, replace.

Reassembly

Position output shaft in ring gear and install retaining snap ring. Install new seal rings into grooves of output shaft, taking care to stagger ring gaps.

MANUAL LINKAGE

Disassembly

1) Note position of parking pawl spring, then detach spring from pawl. Remove parking pawl shaft from outside of case, and withdraw pawl and spring from inside case. Remove clip from manual shaft and pin retaining detent lever. Withdraw manual shaft, detent lever, spacer, and washers from case.

BORG-WARNER MODEL 66 (Cont.)

2) Disconnect parking rod from parking pawl. Note position of parking pawl operating lever and spring, and detach spring from lever. Using a punch, drive out operating lever pin and withdraw operating lever and spring.

Fig. 17: Using Special Tool to Remove Throttle Cable

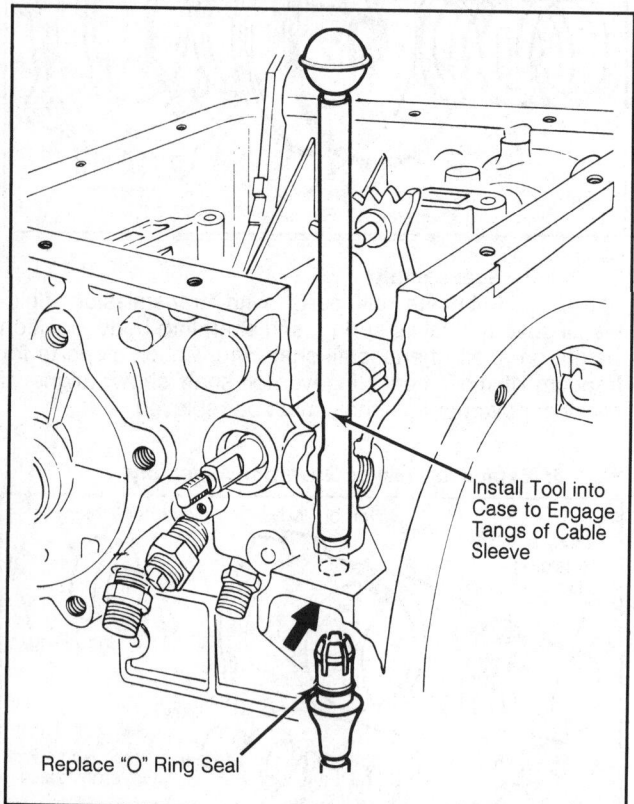

Install Tool into Case to Engage Tangs of Cable Sleeve

Replace "O" Ring Seal

Reassembly

Reverse disassembly procedure. Make sure all parts move freely without binding after reassembly.

THROTTLE CABLE

Removal

Using a removal tool (CBW.62), compress tangs of throttle cable sleeve and remove assembly from transmission case. *See Fig. 17.*

CAUTION: It is not possible to remove throttle cable without compressing retaining tangs; if tangs are broken, cable assembly must be replaced.

Installation

Install a new "O" ring seal on cable sleeve, and push cable assembly into case until sleeve locks into place.

TRANSMISSION REASSEMBLY

1) Coat large tabbed thrust washer with petrolatum and install into case, making sure tabs engage slots in case. Install output shaft and ring gear assembly into case and through thrust washer, making sure washer is not displaced. Place front and rear bands in position in case. While holding clutch assemblies (previously assembled), install large needle thrust bearing and race onto sun gear shaft, with flange facing away from clutches.

2) Install center support, clutch and sun gear assembly into planet carrier. Rotate center support until holes on outer diameter are in approximate alignment with center support bolt holes in case, then install entire assembly (clutches, planetary carrier, and support) into transmission case.

Fig. 18: Exploded View of Manual Linkage Components

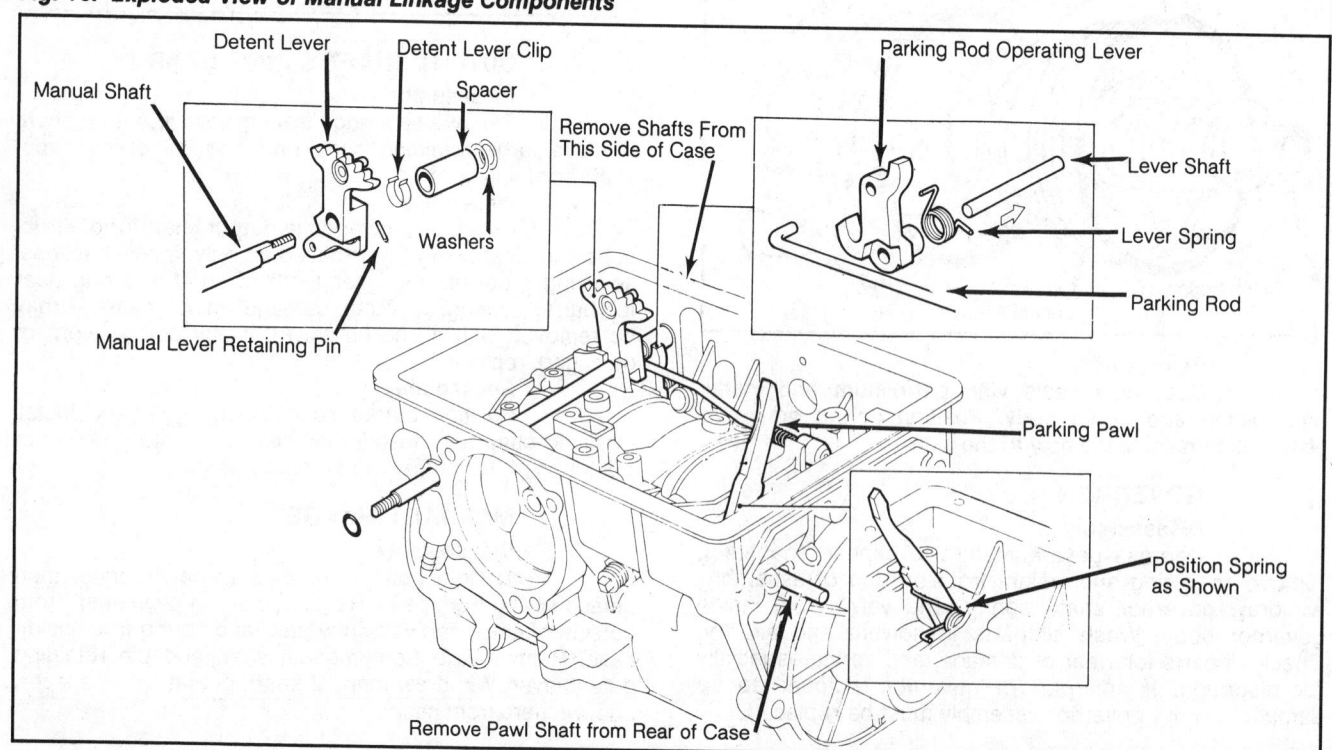

Detent Lever

Manual Shaft

Detent Lever Clip

Spacer

Washers

Manual Lever Retaining Pin

Remove Shafts From This Side of Case

Parking Rod Operating Lever

Lever Shaft

Lever Spring

Parking Rod

Parking Pawl

Position Spring as Shown

Remove Pawl Shaft from Rear of Case

BORG-WARNER MODEL 66 (Cont.)

Fig. 19: Installation of Output Shaft Into Transmission Case

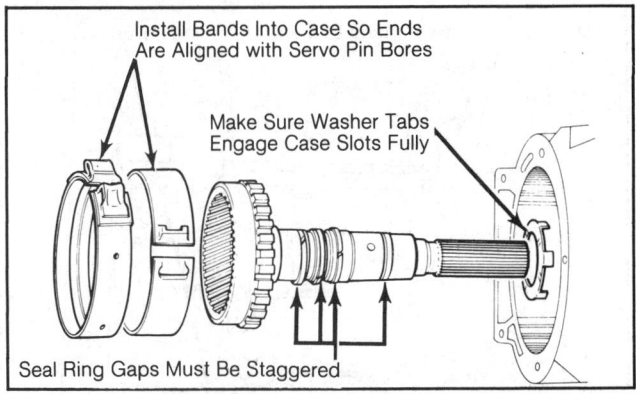

Install Bands Into Case So Ends Are Aligned with Servo Pin Bores

Make Sure Washer Tabs Engage Case Slots Fully

Seal Ring Gaps Must Be Staggered

Fig. 20: Installing Oil Pump Onto Transmission Case

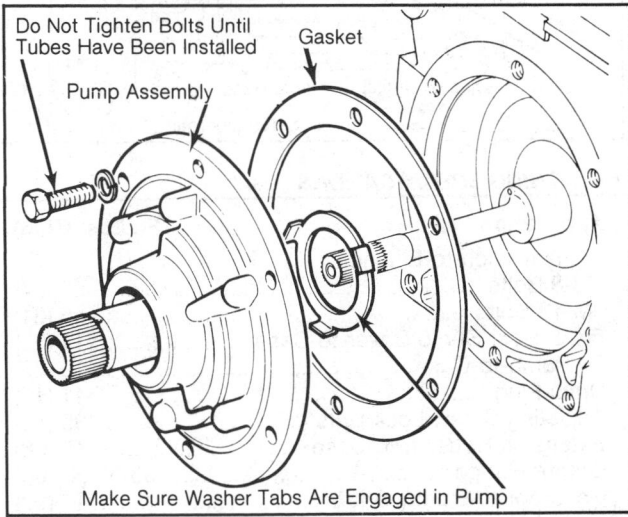

Do Not Tighten Bolts Until Tubes Have Been Installed

Gasket

Pump Assembly

Make Sure Washer Tabs Are Engaged in Pump

Fig. 21: Installing Oil Tubes Into Case

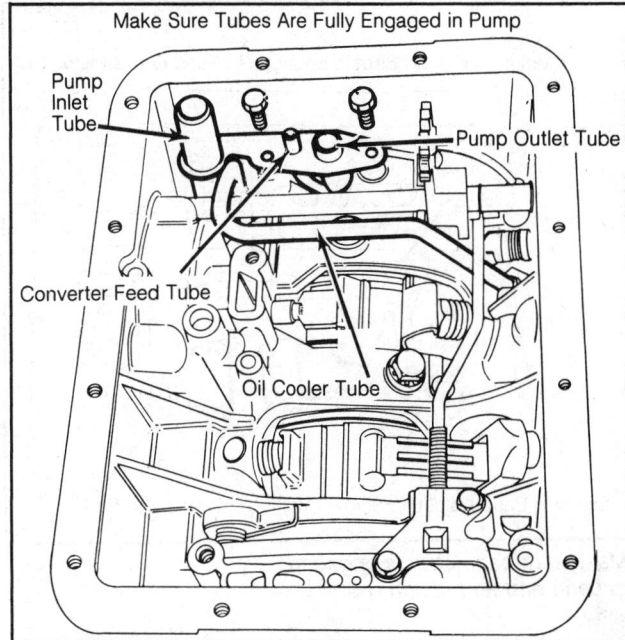

Make Sure Tubes Are Fully Engaged in Pump

Pump Inlet Tube

Pump Outlet Tube

Converter Feed Tube

Oil Cooler Tube

Make sure tubes are fully engaged in pump.

3) Position a new thrust washer and gasket onto rear of oil pump, mount oil pump to transmission case, and install but do not tighten attaching bolts. Install a new "O" ring seal on pump inlet tube, then install inlet tube along with outlet tube and converter feed tube into oil pump housing (inside case). Make sure tubes are correctly positioned, install tube retaining plate and attaching bolts, then tighten oil pump-to-case bolts. At this time, also install oil cooler tube into case.

CAUTION: To prevent damage to internal parts, do not allow components to separate when installing.

4) On rear of case, install 3 oil tubes into case and governor support. Slide governor unit onto output shaft and install plug and spring washer, making sure plug enters BLIND hole in output shaft.

5) Install speedometer drive gear onto output shaft and against governor. Install a new seal into extension housing, position a new extension-to-case gasket, then install housing onto case, tightening nuts and bolts in a diagonal sequence. Install output flange onto shaft, engage parking pawl with parking gear, then install flange attaching bolt or nut and tighten.

6) Position a dial indicator assembly on front of transmission case with button of indicator contacting turbine shaft. With a screwdriver inserted between front clutch and front of case, pry gear train fully rearward. Zero dial indicator. Next, with screwdriver between parking gear and rear clutch, pry gear train forward and note reading on gauge. Reading should be .008-.029" (.20-.73 mm); if not, repeat steps **3)**, **4)** and **5)**, installing a thicker or thinner washer as required behind oil pump.

7) Coat a new "O" ring with petrolatum and install onto speedometer driven gear housing. Install driven gear assembly into extension housing and install retainer. Position a new gasket on front servo, mount servo on case, and install attaching bolts. Install front band strut into servo rod and band, then screw in front band adjusting screw until it engages band end. Do not tighten screw or lock nut at this time.

Fig. 22: Measuring Gear Train End Play Using a Dial Indicator

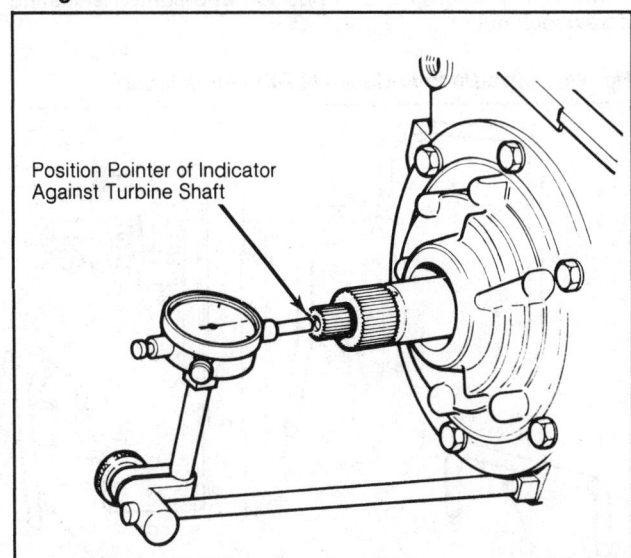

Position Pointer of Indicator Against Turbine Shaft

Automatic Transmissions

BORG-WARNER MODEL 66 (Cont.)

Fig. 23: *Installing Front Band Strut and Adjusting Screw*

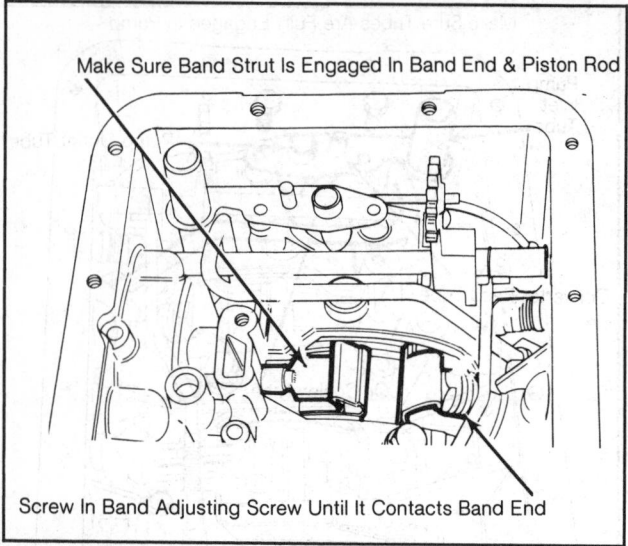

Make Sure Band Strut Is Engaged In Band End & Piston Rod

Screw In Band Adjusting Screw Until It Contacts Band End

*Make sure band strut is engaged
in band end and piston rod.*

Fig. 25: *Installing Rear Band Strut and Adjusting Screw*

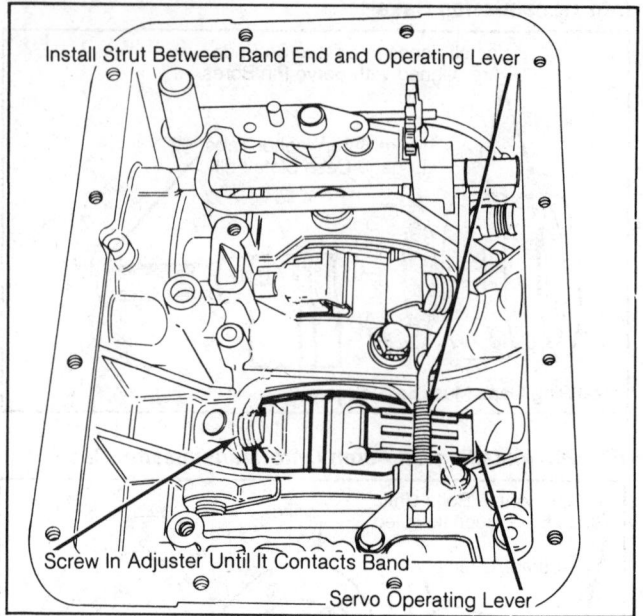

Install Strut Between Band End and Operating Lever

Screw In Adjuster Until It Contacts Band

Servo Operating Lever

8) If removed, install rear servo operating lever in transmission case. Install new "O" rings and gasket on rear servo body and mount servo on case. Ensure servo rod engages operating lever. Install rear band strut between band end and operating lever, screw in band adjusting screw until contact is just made with band, then tighten servo body-to-case bolts. At this time, install the one oil tube which will be partially covered by valve body. *See tube "D" in Fig. 24.*

9) Install valve body into case, making sure manual valve engages detent lever and that valve body fully engages oil pump tubes. Install valve body-to-case bolts, noting that shortest bolt is installed at front. Connect kickdown cable to cam, then install valve body oil tubes. *See Fig. 24.*

10) Install oil pan using a new gasket. Install converter housing, oil filler tube, and breather. To complete assembly, adjust both bands as follows: Tighten band adjusting screw to 60 INCH lbs. (7 N.m.), back out screw 3/4 of a turn, hold in position and tighten adjusting screw lock nut.

TIGHTENING SPECIFICATIONS

Application	Ft. Lbs. (N.m)
Transmission-to-Engine	
M-8 Bolts	25 (34)
M-12 Bolts	45 (61)
Frt. & Rear Servo Cover-to-Case	17 (23)
Oil Pump-to-Case	19 (26)
Drain Plug	11 (15)
Adjusting Screw Lock Nuts	35 (48)
Extension Housing-to-Case	43 (58)
Output Flange	35-50 (47-68)
Governor-to-Output Shaft	17 (23)
	INCH Lbs. (N.m.)
Oil Pan-to-Case	72 (8.1)
Oil Pump Cover-to-Housing Screw	25 (3.0)
Pressure Test Plug	84 (9.5)
Valve Body-to-Case	84 (9.5)
All Other Valve Body Screws	24 (3.0)
Oil Pump Tube Plate	24 (3.0)
Parking Pawl Plate	60 (6.8)

Fig. 24: *Valve Body-to-Case Oil Tube Installation*

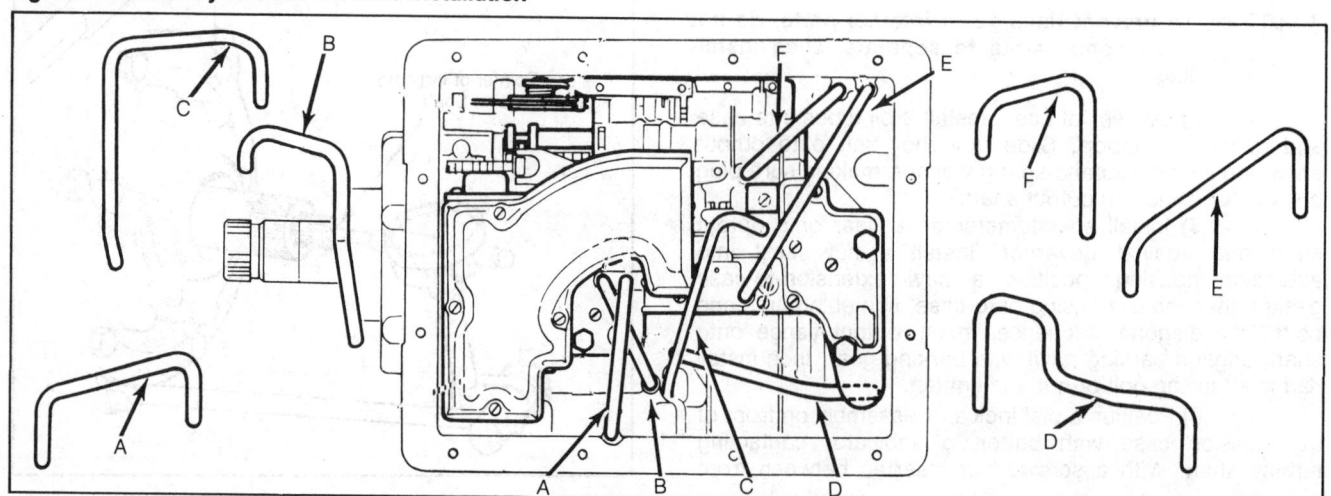

CHAMP & COLT

DESCRIPTION

The Champ and Colt KM170 automatic trans-axle assembly consists of: Automatic transmission; torque converter; transfer assembly; and the differential. The complete transaxle assembly is contained in a single housing. Both units use a common oil sump and oil supply. The automatic transmission consists of a front and rear clutch, kickdown band, low-reverse brake, one-way clutch, valve body and a planetary gear set. Transfer assembly consists of a drive gear, idler gear, driven gear and a transfer shaft. The differential consists of a differential case, ring gear, pinion shaft and gears, speedometer gear and 2 side gears.

LUBRICATION & ADJUSTMENT

See the appropriate article in AUTOMATIC TRANSMISSION SERVICING Section.

SERVICE (IN-VEHICLE)

AXLE SHAFTS

Removal

1) Remove front wheel dust cap and loosen lock nut. Raise vehicle and remove tires and undercover panel. Remove lower ball joint and strut from lower control arm. Drain transaxle fluid.

2) Insert pry bar between transaxle case and Double Offset Joint (D.O.J.) or Tripod Joint (T.J.). Apply pressure to the tool handle and force axle shaft from transaxle.

Fig. 1: View of Drive Axle Removal

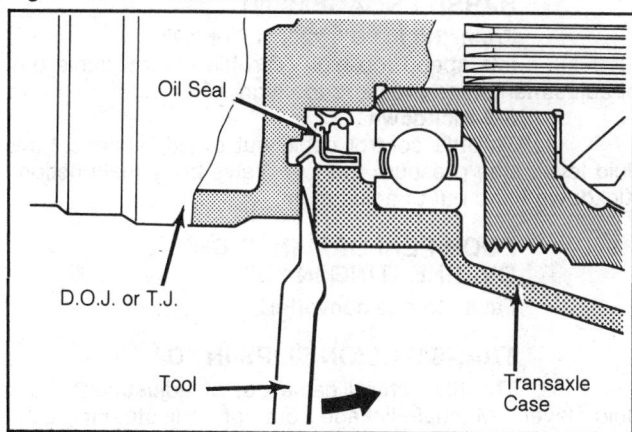

NOTE: **Replace side retainer ring each time the drive shaft is removed from transaxle case.**

3) Force drive shaft out of hub with axle puller (CT-1003). When the drive shaft is forced out, do not let spacer fall out of hub (inner side).

Disassembly (Birfield Joint Type)

Remove inner joint boot. Remove circlip from joint and remove outer race. Remove snap ring and inner race. Remove cage and balls as an assembly.

NOTE: **Do not disassemble inner bearing assembly as they are mated parts and should not be disturbed.**

Fig. 2: Exploded View of Drive Shaft (Birfield Joint Type)

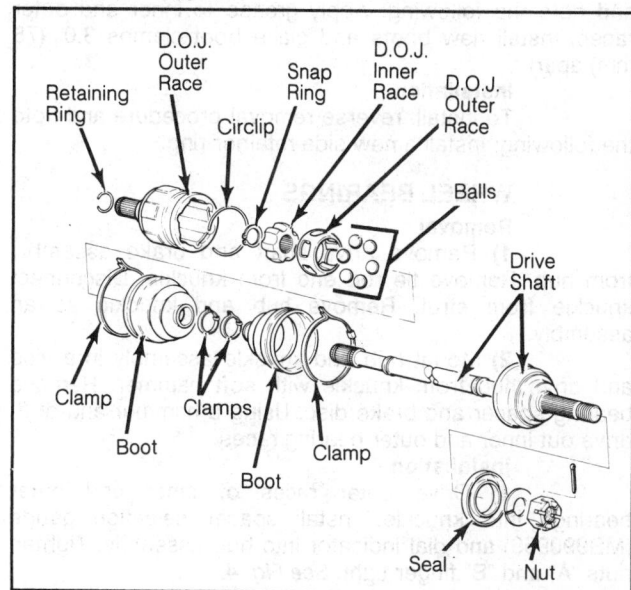

Reassembly

To assemble, reverse disassembly procedure and note the following: Apply grease to inner and outer races. Install CV joint assembly on shaft with chamfered edge of inner race facing outer edge of shaft. Install new boots and place boot clamps 3.5" (90 mm) apart.

Disassembly (Tripod-Rzeppa Joint Type)

Remove inner joint boots. Pull drive shaft out from inner case. Remove snap ring and take out spider assembly. Clean, but do not disassemble, spider assembly. Remove remaining boots.

Fig. 3: Exploded View of Drive Shaft (Tripod-Rzeppa Joint Type)

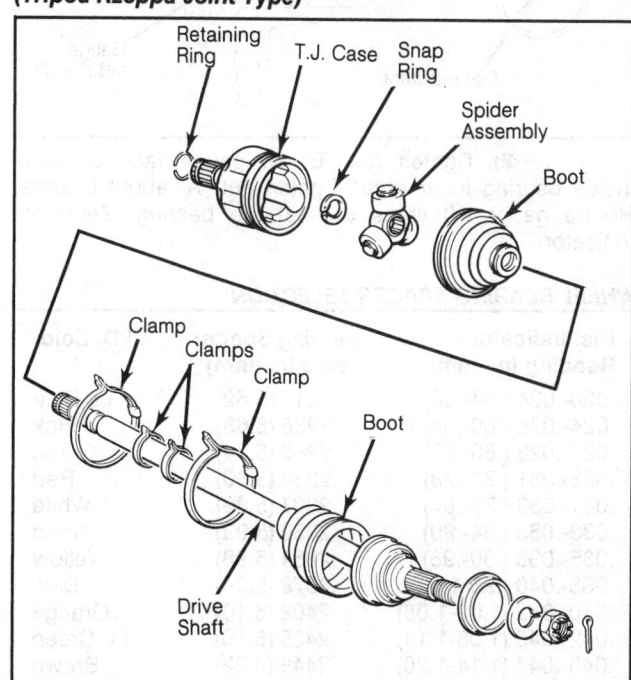

CHAMP & COLT (Cont.)

Reassembly

To assemble, reverse disassembly procedure and note the following: Apply grease to inner and outer races. Install new boots and place boot clamps 3.0" (75 mm) apart.

Installation

To install, reverse removal procedure and note the following: Install a new side retainer ring.

WHEEL BEARINGS

Removal

1) Remove drive shaft and brake assembly from hub. Remove tie rod end from knuckle. Disconnect knuckle from strut. Remove hub and knuckle as an assembly.

2) Mount hub and knuckle assembly in a vise and drive hub from knuckle with soft hammer. Remove bearing spacer and brake disc. Using a hammer and drift, drive out inner and outer bearing races.

Installation

1) Drive outer races of inner and outer bearings into knuckle. Install spacer selection gauge (MB990959) and dial indicator into hub assembly. Tighten nuts "A" and "B" finger tight. *See Fig. 4.*

Fig. 4: Installing Gauge to Measure Bearing Spacer Selection

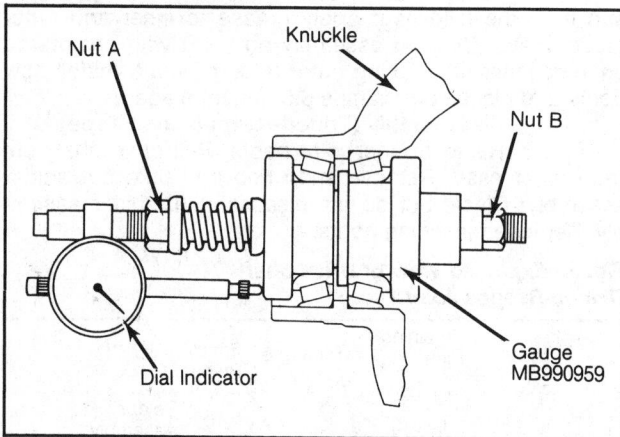

2) Tighten nut "B" so gauge face contacts inside bearing inner race. Tighten nut "A" about 5 turns. Rotate gauge 10 times to seat the bearing. Zero dial indicator.

WHEEL BEARING SPACER SELECTION

Dial Indicator Reading In. (mm)	Bearing Spacer Size In. (mm)	I.D. Color
.020-.024 (.54-.60)	.2212 (5.62)	Lt. Blue
.024-.026 (.60-.66)	.2236 (5.68)	Pink
.026-.028 (.66-.72)	.2260 (5.74)	Green
.028-.031 (.72-.78)	.2283 (5.80)	Red
.031-.033 (.78-.84)	.2307 (5.86)	White
.033-.035 (.84-.90)	.2330 (5.92)	None
.035-.038 (.90-.96)	.2354 (5.98)	Yellow
.038-.040 (.96-1.02)	.2378 (6.04)	Blue
.040-.042 (1.02-1.08)	.2402 (6.10)	Orange
.042-.045 (1.08-1.14)	.2425 (6.16)	Lt. Green
.045-.047 (1.14-1.20)	.2449 (6.22)	Brown
.047-.050 (1.20-1.26)	.2472 (6.28)	Gray
.050-.052 (1.26-1.32)	.2496 (6.34)	Navy Blue
.052-.054 (1.32-1.38)	.2520 (6.40)	Vermilion

3) Loosen nut "B" until pointer of dial indicator stops, and read dial indicator. Select proper size bearing spacer according to the following table.

4) Remove special tool, dial indicator and bearing inner races from the knuckle. Apply grease to knuckle, oil seals and bearings. Mount brake disc to hub and tighten bolts evenly.

5) Install outer wheel bearing, then press in outer oil seal. Hold inner race of outer bearing with bearing holder (MB990776-A), then press hub into knuckle.

TROUBLE SHOOTING

NO STARTER OPERATION IN "P" OR "N"

Faulty or misadjusted inhibitor switch. Manual linkage out of adjustment.

NO DRIVE IN "D"

Throttle control cable out of adjustment. Low fluid level. Manual linkage out of adjustment. Line pressure too low. Faulty rear clutch and piston. Faulty overrunning clutch. Valve body malfunction. Defective oil pump.

NO DRIVE IN "R"

Throttle control cable out of adjustment. Low fluid level. Manual linkage out of adjustment. Line pressure too low. Valve body malfunction. Faulty front clutch and piston. Faulty low reverse brake and piston. Missing "O" ring in front clutch circuit between valve and body case. Defective oil pump.

HARSH ENGAGEMENT

From "N" to "D", "2", "L" or "R"

Idle speed too high. Throttle control cable out of adjustment. Line pressure too high.

3-2 Kickdown

Throttle control cable out of adjustment. Low fluid level. Line pressure too low. Valve body malfunction. Kickdown band out of adjustment.

POOR PERFORMANCE OR OVERHEATING IN "D"

Faulty torque converter.

TRANSMISSION SLIPS IN "D"

Throttle control cable out of adjustment. Low fluid level. Manual linkage out of adjustment. Line pressure too low. Faulty rear clutch and piston. Faulty overrunning clutch. Valve body malfunction.

TRANSMISSION SLIPS IN "R"

Throttle control cable out of adjustment. Low fluid level. Manual linkage out of adjustment. Line pressure too low. Valve body malfunction. Faulty front clutch and piston. Faulty low-reverse brake and piston. Missing "O" ring in front clutch circuit between valve body and case.

TRANSMISSION SLIPS ON 1-2 UPSHIFT

Throttle control cable out of adjustment. Low fluid level. Line pressure too low. Valve body malfunction. Faulty kickdown band or servo. Kickdown band out of adjustment.

CHAMP & COLT (Cont.)

Fig. 5: *Cross-Sectional View of Champ and Colt KM170 Automatic Transaxle Assembly*

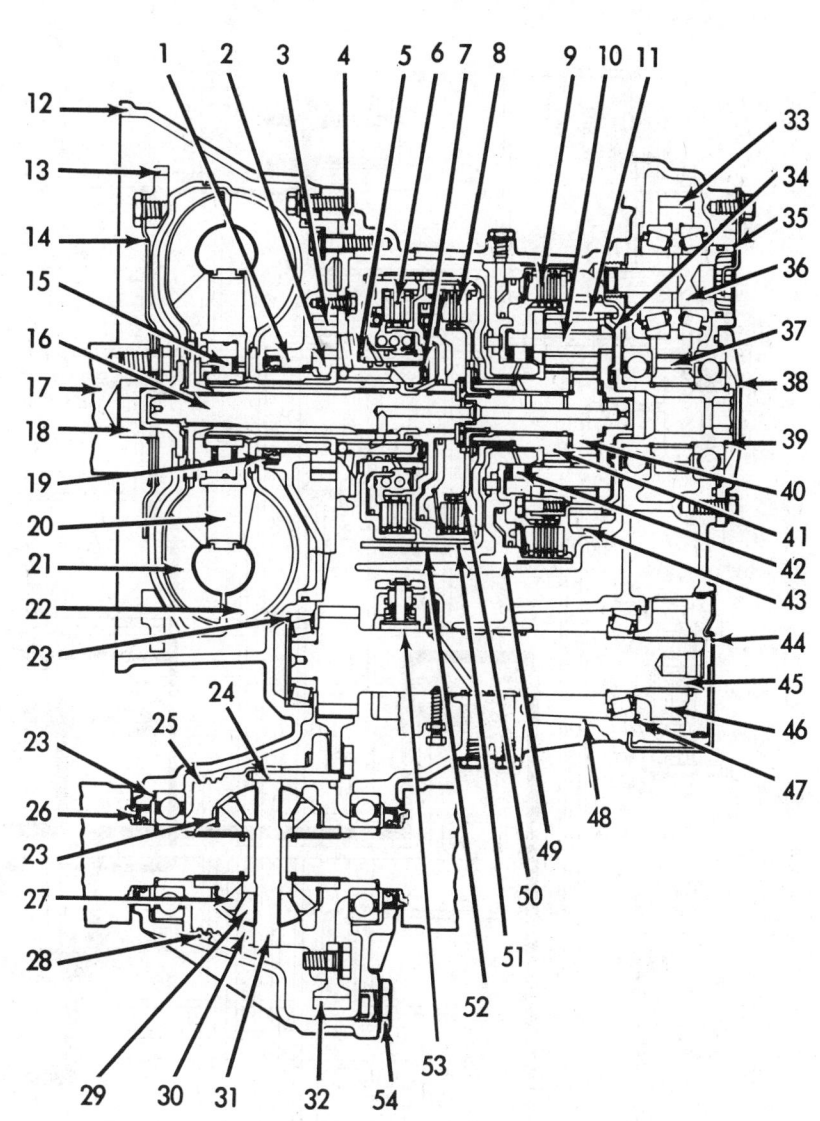

1. Oil Pump Housing	19. Oil Seal	37. Transfer Drive Gear
2. Oil Pump Drive Gear	20. Stator	38. Bearing Retainer
3. Oil Pump Driven Gear	21. Turbine	39. Selective Snap Ring
4. Reaction Shaft Support	22. Impeller	40. Forward Sun Gear
5. Selective Thrust Washer	23. Selective Spacer	41. Reverse Sun Gear
6. Front Clutch	24. Pinion Shaft Lock Pin	42. One-way Clutch
7. Selective Thrust Race	25. Speedometer Drive Gear	43. Parking Sprag
8. Rear Clutch	26. Oil Seal	44. Cover
9. Low-Reverse Brake	27. Side Gear	45. Transfer Shaft
10. Planetary Gear Set	28. Speedometer Driven Gear	46. Transfer Driven Gear
11. Annulus Gear	29. Pinion Gear	47. Snap Ring
12. Converter Housing	30. Differential Case	48. Transaxle Case
13. Starter Ring Gear	31. Pinion Shaft	49. Center Support
14. Flexible Plate	32. Differential Ring Gear	50. Clutch Hub
15. One-way Clutch	33. Transfer Idle Gear	51. Kickdown Drum
16. Input Shaft	34. Output Flange	52. Kickdown Band
17. Crankshaft	35. Lock Plate	53. Governor
18. Bushing	36. Transfer Idle Shaft	54. Drain Plug

Automatic Transmissions

CHAMP & COLT (Cont.)

Fig. 6: *Champ and Colt Model KM170 Hydraulic Circuits Diagram*

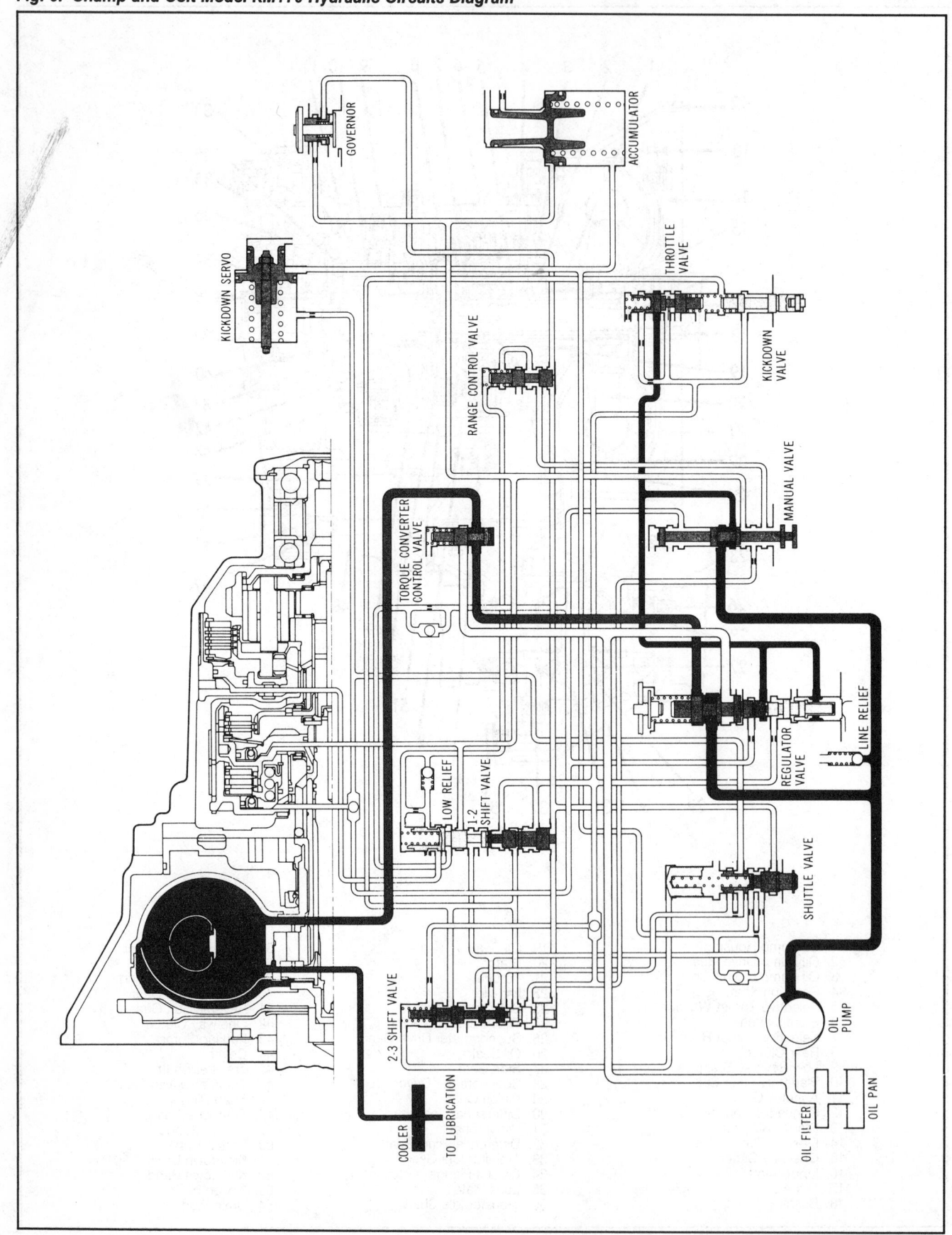

CHAMP & COLT (Cont.)

TRANSMISSION SLIPS ON 2-3 UPSHIFT

Throttle control cable out of adjustment. Low fluid level. Line pressure too low. Valve body malfunction. Faulty front clutch and piston.

TRANSMISSION SLIPS OR SHUDDERS ON STARTS IN "L"

Throttle control cable out of adjustment. Low fluid level. Manual linkage out of adjustment. Valve body malfunction.

NO DOWNSHIFT IN "D" TO "L" SHIFT

Manual shift linkage out of adjustment. Valve body malfunction. Faulty kickdown band or servo. Kickdown band out of adjustment.

NO 1-2 UPSHIFT OR WRONG SPEED 1-2 UPSHIFT

Throttle control cable out of adjustment. Low fluid level. Line pressure too low. Valve body malfunction. Governor valve malfunction. Faulty kickdown band or servo. Kickdown band out of adjustment.

NO 2-3 UPSHIFT OR WRONG SPEED 2-3 UPSHIFT

Throttle control cable out of adjustment. Low fluid level. Line pressure too low. Valve body malfunction. Faulty front clutch or piston. Governor valve malfunction.

UPSHIFT IN "L"

Manual linkage out of adjustment.

"P" WILL NOT ENGAGE

Manual linkage out of adjustment. Faulty parking mechanism.

CONVERTER NOISE

Loose converter bolts or warped flex plate. Defective oil pump. Interference of oil pump gear teeth, and wear of bushing.

TESTING

ROAD TEST

1) Before road testing, be certain that fluid level and condition, and control linkage adjustments have been checked and corrected as necessary. During test, transmission should upshift and downshift at approximately the same speeds as shown in *Shift Speeds chart.* All shifts may vary slightly due to production tolerances or tire size. The important factor is the quality of the shifts. All shifts should be smooth, responsive, and with no slippage or engine speed runaway.

2) Slippage or engine runaway in any gear usually indicates clutch or band problems. The slipping clutch or band in a particular gear can usually be identified by noting transmission operation in other selector positions and comparing internal units which are applied in these positions. *See Clutch and Band Application chart.*

3) The diagnoses process given can be used to detect any unit which slips and to confirm proper operation of good units. More testing is needed, if actual cause of a malfunction cannot be easily decided.

SHIFT SPEEDS CHART

Application	Shift Points (MPH)
Minimum Throttle	
1-2 Upshift	7-12
2-3 Upshift	11-16
3-1 Downshift	5-9
Full Throttle	
1-2 Upshift	30-37
2-3 Upshift	58-64
Kickdown	
3-2 Full Throttle	52-58
3-1 Full Throttle	24-29
3-2 Half Throttle	32-40

4) Practically any condition can be caused by leaking hydraulic circuits or sticking valves. Unless an obvious condition exists, transmission should never be

CLUTCH AND BAND APPLICATION CHART (ELEMENTS IN USE)

Selector Lever Position	Forward Clutch	Direct-Reverse Clutch	First-Reverse Brake	Second Gear Band	One-Way Clutch
D — DRIVE					
First Gear		X			X
Second Gear		X		X	X
Third Gear	X	X			
2 — INTERMEDIATE					
First Gear		X			X
Second Gear		X		X	
1 — LOW (First)		X	X		
R — REVERSE	X		X		

NEUTRAL OR PARK — All clutches, brakes, and bands released and/or ineffective.

CHAMP & COLT (Cont.)

disassembled until hydraulic pressure tests have been made.

STALL TEST

Testing Precautions

When making stall test, do not hold throttle open any longer than 10 seconds to obtain steady gauge reading. After each stall test, move selector lever to "N" and run engine at 1000 RPM for at least 1 minute to cool down engine and transmission. If engine speed exceeds limits shown in *Stall Speed table,* release accelerator immediately as clutch or band slippage is indicated.

Testing Procedure

With engine at normal operating temperature, tachometer installed, and parking and service brakes applied, make transmission stall test in "D" and "R" ranges at full throttle and note maximum RPM obtained. Engine speed should be within limits shown in *Stall Speed table.*

STALL SPEEDS

Application	Stall RPM
All Models	1650-2050

Stall Speed Too High

In all ranges: general transmission problems are indicated and a control pressure test should be made to locate faulty unit(s). In "D"; Stator overrunning clutch is defective, rear clutch is slipping, line pressure is low or overrunning clutch in planetary gear is defective. In "R"; front clutch or low-reverse brake is slipping, line pressure is low or stator overrunnning clutch is defective.

Stall Speed Too Low

Torque converter is faulty, engine output is not sufficient.

NOTE: **Make sure engine performance is satisfactory before condemning converter assembly. Converter cannot be overhauled and must be replaced if defective.**

HYDRAULIC PRESSURE TESTS

NOTE: **Make sure transmission fluid level is to specifications, control cable is adjusted correctly and transmission is at normal operating temperature. Connect a tachometer, disconnect throttle control cable from carburetor and raise vehicle on a hoist so front wheels are off ground.**

Line Pressures

1) Connect oil pressure gauge(s) to each of the following: line pressure port, low-reverse brake pressure port, front clutch pressure port, and "tee" into transmission "To Cooler" line. *See Fig. 7* for pressure port locations. *See Hydraulic Pressure chart for pressure specifications.*

2) Place manual control lever to "L" position (all the way rearward). Take pressure reading at idle, half throttle then with full throttle (engine speed should be at stall speed). Also note low-reverse brake pressure.

3) Place manual control lever to "2" position (1 detent forward). Note pressures at idle, half and full throttle. Also note lubrication (from "to Cooler" line) pressure.

Fig. 7: Pressure Test Hookup Locations

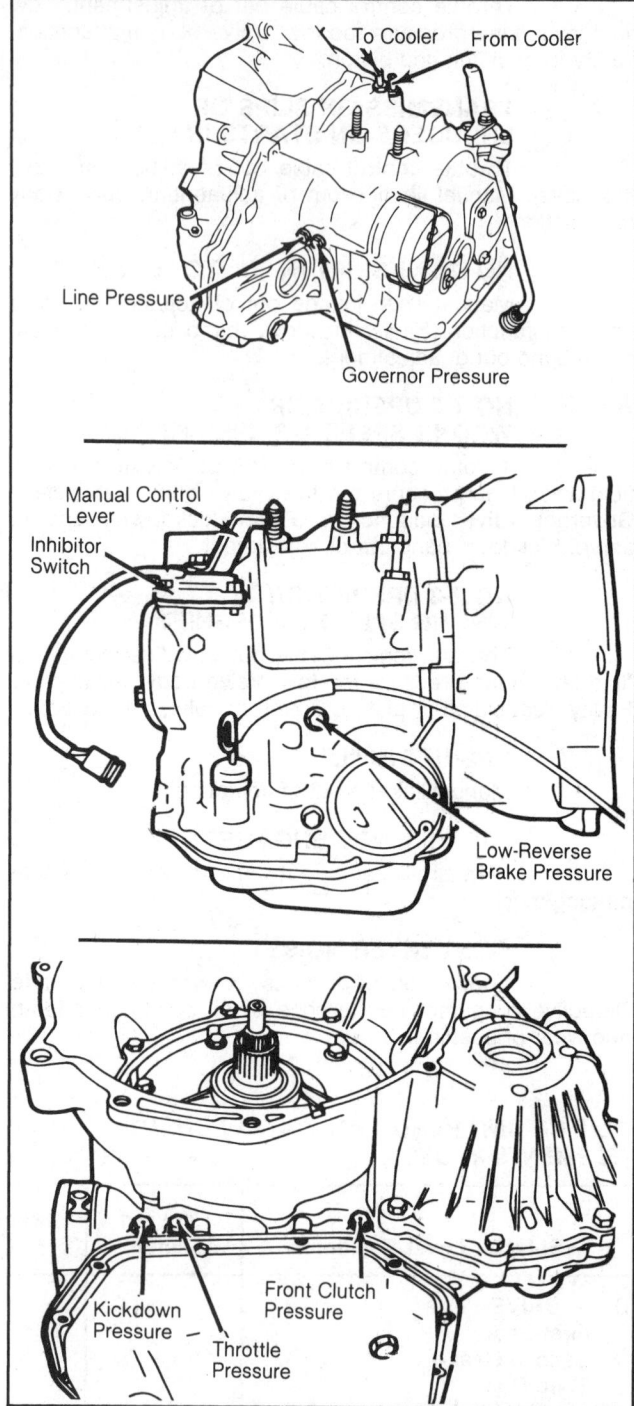

4) Place manual control lever in "D" position (2 detents forward). Note pressures at idle, half and full throttle.

5) Place manual control lever in "R" position (4 detents forward). With pressure gauge attached to low-reverse pressure port, note pressures at idle, half and full throttle.

Line Pressure Test Results

1) If line pressure was to specifications in any one test, pump and pressure regulator are working properly.

CHAMP & COLT (Cont.)

HYDRAULIC PRESSURES

Application	psi (kg/cm²)
Line Pressure in All Ranges	
Idle	58-67 (4.1-4.7)
Half Throttle	96 (6.7)
Full Throttle [1]	98-100 (6.9-7.0)
Low-Reverse Brake Pressure	
In "L"	24-33 (1.7-2.3)
In "R"	199-284 (14.0-20.0)
Lubrication Pressure	
In "2"	7-21 (.5-1.5)

[1] — Pressure should increase as cable is moved from idle to full throttle. Full throttle should be at stall speed specification.

2) A low pressure reading in "L", "2" and "D" but correct pressure in "R" indicates rear clutch circuit leakage.

3) A low pressure reading in "D" and "R" but correct pressure in "L" indicates front clutch circuit leakage.

4) A low pressure reading in "L" and "R" but correct pressure in "2" indicates low-reverse brake circuit leakage.

5) Low pressure readings in all positions indicates a defective pump, clogged filter or a stuck pressure regulator valve.

Governor Pressure Test

1) Make this test only if vehicle shifts at wrong speeds with throttle cable properly adjusted. Connect pressure gauge to governor pressure port. *See Fig. 7.*

2) Place manual control lever in "D" position and increase vehicle speed and note pressures at which transmission shifts. Transmission should shift at indicated speeds and governor pressure should be as indicated in *Governor Pressure chart.* If not, governor valve is sticking, or filter in governor body is clogged.

GOVERNOR PRESSURE

Speed (MPH)	psi (kg/cm²)
Vehicle Stopped	0-2.8 (0-.2)
16-19	14 (1.0)
32-35	43 (3.0)
53-57	71 (5.0)

Throttle Pressure Test

Connect pressure gauge to throttle pressure port. *See Fig. 7.* Note pressure readings at idle, half throttle and at full throttle (stall speed). Pressure readings should be as indicated in *Throttle Pressure chart.*

THROTTLE PRESSURE

Application	psi (kg/cm²)
Idle	0-1.4 (0-.1)
Half Throttle	41-51 (2.9-3.6)
Full Throttle	98-100 (6.9-7.0)

REMOVAL & INSTALLATION

See the appropriate article in MANUAL TRANSMISSION REMOVAL Section.

TORQUE CONVERTER

NOTE: Torque converter is a sealed unit and cannot be disassembled for service. Replace if found to be defective.

TRANSAXLE DISASSEMBLY

1) Remove torque converter, speedometer pinion adapter, manual control lever and inhibitor switch. Attach dial indicator to measure input shaft end play. *See Fig. 8.* Record end play measurement.

Fig. 8: Measuring Input Shaft End Play

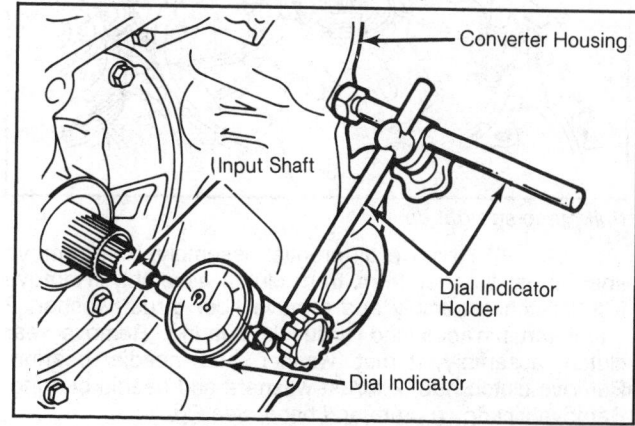

2) Remove oil pan and filter. Disconnect throttle cable. Remove valve body, being careful that manual shift valve does not fall out of valve body.

NOTE: Low-reverse brake clutch "O" ring is attached to valve body by petroleum jelly, be careful not to dislodge or misposition seal when removing or installing valve body.

3) Remove throttle cable, accumulator and spring, being careful not to damage cable or retainer end.

4) Remove transfer shaft cover then attach dial indicator to measure transfer shaft end play. *See Fig. 9.* Record measurement. Rotate transaxle assembly so converter housing is up and remove converter housing.

Fig. 9: Measuring Transfer Shaft End Play

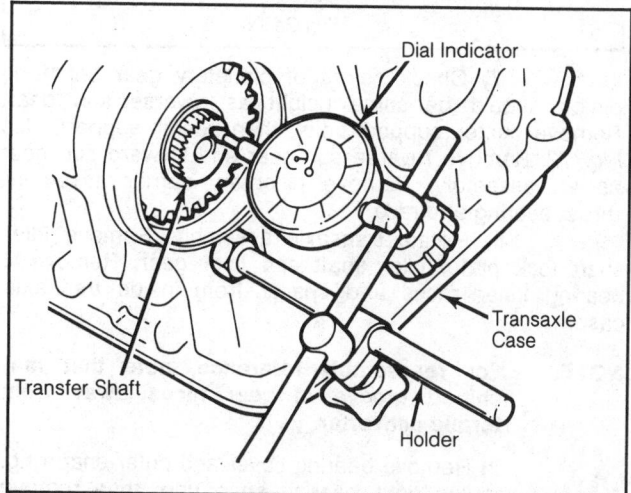

Automatic Transmissions

CHAMP & COLT (Cont.)

5) Remove oil pump bolts and install pump remover tools (MD998333) into pump removing holes (located in pump housing). *See Fig. 10.* Pump may tilt up (side B) when removing. If so, tap on pump (side A) with a soft mallet. *See Fig. 10.*

Fig. 10: *Removing Oil Pump from Transaxle Housing*

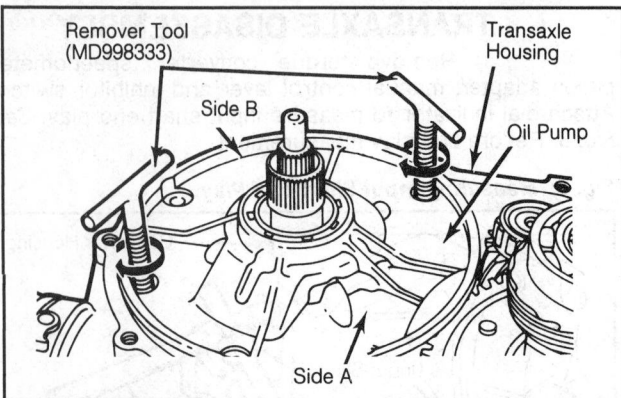

Pull pump straight up.

6) Remove differential assembly, then remove fiber thrust washer from front clutch assembly. Remove front clutch assembly and remove fiber thrust washer, 2 metal thrust races and 1 needle bearing. Remove rear clutch assembly, thrust washer and needle bearing. Remove clutch hub, 2 thrust washers and needle bearing. Remove kickdown drum and band. *See Fig. 11.*

Fig. 11: *Removing Kickdown Band*

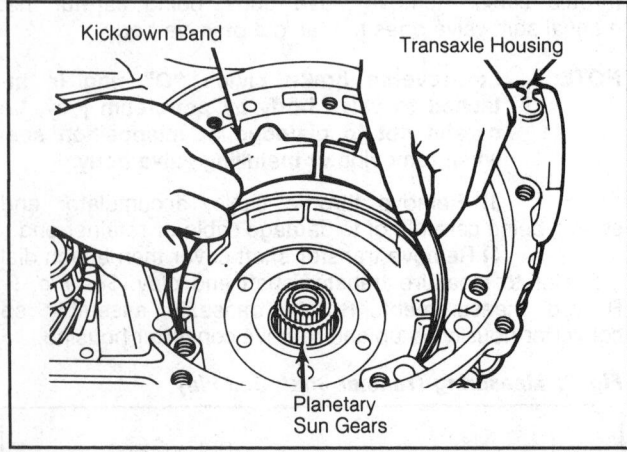

7) Check height of planetary gear set; long pinion should be same height as reverse sun gear. Remove center support bolts, then center support. *See Fig. 12.* Remove reverse sun gear and forward sun gear as an assembly. Remove planetary carrier assembly, thrust bearing and race.

8) Rotate transaxle assembly. Remove idler shaft lock plate, idler shaft and idler gear. Remove 2 bearing inner races and spacer from inside transaxle case.

NOTE: For reassembly reference, note that machined groove in gear faces away from torque converter.

9) Remove bearing cover and outer snap ring. Remove annulus gear bearing snap ring, then remove

Fig. 12: *Center Support Bolt Location*

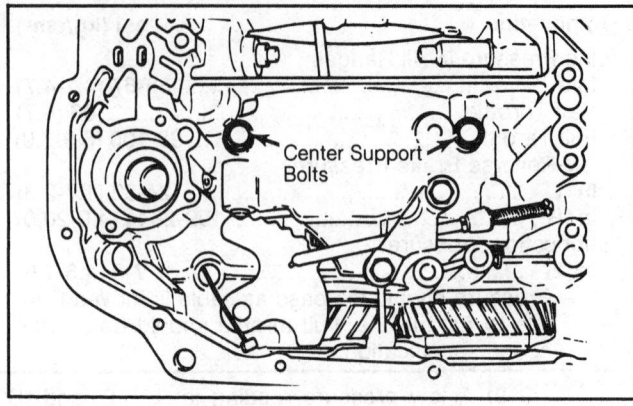

Bolt head has mark "8" on top.

annulus gear, output flange, transfer drive gear and bearing as an assembly.

10) Remove transfer rear end snap ring. Use a brass drift to drive transfer shaft out toward engine mounting surface. Remove snap ring from transaxle case, then remove bearing inner and outer races.

COMPONENT DISASSEMBLY & REASSEMBLY

OIL PUMP

Disassembly

1) Remove bolts to separate pump housing from reaction shaft support. If pump gears are to be reused, mark gears (with felt pen, do not scribe) so they can be reinstalled in original position.

2) Remove drive and driven gears from pump housing. Remove steel ball from pump housing then remove 2 steel rings from reaction shaft support. Pry out pump housing oil seal.

Reassembly

1) Apply DEXRON II fluid to oil seal and install oil seal to pump housing. Lubricate pump gears with DEXRON II fluid, then install to pump housing. If original gears are being reinstalled, install them in original positions using marks made upon disassembly as a guide.

2) Make the following measurements of pump gears to pump housing: driven gear-to-pump housing clearance, driven gear-to-crescent clearance, driven gear side clearance, drive gear-to-crescent clearance and drive gear side clearance. If clearances are incorrect, replace components as necessary.

OIL PUMP CLEARANCES

Application	Clearance In. (mm)
Driven Gear-to-Housing	.003-.006 (.08-.15)
Driven Gear-to-Crescent	.004-.009 (.11-.24)
Driven Gear Side Clearance	.001-.002 (.025-.05)
Drive Gear-to-Crescent	.009-.013 (.24-.34)
Drive Gear Side Clearance	.001-.002 (.025-.05)

3) Install steel ball in pump housing, then install 2 seal rings (coated with DEXRON II fluid) to

CHAMP & COLT (Cont.)

reaction shaft support. Place reaction shaft support to pump housing, then tighten bolts finger tight.

    4) Install guide pin (MD998336) and pump band (C-3759) to assembled pump, then fully tighten pump bolts to 90-102 INCH lbs. (10-12 N.m) *See Fig. 13.* After tightening bolts, make sure pump gear turns freely. If not, disassemble and recheck reassembly procedures and clearances. Install a new large "O" ring to outside circumference of pump and lubricate with petrolatum.

Fig. 13: Assembling Oil Pump
with Special Tools

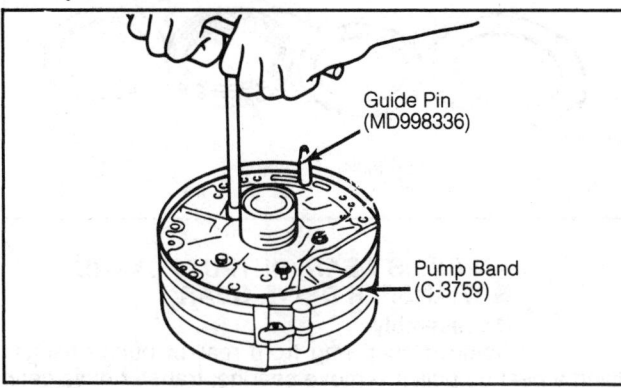

Guide Pin
(MD998336)

Pump Band
(C-3759)

Tighten all the bolts evenly.

FRONT CLUTCH
Disassembly

    1) Remove snap ring, then remove 3 steel plates and 2 lined plates. If plates are to be reused, keep them in order and direction (as removed) for reassembly. *See Fig. 14.*

Fig. 14: Front Clutch Components

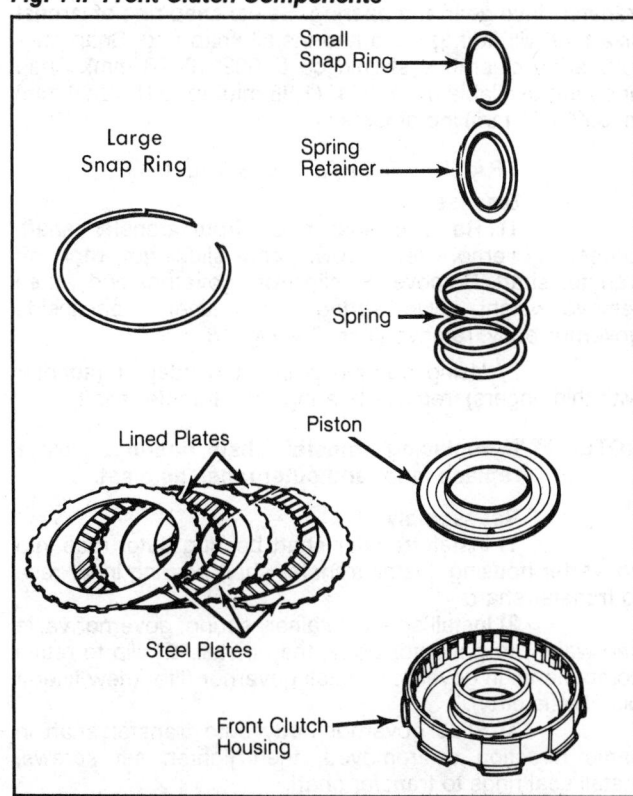

Small
Snap Ring

Large
Snap Ring

Spring
Retainer

Spring

Lined Plates

Piston

Steel Plates

Front Clutch
Housing

    2) Compress return spring, remove snap ring, spring retainer and return spring. Remove piston from front clutch. Remove "D" section rings from outside of piston and front clutch retainer.

Reassembly

    1) Install "D" section rings to piston with round side facing out. Lubricate rings with DEXRON II fluid and install piston in rear clutch retainer by hand. Be careful not to damage rings.

    2) Compress spring and spring retainer to clutch retainer. Install small snap ring to hold spring to clutch retainer. Install 3 steel plates and 2 lined plates, starting with steel plate and alternating with a lined plate. If old plates are reinstalled, install them in same order and direction as removed.

NOTE: **Soak new lined plates in DEXRON II fluid for at least 2 hours before installation.**

    3) Install large snap ring to clutch retainer and measure clearance between snap ring and steel plate. Clearance should be .016-.024" (.4-.6 mm). If clearance is not to specifications, install a selective snap ring to give correct clearance. Snap rings are available in thicknesses from .063" (1.6 mm) to .118" (3.0 mm) in .008" (.2 mm) increments.

REAR CLUTCH
Disassembly

    1) Remove large snap ring, reaction plate, 2 lined plates, clutch plate and pressure plate from rear clutch retainer. If plates are to be reused, keep them in order and direction (as removed) for reassembly.

    2) Remove seal ring, small snap ring and thrust race. Use a press to compress piston, then remove waved snap ring. Release pressure from press and remove waved snap ring, return spring and piston. Remove the 2 "D" section rings from piston.

Reassembly

    1) Install "D" section rings to piston and front clutch retainer (round side of ring facing out), then lubricate rings with DEXRON II fluid. Push piston into front clutch retainer by hand, being careful not to damage rings.

    2) Install return spring with waved snap ring to clutch retainer. Use a press to compress return spring until waved snap ring seats in groove of clutch retainer. Install pressure plate, lined plate, clutch plate, lined plate and, finally, the reaction plate. *See Fig. 15.*

Fig. 15: Rear Clutch Components

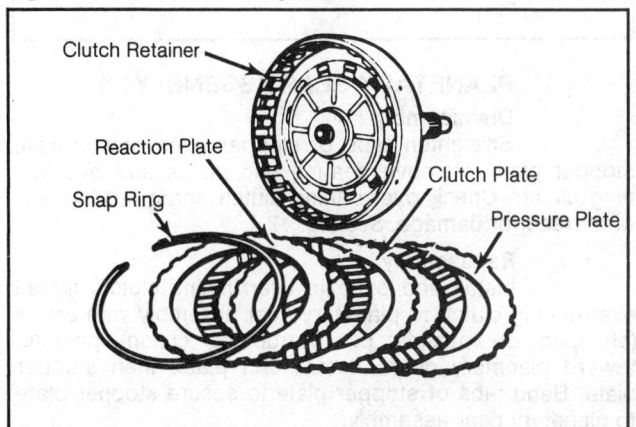

Clutch Retainer

Reaction Plate

Snap Ring

Clutch Plate

Pressure Plate

CHAMP & COLT (Cont.)

NOTE: Soak new lined plates in DEXRON II fluid for at least 2 hours before installation.

3) Install large snap ring to clutch retainer and measure clearance between reaction plate and snap ring. Clearance should be .012-.020" (.3-.5 mm). If clearance is not to specifications, selective snap rings are available in thicknesses from .063" (1.6 mm) to .118" (3.0 mm) in .008" (.2 mm) increments. Install thrust race, small snap ring and new seal ring.

LOW-REVERSE BRAKE
Disassembly
1) Remove snap ring. Remove reaction plate, 4 lined plates, 3 steel plates and the pressure plates. If plates are to be reused, keep them in order and direction (as removed) for reassembly.

2) Compress piston and remove piston snap ring, then remove return spring and waved spring. Remove piston, then remove "D" section rings from piston.

Reassembly
1) Install "D" section rings to piston with round side of ring out. Lubricate rings with DEXRON II fluid and install piston by hand, being careful not to damage rings. Install waved spring and return spring. Compress springs and install snap ring. Install pressure plate, then install plates starting with a lined plate and alternating with steel plates, ending with reaction plate. *See Fig. 16.*

2) Install large snap ring and measure clearance between reaction plate and snap ring. Clearance should be .031-.040" (.8-1.0 mm). If clearance is not to specifications, selective snap rings are available from .063" (1.6 mm) to .118" (3.0 mm) in .008" (.2 mm) increments.

Fig. 16: Low-Reverse Brake Components

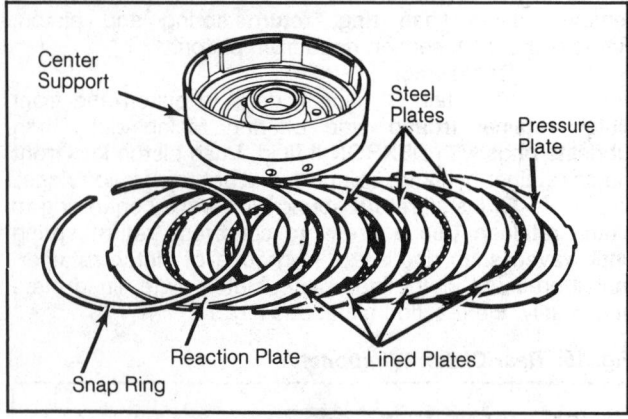

PLANETARY GEAR ASSEMBLY
Disassembly
Straighten tabs of stopper plate and remove stopper plate. Remove bearing end plates and overrunning clutch. Check overrunning clutch sprag, spring and outer race for damage. *See Fig. 17.*

Reassembly
Install end plate to overrunning clutch. Install overrunning clutch to planetary gear assembly with arrow (stamped on outside of overrunning clutch) pointing toward planetary gears. Install end plate, then stopper plate. Bend tabs of stopper plate to secure stopper plate to planetary gear assembly.

Fig. 17: Planetary Gear and Overrunning Clutch Assembly

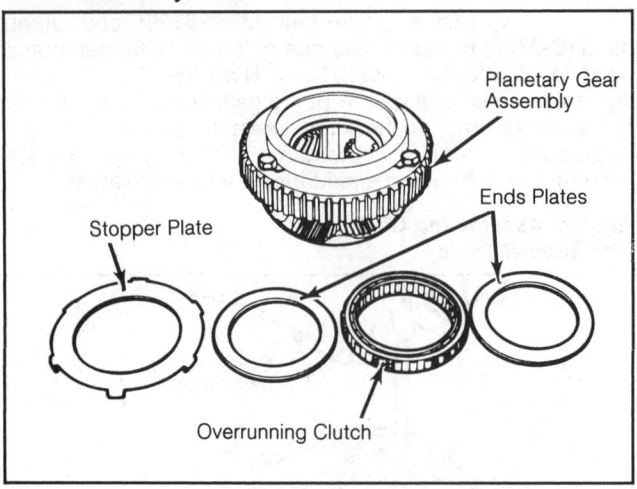

ANNULUS GEAR, OUTPUT FLANGE & TRANSFER DRIVE GEAR
Disassembly
Remove snap ring from rear of output flange. Using a bearing puller, remove bearing, transfer drive gear and bearing. Remove snap ring and separate annulus gear from output flange.

NOTE: Annulus gear and output flange are a matched set. If one is damaged, replace both components.

Reassembly
Install annulus gear to output flange and install snap ring. Using a bearing installer, install bearing, transfer drive gear and bearing. Select snap ring of largest size that will fit in groove and install snap ring. Snap ring-to-bearing clearance should be 0-.002" (0-.06 mm). Snap rings are available from .074" (1.88 mm) to .081" (2.06 mm) in .002" (.06 mm) increments.

TRANSFER SHAFT & GOVERNOR
Disassembly
1) Remove seal rings from transfer shaft. Loosen governor set screws and slide governor off transfer shaft. Remove "E" clip from governor body, then remove weight, valve, spring and retainer. From inside governor body, remove filter. *See Fig. 18.*

2) Using bearing puller and adapter (adapter with thin fingers), remove bearing from transfer shaft.

NOTE: If replacing transfer shaft bearing, always replace inner and outer races as a set.

Reassembly
1) Install transfer shaft bearing outer race into converter housing. Install transfer shaft bearing inner race to transfer shaft.

2) Install spring retainer, spring, governor valve and weight to governor body, then install "E" clip to retain components in governor. Install governor filter (new filter if old filter is dirty).

3) Slide governor body onto transfer shaft in same direction as removed, then tighten set screws. Install seal rings to transfer shaft.

CHAMP & COLT (Cont.)

Fig. 18: *Transfer Gear Shaft and Governor Assembly*

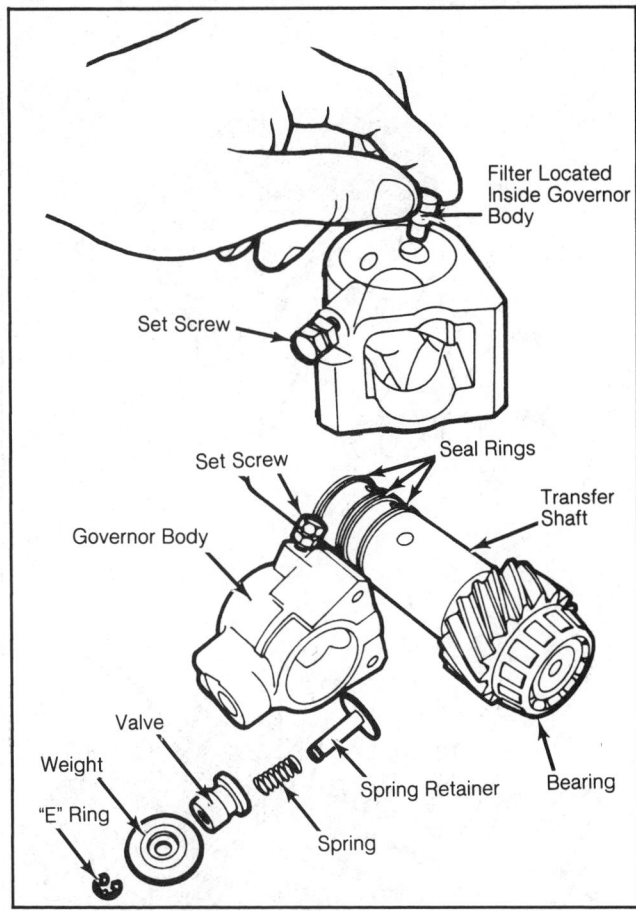

Note the location of the governor filter.

VALVE BODY

NOTE: **When disassembling valve body, place each component in order and relation to removal sequence for reassembly reference.**

Disassembly

1) Remove bolts securing throttle cam to valve body and remove throttle cam assembly. Remove the 19 bolts (1 shorter than others) attaching separating plate to transfer plate, then separate plates.

2) Remove stiffener plate, then separating plate. Remove line relief and low relief steel balls with their springs. See Fig. 20. Remove manual valve, kickdown valve, throttle valve and 2 springs. Remove the 2 regulator plugs.

3) Remove rear end cover and gasket. Remove 1-2 shift valve and 2-3 shift plug. Remove front end cover. Remove all valves, springs and plugs (lay components out in order). Remove snap ring, then remove shuttle valve.

Reassembly

1) Install 2-3 shift valve and spring to valve body. Install shuttle valve, spring and plug, then install snap ring to retain shuttle valve components.

2) Install 1-2 shift plug and spring. Install regulator valve, spring and adjusting screw. Install torque converter valve and spring, then the range control valve and spring. See Fig. 20.

NOTE: For spring identification, see Valve Body Spring Identification table.

Fig. 19: *Transfer Plate, Separating Plate and Stiffener Plate with Line and Low Relief Ball Locations*

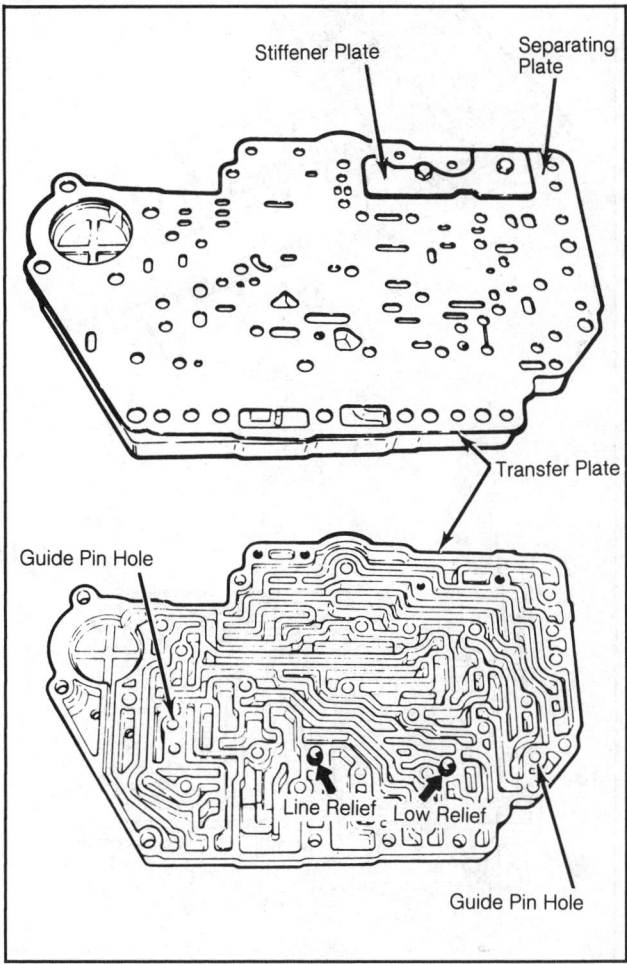

Top view of the assembly shown.

3) Install 2-3 shift plug, then 1-2 shift valve to valve body. Install rear end cover and gasket. Install 2 regulator plugs (small one first), then install manual valve to valve body.

4) Install kickdown spring, throttle valve, throttle spring and kickdown valve into valve body. Install stopper plate to valve body, then install 4 steel balls to valve body. See Fig. 20.

5) Install line relief and low relief steel balls, with their springs, to transfer plate. See Fig. 19. Install guide pins to transfer plate and install separating plate to transfer plate. Install stiffener plate and bolts.

6) Remove guide pins from transfer plate and install them in the valve body. Using guide pins as a guide, install transfer/separating plates to valve body and install the 19 retaining bolts (1 short and 18 long). Install throttle cam assembly.

NOTE: **Make sure short valve body bolt is installed in its proper location. Long bolts will not tighten down properly.**

Automatic Transmissions
CHAMP & COLT (Cont.)

Fig. 20: *Exploded View of Throttle Body and Components*

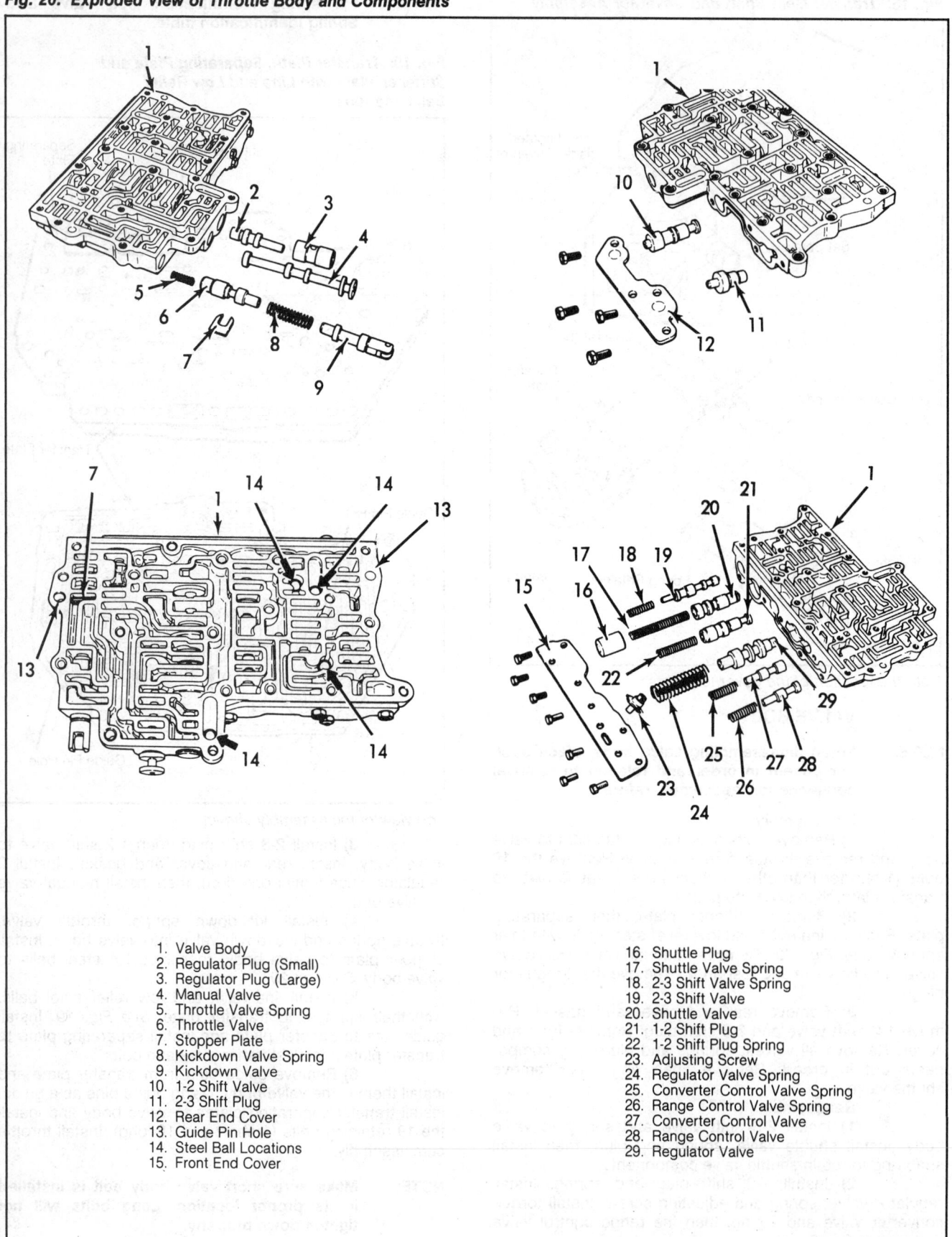

1. Valve Body
2. Regulator Plug (Small)
3. Regulator Plug (Large)
4. Manual Valve
5. Throttle Valve Spring
6. Throttle Valve
7. Stopper Plate
8. Kickdown Valve Spring
9. Kickdown Valve
10. 1-2 Shift Valve
11. 2-3 Shift Plug
12. Rear End Cover
13. Guide Pin Hole
14. Steel Ball Locations
15. Front End Cover
16. Shuttle Plug
17. Shuttle Valve Spring
18. 2-3 Shift Valve Spring
19. 2-3 Shift Valve
20. Shuttle Valve
21. 1-2 Shift Plug
22. 1-2 Shift Plug Spring
23. Adjusting Screw
24. Regulator Valve Spring
25. Converter Control Valve Spring
26. Range Control Valve Spring
27. Converter Control Valve
28. Range Control Valve
29. Regulator Valve

CHAMP & COLT (Cont.)

VALVE BODY SPRING IDENTIFICATION

Location of Spring	Diameter In. (mm)	Length In. (mm)
Throttle Spring	.374 (9.5)	1.276 (32.4)
Kickdown Spring	.252 (6.4)	1.028 (26.1)
Converter Control Spring	.331 (8.4)	.949 (24.1)
Range Control Spring	.331 (8.4)	.949 (24.1)
Regulator Spring	.606 (15.4)	2.024 (51.4)
1-2 Shift Spring	.299 (7.6)	1.535 (39.0)
Shuttle Spring	.260 (6.6)	2.343 (59.5)
2-3 Shift Spring	.268 (6.8)	1.189 (30.2)
Low Relief Spring	.260 (6.6)	.661 (16.8)
Line Relief Spring	.276 (7.0)	.961 (24.4)

DIFFERENTIAL

Disassembly

1) Straighten ring gear lock washers and remove ring gear bolts, then remove ring gear. Remove pinion shaft lock pin, pinion shaft, pinion gears and washers.

2) Remove side gears and spacers. Keep right side gear and spacer separate from left side gear and spacer. Remove differential carrier side bearings if necessary.

Reassembly

1) Install differential carrier side bearing if removed. Install side gears and spacers. If original side gears are reused, make sure they are installed in their original positions. If new side gears are used, use new spacers of .040" (1.0 mm) thickness.

2) Place washers to back of pinion gears, then install pinion gears at same time. Rotate pinion gears to mesh them with side gears. Install pinion shaft.

3) Measure backlash between side gears and pinion gears (measure both right and left side gear backlash). See Fig. 21. Backlash should be 0-.003" (0-.08 mm) on both sides. If backlash is not to specifications, remove pinion and side gears and install thicker or thinner spacers behind side gears to achieve correct backlash. See Side Gear Spacers chart for spacer sizes available.

Fig. 21: Measuring Side Gear-to-Pinion Gear Backlash

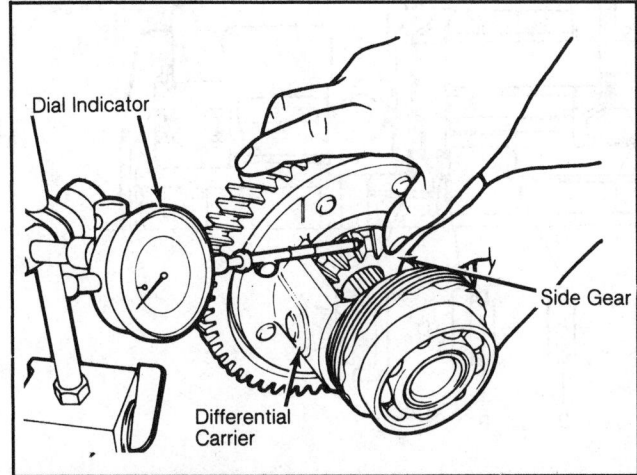

Check both right and left sides.

SIDE GEAR SPACERS

Shim Part No.	Thickness In. (mm)
MA 180862	.030-.033 (.75-.82)
MA 180861	.033-.037 (.82-.92)
MA 180860	.037-.040 (.92-1.0)
MA 180875	.040-.043 (1.0-1.08)
MA 180876	.043-.046 (1.08-1.16)

4) Install ring gear. Install pinion shaft lock pin, then install new lock washers and ring gear bolts. Make sure one of the lock washers retains the pinion shaft lock pin. See Fig. 22.

Fig. 22: Installation of Ring Gear Bolts and Lock Washer That Retains Pinion Shaft Lock Pin

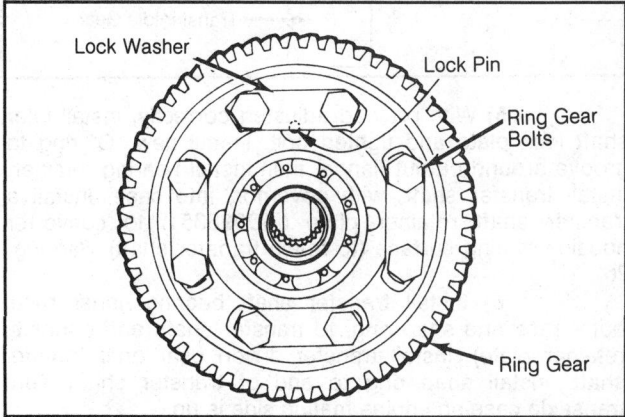

Tighten all the bolts in a star pattern.

5) Tighten ring gear bolts and bend lock washers along a flat of ring gear bolts. Make sure lock washers are not cracked along bend.

TRANSAXLE REASSEMBLY

NOTE: Handle all parts carefully to avoid damaging bearing and mating surfaces. Lubricate all components with DEXRON II fluid prior to reassembly. Gaskets and thrust washers may be held in place with petrolatum.

1) Place transaxle case on bench with oil pan mounting surface up. Install annulus gear and output flange assembly (with bearings and transfer drive gear attached) to inside of transaxle case. Install snap ring to bearing.

2) Install bearing outer races, inner races and spacer (in correct direction) to transfer idle gear. See Fig. 23.

3) Install transfer idle gear assembly to transaxle case. Insert idler shaft from outside case, then screw in and tighten idler shaft to transaxle case. Install new "O" ring to idler shaft.

4) Using a torque wrench and socket, measure output flange turning torque (preload). See Fig. 24. Preload should be 12 INCH lbs. (1.4 N.m). If preload is not to specification, tighten or loosen transfer idler shaft until correct specification is obtained.

Automatic Transmissions

CHAMP & COLT (Cont.)

Fig. 23: Installation of Transfer Gear, Bearings and Spacer

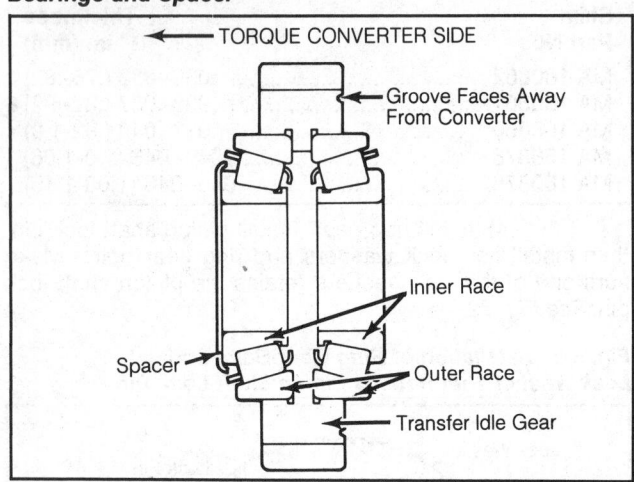

Fig. 24: Measuring Output Flange Preload

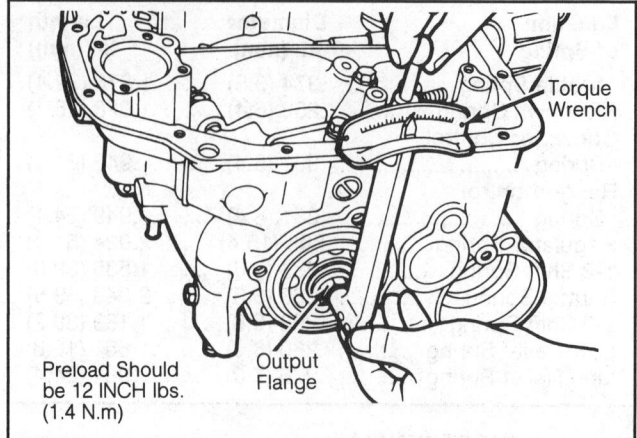

Rotate bearing several times to check preload.

5) With preload adjusted correctly, install idler shaft lock plate and tighten bolt. Install new "O" ring to groove around output flange, then install bearing retainer. Install transfer shaft, with governor, into case. Install a transfer shaft retainer plate (MD998351) to converter housing mating surface (to retain transfer shaft). *See Fig. 26.*

6) Install transfer shaft bearing, inner race, outer race and snap ring, to transfer shaft (end opposite retainer plate). Install transfer driven gear onto transfer shaft. Install snap ring to end of transfer shaft. Turn transaxle case so engine mating side is up.

NOTE: Refer to Fig. 25 for location of thrust bearings, thrust races and thrust washers. Refer to Thrust Bearing, Thrust Race and Thrust Washer chart for components available.

NOTE: Coat thrust races, thrust bearings and thrust washers with petrolatum to hold them in place during installation.

7) Install thrust race "E" to output flange. Attach thrust races "D" and "J" with thrust bearings "A" and "B" to front and rear of planetary gear carrier. *See Fig. 25.* Install planetary gear carrier to transaxle case.

Fig. 25: Cross-Sectional View Showing Locations of Thrust Bearings, Thrust Races and Thrust Washers.

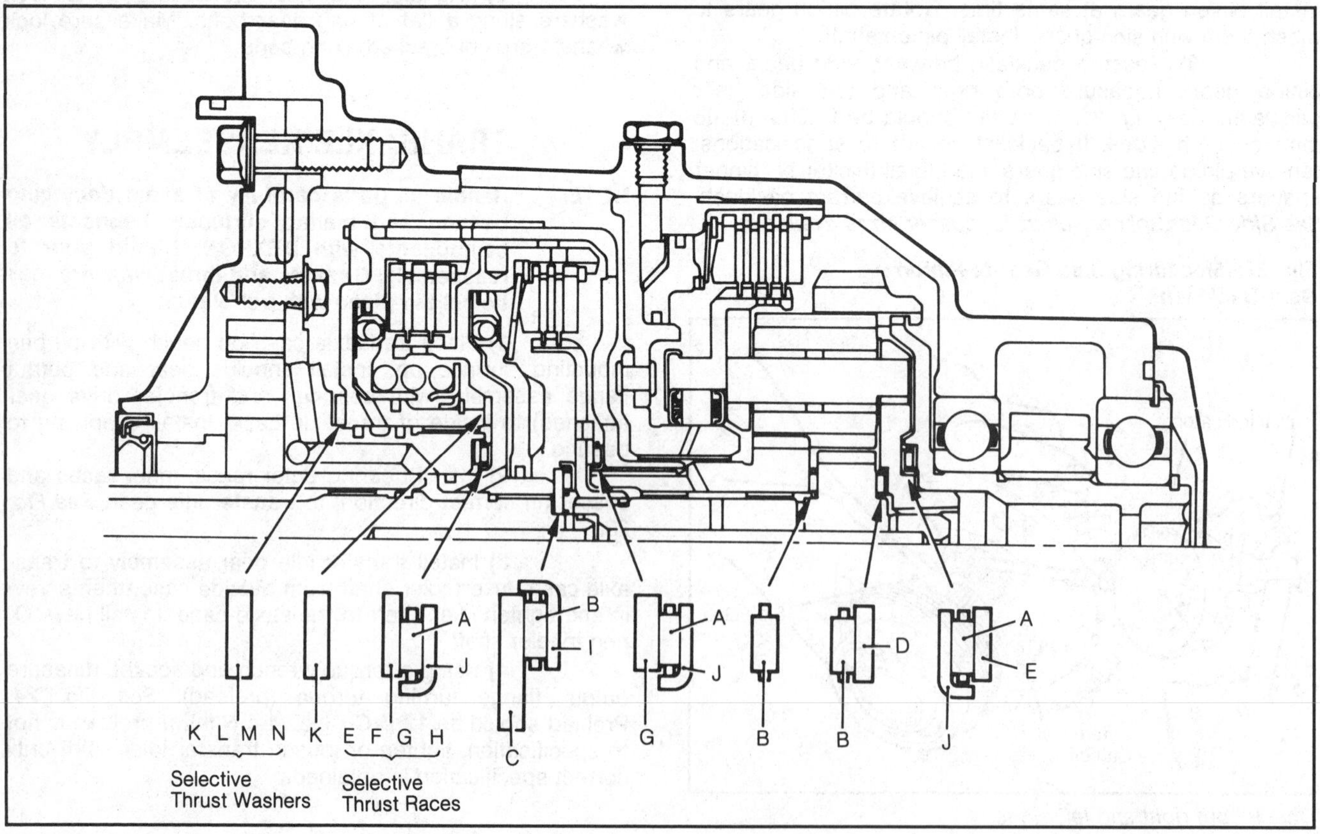

CHAMP & COLT (Cont.)

Fig. 26: Transfer Shaft Retainer Plate

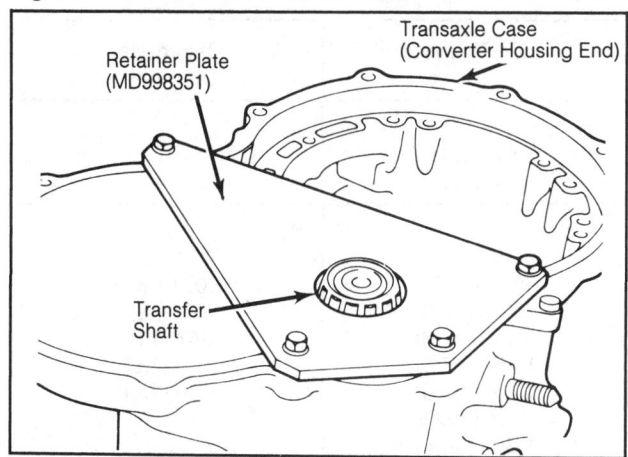

25 for locations of thrust races and bearings. Install planetary gear carrier to transaxle case.

8) Assemble forward sun gear with reverse sun gear and install into planetary gear carrier. Make sure reverse sun gear toothed area is approximately same height as planetary gear long pinion.

9) Lubricate overrunning clutch area of low-reverse brake (center support) with Dexron II, then install low-reverse brake to case. Install the 2 low-reverse brake (center support) lock bolts.

CAUTION: Do not turn transaxle case upside down or thrust washers will fall out of place.

10) Insert manual control shaft to case, pushing it fully toward manual control lever. After shaft is installed, install a new "O" ring to manual control shaft. See Fig. 27.

Fig. 27: Installation of Manual Control Shaft

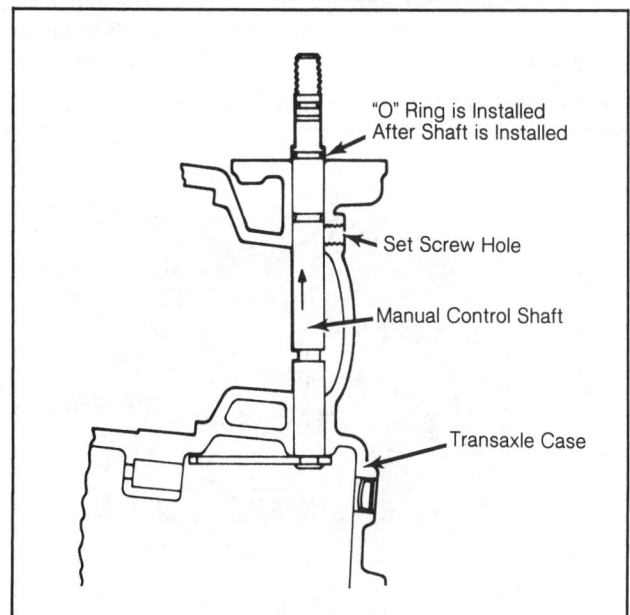

NOTE: If "O" ring is installed before shaft is pushed into case, "O" ring will be damaged by the set screw hole.

11) Pull manual control shaft back into case until set screw groove is aligned with set screw hole and install set screw with gasket. Install detent ball and spring at same time as shaft is pulled back to install set screw. See Fig. 28.

Fig. 28: Installation of Set Screw, Detent Ball And Spring to Manual Control Shaft

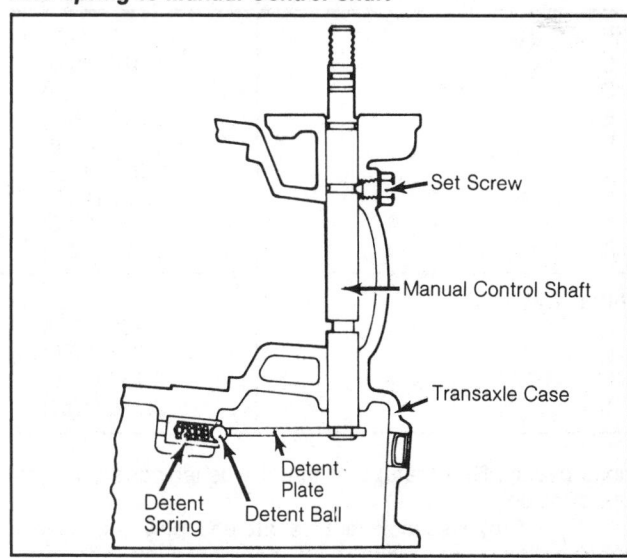

12) Install kickdown servo spring, piston and sleeve into case. Install large and small "D" section rings to piston and a new "O" ring to sleeve before installation of piston. Using spring compressor, compress piston spring and install snap ring.

13) Install kickdown band; attach band ends to end of anchor rod and servo piston adjusting screw. Install kickdown drum, meshing splines with reverse sun gear. Place kickdown band on kickdown drum and tighten kickdown servo adjusting screw to hold band in place.

14) Install thrust race "J" and a thrust bearing "A" to kickdown drum. Refer to Fig. 25. Install thrust races "I" and "G" to both ends of clutch hub. Attach thrust bearing "B" to engine side of thrust race and install clutch hub to forward sun gear splines.

15) Install rear clutch assembly. Install thrust washer "K" to rear clutch retainer. Install thrust race "J" and a thrust bearing "A" to rear clutch retainer. Install front clutch assembly and differential assembly. Install a new oil pump gasket and install thrust washer to rear end of oil pump assembly.

16) If end play, measured at disassembly, is out of specification of .020-.055" (.5-1.4 mm), install selective thrust race (E,F,G or H) to obtain correct end play. Refer to Thrust Bearing, Thrust Race and Thrust Washer Chart for thrust race thicknesses.

NOTE: If thrust race was replaced with one of a different thickness, also replace the thrust washer located between oil pump and front clutch. Replacement thrust washer should be .040" (1.0 mm) thicker than thrust race.

17) Install new selected thrust washer, determined in preceding step, to front clutch. Install new "O" ring to oil pump groove and lubricate it with Dexron II. Install oil pump assembly by tightening the 6 oil pump

Automatic Transmissions

CHAMP & COLT (Cont.)

THRUST BEARING, THRUST RACE AND THRUST WASHER DIMENSIONS

Component I.D. Mark	Outside Diameter In. (mm)	Inside Diameter In. (mm)	Thickness In. (mm)
Thrust Bearing			
A	1.894 (48.1)	1.417 (36.0)	.....
B	1.437 (36.5)	.874 (22.2)	.....
Thrust Race			
C	1.378 (35.0)	.496 (12.6)	.094 (2.4)
D	1.457 (35.0)	.925 (23.5)	.031 (.8)
E	1.925 (48.9)	1.457 (37.0)	.031 (.8)
F	1.925 (48.9)	1.457 (37.0)	.047 (1.2)
G	1.925 (48.9)	1.457 (37.0)	.063 (1.6)
H	1.925 (48.9)	1.457 (37.0)	.080 (2.0)
I	1.496 (38.0)	.925 (23.5)	.....
J	1.482 (47.0)	1.354 (34.4)	.....
Thrust Washer			
K	2.756 (70.0)	2.193 (55.7)	.071 (1.8)
L	2.756 (70.0)	2.193 (55.7)	.087 (2.2)
M	2.756 (70.0)	2.193 (55.7)	.102 (2.6)
N	2.756 (70.0)	2.193 (55.7)	.118 (3.0)

bolts evenly. Be careful that thrust washer does not drop out of place.

18) Recheck input shaft end play for correct specification, also make sure transfer shaft end play (measured upon disassembly) is to specifications. End play should be between a loose .001" (.025 mm) and a tight .001" (.025 mm). If not to specifications, install selective spacer. Spacers are available from .072" (1.84 mm) to .106" (2.68 mm) in .001" (.025 mm) increments. If selective spacer is to be installed, remove bearing outer race from transaxle case and replace old spacer with new selected spacer. Reinstall bearing outer race.

19) Place spacer (removed upon disassembly) on differential bearing outer race. Install new gasket to transaxle case and install converter housing. Check differential case end play. End play should be 0-.006" (0-.15 mm). Also recheck input shaft and transfer shaft end play. If any end play measurements are not to specifications, readjust.

20) Install transfer shaft cover and holder. Turn transaxle case so oil pan mounting surface is facing up. Install parking sprag rod to detent plate of manual control shaft. Install parking sprag rod support. See Fig. 29.

21) Install accumulator piston and spring. Install "O" ring at center of top of valve body assembly (brake oil pressure passage). Install valve body to transaxle case, fitting detent plate pin (for manual control shaft) in slot of manual valve. Install and tighten valve body bolts noting that 1 bolt (A) is shorter than the others (B). See Fig. 30.

22) Insert throttle cable into transaxle case and connect throttle cable inner cable to throttle cam. Install oil filter, oil pan gasket and oil pan. Install drive shaft oil seals to transaxle.

Fig. 30: Valve Body Bolt Installation Locations

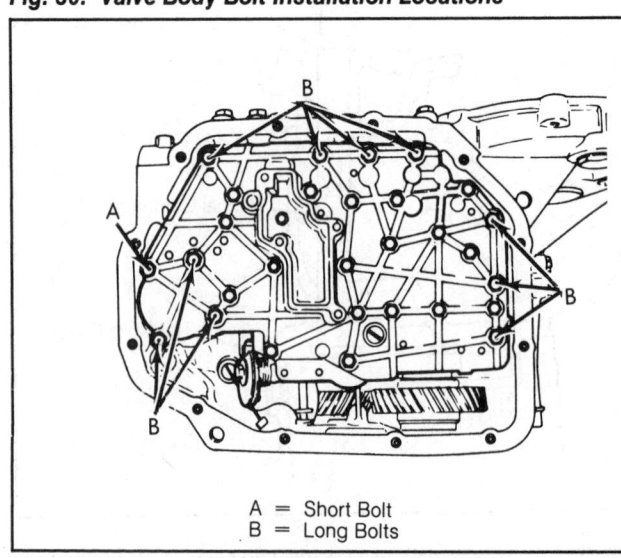

A = Short Bolt
B = Long Bolts

Fig. 29: Parking Sprag Rod and Support Installation

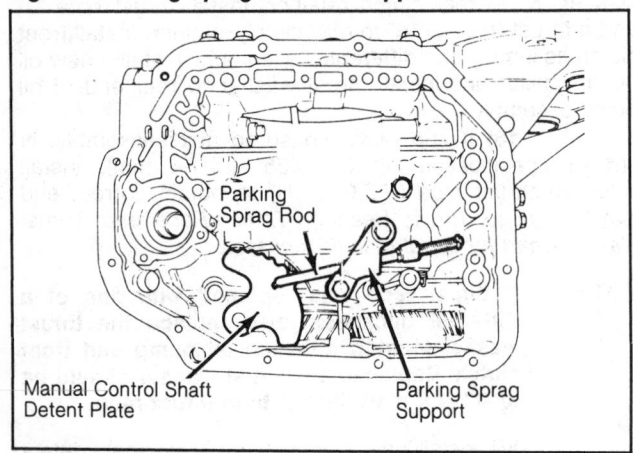

Parking Sprag Rod

Manual Control Shaft Detent Plate

Parking Sprag Support

CHAMP & COLT (Cont.)

23) Install inhibitor switch and manual lever, then adjust inhibitor switch. Lubricate torque converter surface (where converter slides into oil pump) with DEXRON II fluid and carefully install converter.

24) After torque converter installation, measure distance from mating surface of converter housing to torque converter. If measurement is not more than .6" (.15 mm), torque converter is not installed completely. Remove converter and check alignment of converter to oil pump.

TIGHTENING SPECIFICATIONS

Application	Ft. Lbs. (N.m)
Axle Shaft Nut	87-130 (118-177)
Center Support (Low-Reverse Brake)	15-19 (20-26)
Differential Carrier-to-Ring Gear	47-54 (64-73)
Drive Plate-to-Converter	26-30 (35-41)
Idler Shaft Lock Plate	15-19 (20-26)
Oil Pump Assembly	11-15 (15-20)
Rear Cover	14-17 (19-23)
Sprag Rod Support Bolts	15-19 (20-26)
Sway Bar Coupling Bolts	22-30 (30-41)
Transaxle-to-Engine	
M8 Bolts	21-25 (29-34)
M10 Bolts	31-40 (42-54)
Transaxle-to-Mount Bracket	36-43 (49-58)

DESCRIPTION

The Sentra and 310 transaxles consist primarily of a 3-element hydraulic torque converter, 2 planetary gear sets and final gear. Desired function of the 2 planetary gear sets is obtained by 2 multiple-disc clutches, a multiple-disc brake, brake band and 1-way clutch. Both use a hydraulic control system to operate friction elements and shift controls.

Both models are equipped with a non-serviceable torque converter. The Sentra transaxle has a lock-up converter (model RL3F01A); the 310 transaxle (model RN3F01A) is not a lock-up converter.

LUBRICATION & ADJUSTMENT

See the appropriate article in AUTOMATIC TRANSMISSION SERVICING Section.

SERVICE (IN VEHICLE)

AXLE SHAFTS

Removal (Sentra)

1) Raise and support vehicle. Remove wheel and tire. Remove brake caliper and pry cotter pin out of hub. Loosen, do not remove, wheel hub nut from axle shaft while preventing hub from turning. Remove tie rod end from steering knuckle.

2) Remove lower ball joint and discard nut. Drain gear oil from transaxle case. Remove axle shaft from transaxle and discard axle shaft snap ring. Do not damage oil seal during axle shaft removal. Insert a bar or equivalent tool into each side of differential case to prevent dropping of side gear.

3) Remove knuckle attaching bolts and remove hub, knuckle and axle shaft as an assembly. Remove hub nut and pull hub off shaft. Using a ball joint remover, separate lower ball joint from knuckle, if necessary.

Fig. 1: Exploded View of Sentra Front Axle Assembly

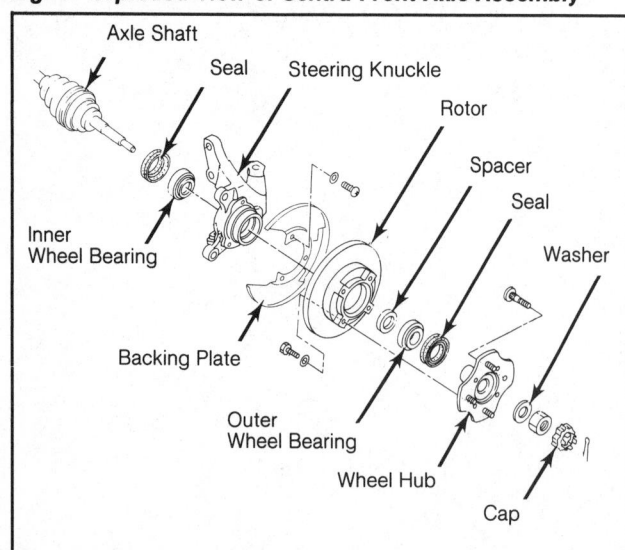

Disassembly

NOTE: **Manufacturer does not recommend disassembly of CV joints. Replace joint assemblies as complete components, if defective.**

1) Place axle shaft in soft-jawed vise with inner CV joint facing up. Remove and discard boot bands from inner boot. Remove inner CV joint housing and stub axle from axle shaft.

2) Mark spider assembly-to-shaft position for reassembly reference. Remove and discard snap ring and press off spider assembly without dropping axle shaft. Remove dust boot. Using a saw blade, make several cuts down side of CV joint cover. Remove and discard cover by bending it off housing. Remove and discard "O" ring.

3) Turn axle shaft in vise so outer CV joint faces up. Remove and discard boot bands. Mark outer CV joint-to-shaft position for reassembly reference. Lightly tap joint with plastic mallet to separate joint from axle shaft. Remove and discard snap ring. Remove boot.

Fig. 2: Exploded View of Sentra Axle Shaft

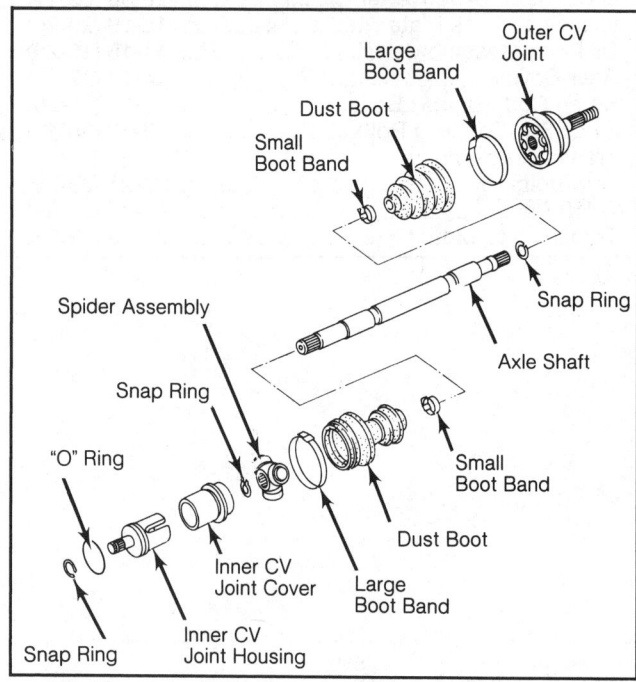

Note differences for inner and outer CV joints.

Inspection

1) Thoroughly clean all parts in solvent and blow dry with compressed air. Replace axle shaft if cracked or twisted. Replace outer CV joint if damaged or deformed. Replace cracked or worn boots.

2) Check inner CV joint for worn or damaged needle bearings. Check splines on axle shaft and spider assembly for wear. Check roller bearing surfaces of spider assembly for damage, scratches and wear. Replace defective components as required.

Reassembly

1) Mount axle shaft in soft-jawed vise with outer end facing out. Position dust boot and new small boot band on shaft without tearing boot on shaft splines. Slide outer CV joint onto shaft, aligning marks made during disassembly. Seat joint by lightly tapping with plastic mallet. Retain joint with new snap ring.

2) Pack joint assembly with grease (1/2 oz. on outer side and 3 oz. on inner side). Install new large boot band. Wrap band around boot 2 times and tighten using screwdriver and pliers. Using a punch, lock band in position. Cut off excess band, leaving amount equal to band width. Bend excess back over itself.

DATSUN/NISSAN SENTRA & 310 (Cont.)

3) Position dust boot on shaft so its length is 3.94" (100 mm). Secure small band in position without deforming or buckling dust boot. Turn axle shaft in vise so inner end faces up.

4) Coat new "O" ring with grease and install on CV joint housing. Install new cover on housing and bend outer edge at 2 points (180° apart) using block of wood to prevent damage. Housing cover should not rattle. Apply sealant at outer edge of housing and cover.

5) Position boot and new small band on axle shaft. Slide spider assembly onto shaft, aligning marks made during disassembly. Press spider assembly into position with splined chamfer facing axle shaft. Retain in position with new snap ring (round surface facing spider assembly).

6) Pack CV joint assembly with 6.5 oz. of grease. Install new large boot band and secure in same manner as for inner CV joint. Position dust boot on shaft so its length is 4.17" (106 mm). Secure small band in position without deforming or buckling dust boot.

Installation

To install, reverse removal procedure and note the following:

1) Place axle shaft in knuckle, aligning splines with hub splines. Place assembly in vise and draw shaft into hub by tightening hub nut. Check and adjust wheel bearing preload. *See Wheel Bearings in this article.* Install new cotter pin in hub nut.

2) Install new differential seals, if required. Install new snap ring on axle shaft. Remove tool (installed during removal) from side of differential case. Install axle shaft, aligning splines, by tapping on inner CV joint cover flange or press-fitting.

3) After installation into differential case, try to pull flange out of inner CV joint housing by hand to ensure proper engagement of snap ring. Use new cotter pins and lower ball joint nuts. Bleed brake system and replace transaxle fluid.

Removal (310)

1) Raise and support vehicle. Remove wheel and tire. Pry cotter pin out of hub. Loosen, do not remove, wheel hub nut from axle shaft while preventing hub from turning. Disconnect lower ball joint from transverse link.

2) Drain gear oil from transaxle case. Disconnect side rod ball stud at steering knuckle arm. Remove axle shaft from transaxle. Do not damage oil seal during axle shaft removal. Insert a bar or equivalent tool into

Fig. 3: Exploded View of 310 Front Axle Assembly

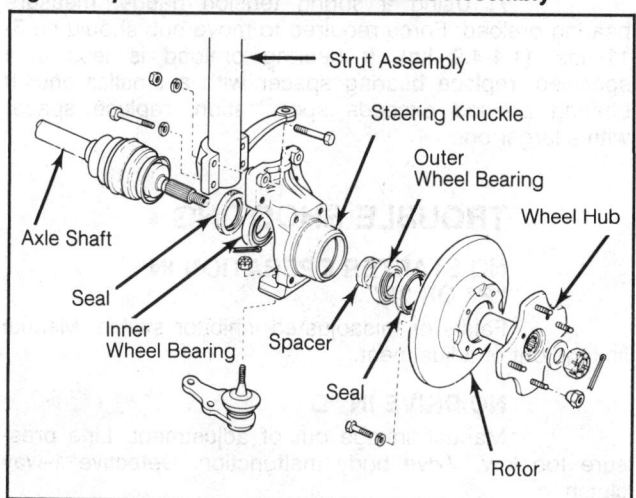

each side of differential case to prevent dropping of side gears.

3) Disconnect brake tube. Remove steering knuckle bolts from strut and separate knuckle from strut. Remove axle shaft, hub, knuckle and caliper as an assembly. Remove hub nut. Mount axle shaft in a vise. Using a puller, separate hub from shaft without damaging knuckle seal. Remove and discard axle shaft snap ring.

Disassembly

NOTE: Manufacturer does not recommend disassembly of outer CV joint. Replace both joint assemblies as complete components, if defective.

1) Place axle shaft in soft-jawed vise with inner CV joint facing out. Straighten and remove large boot band with screwdriver. Detach dust boot from CV joint housing.

2) On inner side of CV joint, remove large snap ring. Pull off housing and stub shaft. Wipe grease off cage and pop balls out of cage with a screwdriver. Rotate cage about 1/2 turn and remove.

3) Remove small snap ring and tap inner ring with plastic mallet to remove. Remove small boot band and slide off dust boot.

Fig. 4: Exploded View of 310 Axle Shaft Assembly

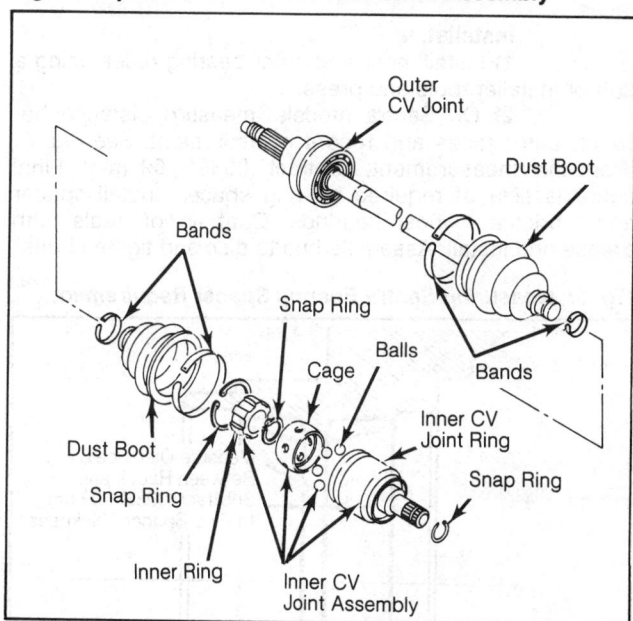

Note differences for inner and outer CV joints.

Inspection

Thoroughly clean all parts in solvent and blow dry with compressed air. Replace axle shaft if cracked or twisted. Replace CV joint if damaged, deformed, or if rust or excessive play are apparent. Replace dust boot if cracked or worn.

Reassembly

To reassemble, reverse disassembly procedure and note the following: Pack joint with grease. Install new bands. Wrap band around boot 2 times and bend it back over itself. Lock band in position and cut off excess, leaving amount equal to band width.

Installation

To install, reverse removal procedure and note the following:

1) Place axle shaft in knuckle, aligning splines with hub splines. Place assembly in vise and draw shaft into hub by tightening hub nut. Check and adjust wheel bearing preload. *See Wheel Bearings in this article.* Install new cotter pin in hub nut.

2) Install new differential seals, if required. Install new snap ring on axle shaft. Remove tool (installed during removal) from side of differential case. Install axle shaft, aligning splines. Bleed brake system and replace transaxle fluid.

WHEEL BEARINGS

NOTE: **Bearing spacers are available in size ranges of .291-.293" (7.381-7.440 mm) to .331-.333" (8.40-8.46 mm). Spacers are stamped with a 2-digit number for identification.**

Removal

1) Remove axle shaft and hub assembly. *See Axle Shafts in this article.* On Sentra models, separate hub from knuckle using a slide hammer. On 310 models, remove brake caliper. On all models, remove hub-to-rotor bolts and press out hub. Remove backing plate.

2) Remove and discard inner and outer grease seals. Remove bearing spacer and set aside. Using a bearing puller, remove outer wheel bearing. Using a hammer and brass drift, drive out inner and outer bearing races.

Installation

1) Install inner and outer bearing races using a drift or installer tools and press.

2) On Sentra models, measure distance between outer races and record measurement. *See Fig. 5.* From this measurement, subtract .0035" (.09 mm). Final figure is size of required bearing spacer. Install spacer and lubricated wheel bearings. Coat lip of seals with grease and install. Assemble hub to disc and tighten bolts.

Fig. 5: Measuring Sentra Bearing Spacer Requirement

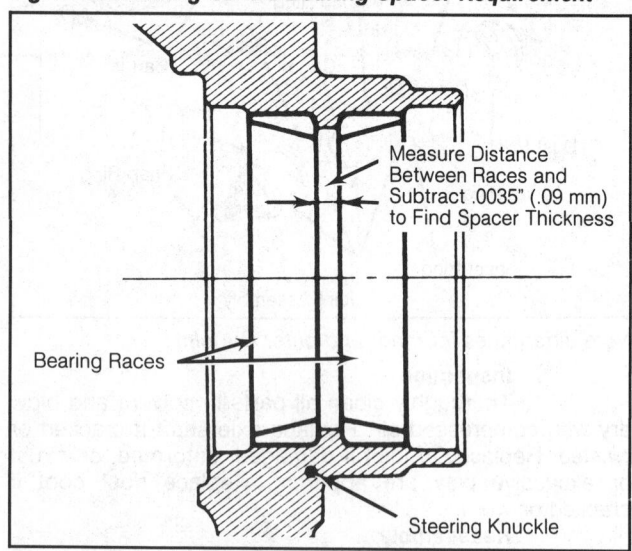

Measure Distance Between Races and Subtract .0035" (.09 mm) to Find Spacer Thickness

Bearing Races

Steering Knuckle

Measure gap between outer bearing races.

3) On 310 models, place outer bearing on base (KV40100700-3) and install knuckle so bearing seats in its race. Install inner wheel bearing over dummy shaft (KV40100700-1) and position assembly in knuckle. Place weight (KV40100700-2) over dummy shaft so it is resting in knuckle. *See Fig. 6.*

Fig. 6: Measuring 310 Bearing Spacer Requirement

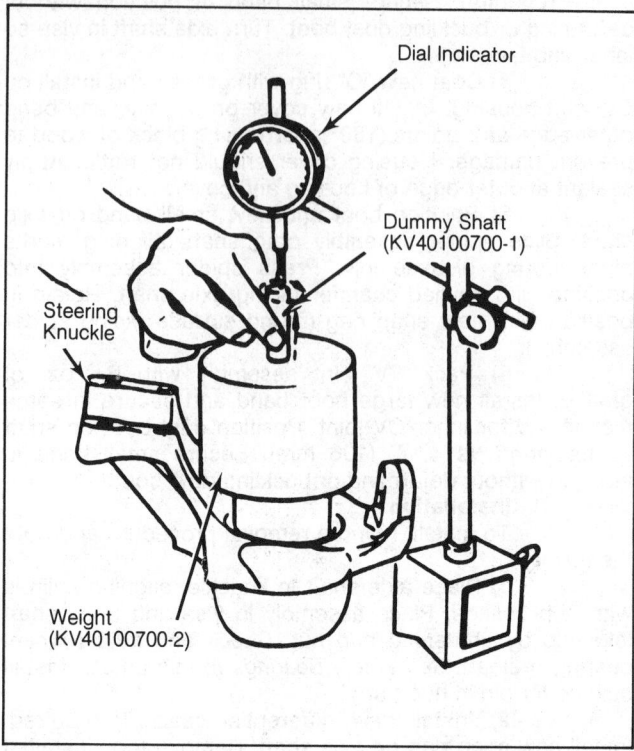

Dial Indicator

Dummy Shaft (KV40100700-1)

Steering Knuckle

Weight (KV40100700-2)

Note dial indicator reading and add dummy shaft thickness.

4) Rotate knuckle 10 times in each direction to properly seat bearings. Mount dial indicator on holding fixture. Place indicator tip on top of dummy shaft. Lift dummy shaft and rotate 1 full turn, recording dial indicator reading. Add metric dimension stamped on dummy shaft to this reading to determine required bearing spacer thickness.

5) Remove measuring tools and bearings. Assemble wheel hub to disc and tighten bolts. Press lubricated outer wheel bearing into hub and install backing plate. Install correct bearing spacer and press in lubricated inner bearing. Coat lip of seals with grease and install.

6) On all models, place axle shaft in knuckle, and place knuckle in soft-jawed vise. Place hub and rotor assembly on axle shaft, aligning splines. Install hub nut and tighten. Rotate hub several times in both directions.

7) Using a spring tension gauge, measure bearing preload. Force required to move hub should be 3-11 lbs. (1.4-4.9 kg). If bearing preload is less than specified, replace bearing spacer with a smaller one. If bearing preload exceeds specification, replace spacer with a larger one.

TROUBLE SHOOTING

NO STARTER OPERATION IN "P" OR "N"

Faulty or misadjusted inhibitor switch. Manual linkage out of adjustment.

NO DRIVE IN "D"

Manual linkage out of adjustment. Line pressure too low. Valve body malfunction. Defective 1-way clutch.

DATSUN/NISSAN SENTRA & 310 (Cont.)

NO DRIVE IN "R"

Manual linkage out of adjustment. Line pressure too low. Valve body malfunction. Faulty rear clutch. Faulty high-reverse (front) clutch. Faulty low-reverse brake. Leak in oil passage. Faulty front clutch check ball.

NO DRIVE IN ANY FORWARD RANGE

Manual linkage out of adjustment. Line pressure too low. Valve body malfunction. Faulty rear clutch. Faulty front clutch. Leak in oil passage.

HARSH ENGAGEMENT
From "N" to "D"

Idle speed too high. Throttle control cable out of adjustment. Line pressure too high. Valve body malfunction. Faulty rear clutch.

From "1" to "2"

Throttle control cable out of adjustment. Stall speed too high. Valve body malfunction. Faulty band servo. Faulty brake band.

From "2" to "3"

Throttle control cable out of adjustment. Line pressure too high. Valve body malfunction. Faulty band servo. Faulty front clutch.

POOR ACCELERATION

Low fluid level. Manual linkage out of adjustment. Line pressure too low. Stall speed too low. Valve body malfunction. Faulty band servo. Faulty rear clutch. Faulty front clutch. Faulty brake band. Faulty low-reverse brake. Defective oil pump.

TRANSAXLE OVERHEATS

Low fluid level. Line pressure too low. Stall speed too low. Valve body malfunction. Faulty band servo. Faulty front clutch. Faulty brake band. Faulty low-reverse brake. Faulty torque converter 1-way clutch. Faulty planetary gear set. Defective oil pump or oil passage leak.

TRANSMISSION SLIPS ON "1-2" UPSHIFT

Low fluid level. Manual linkage out of adjustment. Throttle control cable out of adjustment. Line pressure too low. Valve body malfunction. Faulty band servo. Faulty brake band. Leak in oil passage.

TRANSMISSION SLIPS ON "2-3" UPSHIFT

Low fluid level. Manual linkage out of adjustment. Throttle control cable out of adjustment. Line pressure too low. Valve body malfunction. Faulty band servo. Faulty front clutch. Leak in oil passage. Faulty front clutch check ball.

TRANSMISSION SLIPS ON STARTS

Low fluid level. Manual linkage out of adjustment. Throttle control cable out of adjustment. Valve body malfunction. Defective oil pump or oil passage leak.

NO DOWNSHIFT FROM "3" TO "2" OR "3" TO "1"

Throttle control cable out of adjustment. Valve body malfunction. Faulty governor. Faulty band servo. Faulty brake band. Faulty transaxle 1-way clutch.

NO "1-2" UPSHIFT

Manual linkage out of adjustment. Throttle control cable out of adjustment. Faulty detent valve. Valve body malfunction. Faulty governor. Faulty band servo. Faulty brake band. Leak in oil passage.

NO "2-3" UPSHIFT

Manual linkage out of adjustment. Throttle control cable out of adjustment. Faulty detent valve. Valve body malfunction. Faulty governor. Faulty band servo. Faulty front clutch. Faulty front clutch check ball. Leak in oil passage.

TORQUE CONVERTER DIAGNOSIS (SENTRA ONLY)
Converter Not Locked-Up

Faulty governor. Line pressure too low. Defective input shaft "O" ring. Defective converter. Faulty speed cut valve or lock-up control valve. Defective oil pump.

Lock-Up Piston Slip

Line pressure too low. Defective input shaft "O" ring. Defective converter or oil pump.

Lock-Up Point Too High or Too Low

Faulty governor. Faulty speed cut valve or lock-up control valve.

Transaxle Overheats

Line pressure too low. Defective input shaft "O" ring. Defective converter or oil pump.

TESTING

ROAD TEST

1) Before road testing, ensure fluid level and condition, and control linkage adjustments have been checked and corrected as necessary. During test, transmission should upshift and downshift at approximately the same speeds as shown in *Shift Speeds* chart.

2) All shifts may vary slightly due to production tolerances or tire size. The important factor is the quality of the shifts. All shifts should be smooth, responsive, and with no slippage or engine speed runaway.

3) Slippage or engine runaway in any gear usually indicates clutch or band problems. The slipping clutch or band in a particular gear can usually be identified by noting transmission operation in other selector positions and comparing internal units which are applied in these positions. See *Clutch and Band Application* chart.

SHIFT SPEEDS SPECIFICATIONS

Application	MPH
Minimum Throttle	
1-2 Upshift	7-12
2-3 Upshift	14-19
3-2 Downshift	12-16
2-1 Downshift	6-12
Full Throttle	
1-2 Upshift	29-34
2-3 Upshift	57-62
3-2 Downshift	55-59
2-1 Downshift	17-26
Lock-Up Shift Points (Sentra Only)	
Engaged	39-46
Disengaged	37-44

CLUTCH AND BRAKE APPLICATION CHART (ELEMENTS IN USE)

Selector Lever Position	Clutch		Low-Reverse Brake	1-Way Clutch	Band Servo	
	High-Reverse (Front)	Forward (Rear)			Operation	Release
D — DRIVE						
Low		X	[1]	X		
Second		X			X	
Third [2]	X	X			(X)	X
2 — Second Gear						
Low		X		X		
Second		X			X	
1 — First Gear						
Low		X	X	X		
Second		X			X	
R — Reverse	X		X			

NEUTRAL OR PARK — All clutches and brakes released and/or ineffective.

[1] — Low & reverse brake applied to prevent free wheeling while coasting to provide engine braking.
[2] — Lock-up converter engaged on Sentra only.

STALL SPEED TEST

Stall Test Precautions

Before making a stall speed test, ensure that line pressure is correct. If line pressure is too low when performing a stall test, transmission can be damaged. Also, during stall test, do not hold throttle open for more than 5 seconds at a time.

Stall Test Procedure

1) Road test vehicle and warm transmission to normal operating temperature. Connect tachometer to engine. Position tachometer so that it can be read from driver's seat.

2) Set parking and service brakes. Start engine and place selector lever in "D". Depress accelerator pedal completely and note maximum RPM obtained. RPM should be approximately as shown in *Stall Speed* chart.

3) Place selector lever in "N" and allow engine to idle to cool off transmission. Then, place selector lever in "R" and repeat stall test. Stall RPM should be approximately as shown in *Stall Speed* chart.

STALL SPEED SPECIFICATIONS

Application	Stall Speed (RPM)
Sentra	1800-2100
310	1650-1950

Stall Test Results

1) If stall test RPM is about 600 RPM lower than specifications, torque converter 1-way clutch is slipping and torque converter should be replaced. If stall RPM is about 300 RPM lower than specifications, engine performance may be unsatisfactory.

2) If stall test RPM is about 300 RPM above specifications in "R", low-reverse brakes are faulty. If RPM is about 300 RPM above specifications in "D", front clutch is slipping.

LINE PRESSURE TEST

1) Road test vehicle to bring transmission to normal operating temperature. Connect a pressure gauge to test port. Connect gauge to port "1" to test all forward range line pressures. *See Fig. 7*. Place gauge so that it is visible from driver's seat. Connect tachometer to engine.

Fig. 7: Transaxle Case Pressure Test Port Locations

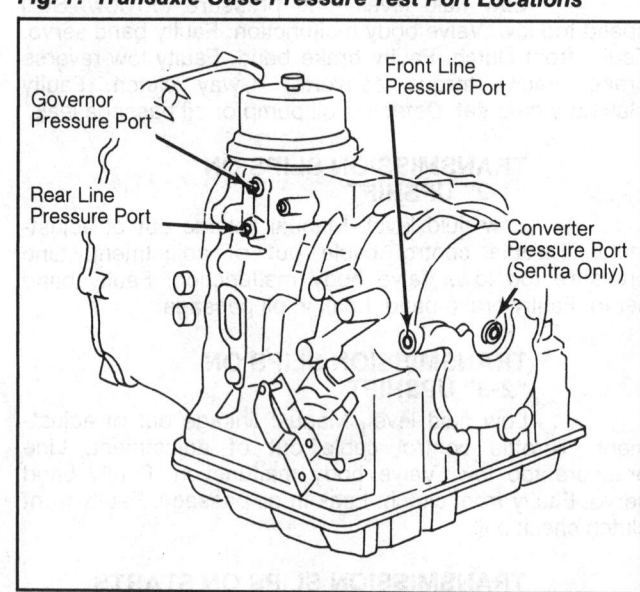

Connect pressure gauge to proper test port.

2) Start engine and if necessary, adjust idle speed. Depress brake pedal and place selector lever in "D". Note line pressure reading on gauge. Repeat procedure for each forward range. Pressure should be approximately as shown in *Line Pressure* chart.

DATSUN/NISSAN SENTRA & 310 (Cont.)

3) Connect gauge to port "2" to test reverse range line pressure. *See Fig. 7.* Repeat line pressure test with selector lever in "R". Pressure should be approximately as shown in *Line Pressure* chart.

4) After testing at idle, road test vehicle and note readings at full throttle position. Pressure should be approximately as shown in *Line Pressure* chart.

LINE PRESSURE SPECIFICATIONS

Application	psi (kg/cm²)
Sentra	
Idle	
In All Forward Ranges	36-50 (2.5-3.5)
In "R"	185-213 (13-15)
Full Throttle	
In All Forward Ranges	80-101 (5.6-7.1)
In "R"	185-213 (13-15)
310	
Idle	
In "D" & "1"	40-50 (2.8-3.5)
In "2"	78-92 (5.5-6.5)
In "R"	85-107 (6.0-7.5)
Full Throttle	
In "D" & "1"	78-92 (5.5-6.5)
In "2"	80-92 (5.6-6.5)
In "R"	192-206 (13.5-14.5)

LINE PRESSURE TEST RESULTS

Pressure Too High

If pressure is too high, check throttle cable adjustment. If cable is correctly adjusted and pressure is still high, regulator valve or throttle valve may be seized.

Pressure Too Low

If line pressure is too low, check for seizing of regulator valve or throttle valve in valve body. If valves are not seized, check pressure relief valve and oil pump assembly for damage. A defective oil pump assembly will usually make noise.

GOVERNOR PRESSURE TEST

NOTE: **Governor pressure is a "modified" line pressure. Therefore, governor pressure will be incorrect if line pressure is incorrect. Line pressure must be correct before checking governor pressure.**

Testing Procedures

Road test vehicle to warm transmission to normal operating temperature. Connect pressure gauge to pressure port "3" on transmission case. *See Fig. 7.* Position gauge so it is visible from driver's seat. Test drive vehicle in "D" and note pressure readings. Pressures should be less than line pressure readings.

TORQUE CONVERTER LOCK-UP TEST (SENTRA ONLY)

Road test vehicle to warm transmission to normal operating temperature. Connect pressure gauge to port "4" on transmission case. *See Fig. 7.* Position gauge so it is visible from driver's seat. Test drive vehicle in "D" and note pressure readings. Pressure should be approximately as shown in *Torque Converter Lock-Up Pressure* chart.

TORQUE CONVERTER LOCK-UP PRESSURE SPECIFICATIONS

Application	psi (kg/cm²)
Sentra Only	
Lock-Up Engaged	Less than 7.0 (0.5)
Lock-Up Disengaged	Greater than 28.0 (2.0)

REMOVAL & INSTALLATION

See the appropriate article in AUTOMATIC TRANSMISSION REMOVAL Section.

TORQUE CONVERTER

Torque converter is a sealed unit and cannot be disassembled for service. Replace if defective.

TRANSAXLE DISASSEMBLY

1) Remove hex plug and drain fluid. Mark position of torque converter in housing and remove torque converter. Remove oil pump shaft and input shaft. Remove snap ring, governor cap with breather hose (if equipped) and "O" ring. Remove oil pan guard and oil pan.

2) Remove valve body bolts and valve body. Remove particle magnet and manual valve. Remove gear selector shaft retaining nuts. Pull out retaining pin and remove throttle lever, selector plate, selector shaft, selector lever and parking rod assembly.

3) Disconnect throttle cable from throttle lever and remove cable. Remove parking actuator support from case. Loosen brake band piston stem lock nut and back off piston stem several turns. Apply compressed air to oil supply hole to remove accumulator piston. Place rag over piston to prevent it from jumping out of bore. *See Fig. 9.*

Fig. 9: Removing Accumulator Piston

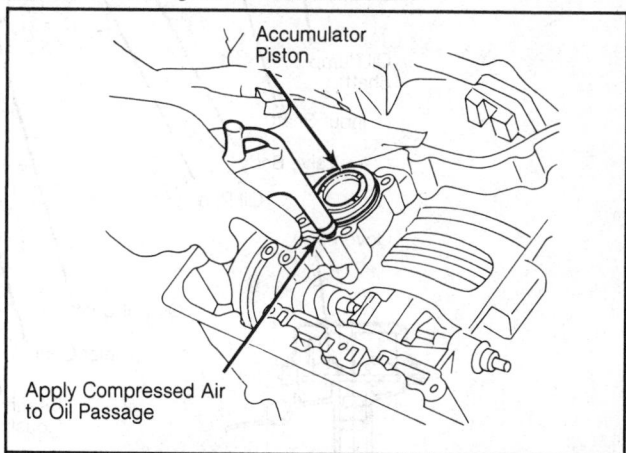

Accumulator Piston

Apply Compressed Air to Oil Passage

Place rag over piston to prevent it from jumping out of bore.

4) Remove converter housing retaining bolts. Tap converter housing with plastic mallet to separate it from transaxle case. DO NOT drop final drive assembly. Remove final drive assembly and place aside. Pull out parking pawl shaft. Remove parking pawl and return spring.

5) Using a chisel and hammer, straighten tang on idler gear bolt lock washer. Remove idler gear bolt and

Automatic Transmissions

DATSUN/NISSAN SENTRA & 310 (Cont.)

Fig. 8: Sectional View of Datsun/Nissan Sentra and 310 Transaxle Assembly

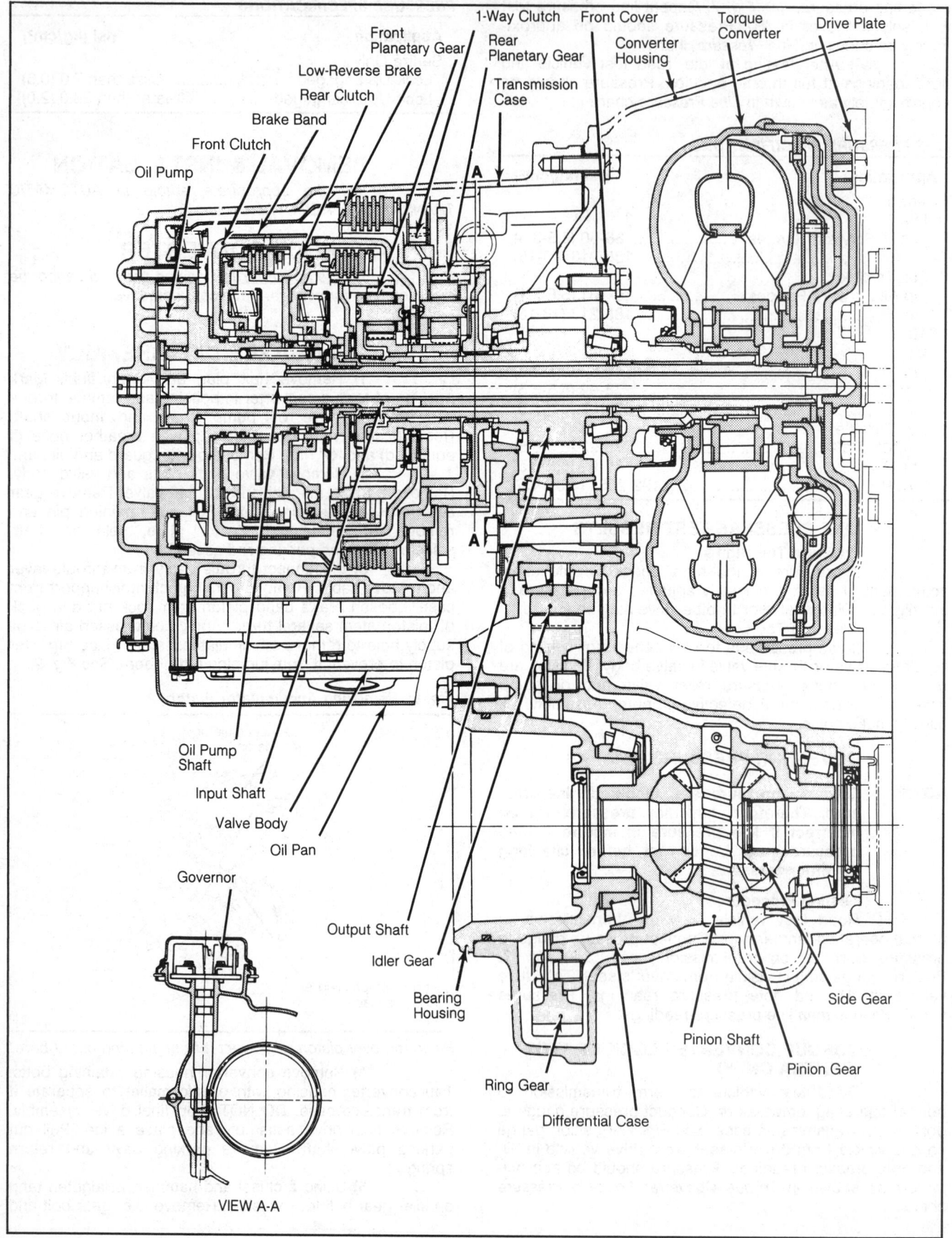

VIEW A-A

DATSUN/NISSAN SENTRA & 310 (Cont.)

lock washer. Turn transaxle case over and remove front cover retaining bolts. Hold front cover and tap output shaft with plastic mallet to loosen. Remove output shaft and front cover as an assembly. DO NOT lose adjusting shim on output shaft.

6) Remove front cover gasket. Tap out idler gear, idler gear shaft and bearings with drift and hammer. Remove planetary gear set seal bushing from case. Turn case so torque converter housing faces up. Remove governor shaft retaining bolt and pull out governor shaft. Remove rear internal gear, bearing race and thrust washer.

7) Remove 1-way clutch snap ring and lift out 1-way clutch assembly with rear carrier assembly. Remove bearing race and thrust washer. Remove snap ring and connecting shell. Remove snap ring, thrust bearing and bearing race. Lift out planetary gear set. Remove thrust bearing and race. Lift out front carrier assembly and internal gear as an assembly.

Fig. 10: Brake Band Securing Clip Installation

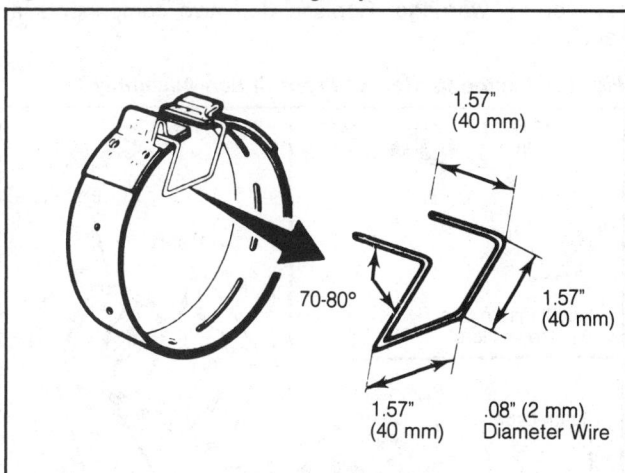

Use specifications shown to fabricate clip.

8) Lift out rear clutch assembly and plastic thrust washer. Remove low-reverse brake retaining plate, discs and plates all at the same time. Rotate and remove front clutch assembly.

Fig. 11: Low-Reverse Brake Piston Removal

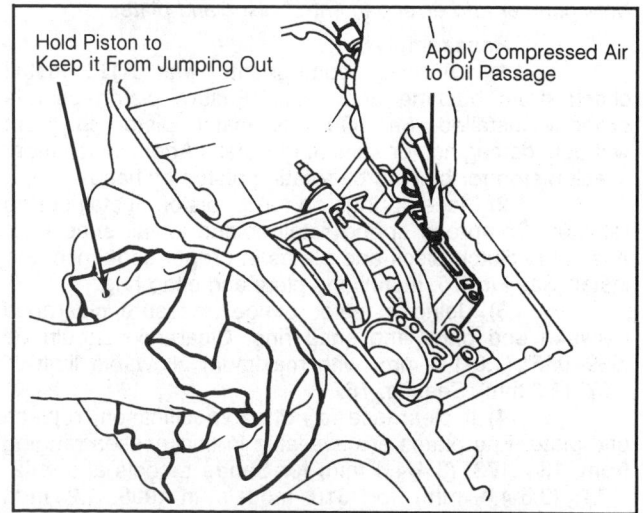

Apply compressed air and hold cloth over piston.

NOTE: If front clutch seal rings have expanded, front clutch assembly will be difficult to remove. DO NOT force out clutch assembly as seal damage may occur.

9) Install securing clip into ends of brake band and remove brake band. Securing clip can be fabricated from .08" (2 mm) diameter wire stock. See Fig. 10.

10) Remove low-reverse brake retainer. Apply compressed air to oil passage to remove low-reverse brake piston. Place cloth over piston to prevent it from jumping out. See Fig. 11. If compressed air is not available, use a screwdriver to remove piston.

11) Remove oil pump assembly, nylon washer and thrust bearing by lifting straight out of case. Use care in lifting out oil pump; clearance is very close even though pump fits loosely. Remove inhibitor switch. Remove band servo piston and return spring.

COMPONENT DISASSEMBLY & REASSEMBLY

OIL PUMP ASSEMBLY

Disassembly

Remove bearing and thrust washer. Remove oil pump plate. Mark pump drive and driven gears for reassembly in same position. DO NOT punch marks. Remove gear hub and gears from pump housing. Remove steel ball and pressure relief spring from its bore.

Fig. 12: Exploded View of Oil Pump Assembly

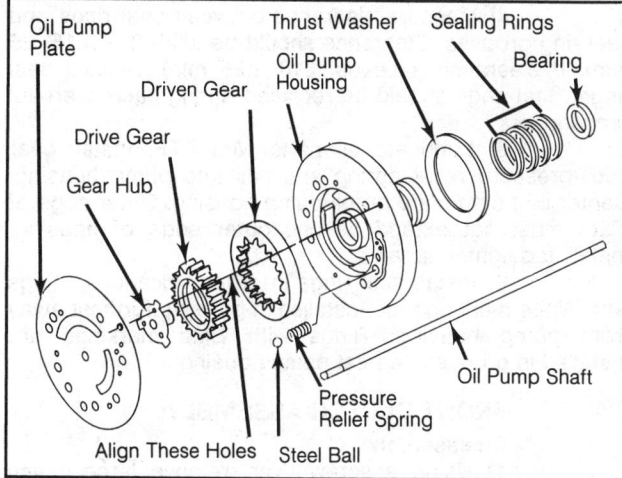

Mark gears for reassembly reference.

Inspection

Thoroughly clean all parts and dry with compressed air. Inspect all parts for wear, cracks, or scoring. If pump housing, cover, drive gear or driven gear requires replacement, complete oil pump assembly must be replaced as a matched set.

Reassembly

1) Install drive and driven gear into housing, aligning marks made at disassembly. Using a feeler gauge, measure clearance between pump driven gear and pump housing. Clearance should be .008-.012" (.20-.30 mm) for Sentra models and .003-.008" (.05-.20 mm) for 310 models. If clearance exceeds .014" (.35 mm) on Sentra models or .010" (.25 mm) on 310 models, replace oil pump assembly.

2) Check clearance between driven gear and crescent. Clearance should be .008-.012" (.20-.30 mm) for Sentra models and .006-.008" (.14-.20 mm) for 310 models. If clearance exceeds .014" (.35 mm) for Sentra models or .010" (.25 mm) for 310 models, replace oil pump.

Fig. 13: Measuring Housing-to-Gear Face Clearance

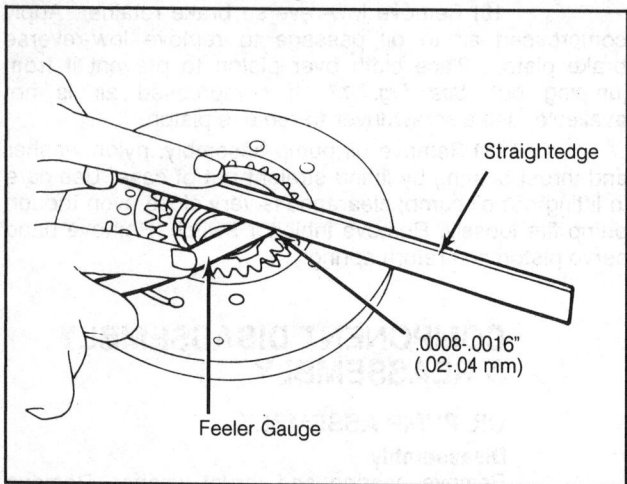

Use straightedge and feeler gauge.

3) Using a straightedge and feeler gauge, check pump housing face-to-gear face clearance. Clearance should be .0008-.0016" (.02-.04 mm) for all models. If clearance exceeds .003" (.08 mm), replace oil pump assembly.

4) Measure clearance between seal rings and seal ring grooves. Clearance should be .006-.010" (.15-.25 mm). If clearance exceeds .010" (.25 mm), replace seal rings. Seal rings should be replaced during each overhaul procedure.

5) Lubricate all parts with ATF. Install gear hub, pressure relief spring and ball into pump housing. Center oil pump plate on oil pump housing. Outer edge of plate must not extend beyond outer edge of housing. Install and tighten screws.

6) Install seal rings in proper locations. Rings with White markings are installed in grooves furthest away from pump housing. Rings with Blue markings are installed in grooves nearest pump housing.

FRONT CLUTCH ASSEMBLY
Disassembly

1) Using a screwdriver, remove large clutch retaining snap ring. Remove clutch plates, noting number and arrangement of discs and plates. Using a spring compressor, compress clutch springs and remove snap ring from spring retainer. Remove spring retainer and lift out springs.

2) Using an air gun with a rubber tip, apply compressed air to oil passage hole to remove clutch piston from drum. Use care in removing piston so it is not damaged. See Fig. 14. Remove and discard seals. Remove drum bushing and set aside.

Inspection

Check clutch discs for wear or damage. Measure plate thickness. Plate thickness should be .059-.065" (1.50-1.65 mm). Replace plate if any thickness measures less than .055" (1.4 mm). Check snap ring for wear, springs for weakness or broken coils, and spring

Fig. 14: Removing Front Clutch Piston

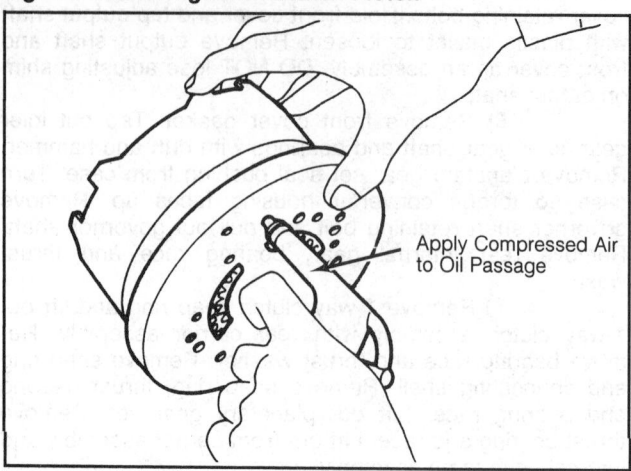

Apply Compressed Air to Oil Passage

Apply compressed air to oil passage.

retainer for warpage. Replace defective components as required.

Fig. 15: Exploded View of Front Clutch Assembly

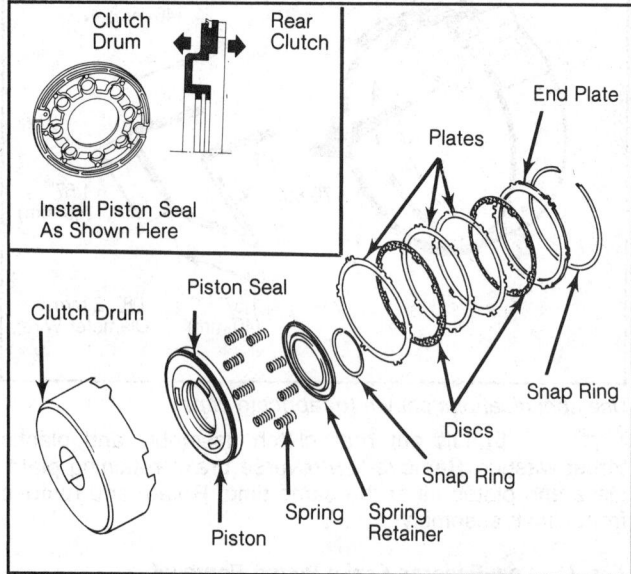

Note number and arrangement of discs and plates.

Reassembly

1) Lubricate components with ATF. Install clutch drum bushing and seals. Ensure piston seal is properly installed. See Fig. 15. Install piston in drum without damaging or pinching seal. After installation, check piston for binding by rotating piston by hand.

2) Place springs on top of piston. Install spring retainer. Compress spring retainer and install snap ring. Assemble clutch discs and plates in proper sequence and install. See Fig. 15. Install end plate and snap ring.

3) Using a feeler gauge, measure clearance between end plate and snap ring. Clearance should be .039-.055" (1.0-1.4 mm) with maximum allowable limit of .087" (2.2 mm). See Fig. 16.

4) If clearance is not to specification, replace end plate. End plates are available in thicknesses ranging from .134-.173" (3.4-4.4 mm) for Sentra models and .142-.173" (3.6-4.4 mm) for 310 models in .008" (.2 mm) increments.

DATSUN/NISSAN SENTRA & 310 (Cont.)

Fig. 16: Measuring End Plate-to-Snap Ring Clearance

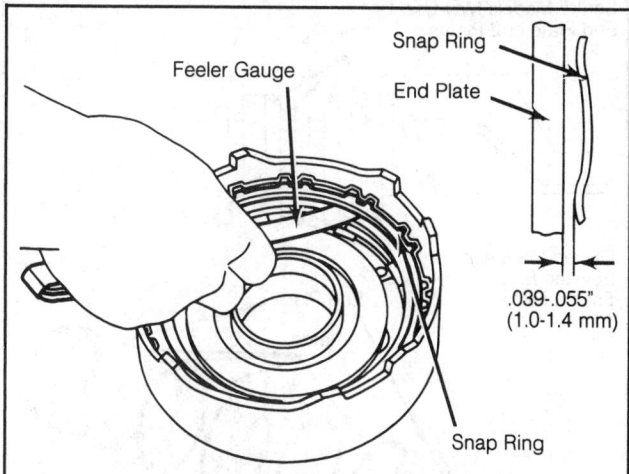

.039-.055"
(1.0-1.4 mm)

Replace end plate if clearance is not to specification.

5) After complete assembly of front clutch, test clutch operation with compressed air. Engagement of piston should be heard when compressed air is applied to oil passage hole. *See Fig. 14.*

REAR CLUTCH ASSEMBLY

Disassembly

1) Using a screwdriver, remove large clutch retaining snap ring. Remove clutch plates, noting number and arrangement of discs and plates. Using a spring compressor, compress clutch springs and remove snap ring from spring retainer. Remove spring retainer and lift out springs.

2) Using an air gun with a rubber tip, apply compressed air to oil passage hole to remove clutch piston from drum. Use care in removing piston so it is not damaged. *See Fig. 17.* Remove and discard seals. Remove drum bushing and set aside.

Fig. 17: Removing Rear Clutch Piston

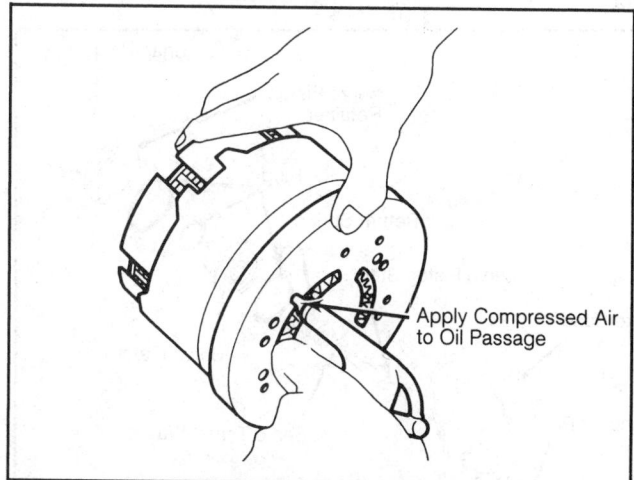

Apply Compressed Air to Oil Passage

Apply compressed air to oil passage.

Inspection

Check clutch discs for wear or damage. Measure plate thickness. Plate thickness should be .059-.065" (1.50-1.65 mm). Replace plate if any thickness measures less than .055" (1.4 mm). Check snap ring for wear, springs for weakness or broken coils, and spring

retainer for warpage. Replace defective components as required.

Fig. 18: Exploded View of Rear Clutch Assembly

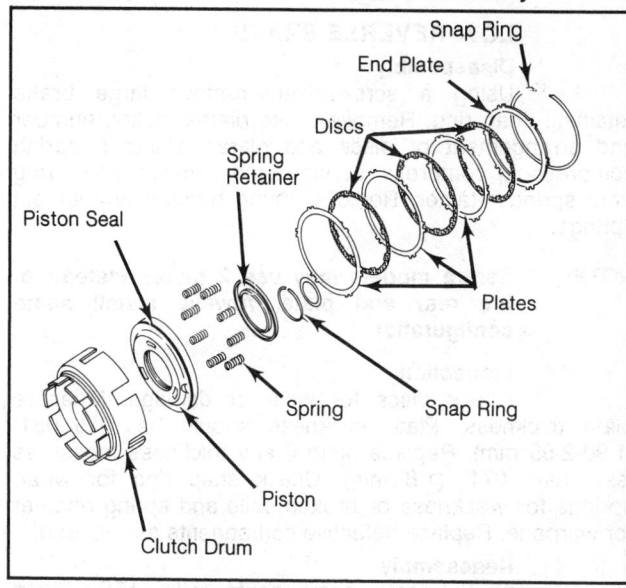

Note number and arrangement of discs and plates.

Reassembly

1) Lubricate components with ATF. Install clutch drum bushing and seals. Ensure piston seal is properly installed. Install piston in drum without damaging or pinching seal. After installation, check piston for binding by rotating piston by hand.

2) Place springs on top of piston and install spring retainer. Compress spring retainer and install snap ring. Install dished plate with beveled end facing piston. Assemble clutch discs and plates in proper sequence and install. *See Fig. 18.* Install end plate and large snap ring.

3) Using a feeler gauge, measure clearance between end plate and snap ring. Clearance should be .031-.047" (0.8-1.2 mm) with maximum allowable limit of .110" (2.8 mm). *See Fig. 19.*

4) If clearance is not to specification, replace end plate. End plates are available in thicknesses ranging from .134-.173" (3.4-4.4 mm) for Sentra models and .142-.173" (3.6-4.4 mm) for 310 models in .008" (.2 mm) increments.

Fig. 19: Measuring End Plate-to-Snap Ring Clearance

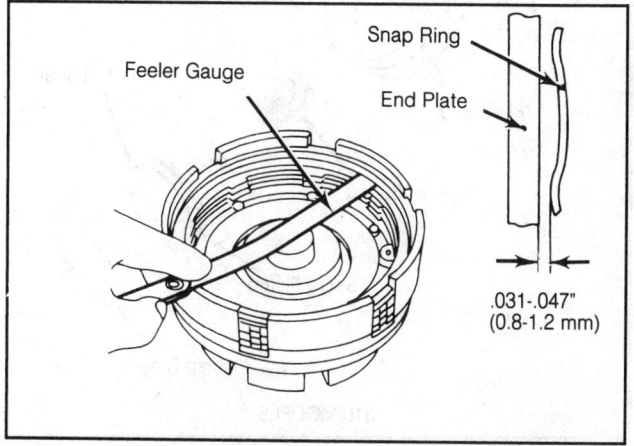

.031-.047"
(0.8-1.2 mm)

Replace end plate if clearance is not to specification.

DATSUN/NISSAN SENTRA & 310 (Cont.)

5) After complete assembly of rear clutch, test clutch operation with compressed air. Engagement of piston should be heard when compressed air is applied to oil passage hole. *See Fig. 17.*

LOW-REVERSE BRAKE

Disassembly

Using a screwdriver, remove large brake retaining snap ring. Remove brake plates, noting number and arrangement of discs and plates. Using a spring compressor, compress springs and remove snap ring from spring retainer. Remove spring retainer and lift out springs.

NOTE: **Sentra models may use 2 plates instead of the rear end plate. Always install same configuration.**

Inspection

Check discs for wear or damage. Measure plate thickness. Plate thickness should be .075-.081" (1.90-2.05 mm). Replace plate if any thickness measures less than .071" (1.8 mm). Check snap ring for wear, springs for weakness or broken coils and spring retainer for warpage. Replace defective components as required.

Reassembly

1) Lubricate components with ATF. Place springs in piston and install spring retainer. Compress spring retainer and install snap ring. Install dished plate with beveled end facing piston (Sentra only). Assemble clutch discs and plates in proper sequence and install. *See Fig. 20.* Install end plate and large snap ring.

2) Using a feeler gauge, measure clearance between end plate and snap ring. Clearance should be .031-.043" (0.8-1.2 mm) on 310 models. Clearance on Sentra models should be .075-.087" (1.9-2.2 mm) with maximum allowable limit of .15" (3.8 mm).

3) If clearance is not to specification, replace end plate. End plates are available in thicknesses ranging from .142-.173" (3.6-4.4 mm) in .008" (.2 mm) increments.

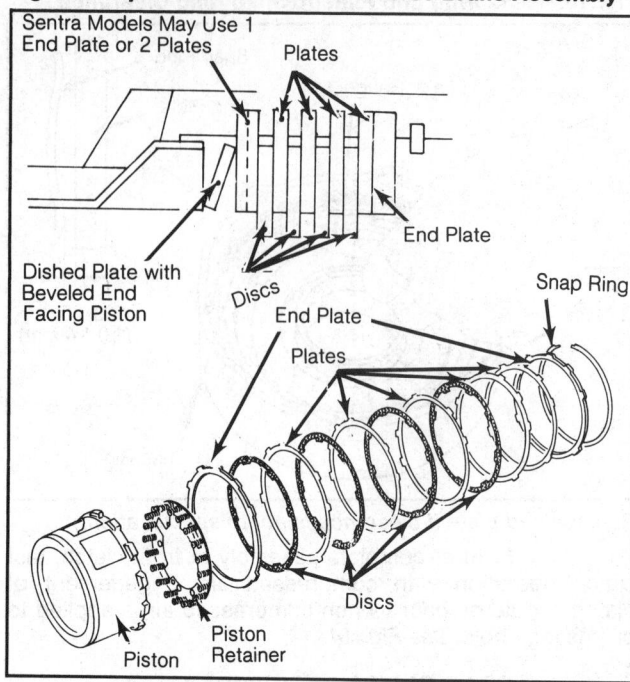

Fig. 20: *Exploded View of Low-Reverse Brake Assembly*

Note number and arrangement of discs and plates.

BRAKE BAND & BAND SERVO

Disassembly

1) On Sentra models, remove adjusting nut and washer from anchor pin. Remove anchor pin and pull off band servo assembly. Remove snap ring and separate servo piston retainer from piston. Disassemble piston assembly and discard "O" rings.

2) On 310 models, remove piston stem and washer. Pull off servo piston assembly. Remove snap ring and separate piston components. Remove and discard "O" rings.

Fig. 21: *Exploded View of Brake Band and Band Servo Assemblies*

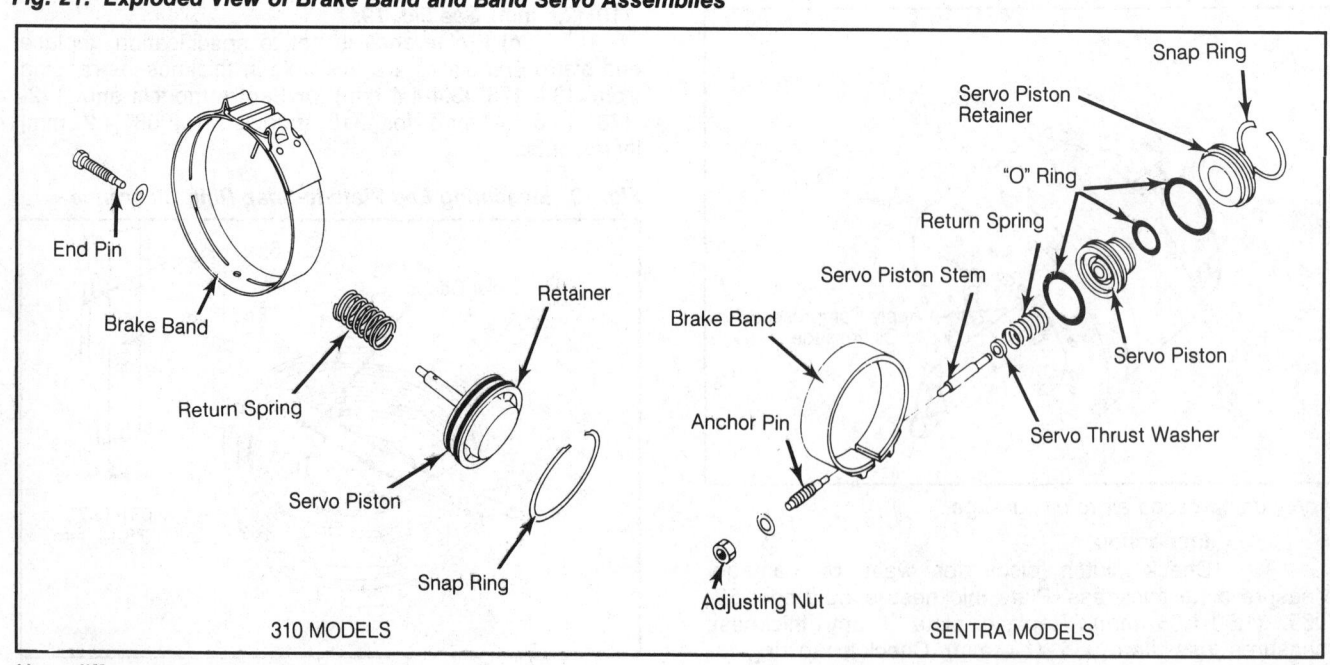

Note difference between models.

DATSUN/NISSAN SENTRA & 310 (Cont.)

Inspection

Check and replace brake band if cracked, chipped or burnt. Check band servo components and replace if worn or scored.

Reassembly

To reassemble, reverse disassembly procedure and note the following: Install new "O" rings and ensure snap ring is properly seated. Perform band adjustment during transaxle reassembly.

PLANETARY GEAR SET

Manufacturer does not recommend disassembly of planetary gear set. Measure clearance between planetary carrier and pinion washer. Normal clearance should be .008-.028" (.20-.70 mm). If clearance exceeds .032" (.80 mm) or gear set is worn or damaged, replace planetary gear set. Heat damage is revealed by Blue discoloration of gear sets.

GOVERNOR ASSEMBLY

Disassembly

Remove governor body-to-governor shaft bolts. Mount governor shaft in a soft-jawed vise and drive out gear retaining pin. Remove drive gear. Disassemble governor valve body and place components in order of disassembly. DO NOT interchange primary and secondary governor components.

Inspection

Check governor valves for burns and scratches. Check springs for weakness and burning. Replace defective components as required.

Fig. 22: Exploded View of Governor Assembly

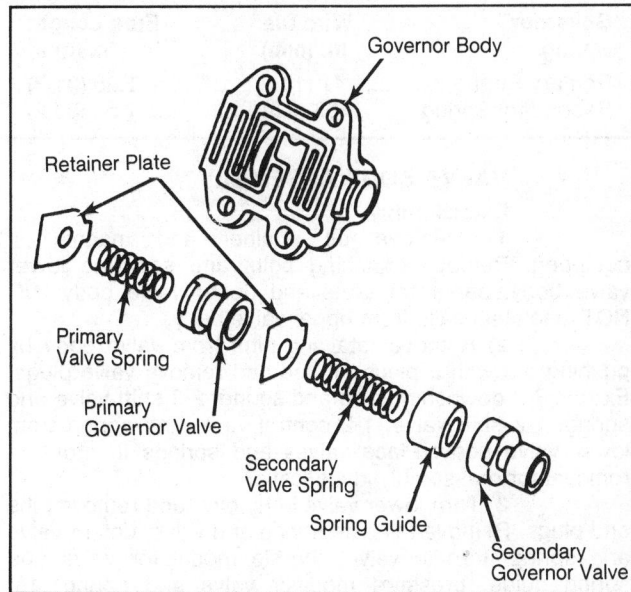

Do not interchange valve components.

Reassembly

To reassemble, reverse disassembly procedure and note the following: Make sure primary and secondary governor springs are properly installed. *See Governor Valve Spring chart.*

Fig. 23: Exploded View of Lower Valve Body

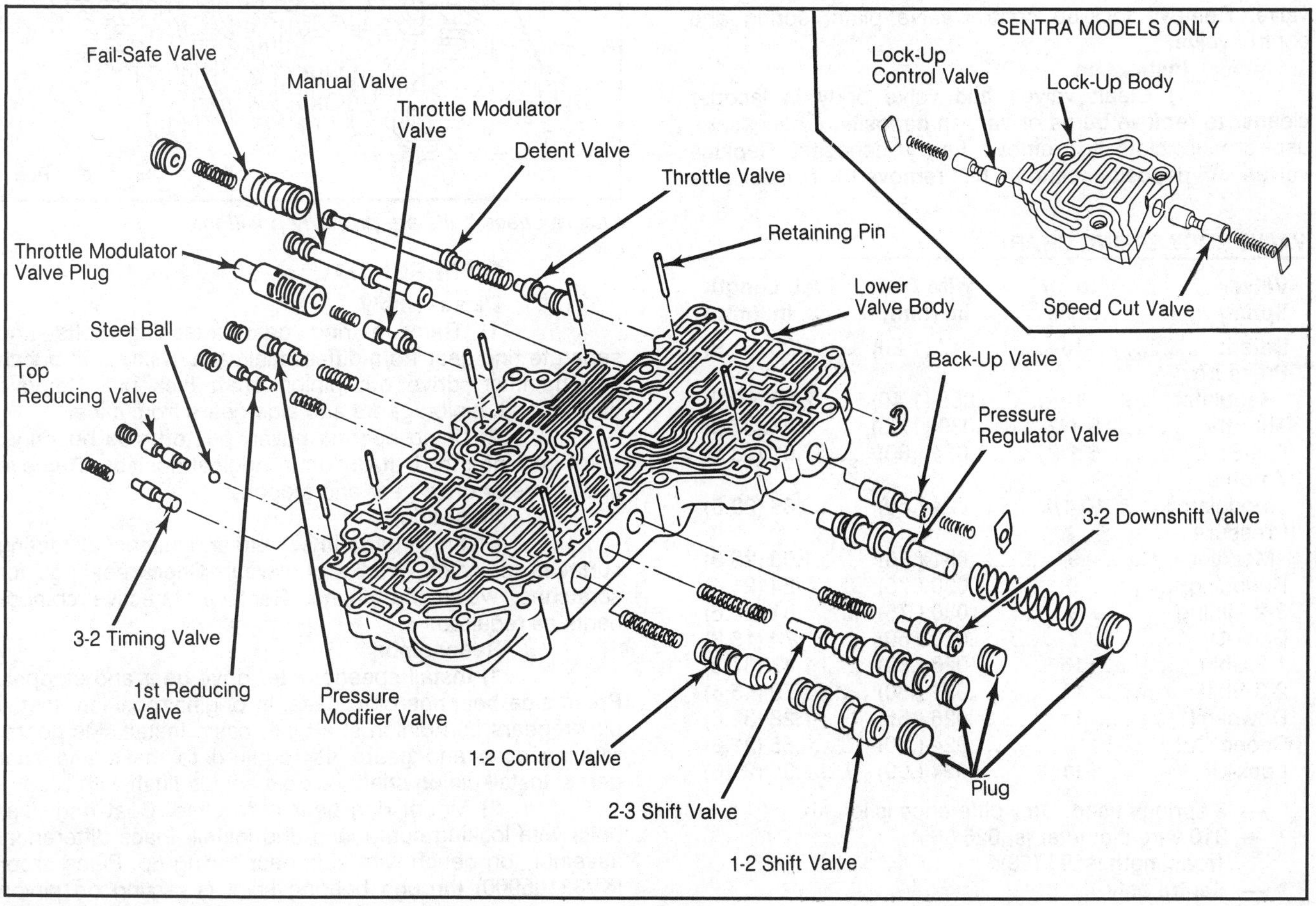

Note location and configuration of components.

GOVERNOR VALVE SPRING CHART

Governor Spring	Wire Dia. In. (mm)	Free Length In. (mm)
Primary Spring	.41 (10.5)	1.25 (31.7)
Secondary Spring	.03 (0.8)	1.50 (38.2)

VALVE BODY ASSEMBLY
Disassembly

1) Remove oil strainer and magnet, if equipped. Remove attaching bolts and separate lower valve body, separator plate and upper valve body. DO NOT lose steel balls from upper valve body.

2) Remove retaining pins from valve body by pushing out with a piece of wire and remove valve plugs. Extract 3-2 downshift valve and spring, 2-3 shift valve and spring, 1-2 shift valve, 1-2 control valve and spring from lower valve body. Place valves and springs in order of removal for reassembly identification.

3) Turn lower valve body over and remove pins and plugs. Remove fail-safe spring and valve, detent valve and spring, throttle valve, throttle modulator valve and spring guide, pressure modifier valve and spring, 1st reducing valve and spring, top reducing valve and check ball, 3-2 timing valve and spring. Place components in order of removal for reassembly identification.

4) Using a small screwdriver, depress back-up valve retaining plate and remove retaining pin. Remove retaining plate, spring and valve. Remove pressure regulator pin, plug spring and valve.

5) On Sentra models, disassemble lock-up valve body. Remove speed cut valve retainer, spring and valve. Remove lock-up control valve plate, spring and control valve.

Inspection

1) Clean valves and valve body in lacquer cleaner to remove burns or varnish deposits. If necessary, use crocus cloth to remove heavy deposits. Replace valves if deposits cannot be removed. If clearance

VALVE BODY SPRING CHART

Valve Spring	No. of Coils	Wire Dia. In. (mm)	Free Length In. (mm)
Detent	16	.047 (1.20)	1.26 (31.9)
Pressure Regulator	10	.055 (1.40)	2.36 (60.0)
Throttle	9 1/2	.039 (1.00)	1.27 (32.3)
Fail-Safe	6 1/2	.024 (.60)	.91 (23.1)
Throttle Modulator	10 1/2	.024 (.60)	.89 (22.5)
Pressure Modifier [1]	9	.031 (.80)	1.00 (25.3)
Reducing	9	.030 (.75)	.84 (21.4)
3-2 Timing [2]	9	.030 (.75)	.81 (20.6)
Back-Up	7	.020 (.50)	.74 (18.8)
1-2 Shift	16	.026 (.66)	1.47 (37.3)
2-3 Shift	17	.031 (.80)	1.79 (45.4)
Downshift	11	.026 (.65)	1.28 (32.6)
Speed Cut [3]	11	.024 (.60)	.85 (21.6)
Lock-Up [3]	11	.024 (.60)	.85 (21.6)

[1] — 3 springs used. Only difference is length.
[2] — 310 wire diameter is .026 (.65);
    free length is .91 (23).
[3] — Sentra only.

between valves and valve bores exceeds .001" (.03 mm), replace entire valve body assembly.

2) Check valves for rounded edges. If edges are not sharp, replace valve. Check separator plate and valve body oil passages for scratches or damage. Test valve springs for weakness. Replace defective components as required.

Reassembly

1) Install valves and springs in correct locations. Place 6 steel check balls in correct position in upper valve body. See Fig. 24. Assemble separator plate and valve bodies. Install reamer bolts first, then install and tighten remaining bolts. Install oil strainer and magnet, if equipped.

2) Install manual valve after valve body is mounted on transaxle. Shift point fine adjustment screw should be adjusted so that the distance from end of shaft to lock nut on valve body is .49-.51" (12.5-13.0 mm). Adjusting this screw changes shift points, except in kickdown mode.

Fig. 24: Upper Valve Body Check Ball Locations

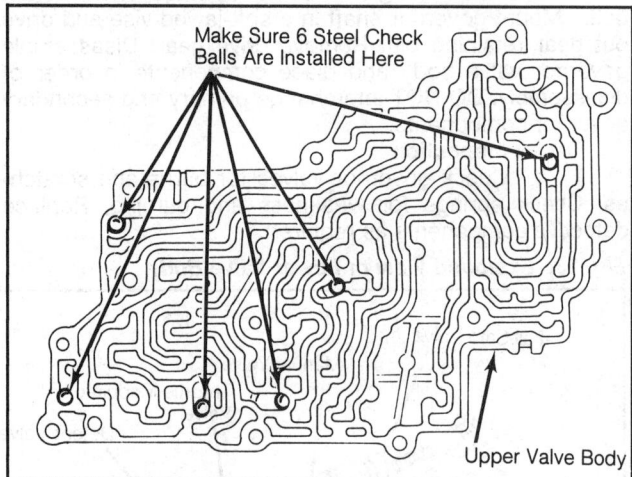

Ensure check balls are properly positioned.

DIFFERENTIAL
Disassembly

1) Remove ring gear attaching bolts and separate ring gear from differential case. Using drift punch and hammer, drive out pinion shaft lock pin. Remove pinion shaft, pinion gears and side gears from case.

2) Using bearing puller, pull off side bearings. Mark bearings for installation in original position. Remove speedometer drive gear and stopper.

Inspection

Clean all parts in solvent and inspect all mating surfaces for chips, cracks and wear. Check bearings for scratches, wear and pitting. Replace defective components as required.

Reassembly

1) Install speedometer drive gear and stopper. Press side bearings onto case, in original position. Install pinion gears and pinion shaft into case. Install side gears, rotating case and gears as required to mesh and seat gears. Install pinion shaft lock pin so it is flush with case.

2) Mount ring gear onto case. Coat ring gear bolts with locking compound and install. Place differential assembly on bench with side gear facing up. Place arbor (KV38105900) through bearing so it is resting on pinion

DATSUN/NISSAN SENTRA & 310 (Cont.)

shaft. Mount dial indicator on holding fixture so indicator tip rests on top of arbor.

3) Measure side bearing-to-pinion gear backlash. Move side bearing up and down and record dial indicator reading. Repeat operation on opposite side gear. If clearance exceeds .020" (.5 mm), replace differential case, side gears and pinion gears as a set.

OUTPUT SHAFT & IDLER GEAR

Disassembly & Inspection

Using bearing puller, pull bearings off output shaft. Place idler gear on wooden blocks and drive out bearings. Thoroughly clean components in solvent and blow dry with compressed air. Replace idler gear if chipped, cracked or worn. Replace output shaft if bent, cracked or splines are worn. Replace bearing if cracked, pitted or does not roll freely.

Reassembly

Press bearings into idler gear. Press bearings onto output shaft. Make sure bearings are properly seated and rotate without binding after installation.

TRANSMISSION CASE

Disassembly & Reassembly

Remove bearing housing from transmission case. Press bearing off housing. Press out oil seal and remove "O" ring. Coat new seal and "O" ring with gear oil and press into position. Press bearing into housing and install housing in transmission case.

TRANSAXLE ADJUSTMENTS

DIFFERENTIAL SIDE BEARING HEIGHT

1) Press differential side bearing outer race into converter housing bore. Place gasket on converter housing and install differential assembly into housing. Turn differential assembly several times in each direction to properly seat bearings.

2) Place counterweight on top of differential assembly. Mount holding bracket onto converter housing and tightening alignment bolts. Install micrometer to bracket and measure distance from upper gasket surface of converter housing to differential side bearing outer race. See Fig. 25. Record reading and subtract thickness of holding bracket to obtain actual measurement.

Fig. 25: Set-Up and Measuring Clearance Between Converter Housing and Differential Side Bearing

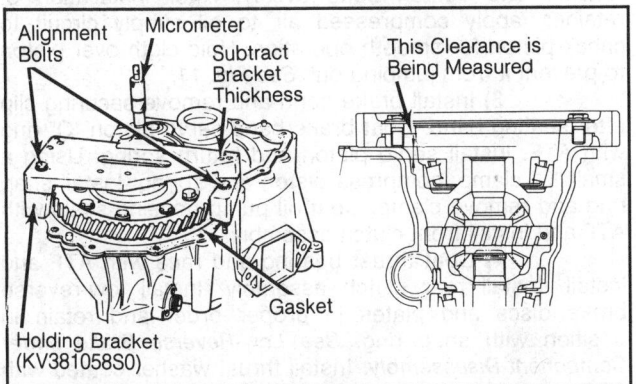

Subtract thickness of bracket to obtain actual distance.

3) Remove holding bracket and counterweight. With bearing housing installed in transmission case, rotate

bearing several times in each direction to seat bearing. Mount holding bracket on transmission case. Install micrometer to bracket and measure distance to bearing race. See Fig. 26. Record reading and subtract thickness of holding bracket to obtain actual measurement.

Fig. 26: Set-Up and Measuring Clearance to Bearing Race in Transmission Case

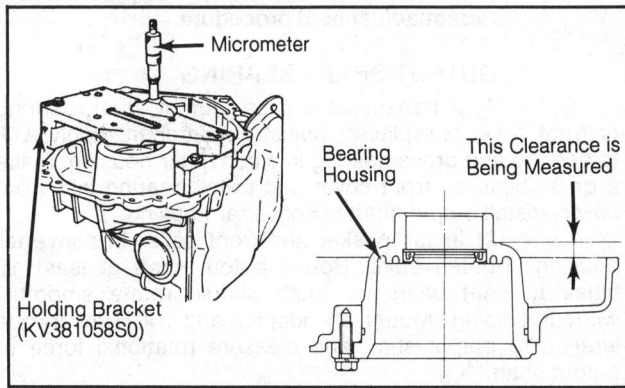

Subtract thickness of bracket to obtain actual distance.

4) Subtract measurement obtained in step 3) from reading obtained in step 2). Using this measurement, find proper shim (or shims) necessary to properly set differential side bearing height. See Differential Side Bearing Shim chart.

DIFFERENTIAL SIDE BEARING SHIM SPECIFICATIONS

Measured Distance In. (mm)	Required Shim In. (mm)
0-.0028 (0-.07)	.0150 (.38)
.0028-.0059 (.07-.15)	.0181 (.46)
.0059-.0091 (.15-.23)	.0213 (.54)
.0091-.0122 (.23-.31)	.0244 (.62)
.0122-.0154 (.31-.39)	.0276 (.70)
.0154-.0185 (.39-.47)	.0307 (.78)
.0185-.0217 (.47-.55)	.0339 (.86)
.0217-.0248 (.55-.63)	.0370 (.94)
.0248-.0280 (.63-.71)	.0402 (1.02)
.0280-.0311 (.71-.79)	.0433 (1.10)
.0311-.0343 (.79-.87)	.0465 (1.18)
.0343-.0374 (.87-.95)	.0496 (1.26)
.0374-.0406 (.95-1.03)	.0528 (1.34)
.0406-.0437 (1.03-1.11)	.0559 (1.42)
.0437-.0469 (1.11-1.19)	.0591 (1.50)
.0469-.0500 (1.19-1.27)	.0622 (1.58)
.0500-.0531 (1.27-1.35)	.0654 (1.66)

5) Remove bearing housing from transmission case. Remove bearing and "O" ring. Install selected shim(s) on bearing housing and install bearing. Coat "O" ring with vaseline and install. Install bearing housing to transmission case.

6) Install differential in transmission case. Place gasket on converter housing and attach converter housing to transmission case. Install and tighten all bolts. Seat differential assembly by rotating it at least 10 times in each direction.

7) Insert preload adapter (KV38105900) into differential assembly. Using an INCH lb. torque wrench, measure rotational force of differential side bearings. If rotational force exceeds 52-65 INCH lbs. (5.7-7.2 N.m),

DATSUN/NISSAN SENTRA & 310 (Cont.)

disassemble transmission case and remove differential assembly.

8) Repeat adjustment procedures and recheck rotational force. Separate case and housing and remove differential assembly.

NOTE: If rotational force reading varies 8.7 INCH lbs. (1.0 N.m) or binds during any revolution, repeat adjustment procedure.

OUTPUT SHAFT BEARING

1) If transmission case, output shaft, bearing or front cover is replaced, adjust output shaft. Apply ATF to bearing and press bearing into converter housing. Place 2 or 3 shims on front cover and press bearing into front cover. Install output shaft in converter housing.

2) Install gasket and front cover in converter housing. Tighten bolts. Rotate output shaft at least 10 times to seat bearings. Shaft should rotate smoothly without binding. Mount an adapter and INCH lb. torque wrench to output shaft and measure rotational force of output shaft.

3) If rotational force exceeds 3-4 INCH lbs. (.3-.4 N.m), remove front cover and output shaft. Remove or add shims as required to increase or decrease rotational force. See Output Shaft Bearing Shims chart.

4) Shims are available in following sizes: .0043" (.11 mm), .0051" (.13 mm), .0059" (.15 mm), .0067" (.17 mm), .0075" (.19 mm), .0118" (.30 mm), .0157" (.40 mm), .0197" (.50 mm), .0236" (.60 mm), .0276" (.70 mm), .0315" (.80 mm), .0354" (.90 mm) and .0394" (1.00 mm) for Sentra models and .0472" (1.20 mm) for 310 models.

OUTPUT SHAFT END PLAY

1) After adjusting rotational force of output shaft bearing, measure output shaft end play. Install idler gear on idler shaft. Install idler gear and output shaft assembly in converter housing.

2) Clean front cover bolt threads and converter housing with solvent. Install front cover gasket and front cover on converter housing. Install and tighten bolts. Install idler gear bolt and lock washer. Tighten idler gear bolt to 20-27 ft. lbs. (26-36 N.m).

Fig. 27: Installing Solder on Internal Gear

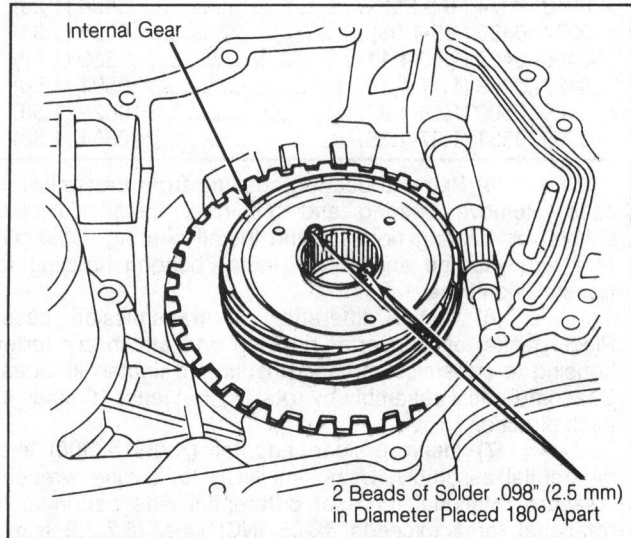

Internal Gear

2 Beads of Solder .098" (2.5 mm) in Diameter Placed 180° Apart

Solder is used in same manner as Plastigage.

3) Turn output shaft at least 5 complete revolutions. Install rear internal gear. Assemble governor shaft assembly, parking pawl, return spring and parking pawl shaft. Install governor shaft retaining bolt.

4) Place 2 beads of solder .098" (2.5mm) in diameter on internal gear, or use a soldering plate that is .098" (2.5 mm) thick and .20" (5 mm) in length. See Fig. 27. Solder is used in same manner as using Plastigage.

5) Install converter housing, with output shaft assembly installed, on transmission case. Install all converter housing-to-transmission case bolts and tighten. Remove converter housing. Remove governor shaft retaining bolt. Remove parking pawl shaft, return spring, parking pawl and governor shaft assembly.

6) Remove rear internal gear and disassemble output shaft. Measure thickness of solder or soldering plate. Subtract .002" (.05 mm) from soldering plate measurement. Select proper shim from Output Shaft Shim chart to set output shaft end play at .0098-.0217" (.25-.55 mm) and place aside for use during reassembly.

OUTPUT SHAFT SHIM SPECIFICATIONS

Measured Thickness [1] In. (mm)	Required Shim In. (mm)
.0217-.0335 (.55-.85)	.012 (.3)
.0295-.0413 (.75-1.05)	.020 (.5)
.0374-.0492 (.95-1.25)	.028 (.7)
.0453-.0571 (1.15-1.45)	.035 (.9)
.0531-.0650 (1.35-1.65)	.043 (1.1)
.0610-.0728 (1.55-1.85)	.051 (1.3)
.0689-.0807 (1.75-2.05)	.059 (1.5)
.0768-.0886 (1.95-2.25)	.067 (1.7)

[1] — After subtracting .002" (.5 mm) from plate measurement.

TRANSAXLE REASSEMBLY

1) All components must be clean before reassembly. Blow out with compressed air. New seals and "O" rings should be used during reassembly. Coat outer diameter of oil pump assembly with ATF. Align 5 bolt holes in oil pump with holes in transmission case. Install pump, nylon washer and thrust bearing.

2) Apply ATF to low-reverse brake piston seal. Tap piston evenly to install. Install low-reverse piston retainer and tighten bolts evenly. After installation of retainer, apply compressed air to oil supply circuit to check piston for smooth operation. Hold cloth over piston to prevent it from jumping out. See Fig. 11.

3) Install brake band and remove securing clip after seating band. Coat brake band servo piston "O" ring with ATF. Install servo piston and return spring. Using a small "C" clamp, compress piston and spring. Install snap ring and remove clamp. Coat oil pump housing seals with ATF and install front clutch assembly.

4) Coat thrust bearing and race with ATF and install. Install rear clutch assembly. Install low-reverse brake discs and plates in proper order and retain in position with snap ring. See Low-Reverse Brake under Component Disassembly. Install thrust washer coated with ATF and front internal gear.

5) Apply ATF to thrust bearing and bearing race and install. Install planetary gear set. Coat bearing race and needle bearing with ATF and install. Install snap

DATSUN/NISSAN SENTRA & 310 (Cont.)

Fig. 28: Exploded View of Transaxle Assembly

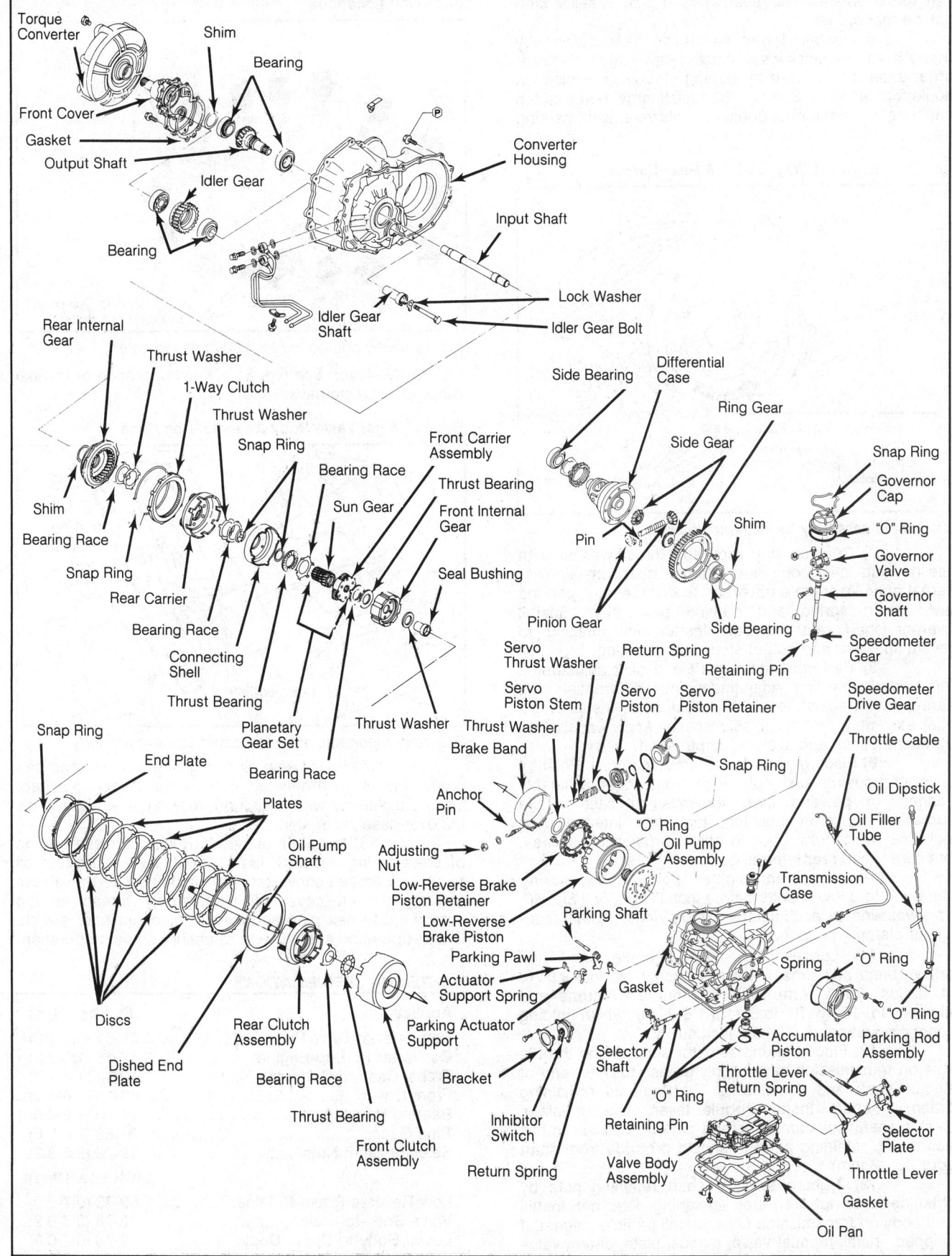

ring. Install connecting shell and retain with snap ring. Coat thrust washer and bearing race with vaseline and stick on rear carrier.

    6) Install 1-way clutch on rear carrier by turning it counterclockwise. Install 1-way clutch and rear carrier assembly in case by turning clockwise. Projection should face upward. *See Fig. 29.* Install large 1-way clutch snap ring so bent end does not interfere with parking pawl.

Fig. 29: *Installing 1-Way Clutch & Rear Carrier*

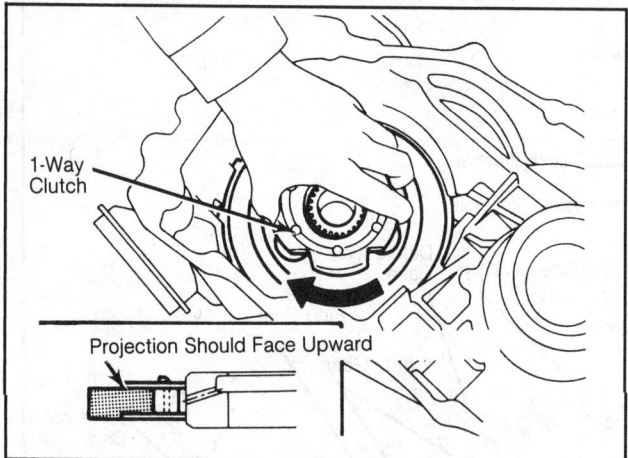

Install as an assembly by rotating clockwise.

    7) Coat bearing race and thrust washer with vaseline and stick on rear internal gear. Install rear internal gear. Assemble governor shaft assembly, parking pawl, return spring and parking pawl shaft. Install governor shaft retaining bolt. Install seal bushing to prevent sun gear and output shaft from jamming.

    8) Perform output shaft end play adjustment, output shaft bearing adjustment and differential side bearing height adjustment. *See Adjustments.* Install differential assembly on transmission case. Apply vaseline to output shaft shim and stick on output shaft.

    9) Place gasket on transmission case. Position converter housing assembly, with front cover assembly attached, in position over transmission case. While supporting converter housing, turn rear internal gear clockwise with screwdriver to align output shaft splines, front carrier and rear internal gear.

    10) Install and tighten bolts. Apply locking compound to 3 lower bolts before installation. *See Fig. 30.* Apply vaseline to accumulator piston rings. Install accumulator piston and spring.

    11) Loosen lock nut on brake band and perform band adjustment. Tighten anchor pin lock nut to 3-4 ft. lbs. (.3-.4 N.m). Back off nut 2 1/2 turns and retighten to 12-16 ft. lbs. (1.3-1.8 N.m) while holding anchor pin stationary. Tighten lock nut.

    12) Place parking actuator support and throttle cable on transmission case. Apply grease to outer end of selector shaft and vaseline to "O" ring and remaining portion of shaft. Install throttle lever, selector plate, selector shaft, selector lever and parking rod assembly. Secure with retaining pin. Pin should protrude from shaft about .12" (3 mm).

    13) Tighten selector shaft retaining nuts by tightening inner nut first, then tightening outer nut. Install valve body on transmission case. Install particle magnet, if equipped. Install manual valve, manual plate, detent valve

Fig. 30: *Converter Housing-to-Transmission Case Bolt Locations*

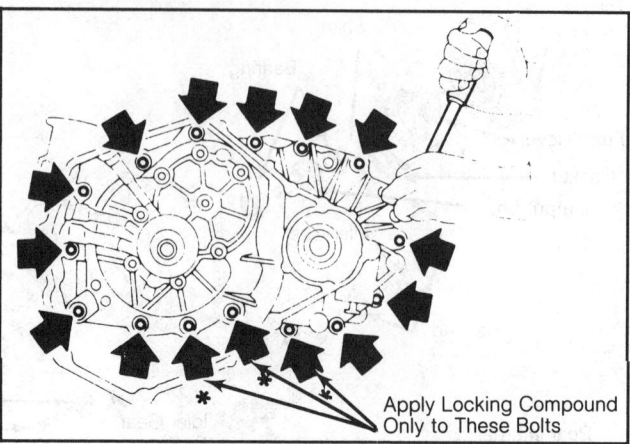

Apply Locking Compound Only to These Bolts

Apply locking compound to 3 bolts as indicated.

and throttle lever. *See Fig. 31.* Check operation of manual valve and parking pawl.

Fig. 31: *Final Valve Body Assembly on Case*

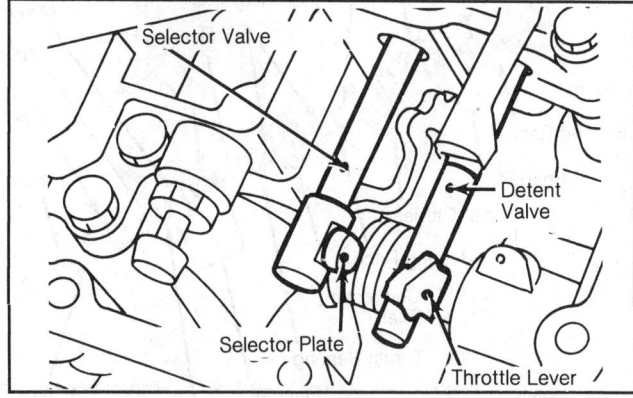

Selector Valve

Detent Valve

Selector Plate

Throttle Lever

Ensure components are secure and operate properly.

    14) Install new oil pan gasket, oil pan and pan guard. Install governor cap seal ring and governor cap. Secure assembly with snap ring, making sure cap recess fits over case protrusion.

    15) Install oil pump shaft with concave portion of shaft facing outward. Install input shaft. Lubricate oil pump seal lip and converter neck. Install converter without scratching front cover oil seal. Apply thread locking compound to hex plug and install. Install inhibitor switch. Check operation of shift lever to ensure smooth operation.

TIGHTENING SPECIFICATIONS

Application	Ft. Lbs. (N.m)
Converter-to-Drive Plate	36-51 (5.0-7.0)
Converter Hsg.-to-Engine	12-16 (1.6-2.2)
Trans. Case-to-Converter Hsg.	10-13 (1.4-1.8)
Front Cover	10-13 (1.4-1.8)
Bearing Housing	14-18 (1.9-2.5)
Ring Gear	51-58 (7.0-8.0)
Selector Shaft Nuts	19-23 (2.6-3.2)

	INCH Lbs. (N.m)
Low-Reverse Brake Retainer	60-78 (0.7-0.9)
Valve Body-to-Case	60-78 (0.7-0.9)
Lower Body-to-Upper Body	60-78 (0.7-0.9)

GM TURBO HYDRA-MATIC 180 — FIAT

Fiat Spider

DESCRIPTION

Transmission is a fully automatic unit consisting of a three-element hydraulic torque converter and a compound planetary gear set. Three multiple disc clutches, 1 sprag clutch and 1 band provide friction elements required to obtain desired function of the planetary gear set. A hydraulic system pressurized by a gear type pump provides working pressure required to operate friction elements and automatic controls.

LUBRICATION & ADJUSTMENT

See the appropriate article in AUTOMATIC TRANSMISSION SERVICING section.

TROUBLE SHOOTING

NO DRIVE

In Any Range

Low oil level. Clogged suction screen. Inner manual valve linkage disconnected. Input shaft broken. Pressure regulator stuck in open position. Defective oil pump.

In Forward Ranges Only

Band worn or incorrectly adjusted. Band servo seal ring cracked.

No Drive in "D" or "2" ("1" and "R" OK)

Input sprag faulty or installed backwards.

No Drive in "R" (All Other Ranges OK)

Reverse clutch failure.

LOW OIL PRESSURE

Low oil level. Clogged suction screen. Leak in pump suction circuit or internal leak in pressure circuit. Priming valve sticking. Pressure regulator failure.

HIGH OIL PRESSURE

Broken or disconnected vacuum line to transmission. Vacuum modulator failure or valve stuck. Leak in engine or accessory vacuum system. Pressure regulator failure.

NO SHIFT AT ANY SPEED

Governor valves sticking. 1-2 shift valve sticking in downshift position. Large leak in governor pressure passage.

UPSHIFTS ONLY AT PART THROTTLE

Detent pressure regulator valve sticking. Detent cable broken or out of adjustment.

NO PART THROTTLE 3-2 DOWNSHIFT AT LOWER SPEEDS

3-2 downshift control valve sticking.

UPSHIFTS FROM 1-2 ONLY

2-3 shift valve sticking.

SUDDEN ENGAGEMENT AFTER INCREASE IN RPM

Band servo piston binding.

SLIPPING 1-2 UPSHIFTS

Low oil pressure. 1-2 accumulator valve sticking. Second clutch piston seals leaking, check ball stuck open, or piston cracked or broken.

SLIPPING 2-3 UPSHIFTS

Low oil pressure. Third clutch piston seals leaking, check ball stuck open or piston cracked or broken. Input shaft bushing worn.

HARSH 1-2 UPSHIFT

High oil pressure. 1-2 accumulator valve sticking. Governor valve sticking.

HARSH 2-3 UPSHIFT

High oil pressure. Governor valve sticking.

HARSH 3-2 FORCED DOWNSHIFT AT HIGH SPEED

High speed downshift timing valve sticking.

HARSH 3-2 COAST DOWNSHIFT

Low speed downshift timing valve sticking.

TESTING

ROAD TEST

Oil Pressure Test

1) Connect a tachometer to engine and a pressure gauge to transmission. Connect a vacuum gauge in line to modulator. Place gauges in position where they can be read while driving.

2) With engine and transmission at normal operating temperatures, place selector in "D". Allow engine to idle at 750-850 RPM. Oil pressure should be 61-70 psi (4.3-4.9 kg/cm²).

3) With selector still in "D" position, press accelerator pedal down past "kickdown" position. Transmission should upshift when oil pressure is 108-119 psi (7.5-8.4 kg/cm²). Vacuum gauge should read .86 in. Hg.

4) Stop vehicle and place selector in "1" position. Oil pressure should now read 98-109 psi (6.9-7.7 kg/cm²) with approximately 12 in. Hg of vacuum.

Stall Test

With pressure gauge and tachometer installed as for road test, engage parking brake and service brake. Place selector in "1" or "R" position and push accelerator pedal to the floor. Read oil pressure gauge at maximum engine speed. Pressure should be 156-160 psi (10.9-11.7 kg/cm²). Stall speed should be 2200-2300 RPM.

CAUTION: DO NOT maintain stall speed for more than a few seconds at a time. If more than 1 stall test is required, allow engine to idle in neutral for at least 30 seconds between tests to cool transmission fluid.

TRANSMISSION REMOVAL & INSTALLATION

See the appropriate article in AUTOMATIC TRANSMISSION REMOVAL Section.

Automatic Transmissions

GM TURBO HYDRA-MATIC 180 — FIAT (Cont.)

Fig. 1: Cutaway View of GM Automatic Transmission Used in Fiat Spider

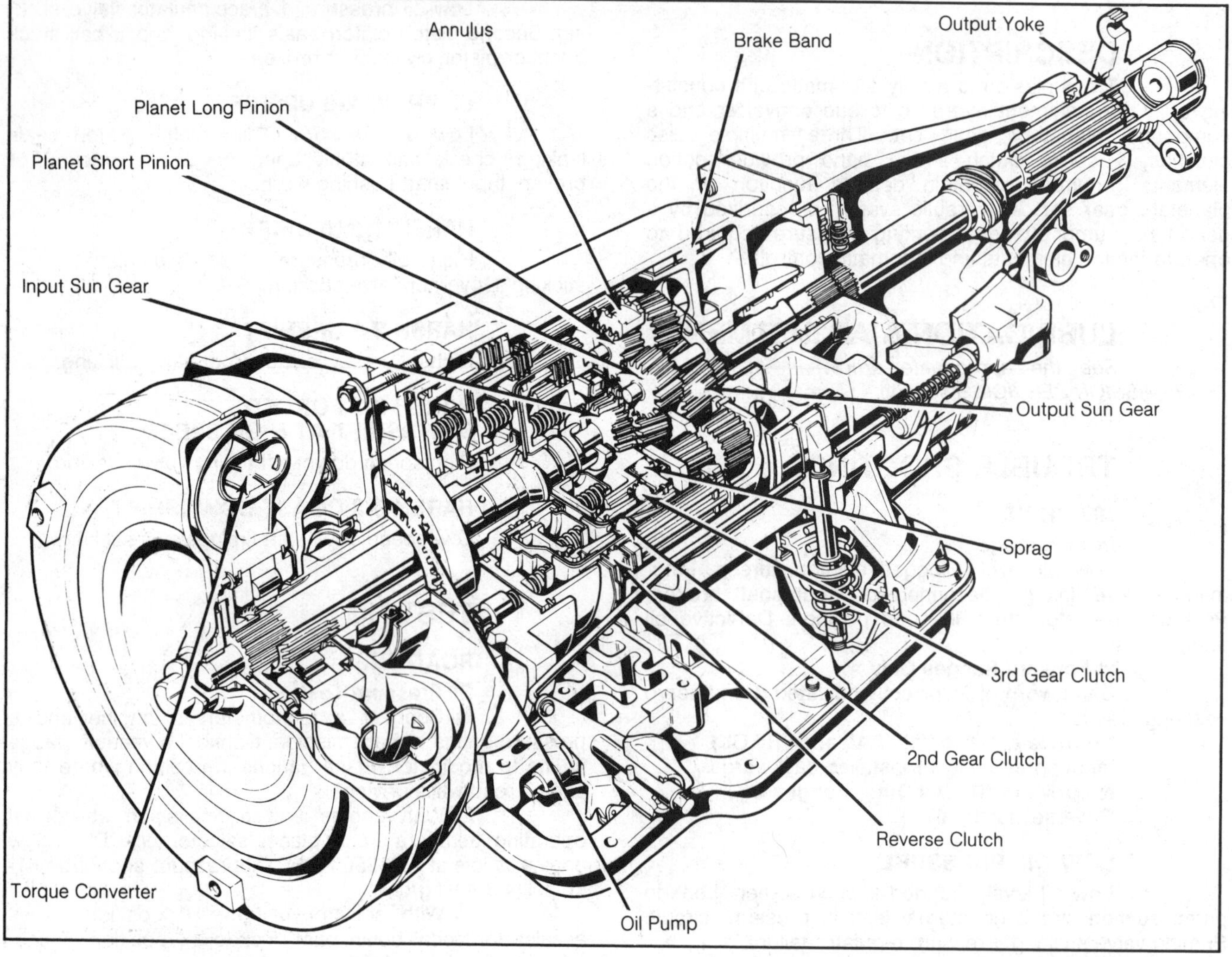

Annulus

Brake Band

Output Yoke

Planet Long Pinion

Planet Short Pinion

Input Sun Gear

Output Sun Gear

Sprag

3rd Gear Clutch

2nd Gear Clutch

Reverse Clutch

Torque Converter

Oil Pump

TORQUE CONVERTER

LEAKAGE TEST

Drain converter and check fluid for clutch material or foreign matter. If foreign matter or clutch material is found, replace converter. Install test tool on converter and pressurize to 71-85 psi (5.0-5.8 kg/cm²). Submerge converter in water and check for leaks.

Fig. 2: Tool Set-Up for Torque Converter Leak Test

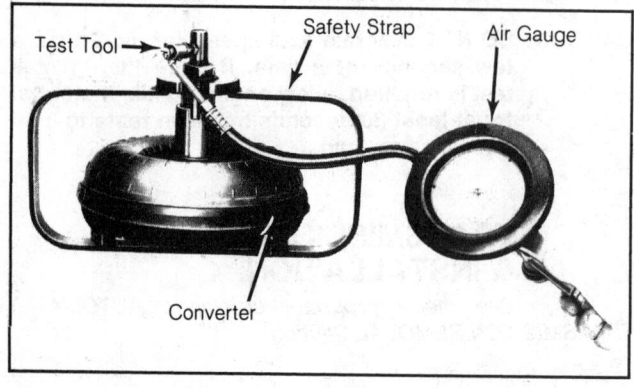

Test Tool

Safety Strap

Air Gauge

Converter

TRANSMISSION DISASSEMBLY

1) Drain transmission, if not already drained. Remove converter from housing and place transmission in holding fixture. Remove speedometer driven gear and gasket. Turn transmission over and remove oil pan bolts. Remove pan and gasket.

2) Remove detent spring, then remove bolts and lift off oil filter and gasket. Remove transfer plate and servo cover retaining bolts. Lift off transfer plate, servo cover and cover gasket. Remove remaining bolts and carefully remove valve body, gasket and transfer plate. Hold manual valve link and disconnect it from selector lever. Remove check ball from oil passage.

3) Using compressor tool (23075), compress servo piston assembly and remove retaining snap ring. Loosen compressor tool slowly since servo piston assembly is under high spring pressure, then remove tool and piston assembly from case.

4) Remove vacuum modulator, gasket and modulator plunger. Remove modulator valve and sleeve. Carefully remove retaining pin holding kickdown valve assembly, then remove kickdown sleeve, valve, spring seat and spring case.

GM TURBO HYDRA-MATIC 180 — FIAT (Cont.)

CLUTCH AND BAND APPLICATION CHART (ELEMENTS IN USE)

Selector Lever Position	Reverse Clutch	Second Clutch	Third Clutch	Sprag Clutch	Low Band
D — DRIVE					
First Gear				X	X
Second Gear		X			X
Third Gear		X	X		
2 — INTERMEDIATE					
First Gear				X	X
Second Gear		X			X
1 — LOW			X		X
R — REVERSE	X		X		

NEUTRAL OR PARK — All clutches and bands released and/or ineffective.

Fig. 3: Removing Servo Piston Snap Ring

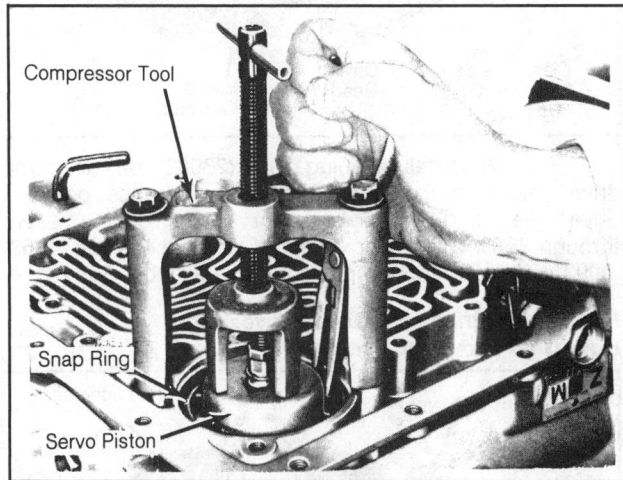

Release tool slowly and remove servo piston assembly.

5) Remove snap ring from end of output shaft. Then remove seal ring, spring, nut and washer. Pull off output yoke. Remove extension housing. Remove snap ring and slide collar and speedometer gear off shaft. Remove governor retaining bolts (4) and remove governor and gasket. Remove governor hub retaining snap ring and slide hub off output shaft.

6) Turn transmission on work stand so converter housing faces up. Break converter housing-to-oil pump bolts loose but do not remove. Remove outer housing-to-case attaching bolts and seal washers (7). Discard washers. Lift housing (with pump) out of case. If pump will not pull free, strike side of housing sharply with rubber mallet to loosen pump.

7) Grasp input shaft and lift third clutch assembly and second clutch drum from case. Remove selective washer from input shaft. Remove reverse clutch and reaction plates from case. Lift planetary carrier and output shaft out of case, being careful not to lose needle bearing and inner race.

8) Pull reaction sun gear and drum straight out of case. Remove needle bearing and race from rear of case, if they did not come out with sun gear and drum. Compress band slightly and pull from case. Turn case so oil passages are up.

9) Remove nut attaching selector lever to shaft and pin holding shaft in case. Remove lever and slide out shaft. Park lock actuator should come out with selector lever. Separate lever from actuator by aligning slot in lever with tab on actuator.

Fig. 4: Removing Selector Lever and Shaft

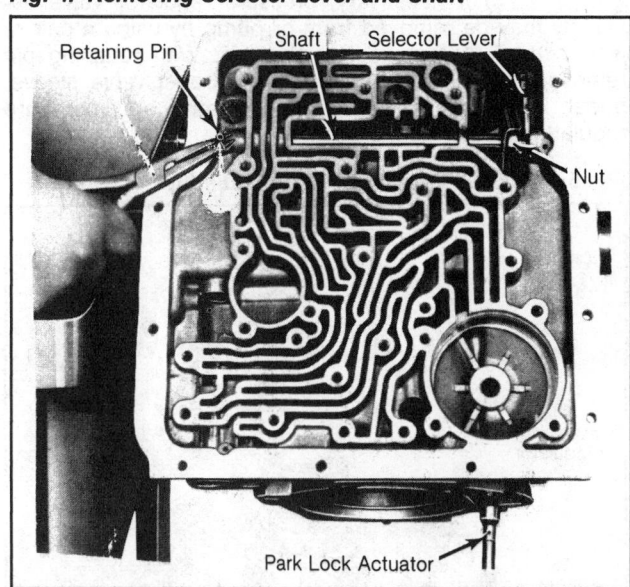

COMPONENT DISASSEMBLY & REASSEMBLY

CONVERTER HOUSING, OIL PUMP & REVERSE CLUTCH

Disassembly

1) Remove outer oil seal from oil pump. Remove attaching bolts (5) and separate oil pump from converter housing. Remove converter housing oil seal, and if necessary, remove housing bushing using driver.

2) Remove oil pump wear plate. Mark relative location of oil pump gears and remove gears from oil pump body. Using compressor tool, compress reverse clutch piston return springs and remove snap ring. Loosen compressor tool and remove clutch retaining ring and the 24 piston return springs, then remove piston. If necessary, remove priming valve assembly from oil pump body using a drift inserted through hole at rear of oil pump.

Fig. 5: Oil Pump Gears

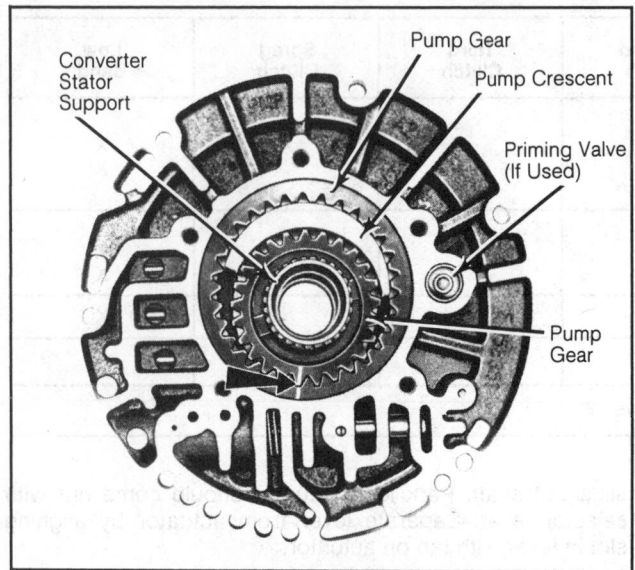

3) If necessary, pressure regulator valve assembly may be removed from oil pump by using a pair of wire cutters to remove retaining pin. With retaining pin removed, lift out pressure regulator boost valve sleeve, boost valve, spring, both spring seats and pressure regulator valve.

Fig. 6: Pressure Regulator Valve Assembly

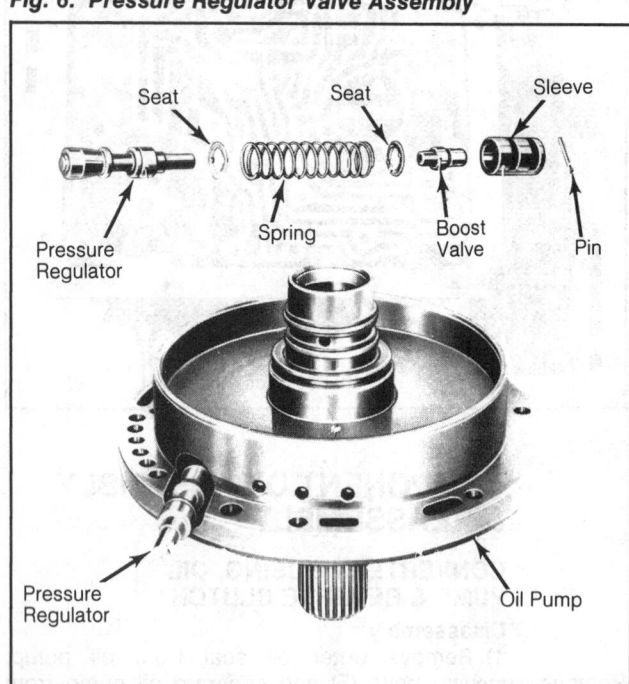

Inspection

1) Wash all parts in clean solvent and blow dry with compressed air. Inspect parts for wear, damage or scoring and replace as necessary. Install gears into pump body and check pump body-to-gear face clearance using a feeler gauge and straightedge; clearance should be .0005-.0015" (.013-.038 mm). If clearance is not within specifications, replace complete oil pump assembly. See Fig. 7.

Fig. 7: Checking Pump Body-to-Gear Face Clearance Using a Feeler Gauge

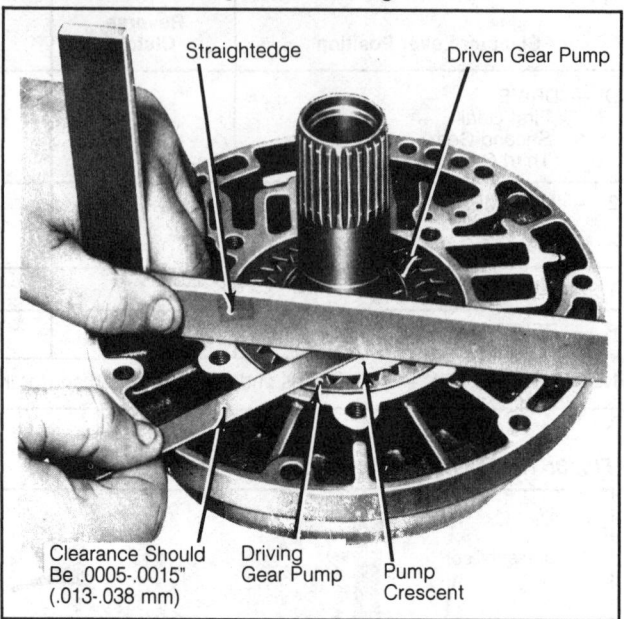

2) Install aligning tool (23082) on oil pump drive gear-to-center gear. Measure clearance between drive gear and pump crescent while rotating gears through 360°. Use feeler gauge. If clearance is not .0053-.0093" (.135-.235 mm), replace pump assembly. See Fig. 8.

Fig. 8: Measuring Clearance Between Drive Gear and Pump Crescent

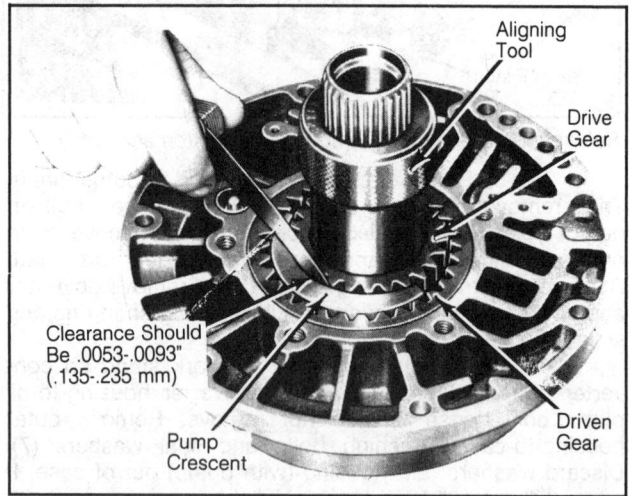

3) Measure clearance between outside of driven gear and pump housing. Rotate gear through 360° while measuring. If clearance is not .0027-.0065" (.069-.165 mm), replace pump assembly. See Fig. 9.

4) Measure clearance between inside of driven gear and pump crescent. Rotate gear through 360°. If clearance is less than .005" (.125 mm), replace pump assembly.

Oil Pump Hub Bushing Replacement

1) To remove, thread standard pipe tap into bushing. With a drift between tap and arbor press, press bushing from hub.

GM TURBO HYDRA-MATIC 180 — FIAT (Cont.)

Fig. 9: Measuring Oil Pump Driven Gear Clearances

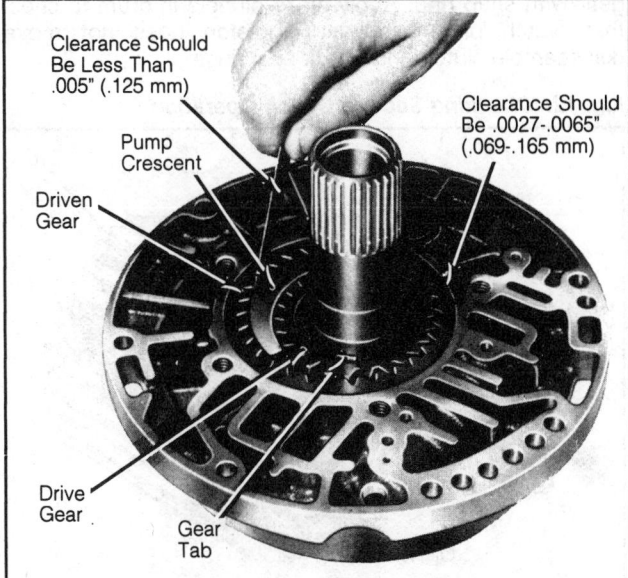

Clearance Should Be Less Than .005" (.125 mm)

Pump Crescent

Driven Gear

Clearance Should Be .0027-.0065" (.069-.165 mm)

Drive Gear

Gear Tab

Measure clearance between outside of gear and case, and between gear teeth and pump crescent.

2) To install, position oil pump with pump shaft hole facing downward. *See Fig. 10.* Scribe an alignment mark on oil pump shaft inner diameter at center of oil groove to right of hole "A". Scribe mark on outer edge of bushing through the centers of small and large drilled holes "B". Place bushing into pump shaft with small hole up and scribe marks on bushing and pump shaft aligned. Use arbor press to drive bushing into pump shaft until firmly seated in bore.

Reassembly

1) If removed, coat pressure regulator valve assembly with transmission fluid, then install pressure regulator valve, spring seats, spring, boost valve and sleeve into pump body bore. Depress boost valve sleeve until back end lines up with pin hole and insert new retaining pin.

2) Install new oil seals on reverse clutch piston, then install piston onto rear face of oil pump. Inspect piston return springs. If any spring(s) is damaged, replace all 24 springs. Install return springs and spring retaining seat. Using same compressor tool as was used

Fig. 10: Installing Oil Pump Hub Bushing

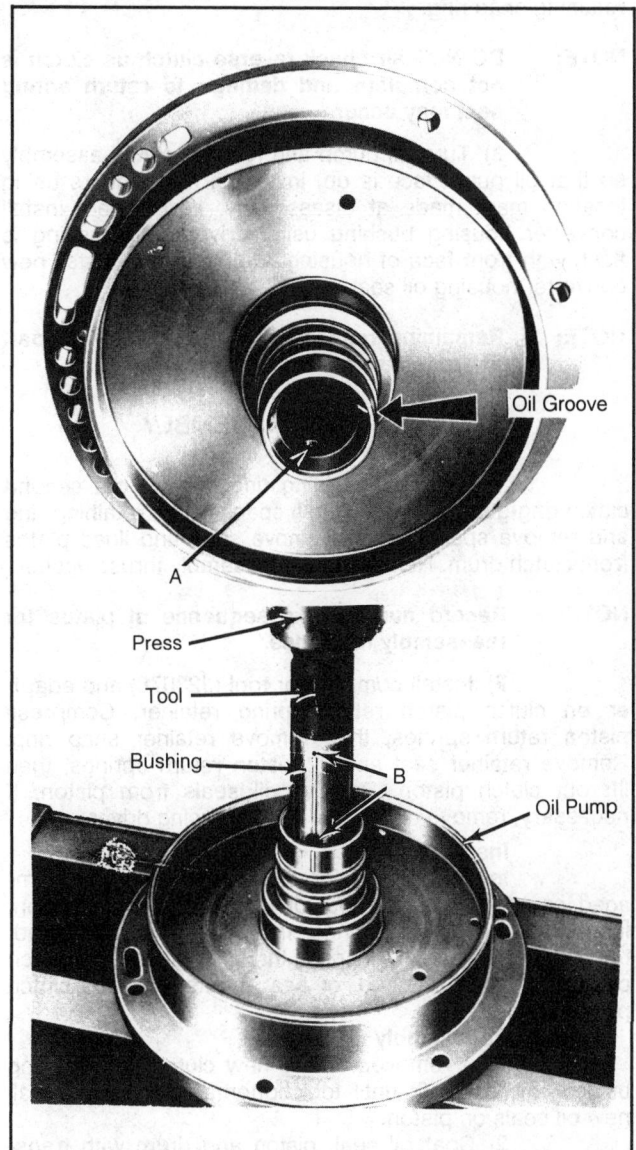

Oil Groove

A

Press

Tool

Bushing

B

Oil Pump

Align scribe marks on bushing and pump shaft when installing bushing.

Fig. 11: Exploded View of Second Clutch Assembly

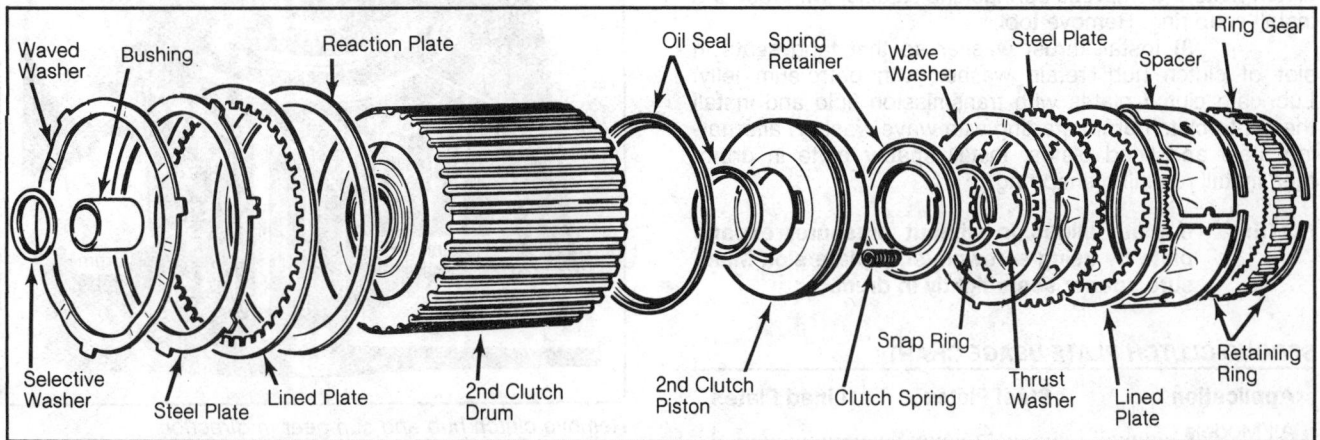

Waved Washer

Bushing

Reaction Plate

Oil Seal

Spring Retainer

Wave Washer

Steel Plate

Spacer

Ring Gear

Selective Washer

Steel Plate

Lined Plate

2nd Clutch Drum

2nd Clutch Piston

Clutch Spring

Snap Ring

Thrust Washer

Lined Plate

Retaining Ring

GM TURBO HYDRA-MATIC 180 — FIAT (Cont.)

for disassembly, compress return springs and install retaining snap ring.

NOTE: **DO NOT air check reverse clutch as clutch is not complete and damage to return spring seat may occur.**

3) Turn oil pump and reverse clutch assembly so that oil pump face is up. Install oil pump gears using location mark made at disassembly. If removed, install converter housing bushing using driver until bushing is flush with front face of housing. Lubricate and install new converter housing oil seal.

NOTE: **Remaining reassembly is performed as part of Transmission Reassembly.**

SECOND CLUTCH ASSEMBLY
Disassembly
1) Remove retaining ring and lift out second clutch ring gear. Remove clutch spacer plate retaining ring and remove spacer plate. Remove steel and lined plates from clutch drum. Remove clutch assembly thrust washer.

NOTE: **Record number and sequence of plates for reassembly reference.**

2) Install compressor tool (J23078) and adapter on clutch piston return spring retainer. Compress piston return springs, then remove retainer snap ring. Remove retainer seat and 22 piston return springs, then lift out clutch piston. Remove oil seals from piston. If necessary, remove clutch hub bushing using driver.

Inspection
Inspect piston for damage. If piston is damaged or check ball falls out or is stuck, replace piston. Inspect piston return springs. If any spring is damaged, replace complete set. Inspect thrust washer and clutch plates for wear, damage, or heat marks. Replace clutch pack if damaged.

Reassembly
1) If removed, install new clutch hub bushing using tool (23130-6) until tool bottoms on bench. Install new oil seals on piston.
2) Coat oil seal, piston and drum with transmission fluid. Place tool (23080) on piston to protect oil seal and install piston and tool in drum. Push down until tool seats. Then push piston furthur until it seats. Remove tool. Install piston return springs (22) and retaining seat on clutch piston. Compress springs and retainer with tool and install snap ring. Remove tool.
3) Install thrust washer so that tang seats in slot of clutch hub; retain washer with petroleum jelly. Lubricate clutch plates with transmission fluid and install them into clutch drum starting with wave washer, alternating steel and lined plates. Install spacer plate in drum, then install retaining snap ring.

NOTE: **If plate slides in without pressure, expand plate by using screwdriver in plate slot. Make sure spacer seats tightly in drum.**

SECOND CLUTCH PLATE USAGE CHART

Application	Steel Plates	Lined Plates
All Models	4	3

4) Install ring gear in drum, then secure ring gear with snap ring. Apply air to oil hole in drum to check that clutch piston moves. If piston does not move, disassemble clutch and check seal rings.

Fig. 12: *Checking Second Clutch Operation*

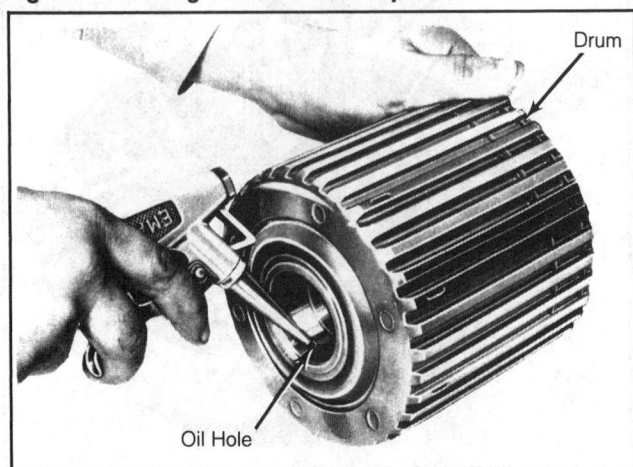

Apply compressed air at oil hole indicated. Clutch movement should be detected.

THIRD CLUTCH ASSEMBLY
Disassembly
1) Compress retaining ring holding third clutch sprag race and retainer in drum. Remove input sun gear with clutch hub. Remove sprag race and retainer from clutch hub, then push sprag race out of retainer.
2) Remove 3rd clutch plates from drum, keeping plates in same order for later reassembly. Remove thrust bearing and washer from input shaft. Using compressor and arbor press, compress piston return springs and remove retaining snap ring. Remove spring retainer and 12 return springs. Lift out clutch piston. Remove oil seals from piston and input shaft in drum.

Fig. 13: *Third Clutch Assembly*

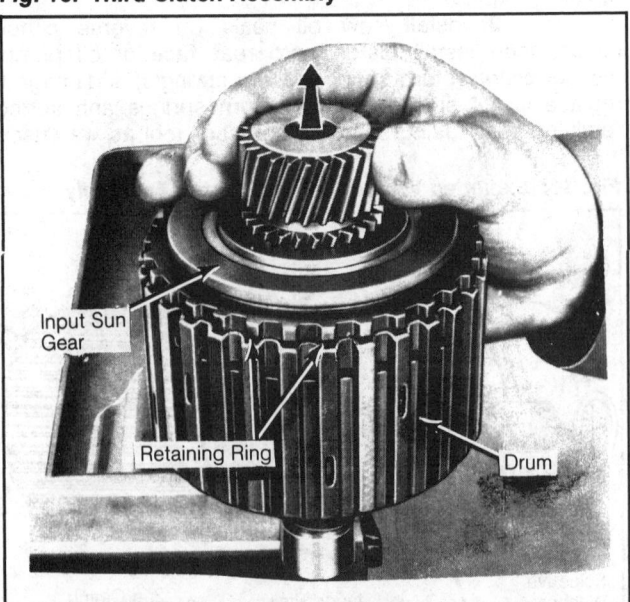

Remove clutch hub and sun gear in direction of arrow while holding retaining ring down.

GM TURBO HYDRA-MATIC 180 — FIAT (Cont.)

Inspection

Inspect piston for damage. If check ball is missing or falls out, replace piston. Clean and inspect clutch drum and thrust washer. Replace if scored or damaged. Inspect piston return springs. If any spring is damaged, replace complete set. Inspect clutch plates for wear, damage, or heat marks. Replace clutch pack if damaged. Check sprag assembly for wear, damage, or sprags that fall out of cage.

Reassembly

1) Coat new oil seals for piston and input shaft with transmission fluid. Lubricate inside of drum with transmission fluid. Install oil seals, then install piston into drum with tool (23084). If tool is not available, push piston down until it reaches inside drum. Use a .020" (.5 mm) feeler gauge to guide oil seal into drum.

Fig. 14: Installing Oil Seals

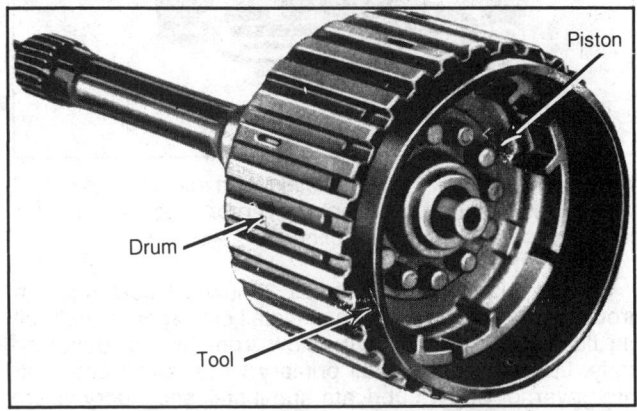

2) Install 12 piston return springs and spring retainer. Compress return springs and install retaining snap ring.

3) Install thrust washer and needle thrust bearing onto input shaft and retain in place with petroleum jelly. Install sprag onto clutch hub with groove on sprag cage outer diameter toward input sun gear. Install sprag race and retainer assembly over sprag assembly.

4) Check sprag lock up by holding sun gear stationary and turning sprag race in direction of arrow "A". See Fig. 15. Sprag should lock up. Turn sprag race in direction of arrow "B" and sprag should rotate freely.

5) Lubricate clutch plates with transmission fluid. Install waved washer in drum. Install steel clutch plate and lined clutch plate, alternating until all plates are installed.

Fig. 15: Checking Sprag Operation

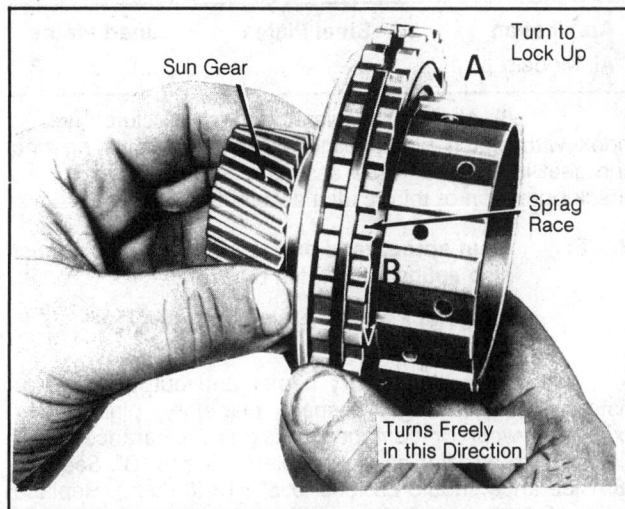

Race should lock up when turned in direction "A" and turn freely in direction "B".

Fig. 16: Checking Third Clutch Operation

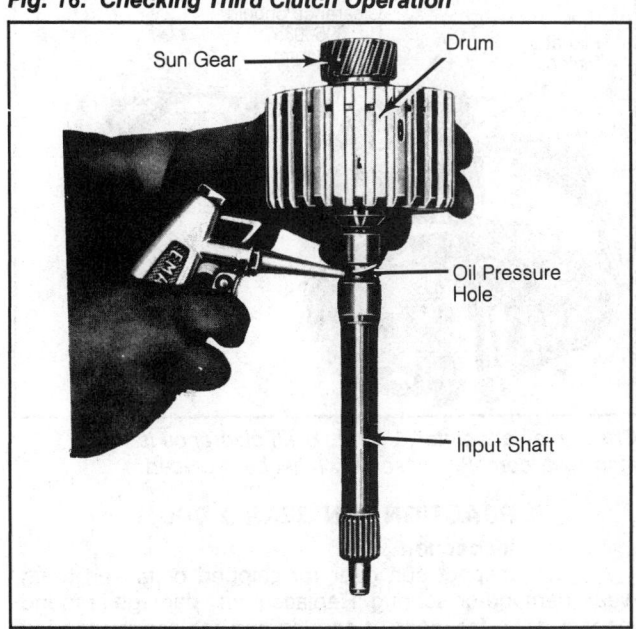

Apply compressed air at oil hole in input shaft. Clutch should move in drum.

Fig. 17: Exploded View of Third Clutch Assembly

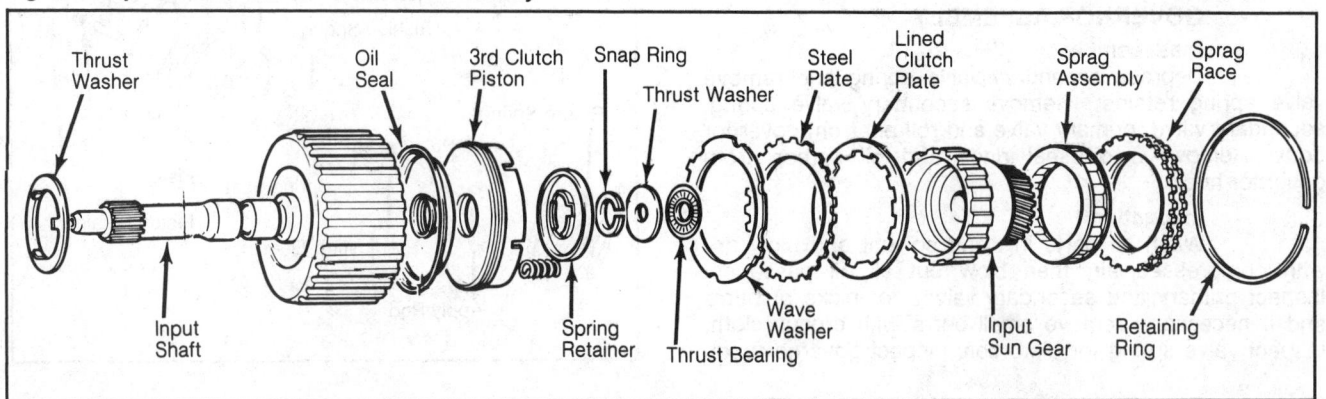

GM TURBO HYDRA-MATIC 180 — FIAT (Cont.)

THIRD CLUTCH PLATE USAGE CHART

Application	Steel Plates	Lined Plates
All Models	4	3

6) Align clutch plates and install clutch hub to index with clutch plate splines. Compress retaining ring and seat input sprag race assembly into clutch drum. Air check operation of third clutch assembly. *See Fig. 16.*

NOTE: **Input sprag, race and retainer assembly must also spline into clutch drum.**

PLANETARY CARRIER ASSEMBLY
Inspection
Inspect planetary carrier and output shaft for distortion or damage. Inspect planetary pinions for excessive wear or damage. Check end clearance of all pinions with a feeler gauge at points "A" and "B". *See Fig. 18.* Clearance should be .005-.035" (.13-.89 mm). Replace entire planetary carrier assembly if damage or excessive wear is noted.

Fig. 18: Checking Planetary Pinion End Play

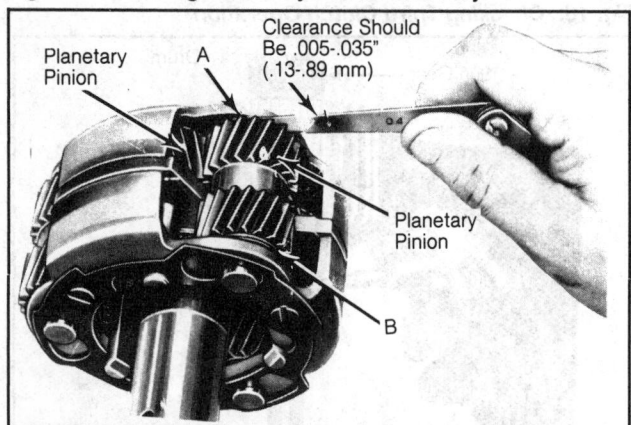

Check play at points "A" and "B". If clearance is incorrect, complete assembly must be replaced.

REACTION SUN GEAR & DRUM
Inspection
Inspect sun gear for chipped or nicked teeth, wear, damage or scoring. Replace if any damage is found. Inspect drum for wear or scoring and replace as needed. Inspect drum bushing and replace if damaged. When installing new bushing, ensure it is flush with rear face of drum hub.

GOVERNOR ASSEMBLY
Disassembly
Depress secondary valve spring and remove valve spring retainer. Remove secondary valve spring, secondary valve, primary valve and roll pin from governor body. Remove 3 oil seal rings and oil screen from governor hub.

Inspection
Wash all parts in clean solvent and blow dry with compressed air, then blow out all oil passages. Inspect primary and secondary valves for nicks or burrs and if necessary, remove small burrs with crocus cloth. Inspect valve spring for distortion. Inspect governor body

Fig. 19: Exploded View of Governor Body Assembly

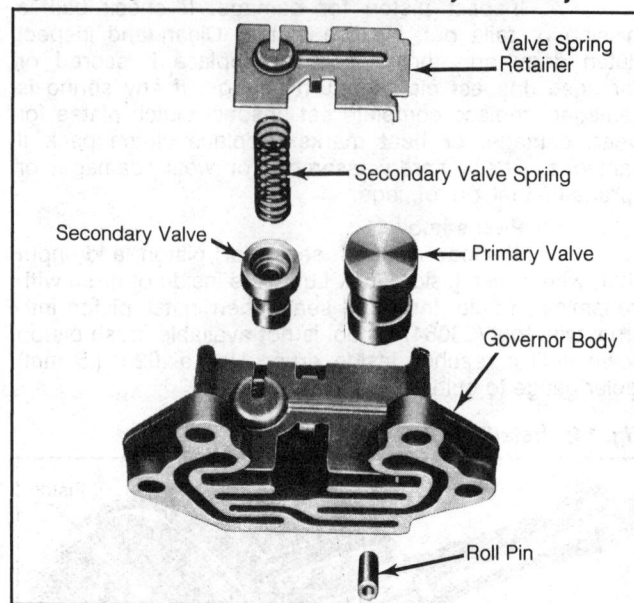

for nicks, burrs or varnish build-up in oil passages and replace as needed. Inspect governor hub splines for cracks or chipped teeth in splines.

Reassembly
Lubricate and install 3 new oil seal rings in grooves on governor hub, then install oil screen. Install roll pin flush to .010" (.25 mm) below front face of governor body. Lubricate and install primary valve, small end first, into governor body. Lubricate and install secondary valve, small spool portion first, into body. Install valve spring. Depress spring and install retainer.

SERVO PISTON ASSEMBLY
Disassembly
Remove servo piston apply rod. Hold servo piston sleeve at flat portion, then loosen and remove adjusting bolt lock nut. Depress piston sleeve and remove sleeve retaining ring. Push sleeve through piston and remove cushion spring and spring retainer. Remove piston ring.

Fig. 20: Exploded View of Servo Piston Assembly

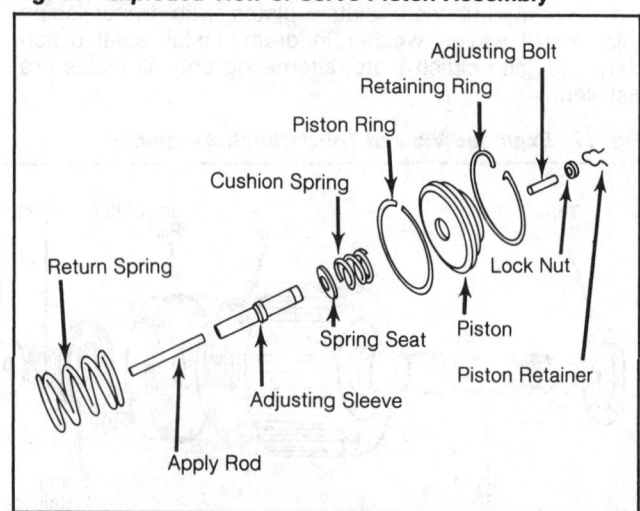

GM TURBO HYDRA-MATIC 180 — FIAT (Cont.)

Fig. 21: *Exploded View of Valve Body Assembly*

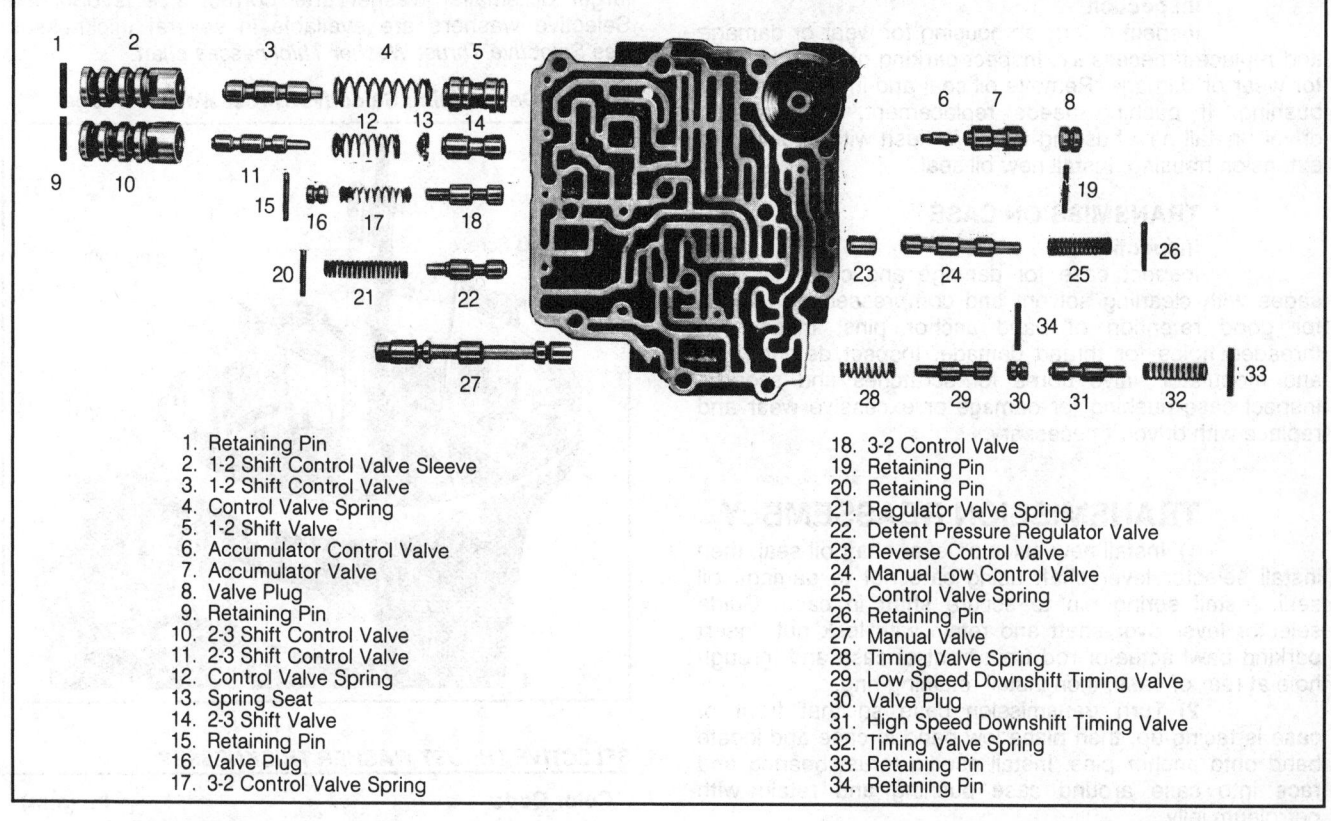

1. Retaining Pin
2. 1-2 Shift Control Valve Sleeve
3. 1-2 Shift Control Valve
4. Control Valve Spring
5. 1-2 Shift Valve
6. Accumulator Control Valve
7. Accumulator Valve
8. Valve Plug
9. Retaining Pin
10. 2-3 Shift Control Valve
11. 2-3 Shift Control Valve
12. Control Valve Spring
13. Spring Seat
14. 2-3 Shift Valve
15. Retaining Pin
16. Valve Plug
17. 3-2 Control Valve Spring

18. 3-2 Control Valve
19. Retaining Pin
20. Retaining Pin
21. Regulator Valve Spring
22. Detent Pressure Regulator Valve
23. Reverse Control Valve
24. Manual Low Control Valve
25. Control Valve Spring
26. Retaining Pin
27. Manual Valve
28. Timing Valve Spring
29. Low Speed Downshift Timing Valve
30. Valve Plug
31. High Speed Downshift Timing Valve
32. Timing Valve Spring
33. Retaining Pin
34. Retaining Pin

Inspection

Inspect cushion spring, adjusting bolt, and sleeve for damage. Inspect piston for damage and piston ring for side wear. Replace as needed.

Reassembly

Reverse disassembly procedure to assemble servo piston.

VALVE BODY ASSEMBLY

To simplify valve body reassembly, place individual valves, springs, etc. in correct order (in relation to position in valve body) as each valve train is removed from its bore.

Valves and springs are not interchangeable; all parts must be installed in correct order in proper valve body bore. *See Fig. 21.*

Disassembly

1) Remove manual valve and valve link from valve body. Turn valve body so that transfer plate is facing up, then remove 2 attaching bolts and lift off transfer plate and gasket.

2) Using a small "C" clamp, compress accumulator piston and remove retaining ring. Loosen clamp slowly and remove accumulator piston and spring. Remove oil ring from piston.

3) Remove 1-2 shift control valve retaining pin. Remove 1-2 shift control valve sleeve, control valve, spring and valve. Remove 2-3 shift control valve retaining pin. Remove 2-3 shift control valve, spring, spring seat and 2-3 shift valve.

4) Remove 3-2 control valve retaining pin. Remove 3-2 control valve plug, spring and control valve. Remove retaining pin, then remove detent pressure regulator spring and valve.

5) Remove high speed downshift timing valve retaining pin. Remove high speed downshift timing valve spring and valve. From the same bore, remove second retaining pin, low speed downshift timing valve plug, valve and spring.

6) Remove manual low and reverse control valve retaining pin. Remove spring, manual low control valve and reverse control valve. Remove 1-2 accumulator valve plug retaining pin. Remove plug, accumulator valve and control valve.

Inspection

1) Inspect each valve for free movement in its respective bore in valve body. Inspect valves for burrs and if necessary remove small burrs with crocus cloth.

NOTE: **DO NOT remove the sharp edges from valves as they perform a cleaning action in valve bore.**

2) Inspect valve springs for distortion or collapsed coils and replace as necessary. Replace entire valve body assembly if any valve on the valve body is damaged.

Reassembly

Reassemble valves, springs, plugs and retaining pins in their proper location and order into valve body using a liberal amount of transmission fluid. Install new oil ring on accumulator piston. Install spring and piston in valve body, compress piston and install retaining ring. Install valve body gasket and transfer plate. Install attaching bolts.

GM TURBO HYDRA-MATIC 180 — FIAT (Cont.)

EXTENSION HOUSING

Inspection

Inspect extension housing for wear or damage and replace if necessary. Inspect parking pawl and spring for wear or damage. Remove oil seal and inspect housing bushing. If bushing needs replacement, remove with driver. Install new bushing until it is flush with shoulder of extension housing. Install new oil seal.

TRANSMISSION CASE

Inspection

Inspect case for damage and clean oil passages with cleaning solvent and compressed air. Check for good retention of band anchor pins. Inspect all threaded holes for thread damage. Inspect detent valve and modulator valve bores for scratches and scoring. Inspect case bushing for damage or excessive wear and replace with driver if necessary.

TRANSMISSION REASSEMBLY

1) Install new selector lever shaft oil seal, then install selector lever shaft using care not to damage oil seal. Install spring pin to secure shaft in case. Guide selector lever over shaft and retain with lock nut. Insert parking pawl actuator rod from front of case and through hole at rear of case, then install retaining ring.

2) Turn transmission case so that front of case is facing up, then place low band in case and locate band onto anchor pins. Install needle thrust bearing and race into case around case bushing and retain with petroleum jelly.

3) Install reaction sun gear and drum into low band with sun gear facing up. Install needle thrust bearing and race onto front face of sun gear and retain with petroleum jelly.

4) Install input sun gear-to-planetary carrier washer and bearing into carrier and retain with petroleum jelly. Insert output shaft and planetary carrier assembly into case. Align second clutch drive plates in clutch drum.

5) Insert third clutch drum and input shaft through top of second clutch drum, seating third clutch drum splines into second clutch plate splines. Hold clutch assemblies by input shaft and lower into case. As clutch assemblies are lowered into place, turn drum and shaft to align ring gear and input sun gear with planetary pinions.

6) Install reverse clutch reaction plate into case. Lubricate reverse clutch plates. Install a steel plate then a lined plate, and continue alternating steel and lined plates until all clutch plates are installed.

REVERSE CLUTCH PLATE USAGE CHART

Application	Steel Plates	Lined Plates
All Models	4	3

7) Install reverse clutch cushion plate (waved washer) into case. Determine correct thickness of selective thrust washer to be installed. To determine which selective washer to use, place gauging tool (23085) on case flange and against input shaft. Loosen thumb screw on tool to allow inner shaft to drop on second clutch drum hub. Tighten thumb screw and remove tool.

8) Place selective washer removed from transmission against inner shaft of tool. Selective washer

should be flush with top face of shaft. If not, select next larger or smaller washer until correct size is obtained. Selective washers are available in several thicknesses. *See Selective Thrust Washer Thicknesses chart.*

Fig. 22: Determining Selective Thrust Washer Usage

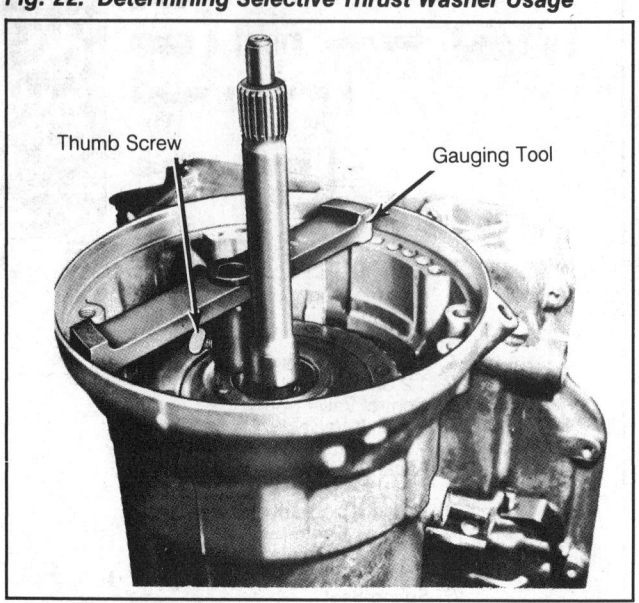

SELECTIVE THRUST WASHER THICKNESSES

Color Code	In. (mm)
Yellow	.070-.074 (1.78-1.88)
Blue	.076-.080 (1.93-2.03)
Red	.081-.085 (2.06-2.16)
Brown	.086-.090 (2.18-2.28)
Green	.091-.095 (2.31-2.41)
Black	.097-.101 (2.46-2.56)

9) Install wear plate on oil pump, then insert guide pin into oil pump for alignment of converter housing and lower housing into pump. Install new oil seal washers on converter housing-to-oil pump attaching bolts, then loosely install bolts into converter housing. Use an aligning tool, align converter housing to oil pump. Tighten attaching bolts and remove tool.

10) Install new converter housing-to-case oil seal and new oil pump flange gasket. Place end play selective washer, previously determined, onto oil pump shaft and retain with petroleum jelly. Install 2 guide pins in case and lower converter housing and oil pump onto case.

11) Install new oil seal washers on housing-to-case attaching bolts, then install and tighten bolts. Check for correct assembly by turning input shaft by hand and making sure assembly rotates freely.

12) Turn transmission so that bottom of case is facing up. Lubricate oil seal rings and install governor hub onto output shaft. Install retaining snap ring. Install governor body gasket, then install governor body to governor hub and tighten attaching bolts.

NOTE: Make sure governor valves move freely after governor body bolts are tightened.

13) Slide speedometer drive gear and collar into position on shaft, and install snap ring. Install new

GM TURBO HYDRA-MATIC 180 — FIAT (Cont.)

gasket, then slide extension housing over output shaft and align holes. Align parking pawl shaft into extension housing. Install and tighten housing-to-case attaching bolts.

14) Install speedometer driven gear into extension housing and install retainer. Lubricate and install detent valve, sleeve, spring and spring seat into case bore. Compress spring and install retaining pin into sleeve hole.

NOTE: Install sleeve with slots facing oil pan.

15) Install modulator valve (small end first) into sleeve, then install sleeve in case. Place new gasket on modulator, install plunger in modulator and thread modulator into case.

Fig. 23: Adjusting Servo Apply Rod

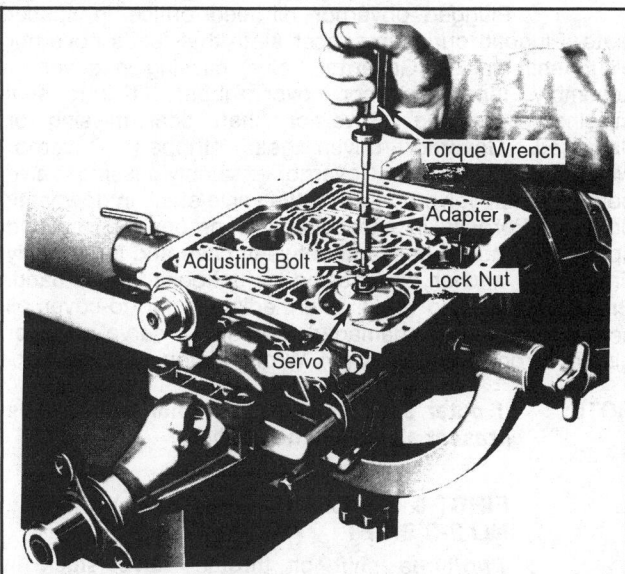

Tighten bolt to 40 INCH lbs. and back off exactly 4 turns.

16) Lubricate and install servo assembly apply rod, spring and piston into case. Compress piston spring with tool. Lightly tap on piston while compressing, until piston is seated, to avoid damage to oil seal ring. Install retaining ring and remove tool.

Fig. 24: Check Ball Location in Transmission Case

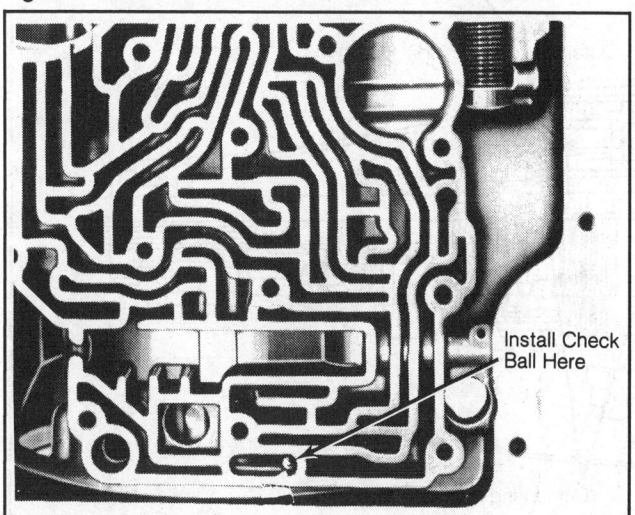

Install Check Ball Here

17) To adjust servo apply rod, use a 3/16" hex head wrench and tighten adjusting bolt to 40 INCH lbs. (4.5 N.m). Back off bolt exactly 4 turns. Hold adjusting bolt and sleeve stationary while tightening lock nut.

18) Install check ball in oil passage in transmission case. *See Fig. 24.* Install new transfer plate gasket. Lubricate and install manual valve into valve body bore, then install long side of manual valve link into valve. Install small end of valve link into selector lever, then install valve body and transfer plate onto gasket and casing. Loosely install 8 valve body-to-transmission case bolts.

19) Position servo cover gasket, servo cover and reinforcement plate on transfer plate and install retaining bolts loosely. Tighten all valve body assembly bolts starting from center of valve body and working outward. Install oil filter with new gasket. Install manual detent spring. Install oil pan with new gasket.

20) Slide output shaft flange on by hand. Slide torque converter over stator shaft and input shaft. Be sure that keyway on converter hub seats in drive lugs on oil pump. Rotate converter to check that it is fully seated. Install gasket, speedometer driven gear, bolt and lock washer.

TIGHTENING SPECIFICATIONS

Application	Ft. Lbs. (N.m)
Converter Housing-to-Case	22-26 (30.8-36.4)
Converter Housing-to-Oil Pump	13-17 (18.2-23.8)
Extension Housing-to-Case	20-25 (28.0-35.0)
Flange Nut	51 (71.4)
Servo Cover-to-Body	17-19 (23.8-26.6)
	INCH Lbs. (N.m)
Filter-to-Case Bolt	156-180 (18.2-21.0)
Governor Body-to-Governor	72-84 (8.4-9.8)
Oil Pan-to-Case	84-108 (9.8-12.6)
Reinforcement Plate-to-Case	156-180 (18.2-21.0)
Selector Lever-to-Shaft	96-132 (11.2-15.4)
Servo Adjusting Bolt	40 (4.7)
Servo Adjusting Bolt Lock Nut	144-180 (16.8-21.0)
Transfer Plate-to-Valve Body	72-96 (8.4-11.2)
Valve Body-to-Case	156-180 (18.2-21.0)

TURBO HYDRA-MATIC 200

Isuzu P'UP

DESCRIPTION

Transmission is a fully automatic 3-speed unit consisting primarily of a three-element hydraulic torque converter and a compound planetary gear set. Three multiple-disc clutches, a roller clutch, and one brake band provide the friction elements required to obtain the desired function of the planetary gear set. A hydraulic system pressurized by a gear-type pump provides the working pressure required to operate the friction elements and automatic controls.

LUBRICATION & ADJUSTMENT

See the appropriate article in AUTOMATIC TRANSMISSION SERVICING Section.

TROUBLE SHOOTING

NO DRIVE IN DRIVE RANGE

Incorrect fluid level, fluid leakage. Manual linkage out of adjustment. Low oil pressure: Plugged or restricted oil screen, screen gasket out of position, pump assembly or pressure regulator faulty, pump drive gear tangs damaged by converter, case porosity in intake bore area. Valve body manual valve disconnected from lever pin. Forward clutch: Piston cracked, seals missing or damaged, clutch plates burned, or snap ring out of groove; forward clutch seal rings missing or damaged on turbine shaft, leak in feed circuits, pump-to-case gasket out of position, ball check stuck or missing in clutch housing. Cup plug leaking or missing in rear of turbine shaft in clutch apply passage, wrong piston or number of clutch plates in forward clutch housing. Cup plug leaking or missing in rear of turbine shaft in clutch apply passage, wrong piston or number of clutch plates in forward clutch

housing, or feed orifice plugged in turbine shaft. Roller clutch assembly: Springs missing in roller clutch, or rollers galled or missing.

1-2 SHIFT AT FULL THROTTLE ONLY

Throttle valve cable binding, unhooked, broken, or misadjusted. Throttle valve lever and bracket assembly binding or unhooked. T.V. exhaust ball lifter or No. 5 ball binding, out of position, or unhooked. Throttle valve and plunger binding. Control valve body gaskets leaking, damaged, or incorrectly installed. Case porosity.

NOTE: Allowing No. 5 ball to seat causes full T.V. pressure regardless of throttle valve position.

FIRST SPEED ONLY, NO 1-2 SHIFT

Plugged governor oil feed orifice in spacer plate. Plugged orifice in spacer plate that feeds governor oil to shift valves. Governor ball(s) missing in governor assembly. Inner governor cover rubber "O" ring seal missing or leaking. Governor shaft seal missing or damaged. Governor driven gear stripped. Governor weights binding on pin. Governor assembly missing. Valve body 1-2 shift valve or 1-2 throttle valve stuck in downshfit position. Porosity in case channels or undrilled second speed feed holes. Leakage between case and band apply ring. Band anchor pin missing or unhooked from band. Broken or missing band. Intermediate servo-to-cover oil seal ring missing or damaged. Porosity in servo cover or piston. Wrong band apply pin. Wrong piston and/or cover.

NOTE: If outer seal leaks, an external leak will be present along with no upshifts.

FIRST & SECOND SPEEDS ONLY, NO 2-3 SHIFT

Two/three shift or throttle valve stuck in downshift position. Direct clutch feed orifice in spacer

Fig. 1: Cutaway View of Turbo Hydra-Matic 200 Automatic Transmission Assembly

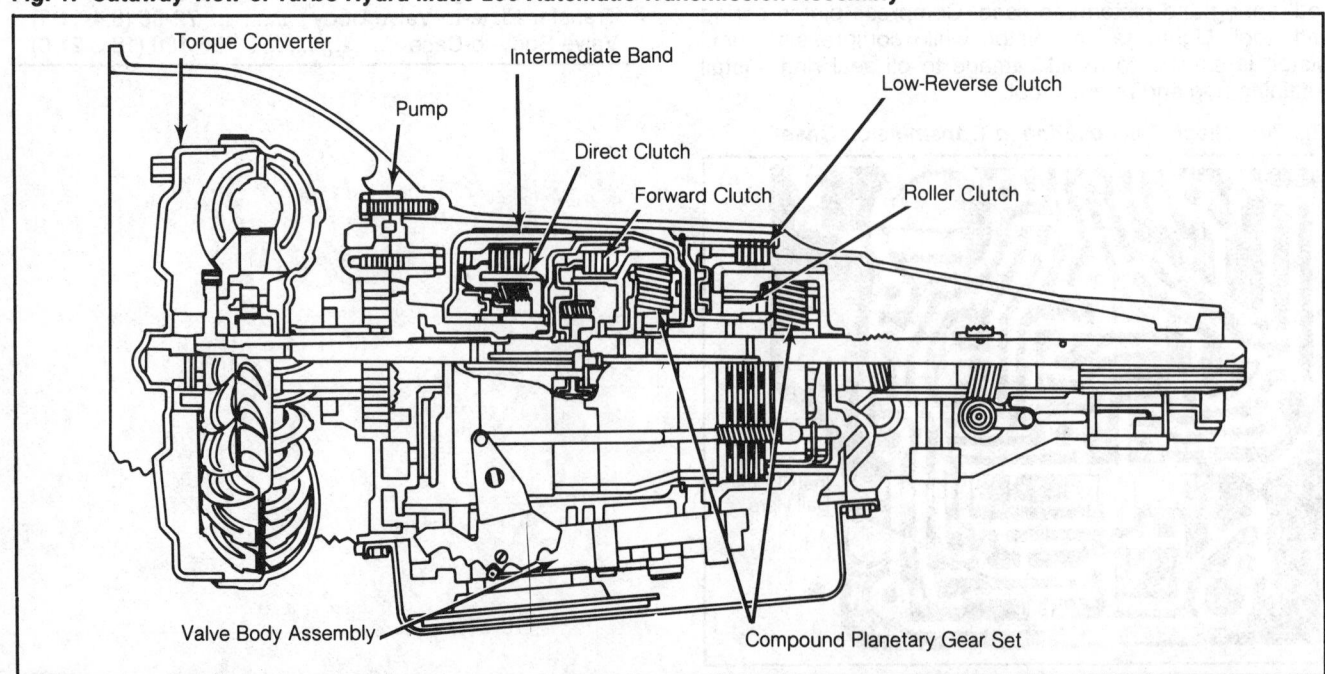

TURBO HYDRA-MATIC 200 (Cont.)

Fig. 2: Turbo Hydra-Matic 200 Hydraulic Circuits Diagram

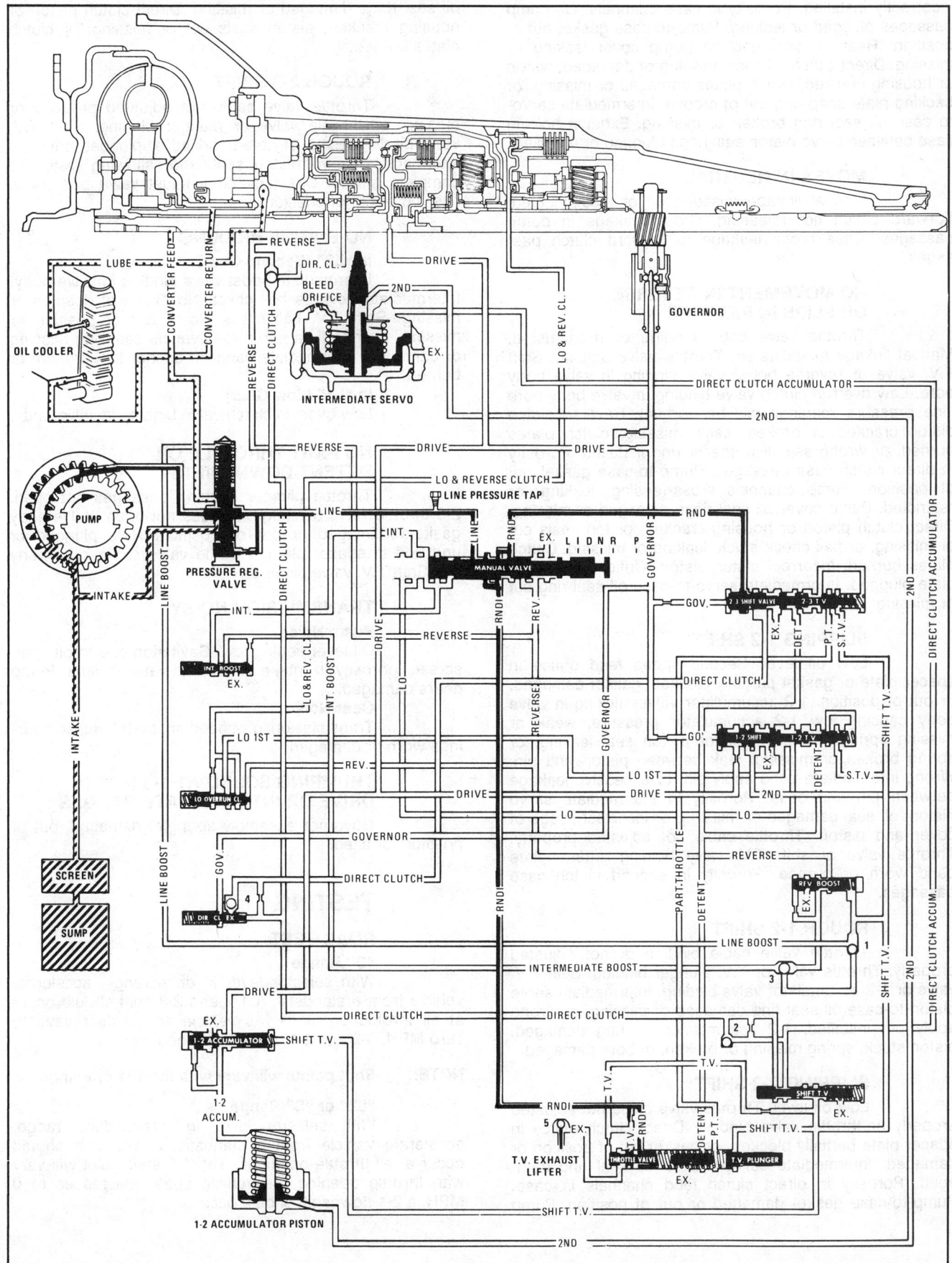

TURBO HYDRA-MATIC 200 (Cont.)

plate plugged. Valve body gaskets leaking, damaged, or incorrectly installed. Porosity in case channels. Oil pump passages plugged or leaking. Pump-to-case gasket out of position. Rear oil seal ring on pump cover leaking or missing. Direct clutch oil seals missing or damaged, piston or housing cracked, clutch plates damaged or missing, or backing plate snap ring out of groove. Intermediate servo-to case oil seal ring broken or missing. Exhaust hole in case between servo piston seal rings plugged or undrilled.

MOVES IN NEUTRAL

Manual linkage misadjusted or disconnected. Forward clutch not releasing. Cross leakage in pump passages. Case cross leakage to forward clutch passages.

NO MOVEMENT IN REVERSE, OR SLIPS IN REVERSE

Throttle valve cable binding or misadjusted. Manual linkage misadjusted. Throttle valve binding. Shift T.V. valve or reverse boost valve binding in valve body bore. Low overrun clutch valve binding in valve body bore (line pressure readings will be normal). Reverse clutch piston cracked or broken, seals missing, clutch plates burned, or wrong selective spacer ring installed. Porosity in direct clutch case passages. Pump-to-case gasket out of position. Pump channels cross-feeding, leaking, or restricted. Pump cover oil seal rings damaged or missing. Direct clutch piston or housing cracked, piston seals cut or missing, or ball check stuck, leaking or missing. Clutch plates burned. Incorrect clutch piston. Orifices in spacer plate plugged. Intermediate servo-to-case oil seal ring cut or missing.

SLIPPING 1-2 SHIFT

Low oil level. Second speed feed orifice in spacer plate or gasket partially blocked, gasket damaged, or out of position. 1-2 accumulator valve sticking in valve body causing low 1-2 accumulator pressure; weak or missing spring. 1-2 accumulator piston seal leaking, or spring broken or missing; leak between piston and pin. Wrong intermediate band apply pin, or excessive leakage between pin and case. Porosity in intermediate servo piston, oil seal damaged or missing, or incorrect usage of cover and piston. Throttle cable not adjusted properly. Throttle valve or shift T.V. valve binding. Intermediate band worn or burned. Porosity in second clutch case passages.

ROUGH 1-2 SHIFT

Throttle valve cable binding or not adjusted properly. Throttle valve or T.V. plunger binding. Shift T.V. valve or 1-2 accumulator valve binding. Intermediate servo piston-to-case oil seal ring damaged or missing, or wrong apply pin installed. 1-2 accumulator oil ring damaged, piston stuck, spring missing or broken, or bore damaged.

SLIPPING 2-3 SHIFT

Low oil level. Throttle valve cable not adjusted properly or throttle valve binding. Direct clutch orifice in spacer plate partially blocked, or gasket out of position or damaged. Intermediate servo-to-case oil seal ring damaged. Porosity in direct clutch feed channels in case. Pump-to-case gasket damaged or out of position. Pump

channels cross feeding, leaking, or restricted. Pump cover oil seal rings damaged or missing. Direct clutch piston or housing cracked, piston seals cut or missing, or clutch plates burned.

ROUGH 2-3 SHIFT

Throttle valve cable not adjusted properly or binding, or throttle valve or plunger binding. Shift T.V. valve binding. Exhaust hole undrilled or plugged between intermediate servo piston seals, not allowing piston to complete stroke. Direct clutch exhaust valve ball check missing or out of position.

NO ENGINE BRAKING

In "L2" (Second Gear)

Intermediate boost valve binding in valve body. Intermediate-Reverse ball check No. 3 out of position or missing. Shift T.V. ball check No. 1 out of position or missing. Intermediate servo-to-cover oil seal ring missing or damaged. Intermediate band off anchor pin, broken, or burned.

In "L1" (Low Gear)

Low overrun clutch valve binding in valve body.

NO PART THROTTLE OR DETENT DOWNSHIFTS

Throttle plunger bushing passages not open. 2-3 throttle valve bushing passages not open. Valve body gaskets damaged or out of position. Hole plugged or undrilled in spacer plate. Throttle valve cable improperly set. Shift T.V. valve binding.

TRANSMISSION NOISY

Pump Noise

Oil lever setting low. Cavitation due to plugged screen, porosity in intake circuit, or water in fluid. Pump gears damaged.

Gear Noise

Transmission grounded to body. Roller bearings worn or damaged.

THUMPING SOUND AT 1-5 MPH IN DRIVE OR INTERMEDIATE RANGES

Governor assembly spring(s) damaged, out of position, or tilted.

TESTING

ROAD TEST

"D" Range

With selector lever in drive range, accelerate vehicle from a standstill. A 1-2 and 2-3 shift should occur at all throttle openings. As vehicle speed decreases to zero MPH, 3-2 and 2-1 downshifts should occur.

NOTE: Shift points will vary with throttle openings.

"L2" or "S" Range

With selector lever in intermediate range, accelerate vehicle from a standstill. A 1-2 shift should occur at all throttle openings. The 1-2 shift point will vary with throttle opening. As vehicle speed decreases to 0 MPH, a 2-1 downshift should occur.

TURBO HYDRA-MATIC 200 (Cont.)

NOTE: No 2-3 upshift or 3-2 downshift can be obtained in this range.

"L1" or "L" Range

Place selector lever in low range and accelerate vehicle from a standstill. No upshift should occur in this range.

2nd Gear ("L2" or "S") Overrun Braking

With selector lever in drive range, lift foot off accelerator and move selector lever to intermediate range ("L2" or "S"). An increase in engine RPM and an engine braking effect should be noted.

1st Gear ("L1" or "L") Overrun Braking

With selector lever in intermediate range, and vehicle speed approximately 30 MPH at constant throttle, move selector lever to low range ("L1" or "L"). An increase in engine RPM and an engine braking effect should be noted.

Fig. 3: View of Transmission Showing Location of Line Pressure Take-Off Point

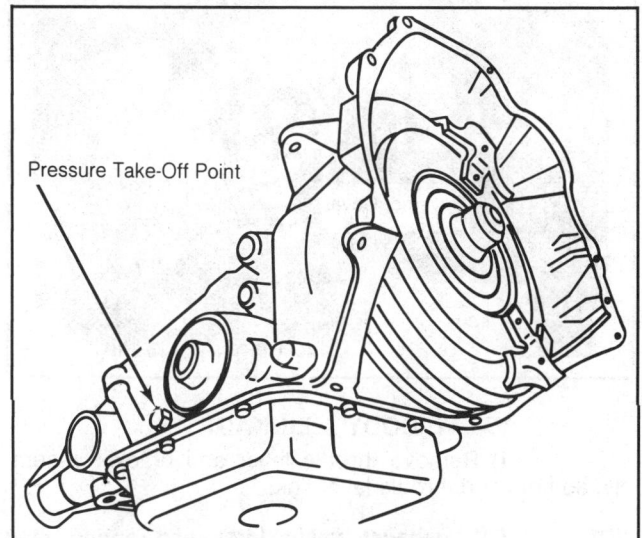

Pressure Take-Off Point

CONTROL PRESSURE CHECK

Connect a tachometer to engine, and a pressure gauge to line pressure take-off point in transmission. With transmission fluid at correct level and at operating temperature, pressure in each range can be checked by running engine at indicated RPM. Pressures should be within limits of table.

CONTROL PRESSURE SPECIFICATIONS

Range@RPM	psi (kg/cm²)
Park@1000	50-60 (3.5-4.2)
Reverse@1000[1]	100-115 (7.0-8.1)
Neutral@1000	55-60 (3.9-4.2)
Drive@1200[1]	60-75 (4.2-5.3)
Int.@1000[1]	85-100 (6.0-7.0)
Low@1000[1]	85-100 (6.0-7.0)

[1] — Total running time for tests with vehicle in gear must not exceed 2 minutes.

REMOVAL & INSTALLATION

See the appropriate article in AUTOMATIC TRANSMISSION REMOVAL Section.

TORQUE CONVERTER

NOTE: Torque converter is a seal unit and cannot be disassembled for service.

LEAKAGE CHECK

1) Install pressure test plug tool (J-21369) into torque converter hub. Tighten hex nut to expand tool. Install safety strap to prevent tool from blowing out when air pressure is applied.

2) Apply 80 psi (5.6 kg/cm²) air pressure to air valve in tool. Submerge converter in water and check for leaks.

CLUTCH AND BAND APPLICATION CHART (ELEMENTS IN USE)

Selector Lever Position	Direct Clutch	Forward Clutch	Low & Reverse Clutch	Intermediate Band	Low Roller Clutch
D — DRIVE					
First Gear		X			X
Second Gear		X		X	
Third Gear	X	X			
S or L2 — INTERMEDIATE					
First Gear		X			X
Second Gear		X	X		X
L or L1 — LOW		X	X		X
R — REVERSE	X		X		

NEUTRAL OR PARK — All clutches, brakes, and bands released and/or ineffective.

Fig. 4: *Installation of Special Tool for Torque Converter Leakage Check*

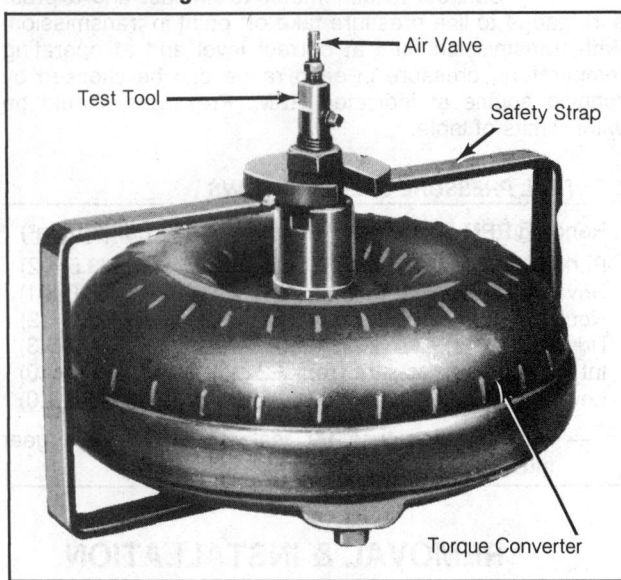

- Air Valve
- Test Tool
- Safety Strap
- Torque Converter

END CLEARANCE CHECK

1) Install end clearance checking tool (J-25020) into converter hub until collet end of tool bottoms. Tighten tool cap nut to 5 ft. lbs. (.7 mkg). Install support collar (J-21371-3) and tighten hex nut to 3 ft. lbs. (.4 mkg). *See Fig. 5.*

Fig. 5: *Installation of Torque Converter End Clearance Checking Tools*

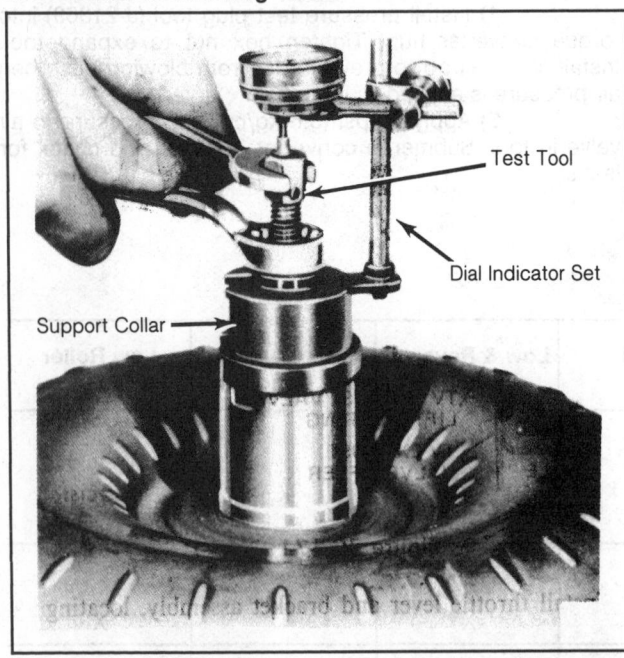

- Test Tool
- Dial Indicator Set
- Support Collar

2) Install a dial indicator and set it at zero while its plunger rests on cap nut of checking tool. Loosen hex nut while holding cap nut stationary. When hex nut is fully loosened, the indicator reading obtained will be torque converter end clearance.

3) Torque converter end clearance should be .050" (1.27 mm) or less. If clearance exceeds specifications, torque converter must be replaced.

TRANSMISSION DISASSEMBLY

GOVERNOR, OIL PAN & SCREEN

1) Using a screwdriver, remove governor cover retaining ring. Remove governor cover using pliers. Discard governor cover seal rings.

NOTE: **Governor cover seal rings may remain in transmission case.**

2) Remove governor assembly from case, rotating output shaft counterclockwise to ease removal. Remove oil pan and gasket. Remove oil screen and gasket.

NOTE: **Screen attaching bolts are approximately 3/8" (9.5 mm) longer than valve body bolts and are not interchangeable.**

Fig. 6: *Using Pliers to Remove Governor Cover*

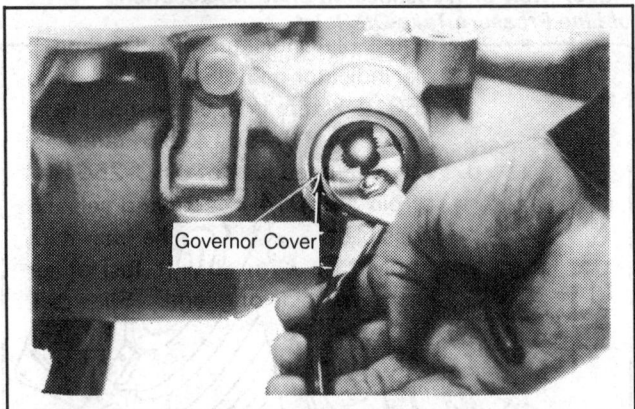

- Governor Cover

VALVE BODY & LINKAGE

1) Remove throttle lever and bracket assembly, do not bend throttle lever link.

NOTE: **T.V. exhaust valve lifter and spring may separate from throttle lever and bracket assembly.**

2) Remove manual detent roller and spring assembly. Remove remaining control valve assembly attaching bolts. Holding manual valve with finger, remove control valve assembly, spacer plate, and gasket together.

3) To prevent dropping of 4 check valves, lay control valve assembly down with spacer plate side up and discard gasket. Remove 1-2 accumulator spring. Remove 1-2 accumulator spring. Remove 5th check ball located in case.

SPEEDOMETER DRIVEN GEAR & INTERMEDIATE SERVO

1) Remove speedometer driven gear bolt, washer and retainer. Withdraw gear from extension housing. Using a small screwdriver, remove intermediate servo cover retaining ring. Using pliers, remove servo cover from case. Discard seal rings from cover, then withdraw servo piston and apply pin assembly from case.

NOTE: **If servo assembly cannot be removed easily, place shop towels and hand over cover and case before applying air pressure.**

TURBO HYDRA-MATIC 200 (Cont.)

Fig. 7: Using Air Pressure to Remove Intermediate Servo Assembly

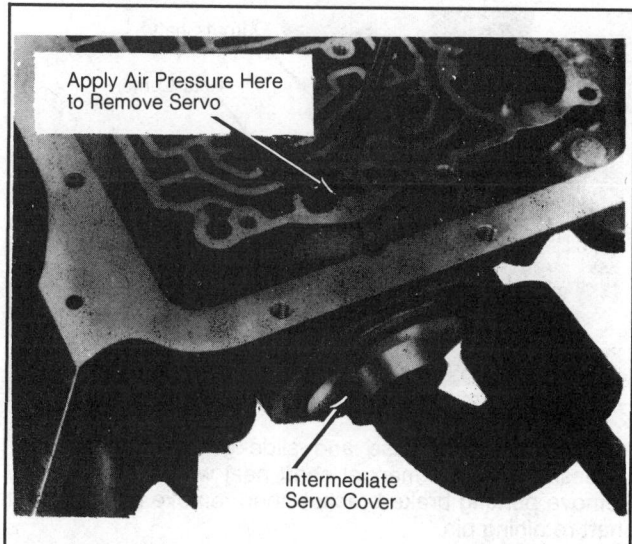

Apply Air Pressure Here to Remove Servo

Intermediate Servo Cover

2) Apply air pressure into direct clutch accumulator port and force servo assembly from case. *See Fig. 7.* Make a band apply pin selection check at this time to determine correct pin for use at reassembly.

Band Apply Pin Selection Check

1) Install special band apply pin gauge (J-25014-2) in intermediate servo bore and retain with servo cover retaining ring. Align ring with gap at case slot. Install gauge pin (J-25014-1) into gauge.

NOTE: Make sure tapered pin end is properly located against band apply lug. Also, make sure band anchor pin is properly located in case and band anchor lug.

2) Install dial indicator as shown in *Fig. 8* and position indicator plunger on top of gauge post. Set dial indicator to zero. Seat gauge pin squarely against servo retaining ring.

Fig. 8: Intermediate Band Apply Pin Selection

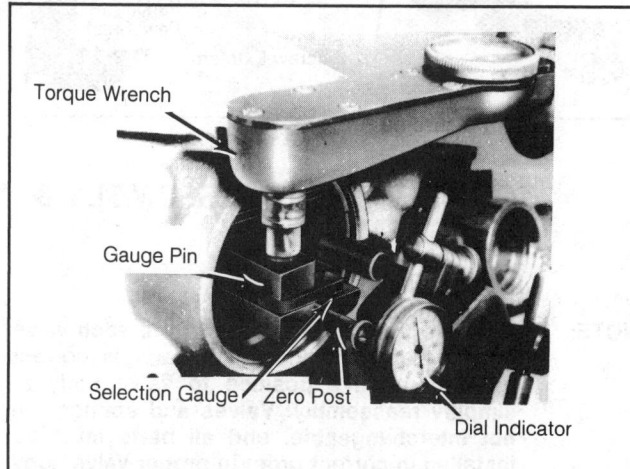

Torque Wrench

Gauge Pin

Selection Gauge   Zero Post

Dial Indicator

3) Align stepped side of gauge pin with torquing arm of selection gauge. Arm must stop against step of gauge pin.

NOTE: If band selection pin does not register between high and low limits, look for possible problem with intermediate band, direct clutch or case.

4) Apply 100 INCH Lbs. (11 N.m.) torque to hex nut on selection gauge. Slide indicator over gauge pin. Read indicator and select correct band apply pin from following chart.

NOTE: Dial indicator travel is reversed, making the indicator readings backwards. On an indicator that ranges from 0-100, a .020" (.5 mm) travel will read .080" (2 mm), a .060" (1.5 mm) travel will read .040" (1 mm).

INTERMEDIATE BAND APPLY PIN SELECTION CHART

Indicator Reading In. (mm)	Apply Pin Identification
.0-.029 (.0-.72)	1 Ring
.029-.057 (.72-1.44)	2 Rings
.057-.086 (1.44-2.16)	3 Rings
.086-.114 (2.16-2.88)	Wide Band

OIL PUMP & FRONT UNIT COMPONENTS

1) Turn transmission so oil pump faces upward. Remove oil pump-to-case bolts and washers, then withdraw oil pump and gasket. Grasp turbine shaft and remove direct and forward clutch assemblies from case. Lift direct clutch assembly off forward clutch assembly.

NOTE: Direct-to-forward clutch thrust washer may stick to end of direct clutch housing.

2) Remove intermediate band and anchor pin from case. Withdraw output shaft-to-turbine shaft front selective thrust washer.

NOTE: Washer may be stuck to end of turbine shaft.

FRONT INTERNAL GEAR

Using snap ring pliers, remove output shaft-to-selective washer snap ring, then withdraw front internal gear, rear selective thrust washer, and tanged thrust washer. Remove front carrier assembly and front internal gear-to-front carrier roller bearing assembly. Remove front sun gear, and front sun gear-to-front carrier roller thrust bearing and thrust race.

NOTE: Bearing may have come out with front carrier.

INPUT DRUM, REAR SUN GEAR & LOW—REVERSE CLUTCH HOUSING

1) Remove input drum and rear sun gear from case, then withdraw input drum-to-low and reverse clutch housing thrust washer from rear of input drum or from clutch housing.

2) Using a No. 14 sheet metal screw, remove housing-to-case cup plug and seal by turning screw in 2 or 3 turns and pulling straight out; discard cup plug and seal.

3) Remove low and reverse clutch housing-to-case beveled snap ring. Using a remover tool (J-25012),

withdraw low and reverse clutch housing from case. Remove low and reverse clutch housing-to-case spacer ring. *See Fig. 10.*

NOTE: Flat side of snap ring is positioned against clutch housing with beveled side up.

Fig. 9: Removing Front Internal Gear

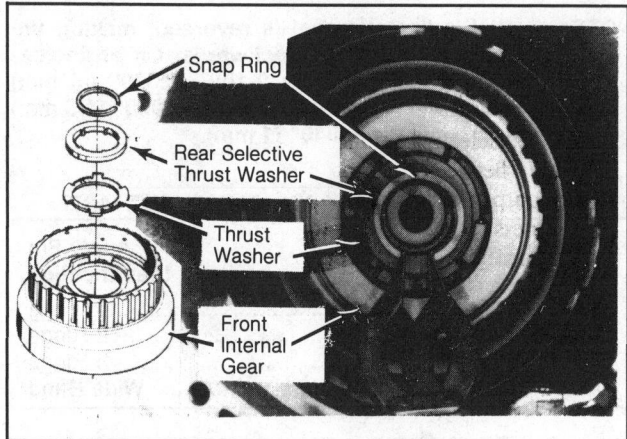

Fig. 10: Removing Low and Reverse Clutch Spacer

REAR GEAR COMPONENTS

1) Make sure governor has been removed. Grasp output shaft, lift out remaining rear unit parts, and place on bench in a horizontal positon. Remove low and reverse clutch selective spacer, roller clutch, and rear carrier from output shaft. Remove rear carrier-to-rear internal gear thrust washer from end of rear carrier or from inside internal gear.

2) Remove low and reverse clutch plates off output shaft, keeping in order for reassembly.

3) Withdraw rear internal gear-to-rear sun gear roller thrust bearing off rear internal gear. Remove rear internal gear from output shaft.

MANUAL SHAFT & PARKING LINKAGE

1) Remove nut retaining inside detent lever to manual shaft, then remove parking brake actuator rod and inside detent lever assembly. Remove manual shaft

Fig. 11: Removing Rear Internal Gear Components

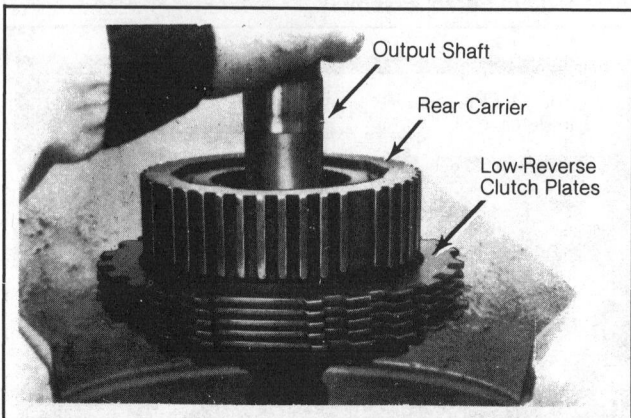

retaining pin from case and slide out manual shaft. If necessary, pry out manual shaft seal with a screwdriver. Remove parking brake bracket, then remove parking pawl shaft retaining pin.

    2) Using a No. 4 screw extractor, withdraw parking pawl cup plug and discard. Then, with a sheet metal screw or No. 3 screw extractor, remove parking pawl shaft. To complete disassembly, withdraw parking pawl and return spring.

Fig. 12: Removing Parking Pawl Shaft

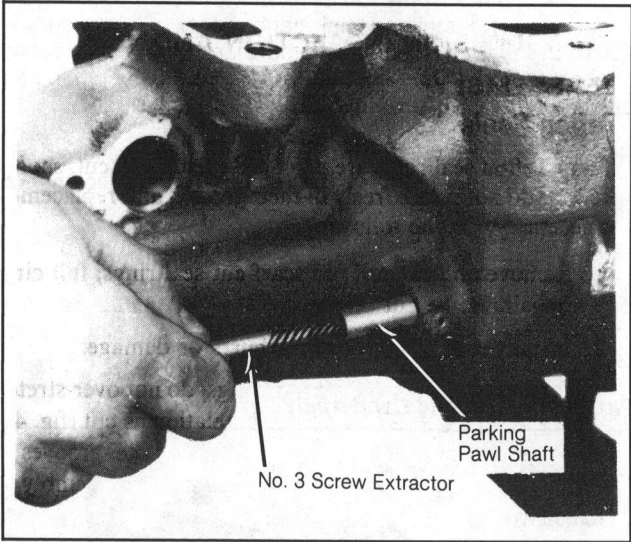

COMPONENT DISASSEMBLY & REASSEMBLY

VALVE BODY

NOTE: As valve trains are removed from each valve body bore, place individual parts in correct order in relative position to valve body to simplify reassembly. Valves and springs are not interchangeable, and all parts must be installed in correct order in proper valve body bore. *See Fig. 15.* Remove all coiled pins except the 2 pins which retain throttle valve train by pushing through from rough case surface side of body.

TURBO HYDRA-MATIC 200 (Cont.)

Disassembly

1) Position valve with cored face upward and 1-2 accumulator pocket at lower left. *See Fig. 15.* Remove four check balls from cored passages of valve body (fifth ball is in case), then remove 1-2 accumulator piston. From upper bore remove manual valve.

2) From upper right side bore, remove the 2-3 valve train. From next bore down, remove the 1-2 valve train. From next bore down, remove the reverse boost valve train.

3) If necessary to remove shift T.V. valve train, remove coiled pin and place valve body with rough casting surface up. Use needle nose pliers and push in on valve then hold in place with a small screwdriver. Position a 1/4" (6.3 mm) diameter rod, 3/8" (9.5 mm) long against end of valve, pry on rod with a screwdriver, remove small screwdriver, and remove plug, spring and valve.

4) From lower right side bore, remove outer coiled pin and withdraw bushing, plunger, spring, and detent pin. Using a 1/16" (1.5 mm) Allen wrench with ground sides to fit inside pin, remove inner coiled pin and throttle valve.

Fig. 13: *Removing Shift T.V. Valve Train*

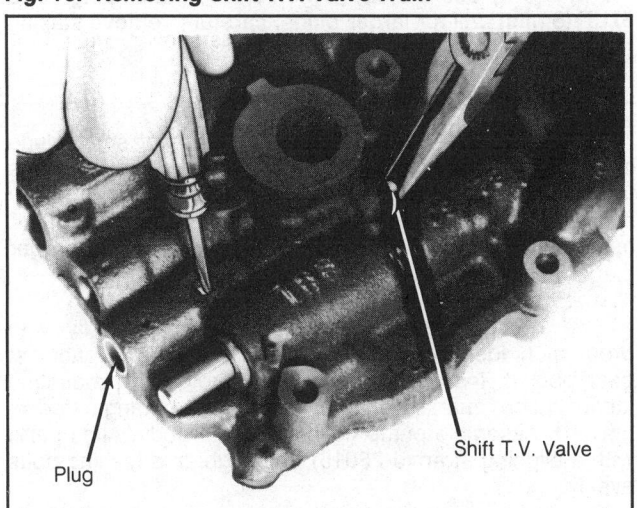

Fig. 14: *Installing Throttle Valve Bushings*

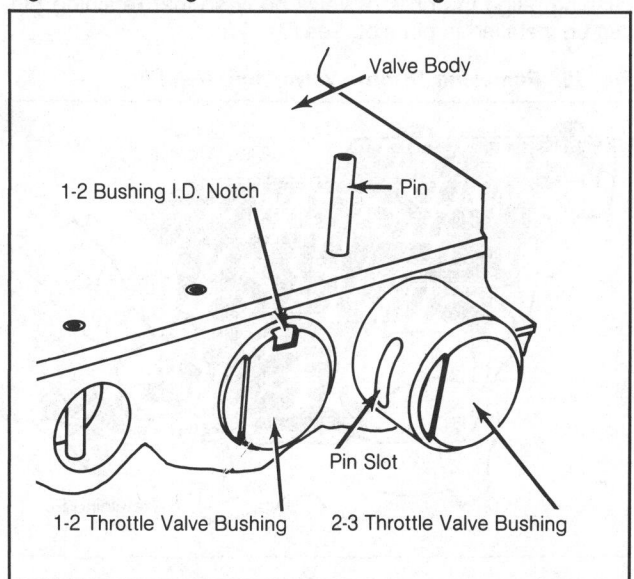

Fig. 15: *Exploded View of Valve Body Assembly*

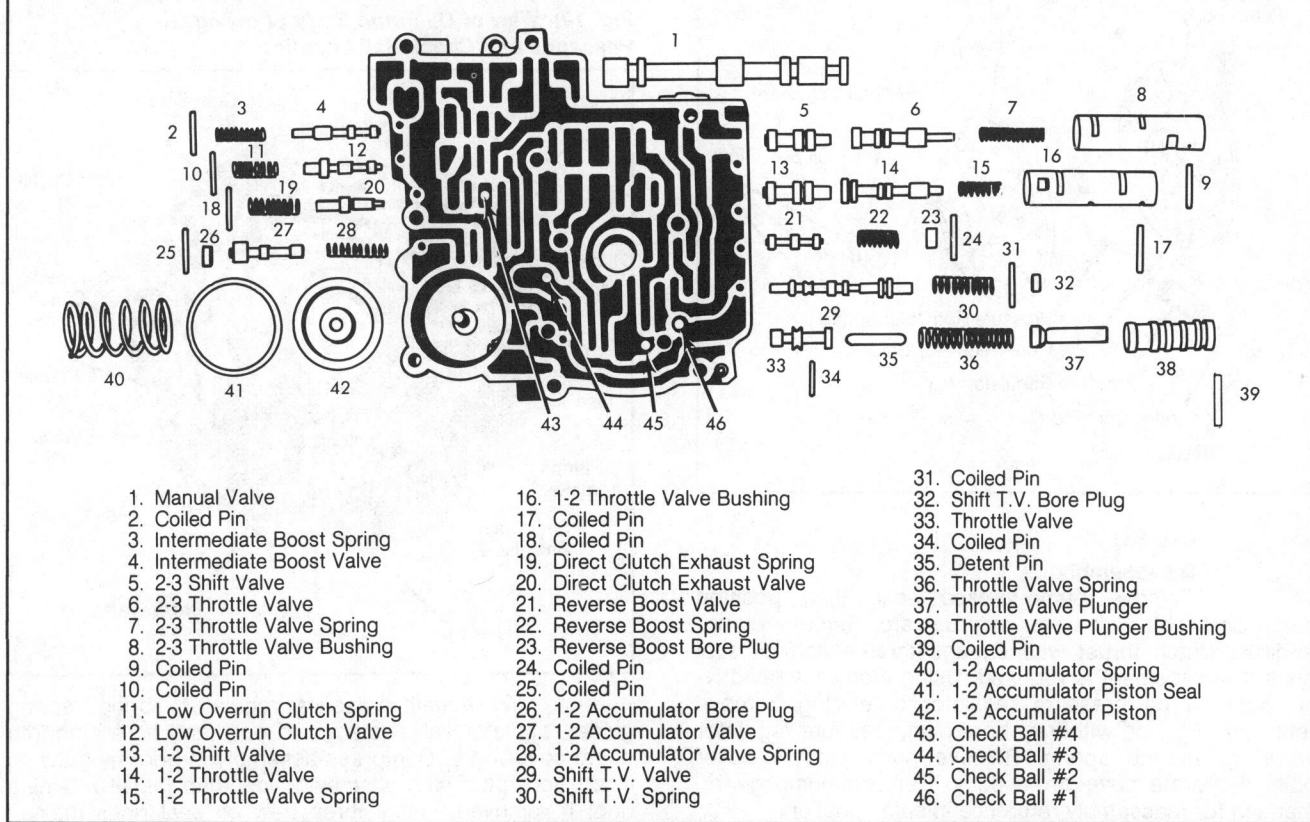

1. Manual Valve	16. 1-2 Throttle Valve Bushing	31. Coiled Pin
2. Coiled Pin	17. Coiled Pin	32. Shift T.V. Bore Plug
3. Intermediate Boost Spring	18. Coiled Pin	33. Throttle Valve
4. Intermediate Boost Valve	19. Direct Clutch Exhaust Spring	34. Coiled Pin
5. 2-3 Shift Valve	20. Direct Clutch Exhaust Valve	35. Detent Pin
6. 2-3 Throttle Valve	21. Reverse Boost Valve	36. Throttle Valve Spring
7. 2-3 Throttle Valve Spring	22. Reverse Boost Spring	37. Throttle Valve Plunger
8. 2-3 Throttle Valve Bushing	23. Reverse Boost Bore Plug	38. Throttle Valve Plunger Bushing
9. Coiled Pin	24. Coiled Pin	39. Coiled Pin
10. Coiled Pin	25. Coiled Pin	40. 1-2 Accumulator Spring
11. Low Overrun Clutch Spring	26. 1-2 Accumulator Bore Plug	41. 1-2 Accumulator Piston Seal
12. Low Overrun Clutch Valve	27. 1-2 Accumulator Valve	42. 1-2 Accumulator Piston
13. 1-2 Shift Valve	28. 1-2 Accumulator Valve Spring	43. Check Ball #4
14. 1-2 Throttle Valve	29. Shift T.V. Valve	44. Check Ball #3
15. 1-2 Throttle Valve Spring	30. Shift T.V. Spring	45. Check Ball #2
		46. Check Ball #1

5) From upper left side bore, remove intermediate boost valve train. From next bore down, remove low overrun clutch valve train. From next bore down, remove direct clutch exhaust valve train. From lower left side bore, remove 1-2 accumulator valve train.

Reassembly

Reverse disassembly procedure and note the following: Install all coiled pins from machined face side except pin retaining throttle valve bushing, plunger, spring, and detent pin; install this coiled pin from rough casting side. When installing 1-2 throttle bushing and 2-3 throttle bushing, align in bores of valve body so that retaining pin can be installed in pin slot. *See Fig. 14.*

Fig. 16: *Removing Throttle Valve Inner Roll Pin*

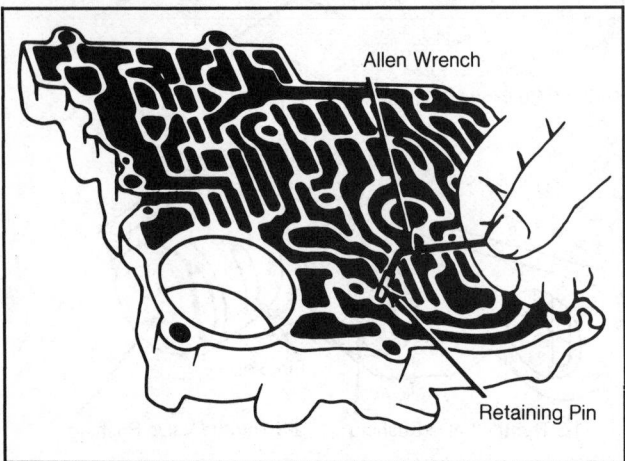

Fig. 17: *Exploded View of Oil Pump Assembly*

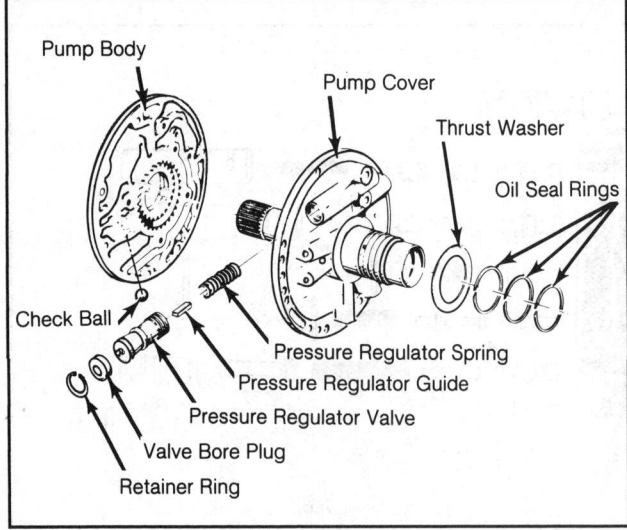

OIL PUMP
Disassembly

Remove pump-to-case seal, then position pump on bench with cover side upward. Remove pump-to-direct clutch thrust washer, and three teflon oil seal rings if replacement is required. Using a small screwdriver, push in on pressure regulator bore plug, remove retaining ring, and withdraw bore plug, pressure regulator valve, guide and spring. Remove pump body-to-cover bolts. Separate cover from body. Remove pump gears, marking for reassembly reference in same postion.

Inspection

Check drive and driven gears for scoring, galling, or other damage. Inspect gear pocket and crescent in body for scoring or damage. Check pump cover and body for nicks, open oil passages and overall flatness. Using a feeler gauge, measure pump body face-to-gear face clearance; clearance should be .0007-.0020" (.020-.055 mm). Inspect pressure regulator valve bore in pump cover and pressure regulator valve assembly for wear or damage, and make sure parts operate freely in bore. Inspect the seven cup plugs in pump cover for damage or leaks; if damaged, replace as follows:

Pump Cover Cup Plug Replacement

1) Use a 9/32" (7 mm) drill for small plugs or a 5/16" (8 mm) drill for larger plugs, carefully remove staking marks around cup plugs.

CAUTION: Do not damage pump cover.

2) Use a No. 4 screw extractor for small plugs or a No. 5 extractor for larger plugs and withdraw plugs from cover. Install plugs into cover 1/32" (.79 mm) below machined surface, then stake in 2 places using a 9/32" (7 mm) rod on small plugs or a 5/16" (8 mm) rod on larger plugs.

Reassembly

1) Install driven gear into pump body with production identification mark facing downward against gear pocket. Install drive gear into body with production identification marks on converter drive tangs facing upward. Assemble pump cover to pump body. Align parts with a aligning strap (J-25015), then tighten attaching bolts evenly.

NOTE: Make sure gears are installed in same position as removed.

Fig. 18: *View of Oil Pump Body Showing Oil Passages and Check Ball Location*

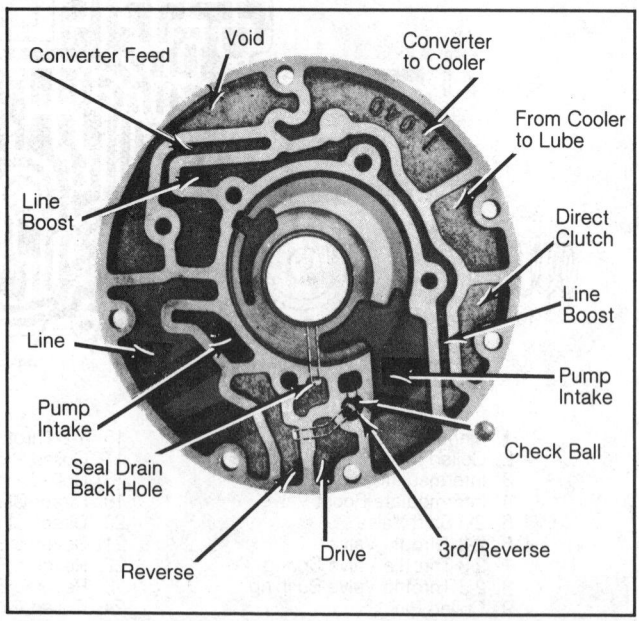

2) Install pressure regulator spring, spring guide, regulator valve (stem end out), and bore plug into pump cover bore. Compress assembly in bore by pushing in on bore plug with a screwdriver, then install retaining ring. If removed, install three new oil seal rings making

TURBO HYDRA-MATIC 200 (Cont.)

sure ends are correctly mated; retain with petrolatum. Install pump-to-case seal ring with chamfered side out, taking care not to twist ring in groove. Install pump-to-direct clutch thrust washer and retain with petrolatum.

Fig. 19: View of Oil Pump Driven Gear Showing Identifcation Marks

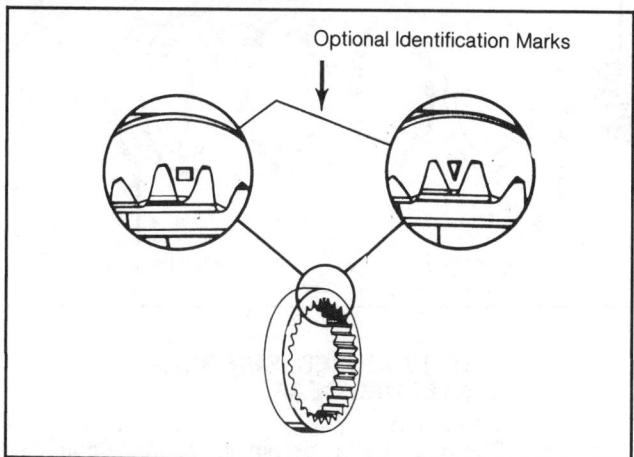

Fig. 20: View of Oil Pump Drive Gear Showing Identification Marks

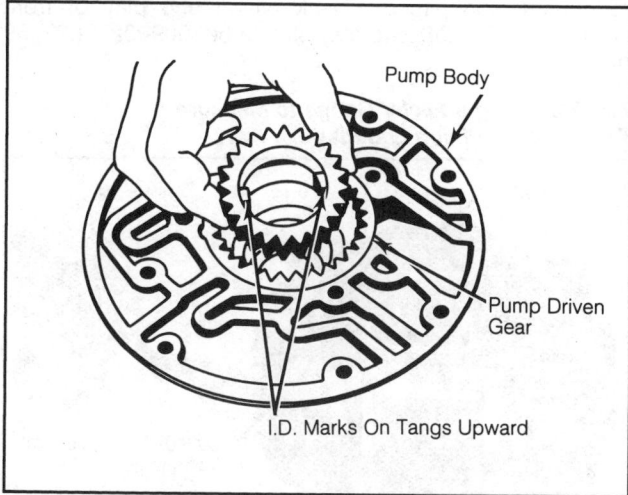

DIRECT CLUTCH

Disassembly

Remove clutch pack snap ring and withdraw backing plate and clutch plates, keeping in order for reassembly. Use compressor tool (J-23327), compress retainer and spring assembly, remove retaining snap ring, then withdraw retainer and spring assembly. Withdraw release spring guide, clutch piston, and apply ring from housing. Remove inner and outer seals from piston, and center seal from clutch housing.

Inspection

Inspect composition plates, steel plates and backing plate for wear, burning, or scoring. Check release springs and retainer for damage or a collapsed condition. Inspect clutch piston assembly for distortion, cracks, and other damage. Check direct clutch housing for cracks, wear, and open passages, and make sure ball check operates freely. Inspect snap ring grooves and bushings in housing for wear or damage.

Fig. 21: Removing Direct Clutch Snap Ring

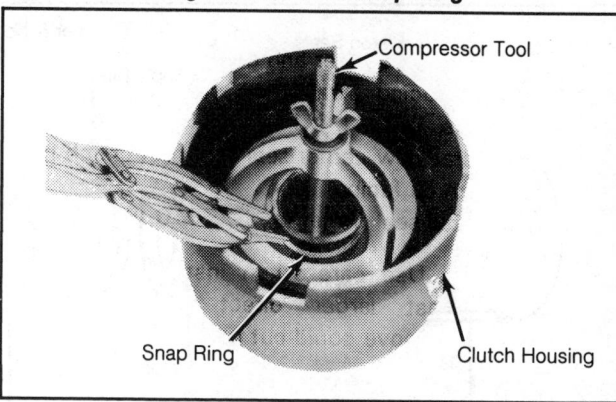

Reassembly

1) Install apply ring on clutch piston, then install new inner and outer seals on piston, with seal lips facing away from clutch apply ring side. Install a new center seal into direct clutch housing, with seal lip facing upward. Install a seal protector (J-25010) over oil seals, lubricate seals with transmission fluid, and install clutch piston.

NOTE: Use care when installing piston past larger snap ring groove as groove could cut outer seal on piston.

2) Install release spring guide with the omitted rib over check ball in piston. Install retainer and spring assembly into housing, making sure all parts are positioned properly.

NOTE: Retainer and spring assembly contain 16 release springs.

3) Using tool used at disassembly, compress release springs and install retainer snap ring. Lubricate with transmission fluid then install one flat steel clutch plate followed by one composition plate until all clutch plates are installed. Install backing plate with chamfered side up and clutch pack retaining snap ring.

NOTE: Make sure composition plates turn freely with clutch assembled.

FORWARD CLUTCH

Disassembly

Remove forward clutch-to-direct clutch thrust washer, then inspect teflon oil seals on turbine shaft for damage and remove if replacement is required. Remove clutch pack snap ring and withdraw backing plate and clutch plates, noting number of plates for reassembly reference. Using an arbor press, compress retainer and spring assembly, remove retaining snap ring, then withdraw retainer and springs from housing. Remove clutch piston from housing, then remove inner and outer seals from piston.

NOTE: Do not remove clutch apply ring from piston unless piston or apply ring requires replacement.

Inspection

Inspect composition plates, steel plates, and backing plate for wear, scores, or other damage. Check

Fig. 22: Exploded View Showing Components of Direct Clutch Assembly

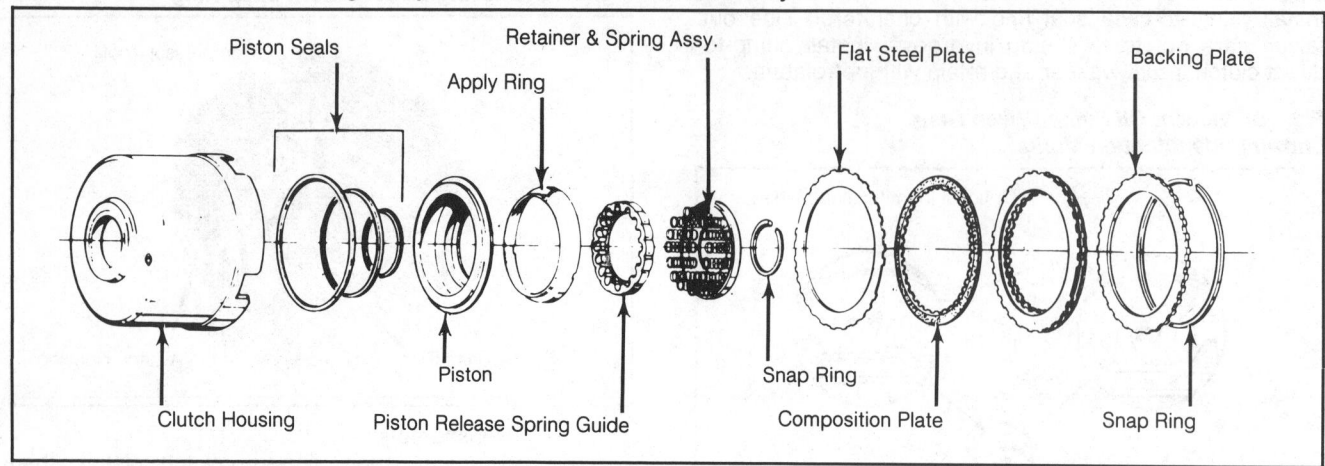

spring retainer and release springs for distortion or collapse. Inspect piston and housing for cracks, distortion, open oil passages, or other damage. Inspect snap ring grooves for wear or damage, and make sure ball check in housing operates freely. Check turbine shaft for open passages on both ends of shaft, and check journals for damage. Inspect clutch housing cup plug and if damaged, remove using a No. 4 screw extractor (grind to fit). Install new cup plug to .039" (1 mm) below surface.

Reassembly
1) Install clutch apply ring on piston, then install new inner and outer seals on piston, with seal lips facing away from apply ring side. Lubricate seals with transmission fluid, then install piston into housing. Install retainer and return spring assembly into housing, compress retainer and springs, and install retaining snap ring.

CAUTION: Use care when installing piston past large snap ring groove as groove could cut outer piston seal.

2) Lubricate with transmission fluid then install one waved steel plate (plate with three missing teeth) into housing, and alternate one composition plate followed by one steel plate until all plates are installed. Install backing plate (chamfered side up) and clutch pack snap ring. If removed, install new turbine shaft seal rings and forward clutch-to-direct clutch thrust washer.

FRONT CARRIER, SUN GEAR & INTERNAL GEAR
Inspection
Check all parts for pitting, scoring, damaged gear teeth, and cracks. Make sure all lubrication holes are open. Check front internal gear thrust washers for wear or other damage, and front carrier roller thrust bearing for roughness and pitting. Check pinion end play of front carrier. *See Fig. 24.* End play should be .009-.027" (.24-.69 mm).

Fig. 24: Using a Feeler Gauge to Measure Front Carrier Pinion End Play

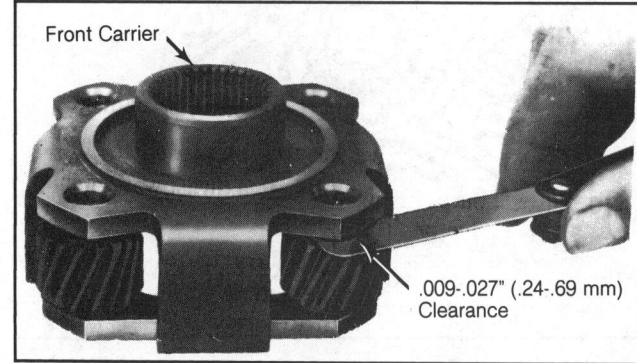

Fig. 23: Exploded View Showing Components of Forward Clutch Assembly

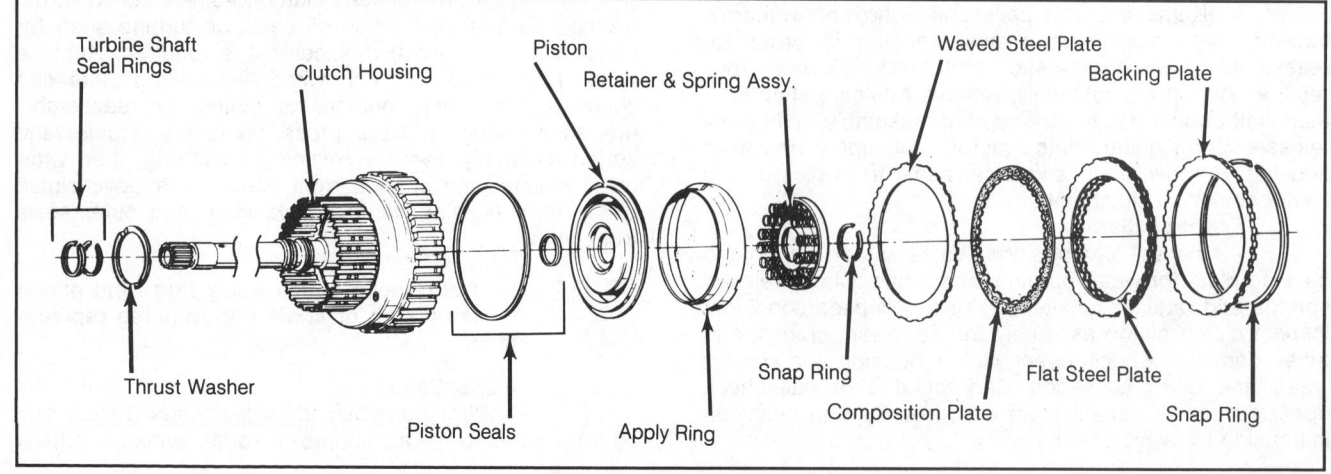

TURBO HYDRA-MATIC 200 (Cont.)

REAR SUN GEAR & INPUT DRUM

Inspection

Check rear sun gear for cracks, splits, spline damage, gear or journal wear, and for plugged lubrication holes. If necessary, remove snap ring and separate sun gear from input drum and inspect drum splines for damage. Check input drum-to-low-reverse clutch housing thrust washer for scoring or distorted tangs.

Fig. 25: Disassembled View of Rear Sun Gear and Input Drum

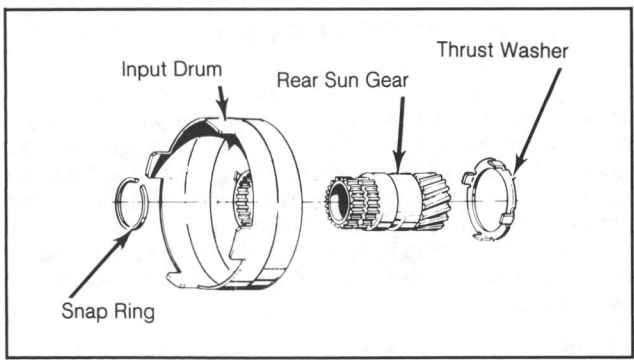

LOW-REVERSE CLUTCH

Disassembly

Compress low-reverse clutch spring retainer, remove snap ring, and check for damage and distortion.

Fig. 26: Installing Low-Reverse Clutch Piston

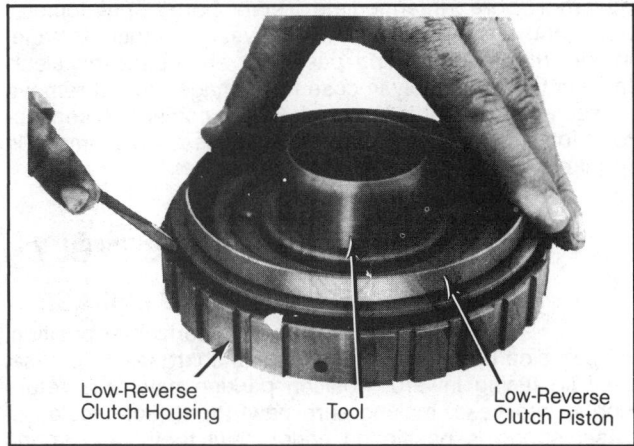

Withdraw retainer, waved spring, and clutch piston from housing. Remove inner and outer seals and clutch apply ring from piston.

Inspection

Check clutch housing for scoring or wear, damaged bushing, and plugged oil feed hole. Inspect splines and snap ring groove for damage or burrs. Check piston assembly for distortion, cracks, or damage. Inspect clutch plates for signs of scoring or burning. Check retainers and spring for damage or distortion.

Reassembly

Install clutch apply ring and new inner and outer seals on clutch piston (seal lips facing away from apply ring side). Lubricate clutch seals with transmission fluid and place a seal protector (J-25011) into clutch housing. Using a flat tip screwdriver to start seal into housing, install clutch piston, rotating while pushing down into bore. Remove seal protector, then install waved spring, retainer (cupped side downward), and snap ring.

REAR CARRIER, ROLLER CLUTCH & INTERNAL GEAR

Inspection

Check rear internal gear splines, teeth, bearing surface, and parking pawl lugs for wear, cracks, or other damage. Inspect roller clutch race and spline for scoring or wear, and roller bearings, cage and springs for wear, scoring, distortion, or collapse. Inspect thrust washers for excessive wear or damaged tangs. Check rear carrier roller clutch cam ramps and bushing for scoring or other damage. Inspect planetary pinions for damage, rough bearing, tilt, and correct end play. End play should be .009-.027" (.24-.69 mm).

Fig. 28: Disassembled View of Rear Carrier and Roller Clutch

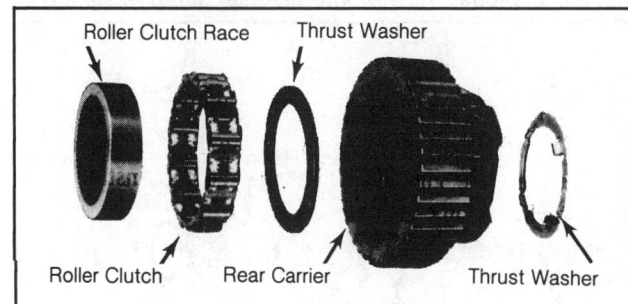

Fig. 27: Exploded View Showing Components of Low-Reverse Clutch Assembly

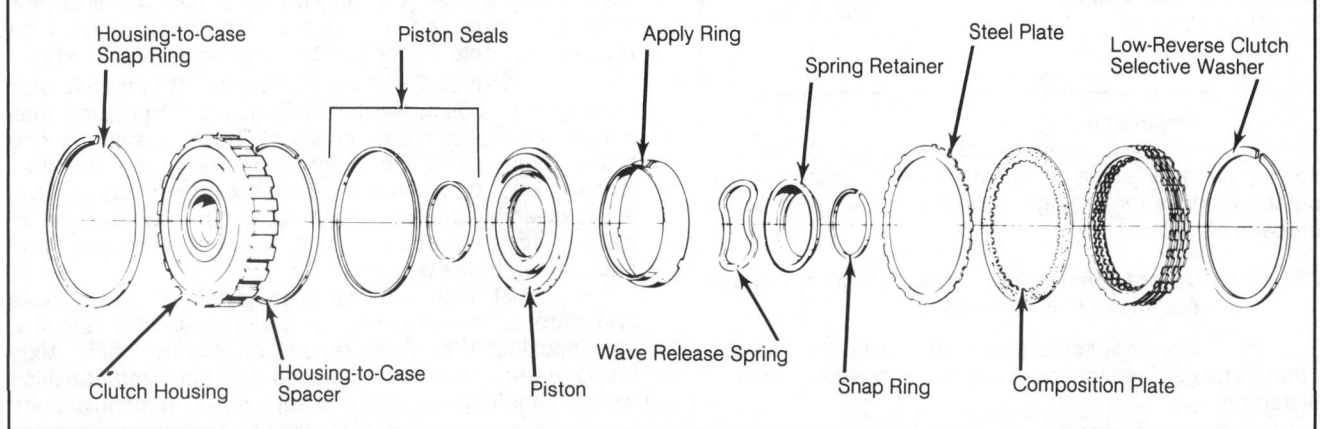

TURBO HYDRA-MATIC 200 (Cont.)

OUTPUT SHAFT

Inspection

Inspect journals and snap ring grooves for wear or damage. Check lubrication holes for being plugged or damaged. Inspect shaft splines and governor drive gear for rough or damaged surfaces. Check speedometer drive gear and retaining clip for wear or damage.

Fig. 29: Output Shaft and Speedometer Drive Gear Assembly

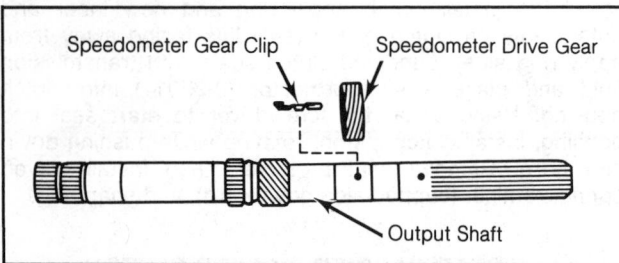

Speedometer Drive Gear Replacement

1) Depress speedometer drive gear retaining clip. Remove gear and clip, tapping gear lightly with a plastic hammer.

2) To install, place speedometer drive clip with tanged end in hole in output shaft. Align slot of gear with clip and install gear.

INTERMEDIATE SERVO

Disassembly

Using a "C" clamp-type compressor tool (J-22269-01), compress servo piston spring, remove servo pin-to-piston retaining ring, remove tool and separate parts.

Fig. 30: Exploded View of Intermediate Servo Assembly

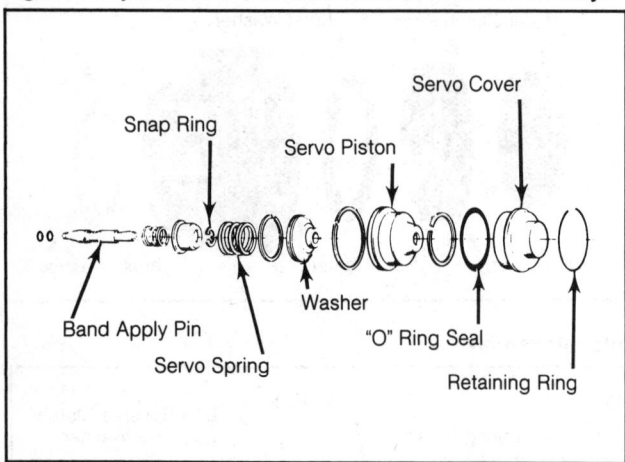

Inspection

1) Check intermediate servo pin for wear or damage, and for proper fit in case bore. Inspect inner and outer seal rings for damage, and for proper fit in seal ring grooves of piston.

CAUTION: Do not remove seal rings from piston unless replacement is required.

2) Check servo piston and cover for cracks or other damage. Inspect servo spring for collapsed coils or distortion.

Reassembly

Install washer on snap ring end of servo pin, position spring on top of washer, then install assembly into servo piston, spring end first. Using compressor tool, compress servo spring and install servo pin-to-piston retaining ring. If removed, install new inner and outer seal rings on piston, making sure cut ends are assembled in same relationship as cut, and that rings are fully seated in grooves. Retain rings with petrolatum. Install a new seal ring on servo cover, lubricate with petrolatum, then install piston assembly into piston cover.

GOVERNOR ASSEMBLY

Inspection

Inspect governor cover for damage, worn bore, or plugged oil passage. Wash governor assembly in cleaning solvent and blow out oil passage. Inspect governor driven gear, weights, spring, shaft, and washer for wear or damage. Inspect governor for presence of two check balls. Check governor shaft seal rings for cuts, damage, and for free fit in groove. If damaged, cut ring off shaft, and install new seal rings. Lubricate seals with petrolatum.

NOTE: **Some governors use one spring, and some use two springs.**

TRANSMISSION CASE

Inspection

Check case assembly for cracks, porosity, and interconnected oil passages. Inspect reverse clutch lugs, governor bore, intermediate servo bore, speedometer bore, and snap ring grooves for wear or other damage. Make sure all vents and passages are open and clear. Inspect vent assembly in case for damage; do not remove unless replacement is required. Check cooler line connectors for damage; do not remove unless replacement is required.

TRANSMISSION REASSEMBLY

MANUAL SHAFT & PARKING LINKAGE

1) Place transmission in a horizontal position, oil pan side up. Install a new manual shaft seal into case, seal lip facing inward. Position parking pawl and return spring into case, making sure pawl tooth faces inside of case, spring is positioned under pawl tooth, and spring ends locate against case pad. Align pawl and spring with shaft bore in case, then install pawl shaft (tapered end first). Using a 3/8" (9.5 mm) diameter rod, install a new shaft cup plug (open end out) into shaft bore, past retaining pin hole. Install parking pawl shaft retaining pin.

2) Install parking brake bracket into case with parking pawl positioned between guides of bracket, then install and tighten two attaching bolts. Install parking brake actuator rod into inside detent lever (on pin side), locating lever between actuator rod tangs. Install rod and lever assembly into case, with lever pin toward center of transmission and actuator plunger between parking pawl and parking brake bracket.

3) Install manual shaft (small I.D. ring groove first) through case. Install manual shaft-to-case retaining pin, indexing with larger groove on manual shaft. Align inside detent lever with flats on manual shaft, position lever on shaft, then install and tighten nut on manual shaft.

TURBO HYDRA-MATIC 200 (Cont.)

Fig. 31: Exploded View of Manual and Parking Linkage

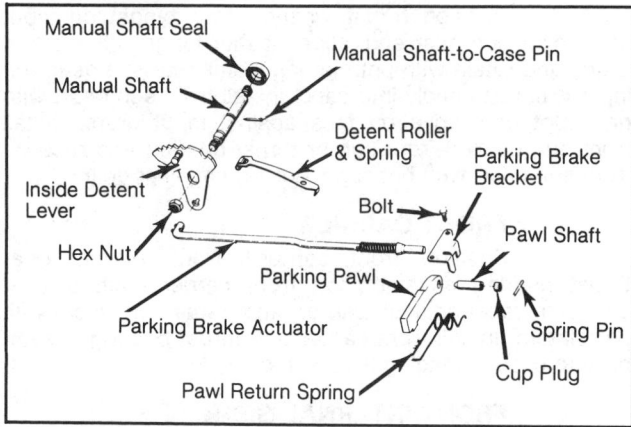

OUTPUT SHAFT & REAR INTERNAL GEAR

If removed, install a new rear internal gear-to-output shaft snap ring into groove on output shaft, then install rear internal gear (hub end first) onto shaft. Position rear internal gear-to-rear sun gear roller thrust bearing assembly over shaft by placing small diameter race against rear internal gear.

Fig. 32: Installing Parking Brake Actuator

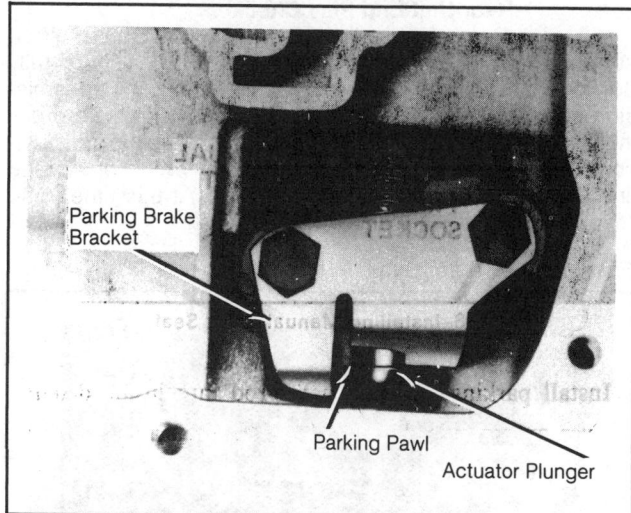

Fig. 33: Installing Rear Internal Gear

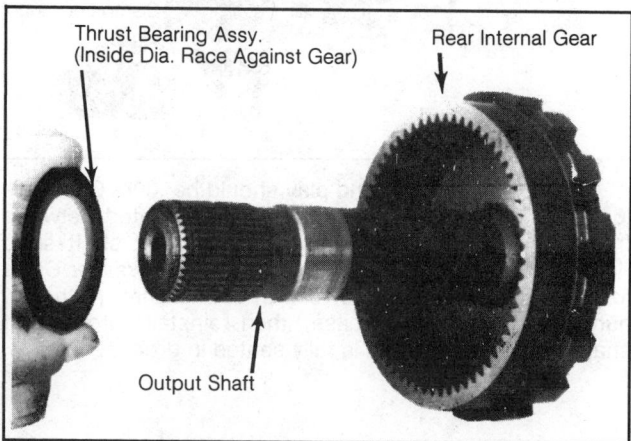

ROLLER CLUTCH & REAR CARRIER

1) Install roller clutch-to-rear carrier thrust washer into rear carrier, then install roller and spring assembly. Install roller clutch race (spline end out), and rotate counterclockwise into position. Install rear carrier-to-rear internal gear thrust washer (four tangs) onto carrier and retain with petrolatum. Position roller clutch and rear carrier assembly over output shaft and install into rear internal gear.

NOTE: Install rollers that may have come out of cage by compressing engergizing spring with forefinger, and inserting roller from outer edge.

2) Install a output shaft support tool (J-25013) on rear of transmission as follows: Place sleeve (J-25013-1) into rear of case, open end first. Then bolt bracket and screw assembly (J-25013-5) into rear mount bolt holes on extension housing. Turn case to a vertical position, pump end upward. Install rear unit parts (output shaft, rear internal gear, and rear carrier previously assembled) into transmission case and into support sleeve (J-25013-1).

Fig. 34: Installing Roller Clutch and Rear Carrier

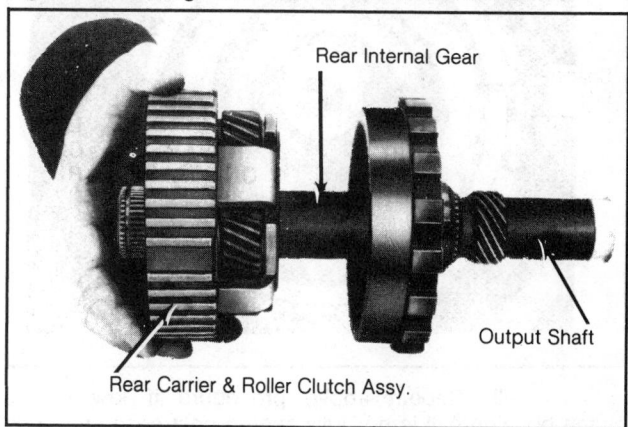

3) Using adjusting screw on tool bracket (J-25013-5) and looking through parking pawl case slot, adjust height of the rear internal gear parking pawl lugs to align flush with the parking pawl tooth.

CAUTION: Make sure speedometer drive gear is visible through speedometer gear bore of case. If drive gear is not visible, it may be located on wrong journal of shaft.

Fig. 35: Installing Output Shaft Support Tools

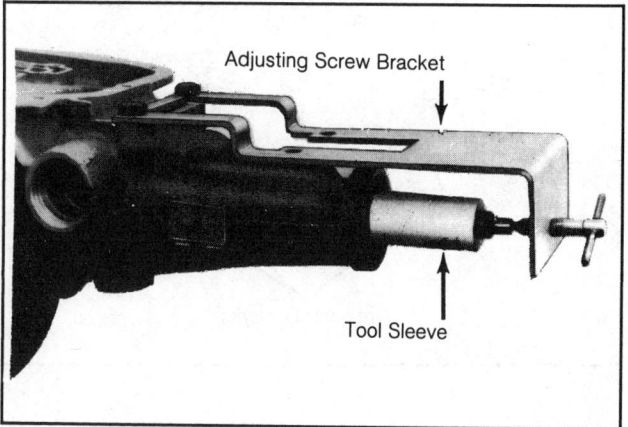

TURBO HYDRA-MATIC 200 (Cont.)

LOW-REVERSE CLUTCH

1) Install low-reverse clutch selective spacer into case. Lubricate with transmission fluid then install low-reverse clutch plates, starting with a flat steel plate, and alternating composition and flat steel plates until all plates are installed.

2) Install low-reverse clutch housing-to-case spacer ring into case, then install low-reverse clutch housing assembly, aligning housing oil feed hole with case oil feed passage. If housing does not seat past snap ring groove, proceed as follows: Install input drum and rear sun gear assembly into case and rotate back and forth to align roller clutch race and low-reverse clutch hub splines, then remove input drum and sun gear.

Fig. 36: *Installing Housing-to-Case Spacer*

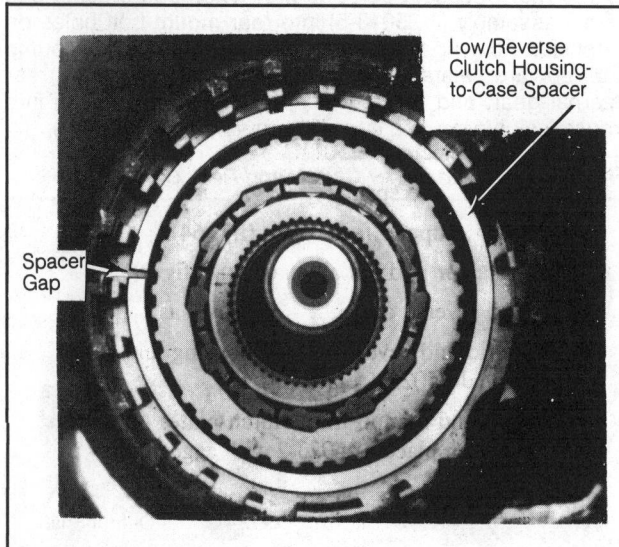

3) Repeat above procedure if low-reverse clutch housing still is not fully seated past case snap ring groove.

NOTE: **It may be necessary to loosen adjusting screw on output shaft support tool to install snap ring.**

4) With parts properly seated, install low-reverse clutch housing-to-case snap ring, with flat side of ring against housing (beveled side upward). Locate snap ring gap opposite parking brake rod.

Fig. 37: *Front Sun Gear Identification Marks*

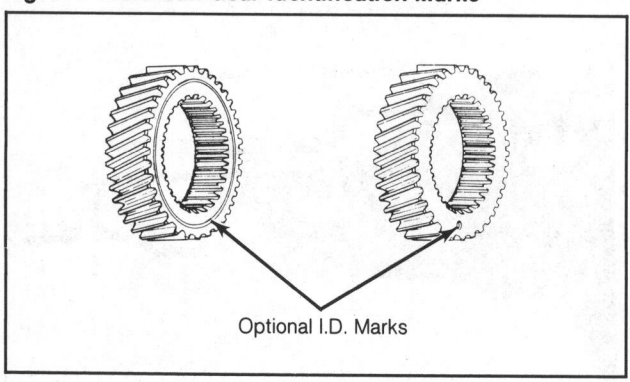

REAR SUN GEAR, INPUT DRUM & FRONT SUN GEAR

Position thrust washer (four tangs) on input drum over sun gear end, align washer tangs with slots in drum, and retain with petrolatum. Install rear sun gear and input drum assembly into case. Install front sun gear, with drill spot or groove on face against input drum. Install front sun gear-to-front carrier thrust bearing and race on front sun gear, with bearing roller side against gear.

FRONT CARRIER

Position front carrier-to-front internal gear thrust bearing assembly on front carrier, with smaller diameter race against carrier and retain in place with petrolatum. Install front carrier and thrust bearing assembly into case, engaging front sun gear.

FRONT INTERNAL GEAR

Install tanged thrust washer on front internal gear and retain with petrolatum, then install front internal gear into case. Install rear unit selective thrust washer on top of tanged thrust washer, then install output shaft-to-thrust washer snap ring.

NOTE: **It may be necessary to lift output shaft upward to install snap ring. At this time, measure rear unit end play to ensure correct selective thrust washer has been installeed.**

Rear Unit End Play Check
1) Loosen adjusting screw on output shaft support tool (J-25013-5) and push output shaft fully downward. Install a dial indicator assembly on transmission so button of indicator rests on output shaft. Zero dial indicator. Move ouput shaft upward by turning adjusting screw on output shaft support tool, until white or scribed line on tool sleeve begins to disappear. At this time, read resulting end play on gauge.

Fig. 38: *Measuring Rear Unit End Play*

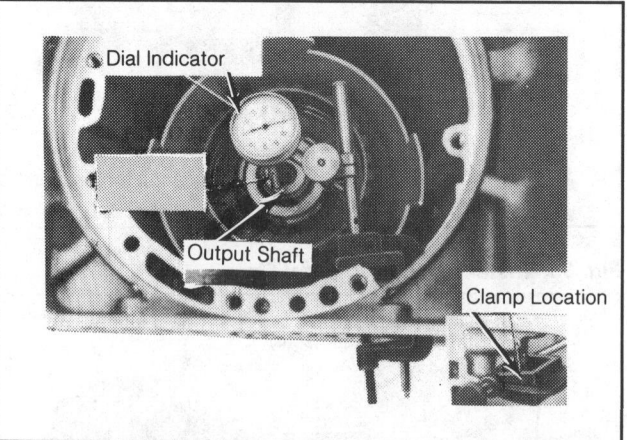

2) Rear unit end play should be .004-.025" (.10-.64 mm). If not, selective thrust washer located between front internal gear thrust washer and output shaft snap ring must be changed. *See Rear Unit Thrust Washer Chart for thicknesses.* Install correct thrust washer (with I.D. number toward front of case), then reinstall output shaft snap ring, making sure it is fully seated in groove.

TURBO HYDRA-MATIC 200 (Cont.)

REAR UNIT THRUST WASHER CHART

Washer Thickness In. (mm)	Identification Number Or Color
.114-.119 (2.9-3.0)	1 Orange
.121-.126 (3.1-3.2)	2 White
.128-.133 (3.3-3.4)	3 Yellow
.135-.140 (3.5-3.6)	4 Blue
.143-.147 (3.6-3.7)	6 Brown
.150-.154 (3.8-3.9)	6 Brown
.157-.161 (4.0-4.1)	7 Green
.164-.168 (4.2-4.3)	8 Black
.171-.175 (4.4-4.5)	9 Purple

DIRECT CLUTCH, FORWARD CLUTCH & INTERMEDIATE BAND

1) Position direct clutch over hole in bench with clutch plate end upward. Make sure forward clutch-to-direct clutch thrust washer is still in place on forward clutch, then install forward clutch (turbine shaft first) into direct clutch. Hold direct clutch housing and rotate forward clutch until forward clutch is seated.

NOTE: When properly seated, end of forward clutch drum will be about 5/8" (15.8 mm) from tang end of direct clutch housing.

Fig. 39: Measuring Forward Clutch Engagement

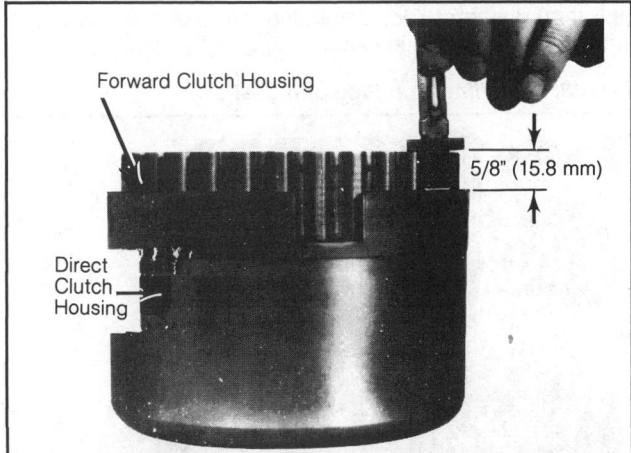

Forward Clutch Housing

5/8" (15.8 mm)

Direct Clutch Housing

2) Position intermediate band into case, locating band apply lug and anchor pin lug in case slots. Install front unit selective thrust washer into end of output shaft (retain with petrolatum), then install direct and forward clutch assemblies into transmission case as a unit, rotating into position.

NOTE: When properly seated, direct clutch housing will be approximately 1 5/16" (33.3 mm) from pump face in case.

OIL PUMP

1) Install new pump-to-case gasket on rear of pump assembly and retain with petrolatum. Install 2 guide pins into pump attaching bolt holes in case, 180° opposite each other. Install pump assembly into case, then install attaching bolts finger tight. Then, gradually tighten bolts, rotating turbine shaft in process.

Fig. 40: Checking Clutch Assembly Installation

Direct Clutch Housing

1 5/16" (33.3 mm)

NOTE: Before installing oil pump, make sure intermediate band anchor pin lug is aligned with band anchor pin hole in case.

2) Remove alignment pins, and install remaining bolts and tighten. At this time, check front unit end play to ensure correct front unit selective thrust washer has been installed.

NOTE: If turbine shaft cannot be rotated as pump is being pulled into place, the forward or direct clutch housings have not been installed properly to index with all the clutch plates. This condition must be corrected before pump is pulled fully into place.

NOTE: Make sure turbine shaft still rotates freely.

Fig. 41: Measuring Front Unit End Play

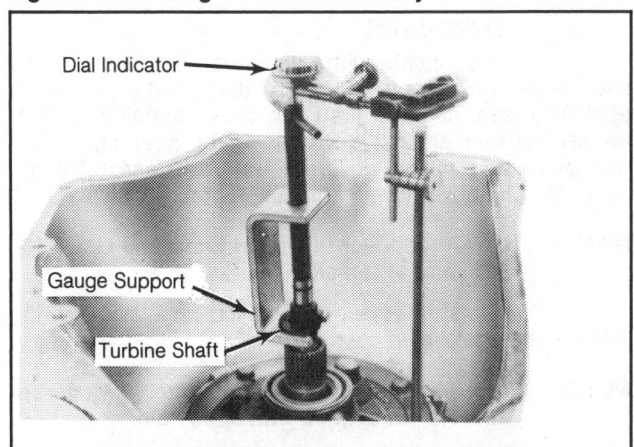

Dial Indicator

Gauge Support

Turbine Shaft

Front Unit End Play Check

1) With transmission in a vertical position (pump side upward), remove one pump-to-case attaching bolt and install a bolt approximately 11" long to support a dial indicator assembly. Push turbine shaft fully downward.

TURBO HYDRA-MATIC 200 (Cont.)

NOTE: Output shaft support tool should still be attached to rear of transmission; if not, reinstall using procedure given in Roller Clutch & Rear Carrier section of Component Disassembly & Reassembly

FRONT UNIT THRUST WASHER CHART

Washer Thickness In. (mm)	Identification Number And/Or Color
.065-.070 (1.66-1.77)	1
.070-.075 (1.79-1.90)	2
.076-.080 (1.92-2.03)	3 Black
.081-.085 (2.05-2.16)	4 Lt. Green
.086-.090 (2.18-2.29)	5 Scarlet
.091-.095 (2.31-2.42)	6 Purple
.096-.100 (2.44-2.55)	7 Cocoa Brown
.101-.106 (2.57-2.68)	8 Orange
.106-.111 (2.70-2.81)	9 Yellow
.111-.116 (2.83-2.94)	10 Lt Blue
.117-.121 (2.96-3.07)	11
.122-.126 (3.09-3.20)	12
.127-.131 (3.22-3.33)	13 Pink
.132-.136 (3.35-3.46)	14 Green
.137-.141 (3.48-3.59)	15 Gray

2) Mount a dial indicator assembly on bolt installed in oil pump, so button of indicator contacts turbine shaft. Move output shaft upward by turning adjusting screw in output shaft support tool until white or scribed line on tool sleeve begins to disappear. Zero dial indicator. Pull turbine shaft upward and read resulting end play on gauge; end play should be .022-.051" (.56-1.3 mm).

3) Selective thrust washer controlling front unit end play is located between output shaft and turbine shaft. If more or less washer thickness is required to bring end play within specifications, remove oil pump and forward and direct clutch assemblies, and install correct thickness washer on end of output shaft. *See Front Unit Thrust Washer Chart for washer thickness and identification.*

GOVERNOR

1) Lubricate with petrolatum and install 2 new seal rings on governor cover, then install governor assembly (seal ring end first) into cover. Install governor-to-case washer against governor driven gear and retain with petrolatum. Install governor and cover assembly into case, rotating governor and output shaft slightly.

NOTE: Governor cover fits tight in bore the last 1/16" (1.5 mm) of travel.

2) Install governor retaining ring, aligning ring with an end showing in case slot.

NOTE: If retaining ring cannot be installed, governor shaft is not aligned with case hole.

BAND ANCHOR PIN & INTERMEDIATE SERVO

Inspect anchor pin for damage, then install pin (stem end first) into its bore in case valve body attaching face (see illustration). Lubricate seals of intermediate servo assembly with petrolatum and install assembly into case tapping with a rubber hammer if necessary. Install

servo retaining ring, locating ring gap with an end showing in case slot.

NOTE: Make sure anchor pin stem locates in hole of intermediate band lug.

Fig. 42: Installing Intermediate Band Anchor Pin

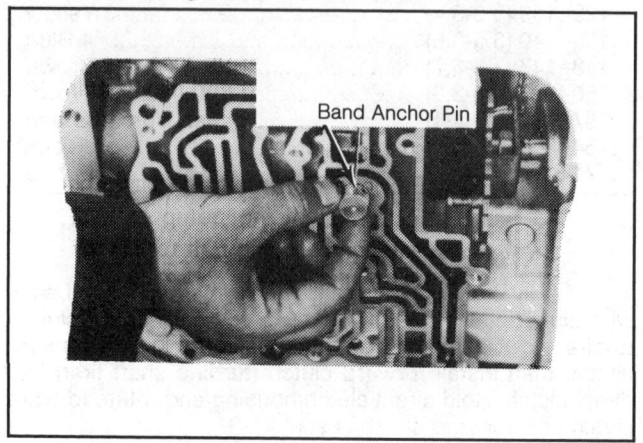

VALVE BODY

1) Before installing valve body assembly, install low-reverse clutch housing-to-case seal and cup plug as follows: Position seal in case passage, then install cup plug (smaller hole end first). *See Fig. 43.* Using a 3/8" (9.5 mm) diameter rod, drive plug into passage until flush with top of plug hole in case.

Fig. 43: Installing Cup Plug and Seal

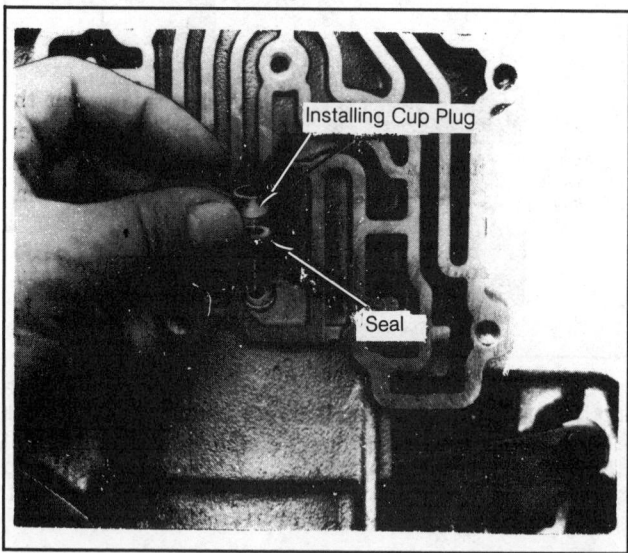

2) Install 5th check ball into case. T.V. exhaust passage. *See Fig. 44.* Install accumulator spring into case accumulator bore. Install 2 guide pins into case to align valve body parts, then install 4 check balls into ball seat pockets in control valve assembly and retain with petrolatum. *See Fig. 15 in Component Disassembly and Reassembly for ball locations.*

3) Place control valve assembly to spacer plate marked "VB" on control valve assembly. Place valve body spacer plate on gasket marked "VB". Place spacer plate to case gasket marked "C" on spacer plate. Insert 2 control valve assembly-to-case attaching bolts through control

TURBO HYDRA-MATIC 200 (Cont.)

Fig. 44: Installing Fifth Check Ball in Case

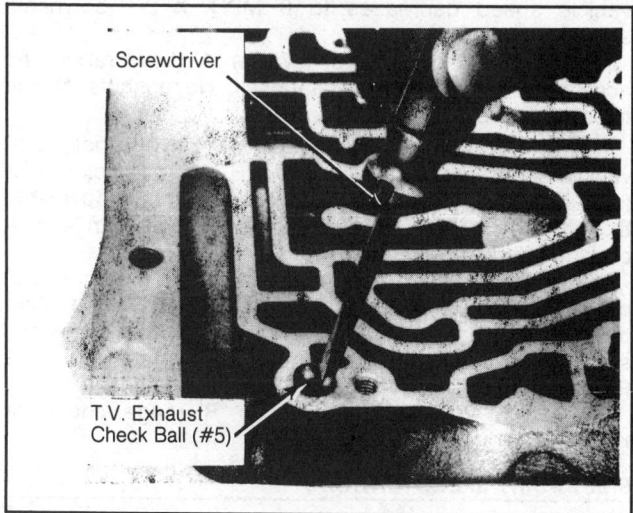

valve assembly, gaskets and spacer plate and install these parts, aligning manual valve with detent lever pin.

CAUTION: Make sure check balls, 1-2 accumulator piston and manual valve do not fall out.

4) Start control valve assembly-to-case attaching bolts, except throttle lever, bracket assembly and oil screen attaching bolts.

NOTE: **The 2 oil screen bolts are approximately 3/8" (9.5 mm) longer than valve body attaching bolts and are not interchangeable.**

5) To install throttle lever and bracket assembly, install spring on top of lifter (if removed), and place lifter (spring first) into bracket. Install parts into case, locating slot in bracket with coiled pin. Align lifter through valve body hole, and link through T.V. linkage case bore, retain with nut. Tighten all valve body retaining bolts to specifications.

Fig. 45: Throttle Lever and Bracket Assembly

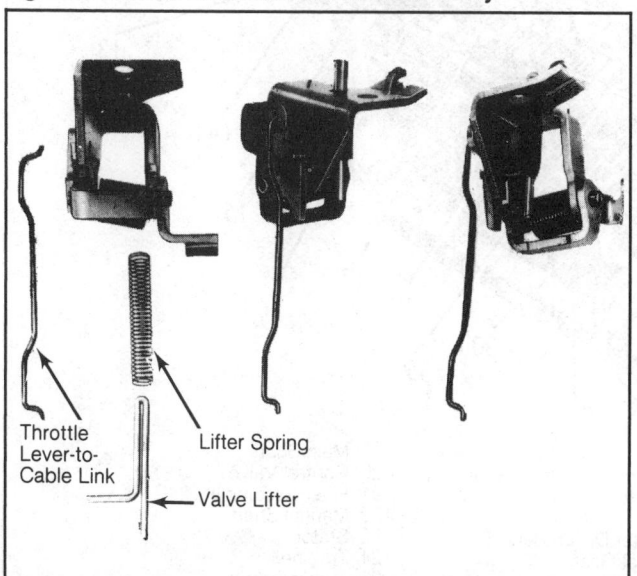

OIL SCREEN, OIL PAN & SPEEDOMETER DRIVEN GEAR

Install a new screen gasket on oil screen, retain with petrolatum, then install screen on valve body and install and tighten attaching bolts. Position a new pan gasket on case, install oil pan and attaching bolts, and tighten. If necessary, install a new "O" ring seal on speedometer driven gear housing, install housing into case, then install retainer and attaching bolt, aligning slot in housing with retainer.

TORQUE CONVERTER

Install torque converter into pump assembly, making sure converter hub drive slots are fully engaged with pump drive gear tangs, and that converter is fully installed towards rear of transmission.

NOTE: **When properly installed, the distance between engine mounting face of case and front face of converter cover drive lugs will be at least 1" (25.4 mm) minimum. Retain converter in case with converter holding tool.**

TIGHTENING SPECIFICATIONS

Application	Ft. Lbs. (N.m.)
Pump Cover Bolts	18 (24)
Pump-to-Case Bolts	18 (24)
Parking Pawl Bracket Bolts	18 (24)
Valve Body-to-Case Bolts	11 (15)
Oil Screen Bolts	11 (15)
Oil Pan-to-Case Bolts	12 (16)
Manual Shaft Nut	23 (31)
Converter-to-Flywheel Bolts	35 (47)
Transission-to-Engine Bolts	25 (34)
Rear Transission Mount	40 (54)
	INCH Lbs. (N.m)
Speedometer Retainer Bolt	96 (11)

Automatic Transmissions

GM TURBO HYDRA-MATIC 400 — JAGUAR

Jaguar XJS

TRANSMISSION DESCRIPTION

Transmission is a fully automatic unit consisting primarily of a 3 element hydraulic torque converter and a compound planetary gear set. Three multiple disc clutches, 2 roller clutches, and 2 bands provide friction elements required to obtain desired function of planetary gear set. A hydraulic system pressurized by a gear type pump provides working pressure required to operate friction elements and automatic controls.

LUBRICATION & ADJUSTMENT

See the apporpriate article in AUTOMATIC TRANSMISSION SERVICING Section.

TESTING

ROAD TEST

1) Place selector lever in "D" range and accelerate vehicle from a standstill. A 1-2 and 2-3 shift should occur at all throttle openings (shift points will vary with throttle openings). As vehicle speed decreases to 0 MPH, a 3-2 and 2-1 downshift should occur.

2) Place selector lever in "2" (Intermediate) range and accelerate from a standstill. A 1-2 upshift should occur at all throttle openings (shift point will vary with throttle opening), and no 2-3 shift should occur. As vehicle speed decreases to 0 MPH, a 2-1 downshift should occur.

3) Place selector lever in "1" (Low) range and accelerate vehicle from a standstill. No upshifts should occur regardless of throttle opening.

4) With selector lever in Drive range, and vehicle speed approximately 35 MPH, move selector lever to "2" (Intermediate) range. Transmission should downshift to 2nd gear; an increase in engine RPM and an engine braking effect should be noticed.

5) With selector lever in "2" (Intermediate) range and vehicle speed approximately 30 MPH (constant throttle), move selector lever to "1" (Low) range. Transmission should downshift to 1st gear; an increase in engine RPM and an engine braking effect should be noticed.

6) With selector lever in "R" range, check for reverse operation.

SHIFT POINT SPECIFICATIONS

Application	Speed (MPH)
Upshift	Minumum
1-2	5
2-3	20
Kick Down	Maximum
3-2	70-85
3-1	28-38
Upshift	Maximum
1-2	40-50
2-3	50-70

Fig. 1: Cutaway View of Turbo Hydra-Matic 400 Automatic Transmission

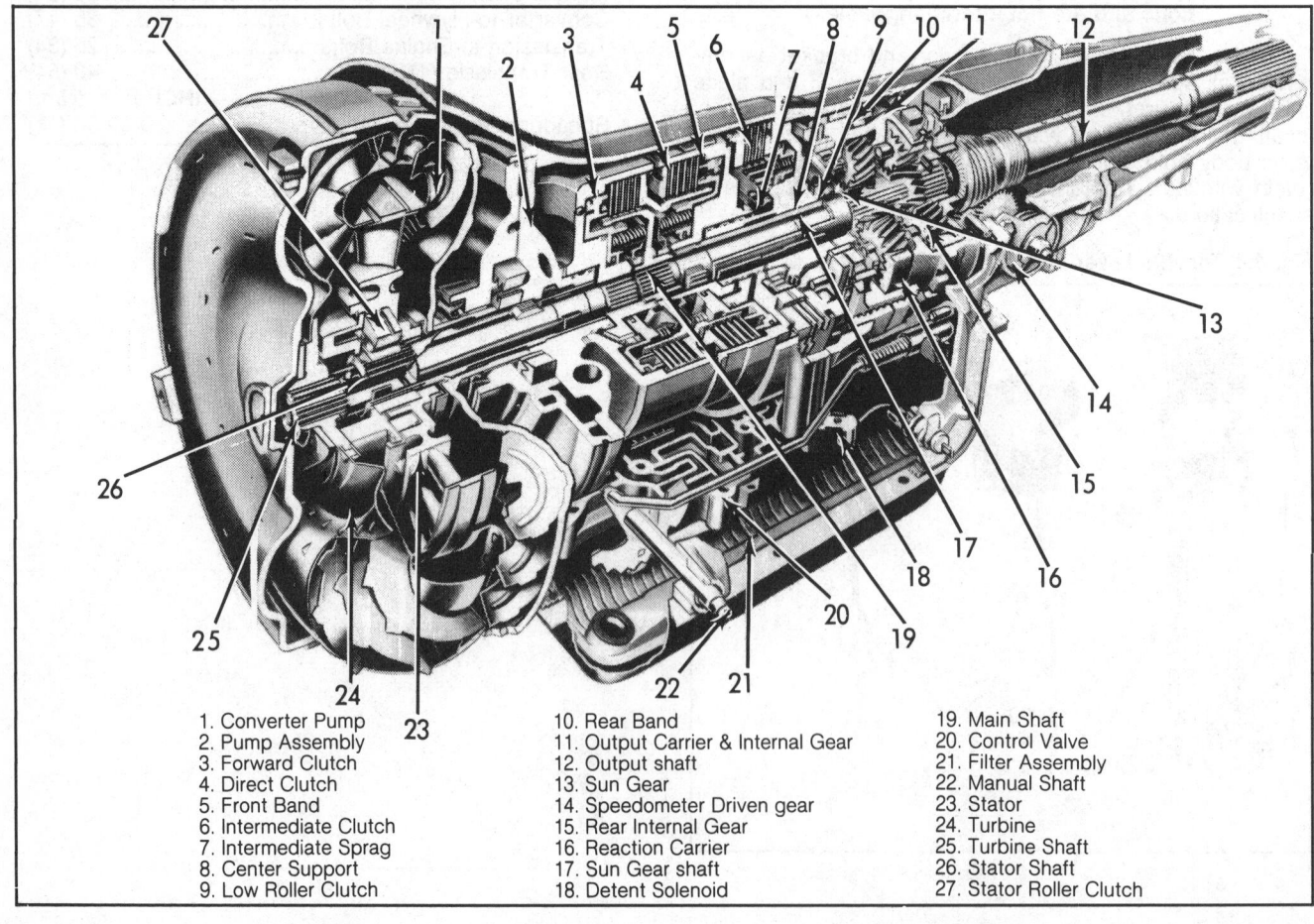

1. Converter Pump	10. Rear Band	19. Main Shaft
2. Pump Assembly	11. Output Carrier & Internal Gear	20. Control Valve
3. Forward Clutch	12. Output shaft	21. Filter Assembly
4. Direct Clutch	13. Sun Gear	22. Manual Shaft
5. Front Band	14. Speedometer Driven gear	23. Stator
6. Intermediate Clutch	15. Rear Internal Gear	24. Turbine
7. Intermediate Sprag	16. Reaction Carrier	25. Turbine Shaft
8. Center Support	17. Sun Gear shaft	26. Stator Shaft
9. Low Roller Clutch	18. Detent Solenoid	27. Stator Roller Clutch

GM TURBO HYDRA-MATIC 400 — JAGUAR (Cont.)

Fig. 2: View of Transmission Case Showing Pressure Take-Off Point

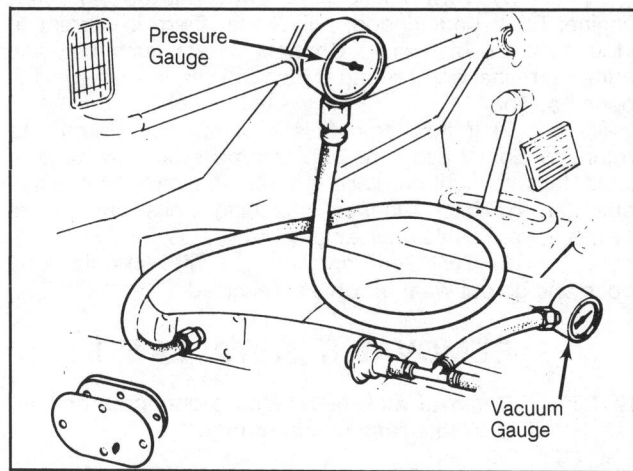

4) If line pressures are normal with external vacuum applied, check engine vacuum and vacuum systems for leaks. If high line pressures are found, refer to Control Pressure Results for causes.

5) When stationary testing is complete, drive vehicle at 30 mph and allow throttle to close completely. Read pressure on gauge. This test may also be conducted on hoist: Driving wheels off ground, selector in drive and brakes released, raise engine RPM to 3000. Close throttle and read pressure between 2000 and 1200 RPM. Pressure should read 55-70 psi (3.8-4.9 kg/cm²).

CAUTION: For control pressure tests, total running time in drive gears is not to exceed 2 minutes. Damage to vehicle may result.

CONTROL PRESSURE CHECK

Install a 0-300 psi pressure gauge to pressure take-off point at left side of transmission near manual lever, then place gauge where it can be seen from driver's seat. With transmission fluid at correct level and operating temperature, hydraulic pressures can be checked.

1) With vehicle stationary, service brakes applied (except as noted), and pressure gauge installed, pressures should check approximately as shown in Hydraulic Pressures Table.

2) On some engines equipped with Exhaust Gas Recirculation, the throttle is open wide enough in drive range at 1000 RPM to cause EGR valve to open, allowing exhaust gas to enter intake manifold which lowers manifold vacuum. With vacuum lowered, transmission oil pressure raises accordingly, and may go above the upper specification limit.

3) Therefore, if high line pressures are obtained, disconnect vacuum line at EGR valve, plug line, and recheck line pressure. If high pressures are still found, check engine vacuum. If low vacuum is found, use a vacuum pump and apply 20 in. Hg vacuum to modulator and recheck pressures.

HYDRAULIC PRESSURES TABLE

Range @ RPM	psi (kg/cm²)
Neutral @ 1000	55-70 (4-5)
Drive @ Idle	60-85 (4.2-6)
Drive @ 1000 [1]	60-90 (4.2-6.3)
Low or "2" @1000 [1]	135-160 (9.5-11.2)
Reverse @1000 [1]	95-150 (6.7-10.5)
Drive @ 1000 [1][2]	90-100 (6.3-7.7)

[1] — Brakes applied.
[2] — Downshift switch activated.

CONTROL PRESSURE RESULTS
Line Pressure Too Low
- Transmission fluid level low. Faulty vacuum modulator assembly. Oil filter blocked or restricted, "O" ring on filter intake pipe omitted or damaged, intake pipe split or leaking.
- Not enough spacers in oil pump pressure regulator. Pressure regulator spring too weak. Oil pump gear clearance incorrect. Oil pump damaged or worn.
- Internal leak in direct clutch circuit (pressure normal in neutral, low, intermediate and drive, but low in reverse).
- Internal leak in forward clutch circuit (pressure normal in neutral and reverse, low in drive).

CLUTCH AND BAND APPLICATION CHART (ELEMENTS IN USE)

Selector Lever Position	Forward Clutch	Direct Clutch	Front Band	Intermed. Clutch	Intermed. Roller Clutch Or Sprag	Low Roller Clutch	Rear Band
D — DRIVE							
First Gear	X					X	
Second Gear	X			X	X		
Third Gear	X	X		X			
2 — INTERMEDIATE							
Second Gear	X		X	X	X		
1 — LOW (First)	X					X	X
R — REVERSE		X					X

NEUTRAL OR PARK — All clutches and bands released and/or ineffective.

GM TURBO HYDRA-MATIC 400 — JAGUAR (Cont.)

Line Pressure Too High

- Vacuum system leak or improper engine vacuum. Water in vacuum modulator. Modulator valve not operating properly or defective. Defective EGR valve.
- Detent switch actuated or shorted, detent solenoid stuck open. Detent feed orifice in spacer plate blocked, detent solenoid loose. Detent valve bore plug damaged. Detent regulator valve pin too short.
- Oil pump pressure regulator and/or boost valve stuck. Incorrect pump pressure regulator spring. Pressure boost valve installed backward. Too many oil pump pressure regulator valve spacers. Oil pump casting defective.
- Control valve assembly-to-spacer gasket out of proportion. Control valve assembly gaskets switched.

GOVERNOR CHECK

1) With vehicle on a hoist (rear wheels off ground), disconnect vacuum line to modulator. Connect pressure gauge to transmission and tachometer to engine.

2) Start engine, keep foot off brake pedal, move selector lever to drive range, and check line pressure at 1000 RPM. Slowly increase engine speed to 3000 RPM and determine if a pressure drop of 10 psi (.7 kg/cm²) or more occurs.

3) If no pressure drop occurs, inspect governor for stuck valve or weight, or a restricted orifice in valve. Check governor feed system for plugged or restricted screen(s), or for restrictions in governor pipe.

4) If pressure drop of 10 psi (.7 kg/cm²) or more occurs, and transmission is malfunctioning, disassemble, clean and inspect control valve assembly.

VACUUM MODULATOR CHECK

Vacuum Diaphragm Leak Check

Insert a pipe cleaner into vacuum connector pipe as far as possible and check for presence of transmission oil. If oil is found, replace modulator.

NOTE: **Gasoline or water vapor may settle in vacuum side of modulator. If this is found without presence of oil, modulator should not be changed.**

Atmospheric Leak Check

1) Apply a liberal coating of soap buble solution to vacuum connector pipe seam (the crimped upper-to-lower housing seam).

2) Using a short piece of rubber hose, apply air pressure to vacuum pipe by blowing into hose and check for leak bubbles. If bubbles appear, replace modulator.

CAUTION: **DO NOT use any method other than human lung power for applying air pressure. Pressures over 6 psi (.4 kg/cm²) may damage modulator.**

Bellows Comparison Check

Where the vacuum bellows is suspect, substitute vacuum modulator in question with a known good modulator.

Sleeve Alignment Check

Roll main body of modulator on a flat surface and observe the sleeve for concentricity to the can. If sleeve is concentric and plunger is free, modulator is acceptable.

KICK-DOWN SOLENOID CHECK

1) Turn ignition to "ON", but do not start engine. From under hood, check that there is current at input terminal of switch. Connect a test lamp between output terminal and ground. Move throttle linkage to wide open position.

2) If test lamp fails to light, allow throttle to return to closed position. Depress the switch by hand. If lamp fails to light, replace switch. If lamp lights when operated by hand, loosen attaching bolts and adjust switch toward cable until lamp lights at W.O.T.

3) Test light should light with throttle wide open and go out when throttle is released.

REMOVAL & INSTALLATION

NOTE: **Removal and installation procedures are not available from manufacturer.**

TRANSMISSION DISASSEMBLY

VACUUM MODULATOR & VALVE

Remove vacuum modulator attaching screw and retainer. Remove modulator and "O" ring seal from case. Discard "O" ring. Withdraw modulator valve from bore in case.

GOVERNOR

Remove attaching screws, cover, and gasket, then remove governor assembly by pulling straight out of case.

SPEEDOMETER DRIVEN GEAR

Remove attaching screw and retainer, then apply slight pressure to remove sleeve and speedometer driven gear assembly from case.

INTAKE PIPE, FILTER & OIL PAN

Remove pan attaching bolts and remove oil pan. Remove filter retaining bolt, withdraw intake pipe and filter assembly, then discard filter and "O" ring seal from intake pipe.

CONTROL VALVE ASSEMBLY

1) Remove control valve assembly attaching bolts and detent roller and spring assembly (do not remove solenoid attaching screws).

NOTE: **If transmission is in vehicle, front servo parts may drop out as control valve assembly is removed.**

2) Remove control valve assembly and governor pipes, using care not to drop manual valve as control valve assembly is removed. Remove governor screen assembly from governor feed pipe hole in case or from end of feed pipe.

3) Remove governor pipes from control valve assembly. Governor pipes are interchangeable and need not be identified. Disconnect detent solenoid wire from electrical connector.

REAR SERVO

Remove servo cover and gasket and discard gasket. Remove servo assembly and accumulator spring.

GM TURBO HYDRA-MATIC 400 — JAGUAR (Cont.)

Make a band apply pin selection check at this time to determine correct pin for use at reassembly. This is equivalent to band adjustment.

Band Apply Pin Selection Check

1) Position ban apply pin selection gauge (J-21370) on transmission case over rear servo bore. *See Fig. 9.* Install gauge with hex nut on side facing toward parking brake linkage. The smaller diameter end of gauge pin (J-21370-5) fits in servo pin bore.

2) Secure gauge with 2 attaching screws, and tighten screws to 18 ft. lbs. (24 N.m). Make sure stepped gauge pin is free to move up and down in both tool and servo pin bore. Stepped side of pin must face front of transmission case.

3) Tighten hex nut on side of gauge to 25 ft. lbs. (34 N.m). This will cause lever on top of gauge to depress stepped gauge pin into servo pin bore, simulating actual operating conditions. Note relation of steps on gauge pin and machined surface on top of gauge. To determine proper size pin, *see Fig. 3.*

4) If new band apply pin is required, make note of pin size for reassembly reference. Remove selection gauge from transmission case.

Fig. 3: Band Apply Pin Selection

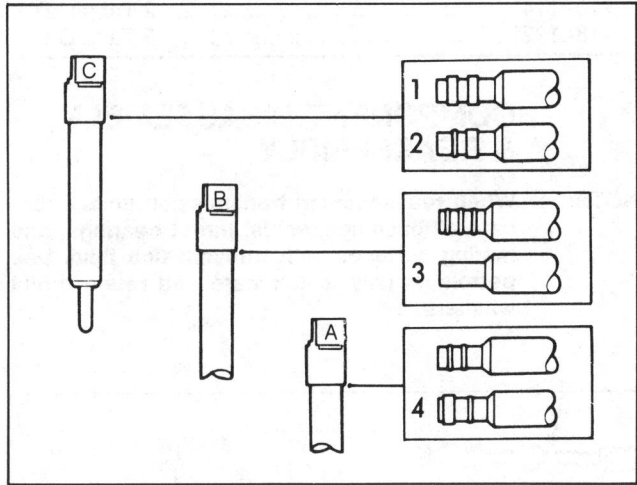

Pins 1, 2, 3 and 4 are factory fitted, but are not available as replacement parts.

DETENT SOLENOID, CONTROL VALVE SPACER & FRONT SERVO

Remove attaching screws and lift off detent solenoid assembly and gasket. Compress connector tangs, and withdraw case sleeve connector and "O" ring seal. Discard seal. Remove control valve spacer plate and gasket. Remove 6 check balls from cored passages in case. Remove front servo piston, retainer ring, servo pin, retainer and spring from case.

REAR OIL SEAL & EXTENSION HOUSING

If replacement is necessary, pry rear oil seal from extension housing. Remove attaching bolts and remove extension housing and gasket from transmission.

NOTE: **Make a front unit End Play Check before proceeding with transmission disassembly. Record end play for later reassembly.**

FRONT UNIT END PLAY CHECK

1) With transmission removed, remove 1 oil pump attaching bolt and bolt seal at either 10 o'clock or 5 o'clock position. Install slide hammer bolt into bolt hole in pump. Mount a dial indicator on rod and index indicator to register with end of turbine shaft.

2) Push turbine shaft rearward and output shaft forward. Zero dial indicator, then pull turbine shaft forward and read resulting end play on indicator. End play should be .003-.024" (.08-.61 mm). If end play is not within specified limits, select correct thickness washer for use at reassembly.

3) The selective thrust washer controlling this end play is located between pump cover and forward clutch housing. Front end play selective thrust washers are available in varing thicknesses and are color coded. *See Front Unit End Play Selective Thrust Washers Chart.*

FRONT UNIT END PLAY SELECTIVE THRUST WASHERS

Washer Thickness [1]	I.D. Number	Color Code
.060-.064"	0	Yellow
.071-.075"	1	Blue
.082-.086"	2	Red
.093-.097"	3	Brown
.104-.108"	4	Green
.115-.119"	5	Black
.126-.130"	6	Purple

[1] An oil soaked washer may tend to discolor, so it will be necessary to measure washer for its actual thickness.

OIL PUMP

If front seal requires replacement, pry seal out before removing pump assembly. Remove pump attaching bolts. Install special tools (18G 1296) or 2 slide hammers into 2 opposite pump bolt holes, and evenly remove pump assembly from case. Remove and discard pump-to-case seal ring and gasket.

TURBINE SHAFT, FORWARD & DIRECT CLUTCH ASSEMBLIES, SUN GEAR SHAFT & FRONT BAND

Remove forward clutch and turbine shaft assembly from case, then remove forward clutch hub-to-direct clutch housing thrust washer. Remove direct clutch and intermediate roller assembly, then remove sun gear shaft and front band.

DETENT LEVER, MANUAL LEVER, SHAFT & PARKING LINKAGE

1) If necessary for parts replacement, remove manual linkage. Loosen jam nut holding detent lever to manual shaft. Remove manual shaft retaining pin from case. Remove jam nut and detent lever from manual shaft. Remove manual shaft.

2) Remove parking pawl actuator rod and detent lever assembly. Remove attaching bolts and parking bracket. Remove parking pawl return spring. Remove parking pawl shaft retainer. Remove parking pawl shaft cup plug. Pry outward to remove plug. Remove parking pawl shaft and parking pawl.

Fig. 4: Detent and Manual Levers, Parking Pawl Assembly

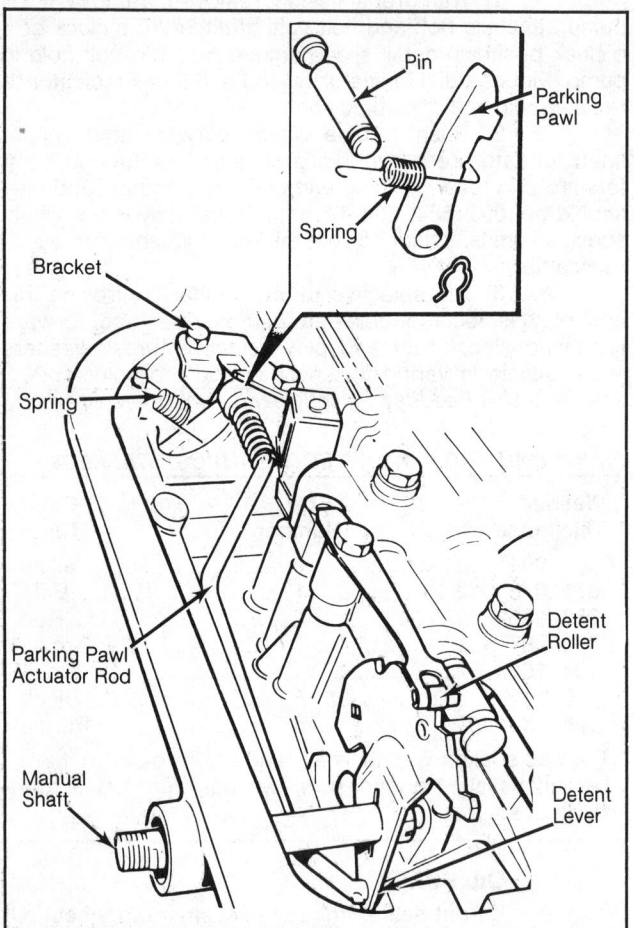

REAR UNIT END PLAY CHECK

1) Install threaded end of a 3/8"-16 rod into one of the extension housing bolt holes in rear of case. Install a dial indicator on rod with button engaging flat surface on end of output shaft. Zero indicator dial, then move output shaft in and out and note end play reading. End play should be .003-.019" (.08-.48 mm). If end play needs adjustment, select a thrust washer that will bring end play within specifications.

2) The selective thrust washer controlling rear unit end play is a steel washer having 3 tabs. It is located between output shaft thrust washer and rear face of transmission case. Notches and/or numerals on tabs of washer identify thickness. *See Selective Thrust Washers Chart.*

SELECTIVE THRUST WASHERS (REAR UNIT END PLAY)

Washer Thickness	I.D. Notches
.080-.082"	None
.086-.090"	1 Tab Side
.094-.098"	2 Tabs Side
.102-.106"	1 Tab O.D.
.110-.114"	2 Tabs O.D.
.118-.122"	3 Tabs O.D.

COMPONENT DISASSEMBLY & REASSEMBLY

NOTE: When reassembling transmission units, lubricate all bushings, seals, thrust bearings, and mating surfaces with transmission fluid. Use petroleum jelly to lubricate and retain thrust washers.

Fig. 5: Exploded View of Control Valve Assembly

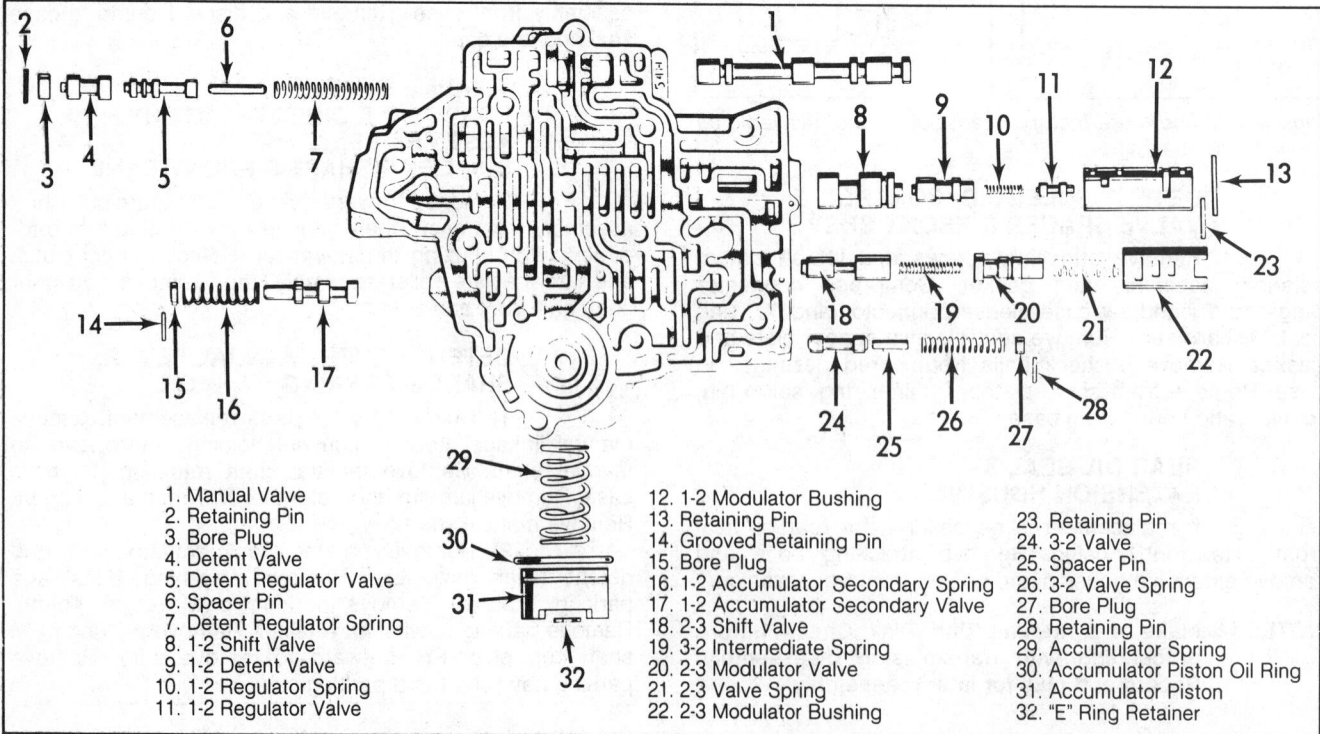

1. Manual Valve
2. Retaining Pin
3. Bore Plug
4. Detent Valve
5. Detent Regulator Valve
6. Spacer Pin
7. Detent Regulator Spring
8. 1-2 Shift Valve
9. 1-2 Detent Valve
10. 1-2 Regulator Spring
11. 1-2 Regulator Valve

12. 1-2 Modulator Bushing
13. Retaining Pin
14. Grooved Retaining Pin
15. Bore Plug
16. 1-2 Accumulator Secondary Spring
17. 1-2 Accumulator Secondary Valve
18. 2-3 Shift Valve
19. 3-2 Intermediate Spring
20. 2-3 Modulator Valve
21. 2-3 Valve Spring
22. 2-3 Modulator Bushing

23. Retaining Pin
24. 3-2 Valve
25. Spacer Pin
26. 3-2 Valve Spring
27. Bore Plug
28. Retaining Pin
29. Accumulator Spring
30. Accumulator Piston Oil Ring
31. Accumulator Piston
32. "E" Ring Retainer

GM TURBO HYDRA-MATIC 400 — JAGUAR (Cont.)

CONTROL VALVE ASSEMBLY

NOTE: As each valve train is removed, place the individual valve train in a separate location relative to its position in valve body. Also, place each part from each valve train in the order that it is removed from valve bore. None of the valves or springs are interchangeable. Keep them in the proper valve train.

Disassembly

1) Position control valve assembly with cored face up and accumulator pocket at bottom. Remove manual valve from upper bore. Install compressor tool (18G 1295) on accumulator piston, compress piston and remove "E" ring, then remove piston and spring.

NOTE: Steps 2) and 3) require using a pin punch to remove retaining pin.

2) From upper right hand bore, remove 1-2 valve train. From center right hand bore, remove 2-3 valve train. From lower right hand bore, remove 3-2 valve train.

3) From upper left hand bore, remove detent valve train. From lower left hand bore, remove 1-2 accumulator valve train.

Inspection

1) Inspect all valves and bushings carefully to make sure they are free from dirt and are not damaged in any way. If burrs are present, remove with a fine stone or fine grade crocus cloth and light oil.

CAUTION: When removing burrs from valves, use care not to round off shoulders of valves.

2) Test all valves and bushings in their bores to make sure they slide freely of their own weight. Manual valve is only valve that can be serviced separately. If other valves require replacement, complete valve body assembly should be replaced.

3) Inspect valve body for cracks or scored bores. Check all springs for distortion or collapsed coils. Inspect accumulator piston and oil ring for damage.

NOTE: Do not remove teflon oil seal from front accumulator piston unless seal needs replacing. For service, the oil seal ring is cast iron.

Reassembly

1) Install front accumulator spring and piston into valve body, then compress piston and spring and install retaining "E" clip.

2) In lower left bore, install 1-2 accumulator primary spring (if required) and 1-2 accumulator valve, stem end out, then install bore plug.

3) Install detent regulator spring and spacer in upper left bore. Install detent regulator valve (stem end out) and detent valve (narrow land first). Install bore plug with open end out and install retaining pin.

4) Install 3-2 valve in lower right bore, then install spacer, valve spring, bore plug (open end out) and retaining pin. In next bore up, install 2-3 shift valve (hole end out) and 3-2 intermediate spring. Install 2-3 modulator valve into bushing and install both parts into valve bore. Install 2-3 valve spring, then install retaining pin.

· 5) In next bore, install 1-2 valve (stem end out). Install 1-2 regulator valve (large stem first), spring and 1-2 detent valve (hole end first) into 1-2 modulator bushing,

aligning spring in bore of detent valve and install parts into valve body bore.

6) Compress bushing against spring and install retaining pin. Install manual valve with detent pin groove to the right.

REAR SERVO

Disassembly

Remove rear accumulator piston from rear servo piston. Remove "E" ring retaining rear servo piston to band apply pin, then remove rear servo piston and seal from pin. Remove washer, spring and retainer.

CAUTION: Do not remove teflon oil seals unless they require replacement. If small ring requires replacement, use service aluminum ring. If large ring requires replacement, use only teflon oil ring.

Fig. 6: Exploded View of Rear Servo Assembly

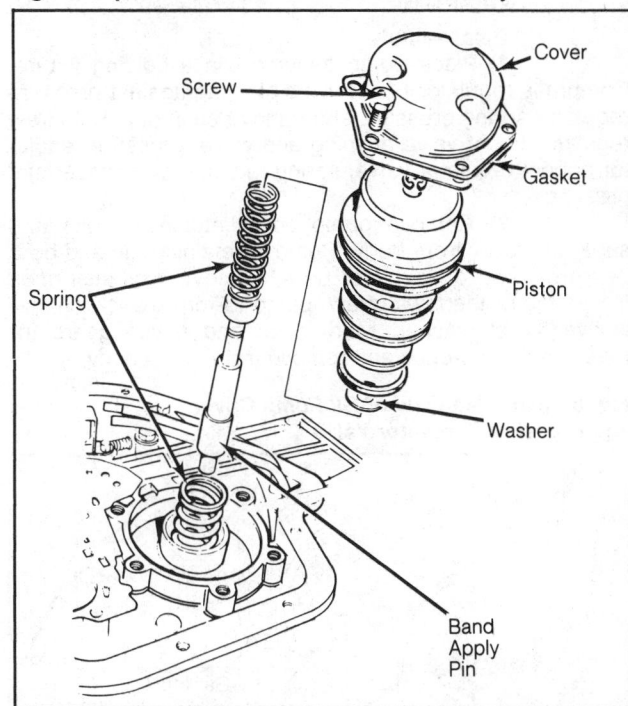

Inspection

Check freedom of accumulator rings in piston and their respective bores. Inspect fit of band apply pin in servo piston and case bore. Inspect band apply pin for scores or cracks. Inspect servo piston for cracks or porosity.

Reassembly

Reverse disassembly procedure.

FRONT SERVO

Inspection

Inspect servo pin, piston and oil seal ring for wear or damage. Check fit of servo pin in piston and in case bore.

NOTE: Do not remove teflon oil seal ring from servo piston unless seal ring requires replacement. For service, replacement oil seal ring is aluminum.

GM TURBO HYDRA-MATIC 400 — JAGUAR (Cont.)

Fig. 7: Exploded View of Front Servo Assembly

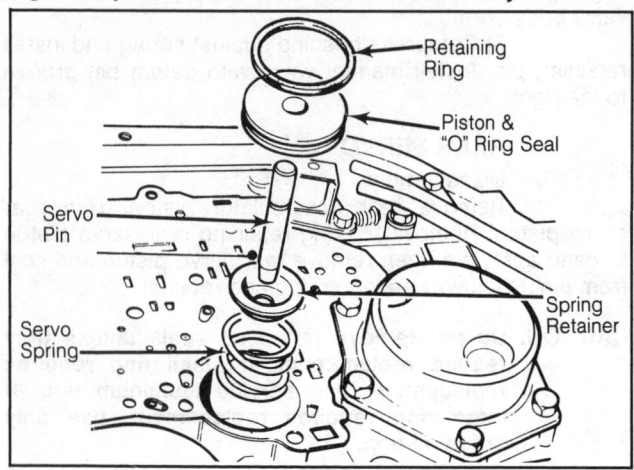

Retaining Ring

Piston & "O" Ring Seal

Servo Pin

Spring Retainer

Servo Spring

OIL PUMP
Disassembly

1) Place pump assembly in a holding fixture. Compress regulator boost valve bushing against pressure regulator spring pressure and remove snap ring. Withdraw regulator boost valve bushing and valve, pressure regulator spring, regulator valve, spring retainer, and spacer(s) if present.

2) Remove pump cover attaching bolts and separate cover from body. Remove retaining pin and bore plug from end of regulator bore. Remove 2 oil seal rings from cover, then withdraw pump-to-forward clutch selective thrust washer. Mark drive and driven gears for reassembly reference and remove from pump body

Fig. 8: Exploded View of Oil Pump Cover and Pressure Regulator Valve

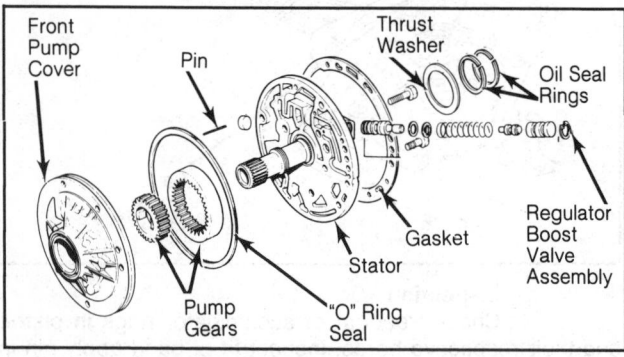

Front Pump Cover

Pin

Thrust Washer

Oil Seal Rings

Stator

Gasket

Regulator Boost Valve Assembly

Pump Gears

"O" Ring Seal

Inspection

1) Inspect all parts for nicks, scoring or galling, wear, or other damage. Install pump gears in pump body, and check pump body-to-gear face clearance with a feeler gauge. Clearance should be .0008-.0035" (.020-.089 mm). Check overall flatness of pump body face.

2) Inspect pump attaching bolt seals for damage and replace if necessary. Make certain all passages are clear and open. Make sure pressure regulator and boost valves are free in bore. Install pump cover oil seal rings in counterbore of forward clutch housing and check for proper fit.

Reassembly
Reverse disassembly procedure and note the following:

1) When installing front unit selective thrust washer, make sure it is the proper thickness as deter-

mined at Transmission Disassembly. When installing gears in pump body, ensure marks made at disassembly are aligned. If correct, converter tangs on drive gear should be upward.

2) When installing pump cover attaching bolts, leave bolts one turn loose, install alignment strap to align cover and body, then tighten attaching bolts.

FORWARD CLUTCH
Disassembly

1) Remove forward clutch housing-to-direct clutch hub snap ring and withdraw hub. Remove forward clutch hub and thrust washers from each side of hub. Withdraw composition and steel clutch plates.

2) If necessary, place clutch housing in an arbor press and press turbine shaft out of housing. Using a compressor tool, compress spring retainer and remove snap ring. Remove tool and lift out spring retainer and 16 clutch release springs.

NOTE: Keep forward clutch release springs separate from direct clutch release springs.

Fig. 9: Exploded View of Forward Clutch Assemby

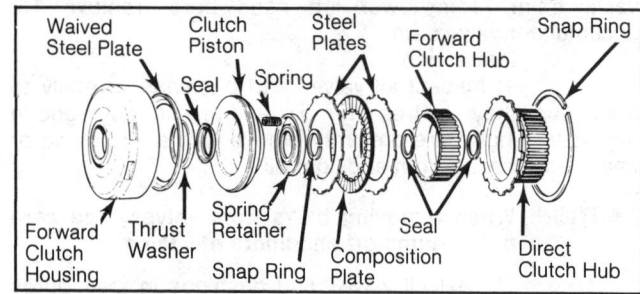

Waived Steel Plate

Clutch Piston

Steel Plates

Forward Clutch Hub

Snap Ring

Seal

Spring

Forward Clutch Housing

Thrust Washer

Spring Retainer

Snap Ring

Seal

Composition Plate

Direct Clutch Hub

3) Remove forward clutch piston from housing. Remove inner and outer seals from piston and center seal from clutch housing.

Inspection

Inspect clutch plates for burning, scoring, or wear. Check release springs for distortion or collapsed coils. Inspect clutch hubs for worn splines and thrust faces, and for clear lubrication passages. Check piston for cracks or porosity. Check turbine shaft and clutch housing for wear, scoring or other damage. Make sure ball check in housing moves freely.

Reassembly

1) Oil and install inner and outer seals on clutch piston with seal lips facing away from spring pockets. Oil and install center seal on clutch housing with seal lips facing upward.

2) Place seal protector tools over clutch hub and into clutch housing, then install piston into housing. Install 16 clutch release springs into piston pockets, place spring retainer and snap ring over springs, then compress springs and install snap ring into groove.

3) If turbine shaft was removed, install shaft into housing using an arbor press. Install forward clutch hub thrust washers. Make sure bronze washer is installed on side of hub facing forward clutch housing. Retain washers in place with petroleum jelly. Place forward clutch hub into clutch housing.

4) Lubricate with transmission fluid and install clutch plates, starting with a waved steel plate (plate with "U" notch), then alternating composition and flat steel plates (plate with "V" notch) until all clutch plates are installed. See Forward Clutch Plate Chart.

GM TURBO HYDRA-MATIC 400 — JAGUAR (Cont.)

5) Install direct clutch hub and retaining snap ring. Place forward clutch housing on oil pump delivery sleeve. Air check operation of forward clutch by applying air through forward clutch passage in pump to actuate piston and move forward clutch.

FORWARD CLUTCH PLATE CHART

Application	Flat Steel [1]	Composition
All Models	5	4

[1] — Steel plates are .0915" (2.3 mm) thick.

DIRECT CLUTCH & INTERMEDIATE ROLLER ASSEMBLY

Disassembly

1) Remove intermediate roller assembly retainer snap ring and retainer. Remove roller outer race and roller assembly. Turn unit over and remove backing plate-to-direct clutch housing snap ring. Remove direct clutch backing plate and clutch pack.

2) Using a compressor tool, compress spring retainer in arbor press and remove snap ring. Remove retainer and piston and 16 clutch release springs. Remove direct clutch piston from clutch housing, then remove inner and outer seals from piston. Remove center piston seal from direct clutch housing.

NOTE: Keep springs separate from forward clutch release springs.

Fig. 10: Exploded View of Direct Clutch and Intermediate Roller Clutch Assembly

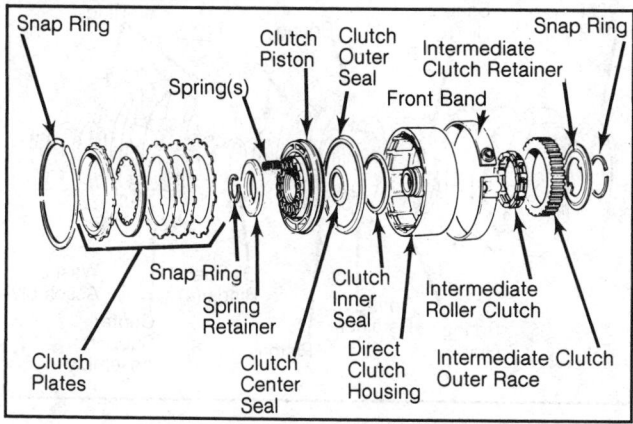

Inspection

1) Inspect roller assembly for popped or loose rollers. Inspect inner cam and outer race for scratches or wear. Inspect clutch housing for cracks, wear, proper opening of oil passages or wear on clutch plate drive lugs. Inspect clutch plates for wear or burning.

2) Inspect backing plate for scratches or damage. Inspect clutch piston for cracks. Inspect clutch housing for free operation of check ball. Check springs for collapsed coils and distortion.

Reassembly

1) Lubricate seals with transmission fluid and install new inner and outer seals on clutch piston with seal lips facing away from spring pockets. Install new center seals on clutch hub with seal lip facing upward. Place seal

protector tool over clutch hub and into clutch housing, then install clutch piston into housing with a rotating motion.

2) If production clutch release springs are being used, install 14 springs into spring pockets of piston, leaving 2 opposite pockets with no springs. If service relacement springs are used, install all 16 springs into spring pockets. Place spring retainer on top of springs and snap ring on top of retainer. Using tool used at disassembly, compress springs and install snap ring.

3) Lubricate clutch plates with transmission fluid. Install plates into clutch housing starting with a waved steel plate (if used). Alternate composition and flat steel plates until all plates are installed. *See Direct Clutch Plate Usage Chart.* Install backing plate and retaining snap ring.

DIRECT CLUTCH PLATE CHART

Application	Flat Steel Plates	Composition Plates
All Models	5	4

4) Install rollers in case by compressing energizing spring and inserting roller from outer side. Turn unit over and install roller clutch assembly onto intermediate clutch inner cam, then install outer race with a clockwise turning motion. Install clutch retainer and snap ring. Place assembly on center support and air check operation of clutch.

GEAR UNIT

Disassembly

1) Remove center support-to-sun gear races and thrust bearing (1 race may have come out with center support). Remove sun gear from output carrier.

2) Remove reaction carrier-to-output carrier thrust washer. Remove front internal gear ring from output carrier assembly. Lift roller clutch assembly out of carrier.

Fig. 11: Exploded View of Gear Unit Assembly and Output Shaft

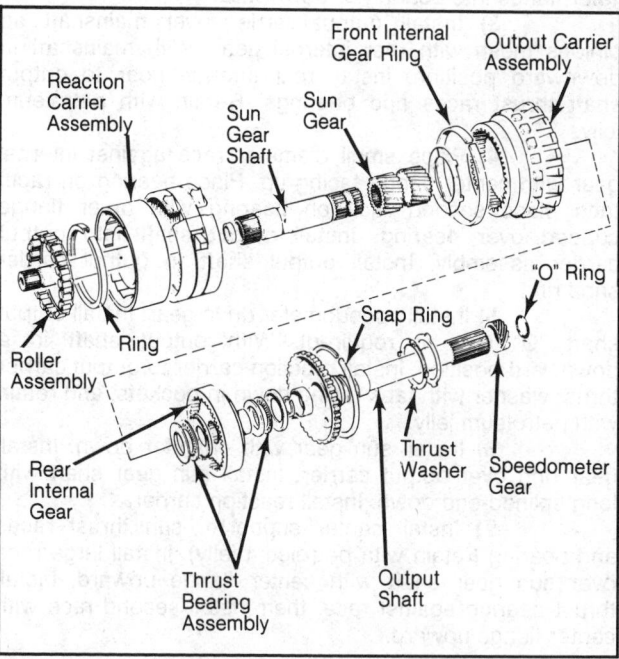

3) Remove "O" ring from output shaft (if equipped). Remove output shaft-to-output carrier snap ring and remove output shaft. Remove output shaft-to-rear internal gear thrust bearing and 2 races. Remove rear internal gear and mainshaft.

4) Remove rear internal gear-to-sun gear thrust bearing and 2 races. If necessary, remove rear internal gear-to-mainshaft snap ring to remove mainshaft.

Inspection

1) If reaction carrier is equipped with a spacer ring in an undercut at bottom of roller cam ramps, inspect ring for wear or damage. Inspect reaction carrier bushing for damage; if bushing is damaged, carrier must be replaced.

2) Check pinions for damage, rough bearings, or tilt. Check pinion end play; end play should be .009-.024" (.23-.61 mm). Inspect band surface on reaction carrier for burning or scoring. Check all other parts for wear, scoring, or other damage. Make sure all lubrication holes are open.

Speedometer Drive Gear Replacement

1) If equipped with a nylon speedometer gear, depress retaining clip and slide gear off shaft. To install, place retaining clip (square end toward flange of shaft) into hole in shaft, align slot in gear with clip, and install gear.

2) If equipped with a steel gear, use a puller and remove gear from shaft. To install, support output shaft on front face and use driver tool to drive gear onto shaft.

3) Drive speedometer gear onto shaft until distance from rear face of gear to end of output shaft is 5 21/32" (83.34 mm).

Reassembly

1) Install rear internal gear on end of mainshaft (end with snap ring groove) and install snap ring. Install sun gear-to-internal gear thrust races and bearing against inner face of rear internal gear. Retain with petroleum jelly.

2) Place large race against internal gear with flange facing forward or upward, place thrust bearing against race, then place small race against bearing with inner flange into bearing or downward.

3) Install output carrier over mainshaft so pinions mesh with rear internal gear. With mainshaft in downward position, install rear internal gear to output shaft thrust races and bearings. Retain with petroleum jelly.

4) Place small diameter race against internal gear with center flange facing up. Place bearing on race, then place second race on bearing with outer flange cupped over bearing. Install output shaft into output carrier assembly. Install output shaft to output carrier snap ring.

5) Install speedometer drive gear. Install output shaft "O" ring (if required). With output shaft in a downward position, install reaction carrier to output carrier thrust washer with tabs facing down in pockets, and retain with petroleum jelly.

6) Install sun gear with chamfer down. Install gear ring over output carrier. Install sun gear shaft with long splined-end down. Install reaction carrier.

7) Install center support-to-sun thrust races and bearing (retain with petroleum jelly). Install large race over sun gear shaft with center flange upward, install thrust bearing against race, then install second race with center flange upward.

8) Install rollers that may have come out of roller case by compressing energizing spring with forefinger and inserting roller from outer side. Install roller clutch into reaction carrier outer race.

9) Install center support-to-reaction carrier thrust washer into recess in center support and retain with petroleum jelly. Install center support into reaction carrier and roller clutch assembly.

10) Install a holding tool to keep units in place, then install output shaft-to-case thrust washers (bent tabs in pockets) and retain with petroleum jelly.

CENTER SUPPORT & INTERMEDIATE CLUTCH

Disassembly

If necessary, remove 4 center support oil seal rings. Compress spring retainer and remove snap ring. Remove spring retainer and 3 clutch release springs. Remove intermediate clutch spring guide and clutch piston from center support. Remove inner and outer piston seals from piston.

Inspection

1) Check all parts for wear, scoring or damage. Inspect release springs for distortion or collapsed coils. Check oil ring grooves and oil rings for wear or damage. Rings should fit freely in grooves.

2) Make sure all passages, lubrication grooves and holes are clear of obstructions. Check roller clutch inner race for scratches and indentations. Make sure constant bleed orifice is open .020" (.51 mm).

Fig. 12: Exploded View of Center Support and Intermediate Clutch

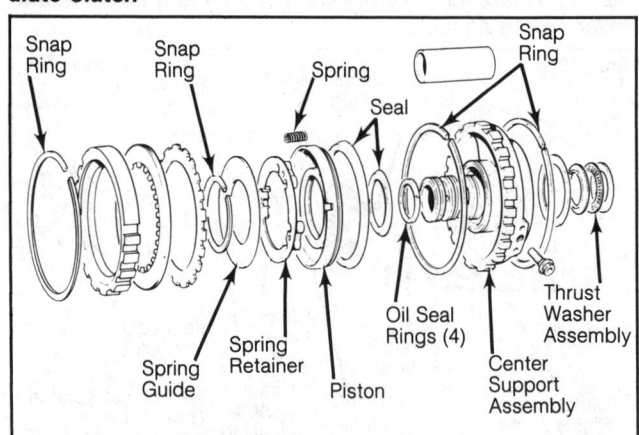

Reassembly

1) Lubricate and install inner and outer seals on piston with seal lips facing away from spring pockets. Place a seal protector tool over center support hub. Install piston indexing spring pockets in drum and piston.

2) Install spring guide and evenly space 3 release springs in spring guides. Place spring retainer and snap ring over springs, then compress springs and install snap ring in groove.

3) If removed, install 4 oil seal rings on center support. Air check operation of intermediate clutch piston by applying air through center oil feed hole to actuate clutch piston.

NOTE: When installing teflon oil seal rings on center support, be sure split ends are assembled in the same relation as cut.

GM TURBO HYDRA-MATIC 400 — JAGUAR (Cont.)

TRANSMISSION CASE

Inspection

Inspect case for cracks, porosity, or interconnected passages. Check governor and modulator valve bores for scratches or scoring. Check band anchor pins for retention, and intermediate clutch driven plate lugs for damage. Inspect snap ring grooves for damage. See that intermediate clutch cup plug is properly staked and sealed.

CAUTION: If case assembly requires replacement, make sure that the center support-to-case spacer and name plate are removed from old case and installed in new case.

EXTENSION HOUSING

Inspection

Check housing for cracks or porosity. Inspect gasket mounting face for burrs or other damage. Make sure rear seal drain-back part is not obstructed. Check rear bushing for wear or damage. Replace as necessary.

TRANSMISSION REASSEMBLY

PARKING PAWL

Install parking pawl, tooth toward inside of case, then install parking pawl shaft and shaft retainer. Install a new cup plug using a 3/8" (9.5 mm) diameter rod, and drive plug into case until shaft bottoms on case rib. Install parking pawl return spring, with square end hooked on pawl and other end on case. Install parking pawl bracket with guides over parking pawl, then install and tighten attaching bolts.

REAR BAND & GEAR UNIT

1) Install rear band so that lugs index with anchor pins and make sure band is seated on lugs. Install support-to-case spacer against shoulder at bottom of case splines and with ring gap adjacent to band anchor pin.

2) Install previously selected rear unit end play washer into slots provided inside rear of case and retain washer with petroleum jelly. Place transmission in a horizontal position and install holding tool on output shaft.

3) Install complete gear unit assembly into case by lining up slots and carefully guiding assembly horizontally into case making sure center support bolt hole is aligned with hole in case.

4) Position transmission vertically and remove output shaft holding tool. Install center support-to-case retaining ring, with beveled side up. Locate gap adjacent to band anchor pin.

5) Lubricate and install intermediate clutch plates, starting with a waved steel plate, then alternating composition and flat steel plates until all clutch plates are installed.

6) Install intermediate clutch backing plate with flat machined surface against clutch plates. Install backing plate-to-case snap ring, locating ring gap opposite band anchor pin. Before proceeding with transmission reassembly, recheck rear unit end play. *See Transmission Disassembly.*

FRONT BAND & CLUTCH ASSEMBLIES

1) Install front band with band anchor hole over band anchor pin and apply lug facing servo hole.

Install direct clutch and intermediate roller assembly. Install forward clutch hub to direct clutch housing thrust washer on forward clutch hub and retain with petroleum jelly.

NOTE: It will be necessary to twist housing to allow roller outer race to index with composition clutch plates.

2) Install forward clutch and turbine shaft, indexing direct clutch hub so end of mainshaft will go all the way into forward clutch hub. When forward clutch is seated, it will be 1-1 1/4" (25.4-31.8 mm) from pump mounting face in case.

OIL PUMP

1) Install new gasket on oil pump and retain in place with petroleum jelly. Lubricate turbine shaft journals and pump oil seal rings. Install pump assembly into case.

2) Install pump attaching bolts with new seals (omit 1 bolt for end play check), and tighten bolts evenly.

CAUTION: If turbine shaft cannot be rotated as pump is being pulled into place, forward or direct clutch housings have not been installed properly to index with all clutch plates. Correct this condition before pulling pump fully into place.

3) Recheck front unit end play as described in Transmission Disassembly. If necessary, adjust end play by changing thrust washer located between pump cover and forward clutch housing.

4) Remove dial indicator and install remaining pump attaching bolt. Apply a non-hardening sealer to outside of new front oil seal. Install seal into pump using a driver.

PARKING LINKAGE, DETENT LEVER & MANUAL SHAFT

If removed, install a new manual shaft seal into transmission case using a 3/4" (19 mm) diameter rod to seat seal. Install actuator rod into manual detent lever from side opposite pin. Install actuator rod plunger under parking bracket and over parking pawl. Install manual shaft through case and detent lever. Install detent retaining lock nut on manual shaft and tighten. Install retaining pin, indexing with groove in manual shaft.

NOTE: It may be necessary to bend manual shaft retaining pin to install. Straighten pin as it is installed.

EXTENSION HOUSING

1) Install a new gasket on extension housing and retain with petroleum jelly. Install housing on transmission case and tighten attaching bolts. If applicable, check "O" ring on output shaft for any nicks or flattening and replace ring if necessary.

2) Apply a non-hardening sealer to outside diameter of rear oil seal, position on extension housing, then seat seal in housing using driver.

CONTROL VALVE SPACER & DETENT SOLENOID

1) Install 2 guide pins opposite each other into 2 control valve assembly attaching bolt holes. Install check

GM TURBO HYDRA-MATIC 400 — JAGUAR (Cont.)

balls into ball seat pockets in case. If transmission is installed in vehicle, install check balls in pockets of spacer plate.

2) Install control valve spacer plate-to-case gasket, gasket with extension for detent solenoid and marked with a "C". Install control valve spacer plate and control valve-to-spacer plate gasket, marked with a "VB". Install detent solenoid gasket, then install solenoid with connector facing outer edge of case. Do not tighten bolts at this time.

NOTE: **Some overhaul kits supply a solenoid gasket. This gasket must not be installed on Jaguar vehicles.**

3) Install "O" ring seal on solenoid connector. Compress connector tangs and install in case with locator tab in notch on side of case. Connect detent solenoid wire to connector terminal.

FRONT SERVO

Install front servo spring and spring retainer into transmission case. Install retainer ring in front servo pin groove and install pin in case so tapered end contacts band. Make sure retainer ring is still installed in groove. Install seal ring on piston. Install piston on pin with flat side of piston positioned toward oil pan.

REAR SERVO

1) Before installing servo, check band apply pin. *See Band Apply Pin Selection Check in Transmission Disassembly.* Also, make certain that rear band apply lug is aligned with servo pin bore in transmission case.

2) Lubricate inner and outer rear servo bores in case with transmission fluid, then install rear accumulator spring in servo inner bore. Install rear servo assembly, install gasket and cover. Install and tighten attaching bolts.

CONTROL VALVE BODY ASSEMBLY

1) Install governor pipes into control valve assembly (pipes are interchangeable). Install governor screen assembly (open end first) into governor feed pipe hole in case (hole nearest center of transmission).

2) Install valve body-to-spacer plate gasket. Using 2 guide pins, install control valve assembly and governor pipes on transmission. Make sure gasket and spacer plate are not moved out of position, that manual valve is indexed properly with pin on detent lever, and that governor pipes are properly seated in case holes.

3) Start control valve body-to-case bolts making sure lead wire clip is installed. Remove guide pins, install detent roller and spring assembly, then install and tighten remaining attaching bolts.

GOVERNOR

Install governor assembly into case. Install cover with new gasket and tighten attaching bolts.

SPEEDOMETER DRIVEN GEAR

If removed, install driven gear into sleeve. Install driven gear assembly into case. Install retainer with tangs in sleeve positioning bosses. Install and tighten attaching bolt.

INTAKE PIPE, FILTER & OIL PAN

Install case-to-intake pipe "O" ring seal on intake pipe. Install pipe into filter assembly. Place filter and intake pipe in case, install retaining bolt and tighten. Install oil pan with new gasket. Install and tighten attaching screws.

VACUUM MODULATOR & VALVE

Install modulator valve into case with stem end out. Install new "O" ring seal on vacuum modulator. Install modulator into case with vacuum hose pipe facing front and angled 5° toward top of case. Install modulator retainer with curved side of tangs inboard. Install and tighten attaching bolt.

CONVERTER ASSEMBLY

Install converter into front pump assembly. Make sure converter hub drive slots are fully engaged with pump drive gear tangs and converter is installed fully toward rear of transmission.

TIGHTENING SPECIFICATIONS

Application	Ft. Lbs. (N.m)
Center Support Bolts	25 (34)
Extension Housing-to-Case Bolts	23 (32)
Transmission-to-Engine Bolts	35 (48)
Converter-to-Drive Plate Bolts	35 (48)
	INCH Lbs.
Pump Cover Bolts	240 (27)
Parking Pawl Bracket Bolts	240 (27)
Pump-to-Case Bolts	240 (27)
Rear Servo Cover Bolts	240 (27)
Detent Solenoid Bolts	84 (10)
Control Valve Body Bolts	96 (11)
Oil Pan Bolts	144 (16)
Modulator Retainer Bolts	240 (24)
Governor Cover Bolts	240 (24)
Manual Lever-to-Manual Shaft Nut	96 (11)
Manual Lever-to-Detent Lever	240 (27)
Line Pressure Take-Off Plug	120 (14)
Filter Retainer Bolt	120 (14)

HONDA 3-SPEED

Accord, Prelude & Civic

TRANSAXLE IDENTIFICATION

Transaxle may be identified by a group of letters and numbers stamped on a pad on top of transaxle. First 2 letters are transaxle type. Next 7 numbers are transaxle serial number.

TRANSAXLE MODEL CODE

Application	Code
Accord & Prelude	AK
Civic	AJ

DESCRIPTION

The Honda 3-speed automatic transaxle is a combination of a 3-phase torque converter, dual shift transmission and a differential-type final drive assembly. Transmission consists of a mainshaft and a countershaft. Transmission is controlled by the main valve body, regulator valve body and the servo valve. Countershaft is in constant mesh with the differential ring gear.

LUBRICATION & ADJUSTMENT

See the appropriate article in AUTOMATIC TRANSMISSION SERVICING Section.

SERVICE (IN-VEHICLE)

AXLE SHAFTS

Removal

1) Drain transmission, then bend tabs on spindle nut washer and loosen nut. Raise and support vehicle. Remove nut and wheel.

2) On Accord models, remove pivot bolt and stabilizer bar bolts on lower control arm. On all other models, remove ball joint nut and separate steering knuckle from ball joint. Pull steering knuckle outward until axle shaft is clear of front hub.

3) Pry constant velocity (CV) joint out of transaxle case approximately 1/2" (12 mm), this will collapse spring clip (on axle shaft inside transaxle case) and allow axle shaft to be withdrawn from case.

4) Pull axle shaft out of transaxle case and out of front hub assembly. Repeat procedures for other axle shaft.

Fig. 1: Exploded View of Axle Shaft Assembly

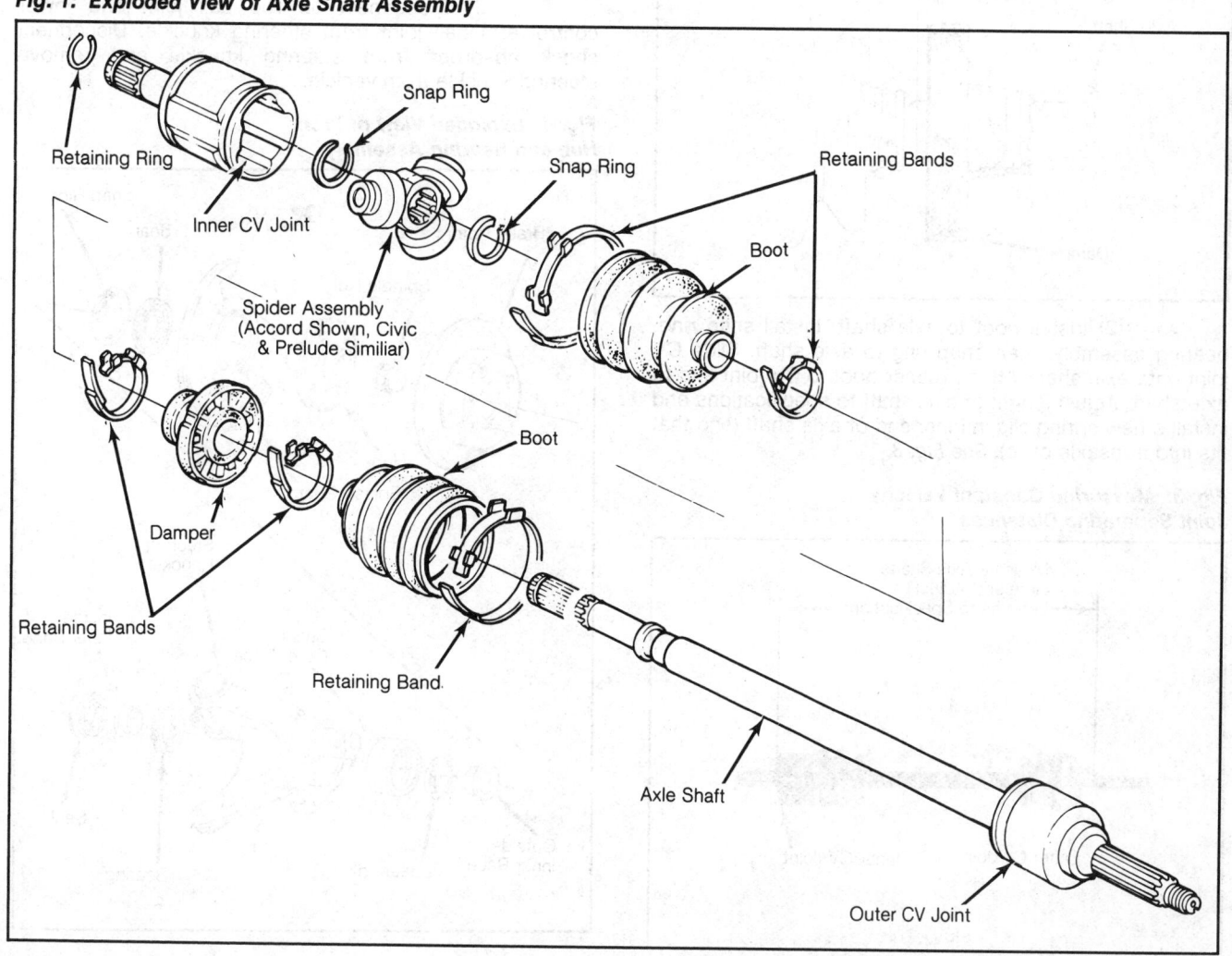

HONDA 3-SPEED (Cont.)

Disassembly

1) Remove metal bands securing rubber boot to axle shaft and inner constant velocity joint. Slide boot back onto axle shaft and remove snap rings. Pull axle shaft from inner constant velocity joint. *See Fig. 1.*

NOTE: Outer constant velocity joint is not removable.

2) Remove retaining ring, then ball bearing cage with bearing race and balls. Remove balls from bearing race by prying out with a screwdriver. Remove band from damper and remove damper toward inside of axle shaft. Remove outer rubber boot. Inspect all parts for wear, pitting or other damage. Replace parts as necessary.

Reassembly

1) Install outer rubber boot and metal bands. Slide damper onto axle shaft and secure damper so that face is .080" (2 mm) from beginning of taper. *See Fig. 2.* Assemble constant velocity joint bearing with cage and insert balls, packed with molybdenum disulfide grease.

Fig. 2: Adjusting Damper Position on Axle Shaft

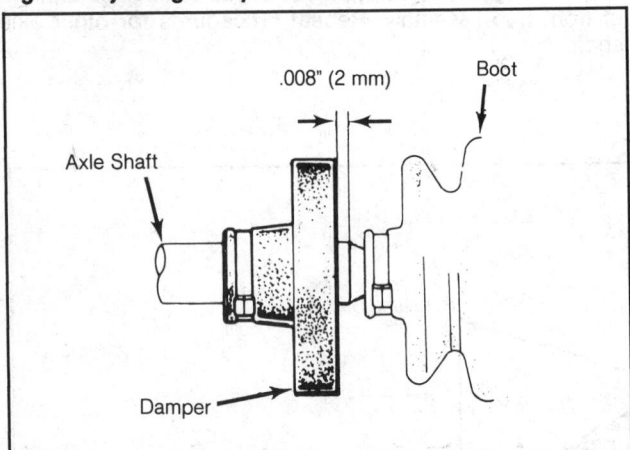

2) Install boot to axle shaft. Install snap ring, bearing assembly, then snap ring to axle shaft. Slide CV joint onto axle shaft. Attach rubber boot to CV joint and to axle shaft. Adjust length of axle shaft to specifications and install a new spring clip in inner end of axle shaft (end that fits into transaxle case). *See Fig. 3.*

Fig. 3: Measuring Constant Velocity Joint Separating Distances

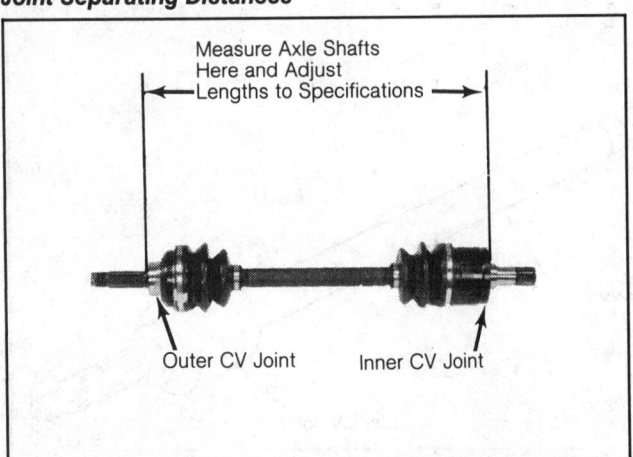

AXLE SHAFT LENGTH

Application	Length In. (mm)
Accord	
Right Axle Shaft	19.2-19.4 (489-493)
Left Axle Shaft	30.1-30.3 (766-770)
Prelude	
Right Axle Shaft	18.7-19.1 (469-479)
Left Axle Shaft	29.8-30.2 (757-767)
Civic	
Right Axle Shaft	18.2-18.4 (462-467)
Left Axle Shaft	29.7-29.9 (755.5-760.5)

NOTE: Pack CV joints with molybdenum disulfide grease before installation of protective rubber boots.

Installation

For installation, reverse removal procedures.

WHEEL BEARINGS

Removal

1) Remove wheel and spindle nut. Remove caliper bolts and hang caliper out of way. Remove 2 brake retaining screws, screw in 2 metric bolts (8 by 1.25 mm) to remove brake rotor from hub.

2) Disconnect tie rod ball joint and lower control arm ball joint from steering knuckle. Disconnect shock absorber from steering knuckle and remove steering knuckle from vehicle.

Fig. 4: Exploded View of Front Hub and Bearing Assembly

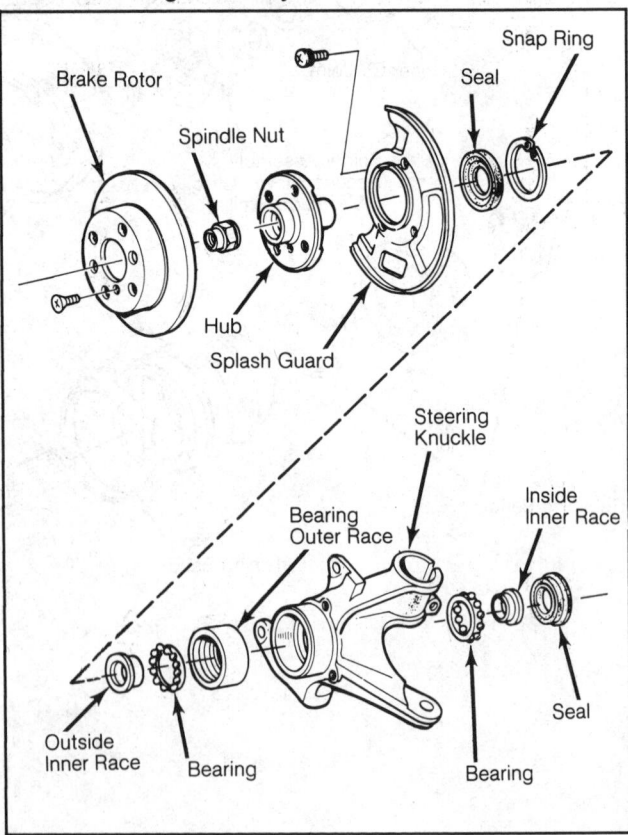

HONDA 3-SPEED (Cont.)

3) Press hub from steering knuckle. Remove splash guard and snap ring from steering knuckle. Remove seal, inner race and bearing from inner side of steering knuckle. Press bearing outer race out of steering knuckle (toward outside). *See Fig. 4.*

4) Using a puller, remove steering knuckle inside inner race from hub, then pry seal from hub.

NOTE: **Pack both wheel bearings with grease before installing. Also, apply grease to lips of seals.**

Installation
1) Press bearing outer race into steering knuckle. Install bearing, outside inner race and snap ring to steering knuckle.

2) Install seal to outside of steering knuckle. Install inner bearing and race to inside of steering knuckle. Install splash guard. Press hub into steering knuckle and install seal.

3) Place steering knuckle in position on vehicle and attach shock absorber. Attach lower control arm ball joint and tie rod ball joint to steering knuckle. Install rotor, caliper and axle shafts to steering knuckle. Install new spindle nut, then wheel.

TROUBLE SHOOTING

NO MOVEMENT
In Any Gear
Low fluid level. Faulty pump. Regulator valve stuck or damaged spring. Servo shaft stuck. Reverse hub splines stuck. Mainshaft damaged. Manual shift cable out of adjustment or broken. Damaged final drive gear. Broken flex plate. Oil filter clogged.

In "D1"; OK in Other Gears
Low fluid level. Manual shift cable out of adjustment. Worn or damaged one-way clutch. Low gear damaged. 1st clutch piston stuck, damaged "O" ring, damaged feed pipe or "O" rings, check valve stuck, worn or burnt clutch discs.

In "2"; OK in Other Gears
Low fluid level. Manual shift cable out of adjustment. 2nd gear damaged. Faulty 2nd clutch.

In "R"; OK in Other Gears
Low fluid level. Servo shaft stuck. Faulty 2nd clutch. Damaged reverse gear.

ENGINE RACES IN "D"
Stall RPM High in "D" and "2"
Low fluid level. Faulty pump. Regulator valve stuck or spring damaged. Manual shift cable out of adjustment. Torque converter check valve.

Stall RPM High in "D" Only
Low fluid level. Faulty pump. Manual shift cable out of adjustment. 1st clutch piston stuck, damaged clutch "O" ring, clutch feed pipe or "O" ring damaged, check valve stuck, worn or burnt clutch discs.

Stall RPM High in "2"
Manual shift cable out of adjustment. Faulty 2nd clutch.

Stall RPM OK
1-2 shift valve faulty. Faulty governor valve. Fluid level too high. Faulty torque converter one-way clutch.

Stall RPM Low
Throttle cable at carburetor out of adjustment. Throttle control cable at automatic transmission out of adjustment. Engine performance not to specifications.

Harsh "D1-D2" UPSHIFT
Faulty 2nd clutch. 2nd accumulator defective. No 2nd ball check valve.

Engine Races in "2"
2nd clutch faulty.

UPSHIFT SPEED TOO HIGH
Governor valve faulty. Throttle cable at carburetor out of adjustment. Defective throttle valve.

JUMPS FROM "D1" TO "D3"
Defective 2-3 shift valve.

UPSHIFT TOO EARLY
"D1-D2" and "D2-D3"
Faulty governor valve. Throttle cable at carburetor out of adjustment. Defective throttle valve. Defective modulator valve.
"D1-D2"
1-2 shift valve faulty.
"D2-D3"
2-3 shift valve faulty.

KICKDOWN TOO LOW
Faulty 1-2 shift valve or 2-3 shift valve.

ENGINE RACES IN "D2-D3" SHIFT
Throttle valve "B" defective. 2nd accumulator, 3rd accumulator or orifice control valve faulty. Main orifice plugged. Faulty 3rd clutch.

ENGINE VIBRATES IN "D2-D3" SHIFT
Orifice control valve faulty or second orifice plugged.

VEHICLE CREEPS IN "N"
Low fluid level. Manual shift cable out of adjustment. Faulty 1st or 2nd clutch. Throttle cable at carburetor out of adjustment. Damaged needle bearing or thrust washer. Improper clutch clearance.

DELAYED ENGAGEMENT
From "N" to "D"
Manual shift cable out of adjustment. Faulty 1st clutch. Low orifice plugged.
From "N" to "R"
Servo shaft stuck. Manual shift cable out of adjustment. Faulty 2nd clutch.

PROBLEMS AFTER REASSEMBLY
Loud Noise in All Selector Positions
Oil pump gear installed backwards. Damaged 3rd gear. Damaged ball bearings.
Vehicle Will Not Move in Any Gear
Fluid level too low. Manual shift control out of adjustment.

HONDA 3-SPEED (Cont.)

No Forward Movement; Movement in Reverse

Faulty 1st clutch assembly. Counter shaft one-way clutch upside down.

Acceleration to 30 MPH Only

Stator assembled backwards in torque converter, or seized.

Vibration in All Gears

Torque converter not fully seated.

No Park Position

Manual shift control out of adjustment or binding. Parking pawl installed back wards.

Vehicle Has 3rd Gear Only

Faulty governor valve.

TESTING

ROAD TEST

1) Before road testing, be certain that fluid level and condition, and control linkage adjustments have been checked and corrected as necessary. During test, transmission should upshift and downshift at approximately the speeds shown in *Shift Speeds chart*. All shifts may vary somewhat due to production tolerances or tire size. The important factor is the quality of the shifts. All shifts should be smooth, responsive and with no slippage or engine speed runaway.

2) Slippage or engine runaway in any gear usually indicates clutch or sprag problems. The slipping unit in a particular gear can usually be identified by noting transmission operation in other selector positions and comparing which internal units are applied in those positions. *See Clutch and Sprag Application chart.*

3) This process of elimination can be used to detect any unit which slips, and to confirm proper operation of good units; however, the actual cause of the malfunction usually cannot be easily decided. Practically any condition can be caused by leaking hydraulic circuits

or sticking valves. Therefore, unless an obvious condition exists, do not disassemble transmission until hydraulic pressure tests have been made.

HYDRAULIC PRESSURE TESTS

1) Before performing pressure tests, be sure that fluid level and condition have been checked and corrected as necessary. With engine at normal operating temperature, connect a tachometer to engine.

2) Connect pressure gauges to the following pressure test points: line pressure port, 1st clutch pressure port, 2nd clutch pressure port and 3rd clutch pressure port. *See Fig. 5.*

Fig. 5: Pressure Test Point Locations

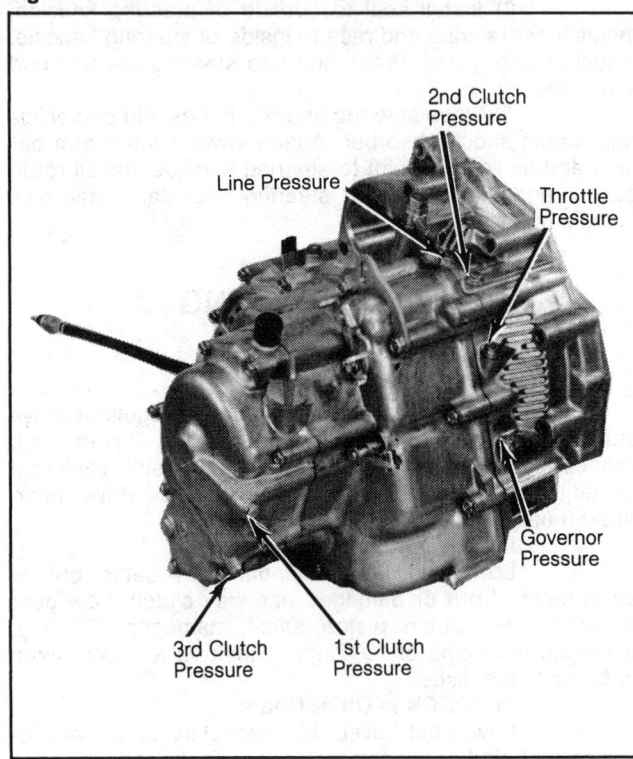

3) Raise front of vehicle so front wheels are off ground and support with safety stands. Start and run engine at 2000 RPM. Place selector lever in the following positions: "P", "N", "D", "2" and "R". Note pressure readings at each selector lever position and compare readings to Pressure Test Specifications chart.

4) If reading in "P" or "N" is not to specifications, check torque converter, oil pump pressure regulator or torque converter check valve. If reading in "D" (high gear) is not to specifications, check 3rd clutch. If reading in "D1" is not to specifications, check 1st clutch. If reading in "2" (manual), is not to specifications. Check 2nd clutch. If reading in "R" is not to specifications, check servo valve.

NOTE: Allow engine to return to idle before changing selector positions.

5) Stop engine and remove pressure gauge connections from transmission. Connect pressure gauge to throttle pressure port and disconnect throttle cable at carburetor. Start engine, place selector lever in "D" and

SHIFT SPEED SPECIFICATIONS

Application	Shift Speed (MPH)
Upshift	
Full Throttle	
1-2 Shift	
Accord & Prelude	35-40
Civic	30-38
2-3 Shift	
Accord & Prelude	60-70
Civic	57-67
Half Throttle	
1-2 Shift	17-22
2-3 Shift	30-45
Closed Throttle	
1-2 Shift	10-15
2-3 Shift	20-27
Downshift	
Full Throttle	
3-2 Shift	50-60
2-1 Shift	25-27
Closed Throttle	
3-2 Shift	15-20
2-1 Shift	5-10

HONDA 3-SPEED (Cont.)

CLUTCH AND BAND APPLICATION CHART (ELEMENTS IN USE)

Selector Lever Position	Low Clutch	Second Clutch	Third Clutch	Sprag Clutch
D — DRIVE				
First	X			X
Second	X	X		
Third	X		X	
2 — MANUAL		X		
REVERSE		X		

NEUTRAL OR PARK — All clutch and sprag clutch released and/or ineffective.

run engine at 1000 RPM. Depress accelerator pedal so throttle control lever is in full throttle position and note pressure reading. Compare reading with Pressure Test specifications chart.

    6) If throttle pressure reading in "D" is not to specifications, check throttle valve "A" or throttle modulator valve.

    7) Stop engine and remove pressure gauge from throttle pressure port and reconnect throttle cable at carburetor. Place vehicle on a chassis dynamomator or raise and support front of vehicle on safety stands. Connect pressure gauge to governor pressure port. Start engine, place selector lever in "D" and increase engine speed to 38 MPH. Note pressure reading and compare it to Pressure Test Specifications chart.

    8) If governor pressure reading was not to specifications, check governor valve.

MAIN HYDRAULIC PRESSURES

Application	psi (kg/cm²)
Line ("P", "N")	
Accord & Prelude	114-121 (8.0-8.5)
Civic	107-114 (7.5-8.0)
1st & 3rd Clutch ("D1", "D2", "D3")	
Accord & Prelude	107-121 (7.5-8.5)
Civic	100-114 97.0-8.0)
2nd Clutch ("D1", "D2", "D3")	
Accord & Prelude	107-121 (7.5-8.5)
Civic	100-114 (7.0-8.0)
Throttle (In "D")	85-88 (6.0-6.2)
Governor (In "D")	
Accord & Prelude	46-47 (3.3-3.4)
Civic	47-49 (3.5-3.6)

STALL SPEED TEST

Testing Precautions

    When making test, do not hold throttle open any longer than the time it takes to read tachometer. Maximum stall speed test time is 10 seconds. Allow engine to run at idle for at least 2 minutes in "N" to cool transmission between tests. If engine speed exceeds limits shown in Stall Speeds chart, release accelerator immediately as clutch slippage is indicated.

Testing Procedure

    With engine at normal operating temperature, connect a tachometer to engine. Start engine and set parking brake and service brakes. Place selector lever in "D". Depress accelerator briefly (6 to 8 seconds) to full throttle and note maximum RPM obtained. Allow 2 minutes for cooling and repeat test in "2" and "R". Engine speed should be within limits shown in Stall Speeds chart.

STALL SPEEDS

Application	Stall RPM
Accord, Prelude	2350-2950
Civic	2100-2700

REMOVAL & INSTALLATION

    See the appropriate article in AUTOMATIC TRANSMISSION REMOVAL Section.

TORQUE CONVERTER

Disassembly

    1) With transmission removed and torque converter pulled off stator shaft, scribe an alignment mark across edge of converter for a reference when reassembling. Remove washer and all torque converter cover-to-pump bolts. Remove torque converter washer and turbine. See Fig. 6.

    2) From stator, remove snap ring. Remove side plate then one-way clutch. Turn stator over and remove other snap ring and side plate. Remove large "O" ring from pump, then remove starter ring gear from pump.

Inspection

    Clean all parts in solvent and dry with compressed air. Blow out all passages with compressed air. Inspect all thrust surfaces for scoring and wear. Always replace "O" rings.

Reassembly

    1) On stator, install a side plate (grooved side facing out) and snap ring. Turn stator over and install one-way clutch ring. Then install cam, rollers and springs. Install second side plate (grooved side facing out) and snap ring.

    2) Using a stator shaft, check that one-way clutch will only turn in a counterclockwise direction. If one-way clutch turns clockwise or in both directions, check stator cam and rollers for proper installation. If installed properly, replace one-way clutch.

Fig. 6: Exploded View of Honda 3-Speed Automatic Transaxle Torque Converter

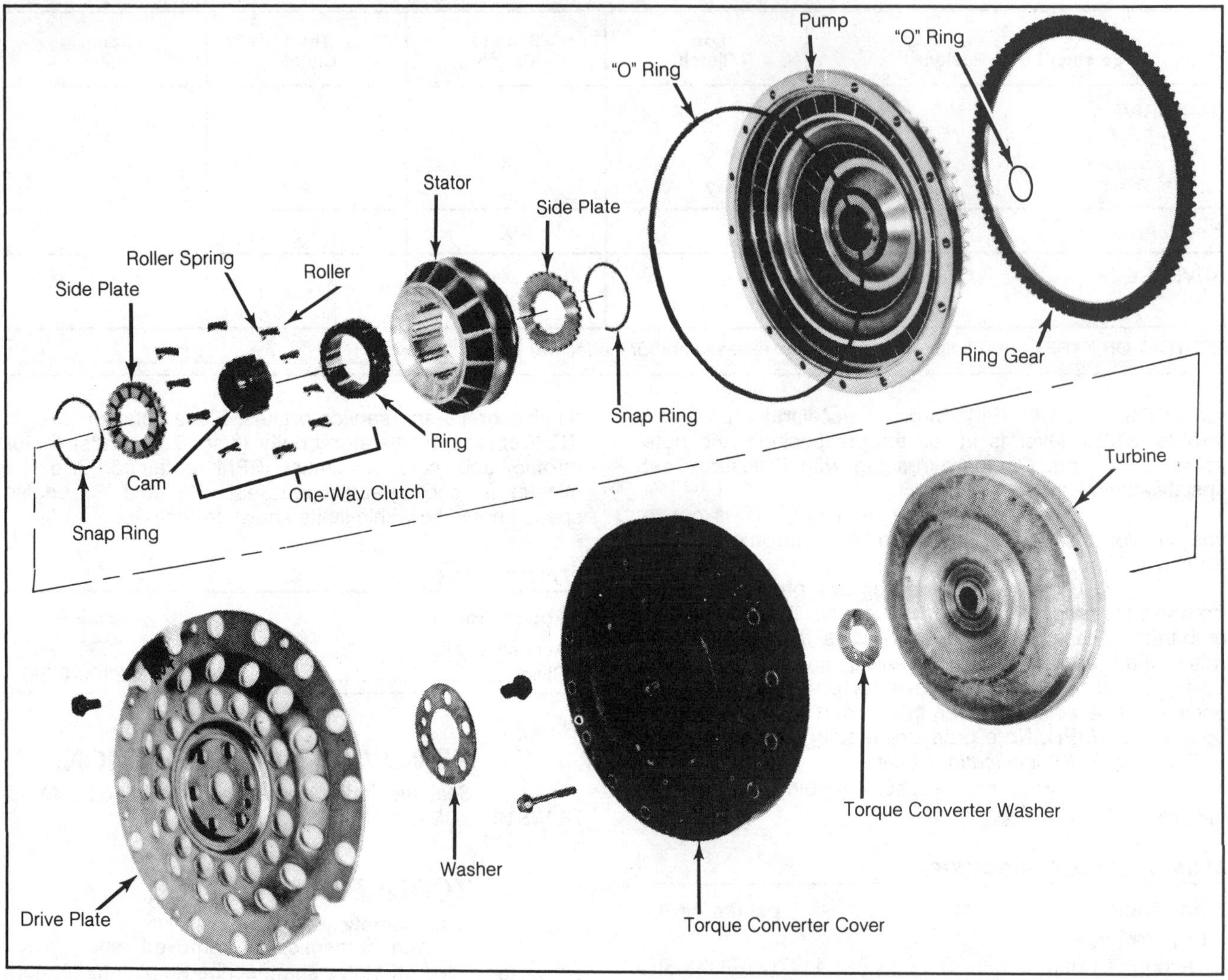

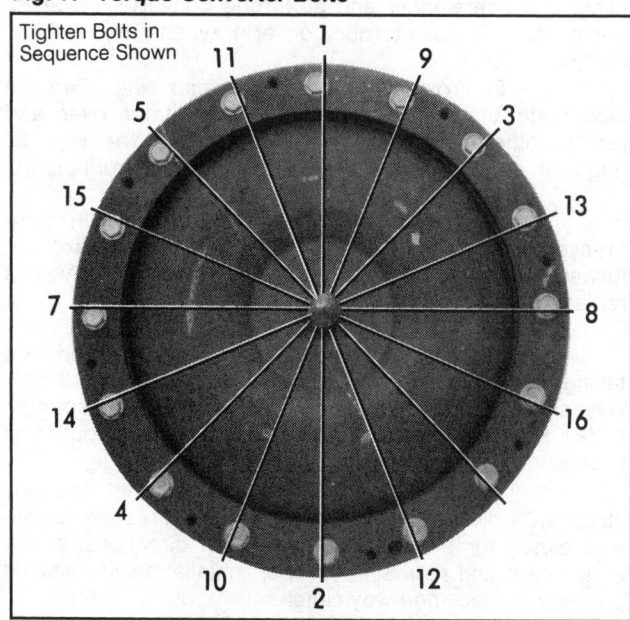

Side Plate

Roller Spring

Roller

Stator

Side Plate

Pump

"O" Ring

"O" Ring

Cam

Ring

Snap Ring

Ring Gear

One-Way Clutch

Snap Ring

Turbine

Drive Plate

Washer

Torque Converter Cover

Torque Converter Washer

Fig. 7: Torque Converter Bolts

Tighten Bolts in Sequence Shown

1
11
9
5
3
15
13
7
8
14
16
4
10
2
12

Tighten bolts in sequence shown.

3) Install new "O" rings into grooves (both sides of pump) of pump. Install stator with thin vanes facing pump, then place turbine on top of pump. Place torque converter washer on turbine.

4) Install torque converter cover on pump, make sure alignment marks (made upon disassembly) are aligned. Install ring gear with flat side towards torque converter, and tighten bolts in a star pattern. *See Fig. 7.*

TRANSAXLE DISASSEMBLY

1) Remove dipstick. Remove bolts from end cover, then remove cover. Shift transmission to "P". Lock mainshaft using holding tool (07923-6890201) as shown in *Fig. 8.*

2) Remove end cover gasket, dowel pins and "O" rings. Pry staked edge of lock nut flange out of notch in 1st clutch. Remove mainshaft lock nut (LEFT HAND thread), then remove 1st clutch. Remove 1st clutch thrust washer, needle bearing and 1st gear. Remove bearing and thrust washer from mainshaft.

3) Pry staked edge of lock nut out of notch in parking gear. Remove coutershaft lock nut and parking pawl stop pin. Remove parking pawl, shaft and spring. Remove parking gear and countershaft 1st gear as a unit.

HONDA 3-SPEED (Cont.)

Remove bearing and 1st gear collar from countershaft. Remove "O" ring and 1st gear collar from mainshaft.

Fig. 8: Locking Mainshaft Using Special Holding Tool

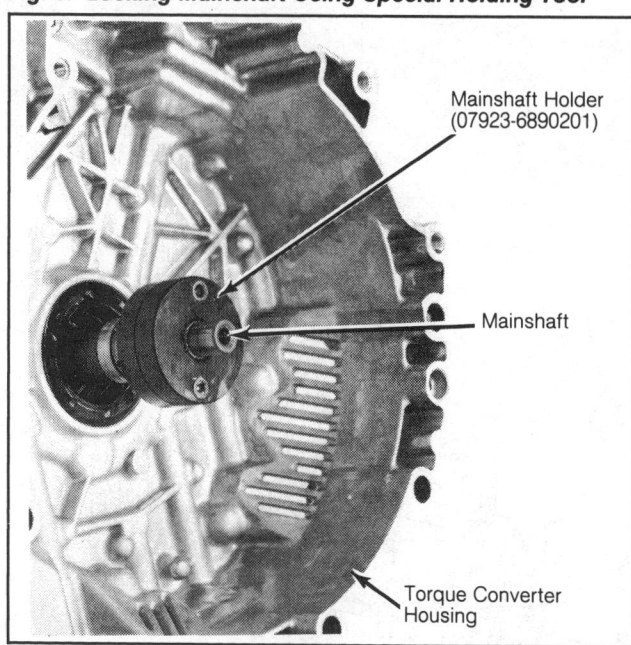

4) Remove reverse idler bearing holder. Bend down tab on lock plate under parking shift arm bolt. Remove bolt and parking shift arm. Lift out parking shift arm, then remove shift arm spring.

Fig. 9: Location of Converter Housing to Transmission Housing Bolts

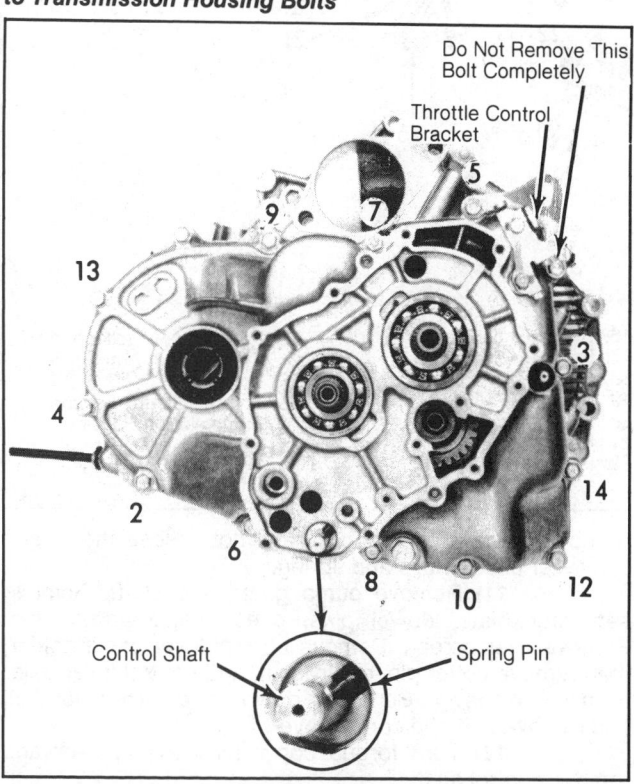

5) Bend down tab on throttle control lever bolt lock plate and remove bolt. Remove throttle control lever and spring from shaft. Remove torque converter housing-to-transmission housing bolts. *See Fig. 9.*

NOTE: Do not remove bolt number 1, just loosen enough so bolt threads are free of torque converter housing. If bolt is removed completely, throttle control bracket will have to be readjusted.

6) Align control shaft spring pin with cutout in transmission housing. Install a puller (that will bolt to transmission housing and press against the countershaft) and separate transmission housing from torque converter housing. After separating housings, remove transmission housing completely.

7) On gear side of torque converter housing, remove gasket, dowel pins and 1st and 3rd oil feed pipes. Remove reverse gear collar, needle bearing and countershaft reverse gear. Bend down tab on lock plate and remove bolt from reverse shift fork. Remove reverse shift fork and selector sleeve as a unit.

8) Remove countershaft 2nd gear. Remove mainshaft and countershaft together. To clear governor, pull shafts up at a slight angle. Bend governor tabs down and remove bolts holding governor to torque converter housing.

CAUTION: Accumulator cover is spring loaded. Hold cover down while removing bolts in a criss cross pattern.

Fig. 10: Removing Accumulator Springs from Servo Valve Body

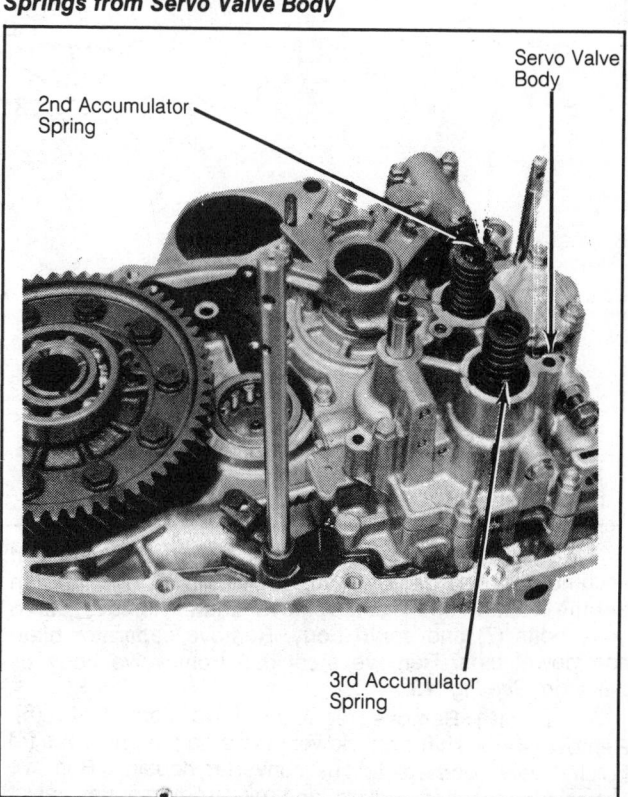

Fig. 11: Exploded View of Transmission Housing and Components

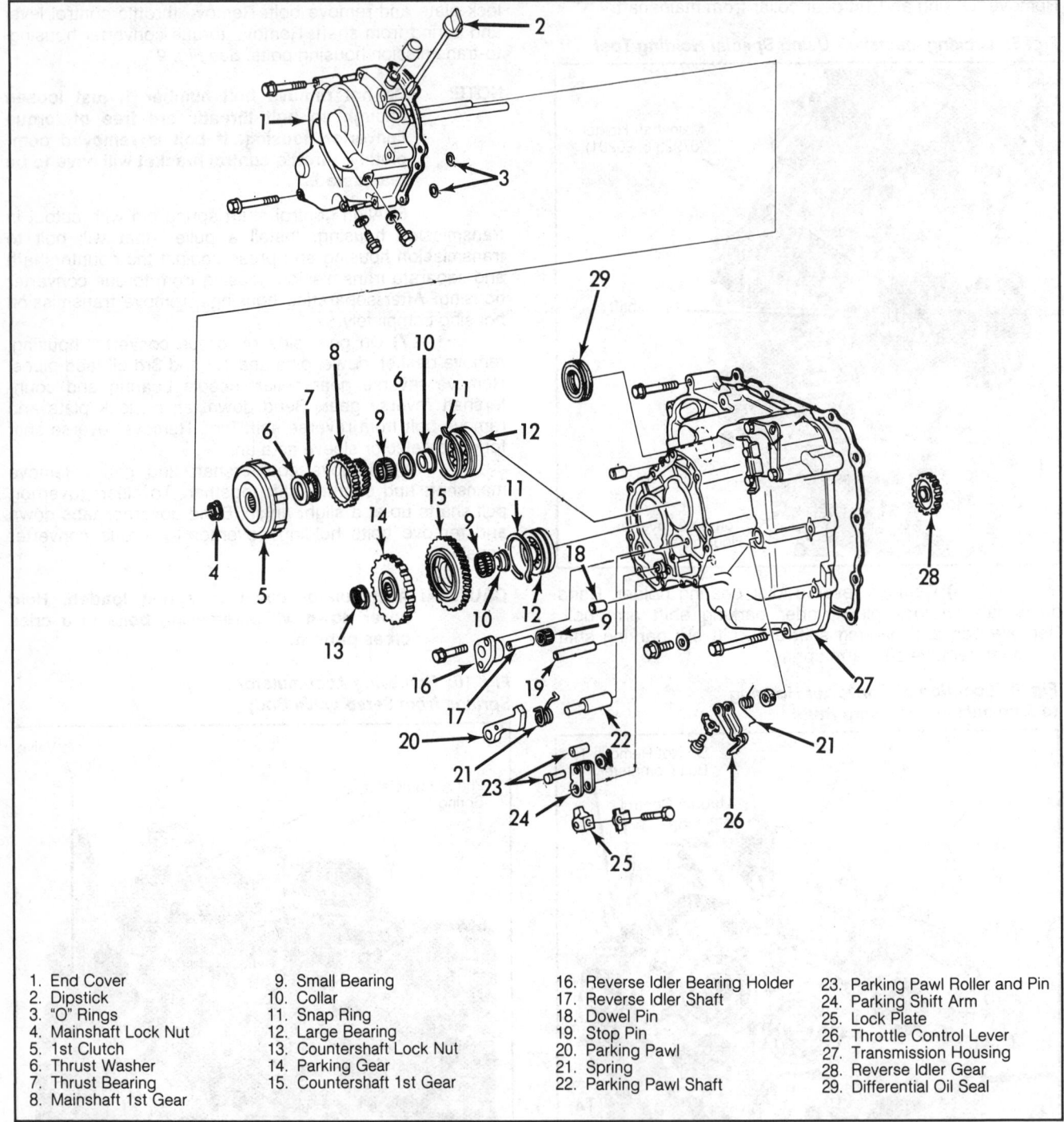

1. End Cover	9. Small Bearing	16. Reverse Idler Bearing Holder	23. Parking Pawl Roller and Pin
2. Dipstick	10. Collar	17. Reverse Idler Shaft	24. Parking Shift Arm
3. "O" Rings	11. Snap Ring	18. Dowel Pin	25. Lock Plate
4. Mainshaft Lock Nut	12. Large Bearing	19. Stop Pin	26. Throttle Control Lever
5. 1st Clutch	13. Countershaft Lock Nut	20. Parking Pawl	27. Transmission Housing
6. Thrust Washer	14. Parking Gear	21. Spring	28. Reverse Idler Gear
7. Thrust Bearing	15. Countershaft 1st Gear	22. Parking Pawl Shaft	29. Differential Oil Seal
8. Mainshaft 1st Gear			

9) Remove accumulator cover, 2nd and 3rd accumulator springs. *See Fig. 10.* Remove "E" clip from throttle control shaft and remove shaft. Remove servo body bolts (7) and servo body. Remove separator plate and dowel pins. Remove steel ball from valve body oil passage. *See Fig. 13.*

10) Remove regulator valve body bolts (6). Remove stator shift arm, dowel pins stop pin and bolts (4) holding valve body to torque converter housing. Remove cotter pin, washer, rollers and pin from manual valve.

Remove valve body, being careful not to lose the torque converter check valve and spring.

11) Remove pump gears and shaft. Remove separator plate, dowel pins, check valve and spring. Remove filter screen. Remove control lever cable holder, then remove cotter pin, control pin, and control lever roller from control lever. Bend tab down on control lever bolt and remove bolt and control lever.

12) Turn torque converter housing over and remove control shaft.

HONDA 3-SPEED (Cont.)

Fig. 12: Exploded View of Torque Converter Housing and Components

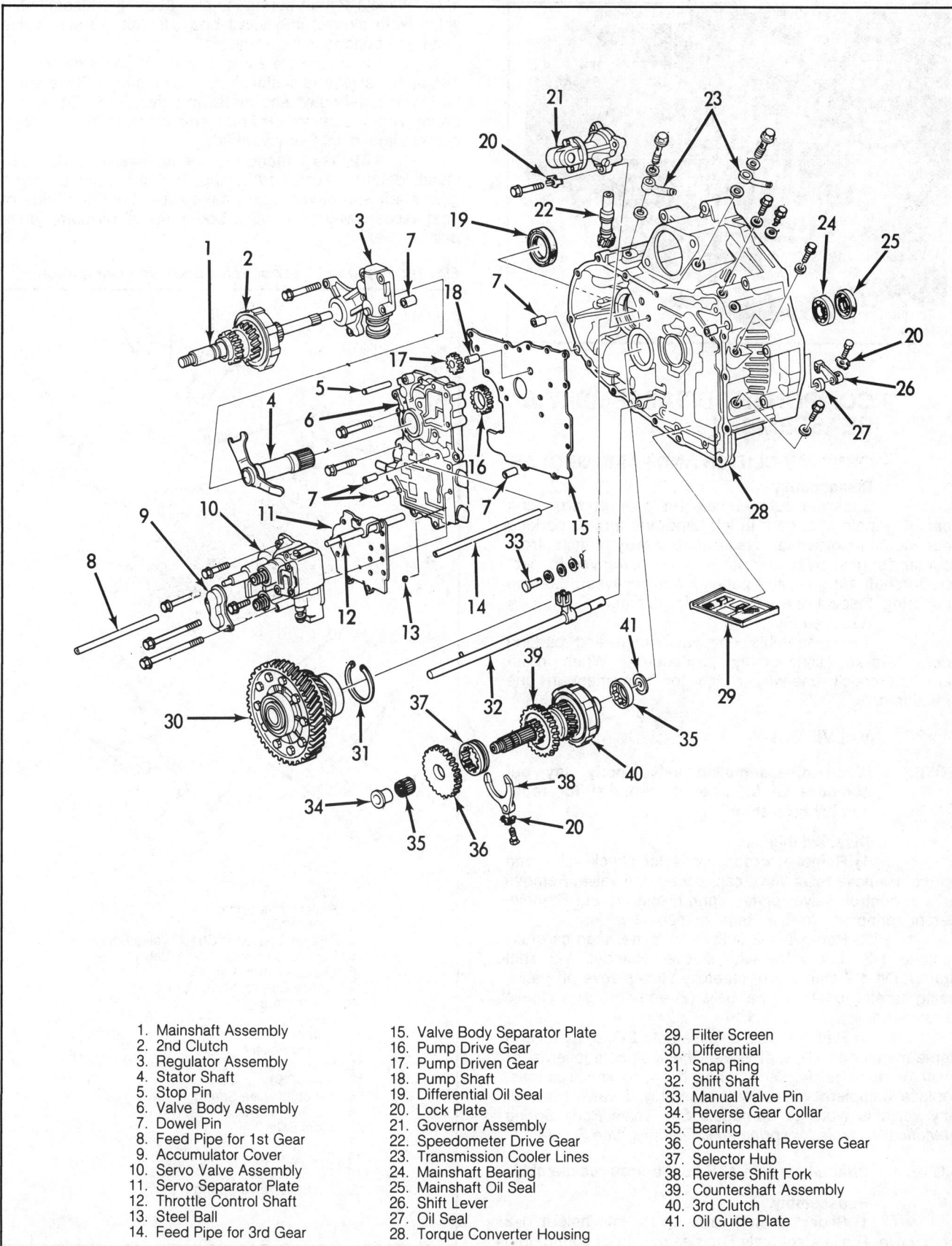

1. Mainshaft Assembly
2. 2nd Clutch
3. Regulator Assembly
4. Stator Shaft
5. Stop Pin
6. Valve Body Assembly
7. Dowel Pin
8. Feed Pipe for 1st Gear
9. Accumulator Cover
10. Servo Valve Assembly
11. Servo Separator Plate
12. Throttle Control Shaft
13. Steel Ball
14. Feed Pipe for 3rd Gear

15. Valve Body Separator Plate
16. Pump Drive Gear
17. Pump Driven Gear
18. Pump Shaft
19. Differential Oil Seal
20. Lock Plate
21. Governor Assembly
22. Speedometer Drive Gear
23. Transmission Cooler Lines
24. Mainshaft Bearing
25. Mainshaft Oil Seal
26. Shift Lever
27. Oil Seal
28. Torque Converter Housing

29. Filter Screen
30. Differential
31. Snap Ring
32. Shift Shaft
33. Manual Valve Pin
34. Reverse Gear Collar
35. Bearing
36. Countershaft Reverse Gear
37. Selector Hub
38. Reverse Shift Fork
39. Countershaft Assembly
40. 3rd Clutch
41. Oil Guide Plate

HONDA 3-SPEED (Cont.)

Fig. 13: Steel Ball Location in Servo Valve Body

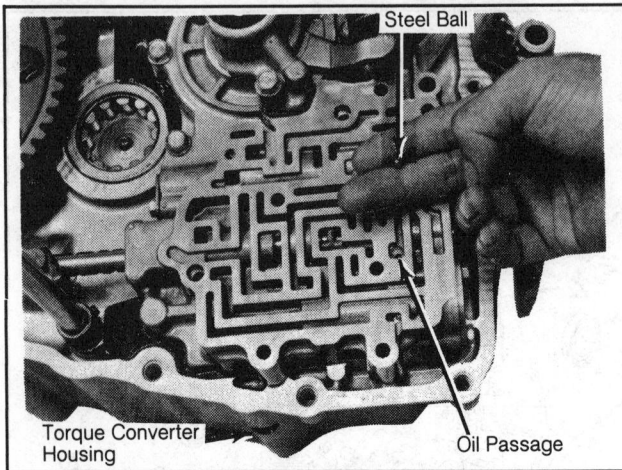

COMPONENT DISASSEMBLY & REASSEMBLY

ONE-WAY CLUTCH AND PARKING GEAR

Disassembly

Separate countershaft 1st gear from parking gear by gripping 1st gear in left hand and turning parking gear counterclockwise. Remove one-way clutch from counter 1st gear by prying out with a screwdriver. Inspect countershaft 1st gear and parking gear for wear, damage or scoring. Inspect one-way clutch for damage.

Reassembly

To reassemble one-way clutch and parking gear, reverse disassembly procedures. When reassembled, check one-way clutch for movement in one direction only.

VALVE BODY

NOTE: When disassembling valve body, lay out components in order of removal for reassembly reference.

Disassembly

1) Remove torque converter check valve and spring. Remove relief valve cap, spring and valve. Remove orifice control valve plate, spring and valve. Remove detent spring and rollers. Remove manual valve.

2) Remove 1-2 shift valve plate, then carefully remove 1-2 shift valve with sleeve. Remove 1-2 shift spring. On 1-2 shift valve, carefully slide sleeve off valve, being careful to catch steel balls (2) and spring as sleeve is removed.

3) Remove and disassemble 2-3 shift valve in same manner as 1-2 shift valve. Check all components for wear or damage. Replace spring if not to specifications, replace complete valve body assembly if valve body or any valve is worn or damaged. *See Valve Body Spring Identification table for spring specifications. See Fig. 14.*

NOTE: Coat all parts in ATF fluid before reassembly.

Reassembly

1) Slide 1-2 shift valve spring into hole in 1-2 shift valve. Press steel balls (1 on each side of spring) into

hole of shift valve and slide sleeve over shift valve and balls. Place 1-2 shift spring in valve body, then install shift valve (with sleeve) into valve body. Install 1-2 shift valve plate and bolts to valve body.

2) Assemble 2-3 shift valve in same manner as 1-2 shift valve and install it to valve body. Place relief spring in relief valve and install in valve body. Compress spring with a screwdriver and insert valve spring cap (with cutout aligned with screwdriver).

3) Install manual valve into valve body, then install detent rollers and spring. Install oil pump driven gear shaft and driven gear (make sure chamfered side of gear faces away from valve body). Install oil pump drive gear.

Fig. 14: Exploded View of Valve Body and Components

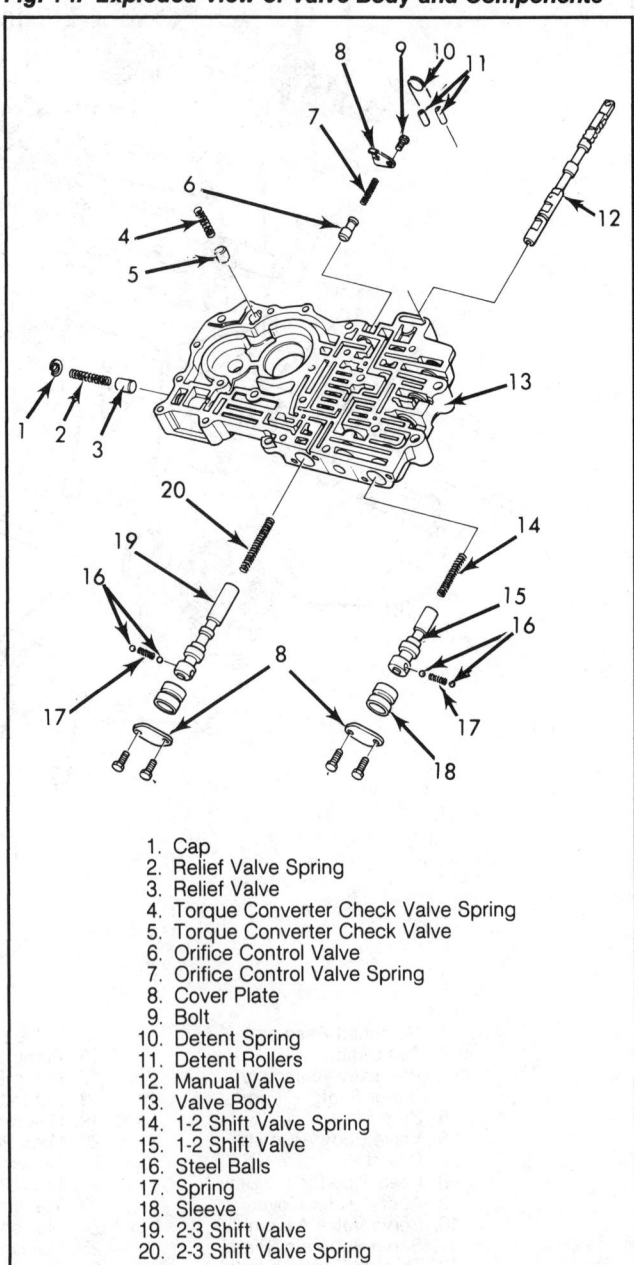

1. Cap
2. Relief Valve Spring
3. Relief Valve
4. Torque Converter Check Valve Spring
5. Torque Converter Check Valve
6. Orifice Control Valve
7. Orifice Control Valve Spring
8. Cover Plate
9. Bolt
10. Detent Spring
11. Detent Rollers
12. Manual Valve
13. Valve Body
14. 1-2 Shift Valve Spring
15. 1-2 Shift Valve
16. Steel Balls
17. Spring
18. Sleeve
19. 2-3 Shift Valve
20. 2-3 Shift Valve Spring

HONDA 3-SPEED (Cont.)

GOVERNOR, REGULATOR, SERVO & VALVE BODY SPRING IDENTIFICATION CHART

Valve Spring	Length In. (mm)	Diameter In. (mm) [1]	Number Of Coils	Wire Thickness In. (mm)
Regulator Valve Outer Spring				
Accord & Prelude	2.84 (71.8)	.59 (15.1)	15	.08 (2.0)
Civic	3.28 (83.2)	.58 (14.7)	17	.07 (1.8)
Regulator Valve Inner Spring	1.73 (44.0)	.38 (9.6)	9	.07 (1.8)
Stator Reacting Spring	1.19 (30.3)	1.51 (38.4)	2	.24 (6.0)
Torque Converter Check Valve Spring	1.53 (38.9)	.35 (8.4)	15	.04 (.9)
Throttle Modulator Valve Spring	1.20 (30.5)	.37 (9.4)	8	.05 (1.2)
Relief Valve Spring	1.86 (47.2)	.33 (8.4)	15	.03 (.8)
Governor Spring	1.11 (28.3)	.74 (18.8)	3.5	.05 (1.2)
Orifice Control Spring	1.28 (32.5)	.27 (6.8)	16	.04 (.9)
Throttle Control Valve "A" Outer Spring	.84 (21.4)	.33 (8.5)	6	.04 (1.0)
Throttle Control Valve "A" Inner Spring	1.18 (29.9)	.24 (6.2)	8	.03 (1.4)
Throttle Control Valve "B" Spring	1.20 (30.5)	.33 (8.5)	8.5	.06 (1.4)
1-2 Shift Spring	1.43 (36.3)	.28 (7.1)	17	.03 (.7)
1-2 Shift Ball Spring	.59 (15.0)	.18 (4.5)	11	.017 (.45)
2-3 Shift Spring	2.03 (51.5)	.30 (7.6)	25	.04 (1.0)
2-3 Shift Ball Spring	.61 (15.4)	.30 (7.6)	10	.02 (.5)
Accumulator Spring	3.70 (94.0)	.81 (20.6)	19.8	Oval Shape
Servo Return Spring	1.24 (31.4)	1.13 (28.6)	2.4	.10 (2.5)

[1] — Outside Diameter of spring coil.

Fig. 15: Measuring Oil Pump-to-Valve Body Gear Clearance

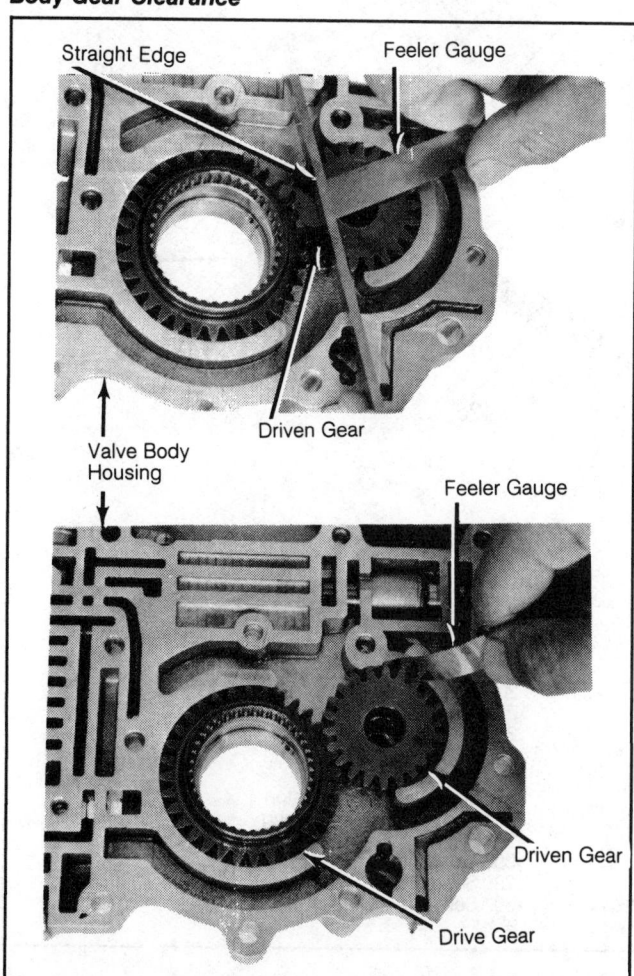

4) Measure driven gear-to-valve body thrust clearance. Clearance should be .001-.002" (.03-.05 mm). Measure side clearance of driven and drive gears. Driven gear side clearance should be .002-.004" (.05-.10 mm), drive gear side clearance should be .004-.005" (.10-.12 mm). See Fig. 15. If clearance is incorrect, check valve body for excessive wear. If wear exists, replace valve body assembly.

SERVO VALVE ASSEMBLY

NOTE: Clean all parts in solvent and blow dry with air. Replace servo valve as an assembly if any parts are worn or damaged.

Disassembly

1) Push out 2nd and 3rd accumulator pistons, then remove "O" rings. Remove servo valve and spring, then remove "O" ring from valve. Remove throttle control valve "B", then separate control valve "B" from inner and outer springs and plug. See Fig. 16.

2) Remove retainer bolt and retainer of throttle control valve "A". Remove plug, outside spring, throttle control valve "A" and inside spring. Remove throttle control cover, then separator plate. Remove oil passage pipe from valve body.

3) Remove plug and washer from servo valve body. Remove modulator valve retainer plate, spring and modulator valve. Inspect all components for wear or damage. Check springs against specifications in Valve Body Spring Identification table. Replace springs that are not to specifications or complete servo assembly if any part is worn or damaged.

NOTE: Do not remove or adjust shift adjustment bolt. Adjustment bolt is factory set and should not be changed or shift points will be changed.

Automatic Transmissions
HONDA 3-SPEED (Cont.)

Fig. 16: Exploded View of Servo Valve Assembly

Shift Point Adjusting Bolt is Factory Adjusted.
DO NOT Remove or Loosen or Shift Points will be Affected.

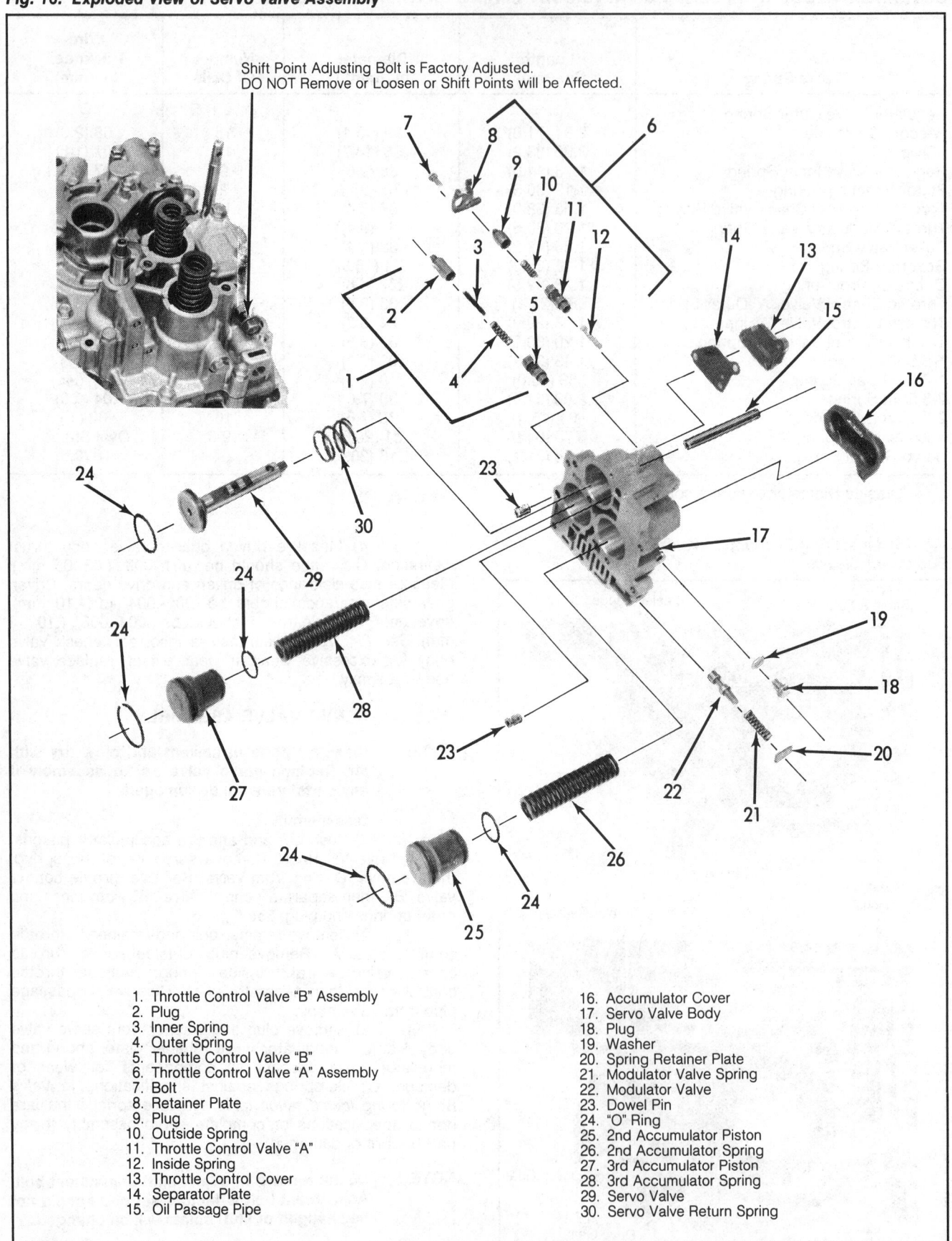

1. Throttle Control Valve "B" Assembly
2. Plug
3. Inner Spring
4. Outer Spring
5. Throttle Control Valve "B"
6. Throttle Control Valve "A" Assembly
7. Bolt
8. Retainer Plate
9. Plug
10. Outside Spring
11. Throttle Control Valve "A"
12. Inside Spring
13. Throttle Control Cover
14. Separator Plate
15. Oil Passage Pipe
16. Accumulator Cover
17. Servo Valve Body
18. Plug
19. Washer
20. Spring Retainer Plate
21. Modulator Valve Spring
22. Modulator Valve
23. Dowel Pin
24. "O" Ring
25. 2nd Accumulator Piston
26. 2nd Accumulator Spring
27. 3rd Accumulator Piston
28. 3rd Accumulator Spring
29. Servo Valve
30. Servo Valve Return Spring

HONDA 3-SPEED (Cont.)

Fig. 17: Exploded View of Governor Assembly

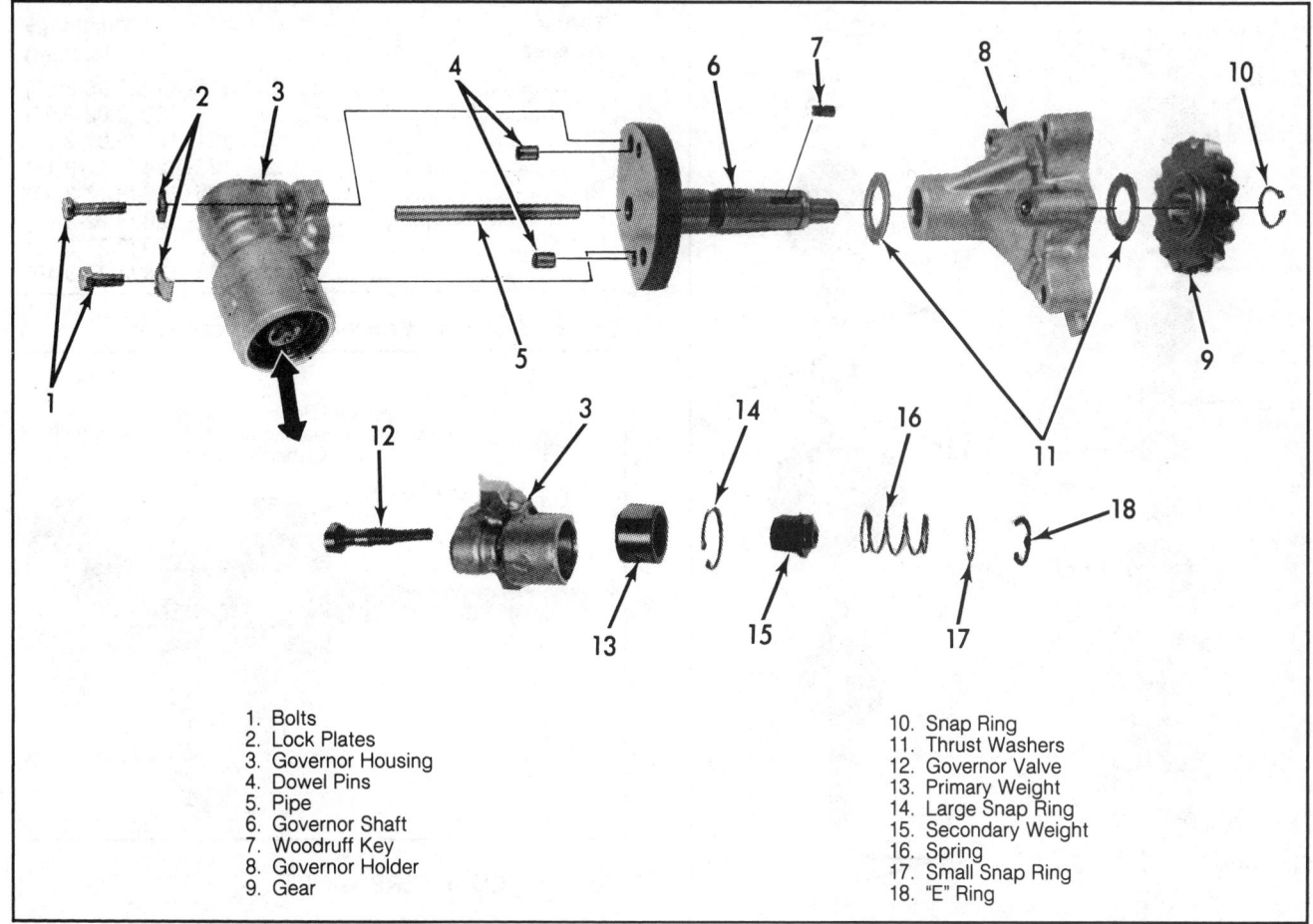

1. Bolts
2. Lock Plates
3. Governor Housing
4. Dowel Pins
5. Pipe
6. Governor Shaft
7. Woodruff Key
8. Governor Holder
9. Gear
10. Snap Ring
11. Thrust Washers
12. Governor Valve
13. Primary Weight
14. Large Snap Ring
15. Secondary Weight
16. Spring
17. Small Snap Ring
18. "E" Ring

Reasembly

To reassemble servo valve, reverse disassembly procedure and note the following. Always replace "O" rings with new ones.

GOVERNOR ASSEMBLY

NOTE: **Replace governor assembly if any part is worn or damaged, or if governor does not operate smoothly.**

Disassembly

1) Remove governor housing lock plate bolts and remove governor housing. Remove "E" ring from governor housing, then remove small snap ring, spring and secondary weight. Remove large snap ring and primary weight. Remove governor valve. *See Fig. 17.*

2) On governor holder, remove snap ring, gear and thrust washer. From governor shaft, remove pipe. Pull governor shaft out of governor holder and remove Woodruff key and thrust washer. Inspect all parts for wear or damage. Check for smooth operation of all parts.

Reassembly

To reassemble governor, reverse disassembly procedure, replace lock plates with new ones and check for smooth operation after reassembly.

REGULATOR VALVE BODY

Disassembly

Hold retainer in place (compressed) while removing lock bolt, then slowly release retainer. Remove retainer, spring seat, stator reaction spring, outer spring, inner spring and pressure regulator valve. Clean all parts and blow dry. Inspect all parts for wear or damage and replace regulator valve if any part is worn or damaged.

Reassembly

To reassemble regulator valve, reverse disassembly procedure, aligning hole in retainer with hole in valve body. Compress retainer until lock bolt can be installed.

MAINSHAFT

NOTE: **Lubricate all parts with ATF fluid during reassembly.**

Disassembly

1) From rear of mainshaft, remove snap ring, bearing, spacer collar and oil seal rings (2). From front of mainshaft, remove lock nut (LEFT HAND thread) and 1st clutch.

2) Remove thrust washer, thrust needle bearing, 1st gear, bearing, thrust washer and spacer collar. Remove bearing, 2 "O" rings, snap ring, washer, thrust needle bearing and 2nd gear.

3) Remove bearings (2), thrust needle bearing and splined thrust washer. Remove 2nd clutch and 2 "O" rings from mainshaft.

NOTE: **When installing thrust needle bearings, install unrolled edge of bearing cage facing thrust washer.**

Automatic Transmissions

HONDA 3-SPEED (Cont.)

Fig. 18: Exploded View of Mainshaft Assembly

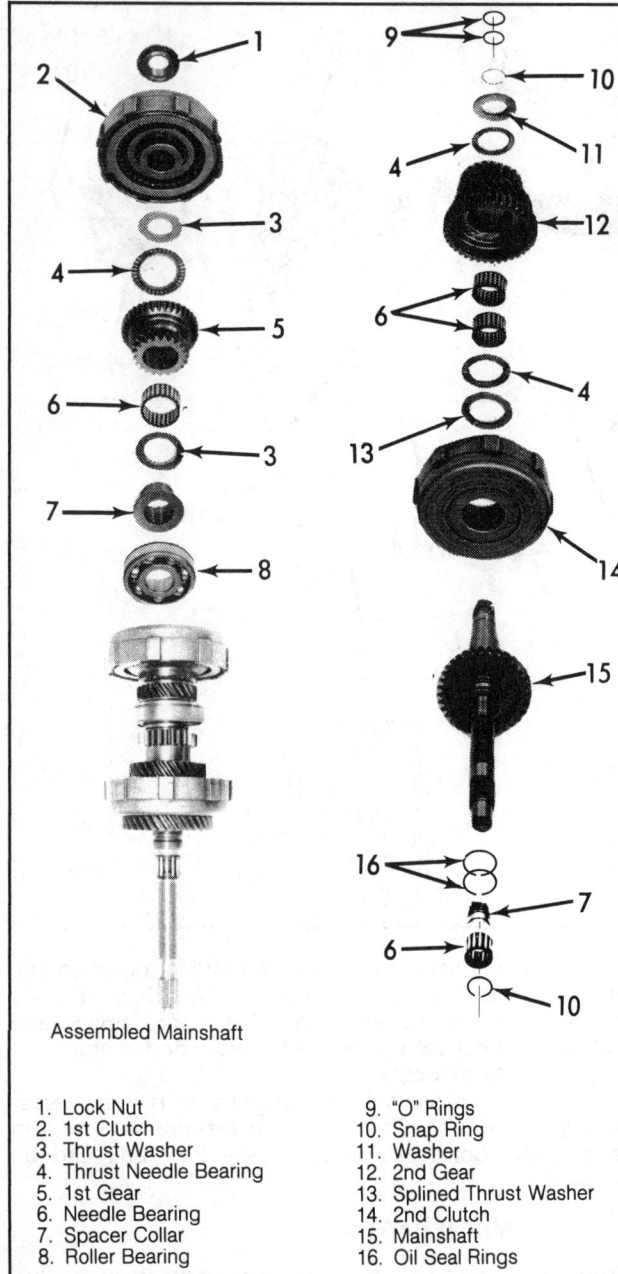

Assembled Mainshaft

1. Lock Nut
2. 1st Clutch
3. Thrust Washer
4. Thrust Needle Bearing
5. 1st Gear
6. Needle Bearing
7. Spacer Collar
8. Roller Bearing
9. "O" Rings
10. Snap Ring
11. Washer
12. 2nd Gear
13. Splined Thrust Washer
14. 2nd Clutch
15. Mainshaft
16. Oil Seal Rings

Reassembly

1) Install mainshaft bearing to transmission housing. Install 2 "O" rings to mainshaft, then install 2nd clutch. Install splined thrust washer then thrust needle bearing with unrolled edge facing thrust washer. Install 2 needle bearings and 2nd gear.

2) Install thrust needle bearing, washer and 2 "O" rings. Install roller bearing, spacer collar and thrust washer. Install needle bearing and 1st gear. Install thrust needle bearing, thrust washer, 1st clutch and lock nut.

3) With mainshaft assembled, measure clearance between thrust needle bearing and shoulder on washer. *See Fig. 19.* Clearance should be .003-.006" (.07-.15 mm), if not, select splined thrust washer of proper thickness to obtain clearance specification. *See Splined Thrust Washer Thickness chart.*

SPLINED THRUST WASHER THICKNESSES

Thrust Washer	Thickness In. (mm)
A	.116-.118 (2.95-3.00)
B	.119-.120 (3.02-3.05)
C	.121-.122 (3.07-3.10)
D	.123-.124 (3.12-3.15)
E	.125-.126 (3.17-3.20)
F	.127-.128 (3.22-3.25)
H	.129-.130 (3.27-3.30)
I	.133-.134 (3.37-3.40)

Fig. 19: Measuring Mainshaft Gear Clearance

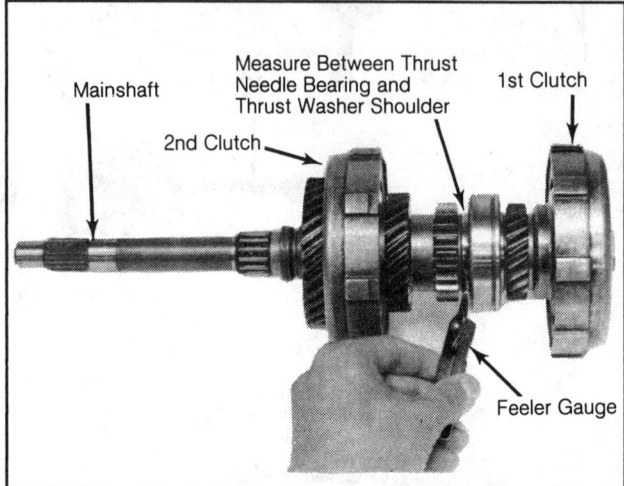

COUNTERSHAFT

NOTE: Lubricate all parts with ATF fluid during reassembly.

Disassembly

1) Remove lock nut, parking gear, 1st gear and roller bearing. Remove reverse gear collar, needle bearing and reverse gear. Remove reverse selector gear, selector hub and 2nd gear with needle bearing.

2) Remove spacer collar, thrust washer, 3rd gear and needle bearing. Remove thrust needle bearing, splined thrust washer and 3rd clutch. Remove 2 "O" rings from countershaft. Remove countershaft bearing from transmission housing.

NOTE: When installing thrust needle bearing, install unrolled edge of bearing cage facing thrust washer.

Reassembly

1) Install countershaft bearing to transmission housing. Install 2 new "O" rings to countershaft. Install splined thrust washer, thrust needle bearing and 3rd gear with needle bearing. Install thrust washer, spacer collar and 2nd gear with needle bearing.

2) Install selector hub, reverse selector gear and reverse gear with needle bearing. Install reverse gear collar, roller bearing, 1st gear, parking gear and lock nut. *See Fig. 20.*

3) With countershaft assembled, measure clearance between selector hub and shoulder on 2nd gear. *See Fig. 21.* Clearance should be .003-.006" (.07-.15

HONDA 3-SPEED (Cont.)

mm). If clearance is more than specifications, install a thrust washer of proper thickness to achieve correct clearance. *See Thrust Washer Thickness chart.*

THRUST WASHER THICKNESSES

Thrust Washer	Thickness In. (mm)
A	.089-.090 (2.27-2.30)
B	.091-.092 (2.32-2.35)
C	.093-.094 (2.37-2.40)
D	.095-.096 (2.42-2.45)
E	.097-.098 (2.47-2.50)
F	.099-.100 (2.52-2.55)
G	.101-.102 (2.57-2.60)

Fig. 20: Exploded View of Countershaft Assembly

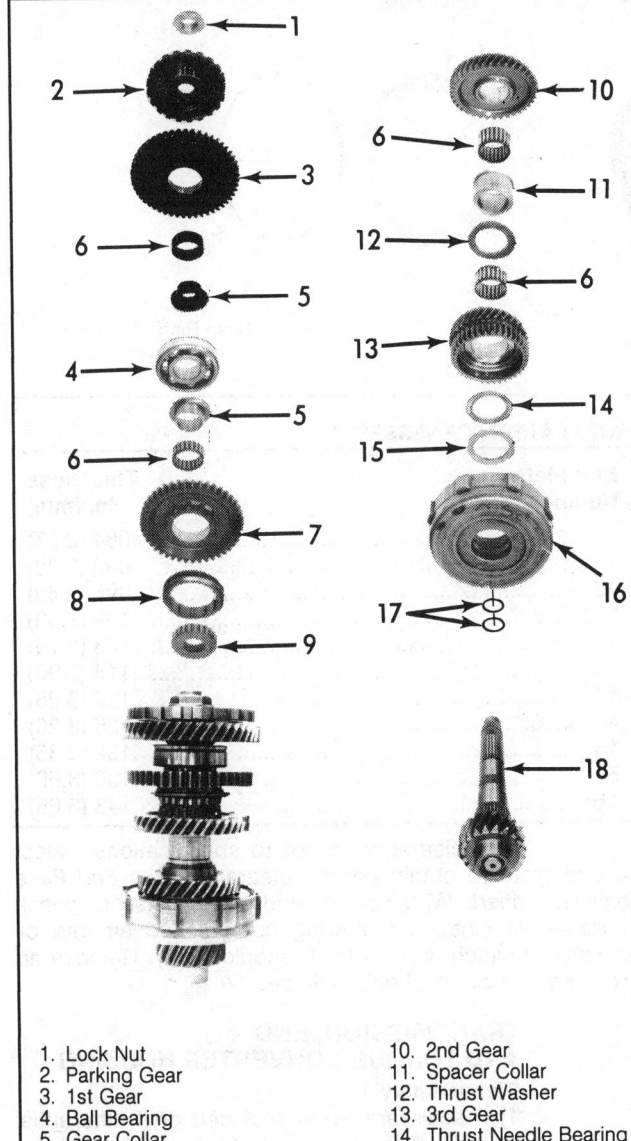

1. Lock Nut
2. Parking Gear
3. 1st Gear
4. Ball Bearing
5. Gear Collar
6. Needle Bearing
7. Reverse Gear
8. Reverse Selector Gear
9. Selector Hub
10. 2nd Gear
11. Spacer Collar
12. Thrust Washer
13. 3rd Gear
14. Thrust Needle Bearing
15. Splined Thrust Washer
16. 3rd Clutch
17. "O" Rings
18. Countershaft

4) Leave feeler gauge of .003-.006" (.07-.15 mm) thickness (standard 2nd gear clearance) installed

Fig. 21: Measuring Countershaft 2nd Gear Clearance

between selector hub and 2nd gear, then install another feeler gauge between thrust washer and shoulder of 3rd gear to measure 3rd gear clearance. *See Fig. 22.* Clearance should be .003-.006" (.07-.15 mm).

5) If clearance is not to specifications, install a splined thrust washer of proper thickness. *Refer to Splined Thrust Washer Thickness chart used in determining mainshaft 2nd gear clearance.*

Fig. 22: Measuring Countershaft 3rd Gear Clearance

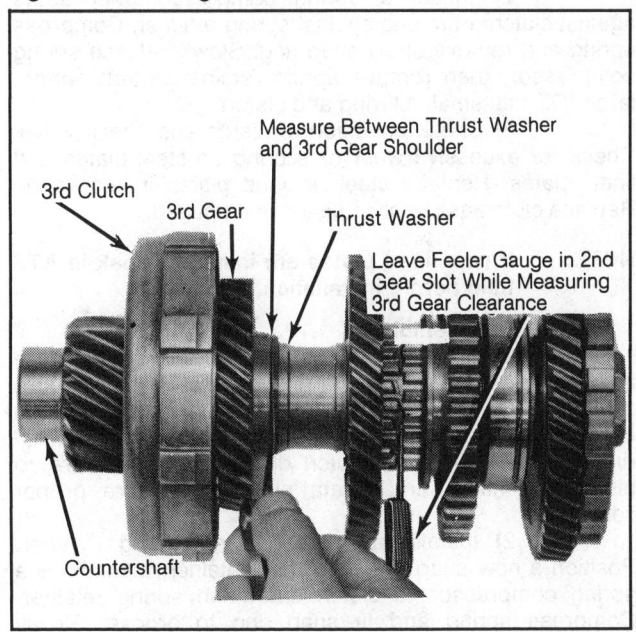

CLUTCH ASSEMBLIES

NOTE: 1st, 2nd and 3rd clutches are identical.

Disassembly

1) Remove large snap ring retaining end plate and clutches. Remove end plate and clutch pack, keep steel plates and lined plates in order removed. *See Fig. 23.*

Fig. 23: Exploded View of 1st, 2nd and 3rd Clutch Assemblies

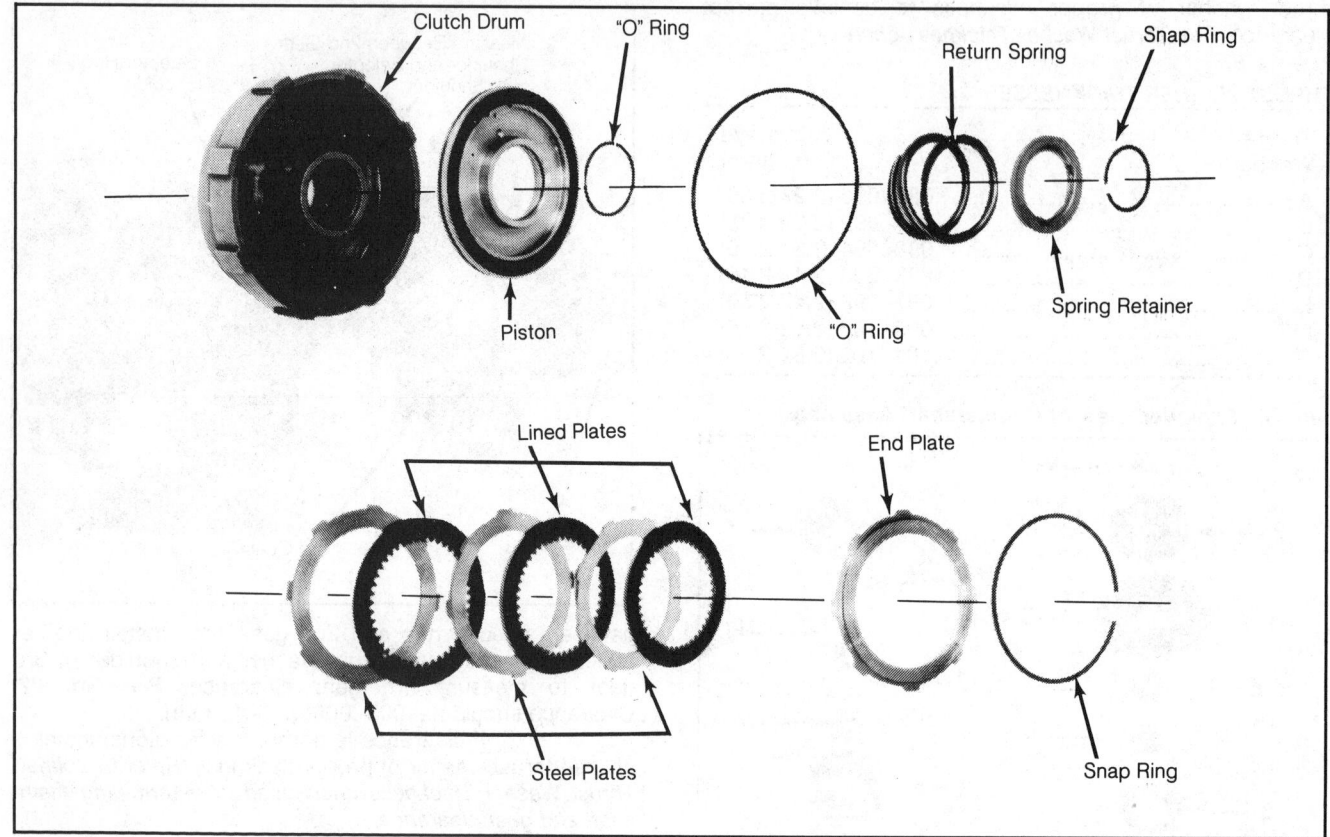

2) Install a spring compressor that seats against clutch drum and against spring retainer. Compress spring and remove small snap ring. Slowly release spring compressor, then remove spring retainer, return spring, large "O" ring, small "O" ring and piston.

3) Check condition of piston and check valve. Check for excessive wear or scoring on steel plates and lined plates. Replace steel or lined plates if necessary. Replace clutch assembly if piston is damaged.

NOTE: If new lined plates are installed, soak in ATF fluid before installation.

Reassembly
1) Lubricate all parts with ATF fluid before assembling. Install new "O" ring on piston. Make sure clutch piston spring washer is installed with high side facing away from clutch drum. Install piston (lubricate "O" ring with ATF fluid) to clutch drum. Apply pressure to piston (by hand) and rotate piston to ensure proper seating.

2) Install return spring and spring retainer. Position a new snap ring on spring retainer, then install a spring compressor to clutch drum and spring retainer. Compress spring and fit snap ring to groove. Slowly release spring compressor and make sure snap ring seats properly.

3) Install clutch pack, starting with a steel plate and alternating with lined plates, ending with the end plate. Install large snap ring to clutch drum. Measure clearance between end plate and lined plate. Clearance should be .016-.028" (.4-.7 mm).

END PLATE THICKNESSES

End Plate Number	Thickness In. (mm)
11	.084 (2.15)
1	.090 (2.30)
12	.096 (2.45)
2	.102 (2.60)
13	.108 (2.75)
3	.114 (2.90)
14	.120 (3.05)
4	.126 (3.20)
15	.132 (3.35)
5	.138 (3.50)
16	.143 (3.65)

4) If clearance is not to specifications, select an end plate to obtain correct clearance. *See End Plate Thickness chart.* With correct end plate installed, check operation of clutch by blowing compressed air into oil passage in clutch drum. Clutch should apply. Remove air pressure and clutch should release.

TRANSMISSION, END AND TORQUE CONVERTER HOUSING
Disassembly
1) If seals are to be replaced or if differential needs repair, lift differential out of torque converter housing. Remove differential seal snap ring and drive seal out.

2) On end cover, remove snap rings to feed pipes "A" and "B". Remove feed pipes with collars, then remove pins and collars from feed pipes. *See Fig. 24*

HONDA 3-SPEED (Cont.)

Fig. 24: Exploded View of End Housing Assembly

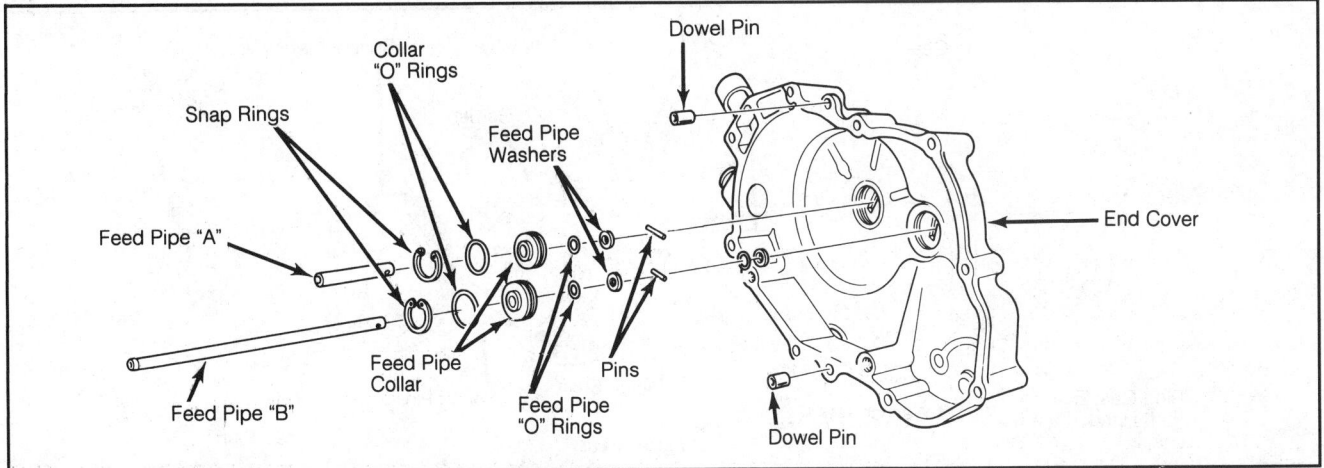

3) On torque converter housing, drive in oil seals and bearings from mainshaft and countershaft. On transmission housing, expand snap rings (do not remove) and push bearings out by hand. Push out idler gear shaft and bearing from inside transmission housing then remove idler gear.

Reassembly

1) Install idler gear, then idler gear shaft and bearing to transmission housing. Expand mainshaft and countershaft bearing snap rings and install bearings to transmission housing. On torque converter housing, drive mainshaft and countershaft bearings and seals into housing.

2) On end housing, install feed pipe "O" rings, collars and washers to feed pipes. Install pins to feed pipes and install feed pipes to end cover. Install snap rings retaining feed pipes.

NOTE: Make sure lugs on feed pipe collars are aligned with slots in end cover housing.

3) To detemine side clearance of differential to transmission, temporarily install snap ring to converter housing (do not install oil seal at this time). Install differential to converter housing.

4) Install mainshaft and countershaft to converter housing. Install new gasket to converter housing, install dowel pins and install transmission housing to converter housing. Install and tighten converter housing-to-transmission bolts.

5) Make sure differential is bottomed in transmission housing, then use a feeler gauge to check clearance between snap ring and outer race of bearing in converter housing. Clearance should be .006" (.15 mm) maximum. If clearance is not to specifications, select snap ring to give proper clearance. *See Side Clearance Snap Ring Thickness chart.*

SIDE CLEARANCE SNAP RING THICKNESSES

Snap Ring	Thickness In. (mm)
1	.096 (2.45)
2	.100 (2.55)
3	.104 (2.65)
4	.108 (2.75)
5	.112 (2.85)
6	.116 (2.95)

6) Disassemble temporarily assembled transmission and install oil seal and correct snap ring to converter housing. Install differential and snap ring to converter housing.

DIFFERENTIAL

Disassembly

1) With differential removed from torque converter housing, place differential in "V" blocks. Install both axle shafts, check backlash of both pinion gears. Backlash should be .002-.006" (.05-.15 mm). *See Fig. 25.* If backlash is not to specifications, disassemble differential and install new thrust washers to obtain correct backlash.

2) Using a bearing puller, remove bearings from both sides of differential. Remove speedometer gear snap ring and speedometer gear. Remove bolts retaining ring gear to carrier and remove ring gear.

CAUTION: Ring gear bolts have left hand threads.

Fig. 25: Checking Backlash of Differential

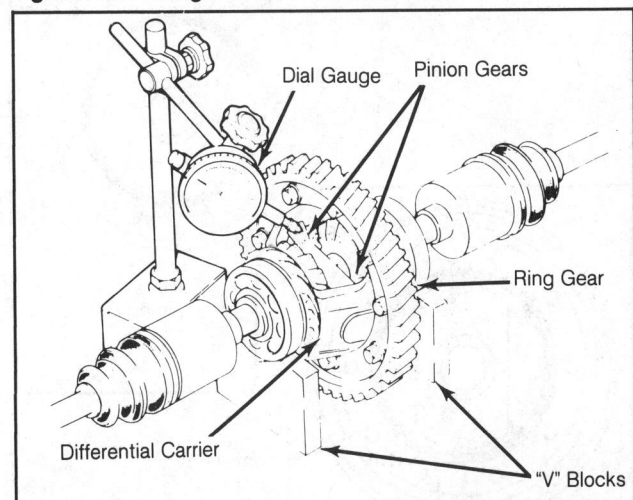

3) Drive out spring pin that retains pinion shaft and remove pinion shaft, pinion gears, side gears and thrust washers. Wash all components and check for excessive wear or damage.

Reassembly

1) Install side gears in differential carrier. Install pinion gears and mesh with side gears. Install

Fig. 26: *Exploded View of Differential Assembly*

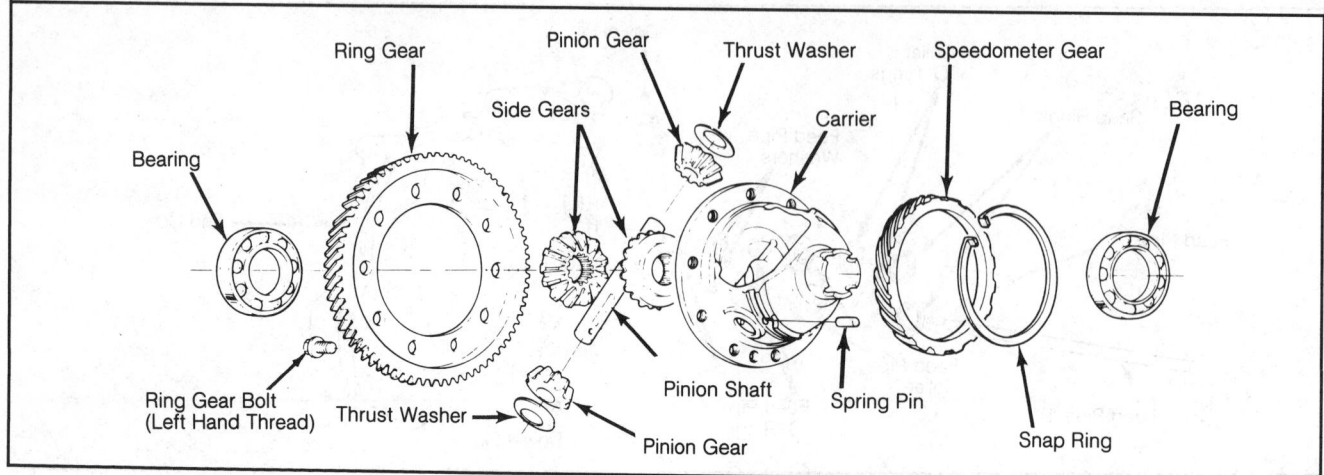

thrust washers of equal and proper thickness to obtain correct backlash. *See Thrust Washer Thickness chart.* Install pinion shaft while rotating gears to align holes in gears with hole in carrier. Align hole in pinion shaft with hole in carrier and install spring pin. *See Fig. 26.*

THRUST WASHER THICKNESSES

Thrust Washer	Thickness In. (mm)
1	.028 (.7)
2	.031 (.8)
3	.035 (.9)
4	.040 (1.0)

Fig. 27: *Installation of Snap Ring on Differential Carrier*

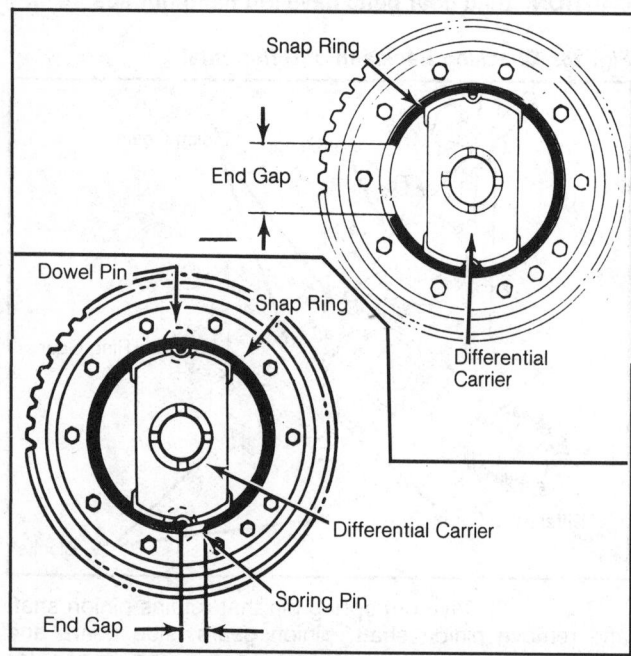

2) With differential assembled with new thrust washers, again measure backlash. If backlash is still not to specifications, replace both pinion gears and recheck

backlash. If still not to specifications, replace both side gears and recheck backlash. If still out of specifications, replace complete carrier assembly.

3) Install bearings to carrier. Install speedometer gear (with chamfer facing carrier) and install snap ring. Make sure snap ring ends do not align with carrier bearing support. *See Fig. 27.*

4) Install ring gear to carrier with chamfer on inside diameter of ring gear facing carrier. Install ring gear bolts (left hand threads) and tighten.

TRANSAXLE REASSEMBLY

NOTE: **Lubricate all parts with ATF fluid during reassembly.**

1) Install differential assembly. Assemble manual valve lever on control shaft, then install torque converter housing. Install control lever and new lock plate on other end of control shaft, install and tighten bolt. Bend tab of lock plate up to prevent bolt from turning.

2) Install new filter screen in converter housing. Install separator plate, dowel pin, oil pump gears and shaft. Make sure chamfered side of driven gear and shouldered side of drive gear is facing down. Install check valve and spring, then install valve body on converter housing.

3) Install and tighten valve body bolts. Install stator shaft arm, stop pin and dowel pins. Install regulator valve. Install steel ball in valve body oil passage. *Refer to Fig. 13.* Install separator plate, throttle control shaft and dowel pins.

4) Install servo. Ensure correct length bolt is installed or servo will not seal to housing. *See Fig. 28.* Place a roller on each side of manual valve stem, then attach valve to lever with pin. Secure with cotter pin.

5) Install 2nd and 3rd accumulator spring in servo body. *Refer to Valve Body Spring Identification chart for accumulator spring diameters and lengths.* Install accumulator cover; compress accumulator springs before tightening bolts.

6) Install governor valve, using new lock plates, then bend lock plate tabs over so bolts will not turn. Install mainshaft and countershaft in converter housing, as an assembly.

HONDA 3-SPEED (Cont.)

Fig. 28: Installation of Servo-to-Converter Housing Showing Attaching Bolt Lengths

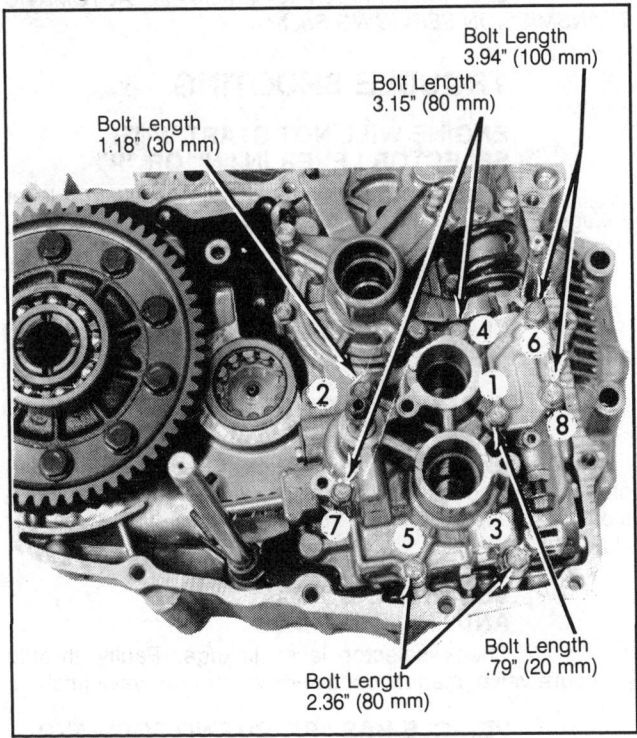

NOTE: Do not tap on shaft ends to force shafts to seat.

7) Remove lock nuts from mainshaft and countershaft, if installed, then install countershaft 2nd gear and reverse selector sleeve with reverse shift fork (assembled before installation). Groove on selector sleeve faces down.

Fig. 29: Transmission Housing-to-Converter Housing Bolt Tightening Sequence

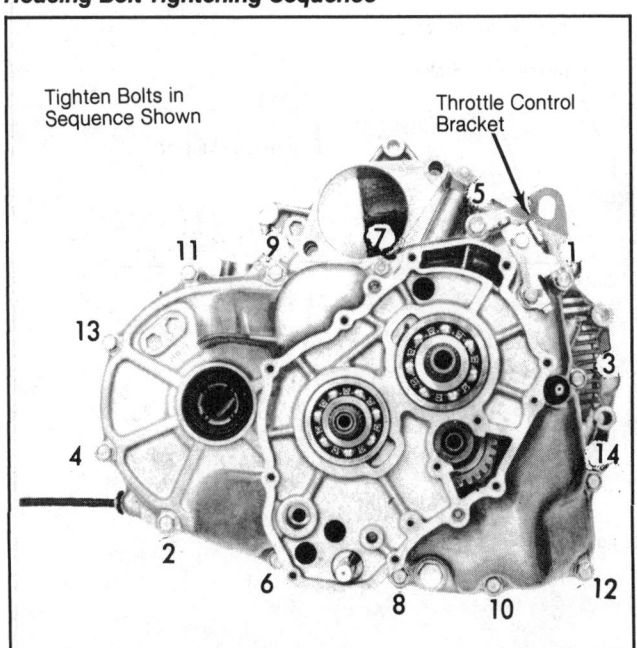

8) Install reverse shift fork over servo valve stem and align hole in stem with hole in fork. Install bolt and new lock plate. Bend tab on lock plate so bolt will not turn. Install countershaft reverse gear, needle bearing and reverse gear collar. Install gasket and 2 dowel pins in converter housing.

9) Place transmission housing on converter housing and install oil feed pipes. Make sure throttle control shaft aligns with hole in converter housing. Tighten bolts in 2 steps in order shown in *Fig. 29*.

10) Install control lever and spring on control shaft, then install bolt and new lock plate. Bend tab against bolt. Install parking shift arm and spring on shift shaft, use new lock tab and bend tab against bolt.

NOTE: Parking shift arm spring should put clockwise tension on shift arm, forcing it against stop pin.

11) Install 1st gear collar and needle bearing on countershaft. Install reverse idler bearing holder then install "O" rings to mainshaft. Install countershaft 1st gear and parking gear on countershaft. Install stop pin, parking pawl shaft, parking pawl and pawl release spring. Spring should put clockwise tension on pawl, forcing it away from parking gear.

12) Shift lever to "P" and install mainshaft holder. Install new countershaft lock nut. Stake lock nut flange into gear groove. Install needle bearing and thrust washer on mainshaft. Install 1st gear, needle bearing and thrust washer on mainshaft.

13) Install 1st clutch on the mainshaft. Attach mainshaft holder from underside of converter housing, then install new mainshaft lock nut. Stake lock nut to groove in 1st clutch.

14) Install gasket, dowel pins and "O" rings on transmission housing. Install end cover and bolts. Install dipstick, coller fittings. Do not tighten cooler fittings until transmission is installed in vehicle.

TIGHTENING SPECIFICATIONS

Application	Ft. Lbs. (N.m)
Converter Hsg.-to-Engine	
8 mm	20 (27)
10 mm	28 (39)
Countershaft Lock Nut	25 (34)
Mainshaft Lock Nut	25 (34)
Ring Gear Bolts	54 (73)
Stabilizer Bar	28 (38)
Starter Bolts	33 (45)
Torque Rods	54 (73)
Transmission Mounting Bolts	33 (45)
Transmission-to-Converter Hsg.	20 (27)

	INCH Lbs. (N.m)
Valve Body	106 (12)
Regulator Body	106 (12)
Governor Body	106 (12)
Ring Gear-to-Converter	106 (12)

Automatic Transmissions

JATCO L3N71B & 3N71B

Model L3N71B
Datsun/Nissan
  200SX
  210
  Maxima
Mazda
  GLC Wagon
  626

Model 3N71B
Courier
Datsun/Nissan
  280ZX
  Pickup
Mazda
  RX7

TRANSMISSION IDENTIFICATION

Transmission type may be identified by a group of numbers stamped into transmission case casting on left side; characters correspond to transmission type: L3N71B or 3N71B. Transmission model may be identified by metal plate attached to right side of transmission case. Plate lists model code and serial number.

DESCRIPTION

The JATCO (Japan Automatic Transmission Company) L3N71B and 3N71B transmissions are 3-speed units, consisting basically of a 3 element torque converter and 2 planetary gear sets. The primary difference between the 2 models is that the L3N71B uses a lock-up type torque converter while the 3N71B uses a conventional type converter.

Two multiple disc clutches, 1 multi-disc brake, 1 brake band, and a one-way clutch provide the friction elements required to obtain the desired function of planetary gear sets. The hydraulic system, pressurized by a gear-type pump, provides working pressure required to operate friction elements and automatic controls.

LUBRICATION & ADJUSTMENT

See the appropriate article in AUTOMATIC TRANSMISSION SERVICING Section.

TROUBLE SHOOTING

ENGINE WILL NOT START WITH SELECTOR LEVER IN "N" OR "P"

Check ignition system. Adjust selector lever linkage. Check inhibitor switch and wiring.

ENGINE STARTS IN POSITIONS OTHER THAN "N" OR "P"

Check selector lever linkage, inhibitor switch and wiring.

SHARP SHOCK WHEN SHIFTED FROM "N" TO "D"

High engine idle RPM. Check vacuum diaphragm and hoses. Faulty throttle valve. Check transmission oil pressure. Faulty manual control valve or rear clutch.

VEHICLE HAS "2", "1", AND "R", BUT NO "D"

Check selector lever linkage. Faulty throttle pressure valve, manual control valve, or one-way clutch.

VEHICLE HAS "R", BUT NO FORWARD GEARS. TRANSMISSION SLIPS BADLY, POOR ACCELERATION

Check oil level and adjust selector lever. Faulty throttle pressure valve, manual control valve, rear clutch, or oil passage leak.

Fig. 1: Cutaway View of Jatco Automatic Transmission

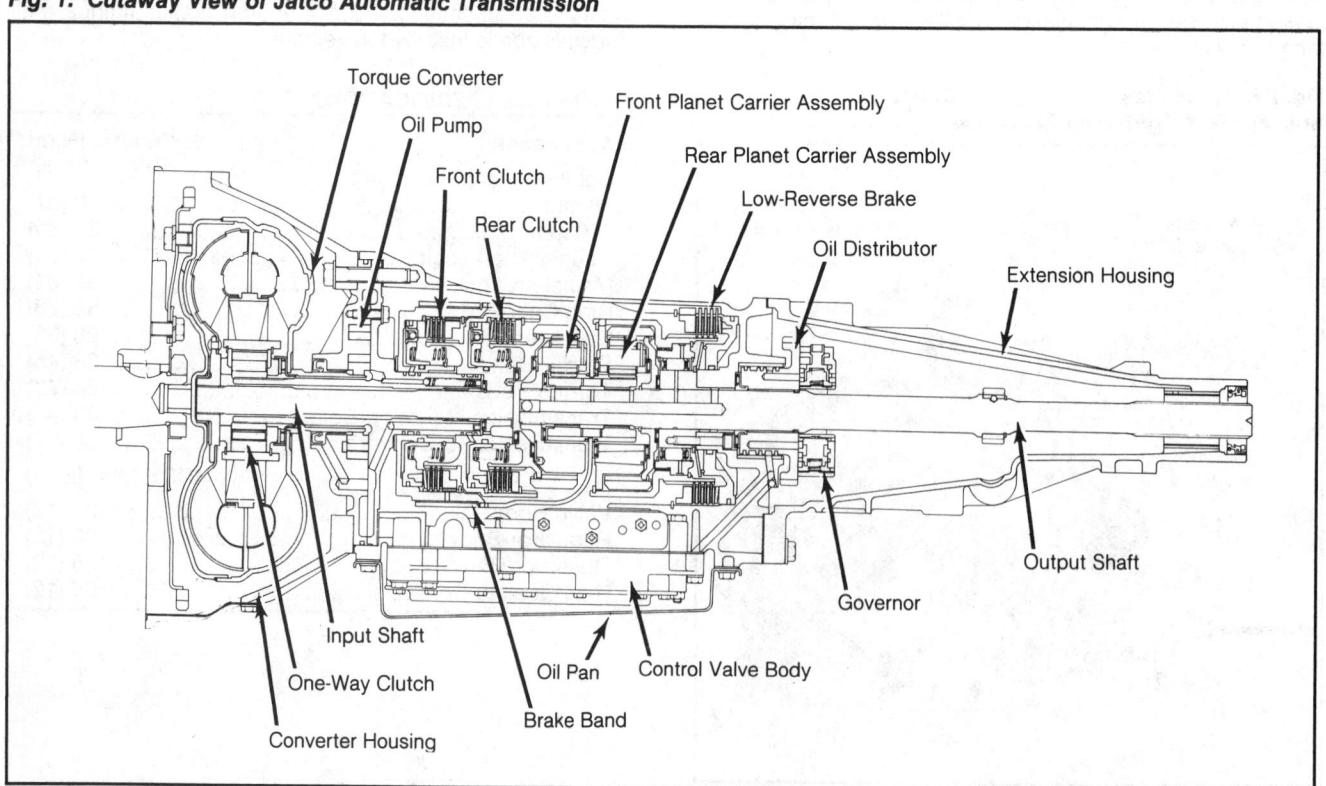

JATCO L3N71B & 3N71B (Cont.)

NO MOVEMENT IN ANY RANGE

Check oil level. Adjust selector lever linkage. Faulty throttle pressure valve, manual control valve, rear clutch, or oil passage leak. Park linkage failure.

SLIPPAGE OF CLUTCHES OR BRAKES WHEN STARTING AWAY

Check oil level. Faulty throttle valve pressure, manual control valve, vacuum diaphragm. Check hoses. Faulty oil pump or oil passage leak.

VEHICLE MOVES IN "N" OR "P"

Adjust selector linkage. Check oil level. Faulty manual control valve or rear clutch.

POOR ACCELERATION, VEHICLE WILL NOT ATTAIN TOP SPEED

Check oil level and selector lever linkage. Faulty throttle pressure valve. Incorrect stall RPM. Faulty band servo, manual control valve, engine or brakes. Low-reverse brake, band brake, rear clutch, front clutch or oil pump faulty or damaged.

VEHICLE BRAKES WHEN SHIFTED INTO "R"

Check oil level and transmission pressure. Faulty band servo, rear clutch, band brake, or "P" linkage.

VEHICLE HAS EXCESSIVE "CREEP"

Adjust idle RPM.

VEHICLE WILL NOT "CREEP"

Check oil level and selector lever adjustment. Adjust engine idle RPM. Faulty manual control valve, oil pump, oil passage leakage, rear clutch, or front clutch.

NO SHIFT FROM 2ND TO 3RD

Check selector lever linkage, vacuum diaphragm and hoses. Faulty downshift solenoid, kickdown switch or wiring. Check oil level. Defective manual control valve or governor valve. Check line and governor pressure. Faulty band servo, band brake or oil passage leak.

NO SHIFT FROM 1ST TO 2ND IN "D"

Adjust selector linkage. Check vacuum diaphragm and hose. Inspect downshift solenoid, kickdown switch and wiring. Check oil level. Faulty manual control valve, governor valve, or inadequate transmission pressure. Defective band servo, front clutch, oil passage leakage or front clutch check ball.

1-2 AND 2-3 SHIFT POINTS TOO HIGH IN "D"

Check vacuum diaphragm and hoses. Check downshift solenoid, kickdown switch and wires. Faulty oil pressure. Check oil drain. Defective manual control valve, governor valve or leak in hydraulic passages.

SHIFTS FROM 1ST TO 3RD, SKIPS 2ND

Check oil drain. Faulty manual control valve. Faulty governor valve or brake band. Leak in hydraulic passages.

SHIFT SHOCK FROM 1ST TO 2ND

Faulty vacuum diaphragm and hoses. Excessive engine RPM. Check oil quantity. Faulty manual control valve, band servo, or band brake.

SHIFT SHOCK FROM 2ND TO 3RD

Faulty vacuum diaphragm and hoses. Defective downshift solenoid, kickdown switch and wiring. Check oil pressure. Faulty manual control valve or band servo. Check oil level.

LITTLE OR NO SHIFT SHOCK. EXCESS SLIPPAGE FROM 1ST TO 2ND

Check oil level and pressure. Adjust selector lever. Check vacuum diaphragm and hoses. Make oil drain check. Faulty manual control valve. Faulty band servo, brake band or hydraulic passage leakage.

LITTLE OR NO SHIFT SHOCK. EXCESSIVE SLIP AND ENGINE RUNAWAY ON 2-3 SHIFT

Check oil level and pressure. Adjust selector lever. Check vacuum diaphragm and hoses. Check drain plug. Faulty manual control valve. Defective band servo or front clutch. Check for hydraulic passage leaks. Damaged front clutch check ball.

VEHICLE BRAKES ON 1-2 SHIFT

Make oil drain check. Faulty manual control valve, low-reverse brake, front clutch or one-way clutch in power train.

NO 3-2 SHIFT

Faulty vacuum diaphragm and hoses. Make oil drain check. Defective manual control valve or governor valve. Faulty band servo, front clutch, brake band or hydraulic passage leaks.

NO 2-1 OR 3-1 SHIFT

Faulty vacuum diaphragm and hoses. Take oil drain check. Defective manual control valve or governor valve. Faulty band servo, brake band or one-way clutch in power train.

SHIFT SHOCK FELT ON DECELERATION

Check selector lever linkage. Faulty vacuum diaphragm and hoses, downshift solenoid, kickdown switch and wiring. Check oil pressure, manual control valve, governor valve or hydraulic passage leak.

3-2 AND 2-1 SHIFT POINTS TOO HIGH

Check selector lever linkage. Check vacuum circuit, diaphragm and hoses. Faulty downshift solenoid, kickdown switch and wiring. Check oil pressure, manual control valve, governor valve or hydraulic passage leak.

NO KICKDOWN AT NORMAL SPEEDS IN "D"

Faulty downshift solenoid, kickdown switch and wiring, vacuum diaphragm and hoses. Make oil drain check. Defective manual control valve, governor valve, brake band or hydraulic passage leak.

Automatic Transmissions

JATCO L3N71B & 3N71B (Cont.)

EXCESSIVE ENGINE RPM WHEN ACCELERATING IN "D" ABOVE KICKDOWN SPEED

Check selector lever linkage, vacuum diaphragm and hoses. Check oil pressure. Check oil drain. Defective manual control valve or governor valve. Faulty front clutch or hydraulic passage leak.

ENGINE SLIP OR RUNAWAY ON "D3" TO "D2" KICKDOWN

Check vacuum diaphragm and hoses. Check oil pressure. Check oil drain. Faulty manual control valve, band servo, brake band or leak in hydraulic passages. Check front clutch and front clutch check ball.

NO ENGINE BRAKING IN "1" RANGE

Check selector lever linkage. Faulty oil pressure. Make oil drain check. Defective manual control valve. Faulty low-reverse brake. Hydraulic passage leak.

TRANSMISSION OVERHEATS

Check oil level. Faulty rear lubrication or oil pressure. Incorrect engine stall speed. Make oil drain check. Defective manual control valve. Faulty band servo, front clutch, band brake, low-reverse brake, oil pump. Possible hydraulic passage leaks. Defective one-way clutch in torque converter, or planetary gear. In addition, on L3N71B models, check "O" ring on input shaft and lock-up orifice in oil pump cover. Faulty torque converter.

TRANSMISSION NOISY IN "P" AND "N"

Check fluid level. Faulty oil pressure or pump.

TRANSMISSION NOISY IN "R" AND ALL "D" RANGES

Check fluid level. Faulty oil pressure, rear clutch, oil pump, one-way clutch in power train, or planetary gear.

NOTE: The following problems and possible causes apply to L3N71B transmission only.

TORQUE CONVERTER DOES NOT LOCK UP

Governor tube disconnected or damaged. Governor faulty. Incorrect oil pressure. Check "O" ring on input shaft and oil pump condition. Speed cut valve or lock-up control valve faulty or defective. Check lock-up orifice in oil pump cover. Faulty torque converter.

LOCK-UP PISTON SLIPS

Incorrect oil pressure. Check condition of "O" ring on input shaft and lock-up orifice in oil pump cover. Check oil pump condition. Faulty torque converter.

LOCK-UP POINT TOO HIGH OR TOO LOW

Governor tube disconnected or damaged. Governor faulty. Check speed cut valve and lock-up control valve condition.

ENGINE STOPPED IN ANY GEAR RANGE

Faulty lock-up control valve. Faulty or defective torque converter.

TESTING

ROAD TEST

1) Before performing road test, be sure that fluid level, shift linkage, control linkage and detent cable adjustments have been checked and adjusted as needed.

2) Check half-throttle upshift in "D". Transmission should start in 1st gear, shift to 2nd and then to 3rd at shift points specified in *Shift Speed Chart*.

3) With transmission still in 3rd gear, depress accelerator to floor (Kickdown). Transmission should shift from 3rd to 2nd or 3rd to 1st depending on vehicle speed. Compare kickdown speeds with those in chart.

4) Check closed throttle downshift from 3rd to 1st by coasting down from about 30 MPH in 3rd gear. Shift should occur within limits specified in *Shift Speed Chart*.

SHIFT SPEED CHART (MPH)

Application	KICKDOWN				HALF-THROTTLE		CLOSED THROTTLE	
	D1-D2	D2-D3	D3-D2	D2-D1	D1-D2	D2-D3	D3-D1	1_2-1_1 [1]
Courier	31-43	55-71	50-64	22-32	8-17	16-37	7-14	26-34
Datsun								
200SX	38-42	66-71	65-60	33-28	14-19	39-44	.....	33-29
210								
California	30-34	53-57	52-48	26-22	11-15	33-37	.....	27-22
All Others	31-36	55-60	54-50	28-23	12-16	32-37	.....	28-24
280ZX	38-43	65-70	64-59	34-29	12-17	37-42	.....	34-29
280ZX Turbo	38-43	57-62	57-52	29-24	16-21	46-51	.....	29-24
810	36-41	63-68	62-57	31-26	14-18	37-42	.....	32-27
810 Diesel	28-34	56-62	56-51	28-23	10-15	35-41	.....	28-23
Pickup	35-39	62-66	61-56	31-26	13-18	36-41	.....	31-27
Mazda								
RX7	31-44	57-74	49-63	20-30	7-19	18-39	6-12	24-32
All Others	29-41	51-69	44-60	20-31	7-17	14-36	6-13	23-31

[1] — Obtained by shifting to "1" range, directy from "D".

JATCO L3N71B & 3N71B (Cont.)

CLUTCH AND BAND APPLICATION CHART (ELEMENTS IN USE)

Selector Lever Position	Front Clutch	Rear Clutch	Low-Reverse Brake	Brake Band	One-Way Clutch
P — PARK			X		
R — REVERSE	X		X		
D — DRIVE					
First		X			X
Second		X		X	
Direct	X	X			
2 — SECOND		X		X	
1 — LOW					
First		X	X		
Second		X		X	

NEUTRAL — All clutches and bands released and/or ineffective.

5) Shift points should be smooth and without excess shock. No excessive "creep" should be noted. A slight "creep" in each range is acceptable.

HYDRAULIC PRESSURE TESTS

Line Pressure Tests

1) Make sure transmission fluid is at correct level and operating temperature. Connect pressure gauges to line pressure test ports at front and rear of transmission. *See Fig. 2.*

NOTE: Front port is used to check pressure in "R" range, rear port is used for forward ranges.

2) Block front and rear wheels and securely set parking brake, place selector lever in range to be checked and note pressure reading on gauge at idle. Gradually increase throttle opening until wide open and check pressure reading again. Pressure should be as indicated in *Line Pressure Specifications* charts.

CAUTION: Do not hold throttle open longer than 5 seconds at a time.

Governor Pressure Test

Governor pressure test should only be used if vehicle shift speeds are different than those indicated in *Shift Speed Chart.* Connect pressure gauge to governor pressure port on transmission case. *See Fig. 2.* Read pressure with vehicle running at speeds indicated in *Governor Pressure Specifications* table. If pressures are incorrect, disassemble and clean governor assembly.

LINE PRESSURE SPECIFICATIONS (COURIER & MAZDA)

Application	psi (kg/cm²)
At Idle Speed	
In "R"	57-100 (4.0-7.0)
In "D"	43-57 (3.0-4.0)
In "2"	114-171 (8.0-12.0)
In "1"	43-57 (3.0-4.0)
At Stall Speed	
In "R"	228-270 (16.0-19.0)
In "D"	128-156 (9.0-11.0)
In "2"	114-171 (8.0-12.0)
In "1"	128-156 (9.0-11.0)

LINE PRESSURE SPECIFICATIONS (DATSUN)

Application	psi (kg/cm²)
At Idle Speed	
In "R"	
280ZX	74-101 (5.2-7.1)
280ZX Turbo	57-71 (4.9-5.0)
810 Diesel	105-119 (7.4-8.4)
All Others	60-80 (4.2-5.6)
In "D"	
280ZX	46-54 (3.2-3.8)
280ZX Turbo	43-57 (3.0-4.0)
810 Diesel	55-70 (3.9-4.9)
All Others	46-54 (3.2-3.8)
In "2"	
280ZX	112-196 (7.9-13.8)
280ZX Turbo	85-171 (6.0-12.0)
810 Diesel	85-171 (6.0-12.0)
All Others	85-166 (6.0-11.7)
In "1"	
280ZX	46-54 (3.2-3.8)
280ZX Turbo	43-57 (3.0-4.0)
810 Diesel	55-70 (3.9-4.9)
All Others	46-54 (3.2-3.8)
At Stall Speed	
In "R"	
280ZX	303-347 (21.3-24.4)
280ZX Turbo	313-356 (22.0-25.0)
810 Diesel	279-301 (19.6-21.2)
All Others	203-230 (14.3-16.2)
In "D"	
280ZX	164-185 (11.5-13.0)
280ZX Turbo	259-282 (18.2-19.8)
810 Diesel	148-173 (10.4-12.2)
All Others	141-158 (9.9-11.1)
In "2"	
280ZX	175-196 (12.3-13.8)
280ZX Turbo	259-282 (18.2-19.8)
810 Diesel	142-171 (10.0-12.0)
All Others	145-166 (10.2-11.7)
In "1"	
280ZX	164-185 (11.5-13.0)
280ZX Turbo	259-282 (18.2-19.8)
810 Diesel	148-173 (10.4-12.2)
All Others	141-158 (9.9-11.1)

JATCO L3N71B & 3N71B (Cont.)

Fig. 2: Hydraulic Pressure Test Port Locations

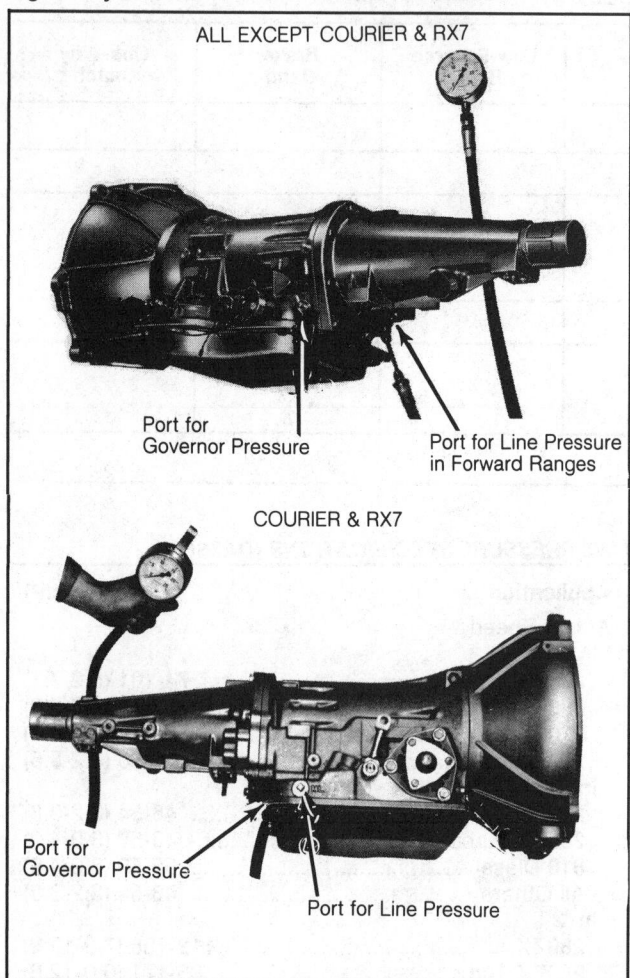

ALL EXCEPT COURIER & RX7

Port for Governor Pressure

Port for Line Pressure in Forward Ranges

COURIER & RX7

Port for Governor Pressure

Port for Line Pressure

GOVERNOR PRESSURE SPECIFICATIONS

Application	psi (kg/cm²)
Courier	
At 20 MPH	12-18 (.8-1.3)
At 35 MPH	24-33 (1.7-2.3)
At 55 MPH	45-60 (3.2-4.2)
Datsun	[1]
Mazda	
GLC Wagon	
At 20 MPH	11-20 (0.8-1.4)
At 35 MPH	26-36 (1.8-2.5)
At 55 MPH	51-70 (3.6-4.9)
RX7	
At 20 MPH	11-18 (0.8-1.3)
At 35 MPH	23-33 (1.6-2.3)
At 55 MPH	48-64 (3.4-4.5)
626	
At 20 MPH	13-20 (0.9-1.4)
At 35 MPH	27-37 (1.9-2.6)
At 55 MPH	57-71 (4.0-5.0)

[1] — Datsun governor pressure should increase directly with vehicle speed and should always be less than line pressure.

STALL TEST

1) Check engine and transmission for proper lubricant levels. Bring engine to normal operating temperature. Attach tachometer to engine and position so that dial is visible from driver's compartment. Block front and rear wheels, and apply hand brake.

2) Place one foot firmly on brake pedal and place selector lever in "D" position. Gradually increase engine speed to wide open throttle. When engine speed will no longer increase, take reading from tachometer and decelerate engine.

NOTE: Do not hold engine at wide open throttle for more than five seconds. Severe transmission damage may result.

3) Move shift lever to "N" or "P" position and run engine at 1200 RPM for at least 1 minute to cool transmission. Repeat stall procedure with shift lever in "2", "1", and "R" ranges.

STALL SPEED SPECIFICATIONS

Application	Stall RPM
Courier	1950-2200
Datsun	
200SX, 810 & Pickup	1800-2100
210	1900-2200
280ZX	2000-2300
280ZX Turbo	2400-2700
Mazda	
GLC Wagon	1900-2150
RX7	2350-2600
626	2000-2250

REMOVAL & INSTALLATION

See the appropriate article in AUTOMATIC TRANSMISSION REMOVAL Section.

TRANSMISSION DISASSEMBLY

1) If not done during transmission removal, drain fluid from transmission. Remove torque converter and place transmission in holding fixture. Separate governor tube from converter housing (if equipped). Remove housing. Remove downshift solenoid, vacuum diaphragm and vacuum diaphragm rod. Remove speedometer lock plate retaining bolt and remove speedometer pinion.

2) Remove oil pan attaching bolts and oil pan. Remove valve body bolts. See Fig. 5. Remove valve body from transmission. Remove manual valve from valve body to prevent it from dropping out accidentally. Loosen brake band adjusting screw lock nut and tighten screw just enough to prevent front clutch drum from dropping out when oil pump is removed.

3) Remove input shaft from oil pump, then remove pump with slide hammers (Courier Part No. T59L-100B, T73L-77103; Datsun No. ST25850000; Mazda No. 49 0378 390). Remove front clutch thrust washer and bearing race from front pump. Back off band servo piston stem to release band.

JATCO L3N71B & 3N71B (Cont.)

Fig. 3: *Jatco Model 3N71B Automatic Transmission Hydraulic Circuits Diagram*

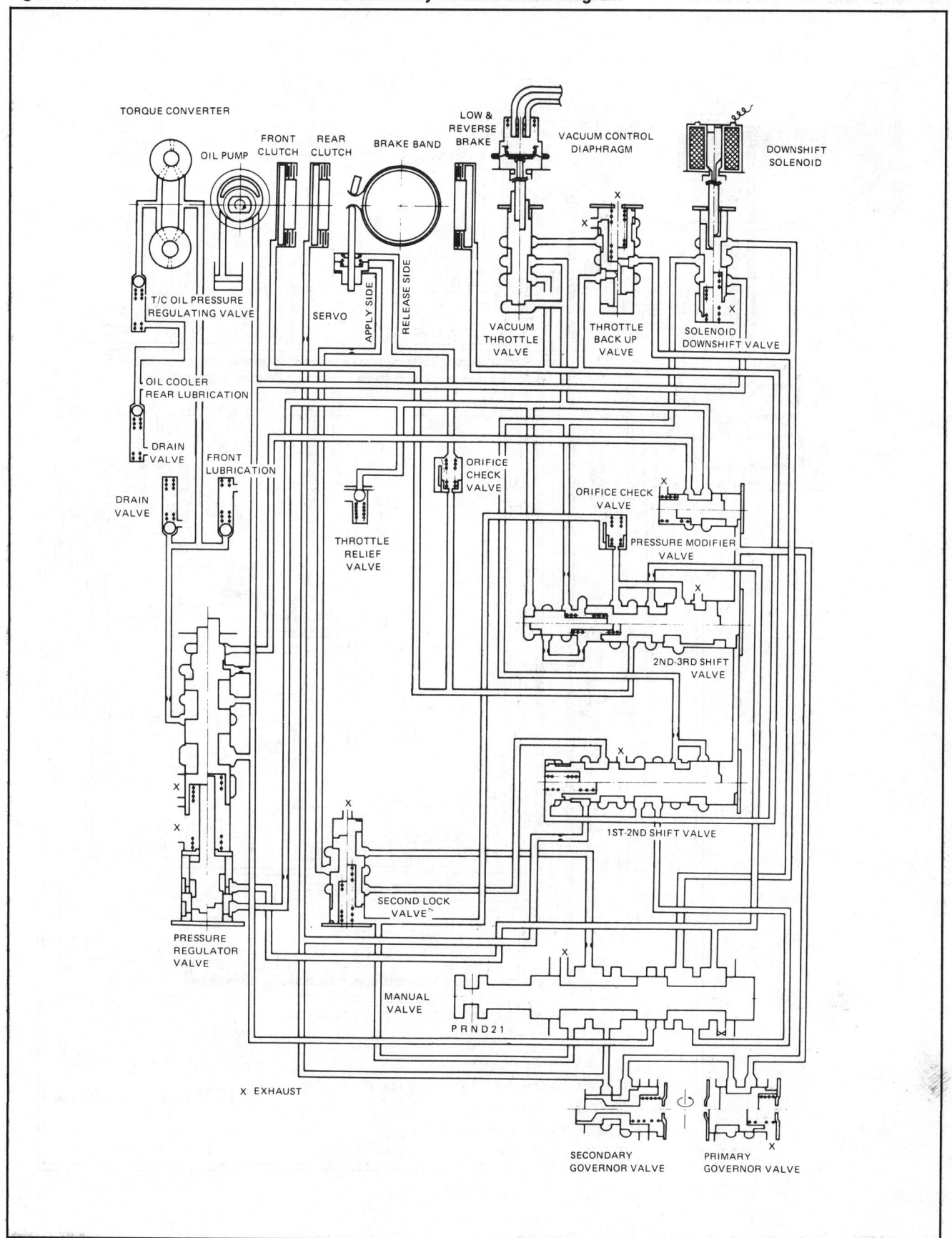

Automatic Transmissions

JATCO L3N71B & 3N71B (Cont.)

Fig. 4: *Jatco Model L3N71B Automatic Transmission Hydraulic Circuits Diagram*

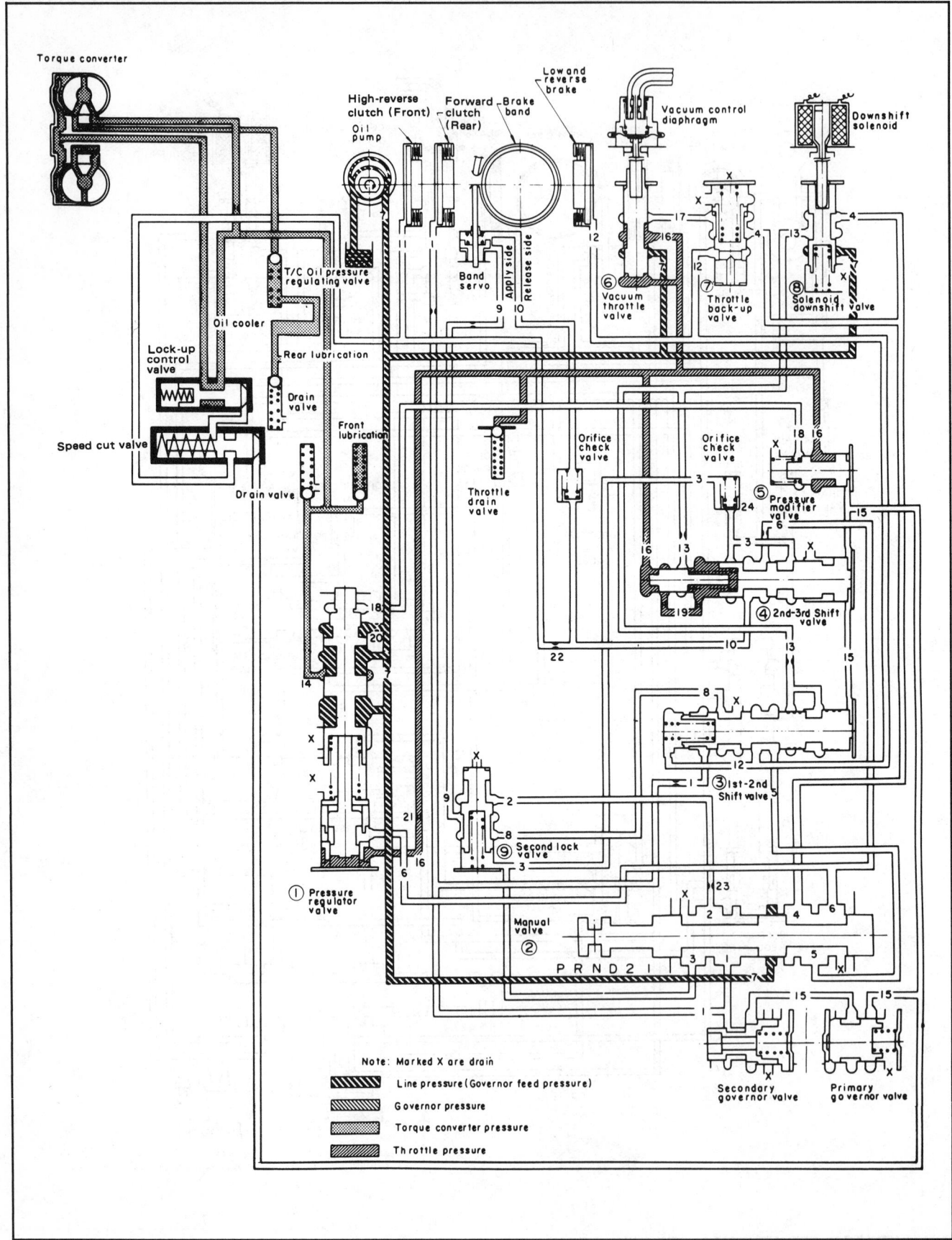

JATCO L3N71B & 3N71B (Cont.)

Fig. 5: *Bottom View of Transmission Case Showing Valve Body-to-Case Bolt Locations*

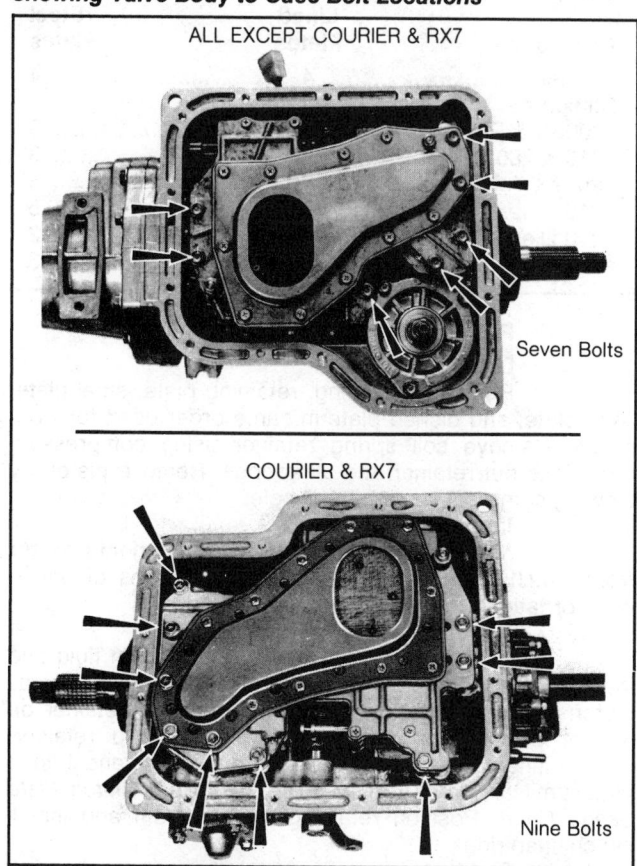

ALL EXCEPT COURIER & RX7

Seven Bolts

COURIER & RX7

Nine Bolts

4) Remove brake band strut. Remove brake band, front clutch and rear clutch as an assembly. Remove front pump thrust bearing and rear clutch thrust washer. Remove rear clutch hub, front planetary carrier and connecting shell. Remove rear clutch thrust bearing, front planetary carrier thrust washer and thrust bearing.

Fig. 6: *Removing Band Servo & Low-Reverse Brake Piston*

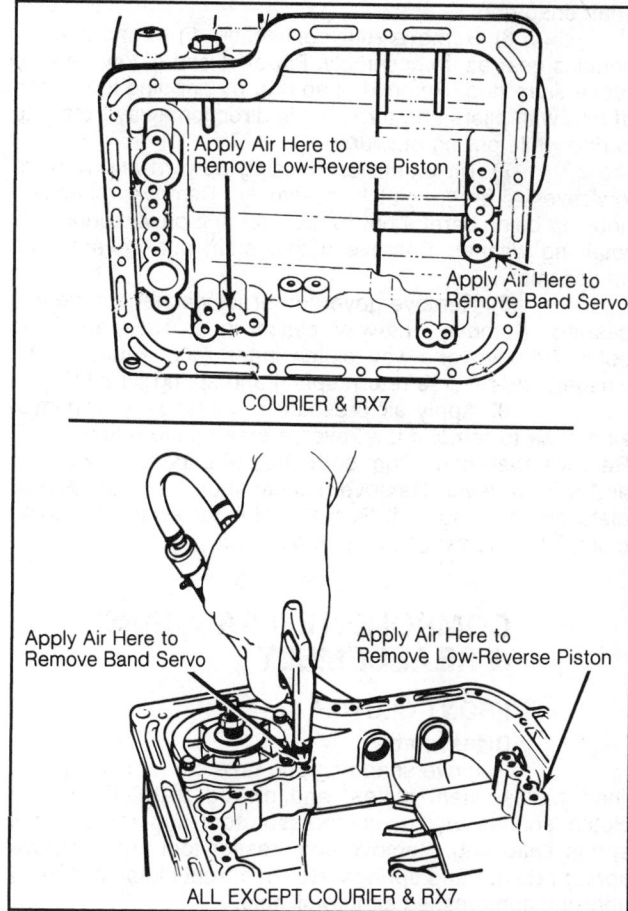

Apply Air Here to Remove Low-Reverse Piston

Apply Air Here to Remove Band Servo

COURIER & RX7

Apply Air Here to Remove Band Servo

Apply Air Here to Remove Low-Reverse Piston

ALL EXCEPT COURIER & RX7

Apply compressed air at passages indicated.

5) Back out, about half way, band servo attaching bolts. Carefully apply air pressure to loosen band servo. *See Fig. 6.* Remove band servo retaining bolts and pull band servo out. Remove rear planetary carrier

Fig. 7: *Exploded View of Front Clutch Assembly*

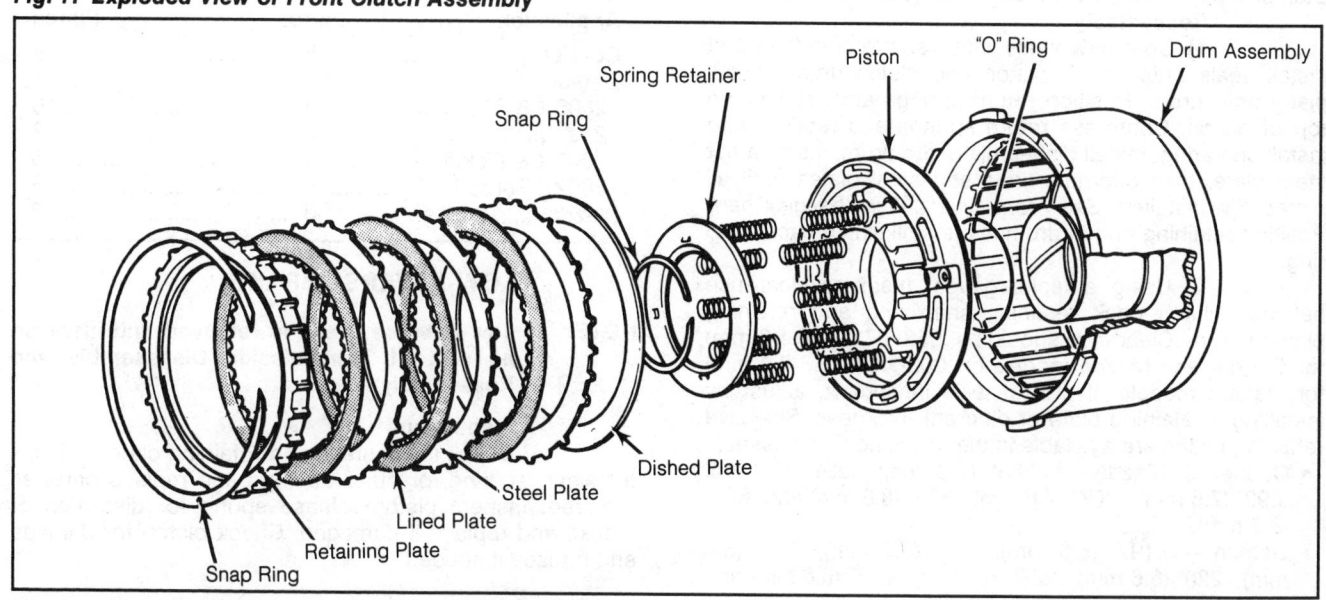

Snap Ring · Spring Retainer · Piston · "O" Ring · Drum Assembly

Snap Ring · Retaining Plate · Lined Plate · Steel Plate · Dished Plate

Number of clutch plates and discs varies with application.

snap ring. Remove rear planetary carrier. Remove output shaft snap ring.

6) Remove rear connecting drum and internal annulus gear as an assembly. Pry off 1 end of low-reverse brake snap ring. Remove snap ring by gripping loose end of ring with pliers and turning it in direction away from gap in ring while pulling outward.

7) Tilt extension housing upward and remove low-reverse brake clutch assembly. Remove extension housing being careful not to lose parking pawl, spring and retaining washer. Remove output shaft and governor as an assembly.

8) Remove governor thrust washer and needle bearing. Remove one-way clutch inner race attaching bolts. Remove one-way clutch inner race, return thrust washer, low-reverse return spring and spring thrust ring.

9) Apply air pressure to passage in transmission case to remove low-reverse brake piston. *See Fig. 6.* Remove snap rings from both ends of parking brake lever and remove lever. Remove manual shaft lock nut, manual plate and parking rod. Remove inhibitor switch attaching bolts, inhibitor switch and manual shaft.

COMPONENT DISASSEMBLY & REASSEMBLY

FRONT CLUTCH

Disassembly

Remove snap ring and take out retaining plate, lined plates, steel plates, and dished plate. Compress clutch springs with a compressor tool and remove coil spring snap ring. Remove compressor tool, then remove spring retainer and springs. Remove front clutch piston by applying compressed air into oil hole.

Inspection

Inspect lined plates for undue wear or fatigue. Check coil spring retainer and replace if deformed. Ensure that coil spring has not lost tension. Inspect seal around piston and "O" ring inside clutch drum for damage. Replace all parts which show undue wear or fatigue. Standard plate thickness in .059-.065" (1.50-1.65 mm).

Reassembly

1) Coat new seals with transmission fluid and install seals onto clutch piston and clutch drum. Install piston into drum. Position return springs and retainer on top of piston. Compress return springs and retainer and install snap ring. Install dished plate into drum. Install a flat steel plate, then alternate lined and steel plates until all plates are installed. *See Front Clutch Plate Usage Chart.* Position retaining ring in drum and install clutch pack snap ring.

2) Using a feeler gauge, measure clearance between clutch pack retaining snap ring and retaining plate in drum. Clearance should be .063-.071" (1.6-1.8 mm) for Courier and Mazda models or .063-.079" (1.6-2.0 mm) for Datsun models. If clearance is inncorrect, adjust by installing a retaining plate of different thickness. Selective retaining plates are available in the following thicknesses:

- Courier & Mazda — .283" (7.2 mm), .291" (7.4 m), .299" (7.6 mm), .307" (7.8 mm), .315" (8.0 mm) and .323" (8.2 mm).
- Datsun — .197" (5.0 mm), .205" (5.2 mm), .213" (5.4 mm), .220" (5.6 mm), .228" (5.8 mm), .236" (6.0 mm) and .244" (6.2 mm).

FRONT CLUTCH PLATE USAGE CHART

Application	Lined Plates	Steel Plates
Courier	4	4
Datsun		
200SX & Pickup	3	5
210 & 280ZX	3	3
280ZX Turbo	4	5
810	3	5
810 Diesel	3	3
Mazda	3	3

REAR CLUTCH

Disassembly

Remove snap ring, retaining plate, steel plate, lined plate, and dished plate in same order used for front clutch. Remove coil spring retainer using compressing tool. Take out retainer and all springs. Remove piston by blowing compressed air into oil hole.

Inspection

Make same inspection of components as for front clutch. Replace any parts showing signs of undue wear or fatigue.

Reassembly

1) Coat new seals with transmission fluid and install seals on clutch piston and clutch drum. Install piston into drum. Position return springs and retainer on top of piston. Compress return springs and retainer. Install dished plate, then alternate 1 steel plate and 1 lined plate until all plates are installed. *See Rear Clutch Plate Usage Chart.* Position retaining ring in drum and install clutch snap ring.

2) Measure clearance between clutch pack retaining snap ring and retaining plate in drum. Clearance should be .031-.063" (.8-1.6 mm). If clearance is not to specification, check all clutch components for wear and replace as necessary.

REAR CLUTCH PLATE USAGE CHART

Application	Lined Plates	Steel Plates
Courier	5	5
Datsun		
200SX & 810	6	6
210	3	3
280ZX & Pickup	5	5
280ZX Turbo	6	6
Mazda	3	3

LOW-REVERSE BRAKE

NOTE: Low-Reverse brake is removed and installed as part of Transmission Disassembly and Reassembly.

Inspection

Check lined, steel, and retaining plate surfaces for wear, scoring, or other damage and replace parts as required. Inspect piston release spring for distortion or cracks and replace if damaged. Check piston for damage and replace if needed.

JATCO L3N71B & 3N71B (Cont.)

Fig. 8: *Exploded View of Rear Clutch Assembly*

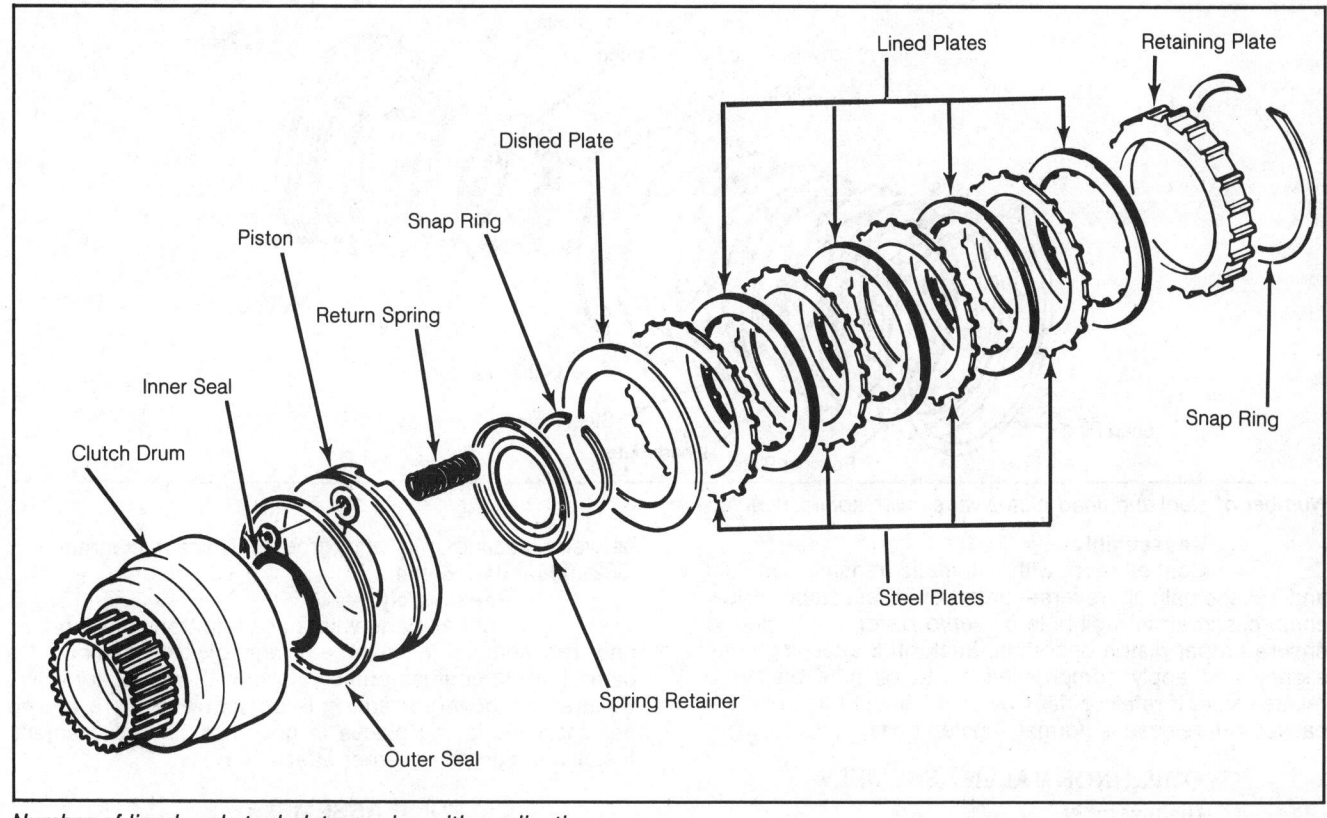

Number of lined and steel plates varies with application.

BAND SERVO PISTON

Disassembly

Remove 3 bolts attaching band servo retainer to transmission case. Take out retainer and servo piston. Lift out return spring. If servo retainer is difficult to free from case, remove by forcing compressed air into oil hole on piston release side. Blow compressed air into oil hole on apply side of servo piston to remove piston from retainer.

Fig. 9: *Exploded View of Band Servo Assembly*

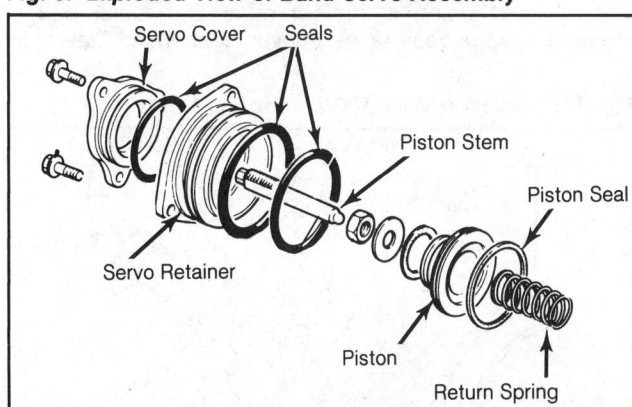

Mazda model shown. Other models are similar.

Inspection

Ensure that 2 "O" rings on servo retainer and rubber seal on servo piston are not damaged. Check all parts for undue wear or fatigue, inspect return spring for adequate tension and brake band lining for excessive wear or damage. Replace parts as needed.

Fig. 10: *Checking Band Servo Operation*

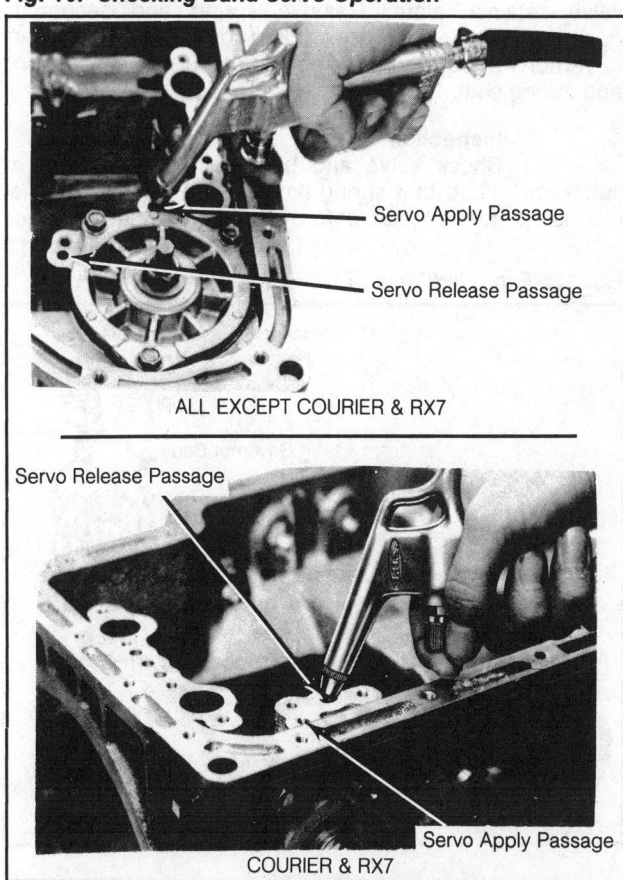

Fig. 11: Exploded View of Low-Reverse Brake Assembly

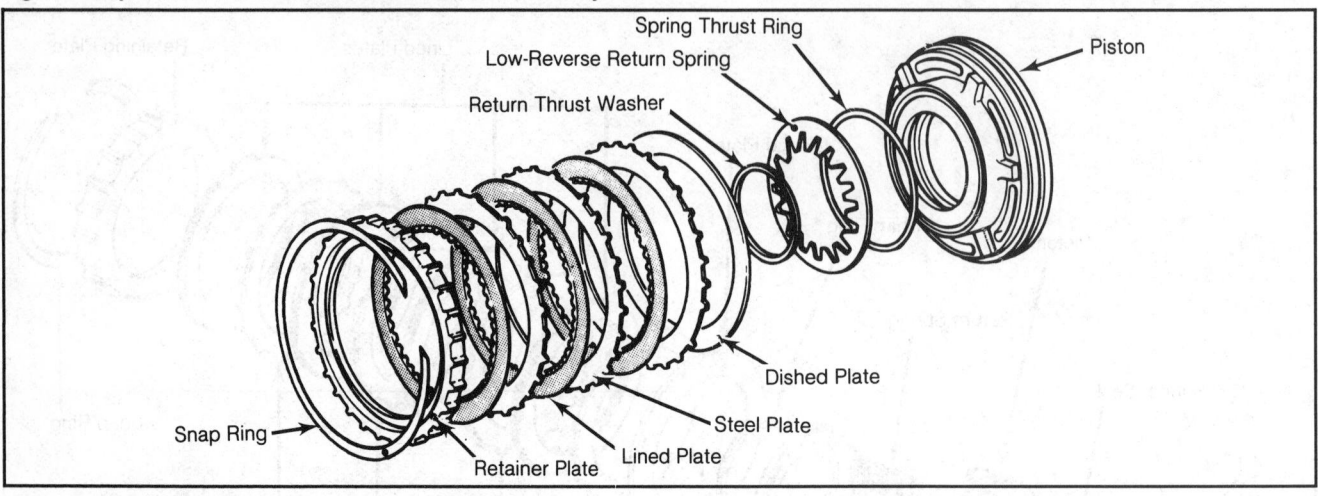

Number of steel and lined plates varies with application.

Reassembly

Coat all parts with automatic transmission fluid and reassemble in reverse order of disassembly. Blow compressed air into oil hole on servo piston apply side to ensure proper piston operation. Back off 3 attaching bolts slightly and apply compressed air to oil hole on servo release side. If retainer rises by same amount as bolts are backed off, release is normal. Tighten bolts.

GOVERNOR VALVE ASSEMBLY

Disassembly

Separate governor from oil distributor by removing 4 attaching bolts. Remove secondary governor valve retainer plate. Remove spring and secondary governor valve from governor body. Remove primary governor valve spring seat, primary governor valve, spring and spring seat.

Inspection

Check valve and body for valve sticking or catching. Ensure that spring has not lost tension and that retainer plates are not deformed. Check side clearance

between sealing ring and groove. Correct clearance is .002-.006" (.04-.16 mm).

Reassembly

Coat all parts with automatic transmission fluid and reassemble in reverse order of disassembly. Be careful not to confuse primary valve with secondary valve. Ensure that governor spring is straight and there are no sticking or catching places in governor valve movement. Install and tighten governor attaching bolts.

OIL PUMP ASSEMBLY

Disassembly

Take pump cover off pump housing by removing 5 bolts. On L3N71B models, remove speed cut valve and lock-up control valve. On all models, mark inner and outer gears with quick-drying ink or paint for reassembly reference, then remove gears from housing. Remove large seal ring from outside diameter of pump housing, and seal rings from stator support.

Inspection

1) Check gear teeth for excessive wear or damage. Replace rubber seal ring if worn. Check oil pump clearances as follows:

2) Using a straight edge and feeler gauge, measure pump gear face-to-cover clearance. Clearance

Fig. 12: Exploded View of Governor Assembly

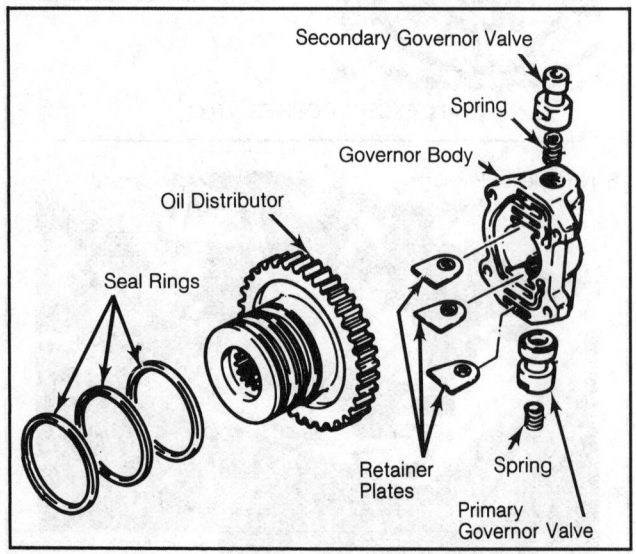

Fig. 13: Exploded View of Oil Pump Assembly

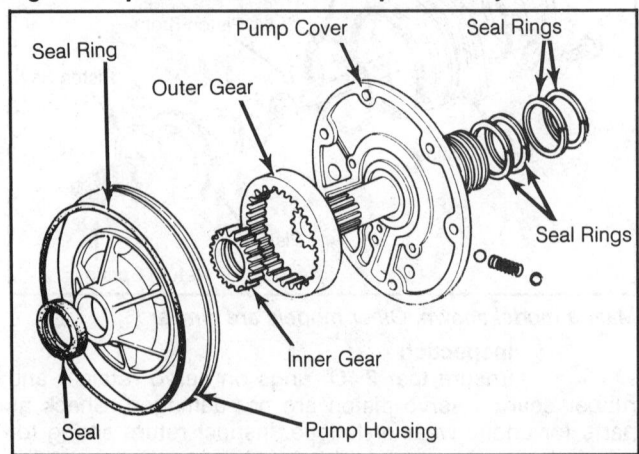

JATCO L3N71B & 3N71B (Cont.)

should be .0008-.0016" (.02-.04 mm). If clearance exceeds .003" (.08 mm), replace gears.

3) Measure clearance between outer gear and crescent. Clearance should be .006-.008" (.14-.21 mm). If clearance exceeds .010" (.25 mm), replace gears.

4) Measure clearance between outer gear and pump housing. Clearance should be .002-.008" (.05-.20 mm). If clearance exceeds .010" (.25 mm), replace gears.

5) Check all parts for wear, cracks or other damage. Replace any defective parts. Ensure that oil seal rings and oil feed grooves are not damaged, and rings still have tension. Check side clearance of oil rings. Clearance should be .002-.006" (.04-.16 mm).

Reassembly

1) Place pump housing in torque converter. Fit inner and outer gears in housing as when disassembling. On L3N71B models, install speed cut valve, lock-up control valve and springs into pump cover. Tap retaining pins.

2) On all models, check pump cover runout. Support pump housing in tool (Datsun No. ST25580001; Mazda No. 49 2113 025A). Temporarily assemble pump cover and housing. DO NOT tighten bolts completely at this time. Attach dial indicator as shown in *Fig. 14* and measure total pump cover runout. Total runout must not exceed .003" (.07 mm). Runout can be adjusted by tapping cover lightly with a plastic hammer.

Fig. 14: Checking Oil Pump Cover Runout

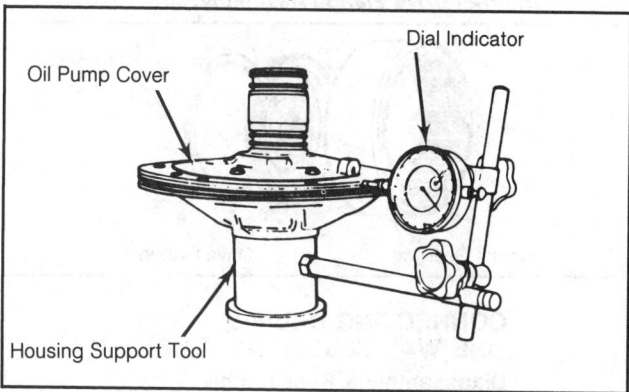

Adjust runout to maximum of .003" (.07 mm).

3) Tighten pump cover bolts. Recheck runout. Install seal rings on stator support and a new large seal ring on pump housing outside diameter.

Fig. 15: Measuring Oil Pump Clearances

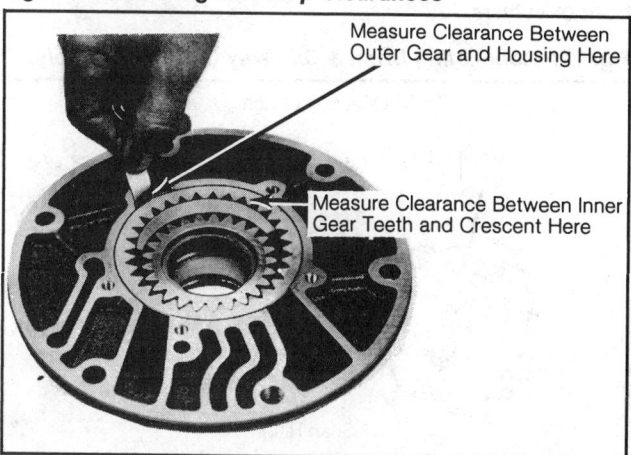

PLANETARY CARRIER

Planetary carrier is one-piece unit. The only clearance check is between pinion washer and carrier. Standard clearance is .008-.028" (.20-.70 mm). If clearance exceeds .031" (.80 mm), replace carrier.

VALVE BODY ASSEMBLY

Disassembly

1) Remove oil screen attaching bolts and oil screen. Remove bolts attaching upper body to lower body. Separate upper body and separator plate from lower body, taking care not to lose check valves and springs in lower body. Slide manual valve out if not already removed.

2) Remove side cover "A" as shown in *Fig. 16*. Remove pressure regulator plug, sleeve, spring seat and spring, and pressure regulator valve. Remove second lock valve and spring.

3) Remove side cover "B", then remove vacuum throttle valve, throttle back-up valve spring and throttle back-up valve. Remove kickdown valve and spring. Remove side cover "C". Lift out 1-2 shift valve and spring. Remove 2-3 shift valve spring and plug, pressure modifier valve and spring.

Inspection

Check all parts for any problem which may cause components to stick. Inspect all valve springs for damage and check for adequate tension. Ensure that no damage has occured to oil strainer. Look over separator plate for abnormal oil passages and check for similar defects in oil passages of valve body. Replace any parts showing signs of abnormal wear or fatigue.

VALVE BODY SPRING IDENTIFICATION CHART

Application	Length In. (mm)	Diameter In. (mm)	Number of Coils
Manual Detent	1.276 (32.4)	.287 (7.3)	15
Pressure Regulator Valve	1.693 (43.0)	.461 (11.7)	13
Pressure Modifier Valve	0.728 (18.5)	.331 (8.4)	5
1-2 Shift Valve	1.260 (32.0)	.260 (6.6)	16
2-3 Shift Valve	1.614 (41.0)	.272 (6.9)	18
Throttle Back-Up Valve	1.417 (36.0)	.287 (7.3)	14
Solenoid Down-Shift Valve	0.866 (22.0)	.219 (5.6)	12
Second Lock Valve	1.319 (33.5)	.219 (5.6)	16
Throttle Relief Check Valve	1.055 (26.8)	.256 (6.5)	14
Orifice Check Valve	0.610 (15.5)	.197 (5.0)	12
Servo Orifice Check Valve	0.610 (15.5)	.197 (5.0)	12

Fig. 16: Exploded View of Valve Body Assembly

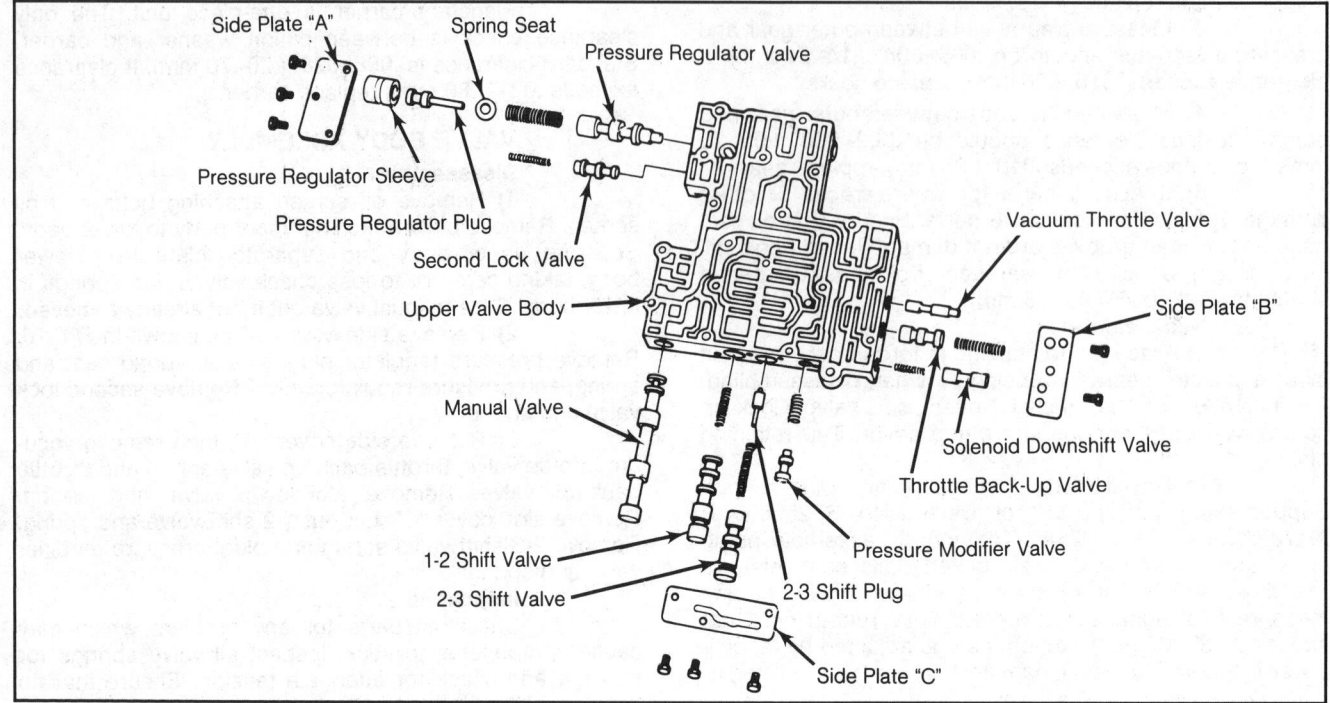

Reassembly
Replace all parts in reverse order of removal after coating parts with automatic transmission fluid. Use *Fig. 16* as a guide to confirm location and position of valves and springs. Do not force any part which seems difficult to place or insert. Use light, straight pressure to fit parts.

INPUT SHELL & SUN GEAR ASSEMBLY
Disassembly & Reassembly
Remove external snap ring from sun gear, withdraw thrust washer, then remove sun gear from shell. Remove internal snap ring from sun gear. To assemble, coat all parts with transmission fluid and reverse disassembly procedure.

Fig. 17: Input Shell & Sun Gear Assembly

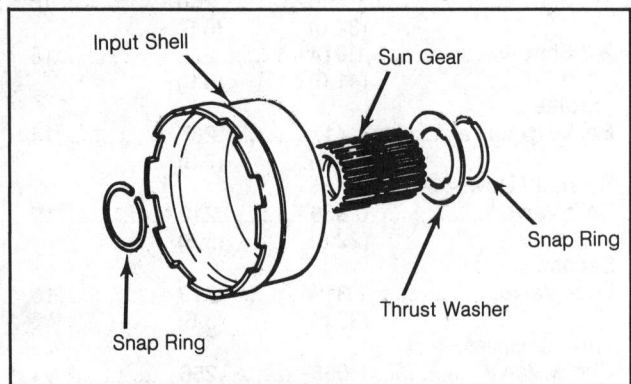

INTERNAL DRIVE FLANGE ASSEMBLY
Disassembly & Reassembly
Remove snap ring and disconnect flange from internal gear. Inspect part for wear or fatigue. Reverse disassembly procedure to assemble after coating all parts with automatic transmission fluid.

Fig. 18: Internal Drive Flange Assembly.

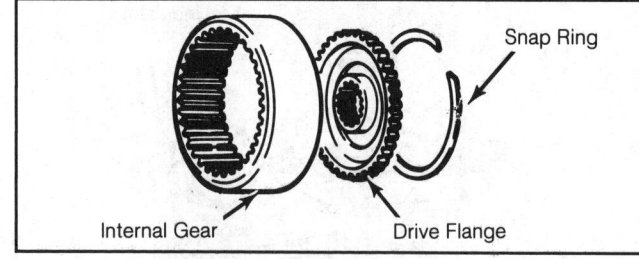

CONNECTING DRUM & ONE-WAY CLUTCH ASSEMBLY
Disassembly & Reassembly
Draw out one-way clutch by removing snap ring from each end. Remove outer race snap ring and draw outer race rearward out of drum. Inspect one-way clutch for undue wear or damage. Check contacting surfaces of inner and outer races. When reassembling one-way clutch, ensure that arrow mark is fitted towards front of vehicle.

Fig. 19: Connecting Drum & One-Way Clutch Assembly.

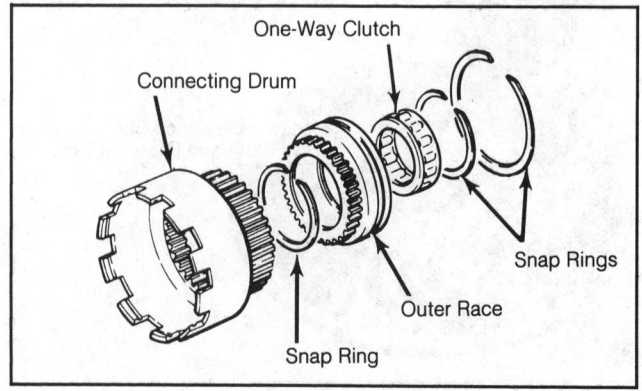

JATCO L3N71B & 3N71B (Cont.)

TRANSMISSION REASSEMBLY

1) Lubricate low-reverse brake piston with transmission fluid and install in transmission case. Position low-reverse support ring, piston return spring, snap ring, and one-way clutch inner race into transmission case. Hold inner race in position and install one-way clutch inner race attaching bolts.

2) Position low-reverse brake dished plate into transmission. Install lined and steel plates alternately, starting with a steel plate, until all plates are installed. *See Low-Reverse Brake Plate Usage Chart.* Install retaining plate and snap ring.

LOW-REVERSE BRAKE PLATE USAGE CHART

Application	Lined Plates	Steel Plates
Courier	4	4
Datsun		
200SX & Pickup	5	5
210	3	3
280ZX & 810	5	5
280ZX Turbo	7	7
810 Diesel	6	6
Mazda		
GLC Wagon	3	3
RX7	5	5
626	4	4

3) Check clearance between retaining plate and snap ring. Clearance should be .032-.049" (.80-1.25 mm). If clearance is incorrect, it may be adjusted by installing a retaining plate of a different thickness. Plates are available in sizes from .307" (7.8 mm) to .346" (8.8 mm)

in .008" (.2 mm) increments. Install correct plate and recheck clearance.

4) Install connecting shell in case. Rotate shell clockwise to mesh low-reverse brake plates with splines. Mount needle bearing and race for front face of oil distributor assembly on transmission case side. Install oil distributor assembly with governor in case, using care to avoid any damage to ring seals.

5) Install output shaft. Mount needle bearings on front and rear faces of internal drive flange, fit flange on output shaft and lock in place with snap ring.

Fig. 20: *Measuring Low-Reverse Brake Clearance in Case*

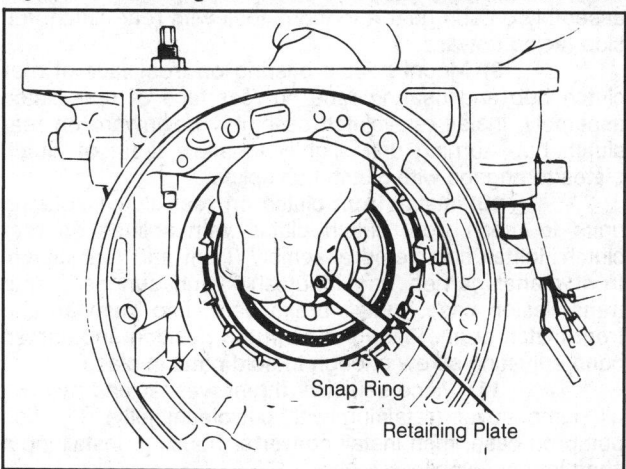

Snap Ring
Retaining Plate

6) Mount bearing race on rear face of rear planet carrier and place needle bearing on front face. Fit rear planet carrier into internal drive flange and lock carrier by placing snap ring on connecting drum. Push

Fig. 21: *Exploded View of Jatco Automatic Transmission*

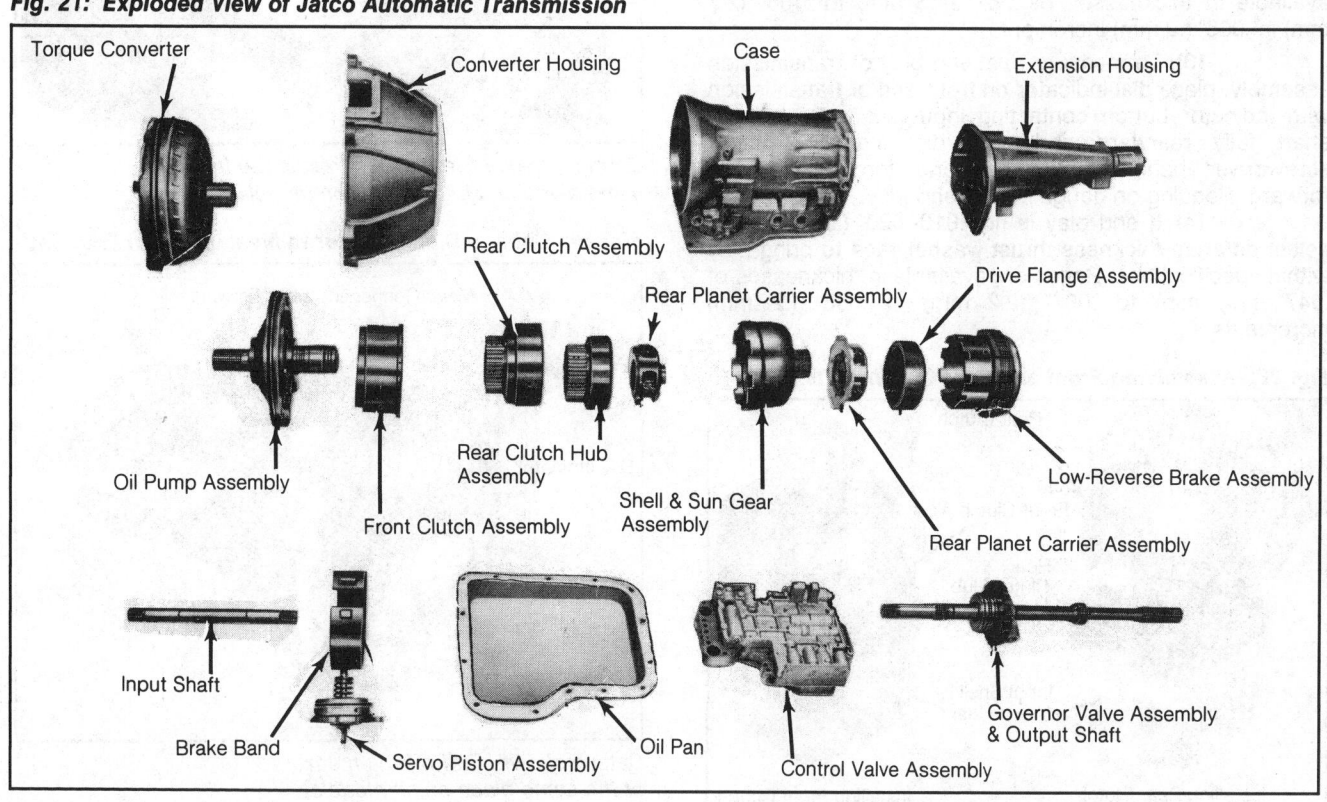

Torque Converter
Converter Housing
Case
Extension Housing
Rear Clutch Assembly
Rear Planet Carrier Assembly
Drive Flange Assembly
Rear Clutch Hub Assembly
Oil Pump Assembly
Front Clutch Assembly
Shell & Sun Gear Assembly
Low-Reverse Brake Assembly
Rear Planet Carrier Assembly
Input Shaft
Brake Band
Servo Piston Assembly
Oil Pan
Control Valve Assembly
Governor Valve Assembly & Output Shaft

JATCO L3N71B & 3N71B (Cont.)

manual shaft into case while tightening spacer and manual plate with nut. Mount parking lever and parking rod.

7) Install servo return spring, piston, and servo retainer into case. Hold retainer in place while installing and tightening attaching bolts. Place spacer, return spring and parking pawl onto shaft in extension housing. Install new gasket on extension housing face. Fit rear end of parking rod between 2 balls in support, then mount extension housing on case. Install and tighten attaching bolts.

8) Mount needle bearing on rear face of rear clutch hub and bearing race on front face of front planet carrier. Assemble rear clutch hub and planet carrier. Install assembly on sun gear and input shell with rear clutch hub side facing upward.

9) Mount needle bearing on front face of rear clutch hub and bearing race on rear face of rear clutch assembly. Install rear clutch assembly downward on rear clutch hub, turning unit slightly to allow teeth of clutch plates to engage with clutch hub spline.

10) Install front clutch on rear clutch, rotating units to mesh front clutch plates with splines on rear clutch. Install completed assembly (front and rear clutch, front planet carrier, and input shell and sun gear) into transmission case. Install brake band into case around front clutch drum. Place band strut in position and tighten band adjusting screw enough to hold band in place.

11) Place selective thrust washer and race on oil pump cover (retaining with petroleum jelly). Position pump on case, then install converter housing. Install input shaft into assembly.

12) To check pump cover-to-front clutch drum end play, insert feeler gauge between front clutch drum and shell. Clearance should be .020-.032" (.5-.8 mm). If not, select a different selective thrust washer that will bring clearance to specification. Thrust washers are available in thicknesses of .051" (1.3 mm) to .106" (2.7 mm) in .008" (.2 mm) increments.

13) To measure total end play of transmission assembly, place dial indicator on front end of transmission with indicator button contacting input shaft. Push input shaft fully rearward and zero dial indicator. Insert screwdriver behind input shell and force gear train forward. Reading on gauge is total end play.

14) If end play is not .010-.020" (.25-.50 mm), select different thickness thrust washer race to bring play within specifications. Races are available in thicknesses of .047" (1.2 mm) to .087" (2.2 mm) in .008" (.2 mm) increments.

15) Adjust brake band. *See Automatic Transmission Servicing section.* Install valve body on transmission case and tighten attaching bolts evenly. If transmission case, valve body or diaphragm unit have been replaced, measure distance from edge of case to bottom of hole in throttle valve (valve completely compressed in bore). Select correct length rod as indicated in *Diaphragm Rod Selection Chart.* Install vacuum unit, downshift solenoid and oil pan.

DIAPHRAGM ROD SELECTION CHART

If Distance "L" Is In. (mm)	Use This Rod In. (mm)
Under 1.009 (25.55)	1.14 (29.0)
1.010-1.030 (25.65-26.05)	1.16 (29.5)
1.031-1.049 (26.15-26.55)	1.18 (30.0)
1.050-1.069 (26.65-27.05)	1.20 (30.5)
Over 1.070 (27.15)	1.22 (31.0)

Fig. 23: Measuring Pump Cover-to-Front Clutch Clearance

Check Clearance Between Clutch Drum and Input Shell

Courier shown. Clearance is measured in same place on all transmission models.

Fig. 24: Using a Dial Indicator to Measure Total End Play

Move Connecting Shell Forward

Dial Indicator

Datsun shown. End play is measured at the same place on all models.

Fig. 22: Assembling Front and Rear Clutch Units

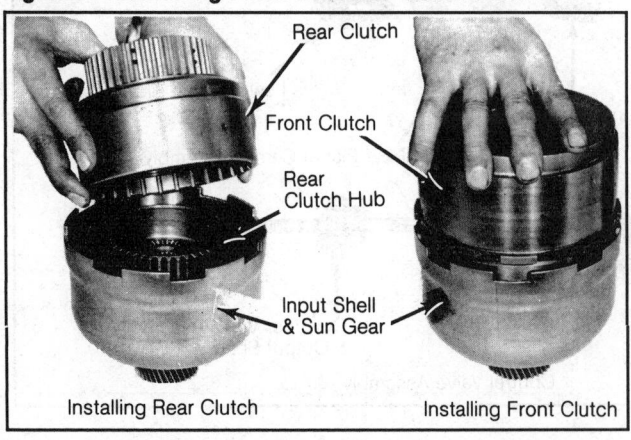

Rear Clutch

Front Clutch

Rear Clutch Hub

Input Shell & Sun Gear

Installing Rear Clutch   Installing Front Clutch

JATCO L3N71B & 3N71B (Cont.)

Fig. 25: Measuring Throttle Valve Depth

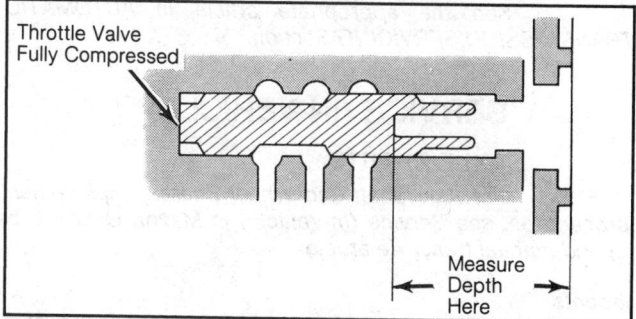

Measure depth with throttle valve completely compressed in bore. Measurement determines diaphragm rod selection.

TIGHTENING SPECIFICATIONS

Application	Ft. Lbs. (N.m)
Band Piston Stem Lock Nut	11-29 (15-39)
Converter Housing-to-Engine	
Datsun	29-36 (39-49)
All Other Models	23-34 (31-46)
Converter Housing-to-Trans. Case	
626	29-36 (39-49)
All Other Models	33-40 (45-54)
Drive Plate-to-Crankshaft	
Courier	54-64 (73-87)
Datsun	101-116 (137-157)
GLC Wagon & RX7	60-69 (81-94)
626	112-118 (152-160)
Drive Plate-to-Torque Converter	29-36 (39-49)
Manual Shaft Lock Nut	22-29 (30-39)
Oil Cooler Pipe Set Bolt	
Courier	12-17
All Others	17-26 (23-35)

	INCH Lbs. (N.m)
Governor Body-to-Oil Distributor	43-60 (4.9-6.8)
Inhibitor Switch-to-Trans. Case	43-60 (4.9-6.8)
Oil Pan-to-Trans. Case	43-60 (4.9-6.8)
Oil Pressure Test Plugs	
Courier, GLC Wagon & RX7	43-86 (4.9-9.7)
Datsun	120-180 (13.6-20.3)
626	84-132 (9.5-14.9)
Oil Pump Cover-to-Pump Housing	52-70 (5.9-7.9)
Oil Screen-to-Valve Body	26-35 (2.9-4.0)
One-Way Clutch Inner Race	108-156 (12.2-17.6)
Servo Piston Retainer-to-Trans. Case	
Courier & Mazda	84-132 (9.5-14.9)
Datsun	43-61 (4.9-6.9)
Valve Body-to-Trans. Case	48-65 (5.4-7.3)
Lower-to-Upper Valve Bodies	22-30 (2.5-3.4)
Valve Body Cover Plates	22-30 (2.5-3.4)
Extension Housing-to-Trans. Case	168-216 (19-24)

Automatic Transaxles

MAZDA F3A 3-SPEED

GLC (FWD)

DESCRIPTION

The transaxle consists of 3 main units: Automatic transmission, torque converter and differential assembly. The automatic transmission consists of front, rear and one-way clutches, low-reverse brake assembly, oil pump and hydraulic controls (valve body and servo piston assemblies). The torque converter and differential are housed together in the torque converter housing.

LUBRICATION & ADJUSTMENT

See the appropriate article in AUTOMATIC TRANSMISSION SERVICING Section.

SERVICE (IN VEHICLE)

AXLE SHAFTS

For Axle Shaft and Wheel Bearing replacement procedures, see Service (In-Vehicle) in Mazda GLC 4 & 5-Speed manual transaxle article.

Fig. 1: Exploded View of Transmission Housing & Primary Components

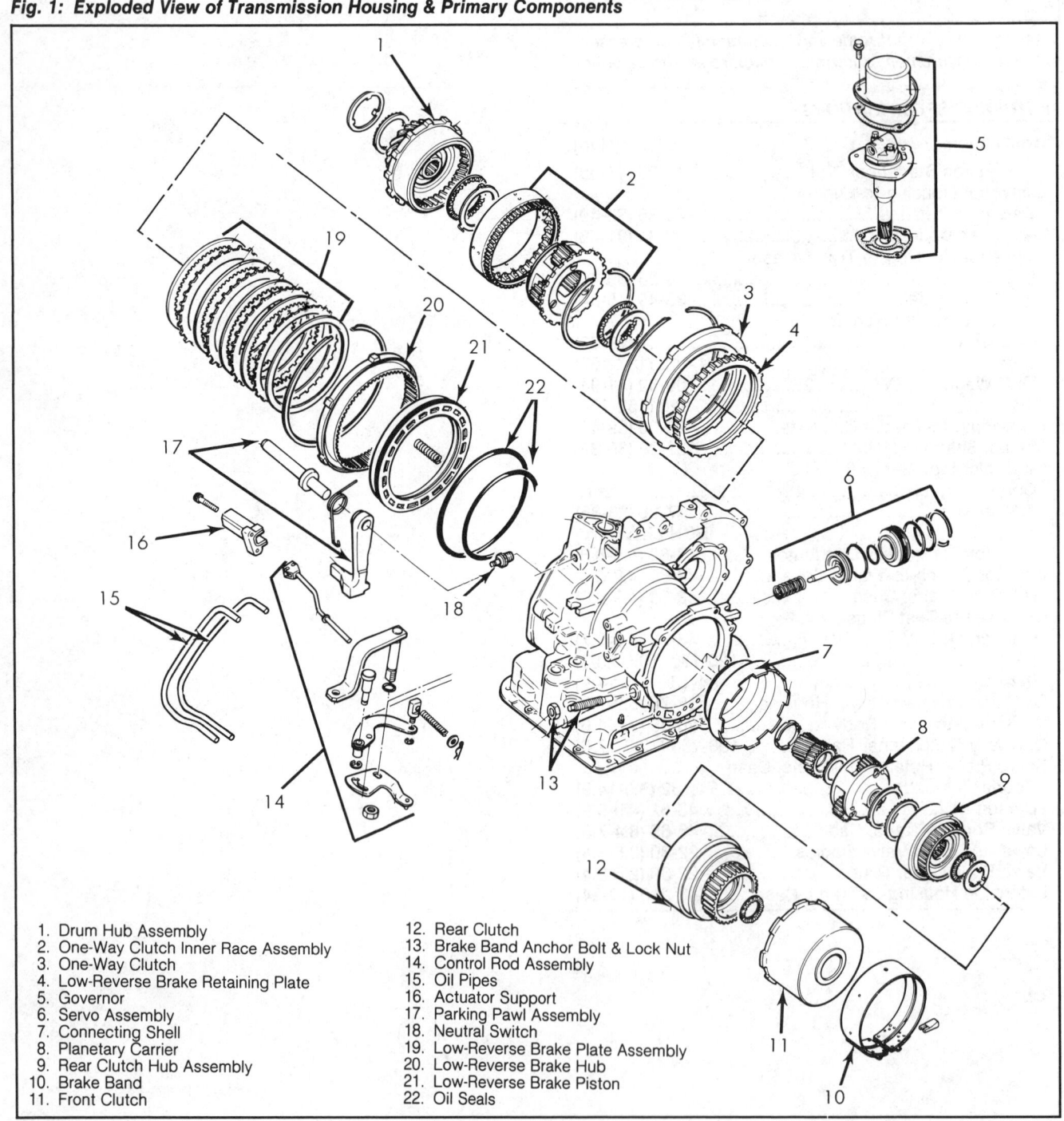

1. Drum Hub Assembly
2. One-Way Clutch Inner Race Assembly
3. One-Way Clutch
4. Low-Reverse Brake Retaining Plate
5. Governor
6. Servo Assembly
7. Connecting Shell
8. Planetary Carrier
9. Rear Clutch Hub Assembly
10. Brake Band
11. Front Clutch
12. Rear Clutch
13. Brake Band Anchor Bolt & Lock Nut
14. Control Rod Assembly
15. Oil Pipes
16. Actuator Support
17. Parking Pawl Assembly
18. Neutral Switch
19. Low-Reverse Brake Plate Assembly
20. Low-Reverse Brake Hub
21. Low-Reverse Brake Piston
22. Oil Seals

Automatic Transaxles

MAZDA F3A 3-SPEED (Cont.)

TROUBLE SHOOTING

ENGINE STARTS IN "D", "2", "1" OR "R", OR WILL NOT START IN "N" OR "P"
Check ignition and starter circuit. Shift linkage faulty or installed improperly. Leak in vacuum circuit.

NO MOVEMENT
In Any Gear
Incorrect fluid level. Shift linkage faulty, out of adjustment or incorrectly installed. Incorrect oil pressure. Manual control valve faulty. Faulty oil pump. Leak in hydraulic system. Parking linkage improperly adjusted.

In "D", OK in Other Gears
Shift linkage faulty, out of adjustment or improperly installed. Incorrect oil pressure. Manual control valve faulty. Faulty one-way clutch.

In "D", "2" OR "1", OK in "R"
Incorrect fluid level. Shift linkage faulty, out of adjustment or incorrectly installed. Incorrect oil pressure. Manual control valve faulty. Transmission fluid contaminated. Engine not performing to specifications or brakes improperly adjusted. Faulty front or rear clutch. Leak in hydraulic system.

In "R", OK in Other Gears
Transmission level incorrect. Shift linkage out of adjustment or faulty. Incorrect oil pressure. Manual control valve faulty. Transmission fluid contaminated. Faulty rear clutch, front clutch or low-reverse brake. Leak in hydraulic system.

VEHICLE "CREEPS" IN "N"
Shift linkage faulty, out of adjustment or incorrectly installed. Manual control valve faulty. Transmission fluid contaminated. Faulty rear clutch.

VEHICLE "CREEPS" EXCESSIVELY
Engine idle speed too high.

VEHICLE WILL NOT "CREEP"
Fluid level incorrect or fluid contaminated. Shift linkage defective, out of adjustment or incorrectly installed. Engine idle too low. Manual control valve faulty. Faulty oil pump. Leak in hydraulic system. Faulty front or rear clutch.

"N" TO "D" ENGAGEMENT HARSH
Engine idle too high. Leak in vacuum circuit. Incorrect oil pressure. Manual control valve faulty. Faulty rear clutch.

TRANSMISSION SLIPS IN FIRST GEAR
Incorrect fluid level. Shift linkage faulty, out of adjustment or incorrectly installed. Incorrect oil pressure. Manual control valve faulty. Transmission fluid contaminated. Incorrect idle speed. Kick-down solenoid, switch or wiring faulty.

EXCESSIVE SHOCK ON 1-2 SHIFT
Leak in vacuum circuit. Engine stall speed incorrect. Transmission fluid contaminated. Manual control valve faulty. Band servo faulty. Brake band damaged or out of adjustment.

EXCESSIVE SHOCK ON 2-3 SHIFT
Leak in vacuum circuit. Kickdown solenoid, switch or wiring faulty. Incorrect oil pressure. Manual control valve faulty. Band servo or front clutch faulty.

SHIFT SHOCK FELT ON DECELERATION
Shift linkage damaged, out of adjustment or incorrectly installed. Leak in vacuum circuit. Kickdown solenoid, switch or wiring faulty. Incorrect oil pressure. Manual control valve faulty. Governor valve faulty. Leak in hydraulic system.

EXCESSIVE 2-1 SHIFT SHOCK WITH LEVER IN "1" POSITION
Leak in vacuum circuit. Engine stall speed incorrect. Manual control valve faulty. Transmission fluid contaminated. Low-reverse brake faulty.

LITTLE OR NO SHIFT SHOCK; EXCESSIVE SLIPPAGE ON 1-2 SHIFT
Transmission fluid level incorrect. Shift linkage damaged, out of adjustment or incorrectly installed. Leak in vacuum circuit. Oil pressure incorrect. Manual control valve faulty. Band servo faulty. Transmission fluid contaminated. Brake band faulty. Leakage in hydraulic system.

NO SHIFT SHOCK; EXCESS SLIPPAGE WHEN SHIFTED FROM "1" TO "2"
Incorrect fluid level. Shift linkage damaged, out of adjustment or installed incorrectly. Leak in vacuum circuit. Engine idle speed incorrect. Engine stall speed incorrect. Manual control valve faulty. Transmission fluid contaminated. Brake band out of adjustment or damaged. Oil pump faulty.

MAXIMUM SPEED TOO LOW; POOR ACCELERATION
Incorrect fluid level or fluid contaminated. Shift linkage faulty, out of adjustment or incorrectly installed. Incorrect oil pressure. Engine stall speed incorrect. Manual control valve faulty. Band servo faulty. Engine not performing to specification or brakes incorrectly adjusted. Faulty front or rear clutch. Brake band damaged or out of adjustment. Low-reverse brake faulty. Oil pump faulty.

NO SHIFT FROM 1ST TO 2ND
Shift linkage defective, out of adjustment or incorrectly installed. Leak in vacuum circuit. Faulty kickdown solenoid, switch or wiring. Transmission fluid contaminated. Manual control valve faulty. Governor valve faulty. Band servo faulty. Brake band out of adjustment. Leak in hydraulic system.

NO SHIFT FROM 2ND TO 3RD
Shift linkage defective, out of adjustment or incorrectly installed. Leak in vacuum circuit. Faulty kickdown solenoid, switch or wiring. Transmission fluid contaminated. Manual control valve, governor valve or band servo faulty. Brake band out of adjustment. Front clutch faulty. Leak in hydraulic system.

Automatic Transaxles

MAZDA F3A 3-SPEED (Cont.)

Fig. 2: Mazda F3A Automatic Transmission Hydraulic Circuits Diagram

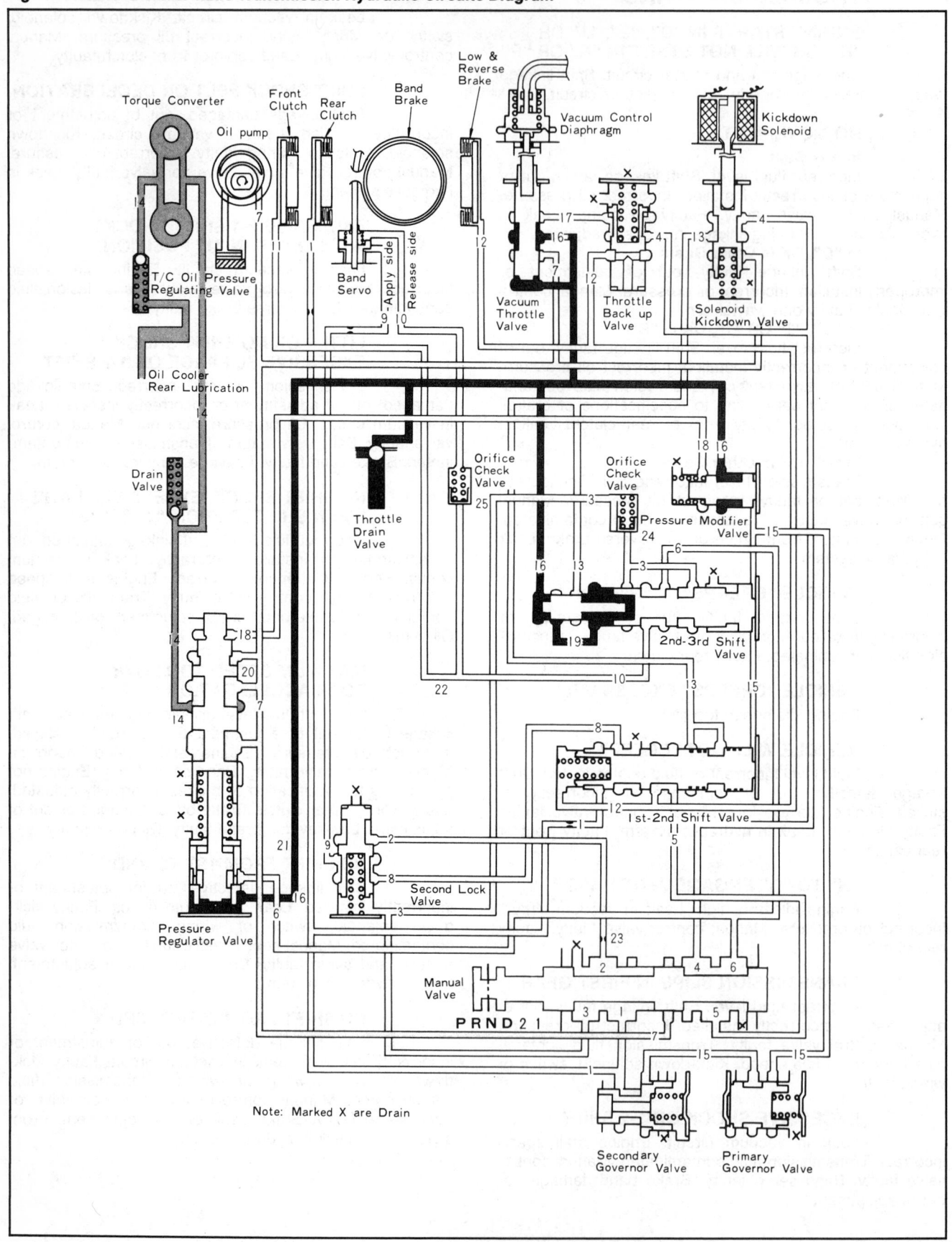

MAZDA F3A 3-SPEED (Cont.)

SHIFTS FROM 1ST TO 3RD; SKIPS 2ND

Transmission fluid contaminated. Manual control valve, governor valve or front clutch faulty. Leak in hydraulic system.

NO 3-2 DOWNSHIFT

Leak in vacuum circuit. Manual control valve, governor valve or band servo faulty. Transmission fluid contaminated. Brake band out of adjustment or damaged. Front clutch damaged. Leak in hydraulic system.

NO 2-1 OR 3-1 DOWNSHIFT

Leak in vacuum circuit. Manual control valve, governor valve or band servo faulty. Transmission fluid contaminated. Brake band out of adjustment or damaged. One-way clutch faulty.

SHIFT POINTS FROM 3RD TO 2ND, 2ND TO 1ST TOO HIGH

Shift linkage damaged, out of adjustment or incorrectly installed. Kickdown solenoid, switch or wiring faulty. Leak in vacuum circuit. Incorrect oil pressure. Manual control valve or governor valve faulty. Leak in hydraulic system.

NO KICKDOWN AT NORMAL SPEEDS IN 3RD GEAR

Leak in vacuum circuit. Kickdown solenoid, switch or wiring faulty. Manual control valve or governor valve faulty. Transmission fluid contaminated. Brake band out of adjustment or damaged. Leak in hydraulic system.

1-2 OR 2-3 GEAR SHIFT IN "1"

Shift linkage damaged, out of adjustment or installed incorrectly. Manual control valve faulty. Leak in hydraulic system.

NO 2-1 SHIFT WHEN SHIFTER MOVED FROM "D" TO "1" POSITION

Incorrect oil pressure. Shift linkage damaged, out of adjustment or installed incorrectly. Transmission fluid contaminated. Manual control valve faulty. Governor valve faulty. Band servo faulty. Leak in hydraulic system. Front clutch damaged. Brake band out of adjustment or damaged.

NO 3-2 DOWNSHIFT WHEN MANUALLY SHIFTED FROM "D" TO "2"

Shift linkage damaged, out of adjustment or installed incorrectly. Incorrect oil pressure. Manual control valve faulty. Band servo faulty. Transmission fluid contaminated. Brake band out of adjustment or damaged. Leak in hydraulic system.

2-1, 2-3 SHIFTS WITH SHIFT LEVER IN "2"

Shift linkage damaged, out of adjustment or installed incorrectly. Incorrect oil pressure. Manual control valve faulty.

EXCESSIVE ENGINE RPM WHEN ACCELERATING IN 3RD GEAR ABOVE KICKDOWN SPEED

Shift linkage damaged, out of adjustment or installed incorrectly. Leak in vacuum circuit. Oil pressure incorrect. Manual control valve or governor valve faulty. Transmission fluid contaminated. Front clutch faulty. Leak in hydraulic system.

ENGINE RUNAWAY OR TRANSMISSION SLIPPAGE ON 3-2 KICKDOWN

Leak in vacuum circuit. Oil pressure incorrect. Manual valve faulty. Band servo faulty. Transmission fluid contaminated. Front clutch faulty. Brake band out of adjustment or damaged. Leak in hydraulic system.

TRANSMISSION BRAKES IN "R"

Band servo faulty. Transmission fluid contaminated. Faulty rear clutch. Brake band damaged or out of adjustment. Parking linkage damaged or improperly adjusted.

VEHICLE BRAKES ON 1-2 SHIFT

Manual control valve faulty. Transmission fluid contaminated. Front clutch or low-reverse brake faulty. One-way clutch faulty.

VEHICLE BRAKES ON 2-3 SHIFT

Manual control valve faulty. Band servo faulty. Transmission fluid contaminated. Brake band out of adjustment or damaged.

NO ENGINE BRAKING IN "1"

Shift linkage damaged, out of adjustment or installed incorrectly. Incorrect oil pressure. Manual control valve faulty. Transmission fluid contaminated. Low-reverse brake faulty. Leak in hydraulic system.

VEHICLE MOVES IN "P"; PARKING GEAR REMAINS ENGAGED WHEN SHIFTED OUT OF "P" POSITION

Shift linkage damaged, out of adjustment or incorrectly installed. Parking linkage out of adjustment or damaged.

TRANSMISSION OVERHEATS

Incorrect fluid level or oil pressure. Incorrect stall speed. Insufficient rear lubrication. Manual control valve faulty. Faulty band servo. Transmission fluid contaminated. Faulty front clutch, low-reverse brake, oil pump or torque converter one-way clutch. Brake band out of adjustment or damaged. Leak in hydraulic system. Planetary gear faulty.

TRANSMISSION NOISY

In "P" or "N"

Incorrect fluid level. Incorrect oil pressure. Faulty oil pump.

In All Other Drive Ranges

Incorrect fluid level. Incorrect oil pressure. Rear clutch, oil pump, one-way clutch or planetary gear faulty.

TESTING

ROAD TEST

1) Before road test, ensure that fluid level, condition and control linkage adjustments have been checked and corrected as necessary. During test, trans-

Automatic Transaxles
MAZDA F3A 3-SPEED (Cont.)

mission should upshift and downshift at approximately same speed as shown in *Shift Speeds Chart*. All shifts may vary slightly due to production tolerances or tire size. The important factor is the quality of the shifts. All shifts should be smooth, responsive and with no slippage or engine speed runaway.

2) Slippage or engine speed runaway in any gear usually indicates clutch or band problems. The slipping clutch or band in a particular gear can usually be identified by noting transmission operation in other selector positions and comparing internal units which are applied in these positions. *See Clutch and Band Application Chart.*

3) With vehicle at a standstill, accelerate under half and full throttle conditions to ensure that 1-2 and 2-3 shifts occur within specified range.

4) With shift lever in "D" position and vehicle speed at about 55 MPH, depress accelerator pedal to floor and ensure that a 3-2 downshift occurs. Slow vehicle to about 25 mph. Repeat and ensure that a 2-1 downshift occurs.

STALL TEST
Testing Precautions
When making test, do not hold throttle open any longer than 5 seconds. Shift to "N" and allow engine to idle for at least 1 minute between tests to cool transmission. If engine speed exceeds maximum limit shown in *Stall Speed Specifications* table, release accelerator immediately as clutch or band slippage is indicated.

SHIFT SPEED CHART

Application	Shift Points (MPH) Half Throttle	Full Throttle
1-2 Upshift	9-21	30-43
2-3 Upshift	17-38	54-74
3-2 Downshift	[1] 6-13	[2] 48-64
2-1 Downshift	[3] 23-32	[2] 13-29

[1] — Coastdown. Throttle fully closed.
[2] — Kickdown.
[3] — Shift lever in "1" position. Throttle fully closed.

Testing Procedures
With engine at normal operating temperature, tachometer installed and parking and service brakes applied, make transmission stall test in "D", "2", "1" and "R" ranges at full throttle and note maximum RPM obtained.

STALL SPEED SPECIFICATIONS

Application	Stall RPM
All Models	2200-2450

Stall Test Results
If stall speed is below specifications, engine performance is unsatisfactory or torque converter one-way clutch is faulty (slipping). If stall speed is high in all drive ranges, oil pressure is incorrect. Check oil pump (weak), oil pump control valve and transmission case for leaks. Check pressure regulator valve (sticking). If stall speed is high in forward gears only, the rear clutch is slipping; in "D" only, the one-way clutch is slipping; in "2" only, the brake band is slipping. If high in "R" only, either the low-reverse brake or the front clutch is slipping.

HYDRAULIC PRESSURE TESTS
Line Pressure
1) Attach oil pressure gauge at line pressure checking plug located at rear of transaxle case on left side. *See Fig. 3.* Attach tachometer. Position gauges so that they may be observed from the driver's seat.

Fig. 3: Transaxle Assembly

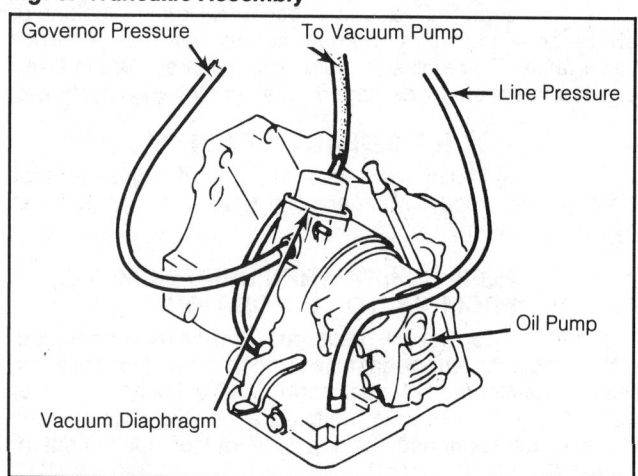

Attach lines as shown for hydraulic pressure tests.

CLUTCH AND BAND APPLICATION CHART (ELEMENTS IN USE)

Selector Lever Position	Front Clutch	Rear Clutch	Low-Reverse Brake	Brake Band	One-Way Clutch
D — DRIVE					
First		X			X
Second		X		X	
Third	X	X			
2 — INTERMEDIATE		X		X	
1 — LOW					
Second		X		X	
First		X	X		
R — REVERSE	X		X		
P — PARK			X		

NEUTRAL — All clutches and bands released and/or ineffective.

MAZDA F3A 3-SPEED (Cont.)

2) With engine at normal operating temperature, transmission fluid level correct and transmission in "D", check line pressure at idle and stall speed. Repeat test in "2" and "R", allowing sufficient time for engine and transmission to cool between tests. Record results.

3) Disconnect line from vacuum diaphragm and connect a vacuum pump at connection. With shift lever in "D", increase engine RPM gradually and observe gauge reading. If line pressure drops abruptly, check governor pressure.

LINE PRESSURES TABLE

| Gear Range | Line Pressure In psi (kg/cm²) | |
	At Idle	At Stall Speed
"D"	43-57	128-156
	(3.0-4.0)	(9.0-11.0)
"2"	114-171	114-171
	(8.0-12.0)	(8.0-12.0)
"R"	57-110	228-270
	(4.0-7.7)	(16.0-19.0)

Governor Pressure Tests

1) Attach vacuum pump at vacuum diaphragm and oil pressure gauge at governor port. With gauge on pump at zero, check governor pressure and record result. Increase vacuum to 7.9 in. Hg (200 mm Hg) and record gauge reading. Pressure observed should be 14-23 psi (1.0-1.6 kg/cm²) at zero and 6-14 psi (.4-1.0 kg/cm²) at 7.9 in. Hg. If readings are not to specifications, check that the vacuum diaphragm rod is installed correctly and check that the manual control valve is not sticking.

2) With oil pressure gauge attached as in step 1) and shift lever in "D", accelerate vehicle smoothly and record governor pressure readings at 20, 35 and 55 MPH. If recorded results are not to specifications as given in *Governor Pressures* table, check for fluid leakage from the line pressure hydraulic circuit and/or the governor pressure hydraulic circuit. Check for faulty governor.

GOVERNOR PRESSURES

Vehicle Speed (MPH)	Pressure on Gauge Psi (kg/cm²)
20	11-20 (.8-1.4)
35	24-34 (1.7-2.4)
55	48-64 (3.4-4.5)

TRANSAXLE REMOVAL & INSTALLATION

See the appropriate article in AUTOMATIC TRANSMISSION REMOVAL Section.

TORQUE CONVERTER

The torque converter is a sealed unit and cannot be disassembled for service. If the converter or any component thereof is found to be faulty, the entire assembly must be replaced.

TRANSAXLE DISASSEMBLY

Whenever working with transmission, it is important that normal standards of cleanliness be ob-

served. Complete transaxle assembly should be thoroughly steam cleaned before beginning any disassembly. Disassemble only those parts which require repair or replacement. Compressed air is preferred for drying components and oil passages, however, nylon cloth may be used. Never use fluffy rags or cloths to wipe parts dry.

Fig. 4: Transaxle Outer Components

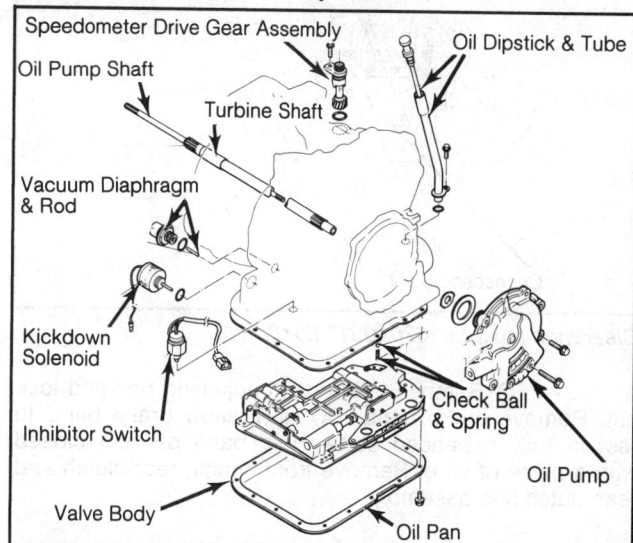

Use care when removing valve body so as not to lose check ball and spring.

1) Remove torque converter. Attach transaxle to hanger (49 F401 495) and place on engine stand. Remove inhibitor switch, kickdown solenoid and vacuum diaphragm with rod, from transmission case. Remove oil dipstick and tube. Remove speedometer drive gear retaining bolt and lift out gear assembly.

2) Remove oil pump drive shaft and turbine shaft. Remove oil pan. Remove valve body, being careful not to lose check ball and spring. Measure and record front clutch drum end play. To determine front clutch drum end play, pry clutch drum toward oil pump with screwdriver and measure gap between drum and the connecting shell.

3) End play should be .020-.031" (.5-.8 mm). Determine adjusting shims required to bring end play to specifications and record for reassembly. Shims are available in thicknesses of .051" (1.3 mm) to .106" (2.7 mm) in increments of .008" (.02 mm).

4) Remove oil pump. If oil pump is difficult to remove, tighten brake band adjusting bolt until front clutch locks, then remove pump. Measure total end play. To do so, remove pump cover from oil pump. Place bearing in front brake drum. Fit bearing outer race on pump cover and install in front brake drum.

5) Place straightedge on face of transmission case and measure distance between straightedge and pump cover or straightedge and transmission case. Pump cover should be between .004" (.10 mm) below transmission case and .006" (.15 mm) above case. Limits are .008" (.20 mm) and .012" (.30 mm), respectively.

6) If end play is not to specifications, select new bearing race as needed to obtain correct end play. Selective bearing races are available in thicknesses of .047" (1.2 mm) to .087" (2.2 mm) in increments of .008" (.2 mm). Record race chosen for reassembly reference.

MAZDA F3A 3-SPEED (Cont.)

Fig. 5: Measuring Front Clutch Drum End Play

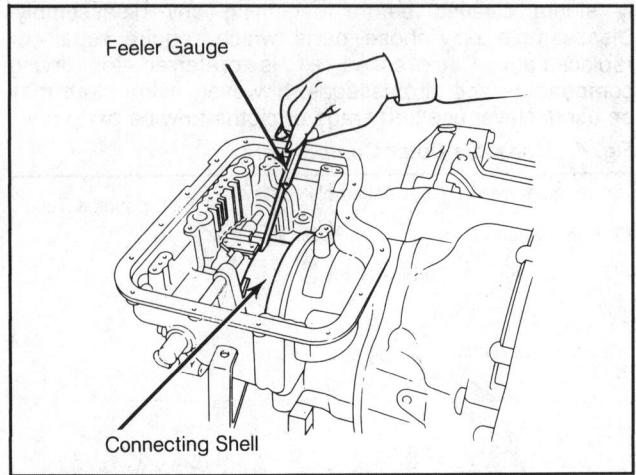

Clearance must be .020-.031" (.5-.8 mm).

7) Remove brake band adjusting bolt and lock nut. Remove brake band. DO NOT allow brake band to rest in fully expanded state. Hold band partially closed with a piece of wire. Remove front clutch, rear clutch and rear clutch hub assembly.

Fig. 6: Measuring Transaxle Total End Play

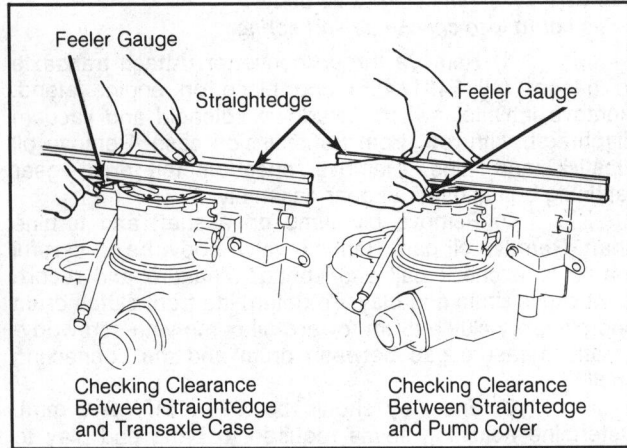

Checking Clearance Between Straightedge and Transaxle Case

Checking Clearance Between Straightedge and Pump Cover

8) Remove planetary gear carrier, sun gear with spacer and connecting shell. Compress servo piston with "C" clamp and remove snap ring. Release "C" clamp and remove servo piston.

9) Separate transmission case from torque converter case. Remove neutral switch and governor assembly from transmission case. Remove oil pipes and parking pawl assembly. Remove drum hub assembly. Remove one-way clutch inner race assembly.

10) Attach dial indicator and measure clearance between one-way clutch and low-reverse brake assembly. With gauge pin resting on drive plate, move plate up and down by hand while observing indicator dial. Clearance should be .031-.041" (.80-1.05 mm).

11) If clearance is not to specifications, select a retaining plate of different thickness to obtain correct clearance. Retaining plates are available in thicknesses of .181" (4.6 mm) to .221" (5.6 mm) in increments of .008" (.2 mm). Record plate chosen for reassembly reference.

Fig. 7: Removing Servo Piston.

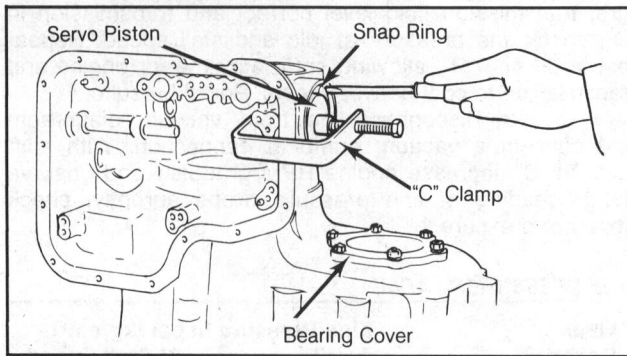

Compress piston with "C" clamp while removing snap ring.

Fig. 8: Checking Low-Reverse Brake Clearance

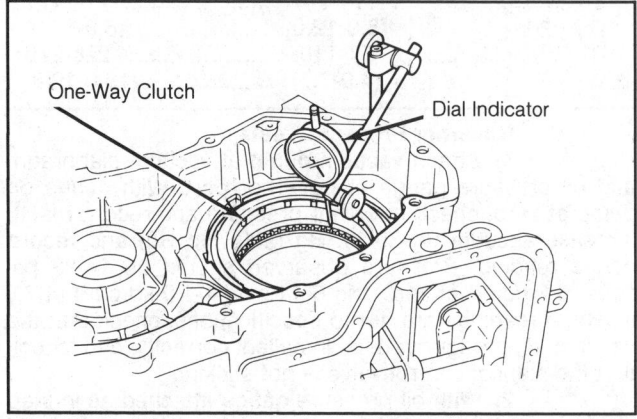

Clearance must be .031-.041" (.80-1.05 mm).

12) Remove snap ring, one-way clutch and low-reverse brake retaining plate. Remove low-reverse brake plates. Attach low-reverse brake hub and piston removal tool (49 FT01 377). Remove snap ring with screwdriver, then remove brake hub and piston.

13) Drive out manual shaft retaining spring pin and remove manual shaft assembly. Do not lose check ball and spring. Remove shift control rod assembly and assembly support. Retain all components in correct order to aid in installation procedures.

Fig. 9: Removing Low-Reverse Brake Hub & Piston

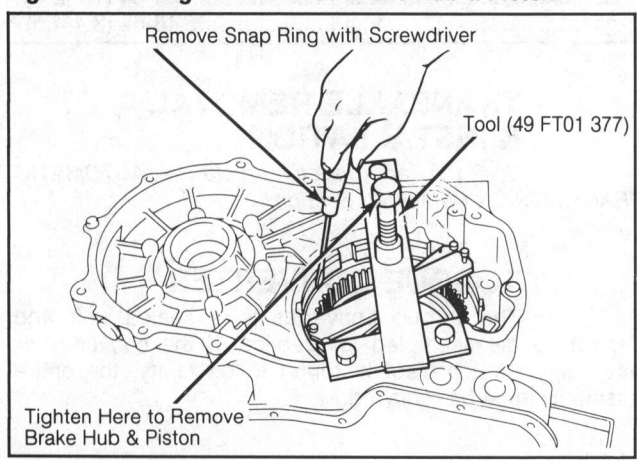

Tighten tool slowly as brake and piston assembly is removed.

MAZDA F3A 3-SPEED (Cont.)

14) Remove differential assembly from torque converter housing. Remove bearing housing assembly (with idler and output gears). If necessary, strike idler shaft lightly with soft hammer to ease bearing housing removal. Drive out idler gear retaining spring pin and remove idler from bearing housing. Remove output gear assembly and press off bearing race. Save adjusting shim for reassembly.

Fig. 10: Torque Converter Housing Components

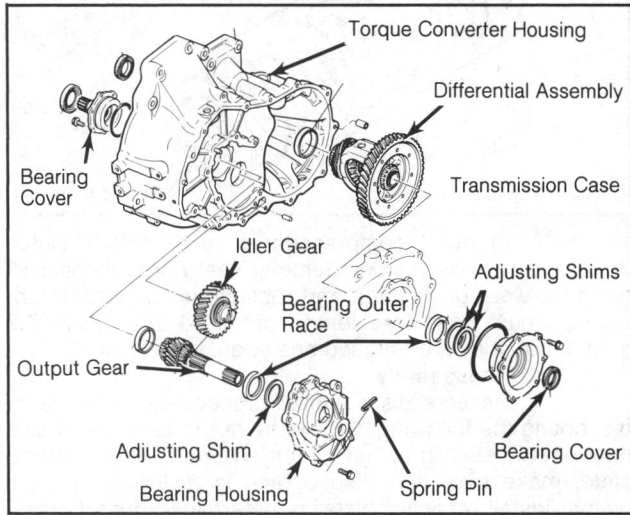

15) Remove 6 bearing cover-to-transmission case retaining bolts and remove bearing cover. Press off bearing race. Remove and retain adjusting shims for reassembly. Drive out oil seal. Remove bearing cover from torque converter side of torque converter housing. Press out bearing race. Drive oil seal from last bearing cover removed. Remove bearing race from differential assembly.

COMPONENT DISASSEMBLY & REASSEMBLY

When reassembling transaxle components, observe the folllowing practices and precautions:
- Wash all parts thoroughly.
- Use new drive plates in all clutch assemblies.
- Soak drive plates and brake band in ATF for at least 2 hours before assembly in the transaxle.
- Use petroleum jelly as needed to hold thrust bearings and/or washers in place during installation. Do not use grease.

OIL PUMP
Disassembly
1) Remove pump cover retaining bolts and separate cover from pump body. Remove pump flange. If gears are to be reused, scribe marks on gears to ensure reassembly in same position. Remove drive and driven gears.

2) Check condition of gear teeth and surfaces. Check seal ring for cracks or breaks and replace as needed. Check condition of pump housing sleeve and inner gear bushing. Check sleeve outer diameter and bushing inner diameter. If sleeve diameter is less than 1.499" (38.075 mm) or bushing diameter is greater than 1.492" (37.90 mm), replace sleeve and bushing as a set.

Fig. 11: Exploded View of Oil Pump Assembly

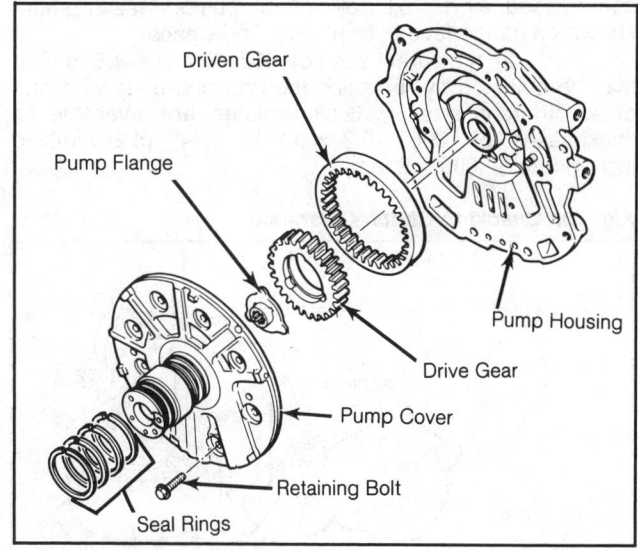

OIL PUMP CLEARANCES

Application	[1] Clearance In. (mm)
Drive/Driven Gear-to-Housing	.001-.002 (.02-.04)
Driven Gear-to-Crescent	.006-.008 (.15-.20)
Driven Gear Side Clearance	.002-.008 (.04-.20)
Seal Ring Side Clearance	.002-.006 (.04-.15)

[1] — Clearances given are standard values. Wear limits are .003" (.08 mm), .010" (.25 mm), .010" (.25 mm) and .016" (.40 mm), respectively.

Reassembly
Reverse disassembly procedures to reassemble, noting the following: Make sure match marks on gears are properly aligned. Before installing pump flange or cover, check pump clearances and compare with values shown in *Oil Pump Clearances* table. With assembly complete, install oil pump drive shaft and check that gears rotate smoothly.

FRONT CLUTCH
Disassembly
1) Before disassembling clutch, check clearance. Place front clutch on oil pump, install dial indicator

Fig. 12: Exploded View of Front Clutch

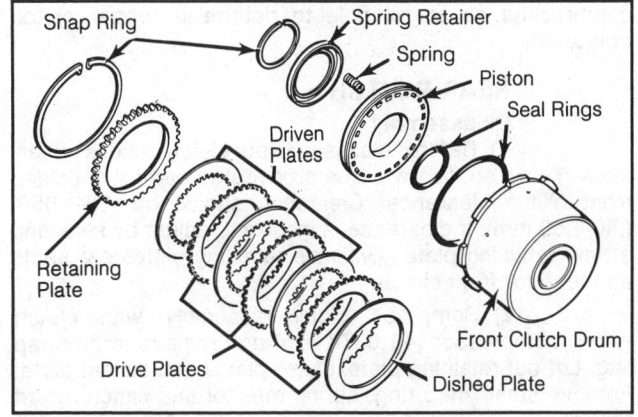

so that the plunger rests on retaining plate and apply compressed air to oil hole of oil pump. Measurement shown on gauge face is front clutch clearance.

2) If clearance is not .063-.071" (1.6-1.8 mm), it may be adjusted by replacing the retaining plate with one of a different size. Retaining plates are available in thicknesses of .205" (5.2 mm) to .244" (6.2 mm) in increments of .008" (.2 mm).

Fig. 13: Checking Clutch Clearance

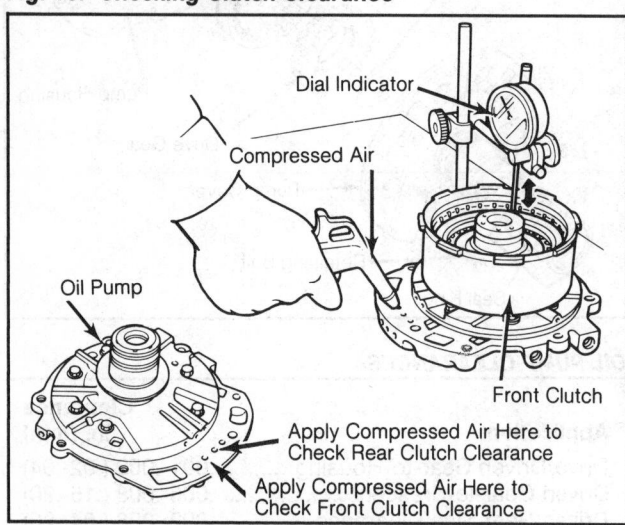

Apply compressed air at oil passages indicated.

3) Compress clutch assembly with clutch spring compressor (49 0378 375) and remove large snap ring. Lift out retaining plate, clutch plates and dished plate. Remove small snap ring, spring retainer and clutch return springs. Apply compressed air at oil hole in clutch drum and remove piston. Remove seal rings.

4) Inspect all parts for wear or damage and replace as needed. Return springs must have free length of .992-1.071" (25.2-27.2 mm). If not, they are fatigued and should be replaced. Check inside diameter of clutch drum bushing. If diameter exceeds 1.735" (44.075 mm), replace bushing.

Reassembly

Reverse disassembly procedures to reassemble, noting the following: Be careful to avoid damage to oil seal ring when installing clutch piston. When installing dished plate, make sure that dished face is away from piston. Install retaining plate as determined during disassembly. Place clutch assembly on oil pump and apply compressed air to oil hole to determine proper clutch operation.

REAR CLUTCH
Disassembly

1) Before disassembling clutch, check clearance. To do so, follow same procedure used for checking front clutch clearance. Clearance should be .031-.059" (.80-1.50 mm). If clearance is incorrect, adjust by selecting a new retaining plate. Available retaining plates are same as those for front clutch.

2) Compress clutch assembly with clutch spring compressor (49 0378 375) and remove large snap ring. Lift out retaining plate, clutch plates and dished plate. Remove small snap ring, spring retainer and clutch return springs.

Fig. 14: Exploded View of Rear Clutch

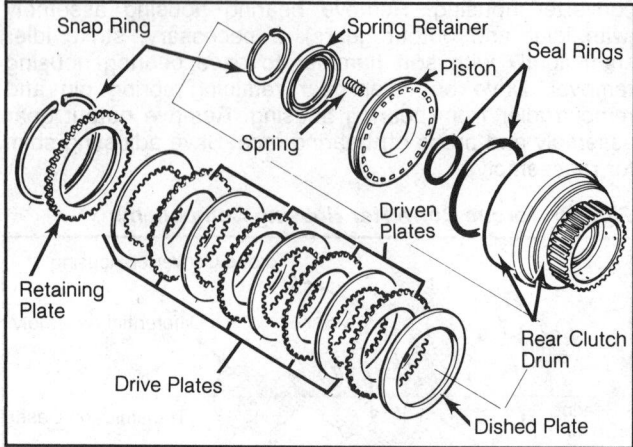

3) Apply compressed air to oil hole in clutch drum and remove piston. Remove seal rings. Inspect all parts for wear or damage and replace as needed. Return springs must have free length of .992-1.071" (25.2-27.2 mm). If not, they are fatigued and should be replaced.

Reassembly

Reverse disassembly procedures to reassemble, noting the following: Be careful not to damage oil seal ring when installing clutch piston. When installing dished plate, make sure that dished face is facing away from piston. Install retaining plate as determined during disassembly. Place clutch assembly on oil pump and apply compressed air at oil hole in pump to determine proper clutch operation.

DRUM HUB
Disassembly

Remove parking gear spring. Push in parking gear retaining pin with screwdriver and remove parking gear. Remove snap ring and lift internal gear assembly from drive hub. Check gears for excessive wear or damage and replace if needed.

Fig. 15: Exploded View of Drum Hub Assembly

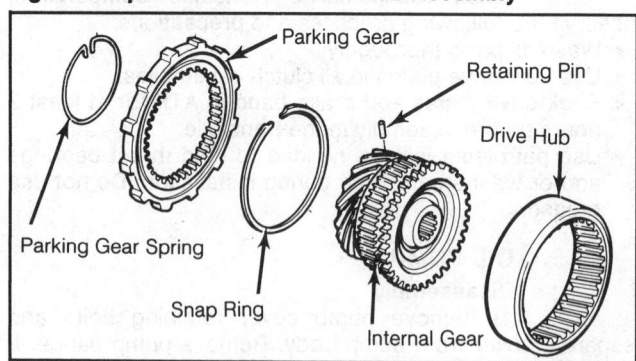

Reassembly

Reverse disassembly procedures to reassemble drum hub.

REAR CLUTCH HUB
Disassembly & Reassembly

Remove snap ring and separate hub from internal gear. Check for worn or damaged snap ring or gear. Replace as needed. Reassemble in reverse order of disassembly.

MAZDA F3A 3-SPEED (Cont.)

ONE-WAY CLUTCH

Disassembly

1) One-way clutch and one-way clutch inner race are removed from transmission case separately. The clutch requires no further disassembly. The inner race is disassembled by removing the snap ring and separating the inner race from the planetary carrier.

2) Check for worn or damaged gears on inner race. Check pinion operation in planetary carrier. Check clearance between the pinion washer and planetary carrier. Clearance must not exceed .031" (.8 mm).

Reassembly

Reverse disassembly procedures to reassemble, noting the following: Install one-way clutch in inner race and ensure that it will turn in one direction only.

LOW-REVERSE BRAKE

Disassembly

Low-Reverse brake assembly was disassembled during transaxle disassembly. Check all components for signs of damage or excessive wear. Check return springs free length. If length is not 1.051-1.130" (26.7-28.7 mm), the spring is fatigued and should be replaced.

Reassembly

Reassembly will be accomplished when transaxle is reassembled. See Transaxle Reassembly.

GOVERNOR ASSEMBLY

Disassembly

Remove 2 governor housing retaining bolts and separate governor body with shaft from housing. Separate body from shaft using care not to lose filter. Disassemble governor body and retain components in correct order for reassembly. Check filter and clean if clogged. Check return springs free length and outside diameter. If not to specification, replace spring.

Fig. 16: Exploded View of Governor Assembly

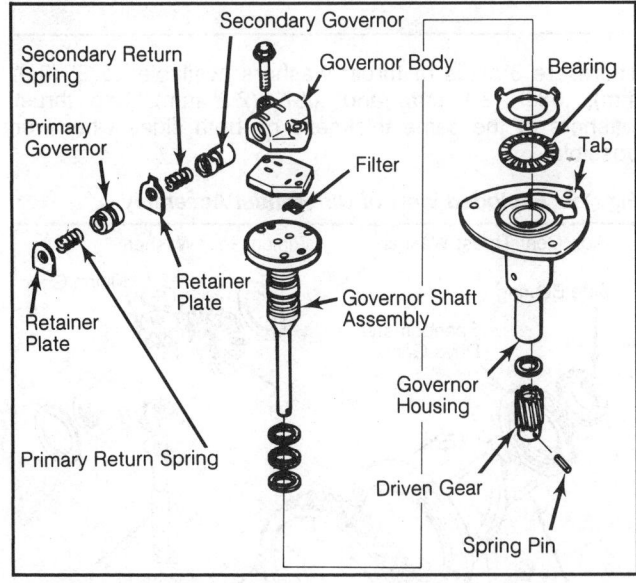

Reassembly

Reverse disassembly procedure to assemble, noting the following: Apply compressed air at top oil hole in housing and ensure that valve is operating properly.

GOVERNOR RETURN SPRING SPECIFICATIONS

Application	Free Length In. (mm)	Diameter In. (mm)
Primary Spring	.650-.728 (16.5-18.5)	.350-.366 (8.7-9.3)
Secondary Spring	.488-.567 (12.4-14.4)	.352-.396 (8.95-9.55)

VALVE BODY

Many components of the valve body assembly are very similar in appearance. Therefore, care should be taken that the different components are kept separate from each other during disassembly. Arrange valves, springs and plugs relative to their positions in the valve body to aid in reassembly.

Disassembly

1) Remove manual control valve. Remove oil stainer retaining bolts and remove oil strainer. Remove upper-to-lower valve body retaining bolts. Separate valve bodies, separator plate and sub-body. Use care not to lose check balls and springs or orifice valve and spring.

Fig. 17: Check Ball and Valve Locations

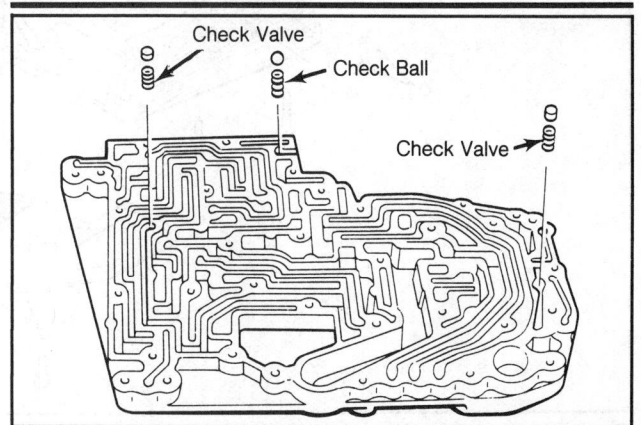

2) Remove side plate. Remove vacuum throttle valve, throttle backup valve and spring, and downshift valve and spring. Remove end plate. Remove pressure modifer valve and spring, 2-3 shift valve, spring and plug, and 1-2 shift valve and spring.

VALVE BODY SPRING IDENTIFICATION

Spring	Outer Diameter In. (mm)	Free Length In. (mm)
Throttle Backup Valve	.287 (7.3)	1.417 (36.0)
Downshift Valve	.218 (5.55)	.866 (22.0)
Pressure Modifier Valve	.331 (8.4)	.728 (18.5)
2-3 Shift Valve	.272 (6.9)	1.164 (41.0)
1-2 Shift Valve	.258 (6.55)	1.260 (32.0)
Second Lock Valve	.218 (5.55)	1.319 (33.5)
Pressure Regulator Valve	.461 (11.7)	1.693 (43.0)
Steel Check Ball Spring	.256 (6.5)	1.516 (26.8)
Orifice Check Valve	.197 (5.0)	.846 (21.5)

Fig. 18: Exploded View of Valve Body and Main Controls

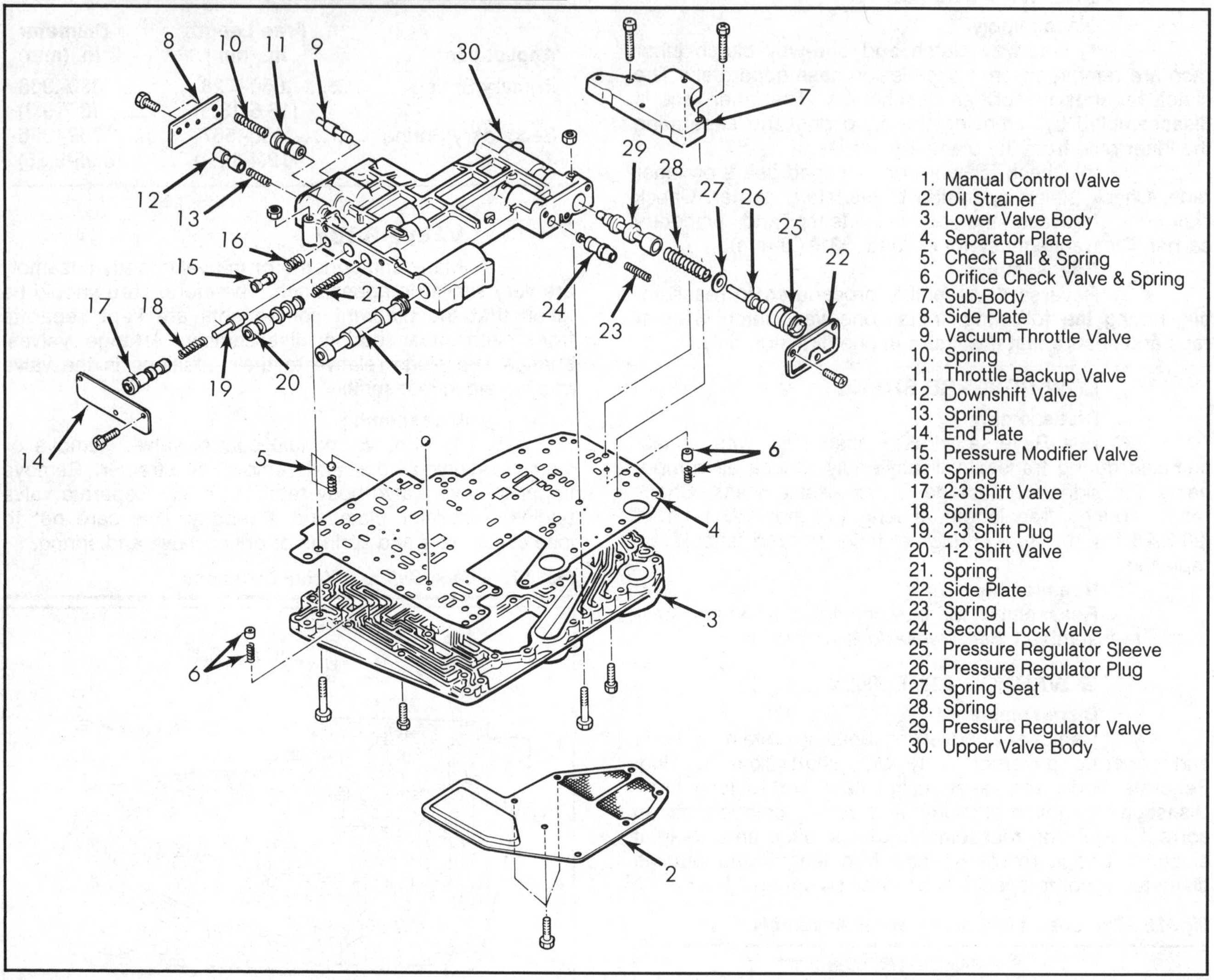

1. Manual Control Valve
2. Oil Strainer
3. Lower Valve Body
4. Separator Plate
5. Check Ball & Spring
6. Orifice Check Valve & Spring
7. Sub-Body
8. Side Plate
9. Vacuum Throttle Valve
10. Spring
11. Throttle Backup Valve
12. Downshift Valve
13. Spring
14. End Plate
15. Pressure Modifier Valve
16. Spring
17. 2-3 Shift Valve
18. Spring
19. 2-3 Shift Plug
20. 1-2 Shift Valve
21. Spring
22. Side Plate
23. Spring
24. Second Lock Valve
25. Pressure Regulator Sleeve
26. Pressure Regulator Plug
27. Spring Seat
28. Spring
29. Pressure Regulator Valve
30. Upper Valve Body

3) Remove side plate. Remove second lock valve and spring. Remove pressure regulator valve assembly (sleeve, plug, seat, spring and valve).

Reassembly

Reverse order of disassembly, noting the following: Coat all parts with clean transmission fluid. When tightening parts, be sure to observe the specified torque values. Do not force valves into position. They should push lightly into place by hand. Ensure orifice check valve, check ball and springs are located correctly. Put separator plate in place and hold there with hand clamps. Install upper valve body and bolt in place.

DIFFERENTIAL

Disassembly

1) Measure side gear and pinion gear backlash before disassembling differential assembly. To do so, insert both drive shafts into differential and support by shafts in "V" blocks. Position dial indicator with plunger resting on teeth of pinion gear. Measure backlash. Repeat procedure with plunger on other pinion gear.

2) Backlash readings should be less than .004" (.1 mm). If not, adjust by changing thrust washers.

There are 3 sizes of thrust washers available: .079" (2.0) mm), .083" (2.1 mm) and .087" (2.2 mm). Use thrust washers of the same thickness on both sides whenever possible.

Fig. 19: Exploded View of Differential Assembly

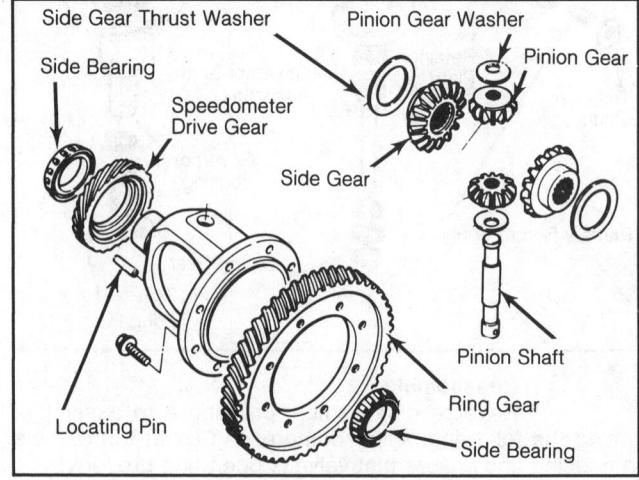

MAZDA F3A 3-SPEED (Cont.)

3) Disassemble differential assembly. Remove ring gear retaining bolts, knock out locating pin and remove right gear. Push out pinion gear shaft. Remove pinion and side gears, with washers, from case. Place differential housing in press and support by bearing on opposite side from ring gear. Press differential case out from bearing. Remove ring gear side bearing with a bearing puller.

4) Side bearings are severely damaged when removed, therefore, new bearings must always be used when differential is reassembled. Remove speedometer drive gear. Check all gears for signs of excessive wear or damage. Check differential gear case for cracks or other damage. Replace as needed.

Reassembly

DO NOT reuse side bearings. Press on new side bearings. Reverse removal procedures to complete reassembly.

IDLER GEAR ASSEMBLY

Disassembly

Attach idler shaft holder (49 FT01 439) to idler shaft and support assembly in vise. Remove lock nut. Remove bearing, spacer, idler gear, adjusting shim(s) and remaining bearing. Press bearing outer races from idler gear. Check all gear teeth for wear or damage and bearings for breakage or signs of unusual wear.

Fig. 20: Exploded View of Idler Gear Assembly

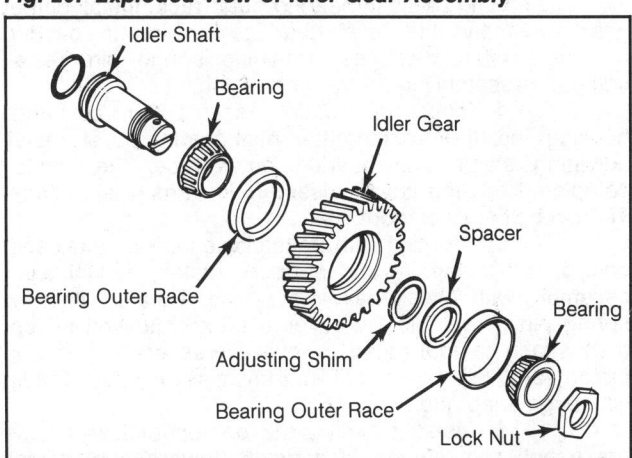

Reassembly

1) Reverse disassembly procedures to reassemble, noting the following: Check bearing preload. Clamp idler gear assembly in a soft-jawed vise and tighten lock nut to 130 ft. lbs. (177 N.m). Attach idler shaft holder (49 FT01 439) and preload attachment (49 0180 510A) to idler shaft. Connect spring scale to preload attachment and measure bearing preload.

2) Bearing preload should be .07-2.1 lbs. (.03-.95 kg). If preload is too high, loosen lock nut to a minimum of 94 ft. lbs. (128 N.m) to obtain correct reading. If correct preload cannot be obtained within these torque specifications, further adjustment is possible by changing the number and/or thickness of adjusting shims used.

3) Five adjusting shims are available in thicknesses of .004" (.09 mm) to .018" (.45 mm) in increments of .001" (.03 mm). Do not use more than 7 shims to obtain correct preload. Increasing thickness of shim pack will reduce the bearing preload.

TRANSAXLE REASSEMBLY

OUTPUT GEAR PRELOAD

If output gear, bearing housing, bearing cover, output gear bearings and/or converter housing is replaced, output gear bearing preload must be checked and adjusted before transaxle reassembly.

1) To check preload, the following special tools are required: Bearing selector (49 FT01 383), preload adaptor (49 FT01 389 and attachment, 49 0180 510A), spacers (49 FT01 384), bars (49 F401 385) and bolt set (49 FT01 386).

2) Remove bearing outer race and adjusting shims from bearing housing. Set output gear assembly in converter housing. Place outer race on bearing selector and attach selector with race to output gear assembly. Turn halves of selector to eliminate gap between them.

3) Install bearing housing on selector. Place 4 spacers between converter housing and bearing housing and install bolts through bearing housing, spacers and into converter housing. Tighten bolts to 14-19 ft. lbs. (19-26 N.m). *See Fig. 21* for proper positioning of spacers.

4) To seat bearing, insert bars in holes in each half of bearing selector. Turn halves as gap between them widens. Continue to increase gap until selector stops. Reverse direction and close gap.

Fig. 21: Measuring Output Gear Bearing Preload

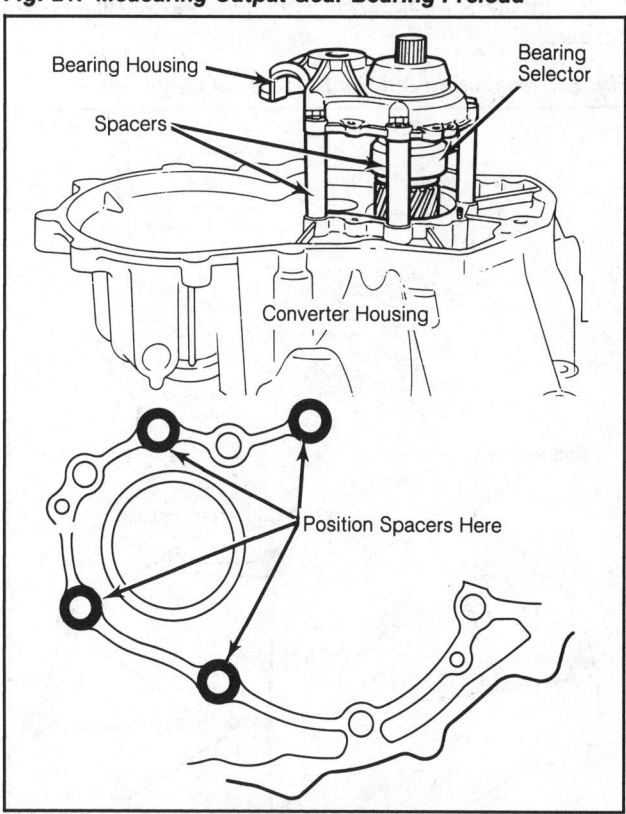

Position spacers between converter and bearing housings in positions as shown.

5) Set preload adapter and attachment on output gear. Measure bearing preload while gradually increasing gap in bearing selector. When preload is 1.1-2.0 lbs. (.5-.9 kg), measure gap in selector (check at several different points). Select adjusting shims to fill gap

Automatic Transaxles

MAZDA F3A 3-SPEED (Cont.)

at widest point. Shims are available in thicknesses of .004" (.10 mm) to .008" (.20 mm) in .001" (.002 mm) increments, and .020" (.50 mm). Do not exceed 7 shims in the pack.

6) Remove selector, install shims and install bearing housing. Check that preload with components properly installed is .07-.20 lbs. (.03-.09 kg).

DIFFERENTIAL SIDE BEARING PRELOAD

If differential gear case, side bearing(s), bearing cover, torque converter housing and/or transmission case is replaced, differential side bearing preload must be checked and adjusted before transaxle reassembly.

1) To check preload, the following special tools will be required: Bearing selector (49 F401 381), preload adapter (49 FT01 515), spacers (49 F401 384), bars (49 F401 385) and bolt set (49 FT01 387).

2) Remove bearing outer race and adjusting shims from differential bearing cover. Place differential assembly in converter housing. Place outer race on bearing selector and place selector with race in differential assembly. Turn halves of selector to eliminate gap between them.

3) Install transmission case on selector using 6 spacers between transmission case and torque converter housing. Install bolts through transmission case, spacers and into converter housing. Tighten bolts to 23-34 ft. lbs. (32-47 N.m). See *Fig. 22* for proper positioning of spacers.

Fig. 22: Measuring Differential Side Bearing Preload

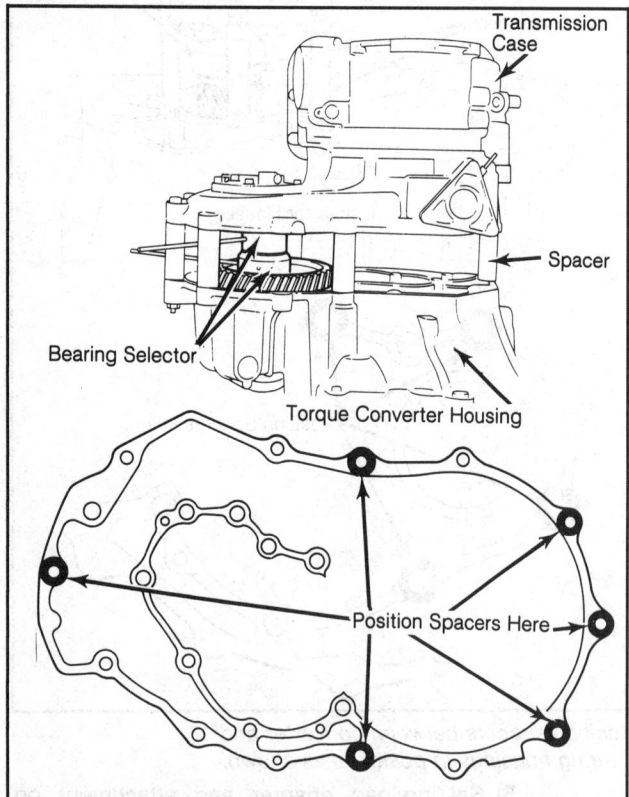

Position spacers between transmission case and converter housing as shown.

4) To seat bearing, insert bars in holes in each half of bearing selector and turn so that gap between

them widens. Continue to increase gap until selector stops. Reverse direction and close gap.

5) Set preload adapter and attachment on output gear. Measure bearing preload while gradually increasing gap in bearing selector. When preload is 1.1-2.0 lbs. (.5-.9 kg), measure gap in selector (check at several different points). Select adjusting shims to fill gap at widest point. Shims are available in thicknesses of .004" (.10 mm) to .008" (.20 mm) in .001" (.02 mm) increments, and .020" (.50 mm). Do not exceed 7 shims in the pack.

6) Remove selector, install shim pack and install transmission case. Check that preload with components properly installed is .07-1.7 lbs. (.03-.76 kg).

TRANSAXLE REASSEMBLY

1) Throughout reassembly procedure, handle all parts carefully to avoid damaging bearing and mating surfaces. Lubricate all components with ATF fluid. Gaskets and thrust washers may be held in place with petroleum jelly where needed. DO NOT use grease. Install all new gaskets and seals.

2) Install oil seal on output gear bearing cover and in opening in converter case adjacent to differential assembly. Press differential bearing outer race into bearing cover. Press output gear bearing outer race into bearing cover. Install output gear bearing cover on torque converter housing and place housing on stand.

3) Install output gear adjusting shims in bearing housing and press in bearing outer race. Install output gear assembly and idler gear assemblies in bearing housing. Install idler gear retaining spring pin. Install complete assembly in converter housing.

4) Install differential assembly in converter housing. Install oil seal in differential bearing cover. Install adjusting shims and bearing outer race, then install completed bearing cover assembly in transmission case. Tighten bolts in a diagonal pattern.

5) Working with transmission case, install shift control rod assembly and support. Install manual shaft assembly with check ball and spring. Retain with new spring pin. Assemble low-reverse brake hub and piston, then attach to tool (used in low-reverse brake hub and piston removal) and install in transmission case. Retain with large snap ring.

6) Install dished plate on top of low-reverse brake hub with dished face down (toward hub). Install drive and driven plates beginning with internally lugged plate and alternating with an externally lugged plate until all plates have been installed.

7) Install correct retaining plate as determined in step **7)** of *Transaxle Disassembly*. Install one-way clutch with bushing side toward retaining plate. Retain with snap ring. Install washer, bearing and one-way clutch inner race assembly. Install washer, bearing, drum hub assembly and last washer and bearing. Install parking pawl assembly and oil pipes.

8) Install governor assembly. Governor is installed correctly when tab on governor sleeve is aligned with mark on transmission case. See *Fig. 16*. Install neutral switch. Apply a thin film of sealer on contact surfaces of transmission case and converter housing.

9) Assemble transmission case to torque converter housing. Place servo assembly in position in case and compress with "C" clamp. Install retaining snap ring and remove "C" clamp.

MAZDA F3A 3-SPEED (Cont.)

10) Install connecting hub, sun gear with spacer and planetary gear carrier assembly. Install rear clutch hub assembly, rear clutch and front clutch. Install bearing race used for end play adjustment as determined during oil pump disassembly.

11) Install brake band. Install and adjust brake band adjusting bolt. Install bolt and tighten to 9-11 ft. lbs. (12-15 N.m). Loosen exactly 2 turns. Tighten lock bolt.

12) Install oil pump. Install steel check ball and spring in case, then install valve body assembly. Install oil pan. Install turbine and oil pump shafts. Install speedometer drive gear, oil dipstick and tube, and vacuum diaphragm. A check must be made to determine which rod to install. Measure dimension "A" shown in *Fig. 23*, and compare to *Diaphragm Rod Chart* to determine which rod to install. Install kickdown solenoid and inhibitor switch.

DIAPHRAGM ROD CHART

Dimension "A" In. (mm)	Rod Size In. (mm)
Less than 1.006 (25.55)	1.14 (29.0)
1.010-1.026 (25.65-26.05)	1.16 (29.5)
1.030-1.045 (26.15-26.55)	1.18 (30.0)
1.049-1.065 (26.65-27.05)	1.20 (30.5)
Over 1.069 (27.15)	1.22 (31.0)

Fig. 23: Vacuum Diaphragm Installation

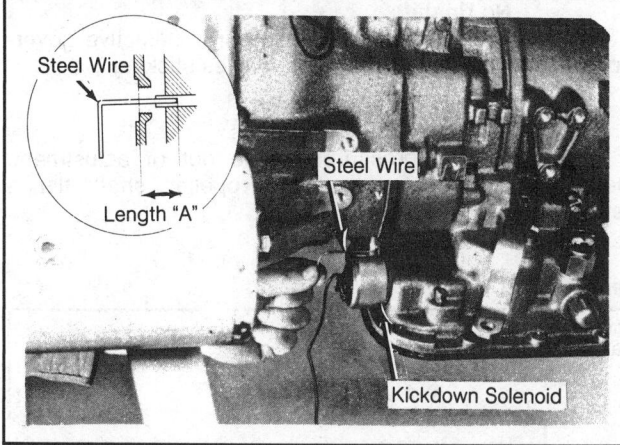

Check length "A" to determine diaphragm rod usage.

CAUTION: Install vacuum diaphragm and kickdown solenoid hand tight only. Do not use any type of wrench or other tool when installing.

13) Install torque converter in torque converter housing. With converter properly installed, dimension "A" in *Fig. 24* should be .425-.492" (10.8-12.5 mm).

Fig. 24: Torque Converter Installation

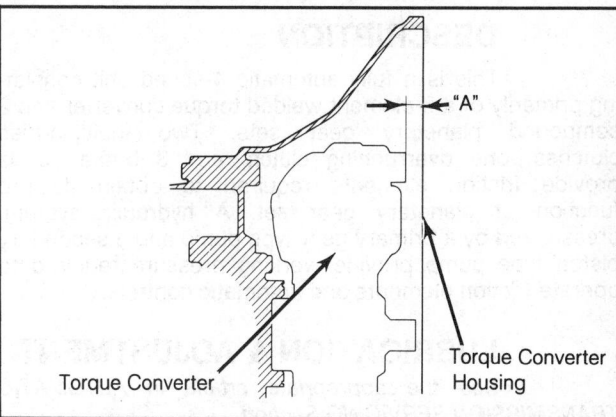

Dimension "A" will be .425-.492" (10.8-12.5 mm) with converter properly installed.

TIGHTENING SPECIFICATIONS

Application	Ft. Lbs. (N.m)
Torque Converter-to-Drive Plate	25-36 (34-49)
Drive Plate-to-Crankshaft	60-69 (82-94)
Trans. Case-to-Converter Housing	27-40 (36-54)
Converter Housing-to-Engine	
12 mm Bolts	47-69 (64-94)
14 mm Bolts	65-87 (88-118)
Idler Gear Lock Nut	94-130 (128-177)

	INCH Lbs. (N.m)
Bearing Cover-to- Transmission Case	168-228 (19-26)
Bearing Cover-to- Converter Housing	168-228 (19-26)
Bearing Housing-to- Converter Housing	96-120 (11.14)
Governor Cover-to-Transmission Case	48-72 (5-8)
Valve Body Bolts	72-96 (8-11)
Lower Valve Body-to-Upper Valve Body	24-36 (3-4)
Side Plate-to-Valve Body	24-36 (3.4)
Oil Pump Cover	96-120 (11-14)
Oil Pump-to-Transmission Case	168-228 (19-26)

MERCEDES-BENZ TYPE W 4 A 040

300 Series, 380 Series

DESCRIPTION

This is a fully automatic 4-speed unit consisting primarily of a 3-element welded torque converter and 2 compound planetary gear sets. Two multiple-disc clutches, one overrunning clutch, and 3 brake bands provide friction elements required to obtain desired function of planetary gear set. A hydraulic system, pressurized by a primary gear type pump and a secondary piston type pump provide working pressure required to operate friction elements and automatic controls.

LUBRICATION & ADJUSTMENT

See the appropriate article in AUTOMATIC TRANSMISSION SERVICING Section.

TROUBLE SHOOTING

TRANSMISSION SLIPS

Slips In All Selector Positions

Incorrect modulating pressure. Modulating pressure control valve or pressure relief valve for modulating pressure dirty or sticking. Line to transmission vacuum unit clogged or leaking. Working pressure control valve dirty or sticking. Defective primary pump.

Transmission Slips in 1st & 2nd Gear When Starting Off or Starting Off Impossible, Okay in Reverse

Band B-2 shift valve sticking. Valve body malfunction. Band B-2 piston worn or damaged. Band B-2 adjustment incorrect, worn or damaged.

Transmission Slips in 2nd Gear Or Shifts from 1st to 3rd

Band B-1 control valve sticking. Valve body malfunction. Band B-1 piston sealing ring worn or damaged. Band B-1 worn or damaged.

Transmission Slips When Upshifting from 2nd to 3rd or from 3rd to 4th Gear

Governor and/or working pressure incorrect. Valve body assembly worn or damaged. Defective front or rear clutch assembly.

No Positive Engagement In Reverse

Front band out of adjustment. Sealing ring on rear band piston worn or damaged. One-way roller clutch in gear assembly worn or damaged.

SHIFT JERK

Rough Jerks When Changing Gears

Incorrect modulating pressure. Incorrect working pressure. If working pressure is too high, replace valve body assembly. Vacuum line to modulator leaking. Control pressure linkage out of adjustment. Control valve converter adjustment incorrect.

Jerk When Engaging "D" or "R"

Engine idle speed too high. Modulating and/or working pressure incorrect. Leak in vacuum modulator vacuum line. Pressure receiving piston in extension housing worn, damaged, or installed incorrectly. Feed bore in pressure receiving piston plugged.

Rough Jerk on 4-3 Downshift

Sealing ring on release end of band B-2 worn or damaged. Band B-2 piston worn or damaged.

UPSHIFTS & DOWNSHIFTS

No Upshift

Incorrect governor pressure. Defective governor assembly. Valve body dirty or valves sticking.

Upshifts Only In Upper Speed Range Of Gears

Control pressure linkage out of adjustment. Defective governor assembly. Propeller shaft flange retaining nut loose.

Fig. 1: Sectional View of Mercedes-Benz W 4 A 040 Automatic Transmission

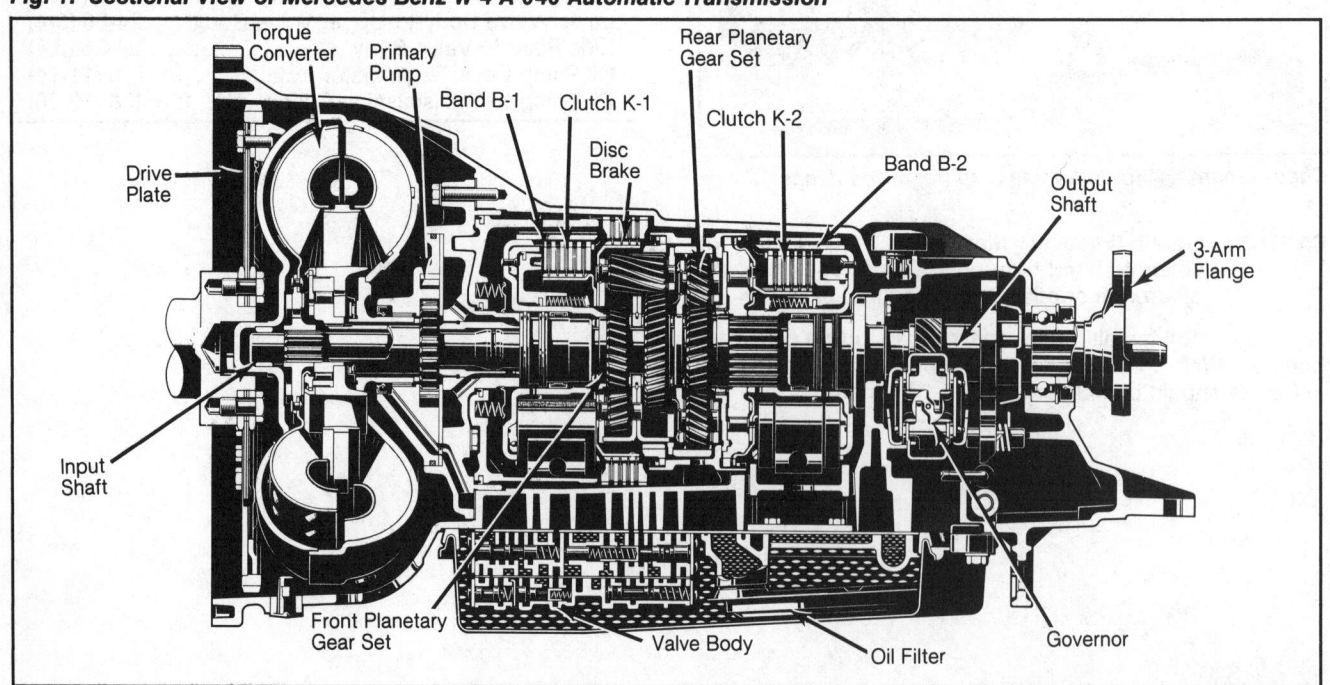

MERCEDES-BENZ TYPE W 4 A 040 (Cont.)

**Upshifts Only In Lower
Speed Range Of Gears**

Control pressure linkage damaged or out of adjustment. Accelerator linkage out of adjustment. Defective governor assembly.

No Kickdown Shifts

Fuse for power supply to solenoid valve blown. Defective solenoid valve. Control pressure linkage damaged or out of adjustment. Kickdown control valve in valve body sticking.

No Brake Shifts (4-3 & 3-2)

Control pressure out of adjustment. Make brake shaft piston operable and exchange shift valve housing, if required.

TESTING

ROAD TEST

NOTE: Before road testing, make sure fluid level and condition, and control linkage adjustments have been checked and corrected as necessary.

1) During road test, transmission should upshift and downshift at approximately the speeds shown in *Shift Speeds Chart.* All shifts may vary somewhat due to production tolerances or tire size. The important factor is quality of shifts. All shifts should be smooth, responsive, and with no engine speed flare-up.

NOTE: Shifts at full throttle and kickdown are somewhat firmer than part throttle shifts.

2) Slipping or engine speed flare-up in any gear usually indicates clutch or band problems. The slipping clutch or band in a particular gear can usually be identified by noting transmission operation in all selector positions and comparing which internal units are applied in those positions. *See Clutch and Band Application Chart.*

3) Although this process of elimination can be used to detect any unit which slips, and to confirm proper operation of good units, actual cause of malfunction usually cannot be decided. Practically any condition can be caused by leaking hydraulic circuits or sticking valves. Therefore, unless an obvious condition exists, transmission should never be disassembled until hydraulic pressure tests have been made.

Fig. 2: Pressure Test Take-Off Points

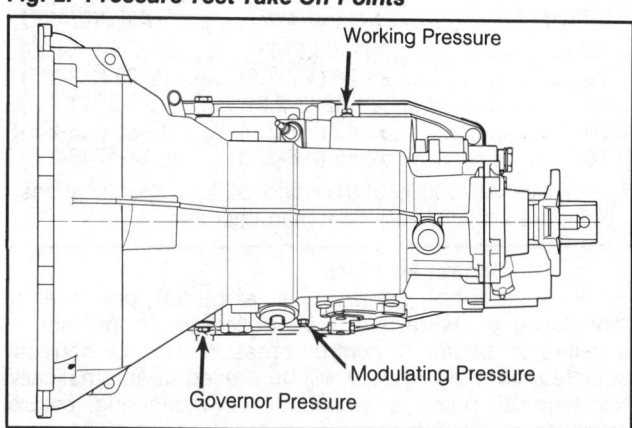

SHIFT SPEED SPECIFICATIONS (MPH)

Application	300SD	300D 300TD 300CD	380SEL 380SL 380SLC
Min. Throttle			
In "D"			
1-2 Upshift	6	9	11
2-3 Upshift	14	17	17
3-4 Upshift	24	23	27
4-3 Downshift	18	17	19
3-2 Downshift	10	12	11
2-1 Downshift			
In "S"			
1-2 Upshift	22	25	
2-3 Upshift	14	17	17
3-2 Downshift	10	12	11
2-1 Downshift			
In "L"			
1-2 Upshift	22	25	
2-1 Downshift	11	9	
Full Throttle			
In "D"			
1-2 Upshift	16	22	35
2-3 Upshift	32	43	55
3-4 Upshift	58	73	99
4-3 Downshift	34	43	71
3-2 Downshift	18	20	32
2-1 Downshift	5	8	17
In "S"			
1-2 Upshift	16	22	35
2-3 Upshift	32	43	55
3-2 Downshift	18	20	32
2-1 Downshift	5	8	18
In "L"			
1-2 Upshift	21	26	35
2-1 Downshift	12	12	17
Kickdown			
In "D"			
1-2 Upshift	16	26	39
2-3 Upshift	32	43	63
3-4 Upshift	58	73	107
4-3 Downshift	56	63	94
3-2 Downshift	30	33	51
2-1 Downshift	11	11	29
In "S"			
1-2 Upshift	16	26	39
2-3 Upshift	32	35	63
3-2 Downshift	28	32	51
2-1 Downshift	12	12	29
In "L"			
1-2 Upshift	30	26	39
2-1 Downshift	18	18	29

NOTE: Modulating pressure must be measured (and corrected if necessary) before making working pressure and governor pressure tests.

Modulating Pressure Test

Accelerate vehicle on the road or on a dynamometer to 53 MPH. Run engine at full throttle and keep speed at 30 MPH by lightly applying service brakes. Read resulting pressure on gauge attached to modulating pressure take-off point on transmission. Pressure should check as shown in *Modulating & Working Pressure* chart. Adjust as needed.

MERCEDES-BENZ TYPE W 4 A 040 (Cont.)

CLUTCH AND BAND APPLICATION CHART (ELEMENTS IN USE)

Selector Lever Position	Band B-1	Band B-2	Disc Brake	Clutch K-1	Clutch K-2	One-Way Clutch
First Gear		X			X	X
Second Gear	X	X				
Third Gear		X		X		
Fourth Gear				X	X	
Reverse			X		X	X

NEUTRAL OR PARK — All clutches and bands released and/or ineffective.

HYDRAULIC PRESSURE TESTS

Preparation For Tests

Before making tests, be sure that fluid level and condition, manual and throttle linkages, EGR system, and neutral safety/back-up light switch have been checked and adjusted or corrected as necessary. Connect a pressure gauge test set (123 589 04 21 00) to pressure take-off points on transmission. *See Fig. 2.*

NOTE: Make sure pressure gauge hoses do not drag on pavement or contact exhaust system.

Fig. 3: Bottom View of Transmission Case Showing Location of Leaf Spring

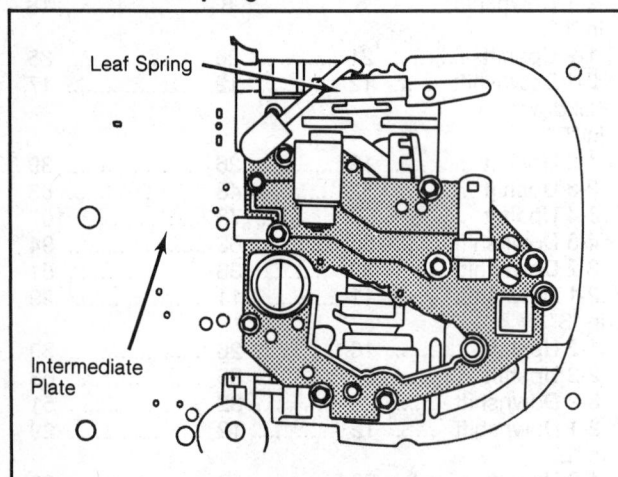

Modulating Pressure Adjustment

1) Compress circlip and remove vacuum modulator cover. Pull locking plate out of locking slots.

2) The adjusting screw in vacuum modulator can now be turned with the locking plate. One turn of adjusting screw changes modulating pressure approximately 6 psi (.4 kg/cm²).

3) After adjustment is completed, press locking plate into the next locking slot to lock adjusting screw in place. Reinstall vacuum modulator cover.

NOTE: Working pressure is not adjustable. Pressure is automatically established with correctly adjusted modulating pressure.

Working Pressure

To check pressure, drive vehicle in indicated range and speed shown in chart, and note pressure readings on gauge.

NOTE: Governor pressure is a partial pressure of the working pressure and is controlled by centrifugal governor on output shaft.

Governor Pressure

Drive vehicle on road or on a chassis dynamometer and compare pressures noted on gauge with pressures given on chart.

NOTE: If values are not within specifications, disassemble and clean governor assembly.

MODULATING & WORKING PRESSURE

Application	psi (kg/cm²)
Modulating Pressure (In "D" at 30 MPH)	
300 Series	42 (3.0)
380 Series	51 (3.5)
Working Pressure (In "D" stationary)	
300 Series	167-196 (11.7-13.7)
380 Series	163-191 (11.4-13.4)

GOVERNOR PRESSURE

Speed (MPH)	300SD [1] psi (kg/cm²)	380 Series psi (kg/cm²)
12	7-10 (.5-.7)	6-9 (.4-.6)
25	25-28 (1.7-1.9)	19-22 (1.3-1.5)
37	29-32 (2-2.2)	26-29 (1.8-2)
56	39-42 (2.7-2.9)	33-36 (2.3-2.5)
75	52-55 (3.6-3.8)	44-47 (3-3.2)

[1] — Models 300D, 300TD and 300CD specifications are not available from manufacturer.

Control Pressure

Control pressure is a partial pressure of modulating pressure and is controlled by the position of accelerator pedal. If control pressure rod is correctly adjusted, control pressure will be arrived at automatically. No take-off point is provided for measuring control pressure.

MERCEDES-BENZ TYPE W 4 A 040 (Cont.)

STALL TEST

Testing Precautions

When making test, do not hold throttle open longer than 5 seconds or severe transmission damage may result from heat generated. If engine speed exceeds maximum limits shown, release accelerator immediately as this is an indication of clutch or band slippage.

Testing Procedure

With engine at normal operating temperature, tachometer installed, and parking and service brakes applied firmly, stall test transmission by pushing accelerator to floor and noting engine speed on tachometer. Engine speed should be within limits in chart.

STALL SPEED SPECIFICATIONS

Application	Stall RPM
300SD & 300TD	2200-2300
380SEL, 380SL & 380SLC	1400-1500

Stall Test Results

If stall speed is higher than specified, general transmission problems are indicated and hydraulic pressure tests should be made to locate faulty units. If stall speed is lower than specified, torque converter roller clutch is faulty.

CAUTION: Make sure engine performance is satisfactory before condemning converter assembly. Torque converter is a sealed unit and cannot be disassembled for service.

SERVICE (IN VEHICLE)

The following units may be removed from transmission without removing transmission from vehicle: Oil Pan and Gasket, Shift Valve Body, Vacuum Modulator Unit, Speedometer Driven Gear Assembly, Secondary Pump Assembly, Extension Housing, Pressure Receiving Piston, Modulating Pressure Housing and Bimetallic Spring, Speedometer Drive Gear, Secondary Pump Eccentric, Governor Assembly, Parking Pawl, and Parking Linkage. *See procedures given in Transmission Disassembly and Transmission Reassembly.*

Fig. 4: Secondary Pump Assembly

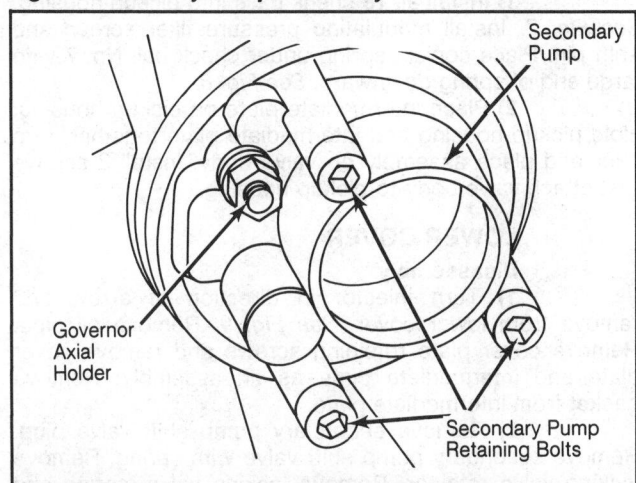

Showing location of nuts and bolts for removal.

4) Remove range selector lever. Remove starter lock-out switch. Remove retaining screws and remove vacuum control unit holding plate. Withdraw vacuum control unit from transmission case. Remove band B-1 thrust body and modulating pressure control valve.

TORQUE CONVERTER

NOTE: Torque converter is a sealed unit and cannot be disassembled for service. If hub of converter is scored, or if metallic particles are found in transmission fluid, replace converter assembly.

TRANSMISSION DISASSEMBLY

1) Position transmission in a holding fixture (116 589 06 59 00 and 126 589 10 63 00) with oil pan facing upward, then remove oil pan and gasket. Remove oil filter and bolts attaching valve body to transmission case, then lift valve body from case.

2) Remove leaf spring screw and remove leaf spring and holder together. *See Fig. 3.* Remove screws and remove lower transmission case cover along with intermediate plate and oil pipe. Remove one-way valve and band B-1 guide. Push in band B-2 piston cover and remove locking ring. Remove band piston cover and pull piston out of bore.

3) Attach compressor (126 589 00 59 00) to transmission housing. Apply compressor to band B-1 piston cover and remove locking ring. Remove compressor and withdraw band B-1 piston cover, piston and back pressure springs. Remove guide for band B-1. Remove closing cover for band B-1 thrust bolt.

4) Remove range selector lever. Remove starter lock-out switch. Remove retaining screws and remove vacuum control unit holding plate. Withdraw vacuum control unit from transmission case. Remove band B-1 thrust body and modulating pressure control valve.

5) Remove kickdown solenoid valve. Remove slot nut and 3-arm flange. Remove bolts attaching rear cover-to-transmission case. Loosen rear cover by lightly tapping cover with a plastic hammer. Remove rear cover.

6) Remove parking lock gear and parking pawl as an assembly. Remove expanding ring. Remove nut from axial holder for governor. Remove Allen head bolts that retain secondary pump and remove pump. *See Fig. 4.* Remove "O" ring and intermediate plate of secondary pump.

7) Remove plastic guide and roller assembly from bottom of transmission case. Push in governor cover and remove retaining ring. Pull cover out of bore. Swivel axial holder back. Remove governor assembly. Remove axial holder. Remove helical gear. *See Fig. 5.*

8) Remove circlip from output shaft. Remove bolts attaching front cover to transmission case. Install 2 longer bolts into threaded holes in front cover (to serve as handles). Pull front cover from transmission case. Hold planetary gear set on input shaft and carefully remove assembly from front of transmission case.

MERCEDES-BENZ TYPE W 4 A 040 (Cont.)

Fig. 5: View of Transmission Case

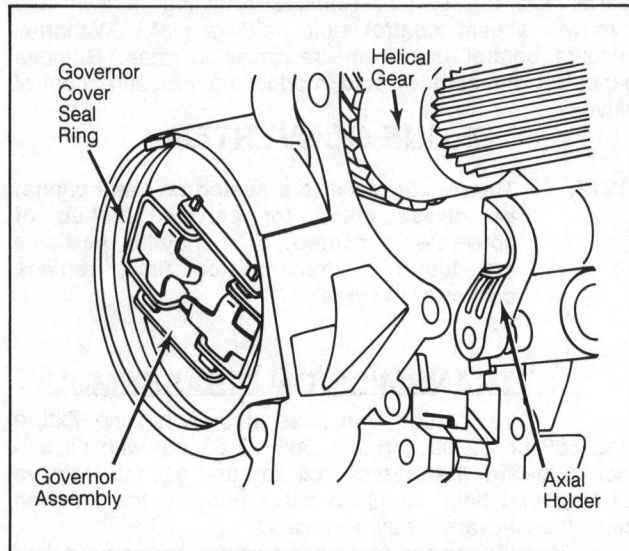

Note location of governor, axial holder and helical gear.

9) Remove clutch K-1 and band B-1 from case as an assembly. Remove disc brake plates. Remove clutch K-2 thrust pin and clutch K-2. Remove bolt retaining detent plate to transmission case. Remove output shaft from transmission case. Remove detent plate.

Fig. 6: View Into Transmission Case

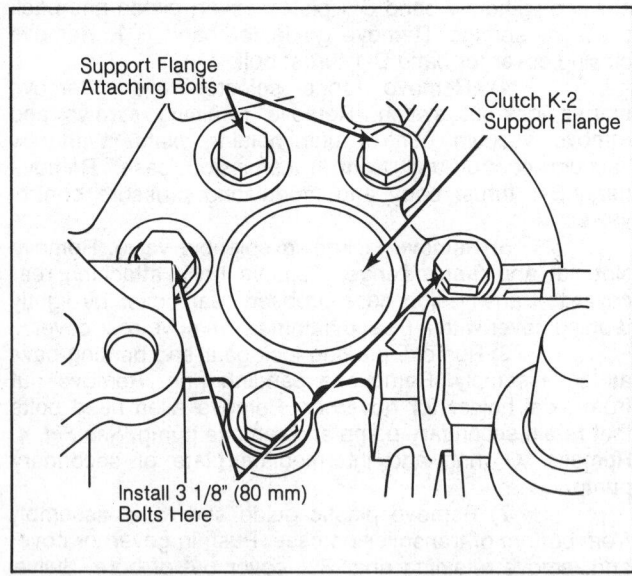

Showing location of clutch K-2 support flange attaching bolts.

10) Tilt band B-2 on an angle and remove from case. Remove band B-2 thrust washer and band B-2 thrust body. Remove bolts attaching clutch K-2 support flange to case. Install 2 bolts, approximately 3 3/8" (80 mm) long, into support flange. Loosen support flange by hitting bolts with hammer. *See Fig. 6.* Remove support flange from case using bolts as handles.

11) Release tabs on detent cable retainer from inside of case. Pull detent cable out of case. Disconnect control pressure cable and remove from case.

COMPONENT DISASSEMBLY & REASSEMBLY

VALVE BODY

Disassembly

Remove 2 screws that attach valve body-to-pickup housing. Hold assembly together and turn over. Lift pickup housing and intermediate plate from valve body. Remove modulating pressure filter screen and shift pin. Remove all check balls.

NOTE: No further valve body information is available from the manufacturer.

Inspection

Wash all parts in clean solvent and blow dry with compressed air. Closely inspect valve body and pickup housing passeges for obstructions or defects. Inspect intermediate plate for damage. Also check all balls for any kind of damage. If internal valve body problems are found or suspected, valve body assembly must be replaced as an assembly.

Fig. 7: Pickup Housing with Valve Body Removed

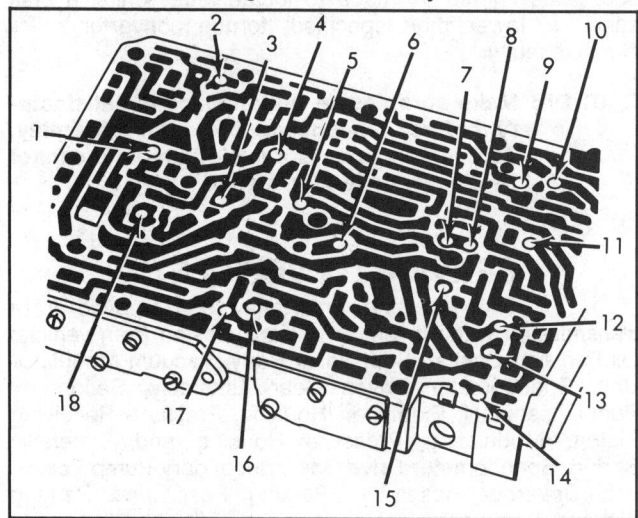

Note location of check balls.

Reassembly

1) Install all 18 check balls into pickup housing. *See Fig. 7.* Install modulating pressure filter screen and shift pin. Place conical spring under check ball No. 7 with large end of spring downward. *See Fig. 8.*

2) Place intermediate plate on pickup housing. Hold pickup housing and intermediate plate together, turn over and place assembly on valve body. Install 2 screws that attach valve body-to-pickup housing.

LOWER COVER

Disassembly

1) Turn injector in direction of arrow and remove from lower cover. *See Fig. 9.* Remove oil pipe. Remove cover plate retaining screws and remove cover plate and intermediate plate as an assembly. Remove gasket from intermediate plate.

2) Remove secondary pump shift valve plug. Remove secondary pump shift valve with spring. Remove locking valve retainer. Remove locking valve, spring and bolt.

MERCEDES-BENZ TYPE W 4 A 040 (Cont.)

Fig. 8: Top View of Pickup Housing

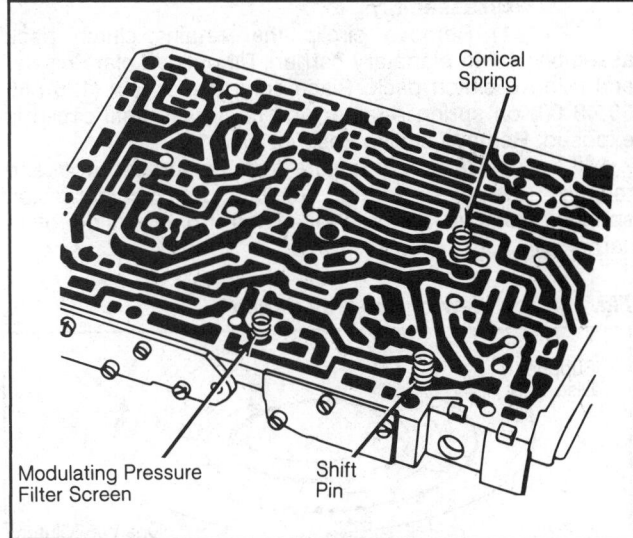

Showing location of conical spring, shift pin and filter screen.

Fig. 9: Injector Located on Bottom of Lower Cover

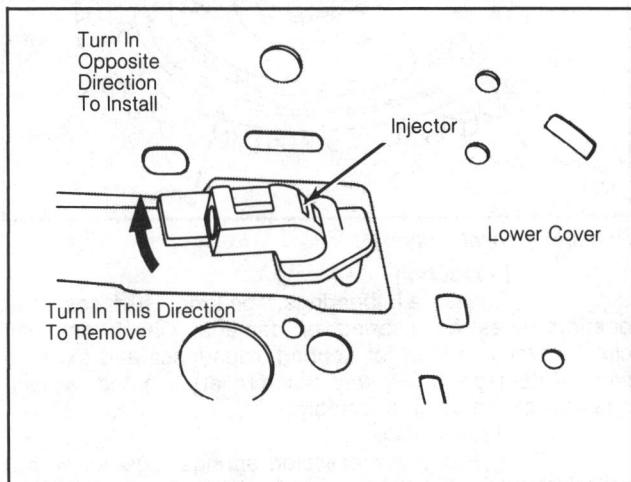

Inspection

Check that intermediate plate is not plugged or distorted in any way. Inspect secondary pump shift valve and spring for damage or distortion. Inspect locking valve and spring for damage or distortion.

Reassembly

1) Install secondary pump shift valve, spring and plug into lower cover. Install locking valve, spring and bolt. Install locking valve retainer. Place intermediate plate, with a new gasket, on lower cover.

2) Install cover plate on intermediate plate and lower cover assembly. Install oil pump. Install injector in lower cover and rotate in opposite direction of arrow. See Fig. 9.

SECONDARY PUMP

Disassembly

Remove pump gears from pump housing. Remove shutoff piston cover retaining ring and cover. Remove shutoff piston with compression spring, spring retainer and ball from pump housing. See Fig. 10.

Inspection

Check pump gears and pump housing for damage or unusual wear. Check compression spring for distortion. Check shutoff piston and piston seal for damage and replace as necessary.

Fig. 10: Exploded View of Secondary Pump

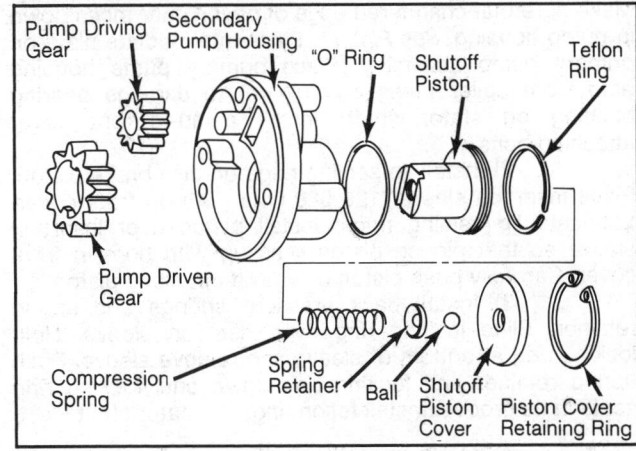

Reassembly

Place "O" ring into pump housing. Install teflon sealing ring on shutoff piston. Install shutoff piston into pump housing. Install compression spring, spring retainer and ball into shutoff piston piston. Install piston cover and piston cover retaining ring. Lubricate pump gears and place in pump housing. See Fig. 10

PRIMARY PUMP

Disassembly

1) Remove 2 teflon rings from stator shaft. Push disc brake spring retainer down and remove locking ring. Remove spring retainer and back pressure springs for disc brake piston.

2) Remove disc brake piston. Remove bolts attaching pump housing-to-front cover and lift pump from cover. Remove both primary pump gears from pump housing. See Fig. 11.

Fig. 11: Removing Driven Gear From Front Pump Housing

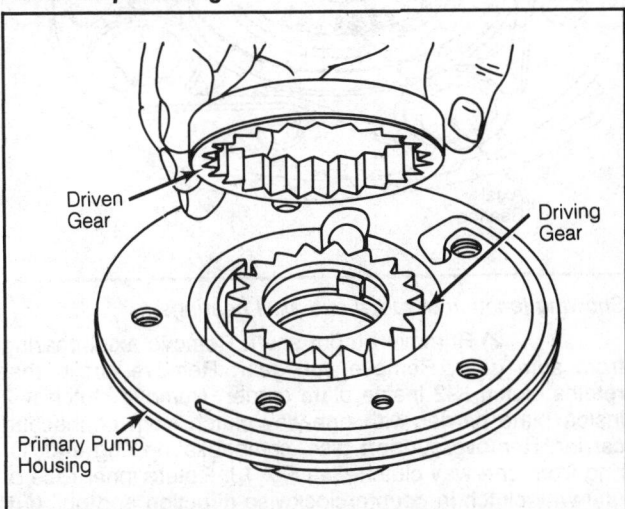

Housing shown with front cover removed.

Automatic Transmissions

MERCEDES-BENZ TYPE W 4 A 040 (Cont.)

Inspection

Check bearing bushing for scores or damage. Check radial sealing ring for damage. Check that "O" ring is properly seated in groove. Check that pump gears are not scored or damaged.

Reassembly

1) Install both pump gears into pump housing. Make sure that chamfered edge of driven gear faces down in pump housing. *See Fig. 11.* Place intermediate plate on primary pump assembly. Place primary pump housing onto front cover being carefull not to damage bearing bushing on stator shaft. Install pump-to-front cover attaching bolts.

2) Install lip sealing rings on disc brake piston. Place insertion sleeve (126 589 04 14 00) on front cover. Lubricate lip sealing rings. Install piston over insertion sleeve so that pin on piston lines up with bore in front cover. Carefully push piston down without tilting piston.

3) Install back pressure springs and spring retainer. Slide locking ring over insertion sleeve. Hold locking ring at bottom of sleeve and remove sleeve. Push spring retainer and locking ring down until locking ring seats in its groove. Install teflon rings on stator shaft.

PLANETARY GEAR SET

Disassembly

1) Clamp gear set in assembly fixture (126 589 00 35 00), at 2 flat sides, in a vice. Place planetary gear set assembly into assembly fixture. Remove circlip that retains planetary gear. Lift front planetary gear set off input shaft. Remove radial bearing and axial bearing. *See Fig. 12.*

Fig. 12: Top View of Inside Plate Carrier

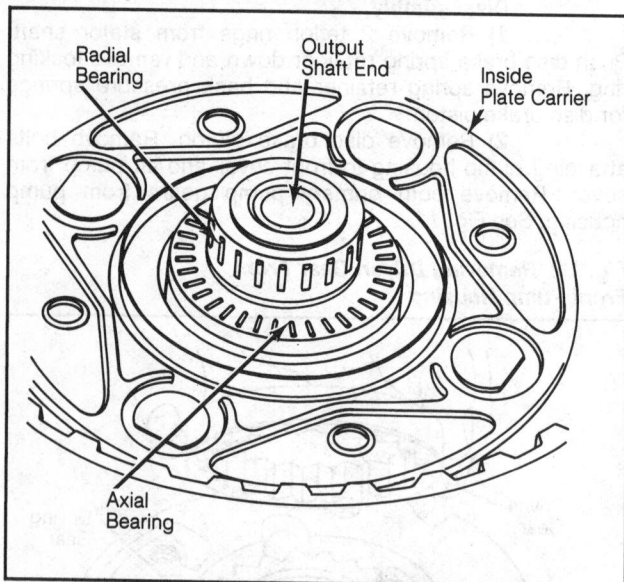

Showing location of radial and axial bearings.

2) Remove output shaft. Remove axial bearing from sum gear. Remove sun gear. Remove circlip that retains clutch K-2 inside plate carrier. Remove clutch K-2 inside plate carrier with one-way clutch from connecting carrier. Remove support disc, compensating ring and "O" ring from one-way clutch. *See Fig. 13.* Rotate inner race of one-way clutch in counterclockwise direction and pull out. Remove one-way clutch and rollers.

CLUTCH K-1

Disassembly

1) Remove circlip that retains clutch pack assembly K-1 in planetary carrier. Tilt outside plate carrier and remove clutch pack. Place compressor tool (126 589 00 43 00) on spring retainer and compress until circlip is exposed. Remove circlip. *See Fig. 17.*

2) Release pressure from compressor tool and remove. Remove spring retainer and compression springs. Remove clutch K-1 piston from outside plate carrier.

Fig. 13: Top View of One-Way Clutch

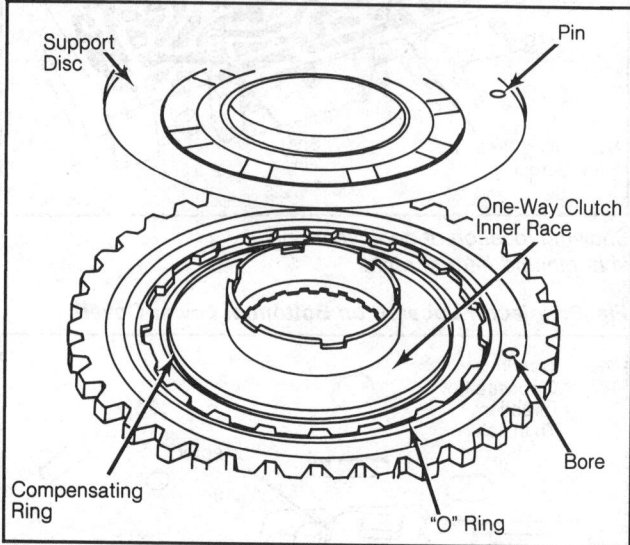

Note component location.

Inspection

Check all bearings, bearing surfaces and bearing races for scoring or damage. Check one-way clutch roller bearings for scoring, roundness and extreme wear. If damage to one-way clutch rollers is noted, replace one-way clutch as an assembly.

Reassembly

1) Press compression springs together with a screwdriver and install one-way clutch rollers. Press rollers against compression springs and insert locking plates with offset pointing outward. *See Fig. 15.* Install one-way clutch inner race. Remove locking plates.

2) Install compensating ring and "O" ring. Mount support plate so that pin on support plate enters in one-way clutch outer race. *See Fig. 13.* Install compensating washers into connecting carrier. Hold one-way clutch together and place assembly into connecting carrier. Install circlip and force into groove with screwdriver.

3) Check clearance between one-way clutch and connecting carrier. *See Fig. 16.* Clearance should be .002-.008" (.05-.20 mm). If clearance is not within limits, add or remove compensating washer until specified clearance is obtained.

4) Place sun gear into one-way roller assembly. One-way clutch should lock when rotated in clockwise direction. Place axial bearing on sun gear. Place one-way clutch on assembly fixture and install output shaft. Place axial and radial bearings on output shaft.

MERCEDES-BENZ TYPE W 4 A 040 (Cont.)

Fig. 14: Exploded View of Planetary Gear Set

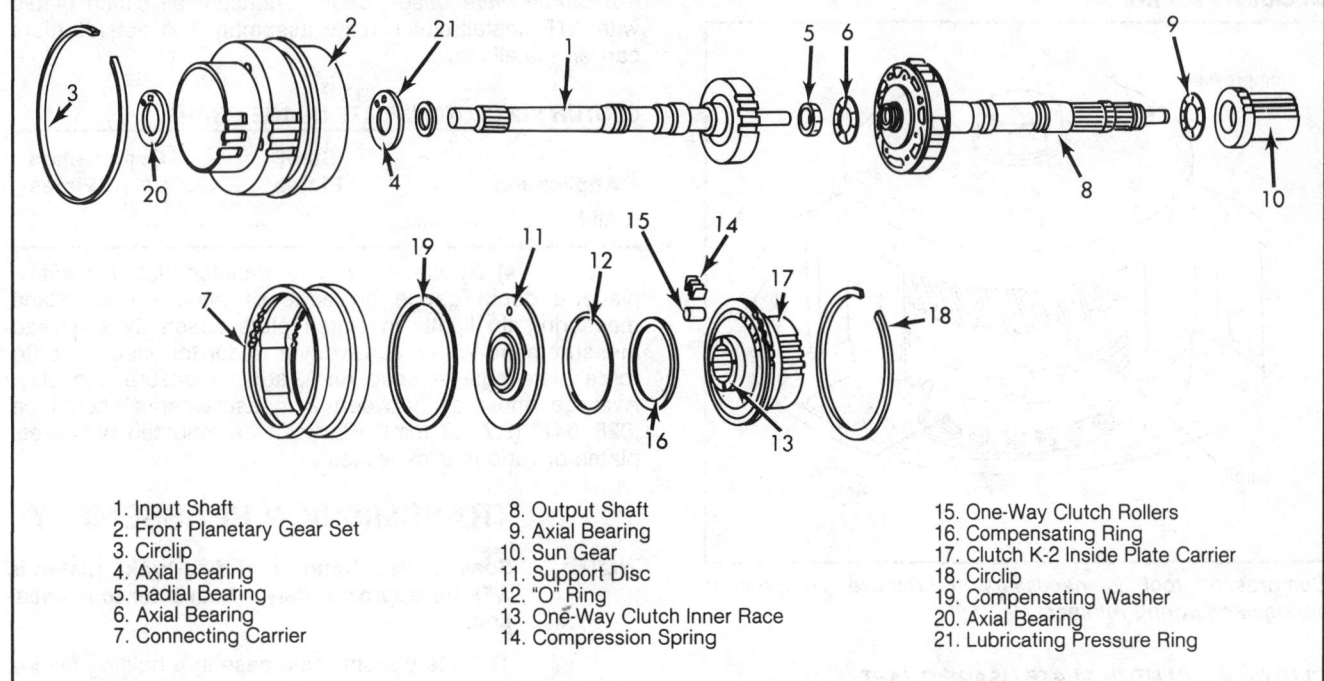

1. Input Shaft
2. Front Planetary Gear Set
3. Circlip
4. Axial Bearing
5. Radial Bearing
6. Axial Bearing
7. Connecting Carrier
8. Output Shaft
9. Axial Bearing
10. Sun Gear
11. Support Disc
12. "O" Ring
13. One-Way Clutch Inner Race
14. Compression Spring
15. One-Way Clutch Rollers
16. Compensating Ring
17. Clutch K-2 Inside Plate Carrier
18. Circlip
19. Compensating Washer
20. Axial Bearing
21. Lubricating Pressure Ring

Fig. 15: View of One-Way Clutch

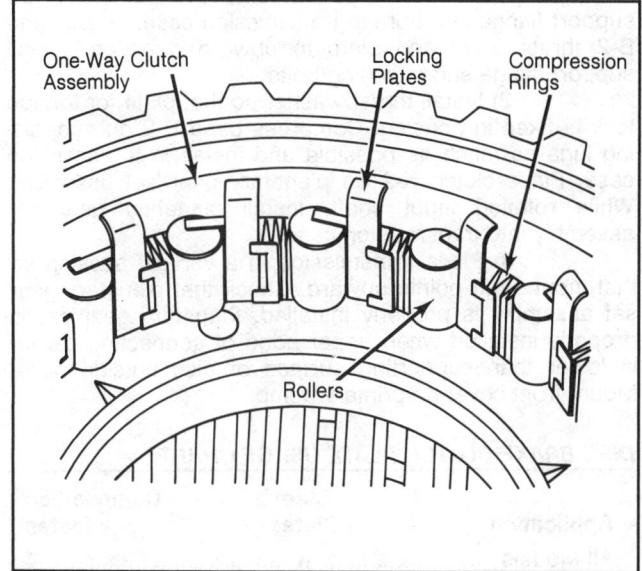

Note location of rollers, compression springs and locking plates.

5) Install input shaft and axial bearing. Install front planetary gear set and secure by forcing circlip into groove. Remove planetary gear set from assembly fixture and install final axial bearing on input shaft.

Reassembly

1) Install new lip sealing rings into piston so that lip of sealing ring points downward. Place installation sleeves (126 589 02 14 00 and 126 589 03 14 00) into outer plate carrier. Lubricate installation sleeves and sealing rings with ATF. Install piston into outer plate carrier being careful not to tilt piston. Remove installation sleeves.

Fig. 16: Measuring One-Way Clutch-to-Connecting Carrier Clearance

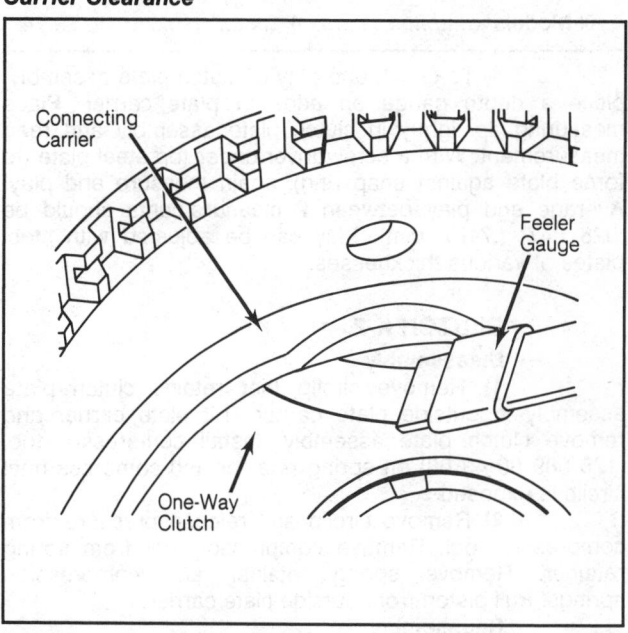

Note position of feeler gauge.

2) Install compression springs into piston. Install spring retainer, making sure that each compression spring is centered by a guide pin. Install compressor tool and compress compression springs. Install circlip and release compressor tool, making sure that circlip is properly seated in groove. Remove compressor tool.

3) Assemble clutch plates as shown in *Clutch K-1 Clutch Plate Usage Chart*. Lubricate all clutch plates with ATF. Install clutch plates into outside plate carrier. Install circlip, making sure that it is fully seated in groove.

MERCEDES-BENZ TYPE W 4 A 040 (Cont.)

Fig. 17: Installing Spring Compressor Tool on Clutch Pack K-1

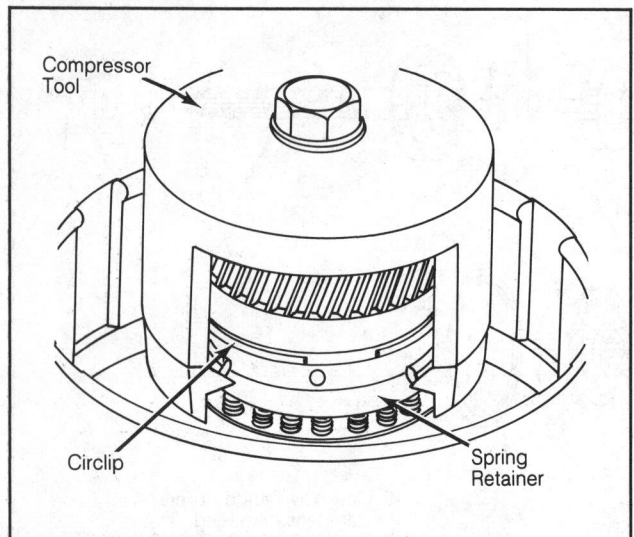

Compressor tool is necessary to remove compressor springs and spring retainer.

CLUTCH K-1 CLUTCH PLATE USAGE CHART

Application	Steel Plates	Composition Plates
All Models	4	4

4) To check end play of clutch plate assembly, place a depth gauge on edge of plate carrier. Place measuring tip lightly in clutch plate assembly and read measurement. With a screwdriver under top steel plate (to force plate against snap ring), again measure end play. Average end play between 2 measurements should be .028-.047" (.7-1.2 mm). Play can be adjusted with steel plates of various thicknesses.

CLUTCH K-2

Disassembly

1) Remove circlip that retains clutch plate assembly in outside plate carrier. Tilt plate carrier and remove clutch plate assembly. Install compressor tool (126 589 00 43 00) on spring retainer and compress until circlip is exposed.

2) Remove circlip and release pressure from compressor tool. Remove compressor tool from spring retainer. Remove spring retainer and compression springs. Pull piston from outside plate carrier.

Reassembly

1) Insert new sealing rings onto clutch piston. Place installation sleeve (126 589 02 14 00) on outside plate carrier. Lubricate installation tool and clutch piston sealing rings with ATF. Carefully place clutch piston over installation tool and slide piston onto outside plate carrier, being careful not to tilt piston in carrier.

2) Place compression springs into clutch piston. Install spring retainer so that each spring is centered by a guide pin. Install compressor tool on spring retainer. Compress spring retainer and install circlip. Be sure that circlip is fully seated in its groove. Remove compressor tool.

3) Assemble clutch plate assembly. See Clutch K-2 Clutch Plate Usage Chart. Lubricate all clutch plates with ATF. Install clutch plate assembly into outside plate carrier. Install circlip.

CLUTCH K-2 CLUTCH PLATE USAGE CHART

Application	Steel Plates	Composition Plates
All Models	4	4

4) To check end play of clutch plate assembly, place a depth gauge on edge of plate carrier. Place measuring tip lightly in clutch plate assembly and read measurement. With a screwdriver under top steel plate (to force plate against snap ring), again measure end play. Average end play between 2 measurements should be .028-.047" (9.7-1.2 mm). Play can be adjusted with steel plates of various thicknesses.

TRANSMISSION REASSEMBLY

NOTE: Soak all new bands and disc brake plates in ATF for approximately 1 hour prior to installation.

1) Place transmission case in a holding fixture. Install "O" ring and radial sealing ring into selector lever shaft bores. Install closing plug with a new aluminum sealing ring. Install "O" rings and teflon seals on clutch K-2 support flange and bore in transmission case. Install band B-2 thrust body and plate in upward direction. Install support flange and attaching bolts.

2) Install thrust washer so that plate for torsion lock is fixed in housing. Compress band B-2 on supporting lugs as much as possible and install in transmission case. Place clutch K-2 on planetary gear set assembly. While rotating input shaft, install planetary gear set assembly into transmission case.

3) Place transmission in a vertical position so that input shaft points upward. Check that planetary gear set assembly is properly installed. Planetary gear set is properly installed when upper edge of connecting carrier is lower than supporting surface of disc outside plate. Mount front cover on primary pump.

DISC BRAKE CLUTCH PLATE USAGE CHART

Application	Steel Plates	Composition Plates
All Models	4	4

4) Install disc brake clutch plates. See Disc Brake Clutch Plate Usage Chart. Place a parallel bar on machined surface of transmission case. Place top of depth gauge on bar and tip of depth gauge on compensating washer. See Fig. 18. Measure and record distance.

5) Place parallel bar on top of disc brake piston. Place top of depth gauge on parallel bar and tip of depth gauge on piston gasket. See Fig. 19. Measure and record distance. Difference between this measurement and measurement taken in step 4) is disc brake release clearance. Clearance should be .059-.079" (1.5-2.0 mm). Clearance can be adjusted with compensating washers and steel plates of various thickness.

MERCEDES-BENZ TYPE W 4 A 040 (Cont.)

Fig. 18: *Measuring Disc Brake Release Clearance*

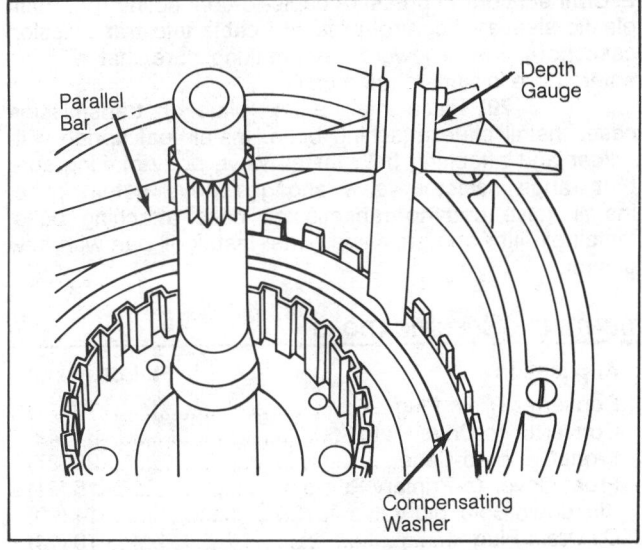

Measurement is taken in case.

Fig. 19: *Measuring Disc Brake Release Clearance*

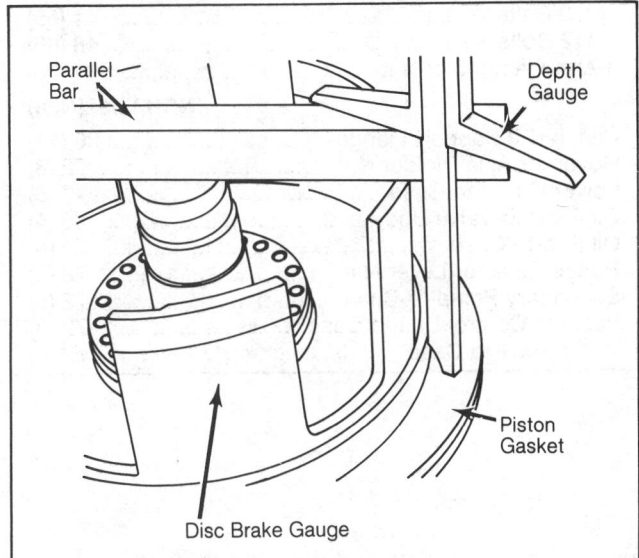

Measurement is taken on piston.

Fig. 20: *Measuring Clutch K-1 End Clearance*

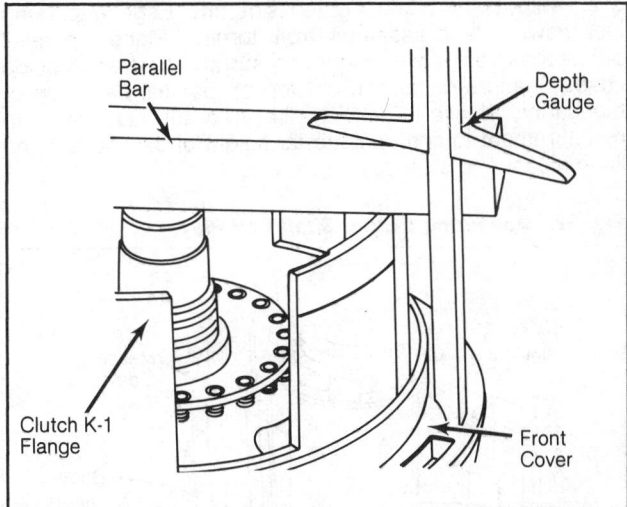

Measurement taken on clutch piston.

Fig. 21: *Measuring Clutch K-1 End Clearance*

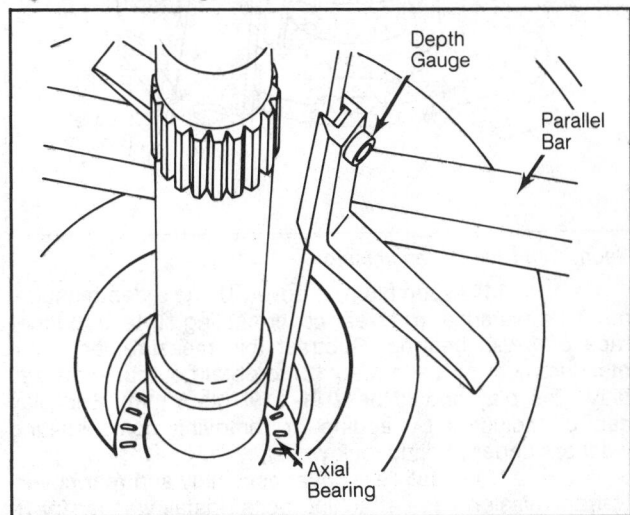

Measurement taken in transmission case.

6) Place axial bearing into planetary gear carrier. Pack groove in input shaft with grease and install grease pressure ring. Connect assembly lock to band B-1. Rotate clutch K-1 to provide meshing of teeth. Install band B-1 so that pin of assembly lock is facing toward band B-1 thrust body. Install axial bearing.

7) Place gasket on front cover. Place a parallel bar on clutch K-1 flange. Place top of depth gauge on bar and tip of depth gauge on gasket of front cover. *See Fig. 20.* Measure and record distance.

8) Place parallel bar on machined surface of transmission case. Place top of depth gauge on bar and tip of depth gauge on roller of axial bearing. *See Fig. 21.* Measure and record distance. Difference between this measurement and measurement taken in step **7)** is clutch K-1 end clearance. Clearance should be .031" (.8 mm). Clearance can be adjusted with compensating washers under washer for axial bearing.

9) Position front cover on transmission case. Install front cover-to-transmission case attaching bolts. Position transmission case so that output shaft is pointing upward. Place circlip into its groove on output shaft. Install helical gear on output shaft. Install governor axial holder.

10) Install "O" ring in governor bore and install governor. Swivel axial holder toward governor so that it will enter groove in governor shaft. Install governor and retaining ring. Pull cover out so that it rests on retaining ring all the way around.

11) Install intermediate plate and "O" ring. Install secondary pump and pump attaching bolts. Check that governor axial holder is properly seated. Install governor axial holder nut. Install oil pipe and attaching bolt. Install detent plate and shaft. Install detent plate-to-case attaching bolt.

12) Mount resilient linkage on detent plate. Mount roller on resilient linkage. Install plastic guide over roller. Place compensating washers on helical gear. Mount parking lock pawl, insert expanding spring and attach spring to parking lock pawl. Install parking lock wheel.

MERCEDES-BENZ TYPE W 4 A 040 (Cont.)

13) Install measuring sleeve (126 589 06 14 00) over output shaft and tighten slot nut. Engage parking lock pawl to hold assembly from turning. Place a parallel bar across rear cover mounting surface on transmission case. Measure distance from top on parallel bar to lip of measuring sleeve. *See Fig. 22.* Add .59" (15 mm) to measurement to compensate for height of parallel bar and lip in measuring sleeve.

Fig. 22: Measuring Output Shaft End Play

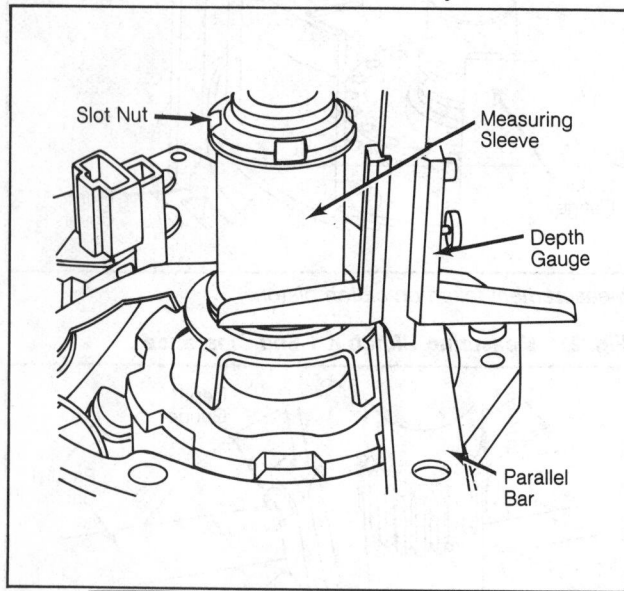

Slot Nut

Measuring Sleeve

Depth Gauge

Parallel Bar

Seen from rear of transmission.

14) Assemble rear cover. Using a depth gauge, measure distance from rear cover sealing surface to inner race of radial bearing. Subtract this measurement from measurement made in step **13)** to obtain output shaft end play. End play should be .011-.019" (.3-.5 mm). End play can be adjusted by adding or removing compensating washers under parking lock wheel.

15) Install rear cover assembly and rear cover-to-transmission case attaching bolts. Install washer for 3-arm flange on output shaft. Insert "O" ring into 3-arm flange. Slide 3-arm flange onto output shaft and install slot nut. Install kickdown solenoid valve. Stake 3-arm flange slot nut into groove in output shaft.

16) Install thrust pin in band B-1 thrust body. Install thrust body in transmission case. Install modulating pressure control valve. Install vacuum control unit and retaining plate. Install starter lock-out switch. Install range selector lever. Install range selector lever retaining bolt and nut. Install cotter pin in range selector lever.

17) Install band B-1 guide into transmission case. Install lip seal on band B-1 piston. Using a compressor tool, install band B-1 compression spring and piston. Install locking ring and remove compressor tool. Insert thrust pin for band B-2 into transmission case. Make sure large end of pin is toward band.

18) Install teflon ring onto band B-2 piston. Install thrust pin in piston. Place band B-2 piston into transmission case bore making sure that thrust pin enters band B-2. Install band B-2 piston cover and locking ring. Measure release clearance of band from inside transmission case. Band B-2 release clearance should be .24-.28" (6-7 mm). Adjust clearance by exchanging thrust pins.

19) Install one-way valve and guide for band B-2. Connect control pressure cable-to-connecting rod. Push plastic sleeve of control pressure cable into transmission case bore. Install lower cover making sure that oil pipe enters bore in transmission case.

20) Place intermediate plate on transmission case. Install plate attaching bolts. Install leaf spring with holder and attaching bolt. Install valve body making sure that range selector valve engages drive detent plate. Install valve body-to-transmission case attaching bolts. Install oil filter and attaching bolts. Install oil pan with new gasket.

TIGHTENING SPECIFICATIONS

Application	Ft. Lbs. (N.m)
Converter Drain Plug	10 (14)
Converter-to-Drive Plate	31 (42)
Front Cover-to-Case	20 (27)
Front Cover-to-Primary Pump	15 (21)
Kickdown Solenoid Valve	14 (20)
Oil Drain Plug	10 (14)
Propeller Shaft Clamping Nut	22 (30)
Rear Cover-to-Case	14 (20)
Transmission-to-Engine	
M10 Bolts	41 (55)
M12 Bolts	48 (65)
3-Arm Flange Slot Nut	89 (120)

	INCH Lbs. (N.m)
Clutch K-2 Support Flange-to-Case	96 (11)
Governor Axial Holder Nut	72 (8)
Lower Cover-to-Case	72 (8)
Oil Filter-to-Valve Body	36 (4)
Oil Pan-to-Case	72 (8)
Range Selector Lever Nut	72 (8)
Secondary Pump-to-Case	72 (8)
Vacuum Control Unit-to Case	72 (8)
Valve Body-to-Case	72 (8)

MERCEDES-BENZ TYPE W 4 B 025

240D

TRANSMISSION IDENTIFICATION

An identification tag is riveted to transmission case, near center servo cover. Top line of tag shows transmission assembly part number, and lower line is sequence built number.

DESCRIPTION

Transmission is a fully automatic 4-speed unit consisting primarily of a 3 element welded torque converter and a compound planetary gear set. Two multiple disc clutches, an overrunning clutch, and 3 bands provide friction elements required to obtain desired function of planetary gear set. A hydraulic system, pressurized by a primary gear type pump and secondary piston type pump provides working pressure required to operate friction elements and automatic controls.

LUBRICATION & ADJUSTMENT

See the appropriate article in AUTOMATIC TRANSMISSION SERVICING Section.

TROUBLE SHOOTING

TRANSMISSION SLIPS IN ALL SELECTOR LEVER POSITIONS

Incorrect modulating pressure. Modulating pressure control valve sticking. Intake manifold-to-vacuum modulator vacuum line plugged. Working pressure control valve sticking. Defective primary pump.

TRANSMISSION GRABS OR VEHICLE SHAKES WHEN STARTING OFF

Incorrect modulating pressure. Check vacuum modulator for presence of fluid; if transmission fluid is found, replace modulator; if fuel is found, check and adjust carburetor or fuel injection system.

TRANSMISSION SLIPS IN 2ND GEAR OR SHIFTS FROM 1ST TO 3RD GEAR

Center band control valve sticking or worn. Center band piston sealing ring worn or damaged. Center band worn or damaged. Bleed valves in front clutch supporting flange leaking.

TRANSMISSION SLIPS WHEN SHIFTING FROM 2ND TO 3RD OR FROM 3RD TO 4TH GEAR

Modulating and/or working pressure incorrect. Valve body assembly worn or damaged. Defective front or rear clutch assembly.

TRANSMISSION SLIPS IN 4TH GEAR, NO 1ST GEAR ENGINE BRAKING

Sealing bushings on pipes of valve body worn or damaged. Rear clutch defective.

TRANSMISSION SLIPS IN 1ST & 2ND WHEN STARTING OFF

Rear band badly worn or damaged. Incorrect rear band pressure pin.

TRANSMISSION SLIPS IN ALL GEARS

Incorrect modulating pressure. Modulating pressure control valve worn or sticking. Modulating pressure relief valve worn, dirty or sticking.

NO POSITIVE ENGAGEMENT IN REVERSE

Front band out of adjustment. Sealing ring on rear band piston worn or damaged. One-way roller clutch in gear assembly worn or damaged.

ROUGH JERK WHEN ENGAGING "D"

Engine idle speed too high. Modulating and/or working pressure incorrect. Leak in vacuum modulator vacuum line. Pressure receiving piston in extension housing worn, damaged, or installed incorrectly. Feed bore in pressure receiving piston plugged.

NOTE: If a rough jerk results when shifting for short periods back and forth between "N" and "D", there is no reason for a complaint. The pressure receiver requires approximately 2 seconds to operate.

ROUGH JERKS WITH CHANGING GEARS

Incorrect modulating pressure. Incorrect working pressure. If working pressure is too high, replace valve body assembly. Vacuum line to vacuum modulator leaking. Control pressure linkage out of adjustment. Control valve converter adjustment incorrect.

NO UPSHIFTS

Worn or damaged governor assembly. Valve body assembly dirty and causing valves and springs to stick. Incorrect governor pressure.

UPSHIFTS ONLY IN UPPER SPEED RANGE

Control pressure linkage out of adjustment. Governor assembly worn or damaged. Control pressure control valve inoperable. Propeller shaft flange retaining nut loose.

UPSHIFTS ONLY IN LOWER SPEED RANGE

Clamping screw for control pressure lever on transmission loose. Control pressure linkage out of adjustment. Throttle valve out of adjustment. Defective governor causing high governor pressure.

NO KICKDOWN SHIFTS

Fuse for power supply to solenoid valve blown. Defective solenoid valve. Clamping screw for control pressure lever on transmission loose. Kickdown control valve in valve body worn or sticking.

MERCEDES-BENZ TYPE W 4 B 025 (Cont.)

NO BRAKE SHIFTS (4-3 AND 3-2)

Control pressure out of adjustment. Make brake shaft piston operable and exchange shift valve housing, if required.

DOWNSHIFT WITHOUT USING KICKDOWN SWITCH

Check kickdown solenoid valve and "O" ring. Check kickdown solenoid switch and replace if bad (stuck down or open). Check control pressure valve.

SHIFT SPEED SPECIFICATIONS

Shift Condition	Speed MPH
Minimum Throttle	
In "D"	
1-2 Upshift	....
2-3 Upshift	19
3-4 Upshift	26
4-3 Downshift	22
3-2 Downshift	1
2-1 Downshift	....
In "S"	
1-2 Upshift	....
2-3 Upshift	20
3-2 Downshift	13
2-1 Downshift	....
In "L"	
1-2 Upshift	21
2-1 Downshift	5
Full Throttle	
In "D"	
1-2 Upshift	....
2-3 Upshift	30
3-4 Upshift	56
4-3 Downshift	31
3-2 Downshift	31
2-1 Downshift	....
In "S"	
1-2 Upshift	....
2-3 Upshift	32
3-2 Downshift	14
2-1 Downshift	....
In "L"	
1-2 Upshift	21
2-1 Downshift	11
Kickdown	
In "D"	
1-2 Upshift	20
2-3 Upshift	30
3-4 Upshift	56
4-3 Downshift	47
3-2 Downshift	27
2-1 Downshift	12
In "S"	
1-2 Upshift	19
2-3 Upshift	30
3-2 Downshift	28
2-1 Downshift	12
In "L"	
1-2 Upshift	21
2-1 Downshift	19

TESTING

ROAD TEST

NOTE: Before road testing, be certain that fluid level and condition, and control linkage adjustments have been checked and corrected as necessary.

1) During road test, transmission should upshift and downshift at approximately the speeds shown. *See Shift Speeds Charts.* All shifts may vary somewhat due to production tolerances or tire size. The important factor to note is the quality of the shifts. All shifts should be smooth and responsive with no engine speed flare-up.

NOTE: Shifts at full throttle and kickdown are somewhat firmer than part throttle shifts.

2) Slipping or engine speed flare-up in any gear usually indicates clutch or band problems. The slipping clutch or band in a particular gear can usually be identified by noting transmission operation in all selector positions and comparing which internal units are applied in those positions. *See Clutch and Band Application Chart.*

3) Although this process of elimination can be used to detect any unit which slips, and to confirm proper operation of good units, actual cause of malfunction usually cannot be decided. Practically any condition can be caused by leaking hydraulic circuits or sticking valves. Therefore, unless an obvious condition exists, transmission should never be disassembled until hydraulic pressure tests have been made.

STALL TEST

Testing Precautions

When making test, do not hold throttle open longer than 5 seconds or severe transmission damage may result from heat generated. If engine speed exceeds maximum limits shown, release accelerator immediately as this is an indication of clutch or band slippage.

NOTE: In order to get an accurate RPM reading, a separate tachometer is to be used.

Testing Procedure

With engine at normal operating temperature, tachometer installed, and parking and service brakes applied firmly, stall test transmission by pushing accelerator to floor and noting engine speed on tachometer. Engine speed should be within limits in chart.

STALL SPEED SPECIFICATIONS

Application	Stall RPM
240D	1500-1600

Stall Test Results

If stall speed is higher than specified, general transmission problems are indicated and hydraulic pressure test should be made to locate faulty units. If stall speed is lower than specified, torque converter roller clutch is faulty.

MERCEDES-BENZ TYPE W 4 B 025 (Cont.)

CAUTION: Make sure engine performance is satisfactory before condemning converter assembly. Torque converter is a sealed unit and cannot be disassembled for service.

HYDRAULIC PRESSURE TESTS
Preparation for Tests
Before making tests, check fluid level and condition. Control linkage adjustments must be checked and corrected as necessary. Connect a pressure test gauge set (116 589 04 21 00) to pressure take off points on transmission. *See Fig. 1.*

CAUTION: Make sure pressure hoses do not drag on pavement or contact exhaust system.

Fig. 1: View of Transmission Case Showing Hydraulic Pressure Test Points

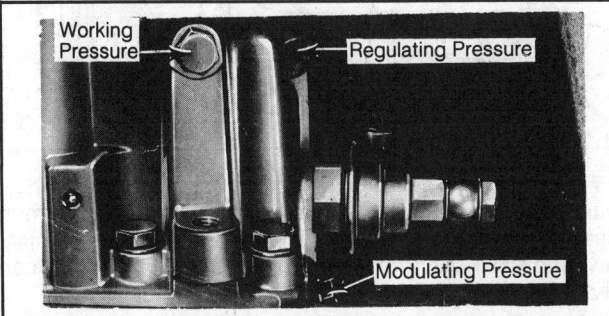

NOTE: Modulating pressure must be measured (and adjusted if necessary) before making working pressure and governor pressure tests.

Modulating Pressure
Accelerate vehicle on the road or on a dynamometer to 40 MPH. Run engine at full throttle, and keep speed at 40 MPH by lightly applying service brakes. Read resulting pressure on gauge attached to modulating pressure test point on transmission. Compare pressure to *Hydraulic Pressure Specifications* and adjust if necessary.

Modulating Pressure Adjustment
1) Compress circlip and remove vacuum modulator cover. Pull locking plate out of locking slots.

2) The adjusting screw in vacuum modulator can now be turned with the locking plate. One complete turn of adjusting screw will change modulating pressure approximately 3 psi (.2 kg/cm²).

HYDRAULIC PRESSURE SPECIFICATIONS

Application	Psi (kg/cm²)
Modulating Pressure (In "D")	
At 40 MPH	41 (2.9)
Stationary [1]	61-67 (4.3-4.7)
Working Pressure (In "D") [1]	
At 40 MPH	73-78 (5.1-5.5)
Stationary	
In "D"	99-110 (7-7.7)
In "R" [2]	261 (18.3)
Governor Pressure	
At 12 MPH	7-10 (.5-.7)
At 25 MPH	22-25 (1.5-1.8)
At 37 MPH	33-36 (2.3-2.6)
At 56 MPH [1]	49-52 (3.4-3.7)
At 75 MPH [1]	70-75 (4.9-5.3)

[1] — Can be measured at full throttle only.
[2] — Specifications given are minimum pressures.

Fig. 2: Rear View of Transmission Showing Vacuum Modulator Assembly

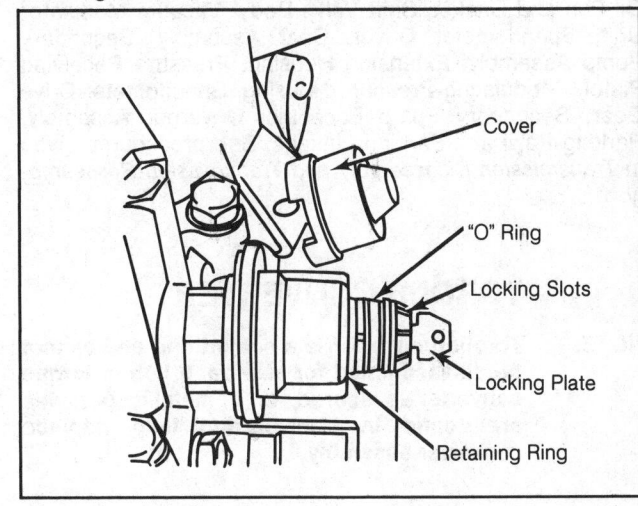

CLUTCH AND BAND APPLICATION CHART (ELEMENTS IN USE)

Selector Lever Position	Front Clutch	Rear Clutch	Front Band	Center Band	Rear Band	Overrunning Clutch
First Gear					X	X
Second Gear				X	X	
Third Gear	X				X	
Fourth Gear	X	X				
Reverse			X			X

NEUTRAL OR PARK — All clutches and bands released and/or ineffective.

3) After adjustment is completed, press locking plate into next locking slot to lock adjusting screw in place. Reinstall vacuum modulator cover.

NOTE: Working pressure is not adjustable. Pressure is automatically established with correctly adjusted modulating pressure.

Working Pressure
To check pressure, drive vehicle in indicated range and speed, and note pressure reading on gauge.

NOTE: Governor pressure is a partial pressure of working pressure and is controlled by centrifugal governor on output shaft.

Governor Pressure
Drive vehicle on road or on chassis dynamometer and compare pressures noted on gauge with pressures given in chart.

NOTE: If values are not within specifications, disassemble and clean governor assembly.

SERVICE (IN VEHICLE)

The following units may be removed from transmission without removing transmission from vehicle: Oil Pan and Gasket, Shift Valve Body, Vacuum Modulator Unit, Speedometer Driven Gear Assembly, Secondary Pump Assembly, Extension Housing, Pressure Receiving Piston, Modulating Pressure Housing, Speedometer Drive Gear, Secondary Pump Eccentric, Governor Assembly, Parking Pawl and Parking Linkage. See procedures given in *Transmission Disassembly and Transmission Reassembly.*

TORQUE CONVERTER

NOTE: Torque converter is a sealed unit and cannot be disassembled for service. If hub or torque converter is scored, or if metallic particles are found in transmission fluid, replace converter assembly.

TRANSMISSION DISASSEMBLY

1) Position transmission on a work bench with oil pan facing upward, then remove oil pan and gasket. Remove bolts attaching shift valve body to transmission case. Move range selector lever between park and reverse positions. Lift shift valve body from case. Remove oil distributor pipes from transmission case. Withdraw sealing caps from pipes.

2) Position transmission so extension housing faces upward. Remove vacuum modulator unit and thrust pin from extension housing. Remove adjusting screw and compression spring from extension housing. Using a special socket (116 589 00 11 00), remove plug for secondary pump and withdraw compression spring from housing

3) Remove nut attaching propeller shaft flange to transmission output shaft, then use a hammer to tap flange from shaft. Remove extension housing attaching bolts, and use a hammer to tap housing from transmission.

Fig. 3: Bottom View of Transmission Showing Location of Valve Body Attaching Bolts

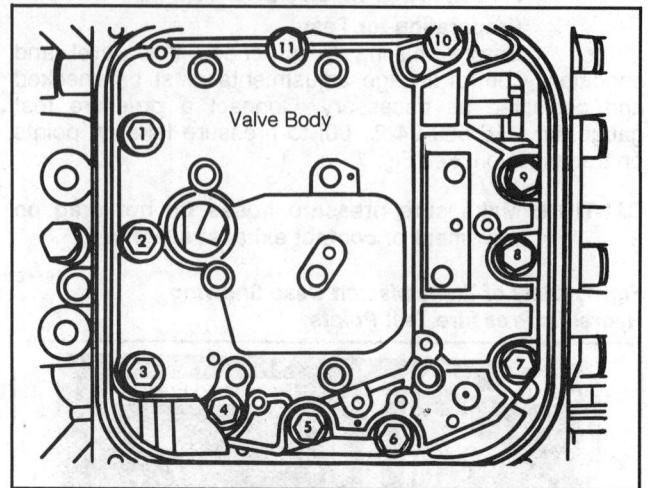

4) Remove plate spring, speedometer drive gear, eccentric ring for secondary pump, and governor assembly from transmission output shaft. Remove parking pawl and pawl spring from rear of case. Pull parking gear off output shaft.

Fig. 4: Removing Secondary Pump Plug From Extension Housing

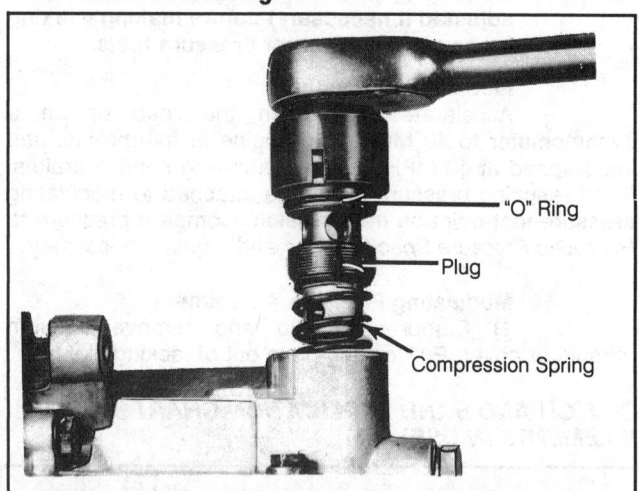

5) Remove bolts attaching converter housing to front of case, then use a hammer to tap housing free. Place transmission in a horizontal position and remove solenoid valve and control pressure lever (if not done previously). Remove retaining ring for rear servo cover, remove cover from transmission, then withdraw rear servo piston from cover.

6) Mount a compressor tool on transmission case over center servo assembly and compress servo cover. Remove retaining ring. Release tool and withdraw servo cover, servo piston and both compression springs.

MERCEDES-BENZ TYPE W 4 B 025 (Cont.)

Fig. 5: Rear View of Transmission Case With Extension Housing Removed

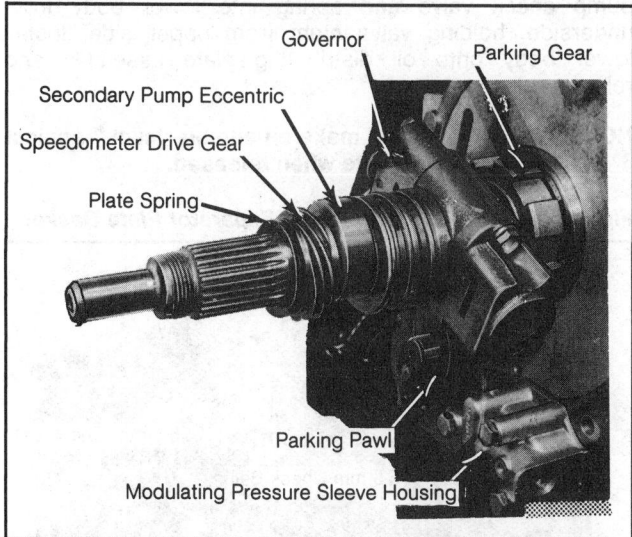

Fig. 6: Bottom View of Transmission Showing Position of Band Pressure Bodies and Thrust Pins

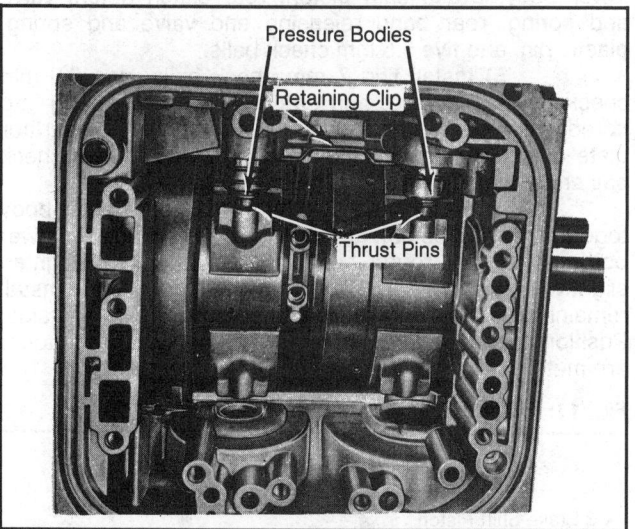

7) Inside transmission case, remove thrust pins for center and rear bands. Loosen front band adjusting screw lock nut, screw out band adjusting screw, remove 2 band thrust pins. Withdraw front band through front of transmission case.

8) Using rear servo cover retaining ring, clamp center band on gear unit. Withdraw gear unit from transmission case. Remove rear band from inside case. Remove bolts attaching modulating pressure sleeve housing to rear of case.

9) Remove housing and extension housing gasket. Remove detent parking lock and leaf spring from rear of case, lock bolt on detent plate, detent plate, linkage arm, and needle bearing.

10) On right side of case, remove retaining clip and plastic washer from control pressure shaft. Withdraw shaft from case. On left side of case, remove attaching screws and withdraw neutral safety and back-up light switch. Remove front servo retaining ring and withdraw servo cover, servo piston, and spring.

Fig. 7: Withdrawing Gear Unit Through Front of Transmission Case

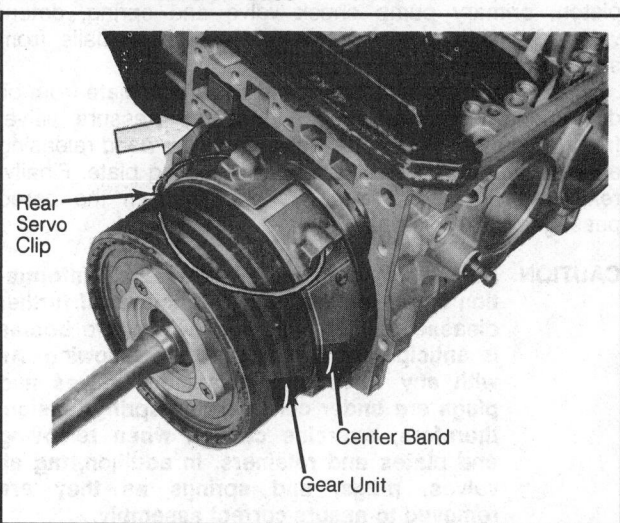

11) From front of case, remove retaining clip from front band lever, knock out lever pin. Withdraw lever from case. Remove lock clip and withdraw center and rear band pressure bodies from bores inside case.

Fig. 8: Removing Front Servo Assembly From Left Side of Transmission Case

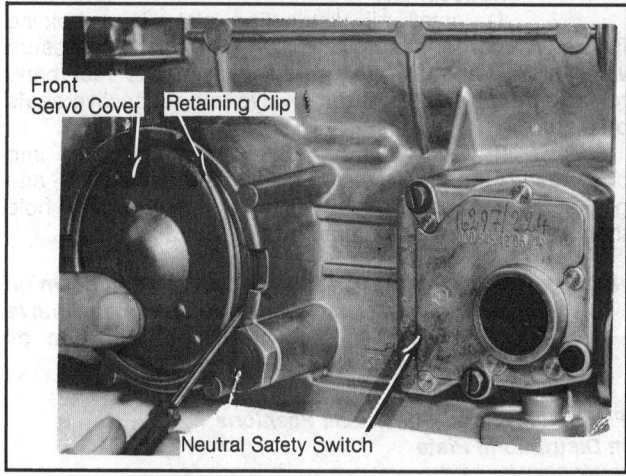

COMPONENT DISASSEMBLY & REASSEMBLY

SHIFT VALVE BODY

Disassembly

1) Remove brake band guide (if non-integral type). Loosen all valve body assembly through bolts and remove all except 2. Position assembly in a holding fixture with oil distributing plate downward. Remove 2 remaining through bolts.

2) Hold upper valve body and separator plate together, remove from assembly, and place on bench with separator plate. Remove strainer filter and spring, two 7 mm check balls, and one 5.5 mm check ball and spring from upper body.

MERCEDES-BENZ TYPE W 4 B 025 (Cont.)

3) Lift lower body off assembly, and remove 5 check balls from cored passages. Remove brake shift piston, primary pump check valve and spring, detent valve, 3-4 shift pin, and two 5.5 mm check balls from surface of separator plate gasket.

4) Remove gasket and separator plate from oil distributing plate. Withdraw lubricating pressure valve, front band one-way throttle valve, and rear band releasing end one-way throttle valve from distributing plate. Finally, remove the two 5.5 mm check balls from the cored passages of the distributing plate.

CAUTION: **No further valve body disassembly information is available from manufacturer. If further disassembly of upper or lower valve bodies is anticipated, please note the following: As with any valve body assembly, valves and plugs are under considerable spring tension; therefore, exercise caution when removing end plates and retainers. In addition, tag all valves, plugs, and springs as they are removed to assure correct assembly.**

Inspection

Wash all parts in clean solvent and blow dry with compressed air. Check all valves for ease of movement in bores. If necessary, remove any minor damage on valves with crocus cloth, taking care not to round off the sharp self-cleaning edges of the valves.

Reassembly

1) Install oil distributing plate in a holding fixture with cored face upward. Install lubricating pressure valve, front band one-way throttle valve, and rear band releasing end one-way throttle valve into respective seats on plate.

2) Place the two 5.5 mm check balls into countersunk seats in plate, place separator plate and gasket over oil distributing plate, and temporarily hold them in place using 2 clamps.

NOTE: **After installing separator plate, push down on valves and check for free operation; valve retainers must not be caught between oil distributing plate and separator plate.**

Fig. 9: Valve and Check Ball Positions in Distributing Plate

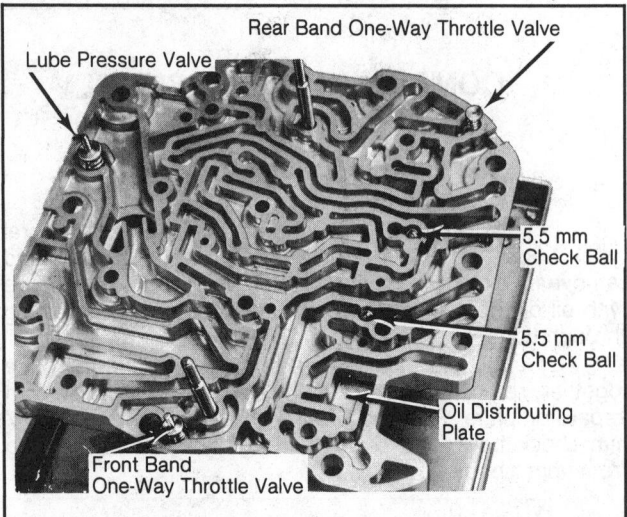

3) Place two 5.5 mm check balls on top of separator plate gasket *See Fig. 10.* Install the primary pump check valve and spring into lower body from underside, holding valve stem from upper side. Install lower body onto oil distributing plate assembly and release valve stem.

NOTE: **Valve should make an audible "click" against separator plate when released.**

Fig. 10: Check Ball Positions on Separator Plate Gasket

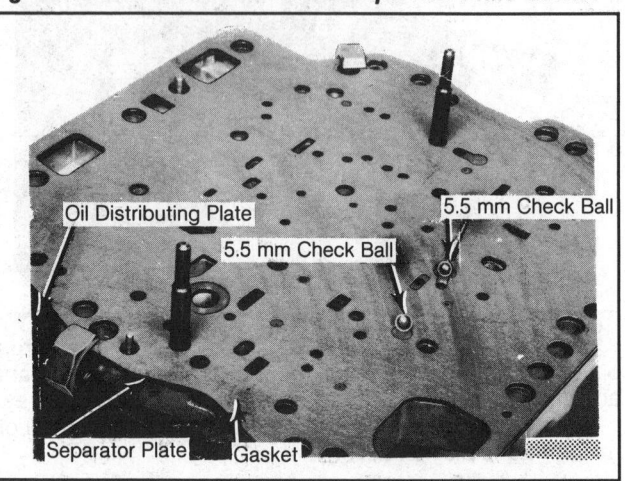

4) Install the following into cored passages of lower body: Brake shift piston, rear clutch detent valve and spring, rear band releasing end valve and spring, plastic pin, and five 5.5 mm check balls.

5) Install two 7 mm check balls, one 5.5 mm check ball and spring, and strainer filter and spring into cored passages of upper body. Place remaining separator plate over upper body, making sure spring loaded check ball and filter are correctly seated.

6) Firmly hold separator plate and upper body together, turn assembly upside down, and place on lower body. Install 2 through bolts into assembly and tighten slightly. Remove valve body from holding fixture, install remaining bolts, and tighten from inside to outside. Position brake guide to valve body making sure contours are mated.

Fig. 11: Valve Locations in Lower Valve Body

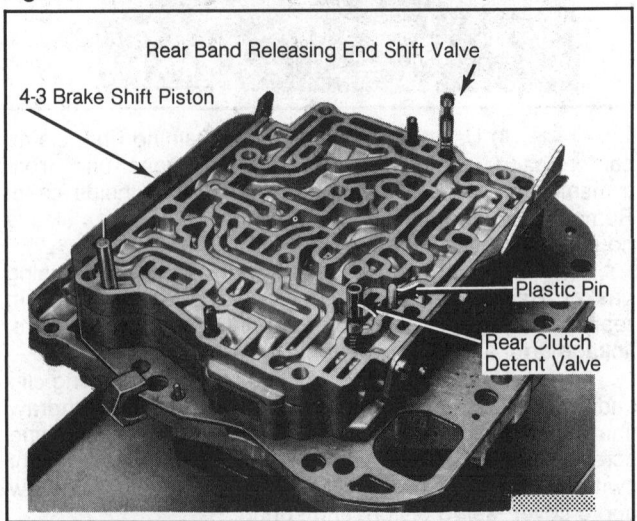

MERCEDES-BENZ TYPE W 4 B 025 (Cont.)

Fig. 12: Exploded View of Valves and Check Balls in Valve Body Assembly

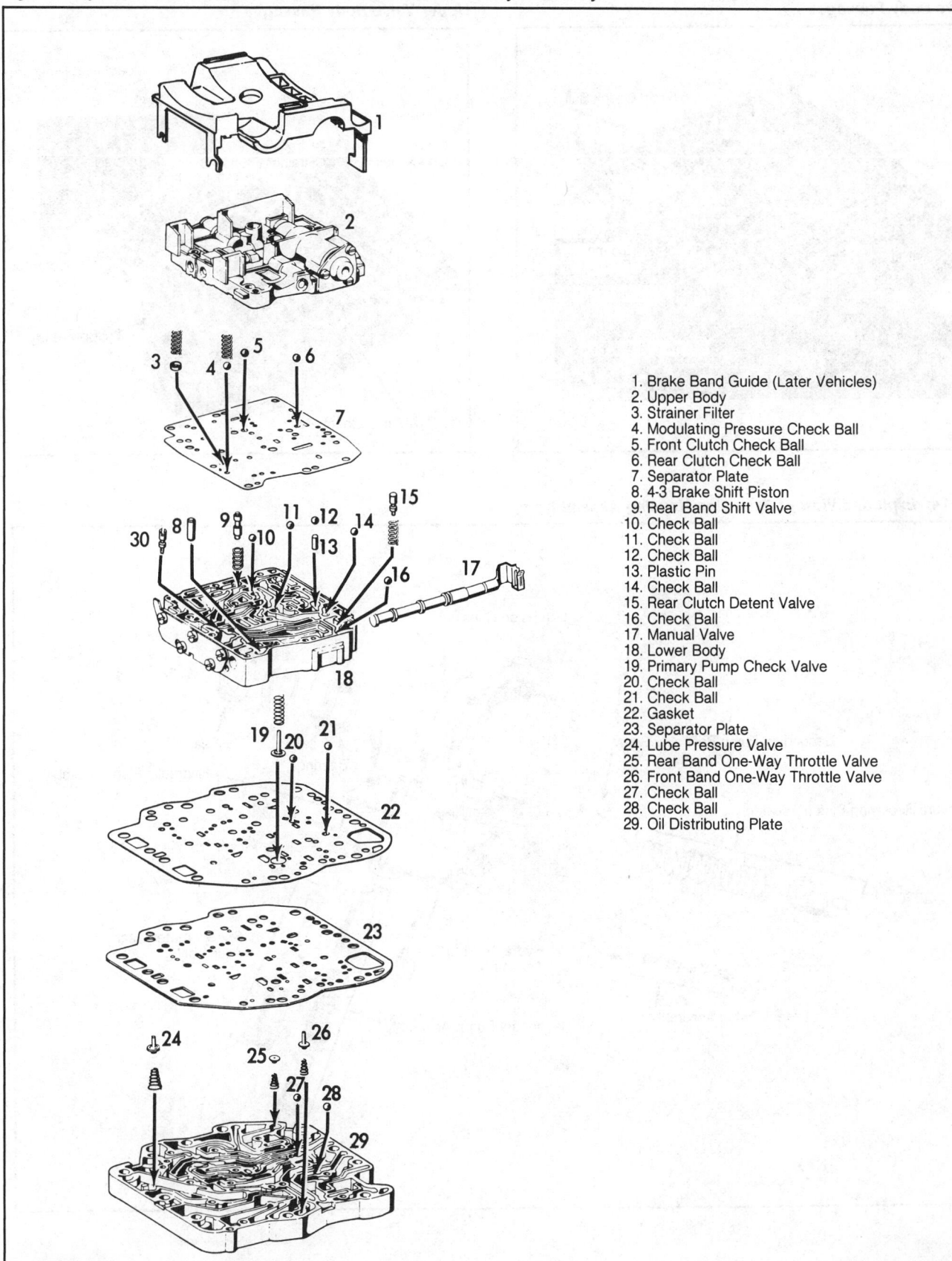

1. Brake Band Guide (Later Vehicles)
2. Upper Body
3. Strainer Filter
4. Modulating Pressure Check Ball
5. Front Clutch Check Ball
6. Rear Clutch Check Ball
7. Separator Plate
8. 4-3 Brake Shift Piston
9. Rear Band Shift Valve
10. Check Ball
11. Check Ball
12. Check Ball
13. Plastic Pin
14. Check Ball
15. Rear Clutch Detent Valve
16. Check Ball
17. Manual Valve
18. Lower Body
19. Primary Pump Check Valve
20. Check Ball
21. Check Ball
22. Gasket
23. Separator Plate
24. Lube Pressure Valve
25. Rear Band One-Way Throttle Valve
26. Front Band One-Way Throttle Valve
27. Check Ball
28. Check Ball
29. Oil Distributing Plate

MERCEDES-BENZ TYPE W 4 B 025 (Cont.)

Fig. 13: *Check Ball Positioning in Lower Valve Body Passages*

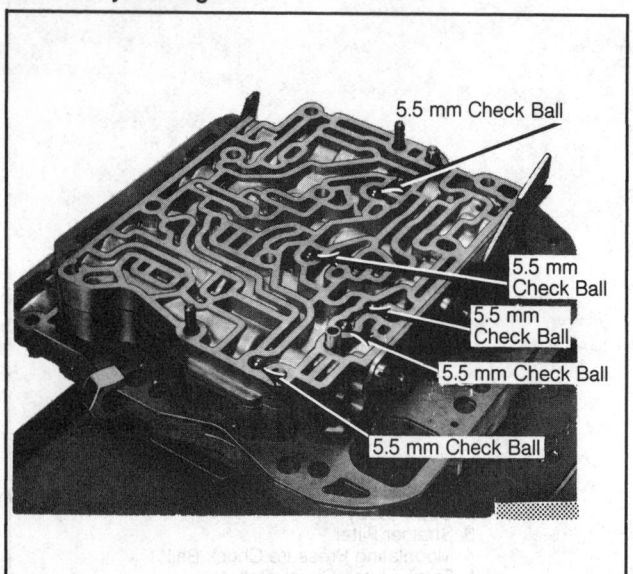

5.5 mm Check Ball

5.5 mm Check Ball

5.5 mm Check Ball

5.5 mm Check Ball

5.5 mm Check Ball

Fig. 15: *Check Ball Positioning in Upper Valve Body Passages*

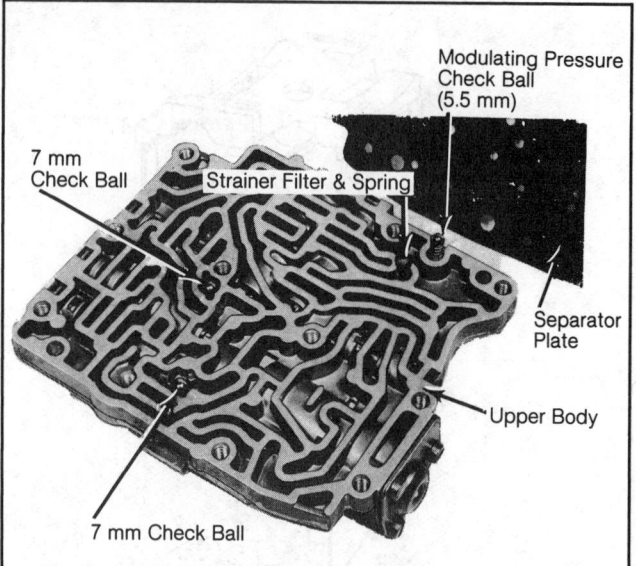

Modulating Pressure Check Ball (5.5 mm)

7 mm Check Ball

Strainer Filter & Spring

Separator Plate

Upper Body

7 mm Check Ball

Fig. 14: *Exploded View of Extension Housing Assembly*

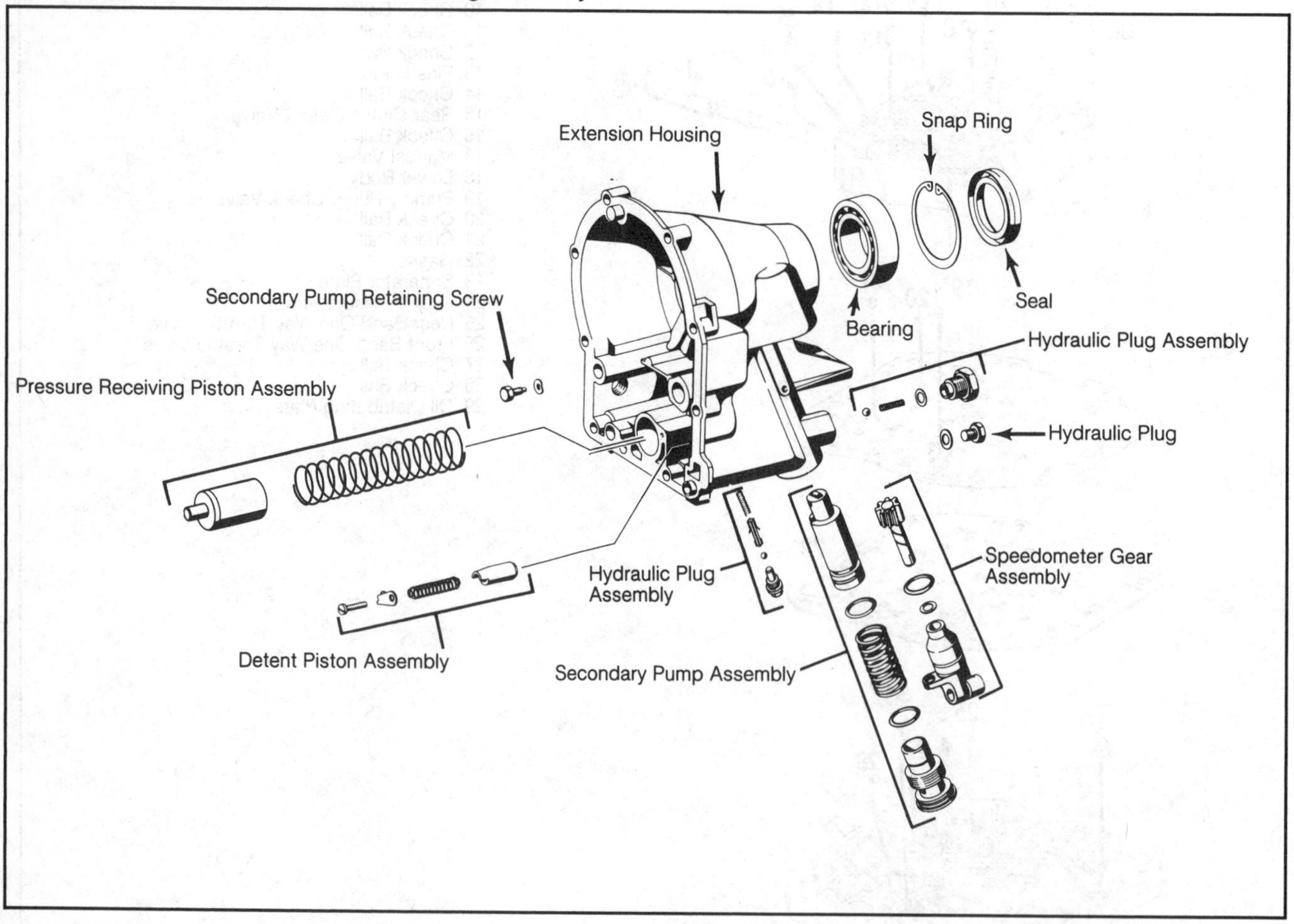

Extension Housing

Snap Ring

Secondary Pump Retaining Screw

Bearing

Seal

Hydraulic Plug Assembly

Pressure Receiving Piston Assembly

Hydraulic Plug

Hydraulic Plug Assembly

Speedometer Gear Assembly

Detent Piston Assembly

Secondary Pump Assembly

MERCEDES-BENZ TYPE W 4 B 025 (Cont.)

EXTENSION HOUSING
Disassembly
1) Remove locking piston retaining bolt and cover plate. Withdraw locking piston and spring. Withdraw pressure receiving piston assembly, noting part position for reassembly reference. Remove speedometer driven gear retaining bolt, withdraw assembly from extension housing and remove driven gear from body.

2) Remove secondary pump retaining bolt from inside extension housing. Withdraw pump assembly. Remove rear seal and rear bearing retaining ring. Use a press and remove rear bearing from housing. Remove all hydraulic pressure plugs, check balls, and springs.

Reassembly
1) Install rear bearing, snap ring and rear seal into extension housing. Install locking piston and spring into housing. Install cover plate and retaining screw. Install secondary pump into housing, align locking hole of pump with retaining screw bore in housing. Install and tighten pump retaining screw.

2) Install new "O" rings into speedometer gear body, install speedometer gear into body. Install body into extension housing. Install and tighten attaching bolt. Install and tighten all hydraulic plug assemblies. Install pressure receiving spring into bore of housing. Install pressure receiving piston.

Fig. 16: Installing Secondary Pump in Extension Housing

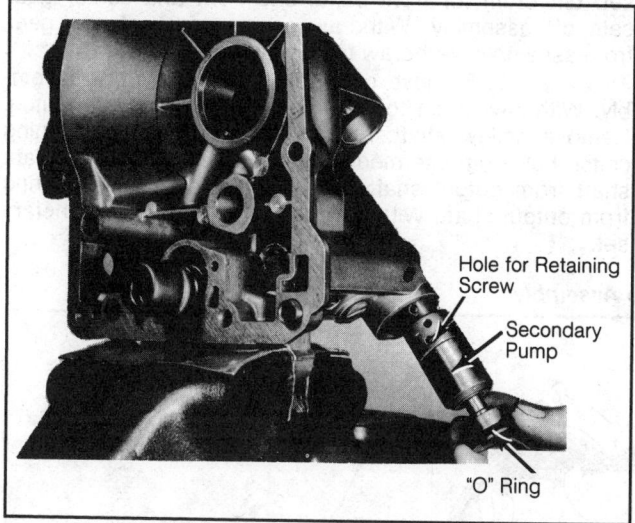

Hole for Retaining Screw

Secondary Pump

"O" Ring

GOVERNOR
Disassembly
1) If necessary, remove oil seal rings from governor flange. Remove 4 attaching bolts and separate shift valve housing and governor housing from flange. Remove lock washer. Withdraw compression spring and shift valve from shift valve housing.

2) Remove spring plate from governor housing assembly. Withdraw weight, compression spring, and spring guide from upper end of housing. From lower end of housing, withdraw heavier compression spring, compensating washers and governor valve.

Inspection
Wash all parts in clean solvent and blow dry with compressed air. Check shift valve and governor valve for free movement in respective housings. Remove and clean oil strainer located in governor flange. If any part is found damaged, replace complete governor assembly.

Reassembly
1) Insert governor valve into housing. Install light compression spring, spring guide, and weight into opposite end of housing. Push weight through governor valve. Install compensating washers and heavier compression spring over governor valve.

NOTE: Do not alter number of compensating washers in assembly.

2) Install spring retainer into assembly, making sure it is fully seated over spring. Install shift valve and compression spring into shift valve housing, then install lock washer, making sure the ends are not distorted in valve groove.

3) Position shift valve housing on governor flange. Make sure oil slots of housing face oil sealing rings on flange and oil passages in both parts are aligned. Install attaching bolts and tighten.

Fig. 17: Exploded View of Governor Assembly

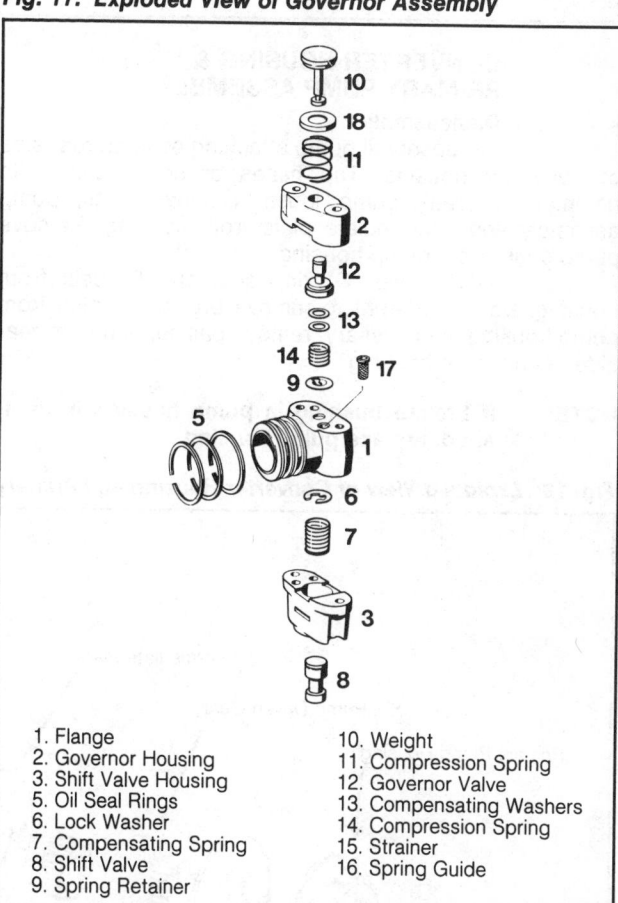

1. Flange
2. Governor Housing
3. Shift Valve Housing
5. Oil Seal Rings
6. Lock Washer
7. Compensating Spring
8. Shift Valve
9. Spring Retainer
10. Weight
11. Compression Spring
12. Governor Valve
13. Compensating Washers
14. Compression Spring
15. Strainer
16. Spring Guide

4) Install oil strainer into passage in governor housing end of governor flange, then position governor housing on assembly. Make sure oil slots of housing face oil seal rings on flange and that oil passages in both parts are aligned. Install attaching bolts and tighten. If removed during disassembly, install oil seal rings on governor flange and lock ends.

Fig. 18: Correct Position of Housings on Governor Flange

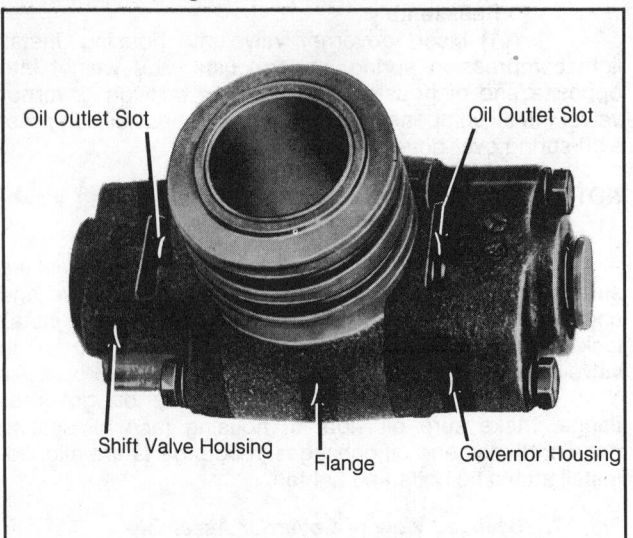

CONVERTER HOUSING & PRIMARY PUMP ASSEMBLY

Disassembly

1) Loosen oil pump attaching bolts on rear side of converter housing. Tap heads of bolts lightly with hammer to break pump loose. Remove bolts, pump assembly and intermediate plate from housing. Remove pump gears from pump housing.

2) Remove "O" ring seal and lip seal from housing. Do not attempt to remove bronze bushing from pump housing. If necessary, remove ball bearing from rear side of converter housing.

NOTE: If bronze bushing in pump housing is damaged, replace pump housing.

Inspection

Wash all parts in clean solvent and blow dry with compressed air. Inspect all parts for wear or damage and replace as necessary.

Reassembly

1) Install a new "O" ring and converter oil seal into pump housing. Lubricate gears with automatic transmission fluid. Install gears into housing.

NOTE: Make sure the bevelled outer edge of ring gear faces bronze bushing.

2) Install intermediate plate into converter housing, aligning bolt and hydraulic passages. Install special installation sleeve (116 58 19 61 00) on stator shaft, then place 2 aligning studs into pump housing.

3) Install pump into converter housing, remove aligning studs, and install and tighten attaching bolts. If removed, install ball bearing onto converter housing.

GEAR UNIT DISASSEMBLY

1) Remove output shaft with rear planetary gear set from assembly. Withdraw caged needle bearing and thrust bearing. Position gear unit in a holding fixture with input shaft upward, remove 3 countersunk retaining screws from supporting flange. Withdraw flange and input shaft/sun gear from front planetary gear set.

2) Remove small snap ring retaining gear sets on intermediate shaft and large snap ring retaining gear set. Lift drum for front band, and front and center gear sets off assembly. Withdraw center gear set sun gear from assembly. Withdraw front clutch assembly.

3) Remove oil distributor sleeve from assembly. Withdraw drum for rear band along with rear clutch. Remove hollow shaft, rear clutch hub, and overrunning clutch hub from intermediate shaft. Separate intermediate shaft from output shaft. Using a puller, remove bearing from output shaft. Withdraw sun gear from rear planetary set.

Fig. 19: Exploded View of Converter Housing and Primary Pump Assembly

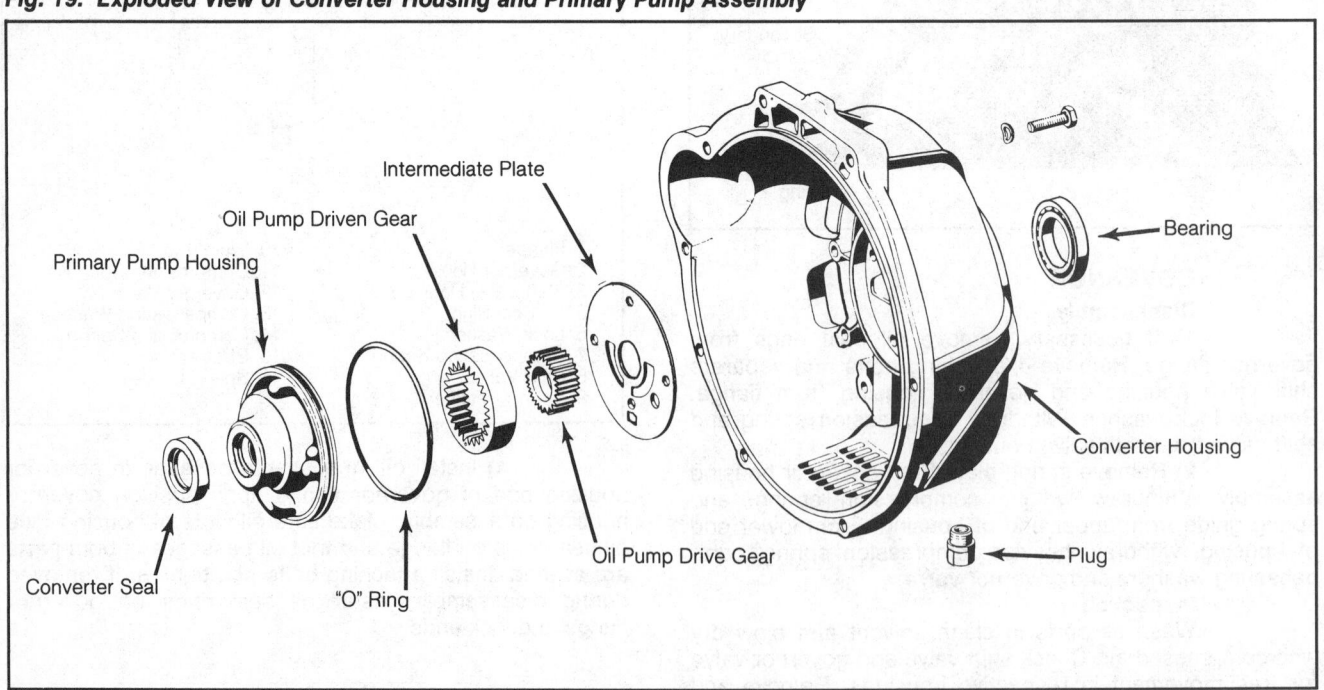

MERCEDES-BENZ TYPE W 4 B 025 (Cont.)

Fig. 20: Removing Snap Ring for Disassembly of Gear Unit

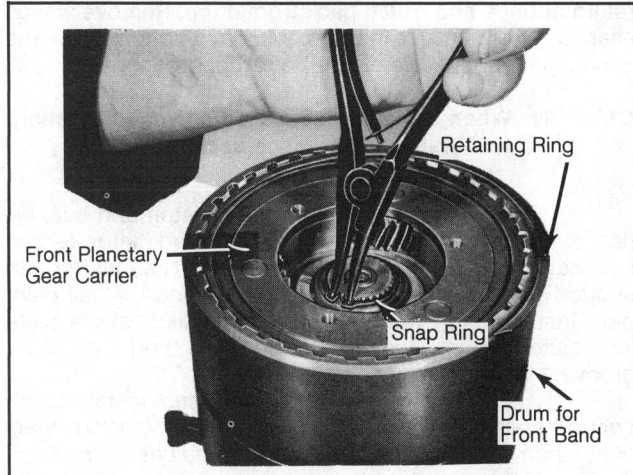

Release pressure on spring retainer and make sure snap ring seats fully in groove.

    3) Install 1 selective steel plate into drum, followed with 1 lined plate, then alternate 1 selective steel and 1 lined plate until all plates are installed. Install end plate and retaining snap ring. Make sure snap ring is fully seated.

NOTE: **Do not confuse front clutch snap ring with rear clutch snap ring. Front clutch snap ring has 6 waves.**

Fig. 22: Clutch Plate Installation in Front Clutch Assembly

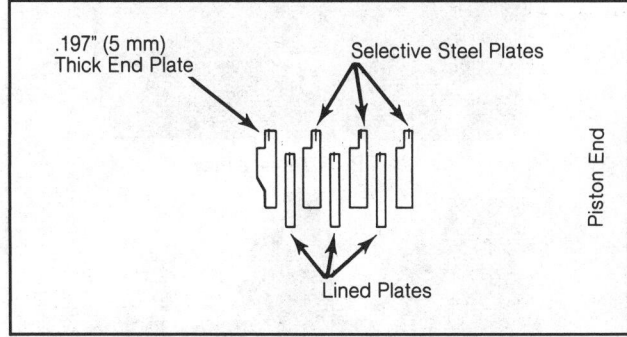

    4) Check release play of clutch pack as follows: Using a depth gauge, measure distance between top of clutch drum and end plate (press downward lightly on plate). Lift end plate up against ring and again measure distance from top of clutch drum to end plate. Subtract second measurement from first measurement; remainder is release play.

    5) Play should be .031-.047" (.8-1.2 mm). If not, replace one or more selective steel plates in drum with correct thickness plate(s). Selective steel plates are available in thicknesses of .177" (4.5 mm) and .197" (5 mm).

FRONT CLUTCH

Disassembly

    Remove large snap ring retaining clutch pack in drum. Withdraw lined and steel clutch plates. Compress spring retainer using a press. Retain snap ring then release press. Remove spring retainer and piston return springs. Withdraw piston from drum. Remove center seal from drum and large piston seal from piston.

Reassembly

    1) Install new center seal on clutch drum and new seal on piston. Make sure lips of both seals face down into clutch drum. Lubricate seals with transmission fluid, then using an installing sleeve (116 589 01 61 00), carefully install piston into clutch drum.

    2) Insert piston return springs into pockets of piston, position spring retainer on top of springs, compress spring retainer and install retaining snap ring.

Fig. 21: Exploded View of Front Clutch Assembly

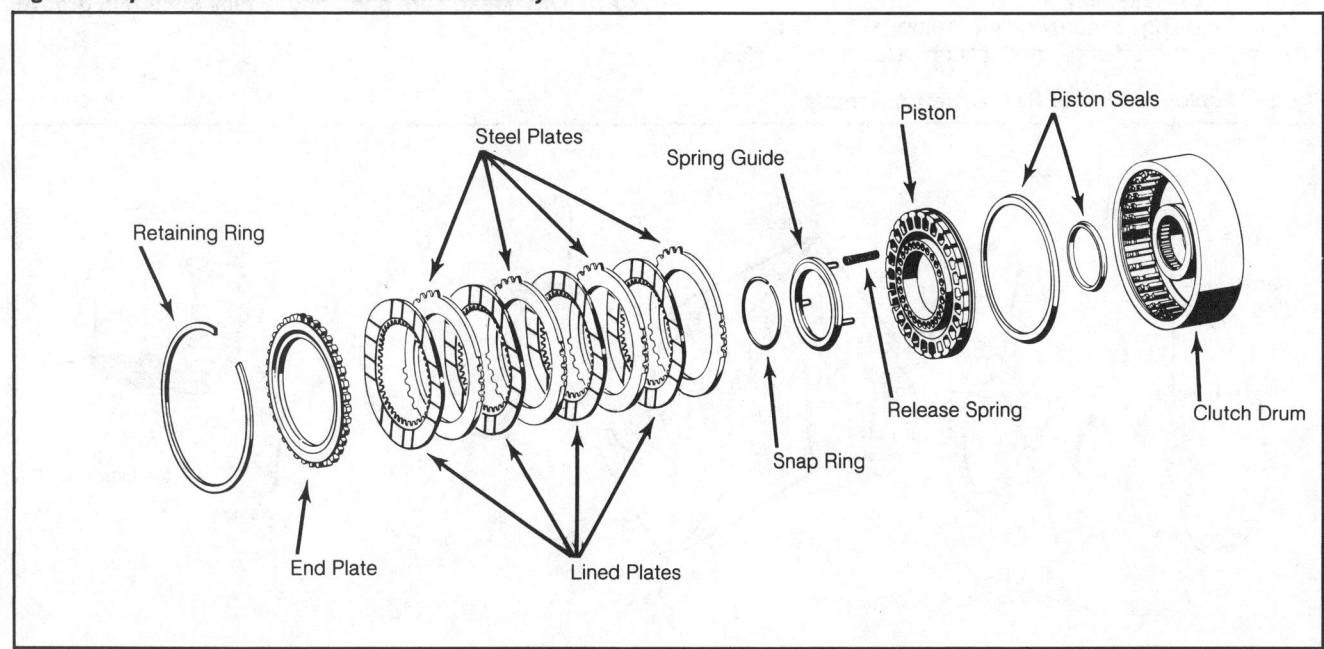

Automatic Transmissions

MERCEDES-BENZ TYPE W 4 B 025 (Cont.)

Fig. 23: Measuring Front Clutch Release Play Using a Depth Gauge

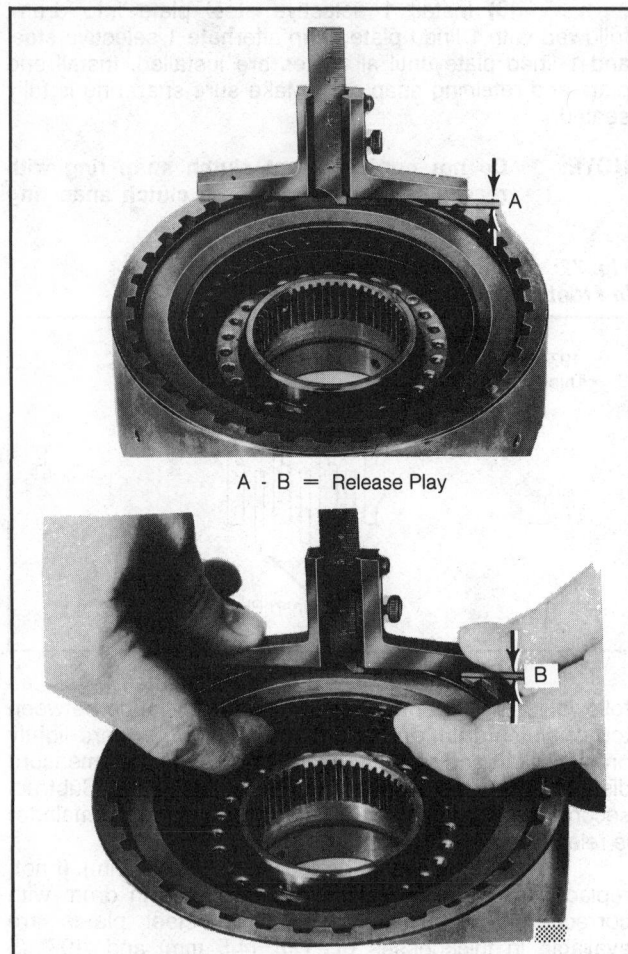

A - B = Release Play

REAR CLUTCH
Disassembly
Using a screwdriver, remove flat snap ring retaining support flange and piston assembly in clutch drum. Withdraw piston and flange assembly from drum, taking care to hold parts together. Remove clutch piston return springs and clutch pack from drum. Remove waved snap ring from groove in drum. Withdraw bottom plate and spring guide. Separate piston from support flange.

CAUTION: When replacing seals, do not use any sharp tool that would damage seal lip.

Reassembly
1) Install new oil seals, on piston and support flange, with seal lips facing downward into flange. Lubricate seals with transmission fluid. Install piston into support flange, starting seal lip with a pencil or ball point pen. Install piston return spring guide and bottom plate into clutch drum. Position waved snap ring into drum groove.

2) Turn clutch drum over and install clutch pack: Install 1 lined plate, follow with 1 selective steel plate, then alternate lined and steel plates until 3 lined and 2 steel plates are installed in drum. Finally, install one .118" (3 mm) steel plate.

NOTE: Rear clutch selective steel plates are available in thicknesses of .177" (4.5 mm) and .197" (5 mm).

3) Check clutch pack clearance as follows: Using a depth gauge, measure distance from top of clutch drum to top steel plate in drum. From this measurement, subtract the distance from top of clutch drum to contacting face of support flange. See Fig. 26.

4) Resulting measurement is clutch pack clearance. Clearance should be .031-.047" (.8-1.2 mm). If clearance is outside of specifications, adjust clearance by varying thicknesses of selective clutch plates in drum.

5) With clutch pack clearance adjusted, install clutch piston return springs into drum on guide pins. Install supporting flange and piston assembly into drum, press down on assembly, and install flat retaining snap ring.

CAUTION: Make sure snap ring is fully seated in groove.

Fig. 24: Exploded View of Rear Clutch Assembly

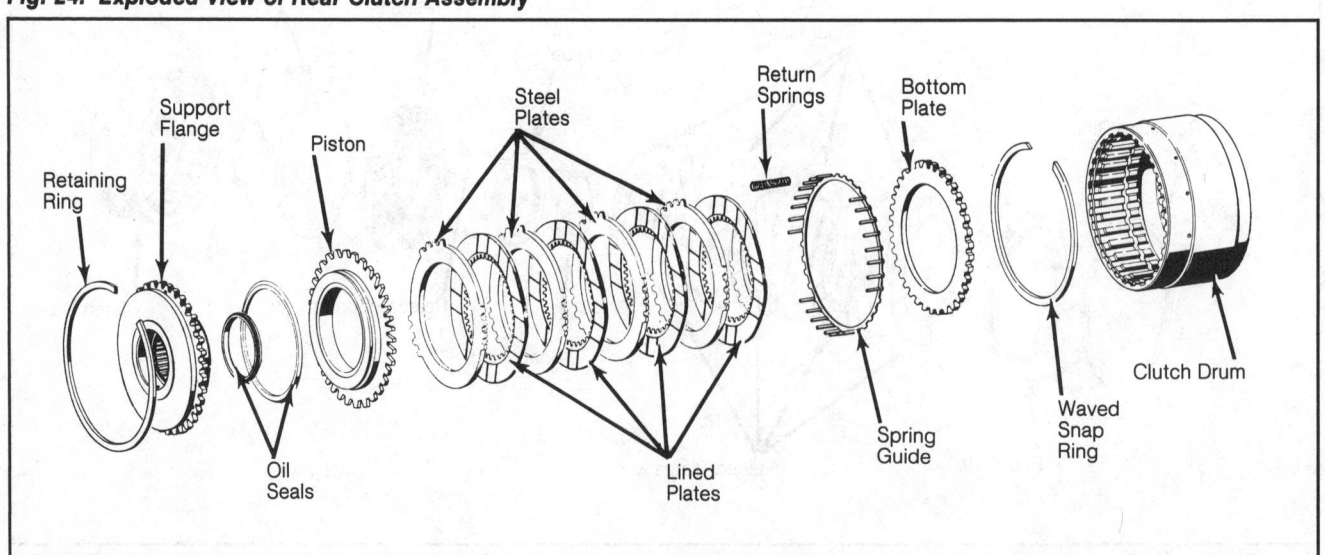

Retaining Ring • Support Flange • Piston • Oil Seals • Steel Plates • Lined Plates • Return Springs • Spring Guide • Bottom Plate • Waved Snap Ring • Clutch Drum

MERCEDES-BENZ TYPE W 4 B 025 (Cont.)

Fig. 25: *Positioning of Clutch Plates in Rear Clutch Assembly*

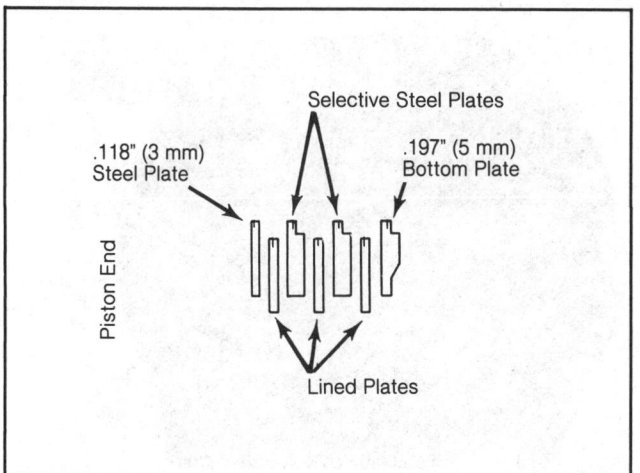

Fig. 26: *Measuring Rear Clutch Pack Clearance Using a Depth Gauge*

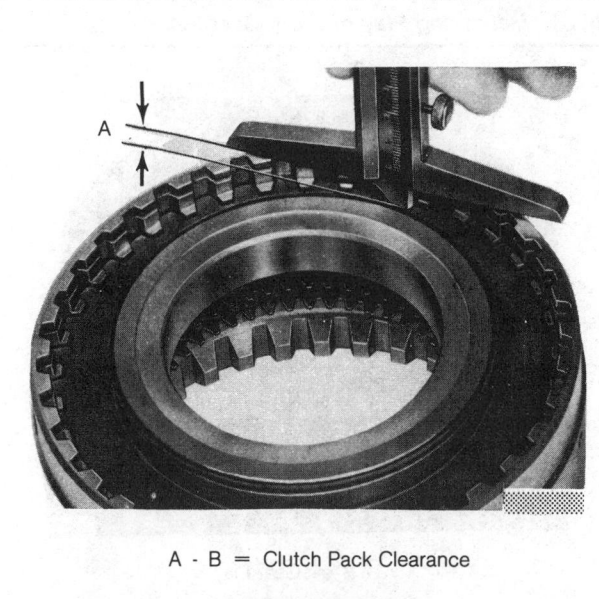

A - B = Clutch Pack Clearance

Fig. 27: *Installation of Rear Clutch Assembly Return Springs*

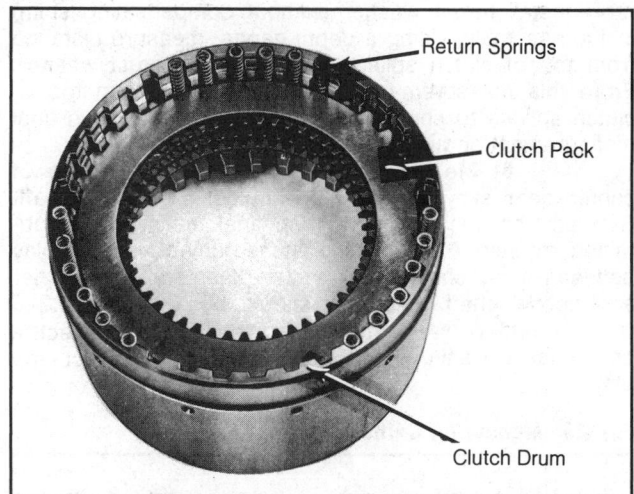

GEAR UNIT REASSEMBLY

NOTE: When installing thrust washer, make sure stepped face of thrust washer is positioned against sun gear.

1) Coat needle thrust bearing and split needle bearing with grease and install onto output shaft. Insert sun gear for rear gear set onto output shaft, then position thrust washer on top of gear. Position ball bearing and parking gear on shaft and press into place.

2) Position 2 greased needle bearings into ring gear end of intermediate shaft. Mate output and intermediate shafts. Place assembly in a holding fixture. Install needle bearing and thrust washer onto intermediate shaft.

3) Place hollow shaft into rear clutch assembly. Make sure all clutch plates are engaged. Place rear clutch/hollow shaft assembly on intermediate shaft. Install needle bearing into overrunning clutch.

4) Check seal rings of oil distributor sleeve for correct position. Insert distributor sleeve into support flange of rear clutch assembly. Position front clutch on oil distributor sleeve. Install needle bearing over hollow shaft. Insert sun gear of center gear unit into front clutch.

Fig. 28: *View of Assembled Gear Unit*

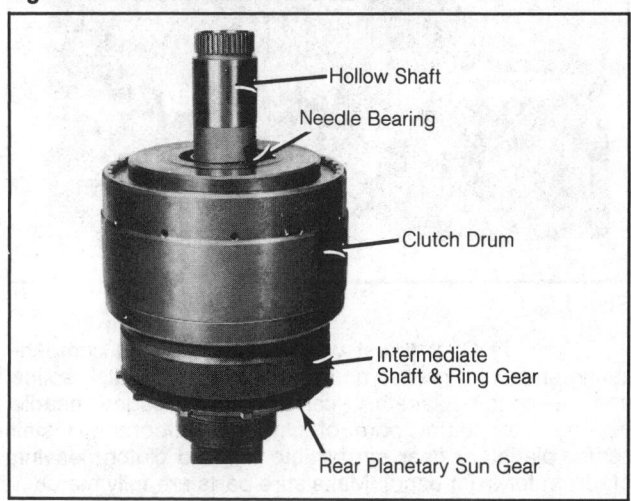

MERCEDES-BENZ TYPE W 4 B 025 (Cont.)

5) Place planetary gear carrier of center gear set on bench with forward clutch splines upward. Temporarily install thrust washer (without compensating shim) inside assembly. Using a depth gauge, measure distance from top of clutch splines to surface of thrust washer. From this measurement, subtract distance from top of clutch splines to shoulder of inner hub. Write down final measurement obtained.

6) Measure distance from thrust surface of center gear set sun gear to shoulder of hollow shaft. Subtract this measurement from final measurement obtained in step **5)**. Resulting measurement is end play between inner shoulder of center planetary gear carrier and hollow shaft. End play should be .008-.012" (.2-.3 mm). If end play is not within specifications, select a compensating shim of correct thickness to correct end play.

Fig. 29: *Measuring Center Sun Gear Play*

Step 1.

7) Coat thrust washer and selected compensating shim with grease and position in front clutch spline end of center planetary carrier. Install caged needle bearing into center bore of carrier. Temporarily install center planetary gear carrier into forward clutch (leaving off drum for front band). Make sure parts are fully mated.

Fig. 30: *Measuring Center Sun Gear Play*

Step 2.

Fig. 31: *Measuring Play of Front Gear Set*

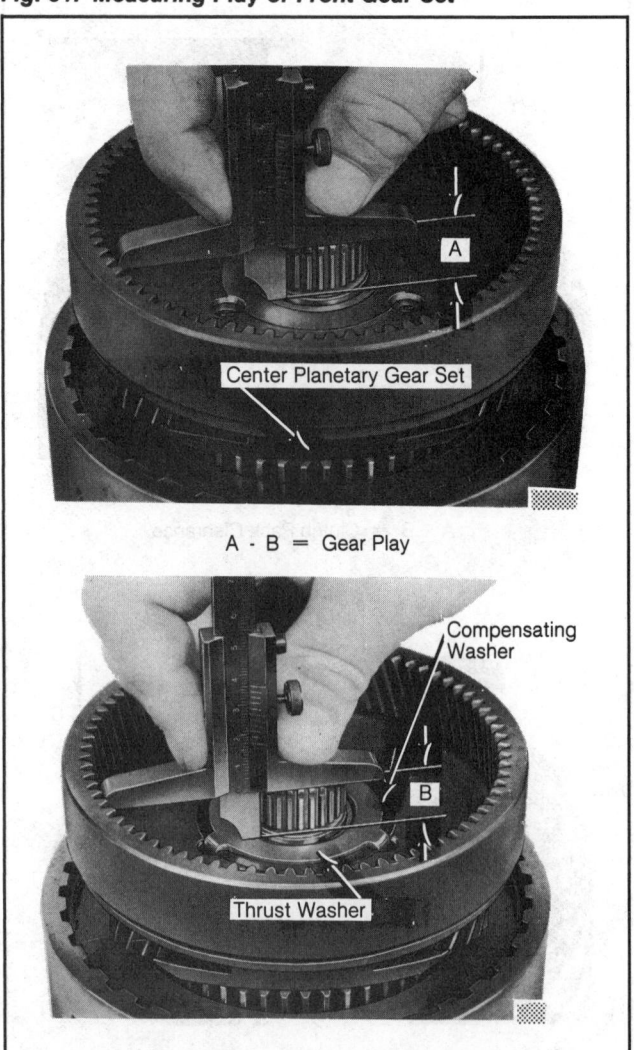

MERCEDES-BENZ TYPE W 4 B 025 (Cont.)

8) Using a depth gauge, measure distance from top of intermediate shaft to shoulder of intermediate shaft. Temporarily install thrust washer into assembly. Measure distance from top of intermediate shaft to thrust washer. Subtract second measurement from first measurement; remainder should be .008-.012" (.2-.3 mm). If not, select a compensating shim of correct thickness to bring end play within specifications. Remove center planetary carrier from gear unit.

9) Coat thrust washer and selected compensating washer with grease and install into ring gear end of center planetary carrier. Mesh center planetary carrier with drum for front band. Install assembly onto gear unit, meshing center planetary carrier with front clutch plates. Install front planetary carrier into assembly, secure to intermediate shaft with small snap ring. Push drum for front band upward. Secure gear unit with large retaining ring.

10) Insert thrust washer into front planetary carrier. Install input shaft/sun gear assembly. Position thrust washer on underside of supporting flange and position flange on gear unit. Coat threads of flange retaining screws with sealer, install and tighten. Install oil seal ring on input shaft, lock ends and check for free movement of ring in groove.

Fig. 32: Installing Supporting Flange onto Gear Unit

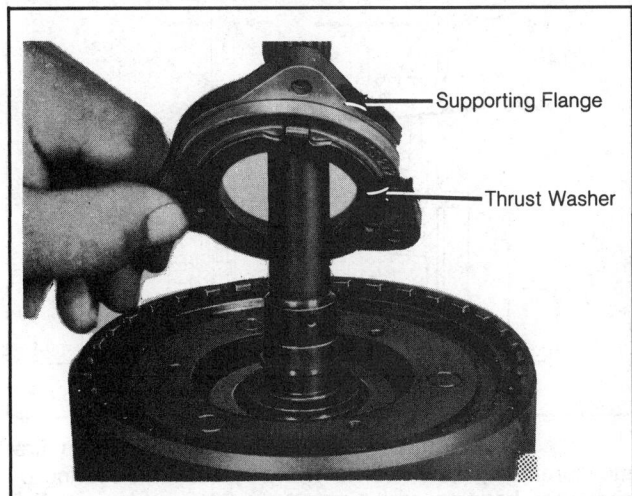

Supporting Flange

Thrust Washer

TRANSMISSION REASSEMBLY

1) Position transmission case in a holding fixture with pan attaching face upward. Insert front band lever into case, install lever pin, and secure with retaining clip. Install new "O" rings into center and rear band pressure body bores. Install new seal into selector lever bore. Position neutral safety and back-up light switch on transmission. Install and tighten attaching screws.

2) Install a new seal on front servo piston, position piston and return spring into case, then install servo cover and retaining ring. Position detent plate on rear of case. Install selector lever and shaft through case and plate. Tighten clamp screw.

3) Place selector lever in neutral position and loosen adjusting screw of neutral safety switch. *See Fig. 33.* Install an alignment pin through link and into bore of housing. Tighten adjusting screw and remove pin.

Fig. 33: Adjusting Neutral Safety Switch

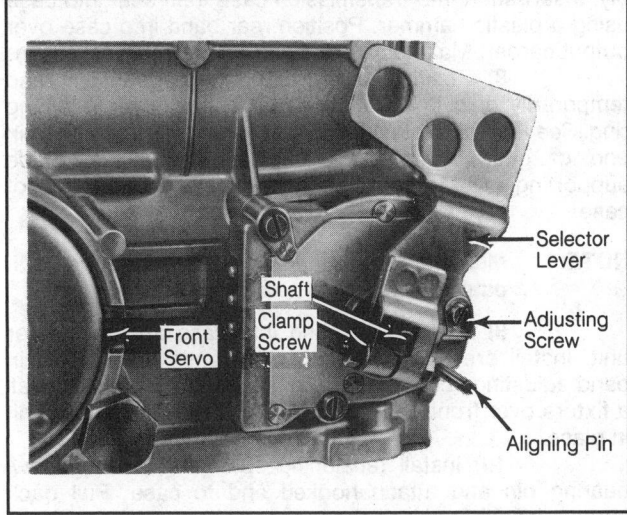

Selector Lever

Shaft

Clamp Screw

Front Servo

Adjusting Screw

Aligning Pin

4) Install control pressure shaft into case bore, insert plastic washer and secure with "E" clip. Install sealing ring into rear servo bore. Make sure seal is flush with bore in housing. Install pressure bodies into center and rear band pressure body bores in case. Secure bodies in case with retaining clip.

CAUTION: Center and rear band pressure bodies are not interchangeable. Center band body has identification grooves; rear band body has no grooves.

5) On rear of case, install linkage arm, washer, and roller. Position leaf spring on case and over detent plate, then install needle bearing supported roller. Install parking lock bracket and retaining bolt.

6) If removed, install parking pawl bearing pin. Position extension housing gasket on rear case face, and center over bores for fitted pins. Mount modulating pressure valve housing on rear of case. Install and tighten attaching bolts. Check valve for free operation.

Fig. 34: Rear View of Transmission Case Showing Installation of Control Linkage

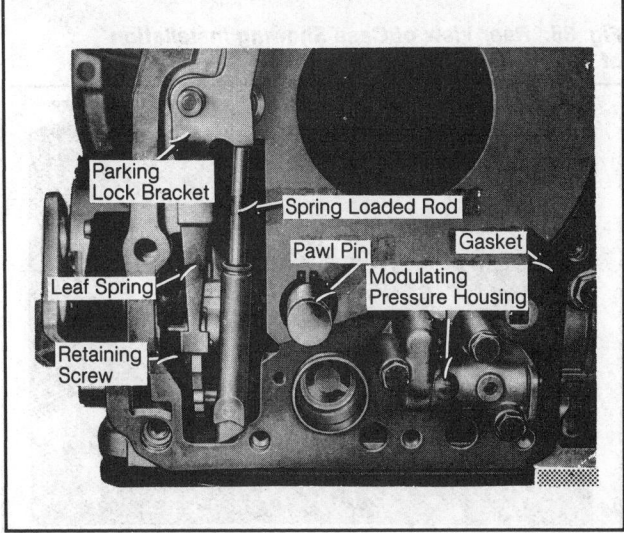

Parking Lock Bracket

Spring Loaded Rod

Pawl Pin

Gasket

Leaf Spring

Modulating Pressure Housing

Retaining Screw

Automatic Transmissions

MERCEDES-BENZ TYPE W 4 B 025 (Cont.)

7) Remove output shaft from gear unit assembly. Insert shaft into transmission case then seat into case using a plastic hammer. Position rear band into case over output carrier. Make sure band end engages pressure pin.

8) Position center band over gear unit and temporarily hold in place with rear servo cover retaining ring. *See Fig. 35.* Make sure bearings are still positioned in end of gear unit. Install gear unit into case, guide supporting lever of oil distributor sleeve into groove of case.

NOTE: Make sure gear unit is fully engaged with output shaft.

9) Insert front band into case and over gear unit. Install pressure pins into band ends then screw in band adjusting screw until band is secured in place. Install a fixture over front of transmission case to retain gear unit in place.

10) Install tensioning spring on parking pawl bearing pin and attach hooked end to case. Pull back spring, install parking pawl and release spring. Check operation of parking lock. Install governor, eccentric for secondary pump, speedometer drive gear, and plate spring on output shaft.

Fig. 35: Installing Gear Unit Through Rear of Case

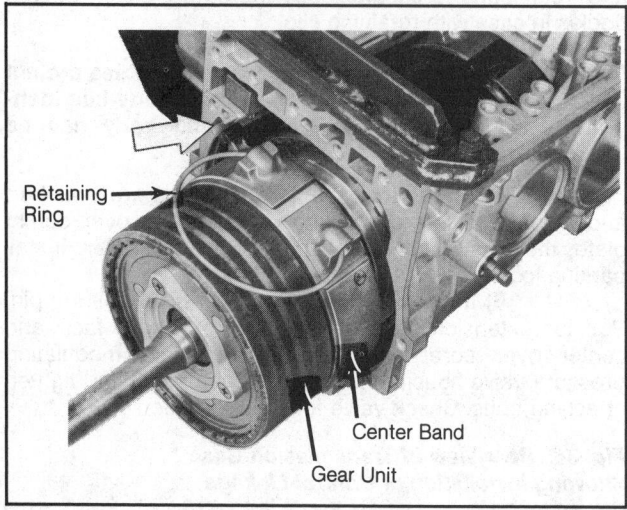

Fig. 36: Rear View of Case Showing Installation of Parking Pawl Spring

11) Make sure pressure receiving piston assembly is correctly positioned in extension housing, mount extension housing on transmission, and install and tighten attaching bolts. Install a new "O" ring seal on secondary pump plug. Install compression spring and plug into extension housing.

12) Place a new sealing washer on adjusting screw. Install screw and compression spring into extension housing. Install flange on output shaft. Install and tighten retaining nut. Stake nut to secure in place.

13) Determine end play between gear unit and converter housing as follows: Place a measuring bar (116 589 00 21 00) on transmission case. Measure distance from top of bar to bearing surface of supporting flange in gear unit. Install new gasket on rear of converter housing. Place measuring bar on housing and measure distance from top of bar to bearing race.

NOTE: After subtracting thickness of bar, resulting measurements are: Distance from face of transmission case to bearing surface of supporting flange and distance from gasket surface to bearing race.

Fig. 37: Gear Unit-to-Housing Clearance Diagram

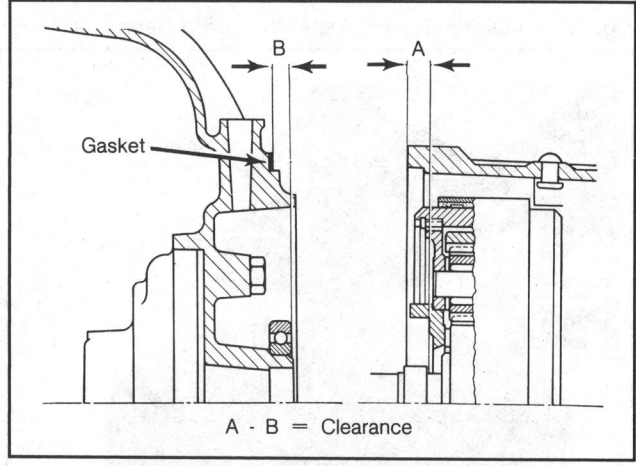

14) Subtract second measurement from first measurement; remainder is end play between bearing on converter housing and support flange in gear unit. End play should be .012-.020" (.3-.5 mm). If end play needs adjustment, install compensating shims into support flange in gear unit to bring end play within specifications.

15) Make sure gasket on converter housing is correctly positioned and mount converter housing on transmission case. Coat converter housing attaching bolts with sealer, install and tighten.

16) Using a ring compressor, install rear servo piston into transmission case making sure piston stem engages bore of band. Position a new "O" ring on servo cover, position compression spring (if used) over piston. Make sure small end of spring is positioned against servo piston. Install servo cover and retaining ring.

17) Place new seal rings on center servo secondary piston and install into servo piston cover. Install new seals on cover, place on secondary piston and secure with retaining ring. Install new sealing "O" rings on assembly, position compression springs on piston stem and insert into case. Compress assembly into case and install retaining ring.

MERCEDES-BENZ TYPE W 4 B 025 (Cont.)

18) Check freeplay of center and rear bands as follows: Introduce air pressure into rear band release pressure passage in case. *See Fig. 40.* Mark position of band end on drum. Introduce air pressure to rear band apply pressure passage in case. Mark position of band end on drum.

19) Measure distance between 2 marks; measurement is rear band freeplay. For center band freeplay, first mark position of band end on drum in released position (spring pressure holds band in released position). Apply air pressure to center servo apply passage in case and again mark position of band end on drum. Distance between 2 marks is center band free play.

Fig. 38: Exploded View of Gear Unit Assembly

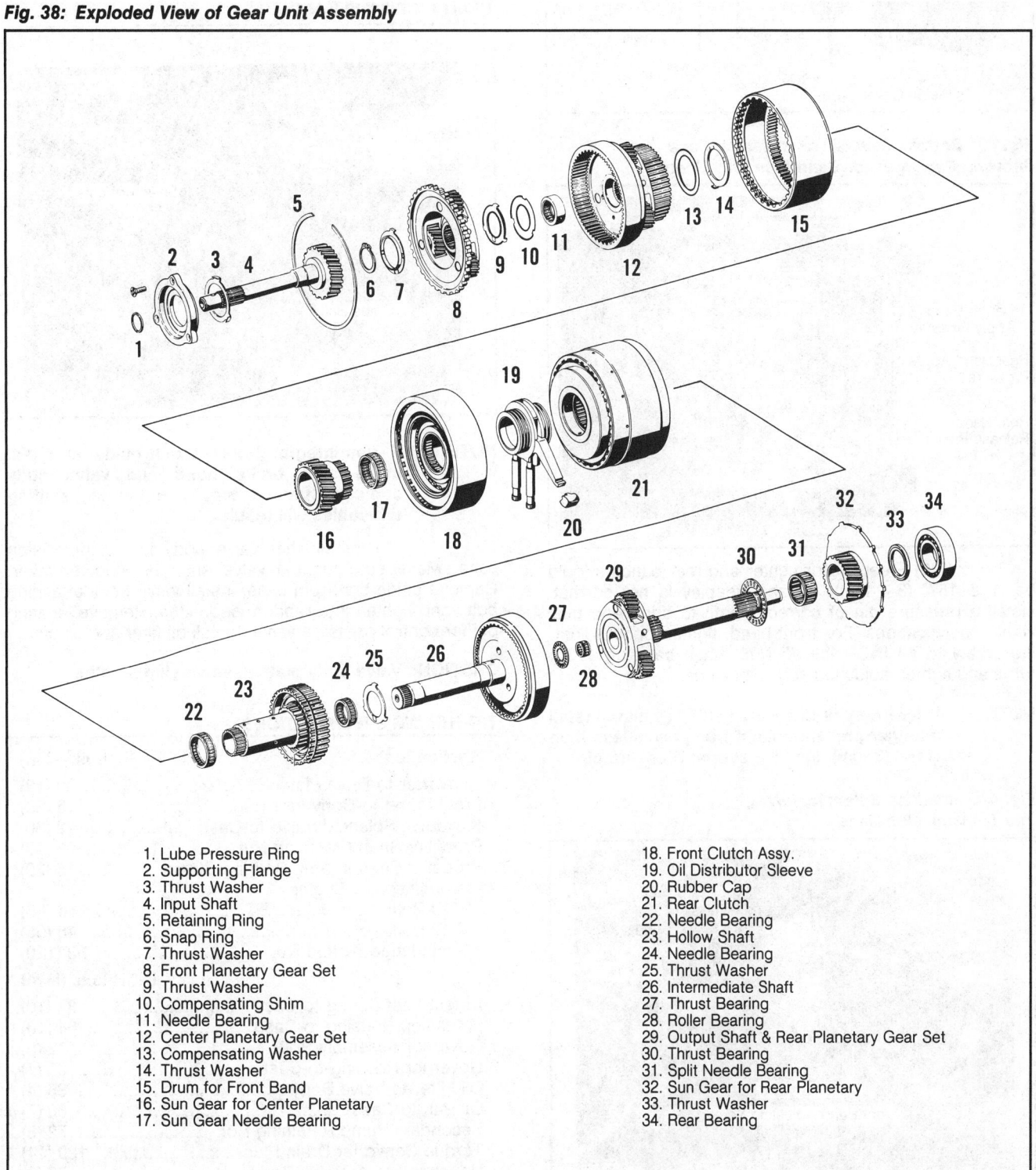

1. Lube Pressure Ring
2. Supporting Flange
3. Thrust Washer
4. Input Shaft
5. Retaining Ring
6. Snap Ring
7. Thrust Washer
8. Front Planetary Gear Set
9. Thrust Washer
10. Compensating Shim
11. Needle Bearing
12. Center Planetary Gear Set
13. Compensating Washer
14. Thrust Washer
15. Drum for Front Band
16. Sun Gear for Center Planetary
17. Sun Gear Needle Bearing
18. Front Clutch Assy.
19. Oil Distributor Sleeve
20. Rubber Cap
21. Rear Clutch
22. Needle Bearing
23. Hollow Shaft
24. Needle Bearing
25. Thrust Washer
26. Intermediate Shaft
27. Thrust Bearing
28. Roller Bearing
29. Output Shaft & Rear Planetary Gear Set
30. Thrust Bearing
31. Split Needle Bearing
32. Sun Gear for Rear Planetary
33. Thrust Washer
34. Rear Bearing

MERCEDES-BENZ TYPE W 4 B 025 (Cont.)

Fig. 39: Exploded View of Center Servo Assembly

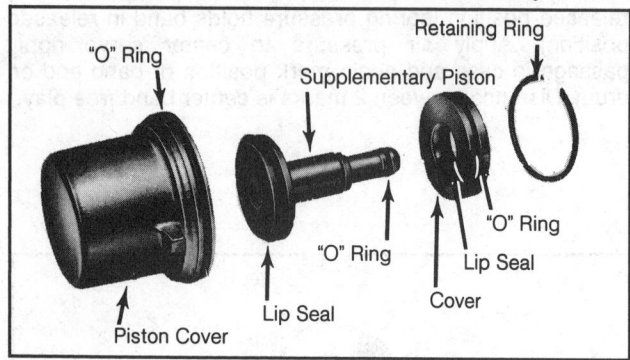

Fig. 40: Bottom View of Transmission Case Showing Passages for Band Free Play Check

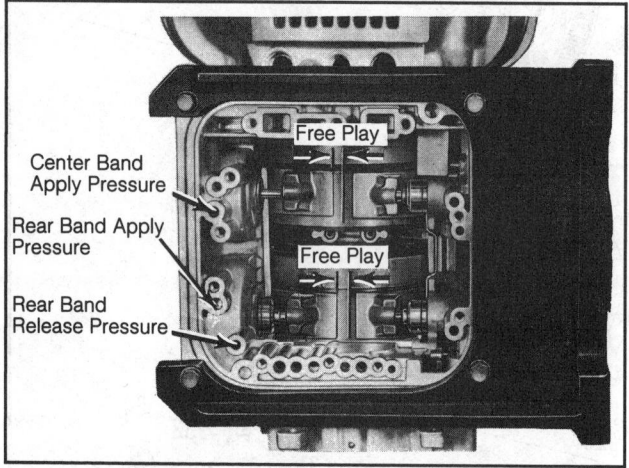

20) Freeplay for center and rear bands should be .118-.157" (3-4 mm). If band freeplay is not correct, install a pressure pin of correct length to bring end play within specifications. For front band, tighten band adjusting screw to 43 INCH lbs. (5 N.m), then back off 1 3/4 turns and tighten adjusting screw lock nut.

NOTE: If free play is more than .157" (4 mm), install a longer pressure pin; if free play is less than .118" (3 mm), install a shorter pressure pin.

Fig. 41: Installing Solenoid Valve into Transmission Case

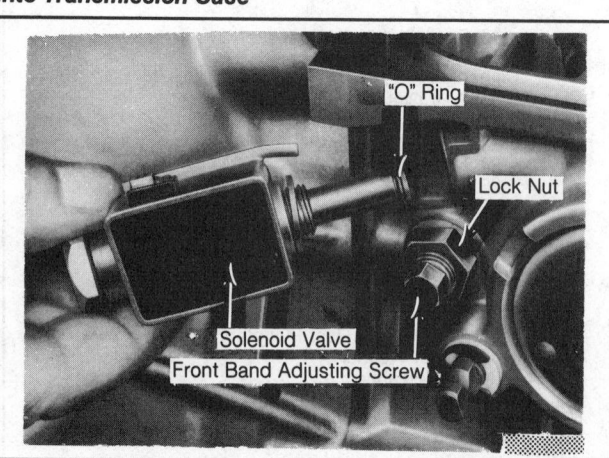

21) Install a new sealing washer and "O" ring on solenoid valve and install assembly into case. Install both oil feed pipes into oil distributor sleeve, and place new seals on pipes. Move selector lever between park and reverse positions. Install a locating pin for control pressure valve into valve body and a guide bolt into transmission case. *See Fig. 42.*

Fig. 42: Installing Valve Body Assembly into Transmission Case

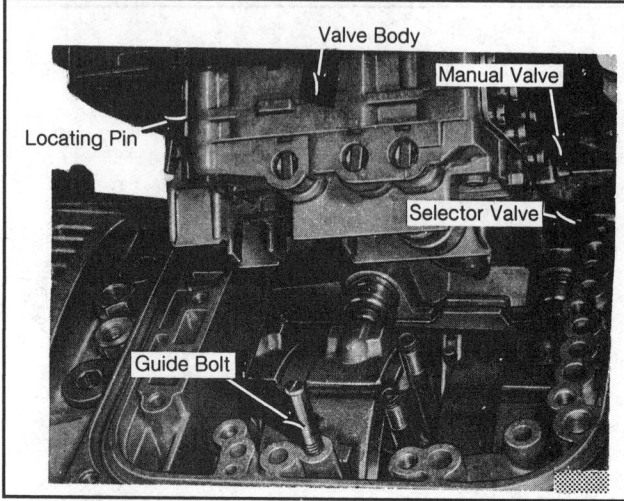

NOTE: If non-integral brake band guide is used, make sure brake band and valve body contours match. If they do not match, shifting difficulties will result.

22) Install shift valve body into transmission case. Make sure manual valve engages selector lever. Remove guide bolt from case, install valve body attaching bolts and tighten in a random sequence. Remove locating pin for control pressure valve. Install oil filter and oil pan.

CAUTION: Valve body bolts have varying lengths.

TIGHTENING SPECIFICATIONS

Application	Ft. Lbs. (N.m)
Converter-to-Drive Plate	30 (42)
Front Pump-to-Converter Hsg	15 (20)
Kickdown Solenoid Valve-to-Case	22 (30)
Propeller Shaft Clamping Nut	22 (30)
Propeller Shaft Interm. Bearing Clamp	15 (20)
Transmisson-to-Engine	
M 10 Bolts	41 (55)
M 12 Bolts	48 (65)
3-Arm Flange Slotted Nut	89 (120)

	INCH Lbs. (N.m)
Detent Leaf Spring-to-Case	84 (10)
Extension Housing-to-Case	84 (10)
Governor Assembly Bolts	72 (8)
Governor Housing-to-Case	60 (7)
Oil Filter-to-Valve Body	36 (4)
Oil Pan-to-Case	60 (7)
Secondary Pump Retaining Bolt	72 (8)
Torque Converter Drain Plug	120 (14)
Upper-to-Lower Valve Body	72 (8)

PORSCHE 928

DESCRIPTION

Transaxle assembly consists of 3 main units: Automatic transmission, torque converter and final drive assembly. Automatic transmission is an A22.01 fully automatic 3-speed, planetary gear type and consists of 2 planetary gear sets, 3 brake bands, 2 multiple-disc clutches, oil pump, valve body and input and output shafts.

Torque converter is located on front of transmission and is housed in a 2 piece bell housing. Final drive is attached to rear of transmission case and contains a ring and pinion gear, side gears and pinion gears. The operation of final drive is the same as conventional differentials.

LUBRICATION & ADJUSTMENT

See the appropriate article in AUTOMATIC TRANSMISSION SERVICING Section.

TROUBLE SHOOTING

SLIPS IN ALL SELECTOR POSITIONS

Incorrect modulating pressure. Modulating pressure control valve or pressure relief valve for modulating pressure dirty or sticking. Line to transmission vacuum unit clogged or leaking. Working pressure control valve dirty or sticking. Defective pump.

TRANSMISSION GRABS OR VEHICLE SHAKES WHEN STARTING OFF

Incorrect modulating pressure. Check transmission vacuum unit; if transmission fluid is found in vacuum unit, replace unit. If fuel is found in vacuum unit, check injection system and adjust.

TRANSMISSION SLIPS IN FIRST GEAR

Dirty or sticking valves in valve body. Defective center servo piston or piston sealing ring damaged. Defective center band or thrust body.

TRANSMISSION SLIPS ON UPSHIFT

Incorrect modulating pressure. Faulty valve body assembly (replace sealing bushings on plug pipes). Defective front or rear clutch. Oil distribution sleeve damaged.

TRANSMISSION SLIPS IN THIRD GEAR

Valve body sealing bushings worn or damaged. Defective rear clutch assembly. Oil distributing sleeve damaged.

TRANSMISSION SLIPS IN FIRST AND SECOND GEARS

Rear band worn or damaged. Adjust brake band by installing a longer thrust pin.

TRANSMISSION SLIPS IN ALL GEARS

Incorrect modulating pressure. Defective modulating pressure relief valve or control valve.

TRANSMISSION WILL NOT ENGAGE PROPERLY

Torque converter not installed correctly. Driver not correctly engaging in drive gear.

NO POSITIVE ENGAGEMENT IN REVERSE

Front band out of adjustment. Front servo piston sealing ring worn or damaged. Defective one-way clutch in gear unit assembly.

Fig. 1: 928 Automatic Transaxle Assembly

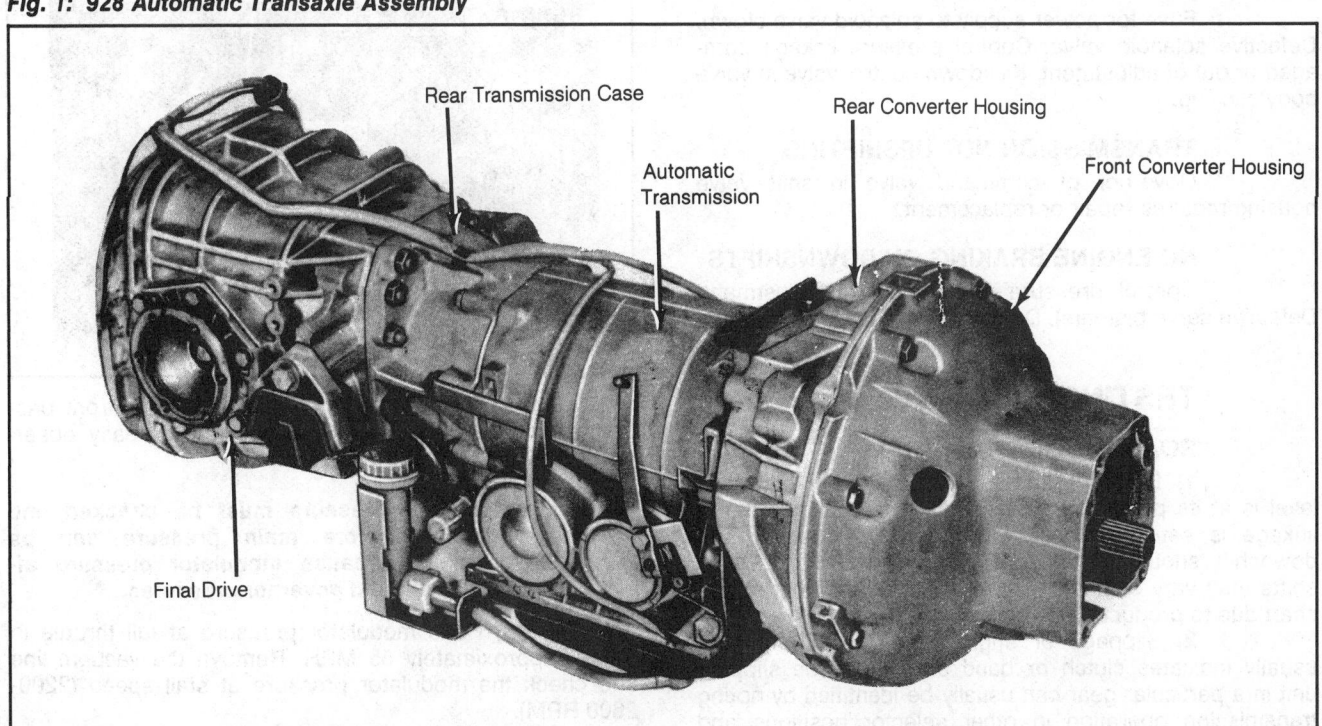

ROUGH JERK WHEN ENGAGING SELECTOR LEVER POSITION "D"

Adjust engine idle speed and emissions as specified. Incorrect modulating and/or working pressure. Vacuum leak. Defective pressure receiving piston in extension housing.

ROUGH JERK WHEN CHANGING GEAR

Check modulating pressure and working pressure and adjust modulating pressure if necessary. If working pressure is too high, replace valve body assembly. Vacuum lines or connections leaking. Control pressure linkage out of adjustment.

ROUGH JERK ON 3-2 DOWNSHIFT

Rear servo piston sealing ring worn or damaged. Defective rear servo piston.

NO UPSHIFTS

Incorrect governor pressure. Defective governor assembly.

UPSHIFTS ONLY IN UPPER SPEED RANGE OF GEARS

Control pressure linkage out of adjustment. Defective governor assembly.

UPSHIFTS ONLY IN LOWER SPEED RANGE OF GEARS

Control pressure linkage damaged or out of adjustment. Accelerator linkage out of adjustment. Defective governor assembly.

POOR ACCELERATION AT START

Check stalling speed. If speed drops 400/700 RPM, replace torque converter.

NO KICKDOWN SHIFTS

Fuse for power supply to solenoid valve blown. Defective solenoid valve. Control pressure linkage damaged or out of adjustment. Kickdown control valve in valve body sticking.

TRANSMISSION NOT UPSHIFTING

Governor or command valve in shift valve housing requires repair or replacement.

NO ENGINE BRAKING ON DOWNSHIFTS

Control pressure linkage out of adjustment. Defective servo piston(s). Defective valve body assembly.

TESTING

ROAD TESTING

1) Before road testing, be certain that fluid level is at its proper level. Also make certain the control linkage is set properly. During road test, upshift and downshift should be smooth and without slippage. All shifts may vary somewhat from the following shift speed chart due to production tolerances or tire size.

2) Slippage or engine runaway in any gear usually indicates clutch or band problems. The slipping unit in a particular gear can usually be identified by noting transmission operation in other selector positions and comparing which internal units are applied in those positions. See Clutch and Band Application Chart.

3) This process of elimination can be used to detect any unit which slips, and to confirm proper operation of good units. The actual cause of the malfunction usually cannot be determined. Practically any condition can be caused by leaking hydraulic circuits or sticking valves. Therefore, unless an obvious condition exists, do not disassemble transmission until a hydraulic pressure check has been completed.

SHIFT SPEEDS

Application	Shift Points (MPH)	
	Upshift	Downshift
Part Throttle		
1-2-1	16-21	10-14
2-3-2	26-30	20-23
Full Throttle		
1-2-1	60-65	28-32
2-3-2	93-98	35-53
Kickdown		
3-2		76-83
2-1		36-48

HYDRAULIC PRESSURE TEST

1) Connect 0-350 psi (0-24.1 kg/cm²) pressure gauge to main pressure check point. Connect 0-140 psi (0-9.6 kg/cm²) pressure gauge to governor pressure check point. Connect 0-140 (0-9.6 kg/cm²) pressure gauge to modulator pressure check point. See Fig. 2.

Fig. 2: View of Transmission Case Showing Pressure Test Connections

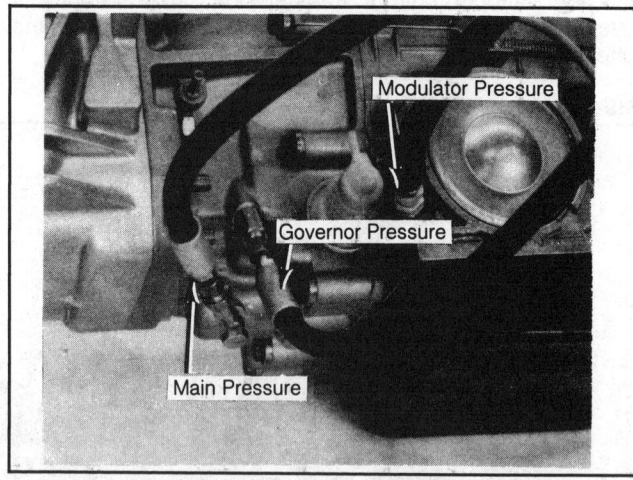

2) Route pressure gauges through front passenger window and place in a position for easy observation.

NOTE: Modulator pressure must be checked and adjusted before main pressure can be checked, because modulator pressure affects main and governor pressures.

3) Read modulator pressure at full throttle in "D", at approximately 55 MPH. Remove the vacuum line and check the modulator pressure at stall speed (2200-2600 RPM).

PORSCHE 928 (Cont.)

4) To adjust, remove modulator pressure cover. Slightly pull adjusting key out. To increase pressure, turn key to the right; to decrease pressure, turn key to the left. After adjustment is made, push key into nearest slot and install modulator cover.

5) Check main pressure as follows: With vacuum line disconnected, gear selector in "D" and vehicle at stall speed (2200-2600), read main line pressure. Next, repeat above in "R" and read main line pressure. Final main line pressure check is performed at full throttle in "D" at approximately 55 MPH and vacuum line connected.

6) Governor pressure is checked at designated speeds with vacuum line disconnected. *See Operating Pressure Chart.*

TRANSMISSION OPERATING PRESSURES

Application	Psi (kg/cm²)
Modulating Pressure	
"D" @ 55 MPH	44-45 (3.0-3.1)
At Stall Speed in "D" ¹	65-70 (4.5-4.8)
Main Pressure	
At Stall Speed in "D" ¹	145-168 (10.0-11.6)
At Stall Speed in "R" ¹	278-294 (19.2-20.3)
At Full Throttle in "D" 62 MPH	80-86 (5.6-5.9)
Governor Pressure	
At 12 MPH	7-9 (.4-.6)
At 31 MPH	21-24 (1.4-1.6)
At 47 MPH	30-31 (2.0-2.1)
At 62 MPH	36-37 (2.4-2.5)
At 81 MPH	44-47 (3.0-3.2)
AT 99 MPH	55-58 (3.7-3.9)

¹ — Vacuum line disconnected.

STALL SPEED

Testing Precautions

Set parking brake, block wheels, and apply foot brake. Maximum stall speed test time is 5 seconds. If engine speed exceeds limits shown in *Stall Speed Table*, release accelerator immediately as clutch or band slippage is indicated.

Testing Procedure

Connect tachometer to engine and place in a position for easy observation. Run engine at 2000 RPM for 2 minutes in Neutral before testing. Place selector lever in "D" and depress accelerator pedal. Read stall speed on tachometer.

Test Result

If stall speed is higher than specified by 300 RPM, slippage in transmission is indicated. If stall speed drops by approximately 400 to 700 RPM, one-way clutch in torque converter is slipping. If stall speed is correct and top speed is not reached, one-way clutch is locking up.

NOTE: Stall speed will drop approximately 125 RPM for every 3900 feet of altitude above sea level. Also high outside temperatures could cause stall speed to drop slightly.

STALL SPEEDS

Application	Stall RPM
All Models	2200-2600

SERVICE (IN-VEHICLE)

REAR WHEEL BEARINGS

Removal

With brake calipers off and drive shaft disconnected at axle flange, press shaft from housing, remove circlip and drive grooved ball bearing and roller bearing out with soft drift.

Installation

Press grooved ball bearing in inner end of housing and replace circlip. Put spacer in housing and drive roller bearing in place (flanged side facing out). Install seal in inboard side of housing. Put outer spacer in shaft and press in along with bearing inner race using castellated nut and driver.

AXLE DRIVE SHAFTS

Removal & Installation

Raise vehicle on hoist. Remove bolts from constant velocity joint-to-mating flange and remove drive axle from vehicle. To install, reverse removal procedure and tighten to specifications.

CONSTANT VELOCITY JOINTS

NOTE: Axle shafts must be removed from vehicle before servicing.

Removal

Clamp axle shaft in a vise with soft jaws. Remove boot clamp and push boot to center of axle.

CLUTCH AND BAND APPLICATION CHART (ELEMENTS IN USE)

Selector Lever Position	Front Clutch	Rear Clutch	Front Band	Center Band	Rear Band	Overrunning Clutch
FIRST GEAR				X	X	X
SECOND GEAR	X				X	
THIRD GEAR	X	X				
REVERSE			X			X

NEUTRAL OR PARK — All clutches and bands released and/or ineffective.

PORSCHE 928 (Cont.)

Remove circlip from axle shaft, press joint from axle shaft using special tools VW 401 and VW 408.

Disassembly

Swing ball and ball cage from joint and press out in direction of arrow. *See Fig. 3.* Tilt ball hub out of ball cage via ball groove. *See Fig. 4.* Clean all parts in a cleaning solvent and blow dry. Inspect for wear and damage.

NOTE: **Ball hub and joint are paired. Do not mix parts. The 6 balls are also mated together and cannot be mixed with others.**

Fig. 3: Ball Hub and Ball Cage Removal

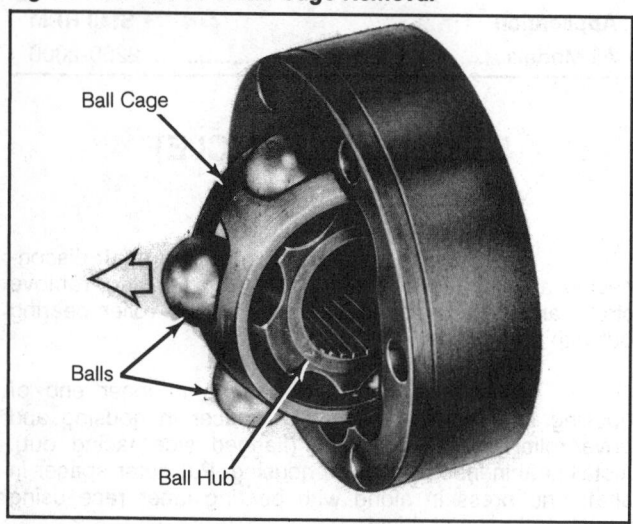

Fig. 4: Removal of Ball Hub from Cage

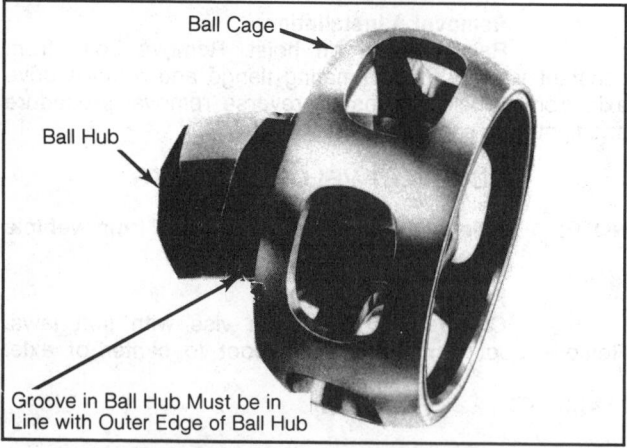

Reassembly

Place ball hub in ball cage. Press balls into cage. Install hub with cage and balls into joint and swing into assembled position. Check for smooth operation.

Installation

Reverse removal procedure and note the following: Install a new gasket on flange cover. Pack joint with molybdenum grease.

FLANGE SHAFT SEAL

Removal

Remove axle drive shaft. Remove inner flange bolt while holding flange with tool. Remove flange and seal using tools.

Installation

Fill cavity between sealing, dust lips with multi-purpose grease and drive seal in place with tool. Replace flange and axle drive shaft and tighten to specifications.

TORQUE CONVERTER

NOTE: **The torque converter is a sealed unit and cannot be disassembled for service.**

REMOVAL & INSTALLATION

See the appropriate article in AUTOMATIC TRANSMISSION REMOVAL Section.

TRANSMISSION DISASSEMBLY

NOTE: **Transmission has to be separated from final drive before it can be disassembled.**

1) Detach final drive assembly and remove bearing and pinion assembly. Remove final drive housing, centrifugal governor and modulating pressure housing.

NOTE: **Vacuum modulator must be removed before removing final drive housing.**

2) Pull parking lock gear off output shaft. Remove front torque converter housing and torque converter. Remove oil pan, valve body and kickdown solenoid. Remove snap ring for number 2 brake band piston and remove cover. Install special tool (9305) and press out piston. Attach special tool (9304) for number 1 brake band piston, preload piston and remove snap ring. Release special tool and remove cover, piston and springs.

3) Mark pins for brake bands 1 and 2, then remove pins. Position transmission in horizontal position. Remove number 3 brake band adjusting screw and take out both pins. Pull number 3 brake band forward slightly. Remove input shaft from gear assembly by using snap ring from number 2 piston cover. *See Fig. 5.*

4) Remove gear assembly from case by pulling forward. Output shaft is removed from case by driving it forward with a plastic hammer.

Fig. 5: Gear Assembly Removal

PORSCHE 928 (Cont.)

Fig. 6: Exploded View of Transmission Case and Main Components

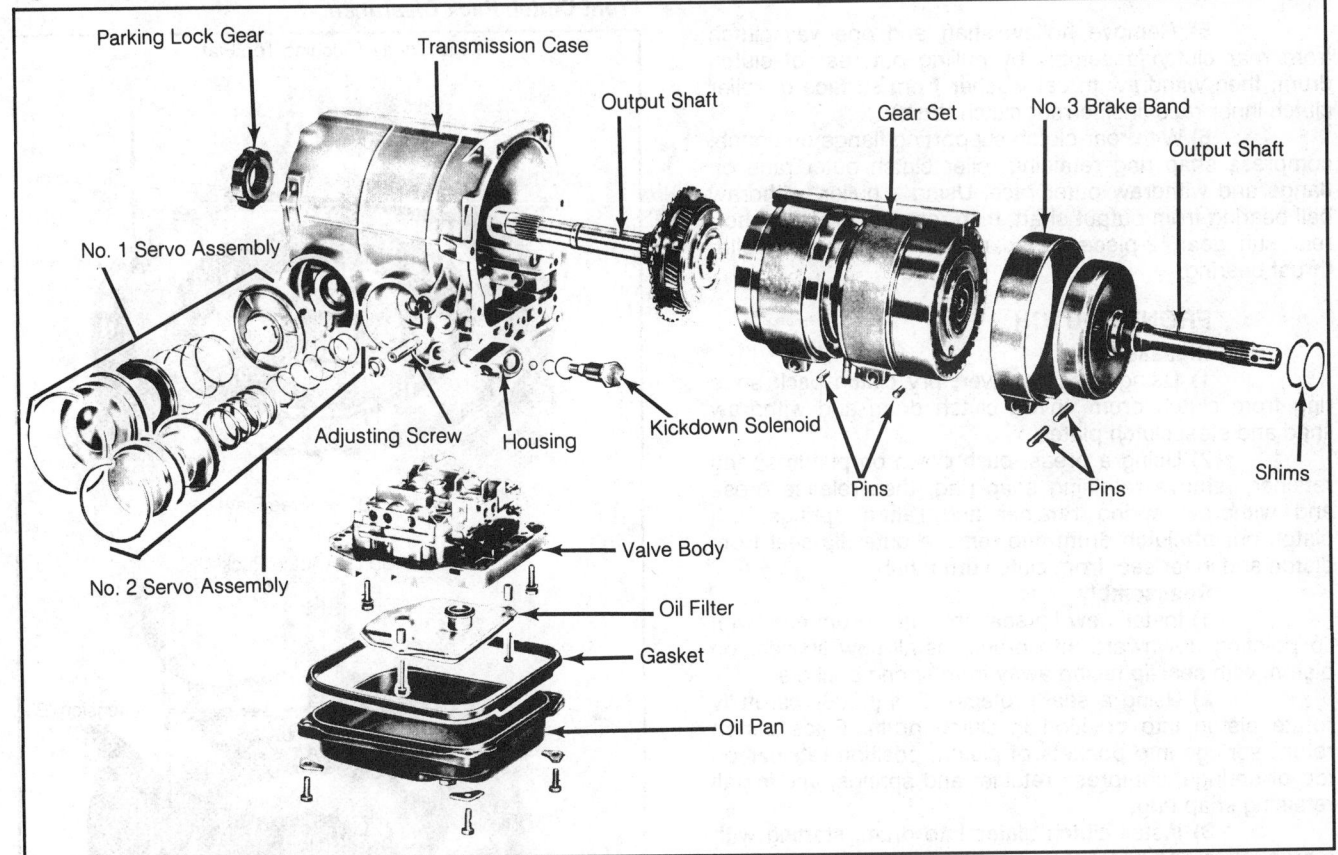

COMPONENT DISASSEMBLY & REASSEMBLY

VALVE BODY

NOTE: Manufacturer does not supply information on valve body disassembly. If transmission fluid smells burnt or there are metal particles or sludge in oil pan, manufacturer suggests that entire torque converter and transmission should be replaced. Also oil cooler and lines will have to be cleaned.

GOVERNOR

Disassembly

1) Remove sealing rings from governor flange. Remove retaining bolts for shift housing and governor housing, then separate housing from governor flange.

2) Remove lock washer, compression spring, and shift valve from shift valve housing.

3) From governor housing, remove the spring plate, then withdraw centrifugal weight and thin compression spring from top of housing. Remove remaining spring, compensating shims, and control valve through bottom of housing.

Reassembly

1) Clean all parts in solvent and air dry. Make sure valves slide easily in bores. Insert control valve into governor housing.

2) Install centrifugal weight and thin compression spring into control valve, install compensating washers and remaining spring into assembly, then attach spring plate to centrifugal weight stem, making sure it is correctly seated.

3) Insert shift valve and spring into shift valve housing and retain with snap ring. Position shift housing on governor flange so that oil slot of housing faces seal rings on flange, and oil passages are aligned in housing and flange.

4) Position strainer into slot on opposite end of flange, then install governor housing into flange so that slot of housing faces seal rings of flange. Install oil seal rings onto flange and hook ends to secure.

GEAR UNIT DISASSEMBLY

1) Remove output shaft and rear planetary assembly by pulling straight out of gear unit, then withdraw caged needle bearing and needle thrust bearing from inside rear internal gear.

2) Place gear unit on bench with input shaft facing upward. Withdraw input shaft and front internal gear from assembly, then remove caged needle bearing from front planetary gear set.

3) Pull front planetary gear carrier from unit, then withdraw front sun gear and its caged needle bearing. Remove snap ring from hollow shaft, then withdraw compensating washers and front clutch assembly.

4) Grasp oil distributing sleeve and pull sleeve and rear clutch support flange from rear clutch and hollow shaft. Remove hollow shaft and rear clutch assembly from intermediate shaft by pulling straight up, then withdraw

PORSCHE 928 (Cont.)

caged needle bearing and thrust washer from intermediate shaft.

5) Remove hollow shaft and one-way clutch from rear clutch assembly by pulling out rear of clutch drum, then withdraw thrust washer from surface of roller clutch inner race (inside rear clutch drum).

6) With rear clutch supporting flange on bench, compress snap ring retaining roller clutch outer race on flange and withdraw outer race. Using a puller, withdraw ball bearing from output shaft, then remove thrust washer, rear sun gear, 2-piece caged needle bearing and roller thrust bearing.

FRONT CLUTCH

Disassembly

1) Using a screwdriver, pry clutch pack snap ring from clutch drum. Invert clutch drum and withdraw lined and steel clutch plates.

2) Using a press, push down on piston spring retainer, remove retaining snap ring, then release press and withdraw spring retainer and return springs. Lift piston out of clutch drum and remove outer lip seal from piston and inner seal from clutch drum hub.

Reassembly

1) Install new lip seal on clutch drum hub, with lip pointing downward into drum. Install new lip seal on piston, with seal lip facing away from spring pockets.

2) Using a seal protector tool (9308), carefully rotate piston into position in clutch drum. Place piston return springs into pockets of piston, position retainer on top of springs, compress retainer and springs, and install retaining snap ring.

3) Install clutch plates into drum, starting with a steel plate and alternating lined and steel plates until all plates are installed. Next, install top plate with inner bevelled edge facing upward. Install snap ring into drum to secure clutch pack.

NOTE: If new lined plates are used, soak them in transmission fluid before installation.

4) Measure clutch pack free play as follows: Using a depth gauge, measure distance from top of clutch drum to flat surface of top plate. Next, pull clutch up

Fig. 7: Using a Depth Gauge to Measure Front Clutch Pack Clearance

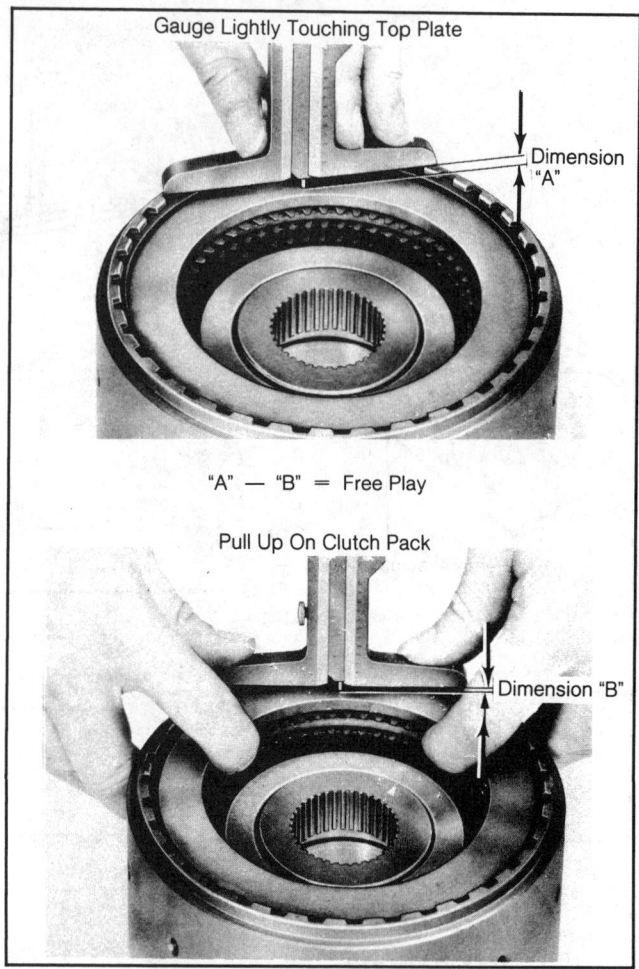

Gauge Lightly Touching Top Plate

Dimension "A"

"A" — "B" = Free Play

Pull Up On Clutch Pack

Dimension "B"

against snap ring and again check distance between top of clutch drum and surface of top plate.

5) Clutch pack free play is determined by subtracting second measurement from first measurement. Resulting free play should be .032-.047" (.8-1.2 mm).

Fig. 8: Exploded View of Front Clutch Assembly

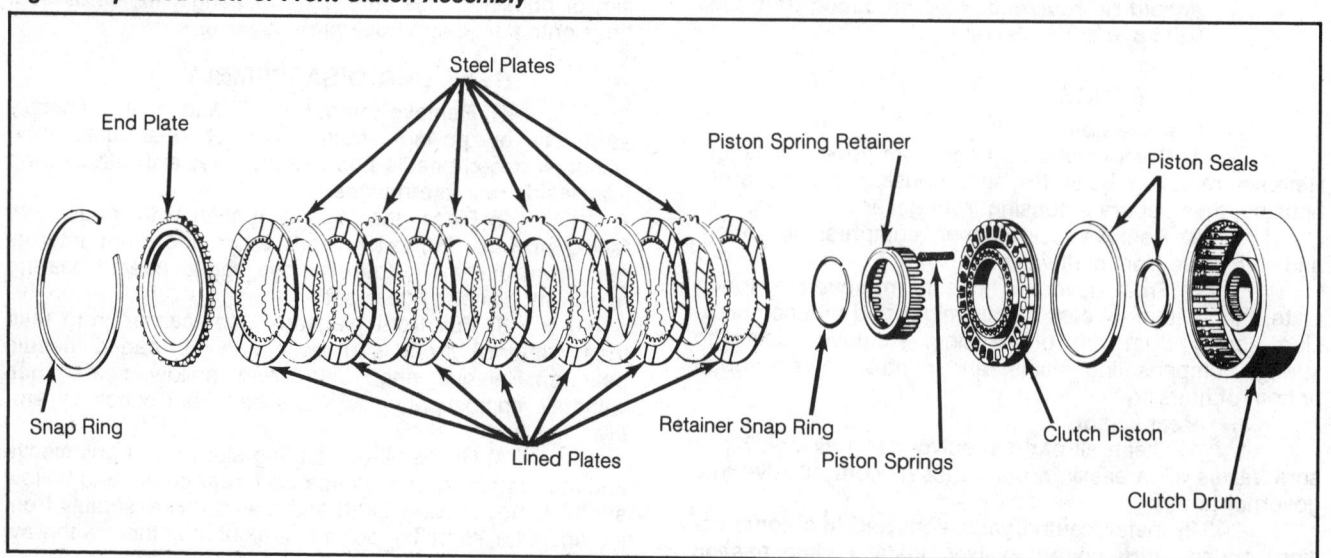

End Plate

Steel Plates

Piston Spring Retainer

Piston Seals

Snap Ring

Lined Plates

Retainer Snap Ring

Piston Springs

Clutch Piston

Clutch Drum

PORSCHE 928 (Cont.)

6) If free play is not within specifications, install a thicker or thinner steel plate (as necessary) to bring clearance within specifications. Selective steel plates are available in thicknesses of .118" (3.0 mm) and .138" (3.5 mm).

REAR CLUTCH
Disassembly
1) With supporting flange end of rear clutch upward, remove flat snap ring from clutch drum and withdraw supporting flange and piston assembly.

CAUTION: Do not allow piston to separate from flange as damage may result.

2) Remove piston return springs and lined and steel clutch plate from clutch drum. Invert clutch drum and remove the waved snap ring from bottom of clutch drum.

3) Withdraw steel plate with bevelled inside diameter and guide ring for piston return springs. Remove piston from supporting flange, then remove inner and outer piston lip seals.

Reassembly
1) Install waved snap ring into bottom groove of rear clutch drum, then install bottom plate (with bevel on inside diameter downward) and piston spring guide ring.

2) Install clutch pack assembly into drum as follows: Install 1 lined plate, follow with thicker selective steel plate, then alternate 1 lined plate and 1 thinner steel plate until all plates are installed.

NOTE: If new lined plates are being installed, soak in transmission fluid prior to assembly.

3) Place clutch piston into clutch drum on top of clutch plates. Using a depth gauge, measure distance from top of clutch drum to flat surface of clutch piston.

4) Remove piston from drum and measure distance from top of clutch drum supporting flange contacting surface of clutch drum splines. Subtract

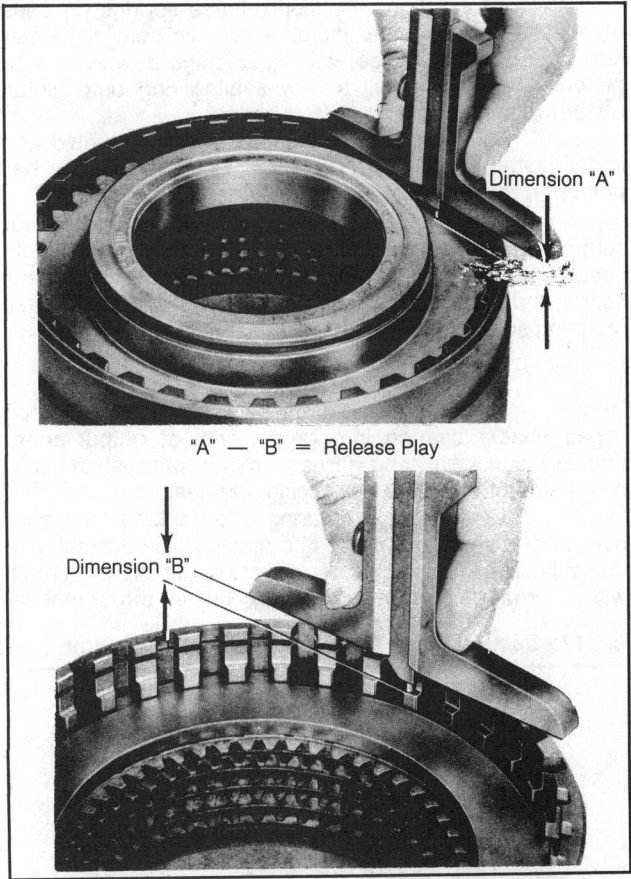

Fig. 9: Using a Depth Gauge to Measure Rear Clutch Pack Clearance

Dimension "A"

"A" — "B" = Release Play

Dimension "B"

second measurement from first measurement; resulting measurement is clutch piston release play.

5) Clutch pack clearance should be .032-.047" (.8-1.2 mm). If not, selective thickness clutch plates are available to correct clearance. Install thicker or thinner

Fig. 10: Exploded View of Rear Clutch Assembly

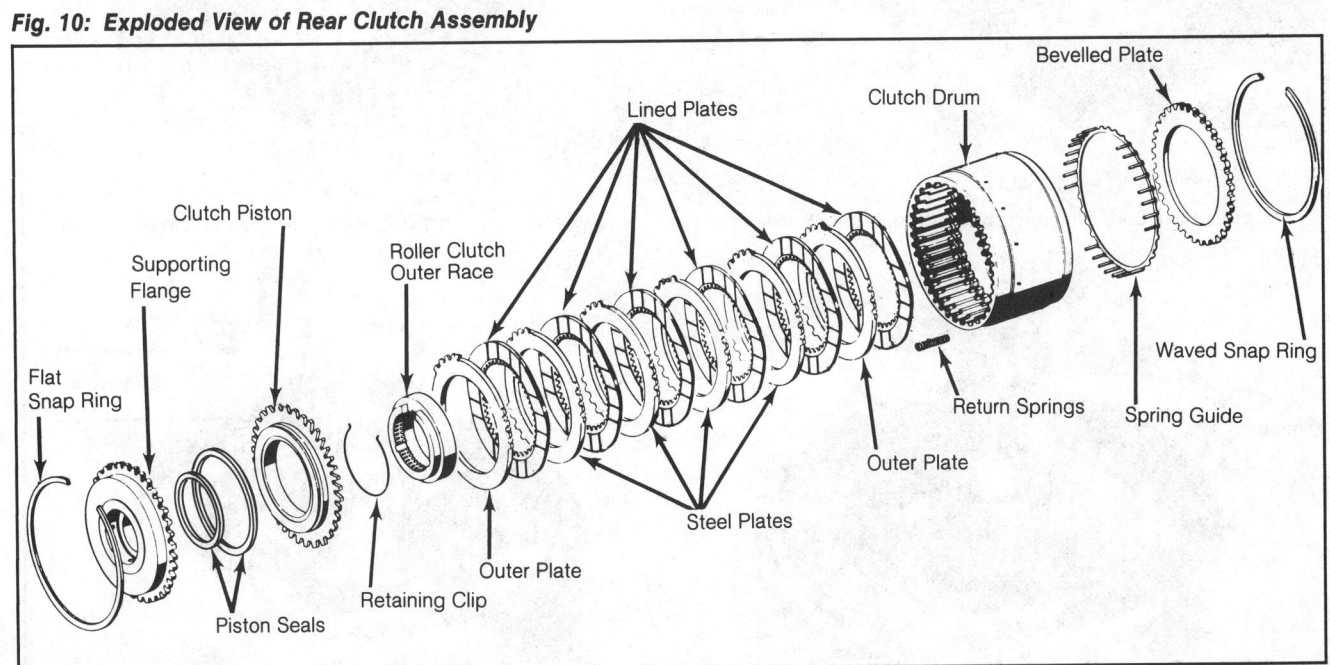

Lined Plates

Clutch Drum

Bevelled Plate

Clutch Piston

Supporting Flange

Roller Clutch Outer Race

Waved Snap Ring

Flat Snap Ring

Return Springs

Spring Guide

Outer Plate

Piston Seals

Retaining Clip

Outer Plate

Steel Plates

plates as necessary to bring clutch pack clearance within specifications.

6) Position all piston release springs on pegs of release spring guide. Install a new lip seal on center hub of supporting flange, with lip pointing downward into piston well. Also install a new sealing ring onto clutch piston, with lip facing away from splines.

7) Lubricate seals with transmission fluid and install piston into supporting flange, using a pencil or ball point pen to start lip of seal into flange.

8) Install snap ring into upper groove of supporting flange, compress snap ring ends with needle nose pliers, then install one-way clutch outer race. Install flange and piston assembly into clutch drum, then install retaining snap ring.

GEAR UNIT REASSEMBLY

1) Install needle thrust bearing and 2-piece caged needle bearing into gear cavity of output shaft. Position sun gear and thrust washer onto shaft, with offset side of thrust washer facing sun gear.

2) Install ball bearing and parking lock gear over output shaft and press into place. Place assembly to the side. Next, position intermediate shaft on the bench with internal gear facing downward. Install thrust washer

and caged needle bearing into assembly, then place this assembly to the side.

3) Position rear clutch on the bench with supporting flange downward (rear end of clutch facing upward). Coat thrust washer with grease and install into one-way clutch outer race (inside rear clutch).

4) Install one-way clutch roller assembly into outer race, making sure edge with outer bead faces out of outer race. Install hollow shaft into one-way clutch assembly, rotating counterclockwise to ease assembly.

NOTE: **When looking from bottom of rear clutch, hollow shaft should freewheel when rotated counterclockwise, and lock up when rotated clockwise.**

5) Insert intermediate shaft into rear clutch and hollow shaft, rotating so assembly meshes with rear clutch lines plate splines. Place assembly on bench with shafts pointing upward.

6) Install caged needle bearing over hollow shaft and into rear clutch supporting flange, then install oil distributing sleeve into flange, making sure sealing rings are fully engaged. Install front clutch onto assembly, making sure it engages fully with seal rings on distributing sleeve.

Fig. 11: Using a Depth Gauge to Determine Gear Unit End Play

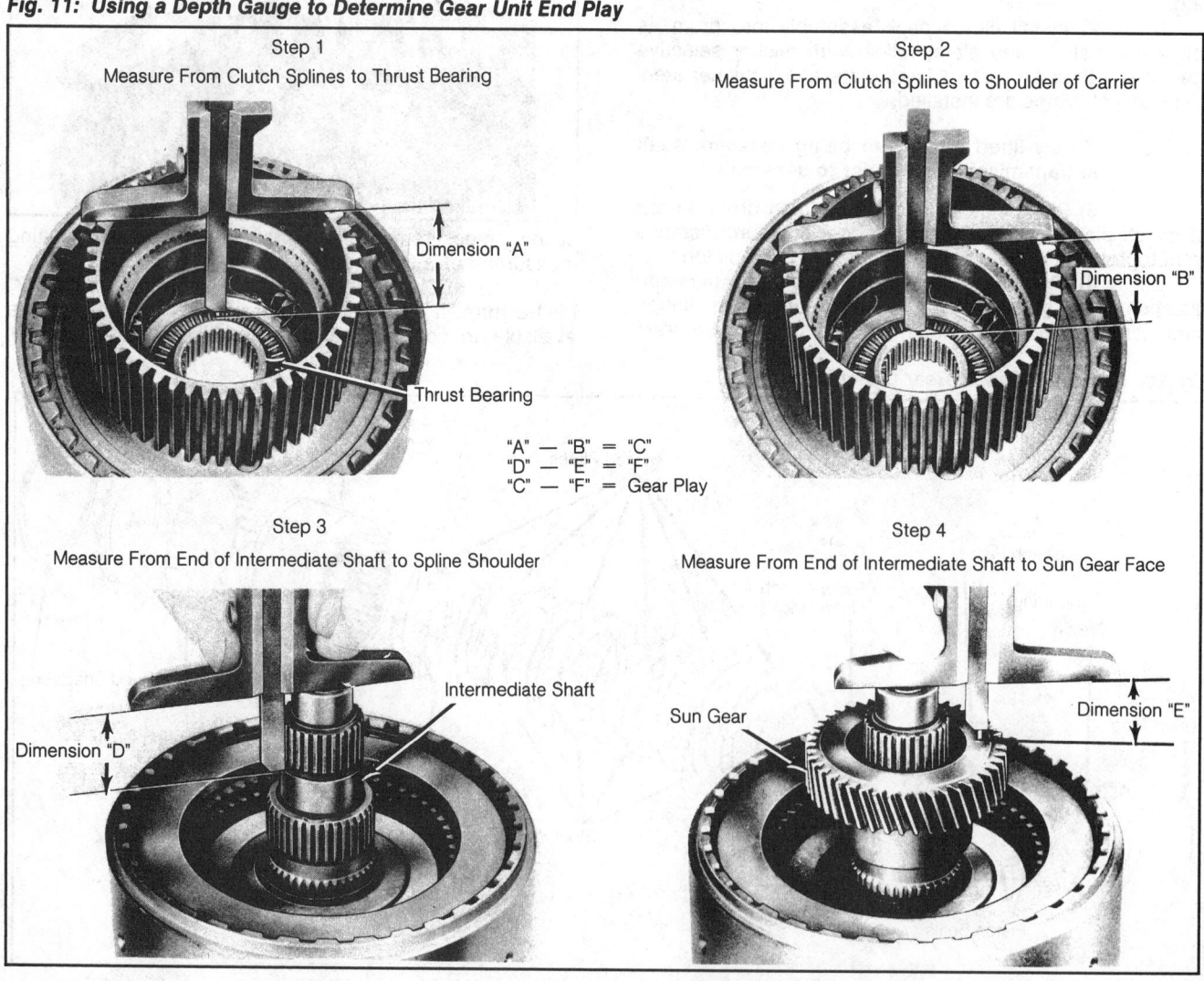

Step 1
Measure From Clutch Splines to Thrust Bearing

Dimension "A"

Thrust Bearing

Step 2
Measure From Clutch Splines to Shoulder of Carrier

Dimension "B"

"A" — "B" = "C"
"D" — "E" = "F"
"C" — "F" = Gear Play

Step 3
Measure From End of Intermediate Shaft to Spline Shoulder

Intermediate Shaft

Dimension "D"

Step 4
Measure From End of Intermediate Shaft to Sun Gear Face

Dimension "E"

Sun Gear

PORSCHE 928 (Cont.)

Fig. 12: Using a Feeler Gauge to Measure Front Clutch Hub-to-Snap Ring Clearance

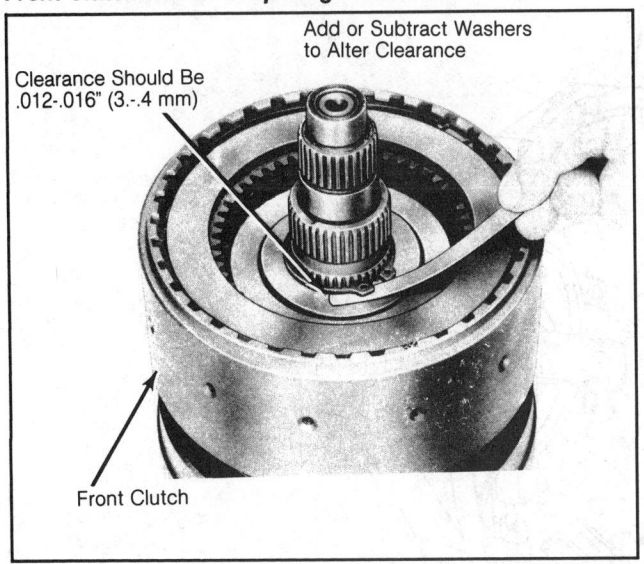

Clearance Should Be .012-.016" (3.-.4 mm)

Add or Subtract Washers to Alter Clearance

Front Clutch

7) Install retaining snap ring, then measure clearance between snap ring and hub of front clutch drum. Clearance should be .012-.016" (.3-.4 mm); if not, install compensating washers between snap ring and clutch drum hub.

8) With front planetary gear carrier on the bench (clutch spline end upward), coat gear carrier-to-sun gear roller thrust bearing with grease and install into carrier.

9) Using a depth gauge, measure distance from top of clutch splines on carrier to top of one of the rollers on thrust bearing; this is dimension "A" (write down for future reference). Next, measure distance from top of carrier splines to shoulder of hub inside carrier; this is dimension "B".

10) Measure distance from top of intermediate shaft to shoulder of the shaft (just below first set of splines); this is dimension "D".

11) Install forward sun gear into intermediate shaft, then install caged needle bearing over shaft and into sun gear.

12) Measure distance from top of intermediate shaft to top face of sun gear; this is dimension "E". Subtract dimension "B" from "A"; this is dimension "C". Next, subtract dimension "E" from dimension "D"; this is dimension "F".

13) Subtract dimension "F" from dimension "C"; the result is gear unit end play. Gear play should be .008-.012" (.2-.3 mm); if not, add or subtract compensating washers under needle thrust bearing on front planetary carrier as necessary to bring play within specifications.

14) With proper compensating washer installed under thrust bearing, install forward planet carrier onto front clutch assembly, rotating carrier so it engages splines of front clutch lines plates. With carrier in place, install caged needle bearing onto intermediate shaft end, then install input shaft into carrier.

15) Install a new metal seal onto input shaft and lock ends. Lay entire gear unit on its side and install caged needle bearing and needle thrust bearing into internal gear of intermediate shaft. Install output shaft into internal gear to complete assembly.

Fig. 13: Exploded View Showing Components of Gear Unit Assembly

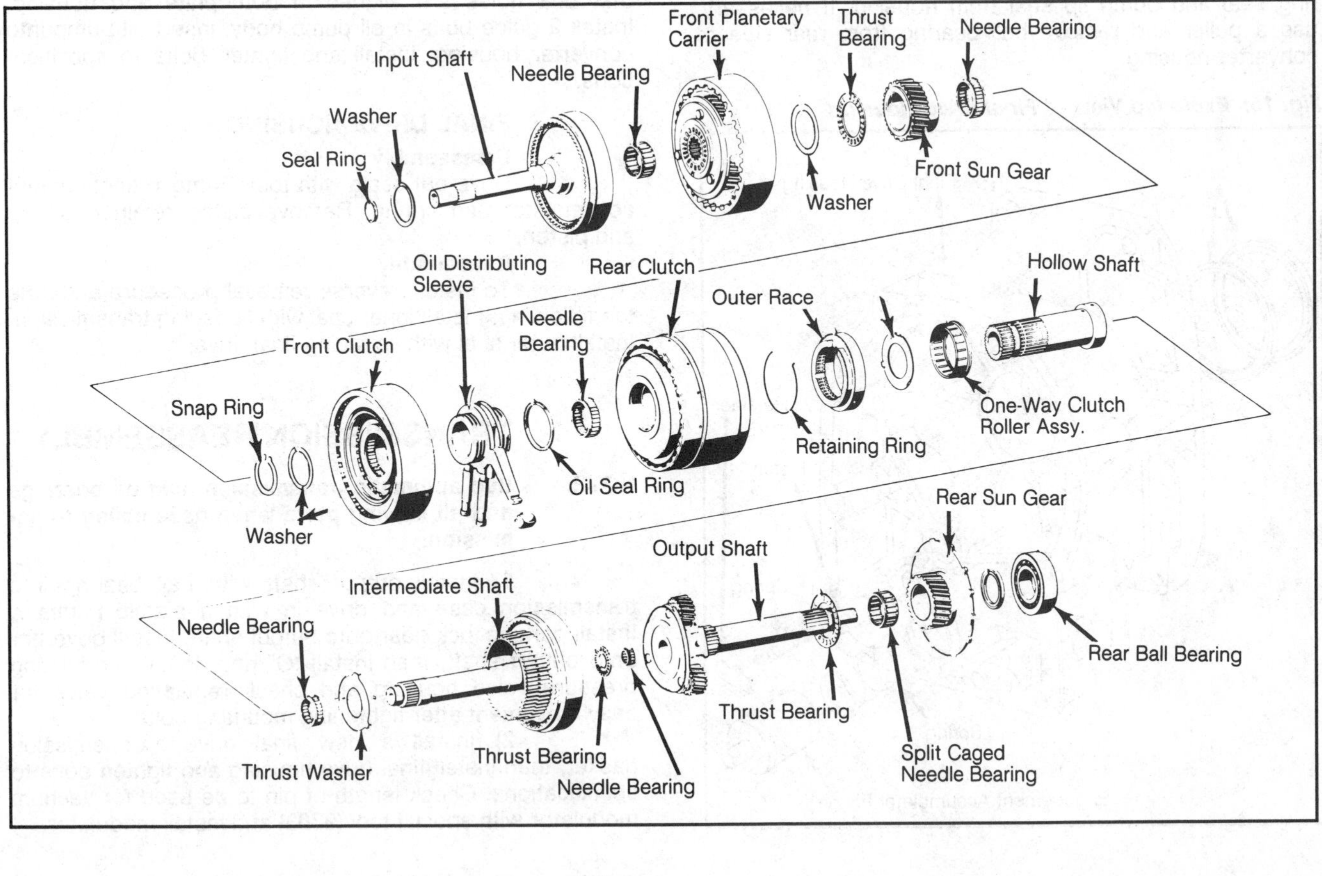

Input Shaft · Needle Bearing · Front Planetary Carrier · Thrust Bearing · Needle Bearing · Washer · Seal Ring · Washer · Front Sun Gear

Oil Distributing Sleeve · Rear Clutch · Hollow Shaft · Front Clutch · Needle Bearing · Outer Race · Snap Ring · Washer · Oil Seal Ring · Retaining Ring · One-Way Clutch Roller Assy.

Intermediate Shaft · Output Shaft · Rear Sun Gear · Needle Bearing · Thrust Washer · Thrust Bearing · Needle Bearing · Thrust Bearing · Split Caged Needle Bearing · Rear Ball Bearing

Automatic Transmissions

PORSCHE 928 (Cont.)

Fig. 14: *Exploded View of Torque Converter Housing and Pump Housing*

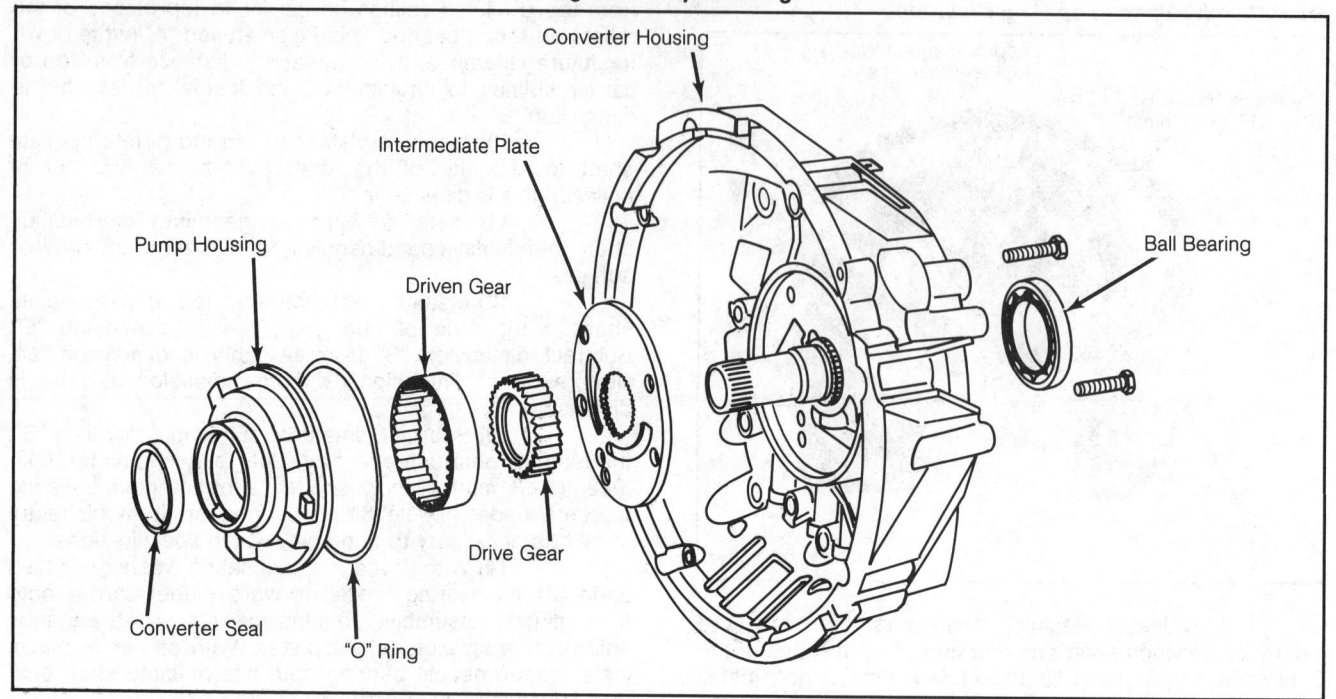

CONVERTER HOUSING & OIL PUMP ASSEMBLY

Disassembly

Remove oil pump attaching bolts at rear of pump. Install 2 bolts, 2" (50 mm) long, in oil pump bolt holes and tap lightly to remove oil pump. Withdraw "O" ring seal and pump lip seal from housing. If necessary, use a puller and remove ball bearing from rear side of converter housing.

Fig. 15: *Exploded View of Final Drive Housing*

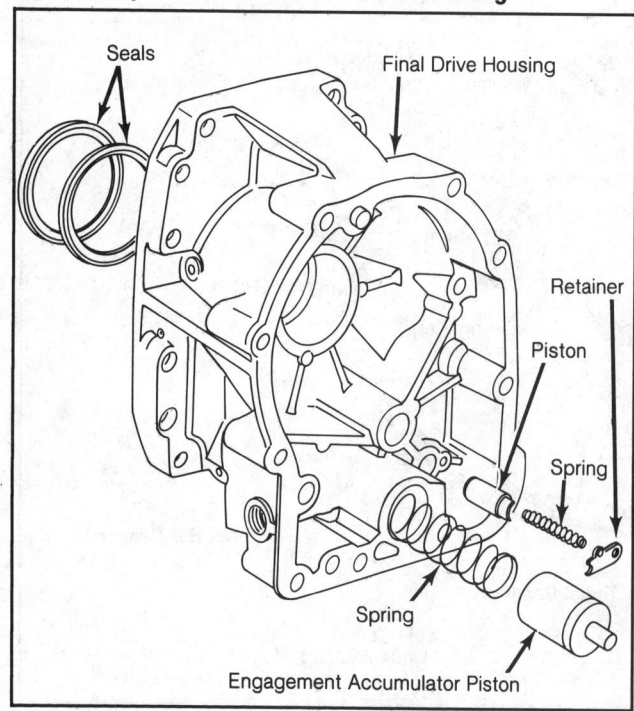

Reassembly

1) Install a new "O" ring seal on outside diameter of pump housing, and a new lip seal in front cavity of housing. Lubricate pump gears with transmission fluid and install into housing.

2) Install intermediate plate onto housing so that bolt holes are aligned in both plate and housing. Install 2 guide bolts in oil pump body, insert oil pump into converter housing, install and tighten bolts to specifications.

FINAL DRIVE HOUSING

Disassembly

Drive out seals with tool. Remove engagement accumulator and spring. Remove piston retainer, spring and piston.

Reassembly

To install, reverse removal procedure and note the following: Install inner seal with lip facing transmission. Install outer seal with lip facing final drive.

TRANSMISSION REASSEMBLY

NOTE: Use automatic transmission fluid on bearings and all moving parts when assembling transmission.

1) Install output shaft with ball bearing into transmission case and drive in with a plastic hammer. Install parking lock gear onto output shaft. Install governor onto output shaft, then install "O" ring. Install modulating pressure valve housing and check regulating valve for easy movement after tightening mounting bolts.

2) Install a new final drive-to-transmission gasket, then install final drive housing and tighten bolts to specifications. Check length of pin to be used for vacuum modulator with special tool (9303) and install modulator.

PORSCHE 928 (Cont.)

NOTE: **The pinion assembly has to be checked for proper end play adjustment any time it is removed.**

3) Use a depth gauge to measure the distance from the tapered roller bearing surface to bearing flange surface. The proper end play is 1.38" ± .020" (35 ± .5 mm). *See Fig. 16.*

Fig. 16: Measuring Pinion Bearing End Play

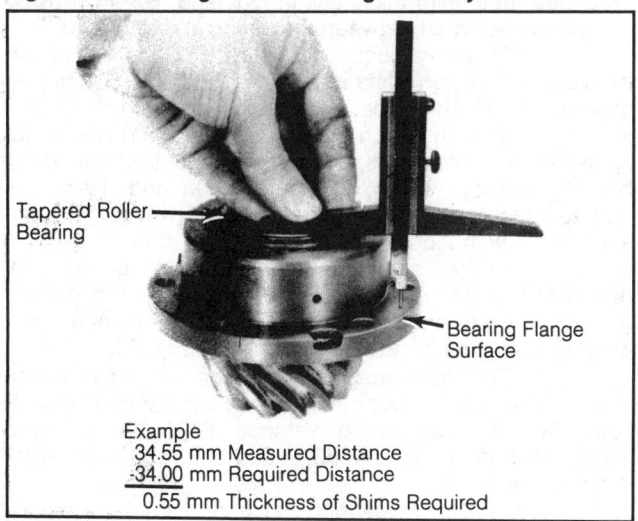

Tapered Roller Bearing

Bearing Flange Surface

Example
34.55 mm Measured Distance
-34.00 mm Required Distance
0.55 mm Thickness of Shims Required

4) Install pinion assembly on final drive case and tighten bolts to specifications. Install number 2 brake band guide and band in transmission case. Position number 1 brake band over gear unit, and temporarily hold in place with rear servo retaining ring.

5) Make sure thrust bearings are still positioned in end of gear unit, then install gear unit into case, guiding supporting lever of oil distributing sleeve into groove of case.

NOTE: **Make sure gear unit is seated in output shaft.**

6) Make sure bearings are still in position on front of gear unit, then install input shaft into assembly. Insert number 3 brake band into case and over gear unit, install pressure pins into band ends, then screw in band adjusting screw until band is secured in place. Turn transmission until input shaft faces up.

7) Determine end play between gear unit and converter housing as follows: Measure the distance from upper edge of input shaft-to-upper edge of stator shaft with a depth gauge. This distance is "A".

8) Pull up on input shaft and repeat measurement. This measurement is "B". End play is the difference between "A" and "B". Install compensating washers onto input shaft thrust surface to bring end play within specifications.

9) Install pins from number 1 and 2 brake bands. Install number 2 brake band piston into transmission case with special tool (9305). Install new 'O' ring on number 2 brake band cover, place in case and secure with snap ring.

10) Install piston and cover for number 1 brake band into transmission case with special tool (9304) and secure with snap ring.

11) Check free play of number 1 and 2 brake band as follows: Apply air pressure into number 1 brake band release port in case and mark position of band on drum. *See Fig. 17.* Next, introduce air pressure to number 1 brake apply port and again mark position of band position on drum.

12) Measure distance between 2 marks; measurement is number 1 band free play.

13) For number 2 band adjustment, first measure position of band end on drum in released position (spring pressure holds band in released position). Next, apply air pressure to number 2 apply port in case and again mark position of band end on drum.

14) Distance between 2 marks is band free play. Free play for number 1 and 2 bands is .118-.157" (3-4 mm).

Fig. 17: Bottom View of Case Showing Measurement of Band Free Play

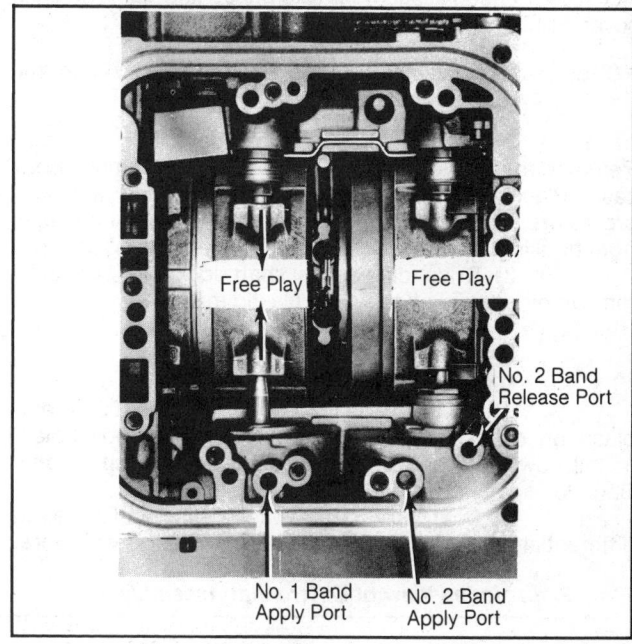

Free Play

Free Play

No. 2 Band Release Port

No. 1 Band Apply Port

No. 2 Band Apply Port

15) For number 3 band adjustment, tighten band adjusting screw to 48 INCH lbs. (5.4 N.m), then check gap, unscrew adjusting screw 1 3/4 turns, recheck gap, difference between both measurements is free play, which should be .118" (3 mm). Tighten lock nut to specification.

Fig. 18: Using Punch to Hold Throttle Pressure Valve

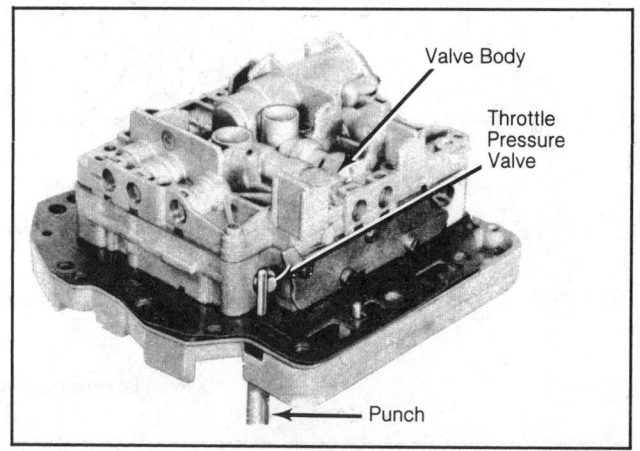

Valve Body

Throttle Pressure Valve

Punch

16) Install both oil feed pipes into oil distributing sleeve and place new valve body seals on pipes. Screw 2 centering pins into transmission case. Install centering pin (punch) for throttle pressure valve into valve body. *See Fig. 18.*

17) Guide valve body in place, making sure manual valve engages correctly in plate. Install valve body-to-case bolts and tighten to specifications. Install valve body, oil fitler and oil pan.

FINAL DRIVE

DISASSEMBLY

1) Place final drive housing in holding fixture. Remove axle flange bolts and remove axle flanges. Mark side covers for reassembly reference, and remove side cover bolts and side covers.

NOTE: **Record number and thickness of shims for reassembly reference on each side.**

2) Remove oil seals from side covers with tool. Remove rear cover and pull differential assembly from case. Place differential assembly in vise fitted with jaw protectors. Remove ring gear bolts and drive ring gear from housing. Remove bearings (if required) using puller.

3) Drive differential shaft lock pin out, then remove differential shaft with a plastic mallet.

REASSEMBLY & ADJUSTMENTS

Differential Assembly

1) Heat ring gear to about 212°F (100°C) and place on case using centering pins to align bolt holes. Install new bolts and tighten crosswise to specifications. Bend lock plate ends over side of bolt heads.

2) Coat large gears with grease and install in differential carrier. Install small gears and align with bore, then insert shaft, position correctly and install locking pin. Drive tapered roller bearings on carrier with tool.

Pinion Gear Adjustment

1) When adjusting pinion and ring gear, the following sequence should be used:
* Determine the total shim thickness ("S1" + "S2") for the specified preload of the tapered roller bearing differential.
* Determine shim thickness ("S3").
* Divide total shim thickness in "S1" and "S2" to provide correct backlash between the pinion and ring gear.

2) The adjustment distance "E" is calculated from known design distance "R" = 2.86" (72.20 mm) + deviation "r" which is located on face of pinion.

3) With pinion bearing adjusted and pinion nut tightened to proper specifications, install final drive housing (without shims) to transmission and tighten all nuts to specifications. Install 1 side cover (without "O" ring) and secure with 2 bolts.

4) Set adjusting ring of master gauge (VW 385/1) at 1.61" (41 mm). *See Fig. 21.* Install centering discs (VW 385/4) on master gauge and attach plunger (VW 385/14) with dial indicator extension. *See Fig. 22.*

5) Install measuring gauge in case, install second side cover (without "O" ring) and secure with 2 bolts. Set dial indicator to distance "E" + .20" (5 mm). Install measuring bar (VW385/1) and set at "O" with .004" (1 mm) preload.

6) Turn measuring bar until dial gauge extension is vertical to face of pinion head. *See Fig. 23.* At this moment, dial gauge needle will reach its point of reversal (highest point) and dial gauge should be read. Install determined shim thickness ("S3") between the transmission case and final drive housing. Recheck distance after installation of shims. A deviation of ±.0012" (.03 mm) is permissible.

Fig. 19: Exploded View of Differential Assembly

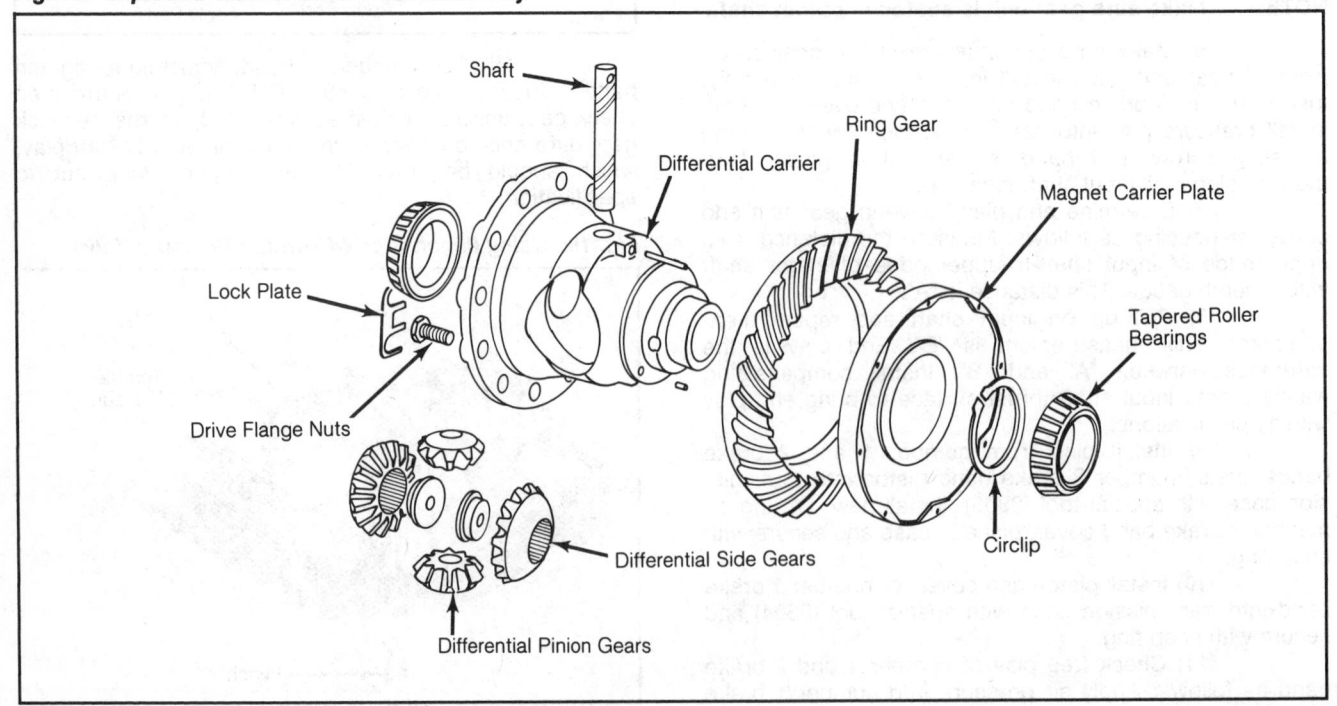

PORSCHE 928 (Cont.)

Fig. 20: Manufacturer's Codes Stamped in Pinion and Ring Gears

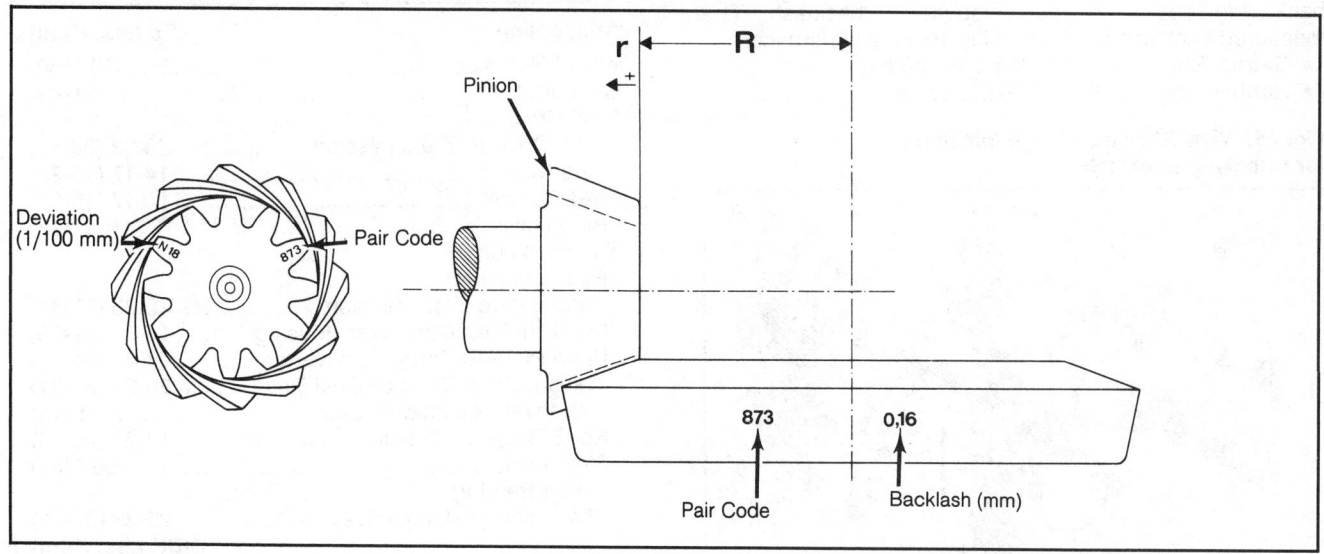

Fig. 21: Universal Master Measuring Gauge

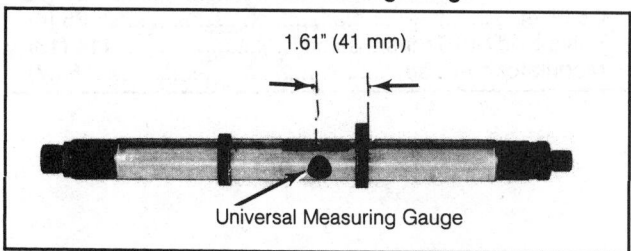

Fig. 22: Universal Master Measuring Gauge with Dial Indicator and Centering Discs Attached

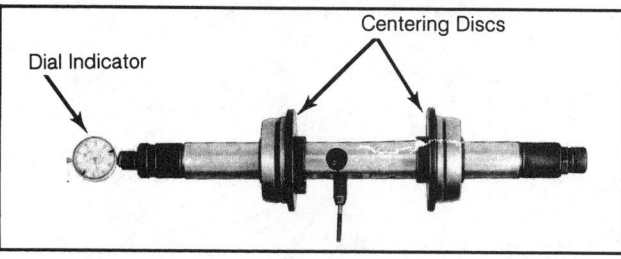

Fig. 23: View Showing Dial Gauge in Contact with Pinion Head

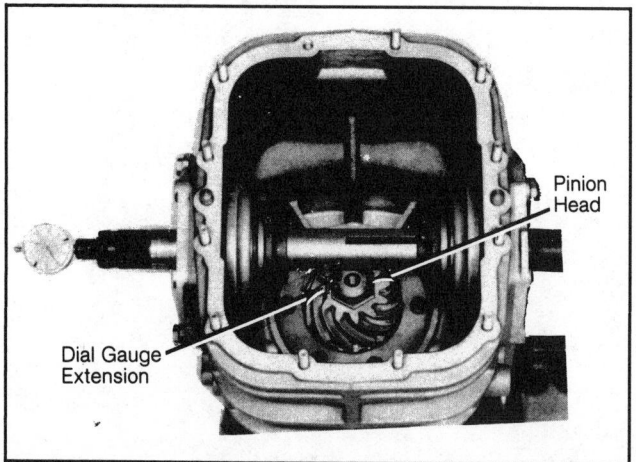

Ring Gear Adjustment

1) Clamp final drive in a vise. Install differential with ring gear into final drive housing. Install side cover (without shims) and tighten all bolts to specifications.

2) Guide second cover (without shims) into place on the case and check gap between case and side cover. *See Fig. 24.* Then, determine shim thickness by subtracting bearing preload .012" (.30 mm) from gap measurement. Resulting shim thickness is "S" total.

Fig. 24: Checking for Shim Thickness Between Final Drive Case and Side Cover

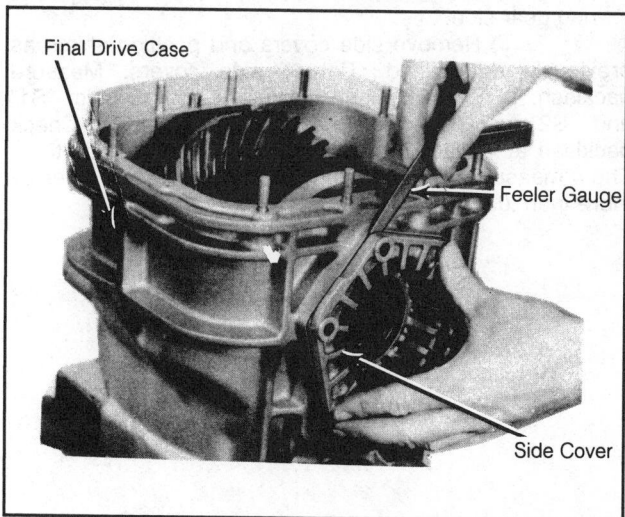

Ring Gear Backlash Adjustment

1) Place shims determined for pinion adjustment between transmission case and final drive case. Install final drive to transmission and tighten all mounting bolts to specifications. Install differential assembly into case, install side covers with shims on ring gear side and tighten all bolts to specifications.

2) Turn differential in both directions several times to settle bearings. Install dial indicator (VW388) and set to 3.1" (mm). *See Fig. 25.* Engage parking lock, turn ring gear by hand against stop and set dial indicator to zero.

Automatic Transmissions

PORSCHE 928 (Cont.)

3) Hold pinion with locally made tool and turn back ring gear and read amount of backlash. The measured backlash must be within specified tolerance:
- Getrag Pinion — .006-.008" (.15-.20 mm)
- Hurth Pinion — .008-.010" (.20-.25 mm)

Fig. 25: View Showing Gauge Installation for Checking Backlash

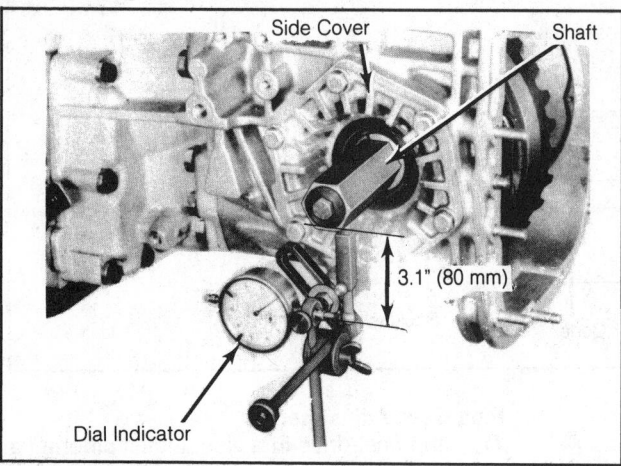

4) The splitting and positioning of shims is determined by the following:
- Ring gear side — Take total shim thickness ("S total", subtract measured backlash, add inscribed backlash, then multiply by .026" (.66 mm). The result is the proper shim amount to be placed on ring gear side ("S1").
- Opposite ring gear side — Subtract ring gear side ("S1") from total shim thickness ("S total") the result is ("S2") which is the amount of shims placed opposite ring gear side.

5) Remove side covers and position shims as previously determined. Tighten side covers. Measure backlash. If not within specifications, change shim "S1" and "S2" until specified backlash is obtained. Check backlash at 4 places by turning ring gear 90° each time. The 4 measurements must not deviate from each other by more than .002" (.05 mm).

TIGHTENING SPECIFICATIONS

Application	Ft. Lbs. (N.m)
Wheel Hub Nut	333 (460)
CV Joint Bolts	60 (83)
Final Drive	
Final Drive-to-Transmission	28-33 (38-45)
Side Covers	14-17 (19-23)
Rear Cover	14-17 (19-23)
Ring Gear	110-131 (150-178)
Transmission	
Rear Converter	
Housing-to-Transmission	20-23 (27-31)
Front-to-Rear Converter Housing	14-17 (19-23)
Drive Plate-to-Torque Converter	23-28 (31-38)
Transmission Case-to-Final Drive	20-23 (27-31)
Kickdown Solenoid-to-Case	14 (19)
No. 3 Brake Lock Nut	18-22 (25-30)
Pinion Nut	206 (280)
Pinion Bearing	
Assembly-to-Transmission	20-23 (27-31)

	INCH Lbs. (N.m)
Transmission	
Oil Pan	60 (7)
Oil Filter	36 (4)
Valve Body-to-Transmission	114 (13)
Modulator-to-Case	5 (.7)

RENAULT FUEGO & 18i

DESCRIPTION

The Fuego and 18i transaxle is a 3-speed unit consisting basically of torque converter, differential assembly and transmission assembly. Differential consists of ring and pinion gear set, worn gear to drive governor, and step-down gears to change direction of drive centerline.

Transmission assembly consists of a planetary gear train, 2 clutches, 2 brakes and main control systems for transaxle. Mechanical, electrical and hydraulic control systems are used.

LUBRICATION & ADJUSTMENT

See the appropriate article in *AUTOMATIC TRANSMISSION SERVICING* Section.

TROUBLE SHOOTING

ENGINE IDLES ROUGH OR STALLS

Idle speed incorrect. Check ignition timing and spark plug condition. Throttle cable out of adjustment. Leak in vacuum circuit.

VEHICLE CREEPS IN "N"

Shift lever out of adjustment. Defective or damaged E1 clutch.

EXCESSIVE CREEPING IN "A"

Idle speed incorrect. Throttle cable out of adjustment. Torque converter faulty or damaged.

SLIPS IN FORWARD & REVERSE

Incorrect fluid level. Pressure regulator damaged or out of adjustment. Torque converter faulty or damaged.

NO MOVEMENT

In 3rd, OK in Other Gears

E1 clutch faulty or defective. One-way clutch damaged or faulty.

In 3rd, "1" or "R"

Fluid level incorrect. Pressure regulator or shift control mechanism out of adjustment. Oil pump shaft or turbine shaft bent or damaged. Defective oil pump. Torque converter drive plate warped or otherwise damaged. Final drive assembly faulty. Torque converter damaged.

Fig. 1: Cross Sectional View of Renault Fuego & 18i Automatic Transaxle

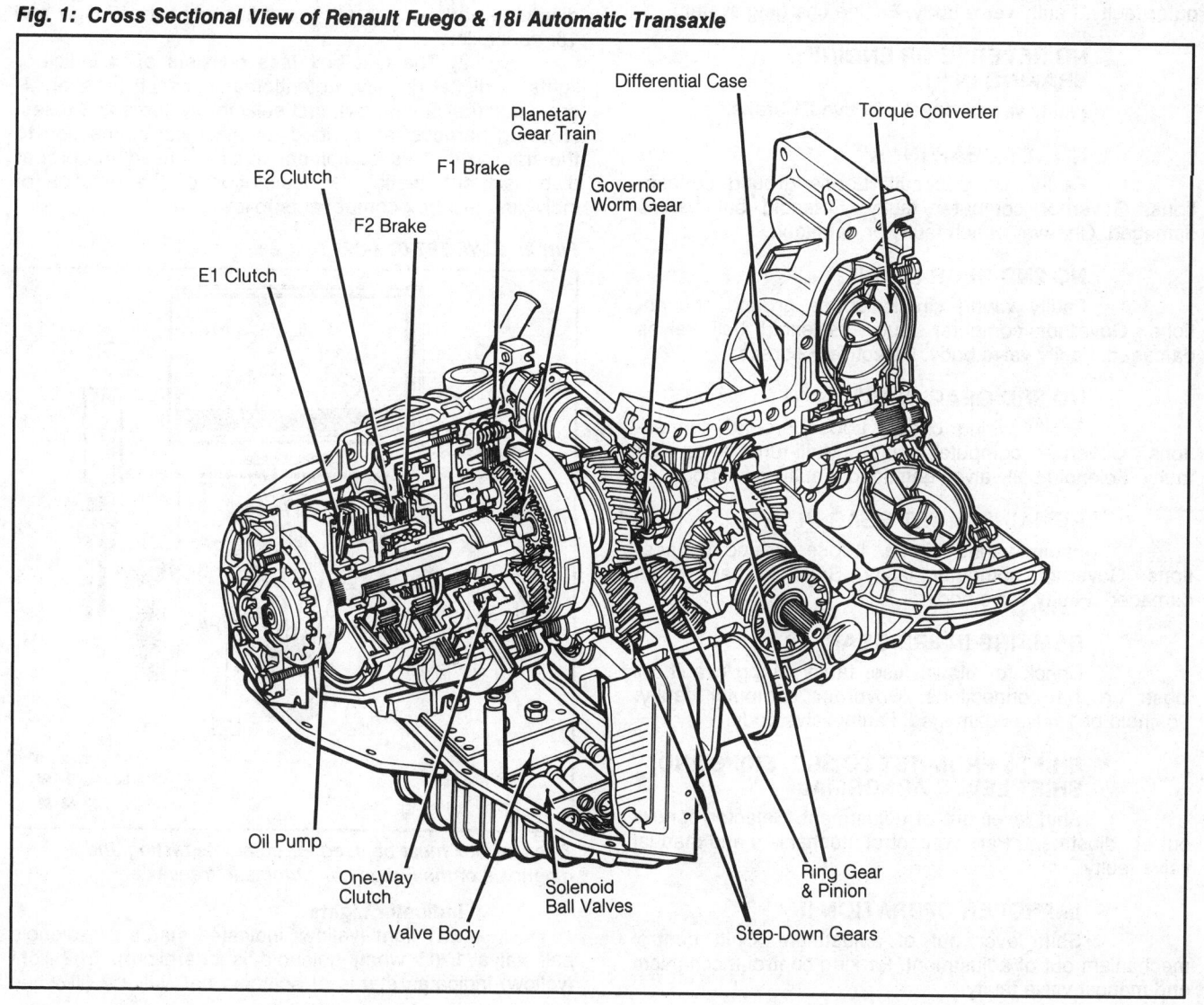

In 3rd or "1"
Defective E1 clutch.
In "R" or 3rd Gear
Faulty valve body. Defective E2 clutch.

SLIPPING ON SHIFTS
Incorrect fluid level. Fluid pressure regulator damaged or out of adjustment. Faulty valve body. Defective E1 or E2 clutch. Defective F1 or F2 brake.

ERRATIC STARTS
Idle speed incorrect. Throttle cable out of adjustment.

EXCESSIVE SHIFT SHOCK BETWEEN GEARS
Incorrect fluid level. Pressure regulator damaged or out of adjustment. Defective F1 brake. Leak in vacuum circuit. Faulty valve body.

SHIFT POINTS INCORRECT
Throttle cable, governor cable or kickdown switch out of adjustment. Governor cable faulty. Faulty wiring circuit. Loose ground connections. Governor computer faulty. Faulty valve body. Engine charging system.

NO REVERSE OR ENGINE BRAKING IN "1"
Faulty valve body. Defective F1 brake.

NO 1ST GEAR IN "A"
Faulty wiring circuit. Loose ground connections. Governor computer faulty. Solenoid ball valves damaged. One-way clutch faulty or damaged.

NO 2ND GEAR IN "A"
Faulty wiring circuit. Loose ground connections. Governor computer faulty. Solenoid ball valves damaged. Faulty valve body. Defective F2 brake.

NO 3RD GEAR IN "A"
Faulty wiring circuit. Loose ground connections. Governor computer faulty. Multi-function switch faulty. Solenoid ball valves damaged. Faulty valve body.

REMAINS IN 1ST GEAR IN "A"
Faulty wiring circuit. Loose ground connections. Governor computer faulty. Solenoid ball valves damaged. Faulty valve body.

REMAINS IN 3RD GEAR
Check for blown fuse, faulty wiring circuit, or loose ground connections. Governor computer faulty. Solenoid ball valves damaged. Faulty valve body.

SHIFTS FROM 1ST TO 3RD, SKIPS 2ND; SHIFT LEVER ABNORMAL
Shift lever out of adjustment. Selector control out of adjustment. Parking control mechanism and manual valve faulty.

IMPROPER OPERATION IN "P"
Shift lever out of adjustment. Shift control mechanism out of adjustment. Parking control mechanism and manual valve faulty.

STARTER NOT WORKING
Faulty wiring circuit. Loose ground connections. Shift lever out of adjustment. Multi-function switch faulty.

BACKUP LIGHTS NOT WORKING
Faulty wiring circuit. Loose ground connections. Multi-function switch faulty.

SLIPS WHEN STARTING OUT IN "A"
One-way clutch damaged or faulty.

TESTING

TESTING EQUIPMENT
1) No special equipment is needed for road testing. Hydraulic testing and transaxle diagnosis require the use of the following special test equipment: Test box B. Vi. 797-01 or -02 and thermometer B. Vi. 524-01. If test box B. Vi. 797-01 is used, intermediate cable B. Vi. 858 is required for hook-up to transaxle. In addition, hydraulic testing requires oil pressure switch B. Vi. 466-04. The test box is equipped with indicator lights and gauges to diagnose various operating conditions of the Fuego and 18i transaxle.

2) The test box face consists of: 4 indicator lights, a digital display, potentiometer, circuit breaker, 4-scale dial (galvanometer), test selector switch and 3 fuses. A wiring harness is provided for electrical connection to the transaxle. This equipment must be used for proper diagnosis and testing. A description of the function of individual test box components follows.

Fig. 2: B. Vi. 797-01 (-02) Test Box

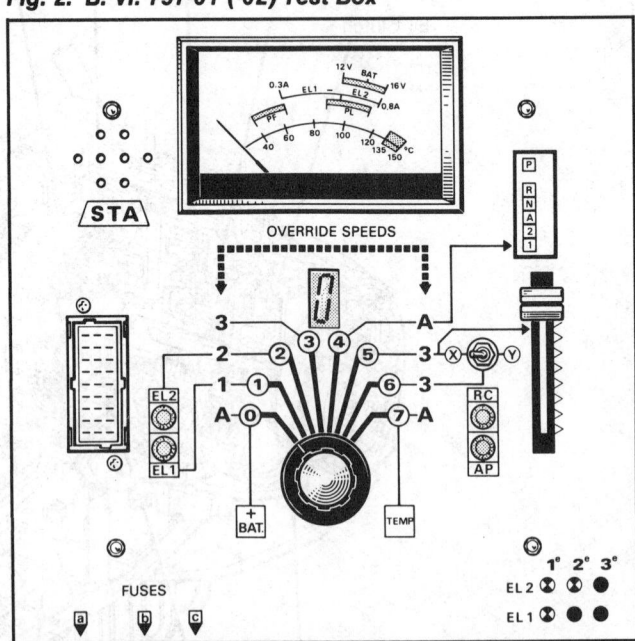

This test box must be used for complete testing and diagnosis of the Fuego/18i automatic transaxle.

Indicator Lights
EL1 light (yellow) indicates status of solenoid ball valve 1 (lit when solenoid is energized). EL2 light (yellow) indicates status of solenoid ball valve 2 (lit when

RENAULT FUEGO & 18i (Cont.)

energized). The AP indicator light (red) indicates whether emission control system is operating (this system not used in these tests). RC light (green) indicates whether the kickdown switch is operating.

Digital Display

Indicates multifunction switch operation and computer condition.

Potentiometer and Circuit Breaker

Systems not used in these tests.

Galvanometer

The galvanometer has 4 scales: BAT scale for reading of battery voltage, EL1-EL2 scale to measure current passing through solenoid ball valves, and temperature scale to measure transmission oil temperature (Red zone indicates maximum operating temperature). The PF and PL scales are not used.

Test Selector Switch

This switch is used to selected desired test made. Position "0" gives battery voltage; "1" measures current and input in EL1; "2" measures current and input in EL2; "3" places vehicle in 3rd gear with shift lever in "A" position (solenoid ball valves not activated); "4", "5" and "6" are not used; "7" measures transmission fluid temperature (with thermometer in place).

Fuses

All fuses are 1 amp capacity. Fuse "a" protects test box, fuse "b" protects EL1 and fuse "c" protects EL2.

ROAD TEST

1) Before road testing, make sure that fluid level and condition and control linkage adjustments have been checked and corrected as needed. During test, transmission should upshift and downshift at approximately the speeds shown in *Shift Speed Specifications* chart.

2) All shifts may vary somewhat due to production tolerances or tire size. What is important is the quality of the shifts. All shifts should be smooth, responsive and with no slippage or engine speed runaway.

3) Note any transmission malfunctions or faulty operating conditions. Slippage or engine runaway in any gear usually indicates clutch or brake problems. Compare noted malfunctions with *Trouble Shooting* section to determine probable cause.

SHIFT SPEED SPECIFICATIONS

Application	Shift Speed (MPH)
Part Throttle	
3-2 Downshift	15
2-1 Downshift	10
Full Throttle	
1-2 Upshift	40
2-3 Upshift	65
Kickdown	
3-2 Downshift	55
2-1 Downshift	35

4) This process should give a good indication of which units are faulty and/or out of adjustment. It will also give a reasonable indication of which units are operating properly; however, it is extremely difficult to determine the exact cause of any particular malfunction. Practically any condition can be caused by leaking hydraulic circuits or sticking valves. Therefore, unless an obvious condition exists, do not disassemble transmission until hydraulic pressure tests have been made.

HYDRAULIC PRESSURE TESTS

Perform tests with transmission fluid at normal operating temperature of about 175°F (80°C). Attach thermometer to test box, remove dipstick from tube and insert thermometer. Hydraulic pressures are checked in 2 steps, "Initial Adjustment" and "Full Throttle Road Test".

Initial Adjustment

1) Connect pressure gauge at rear of transaxle. *See Fig. 3.* Check fluid level and top off if needed. With parking brake engaged, wheels blocked and tachometer attached, place shift lever in "P" and check fluid pressure.

2) With engine running at 800 RPM, pressure should be 58 psi (4.2 kg/cm²). As engine speed is increased, pressure should increase rapidly to a maximum pressure of 189-203 psi (13.3-14.3 kg/cm²).

Fig. 3: Pressure Test Port Location

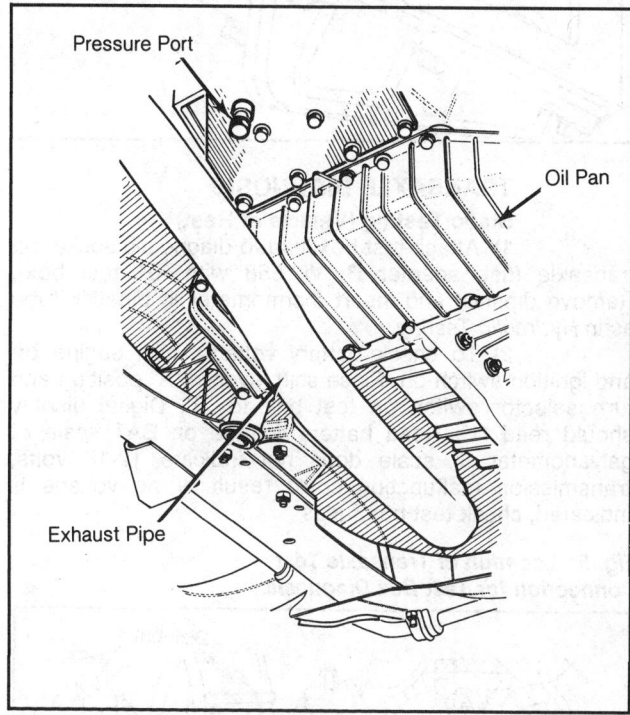

3) Move shift lever to "N", bring engine speed to 800 RPM, and read pressure at partial throttle. If pressure is not 36-39 psi (2.5-2.7 kg/cm²), adjust by turning the vacuum capsule one notch at a time. Changing capsule position by 1 notch will change pressure by about 1.5 psi (.11 kg/cm²). Pressure is increased as the vacuum capsule is screwed in.

Full Throttle Road Test

Reconnect vacuum capsule. Drive car. Place shift lever in "A" and press accelerator pedal to the floor. Read maximum fluid pressure obtained (just before 1-2 upshift). If pressure is not about 58 psi (4.1 kg/cm²), check vacuum capsule and vacuum circuit. *See Service (In Vehicle).* Replace capsule if necessary and adjust full throttle pressure. If pressure will not adjust properly, check for faulty pressure regulator or transmission assembly.

Fig. 4: Vacuum Capsule Location

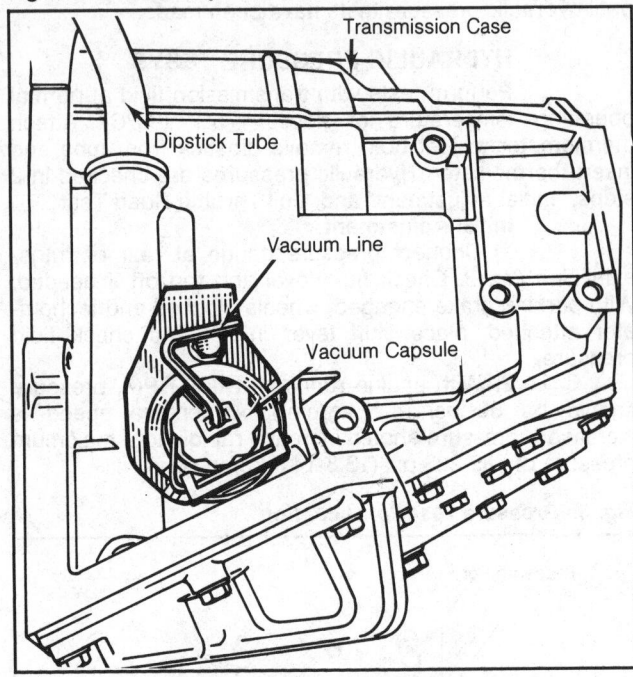

TRANSAXLE DIAGNOSIS

Static Testing (Vehicle at Rest)

1) Attach test box lead to diagnostic socket on transaxle (use adapter B. Vi. 858 with -01 test box). Remove dipstick and insert thermometer in dipstick tube as in *Hydraulic Testing*.

2) To check battery voltage, turn engine off and ignition switch on. Place shift lever in "A" position and turn selector switch on test box to "0". Digital display should read "1". Read battery voltage on BAT scale of galvanometer. If scale does not indicate 12-16 volts, transmission malfunction could result. If no voltage is indicated, check test box fuses.

Fig. 5: Location of Transaxle Test Connection for Test Box Diagnosis

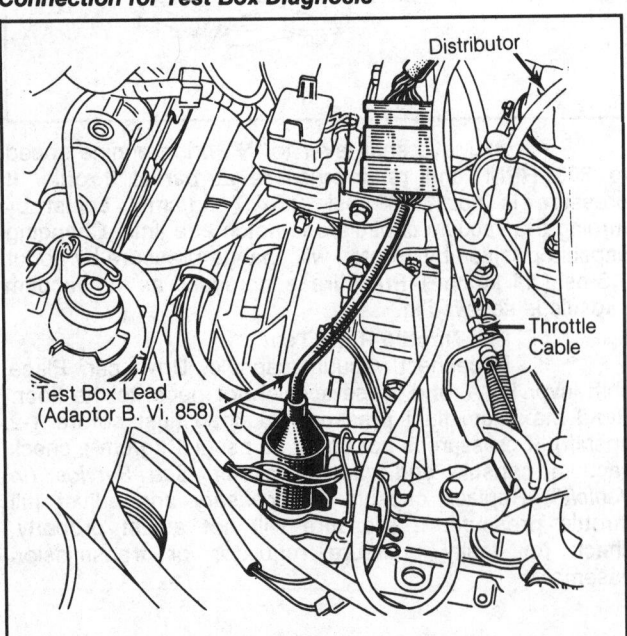

3) To check EL1 solenoid ball valve, move selector switch to "1". Digital display will read "3" and EL1 and EL2 indicator lights should light, indicating that solenoid ball valves are energized. Read current flow on EL1-EL2 scale of galvanometer. Current flow should be .3-.8 amps.

4) If current flow is correct, EL1 solenoid ball valve is in good electrical condition. Go to next step. If current is out of indicated range, check wiring and connecters. If wiring is good, solenoid ball valve is defective. If no current is indicated, check test box fuses.

5) EL2 solenoid ball valve is checked in the same manner as EL1, with the selector switch in the "2" position. If current is correct, go to next test.

6) Move selector switch to "3". Input current should still read .3-.8 amps. If current is incorrect, check test box leads and electrical controls. If input current is correct, transaxle malfunction is not in electrical system. Check hydraulic and mechanical systems.

Dynamic Testing (Vehicle in Motion)

1) With test equipment attached as before, position test box in vehicle so that it may be observed while vehicle is being driven. Start engine, place shift lever in "A" and begin driving with selector switch in "0". Digital display should show "1" and EL1 and EL2 lights should be on.

2) Continue driving. On 1-2 upshift, digital display should go to "2" and EL1 light should go out. Continue driving. On 2-3 upshift, digital display should go to "3" and both EL lights should be out.

3) Reduce speed to 40-45 MPH and move selector switch to "7". Press accelerator pedal to the floor to get 3-2 kickdown. RC light should come on. If it does not, check kickdown switch adjustment, ignition switch and the connecting wire.

SERVICE (IN-VEHICLE)

AXLE SHAFTS & WHEEL BEARINGS

See Service (In Vehicle) in Renault Fuego & 18i 4 & 5-Speed manual transaxle article.

SOLENOID BALL VALVES

Removal

Solenoid ball valves are located on the valve body. To remove, drain transmission fluid, remove inspection plate, oil pan and gasket. Remove solenoid ball valve clips and disconnect wiring. Note color of wire attached to each valve. Remove support plate retaining bolts (2) and remove valves from valve body. *See Fig. 38.*

Installation

Reverse removal procedure to install. Do not reverse valve positions. Be sure to install correct wire to correct valve as noted during removal.

VACUUM CAPSULE

Inspection

1) With test equipment connected as in *Hydraulic Pressure Tests*, connect vacuum pump to vacuum hose on capsule. Apply a vacuum of about 15.7 in. Hg. If needle on test box does not move, check pressure at full and part throttle.

2) If the needle falls, there is a leak in the vacuum circuit and the capsule or its hose must be replaced. Make sure that the vacuum hose connection on the intake manifold is in good condition.

RENAULT FUEGO & 18i (Cont.)

3) Check to make sure that the hose connection to the capsule is tight. An air leak in the capsule or pipe causes a whistling sound, irregular idling, excessive light throttle pressure, and slightly harsh gear shifts under light load.

Removal

Drain transmission fluid. Disconnect vacuum hose from capsule. Move retaining clip out of way and unscrew the capsule, counting the number of turns.

Installation

The vacuum capsule cannot be disassembled and must therefore be replaced as a unit if faulty. Screw in capsule the same number of turns as needed to remove it. Install retaining clip and connect vacuum hose. Refill transmission. Adjust pressure.

KICKDOWN SWITCH

Removal & Installation

Remove accelerator cable. Disconnect wire from kickdown switch. Unscrew 2 retaining bolts and remove switch. Reverse removal procedure to install.

Fig. 6: Accelerator Cable Housing

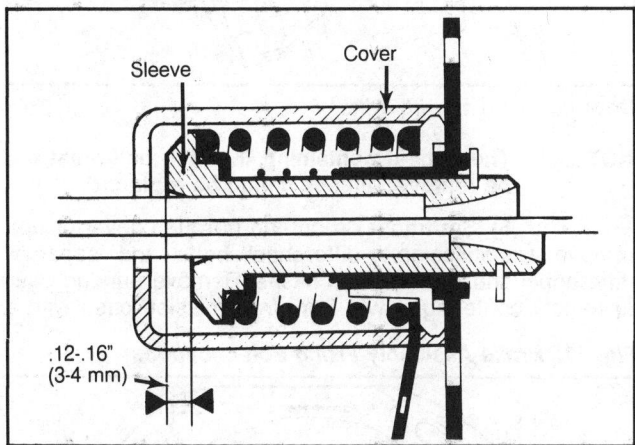

Adjust to allow .12-.16" (3-4 mm) free play in housing.

Adjustment

Adjustment is made with the accelerator cable. Make sure that the accelerator cable has enough play in it to allow .12-.16" (3-4 mm) movement in the sleeve when the accelerator pedal is depressed. Make sure that the cover is positioned correctly to prevent tarnishing of the contacts.

DIFFERENTIAL BEARING NUT & OIL SEAL

Removal

1) Raise and support vehicle. Disconnect battery. Drain transmission fluid. Disconnect vacuum capsule hose from intake manifold. Disconnect transaxle wiring connectors and remove support. Insert spacer tool (T. Av. 509-01) between lower shock mounting base and lower control arm pivot shaft on each side.

2) Remove drive shaft retaining roll pins with drift. Separate tie rod end ball joints and upper control arm ball joints from steering knuckle using puller. Tilt axle carriers away from transaxle to separate drive shafts from side gears.

3) Mark nut and housing for reassembly to same position. Remove lock nut. Remove nut with tool (B. Vi. 807). Count and record number of turns required to

remove nut. Remove lip seal and "O" ring from nut. Remove "O" ring from side gear.

Fig. 7: Differential Bearing Nut Location

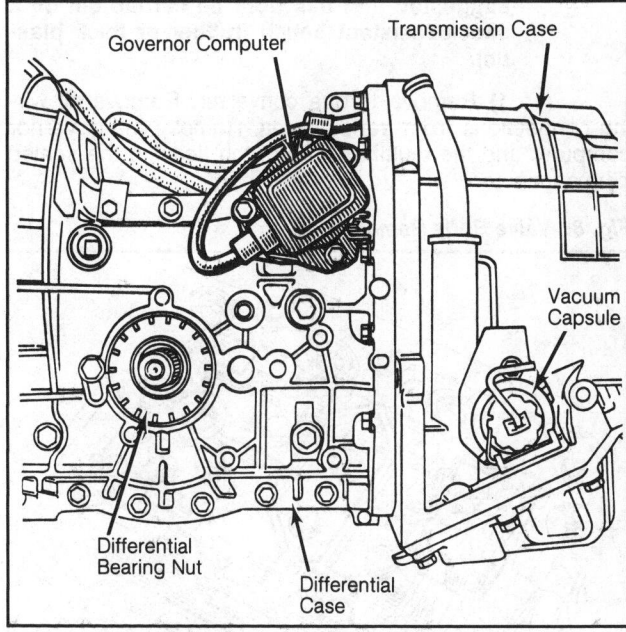

Installation

Install new lip seal and "O" ring on nut. Place tool (B. Vi. 813) around side gear to prevent damage to lip seal on installation. Install nut the same number of turns as was required to remove it. Align mark made during removal. Install nut lock. Remove tool from side gear and install new "O" ring. Reverse removal procedure to complete installation.

TRANSAXLE REMOVAL & INSTALLATION

See the appropriate article in AUTOMATIC TRANSMISSION REMOVAL Section.

TORQUE CONVERTER

Removal

With transaxle removed from vehicle, pull converter straight out. Check general condition of converter components (i.e. input shaft, oil seal surface, converter sleeve, mounting bosses, etc.). If converter is damaged in any way, it must be replaced. Remove old oil seal from transmission case. Install new seal with tool (B. Vi. 465, Ref. A). Use of this tool automatically sets oil seal to correct depth.

Installation

1) Locate sharp-cornered edge on torque converter drive plate (marked with paint). There are 3 mounting bosses on the torque converter. Locate the boss which is directly opposite the hole in converter used as reference point for distributor timing.

2) When assembling torque converter to drive plate, align specified mounting boss with sharp-cornered edge on drive plate. Install new spring washers and tighten converter retaining bolts gradually and in rotation so that the converter is centered.

RENAULT FUEGO & 18i (Cont.)

TRANSAXLE DISASSEMBLY

NOTE: It is very important that all components remain clean throughout operation. It is suggested that this work be carried out on a shock resistant bench (rubber or thick plastic).

1) Remove torque converter. Remove all wiring connections from transmission. Remove the governor computer and the multifunction switch, leaving the sealed plug connected.

Fig. 8: Valve Body Removal

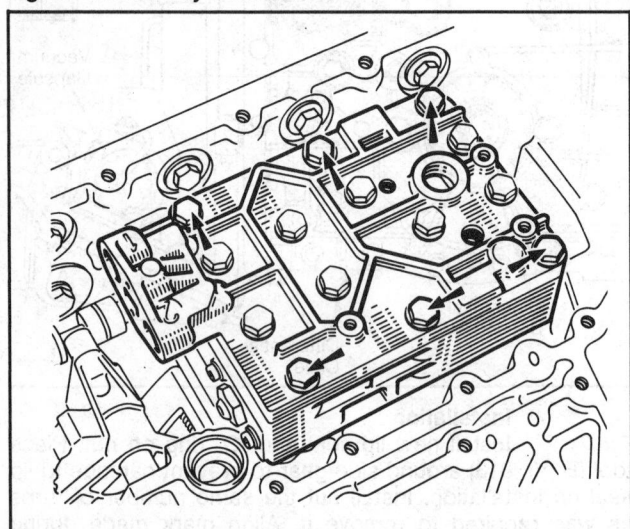

Remove only those bolts (6) indicated by arrows.

2) Remove vacuum capsule, oil pan, bottom cover and gasket. Remove filter and seal. Retain suction tube seal for reassembly. Disconnect sealed plug socket and remove wiring. Remove valve body retaining bolts indicated in *Fig. 8*. Remove valve body.

3) Remove the pump cover and shaft. If the oil pump driven gear is to be reused, mark upper face with felt pen or soft pencil so that it may be reinstalled in the same position. Remove drive gear. Remove 4 inner differential assembly bolts from transmission case. *See Fig. 9.*

Fig. 9: Inner Differential Assembly Bolts

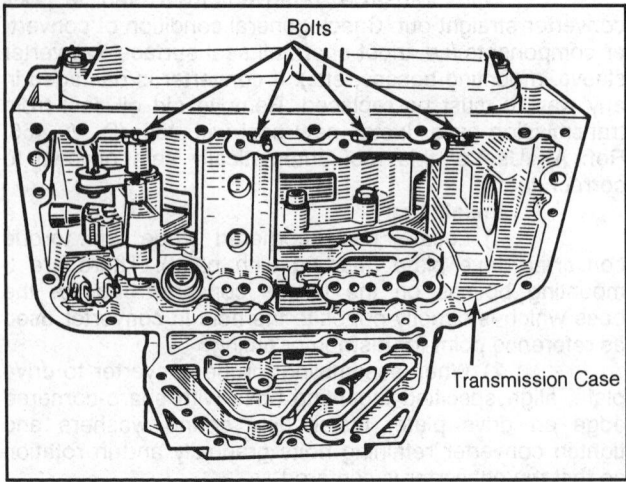

4) Drive out shift shaft roll pin(s) with drift. Remove bolt "A" in *Fig. 10*. Remove shift arm from shaft. Pull out shaft and save toothed wheel. Remove control linkage.

Fig. 10: Removing Shift Shaft Assembly

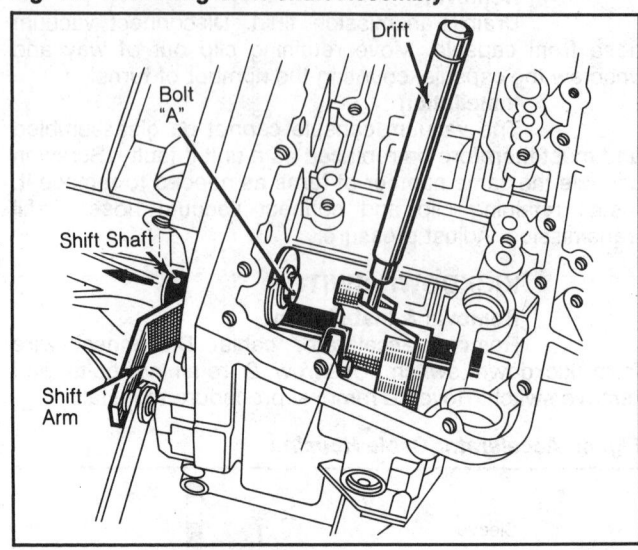

Drive out roll pins with drifts.

NOTE: The socket containing the lock ball must not be removed unless it is to be replaced.

5) Set transaxle on end (torque converter up), remove transmission-to-differential bolts and separate differential and transmission cases. Remove parking pawl assembly centering dowel from transmission case with a

Fig. 11: Brake Assembly Fixing Bolt Locations

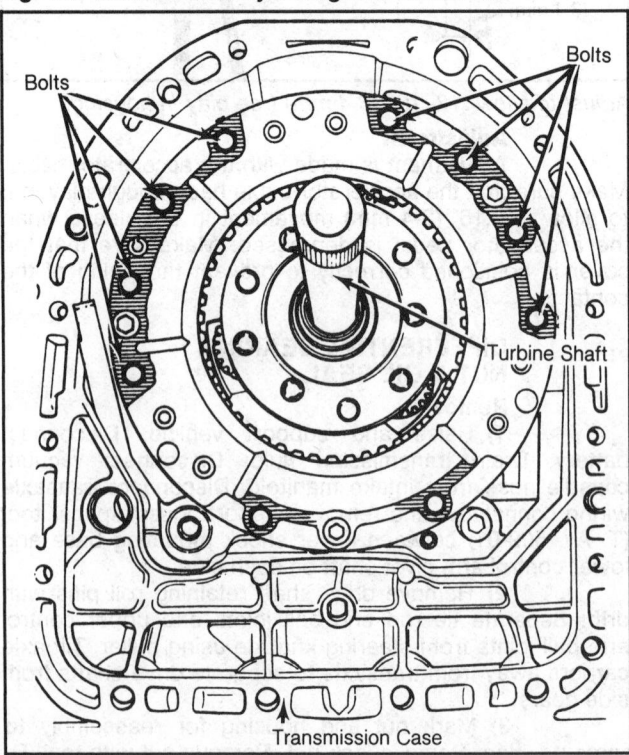

Remove bolts. Lift out drive train assembly by turbine shaft.

RENAULT FUEGO & 18i (Cont.)

slide hammer. Remove pivot shaft, parking pawl and return spring.

6) Remove brake assembly fixing bolts. *See Fig. 11.* Grasp turbine shaft and lift out complete drive train assembly. Ensure that needle thrust bearing remains in case. Support assembly vertically on a 4" tube on bench and remove planetary gear assembly, sun gear and shaft, F1-F2 brake assembly and E2 clutch.

Fig. 12: Drive Train Assembly

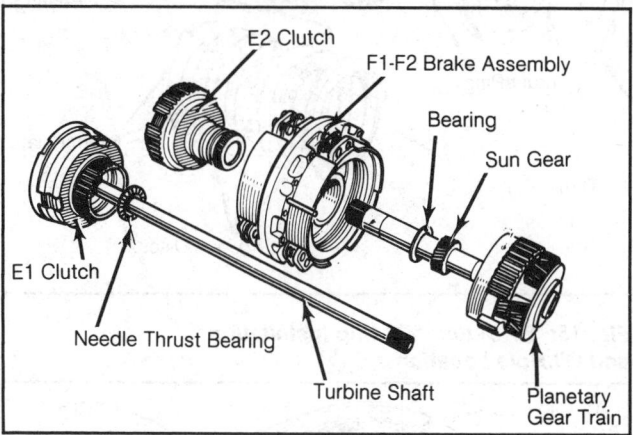

Separate components for disassembly.

COMPONENT DISASSEMBLY, REASSEMBLY & INSPECTION

INSPECTION

1) After disassembly and before reassembly, inspect condition of various components of transaxle. Check all machined surfaces for wear or scratches. Check oil seal and "O" ring surfaces and grooves for smoothness and uniformity of fit.

2) Check all white metal sleeves, as on transmission case, E2 clutch, planetary gear train, and other components. If excessively worn or damaged, replace part.

3) If any parts exhibit signs of excessive wear or damage, they must be replaced. For inspection procedures which apply to a particular component, see procedures below.

Transmission Case

Check condition of oil pump gears and housing, pump drive and cover. The transmission case and oil pump assembly are serviced as a complete unit only. If any one component requires replacement, the entire unit must be replaced.

Clutches & Brakes

1) Check all discs for damage, discoloration or separated linings. Replace as needed. All discs and plates should slide easily on hub splines or in their respective housings.

2) Check waved discs for proper bend. To do this, lay the disc on a flat surface and measure gap between waves and surface with a feeler gauge. Check wave height at all 3 positions on each disc. Do not apply pressure to the disc while making this measurement. Wave heights must be .010-.018" (.25-.45 mm). If disc is not to specification, it must be replaced.

3) Check all plates and thrust plates for signs of excessive wear, damage or overheating and replace as

needed. Generally speaking, if one of the assemblies (E1, E2, F1, F2) has overheated, all intermediate discs and all with damaged linings must be replaced. All oil seals and "O" rings should be systematically replaced during any disassembly procedure.

4) E1 and E2 clutches utilize relief valve check balls which are crimped into place in the piston bodies (2 in E1 clutch, 1 in E2). Check that balls move freely in their sockets and do not stick to seat or crimped side. Total check ball travel should be about .04" (1 mm). If check ball operation is not satisfactory, the entire clutch piston assembly must be replaced.

5) On E1 clutch, check surface condition of piston bore. Check diaphragm spring for breakage, hub for disc marks on splines, fit of 2 sleeves in piston housing, and fit of the turbine shaft. On E2 clutch, check the piston bore and the return spring, spring retainer, and snap ring.

Planetary Gear Train

Check condition of planet gear teeth. Check one-way clutch. Ensure that one-way clutch hub plugs are securely in place. Check center bore and outer clutch track. Inspect needle thrust bearing and bearing plate for scoring or other damage. The one-way clutch or thrust plate may be replaced separately if damaged. If any other component of the gear train is damaged, the entire assembly must be replaced.

Valve Body

The valve body and regulator assembly must not be disassembled. Only the solenoid ball valves may be replaced. Whenever the automatic transmission is disassembled due to damaged clutches or brakes, or because of poor quality gear shifting, the valve body and its regulator must be replaced.

Fig. 13: Assembling Sun Gear Shaft & Planetary Gear Train

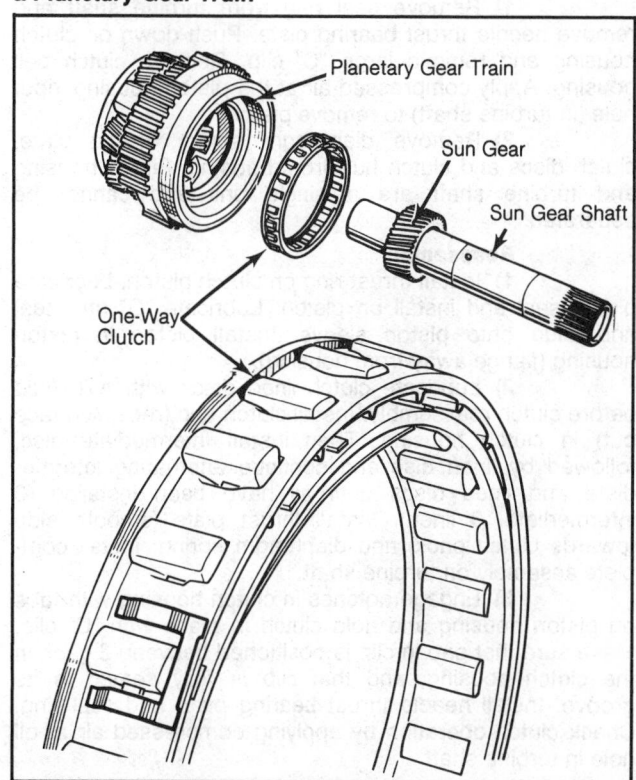

One-way clutch must be installed as shown.

Fig. 14: E1 Clutch and Turbine Shaft Assembly

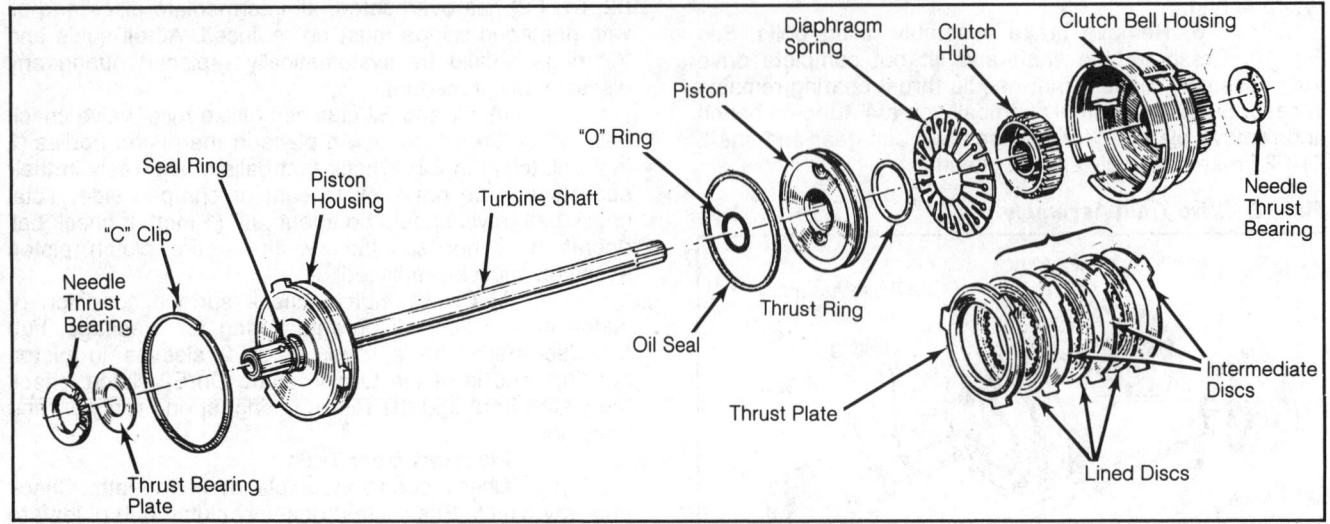

PLANETARY GEAR ASSEMBLY
Disassembly

Remove one-way clutch. Remove adjusting shim, needle bearing plate and needle thrust bearing. Remove remaining needle bearing plate. Leave inner needle thrust bearing in place.

Reassembly

Reverse disassembly procedure to assemble. Make sure one-way clutch is installed with shoulder oriented as shown in *Fig. 13*. Inner needle thrust bearing is centered with sun gear.

E1 CLUTCH
Disassembly

1) Remove seal ring from turbine shaft and remove needle thrust bearing plate. Push down on clutch housing and remove large "C" clip. Remove clutch bell housing. Apply compressed air at the piston housing input hole (in turbine shaft) to remove piston.

2) Remove diaphragm spring, thrust plate, clutch discs and clutch hub from housing. Piston housing and turbine shaft are a single unit and cannot be separated.

Reassembly

1) Install thrust ring on clutch piston. Lubricate piston seal and install on piston. Lubricate "O" ring seal and slide onto piston sleeve. Install piston in piston housing (flange away from housing).

2) Lubricate clutch lined discs with ATF fluid before clutch reassembly. Install clutch hub (recessed face out) in clutch housing. Then install intermediate disc, followed by lined disc and continue alternating intermediate and lined discs until all have been installed (3 intermediate, 3 lined). Install thrust plate (smooth side towards clutch pack) and diaphragm spring. Install complete assembly on turbine shaft.

3) Engage notches in clutch housing with tabs on piston housing and hold clutch in place with "C" clip. Make sure that gap in clip is positioned between 2 gaps in the clutch housing, and that clip is fully seated in its groove. Install needle thrust bearing plate and seal ring. Check clutch operation by applying compressed air at oil hole in turbine shaft.

Fig. 15: E1 Clutch "C" Clip Installation and Oil Hole Location

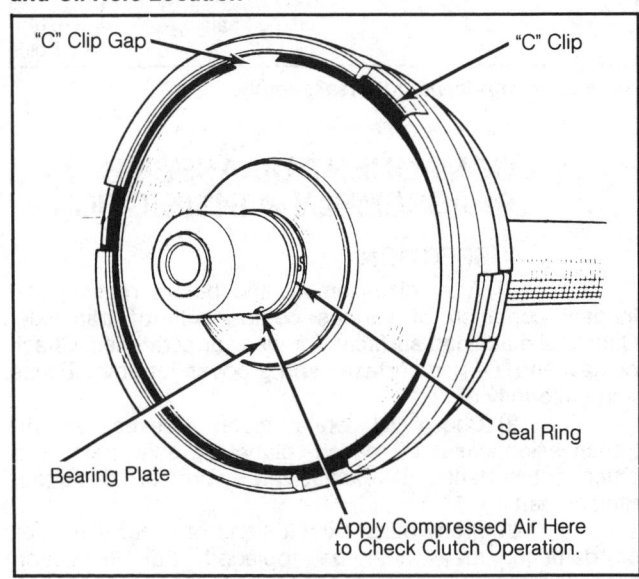

Install "C" clip with gap centered between housing notches.

E2 CLUTCH
Disassembly

Compress clutch return spring with press and tool (B. Vi. 489-14 or -19, Ref. 07) and remove snap ring. Lift out spring retainer and spring. Remove seal rings (3). Remove large "C" clip, thrust plate, clutch discs (3 lined, 2 waved) and flat disc from clutch housing. Remove piston by applying compressed air at oil hole in housing.

Reassembly

1) Install seal rings on clutch housing. Ensure that ring grooves are clean and square before installing rings. Lubricate piston seal and install on piston. Lubricate "O" ring seal and install on piston hub in clutch housing. Ensure that seals are firmly seated in their grooves.

2) Install piston in clutch housing so that slots in piston are aligned with slots in the housing. Install return spring and retainer. Compress spring and install

RENAULT FUEGO & 18i (Cont.)

snap ring. Lubricate lined clutch discs with clean ATF. Install clutch components in housing in order: Thrust plate, lined disc, waved disc, lined disc, waved disc, lined disc, and thrust plate (with punch-marked side out).

Fig. 16: Installing E2 Clutch Piston

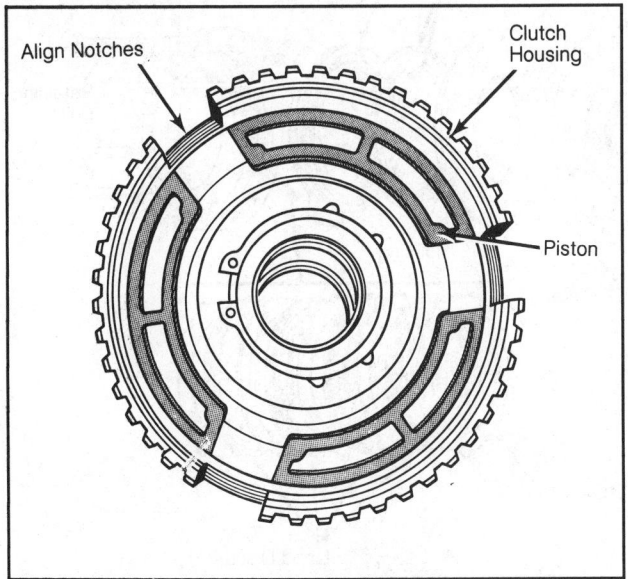

Align slots in piston and housing as shown.

3) Install "C" clip with gap centered between 2 slots in housing. Check clutch operation by applying compressed air at oil hole in housing. Place E2 clutch on a flat surface, large end up. Place flat metal disc (B. Vi. 489-14 or -19, Ref. 06) on top of clutch discs and position dial indicator with tip resting on disc. Zero indicator.

4) Raise clutch pack (at slots in housing) until "C" clip is against top of groove, without compressing waved discs. Read indicator dial. If end play is greater than .083" (2.1 mm), replace thrust plate with one .098" (2.5 mm) thick.

Fig. 18: Installing E2 Clutch "C" Clip

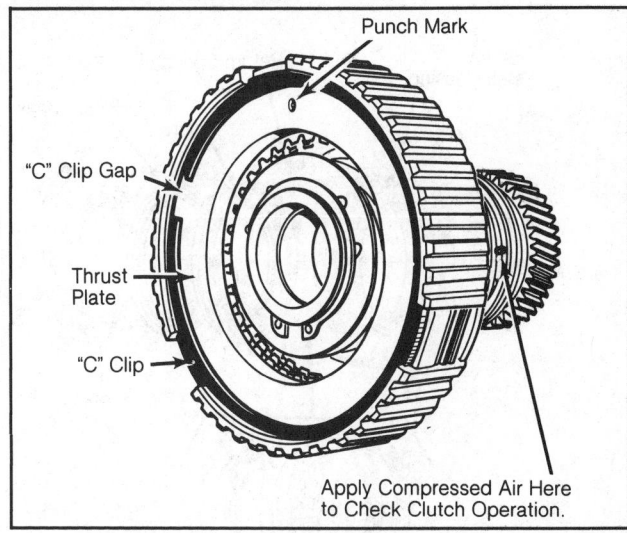

Install clip with gap located between notches in housing.

F1-F-2 BRAKE ASSEMBLY
Disassembly

1) Remove 3 F1 brake bell housing retaining bolts. Remove housing and 6 piston return springs. Remove steel and lined discs, noting relative positions for reassembly reference. Note position of "O" ring between one-way clutch hub and F1 piston housing. Save "O" ring.

2) Remove 3 F2 brake bell housing retaining bolts. Remove housing and 6 piston return springs. Remove steel and lined discs, noting positions for reassembly reference. Note position of the "O" ring between one-way clutch hub and F1 piston housing. Save "O" ring. Apply compressed air at oil input holes to remove pistons. Remove piston seals (F1 and F2).

Reassembly

1) Check F2 brake operating play: Install F2 piston (without seal) in piston housing. Install flat disc

Fig. 17: Exploded View of E2 Clutch Assembly

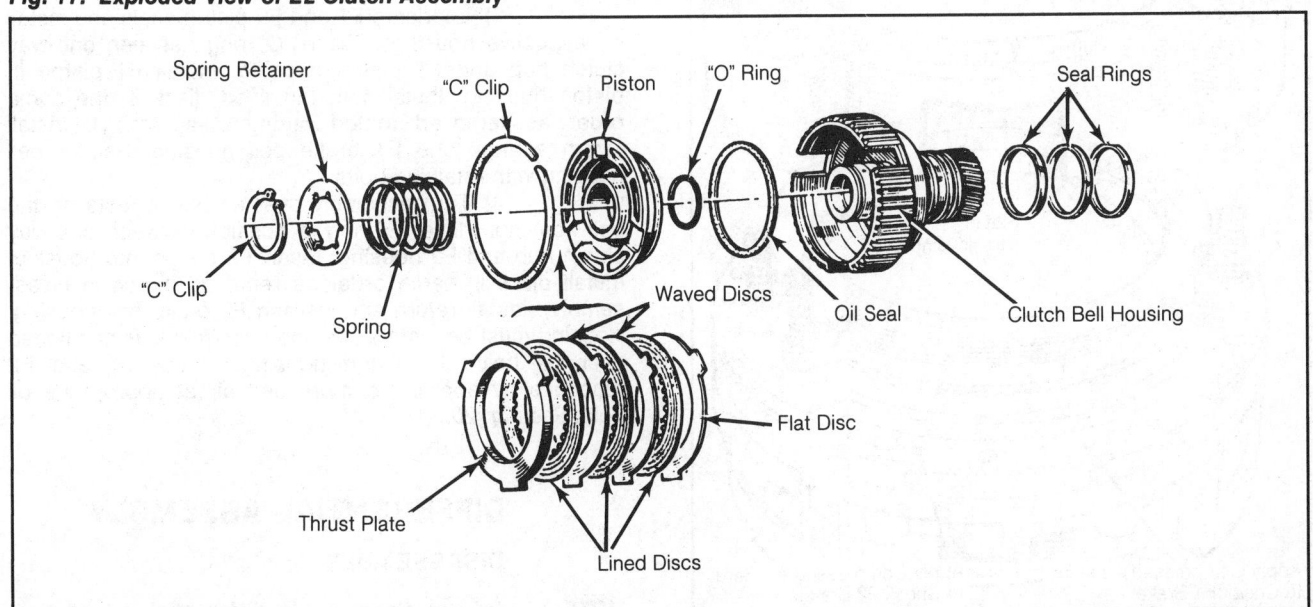

Automatic Transmissions

RENAULT FUEGO & 18i (Cont.)

Fig. 19: Complete F1-F2 Brake Assembly

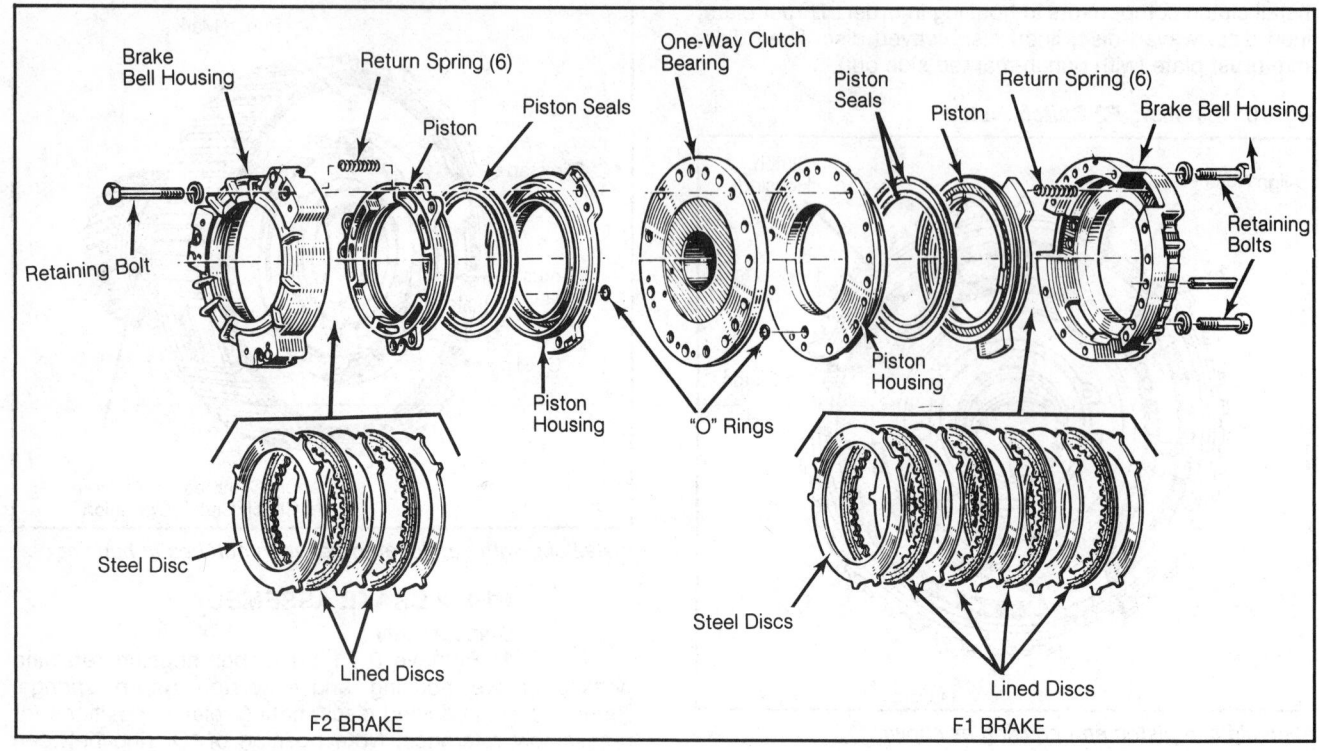

Fig. 20: Installing F2 Brake Bell Housing

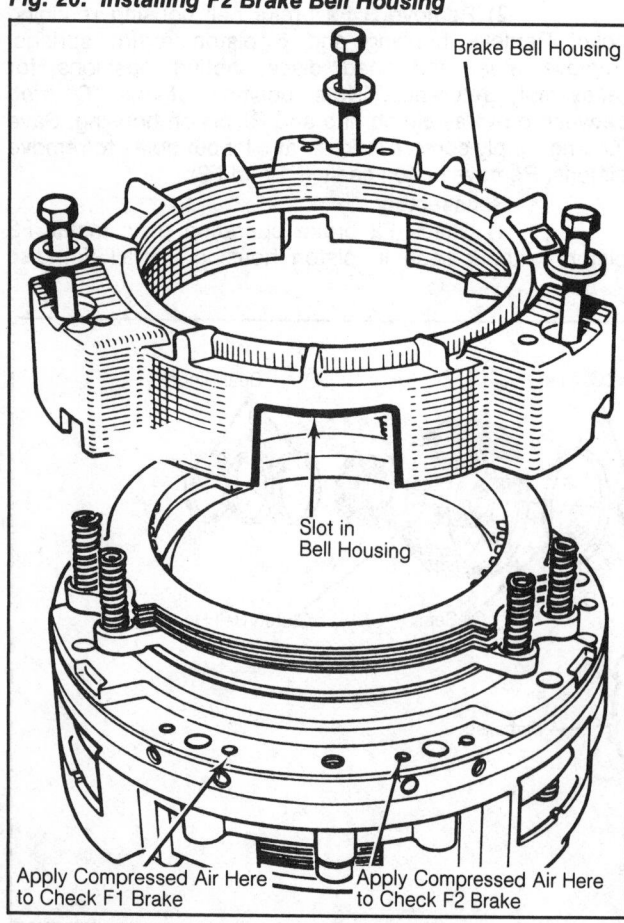

Note position of oil holes and slot in housing.

(.059", 1.5 mm thick), lined disc, waved disc (.079", 2 mm thick), lined disc and another flat disc in housing. Install brake bell housing and attach entire asembly to one-way clutch hub with bolts (3).

2) Position dial indicator with dial pin resting on a spline of the first lined disc. Zero indicator. Lift disc pack until it makes contact with bell housing. Read indicator dial. Take measurements at several points and average readings to obtain F2 operating play. If play is not .028-.067" (.70-1.70 mm), check piston and all discs for damage or distortion and replace as needed. Disassemble components.

3) Lubricate F1 and F2 piston seals and install in respective housings. Place "O" ring between one-way clutch hub and F1 piston housing. Install F1 piston in piston housing. Install flat and lined discs in the same order as removed (noted during disassembly). Install return springs and F1 brake bell housing. Secure bell housing with retaining bolts.

4) Turn assembly over so that it rests on the bell housing. Place "O" ring in position between one-way clutch hub and F2 housing. Insert F2 piston into housing. Install discs in same order as removed (noted in disassembly). Install return springs and F2 brake bell housing. Housing must be installed so that slot in side is positioned over oil holes in piston housing. Check F1 and F2 functions by applying compressed air at appropriate oil hole. *See Fig. 20.*

DIFFERENTIAL ASSEMBLY

DISASSEMBLY

NOTE: Do not disassemble differential unless specific repairs are required.

RENAULT FUEGO & 18i (Cont.)

1) Place differential assembly on engine stand with adaptor (B. Vi. 16-01). Remove output shaft bearing lockplate retaining bolts. Using 2 slightly longer bolts, install fixing tool (B. Vi. 489-04) to lock output shaft in place. Remove drive pinion lock nut.

2) Remove torque converter (if still attached). Pry out converter oil seal with tool (B. Vi. 465, Ref. C). Remove stator support retaining bolts (4) and remove support. Remove side gear "O" rings.

Fig. 21: *Complete Differential Assembly*

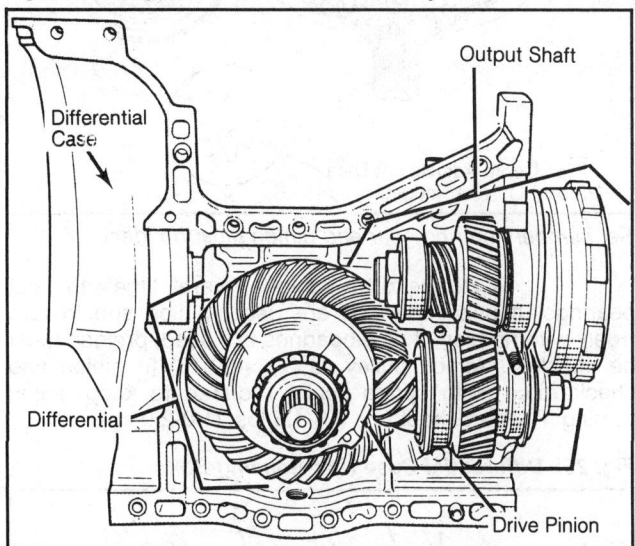

3) Remove bolts which secure the 2 differential half-housings together and separate half-housings (use a rubber mallet if needed). Remove output shaft, differential and drive pinion. Remove differential bearing adjusting nut lock washers, then remove adjusting nuts with tool (B. Vi. 807).

Differential

Remove 2 opposing ring gear-to-differential case retaining bolts. Support differential in soft-jawed vise and remove bearing from ring gear side with puller and clamp (T. Ar. 65 and B. Tr. 02). Turn differential over and remove bearing from opposite side. Remove remaining ring gear-to-case retaining bolts and discard all bolts.

Fig. 22: *Exploded View of Differential*

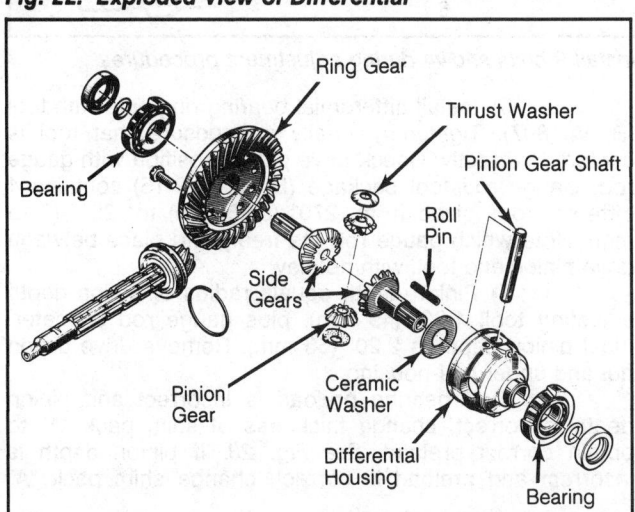

Drive out pinion gear shaft roll pin. Separate pinion gears, side gears and washers from differential housing.

Drive Pinion

Remove in order from pinion: Retaining nut, adjusting shims (note thickness for reassembly), spacer, stepdown gear, and adjusting shims (note thickness for reassembly). Remove bearing with puller and clamp. Check bearing condition.

Fig. 23: *Exploded View of Drive Pinion*

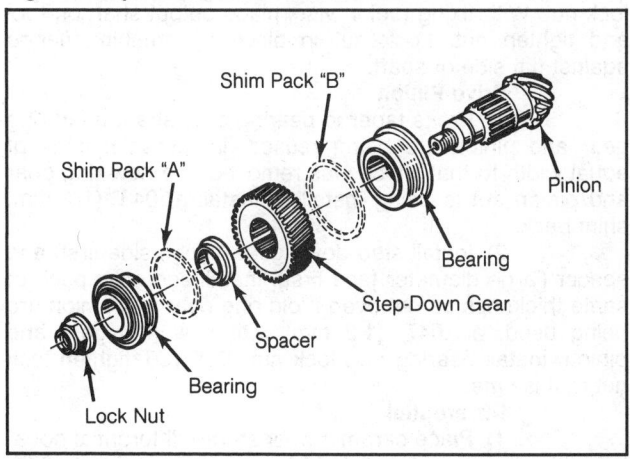

Output Shaft

Clamp fixing tool (B. Vi. 489-04) in vise and fit output shaft over it. Remove nut from end of shaft. Remove gear and bearings with puller, clamp and spacer (Rou. 15-01).

Fig. 24: *Exploded View of Output Shaft*

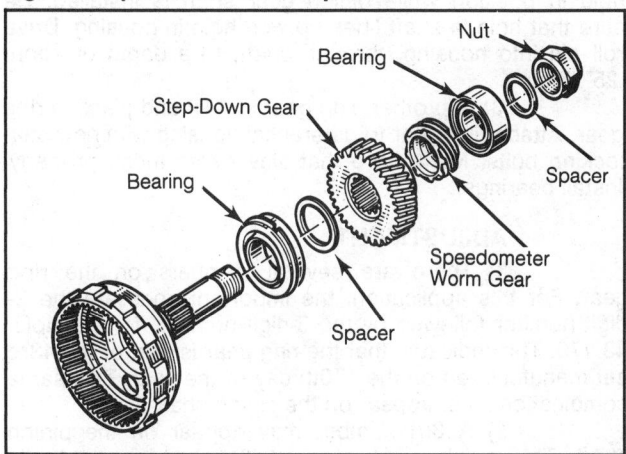

INSPECTION

1) Clean all parts thoroughly and blow dry with compressed air. Also blow out all oil holes and lubrication channels. Lubricate all parts with Dexron II ATF.

2) Check all gear teeth for wear or damage. Check all bearings and step-down gears for excessive wear or damage. Check condition of the 2 white metal bushings on the output shaft.

3) Check contact surfaces in both housings. Check stator support housing and breather. Check differential adjusting nut threads. Replace any damaged parts. The step-down gears are serviced as a complete set only. If either of the gears is damaged, both must be

RENAULT FUEGO & 18i (Cont.)

replaced. Likewise, the ring gear and pinion are manufactured in matched pairs only and must always be replaced as a set.

REASSEMBLY

Output Shaft

Press bearing onto shaft, flange side first. Install parts in order: Spacer, step-down gear (flange towards speedometer worm gear), speedometer worm gear (large diameter bore end first), bearing, shim and lock nut. With fixing tool in vise, place output shaft on tool and tighten nut. Lock nut in place by crushing flange against flat side of shaft.

Drive Pinion

1) Press tapered bearing onto shaft. If old ring gear and pinion are being reused, install shim pack of equal width to that which was removed. If a new ring gear and pinion set is being installed, install a .043" (1.1 mm) shim pack.

2) Install step-down gear (flange side first) and spacer (large diameter face first). Install 2nd shim pack of same thickness as removed if old ring gear and pinion are being used, or .047" (1.2 mm) with new ring gear and pinion. Install bearing and lock nut. DO NOT tighten lock nut at this time.

Differential

1) Place ceramic washer into differential housing with oil groove toward side gear. Use a washer .077-.079" (1.96-2.0 mm) thick, unless side gear to pinion gear backlash is excessive. If so, use a washer .080-.081" (2.03-2.07 mm) thick. Dip side gear in ATF before installing.

2) Place pinion gears and thrust washers in housing (locking tabs on washers in holes in housing) and hold in position while pinion gear shaft is installed. Be sure that hole in shaft lines up with hole in housing. Drive roll pin into housing, through shaft, to a depth of about .25" (5 mm).

3) Dip other side gear in ATF and place in ring gear. Attach ring gear to differential housing with new self-locking bolts. Make sure that side gears mesh properly. Install bearings.

ADJUSTMENT

1) There are several numbers on the ring gear. For this application, the important ones are the 2-digit number followed by the 3-digit number, for example, 43 170. This indicates that the ring gear is part of the 43rd set manufactured on the 170th day of the year. This same combination must appear on the pinion shaft used.

2) A 3rd number may appear on the pinion shaft. This number indicates additional pinion depth (in hundredths of a millimeter) which must be set when the differential is assembled. For example, if the number is 20, pinion depth must be set at standard depth PLUS .20 mm (.008").

3) With governor side half-housing attached to engine stand, install differential bearing races and adjusting nuts on half-housing (make sure nuts are clean). Lubricate tapered faces of pinion depth adjusting tool (B. Vi. 489-12) and install in half-housing. Install drive pinion.

4) Install other half-housing and secure with bolts indicated in *Fig. 26*. Do not tighten bolts at this time. Hold drive pinion with tool (B. Vi. 489-04) and tighten lock nut. Now tighten half-housing bolts to specification.

Fig. 25: *Ring Gear and Pinion Shaft ID Numbers*

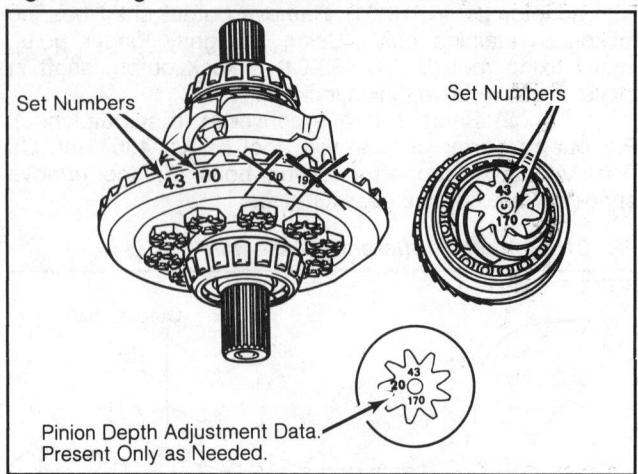

Pinion Depth Adjustment Data. Present Only as Needed.

Set numbers on ring gear and pinion must be identical.

5) Rotate drive pinion several times to seat bearings. If used bearings are used, pinion should turn freely with no play. If new bearings are used, preload must be checked. Attach pulley (B. Vi. 489-13) to pinion and check force (with spring scale) required to keep pinion turning. Preload should be 2.3-4.5 lbs. (1.0-2.0 kg).

Fig. 26: *Differential Case Half-Housing Bolts*

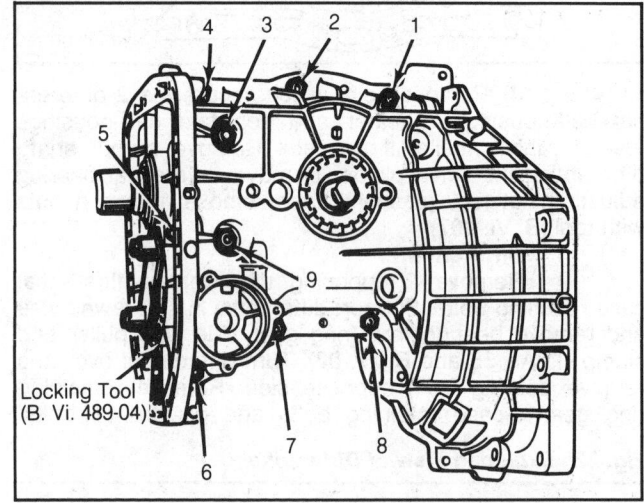

Locking Tool (B. Vi. 489-04)

Install 9 bolts shown during adjustment procedures.

6) Install differential bearing ring nuts with tool (B. Vi. 807). Tighten gradually and ensure that tool is centered correctly. Check drive pinion position with gauge rod. Gauge rod tool package (B. Vi. 489-15) contains 4 different rods sized from .270" (6.85 mm) to .281" (7.15 mm). Note which gauge rod fits freely into place between drive pinion and tool, with no play.

7) Pinion depth equals radius of pinion depth adjusting tool, 1.93" (49 mm), plus gauge rod diameter. Ideal pinion depth is 2.20" (56 mm). Remove drive pinion nut and upper half-housing.

8) If bearing preload is incorrect and pinion depth is correct, change thickness of shim pack "A" to obtain correct preload. *See Fig. 23.* If pinion depth is incorrect and preload is correct, change shim pack "A"

RENAULT FUEGO & 18i (Cont.)

Fig. 27: Checking Drive Pinion Preload

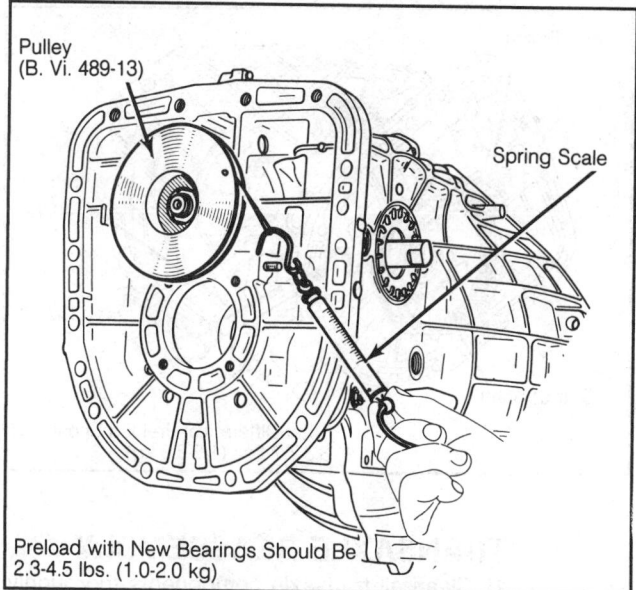

Pulley
(B. Vi. 489-13)

Spring Scale

Preload with New Bearings Should Be
2.3-4.5 lbs. (1.0-2.0 kg)

Preload must be checked when new bearings are installed.

and shim pack "B" by equal, but opposite, amounts: If pinion depth is too great, increase thickness of shim pack "B" and decrease thickness of shim pack "A"; if pinion depth is below specifications, increase "A" and decrease "B". The total combined thickness of shim packs "A" and "B" must remain the same. Change shim pack thickness by amount equal to the difference between measured pinion depth and ideal depth given in step **7**).

Fig. 28: Checking Drive Pinion Depth

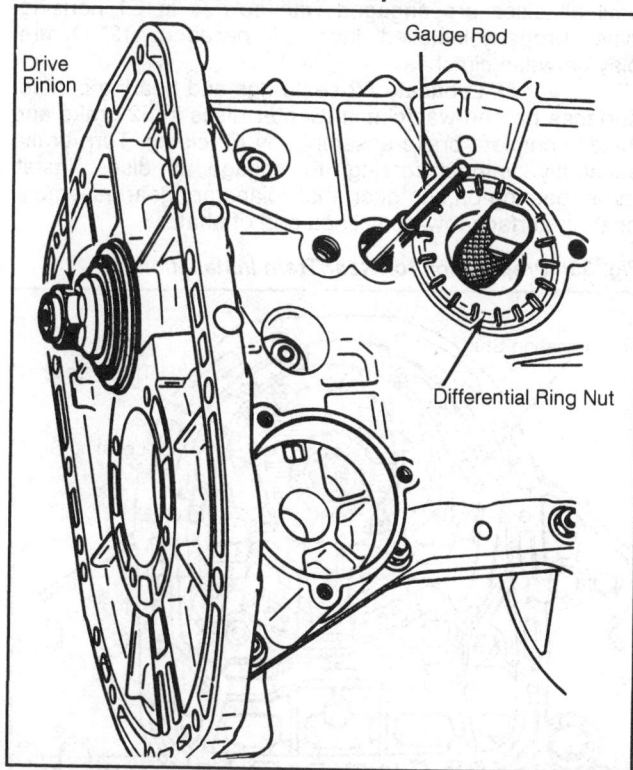

Drive
Pinion

Gauge Rod

Differential Ring Nut

Check depth by placing tool between drive pinion and tapered face of adjusting tool.

9) If pinion depth and bearing preload are both incorrect, adjust preload by changing thickness of shim pack "A" or "B", approximating the pinion depth adjustment as closely as possible. Check new bearing preload. When preload is correct, adjust pinion depth as in step **8**).

10) With half-housings separated, install differential without drive pinion or output shaft. Reassemble half-housings as before. Rotate ring gear several times to seat bearings. Tighten bearing ring nuts same number of turns as was required to remove them and line up match marks. Differential should turn freely with no play.

11) If new bearings are being used, preload must be checked. Run a hook and string through drive pinion hole and around the differential housing (several times) as close as possible to the ring gear. Attach a spring scale and measure the effort required to keep the differential housing turning.

12) Reading on scale should be 2.3-4.5 lbs. (1.0-2.0 kg). Adjust preload by tightening or loosening ring nuts as needed. When proper preload is obtained, mark new position of ring nuts.

Fig. 29: Checking Differential Bearing Preload

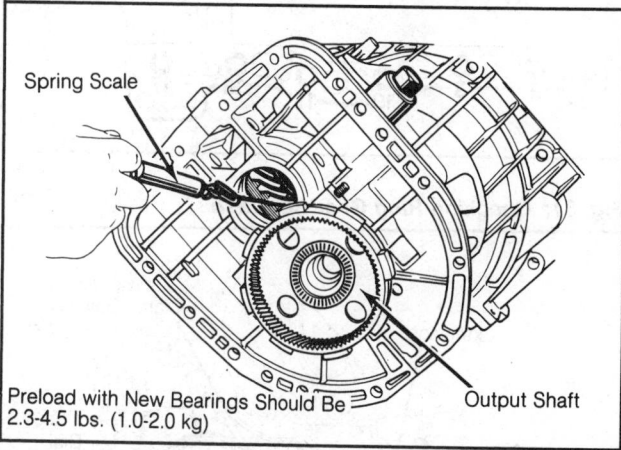

Spring Scale

Output Shaft

Preload with New Bearings Should Be
2.3-4.5 lbs. (1.0-2.0 kg)

Preload must be checked when new bearings are installed.

13) Separate half-housings. Install drive pinion and output shaft. Reassemble differential assembly, aligning ring nuts with match marks. Apply a thick bead of sealer to mating surface of one half-housing before assembly. Tighten bolts in order indicated in *Fig. 30*. Lock output shaft with tool (B. Vi. 489-04) and tighten drive pinion nut. Rotate output shaft a few times to seat bearings.

14) Install dial indicator support (B. Vi. 489-16) in housing as shown in *Fig. 31*. Screw extension onto dial indicator tip (use extension B. Vi. 489-16 if indicator has a 3 mm diameter tip and .60 mm pitch, extension B. Vi. 489-17 for 2.5 mm diameter tip and .45 mm pitch).

15) Fit assembly into support and tighten clamp bolt until dial is snug. Place tip of extension against tooth of ring gear and zero indicator dial. Measure backlash at several places on ring gear. Backlash should be .005-.010" (.12-.25 mm).

16) If backlash is incorrect, adjust by tightening one ring nut and loosening the other the same amount. When final adjustments have been made and backlash is within specifications, mark new position of ring nuts.

17) Remove nuts, counting number of turns. Replace seals and "O" rings. Apply sealer to ring nut

RENAULT FUEGO & 18i (Cont.)

Fig. 30: Differential Case Bolt Tightening Sequence

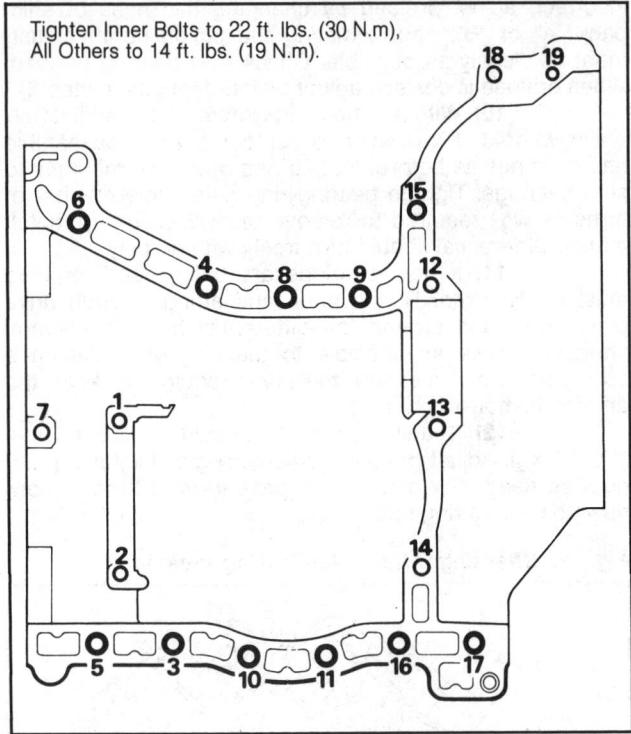

Tighten Inner Bolts to 22 ft. lbs. (30 N.m),
All Others to 14 ft. lbs. (19 N.m).

Fig. 31: Checking Ring Gear Backlash

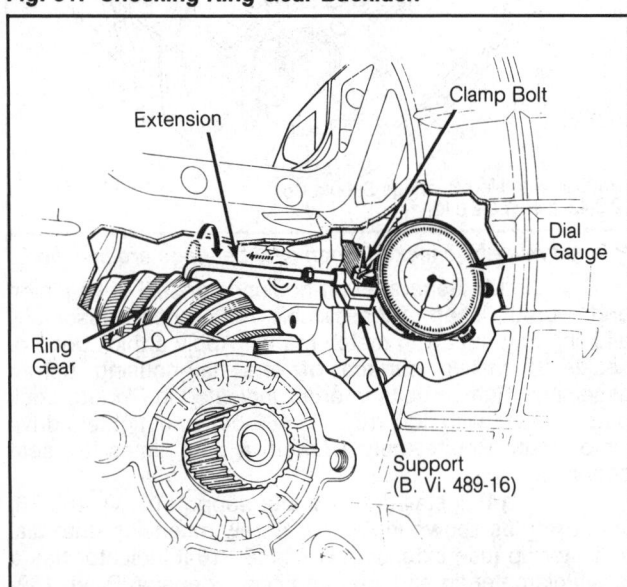

Check backlash at several points on gear.

threads and reinstall ring nuts same number of turns. Line up match marks. Install locks.

18) With adjustments correct and differential assembly assembled, check preload at output shaft. Starting force should be 3.3-7.7 lbs. (1.5-3.5 kg). Check condition of smooth part of stator support.

19) Lightly lubricate seal and tap gently into place with installer tool (B. Vi. 465, Ref. A). The tool will automatically position seal at the correct depth. Install torque converter and secure in place with retaining bracket.

Fig. 32: Checking Differential Assembly Total Preload

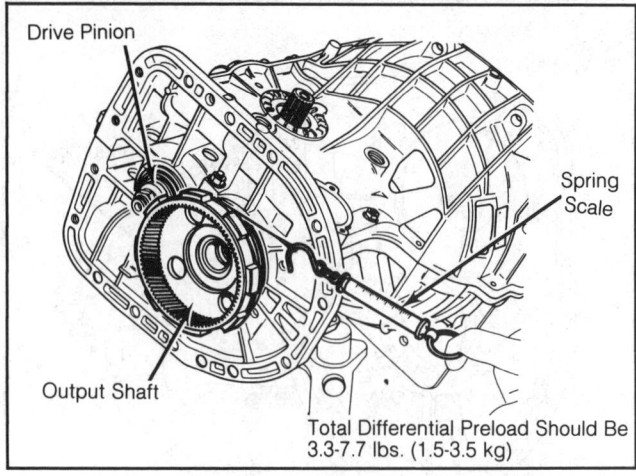

Total Differential Preload Should Be 3.3-7.7 lbs. (1.5-3.5 kg)

TRANSAXLE REASSEMBLY

1) Clean all transaxle components thoroughly. Blow out all oil holes and passages with compressed air. Lubricate all parts with clean ATF fluid before final assembly. Drain torque converter, pump out remaining fluid from center of turbine hub with a syringe and refill with clean fluid. Use Dexron II type transmission fluid only.

2) Support E1 clutch/turbine shaft assembly on a 4" diameter tube, clutch end down, during reassembly. Install needle thrust bearing on turbine shaft, bearing side up. Center clutch discs in E2 clutch and slide clutch assembly into position on turbine shaft.

3) Gently turn clutch assembly, do not force, until all discs are engaged with splines in E1 housing. When properly installed, there will be about .12" (4 mm) play between clutches.

4) Lubricate E2 seal rings and bearing contact surfaces on one-way clutch. Center discs in F2 brake and install complete brake assembly on E2 clutch. Turn brake assembly, without forcing, to engage all discs. Install thrust bearing on sun gear shaft/planetary gear assembly, bearing surface toward splined end of shaft.

Fig. 33: Preparation for Gear Train Installation

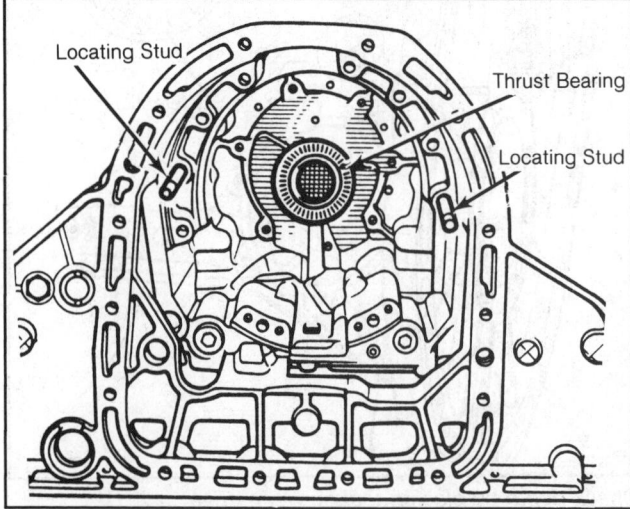

Install thrust bearing and locating studs as shown.

RENAULT FUEGO & 18i (Cont.)

5) Center discs in F1 brake and lower sun gear shaft/planetary gear assembly into place. Turn gently, without forcing, to engage all discs. Install thrust bearing and two .275" (7 mm) diameter locating studs in transmission case. Lubricate seal ring housing and contact surface for one-way clutch hub.

6) Lift gear train assembly by turbine shaft and slowly lower into transmission case. Use locating studs to guide assembly into place. Ensure that one-way clutch hub is lined up properly and fits well up against the case.

7) Remove locating studs. Install retaining bolts removed in step **6)** of *Transaxle Disassembly*. Install parking pawl return spring on shaft. Install parking pawl. Install shaft (threaded hole up), centering dowel and retaining clip.

8) Install main shaft needle thrust bearing in differential housing. Lay a straightedge across output shaft and measure distance "A" from straightedge surface to housing mating surface. Then measure distance "B" from straightedge surface to needle bearing. Subtract "B" from "A" to get distance "C" and record. *See Fig. 34.*

Fig. 34: *Measuring Output Shaft Clearances*

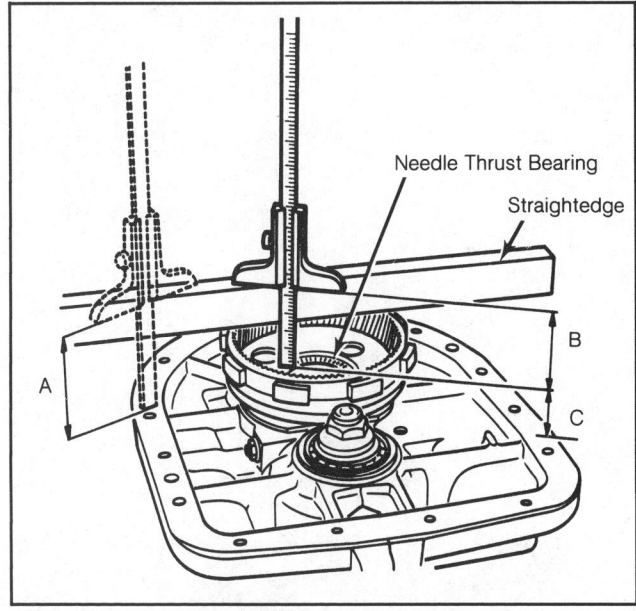

9) Install needle thrust bearing plate onto planetary gear carrier in transmission case. Lay a straightedge across transmission case mating surface and measure distance "E" from straightedge surface to bearing plate. *See Fig. 35.* Subtract straightedge width from "E" to get distance "D" and record. Subtract distance "C" from distance "D" to get total end play.

10) Desired end play is .024" (.6 mm). Subtract .024" (.6 mm) from total end play "D" to determine what thickness adjusting shim to install between needle thrust bearing plate and planetary gear carrier.

11) If end play "D" is less than .024" (.6 mm) or greater than .120" (3.1 mm), check that all needle thrust bearings are in position, sun gears are properly meshed and all discs are properly seated on their splines.

12) Install needle thrust bearing on output shaft in differential case. Install end-play adjusting shim (as determined in previous steps) and needle thrust bearing plate in transmission case. *See Fig. 36.*

Fig. 35: *Measuring Gear Train Clearances*

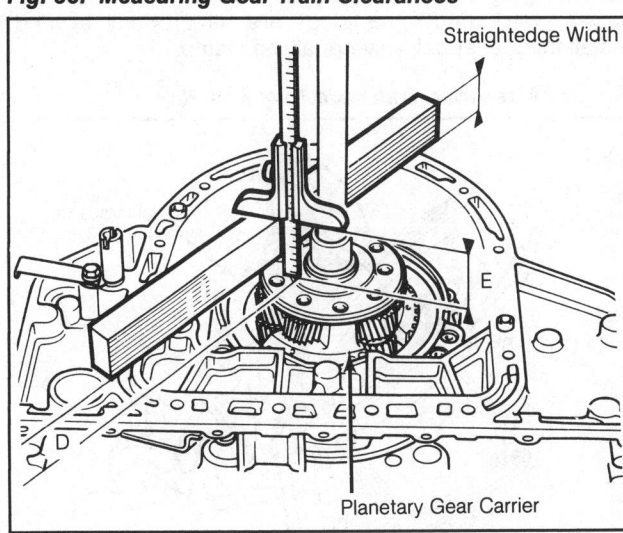

13) Install .28" (7 mm) studs and centering dowels on case. Smear gasket sealer (Perfect Seal) on case surface and install paper gasket (dry). Lubricate turbine shaft and slowly lower differential case onto transmission case.

Fig. 36: *Location of Oil Seal Between Transmission and Differential Cases*

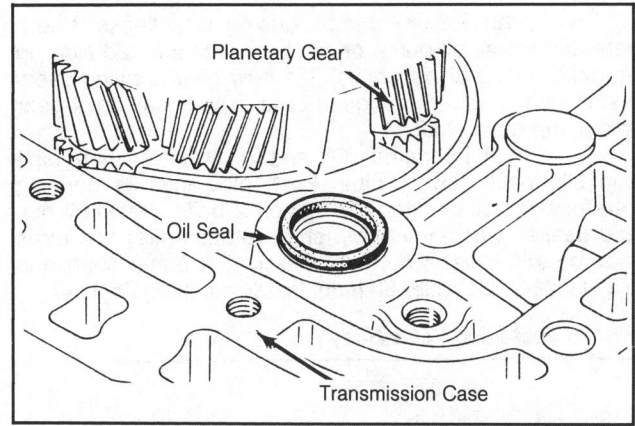

Install seal on transmission case before final assembly.

14) Install a few of the case-to-case retaining bolts and tighten. Install lower cover plate with new gasket (dry). Attach dial indicator to lower cover plate and set indicator tip on E1 clutch shaft. Pull turbine shaft out, zero gauge, push shaft back in and read gauge.

15) End play should be .016-.032" (.4-.8 mm). If play is not to specification, disassemble and replace end play adjusting shim as required. When correct play has been obtained, install remaining case-to-case bolts and tighten.

16) Reverse removal procedures to install shift control linkage and shift shaft. *See Transaxle Disassembly.* Check that valve body mounting surfaces and surfaces on case are clean and smooth. Make sure that centering dowels are in position on valve body and the 2 toothed wheels are properly meshed when in park.

17) Install valve body in housing, engaging the manual valve on shift lever. *See Fig. 38.* Tighten retaining screws in several steps. Install solenoid ball valves and connect plug to sealed plug connector. Check that ball valves, valve body and plugs are all properly aligned. Install magnet at ball valve retaining clamp.

Fig. 37: Measuring Transaxle Total End Play

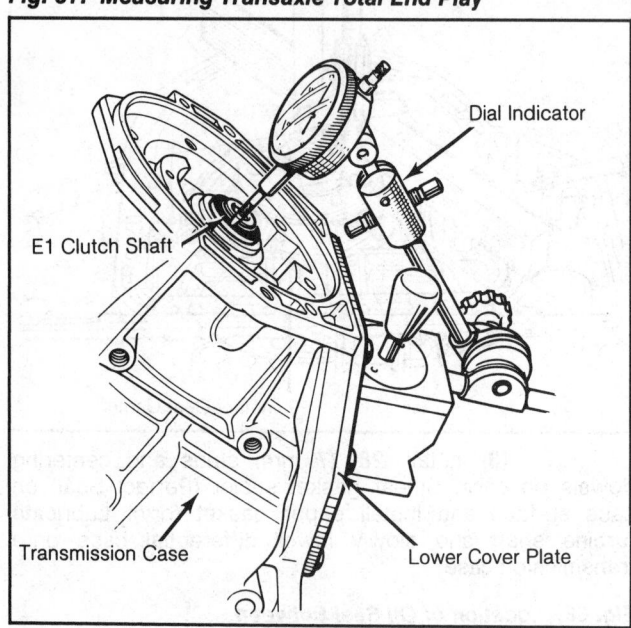

Total end play should be .016-.032" (.4-.8 mm)

18) Ensure pump housing cleanliness. Lubricate and install oil pump driven gear with marked side up (marked during disassembly). If a new gear is being used, install with chamfered edge in case first. Install drive gear and pump drive shaft.

19) Lubricate "O" ring on filter suction pipe and slip over end of pipe. Push pipe into its housing carefully. Install oil filter and tighten 2 bolts. Install oil pan and gasket. Check oil pump shaft rotation (first few turns may be stiff, this is normal). Check that pump shaft end play is .014-.031" (.35-.80 mm). Install pump shaft cover.

Fig. 38 Installing Valve Body

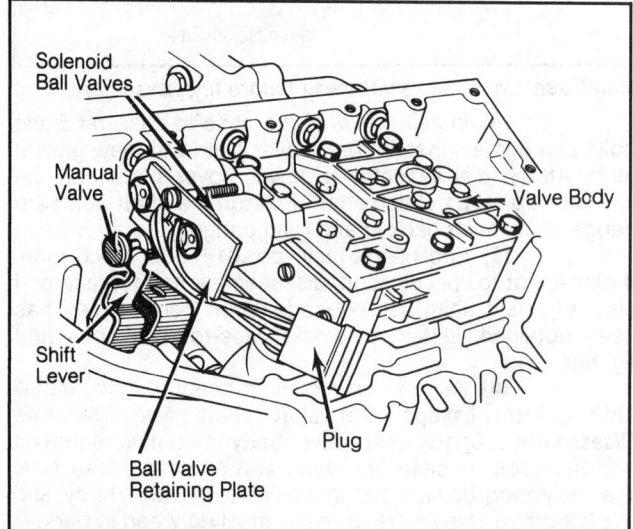

Make sure that shift lever and manual valve are properly engaged.

TIGHTENING SPECIFICATIONS

Application	Ft. Lbs. (N.m)
Torque Converter-to-Drive Plate	
Fuego	30 (42)
18i	24 (33)
Drive Plate-to-Crankshaft	50 (68)
Ring Gear-to-Differential Case	74 (101)
Drive Pinion Lock Nut	110 (150)
Half Housing-to-Half Housing	
Inner	22 (30)
Outer	14 (19)
	INCH Lbs. (N.m)
Transmission Housing-to-Differential Housing	180 (20)
Stator Support	180 (20)
Oil Pump Cover	96 (11)
Valve Body Bolts	60 (7)
Lower Cover Plate	72 (8)
Brake Retaining Bolts	96 (11)

SAAB — BORG-WARNER MODEL 37

900, 900S, 900 Turbo

TRANSAXLE IDENTIFICATION

The transaxle identification number is stamped on a plate attached to torque converter housing near throttle cable.

DESCRIPTION

The transaxle assembly is a three-speed unit mounted beneath the engine. Transaxle assembly consists basically of a three-element torque converter, planetary gear set, two multi-disc clutches, a one-way clutch, two servos and brake bands, an oil pump, a hydraulic control system and a differential-type final drive assembly. Power is transmitted from the turbine shaft of torque converter to the input shaft of transmission via a chain.

LUBRICATION & ADJUSTMENT

See the appropriate article in AUTOMATIC TRANSMISSION SERVICING Section.

TROUBLE SHOOTING

NO DRIVE IN ANY LEVER POSITION

Incorrect fluid level. Manual linkage incorrectly adjusted or assembled. Oil tubes missing or incorrectly installed. Sealing ring missing or broken. Valve body screws missing or improperly tightened. Primary regulator valve sticking. Input shaft broken. Pump drive tangs on converter hub broken. Defective oil pump. Defective converter or one-way clutch. Stator support broken.

NO DRIVE IN FORWARD RANGES

Manual linkage incorrectly adjusted or assembled. Sealing rings missing or broken. Valve body screw missing or improperly tightened. Defective front clutch. One-way clutch slipping or incorrectly installed.

NO DRIVE IN REVERSE RANGE

Manual linkage incorrectly adjusted or assembled. Incorrect rear band adjustment. Oil tubes missing or installed incorrectly. Sealing rings missing or broken. Valve body screws missing or improperly tightened. 1-2 shift valve or 2-3 shift valve sticking. Defective rear clutch or rear band.

HARSH ENGAGEMENT

Downshift valve cable incorrectly assembled or adjusted. Incorrect engine idle speed. Valve body screws missing or improperly tightened. Primary regulator valve sticking. Throttle valve sticking. Defective front clutch. Defective rear clutch.

DELAYED ENGAGEMENT

Incorrect fluid level. Manual linkage incorrectly adjusted or assembled. Incorrect engine idle speed. Oil tubes missing or incorrectly installed. Sealing rings missing or broken. Valve body screws missing or improperly tightened. Primary regulator valve sticking. Converter

Fig. 1: Saab (Borg-Warner Model 37) Hydraulic Circuits Diagram

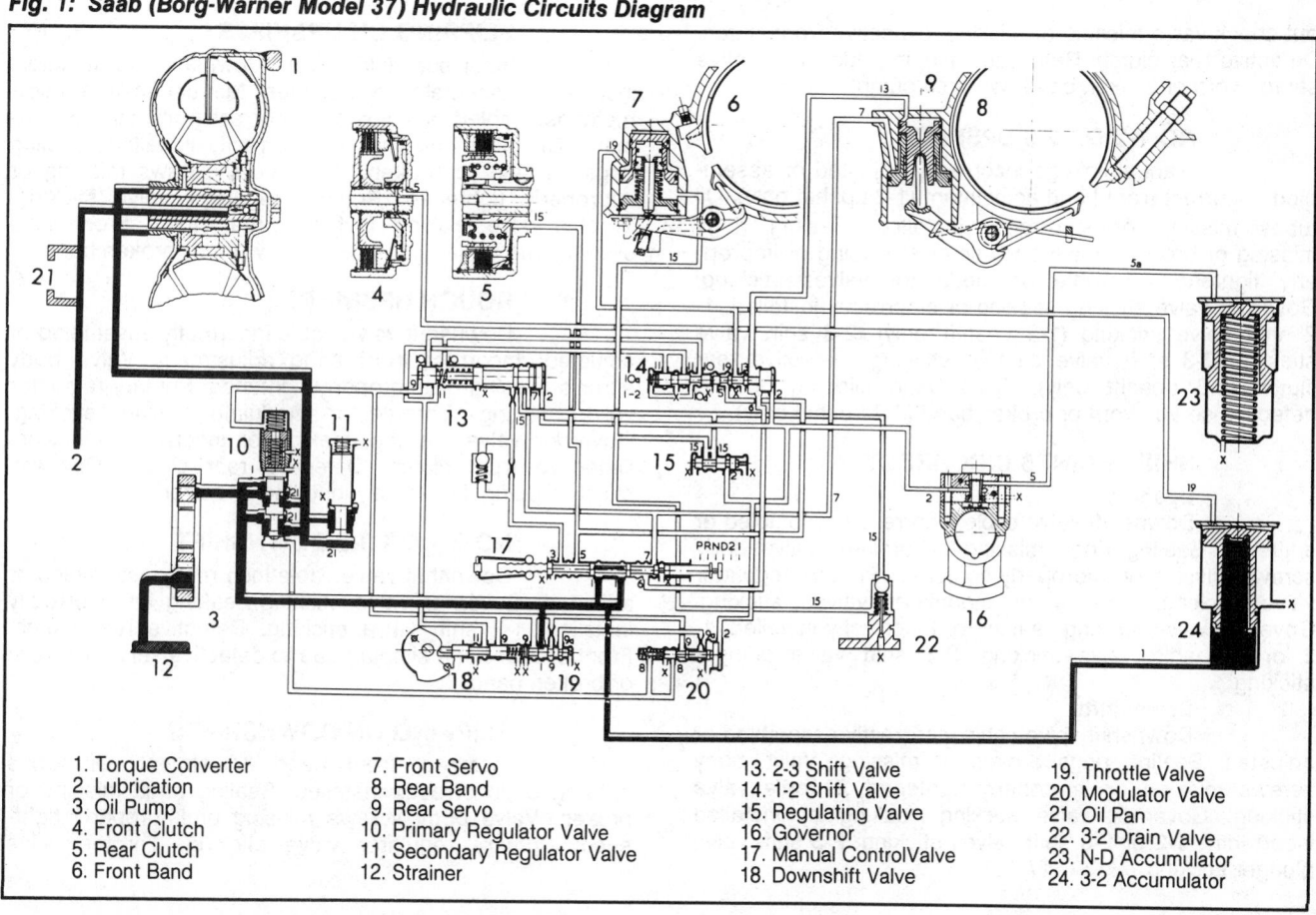

1. Torque Converter	7. Front Servo	13. 2-3 Shift Valve	19. Throttle Valve
2. Lubrication	8. Rear Band	14. 1-2 Shift Valve	20. Modulator Valve
3. Oil Pump	9. Rear Servo	15. Regulating Valve	21. Oil Pan
4. Front Clutch	10. Primary Regulator Valve	16. Governor	22. 3-2 Drain Valve
5. Rear Clutch	11. Secondary Regulator Valve	17. Manual ControlValve	23. N-D Accumulator
6. Front Band	12. Strainer	18. Downshift Valve	24. 3-2 Accumulator

Automatic Transmissions

SAAB — BORG-WARNER MODEL 37 (Cont.)

Fig. 2: *Cutaway View of Saab (Borg-Warner Model 37) Automatic Transaxle Assembly Showing Relative Positions of Clutch Packs, Drive Bands and Major Transmission Components*

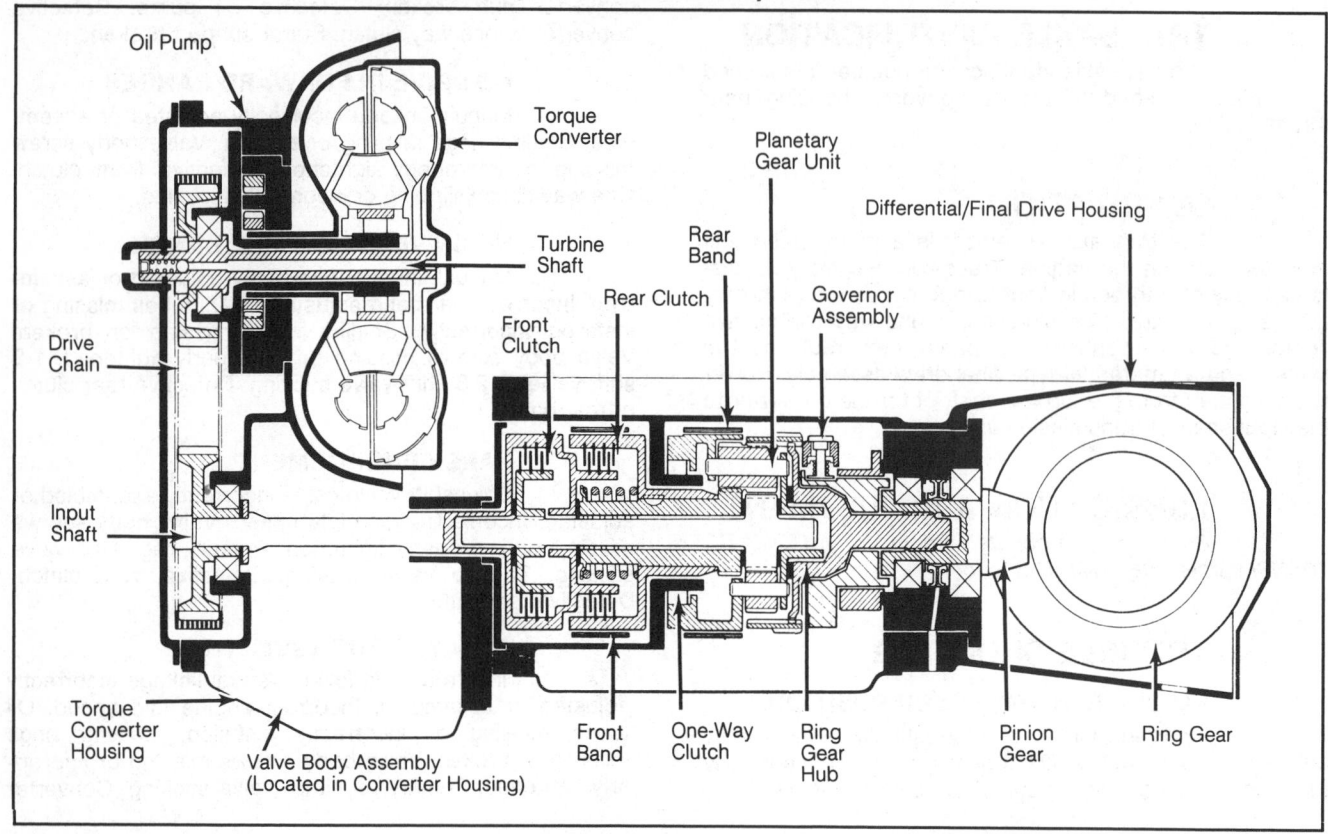

out check valve missing or sticking. Defective front clutch. Defective rear clutch. Rear band slipping due to defective servo, worn or broken band. Worn oil pump.

NO 1-2 OR 2-3 UPSHIFT

Manual linkage incorrectly adjusted or assembled. Incorrect front band adjustment (1-2 upshift only). Oil tubes missing or incorrectly installed. Sealing rings missing or broken. Valve body screws missing or improperly tightened. Throttle or modulator valves sticking. Governor valve sticking, leaking or incorrectly installed. 1-2 shift valve sticking (1-2 upshift only). 2-3 shift valve sticking. 2-3 shift valve plunger sticking. Defective rear clutch (2-3 upshift only). Front band slipping due to defective servo, worn or broken band (1-2 upshift only).

SHIFT POINTS INCORRECT
Upshifts

Downshift valve cable incorrectly assembled or adjusted. Sealing rings missing or broken. Valve body screws missing or improperly tightened. Primary regulator valve sticking. Throttle or modulator valves sticking. Governor valve sticking, leaking or incorrectly installed. 1-2 or 2-3 shift valve sticking. 2-3 shift valve plunger sticking.

Downshifts

Downshift valve cable incorrectly assembled or adjusted. Sealing rings broken or missing. Valve body screws missing or improperly tightened. Throttle valve sticking. Governor valve sticking, leaking or installed incorrectly. 1-2 or 2-3 shift valves sticking. 2-3 shift valve plunger sticking.

SLIPPING ON UPSHIFTS

Incorrect fluid level. Downshift valve cable incorrectly assembled or adjusted. Manual linkage incorrectly assembled or adjusted. Incorrect front band adjustment. Oil tubes missing or incorrectly installed. Sealing rings missing or broken. Valve body screws missing or improperly tightened. Primary regulator valve sticking. Throttle valve sticking. Defective rear clutch. Front band slipping due to defective servo, or worn or broken band.

ROUGH UPSHIFTS

Downshift valve cable incorrectly assembled or adjusted. Incorrect front band adjustment. Valve body screws missing or improperly tightened. Primary regulator valve sticking. Throttle or modulator valves sticking. Governor valve sticking, leaking or incorrectly installed. Defective front clutch. Defective rear clutch. One-way clutch slipping, incorrectly installed or seized.

NO 2-1 OR 3-2 DOWNSHIFT

Downshift valve cable incorrectly assembled or adjusted. Governor valve sticking, leaking or incorrectly installed. 1-2 shift valve sticking. Defective rear clutch. Front or rear band slipping due to defective servo, or worn or broken band.

SLIPPING ON DOWNSHIFTS

Incorrect front band adjustment. Oil tubes missing or incorrectly installed. Sealing rings missing or broken. Valve body screws missing or improperly tightened. Primary regulator valve sticking. Throttle valve

SAAB — BORG-WARNER MODEL 37 (Cont.)

sticking. Orifice control valve sticking. Defective rear clutch. Front clutch slipping due to defective servo, or worn or broken band. One-way clutch slipping.

ROUGH DOWNSHIFTS

Incorrect front band adjustment. Sealing rings missing or broken. Valve body screws missing or improperly tightened. Primary regulator valve sticking. Throttle valve sticking. Orifice control valve sticking. Defective front clutch. Defective rear clutch. Front band slipping due to defective servo, or worn or broken band. One-way clutch slipping or incorrectly installed.

TRANSMISSION OVERHEATING

Incorrect fluid level. Incorrect front or rear band adjustment. Defective converter or one-way clutch. Broken stator support.

TESTING

ROAD TEST

1) Before road test, ensure that fluid level and condition, and control linkage adjustments have been checked and corrected as necessary. During test, transmission should upshift and downshift at approximately same speed as shown in *Shift Speeds Chart*. All shifts may vary slightly due to production tolerances or tire size. The important factor is the quality of the shifts. All shifts should be smooth, responsive, and with no slippage or engine speed runaway.

2) Slippage or engine speed runaway in any gear usually indicates clutch or band problems. The slipping clutch or band in a particular gear can usually be identified by noting transmission operation in other selector positions and comparing internal units which are applied in these positions. *See Clutch and Band Application Chart.*

3) With vehicle at a standstill, accelerate both at minimum and full throttle and ensure a 1-2 and 2-3 shift occurs.

NOTE: At minimum throttle opening, shifts may be difficult to detect. Confirmation that transmis-

sion is in third gear may be obtained by shifting to "2" when a 3-2 downshift should occur.

4) With vehicle at 25 MPH in third gear, depress accelerator to full throttle position (not through detent). Vehicle should accelerate without a downshift. With vehicle at 30 MPH in third gear, depress accelerator through detent. Vehicle should downshift to second gear before accelerating.

5) With vehicle at 40 MPH, release accelerator and move selector lever to "2". Vehicle should downshift to second gear and engine braking should be noticed. Finally, check reverse operation by accelerating at full throttle and check for slipping.

SHIFT SPEEDS CHART

| Application | Shift Points (MPH) | |
	Minimum Throttle	Full Throttle
1-2 Upshift	9-16	40-46
2-3 Upshift		
Turbo Models	12-19	73-81
All Other Models	12-19	67-75
3-2 Downshift		
Turbo Models		[1] 61-72
All Other Models		[1] 56-65
2-1 Downshift	1-11	[1] 27-36

[1] — Kickdown.

STALL TEST

Testing Precautions

When making test, do not hold throttle open any longer than 10 seconds. If engine speed exceeds limits shown in *Stall Speeds table*, release accelerator immediately as clutch or band slippage is indicated.

Testing Procedure

With engine at normal operating temperature, tachometer installed and parking and service brakes applied, make transmission stall test in "D", "1" and "R" ranges at full throttle and note maximum RPM obtained. Engine speed should be within limits shown in *Stall Speeds table*.

CLUTCH AND BAND APPLICATION CHART (ELEMENTS IN USE)

Selector Lever Position	Forward Clutch	Front Band	Rear Clutch	Rear Band	One-Way Clutch
D — DRIVE					
First Gear	X				X
Second Gear	X	X			
Third Gear	X		X		
2 — INTERMEDIATE					
First Gear	X				X
Second Gear	X	X			
1 — LOW (First)	X			X	X
R — REVERSE			X	X	

NEUTRAL OR PARK — All clutches, brakes, and bands released and/or ineffective.

SAAB — BORG-WARNER MODEL 37 (Cont.)

STALL SPEED SPECIFICATIONS

Application	Stall RPM
900, 900S	2150-2550
900 Turbo	2100-2600

Stall Test Results

If stall speed is about 300 RPM below specifications, engine is not operating at full power. If stall speed is about 800 RPM below specifications, stator one-way clutch in torque converter may be damaged or slipping. If stall speed is above specifications in "D", either front clutch or one-way clutch is defective. If stall speed is too high in "1" position, front clutch is slipping, and if too high in "R", either the rear clutch or rear band is slipping.

REMOVAL & INSTALLATION

See the appropriate article in AUTOMATIC TRANSMISSION REMOVAL Section.

Fig. 3: Engine-to-Transaxle Mating Surface Bolt Pattern

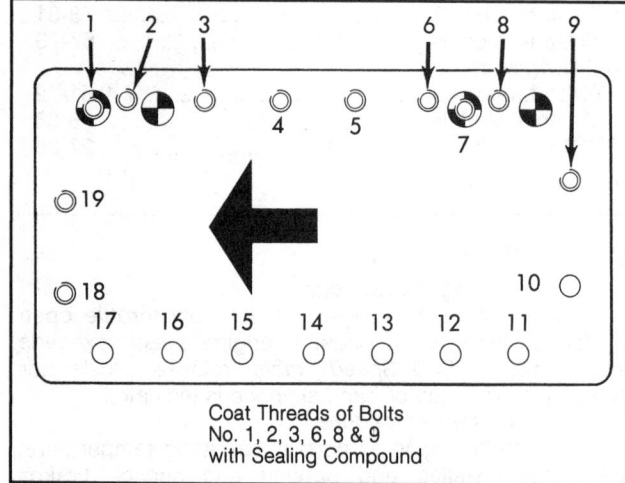

Coat Threads of Bolts
No. 1, 2, 3, 6, 8 & 9
with Sealing Compound

TORQUE CONVERTER

NOTE: Torque converter is a sealed unit and cannot be disassembled for service; therefore it must be replaced as a unit if found defective. Ventilation holes in torque converter housing must be kept free from dirt.

TRANSAXLE DISASSEMBLY

1) Separate transaxle assembly from engine and mount on transmission stand (78 60 794). Attach torque converter support (87 90 255). Drain fluid from transmission and final drive unit. Remove all covers (5) from assembly. Remove sealing ring from turbine shaft. Hold drive chain sprockets stationary and remove sprocket attaching bolts. Remove drive chain and sprockets.

2) Turn transmission upside down. Remove oil screen and magnet. Remove oil tubes connecting front and rear sumps. Remove throttle valve cable. Remove oil pump strainer. Remove all oil tubes except the 2 from drain valve to servo piston. Remove valve body retaining bolts and lift out valve body. Remove accumulator piston

Fig. 4: Removing Drive Chain and Sprockets

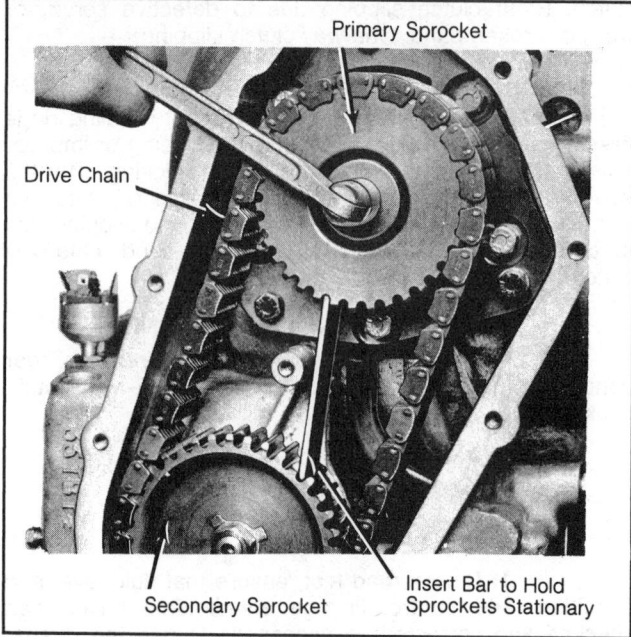

(under valve body). Remove torque converter housing-to-transaxle housing attaching bolts. While holding parking pawl away from gear with screwdriver, remove torque converter housing and gasket. If necessary, tap housing with plastic hammer to separate.

Fig. 5: Bottom View of Torque Converter Case Showing Location of Connecting Tubes, Oil Screen and Oil Pump Strainer

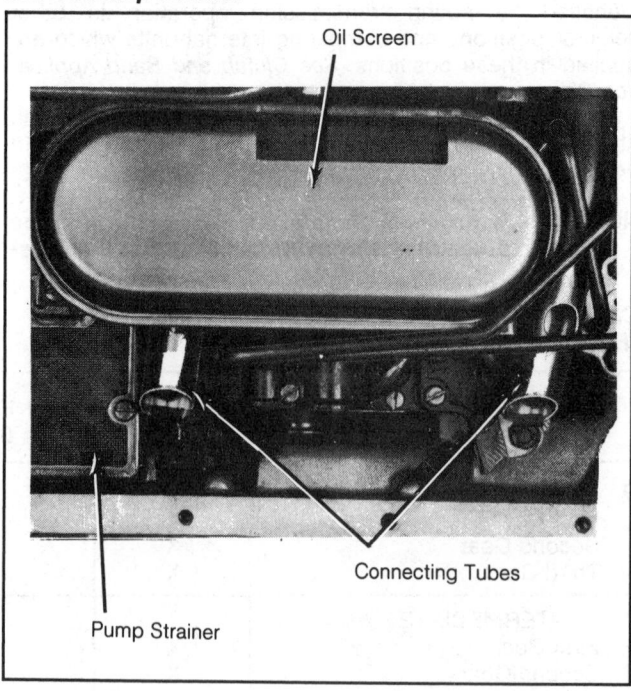

3) Pry out front band pivot shaft with screwdriver. Remove band lever and strut. Remove self adjusting screw. Unhook rear band lever tension spring. Remove pivot shaft toward front of case. Use a strong screwdriver to push out shaft. Remove the band lever and

SAAB — BORG-WARNER MODEL 37 (Cont.)

Fig. 6: Bottom View of Transaxle Case Showing Positions of Band Levers, Rear Band Tension Spring and Pivot Shafts

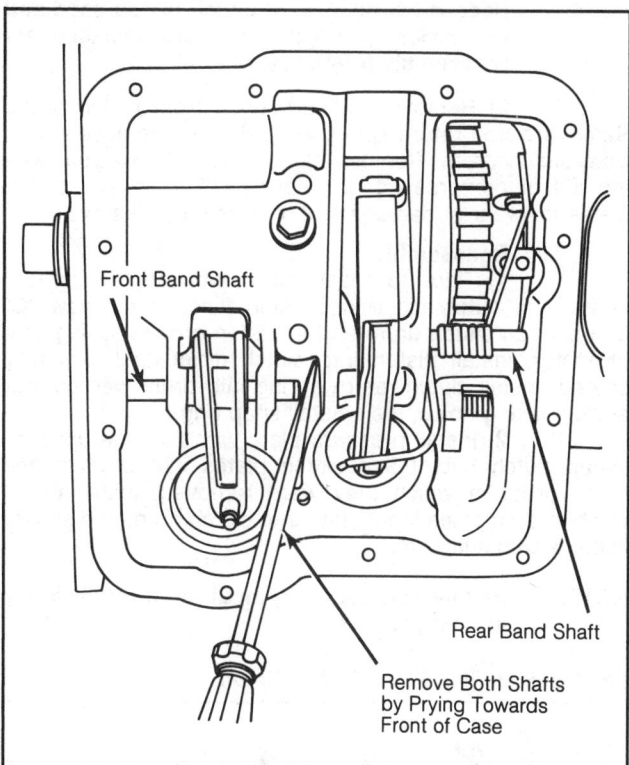

Front Band Shaft

Rear Band Shaft

Remove Both Shafts by Prying Towards Front of Case

the strut. Remove the 3 bolts securing center support to transaxle housing. Attach sprocket and nut to input shaft. Tap sprocket to loosen cover and remove front clutch.

Fig. 7: Removing Front Servo Piston Using Compressed Air

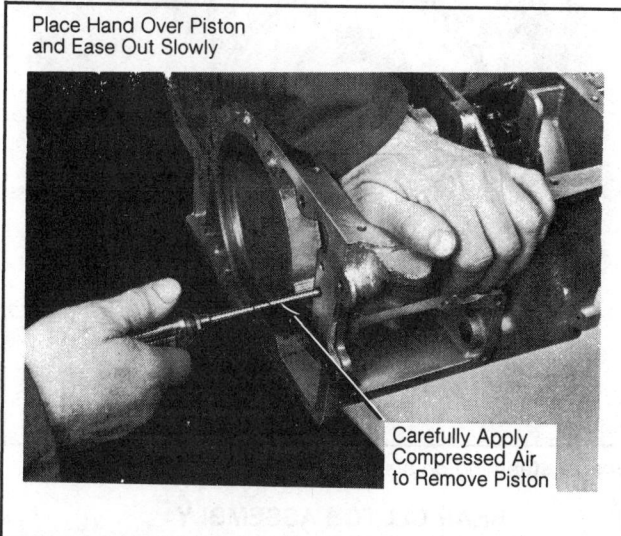

Place Hand Over Piston and Ease Out Slowly

Carefully Apply Compressed Air to Remove Piston

Place hand over piston to prevent possible damage.

4) Remove rear clutch assembly and sun gear shaft. Save shaft bearing and thrust washers for reassembly. Remove front and rear bands, planetary gear assembly and the center support. Remove the front servo snap ring. Using compressed air, remove front servo piston. Remove the rear servo piston in the same manner.

Fig. 8: Using Compressed Air to Remove Rear Servo Piston

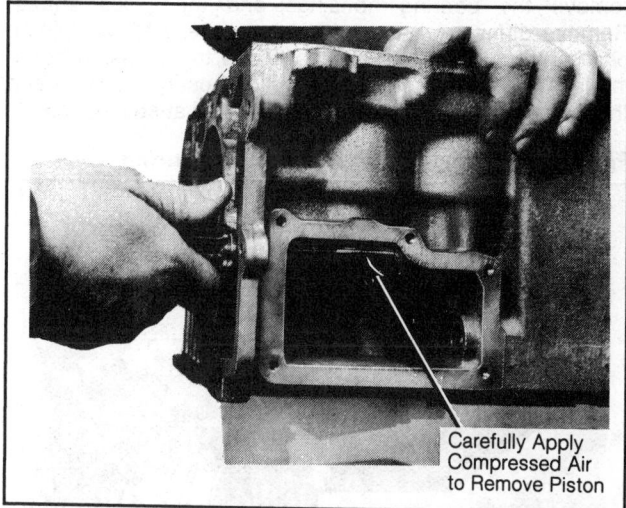

Carefully Apply Compressed Air to Remove Piston

Place hand over piston and ease out gently.

5) Install a long bolt (87 90 958) through middle of ring gear hub. Press off hub, governor and pinion output shaft by slowly tightening bolt. Use parking pawl to hold hub during removal. Do not remove parking pawl unless it is to be replaced. If necessary, remove snap ring from pivot shaft, push out shaft and remove pawl and spring.

NOTE: Before disassembling final drive unit, measure and record backlash and position of the pinion for reassembly reference. *See Adjustment procedures in Transaxle Reassembly.* If ring and pinion gear assembly has been installed for less than 6,000 miles, follow normal adjustment procedures on reassembly. If assembly has been installed for longer than 6,000 miles, adjust to recorded measurements.

Fig. 9: Removing Ring Gear Hub, Governor & Output Shaft

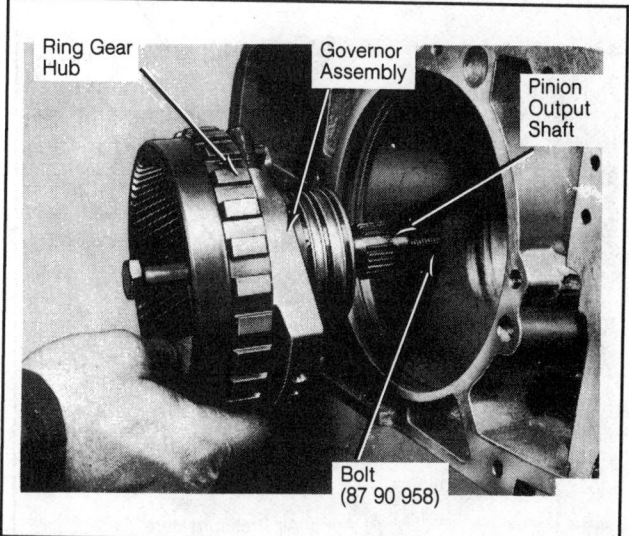

Ring Gear Hub

Governor Assembly

Pinion Output Shaft

Bolt (87 90 958)

Tighten bolt through center of assembly to press off components.

SAAB — BORG-WARNER MODEL 37 (Cont.)

6) Remove differential bearing housing retaining bolts (both sides). Using a puller and slide hammer, remove the bearing housings and their axle shafts. Remove differential assembly from case. Remove pinion bearing housing retaining bolts. Place transmission housing in press and press out the pinion bearing housing and the pinion seal housing (pressure applied at seal housing).

Fig. 10: Removing Differential Bearing Housing

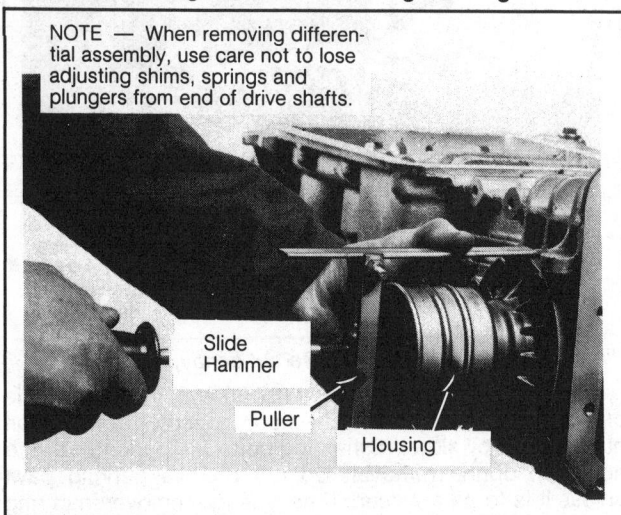

Use slide hammer and puller to detach bearing housing/axle shaft assembly.

COMPONENT DISASSEMBLY & REASSEMBLY

FRONT CLUTCH ASSEMBLY
Disassembly
1) Slide clutch sealing plate from input shaft. Remove snap ring and lift input shaft and thrust washer

Fig. 11: Removing Front Clutch Piston Using Compressed Air

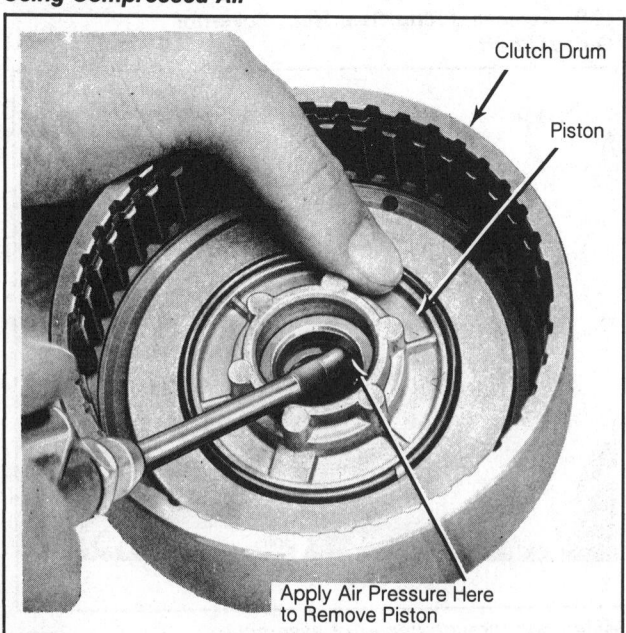

from clutch drum. Lift out clutch hub and clutch plates from drum.

NOTE: Record the number of clutch plates used and the order in which they are installed for reassembly reference.

2) Remove pressure plate from clutch drum. Remove piston return spring snap ring and remove spring from clutch drum. Remove clutch piston from drum with the aid of compressed air. Inspect all seals and clutch plates for wear or damage and replace if necessary.

Reassembly
1) Prior to reassembly, lubricate all components with automatic transmission fluid. Install new "O" ring seal on clutch drum and in piston groove. Using seal protector, install piston into clutch drum until it is fully seated. Install clutch return spring into drum with convex portion facing down, then install snap ring.

2) Install pressure plate with flat side up, then install clutch hub. Place clutch plates into drum in the same order in which they were removed. Install thrust washer, then place input shaft into clutch drum and secure in place with snap ring.

NOTE: Ensure seal rings on input shaft rotate freely in their grooves.

Fig. 12: Installing Front Clutch Piston

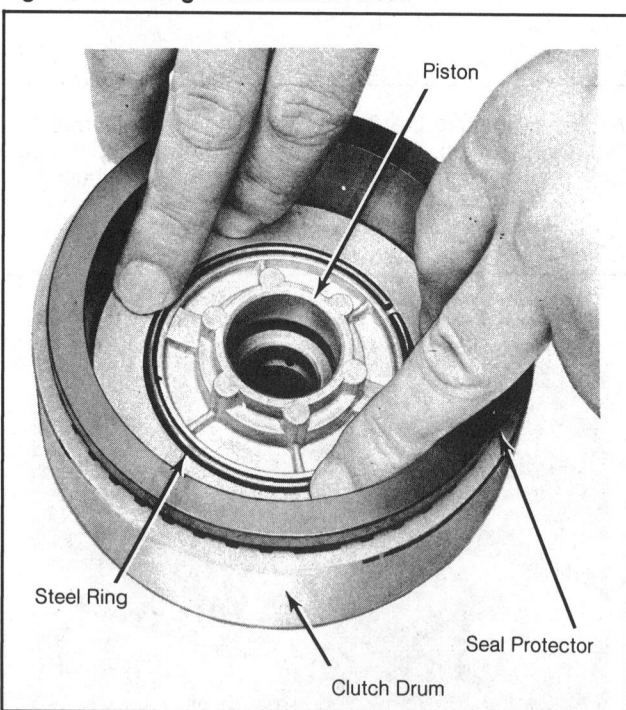

Ensure steel ring on piston is fully seated.

REAR CLUTCH ASSEMBLY
Disassembly
Remove clutch drum snap ring. Remove pressure plate and clutch plates, noting number of clutch plates used and order of installation for reassembly reference. Install clutch spring compressor (87 90 018) and remove clutch return spring snap ring, spring seat and return spring. Use compressed air to remove piston.

SAAB — BORG-WARNER MODEL 37 (Cont.)

Fig. 13: *Exploded View of Front Clutch Assembly and Input Shaft*

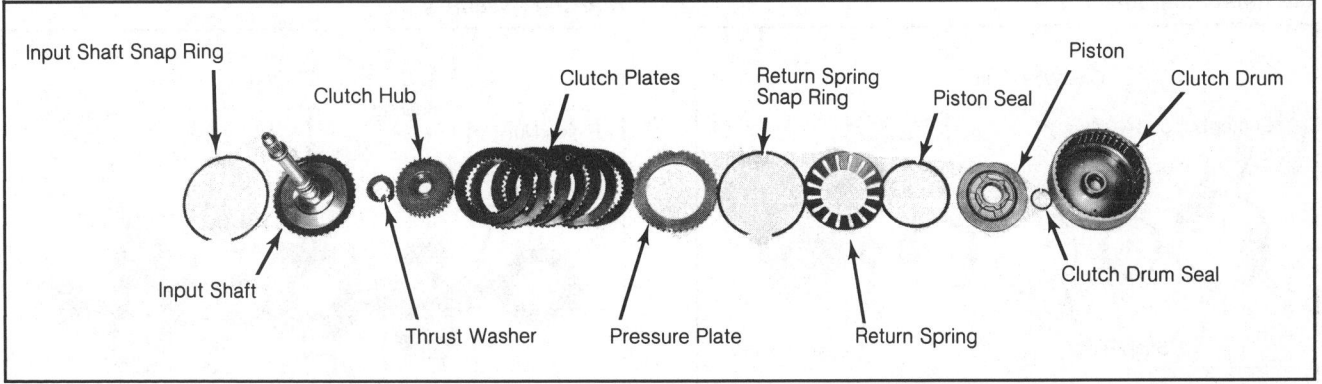

Fig. 14: *Removing Rear Clutch Return Spring Snap Ring Using Clutch Spring Compressor and Snap Ring Pliers*

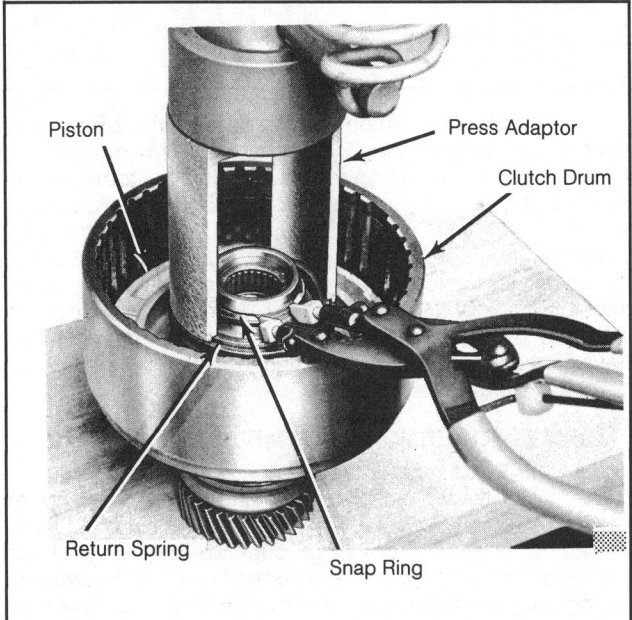

Fig. 15: *Using Compressed Air to Remove Rear Clutch Piston*

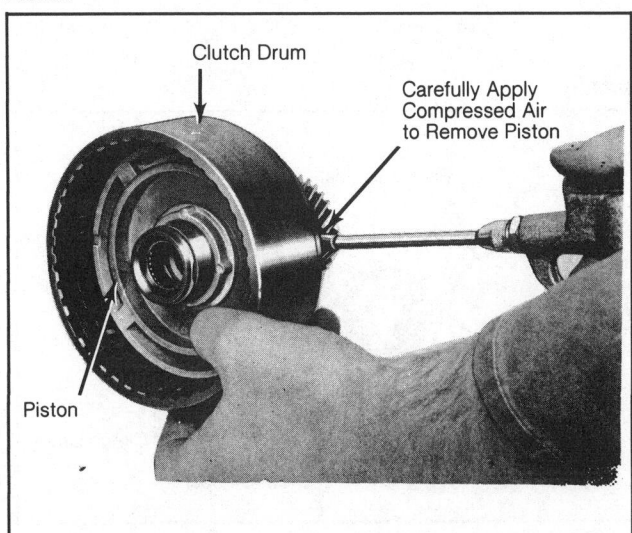

NOTE: Lubricate all parts with ATF fluid before reassembly. Inner clutch plates must be soaked in ATF fluid before final installation.

Reassembly

1) Using a seal protector (87 90 099), install piston (flat side down) until fully seated. Install return spring and spring seat. Compress return spring and install snap ring.

2) Assemble clutch plates, pressure plate and snap ring. Apply load to pressure plate, and measure clearance between pressure plate and snap ring. Clearance should be .025-.045" (.63-1.14 mm). If clearance is .046-.064" (1.17-1.63 mm), install a thicker snap ring. If clearance exceeds .064" (1.63 mm), install 2 thin snap rings. If clearance is below specification, replace the greatly concave plates with slightly flatter plates (one at a time) until correct clearance is obtained.

Fig. 16: *Rear Clutch Plate Positions*

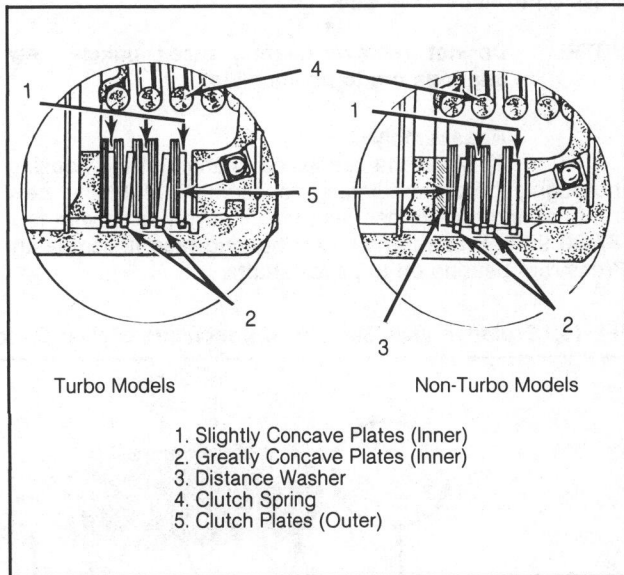

Turbo Models   Non-Turbo Models

1. Slightly Concave Plates (Inner)
2. Greatly Concave Plates (Inner)
3. Distance Washer
4. Clutch Spring
5. Clutch Plates (Outer)

Install plates in order shown.

PLANETARY GEAR ASSEMBLY
Disassembly

Remove center support from planetary gear assembly. Remove one-way clutch from outer race. Remove snap ring for one-way clutch outer race and remove race from planet carrier.

SAAB — BORG-WARNER MODEL 37 (Cont.)

Fig. 17: Exploded View of Gear Unit and Center Support

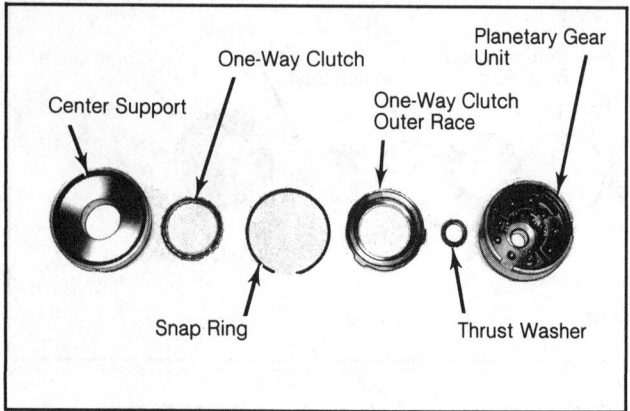

Reassembly

Install one-way clutch outer race and secure in place with snap ring. Install one-way clutch, with flange on inner roller retainer facing outwards, into outer race. Install center support. After reassembly, one-way clutch should rotate in a clockwise direction only.

PINION BEARING HOUSING

Disassembly

1) Remove pinion bearing housing seal cover and "O" ring. Fit housing in holding fixture (87 90 636 and retaining ring 87 90 651) and clamp fixture in vise. Install two 8 mm bolts in holes in holding fixture to act as stops for bearing housing. Remove pinion nut. Remove pinion from housing and press off rear pinion bearing.

2) Heat pinion bearing housing to about 210°F (100°C). Carefully pull out the rear bearing race with tool (87 90 966) and slide hammer. Remove pinion seals, and press off front bearing race.

NOTE: Do not remove bearing races unless new bearings are to be installed.

Reassembly

1) Clean the ventilation channel of the housing thoroughly before beginning reassembly. Press in new front bearing race (if needed). Install pinion seals with tool (87 90 900). Press in new rear bearing race (if removed). Press rear bearing on to pinion shaft.

Fig. 19: Exploded View of Pinion Bearing Housing Assembly

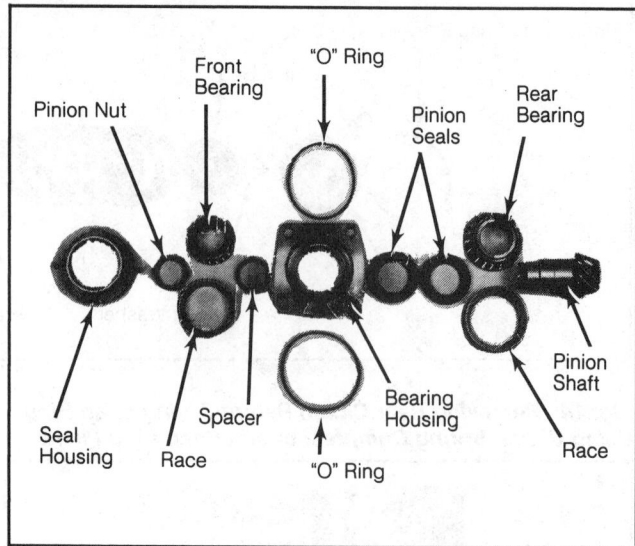

2) Install pinion shaft in bearing housing. Install spacer and front bearing. Oil threads of pinion shaft and install nut. Place complete assembly in tools as in disassembly and place in vise. Oil bearing and torque nut.

3) Check bearing preload. Preload for new bearings should be 19-24 INCH lbs. (2.2-2.7 N.m). For old bearings (with more than 1200 miles service), preload should be 8-13 INCH lbs. (.9-1.5 N.m). Preload can be adjusted by installing a new spacer of difference thickness. Spacers are available in thicknesses of .112 to .149" (2.85 to 3.78 mm).

GOVERNOR ASSEMBLY

Disassembly

Remove screws attaching governor body to housing. Remove cover plate. Remove retaining clip and weight from end of governor shaft. Separate governor body from housing. Remove governor shaft with valve and spring. Inspect all parts for wear or damage. Scratches on governor valve may be cleaned with fine emery cloth.

Fig. 18: Exploded View Showing Components of Rear Clutch Assembly

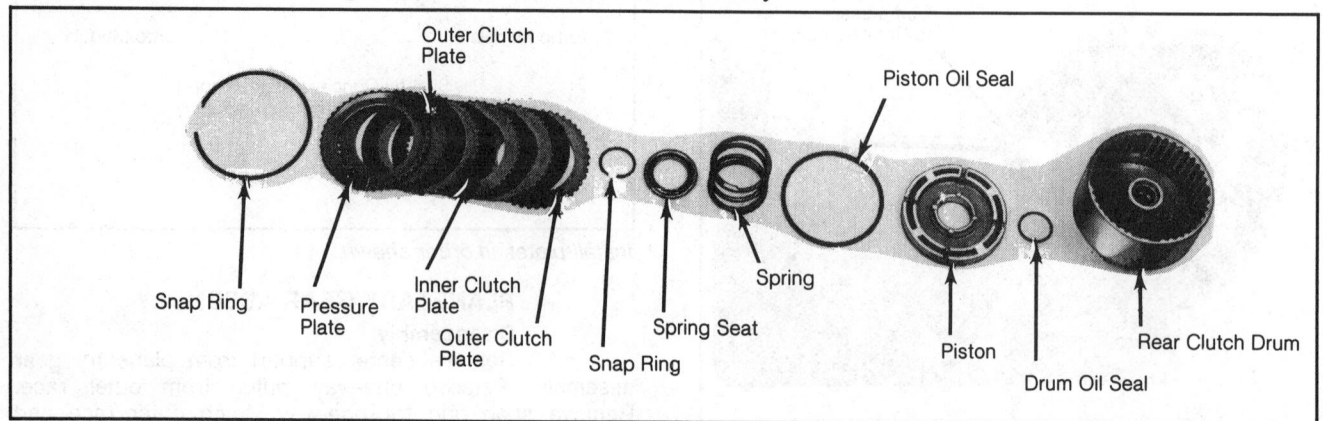

SAAB — BORG-WARNER MODEL 37 (Cont.)

Fig. 20: Exploded View of Governor Assembly

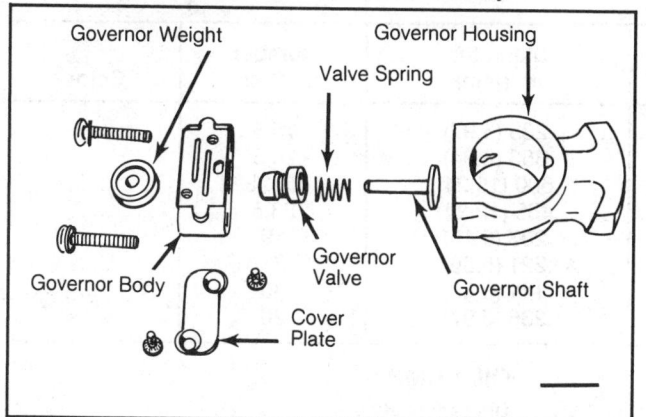

CAUTION: Valves and springs are not interchangeable; all parts must be installed in correct order in proper valve body bore. See Fig. 21.

Disassembly

1) Remove retaining screws and lift off downshift valve carrier and cam assembly. Pull out manual valve. Remove the kickdown valve and the throttle valve and springs. Remove the 7 upper-to-lower valve body retaining screws from the top of the assembly and 2 screws from the bottom. Separate upper and lower valve bodies. Remove 8 oil pipe plate-to-valve body retaining screws. Remove dividing plate, taking care not to lose check ball and spring from lower valve body.

2) Remove orifice control valve stop and valve. Remove modulator valve plug retaining pin. Remove valves and springs. Remove end plate retaining screws (3). Remove the primary and secondary regulator valves. Remove upper valve body cover screws. Remove cover. Remove 1-2 shift valve and 2-3 shift valve assemblies.

Reassembly

Before reassembly, lubricate all parts with automatic transmission fluid. To reassemble, reverse disassembly procedure. After reassembly, ensure governor valve moves freely.

Reassembly

1) Reverse disassembly procedure and note the following: Before reassembly, ensure that all components are thoroughly cleaned and are free from scratches. Small scratches on valves and valve body bores may be removed with fine emery cloth.

VALVE BODY ASSEMBLY

NOTE: As valve trains are removed from each valve body bore, place individual parts in correct order and in relative position to valve body to simplify reassembly.

Fig. 21: Exploded View of Upper and Lower Valve Body Assembly

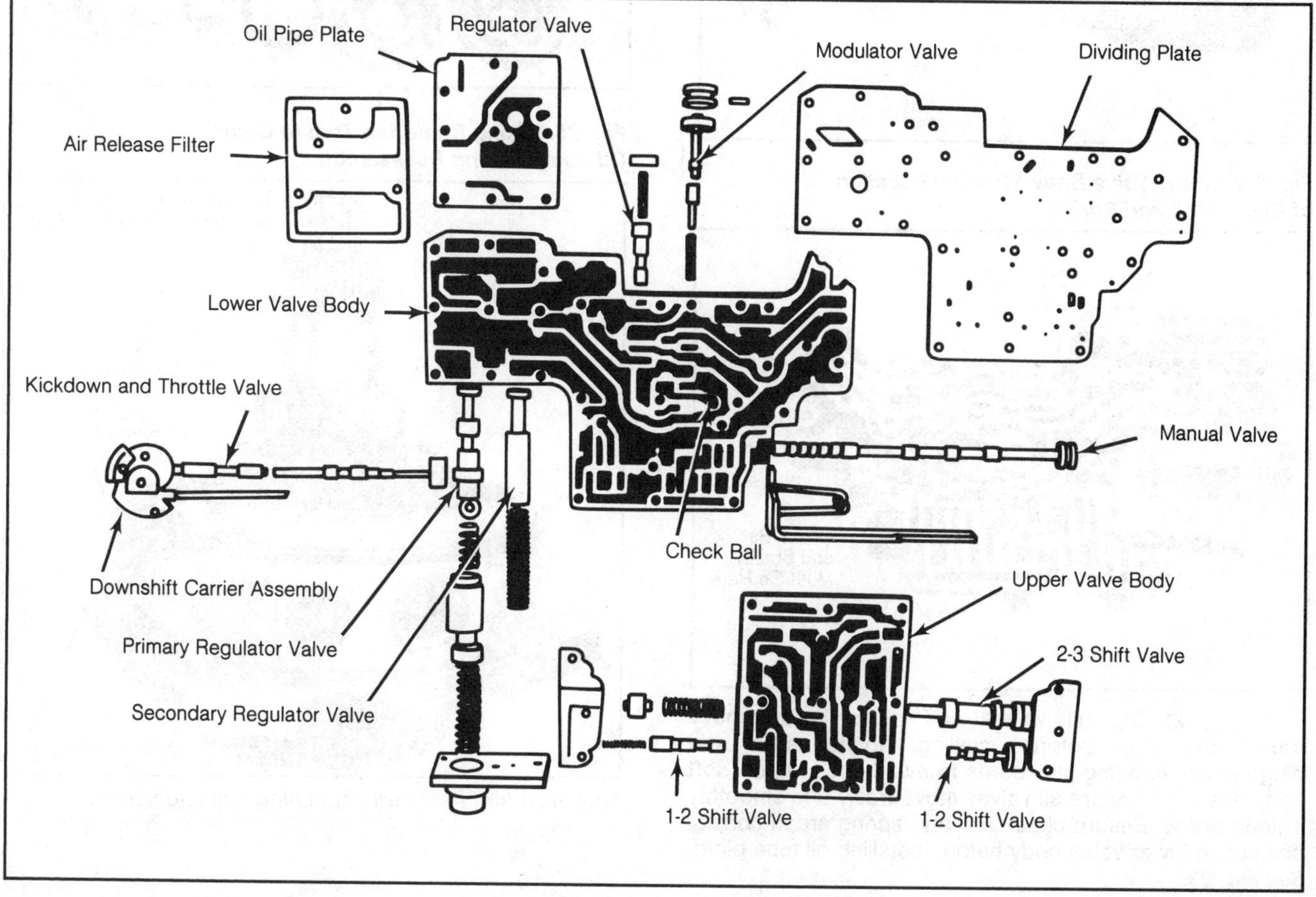

SAAB — BORG-WARNER MODEL 37 (Cont.)

SAAB VALVE BODY SPRING IDENTIFICATION CHART

Valve Spring	Length In. (mm)	Diameter In. (mm)	Number Of Coils	Color
1-2 Shift Valve	1.094 (27.8)	.235 (5.97)	15.5	.....
2-3 Shift Valve	1.590 (40.4)	.352 (8.94)	24.5	.....
Primary Regulator Valve	2.850 (72.4)	.600 (15.24)	16.25	.....
Secondary Regulator Valve	2.593 (65.9)	.485 (12.24)	23.5	.....
Orifice Control Valve	1.005 (25.53)	.203 (5.16)	19	.....
Modulator Valve	1.0069 (27.15)	.221 (5.36)	21	.....
Throttle Valve (Inner)	.807 (20.5)	.141 (3.58)	30	.....
Throttle Valve (Outer)	1.185 (30.1)	.236 (5.97)	20	.....

Fig. 22: View of Lower Valve Body Showing Downshift Carrier Assembly

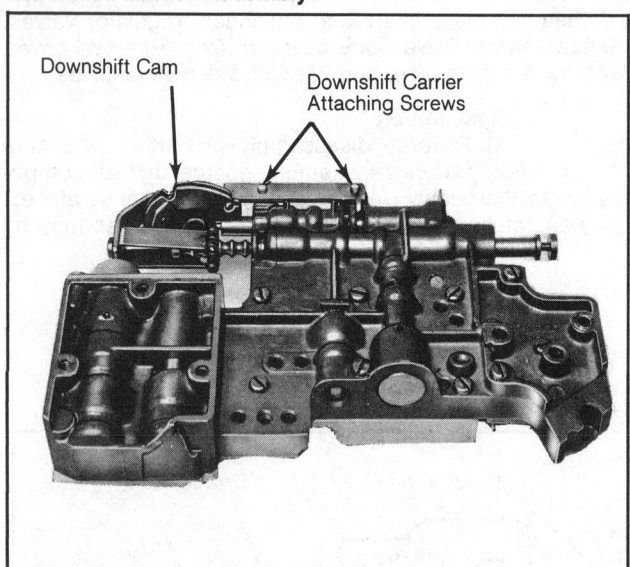

Fig. 23: Lower Valve Body Showing Location of Check Ball and Spring

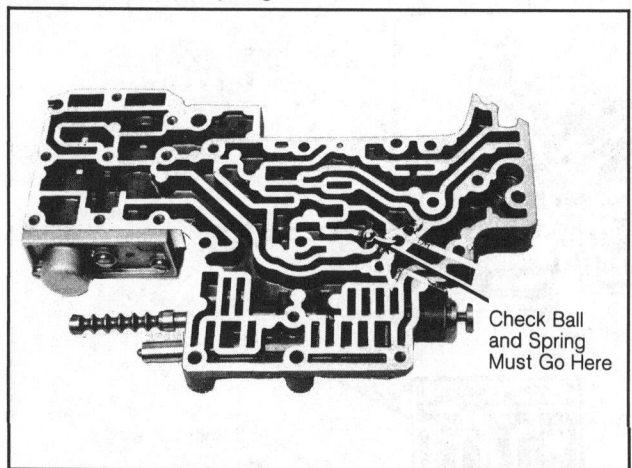

2) Dip all valves and plugs in automatic transmission fluid before installing. Rotate valves and plugs when inserting into bores to avoid shearing off soft body castings. Ensure all valves move freely and smoothly in their bores. Ensure check ball and spring are in correct position in lower valve body before installing oil tube plate. *See Fig. 23.*

OIL PUMP
Disassembly

Remove the 5 attaching screws and separate pump housings. Check back plate for scratches or other damage. Mark pump drive and driven gear for reassembly. DO NOT scribe mark on gears, use chalk or a soft pencil. Remove gears. Inspect gears for scratches or signs of other damage. Inspect bearing and seals for wear, and replace if necessary.

Fig. 24: Disassembled View of Oil Pump Assembly

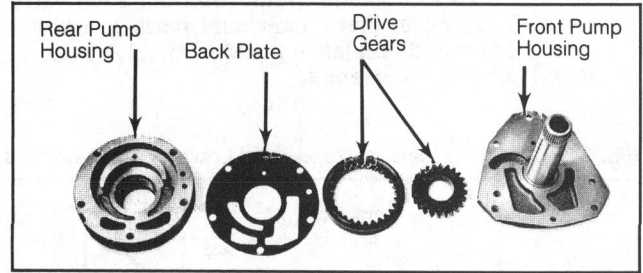

Fig. 25: Using Centering Tool to Center Oil Pump During Reassembly

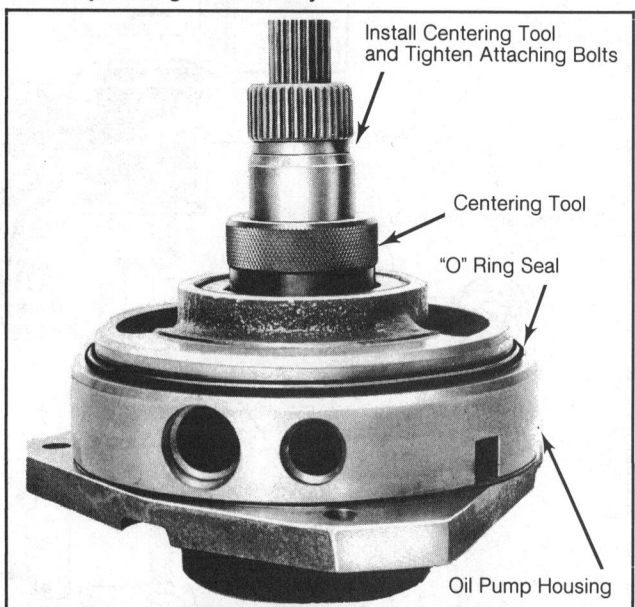

Tool must turn freely with attaching bolts tightened.

SAAB — BORG-WARNER MODEL 37 (Cont.)

Pump Bearing Replacement

Remove snap ring. Gently tap oil pump shaft with a plastic mallet to free shaft and bearing. Remove bearing. Reverse procedure to install new bearing.

Reassembly

Reverse disassembly procedure to reassemble. Use a centering tool (87 90 248) to center oil pump. Install a new "O" ring seal on outside of pump housing.

DIFFERENTIAL ASSEMBLY

Disassembly

1) Remove differential bearings only if they are to be replaced. Remove differential ring gear attaching bolts and separate ring gear from differential housing.

Fig. 26: *Exploded View of Differential Assembly*

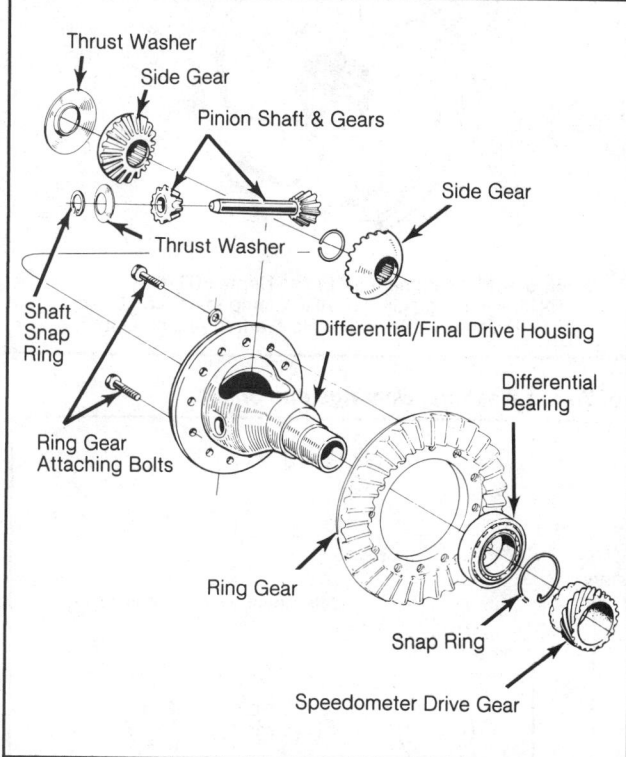

2) Remove snap ring, then push out differential pinion gear shaft. Remove pinion gears and side gears along with thrust washers from housing. If ring gear requires replacement, pinion shaft must also be replaced as they are serviced as a complete set.

NOTE: **Before left side bearing can be removed, speedometer drive gear must be pulled from housing.**

Reassembly

Install pinion gears and side gear along with thrust washers into differential housing, install pinion shaft and lock in place with snap ring. Mount ring gear on differential housing. Install attaching bolts using Loctite.

INNER DRIVE SHAFT ASSEMBLY

Disassembly

Remove drive shaft snap ring and press drive shaft from bearing housing. Using a screwdriver, remove oil seal from housing using care not to damage housing.

On left side bearing housing, remove shaft and pull out speedometer drive assembly. On both sides, press out drive shaft bearing. If new differential bearings are to be installed, remove bearing outer race from housing using a drift.

NOTE: **A washer is located between right side race and bearing housing to improve bearing lubrication.**

Reassembly

Press new drive shaft bearing into bearing housing. If removed, press new differential bearing outer race into bearing housing. Make sure that lubrication washer is installed before right side race. Using a drift, press bearing housing oil seal into housing until it protrudes approximately .08" (2 mm) above face of housing.

Fig. 27: *Exploded View of Inner Drive Shaft Assembly*

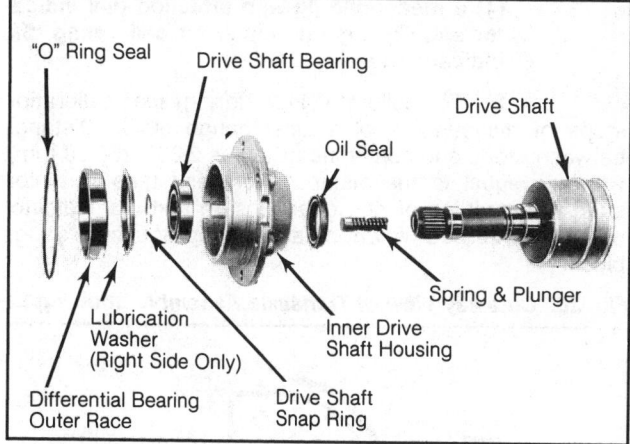

Right side assembly shown.

Fig. 28: *Exploded View of Speedometer Drive Assembly*

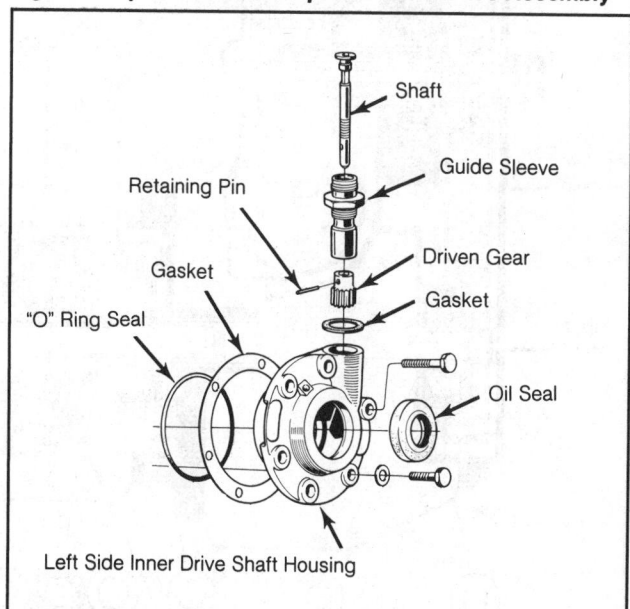

SAAB — BORG-WARNER MODEL 37 (Cont.)

TRANSAXLE REASSEMBLY

NOTE: **Handle all parts carefully to avoid damaging bearing and mating surfaces. Lubricate all components with ATF fluid. Use petrolatum to hold gaskets and thrust washers in place, where required. Replace all worn or damaged parts. See Fig. 30 for thrust washer and bearing locations.**

1) Blow out ventilation channels with compressed air. Install pinion bearing housing locating studs into case. Install pinion bearing shims. Lubricate bearing housing sealing rings. Position complete pinion bearing housing assembly on locating stubs. Place case in press, and press in housing. Remove locating studs and install retaining bolts. Check pinion clearance.

NOTE: **Pinion depth must be measured using Saab metering tool (83 90 155), which consists of (1) a measuring jig with attached dial indicator and (2) a gauge block for calibrating dial indicator. See Fig. 31.**

2) To calibrate indicator, place calibration stops of measuring tool against gauge block. Distance between stops and centerline of tool is 2.362" (60.00 mm), which is equal to the distance from end face of pinion shaft to centerline of ring gear. Ensure that dial indicator pointer is zeroed when measuring tip touches gauge block.

3) Place measuring tool in transaxle case with measuring tip applied to flat end of pinion gear. Take a reading. When pinion gear is correctly positioned, dial indicator should show the number of hundredths of a millimeter (+ or -) stamped into pinion, with a permitted tolerance of .05 mm (.002"). For example, if pinion is stamped +3, indicator should read +3 ± .05 mm.

4) If measured pinion depth reading is not within specifications (stamped on pinion), pinion shaft must be adjusted. To adjust, remove pinion shaft bearing

Fig. 29: *View of Pinion Gear Showing Location of Adjustment Data*

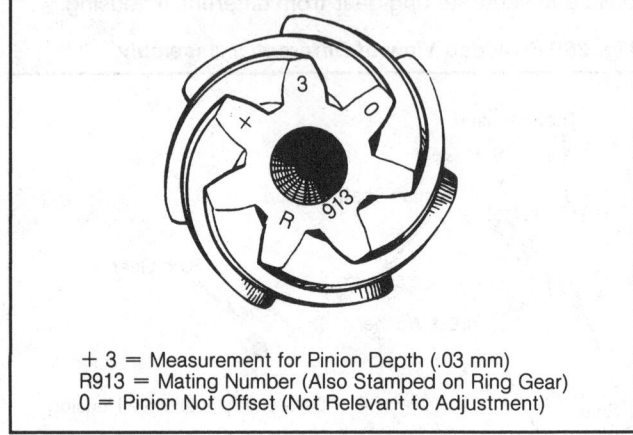

+ 3 = Measurement for Pinion Depth (.03 mm)
R913 = Mating Number (Also Stamped on Ring Gear)
0 = Pinion Not Offset (Not Relevant to Adjustment)

Fig. 30: *Cutaway View of Transaxle Assembly Showing Location of Thrust Washers, Bearings and Shims*

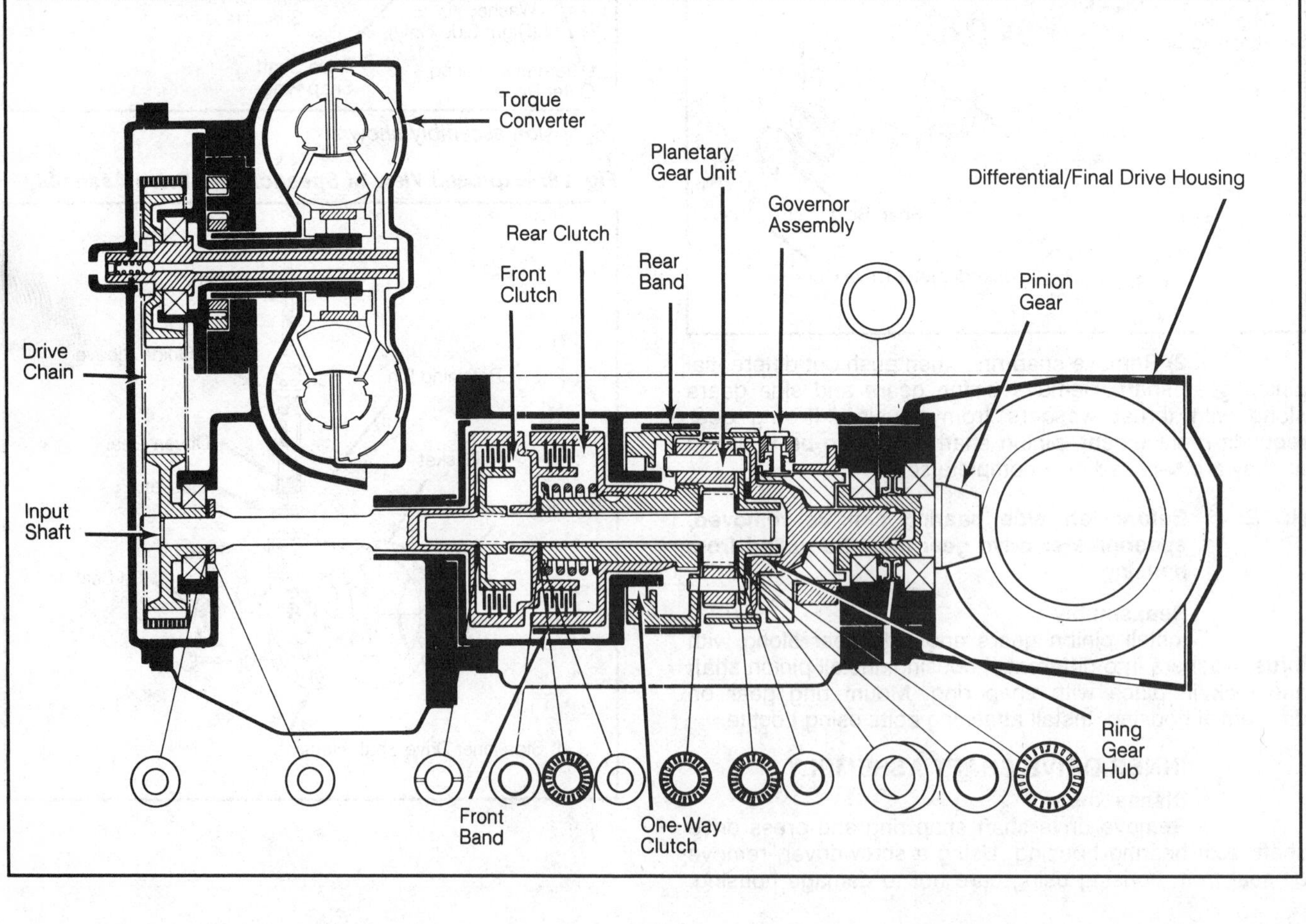

Torque Converter

Planetary Gear Unit

Governor Assembly

Differential/Final Drive Housing

Rear Clutch

Front Clutch

Rear Band

Pinion Gear

Drive Chain

Input Shaft

Front Band

One-Way Clutch

Ring Gear Hub

SAAB — BORG-WARNER MODEL 37 (Cont.)

housing. Add or remove shims between housing and transaxle case as follows: If reading is higher than specifications, reduce shim combination. Reduce or increase shim combination according to difference between measured value and specified value. Pinion depth adjusting shims are available in thicknesses of .004" (.10 mm), .006" (.15 mm) and .012" (.30 mm).

5) Before reinstalling pinion housing and pinion depth adjusting shims, differential bearing preload must be adjusted. Place differential/final drive assembly into transaxle case, then install left side inner drive shaft housing (side with speedometer drive) without shims. Install attaching bolts and tighten to 15-18 lbs. (20-24 N.m). Oil differential bearing, and install right side drive shaft housing without shims. Tighten attaching bolts to 19 INCH lbs. (2.2 N.m) in 2 or 3 steps. Rotate differential assembly while tightening bolts.

Fig. 31: Using Special Tool to Measure Pinion Depth

6) Using a feeler gauge, measure gap between right side drive shaft housing and transaxle case at 2 points opposite each other. Take the average of the 2 readings and select adjusting shims which will equal this value. Then add an additional .008" (.20 mm) in shim thickness to obtain correct bearing preload.

NOTE: Up to 4 shims may be used to obtain correct preload. Adjusting shims are available in thicknesses of .004" (.10 mm), .006" (.15 mm), .012" (.30 mm) and .020" (.50 mm).

7) Remove right side drive shaft housing and lift out differential/final drive assembly. Reinstall pinion shaft housing along with pinion depth adjusting shims. Recheck pinion depth adjustment. Reinstall differential/final drive assembly. Reinstall right side drive shaft housing along with previously selected bearing preload adjusting shims and tighten attaching bolts.

8) Grease the sealing rings on the output shaft. Place transmission housing in vise and support pinion with a drift. Position output shaft on pinion, and carefully press

Fig. 32: Using Feeler Gauge to Measure Differential Bearing Preload

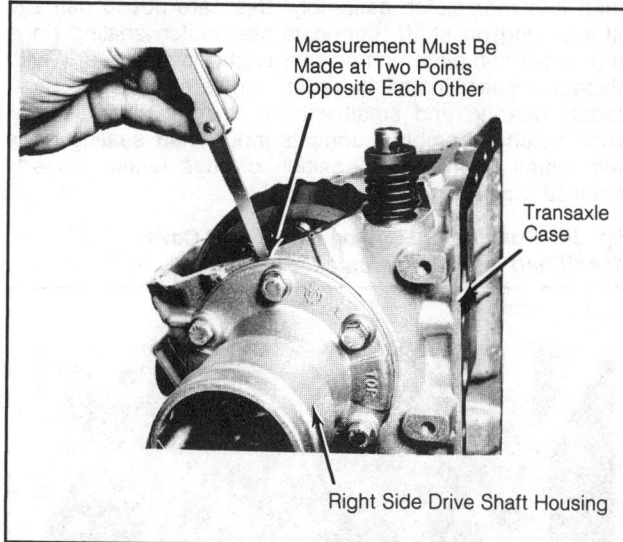

on shaft. Be sure that the shaft and pinion splines are properly aligned. Also be sure that the sealing rings on the output shaft are located correctly in their grooves as they enter the seal housing. Measure assembly depth in case with a large depth gauge. Total depth should be 7.561-7.578" (192.04-192.48 mm) including shims.

Fig. 33: Measuring Depth of Output Shaft/Ring Gear Assembly in Transmission Case

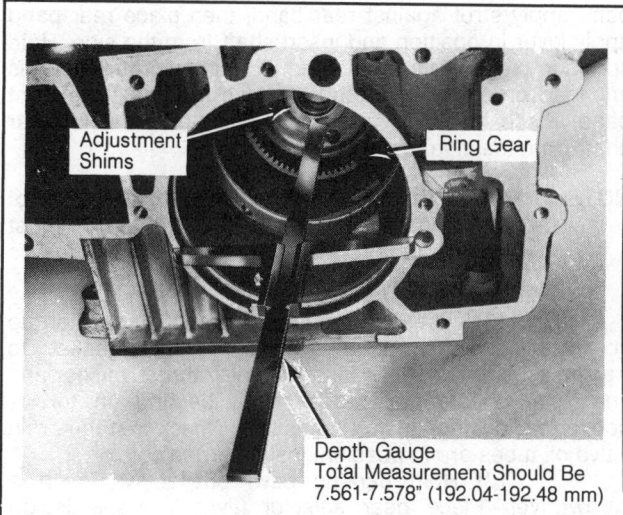

Total depth includes adjustment shims.

9) If the parking pawl was removed during disassembly, reverse removal procedure to install. Grease front and rear servo piston "O" rings. Install pistons into servo cylinders in transaxle case. Install the rear brake band. Install thrust bearing, race and shims in planetary gear assembly. Install planetary gear and center support. Install front brake band.

NOTE: Soak brake bands (front and rear) in ATF fluid before installation.

SAAB — BORG-WARNER MODEL 37 (Cont.)

10) Install a thrust needle bearing on each side of sun gear on sun gear shaft. Carefully insert sun gear shaft into rear clutch assembly. Use care not to damage oil seal ring on shaft. Lubricate rear clutch sealing rings and install complete unit so that teeth mesh properly with planetary gear. Install in order, the large bearing race, needle bearing and small washer in front clutch. Install front clutch assembly. Lubricate input shaft sealing rings and install shaft. Note position of lugs when properly installed. *See Fig. 34.*

Fig. 34: Position of Lugs on Input Shaft Cover When Shaft is Properly Installed

11) Place pin in rear servo piston. Place long band apply strut against rear band, then place rear band apply lever in position and insert shaft from the side. Hold spring in place while sliding shaft into position so that it is engaged on shaft. Place the short strut against the front band. Place the lever in position and press in the lever shaft from the side.

NOTE: When installing the rear servo piston pivot shaft and spring, one end of the spring must be in contact with the lever at all times to prevent scratching the servo cylinder.

12) Grease transmission housing-to-torque converter housing mating surface. Install gasket to transmission housing. Grease axial play thrust washer and shims, and install inside the front bearing (in torque converter housing). Install shims first. Check that the drain valve oil tubes are in position. Install torque converter.

13) Hold parking pawl out of way with a screwdriver. Place gear selector lever in transmission case. Guide front servo oil tube into position while installing torque converter housing-to-transmission case. Install converter housing-to-transmission case attaching bolts, and pull converter housing into position with bolts.

14) Check transaxle gear unit end play. Mount a dial indicator on torque converter housing, so that indicator tip is touching end of input shaft. Zero indicator. Pry forward on planetary gear assembly and read gear end play. End play should be .01-.03" (.25-.75 mm). If end play is not to specifications, adjust by adding or removing shims between thrust washer and front bearing.

15) Install accumulator piston. Place valve body assembly into converter housing and ensure that manual gear selector is properly connected. Center valve body in position with 5 retaining bolts, tighten 2 and

Fig. 35: Using a Dial Indicator to Measure Gear Unit End Play

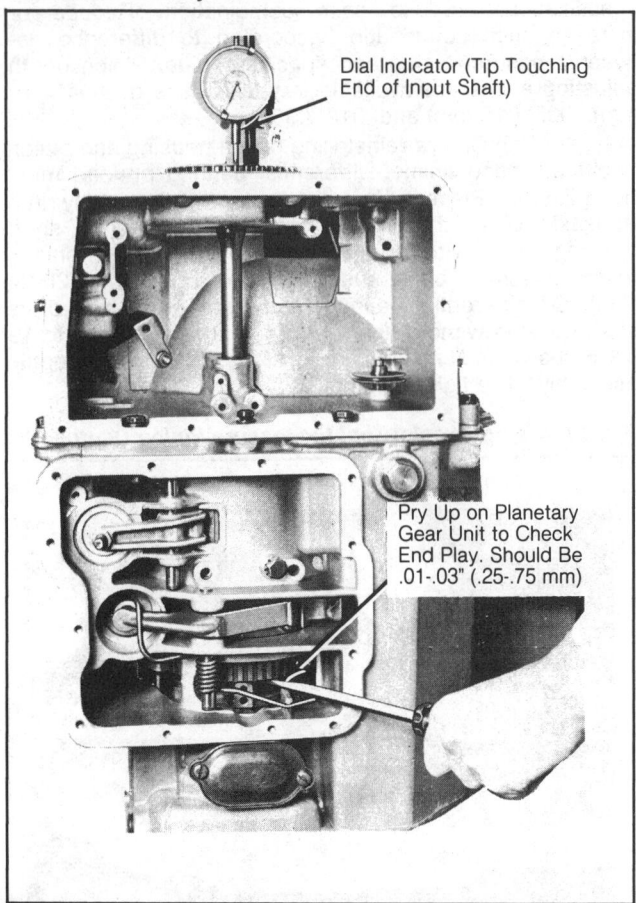

remove the others. *See Fig. 36.* Attach cam disc cable to cam disc on valve body. Check that cable is positioned in pulley groove.

Fig. 36: Positioning Valve Body in Case

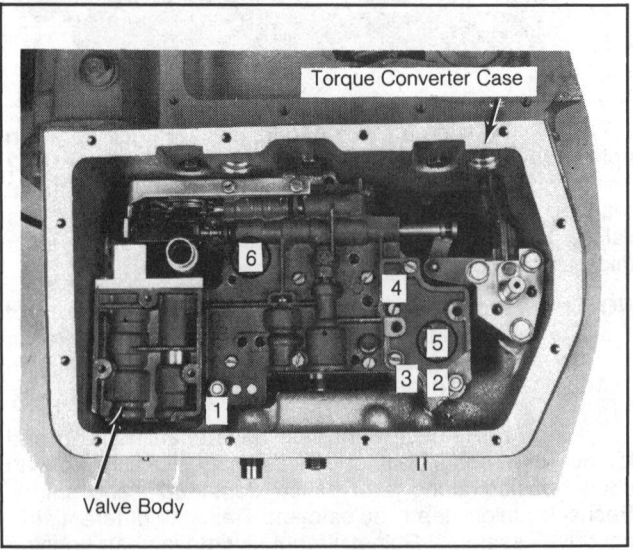

Center with bolts 5 and 6 as shown. Tighten bolts 3 and 4. Remove other bolts for installation with oil pump strainer and air escape pipe.

SAAB — BORG-WARNER MODEL 37 (Cont.)

Fig. 37: Bottom View of Transaxle Showing Location & Routing of Oil Tubes

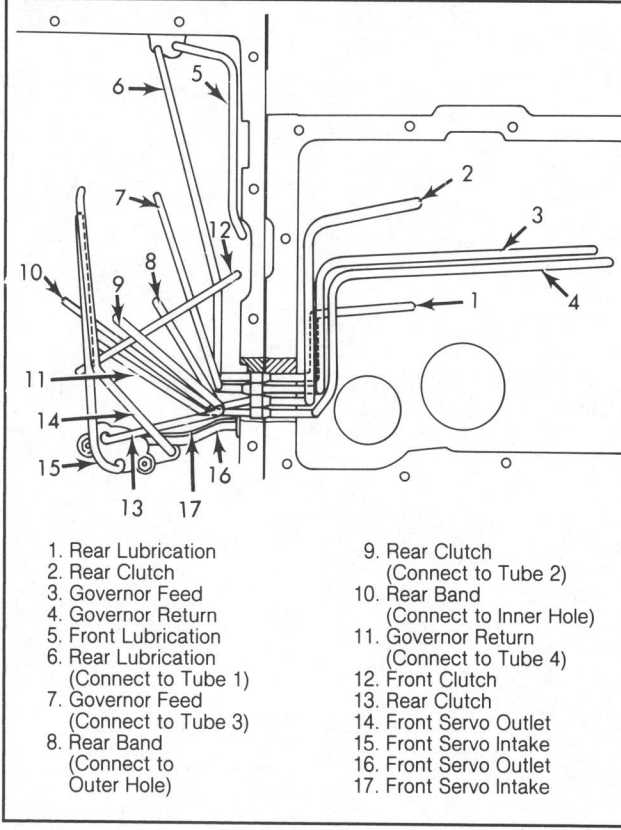

1. Rear Lubrication
2. Rear Clutch
3. Governor Feed
4. Governor Return
5. Front Lubrication
6. Rear Lubrication
   (Connect to Tube 1)
7. Governor Feed
   (Connect to Tube 3)
8. Rear Band
   (Connect to Outer Hole)
9. Rear Clutch
   (Connect to Tube 2)
10. Rear Band
    (Connect to Inner Hole)
11. Governor Return
    (Connect to Tube 4)
12. Front Clutch
13. Rear Clutch
14. Front Servo Outlet
15. Front Servo Intake
16. Front Servo Outlet
17. Front Servo Intake

Install tubes in order given noting procedures in text.

16) Install oil tube in order shown in *Fig. 37.* Tubes 16 and 17 should have been installed with drain valve. When installing tube 12, run it under tube 9 and install tube support (if equipped). Install oil strainer and magnet. Install connection pipes.

17) Adjust rear band: Locate adjusting screw on outer left-hand side of transmission case. Loosen adjusting screw. Tighten screw to 10 Ft. lbs. (14 N.m). Back screw off 3/4 of a turn and tighten lock nut.

Fig. 38: Adjusting Front Band

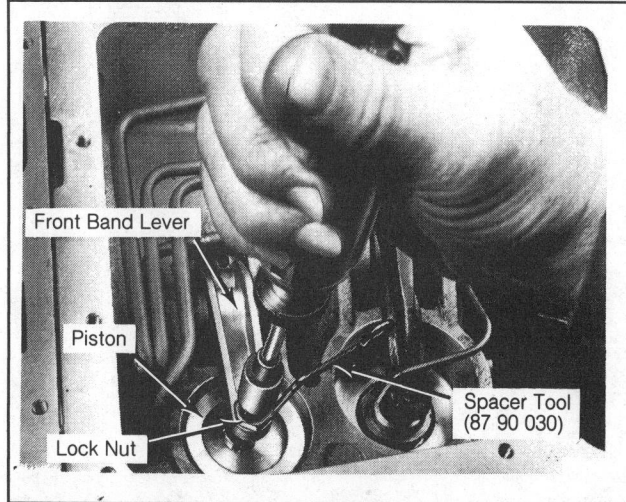

When tightening lock nut, do not allow adjusting screw to change position

18) Adjust front band. Loosen lock nut. Place spacer 87 90 030 (11/32", 8.9 mm rod) between the screw and the piston pin. Tighten adjusting screw to 10 INCH lbs. (1.3 N.m). Remove tool. Hold adjusting screw so it does not move and tighten lock nut.

Fig. 39: Measuring Ring Gear Backlash

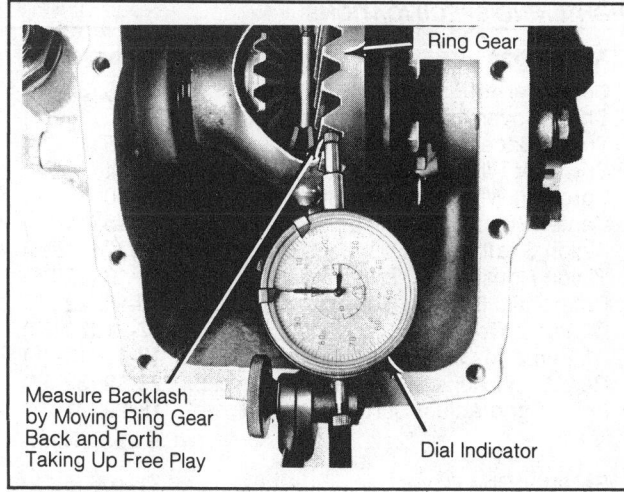

Take backlash measurements of 4 places around ring gear.

19) Install chain and sprockets. Place lock plate under retaining nuts and tighten nuts. Use a bar between sprockets to hold them in place while tightening bolts. Install turbine shaft seal. Install differential assembly and bearing housings. Install complete shim pack under right bearing seat.

20) To check ring gear backlash: Mount dial indicator on transaxle case so that indicator tip is touching ring gear teeth. Measure backlash. Check backlash at 4 different points around the ring gear. Measurements must not vary by more than .002" (.05 mm) from specifications.

NOTE: **Backlash with a new ring and pinion set (or a used set with less than 6,000 miles service) should be to specification which appears on ring gear. See Fig. 40. If a used gear set with MORE than 6,000 miles service is being reinstalled, backlash should be the same as was recorded during transaxle disassembly.**

Fig. 40: View of Ring Gear Showing Adjustment Data

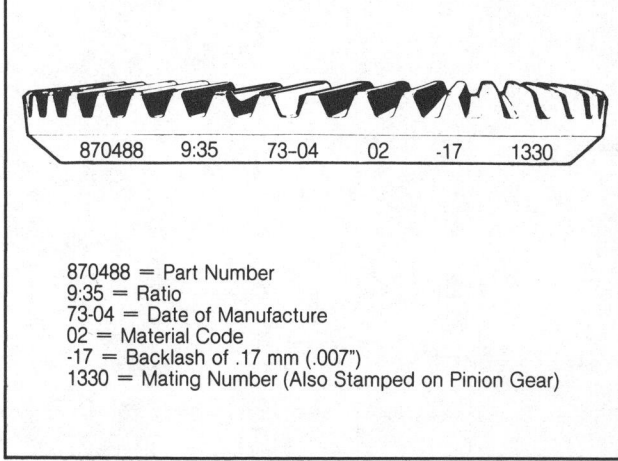

870488 = Part Number
9:35 = Ratio
73-04 = Date of Manufacture
02 = Material Code
-17 = Backlash of .17 mm (.007")
1330 = Mating Number (Also Stamped on Pinion Gear)

Automatic Transmissions

SAAB — BORG-WARNER MODEL 37 (Cont.)

21) Calculate the difference between the measured backlash and the backlash reading desired. Move shims of correct thickness from right bearing housing to the left side housing. DO NOT add or remove any shims. The combination of shims installed has been preselected and must not be changed.

TIGHTENING SPECIFICATIONS

Application	Ft. Lbs. (N.m)
Converter-to-Flywheel	25-30 (33-39)
Chain Cover-to-Converter Hsg.	10-15 (14-21)
Trans. Case-to-Converter Hsg.	10-15 (14-21)
Sprocket Wheel-to-Turbine Shaft	19-24 (26-33)
Sprocket Wheel-to-Input Shaft	25-30 (33-40)
Center Support Bolts	10-18 (14-25)
Pinion Shaft Nut	180-195 (245-265)
Pinion Housing-to-Trans. Case	16-18 (22-25)
Differential Bearing Housing	16-18 (22-25)
Oil Pump Cover	17-21 (23-29)
Oil Pump-to-Converter Housing	13-18 (18-25)
Rear Band Adjust Screw Lock Nut	29-39 (39-53)
Front Band Adjust Screw Lock Nut	15-20 (21-27)
	INCH Lbs. (N.m)
Selector Rod Cover	71-106 (8-12)
Valve Body-to-Trans. Case	53-106 (6-12)

SUBARU MODEL M41A

Subaru 1800

DESCRIPTION

The transaxle assembly consists of 2 main units: automatic transmission and final drive assembly. The transmission housing contains a compound planetary gear unit and one-way clutch, 2 multi-disc clutches, a multi-disc brake, a servo and brake band, an oil pump, and a hydraulic control system. The final drive housing contains the torque converter, governor assembly, ring and pinion gears, and differential assembly.

LUBRICATION & ADJUSTMENT

See the appropriate article in AUTOMATIC TRANSMISSION SERVICING Section.

TROUBLE SHOOTING

NO DRIVE IN ANY RANGE

Fluid level incorrect or fluid contaminated. Manual linkage out of adjustment or improperly installed. Incorrect oil pressure. Leak in hydraulic circuit. Faulty valve body. Defective oil pump or parking linkage.

NO DRIVE IN FORWARD RANGES

Transmission fluid contaminated or level incorrect. Incorrect oil pressure. Manual linkage out of adjustment or incorrectly installed. Faulty valve body. Leak in hydraulic circuit. Faulty oil pump. Parking linkage damaged or incorrectly installed. Poor engine performance. Faulty brakes.

HARSH ENGAGEMENT

From "N" to "D"

Transmission fluid contaminated. Engine idle speed too high. Leak in vacuum circuit. Incorrect oil pressure. Faulty valve body.

From 1st to 2nd Gear

Transmission fluid contaminated. Leak in vacuum circuit. Incorrect oil pressure. Incorrect stall RPM. Brake band out of adjustment or band servo faulty. Faulty valve body.

From 2nd to 3rd Gear

Transmission fluid contaminated. Incorrect oil pressure. Leak in vacuum circuit. Faulty valve body. Servo pipe faulty. Brake band out of adjustment or band servo faulty. Defective reverse clutch.

POOR ACCELERATION & TOP SPEED

Incorrect oil level. Defective stator in torque converter. Manual linkage out of adjustment. Transmission fluid contaminated. Incorrect oil pressure. Incorrect stall RPM. Brake band out of adjustment or band servo faulty. Faulty valve body. Poor engine performance. Defective low-reverse clutch, forward clutch, or reverse clutch. Defective oil pump. Faulty brakes.

VEHICLE BRAKED WHEN SHIFTED INTO "R"

Transmission fluid contaminated. Brake band out of adjustment or band servo faulty. Defective forward clutch. Faulty parking linkage.

Fig. 1: Cross-Sectional View of Subaru Model M41A Automatic Transaxle Assembly

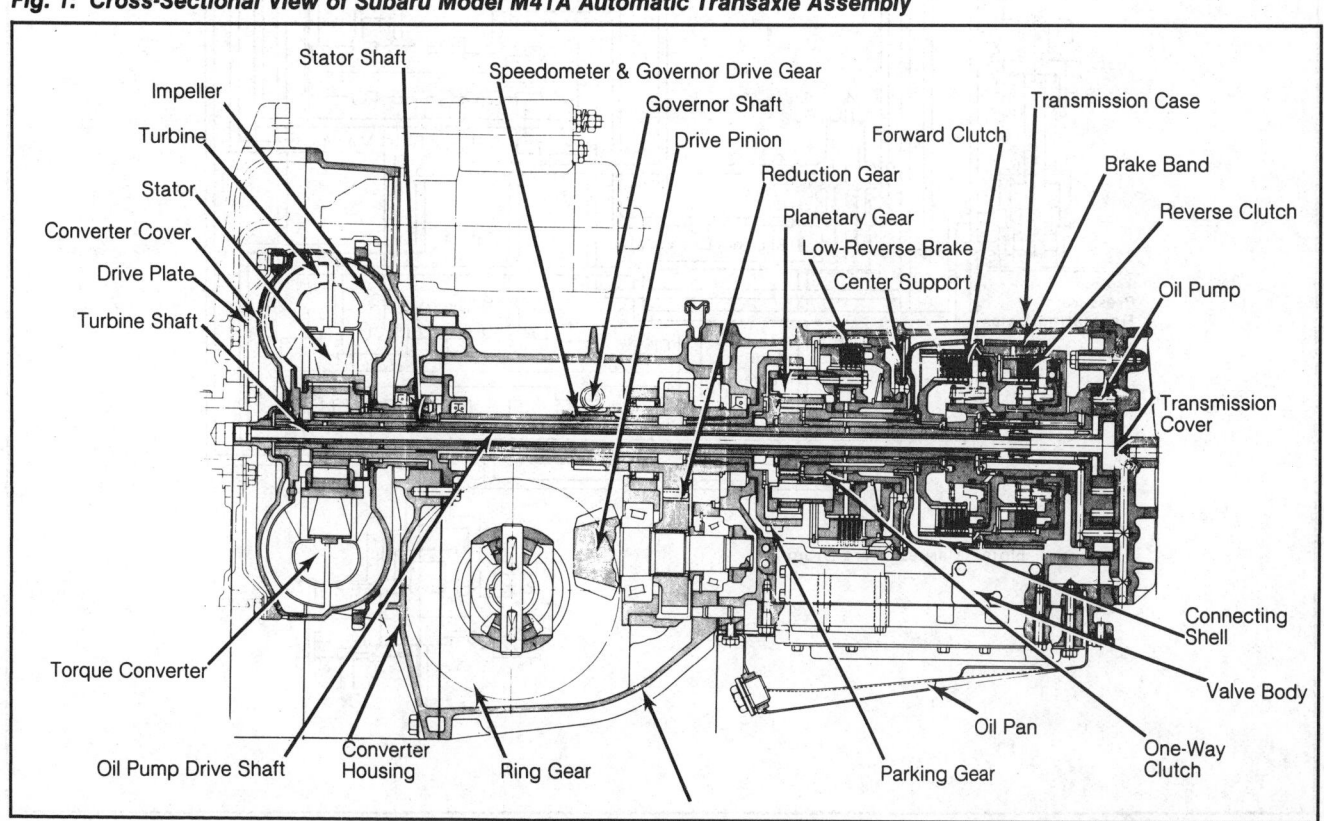

Automatic Transmissions
SUBARU MODEL M41A (Cont.)

Fig. 2: Subaru Model M41A Automatic Transmission Hydraulic Circuits Diagram

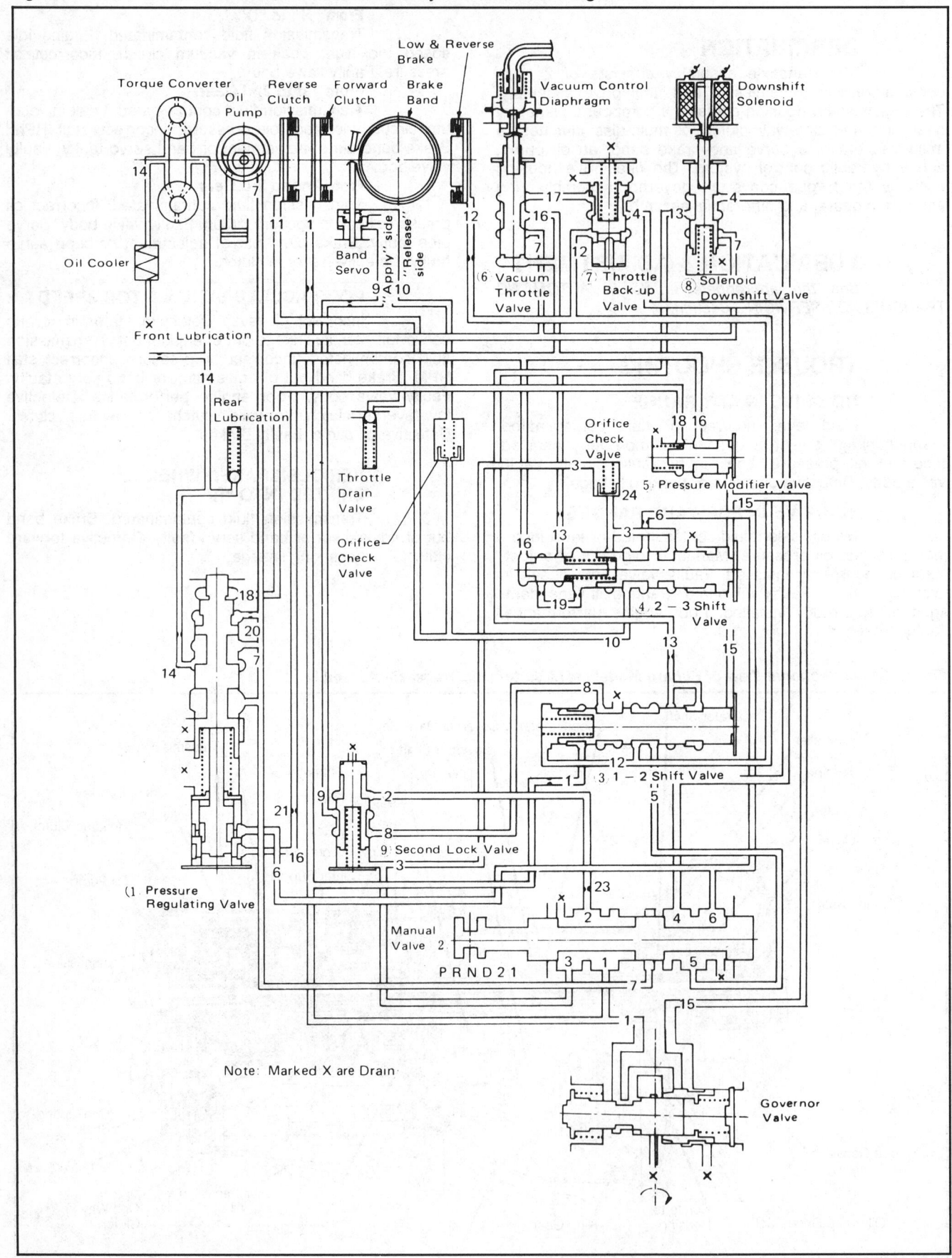

SUBARU MODEL M41A (Cont.)

VEHICLE MOVES IN "N"

Manual linkage out of adjustment. Transmission fluid contaminated. Faulty valve body. Defective forward or reverse clutch.

VEHICLE HAS EXCESSIVE "CREEPING"

Engine idle speed too high.

VEHICLE WILL NOT "CREEP"

Incorrect fluid level. Manual linkage out of adjustment. Incorrect engine idle RPM. Transmission fluid contaminated. Faulty valve body. Defective oil pump. Leak in hydraulic circuit. Defective forward or reverse clutch.

NO SHIFT FROM 1ST TO 2ND GEAR

Manual linkage out of adjustment. Leak in vacuum circuit. Defective downshift solenoid, switch or wiring. Transmission fluid contaminated. Faulty valve body. Faulty governor valve. Brake band out of adjustment or band servo faulty. Nylon gear damaged. Servo pipe faulty. Leak in hydraulic circuit.

NO SHIFT FROM 2ND TO 3RD GEAR

Transmission fluid contaminated. Faulty valve body. Incorrect oil pressure. Faulty governor valve. Brake band out of adjustment. Servo pipe faulty. Defective reverse clutch. Leak in hydraulic circuit. Reverse clutch check ball missing.

SHIFT POINTS TOO HIGH FROM 1ST TO 2ND AND 2ND TO 3RD GEARS

Leak in vacuum circuit. Downshift solenoid, switch or wiring faulty. Incorrect oil pressure. Transmission fluid contaminated. Valve body faulty. Leak in hydraulic circuit.

SHIFTS FROM 1ST TO 3RD, SKIPPING 2ND

Faulty valve body. Incorrect oil pressure. Transmission fluid contaminated. Faulty governor valve. Brake band out of adjustment or band servo faulty. Leak in hydraulic circuit. Servo pipe faulty.

LITTLE OR NO SHIFT SHOCK, EXCESSIVE SLIPPAGE FROM 1ST TO 2ND GEAR

Incorrect oil level. Manual linkage out of adjustment. Leak in vacuum circuit. Incorrect oil pressure. Transmission fluid contaminated. Valve body faulty. Brake band out of adjustment or band servo faulty. Servo pipe faulty. Leak in hydraulic circuit.

LITTLE OR NO SHIFT SHOCK, EXCESSIVE SLIP & ENGINE RUNAWAY FROM 2ND TO 3RD GEARS

Incorrect oil level. Manual linkage out of adjustment. Leak in vacuum circuit. Incorrect oil pressure. Transmission fluid contaminated. Valve body faulty. Brake band out of adjustment. Servo pipe faulty. Defective reverse clutch. Leak in hydraulic circuit. Reverse clutch check ball missing.

VEHICLE IS BRAKED WHEN SHIFTED FROM 1ST TO 2ND GEAR

Transmission fluid contaminated. Valve body faulty. Defective low-reverse clutch. Defective reverse clutch. Defective one-way clutch.

VEHICLE IS BRAKED WHEN SHIFTED FROM 2ND TO 3RD GEAR

Transmission fluid contaminated. Brake band out of adjustment or band servo faulty.

NO 3RD TO 2ND DOWNSHIFT

Leak in vacuum circuit. Transmission fluid contaminated. Valve body faulty. Faulty governor valve. Brake band out of adjustment or band servo faulty. Incorrect oil pressure. Leak in hydraulic circuit. Defective reverse clutch. Servo pipe faulty.

NO 2ND TO 1ST OR 3RD TO 1ST DOWNSHIFT

Leak in vacuum circuit. Transmission fluid contaminated. Faulty valve body. Governor valve faulty. Brake band out of adjustment or band servo faulty. Defective one-way clutch.

SHIFTING SHOCK FELT ON DECELERATION

Manual linkage out of adjustment. Transmission fluid contaminated. Leak in vacuum circuit. Downshift solenoid, switch or wiring faulty. Incorrect oil pressure. Valve body faulty. Governor valve faulty. Leak in hydraulic circuit.

SHIFT POINTS TOO HIGH FROM 3RD TO 2ND OR 2ND TO 1ST GEARS

Manual linkage out of adjustment. Transmission fluid contaminated. Leak in vacuum circuit. Downshift solenoid, switch or wiring faulty. Incorrect oil pressure. Faulty valve body. Governor valve faulty. Leak in hydraulic circuit.

NO KICKDOWN AT NORMAL SPEEDS IN 3RD GEAR

Downshift solenoid, switch or wiring faulty. Leak in vacuum circuit. Transmission fluid contaminated. Faulty valve body or governor valve. Servo pipe faulty. Brake band out of adjustment or band servo faulty. Leak in hydraulic circuit.

EXCESSIVE ENGINE RPM WHEN ACCELERATING IN 3RD GEAR ABOVE KICKDOWN SPEED

Manual linkage out of adjustment. Incorrect oil pressure. Transmission fluid contaminated. Faulty valve body. Faulty governor valve. Defective reverse clutch. Leak in hydraulic circuit.

ENGINE RUNAWAY OR TRANSMISSION SLIPPAGE ON 3RD TO 2ND GEAR KICKDOWN

Leak in vacuum circuit. Incorrect oil pressure. Transmission fluid contaminated. Valve body faulty. Brake band out of adjustment or band servo faulty. Servo pipe faulty. Defective reverse clutch. Leak in hydraulic circuit.

NO ENGINE BRAKING IN 1ST GEAR

Manual linkage out of adjustment. Transmission fluid contaminated. Faulty valve body. Defective low-reverse clutch. Leak in hydraulic circuit. Incorrect oil pressure.

TRANSMISSION OVERHEATS

Incorrect oil level or oil pressure. Incorrect stall RPM. Transmission fluid contaminated. Faulty valve body.

Automatic Transmissions

SUBARU MODEL M41A (Cont.)

Defective reverse clutch, low-reverse clutch, oil pump, forward clutch or planetary gear unit. Converter stator one-way clutch faulty. Brake band out of adjustment or band servo faulty. Leak in hydraulic circuit.

TRANSMISSION NOISY IN "N" OR "P"

Incorrect oil level or oil contaminated. Incorrect oil pressure. Valve body faulty. Defective oil pump.

TRANSMISSION NOISY IN "R" AND ALL DRIVE RANGES

Incorrect oil level. Defective forward clutch, oil pump, one-way clutch, or planetary gear unit. Faulty ring or pinion gear in final drive. Incorrect oil pressure. Faulty reduction gears.

TESTING

ROAD TEST

1) Before road testing, be certain that fluid level and condition, and control linkage adjustments have been checked and corrected as necessary. During test, transmission should upshift and downshift at approximately the same speeds as shown in Shift Speeds table.

2) All shifts may vary slightly due to production tolerances or tire size. The important factor is quality of shifts. All shifts should be smooth, responsive, and with no slippage or engine speed runaway. Slippage or engine runaway in any gear usually indicates clutch or band problems.

3) The slipping clutch or band in a particular gear can usually be identified by noting transmission operation in other selector positions and comparing internal units which are applied in these positions. See Clutch and Band Application Chart.

4) The process of elimination given can be used to detect any unit which slips and to confirm proper operation of good units, but actual cause of a malfunction cannot be easily decided.

6) Practically any condition can be caused by leaking hydraulic circuits or sticking valves. Unless an obvious condition exists, transmission should never be disassembled until hydraulic pressure tests have been made.

SHIFT SPEEDS CHART

Application	Shift Points (MPH)
Kickdown	
1-2 Upshift	31-37
2-3 Upshift	55-62
3-2 Downshift	51-57
2-1 Downshift	23-29
Half-Throttle	
1-2 Upshift	9-14
2-3 Upshift	25-32
3-2 or 3-1 Downshift	8-14
2-1 Downshift	6-11
Full Throttle	
2-1 Downshift [1]	25-32
Minimum Throttle	
2-1 Downshift [1]	25-32

[1] — Shifting selector from "D" to "1" range when vehicle is running at 31 MPH.

STALL TEST

Testing Precautions

When making stall test, do not hold throttle open any longer than 5 seconds to obtain steady gauge reading. After each stall test, move selector lever to "N" and allow engine to idle for at least a minute to cool down engine and transmission. If engine speed exceeds limits shown in Stall Speeds table, release accelerator immediately as clutch or band slippage is indicated.

Testing Procedure

With engine at normal operating temperature, tachometer installed, and parking and service brakes applied, make transmission stall test in "D", "2", "1" and "R" ranges at full throttle and note maximum RPM obtained. Engine speed should be within limits shown in Stall Speeds table.

STALL SPEEDS

Application	Stall RPM
All Models	1800-2100

CLUTCH AND BAND APPLICATION CHART (ELEMENTS IN USE)

Selector Lever Position	Foward Clutch	Reverse Clutch	Low-Reverse Band	Brake Band	One-Way Clutch
P — PARK			X		
R — REVERSE		X	X		
D — DRIVE					
First Gear	X				X
Second Gear	X				
Third Gear	X	X			
2 — SECOND	X			X	
1 — LOW					
First	X		X		
Second	X			X	

N — NEUTRAL — All clutches and bands released and/or ineffective.

SUBARU MODEL M41A (Cont.)

Stall Speed Too High

In all ranges: General transmission problems are indicated and a control pressure test should be made to locate faulty unit(s). In "D", "2" and "1" only: Forward clutch slippage is indicated. In "D" range only: One-way clutch slippage is indicated. In "2" range only: Brake band slippage is indicated. In "R" range only: Slippage of reverse clutch or low-reverse brake is indicated.

Stall Speed Too Low

Converter stator one-way clutch faulty.

NOTE: Make sure engine performance is satisfactory before condemning converter assembly. Converter is a sealed unit and cannot be overhauled, it must be replaced if defective.

HYDRAULIC PRESSURE TESTS

Line Pressure

1) Connect a pressure gauge to line pressure checking plug on rear cover of transmission. *See Fig. 3.* Place gauge in position for viewing from driver's seat.

NOTE: A hole is provided on front of toe-board to route gauge hose from engine compartment into driver's compartment.

Fig. 3: Rear View of Transmission Case Showing Location of Line Pressure Checking Point

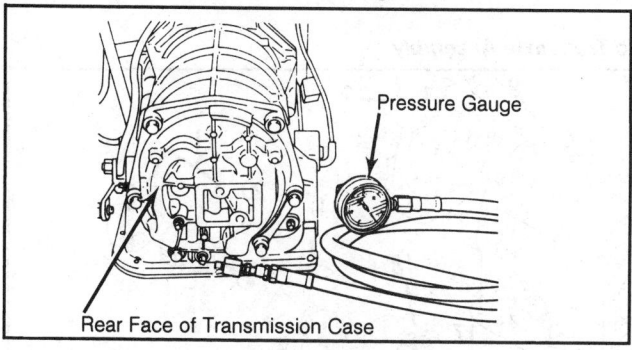

2) With engine at normal operating temperature and transmission fluid at correct level, perform line pressure test in "D", "2" and "R" ranges. Start vehicle from a standstill and slowly increase engine speed and note pressure in each range. Pressures should be approximately as shown in Line Pressure table.

Line Pressure Test Results

1) If line pressure at idle is low in all ranges, faulty pressure feeding line or low oil pump discharge pressure may be assumed, due to the following: Worn oil pump or improperly adjusted internal clearances; oil leakage from oil pump, valve body, governor or transmission case; sticky pressure regulator valve.

2) If oil pressure at idle is low in "D", "2" and "1" ranges only, check for faulty or leaking forward clutch or governor assembly.

3) If oil pressure at idle is low in "P" and "R" ranges only, check for a faulty or leaking low-reverse brake assembly.

4) If oil pressure is high in all ranges, check for the following: Leaky vacuum tube or vacuum diaphragm, or excessive length of vacuum rod; sticky pressure regulator valve.

Fig. 4: View of Final Drive Housing Showing Location of Governor Pressure Checking Point

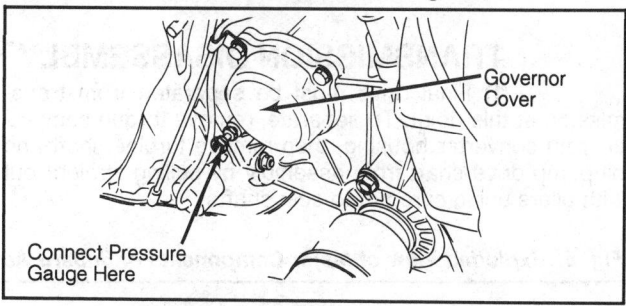

Governor Pressure

Connect pressure gauge to governor pressure plug located on right side of final drive housing, then place gauge in driver's compartment as outlined in line pressure test procedure. With engine at normal operating temperature and transmission fluid level correct, check governor pressure at speeds shown in Governor Pressure chart with transmission in "2".

GOVERNOR PRESSURES CHART

Speed (MPH)	Psi (kg/cm²)
Below 6	0-2.8 (0-.2)
Below 25	18-27 (1.3-1.9)
Below 50	53-67 (3.7-4.7)

SUBARU LINE PRESSURE TABLE — psi (kg/cm²)

Range	Throttle Opening	Before Cut-Back Point (Under 9.5 MPH)	After Cut-Back Point (Over 22 MPH)
"D"	Full Throttle	121-142 (8.5-10.0)	78-93 (5.5-6.5)
	Minimum Throttle	43-57 (3.0-4.0)	43-57 (3.0-4.0)
"2"	Full Throttle	145-168 (10.2-11.8)	84-98 (5.9-6.9)
	Minimum Throttle	145-168 (10.2-11.8)	84-98 (5.9-6.9)
"R"	Full Throttle	200-227 (14-16)	200-227 (14-16)
	Minumum Throttle	67-81 (4.7-5.7)	67-81 (4.7-5.7)

NOTE: Line pressures at each of "D", "2" and "R" ranges will change in steps at certain points (where pressure modifier valve functions) and these points are called the "Cut-Back Point". Before cut-back in the above table implies slow driving condition (less than 9.5 MPH) and after cut-back implies the vehicle speed of more than 22 MPH.

SUBARU MODEL M41A (Cont.)

SERVICE (IN VEHICLE)

WHEEL BEARINGS

See SERVICE (IN VEHICLE) in SUBARU MANUAL TRANSAXLE article in MANUAL TRANSAXLE Section.

AXLE DRIVE SHAFTS

See SERVICE (IN VEHICLE) in SUBARU MANUAL TRANSAXLE article in MANUAL TRANSAXLE Section.

CONSTANT VELOCITY (CV) JOINTS

See SERVICE (IN VEHICLE) in SUBARU MANUAL TRANSAXLE article in MANUAL TRANSAXLE Section.

TORQUE CONVERTER

NOTE: **Torque converter is a sealed unit and cannot be disassembled for service. Replace if found to be defective.**

TRANSMISSION DISASSEMBLY

1) Final drive must be separated from transmission at this point. To separate, remove torque converter from converter housing, then remove turbine shaft and oil pump drive shaft from assembly by pulling straight out with pliers using care not to scar shafts.

2) Remove nuts securing transmission case to final drive case, then disconnect neutral safety switch and clip from downshift solenoid lead wire. Remove bolt securing filler pipe to governor cover.

3) Disconnect vacuum pipe and ground cable. Remove oil supply pipe from transmission after draining fluid. Remove oil cooler pipe. Separate transmission from final drive.

NOTE: **When moving the transmission from one place to another, do not move transmission by holding planetary output gear.**

4) Drain transmission fluid. Place transmission on a work stand with oil pan facing up. Remove oil pan. Unscrew downshift solenoid and vacuum modulator by hand and remove them from transmission case. Pull out modulator rod. Carefully pry servo apply and release tubes from case.

5) Remove attaching screws, and carefully lift out valve body assembly using care not to drop manual valve. Loosen band adjusting screw lock nut, and snugly tighten adjusting screw for convenience in removing transmission rear cover. Remove rear mount from bracket on transmission.

6) Remove bolts securing transmission rear cover, then gently tap rear mount bracket to rotate cover and remove cover and oil pump carrier as an assembly.

Fig. 5: Exploded View of Major Components of Subaru Automatic Transaxle Assembly

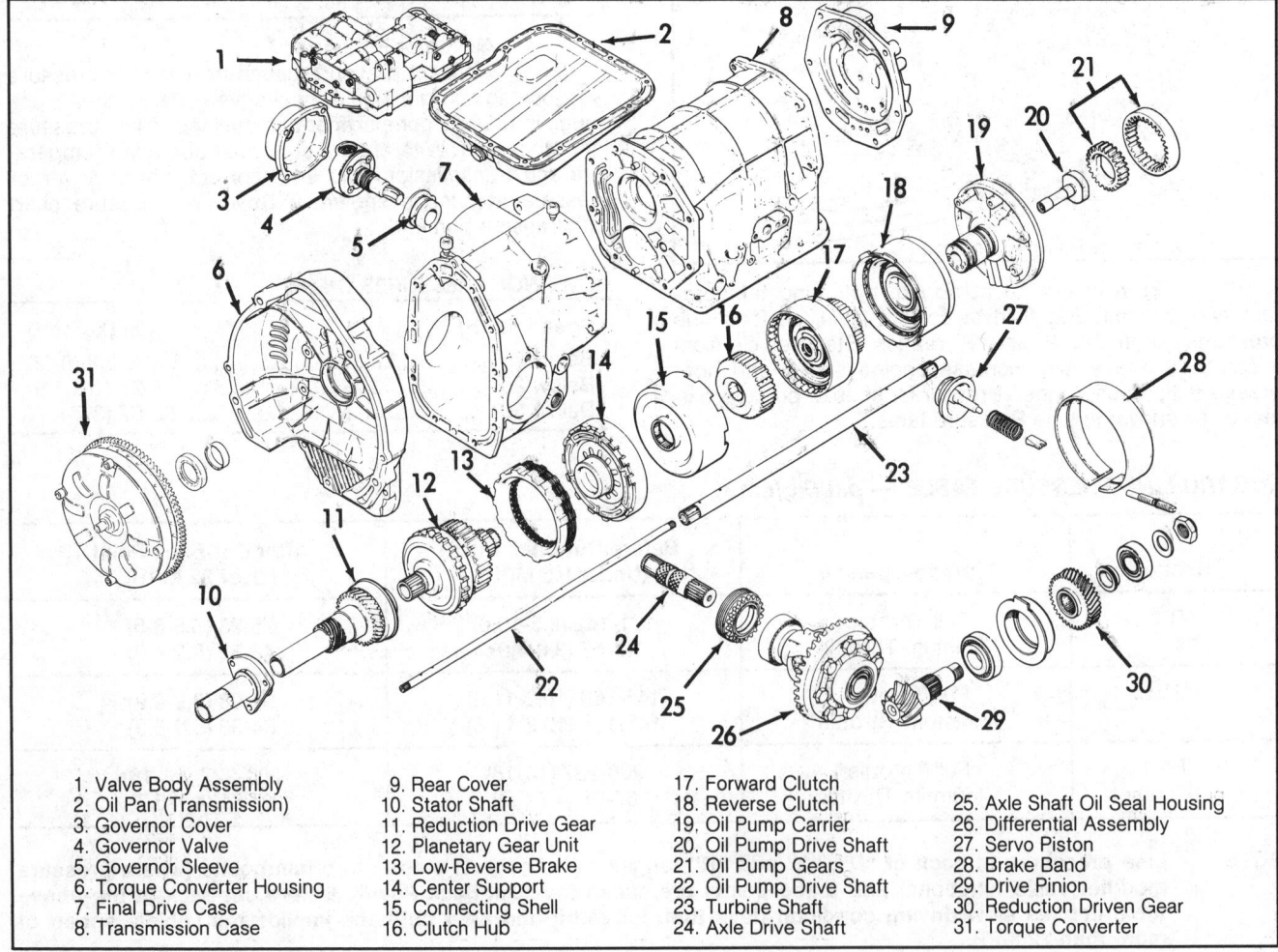

1. Valve Body Assembly	9. Rear Cover	17. Forward Clutch	25. Axle Shaft Oil Seal Housing
2. Oil Pan (Transmission)	10. Stator Shaft	18. Reverse Clutch	26. Differential Assembly
3. Governor Cover	11. Reduction Drive Gear	19. Oil Pump Carrier	27. Servo Piston
4. Governor Valve	12. Planetary Gear Unit	20. Oil Pump Drive Shaft	28. Brake Band
5. Governor Sleeve	13. Low-Reverse Brake	21. Oil Pump Gears	29. Drive Pinion
6. Torque Converter Housing	14. Center Support	22. Oil Pump Drive Shaft	30. Reduction Driven Gear
7. Final Drive Case	15. Connecting Shell	23. Turbine Shaft	31. Torque Converter
8. Transmission Case	16. Clutch Hub	24. Axle Drive Shaft	

SUBARU MODEL M41A (Cont.)

Pry out snap ring securing servo cover. Insert tool into brake band opening and tighten band adjusting screw until servo cover and piston are removed. Loosen band adjusting screw and remove band apply strut.

NOTE: Note positions of washers, thrust washers and needle bearings removed in this step. Use care to avoid losing any of these parts.

Fig. 6: Removing Band Apply Strut

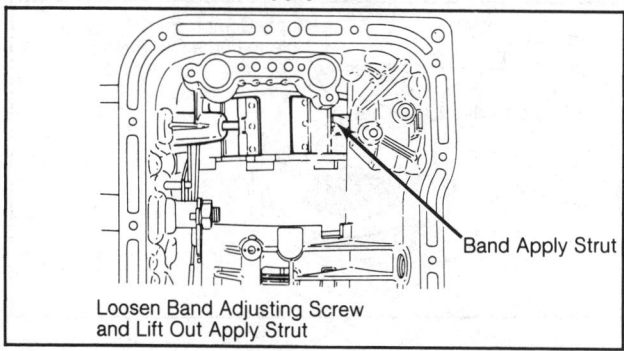

Band Apply Strut

Loosen Band Adjusting Screw and Lift Out Apply Strut

7) Remove brake band, reverse clutch assembly and forward clutch assembly from transmission. Remove clutch hub and connecting shell from transmission case. Pry out snap ring and lift out center support assembly. Remove forward and reverse sun gears.

8) Lift planetary gear assembly and low reverse brake assembly from transmission case, then remove low-reverse brake retaining plate. If not removed with planetary gear unit, remove planetary output shaft.

Fig. 7: Installed View of Manual Shaft and Parking Rod Assembly

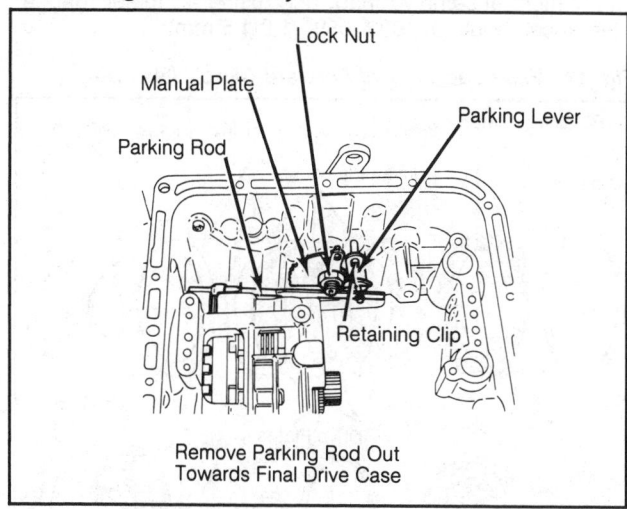

Lock Nut

Manual Plate

Parking Lever

Parking Rod

Retaining Clip

Remove Parking Rod Out Towards Final Drive Case

9) DO NOT remove parking pawl and lever assemblies unless they are damaged or otherwise require replacement. If replacement is necessary, remove lock nut and detach manual plate, spacer, washer, "O" ring and dust seal. Remove parking lever retaining clip, then remove parking rod with lever.

10) Remove retaining clip from parking pawl shaft. Remove parking pawl shaft, parking pawl, parking pawl return spring and parking rod support plate. Remove transmission assembly from stand.

Fig. 8: Disassembled View of Parking Pawl Components

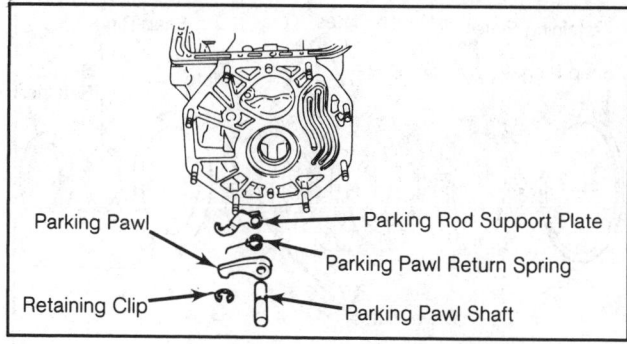

Parking Pawl

Retaining Clip

Parking Rod Support Plate

Parking Pawl Return Spring

Parking Pawl Shaft

COMPONENT DISASSEMBLY & REASSEMBLY

REVERSE CLUTCH ASSEMBLY
Disassembly

1) Remove clutch assembly snap ring and lift out retaining plate, drive plates, driven plates and dished plate from clutch drum. Using a compressor tool, compress clutch assembly return spring and remove retaining snap ring.

2) Remove return spring retainer and return springs. Apply compressed air to oil hole in clutch drum and remove clutch piston. Remove oil seal from clutch piston and drum.

Fig. 9: Using Compressed Air to Remove Reverse Clutch Piston

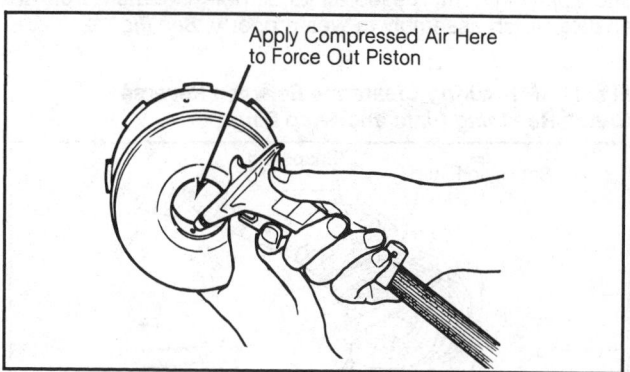

Apply Compressed Air Here to Force Out Piston

Reassembly

1) To reassemble, reverse disassembly procedure. Coat all parts with automatic transmission fluid before installation. When installing clutch plates into drum, start with the dished plate, then install a driven (steel) plate followed by a drive (lined) plate and alternate driven plates and drive plates until all plates are installed.

NOTE: The reverse clutch assembly clutch pack consists of dished plate, 3 driven (steel) plates and 3 drive (lined) plates. When installing driven plates, be sure to align missing tooth portion with oil hole in clutch drum.

2) Using a feeler gauge, check clearance between retaining plate and clutch assembly snap ring.

Fig. 10: Exploded View of Reverse Clutch Assembly

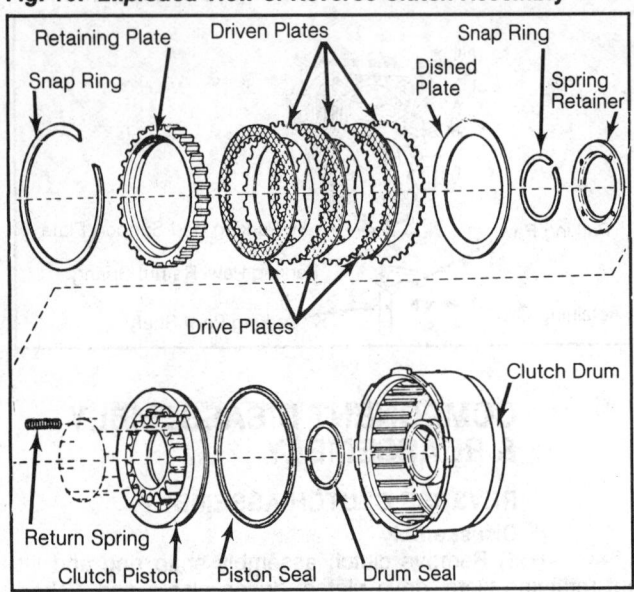

Clearance should be .063-.071" (1.6-1.8 mm). If clearance is not within specifications, correct by installing a retaining plate of different thickness.

3) Reverse clutch retaining plates are available in thicknesses of .417" (10.6 mm) to .457" (11.6 mm) in .008" (.2 mm) increments.

4) After clutch assembly is completed, check operation by installing clutch assembly to oil pump carrier and applying compressed air to oil hole in clutch drum to ensure clutch assembly moves properly. *See Fig. 12.*

Fig. 11: Measuring Clearance Between Reverse Clutch Retaining Plate and Snap Ring

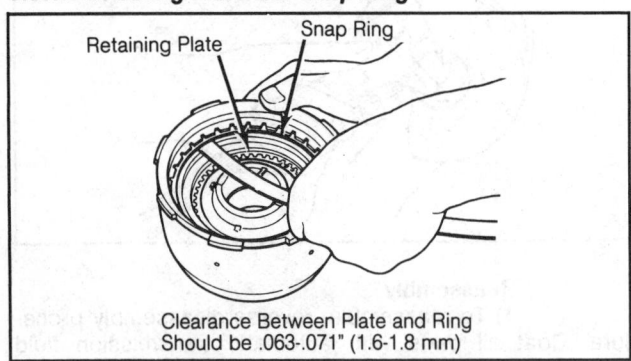

Clearance Between Plate and Ring Should be .063-.071" (1.6-1.8 mm)

Fig. 12: Using Compressed Air to Check Operation of Reverse Clutch Assembly

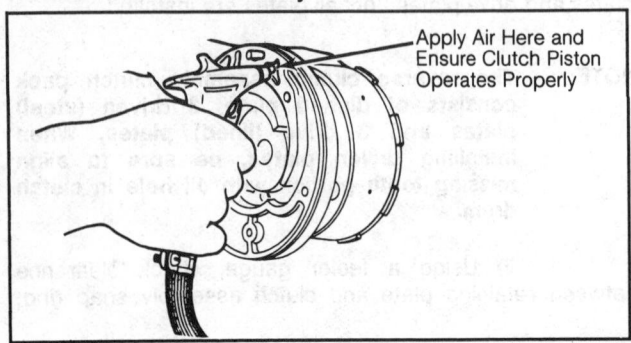

Apply Air Here and Ensure Clutch Piston Operates Properly

FORWARD CLUTCH ASSEMBLY
Disassembly
Remove forward clutch assembly snap ring and lift out retaining plate, drive and driven clutch plates, and dished plate. Compress clutch return springs and remove snap ring. Apply compressed air to oil hole in clutch drum and force out clutch piston.

Fig. 13: Using Compressed Air to Remove Forward Clutch Piston

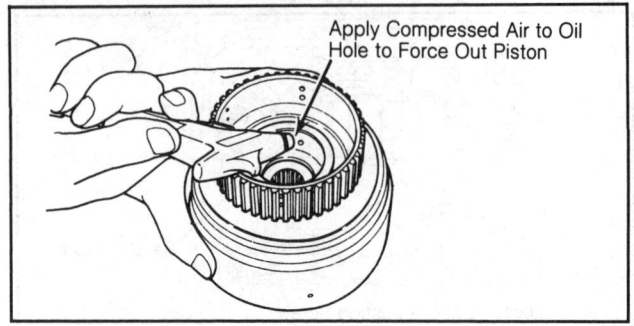

Apply Compressed Air to Oil Hole to Force Out Piston

Reassembly
1) To reassemble, reverse disassembly procedure. Coat all parts with automatic transmission fluid before reassembly. When installing clutch pack into clutch drum, start with the dished plate, then install a driven (steel) plate followed by a drive (lined) plate and alternate driven and drive plates until all clutch plates are installed.

NOTE: **Forward clutch pack consists of 3 driven (steel) and 3 drive (lined) plates.**

2) Check clearance between retaining plate and clutch assembly snap ring using a feeler gauge. Clearance should be .039-.059" (1.0-1.5 mm).

Fig. 14: Exploded View of Forward Clutch Assembly

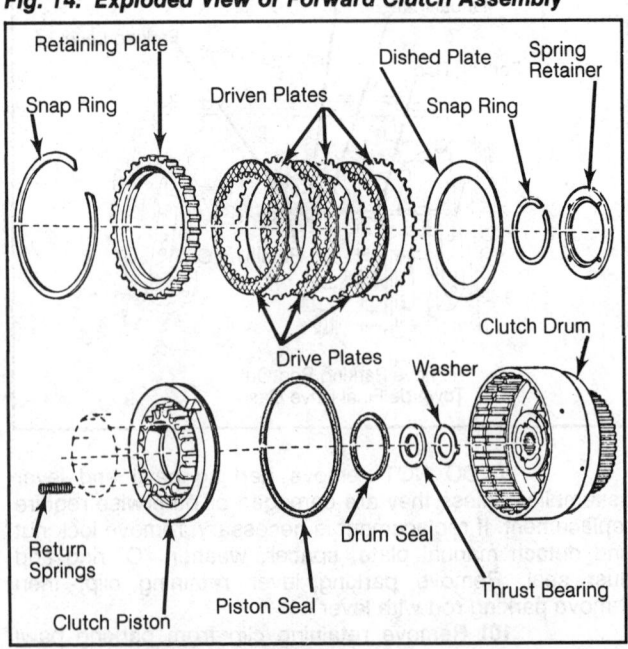

3) With reassembly completed, install forward and reverse clutches on oil pump carrier. Apply compressed air to oil hole in forward clutch drum to make sure clutch piston operates properly.

SUBARU MODEL M41A (Cont.)

Fig. 15: Measuring Clearance Between Forward Clutch Retaining Plate and Snap Ring

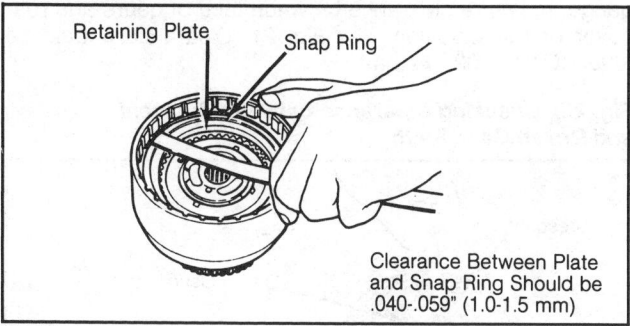

Retaining Plate

Snap Ring

Clearance Between Plate and Snap Ring Should be .040-.059" (1.0-1.5 mm)

Fig. 16: Using Compressed Air to Check Operation of Forward Clutch Assembly

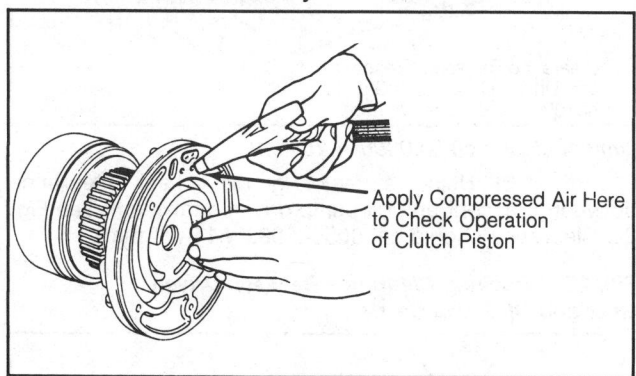

Apply Compressed Air Here to Check Operation of Clutch Piston

CENTER SUPPORT AND LOW-REVERSE BRAKE ASSEMBLY

NOTE: **Low-reverse brake plates were removed at Transmission Disassembly and will be installed at Transmission Reassembly.**

Disassembly

Using a compressor tool, compress low-reverse piston return spring and remove return spring snap ring, then lift out return spring and thrust ring. Apply compressed air to oil hole in center support and force low-reverse brake piston from center support. Remove oil seals from brake piston.

Reassembly

To install, reverse disassembly procedure. Coat all parts with automatic transmission fluid before reassembly. When installing clutch piston to center support, use care not to damage piston oil seals.

GOVERNOR ASSEMBLY

NOTE: **Governor assembly is mounted in final drive case.**

Removal

Remove attaching bolts and lift off governor cover, then pull governor assembly straight out of case. Remove 2 attaching bolts and pull governor sleeve out of case.

Disassembly

Remove "E" clip and snap ring from ends of valve body. Remove valve, springs and related components from valve body. Remove 2 governor shaft-to-valve body retaining bolts and separate valve body from shaft.

Fig. 17: Exploded View of Center Support and Low-Reverse Brake Assembly

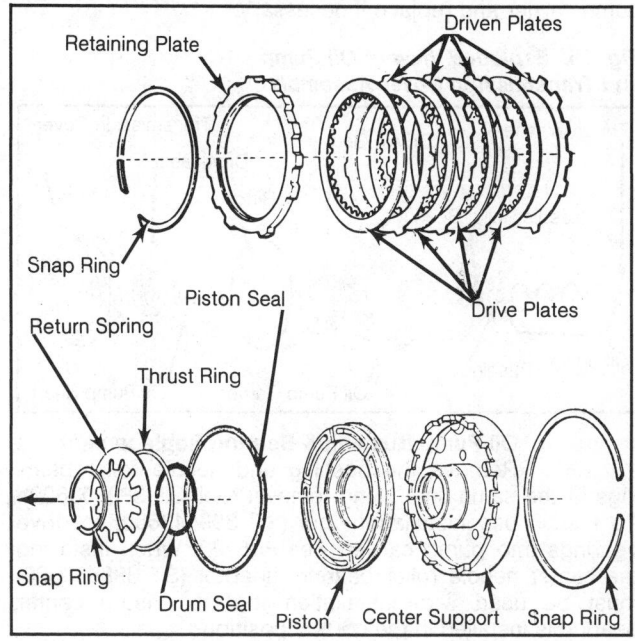

Retaining Plate

Driven Plates

Snap Ring

Piston Seal

Return Spring

Thrust Ring

Drive Plates

Snap Ring

Drum Seal

Piston

Center Support

Snap Ring

Reassembly

To reassemble, reverse disassembly procedure. Inspect all parts for wear or damage and replace as necessary. Make sure large weight moves freely in governor bore when reassembly is completed. Inspect governor shaft oil seals and replace if worn or damaged.

Installation

To install, reverse removal procedure. Use care to prevent damage to oil seals when installing governor assembly.

Fig. 18: Exploded View of Governor Assembly

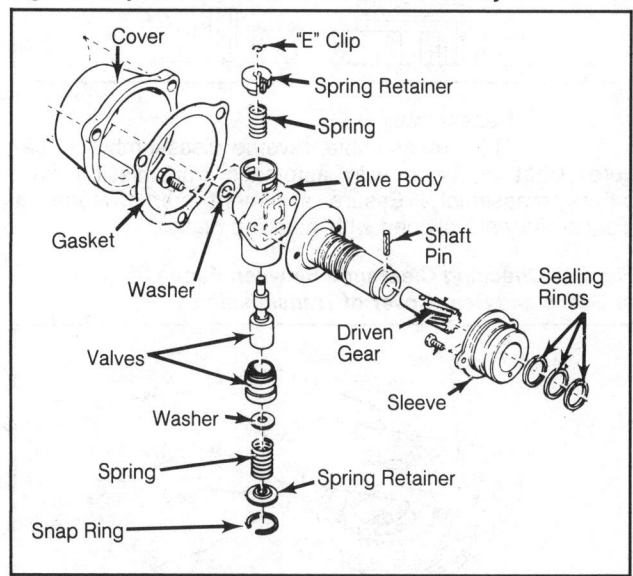

Cover

"E" Clip

Spring Retainer

Spring

Valve Body

Gasket

Shaft Pin

Washer

Sealing Rings

Valves

Driven Gear

Washer

Sleeve

Spring

Spring Retainer

Snap Ring

OIL PUMP

Disassembly

Remove bolts and separate oil pump carrier from transmission rear cover. Mark drive and driven gears for reassembly in their original position. Inspect oil pump gears for wear or damage and replace as necessary. Inspect the bushing and 2 needle roller bearings located in pump carrier and replace if necessary.

Fig. 19: Exploded View of Oil Pump and Transmission Cover Assembly

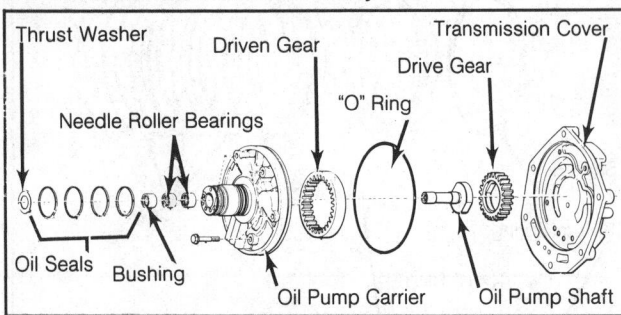

Oil Pump Bushing & Bearing Replacement

Remove the bushing and needle roller bearings at the same time using removal tool (ST 399903600). To install, use installation tool (ST 399543600) to drive bearings into pump carrier. *See Fig. 20.* When installing the center needle roller bearing, adaptor (ST 398863600) must be used with installation tool to ensure center bearing is installed in the correct position.

Fig. 20: Installation of Bushing and Bearings into Oil Pump Carrier

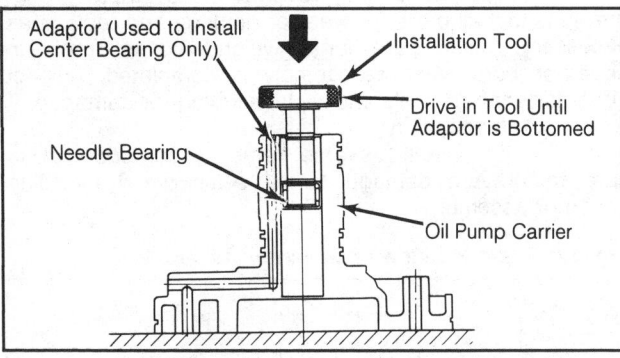

Reassembly

1) To reassemble, reverse disassembly procedure. Coat all parts with automatic transmission fluid before reassembly. Ensure alignment marks made at disassembly are aligned with installing gears.

Fig. 21: Checking Clearance Between Face of Gears and Rear Cover of Transmission

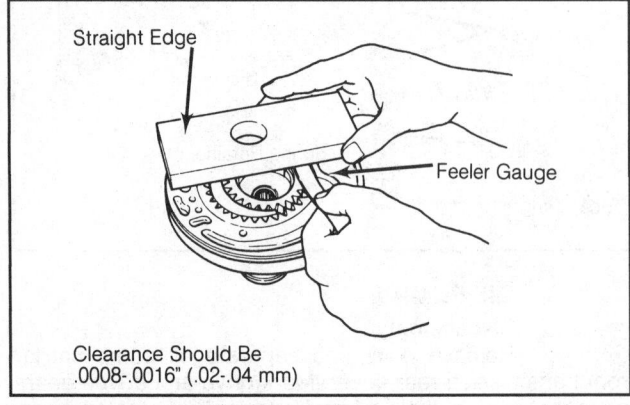

Limit of clearance is .0031" (.08 mm).

2) With drive and driven gears installed, check oil pump clearances. Using a straightedge and feeler gauge, measure clearance between face of gears and rear cover of transmission. *See Fig. 21.* Clearance should be .0008-.0016" (.02-.04 mm).

Fig. 22: Checking Clearance Between Crescent and Driven Gear Teeth

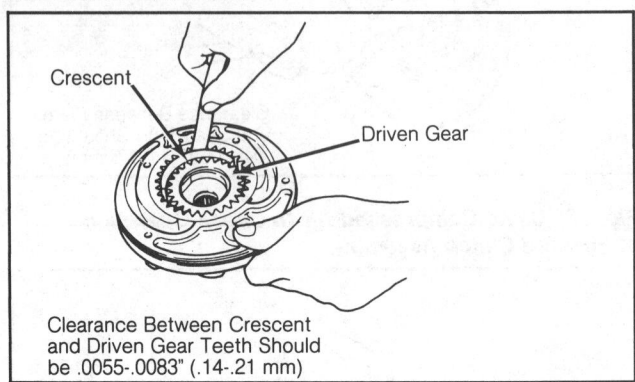

Limit of clearance is .0098" (.25 mm).

3) Using a feeler gauge, check clearance between crescent and oil pump driven gear teeth. *See Fig. 22.* Clearance should be .0055-.0083" (.14-.21 mm).

Fig. 23: Checking Clearance Between Driven Gear and Oil Pump Carrier

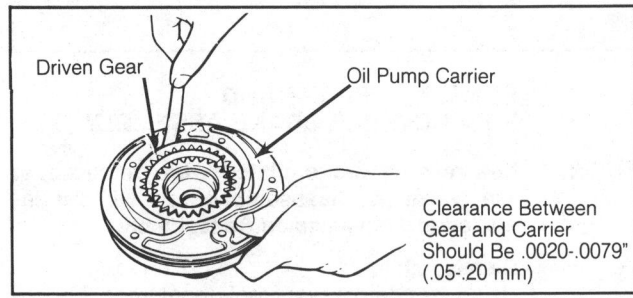

Limit of clearance is .0098" (.25 mm).

4) Using a feeler gauge, check clearance between oil pump driven gear and oil pump carrier. *See Fig. 23.* Clearance should be .0020-.0079" (.05-.20 mm).

5) If clearance obtained in step **2)** exceeds .0031" (.08 mm), replace pump gears. If clearance obtained in step **3)** or **4)** exceeds .0098" (.25 mm), replace pump gears. Pump gears must always be replaced as a matched set.

PLANETARY GEAR UNIT

Disassembly

Remove bolts securing one-way clutch outer race to planetary gear unit and separate one-way clutch from planetary gear unit. Push pinion pins out toward one-way clutch and remove short pinions, long pinions, thrust washers, needle roller bearings, spacers and thrust bearing. Separate one-way clutch from outer race.

Reassembly

1) To reassemble, reverse disassembly procedure. Use illustration for an assembly guide. *See Fig. 24.* Coat all parts with automatic transmission fluid. When installing one-way clutch on outer race, push "T" bar with finger to insert one-way clutch until a snap is felt, then secure retainer to outer race.

SUBARU MODEL M41A (Cont.)

Fig. 24: *Exploded View of Planetary Gear Assembly*

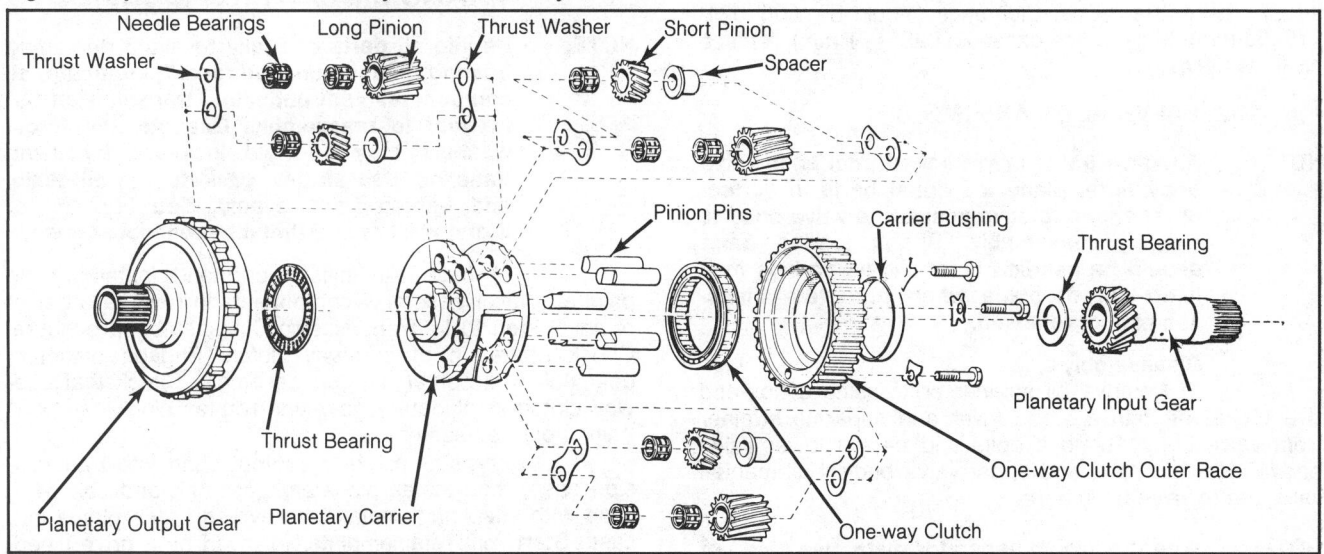

Fig. 25: *Exploded View of Valve Body Assembly*

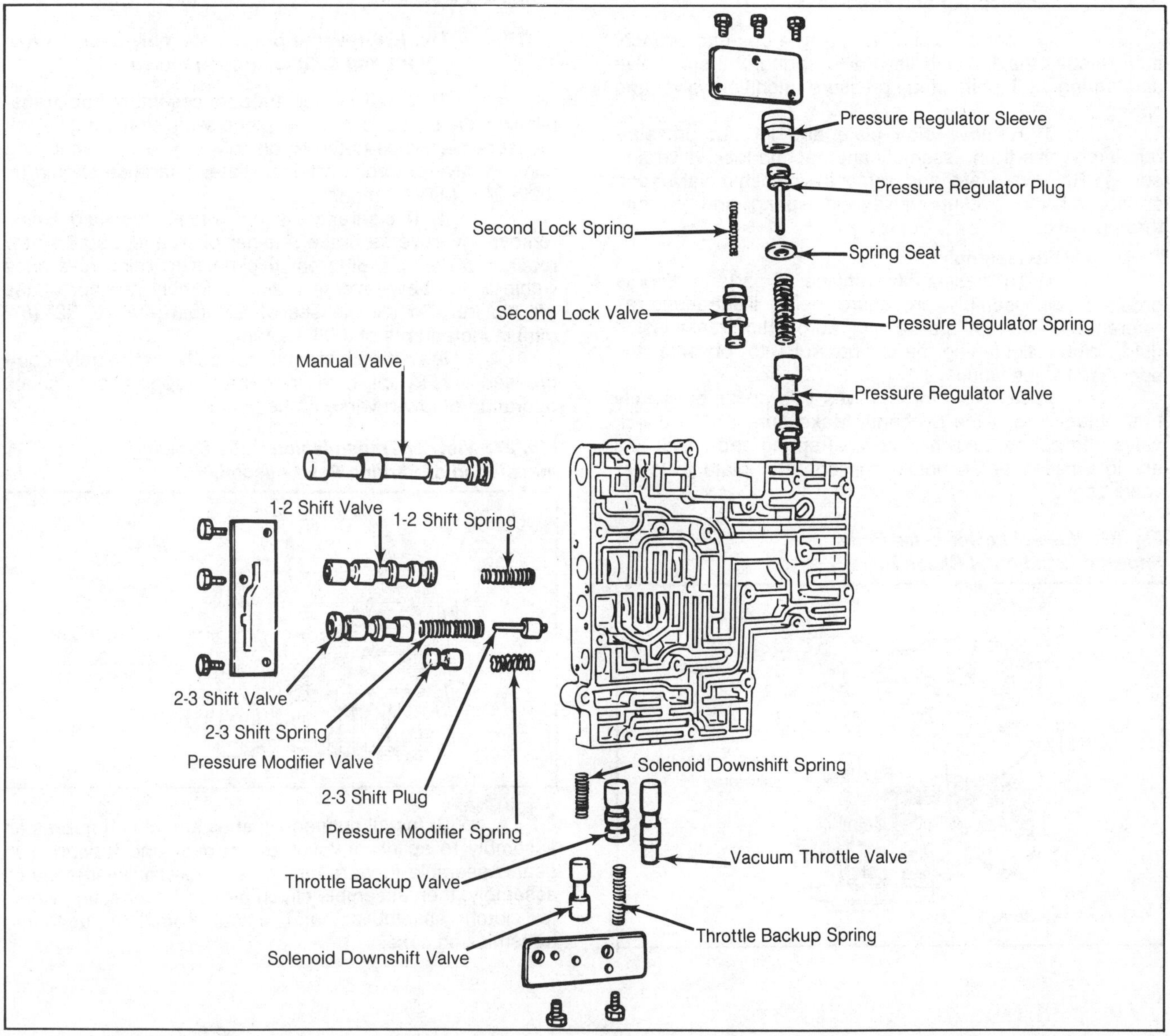

SUBARU MODEL M41A (Cont.)

2) After reassembly, check planetary carrier-to-thrust washer clearance. Clearance should be .006-.024" (.15-.60 mm). If clearance exceeds .028" (.71 mm), replace parts as necessary.

VALVE BODY ASSEMBLY

NOTE: As valve trains are removed from each valve body bore, place individual parts in correct order and in relative position to valve body to simplify reassembly. Spring loaded parts should be handled carefully, as springs may jump out of place when parts are disassembled or removed.

Disassembly

1) Remove oil strainer bolts using a box-end wrench rather than a screwdriver and separate strainer from valve body. Remove bolts and detach lower valve body, separator plate and upper valve body. Pull manual valve out of valve body bore.

NOTE: When removing separator plate, use care not to lose orifice check valve, spring, throttle relief spring and check ball.

2) Remove side plate using a box-end wrench, then remove the 1-2 shift valve and spring, 2-3 shift valve and spring, 2-3 shift plug, pressure modifier valve and spring.

3) Remove side plate and lift out pressure regulator valve train assembly and second lock valve and spring. Remove plate and remove downshift valve and spring, throttle backup valve and spring and vacuum throttle valve.

Reassembly

1) To reassemble, replace all parts in reverse order of disassembly procedure using illustrations as references. Coat all parts with automatic transmission fluid. When tightening parts, be sure to observe the specified torque values.

2) DO NOT force valves into place, but lightly push them into place by hand. Make sure orifice check valve and spring, and throttle relief spring and check ball are in position before installing separator plate to lower valve body.

Fig. 26: View of Lower Valve Body Showing Location of Check Balls

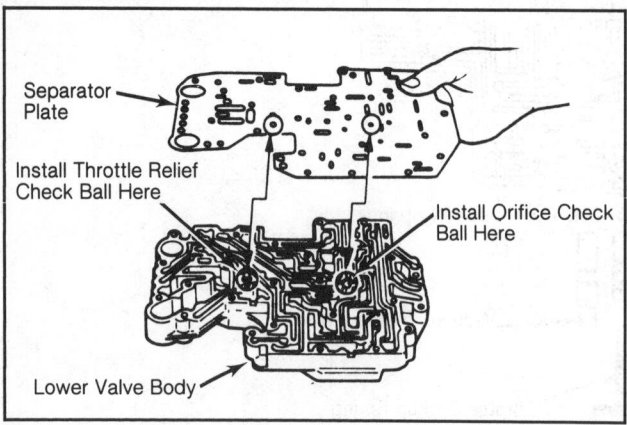

TRANSMISSION REASSEMBLY

NOTE: Handle all parts carefully to avoid damaging bearing and mating surfaces. Lubricate all components with automatic transmission fluid prior to reassembly. Gaskets and thrust washers may be held in place by using Vaseline. Use all new gaskets and oil seals, and tighten bolts evenly. See Fig. 36 for thrust washer and thrust bearing locations.

1) Place transmission on stand. Install parking pawl and lever assembly components in reverse order of removal step **8)** in Transmission Disassembly procedure. Check operation of one-way clutch. Engage planetary gear unit with center support assembly. Check that one-way clutch in planetary gear unit rotates clockwise only, then separate assemblies.

2) Install planetary output shaft into transmission case, then install planetary gear unit and secure in case with snap ring. Install low-reverse brake plates into case. Start with retainer plate, followed by a drive (lined) plate, then alternate driven (steel) plates until all brake plates are installed.

NOTE: The low-reverse brake assembly uses 4 drive (lined) and 4 driven (steel) plates.

3) Install center support assembly into transmission case and secure in place with snap ring. Next, measure clearance between planetary gear unit snap ring and low-reverse brake retainer plate; clearance should be .020-.047" (.50-1.2 mm).

4) If clearance is not within specified limits, remove low-reverse brake retainer plate and install a new retainer plate of a different thickness to bring clearance within limits. Low-reverse brake assembly retainer plates are available in thicknesses of .27" (6.8 mm) to .32" (8.2 mm) in increments of .008" (.2 mm).

5) With clearance correctly set, apply compressed air to oil hole in center support and check operation of low-reverse brake piston.

Fig. 27: View of Transmission Case Showing Installation of Parking Pawl Assembly

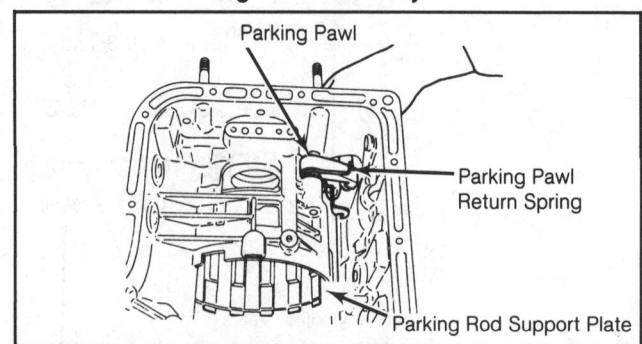

6) Install connecting shell and clutch hub as an assembly to spline of reverse sun gear and forward sun gear. Assemble forward clutch assembly to reverse clutch assembly, then assemble clutch hub and connecting wheel to clutch assemblies and install complete unit into transmission case.

SUBARU MODEL M41A (Cont.)

Fig. 28: *Measuring Clearance Between Snap Ring and Low-Reverse Brake Retainer Plate*

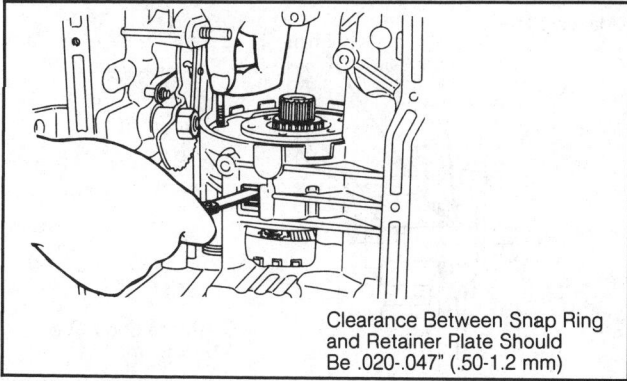

Clearance Between Snap Ring and Retainer Plate Should Be .020-.047" (.50-1.2 mm)

Fig. 29: *Using Compressed Air to Check Operation of Low-Reverse Brake Piston*

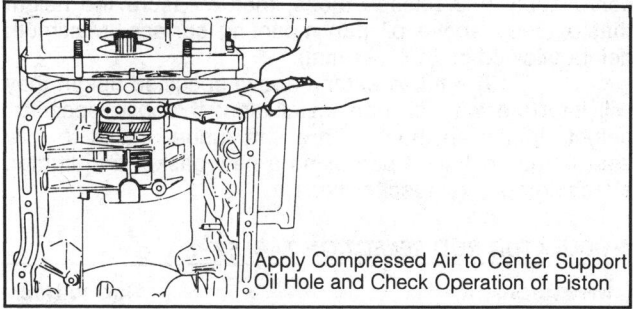

Apply Compressed Air to Center Support Oil Hole and Check Operation of Piston

7) Make sure washer installed between forward clutch assembly and clutch hub is .050" (1.2 mm) thick. Match projected portions of brake band with notches in transmission case to install brake band. Before proceeding with reassembly, it will be necessary to adjust total end play of transmission. Transmission end play is checked and adjusted as follows:

NOTE: Depth gauge block (498147001) and gauge (398643600) must be used to check transmission total end play and reverse clutch end play.

8) Place gauge block on rear face of transmission case, then using depth gauge, measure distance "L" (from forward clutch to top of gauge block). *See Fig. 30.* Next, place gauge block on top of oil pump carrier (with thrust bearing installed).

Fig. 30: *Measuring Distance "L" for Transmission End Play Adjustment*

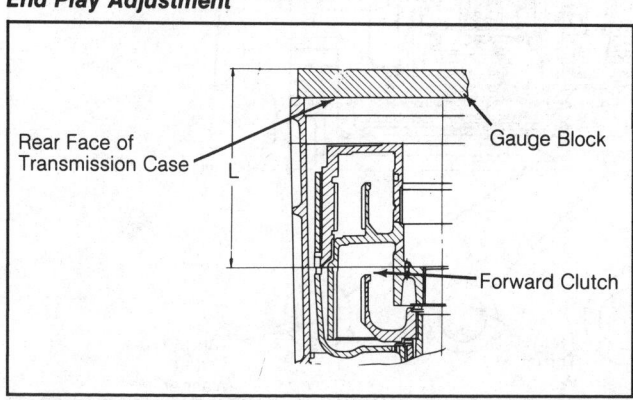

Rear Face of Transmission Case

Gauge Block

L

Forward Clutch

9) Measure distance "I" (from rear cover mounting surface to top of gauge block). *See Fig. 31.* Note both values just obtained for future reference. Add .016" (.4 mm) to distance "L", then subtract the allowable transmission end play of .01-.02" (.25-.50 mm) from this value.

Fig. 31: *Measuring Distance "I" for Transmission End Play Adjustment*

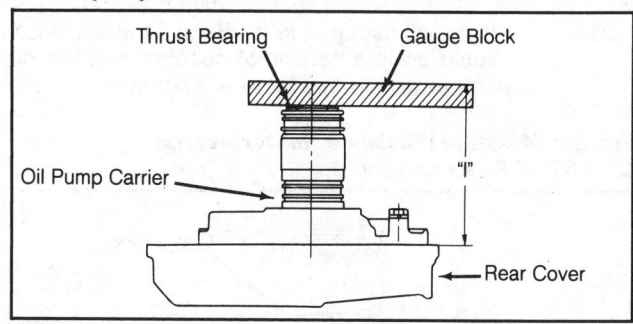

Thrust Bearing   Gauge Block

Oil Pump Carrier

"I"

Rear Cover

10) Next, subtract distance "I" from value just obtained. Final value is thickness of washer to be installed. End play washers are available in thicknesses from .039" (1.0 mm) to .087" (2.2 mm) in increments of .008" (.2 mm).

11) Remove reverse and forward clutch assemblies and install washer between the 2 assemblies, then reassemble clutch assemblies and install them into transmission case. Before installing oil pump carrier and rear cover assembly, reverse clutch drum end play must be checked and adjusted.

12) With oil pump carrier and rear cover on a work bench, place gauge block on rear face of transmission case and measure distance "M" (from rear face of reverse clutch drum to top of gauge block). Next, place gauge block on oil pump face and measure distance "m" (from rear cover mounting surface to top of gauge block). To determine correct thrust washer installation, proceed as follows:

13) Add .016" (.4 mm) to distance "M", then subtract allowable end play of .020-.030" (.5-.8 mm) from this value. Next, subtract distance "m" from value just obtained. Resulting value is thickness of reverse clutch drum thrust washer to be installed. Reverse clutch drum thrust washers are available in thicknesses from .059" (1.5 mm) to .106" (2.7 mm) in increments of .008" (.2 mm).

Fig. 32: *Measuring Distance "M" for Reverse Clutch End Play Adjustment*

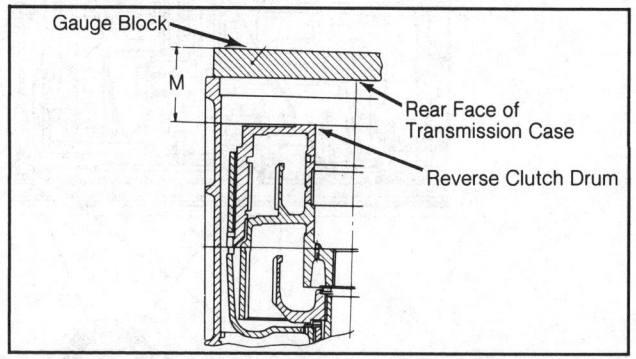

Gauge Block

M

Rear Face of Transmission Case

Reverse Clutch Drum

14) Install correct reverse clutch drum thrust washer on oil pump carrier and retain in place with vaseline. Install oil pump carrier and rear cover assembly

SUBARU MODEL M41A (Cont.)

to transmission case and tighten attaching bolts to specifications. Install servo piston cover assembly into transmission case bore using piston rod as a guide.

15) Be careful when installing servo cover that "O" ring is not damaged. Install brake band apply strut and tighten band adjusting screw just enough to hold apply strut in place. To adjust band, tighten band adjusting screw to 78 INCH lbs. (9 N.m), then back screw off 2 complete turns and tighten lock nut.

NOTE: When adjusting brake band, transmission should be in a horizontal position with the oil pan upward so that band will not jam.

Fig. 33: Measuring Distance "m" for Reverse Clutch End Play Adjustment

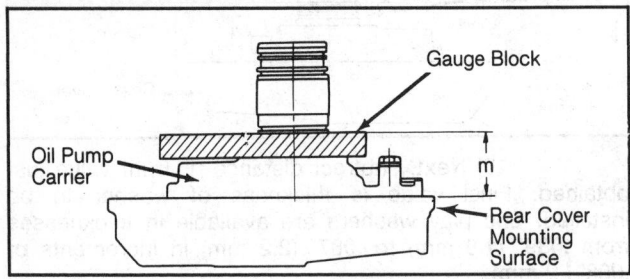

16) Install manual plate onto manual shaft. Using shims, adjust clearance between manual plate and transmission case to .012" (.3 mm). Install neutral safety switch. Install valve body assembly into transmission case, ensuring that groove in manual valve engages notch in manual plate.

17) With valve body installed, fully compress vacuum throttle valve and measure distance from end of valve where modulator rod will seat to outside of transmission case. Resulting measurement will determine length of modulator valve rod to be installed.

Fig. 35: Cross-Section View Showing Manual Plate to Transmission Case Adjustment

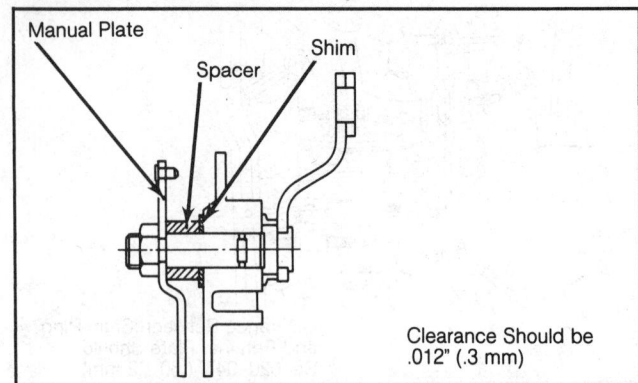

18) Install downshift solenoid assembly into the front hole of the transmission case by hand. Install servo apply and release tubes, then measure the height that extends above oil pan mounting surface. Maximum height allowed in .827" (21 mm).

19) If tubes extend above specified height they will interfere with oil pan installation. If above specified height, lightly tap tubes with a soft rubber mallet to fully seat tubes. Install oil pan using a new gasket and tighten attaching bolts to specifications.

MODULATOR ROD SELECTION TABLE

Measurement In. (mm)	Rod to Use In. (mm)
1.0059 (25.55) or Less	1.14 (29.0)
1.0098-1.0256 (25.65-26.05)	1.16 (29.5)
1.0295-1.0453 (26.15-26.55)	1.18 (30.0)
1.0492-1.0650 (26.65-27.05)	1.20 (30.5)
1.0689 (27.15) or More	1.22 (31.0)

Fig. 34: Cross-Sectional View of Transmission Case Showing Thrust Washer and Thrust Bearing Locations

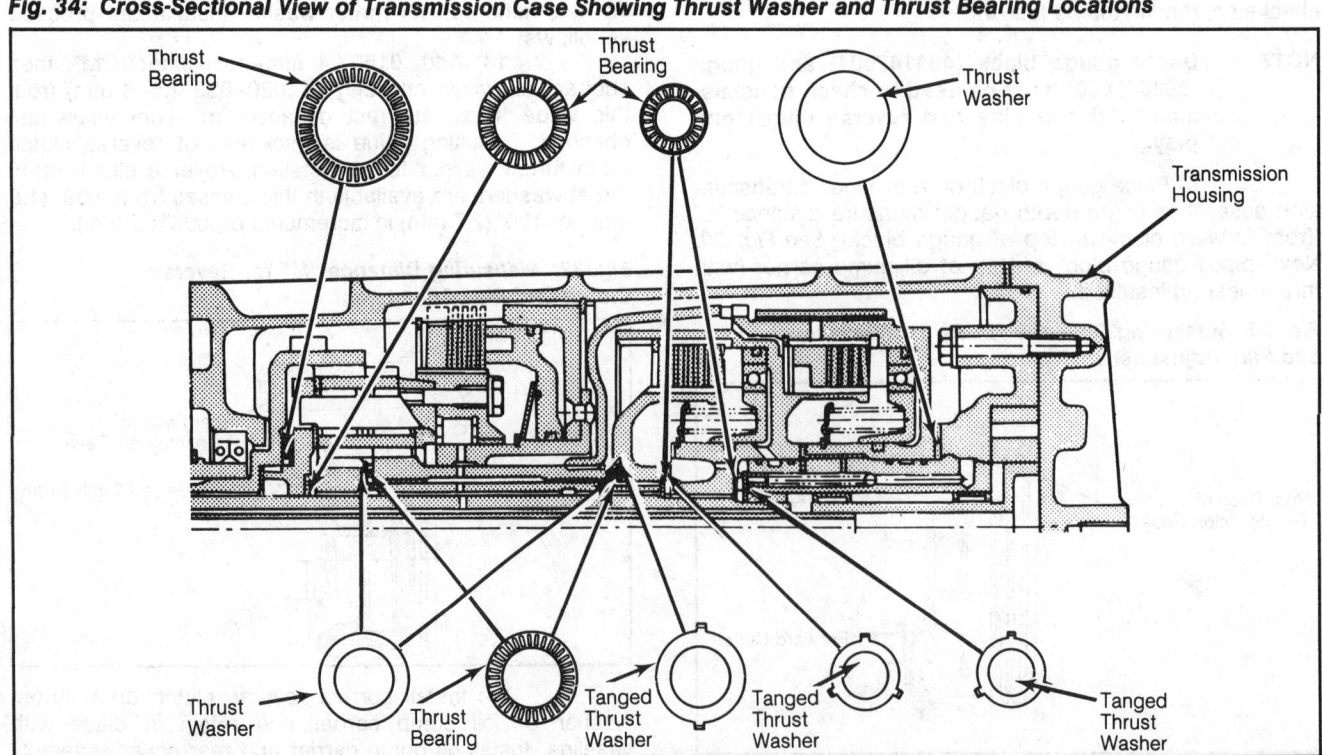

SUBARU MODEL M41A (Cont.)

Fig. 36: Measuring Throttle Valve Depth for Modulator Rod Selection

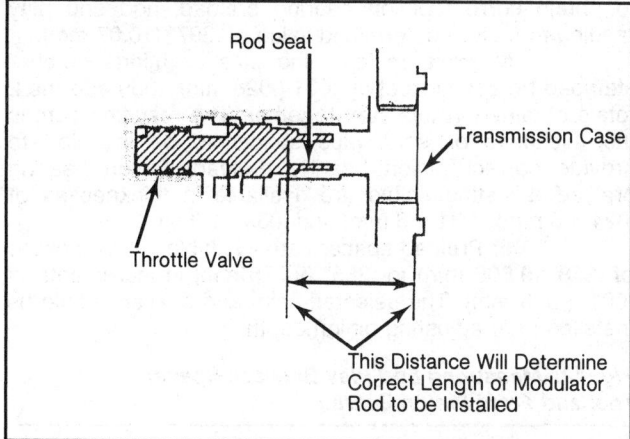

FINAL DRIVE ASSEMBLY

1) Place final drive case on a work stand. Remove bolts attaching torque converter housing to case and separate housing from case. Remove governor cover and pull out governor assembly, then remove attaching bolts and pull out governor sleeve. Remove attaching bolts and lift out parking actuator assembly.

2) Remove axle drive shaft snap rings from inside differential assembly. Wrap vinyl tape over axle shaft splines to protect oil seals. Remove lock plates and remove axle drive shaft oil seal housings and drive shafts as an assembly. Remove oil level gauge. Move differential assembly to one side and lift out of case.

3) Remove snap ring from end of speedometer shaft, and detach driven gear and steel ball. Remove snap ring from speedometer shaft. Lock reduction drive gear in place and remove drive pinion lock nut. Place final drive housing in a press with converter housing mounting surface facing up.

4) Press drive pinion from housing. Press out driven gear and bearing retainer. Invert housing in press and press out reduction drive gear. Remove stator shaft from torque converter housing.

Fig. 37: Pressing Drive Pinion from Final Drive Case

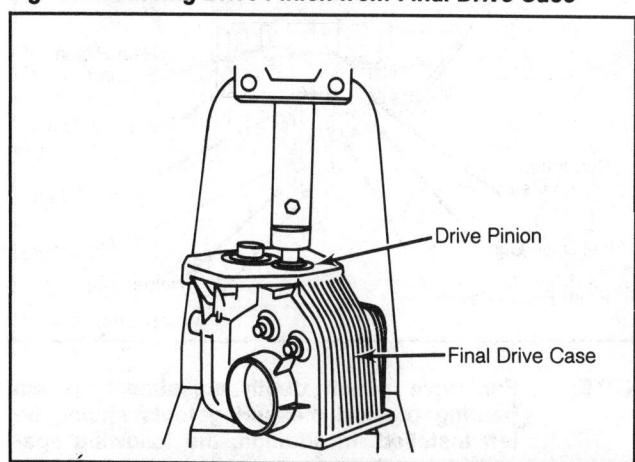

5) Remove right and left side drive shaft retaining snap rings and remove drive shafts from differential assembly. Bend back locking tabs on ring gear

mounting bolt washers, remove mounting bolts and lift ring gear from differential housing.

6) Drive out locking pin and remove differential pinion gear shaft. Lift out pinion gears, side gears and washers. Using a puller, remove differential case bearings.

Fig. 38: Exploded View of Drive Pinion and Reduction Drive Gear Assemblies

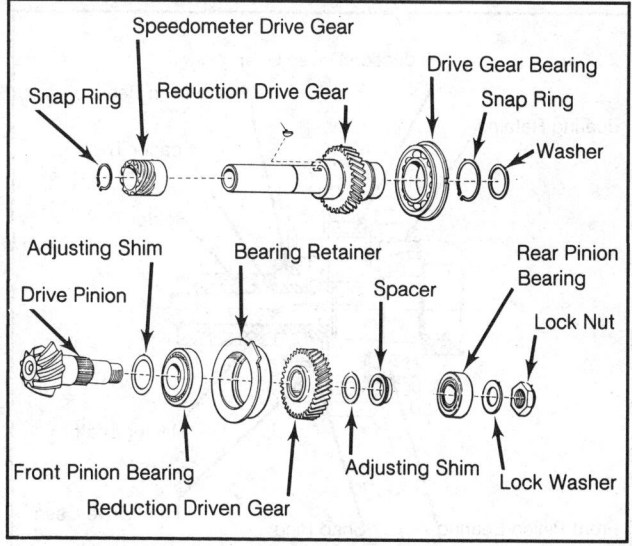

7) If necessary to replace drive pinion front bearing, remove from shaft using puller tool, then drive bearing outer race from final drive case. If necessary to replace reduction drive gear, press from shaft using an arbor press. Check all oil seals and replace as necessary.

Fig. 39: Exploded View of Differential Assembly

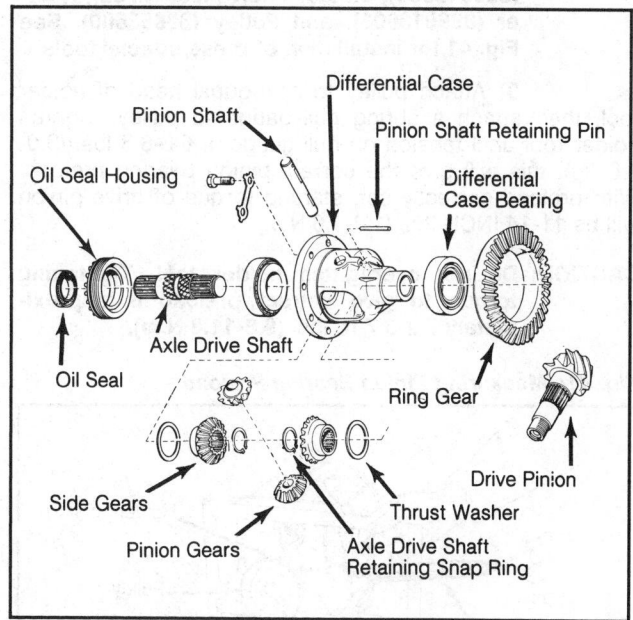

REASSEMBLY & ADJUSTMENT

1) Press drive gear onto reduction drive gear shaft, then install speedometer governor drive gear on shaft and retain with snap ring. Press drive gear shaft into final drive case, then install final drive case on a work stand.

2) To set drive pinion bearing preload, install driven gear and bearing retainer into final drive case. Install front drive pinion bearing, spacer tool, and rear pinion bearing onto master shaft then install master shaft into final drive case. Install holder tool over master shaft, then hold master shaft stationary and tighten holder tool.

Fig. 40: *Installation of Drive Pinion Bearing Preload Measuring Tools*

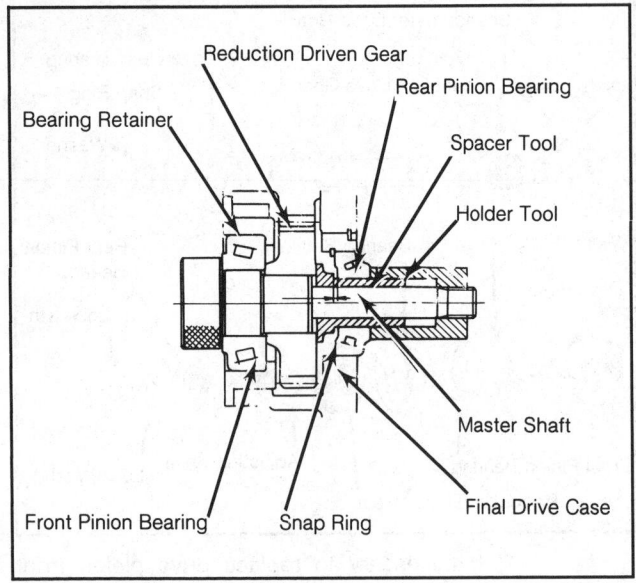

NOTE: Drive pinion bearing preload adjustment must now be performed. The following tools should be used to carry out adjustment: Spacer (399913604), Master Shaft (499912702), Holder (399913603), and Pulley (39853600). See Fig. 41 for installation of these special tools.

3) Attach pulley to hexagonal head of holder tool, then attach a spring pull gauge to pulley. Tighten holder tool until tension on pull gauge is 6.6-8.8 lbs. (3.0-4.0 kg), this will give the correct pinion bearing preload. With preload correctly set, starting torque of drive pinion will be 11-14 INCH lbs. (1.2-1.6 N.m).

CAUTION: Do not overtighten holder tool. Tightening torque to give correct preload is approximately 7.2-8.7 ft. lbs. (9.8-11.8 N.m).

Fig. 41: *Measuring Pinion Bearing Preload*

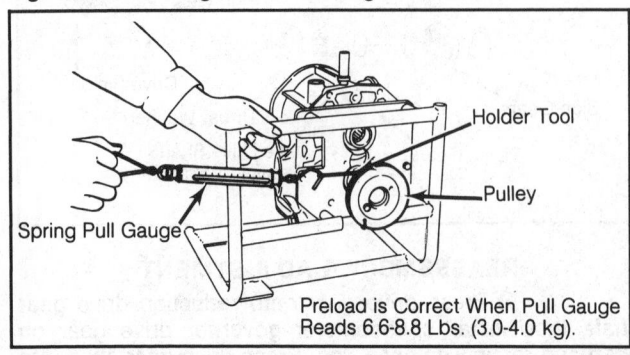

Preload is Correct When Pull Gauge Reads 6.6-8.8 Lbs. (3.0-4.0 kg).

4) With special tools still installed, measure end play between spacer tool (399913604) and front

pinion bearing using dial indicator. *See Fig. 42.* To determine correct combination of shim and spacer needed to obtain correct pinion bearing preload, add end play reading to factory determined value of .397" (10.07 mm).

5) Next, multiply the plus or minus number stamped on spacer tool by .001 (.026 mm), then add the 2 totals obtained in this step together. The resulting sum is the thickness or shim plus spacer to be installed to provide correct pinion bearing preload. Pinion bearing preload adjusting shims are available in thicknesses of .024" (.6 mm), .031" (.8 mm) and .039" (1.0 mm).

6) Preload spacers are available in thicknesses of .378" (9.600 mm) to .385" (9.775 mm) in increments of .001" (.025 mm). The selected shim and spacer should be installed after adjusting pinion depth.

Fig. 42: *Measuring End Play Between Spacer Tool and Front Pinion Bearing*

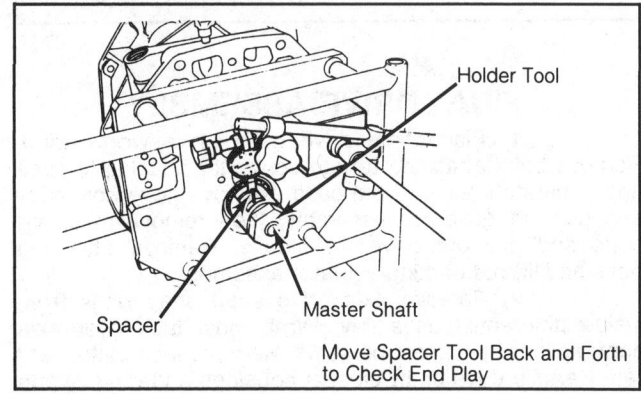

Move Spacer Tool Back and Forth to Check End Play

Fig. 43: *Installation of Drive Pinion Depth Measuring Tools*

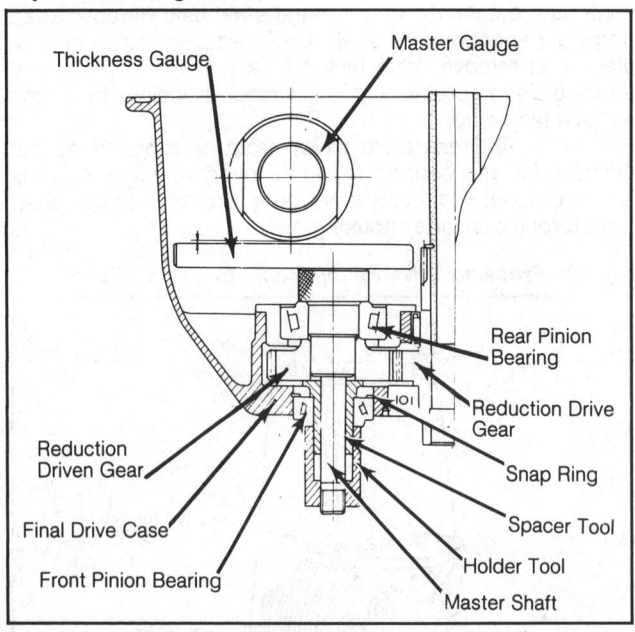

NOTE: For drive pinion depth adjustment, pinion bearing preload measuring tools should be left installed. In addition, the following special pinion depth measuring tools should be installed as shown in Fig. 44: Thickness gauge (398643600) and Master guage (399913601).

SUBARU MODEL M41A (Cont.)

7) To adjust drive pinion depth, leave preload tools installed, then install thickness gauge and master gauge into final drive case. Measure and record clearance between thickness gauge and master gauge. To determine thickness of pinion depth adjusting shim(s) to be installed, proceed as follows:

Step 1: Multiply the plus or minus figure on master gauge (499917002) by .001 and record the result.

Step 2: Multiply the plus or minus figure on thickness gauge (39863600) by .001 and record the result.

Step 3: Measure clearance between master gauge and thickness gauge and record the result. *See Fig. 44.*

Step 4: Add totals of step 1, 2 and 3. The resulting sum is the shim thickness required for correct drive pinion depth.

Fig. 44: *Measuring Clearance Between Master Gauge and Thickness Gauge for Pinion Depth Adjustment*

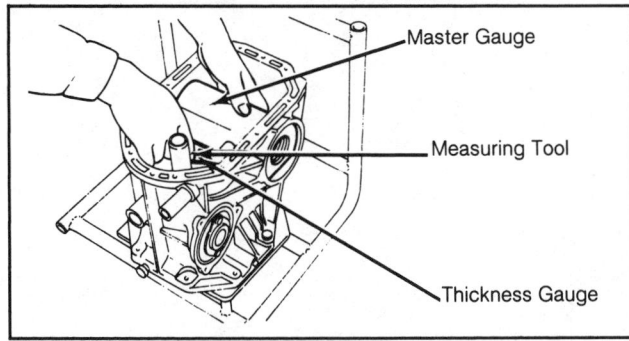

Master Gauge

Measuring Tool

Thickness Gauge

8) Up to 3 adjusting shims may be installed to set pinion depth. Adjusting shims are available in thicknesses from .006" (.15 mm) to .02 (.50 mm) in increments of .001" (.025 mm). Remove and disassemble all measuring tools. Install selected pinion depth adjusting shim(s) onto drive pinion, then press on front pinion bearing.

9) Install drive pinion into final drive case. Install selected pinion bearing preload shim and spacer followed by rear pinion onto drive pinion, then install lock washer and nut and tighten nut to specifications. Install final drive case to a work stand and attach pulley and spring pull gauge to pinion lock nut.

10) Recheck pinion bearing preload and adjust as necessary. To reassemble differential assembly, proceed as follows: Install differential side gears with thrust washers and differential pinion gears into differential housing, then install pinion gear shaft. Using a dial indicator, measure backlash between pinion gears and side gears.

11) Backlash should be .002-.006" (.05-.15 mm). If backlash is not within specifications, correct by installing side gear thrust washers of a different thickness. Side gear thrust washers are available in thicknesses from .036" (.93 mm) to .041" (1.05 mm) in increments of .001" (.025 mm).

12) Align holes in differential housing with hole in pinion gear shaft and install locking pin until it is approximately .040" (1 mm) below hole. Press differential bearings onto differential housing. Place ring gear in position on differential housing.

13) Install NEW lock washers, then install attaching bolts and tighten to specifications. Lock in place by bending up tabs on lock washers. Install differential assembly into final drive case, then install both axle drive shafts and lock in place with snap rings.

14) Check clearance between differential pinion shaft and axle drive shafts using a feeler gauge. Clearance should be .008" (.2 mm) or less. If clearance is greater than specifications, install a snap ring of different thickness. Axle drive shaft snap rings are available in 2 thicknesses: .041" (1.05 mm) and .047" (1.2 mm).

15) Install new oil seals into axle drive shaft oil seal housings. Install ring gear side oil seal housing into final drive case, then turn reduction drive gear shaft several times and screw housing in until it bottoms lightly. Repeat this procedure several times, then screw in housing on opposite side until it bottoms.

16) Install lock plate for oil seal housing on ring gear side of final drive case, then back oil seal housing off approximately 1.5 notches and tighten housing on opposite side of case. Temporarily tighten lock plate on ring gear side, then screw in oil seal housing on other side an additional 1/2 turn to one notch and tighten lock plate.

17) Mount a dial indicator on final drive case with indicator tip touching ring gear teeth and check ring gear back lash; ring gear back lash should be .004-.007" (.10-.18 mm). If back lash is not within specifications, recheck drive pinion depth adjustment and correct as necessary.

18) After ring gear back lash is checked and adjusted (if necessary), tighten axle drive shaft housing locking plates to specifications.

NOTE: As an additional check, a Gear Tooth Pattern test may be performed. See Gear Tooth Contact Pattern in GENERAL SERVICING Section.

19) Install governor assembly sleeve into final drive case with drain hole facing down, then install attaching bolts and tighten to specifications. Apply a coating of Vaseline to governor assembly needle roller bearing and oil seal lips, then install governor assembly to case.

20) Install new gasket and install governor cover and tighten attaching bolts to specifications. Install stator shaft to torque converter housing and tighten attaching bolts, then install a new oil seal on stator shaft with flat face against shaft.

21) Coat drive gear shaft with gear oil, then install a new gasket and attach converter housing to final drive case and tighten attaching bolts to specifications. Install parking actuator assembly into final drive case.

Fig. 45: *Oil Port Positioning*

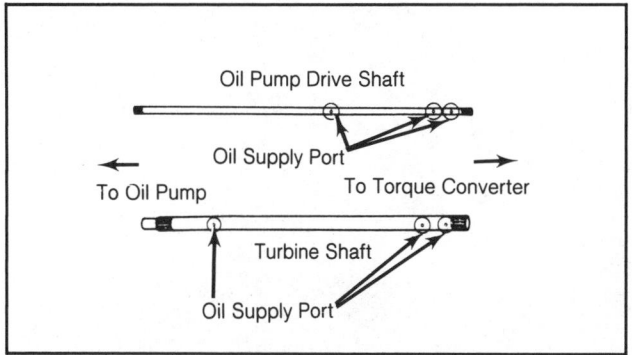

Oil Pump Drive Shaft

Oil Supply Port

To Oil Pump

To Torque Converter

Turbine Shaft

Oil Supply Port

SUBARU MODEL M41A (Cont.)

Final Assembly

1) Place final drive assembly on a flat surface with converter housing facing down. Place a new gasket on final drive case and install transmission case, then install and tighten attaching bolts. Be careful that parking rod and actuator engage properly and sealing lip is not damaged.

2) Make sure that the reduction drive gear and planetary output gear are engaged. Install turbine shaft and oil pump drive shaft into forward side of transmission case, with oil ports arranged as shown. *See Fig. 45.*

3) Install torque converter to stator shaft and ensure that converter is aligned with splines of stator shaft, turbine shaft, and pump drive shaft. Install vacuum pipe, oil supply pipe, ground wire and oil cooler pipe.

TIGHTENING SPECIFICATIONS

Application	Ft. Lbs. (N.m)
Band Adjust Screw Lock Nut	18-21 (24-29)
Converter Hsg.-to-Reduction Gear Case	17-20 (23-27)
Drive Plate-to-Converter	17-20 (23-27)
Drive Plate-to-Crankshaft	36-39 (49-53)
Drive Pinion Lock Nut	68-76 (92-103)
Manual Plate-to-Trans. Case	25-33 (34-45)
Oil Pump Assembly	17-20 (23-27)
Stator Shaft Flange	17-20 (23-27)
Trans. Case-to-Reduction Gear Case	17-20 (23-27)
Transmission-to-Engine	34-40 (46-54)

TORQUEFLITE

Arrow Pickup, Challenger, Ram-50
Pickup, Sapporo

TRANSMISSION IDENTIFICATION

Three groups of numbers, stamped on left side of case just above oil pan mating surface, identify transmission. First group is a 7 digit part number, center group is a 4 digit number code indicating date of manufacture, and last group of numbers are the transmission serial number. This transmission is referred to as a MA-904 for Challenger and Saporro models or a model MA-904A for Arrow Pickup and Ram-50 Pickup models.

DESCRIPTION

Three groups of numbers, stamped on left side of case just above oil pan mating surface, identify transmission. First group is a 7 digit part number, center group is a 4 digit number code indicating date of manufacture, and last group is the transmission serial number. This transmission is referred to as a MA-904 for Challenger and Sapporo models or a model MA-904A for Arrow Pickup and Ram-50 Pickup models.

LUBRICATION & ADJUSTMENT

See the appropriate article in AUTOMATIC TRANSMISSION SERVICING Section.

TROUBLE SHOOTING

HARSH ENGAGEMENT FROM NEUTRAL TO "D" OR "R"

Engine idle speed too high. Valve body malfunction or leakage. Oil pressure too high. Worn or faulty rear clutch.

DELAYED ENGAGEMENT FROM NEUTRAL TO "D" OR "R"

Oil pressure too low. Valve body malfunction or leakage. Low-reverse servo, band or linkage malfunction. Low fluid level. Incorrect shift linkage adjustment. Oil filter clogged. Faulty oil pump. Worn or broken input shaft seal rings. Aerated fluid. Engine idle speed too low. Worn or broken reaction shaft support seal rings. Worn or faulty front clutch. Worn or faulty rear clutch.

RUNAWAY UPSHIFT

Oil pressure too low. Valve body malfunction or leakage. Low fluid level. Oil filter clogged. Aerated fluid. Incorrect throttle rod adjustment. Worn or broken reaction shaft support seal rings. Kickdown servo, band or linkage malfunction. Worn or faulty front clutch.

NO UPSHIFT

Oil pressure too low. Valve body leakage or malfunction. Low fluid level. Incorrect shift linkage adjustment. Incorrect throttle rod adjustment. Governor support seal rings broken or worn. Worn or broken reaction shaft

Fig. 1: Cutaway View of Torqueflite Transmission Showing Major Components

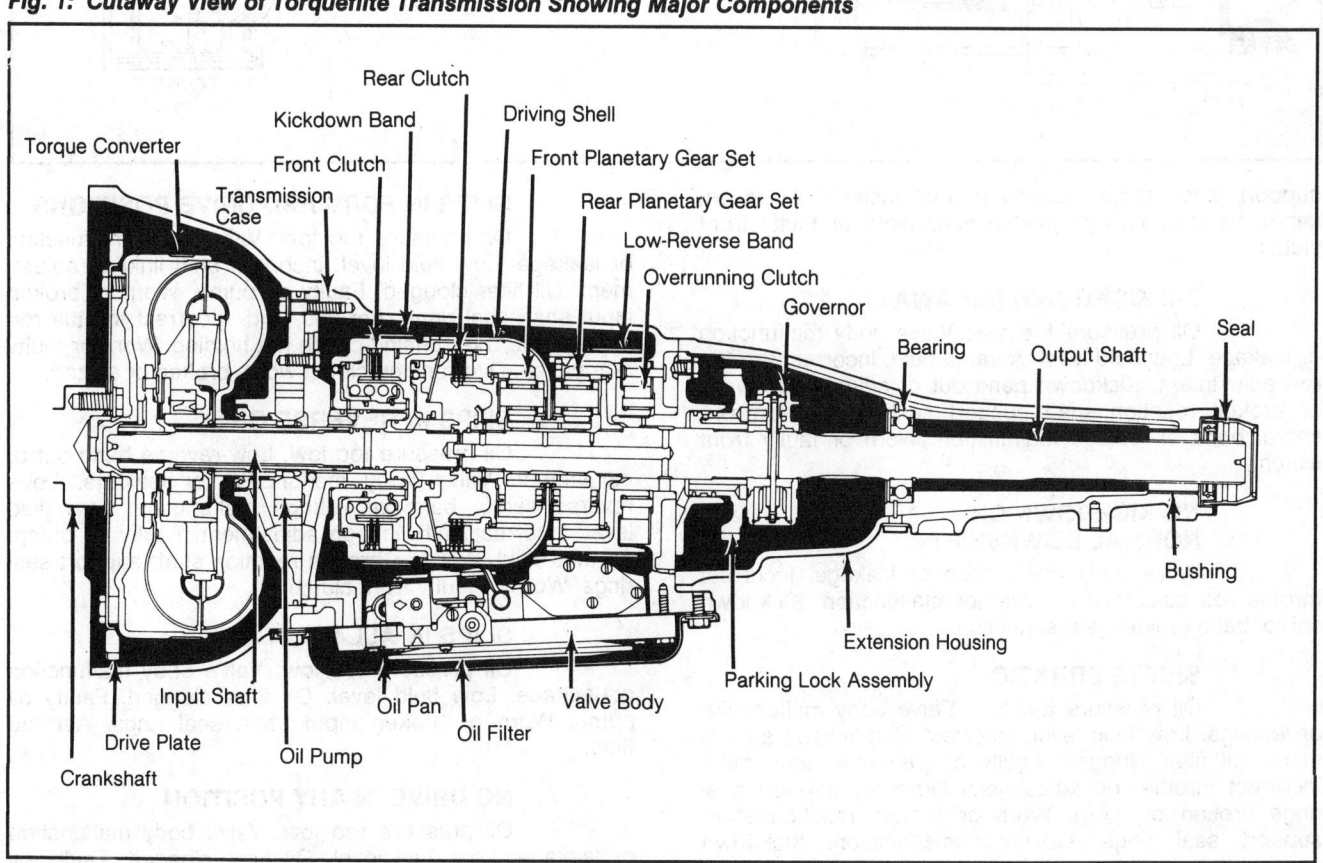

Automatic Transmissions

TORQUEFLITE (Cont.)

Fig. 2: *Torqueflite Automatic Transmission Hydraulic Circuits Diagram*

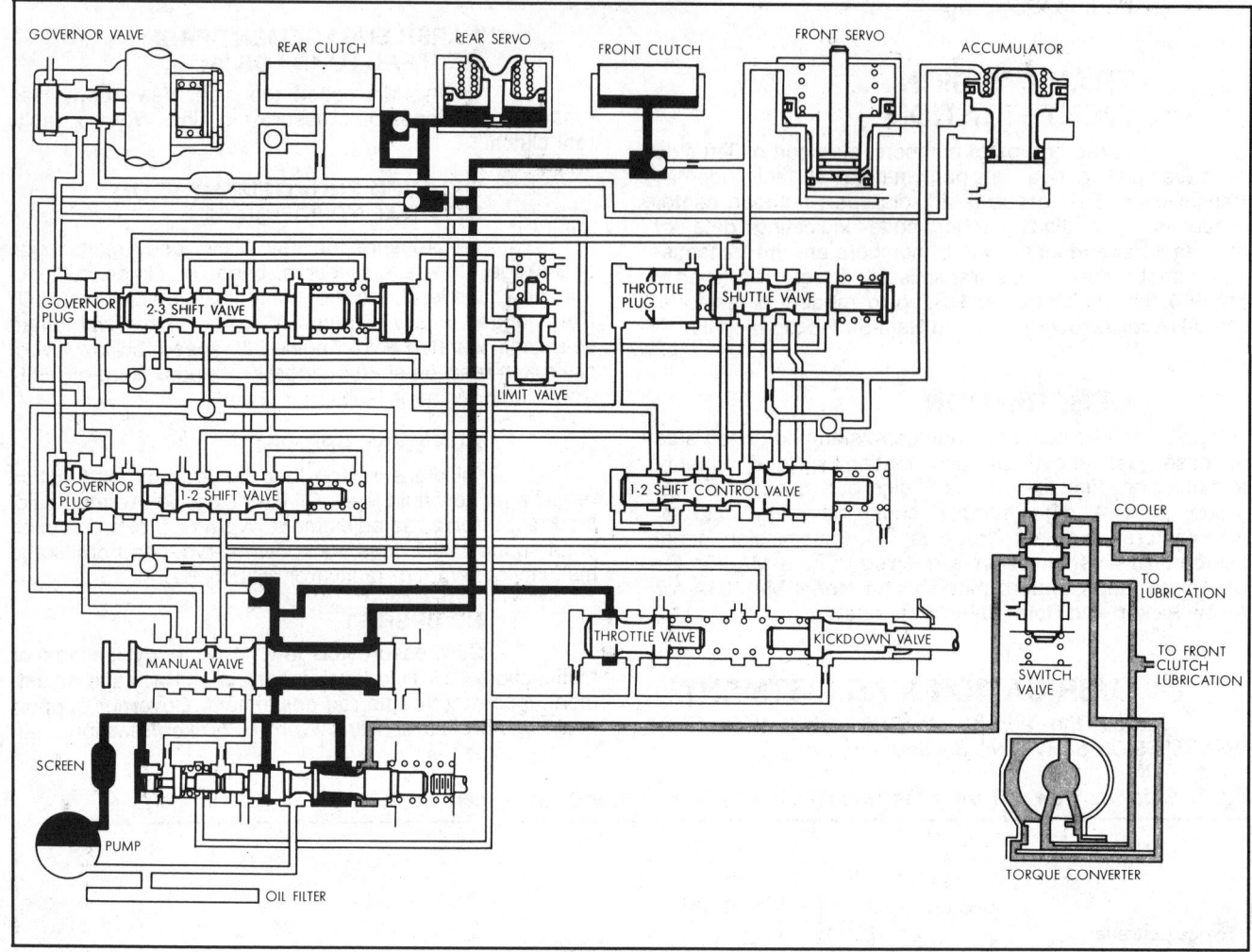

support seal rings. Governor malfunction. Kickdown servo, band or linkage malfunction. Worn or faulty front clutch.

3-2 KICKDOWN RUNAWAY

Oil pressure too low. Valve body malfunction or leakage. Low fluid level. Aerated fluid. Incorrect throttle rod adjustment. Kickdown band out of adjustment. Worn or broken reaction shaft support seal rings. Kickdown servo, band or linkage malfunction. Worn or faulty front clutch.

NO KICKDOWN OR NORMAL DOWNSHIFT

Valve body malfunction or leakage. Incorrect throttle rod adjustment. Governor malfunction. Kickdown servo, band or linkage malfunction.

SHIFTS ERRATIC

Oil pressure too low. Valve body malfunction or leakage. Low fluid level. Incorrect shift linkage adjustment. Oil filter clogged. Faulty oil pump. Aerated fluid. Incorrect throttle rod adjustment. Governor support seal rings broken or worn. Worn or broken reaction shaft support seal rings. Governor malfunction. Kickdown servo, band or linkage malfunction. Worn or faulty front clutch.

SLIPS IN FORWARD DRIVE POSITIONS

Oil pressure too low. Valve body malfunction or leakage. Low fluid level. Incorrect shift linkage adjustment. Oil filter clogged. Faulty oil pump. Worn or broken input shaft seal rings. Aerated fluid. Incorrect throttle rod adjustment. Overrunning clutch not holding. Worn or faulty rear clutch. Overrunning clutch worn, broken or seized.

SLIPS IN REVERSE ONLY

Oil pressure too low. Low-reverse band out of adjustment. Valve body malfunction or leakage. Low-reverse servo, band or linkage malfunction. Low fluid level. Incorrect shift linkage adjustment. Faulty oil pump. Aerated fluid. Worn or broken reaction shaft support seal rings. Worn or faulty front clutch.

SLIPS IN ALL POSITIONS

Oil pressure too low. Valve body malfunction or leakage. Low fluid level. Oil filter clogged. Faulty oil pump. Worn or broken input shaft seal rings. Aerated fluid.

NO DRIVE IN ANY POSITION

Oil pressure too low. Valve body malfunction or leakage. Low fluid level. Oil filter clogged. Faulty oil pump. Planetary gear sets broken or seized.

TORQUEFLITE (Cont.)

NO DRIVE IN FORWARD OR DRIVE

Oil pressure or level too low. Valve body leak or malfunction. Worn or broken input shaft seal rings. Overrunning clutch slipping, worn, broken or siezed. Worn or faulty rear clutch. Planetary gear sets broken or seized.

NO DRIVE IN REVERSE

Oil pressure low. Low-reverse band out of adjustment. Valve body leak or malfunction. Low-reverse servo, band or linkage malfunction. Incorrect shift linkage adjustment. Worn or broken reaction shaft support seal rings. Worn or faulty front or rear clutch. Planetary gear sets broken or seized.

DRIVES IN NEUTRAL

Valve body malfunction or leakage. Incorrect shift linkage adjustment. Insufficient clutch plate clearance. Worn, faulty or dragging rear clutch.

DRAGS OR LOCKS

Low-reverse band out of adjustment. Kickdown band adjustment tight. Planetary gear sets broken or seized. Overrunning clutch worn, broken or seized.

HARSH OR DELAYED UPSHIFT

Oil pressure incorrect. Incorrect throttle rod adjustment. Kickdown band out of adjustment. Governor support or reaction shaft seal rings broken or worn. Governor malfunction. Kickdown servo, band or linkage malfunction. Worn or faulty front clutch.

TRANSMISSION NOISE

Grating, Scraping, Or Growling

Low-reverse band out of adjustment. Output shaft bearing and/or bushing damaged. Planetary gear sets broken or seized. Overrunning clutch worn, broken or seized.

Buzzing

Valve body malfunction or leakage. Low fluid level. Air in fluid. Overrunning clutch inner race damaged.

TESTING

ROAD TEST

1) Before road test, be sure that fluid level and condition, and control linkage adjustments are correct.

During test, transmission should upshift and downshift automatically at approximately the speeds shown chart.

2) Shift speeds may vary somewhat due to production tolerances, rear axle ratio, or tire size. The important factor is the quality of the shifts. All shifts should be smooth, responsive, and with no slipping or engine speed flare-up.

3) Slipping or flare-up in any gear usually indicates clutch, band or overrunning clutch problems. The slipping clutch or band in a particular gear can be identified by noting transmission operation in other selector positions and comparing which internal units are applied in those positions.

4) For example, if transmission slips in "D" third gear, either the front or rear clutch is slipping. By selecting another gear which does not use one of those units, the unit which is slipping can be identified. If transmission slips in reverse, the front clutch is slipping. If transmission does not slip in reverse, the rear clutch is slipping.

5) Although this process of elimination can be used to detect any unit which slips and to confirm proper operation of good units, the actual cause of malfunction usually cannot be decided. Practically any condition can be caused by leaking hydraulic circuits or sticking valves. Therefore, unless an obvious condition exists, transmission should never be disassembled until hydraulic pressure tests have been made.

AUTOMATIC SHIFT SPEEDS & GOVERNOR PRESSURE CHART

Application	[1] MPH
Wide Open Throttle	
1-2 Upshift	35-45
2-3 Upshift	65-75
Kickdown Limit	
3-2 WOT Downshift	52-68
3-1 WOT Downshift	24-34
Governor Pressure	
15 psi	20-21
40 psi	35-40
60 psi	52-57

[1] — All speeds given are approximate. Changes in tire size or axle ratio will correspondingly raise or lower vehicle speed.

CLUTCH AND BAND APPLICATION CHART (ELEMENTS IN USE)

Selector Lever Position	Front Clutch	Rear Clutch	Over-running Clutch	Front (Kickdown) Band	Rear (Low-reverse) Band
D — DRIVE					
First		X	X		
Second		X		X	
Direct	X	X			
2 — SECOND					
First		X	X		
Second		X		X	
L — LOW (First)		X			X
R — REVERSE	X				X

NEUTRAL OR PARK — All clutches and bands released and/or ineffective.

TORQUEFLITE (Cont.)

HYDRAULIC PRESSURE TESTS

Before making pressure tests, be certain that fluid level and condition, and control linkage adjustments have been checked and corrected if necessary. Install an engine tachometer, raise vehicle on hoist which allows rear wheels to turn, and position tachometer so it can be read under vehicle. Disconnect throttle rod and shift rod from transmission levers so they can be controlled under vehicle. Make sure transmission fluid is at normal operating temperature (170°F).

Pressure Test (Selector in "L")

1) Attach 0-100 psi gauges to line and rear servo ports. Operate engine at 1000 RPM for test. Move selector lever on transmission all the way forward ("L" position). Read pressures on both gauges as throttle lever on transmission is moved from full rearward position to full forward position.

2) Line pressure should read 54-60 psi (3.8-4.2 kg/cm²) with throttle lever rearward and gradually increase, as lever is moved forward to 90-95 psi (6.3-6.7 kg/cm²). Rear servo pressure should read the same as line pressure within 3 psi (0.2 kg/cm²). This tests pump output, pressure regulation, and condition of rear clutch and rear servo hydraulic circuits.

Fig. 3: View of Right Side of Transmission Case Showing Pressure Test Ports

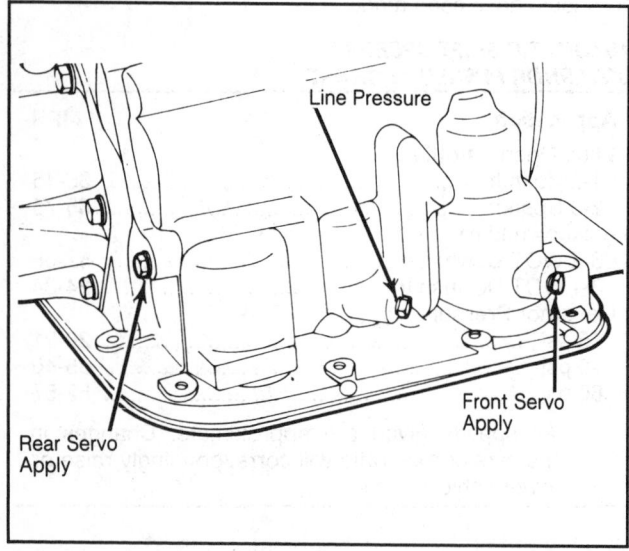

Pressure Test (Selector in "2")

1) Install a "T" connection at rear cooler line fitting. Attach 0-100 psi gauges to "T" connection and line pressure port. Operate engine at 1000 RPM for test. Move selector lever on transmission 1 detent rearward from full forward position (into selector "2" position).

2) Read pressures on both gauges as throttle lever on transmission is moved from full rearward position to full forward position. Line pressure should read 54-90 psi (3.8-6.3 kg/cm²) with throttle lever rearward and gradually increase, as lever is moved forward to 90-96 psi (6.3-6.8 kg/cm²).

3) Lubrication pressure should be 6-16 psi (0.4-1.1 kg/cm²) with lever rearward, and 10-30 psi (0.7-2.1 kg/cm²) with lever forward. This tests pump output, pressure regulation, and condition of rear clutch and lubrication hydraulic circuits.

Pressure Test (Selector in "D")

1) Attach 0-100 psi gauges to line and front servo release ports. Operate engine at 1600 RPM for test. Move selector lever on transmission 2 detents rearward from full forward position (selector in "D" position).

Fig. 4: Rear View of Transmission Case Showing Pressure Test Ports

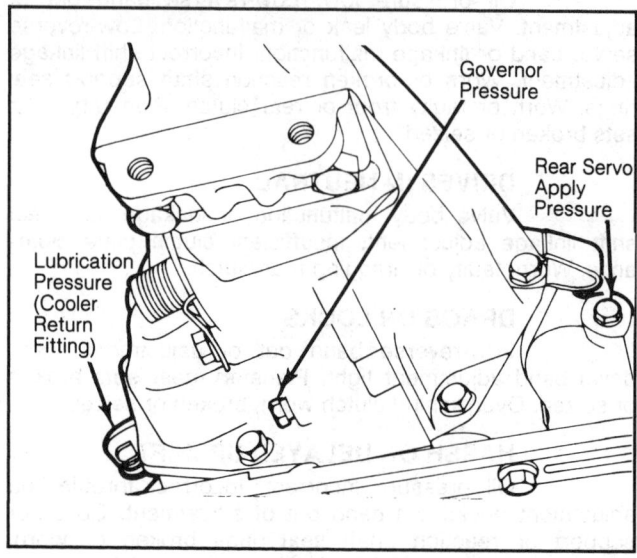

2) Read pressure on both gauges as throttle lever on transmission is moved from full rearward position to full forward position. Line pressure should rear 54-60 psi (3.8-4.2 kg/cm²) with throttle lever rearward and gradually increase, as lever is moved forward.

3) Front servo release is pressurized only in direct drive and should be same as line pressure within 3 psi (.2 kg/cm²), up to downshift point. This tests pump output, pressure regulation, and condition of rear clutch and front clutch hydraulic circuits.

NOTE: A 0-300 psi gauge is required for the following test.

Pressure Test (Selector in Reverse)

1) Attach gauge to rear servo apply port. Operate engine at 1600 RPM for test. Move selector lever on transmission 4 detents rearward from full forward position (into selector "R" position).

2) Rear servo pressure should read 230-260 psi (16.2-18.3 kg/cm²). This tests pump output, pressure regulation, and condition of front clutch and rear servo hydraulic circuits.

3) Move selector lever on transmission to "D" position to check that rear servo pressure drops to zero. This tests for leakage into rear servo, due to case porosity, which can cause reverse band to burn out.

Pressure Test Indication

1) If proper line pressure, minimum to maximum, is found in any one test, the pump and pressure regulator are working properly. Low pressure in "D", "L" and "2" but correct pressure in "R", indicates rear clutch circuit leakage.

2) Low pressure in "D" and "R", but correct pressure in "L", indicates front clutch circuit leakage. Low pressure in "R" and "L", but correct pressure in "2", indicates rear servo circuit leakage, low line pressure in all

TORQUEFLITE (Cont.)

positions indicates a defective pump, clogged filter, or stuck pressure regulator valve.

Governor Pressure

NOTE: **Test only if transmission shifts at wrong vehicle speeds when throttle rod is correctly adjusted.**

1) Connect a 0-100 psi (0-7.0 kg/cm²) gauge to governor pressure port. Operate transmission in third gear to read pressures. *See Automatic Shift Speeds and Governor Pressure Chart.*

2) If governor pressures are incorrect at the given vehicle speeds, governor valve and/or weights are probably sticking. Governor pressure should respond smoothly to changes in MPH and should return to 0-1.5 psi (0-.1 kg/cm²) when vehicle is stopped. High governor pressure at stand still (above 2 psi) will prevent transmission from downshifting.

Throttle Pressure

No gauge port is provided for testing throttle pressure. Incorrect throttle pressure should only be suspected if part throttle upshift speeds are either delayed or occur too early in relation to vehicle speeds. Engine runaway on either upshifts or downshifts can also be an indicator of incorrect (low) throttle pressure setting.

CAUTION: **In no case should throttle pressure be adjusted until transmission throttle rod adjustment has been checked, and corrected if necessary.**

HYDRAULIC PRESSURE ADJUSTMENTS

NOTE: **An incorrect throttle pressure setting will cause incorrect line pressure readings even though line pressure adjustment is correct. Always inspect and correct throttle pressure adjustment before adjusting line pressure.**

Throttle Pressure

1) Remove valve body from transmission. Insert gauge (C-3763) between throttle lever cam and kickdown valve.

Fig. 5: View of Valve Body Showing Throttle Pressure Adjustment

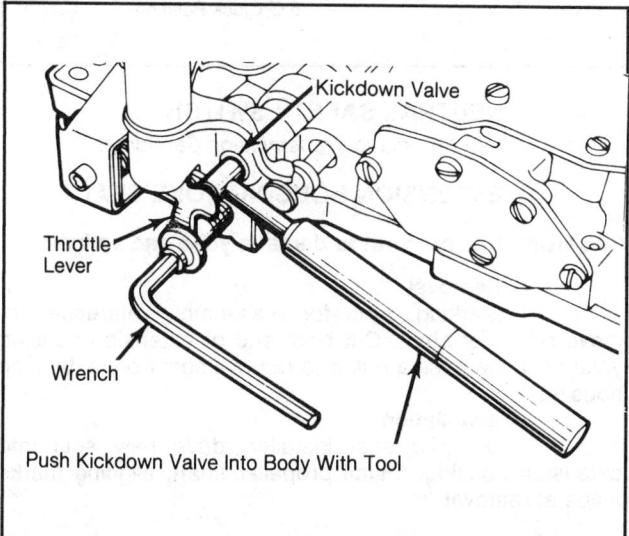

2) By pushing in on tool, compress kickdown valve against spring so valve is completely bottomed inside the valve body. As force is being exerted to compress spring, turn throttle lever stop screw with an Allen wrench until head of screw touches throttle lever tang with throttle lever cam touching tool and throttle valve bottomed.

Line Pressure

1) Turn Allen screw in end of pressure regulator spring bracket so measurement between valve body and inner edge of adjusting nut is 1 5/16". *See Fig. 6.*

NOTE: **Due to manufacturing tolerances, adjustment can be varied to obtain specified line pressure.**

Fig. 6: View of Valve Body Showing Line Pressure Adjustment

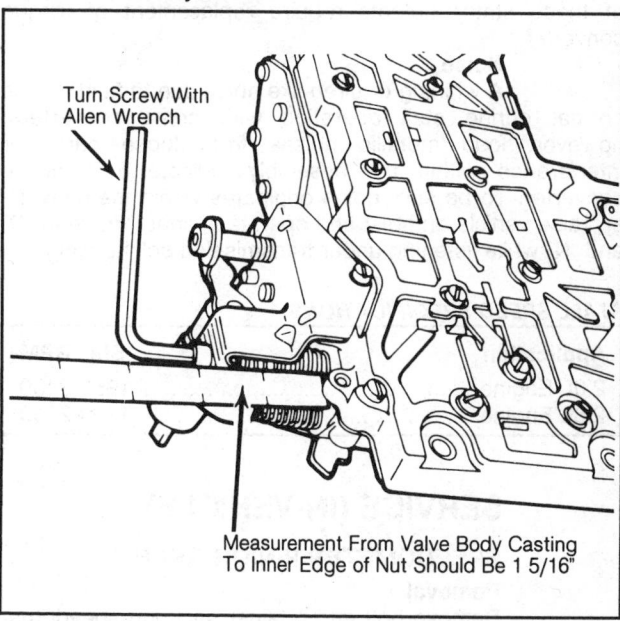

2) One complete turn of adjusting screw changes closed throttle line pressure approximately 1.4 psi (.098 kg/cm²). Turning adjusting screw counterclockwise increases pressure; clockwise decreases pressure.

STALL TEST

CAUTION: **When making the following test, DO NOT let anyone stand in front of the vehicle.**

1) Before making test, check transmission oil level, bring engine to normal operating temperature, and attach a tachometer to engine.

2) Test consists of determining engine speed obtained at full throttle in "D" position. Both parking and service brakes must be fully applied while making test.

CAUTION: **Do not hold throttle open any longer than is necessary to obtain a maximum engine speed reading, and never longer than 5 seconds at a time.**

3) If more than one stall check is required, operate engine at approximately 1000 RPM in neutral for 20 seconds to cool transmission fluid between runs. If engine speed exceeds maximum limits shown, release accelerator immediately since transmission clutch slippage is indicated.

Stall Speed Above Specification

If stall speed exceeds maximum limits shown by more than 200 RPM, transmission clutch slippage is indicated. Make hydraulic pressure and air pressure checks to determine cause of slippage.

Stall Speed Below Specification

1) Low stall speeds (with a properly tuned engine) indicate torque converter stator clutch problems. A road test will be necessary to identify the exact problem.

2) If stall speeds are 250-350 RPM below specifications, and vehicle operates properly at highway speeds, but has poor through-gear acceleration, stator overrunning clutch is slipping.

3) If stall speed and acceleration are normal, but abnormally high throttle opening is required to maintain highway speeds, stator clutch has seized. Both of these stator defects require replacement of torque converter.

Noise

A whining or siren-like noise due to fluid flow is normal during stall operation with some converters; however, loud metallic noises from loose parts or interference within the assembly indicate a defective converter. To be sure noise originates within the converter, raise vehicle on hoist and operate at light throttle in "D" and "N" while listening under transmission bell housing.

STALL SPEED SPECIFICATIONS

Application	Stall RPM
2.0L Engine	1950-2450
2.6L Engine	1800-2200

SERVICE (IN-VEHICLE)

SPEEDOMETER PINION GEAR

Removal

Remove bolt and retainer securing speedometer pinion adapter in extension housing. With cable housing connected, carefully work adapter and pinion out of extension housing.

Fig. 7: Disassembled View of Speedometer Drive

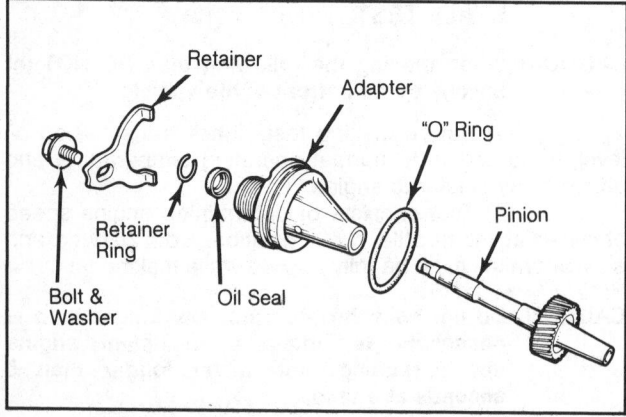

Seal Replacement

If transmission fluid is found in cable housing, replace seal in adapter. Start seal and retainer ring in

adapter, then push into adapter using tool (C-4004) until tool bottoms.

Fig. 8: Speedometer Pinion Seal Installation

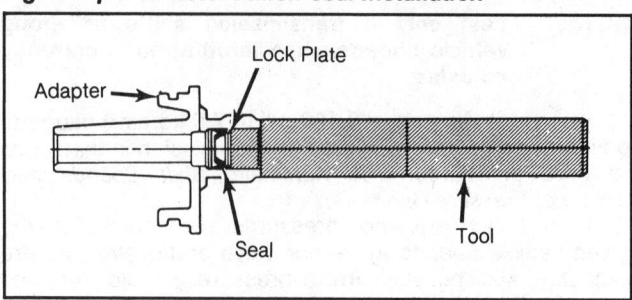

CAUTION: To avoid misalignment, make sure adapter flange and its mating area on extension housing are clean.

Intallation

1) Note number of gear teeth and install speedometer pinion gear into adapter. Rotate pinion gear and adapter assembly so that number on adapter, corresponding with number of teeth on gear, is in 6 o'clock position as assembly is installed.

2) Install retainer and bolt, with tangs in adapter positioning slots. Tap adapter firmly into extension housing, then tighten retainer bolt.

Fig. 9: View of Extension Housing Showing Speedometer Pinion and Adapter Installation

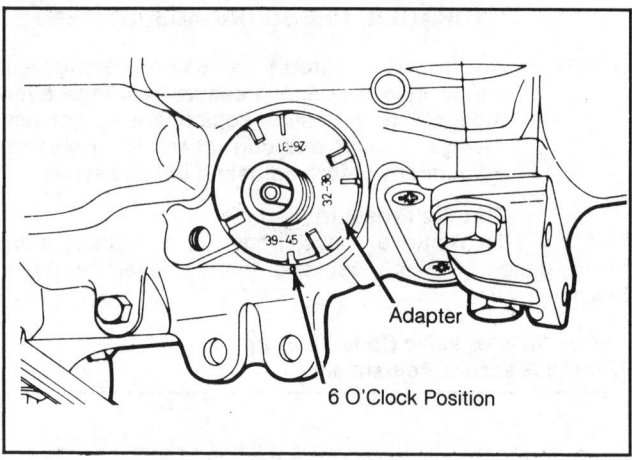

NEUTRAL SAFETY SWITCH

See Automatic Transmission Servicing.

EXTENSION HOUSING YOKE SEAL

CAUTION: Use care not to damage yoke and splines.

Removal

Marking parts for reassembly reference, remove propeller shaft. Cut boot end of extension housing yoke seal, then use a puller to remove seal from extension housing.

Installation

Using a seal installer, drive new seal into extension housing. Install propeller shaft, aligning marks made at removal.

TORQUEFLITE (Cont.)

EXTENSION HOUSING

Removal

1) Marking parts for reassembly reference, remove propeller shaft, then remove extension housing seal. Remove speedometer pinion adapter assembly, then drain approximately 2 quarts of transmission fluid.

2) Remove extension housing-to-crossmember bolts. Raise transmission slightly with service jack, then remove center crossmember and support assembly. Remove extension housing-to-transmission bolts.

Fig. 10: *Bottom View of Extension Housing Showing Removal of Retaining Snap Ring*

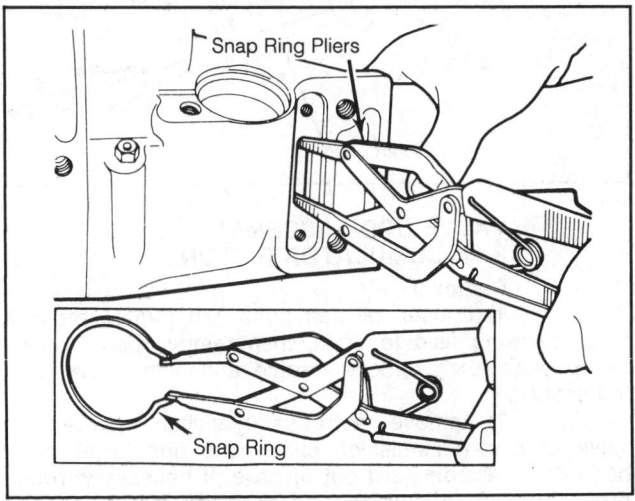

NOTE: When removing or installing extension housing, gearshift lever must be in "L" position, placing parking lock control rod rearward so it can be disengaged or engaged with parking lock sprag.

3) Remove 2 screws, plate and gasket from bottom of housing mounting pad. With large snap ring on output shaft bearing spread as far as possible, tap extension housing off output shaft bearing, then pull carefully rearward to remove parking lock control rod knob past parking sprag and remove housing.

Bearing Replacement

Using heavy duty snap ring pliers, remove output shaft bearing rear snap ring, then remove bearing from shaft. Install new bearing on shaft with outer race ring groove toward front, then install rear snap ring.

Bushing Replacement

Using driver, remove bushing from extension housing. Align hole in new bushing with oil slot in extension housing, drive or press bushing into housing, then install new seal.

Installation

1) Install a new gasket on transmission case. Position output shaft bearing retaining snap ring in extension housing. Slide extension housing on output shaft guiding the parking lock control rod knob past parking sprag. While spreading large snap ring in housing, carefully tap housing into place, then release snap ring.

CAUTION: Make sure snap ring is fully seated in bearing outer race ring groove.

Fig. 11: *Rear View of Transmission Showing Output Shaft Bearing Installation*

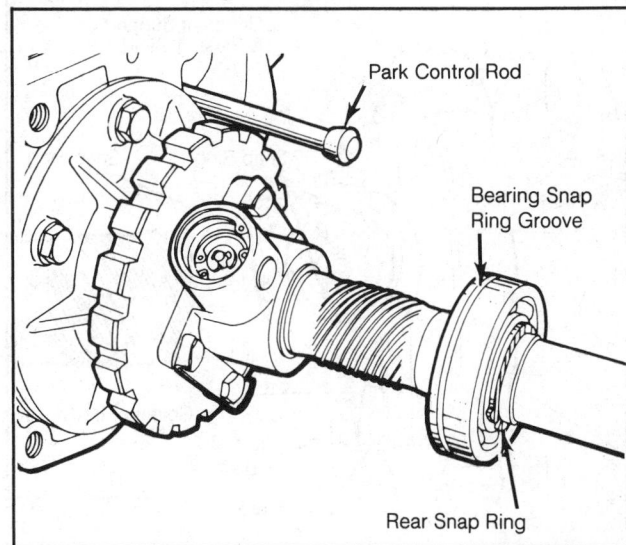

2) Install and tighten extension housing-to-transmission bolts, then install gasket, plate, and screws on bottom of extension housing mounting pad. Install center crossmember and rear mount assembly, then lower transmission and install and tighten extension housing-to-support bolts.

3) Install speedometer pinion and adapter. Carefully guide front universal joint yoke into extension housing and on the output shaft splines. Align marks made at removal and connect propeller shaft to rear axle pinion shaft yoke. Adjust transmission fluid level as necessary.

GOVERNOR & PARKING GEAR

Removal

1) Remove extension housing and output shaft bearings as previously outlined. Carefully pry snap ring from weight end of governor valve shaft, then slide valve and shaft assembly out of governor body.

2) Remove large snap ring from weight end of governor body, then lift out governor weight assembly. Remove snap ring from inside governor weight, then remove inner weight and spring from outer weight.

3) Remove snap ring from behind governor body, then slide governor and support assembly off output shaft. Remove bolts and separate governor body and screen from parking gear.

Inspection

Inspect all parts for wear or damage, and spring for distortion. Weights and valve should fall freely in bores when clean and dry. Remove any roughness with crocus cloth.

Installation

1) Assemble governor body and screen to support and tighten bolts finger tight, making sure oil passage of governor body aligns with passage in support. Position support and governor assembly on output shaft, aligning so valve shaft hole in body mates with hole in output shaft. Slide assembly into place, install snap ring behind governor body, then tighten body-to-support bolts and bend ends of lock straps over bolt heads.

Fig. 12: Installed View of Governor Assembly

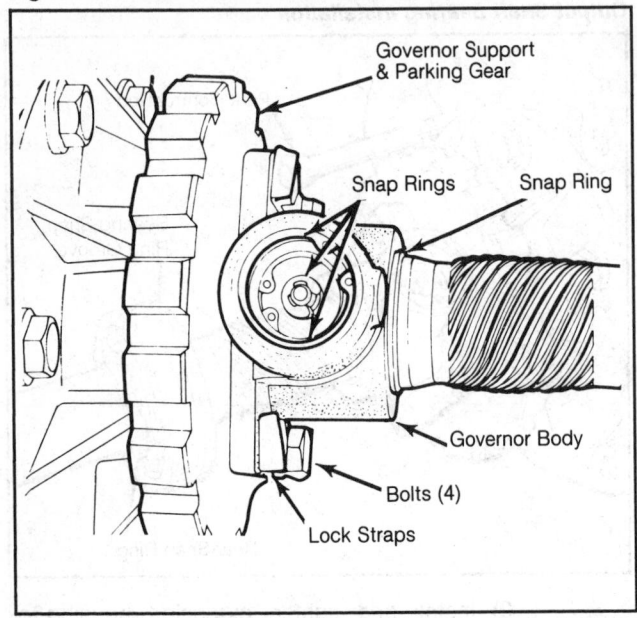

2) Assemble governor weights and spring and secure with snap ring inside of large governor weight, then place assembly in governor body and install snap ring. Place governor valve on valve shaft, insert assembly into body and through governor weights, then install valve shaft retaining snap ring. Inspect valve and weight assembly for free movement, then install output shaft bearing and extension housing.

Fig. 13: Disassembled View of Governor Assembly

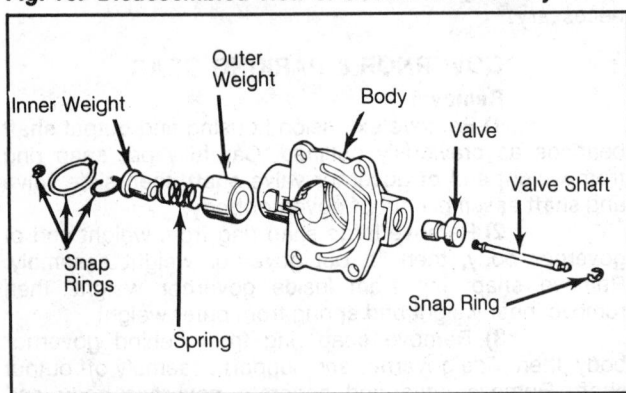

PARKING LOCK
Removal
With extension housing removed, slide shaft out of housing to remove parking sprag and spring. Remove snap ring, then slide reaction plug and pin assembly out of housing.
Installation
Install reaction plug and spring assembly in housing, then secure with snap ring. Position sprag and spring in housing then insert shaft, making sure square lug on sprag is toward parking gear, and spring is positioned so it moves sprag away from gear. Install extension housing.

Fig. 14: Disassembled View Showing Components of Parking Lock Assembly

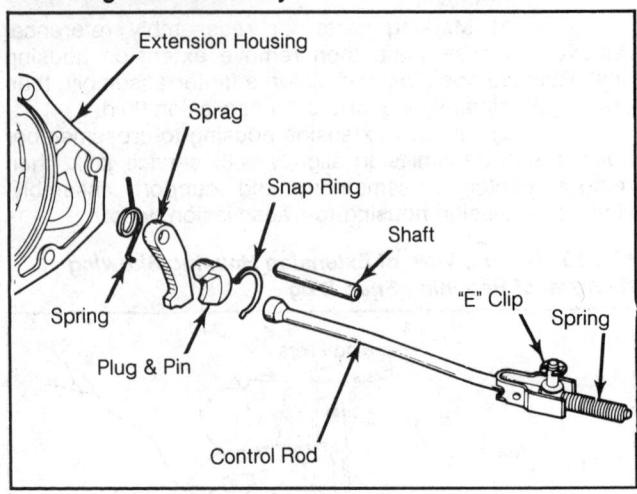

VALVE BODY ASSEMBLY & ACCUMULATOR PISTON
Removal
1) Loosen oil pan bolts, tap pan to break it loose allowing fluid to drain, then remove pan. Loosen clamp bolts, then remove throttle and shift levers from transmission.

2) Remove neutral safety switch, then remove valve body-to-transmission case bolts and lower valve body down and forward out of case. If necessary, rotate propeller shaft to align parking gear and sprag to permit knob on end of parking control rod to pass sprag.

3) Remove accumulator piston and spring from transmission case, then inspect for damage. If valve body manual lever shaft seal requires replacement, drive out of case with punch. Drive new seal into case with a 15/16" socket and hammer.

NOTE: Seal may be replaced without removing valve body from case by using a small screwdriver to pry seal out of case. Take care not to damage shaft or seal bore in case.

Installation
1) With neutral safety switch removed from case, place valve body manual lever in low position to move parking rod to rear position. Use screwdriver to push sprag into engagement with parking gear, turning output shaft to ensure engagement. This will allow knob on end of parking rod to move past sprag as valve body is installed. Install accumulator piston in case. Position accumulator spring between piston and valve body.

2) Place valve body in position, working park rod through opening and past sprag, then install retaining bolts finger tight. Install neutral safety switch, then place manual lever in neutral position, shifting valve body if necessary to center neutral finger over switch plunger.

3) Install and tighten valve body-to-case bolts evenly. Install gearshift lever and tighten clamp bolt. Move lever through all detent positions to ensure shaft does not bind in case. If binding exists, loosen valve body bolts and realign.

TORQUEFLITE (Cont.)

4) Be sure throttle shaft seal is in place, then install flat washer and throttle lever and tighten clamp bolt. Connect throttle and gearshift linkage, adjust as required. Install oil pan with new gasket, then adjust transmission fluid level.

REMOVAL & INSTALLATION

See the appropriate article in AUTOMATIC TRANSMISSION REMOVAL Section.

TORQUE CONVERTER

Converter Pressure Test

Drain all oil from converter. If flushing is required, flush before checking for leakage. Install pressure test tool (C-4102) and tighten. Apply a maximum of 100 psi (7.0 kg/cm²) air pressure to converter, then submerge in a tank of water and observe hub, ring gear and seam welds for bubbles. Five to ten minutes may be required for bubbles to appear from small leaks. If leakage occurs, converter must be replaced.

TRANSMISSION DISASSEMBLY

INPUT SHAFT END PLAY CHECK

Measuring input shaft end play before disassembly will usually indicate when a thrust washer change is required (except when major parts are replaced). Thrust washer is located between input and output shafts. Attach dial indicator to transmission converter housing with plunger seated against end of input shaft. Move input shaft in and out to obtain end play reading. End play should be .022-.091" (.56-2.3 mm). Record end play reading for reassembly reference.

Fig. 15: Using a Dial Indicator to Measure Input Shaft End Play

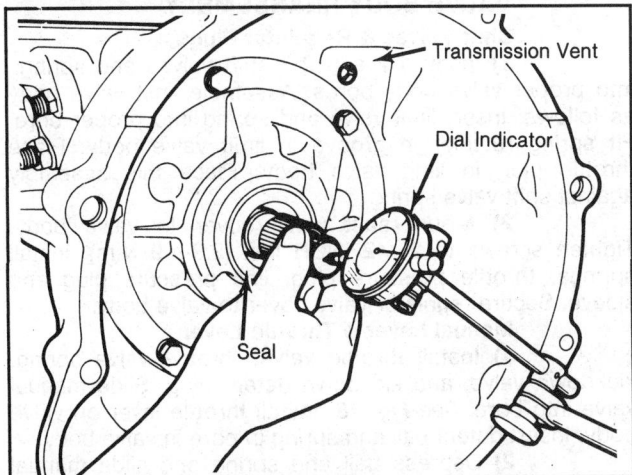

VALVE BODY ASSEMBLY & ACCUMULATOR PISTON

See Service (In Vehicle)

EXTENSION HOUSING

See Service (In Vehicle)

GOVERNOR

See Service (In Vehicle)

OIL PUMP & REACTION SHAFT SUPPORT

Tighten front band adjusting screw until band is tight on front clutch retainer, preventing retainer from coming out with pump, damaging clutches. Remove oil pump housing retaining bolts, then install slide hammers in threaded holes in pump housing flange. Operating both hammers evenly, withdraw pump and reaction shaft support assembly from case.

FRONT BAND & FRONT CLUTCH

Loosen front band adjuster, remove band strut then slide band out of case. Slide front clutch assembly out of case.

INPUT SHAFT & REAR CLUTCH

Grasp input shaft, then slide input shaft and rear clutch assembly out of case.

CAUTION: **Do not lose thrust washer located between rear end of input shaft and forward end of output shaft.**

PLANETARY GEAR ASSEMBLIES, SUN GEAR & DRIVING SHELL

While supporting output shaft and driving shell, carefully slide assembly forward and out through case.

CAUTION: **Do not damage ground surfaces on output shaft during removal.**

REAR BAND & LOW-REVERSE DRUM

Remove low-reverse drum, loosen rear band adjuster and remove band strut and link, then remove band from case.

OVERRUNNING CLUTCH

Note position of overrunning clutch rollers and springs before disassembly to aid in reassembly. Carefully slide out clutch hub, then remove rollers and springs.

KICKDOWN SERVO (FRONT)

Using tool, compress kickdown servo spring, then remove snap ring. Remove rod guide, springs, and piston rod from case, taking care not to damage piston rod or guide during removal. Withdraw piston from transmission case.

LOW-REVERSE SERVO (REAR)

Compress low-reverse servo piston spring using tool, then remove snap ring, spring retainer, spring, and servo piston and plug assembly from case.

COMPONENT DISASSEMBLY & REASSEMBLY

VALVE BODY DISASSEMBLY

NOTE: **Tag all springs for reassembly reference as they are removed.**

TORQUEFLITE (Cont.)

CAUTION: DO NOT clamp any portion of the valve body or transfer plate in a vise. Any distortion of the valve body or transfer plate will result in sticking valves. Always place valve in a repair stand when repair procedures are to be performed.

Filter, Transfer Plate & Pressure Regulators

1) Remove 3 screws from fluid filter and remove filter from valve body. Remove top and bottom screws from adjustment screw bracket. Hold bracket firmly while removing last retaining screw from side of valve body.

Fig. 16: Valve Body Transfer and Separator Plates

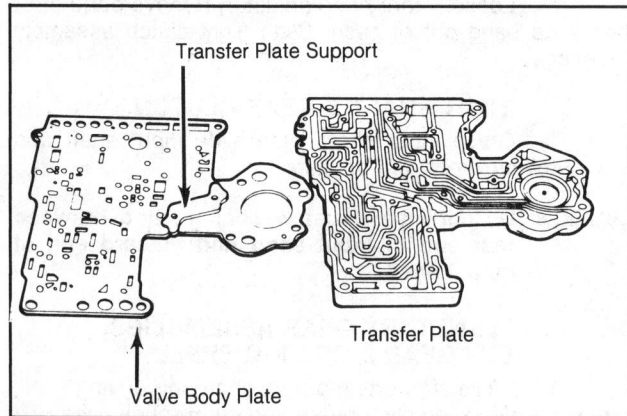

2) Remove bracket with line and throttle pressure adjusting screws (do not disturb screw settings). Also remove regulator valve and switch valve springs. Remove switch valve and regulator valve. Remove transfer plate retaining screws and remove transfer plate and valve body plate. See Fig. 16.

3) Remove 6 screws from transfer plate support and valve body plate and separate parts for cleaning. Remove rear clutch check ball and rear servo check ball from transfer plate. Also remove screen from valve body plate. See Fig. 16. Remove 7 check balls from valve body. See Fig. 20.

Fig. 17: Exploded View of Valve Body Showing Shuttle Valve and Governor Plugs

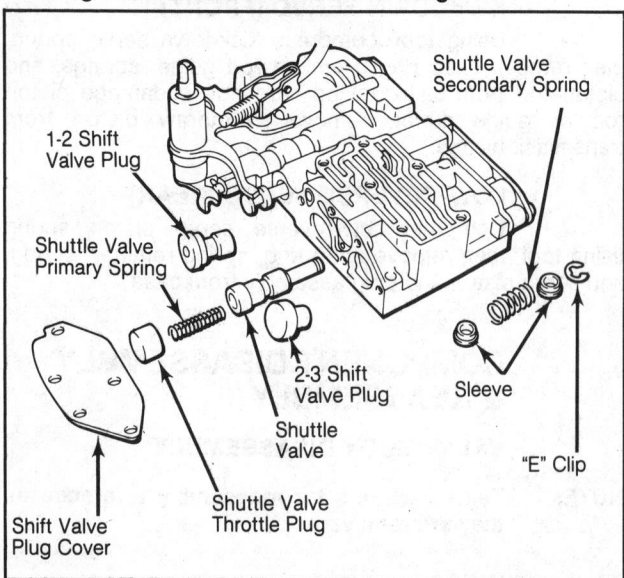

Shuttle Valve & Governor Plugs

1) Turn valve body over. Remove "E" clip and park sprag rod from manual lever. Remove shuttle valve cover plate. Remove shift valve plug cover.

2) Remove 1-2 and 2-3 shift valve plugs. Remove shuttle valve "E" clip and slide shuttle valve, along with the secondary spring and sleeve, from bore.

Manual Lever & Throttle Lever

1) Remove "E" clip and washer from throttle lever shaft. Remove any burrs from shaft, then while holding manual lever detent ball and spring in bore, slide manual lever off throttle shaft.

2) Remove detent ball and spring, then slide manual valve from bore. Slide out kickdown detent, kickdown valve, throttle valve spring, and throttle valve.

Shift Valves & Regulator Plugs

1) Remove regulator valve cover. Slide out sleeve, line pressure plug, throttle pressure plug, and spring. Remove limit valve body and throttle pressure plug.

2) Remove retainer, limit valve and spring. Remove each shift valve and spring. Withdraw 1-2 shift control valve out of its bore.

VALVE BODY INSPECTION

1) Wash all parts in a solvent and blow dry with compressed air. Inspect all parts for nicks, burrs, scratches, or distortion. Small nicks and burrs may be removed with crocus cloth, taking care not to round off any machined sharp edges. Make sure all passages are clean and free from obstructions, and all metering holes in steel plate and valve body are open.

2) Inspect all valve springs for distortion or collapsed coils. Inspect manual and throttle valve operating levers and shafts. If a lever is loose on its shaft, it may be SILVER SOLDERED ONLY, or lever and shaft assembly should be replaced. DO NOT attempt to straighten bent levers. When bores, valves and plugs are clean and dry, valves and plugs should fall freely in their bores.

VALVE BODY REASSEMBLY

Shift Valves & Regulator Plugs

1) Insert 1-2 and 2-3 shift valves and springs into proper valve body bores. Assemble limit valve body as follows: Insert limit valve and spring into proper bore. Fit spring retainer in groove in limit valve body. Place throttle plug in limit valve body. Place this assembly against shift valve spring.

2) Mount shift valve cover to valve body. Tighten screws to 26-42 INCH lbs. (2.9-4.9 N.m). Install springs, throttle pressure plug, line pressure plug and sleeve. Secure regulator valve cover to valve body.

Manual Lever & Throttle Lever

1) Install throttle valve, throttle valve spring, kickdown valve, and kickdown detent plug. Slide manual valve into bore. See Fig. 18. Install throttle lever on valve body. Insert detent ball and spring in bore in valve body.

2) Depress ball and spring and slide manual lever over throttle shaft so it engages manual valve and detent ball. Install seal, retaining washer, and "E" clip on throttle shaft.

Shuttle Valve & Shift Plugs

Place 1-2 and 2-3 shift valve plugs in their bores. Install shuttle valve, spring and shuttle valve throttle plug. Install shift valve end plate. Install "E" clip on end of shuttle valve, then install shuttle valve cover plate.

Install "E" clip on end of shuttle valve, then install shuttle valve cover plate.

Fig. 18: Exploded View of Valve Body Showing Pressure Regulators and Manual Control

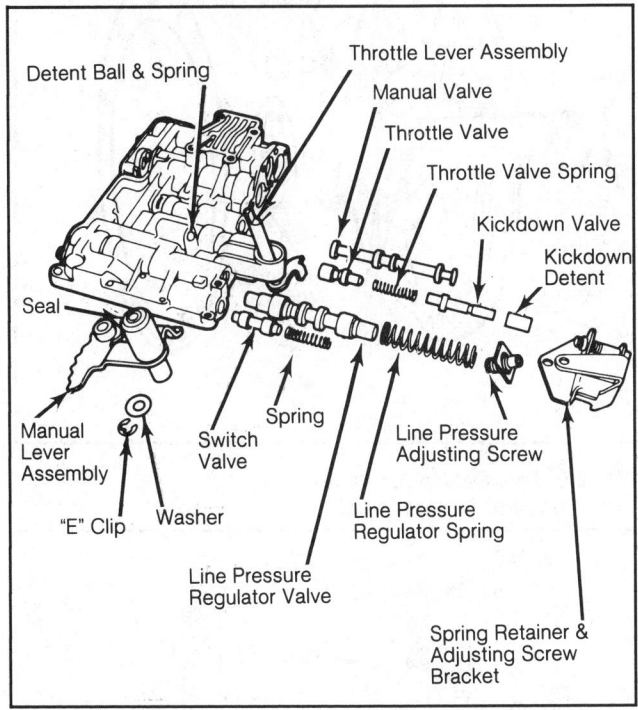

Filter, Transfer Plate, & Pressure Regulators

1) Install 7 check balls in valve body. *See Fig. 20.* Install rear clutch check ball and rear servo check ball in transfer plate. Install regulator valve screen to valve body plate.

2) Assemble transfer plate to valve body plate with 6 screws. Place transfer plate assembly on valve body and install 14 screws. Tighten screws to 26-42 INCH lbs. (2.9-4.9 N.m) working from center screws outward.

Fig. 19: Exploded View of Valve Body Showing Shift Valves and Pressure Regulator Valve Plugs

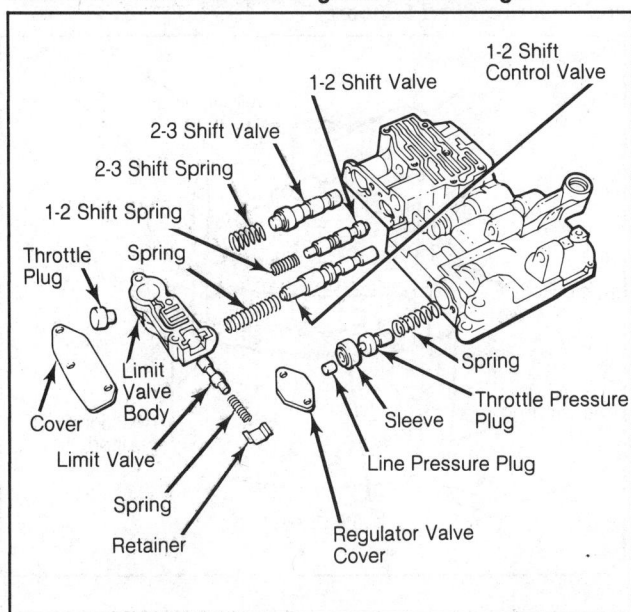

3) Place switch valve, regulator valve and spring in their respective bores. *See Fig. 18.* Place adjustment screw bracket on spring and temporarily install the side mounting screw. After top and bottom screws have been installed and tightened, tighten side screw.

Fig. 20: View of Valve Body Showing Check Ball Locations

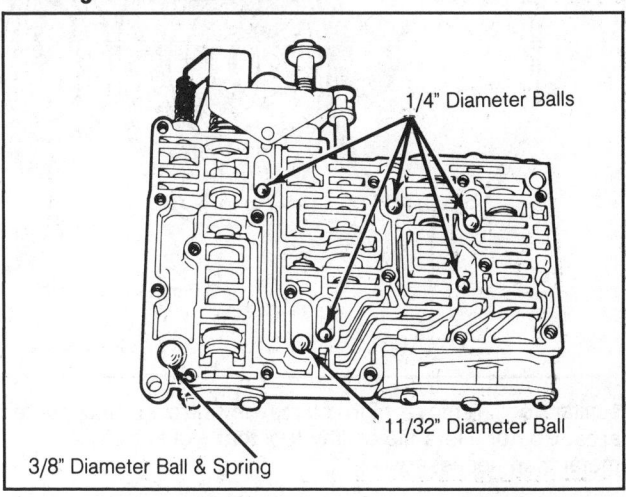

4) Install oil filter and tighten attaching screws. After valve body is completely assembled, measure throttle and line pressure adjustments. If pressures were satisfactory before disassembly, use original settings. Install park sprag rod and "E" clip on manual lever.

OIL PUMP & REACTION SHAFT SUPPORT

Disassembly

Remove bolts from rear side of reaction shaft support, then lift support off pump. Remove rubber seal ring from pump body flange, then drive out oil seal with blunt punch.

Inspection

1) Inspect all parts for wear or damage. Be sure interlocking seal rings turn freely in groves. Inspect front clutch piston retainer to reaction shaft support thrust washer for wear; thickness should be .061-.063" (1.55-1.60 mm), replace if necessary.

NOTE: Seal rings must be removed to allow clearance for thrust washer removal or installation.

2) With rotors installed in pump body, place a straightedge across faces of rotors and pump body. Using a feeler gauge, measure clearance between straightedge and pump rotors. Clearance should be .001-.003" (.03-.08 mm).

3) Rotor tip clearance between inner and outer rotor teeth should be .005-.010" (.13-.25 mm). Clearance between outer rotor and rotor bore in pump body should be .004-.008" (.10-.20 mm)

Pump Bushing Replacement

1) Place pump housing (seal face down) on a clean, smooth surface. Using removing tool (SP-3551) and handle (SP-3549 or C-4171), drive bushing straight down and out of bore, being careful not to cock tool in bore. Using installing head (SP-5117), drive new bushing into place in pump rotor housing.

2) Stake bushing in place using a blunt punch or other similar tool. Using a narrow bladed knife or

Fig. 21: *Exploded View of Oil Pump and Reaction Shaft Support*

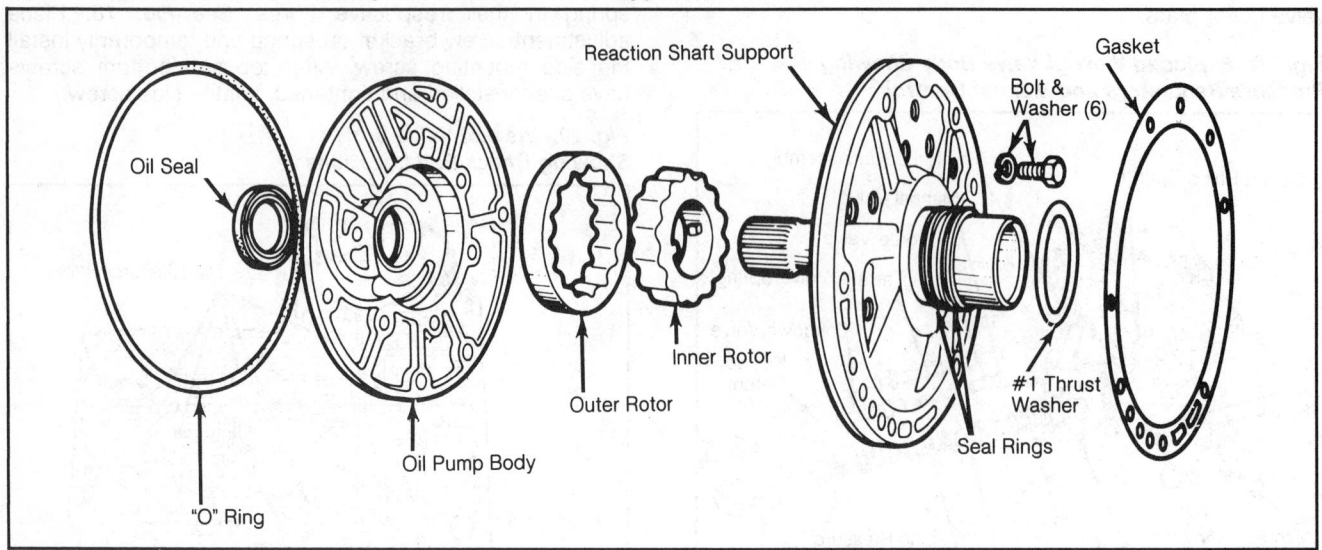

similar tool, remove high points or burrs around staked area. Do not use a file or any tool that would remove more metal than necessary.

Fig. 22: *Rear View of Oil Pump Housing Showing Staking Positions in Bushing*

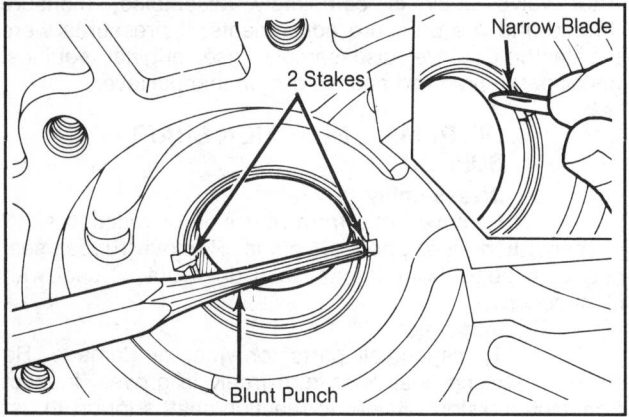

Reaction Shaft Bushing Replacement

Thread a bushing remover tool into bushing. *See Fig. 23.* Withdraw bushing from reaction shaft. Support reaction shaft upright. Using a driving tool, drive new bushing into place in reaction shaft.

NOTE: If bushing failed in service, inspect support for wear from input shaft seal ring lands. If worn or grooved, replace support assembly.

Reassembly

1) Place reaction shaft support in an assembling tool (C-3759) with hub of support and tool on a smooth, flat surface. Install 2 pilot studs in threaded holes in support flange. *See Fig. 24.*

2) Assemble rotors in center of support and lower pump body over pilot studs. Using tool (C-3756), center rotors in pump body. With pump body firmly against reaction shaft support, tighten assembling tool securely.

3) Invert pump and tool assembly. Install support-to-pump bolts and tighten evenly. Remove as-

Fig. 23: *Tool Set-Up for Reaction Shaft Bushing Replacement*

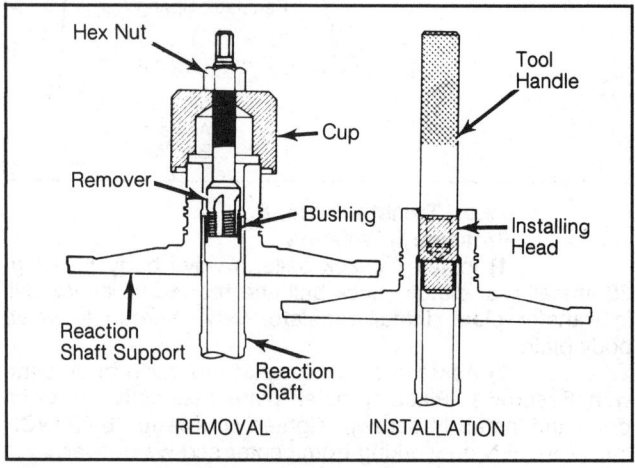

Fig. 24: *Tool Set-Up for Assembling Oil Pump and Reaction Shaft Support*

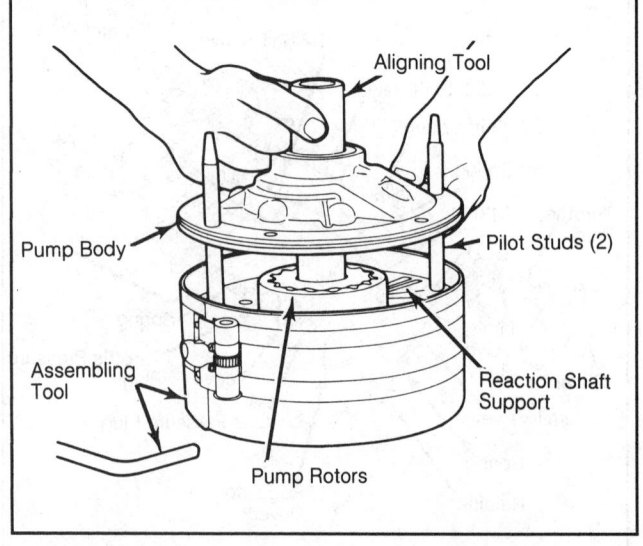

TORQUEFLITE (Cont.)

sembling tool, pilot studs, and aligning tool. Using tool (C-4193), install new pump oil seal.

FRONT CLUTCH

Disassembly

1) Remove large waved snap ring that secures pressure plate in clutch piston retainer. Remove pressure plate, clutch discs and clutch plates from retainer. Install compression tool ((C-3573-A) over piston spring retainer. Compress spring and remove snap ring.

2) Slowly release compressor tool until spring retainer is free from hub. Remove tool, retainer and spring. Invert clutch retainer assembly. Bump assembly on block of wood to remove piston. Remove all seals from piston and clutch retainer hub.

Inspection

1) Inspect plates and discs for flatness; they must not be warped or cone-shaped. Inspect facing material on all driving discs, replace if damaged.

2) Inspect discs and plates for wear on splines or lugs, then check clutch retainer for damaged lug grooves, or damaged band contacting surfaces. Make sure ball check in clutch retainer moves freely.

3) Check neoprene seals for wear, hardness or deterioration. Inspect piston spring(s), retainer and snap ring for distortion.

Front Clutch Retainer Bushing Replacement

Lay clutch retainer (open end down) on a clean smooth surface, then using a removing head tool (SP-3627), drive bushing straight down and out of bore, being careful not to cock tool. To install, lay clutch retainer (open end up) on a clean smooth surface, then using installing head tool (SP-3626), drive bushing into place in clutch retainer bore.

Reassembly

1) Lubricate and install inner seal on hub of clutch retainer, making sure lip of seal faces down and is properly seated in groove. Install outer seal on clutch piston, with lip of seal toward bottom of clutch retainer. Apply a coating of wax type lubricant to outer edge of seal, then place piston assembly in retainer and carefully seat piston in bottom of retainer.

2) Place spring on piston hub and postion spring retainer and snap ring on the spring. Using tool (C-3575-A), compress spring, seat snap ring in hub groove, then remove tool.

3) Lubricate all clutch plates, then install one steel plate followed by one lined disc until number given in Front Clutch Chart is installed. Install pressure plate and snap ring, making sure snap ring is properly seated. Insert a feeler gauge between pressure plate and waved snap ring to measure maximum clearance where snap ring is waved away from pressure plate.

FRONT CLUTCH PLATE USAGE CHART

Application	Plates	Discs
All Models	2	 2

4) With clutch assembly completed, insert a feeler gauge between pressure plate and waved snap ring to measure maximum clearance where snap ring is waved away from pressure plate. Clearance should be .024-.070" (.61-1.78 mm).

Fig. 26: Using a Feeler Gauge to Measure Front Clutch Clearance

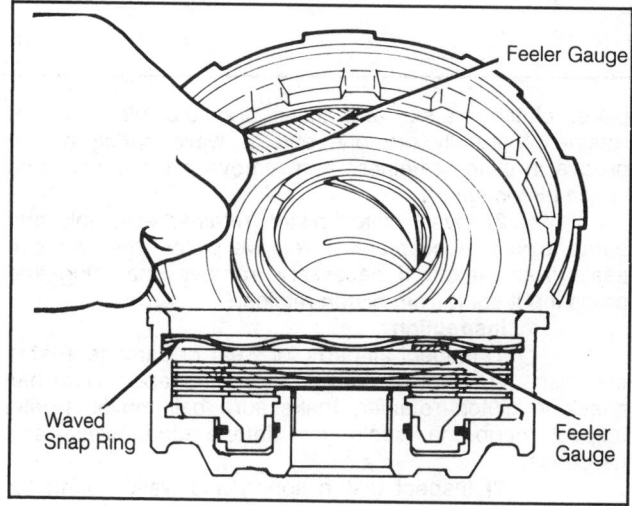

REAR CLUTCH

Disassembly

1) Remove large selective snap ring securing pressure plate in clutch piston retainer, then lift pressure

Fig. 25: Exploded View of Front Clutch Assembly

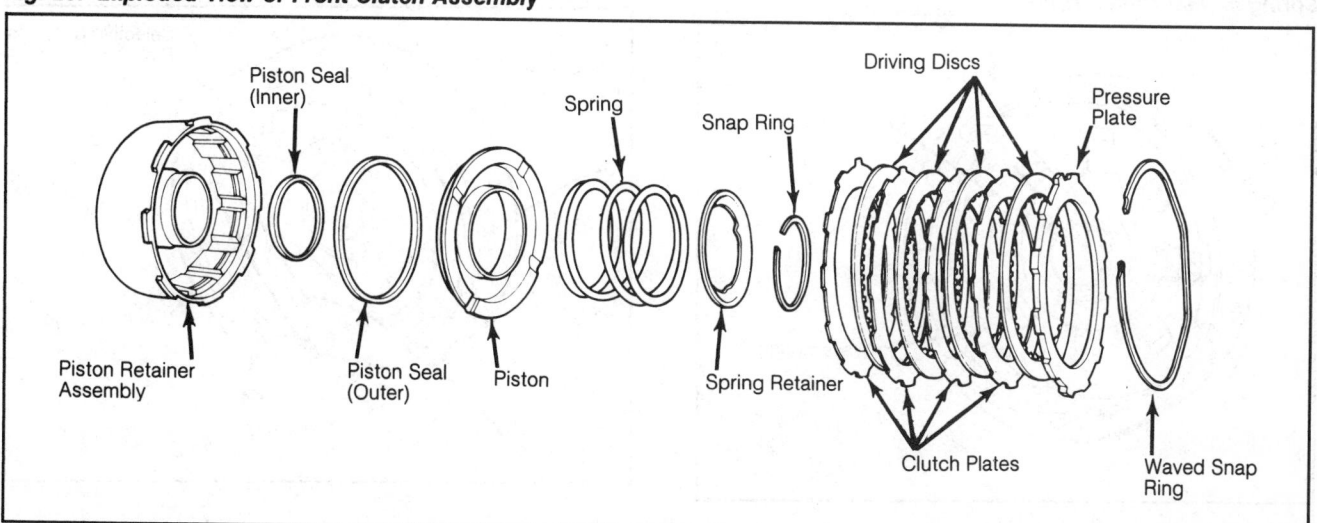

Automatic Transmissions

TORQUEFLITE (Cont.)

Fig. 27: Exploded View of Rear Clutch Assembly

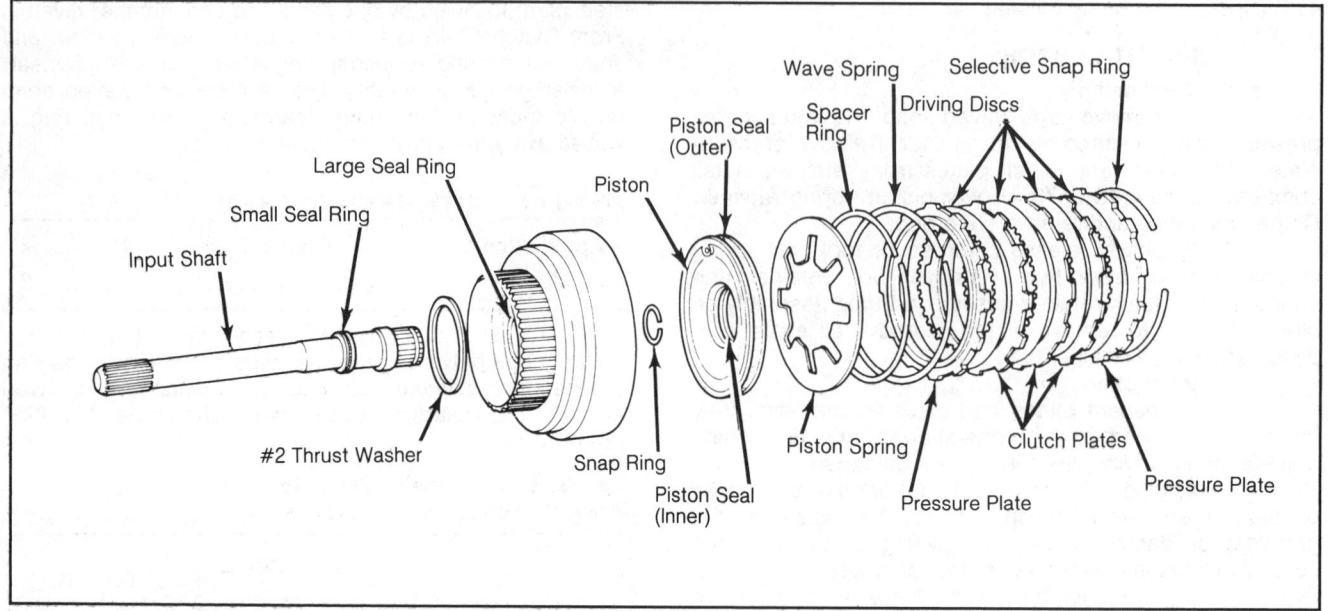

plate, clutch plates, and inner pressure plate out of retainer. Carefully pry one end of wave spring out of groove in clutch retainer, then remove wave spring, and clutch piston spring.

2) Invert clutch piston retainer assembly and bump it on a wood block to remove piston, then remove seals from piston. If necessary, remove snap ring and press input shaft from piston retainer.

Inspection

1) Inspect all parts for wear or damage. Plates and discs must not be warped or cone-shaped. Note ball check in clutch retainer, make sure ball moves freely. Inspect neoprene seals for deterioration, wear and hardness.

2) Inspect piston spring and wave spring for distortion or breakage. Inspect seal rings for wear or breakage, make sure they turn freely in grooves. Inspect rear clutch-to-front clutch thrust washer for wear. Thickness should be .061-.063" (1.55-1.60 mm), replace as necessary.

NOTE: Do not remove rings unless conditions warrant. Replacement seal rings are cast iron hooked joint type.

Reassembly

1) If removed, press input shaft into piston retainer and install snap ring. Lubricate and install inner and outer seals on clutch piston, making sure lips of seals face toward head of clutch retainer and are properly seated in grooves. Place piston assembly in retainer and, with a twisting motion, seat piston in bottom of retainer.

2) Place clutch piston spring on top of piston in clutch retainer. Start one end of wave spring in retainer groove, then progressively push or tap spring into place making sure it is fully seated in groove.

3) Install inner pressure plate in clutch retainer with raised portion of plate resting on spring. Lubricate all clutch plates, then install one lined disc followed by one steel plate until all plates are installed. Install outer pressure plate and selective snap ring.

Fig. 28: Installing Piston Spring and Wave Spring in Rear Clutch Drum

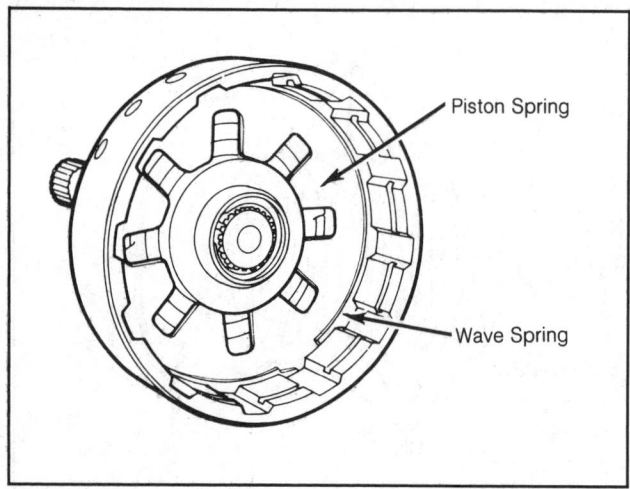

Fig. 29: Using a Feeler Gauge to Measure Rear Clutch Clearance

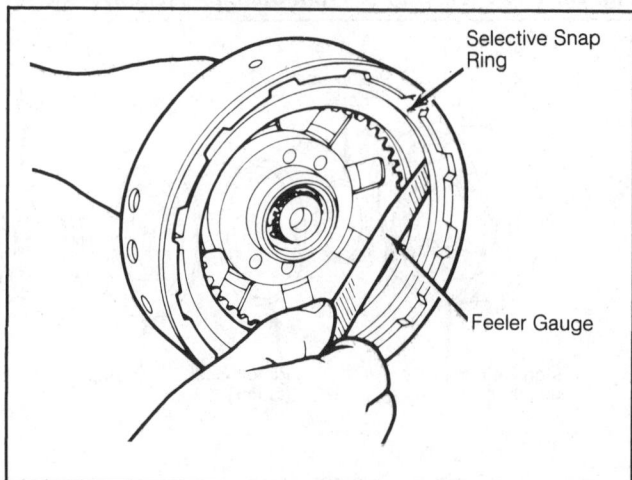

TORQUEFLITE (Cont.)

REAR CLUTCH PLATE CHART

Application	Plates	Discs
All Models	2	3

4) Measure rear clutch clearance by pressing down firmly on outer pressure plate, then inserting a feeler gauge between plate and snap ring. Clearance should be .032-.055" (.82-1.39 mm), with low limit clearance desirable. Install new snap ring of proper thickness to obtain specified clearance. Snap rings are available in thicknesses of .061", .077" and .099" (1.55, 1.96, and 2.51 mm).

PLANETARY GEAR TRAIN
End Play

1) Measure end play of planetary gear assemblies, sun gear and driving shell before removing from ouput shaft. Stand assembly upright with forward end of output shaft on a wood block so that all parts will move forward against snap ring at front of shaft.

2) Insert a feeler gauge between rear annulus gear support hub and shoulder on output shaft. Clearance should be .006-.033" (.16-.83 mm). If clearance exceeds specifications, replace thrust washers and/or necessary parts. *See Fig. 30.*

Fig. 30: Using a Feeler Gauge to Measure Planetary Gear Train End Play

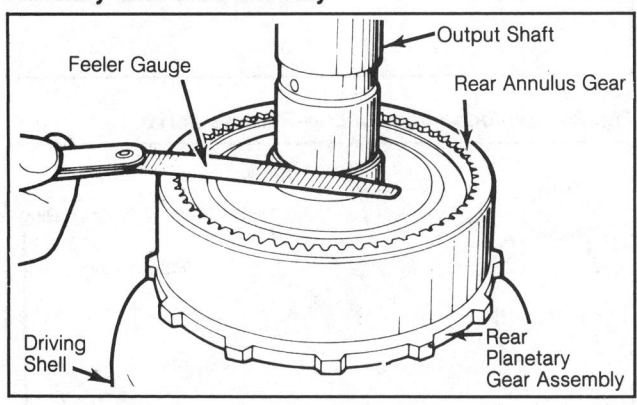

Disassembly

1) Remove selective thrust washer from forward end of output shaft. Remove selective snap ring and thrust washer from forward hub of front planetary gear assembly. Slide front annulus gear and support off planetary gear set.

2) If necessary, remove snap ring from front of annulus gear to separate support from annulus gear. Slide sun gear, driving shell and rear planetary assembly off output shaft, then lift sun gear and driving shell off rear planetary assembly. Remove snap ring and thrust plate from sun gear (rear side of driving shell).

3) Slide sun gear out of driving shell, then remove snap ring and thrust plate from opposite end of sun gear if necessary. Remove thrust washer from forward side of rear planetary assembly, then remove planetary gear set from rear annulus gear. If necessary, remove snap ring from rear of annulus gear to separate support from annulus gear.

Inspection

Inspect all parts for nicks, burrs, scores, or other damage. Light scratches, small nicks or burrs can be removed with crocus cloth or a fine stone. Inspect bushings in sun gear for wear or scores, replace assembly if bushings are damaged. Inspect all thrust washers for wear and scores, replace if damaged or worn below specifications. Make sure oil passages in shaft are open and clean. Replace distorted lock rings.

Reassembly

Reverse disassembly procedure and note following: With all components properly positioned, install selective snap ring on front end of output shaft. Remeasure end play of assembly. Clearance may be adjusted by use of various thickness snap rings. Snap rings are available in thicknesses of .040", .048" and .059" (1.02, 1.22 and 1.50 mm).

OVERRUNNING CLUTCH
Inspection

Inspect clutch rollers for smooth, round surfaces. These surfaces must be free of flat spots and chipped edges. Inspect roller contacting surfaces in cam and race for wear. Inspect roller springs for distortion, wear or other damage.

Fig. 31: Exploded View of Planetary Gear Train and Output Shaft

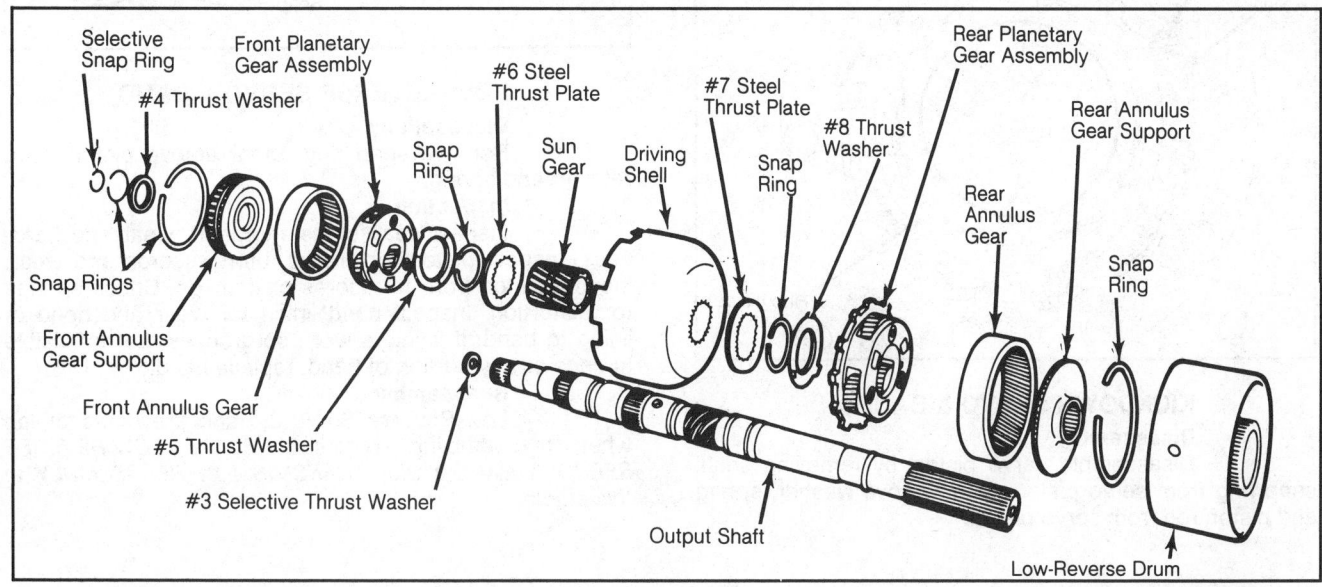

TORQUEFLITE (Cont.)

Fig. 32: Disassembled View of Replacement Type Overrunning Clutch Cam

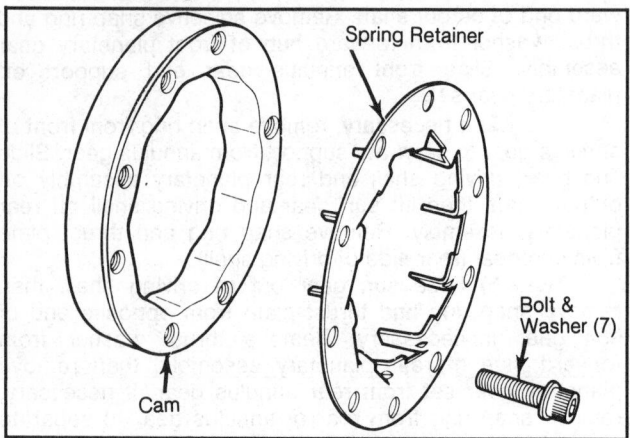

Overrunning Clutch Cam Replacement

1) Remove 4 bolts securing output shaft support to rear of transmission case, then tap support rearward and out of case with soft faced hammer. Center punch rivets exactly in center of each rivet head.

2) Drill through each rivet head with a 3/8" drill, taking care not to drill into transmission case. Chip off rivet heads with small chisel, then drive rivets and cam from case using a blunt punch. Enlarge rivet holes in case using a 17/64" drill. Remove all chips and foreign material from case.

3) To install, position cam and roller spring retainer in case, align cam bolt holes with holes in case, then thread all 7 retaining bolt and washer assemblies into cam a few turns. Cone washers must be installed so inner diameter is coned toward bolt head.

4) Tap cam firmly into case if necessary, then tighten bolts evenly. Screw 2 pilot studs into case, then position support over studs and tap firmly onto place using a soft faced hammer. Remove pilot studs, then install and tighten bolts evenly.

Fig. 33: Installed View of Overrunning Clutch Assembly

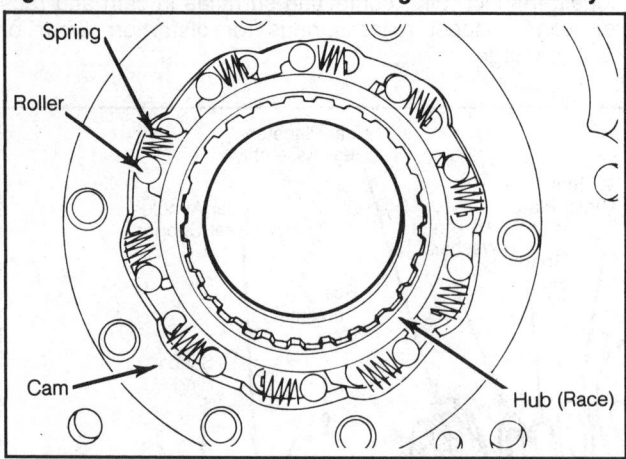

KICKDOWN SERVO & BAND

Disassembly

Disassemble servo piston by removing small snap ring from servo piston, then remove washer, spring and piston rod from servo piston.

Inspection

Inspect all parts for nicks, burrs, wear or damage. Be sure piston and guide seal rings turn freely in grooves. Do not remove seal rings unless conditions warrant. Inspect piston bore in case for scores or other damage. Inspect fit of guide on piston rod, and piston spring for distortion. Inspect band lining for wear or damage. If lining is worn so grooves are not visible at ends or any portion of band, replace band.

Reassembly

Carefully push servo piston into transmission case bore then install piston rod, springs and guide. Compress kickdown servo springs with spring compressor and install snap ring.

Fig. 34: Exploded View of Kickdown Servo

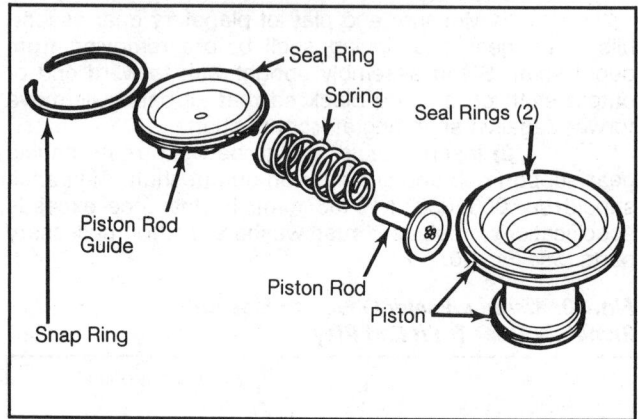

Fig. 35: Exploded View of Low-Reverse Servo

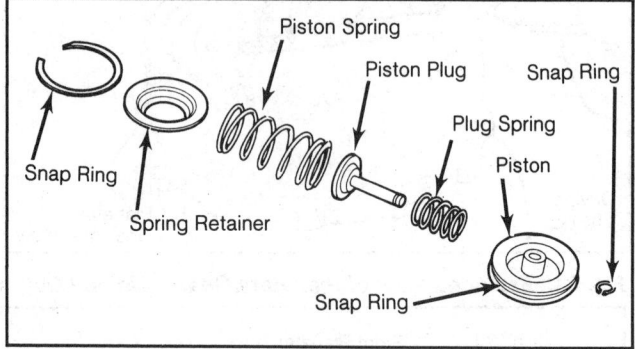

LOW-REVERSE SERVO & BAND

Disassembly

Remove snap ring, then remove piston, plug retainer and spring.

Inspection

Inspect seal for deterioration, wear and hardness. Inspect piston for cracks, burrs, scores and wear. Inspect piston bore for scores or damage. Check springs for distortion. Inspect band lining for wear and bond of lining to band. If lining is worn so grooves are not visible at ends or any portion of band, replace band.

Reassembly

Low-Reverse Servo & Band are reassembled when reassembling transmission. *See LOW-REVERSE SERVO & BAND under TRANSMISSION REASSEMBLY in this article.*

TORQUEFLITE (Cont.)

TRANSMISSION REASSEMBLY

NOTE: Use only Dexron type Automatic Transmission Fluid to lubricate transmission parts during reassembly.

OVERRUNNING CLUTCH

With transmission case in upright position, insert clutch hub inside cam, then install overrunning clutch rollers exactly as shown in *Fig. 33.*

Fig. 36: *Assembled View of Low-Reverse Band and Linkage Assembly*

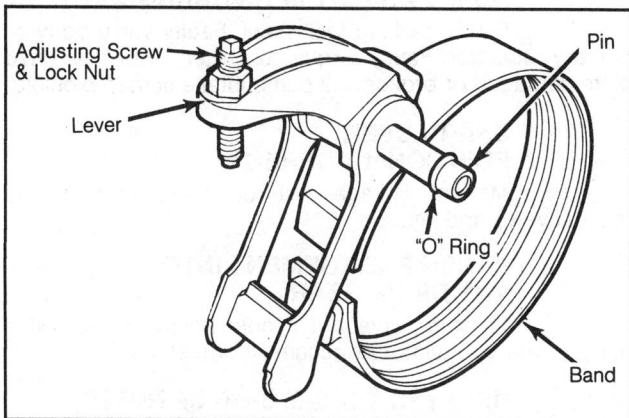

LOW-REVERSE SERVO & BAND

Low-Reverse Servo
Carefully work servo piston into transmission case with a twisting motion, then place spring, retainer and snap ring over piston. Using a spring compressor, compress low-reverse servo piston, then install snap ring.

Low-Reverse Band
Position rear band in transmission case, install short strut, then connect long link and anchor to band. Screw in band adjuster just enough to hold strut in place, then install low-reverse drum. Make sure long link and anchor are installed so as to provide running clearance for low-reverse drum.

PLANETARY GEAR, SUN GEAR & DRIVING SHELL

While supporting assembly in case, insert output shaft through rear support. Carefully work assembly rearward, engaging rear planetary carrier lugs into low-reverse drum slots.

CAUTION: Do not damage ground surfaces on output shaft during installation.

FRONT & REAR CLUTCH ASSEMBLIES

NOTE: Front and rear clutches, front band, oil pump and reaction shaft support are more easily installed with transmission in upright position.

1) Apply a coat of grease to selective thrust washer and install on front end of output shaft. If input shaft end play was not within specifications (.022-.091" or .56-2.3 mm) when tested prior to disassembly, replace thrust washer with one of proper thickness.

2) Align front clutch plate inner splines, then place assembly in position on rear clutch, making sure

front clutch plate splines are fully engaged on rear clutch splines.

3) Align rear clutch plate splines, grasp input shaft, then lower assemblies into case. Carefully work clutch assemblies in a circular motion to engage rear clutch splines over splines of front annulus gear. Make sure front clutch drive lugs are fully engaged in slots of driving shell.

FRONT (KICKDOWN) BAND

Slide front band over front clutch assembly. Install band strut, then screw in adjuster just enough to hold strut and anchor in place.

OIL PUMP & REACTION SHAFT SUPPORT

1) Install thrust washer on reaction shaft support hub.

NOTE: If difficulty was encountered in removing pump assembly due to an exceptionally tight fit, it may be necessary to expand case in pump area with a heat lamp prior to installation.

2) Screw 2 pilot studs into pump opening in case, then install a new gasket over studs. Place a new rubber seal ring in groove on outer flange of pump housing, making sure seal is not twisted.

3) Coat seal ring with grease, then install pump assembly into case, tapping lightly with a soft mallet, if necessary. Remove pilot studs, install bolts and snug down evenly.

4) Rotate input and output shafts to see that no binding exists, then tighten bolts. Check shafts again for free rotation, then adjust both bands.

GOVERNOR

See Service (In Vehicle).

EXTENSION HOUSING

See Service (In Vehicle).

TORQUE CONVERTER

See Transmission Removal & Installation

TIGHTENING SPECIFICATIONS

Application	Ft. Lbs. (N.m)
Transmission Mount Bolts	31-40 (42-54)
Torque Converter-to-Drive Plate	33-36 (45-49)
Drive Plate-to-Crankshaft	83-90 (113-122)
Extension Hsg.-to-Trans. Case	24 (33)
Trans. Insulator-to-Extension Hsg.	50 (68)
Adjusting Screw Lock Nut	
Kickdown Band	35 (47)
Reverse Band	30 (41)
	INCH Lbs. (N.m)
Governor Body-to-Governor Support	100 (11)
Kickdown Lever Shaft Plug	150 (17)
Oil Pan-to-Case	150 (17)
Oil Pump Hsg.-to-Trans. Case	175 (20)
Output Shaft Support Bolt	150 (17)
Pressure Test Plug	110 (12)
Reaction Shaft Support-to-Oil Pump	160 (18)
Valve Body Screws	35 (4)
Valve Body-to-Trans. Case	100 (11)

Automatic Transmissions

TOYOTA A-40, A-40D, A-43D & A-43DL

A-40 3-Speed
  Corolla
A-40D 4-Speed (Overdrive)
  Celica, Corolla, Corona
A-43D 4-Speed (Overdrive)
  Cressida, Pickup
A-43DL 4-Speed (Overdrive)
  Supra

TRANSMISSION IDENTIFICATION

Transmission can be identified by the lack of external adjustment levers or bolts on the transmission case. The oil pan is long and deep.

DESCRIPTION

These automatic transmissions have no bands, eliminating any internal adjustments. The only external adjustments are for throttle cable position and shift linkage adjustment. The A-40 transmission has 3 forward speeds and reverse. The A-40D, A-43D and A-43DL transmissions have 4 forward speeds (overdrive) and reverse.

Control of these shift sequences can be exercised in low or second lever position. The torque converter is a 3-element type. Planetary gears are actuated by 3 multi-disc brakes and 2 clutches. Engine load and speed determine gear changes by use of throttle valve position and output shaft speed. Tests, specifications and repair procedures are the same except where noted.

LUBRICATION & ADJUSTMENT

See the appropriate article in AUTOMATIC TRANSMISSION SERVICING Section.

TROUBLE SHOOTING

NO MOVEMENT IN ANY FORWARD GEAR OR REVERSE

Manual linkage out of adjustment. Faulty valve body or primary regulator.

NO MOVEMENT IN ANY RANGE

Faulty parking lock pawl. Faulty valve body or primary regulator. Faulty torque converter. Converter drive plate damaged or broken. Oil pump intake screen blocked.

SHIFT LEVER POSITION INCORRECT

Manual linkage out of adjustment. Faulty maunal valve and lever.

HARSH ENGAGEMENT INTO ANY DRIVE GEAR

Throttle cable out if adjustment. Faulty valve body, primary regulator or accumulator pistons.

DELAYED 1-2, 2-3, 3-OD UPSHIFTS, OR DOWNSHIFTS FROM OD-3 OR 3-2 THEN BACK TO OD OR 3

Throttle cable out of adjustment or faulty. Faulty governor or valve body.

Fig. 1: Cutaway View of Toyota A-40 Automatic Transmission Assembly

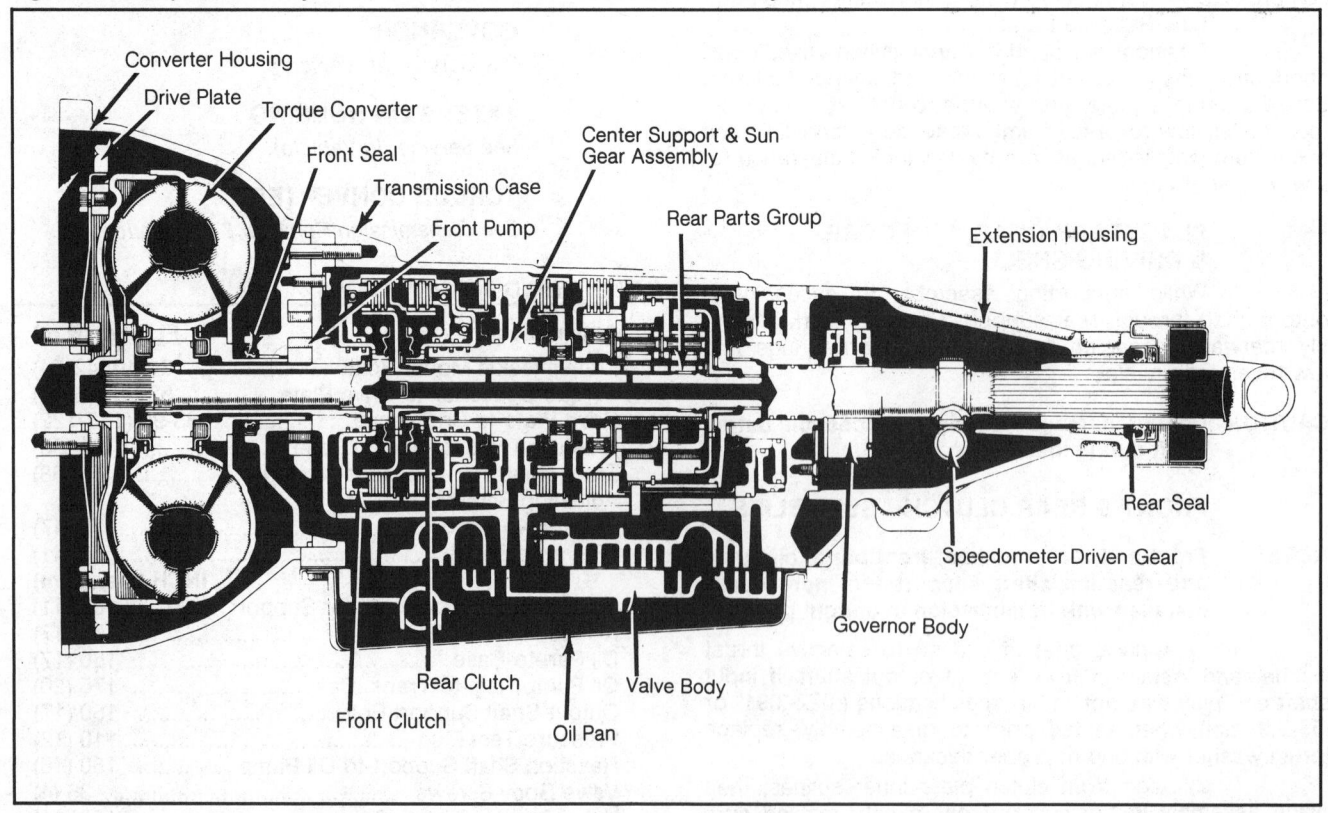

TOYOTA A-40, A-40D, A-43D & A-43DL (Cont.)

Fig. 2: *Cutaway View of Toyota A-40D Automatic Transmission Assembly*

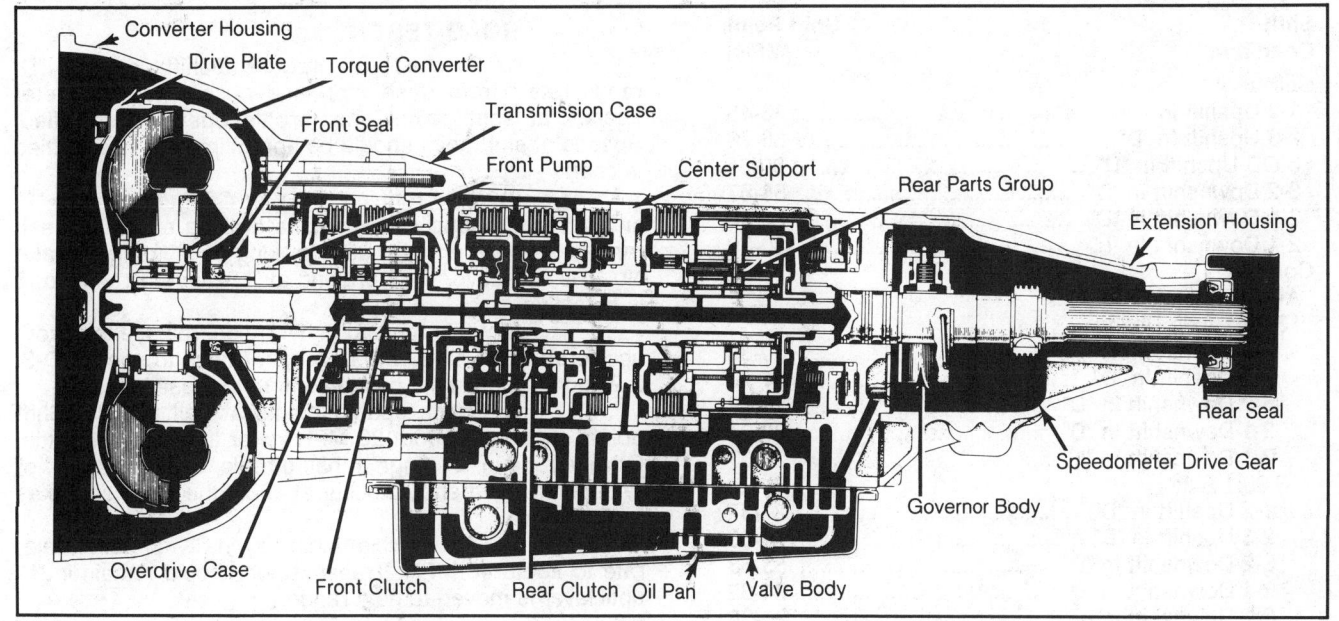

SLIP ON ANY UPSHIFT OR SLIP OR SHUDDER ON TAKEOFF

Manual linkage or throttle cable out of adjustment. Valve body faulty.

HARSH DOWNSHIFT

Throttle cable out of adjustment or faulty. Accumulator pistons or valve body faulty.

NO DOWNSHIFT WHEN COASTING

Faulty governor or valve body

DOWNSHIFTS TOO SOON OR TOO LATE WHEN COASTING

Throttle cable out of adjustment or faulty. Faulty governor or valve body.

NO OD-3, 3-2 OR 2-1 KICKDOWN

Throttle cable out of adjustment. Governor or valve body faulty.

NO ENGINE BRAKING IN "2"

Faulty valve body.

VEHICLE DOES NOT HOLD IN "P"

Manual linkage out of adjustment. Parking lock pawl cam and spring faulty.

CLUTCH AND BAND APPLICATION CHART (ELEMENTS IN USE — A-40 ONLY)

Selector Lever Position	Front Clutch	Rear Clutch	Brake No.1	Brake No. 2	Brake No. 3
D — DRIVE					
First	X [1]				
Second	X			X	
Third	X	X [3]		X	
2 — SECOND (Intermediate)	X		X [5]	X [2]	
L — LOW (First)	X				X [1][4]
R — REVERSE		X		X	

NEUTRAL OR PARK — All clutches, brakes, and bands released and/or ineffective.

[1] — One-way clutch No. 2 applied.   [2] — One-way clutch No. 1 applied.   [3] — Inner piston applied.
[4] — Outer piston applied.   [5] — Applied when engine is braking.

TOYOTA A-40, A-40D, A-43D & A-43DL (Cont.)

SHIFT SPEED SPECIFICATIONS

Shift Condition	Shift Point (MPH)
Celica	
1-2 Upshift in "D"	36-45
2-3 Upshift In "D"	66-76
3-OD Upshift In "D"	[1] 80-85
3-2 Downshift In "D"	58-67
2-1 Downshift In "D"	26-34
2-1 Downshift In "L"	30-39
Corolla	
A-40 Transmission	
3.58:1 Axle Ratio	
1-2 Upshift In "D"	30-39
2-3 Upshift In "D"	61-70
3-2 Downshift In "D"	58-68
2-1 Downshift In "D"	26-34
2-1 Downshift In "L"	28-37
3.90:1 Axle	
1-2 Upshift In "D"	27-37
2-3 Upshift In "D"	56-65
3-2 Downshift In "D"	53-63
2-1 Downshift In "D"	24-32
2-1 Downshift In "L"	25-35
A-40D Transmission	
1-2 Upshift In "D"	30-39
2-3 Upshift In "D"	56-65
3-OD Upshift in "D"	[1] 70-80
3-2 Downshift In "D"	48-58
2-1 Downshift In "D"	24-32
2-1 Downshift In "L"	25-35
Corona	
1-2 Upshift In "D"	34-43
2-3 Upshift In "D"	63-73
3-OD In "D"	[1] 75-80
3-2 Downshfit In "D"	52-35
2-1 Downshift In "D"	32-10
2-1 Downshift In "L"	29-32
Cressida	
1-2 Upshift In "D"	35-45
2-3 Upshift In "D"	65-75
3-OD Upshift in "D"	[1] 23-31
3-2 Downshift In "D"	58-67
2-1 Downshift In "D"	26-35
2-1 Downshift In "L"	28-39
Pickup	
1-2 Upshift In "D"	32-42
2-3 Upshift In "D"	61-70
3-OD Upshift In "D"	[1] 88-92
3-2 Downshift in "D"	57-66
2-1 Downshift In "D"	10-33
2-1 Downshift In "L"	27-36
Supra	
1-2 Upshift In "D"	32-42
2-3 Upshift In "D'"	61-71
3-OD Upshift In "D"	[1] 17-24
3-2 Downshift In "D"	56-65
2-1 Downshift in "D"	22-29
2-1 Downshift In "L"	28-39

[1] — 3-OD upshifts will not occur at full throttle. Shift speed shown are at 85% throttle on Celica, Corona and Pickup models, closed throttle on Corolla, Cressida and Supra.

TESTING

ROAD TEST

1) To check full throttle upshift points in "D" range, start from dead stop and observe speedometer speeds at shift points and throttle openings specified. Speeds at shift point should be approximately as specified in chart.

2) While running in "D" or OD gear, shift to "2" and "L" ranges and check engine braking effect at these ranges. If there is no engine braking at "2" range, Brake No. 1 is defective. If no braking at "L" range, Brake No. 3 is defective.

3) While running in "D" range, release foot from accelerator and shift into "L" range. Check to see if OD-3, 3-2 and 2-1 downshift points confirm to those in chart.

4) Check upshift points at half throttle. Shift points should be about 20 MPH lower than at full throttle. Drive vehicle in "2" range at half throttle. Observe speed of 1-2 upshift. Shift should occur at about the same speed as in "D" range.

5) Start vehicle underway in "L" range. Accelerate to about 40 MPH. Transmission should remain in "L" until lever is moved to next range.

HYDRAULIC PRESSURE TESTS

With transmission fluid at normal operating temperature, raise and support rear of vehicle so that rear wheels are free to turn. Connect pressure gauges to line pressure and governor pressure test ports on transmission as shown in *Fig. 3*. Check hydraulic pressures as follows:

Fig. 3: View of Transmission Case Showing Hydraulic Pressure Test Ports

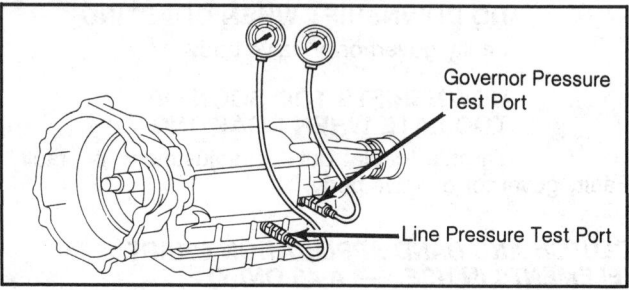

Governor Pressure

1) Start engine and release parking brake. Slowly accelerate engine with transmission in "D" and check governor pressure at speeds specified in "Governor Pressures" table.

2) If governor pressures are not as specified, check for the following: incorrect line pressure; fluid leakage in governor pressure circuit; governor valve operation defective.

GOVERNOR PRESSURE SPECIFICATIONS

Vehicle Speed (MPH)	Output Shaft (RPM)	Pressure psi (kg/cm²)
18-21	1000	12.8-21.3 (0.9-1.5)
34-36	1800	22.8-31.3 (1.6-2.2)
65-70	3500	58.3-75.4 (4.1-5.3)

TOYOTA A-40, A-40D, A-43D & A-43DL (Cont.)

Fig. 4: Toyota A-40 Automatic Transmission Hydraulic Circuits Diagram

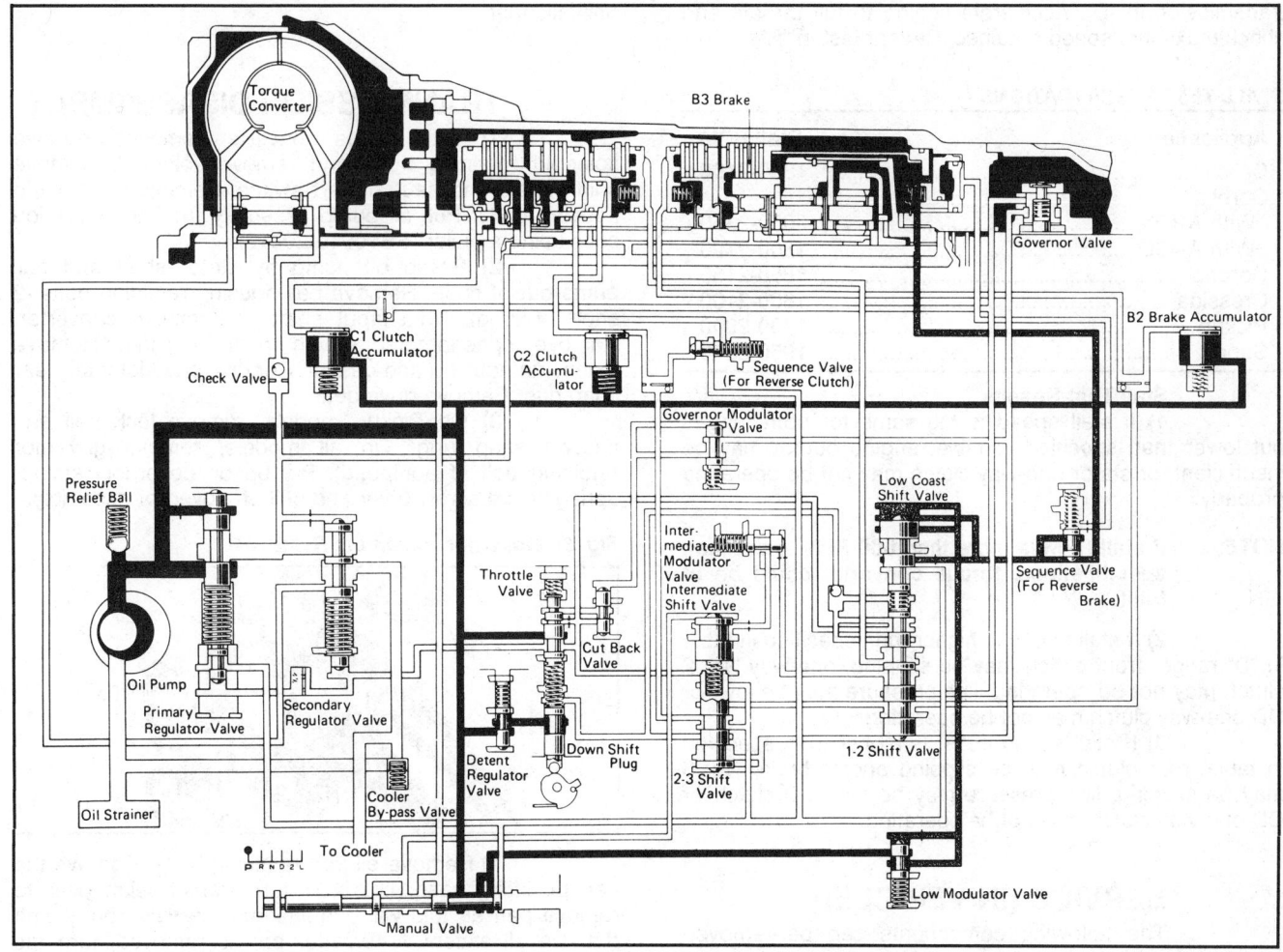

Line Pressure

1) Fully apply parking brake and block all 4 wheels. Start engine and shift transmission into "D". Apply firm pressure to brake pedal and accelerate engine to 1000 RPM. Line pressure should be as shown in "Line Pressures" table.

2) Increase engine to Stall Speed and again check line pressure. If specified line pressures are not obtained, check throttle cable adjustment and repeat test.

3) Repeat line pressure tests with transmission in "R". Line pressure should be as shown in *Line Pressures* table.

Line Pressure Test Results

1) If line pressure in all ranges is higher than specified, check for the following: defective regulator valve, defective throttle valve, or throttle cable out of adjustment.

2) If line pressure is low in all ranges, check for the following: defective oil pump, defective regulator valve, defective throttle valve, throttle cable out of adjustment, or defective OD clutch.

3) If line pressure is low in "D" range only, check for the following: defective front clutch, fluid leak in "D" range circuit, or defective OD clutch.

4) If line pressure is low in "R" range only, check for the following: defective rear clutch, defective No. 3 brake, fluid leak in "R" range circuit, or defective OD clutch.

LINE PRESSURE SPECIFICATIONS

Engine Speed	Pressure psi (kg/cm²)
At 1000 RPM	
"D"	
Cressida & Supra	65-74 (4.6-5.2)
All Other Models	57-64 (4.0-4.5)
"R"	
Cressida & Supra	80-117 (6.4-8.2)
All Others	82-97 (5.8-6.8)
At Stall Speed	
"D"	
Cressida	139-175 (9.8-12.3)
Supra	137-154 (9.6-10.8)
All Other Models	135-171 (9.5-12.0)
"R"	
Cressida & Supra	203-239 (14.3-16.8)
All Other Models	199-242 (14.0-17.0)

STALL TEST

1) With engine and transmission at normal operating temperature, connect a tachometer to engine. Fully apply parking brake and block front wheels.

NOTE: **DO NOT maintain stall RPM for more than 5 seconds.**

Automatic Transmissions

TOYOTA A-40, A-40D, A-43D & A-43DL (Cont.)

2) Start engine, apply brake pedal and place transmission in "D". Accelerate engine to full throttle and check maximum speed obtained. Repeat test in "R".

STALL TEST SPECIFICATIONS

Application	Stall RPM
Celica	1800-2100
Corolla	
With A-40	2050-2350
With A-40D	1800-2100
Corona	1850-2150
Cressida	1800-2100
Pickup	1700-2000
Supra	1950-2250

Stall Test Results

1) If stall speed is the same for both ranges but lower than specified in table, engine output may be insufficient, or stator one-way clutch may not be operating properly.

NOTE: If stall RPM is more than 600 RPM lower than specifications, torque converter could be at fault.

2) If stall speed is higher than specified in table in "D" range, front clutch may be slipping, one-way No. 2 clutch may not be operating, line pressure may be low, or OD one-way clutch may not be operating.

3) If stall speed in "R" is higher than specified in table, rear clutch may be slipping and/or brake No. 3 may be slipping, line pressure may be low, OD clutch or OD one-way clutch may not be operating.

SERVICE (IN VEHICLE)

The following components can be removed from transmission with transmission installed in vehicle: oil pan; valve body assembly; throttle cable; parking pawl assembly; manual valve shaft oil seal; speedometer drive gear; rear oil seal; extension housing; speedometer driven gear; governor assembly.

NOTE: For above components, procedures given in Transmission Disassembly, Component Disassembly and Reassembly, and Transmission Reassembly will apply.

TORQUE CONVERTER

Converter Flushing

If transmission appears contaminated, thoroughly flush converter before reassembly. Use transmission cleaner to flush converter. Clean outside of converter and case.

One-Way Clutch Test

1) With converter placed on work surface, insert special tool kit (SST 09350-20010). Kit consists of 2 pieces; a turning tool and a stopper. Insert turning tool in inner race of one-way clutch, insert stopper to fit in notch of converter hub and other race of one-way clutch.

2) Clutch should lock when turned counterclockwise, but should turn freely when rotated clockwise. Torque required to turn clutch clockwise should be less than 22 INCH lbs. (2.5 N.m). If necessary, clean

converter and retest clutch. Replace converter if clutch still fails test.

TRANSMISSION DISASSEMBLY

1) With torque converter removed, remove solenoid retaining bolts and remove solenoid. Remove shift handle and neutral start switch. Remove front pump housing bolts. Pull oil pump assembly from transmission case using a puller (SST0910-20012).

2) Grasp oil pump by stator shaft and pull pump out of case. Remove bell housing retaining bolts (2 short, 4 long). Hold input shaft and remove converter. Remove speedometer driven gear housing. Remove extension housing and gasket. Remove speedometer gear snap ring. Remove drive gear.

3) On Pickup models, remove lock ball and second snap ring. On all models, remove governor retaining bolt (if equipped). Pry up on governor retainer spring with a screwdriver and pull off governor assembly.

Fig. 5: Governor Assembly Removal

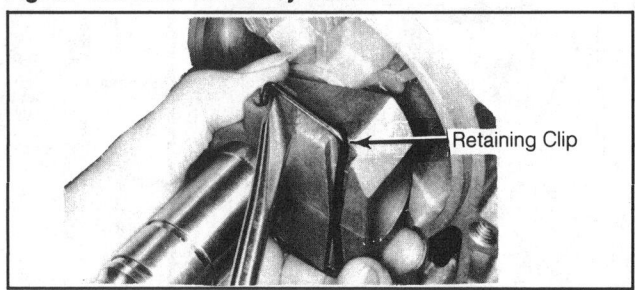

4) Remove oil pan retaining bolts. Remove the pan by lifting case. DO NOT turn transmission over to remove pan as this will contaminate the valve body with dirt. On all except A-40, after pan is removed, turn the transmission over and remove oil tubes. Note installation position for reassembly reference.

5) On all transmissions, remove oil strainer, then remove valve body attaching bolts. Carefully lift up valve body and disconnect throttle cable from throttle cam, then remove valve body assembly from case. Hold throttle cable retainer with a 10 mm socket and pull cable from case.

Fig. 6: Apply Compressed Air at Holes Indicated to Remove Accumulator Pistons and Springs (A-43D and A-43DL Transmissions)

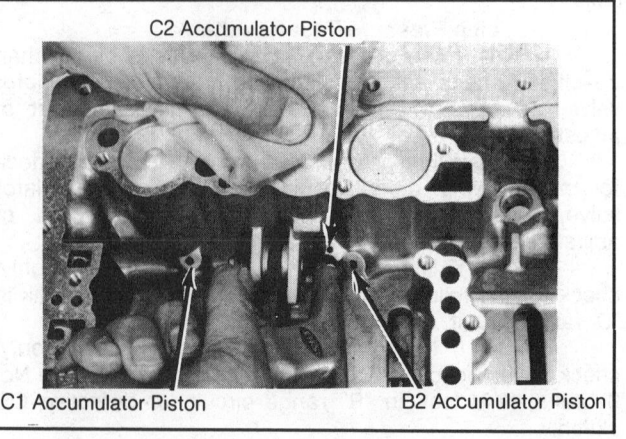

TOYOTA A-40, A-40D, A-43D & A-43DL (Cont.)

Fig. 7: Apply Compressed Air at Holes Indicated to Remove Accumulator Pistons and Springs (A-40 and A-40D Transmissions)

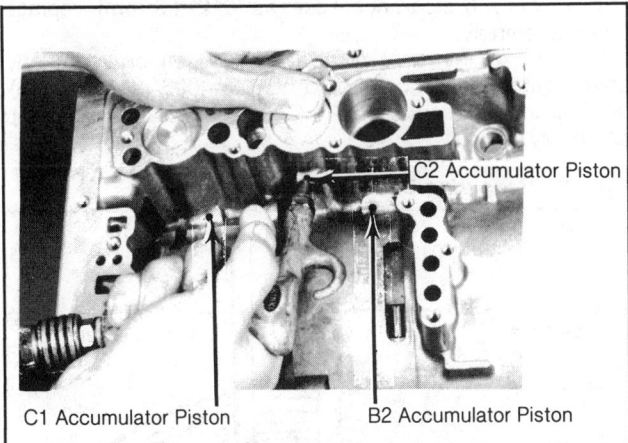

C1 Accumulator Piston   B2 Accumulator Piston

6) Remove accumulator pistons and springs from case by blowing compressed air through holes in case indicated in *Figs. 6 and 7*. Position a rag to catch piston when removing. Identify each accumulator piston and spring for reassembly reference.

7) Remove attaching bolts and parking lock pawl bracket. Remove the lock rod after aligning the lugs with manual valve lever. Remove parking pawl, pivot pin and spring. Pry manual shift lever shaft over to gain access to retaining pin. Drive out pin and remove shaft.

8) On all models except A-40, turn transmission over, grasp shaft and remove OD clutch. Hold both sides of the OD case and remove from transmission case with brake. Watch for bearings and races on both sides of assembly. On all models, remove front clutch and bearings.

9) Remove rear clutch. Remove 2 center support mounting bolts at valve body side of case. Pull center support and sun gear shaft assembly from case. Using screwdriver, remove large snap ring from case groove.

10) Pull rear parts group from transmission case by intermediate shaft. If brake apply tube did not come out with the rear parts group, remove it from case. Remove output shaft thrust bearing and race from inside of case.

Fig. 8: Removing Rear Parts Group

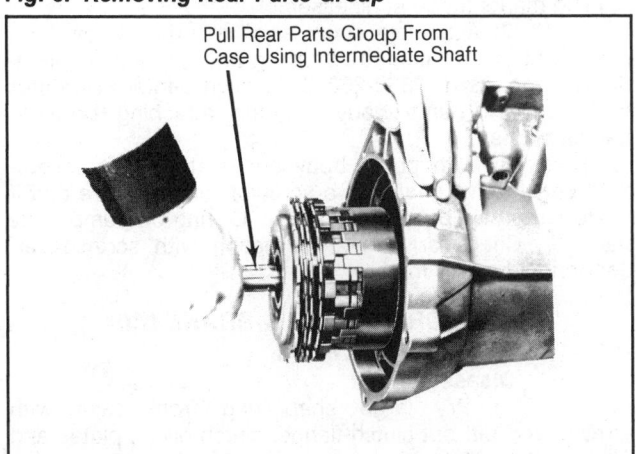

Pull Rear Parts Group From Case Using Intermediate Shaft

COMPONENT DISASSEMBLY & REASSEMBLY

BUSHING SERVICE
Inspection
Using the following tables, check bushings for excessive wear. If a bushing requires replacement, the component containing the bushing must also be replaced.

NOTE: Information on bushings for A-43D and A-43DL was not available from manufacturer.

Fig. 9: View of A-40 Transmission Showing Bushing Locations

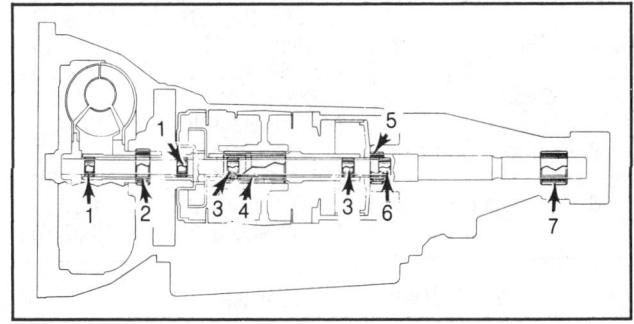

Fig. 10: View of A-40D Transmission Showing Bushing Locations

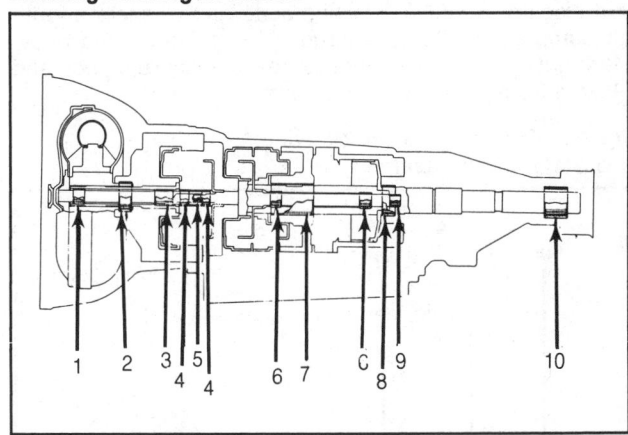

A-40 TRANSMISSION BUSHING SPECIFICATIONS

Bushing	Finish Bore In. (mm)	Bore Limit In. (mm)
1 - Stator Shaft	.8465-.8475 (21.501-21.527)	.8495 (21.577)
2 - Oil Pump	1.5005-1.5015 (38.113-38.138)	1.5035 (38.188)
3 - Sun Gear	.8465-.8475 (21.501-21.527)	.8495 (21.577)
4 - Center Support	1.4325-1.4335 (36.386-36.411)	1.4355 (36.461)
5 - Case	1.5005-1.5015 (38.113-38.138)	1.5035 (38.188)
6 - Output Shaft	.7087-.7096 (18.011-18.025)	.7117 (18.076)
7 - Extension Hsg.	1.4961-1.4970 (38.000-38.025)	1.4990 (38.075)

TOYOTA A-40, A-40D, A-43D & A-43DL (Cont.)

A-40D TRANSMISSION BUSHING SPECIFICATIONS

Bushing	Finished Bore In. (mm)	Bore Limit In. (mm)
1 - Stator Support	.8465-.8475 (21.501-21.527)	.8495 (21.577)
2 - Oil Pump	1.5005-1.5015 (38.113-38.138)	1.5035 (28.188)
3 - Stator Support	.8465-.8475 (21.501-21.527)	.8495 (21.577)
4 - OD Sun Gear	.8480-.8490 (21.538-21.565)	.8509 (21.614)
5 - OD Input Shaft	.4409-.4418 (11.200-11.221)	.4437 (11.271)
6 - Sun Gear	.8465-.8475 (21.501-21.527)	.8495 (21.577)
7 - Center Support	1.4325-1.4355 (36.386-36.411)	1.4355 (36.461)
8 - Case	1.5005-1.5015 (38.113-38.138)	1.5035 (38.188)
9 - Output Shaft	.7087-.7097 (18.001-18.026)	.7117 (18.076)
10 - Extension Hsg.	1.4972-1.4970 (38.000-38.025)	1.5256 (38.075)

OIL PUMP & STATOR SHAFT
Disassembly

Set pump shaft in torque converter while working on pump. Remove 2 oil seals from pump cover and discard. Remove retaining bolts and washers and lift off pump cover. Remove large "O" ring from pump body. Mark drive and driven gears for reassembly reference and remove from pump body. Pry out front oil seal.

Fig. 11: Exploded View of Oil Pump and Stator Shaft Assembly

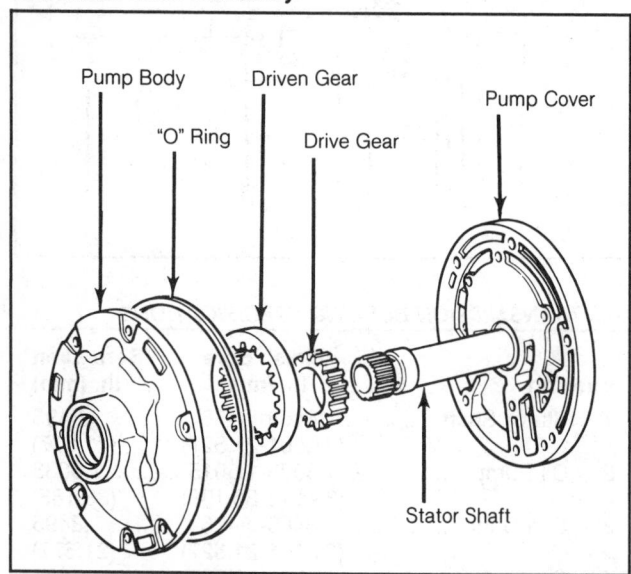

Inspection

1) Wash disassembled parts and blow dry with compressed air. Inspect pump oil seal and transmission seal ring for damage.

2) Inspect contacting surfaces between body and driven gear for ridged wear. Check gears for wear and body crescent for damage. Check pump gear contacting surface on stator shaft for damage and wear.

3) With a feeler gauge, measure clearance between driven gear and oil pump body with gear pushed over fully to the other side. Clearance should be .003-.006" (.07-.15 mm). If clearance exceeds .012" (.3 mm), replace pump assembly.

4) Measure clearance between crescent and driven gear. Clearance should be .004-.006" (.11-.14 mm). If clearance exceeds .012" (.3 mm) replace oil pump assembly.

Fig. 12: Measuring Oil Pump Clearances

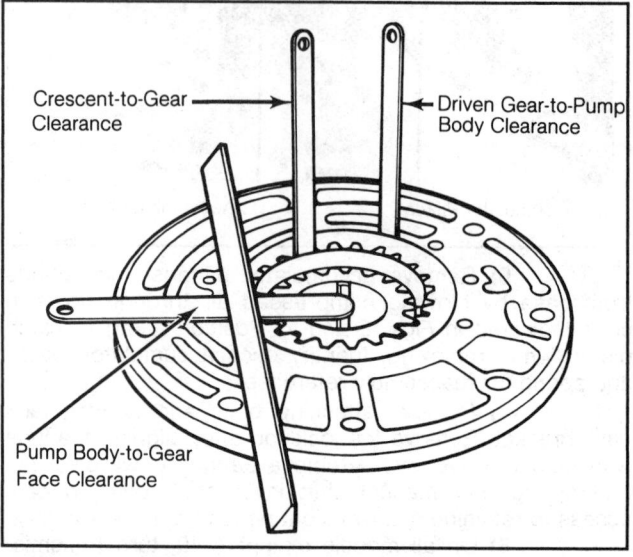

5) Measure clearance between crescent and drive gear. Clearance should be .004-.016" (.11-.14 mm). If clearance exceeds .012" (.3 mm), replace oil pump assembly.

6) Using a feeler gauge and straightedge, measure clearance between pump body face and top of gears. Clearance should be .001-.002" (.02-.05 mm). If clearance exceeds .004" (.1 mm) replace oil pump assembly.

7) Inspect stator shaft splines by inserting stator shaft into torque converter. Shaft should slide in smoothly and there should be no excessive looseness. Replace stator shaft if defective.

Reassembly

1) Coat drive and driven gears with automatic transmission fluid, then install them into pump body, aligning marks made at disassembly.

2) Assemble stator shaft to pump body, then install, but do not tighten attaching bolts. Using oil pump aligning tool (SST09350-20013) to align centers of stator shaft and oil pump body. Tighten attaching bolts to specifications.

3) With pump body and stator shaft assembled, check drive gear with a screwdriver to ensure that it rotates freely. Lubricate and install "O" ring on pump body diameter. Check drive gear opreation with screwdriver. Gear should rotate freely.

OVERDRIVE CASE & BRAKE (B0) (ALL EXCEPT A-40)
Disassembly

1) Pry large snap ring from case with screwdriver. Lift out clutch flange, clutch discs, plates and cushion plate. Retain in correct order for reassembly.

TOYOTA A-40, A-40D, A-43D & A-43DL (Cont.)

2) Remove ring gear. Pry thrust washer from ring gear with screwdriver. Remove thrust bearings and races from case and note order and position for reassembly. Compress piston return springs and remove snap ring. Lift out piston return springs and seat.

3) Remove brake piston from case by applying compressed air. Remove oil seals from case and "O" rings from piston.

Fig. 13: Using Compressed Air to Remove Piston from Overdrive Clutch Case

Apply Air Here to Force Piston From Case

Inspection

1) Wash all parts (except discs) thoroughly in clean solvent. Air dry all parts with compressed air.

2) Inspect all parts for wear or damage and replace as necessary. Inspect clutch plates, discs and flange for signs of burning. Check piston return springs for wear, damage and collapsed coils.

NOTE: New clutch disc must be soaked in ATF fluid for at least 2 hours prior to installation.

Fig. 15: View of Ring Gear Showing Correct Installation of Bearing and Races

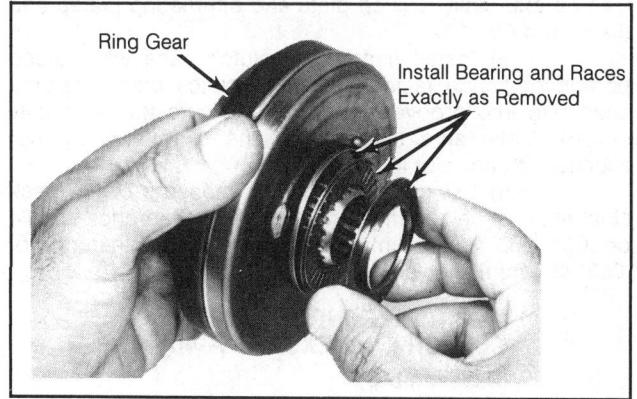

Ring Gear

Install Bearing and Races Exactly as Removed

Reassembly

1) Coat all surfaces with transmission fluid for assembly. Lubricate and install oil seals on piston and

Fig. 14: Exploded View of Overdrive Case and Brake B0

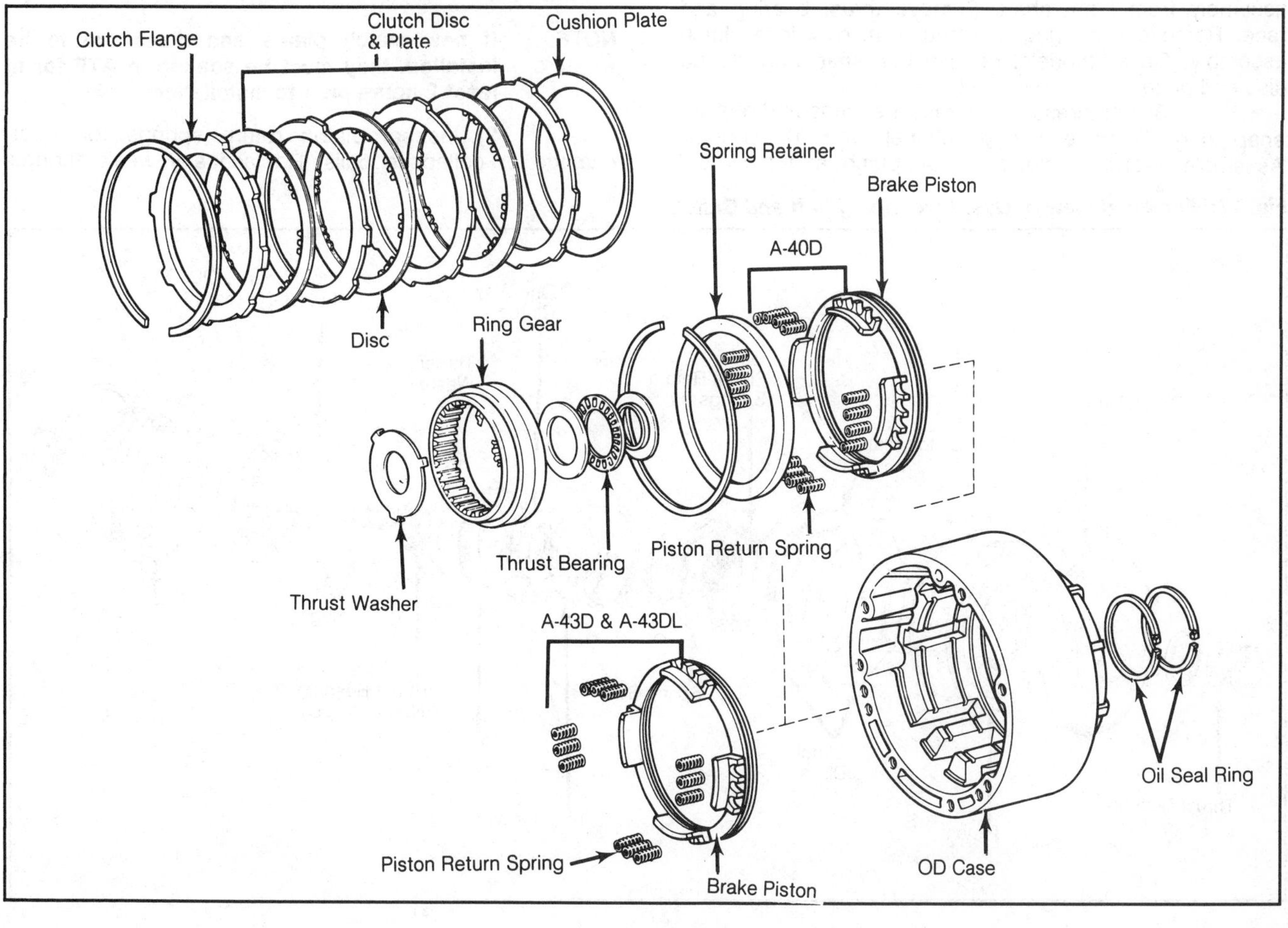

Clutch Flange

Clutch Disc & Plate

Cushion Plate

Disc

Ring Gear

Thrust Bearing

Spring Retainer

A-40D

Brake Piston

Piston Return Spring

Thrust Washer

A-43D & A-43DL

Piston Return Spring

Brake Piston

OD Case

Oil Seal Ring

TOYOTA A-40, A-40D, A-43D & A-43DL (Cont.)

clutch case. Carefully install piston into case. Save thrust washer for installation when transmission is reassembled.

2) Position return springs into pockets of clutch piston, then install spring seat over springs. Compress return springs and install retaining snap ring.

3) Install bearing and races on ring gear in same positions as when disassembled. Install ring gear assembly into clutch case.

4) Install cushion plate into clutch case with beveled side down. Install clutch pack into case starting with an externally splined plate and alternating plates and discs. *See Fig. 14.*

5) Install flange into clutch case with raised portion of flange facing up. Install clutch pack retaining snap ring into groove in case and ensure that it is fully seated. Make sure the ends of the snap ring are not aligned with any slot in housing.

6) Using a feeler gauge, measure clutch pack clearance between flange and snap ring. Clearance should be .014-.063" (.35-1.6 mm), with a maximum clearance of .083" (2.1 mm) allowed.

OVERDRIVE INPUT SHAFT & CLUTCH (ALL EXCEPT A-40)

Disassembly

1) Remove thrust bearings and races from clutch side by hand. Note position of races. Pry thrust washer from planetary gear side with a screwdriver. On A-40D, remove snap ring and hub from overdrive clutch assembly.

2) On A-43D and A-43DL, pull overdrive clutch assembly from input shaft. Remove thrust bearing and race. Remove snap ring and hub from overdrive clutch assembly. On all models, remove thin snap ring, flange disc and plate.

3) Compress piston return springs and remove snap ring. Remove spring retainer and 18 springs. Assemble overdrive clutch on oil pump and blow out

piston with compressed air. *See Fig. 16.* Remove overdrive clutch from the oil pump. Remove clutch piston "O" rings.

Fig. 16: *Removing Overdrive Direct Clutch*

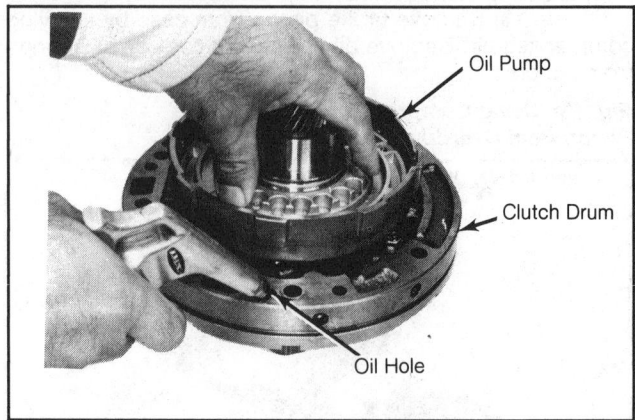

Apply air to oil hole.

4) Remove snap ring from overdrive planetary gear assembly. Remove thrust washers and one-way clutch from planetary gear assembly. Remove plugs with a magnet, being careful not to loose plugs. Remove one-way clutch from outer race.

Inspection

1) Thoroughly clean all parts and inspect them for wear and damage. Check clutch plates for signs of burning. Replace parts as necessary.

NOTE: **If new clutch plates and discs are to be installed, they must be soaked in ATF for at least 2 hours prior to installation.**

2) Inspect piston return springs for wear, damage or collapsed coils. Replace any weak springs.

Fig. 17: *Exploded View of Overdrive Input Shaft and Clutch*

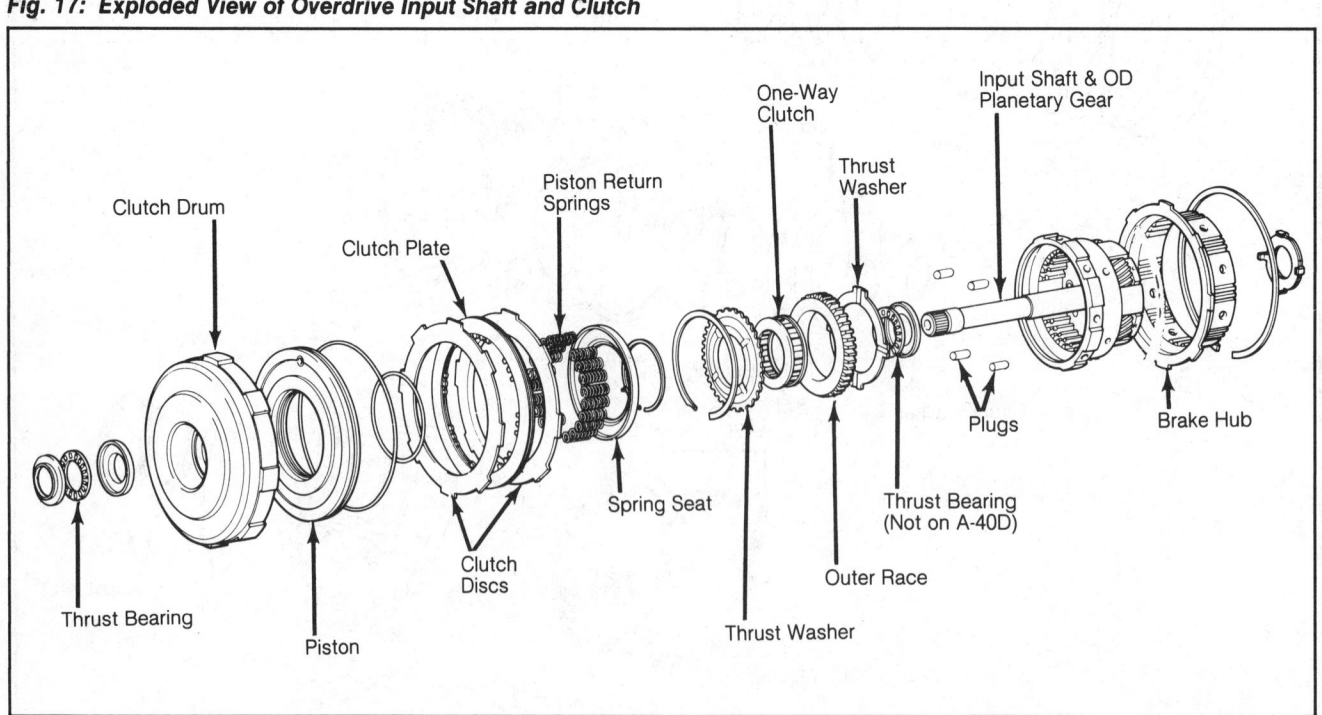

TOYOTA A-40, A-40D, A-43D & A-43DL (Cont.)

Inspect clutch piston and "O" rings for wear or damage. Check clutch piston to ensure that piston check ball is not sticking.

Reassembly

1) Lubricate all parts with transmission fluid prior to installation. Install the 4 plugs. On A-43D and A-43DL, install thrust washer and bearing. Coat parts with petroleum jelly to keep in place and slip bearing and thrust washer on with lip facing outward.

2) On all models, install the one-way clutch into the outer race. Install a retainer on both sides of the one-way clutch. Spring cage side of one-way clutch faces toward the front of transmission. Install thrust washer and one-way clutch.

Fig. 18: View Showing Correct Installation of One-Way Clutch Assembly

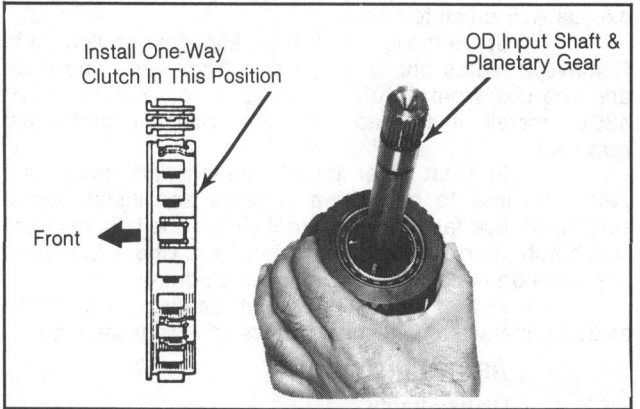

3) On A-40D, install thrust washer with the oil groove facing upward. On all models, install new "O" ring to piston and lubricate with ATF. Press clutch piston into overdrive clutch drum with cup side up. Position return springs into pockets of piston, then install spring seat over springs.

4) Using a compressor tool, compress springs and seat and install retaining snap ring. Install clutch plates and discs into clutch drum in reverse order as removed. DO NOT install thinner retaining snap ring at this time. Piston travel must be checked as follows:

5) Temporarily install overdrive clutch hub and outer snap ring. Install the front clutch drum on the oil pump body. Mount a dial indicator so that indicator tip touches top of clutch piston. See Fig. 19.

Fig. 19: Checking Clutch Piston Travel

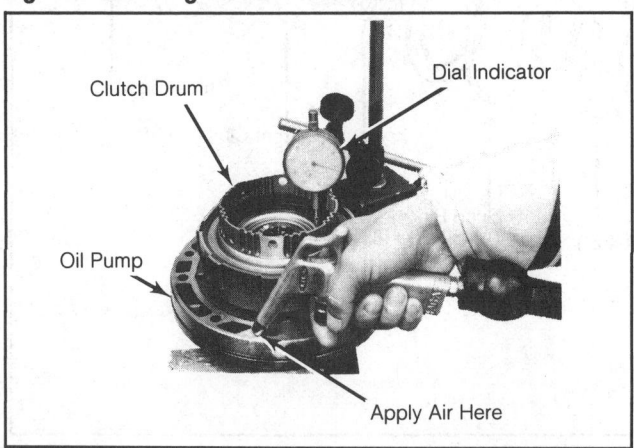

6) Apply pressure to oil hole in oil pump as shown in Fig. 19 and read piston travel on dial indicator. Piston travel with 57-114 psi (4-8 kg/cm²) air pressure applied should be .061-.090" (1.55-2.28 mm). If stroke exceeds limit, clutch pack is probably worn. If stroke is less than specified, parts may be misassembled or there may be excess ATF on discs.

7) Remove dial indicator. Remove overdrive clutch outer snap ring and hub to allow installation of inner snap ring. Install thin inner snap ring in overdrive clutch drum. Check that ends of snap ring are not aligned with cutouts.

8) On A-43D and A-43DL, install hub and outer snap ring. Check that ends of snap ring are not aligned with cutouts. On all models, assemble overdrive clutch drum and overdrive planetary gear. Mesh hub with disc, twisting hub as necessary.

9) On A-40D, install hub and outer snap ring. Check that ends of snap ring are not aligned with cutouts. On all models, check operation of one-way clutch. Hold the clutch drum and turn the input shaft. Input shaft should turn freely clockwise and lock counterclockwise.

FRONT CLUTCH

Disassembly

1) Remove thrust bearing and races from both sides of clutch. Note position of races. Use extension housing as a work stand for remainder of disassembly. Remove snap ring and lift out both clutches together. Remove thrust bearings and races. Remove clutch plate on A-40 and A-40D or disc on A-43D and A-43DL.

2) Remove thin snap ring and pull out remaining clutch plates and discs. Using a compressor tool,

Fig. 20: Removing Front Clutch Piston Using Compressed Air

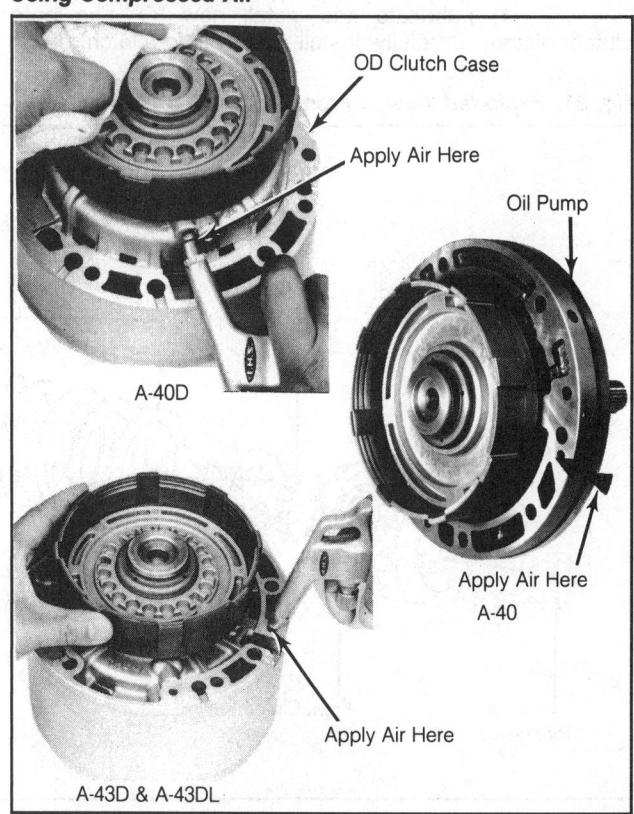

compress piston return spring and remove snap ring. Take out spring seat and return springs.

3) On A-40 transmissions, assemble clutch drum onto oil pump, then remove clutch piston from drum by applying compressed air to oil pump oil hole indicated in *Fig. 20.* Remove "O" rings from piston.

4) On all other transmissions, assemble clutch drum onto overdrive clutch case, then remove piston by applying compressed air to case oil hole as indicated in *Fig. 20.* Remove "O" rings from clutch piston.

Inspection

1) Thoroughly clean all parts and inspect them for wear and damage. Check clutch plates and discs for signs of burning and replace as necessary.

NOTE: **If new clutch plates are to be installed they must be soaked in ATF for at least 2 hours prior to installation.**

2) Check input shaft bearing and bushing contacting surfaces for damage, excessive wear and burning. Insert input shaft into torque converter and ensure that it slides in smoothly and that there is no excessive looseness.

3) Inspect toothed parts of clutch drum and clutch hubs for wear and damage. Inspect piston and clutch drum sliding surfaces for burning.

4) Check return springs for wear, damage or collapsed coils. Check for uniform length of springs and replace if any spring is noticeably shorter than the rest. Replace any worn or damaged springs.

5) Inspect check ball in clutch piston for sticking by shaking piston. Also, apply compressed air from inner side of piston and inspect check ball for air leaks.

Reassembly

1) Lubricate and install new "O" ring onto clutch piston. Carefully install piston into clutch drum.

Position piston return springs and seat on piston, then compress springs and install snap ring.

2) Blow excess ATF off of clutch discs and plates with low pressure compressed air. Install ALL clutch discs and plates into drum without thin snap ring. Install rear clutch hub and outer snap ring. Make sure snap ring ends do not line up with any slot in clutch drum.

3) On A-40 transmissions, install clutch drum on oil pump body. On A-40D and A-40DL, install clutch on the overdrive case. Apply 57-114 psi (4-8 kg/cm²) air pressure to the oil hole in pump body or overdrive case. Assemble a dial indicator with tip touching clutch piston.

4) Travel on A-40 and A-40D models should be .056-.092" (1.42-2.33 mm) and on A-43D and A-43DL should be .072-.092" (1.84-2.33 mm). If stroke is longer, clutch pack may be worn. If stroke is too short, component may be assembled improperly or there may be excess ATF on clutch discs.

5) Remove snap ring and rear clutch hub. Remove 2 plates and a clutch disc from A-40, one plate and one disc from A-40D, or one disc from A-43D and A-43DL. Install thin snap ring and reinstall parts just removed.

6) Coat inner thrust bearing and races with petroleum jelly to hold them in place and install. Make sure lip of race faces toward front clutch body. Install front clutch hub, rear clutch hub and snap ring. Check that snap ring ends do not align with slot in clutch drum.

7) Set remaining thrust bearings and races aside for installation when transmission is reassembled.

REAR CLUTCH

Disassembly

1) Remove snap ring and lift clutch flange, clutch discs and clutch plates from rear clutch drum. Compress piston return spring with compressor tool and remove snap ring. Lift out springs and spring seat.

2) Assemble clutch drum on center support. Apply compressed air to oil hole(s) in center support and

Fig. 21: Exploded View of Front Clutch Assembly

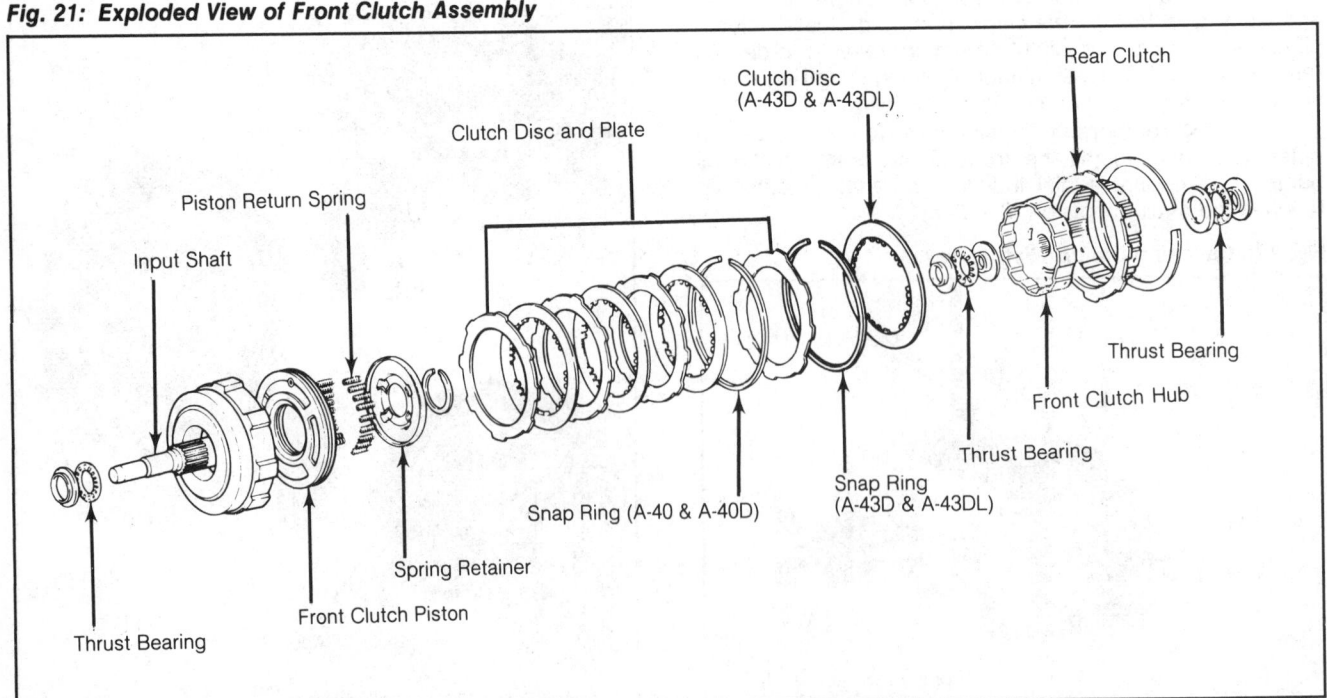

TOYOTA A-40, A-40D, A-43D & A-43DL (Cont.)

remove inner and outer pistons (rear clutch piston on A-43D and A-43DL models) from clutch drum. *See Fig. 22.* Remove "O" rings from piston(s) and discard.

Fig. 22: *Using Compressed Air to Remove Rear Clutch Inner and Outer Pistons*

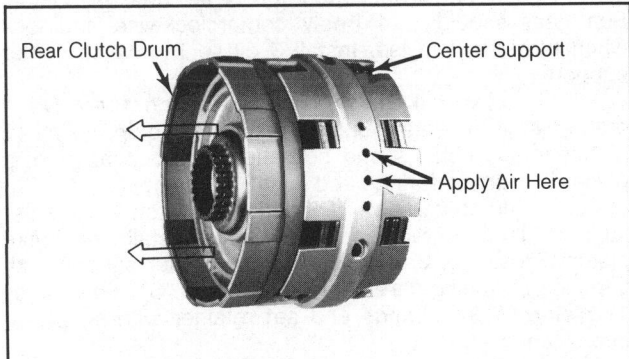

Inspection

1) Thoroughly clean all parts and inspect them for wear and damage. Inspect toothed parts and piston sliding surfaces of clutch drum for wear or damage.

2) Inspect clutch plates and discs for signs of burning. Also check plate and disc splines (teeth) for wear and damage.

3) Inspect clutch pistons for wear and damage. Shake pistons and make sure that check balls are not stuck. Also, apply air pressure to the check balls to see that they do not leak. Check piston return springs as for even length.

Reassembly

1) Install "O" rings on inner and outer pistons. Apply a thin coat of ATF to "O" rings, then insert pistons carefully into clutch drum, making sure not to damage "O" rings.

2) Place piston return springs and spring seat on piston, then compress springs and install snap ring. Install clutch plates, clutch discs and clutch flange into drum in sequence shown in *Fig. 23.* Install clutch pack snap ring.

NOTE: **Make sure that clutch flange is installed with raised portion facing forward.**

3) Install rear clutch onto center support. Apply compressed air pressure of 57-114 psi (4-8 kg/cm²) to oil hole in center support and measure travel with a dial indicator. Piston travel should be .037-.068" (.93-1.72 mm) on A-40, .043-.051" (1.10-1.30 mm) on A-40D and .049-.084" (1.24-2.12 mm) on A-43D and A-43DL.

Fig. 24: *Checking Rear Clutch Piston Travel*

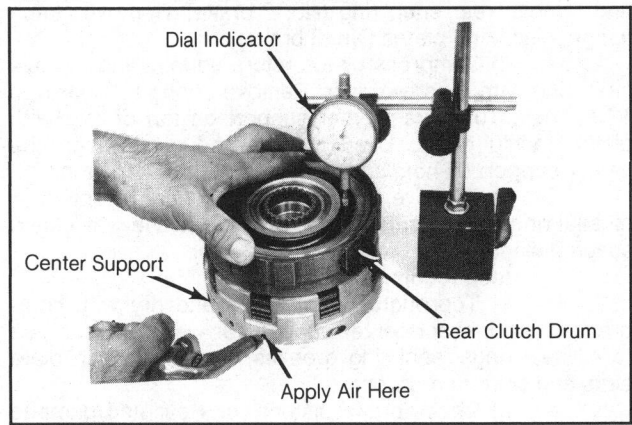

A-40D shown, others similar.

Fig. 23: *Exploded View of Rear Clutch Assembly*

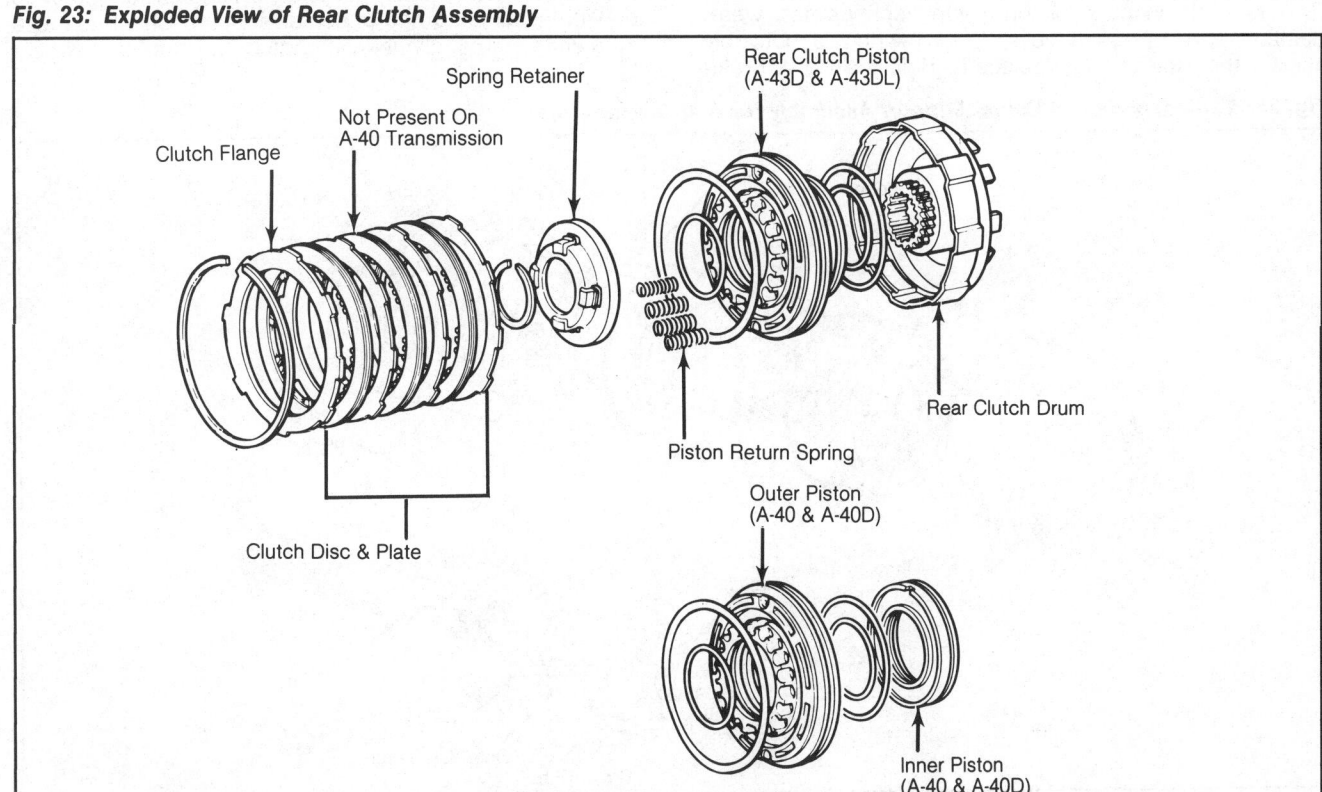

4) Excessive travel indicates clutch pack is worn. If travel is below specifications, components may be misassembled or there could be excess ATF on clutch discs.

CENTER SUPPORT ASSEMBLY
Disassembly (A-40 Transmission)

1) Remove snap ring from end of planetary sun gear, then remove center support assembly from shaft. Remove snap ring from front of center support assembly (No. 1 brake). *See Fig. 25.*

2) Remove clutch flange, disc and plate (No. 1 Brake). Compress piston return springs and remove snap ring. Remove spring retainer and 12 springs. Turn over center support on top of rag, with piston facing down.

3) Blow compressed air through the center support oil hole to remove No. 1 brake piston. Remove brake piston "O" rings. Turn center support assembly over and remove rear snap ring (No. 2 brake). Remove clutch flange, discs and plates (No. 2 brake).

4) Compress piston return springs and remove snap ring with a screwdriver. Remove spring retainer and 12 springs. Turn over center support on top of rag, with piston facing down. Blow compressed air through the center support oil hole and remove No. 2 brake piston.

5) Remove brake piston "O" rings. Remove 3 oil seal rings from center support. Remove one-way clutch assembly and oil seal rings from sun gear.

Inspection

1) Thoroughly clean parts and dry with compressed air. Inspect center support for wear and damage to oil seal rings, seal ring grooves, bushing, clutch plate slots and snap ring groove.

2) Check brake pistons for wear and damage to sliding surfaces. Inspect clutch plates and discs for signs of burning, and for damage to splines.

3) Inspect piston return springs for wear, damage and collapsed coils. If any spring is noticably shorter than the others, replace it. Hold the No. 2 brake

hub and turn the sun gear. The sun gear should turn freely conterclockwise and should lock clockwise. If the one-way clutch does not work properly, replace it.

Reassembly

1) Assemble oil seal rings and one-way clutch on sun gear. Check the operation of the one-way clutch. Sun gear should turn freely conterclockwise and lock when turned clockwise. Install 3 oil seal rings on center support.

2) Install new "O" rings on piston. Press No. 1 brake piston in center support with cup side up. Install 12 piston return springs and set retainer and snap ring in place. Compress springs and install snap ring.

3) Install new "O" rings on piston and center support. Turn center support over and install new brake piston. Press No. 2 brake piston into center support with cup side up, being careful not to damage "O" rings. Install 12 piston return springs and set retainer with snap ring into place.

4) Compress springs and install snap ring with a screwdriver. Turn center support over and install No. 1 brake piston plate, disc and flange (rounded edge down). Install snap ring in center support. Check to make sure that snap ring ends are not aligned with one of the cutouts.

5) Install a dial indicator to measure piston stroke. Apply compressed air to piston oil hole at 57-114 psi (4-8 kg/cm²) and measure stroke. Stroke should be .026-.051" (.65-1.30 mm). Excessive travel indicates clutch pack is worn. If travel is below specifications, components may be misassembled or there could be excess ATF on clutch discs.

6) Turn center support over and install No. 2 brake plates, discs and flange. Use low pressure compressed air to blow excess ATF from discs. Install in this order: Plate, disc, plate, plate, disc, flange (rounded edge down). Install snap ring in center support. Check to make sure ends are not aligned with one of the cutouts.

Fig. 25: Exploded View of Center Support Assembly for A-40 Transmission

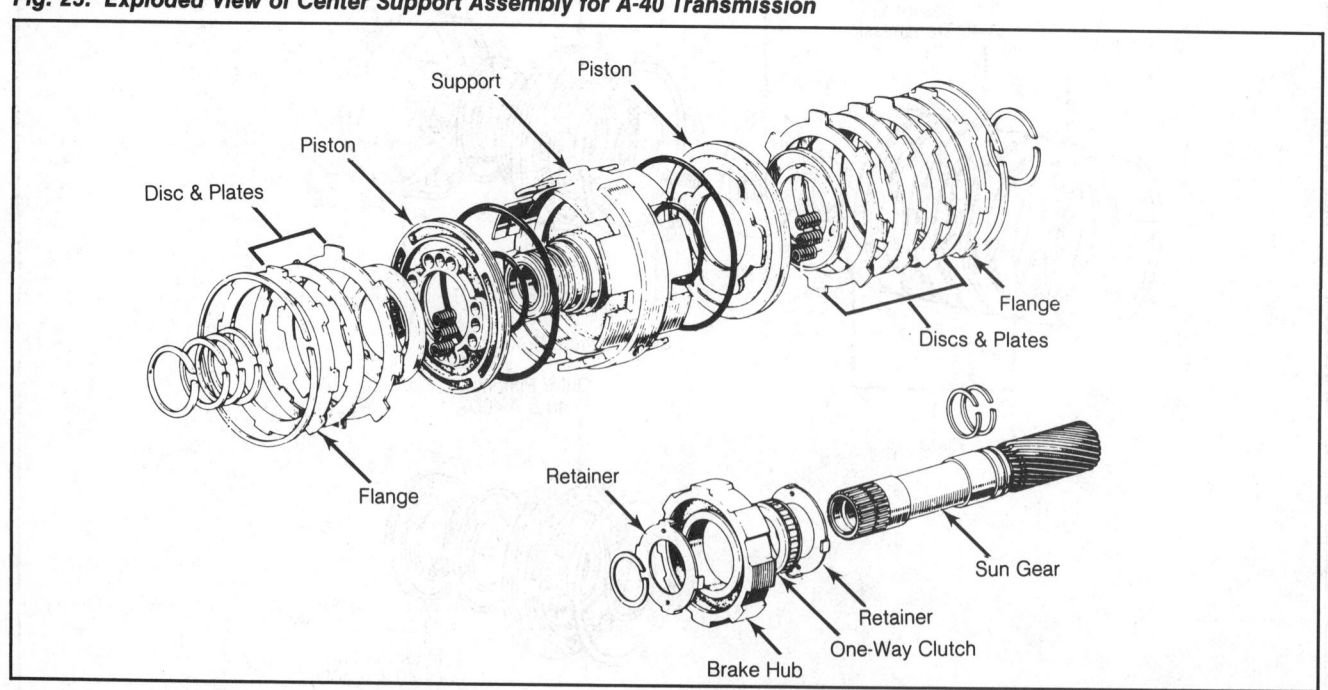

TOYOTA A-40, A-40D, A-43D & A-43DL (Cont.)

Fig. 26: Exploded View Center Support Assembly for A-40D Transmission

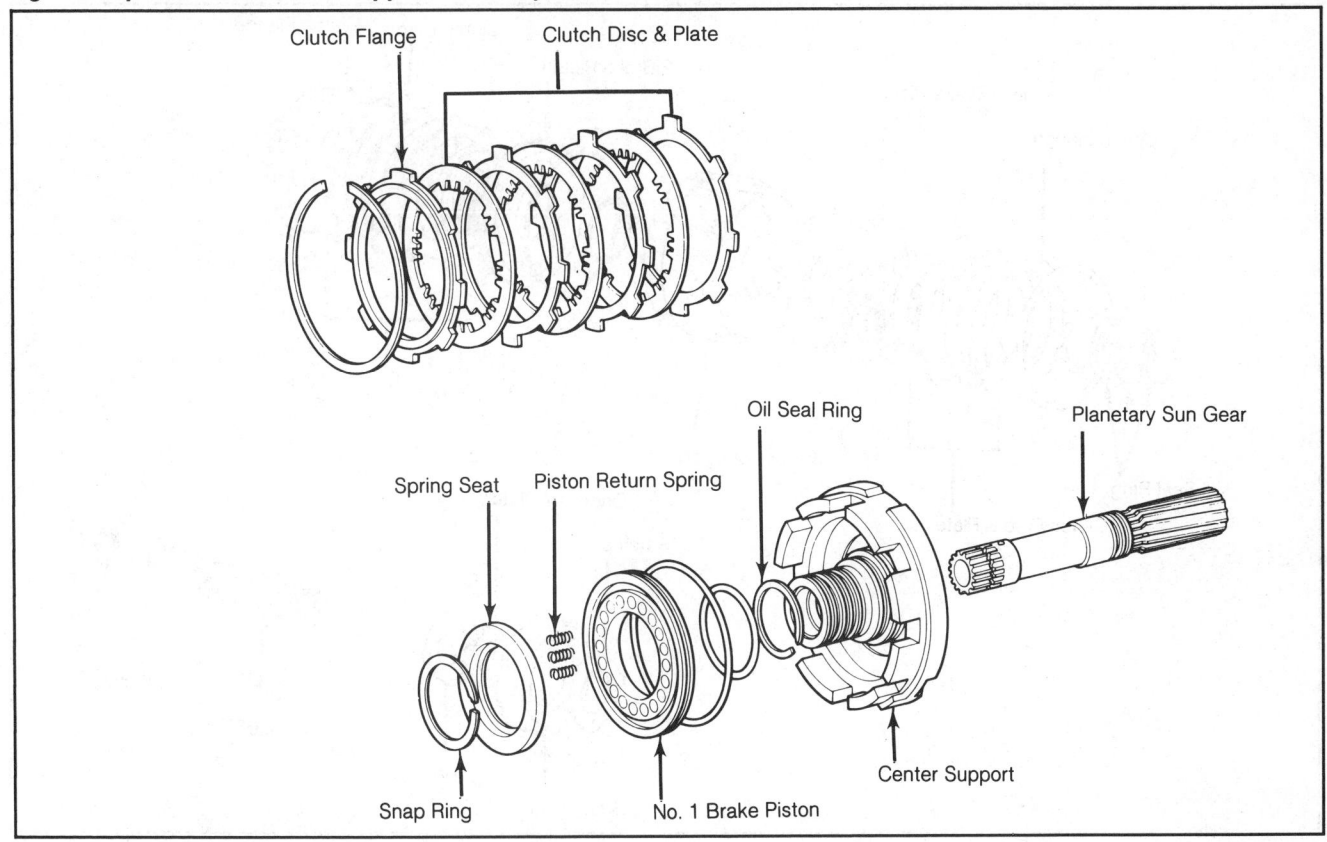

7) Install dial indicator to measure piston stroke of No. 2 brake. Apply compressed air to piston oil hole at 57-114 psi (4-8 kg/cm²) and measure stroke. Stroke should be .037-.068" (.93-172 mm). Excessive travel indicates clutch pack is worn.

8) If travel is below specifications, components may be misassembled or there could be excess ATF on clutch discs. Assemble center support and sun gear shaft. Align No. 2 disc flukes. Mesh brake hub with discs, twisting as necessary. Install snap ring on end of sun gear shaft.

Disassembly (A-40D Transmission)

1) Remove snap ring from end of planetary sun gear, then pull sun gear from center support.

2) Remove retaining snap ring, then lift flange, discs and plates for Brake B1 from center support. Note order for reassembly reference. Compress piston return springs and remove snap ring, then remove return springs and spring seat from center support.

3) Using compressed air, remove Brake B1 piston from center support by blowing in oil holes in center support. Remove "O" rings from piston. Remove oil seal rings from center suppport. Remove oil seal rings from sun gear.

Inspection

Inspect all parts for wear or damage. Check plates and discs for signs of burning. Check free length of return springs. If any spring is noticably shorter than the others, replace it.

Reassembly

1) Install 2 oil seal rings on sun gear. Install 3 oil seal rings on center support. Install new "O" rings on piston and center support. Press No. 1 brake piston into center support with cup side up. Install piston return springs and set retainer with snap ring into place.

2) Compress springs and install snap ring with a screwdriver. Use low pressure compressed air to blow ATF from discs and install No. 1 brake plates, discs and flange. Install in order noted during disassembly. Install flange with flat end down.

3) Install snap ring in center support. Check that ends are not aligned with the cutouts. Install dial indicator to measure piston stroke. Apply compressed air to piston oil hole at 57-114 psi (4-8 kg/cm²) and measure stroke. Stroke should be .039-.047" (1.0-1.2 mm).

4) Excessive travel indicates clutch pack is worn. If travel is below specifications, components may be misassembled or there could be excess ATF on clutch discs. Assemble center support and sun gear shaft. Install snap ring on end of sun gear shaft.

Disassembly (A-43D & A-43DL Transmissions)

1) Remove snap ring from end of sun gear shaft. Pull center support assembly from shaft. Remove snap ring from front of center support assembly. Remove clutch flange, disc and plate (No. 1 brake). Compress piston return springs and remove snap ring.

2) Remove spring retainer and 12 springs. Blow compressed air through center support oil hole to remove No. 1 brake piston. Remove No. 1 piston "O" rings. Turn center support assembly over and remove rear snap ring (No. 2 brake). Remove clutch flange, discs and plates (No. 2 brake).

Automatic Transmissions

TOYOTA A-40, A-40D, A-43D & A-43DL (Cont.)

Fig. 27: Exploded View of Center Support Assembly for A-43D and A-43DL Transmission

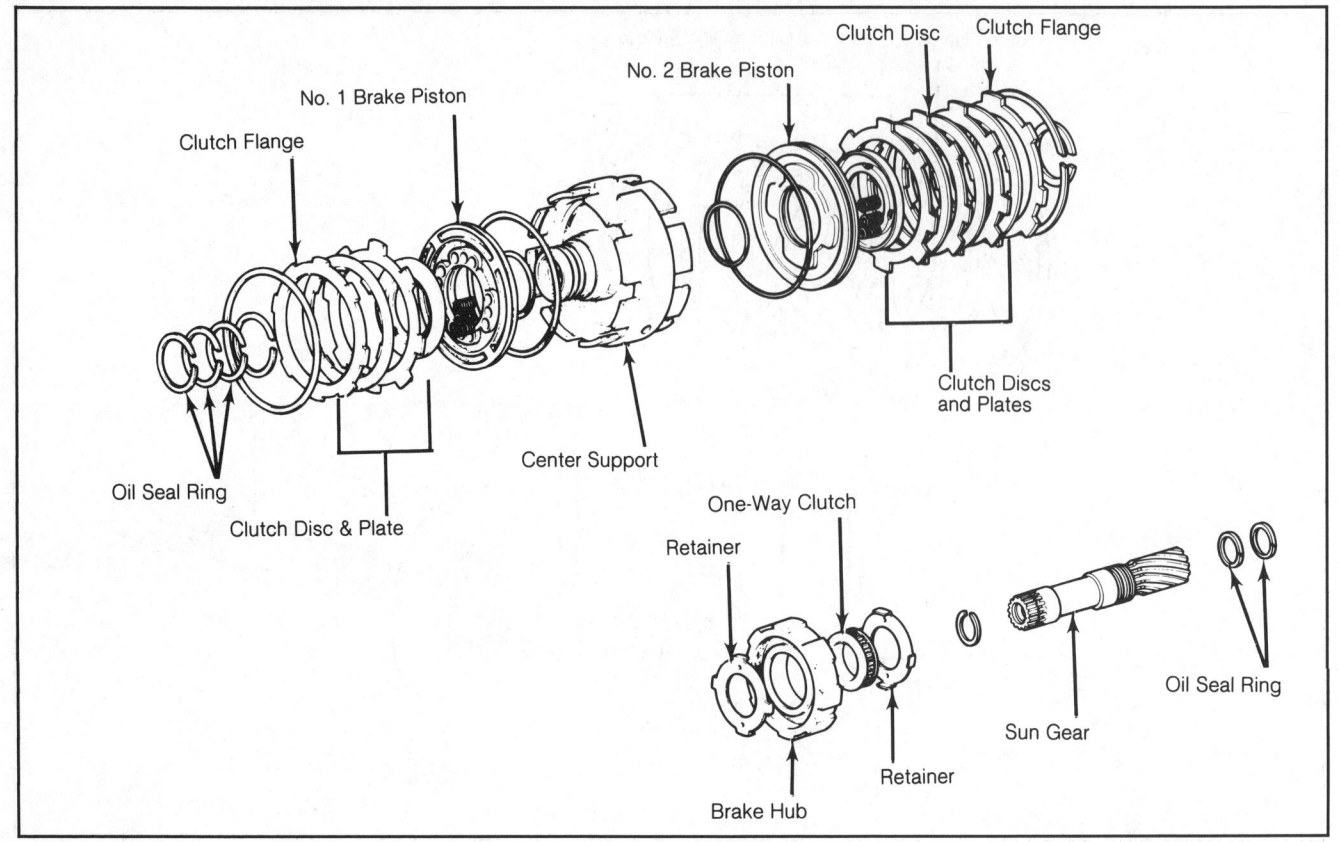

3) Compress piston return springs and remove snap ring. Remove spring retainer and 12 springs. Remove No. 2 brake piston by blowing comressed air through center support oil hole. Remove No. 2 brake piston "O" rings. Remove 3 oil seal rings from center support. Remove one-way clutch assembly and seal rings from sun gear.

Inspection
Inspect all parts for wear or damage. Check plates and discs for signs of burning. Check free length of return springs. If any spring is noticably shorter than others, replace it.

Reassembly
1) Install 2 oil seal rings and one-way clutch assembly on sun gear. Install 3 oil seal rings on center support. Install new "O" rings on piston. Install No. 1 brake piston in center support with cup side up. Install 12 piston return springs and set retainer in place.

2) Compress springs and install snap ring using screwdriver. Install new "O" rings on piston and center support. Turn center support over and install No. 2 brake piston into center support with cup side up. Install 12 piston return springs and retainer. Compress return springs and set snap ring into place with screwdriver.

3) Turn center support over and install No. 1 brake piston plate, disc and flange. Install flange with rounded edge down. Install snap ring to center support. Apply compressed air to piston oil hole at 57-114 psi (4-8 kg/cm²) and measure stroke of B1 brake. Stroke should be .026-.051" (.65-1.30 mm).

4) Excessive travel indicates clutch pack is worn. If travel is below specifications, components may be misassembled or there could be excess ATF on clutch discs. Turn center support over and install No. 2 brake

plates, disc and flange in order removed. Install snap ring in center support, making sure ends are not aligned with one of the cutouts.

5) In the same manner as for B1 brake, test piston stroke of B2 brake. Stroke should be .049-.068" (.93-1.72 mm). Excessive travel indicates clutch pack is worn. If travel is below specifications, components may be misassembled or there could be excess ATF on clutch discs. Align brake no. 2 disc flukes. Assemble the center support and sun gear shaft. Install snap ring on end of sun gear shaft.

PLANETARY GEAR OUTPUT SHAFT
Disassembly
1) Remove No. 3 brake disc/plate pack and front planetary pinion gears. Remove thrust washer from planetary gears. Remove brake discs and plates from planetary gears. Remove reaction plate from planetary gears. Remove snap ring and one-way clutch from planetary gears. Remove nylon thrust washer from planetary gears.

2) Remove apply tube and clutch pressure plate. While pulling up on the ring gear, compress the snap ring with needle nose pliers and remove snap ring from ring gear. Remove ring gear. Remove intermediate shaft from output shaft. Remove thrust bearing and races from output shaft, noting position of races.

3) From output shaft. From intermediate shaft, remove nylon thrust washer on A-40D and A-40, or steel thrust washer on A-43D and A-43DL. Remove race and thrust bearing from intermediate shaft, noting position of race. Invert intermediate shaft and remove set ring. Remove rear planetary ring gear and bearing race from intermediate shaft.

TOYOTA A-40, A-40D, A-43D & A-43DL (Cont.)

Fig. 28: Exploded View of Output Shaft and Planetary Gears

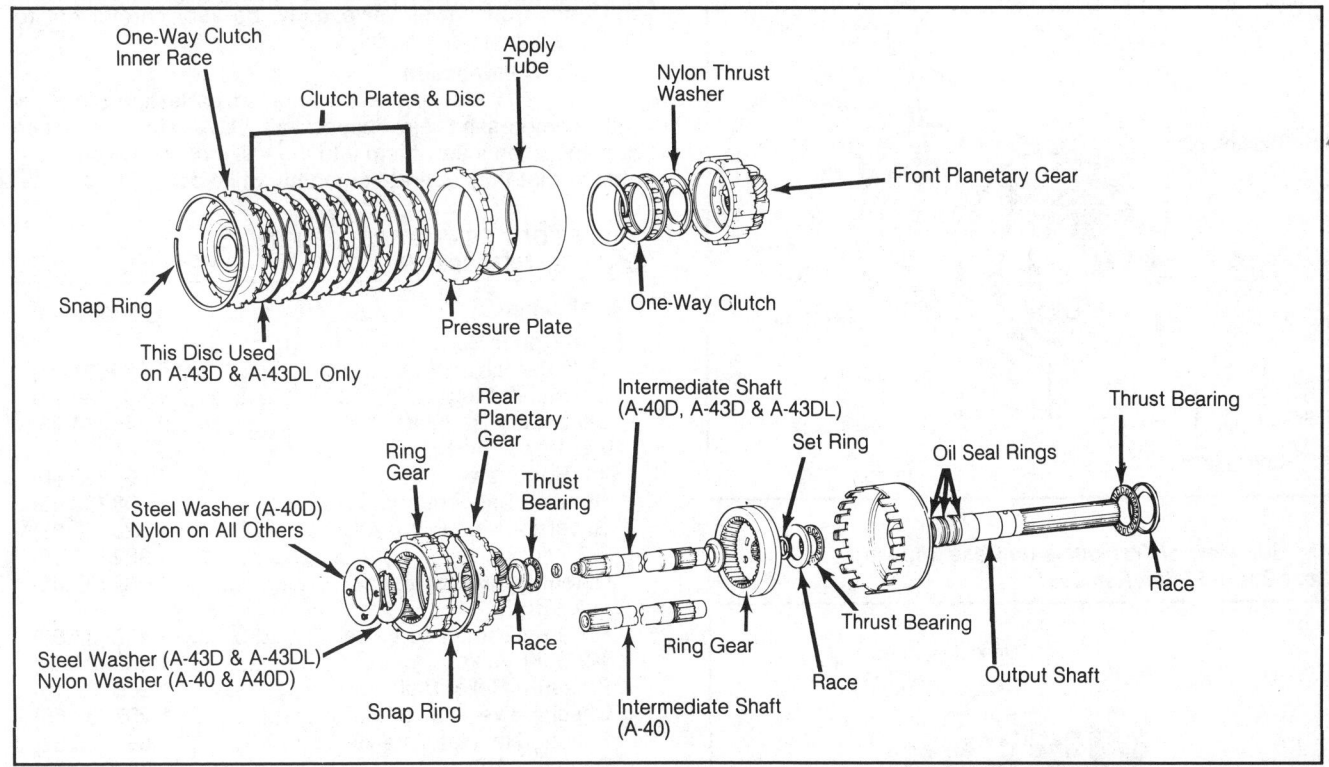

Inspection

1) Wash disassembled parts and blow dry with compressed air. Inspect thrust washers for wear, warpage and burning. Inspect carrier thrust surfaces for warpage and wear. Check planetary pinions for wear and damage.

2) Inspect one-way clutch outer race surface in carrier for wear. Check reaction plate toothed part and sliding surface for wear and damage. Check one-way clutch sliding surface or reaction plate for wear and damage.

Reassembly

1) Install thrust bearing race and rear planetary ring gear on intermediate shaft. Slip thrust bearing race and ring gear onto shaft with exterior splines up. Install set ring on intermediate shaft. Turn over intermediate shaft and install thrust bearing and race.

2) Install pinion gear assembly thrust washer on rear planetary carrier (nylon washer on A-40 and A-40D, steel on A-43D and A-43DL). Install washer with lugs down, fitting into the rear planetary carrier. Make sure lug shapes match opening on plate. Install 3 oil seal rings on output shaft.

3) Using extension housing as an assembly stand, install thrust bearing and race on output shaft. Hold the cup of the race toward the bearing. Install intermediate shaft assembly in output shaft. Install rear planetary carrier in output shaft. Slide into place and make sure lugs interlock.

4) Install snap ring on front planetary ring gear. Align ends of snap ring with wide gap between teeth. Install ring gear on shaft and, while pushing down on ring gear, squeeze ends of snap ring with needle nose pliers and install into groove. When snap ring is fully seated, gap is the width of one lug.

5) Install nylon thrust washer in front planetary gear. Face lugs down and match them with slots in the back of planetary gear. Install the one-way clutch into the outer race with spring cage toward front. Install snap ring. *See Fig. 18.*

6) Temporarily install one-way clutch inner race on planetary gear and check operation of clutch. Planetary gear should freely clockwise and lock when turned counterclockwise. Remove inner race. Install thrust washer on planetary gear, matching lugs with planetary carrier while installing.

7) Hold washer in place with petroleum jelly for later assembly. Install planetary gear assembly gear assembly on intermediate shaft. Make sure pinion gears mesh fully with ring gear. Install the pressure plate with flat surface toward intermediate shaft.

8) Install clutch pack discs and plates in the same order as they were removed. Keep inner race apply tube, thrust bearing and race together to be installed when transmission is reassembled.

REAR BRAKE PISTON

Disassembly

1) Using special compressor tool (SST09350-29913), compress piston return springs and remove snap ring. Remove spring retainer, return springs and compressor tool. Position transmission with front opening facing down.

2) Using 2 air guns, blow SIMULTANEOUSLY through the brake cylinder holes and remove inner piston, outer piston and brake reaction sleeve as a unit. *See Fig. 30.*

Inspection

Wash all parts in clean solvent and blow dry with compressed air. Inspect piston and reaction sleeve for scoring, wear or other damage. Check return springs for uniform height and cracked or broken coils. Replace any damaged parts.

TOYOTA A-40, A-40D, A-43D & A-43DL (Cont.)

Fig. 29: Exploded View of Rear Brake Piston Assembly

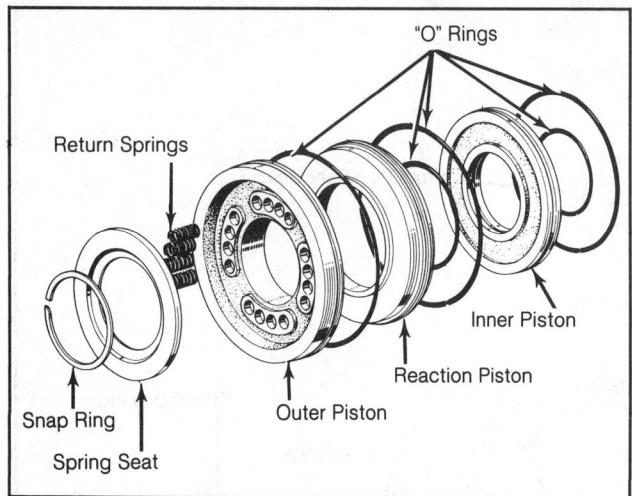

Fig. 30: View of Transmission Case Showing Rear Brake Piston Removal

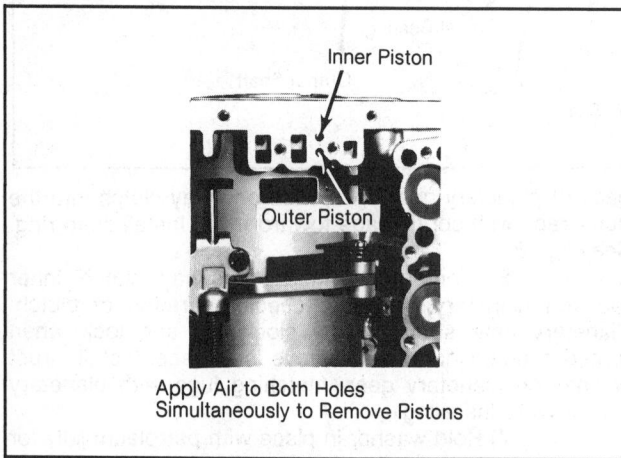

Apply air to holes simultaneously.

Reassembly

1) Install new "O" rings to reaction sleeve and pistons. Thinner "O" ring goes on the outside of reaction sleeve. Install inner and outer pistons on reaction sleeve. Push the inner piston into the cupped side of the reaction sleeve.

2) Push the outer piston onto the other side of the reaction sleeve. Install pistons and sleeve in case by holding the assembly with the outer piston up and push assembly into its bore in the case. Using same tools as for removal, install spring retainer, compress springs and install snap ring.

VALVE BODY

Disassembly

1) Disassembly procedures for all valve bodies are similar. Use appropriate valve body figure as a guide and note the following procedures:

2) As valve trains are removed from each valve body bore, place individual parts in correct order in relative position to valve body in order to simplify reassembly.

3) When disassembling, use care not to damage valve surfaces or form burrs around the valve body bores.

4) When separating upper valve bodies (front and rear) from lower valve body, be very careful not to lose check balls and springs.

Inspection

1) Wash all disassembled parts and blow dry with compressed air. Inspect all valves for wear and damage, then insert them into the valve body and check to ensure that they operate smoothly while being turned.

VALVE BODY SPRING FREE LENGTH (A-40 TRANSMISSION)

Application	In. (mm)
Front Upper Body	
Throttle Valve	.864 (21.24)
Downshift Plug	1.563 (39.71)
Secondary Regulator Valve	2.946 (74.83)
Rear Upper Body	
Int. Reg. Valve	1.008 (25.60)
Reverse Sequence Valve	1.488 (37.55)
Governor Modulator Valve	1.420 (36.07)
2-3 Shift Valve	1.382 (35.10)
Detent Regulator Valve	1.263 (32.08)
Lower Body	
Reverse Sequence Valve	1.478 (37.55)
1-2 Shift Valve	1.363 (34.62)
Pressure Relief Ball	1.265 (32.14)
Check Valve	1.207 (30.65)
Primary Regulator Valve	2.887 (73.32)
Damping Ball	.787 (20.00)

VALVE BODY SPRING FREE LENGTH (A-40D, A43D & A-43DL TRANSMISSIONS)

Application	A40D In. (mm)	A-43D & A-43DL In. (mm)
Front Upper Body		
Throttle Valve	.864 (21.94)	.864 (21.94)
Downshift Plug	1.693 (43.00)	1.563 (39.71)
Sec. Reg. Valve	2.806 (71.27)	2.806 (71.27)
Rear Upper Body		
Int. Mod. Valve		1.073 (27.26)
Sequence Valve	1.478 (37.55)	1.478 (37.55)
Gov. Mod. Valve	1.420 (36.07)	1.420 (36.07)
2-3 Shift Valve	1.420 (36.07)	1.382 (35.10)
2-3 Shift		
Time Valve	1.174 (29.82)	
Det. Reg. Valve	1.198 (30.43)	1.178 (29.93)
Low-Coast		
Mod. Valve	1.667 (42.35)	1.667 (42.35)
3-2 Kick-Down		
Valve	.991 (25.17)	
Lower Body		
1-2 Shift Valve	1.363 (34.62)	1.363 (34.62)
Pressure		
Relief Ball	1.265 (32.14)	1.265 (32.14)
Check Valve	1.312 (33.32)	1.312 (33.32)
Prim. Reg. Valve	2.887 (73.32)	2.409 (61.20)
Damping Ball	.767 (19.50)	.787 (20.00)
3-4 Shift Valve	1.363 (34.62)	.363 (34.62)
OD Clutch		
Exh. Valve	1.224 (31.09)	
Lock-Up		
Relay Valve		728 (18.50)
Lock-Up		
Signal Valve		1.794 (45.56)

TOYOTA A-40, A-40D, A-43D & A-43DL (Cont.)

Fig. 31: *Exploded View of A-40 Transmission Valve Body Assembly*

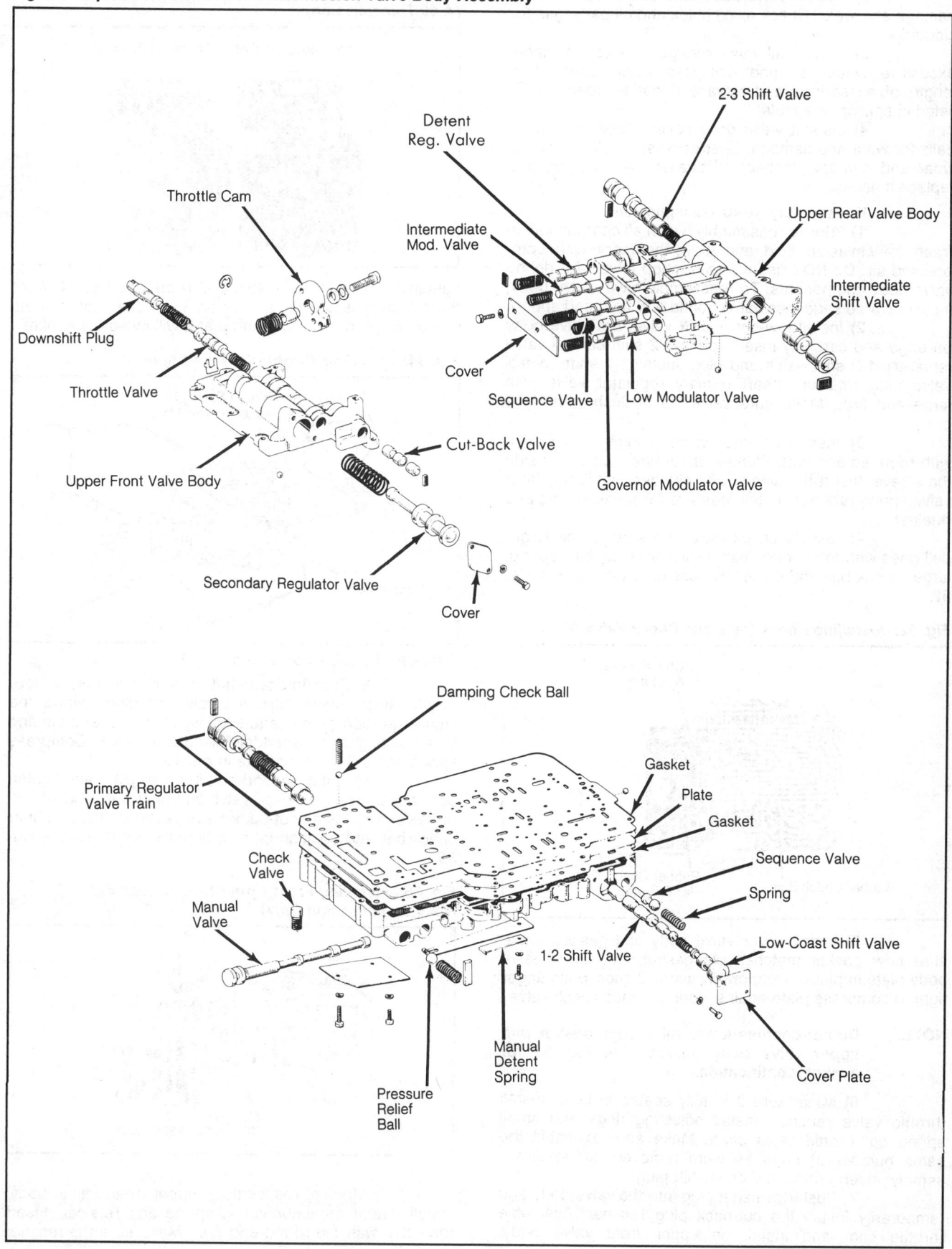

TOYOTA A-40, A-40D, A-43D & A-43DL (Cont.)

2) Inspect valve body bore sliding surfaces for damage and wear. Check all oil holes and oil passages for clogging.

3) Inspect all valve springs for wear, damage, excessive weakness and collapsed coils. Check free length of all springs and replace if not to specification listed in appropriate table.

4) Inspect valve body cover plates and check balls for wear and damage. Check pressure relief valve for wear and damage. Inspect oil strainer for clogging and replace if necessary.

Reassembly (A-40 Transmission)

1) Prior to reassembly, wash all components in fresh transmission fluid and blow them dry with compressed air. Do NOT use waste or shop towels for drying valve body components. To reassemble lower valve body, install reverse sequence valve (round end first) and spring.

2) Install low-coast shift valve. Set valve body on edge and carefully insert spring 1-2 shift control valve (smaller), 1-2 shift valve and plug. Install 1-2 shift control valve plug retainer. Insert primary regulator valve with large end first. Make sure valve fits in flush with valve body.

3) Insert regulator valve plunger into sleeve with rounded end first. Plunger should be recessed inside the sleeve. Insert the sleeve with plunger. Install regulator valve spring retainer. Install pressure relief ball, spring and retainer.

4) Identify check balls and spring. The larger ball goes with the spring. Install smaller check ball, spring, larger check ball and cooler by-pass check valve. *See Fig. 32.*

Fig. 32: Installing Check Balls and Check Valve (A-40)

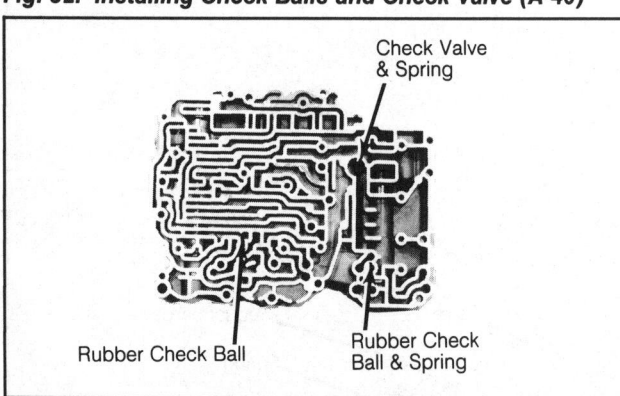

5) Install lower valve body and gasket. Make sure new gasket matches old gasket. Set lower valve body plate in place. Temporarily install 2 short bolts finger tight to compress plate against spring-loaded check valve.

NOTE: Do not confuse lower valve body gasket with upper valve body gasket. See Fig. 33 for gasket identification.

6) Make sure it is fully seated in bore. Install throttle valve retainer. Install adjusting rings and small spring on throttle valve shaft. Make sure to install the same number of rings as were removed during disassembly. Insert spring and downshift plug.

7) Push downshift plug into the valve body and temporarily install the cut-back plug retainer. Assemble throttle cam and install on upper front valve body,

Fig. 33: Valve Body Gasket Identification (A-40 Transmission)

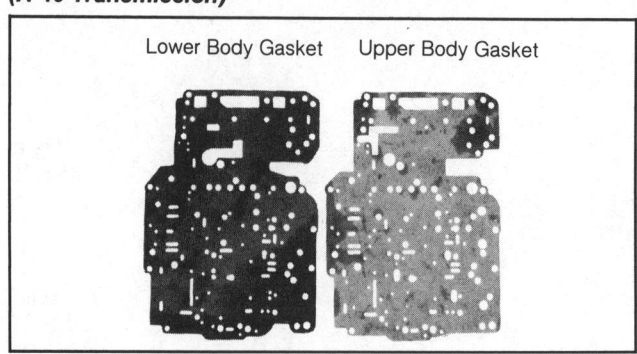

tightening to 53-78 INCH lbs. (6-9 N.m). *See Fig. 34.* After throttle cam is installed, pull on it to see that it turns smoothly without sticking and that it will move full stroke.

Fig. 34: Installing Throttle Cam and Spring

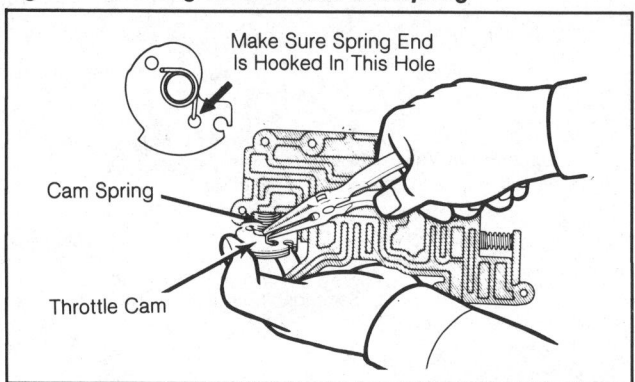

Check for full stroke operation.

8) Push in downshift valve and remove temporary retainer. Make sure the roller or plug follows the smaller portion of the cam. Partially install cover plate and insert spring and secondary regulator valve. Compress spring and swing cover plate into place.

9) Install second bolt in cover plate and tighten both bolts. Insert cut-back valve and plug with smaller end of valve first. Install cut-back valve retainer. Install rubber check ball into position in front upper valve body. *See Fig. 35.*

Fig. 35: Installing Front Upper Body Check Ball (A-40 Transmission Only)

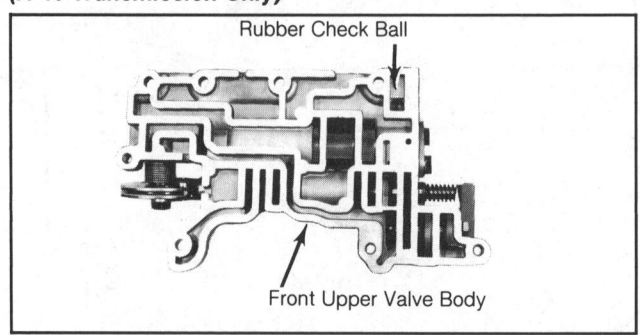

10) To reassemble upper rear valve body, install detent regulator valve, spring and retainer. Insert the valve with the round end first. Make sure the retainer

Automatic Transmissions

TOYOTA A-40, A-40D, A-43D & A-43DL (Cont.)

Fig. 36: Exploded View of A-40D and A-43D Transmission Valve Body

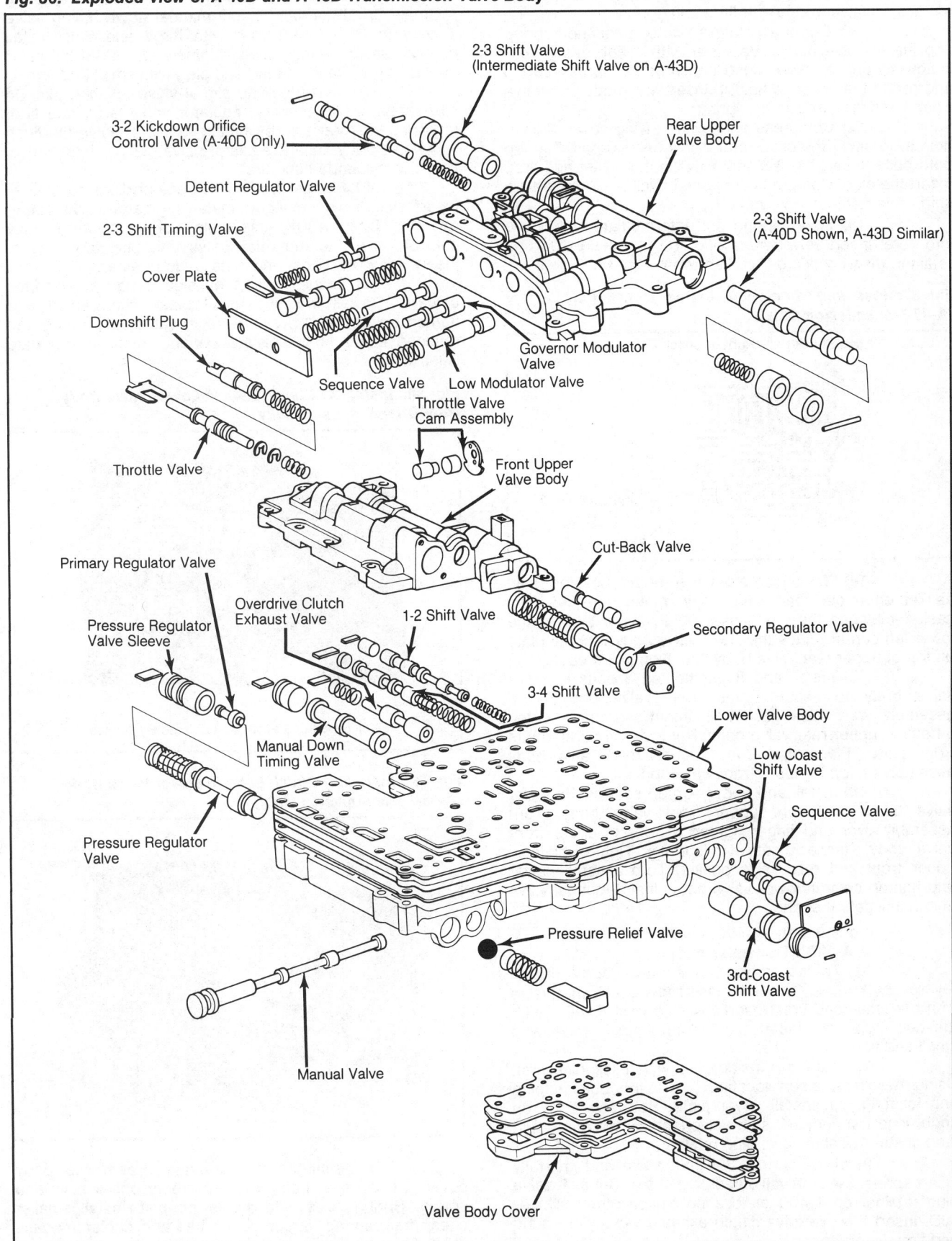

TOYOTA A-40, A-40D, A-43D & A-43DL (Cont.)

fully covers the end of the spring. Insert intermediate modulator valve (round end first) and spring.

11) Compress intermediate modulator spring and install valve body side cover with 1 bolt. Insert rear clutch sequence valve round end first. Compress spring and rotate the cover to hold it. Insert low modulator valve (round end first) and insert spring.

12) Compress spring and swing cover over to hold it. Position the cover and install second bolt. Tighten both bolts. Insert the 2-3 shift valve with smaller end first. Insert the plug. Compress plug and install the intermediate shift valve retainer in valve body.

13) Insert spring and intermediate shift valve into bore. Insert valve with round end up. Insert plug and retainer. Insert check balls as shown in *Fig. 37*.

Fig. 37: *Installing Check Balls in Rear Upper Body (A-40 Transmission Only)*

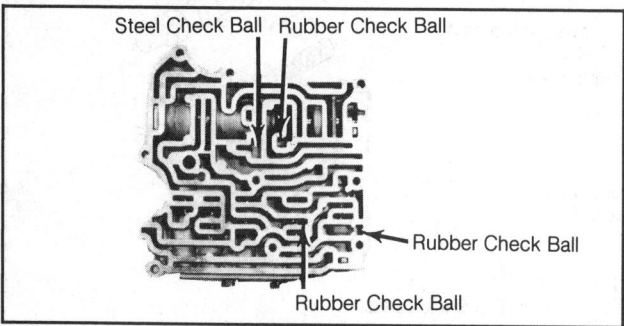

14) To assemble valve body, position new gasket on upper rear valve body. Make sure the new gasket matches the old gasket. Align the gasket at the lower left corner. Place the lower valve body with the plate on top of upper rear valve body and align at left edge.

15) Install and finger tighten 3 bolts in lower valve body to secure upper rear valve body. Turn assembly over, check gasket alignment and finger tighten 5 bolts in upper rear valve body. Remove temporary bolts from plate. Place lower and upper rear valve body assembly on top of upper front valve body.

16) Install and finger tighten set bolts in lower valve body to secure upper front valve body. Turn assembly over and finger tighten 5 bolts in upper front valve body. Recheck gasket alignment. Tighten bolts in upper front and rear valve bodies. Turn assembly over and tighten bolts in lower valve body. Insert manual valve and install detent spring.

Reassembly (A-40D, A-43D & A-43DL Transmissions)

1) To assemble lower valve body, install reverse brake plug. Carefully insert low-coast shift valve with the small end first. Insert 3-4 shift control valve with the cup side first. Insert the 3rd-coast shift valve with small end first.

2) Insert the inside plug with thick face first. Using tweezers, insert locating pin. Insert outside plug and locating pin. Install cover plate. Set valve body on edge, insert spring, 1-2 shift valve (smaller part first) and plug. Install 1-2 shift valve plug retainer.

3) Insert spring, 3-4 shift valve and carefully insert spring, 3-4 shift valve and plug. Install 3-4 shift valve plug retainer on A-40D or locating pin on others. On A-40D, insert the overdrive clutch exhaust valve with round end first. Insert spring.

4) Install overdrive clutch exhaust valve spring retainer. On all models, install manual down timing valve small end first. Insert plug with large end first. Install manual down timing valve retainer. On A-43DL, insert lock-up signal valve, spring and plug with small end first.

5) Install lock-up signal valve locating pin. On all models, insert primary regulator valve large end first. Insert spring. Make sure primary regulator valve fits flush with valve body. Insert regulator valve plunger into sleeve. Insert with rounded end first.

6) Plunger should be recessed inside sleeve. Insert sleeve with plunger. Install regulator valve spring retainer. On A-43DL, assemble spring, lock-up relay control valve, lock-up relay valve and plug into sleeve. Insert sleeve into bore and install plug retainer.

7) Smaller hollow on sleeve side should face upward. On all models, install plate with gasket and tighten bolts. Install pressure relief valve ball, spring and retainer. Install check balls according to the appropriate illustration.

Fig. 38: *Installing Check Balls in Lower Valve Body (A-40D Transmission Only)*

Install Balls into Passages Indicated By Arrows

Fig. 39: *Installing Check Balls in Lower Valve Body (A-43D Transmission Only)*

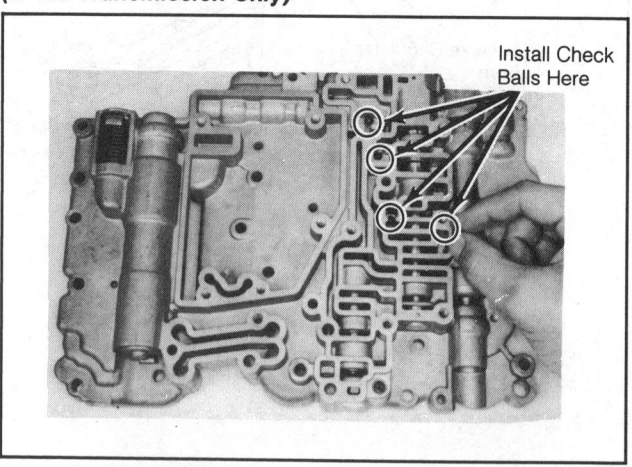

Install Check Balls Here

8) Install gasket, plate, gasket and lower body cover. Install cover bolts. Identify rubber check balls and spring. Spring goes with the larger ball. Install smaller check ball, spring, larger check ball and cooler by-pass check valve according to the appropriate illustration.

TOYOTA A-40, A-40D, A-43D & A-43DL (Cont.)

Fig. 40: *Installing Check Balls in Lower Valve Body (A-43DL Transmission Only)*

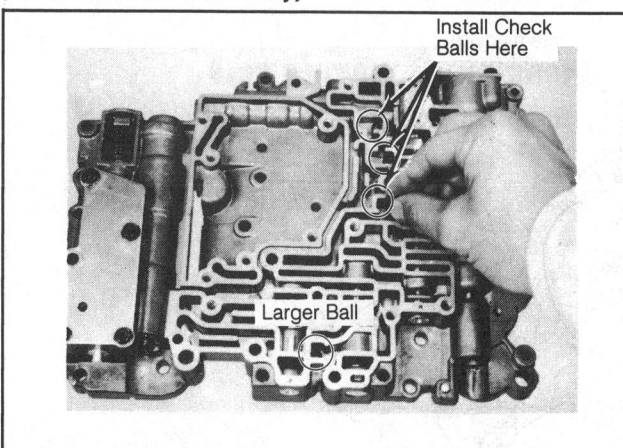

Fig. 41: *Installing Check Balls in Lower Valve Body (A-40D Transmission Only)*

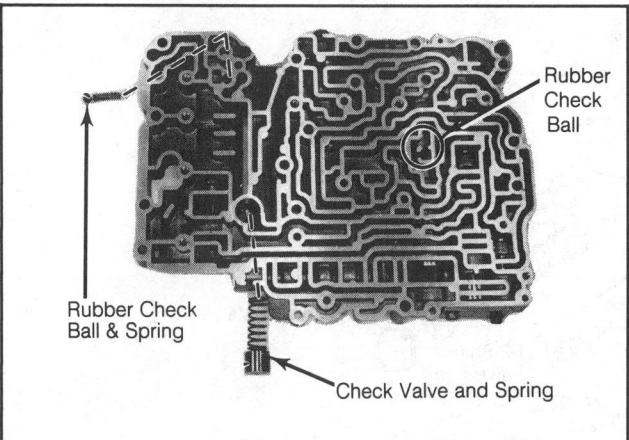

Fig. 42: *Installing Check Balls in Lower Valve Body (A-43D Transmission Only)*

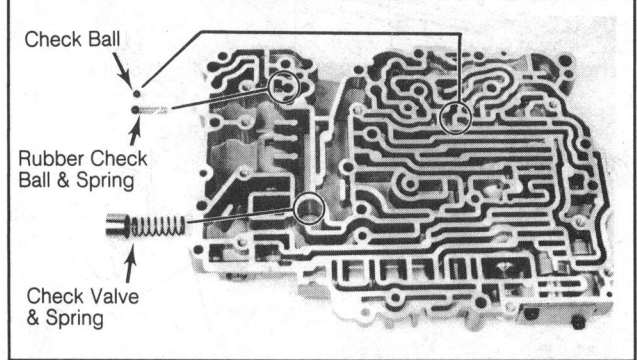

9) Install lower valve body gasket, making sure new gasket matches old gasket. Install lower valve body plate. Set plate into place. Temporarily install 2 bolts finger tight to compress plate against check valve.

10) To reassemble upper front valve body, insert throttle valve. Install throttle valve retainer. Install adjusting rings on throttle valve shaft. Install the same number as removed. Insert spring and shiftdown plug.

11) Temporarily install retainer of cut-back plug to hold downshift plug in place. Assemble throttle

Fig. 43: *Installing Check Balls in Lower Valve Body (A-43DL Transmission Only)*

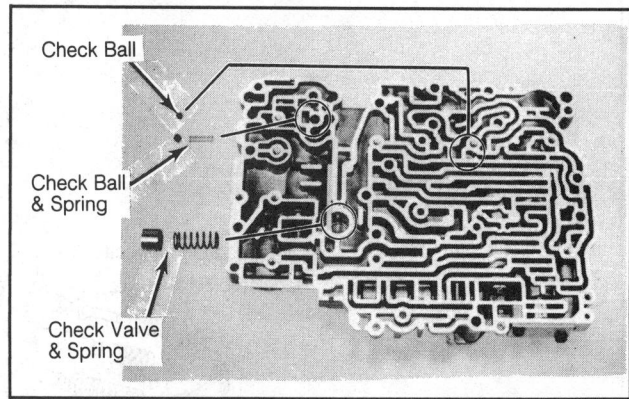

cam assembly. Install throttle cam to upper front valve body, tightening to 53-78 INCH lbs. (6-9 N.m). See Fig. 34.

12) After throttle cam is installed, pull on it to see that it turns smoothly without sticking and that it will move a full stroke. Push in downshift valve and remove temporary retainer. Make sure the roller or plug follows the smaller portion of the cam.

13) Partially install cover plate and insert spring and secondary regulator valve. Compress spring and swing cover plate into place. Install second bolt in cover plate and tighten both bolts. Insert cut-back valve and plug with smaller end of valve first. Install cut-back valve retainer. On all except A-43DL, install rubber check ball into position. See Fig. 44.

Fig. 44: *Installing Check Ball to Front Upper Valve Body*

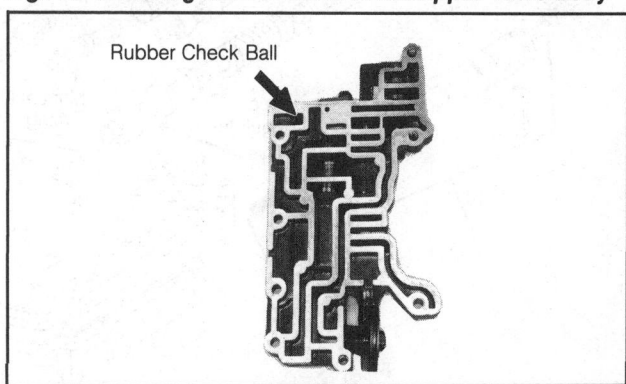

14) To assemble upper rear body, install detent regulator valve with round end first. Compress spring with a screwdriver and slip retainer over edge of spring. Compress spring and allow retainer to fall into place. On A-40D, install spring and 2-3 shift timing valve.

15) On others, install intermediate modulator valve with round end first, then install spring. Install valve body side cover with 1 bolt. Insert rear clutch sequence valve with round end first, then install spring. Insert governor modulator valve with round end first. Insert spring.

16) Insert low modulator valve with round end first. Install modulator valve spring. Position cover and install second bolt. Tighten both cover bolts. On A-40D, insert valve spring, and insert kick-down orifice control valve with longer bevelled end first.

17) Install plug into the bore, using tweezers, and insert the pin into the hole (coat pin with petroleum jelly). Insert the 2-3 shift valve with the large end first. On

Automatic Transmissions

TOYOTA A-40, A-40D, A-43D & A-43DL (Cont.)

Fig. 45: Exploded View of A-43DL Transmisssion Valve Body Assembly

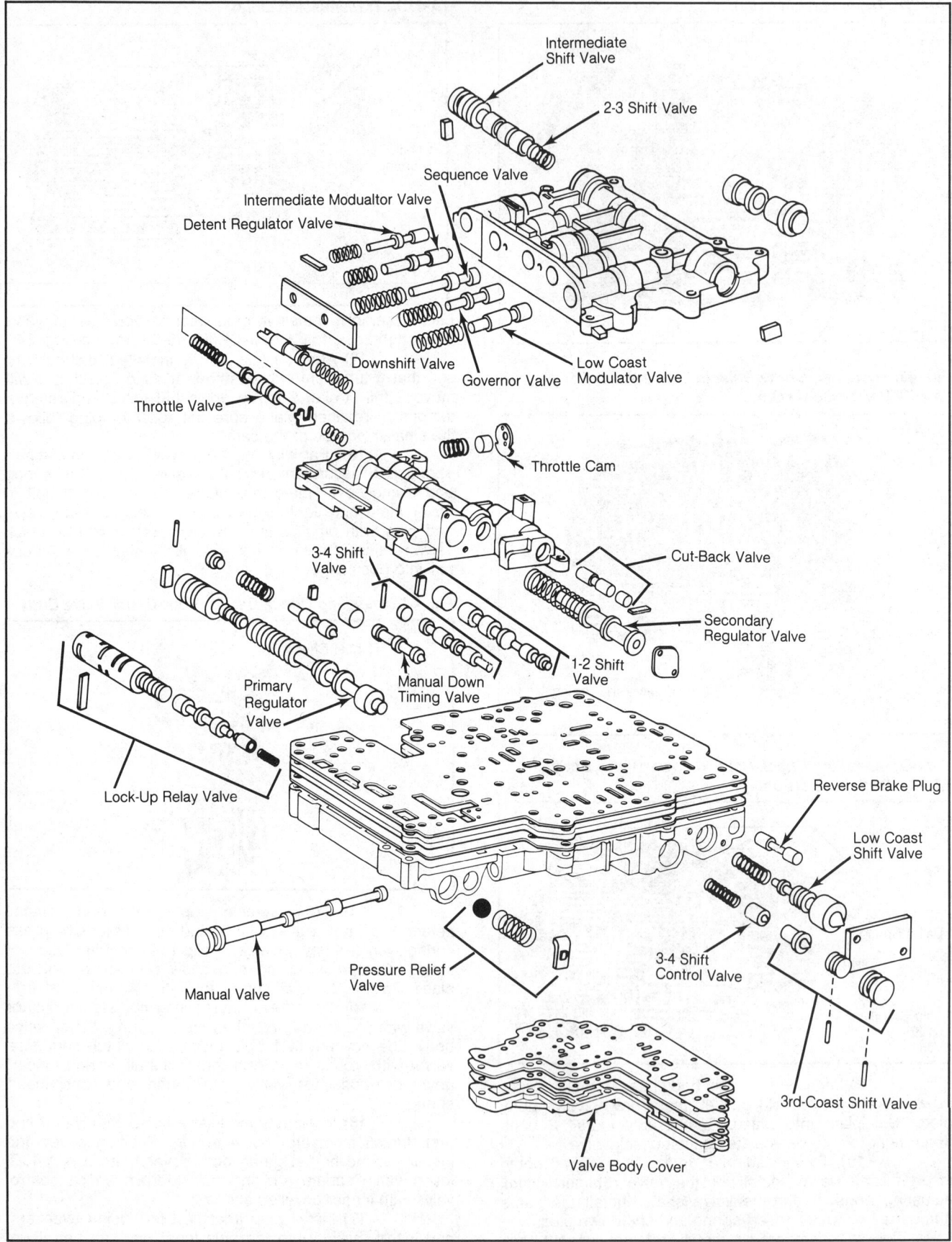

TOYOTA A-40, A-40D, A-43D & A-43DL (Cont.)

all others, insert the 2-3 shift valve with smaller end first, and insert plug.

18) Compress the plug and install the intermediate shift valve retainer in the valve body. On all models, insert spring and intermediate shift valve into bore. On A-40D, insert plug and locating pin. On others, insert plug and retainer. On all models, install check balls as shown in appropriate illustration. A-40D has 1 steel and 4 rubber balls, all others have 1 steel and 3 rubber balls.

19) To reassemble the valve body, make sure new gasket matches old and position on upper rear valve body. Align the gasket at lower left corner. Place the lower valve body with plate on top of upper rear valve body. Install and finger tighten 3 bolts in lower valve body to secure upper rear valve body.

20) Turn assembly over, check gasket alignment, and finger tighten 5 bolts in upper rear valve body. Remove temporary bolts from plate. Place lower and upper rear valve body assembly on top of upper front valve body. Install and finger tighten set bolts in lower valve body to secure upper front valve body.

21) Turn assembly over and finger tighten 5 bolts in upper front valve body. Recheck alignment of gaskets, and tighten bolts in upper front and rear valve bodies. Turn assembly over and tighten bolts in lower valve body. Insert manual valve. Install detent spring.

GOVERNOR VALVE ASSEMBLY

Disassembly

Remove "E" ring and lift off governor weight. Remove governor valve shaft, spring and governor valve from governor body.

Fig. 46: Exploded View of Governor Assembly

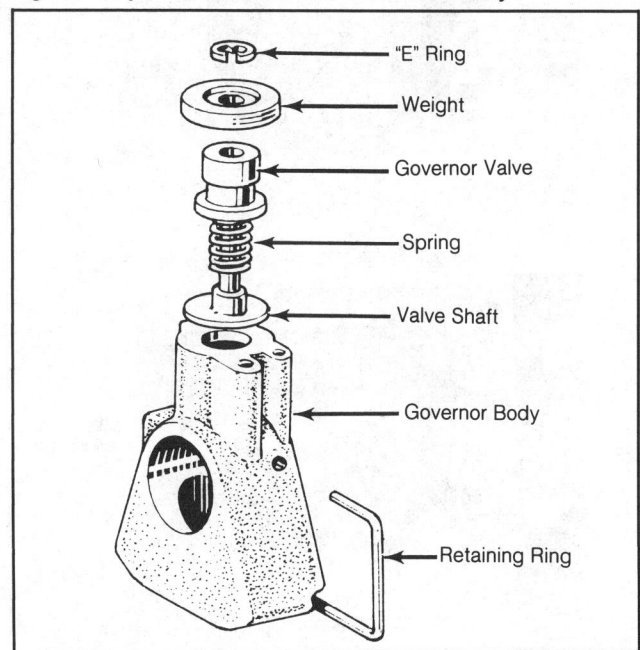

Inspection

Inspect all parts for wear and damage. Insert valve shaft into body and make sure that it slides smoothly. Check oil passage for clogging.

Reassembly

To reassemble governor valve assembly, reverse disassembly procedure.

TRANSMISSION REASSEMBLY

NOTE: During transmission reassembly note the following:

- Dry all parts with compressed air. Never use waste or shop towels.
- Soak new clutch discs in ATF for at least 2 hours prior to installation.
- Apply ATF on all sliding and rotating surfaces before assembly.
- Do not use adhesive cements on gaskets and similar parts.
- Use all new "O" rings and gaskets.

1) Place transmission case on a cylinder with front facing up. Install output shaft thrust bearing and race into case with lip on race facing down over bearing. Install brake apply tube into case. Make sure lips of the tube end are completely inserted in the case.

CAUTION: Install apply tube so that its lip ("A") fits into transmission case at "B". Also, make sure that lip at apply tube end is fitted inside the piston. See Fig. 47.

Fig. 47: View Showing Correct Installation of Brake Apply Tube

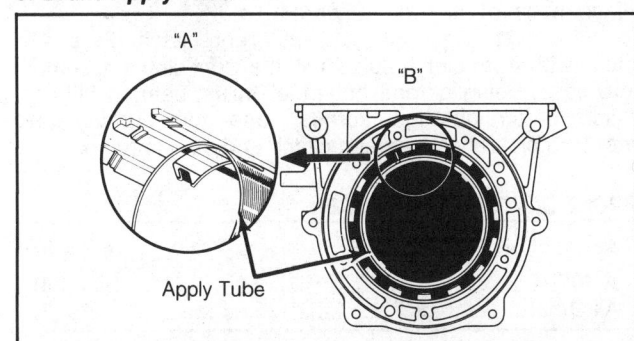

2) Align clutch plates on output shaft. Partially insert output shaft assembly into case. On models with slot in case, align notch in clutch plates with slot in case. Check clutch pack clearance. Measure the depth of the ledge below the snap ring groove. *See Fig. 48.* If clutch pack is not lower than ledge, components may be misassembled or excess ATF may be on discs.

CLUTCH PACK CLEARANCE

Application	In. (mm)
A-40	.031-.087 (.8-2.2)
A-40D	.016-.087 (.4-2.2)
A-42D, A-43DL	.028-.087 (.7-2.2)

3) Position the notched tooth of the reaction plate toward valve body side of the case. Push into place. When correctly installed, snap ring groove will be completely visible. Install reaction plate, positioning notched tooth of the plate toward valve body side of the case. Push the plate into place.

4) Install snap ring by compressing with a large screwdriver and then pushing into position by hand. Work the snap ring around the case. Visually check to make sure snap ring is seated and ends are between lugs. Push center support assembly into case.

Fig. 48: Measuring Rear Brake Clutch Pack Clearance

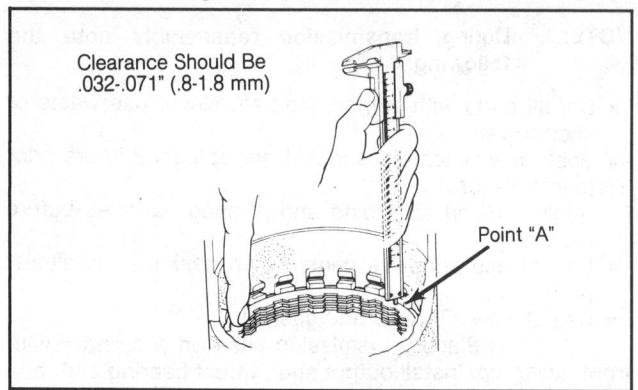

Clearance Should Be
.032-.071" (.8-1.8 mm)

Point "A"

5) Align the oil hole and bolt hole of the center support with those of body side. Align center support with holes in case and install support bolts with wave washers finger tight. Tighten bolts alternately in small increments. Install rear clutch to case. Rotate the clutch to mesh with the center support.

6) When correctly installed, splined center of the clutch will be flush with the end of sun gear shaft. Install needle bearing race over splined end of rear clutch in case. Coat parts with petroleum jelly to hold in place. Place the lip of the race outward.

7) Align flukes of the rear clutch discs and mesh with front clutch hub. Push the front clutch assembly into case, being careful not to let thrust bearing fall out. Place a straightedge across case top surface and measure clearance between clutch and straightedge.

FRONT CLUTCH CLEARANCE

Application	In. (mm)
A-40D	1.34 (34)
All Others	.08 (2)

8) Install guide rods (SST09350-20013) finger tight to the case. Coat thrust bearing with petroleum jelly and install to front clutch. On all except A-40, coat thrust washer with petroleum jelly and install to overdrive case. Lip side should face overdrive case.

9) Insert overdrive case gently through 2 guide pins. Coat thrust washers with petroleum jelly. Install one washer to overdrive case and the other to overdrive clutch. Washer lugs should be inserted to holes. Align flukes of discs in the overdrive case.

10) Align the flukes with slots of the overdrive clutch and press the overdrive clutch into the case. Be careful that thrust washer does not fall out. Place a straightedge across case top surface and measure clearance between overdrive clutch and straightedge.

OVERDRIVE CLUTCH CLEARANCE

Application	In. (mm)
A-40D	.08 (2.0)
All Others	.138 (3.5)

11) Install "O" ring on overdrive case. On all models, install converter housing and tighten bolts. Install thrust washer and bearing on front clutch on A-40 or overdrive clutch on all others. On all models, install thrust washer with lip side facing outward together with bearing.

12) Install thrust washer with lip side toward pump to the front oil pump. Install front oil pump gently through the guide pins. Coat the 5 set bolts with liquid sealer and finger tighten them. Remove guide pins. In place of them, insert 2 set bolts coated with liquid sealer. Tighten set bolts gradually and evenly. Blow low pressure compressed air into passages indicated in *Fig. 49.* to test accumulator piston operation.

Fig. 49: Testing Piston Operation

A-40

A40D

A-40D

A-43D & A-43DL

1. Overdrive Clutch
2. Overdrive Brake
3. Front Clutch
4. Rear Clutch
5. Brake No. 1
6. Brake No. 2
7. Brake No. 3

Blow low pressure air into indicated passages.

TOYOTA A-40, A-40D, A-43D & A-43DL (Cont.)

13) Check input shaft and output shaft. Make sure input shaft has axial play and that it turns. Make sure the output shaft has thrust play in the axial direction. Thrust play should be .012-.035" (.3-.9 mm). Assemble a new collar to the manual valve lever with a new roll pin.

14) Install the manual valve lever shaft to the transmission case through the manual valve lever. Drive in the new roll with the slot at a right angle to the shaft. Match the collar hole to the lever calking hollow and calk the collar to the lever. Install park pawl, pivot pin and spring in case.

15) Install and tighten park pawl bracket on case, making sure collar on control rod is toward the front of transmission. Check the operation of the park lock pawl, making sure the planetary gear output shaft is locked when manual valve lever is in the "P" range.

16) Install new "O" rings on throttle cable fitting. Install throttle cable in case, seating fully. Install accumulator piston and springs. On A-40D, install new "O" rings to transmission case. On all models, place valve body on the transmission. Make sure the accumulator pistons are pressed fully into the bore.

17) Align the manual valve with pin on manual shift lever. Lift the side of the valve body and slip throttle cable into the cam slot. Install attaching bolts for valve body. Install oil screen and bolts. Install oil tubes (if equipped). Install magnet in pan and install oil pan with new gasket.

18) Install drain plug with new gasket. Lift governor body retaining clip with screwdriver and slide governor body onto output shaft. Insert retaining clip end into hole on output shaft. On A-43D and A-43DL, install lock screw and stake lock plate in place.

19) On all models, install speedometer drive gear snap ring and lock ball on output shaft. Slide speedometer drive gear onto shaft and install outer snap ring. Install extension housing and new gasket and tighten bolts. Install "O" rings, bushing and speedometer driven gear to shaft sleeve.

20) Install speeometer driven gear assembly in extension housing. Insert the shaft sleeve assembly into housing. Install lock plate with bolt and lock washer. Slide the neutral start switch onto the control shaft. Install the grommet, facing the groove toward switch body.

21) Install washer and nut. Move the switch so that slit in the switch and neutral base line up. Tighten bolt and nut. Install shift handle. Install solenoid switch with 2 "O" rings.

TIGHTENING SPECIFICATIONS

Application	Ft. Lbs. (N.m)
Transmission-to-Engine	[1] 37-57 (50-78)
Converter Housing-to-Case	
Short Bolts	20-30 (27-41)
Long Bolts	35-49 (48-67)
Extension Hsg.-to-Case	20-30 (27-41)
Oil Pump-to-Case	14-18 (19-25)
Center Support-to-Case	18-20 (25-27)
Oil Pan Drain Plug	11-15 (15-20)
Converter-to-Drive Plate	11-15 (15-20)

Application	INCH Lbs. (N.m)
Oil Pan-to-Case	38-43 (4.3-4.9)
Strainer-to-Valve Body	43-52 (4.9-5.9)
Valve Body-to-Case	69-104 (7.8-11.8)
Lock Pawl Bracket-to-Case	52-78 (5.9-8.8)
Test Plugs-to-Case	52-78 (5.9-8.8)

[1] — Cressida and Supra should be 22-32 Ft. Lbs. (30-44 N.m).

Automatic Transmissions

TOYOTA MODEL A-55

Tercel

DESCRIPTION

The transaxle assembly is a 3-speed unit attached to the back of the engine. The transaxle assembly consists basically of a chain driven 3 element torque converter, 2 clutches, 3 brakes, 2 planetary gear sets, one-way clutch and a final drive assembly.

LUBRICATION & ADJUSTMENT

See the appropriate article in AUTOMATIC TRANSMISSION SERVICING Section.

SERVICE (IN VEHICLE)

AXLE DRIVE SHAFTS
Removal

1) Raise and support vehicle. Remove tire and wheel. Depress brake pedal and loosen axle shaft nut. Remove brake caliper and suspend caliper from frame. DO NOT remove hydraulic line. Disconnect nut holding stabilizer bar end to suspension arm. Remove upper steering knuckle-to-suspension strut bolts. Push down on steering knuckle to separate knuckle from strut.

2) Remove axle shaft nut. Pull axle shaft out of hub with puller (SST09950-20014). Separate steering knuckle from strut and draw out axle drive shaft from rear

of hub. Remove stiffener plate (left side only). Tap shaft out from differential with remover (SST09648-16010) and hammer. Install stopper (SST09563-16010) in differential case to prevent oil leakage.

NOTE: Do not damage rubber boots of axle drive shaft. Always carry and store shaft in level position.

Fig. 2: Exploded View of Axle Drive Shaft Assembly

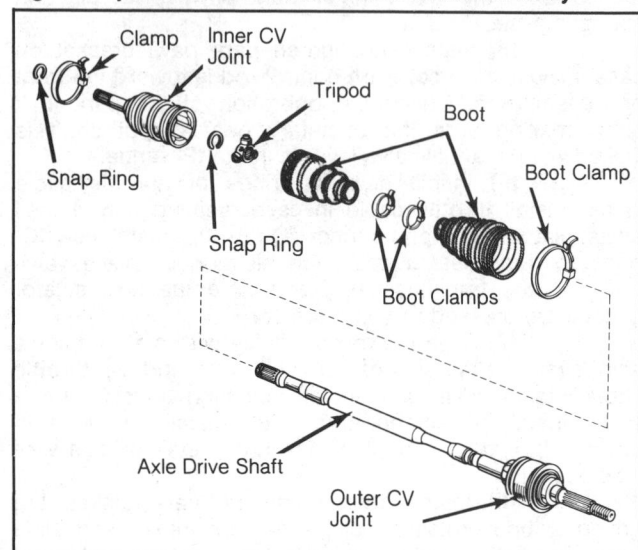

Fig. 1: Cross Sectional View of Toyota Tercel A-55 Automatic Transaxle

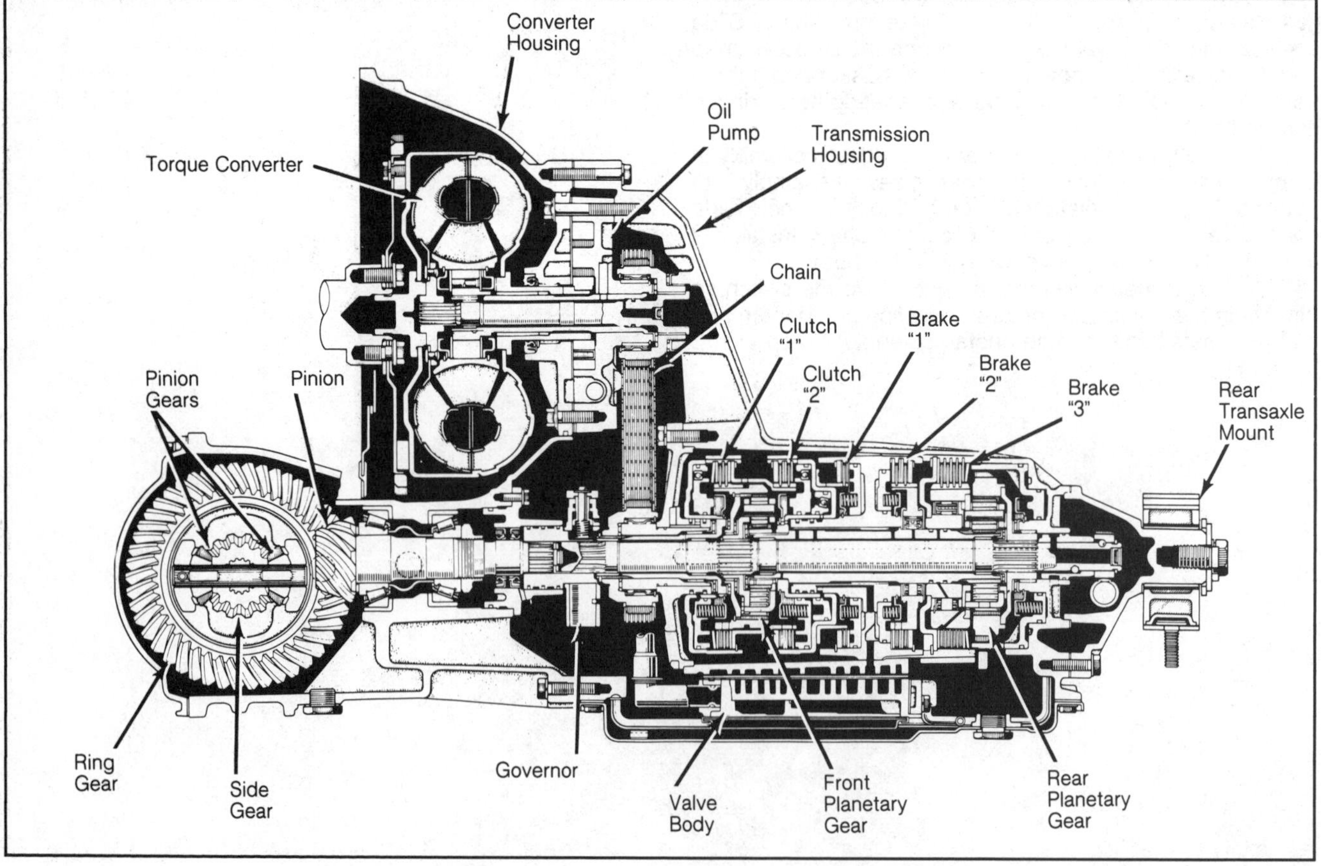

TOYOTA MODEL A-55 (Cont.)

Disassembly

1) Before disassembling axle drive shaft, check outer CV joint for any play. If play exists at outer CV joint, replace complete axle drive shaft assembly. Outer CV Joint cannot be disassembled. Remove boot clamps from boots of inboard shaft.

2) Check to see if joint slides smoothly in thrust direction. Check for excessive play in the radial direction. Draw alignment marks on inner CV joint and shaft with chalk. Remove inner joint from shaft. Place index marks on tripod and axle shaft.

3) Remove snap ring and tap body of tripod to drive tripod off shaft. DO NOT tap on roller. Remove inner CV joint boot. Remove outer CV joint boot clamps and slide boot off axle shaft.

Reassembly

1) Slide new boots onto axle shaft. Place clamping rings loosely over boot with open end of clamp away from direction of rotation. Do not tighten clamps at this time. Place beveled side of tripod onto shaft with beveled splines facing outer joint and align reference marks.

2) Before tapping tripod into final position, align centers of inner and outer joints. See Fig. 3. Tap tripod into position and install new snap ring. Pack outer CV joint with 8.6 ozs. (245 g) of grease (supplied with boot kit). Install outer boot and tighten clamps.

Fig. 3: Sectional View Showing Alignment of Inner and Outer CV Joint Centers

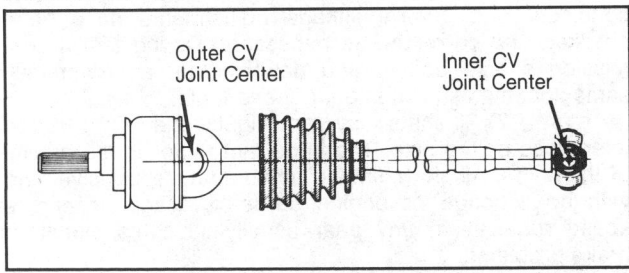

Outer CV Joint Center   Inner CV Joint Center

3) Pack inner CV joint with 5 ozs. (140 g) of grease (supplied with boot kit). Align reference marks made at disassembly and install inner CV joint. Install inner CV joint boot and tighten clamps. Install new snap ring on axle shaft.

NOTE: Right axle shaft is 23.07" (586 mm) long. Left shaft is 27.09" (688 mm) long. If axle shaft does not meet length specification, replace axle shaft assembly.

Installation

To install, reverse disassembly procedure. After installation of shafts, check front wheel alignment. Check boots for damage during installation. Measure the distance between drive shafts at transaxle. Distance should be less than 7.6" (194 mm).

WHEEL BEARINGS

Removal

1) Raise and support vehicle. Remove tire and wheel. Apply brakes and loosen axle shaft nut. Remove brake caliper and suspend from frame with wire. DO NOT remove hydraulic line. Disconnect and remove tie rod end with remover (SST09610-20012). Disconnect stabilizer bar and strut bar from lower arm.

2) Place a jack and block of wood under left lower control arm and slightly lift control arm. Right side does not require lifting. Remove lower control arm-to-crossmember attaching bolt. Disconnect control arm from crossmember. Remove axle shaft nut.

3) Remove nut holding axle hub to shock absorber. Press axle shaft out of hub assembly with puller (SST09950-20014). Separate strut and steering knuckle and remove hub. Remove bolt holding axle hub to lower arm. Separate axle hub and lower arm.

4) Using puller (SST09308-00010), pull oil seal out of axle hub. Pull hub assembly out of steering knuckle with puller (SST09608-16031). Remove inner bearing and spacer steering knuckle. Place reference marks on hub and disc assembly, remove attaching bolts and separate hub and disc.

NOTE: Mark inner and outer bearings for reassembly reference.

5) Place hub in vise and dislodge outer bearing from hub with hammer and chisel. Remove outer bearing with a puller. Remove scratches from hub bearing surface with oil stone. If necessary, replace outer bearing race.

Installation

1) Place inner bearing, spacer and outer bearing onto bearing preload holder (SST09608-16040). Coat bearings and bearing housing of steering knuckle with gear oil. Place assembled bearings into bearing housing and tighten nut to 90 ft. lbs. (122 N.m). Rotate assembly back and forth to seat bearings.

2) Install INCH lb. torque wrench and measure bearing preload while turning nut. Bearing preload should be 3.5-8.7 INCH lbs. (.4-1.0 N.m). See Fig. 4. If preload is not within specifications, select and install spacer and repeat procedure. Spacers are available in 20 thicknesses ranging from .316" (8.03 mm) to .346" (8.79 mm) in .0016" (.04 mm) increments.

Fig. 4: Assembled View of Wheel Bearings and Bearing Preload Adjusting Tool in Wheel Hub Assembly

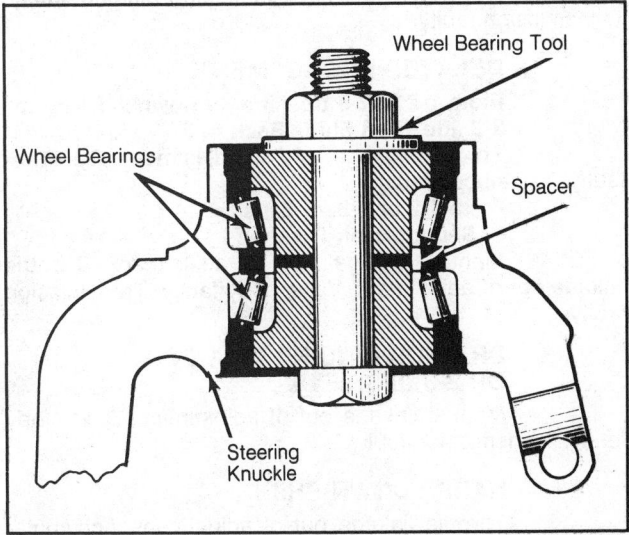

Wheel Bearing Tool

Wheel Bearings

Spacer

Steering Knuckle

3) Mount hub to rotor. Align marks made during removal and tighten hub-to-rotor bolts. Pack bearings and bearing housing with grease. Install outer bearing and oil seal in steering knuckle. Drive oil seal into hub with driver and installer (SST09515-35010).

TOYOTA MODEL A-55 (Cont.)

4) Install preselected spacer and inner bearing in steering knuckle. Place steering knuckle assembly in vise and press hub assembly into knuckle with press and arbor (SST09636-20010). Do not exceed 2200 lbs. (1000 kg) force. With pressure applied, rotate steering knuckle to seat bearings.

5) Attach spring pull scale to steering knuckle stopper and measure frictional force. Frictional force should be .8-1.7 lbs. (.4-.8 kg). Increase force to 7700 lbs. (3500 kg) and turn steering knuckle to seat bearings. Attach spring pull scale to steering knuckle stopper and measure bearing preload.

6) Preload should be .8-2.5 lbs. (.4-1.1 kg). If below specifications, install thinner spacer. If above specification, install thicker spacer. Install inner oil seal with driver and installer (SST09554-22010) until seal is recessed .16" (4 mm) from end surface. Install dust shield. Apply grease to oil seal lip.

7) Complete installation by reversing removal procedure. Install suspension components snugly. Lower vehicle to floor and bounce vehicle several times to seat suspension. Tighten suspension components with vehicle weight resting on suspension system.

TROUBLE SHOOTING

NO DRIVE IN ANY SELECTOR POSITION

Park lock faulty. Valve body or primary regulator faulty. Torque converter faulty. Converter drive plate broken. Oil pump intake screen blocked. Transmission faulty.

NO DRIVE IN FORWARD OR REVERSE RANGES

Manual linkage incorrectly adjusted. Valve body or primary regulator faulty. Transmission faulty.

HARSH ENGAGEMENT

Throttle linkage out of adjustment. Valve body or primary regulator faulty. Accumulator pistons faulty. Transmission faulty.

DELAYED ENGAGEMENT

From 1-2 or 2-3 Upshifts, or Downshifts From 3-2 and Then Shifts Back to 3
Throttle linkage out of adjustment. Governor faulty. Valve body faulty.

From 1-2 or 2-3, or Slips or Shudders on Take-Off
Manual linkage out of adjustment. Throttle linkage out of adjustment. Valve body faulty. Transmission faulty.

DRAG OR BINDING ON 1-2 OR 2-3 UPSHIFTS

Manual linkage out of adjustment. Valve body faulty. Transmission faulty.

HARSH DOWN-SHIFT

Throttle linkage out of adjustment. Accumulator out of adjustment. Accumulator pistons faulty. Valve body faulty. Transmission faulty.

NO DOWN-SHIFT WHEN COASTING

Governor faulty. Valve body faulty.

DOWN-SHIFT OCCURS TOO QUICK OR TOO LATE WHILE COASTING

Throttle linkage out of adjustment. Governor faulty. Valve body faulty.

NO 3-2 OR 2-1 KICKDOWN

Throttle linkage out of adjustment. Governor faulty. Valve body faulty.

NO ENGINE BRAKING IN "2" RANGE

Valve body faulty. Transmission faulty.

VEHICLE DOES NOT HOLD IN "P"

Manual linkage out of adjustment. Parking pawl cam and spring faulty.

SHIFTER LEVER POSITION INCORRECT

Manual linkage out of adjustment. Manual valve and lever faulty. Transmission faulty.

FLUID DISCOLORED OR BURNT

Fluid contaminated. Torque converter faulty. Transmission faulty.

TESTING

ROAD TEST

1) Before road test, ensure that fluid level and condition, and control linkage adjustments have been checked and corrected as necessary. During test, transmission should upshift and downshift at approximately same speed as shown in *Shift Speed* table.

2) All shifts may vary slightly due to production tolerances or tire size. The important factor is the quality of the shifts. All shifts should be smooth, responsive, and with no slippage or engine surge. Slippage or engine speed runaway in any gear usually indicates clutch or brake problems.

3) The slipping clutch or brake in a particular gear can usually be identified by noting transmission operation in other selector positions and comparing internal units which are applied in these positions. *See Clutch and Brake Application* chart.

4) While running in "D" range with accelerator held in at full throttle, check that upshifts take place and shift points are correct. If there is no 1-2 upshift, governor valve may be defective or 1-2 shift valve may be stuck. If there is no 2-3 upshift, 2-3 shift valve may be stuck.

5) If shift point is incorrect, throttle linkage may be misadjusted, or throttle valve, or shift valves may be defective. In the same manner, check the shock and slippage at 1-2 and 2-3 upshifts. If the shock is large, line pressure may be too high, accumulator may be defective, or check ball may be defective.

6) Run at "D" range and and check for abnormal noise or vibration. Check that shiftdown points 2-1, 3-1 and 3-2 are correct. While running in "D" range, shift from 3rd gear to "2" and "L" and check engine braking effect at each of these ranges.

7) If there is no braking at "2" range, brake No. 1 is defective. If there is no braking at "L" range, brake No. 3 is defective. While running in "D" range, release the foot from accelerator and shift into "L" range. Then check to

TOYOTA MODEL A-55 (Cont.)

CLUTCH AND BRAKE APPLICATION CHART

Selector Lever Position	Clutch 1	Clutch 2		Brake 1	Brake 2	Brake 3	
		Inner Piston	Outer Piston			Inner Piston	Outer Piston
D — DRIVE							
First Gear	X						
Second Gear	X				X		
Third Gear	X	X			X		
2 — INTERMEDIATE							
First Gear	X						
Second Gear	X			X	X		
1 — LOW	X					X	
R — REVERSE		X	X			X	X

NEUTRAL OR PARK — All clutches and brakes released and/or ineffective.

see if 3-2 and 2-1 down-shift points are the same as those in chart.

8) Shift to "2" position and run with throttle at half and fully open. Check the 1-2 upshift points against chart. While running in second gear, release accelerator pedal and check engine braking effect.

9) Perform a kick-down from "2" range and check the 2-1 kickdown speed. While in "2" range, check for abnormal noise at acceleration and deceleration and for shock at up and downshifts.

10) While in "L" range, check that there is no upshift to 2nd gear. Release the accelerator pedal and check engine braking effect. Check for abnormal noise at acceleration and deceleration.

11) While running at full throttle in "R" range, check for slipping. Stop vehicle on a gradient and shift into "P". See if parking lock pawl keeps vehicle from moving.

SHIFT SPEEDS TABLE

Application	Half Throttle	Full Throttle
In "D"		
1-2 Upshift	17	28-37
2-3 Upshift	43	54-64
3-2 Downshift	24	51-61
2-1 Downshift	12	23-33
In "L"		
2-1 Downshift		23-33

STALL SPEED TEST
Testing Precautions
When making test, do not hold throttle open any longer than 5 seconds. If engine speed exceeds limits shown in Stall Speeds table, release accelerator immediately as clutch or brake slippage is indicated. Fluid should be at normal operating temperature of 122-176°F (50-80°C).

Testing Procedure
Block wheels. With engine and transmission at normal operating temperature, tachometer installed and parking and service brakes applied, make transmission stall test in "D" and "R" ranges at full throttle and note maximum RPM obtained. Engine speed should be within limits shown in table.

STALL SPEED SPECIFICATIONS

Application	Stall RPM
All Models	2000-2300

Stall Test Results
1) If stall speed is below specifications in both ranges, engine performance may be unsatisfactory or stator one-way clutch is not operating properly. If stall speed is more than 600 RPM below specifications, torque converter could be defective.

2) If stall speed is higher than specification in "D" range, front clutch is slipping, one-way clutch number 2 could be defective or line pressure is low. If stall speed is higher than specification in "R" range, rear clutch could be slipping, brake number 3 could be slipping or line pressure is too low.

SHIFT TIME LAG TEST
Testing Procedure
With engine and transmission at normal operating temperature, shift from "N" to "D" and note time it takes for gear engagement (use a stop watch). Repeat this test 2 or 3 times and take an average time. Repeat this test procedure shifting to "R". Wait 1 minute between tests.

SHIFT TIME LAG SPECIFICATIONS

Application	Time Lag (Seconds)
"N" to "D"	Less Than 1.2
"N" to "R"	Less Than 1.5

Test Results
If time lag is longer than specifications when shifting from "N" to "D", line pressure is too low or front clutch is worn. If time lag is longer than specifications when shifting from "N" to "R", rear clutch is worn, brake number 3 is worn or line pressure is too low.

Automatic Transmissions

TOYOTA MODEL A-55 (Cont.)

HYDRAULIC PRESSURE TESTS

Governor Pressure Test

1) Connect a pressure gauge to governor pressure test port. *See Fig. 6.* Raise and support front of vehicle or place vehicle on a chassis dynomometer. With engine and transmission at normal operating temperature, place selector lever in "D" and note pressure readings at speeds indicated in *Hydraulic Pressure Specifications* table.

2) If pressures are not to specifications, governor valve operation is defective, governor pressure circuit is leaking, governor valve may be defective or line pressure is not to specifications.

Line Pressure Test

1) Connect a pressure gauge to line pressure test port. *See Fig. 6.* Apply parking brake and service brakes, then with engine and transmission at normal operating temperature, place selector lever in "D" and note pressure readings at speeds indicated in *Hydraulic Pressure Specifications* table. Repeat test with selector lever in "R".

Fig. 6: Hydraulic Pressure Test Port Hookup Points

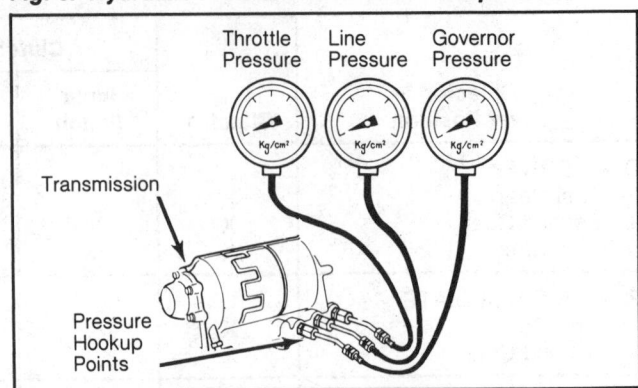

2) If test pressures were higher than specifications in all ranges, regulator valve is defective, throttle valve is defective or throttle link is out of adjustment.

3) If test pressures were lower than specifications in all ranges, oil pump is defective, regulator valve is

Fig. 5: Toyota Tercel Model A-55 Automatic Transmission Hydraulic Circuits Diagram

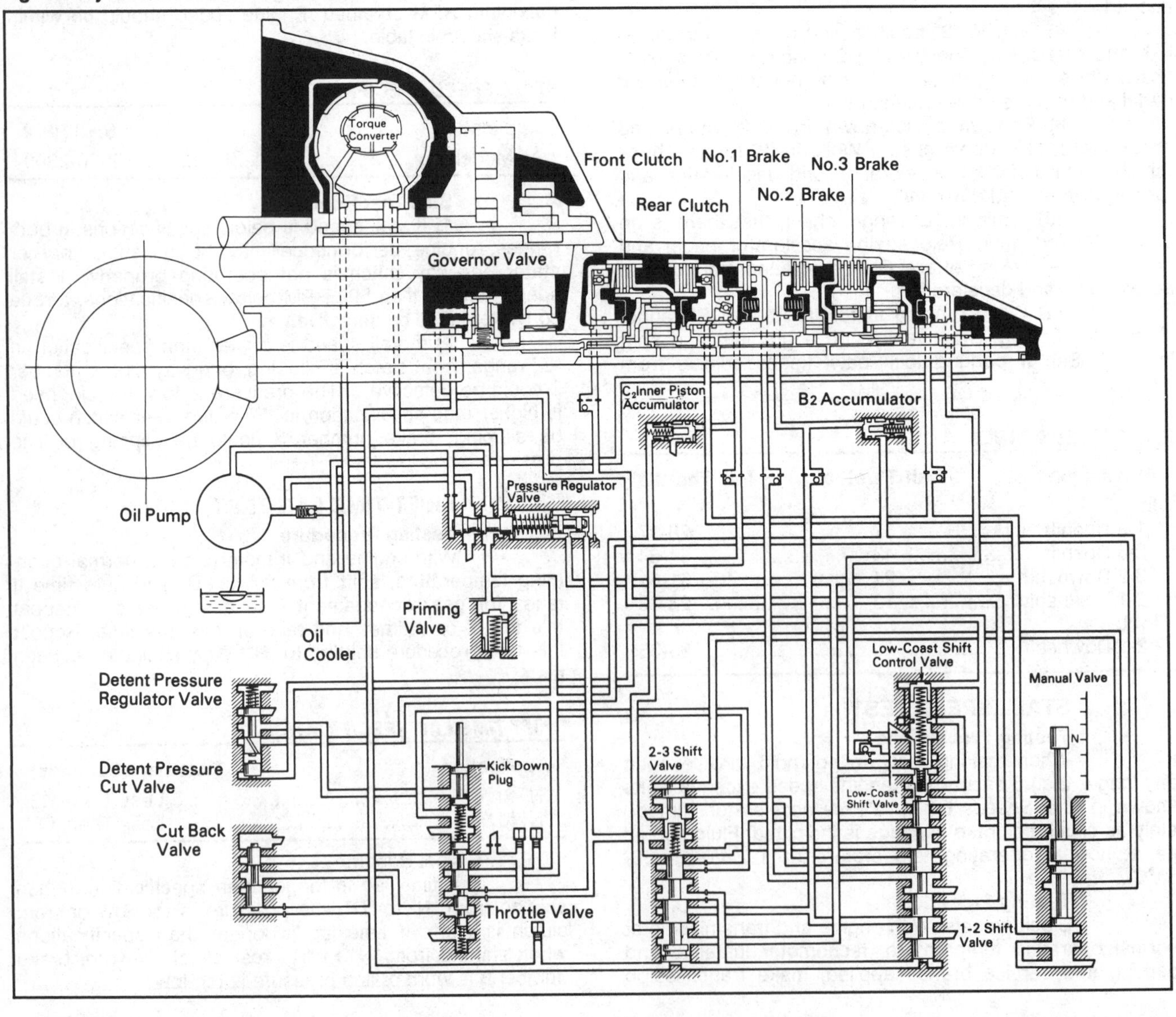

TOYOTA MODEL A-55 (Cont.)

defective, throttle valve is defective or throttle valve link is out of adjustment.

4) If test pressures were low in "D" range, front clutch is defective or "D" range circuit is leaking. If test pressures were low in "R" range, rear clutch is defective, brake number 3 is defective or "R" range circuit is leaking.

HYDRAULIC PRESSURE SPECIFICATIONS

Application	psi (kg/cm²) In "R"	psi (kg/cm²) In "D"
Governor Pressure		
18 MPH		14-23 (1.0-1.6)
33 MPH		24-33 (1.7-2.3)
64 MPH		61-78 (4.3-5.5)
Line Pressure		
At Idle Speed	84-98	54-63
	(5.9-6.9)	(3.8-4.4)
At Stall Speed	205-241	129-157
	(14.4-16.9)	(9.1-11.1)
Throttle Pressure		
At Idle Speed	0-4.3 (0-.3)	0-4.3 (0-.3)
At Stall Speed	110-118	110-118
	(7.7-8.3)	(7.7-8.3)

Throttle Pressure Test

1) Connect a pressure gauge to throttle pressure test port. *See Fig. 6.* Apply parking and service brakes. With engine and transmission at normal operating temperature, place selector lever in "D" and note pressure readings at speeds indicated in *Hydraulic Pressure Specifications* table. Repeat test in "R" range.

2) If pressure readings are higher than specified, throttle valve may be defective or throttle circuit orifice may be clogged. If values are lower that specified, oil pump, throttle valve or regulator valve may be defective.

REMOVAL & INSTALLATION

See the appropriate article in AUTOMATIC TRANSMISSION REMOVAL Section.

TRANSMISSION DISASSEMBLY

1) Remove torque converter from converter housing. Remove converter housing-to-transmission housing bolts and separate housings by tapping with a mallet. Remove oil filler tube, neutral start switch, control rod, speedometer driven gear housing and rear support mounting.

2) Remove extension housing and gasket. *See Fig. 7.* Remove snap ring and slide output shaft with speedometer drive gear out of transmission. Remove speedometer drive gear from output shaft, being careful not to lose the 2 steel balls.

3) Remove oil pan. Turn transmission over so valve body side is up. Remove oil pressure tubes by prying on both ends of tubes. Remove screen. Remove valve body with plate and gasket. Remove 6 steel balls and valve vibrating stopper.

Fig. 7: Exploded View of Transmission and Converter Housing

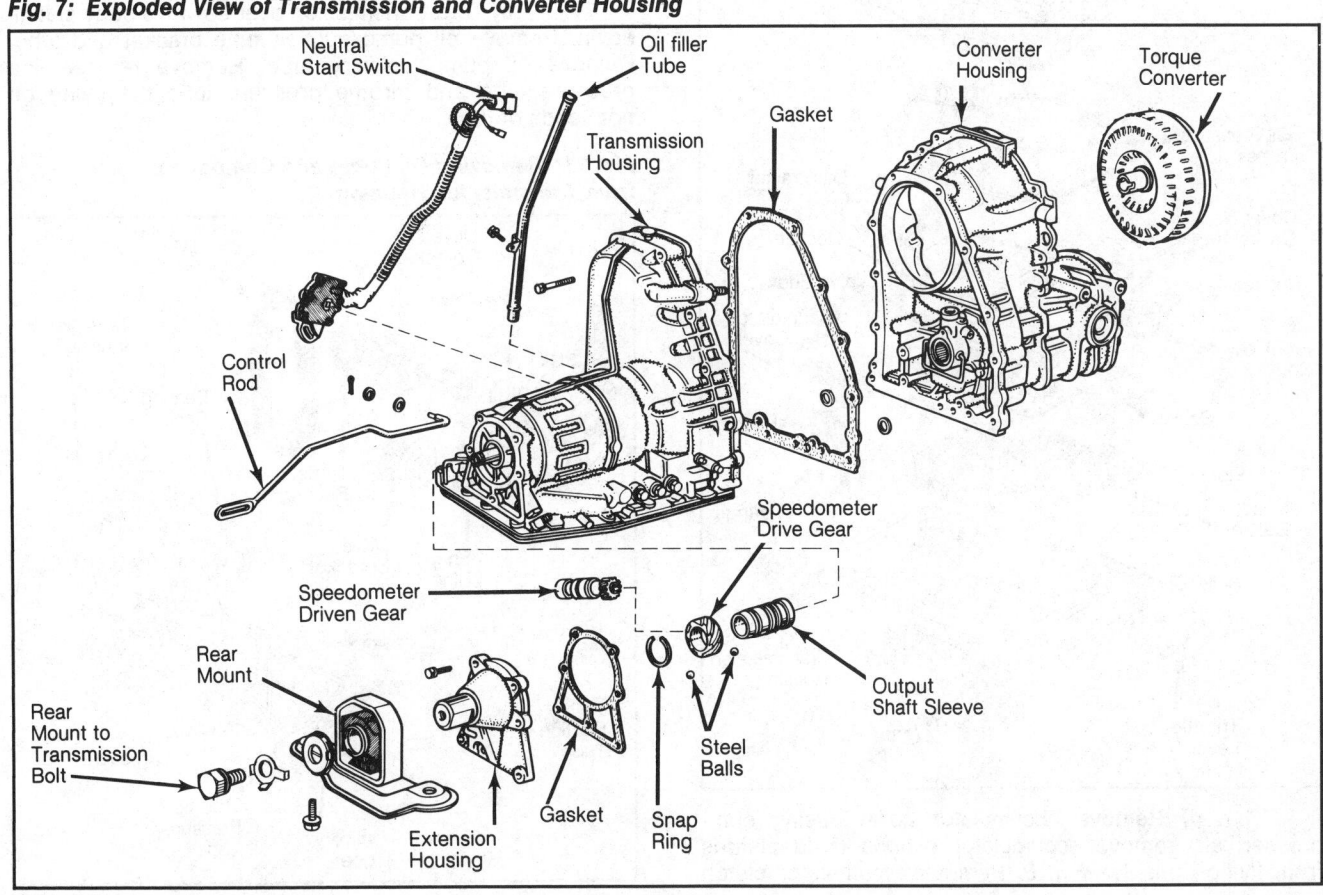

NOTE: After removing pan, examine composition of particles. Steel means bearing, gear and clutch plate wear, while brass means bushing wear.

Fig. 8: Removing Accumulator Pistons with Compressed Air

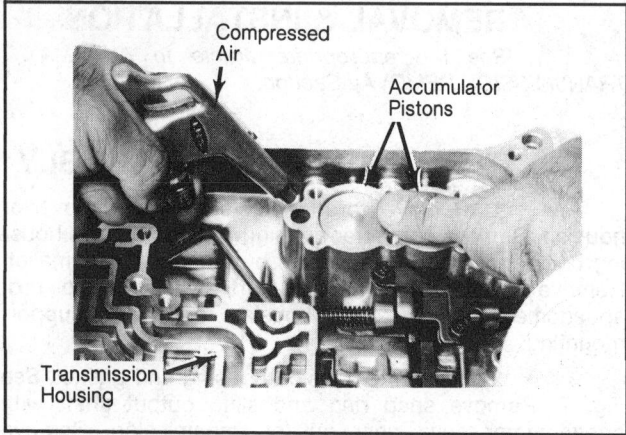

Fig. 9: Exploded View of Transmission Valve Body and Related Components

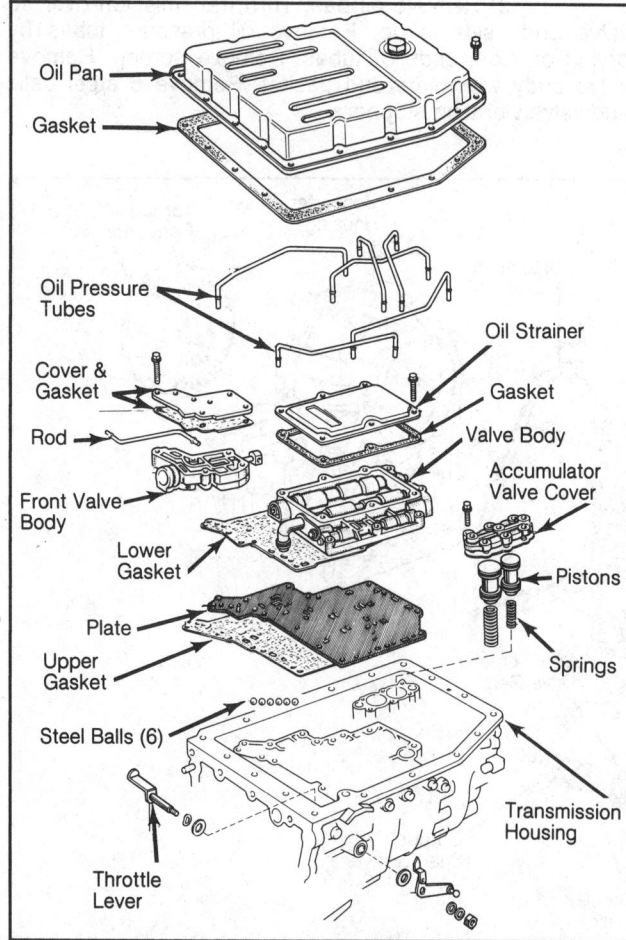

4) Remove accumulator cover. Using compressed air, remove accumulator pistons (hold pistons from flying out). *See Fig. 8.* Remove accumulator piston

springs. Note size and location of accumulator pistons and springs for reassembly reference. *See Fig. 9.*

5) Remove parking lock pawl rod, spring, pivot pin and parking lock pawl. Loosen staked part of ring on manual valve shaft, then rotate ring 90° to align spring pin with slot in ring. Drive out spring pin and remove manual valve shaft. *See Fig. 10.*

Fig. 10: Removing Parking Lock Pawl and Manual Valve Shaft Components

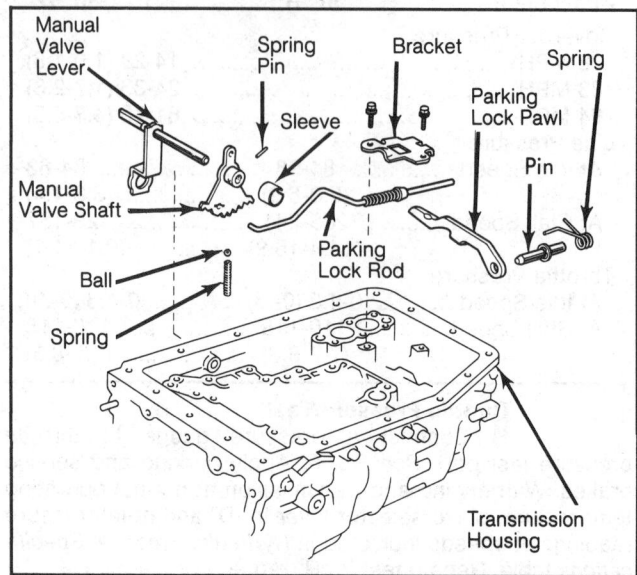

6) Turn transmission over so valve body side is down. Remove oil pump suction tube bracket and tube. Remove oil pump delivery tube. Remove reverse line pressure tube and throttle pressure tube by prying on both ends of tube.

Fig. 11: Removing Oil Pump and Components from Transmission Housing

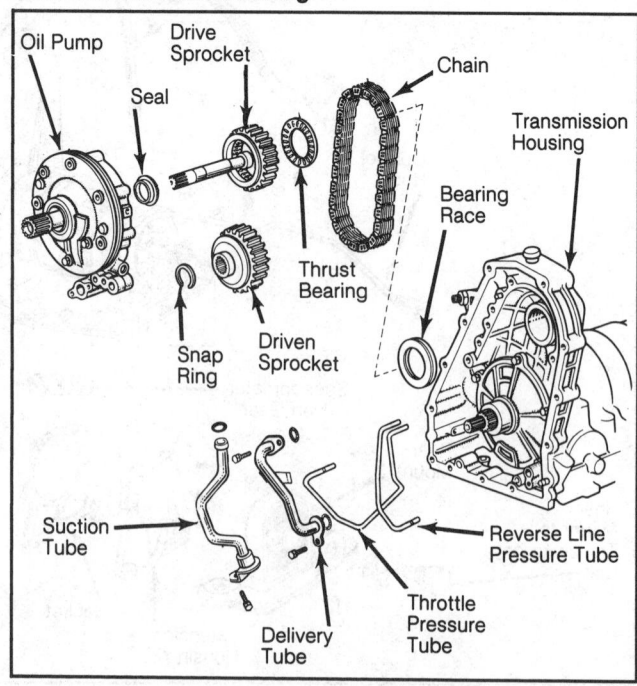

TOYOTA MODEL A-55 (Cont.)

7) Remove oil pump by loosening 3 inside bolts (do not remove) and removing all outside bolts. Remove oil pump seal. Remove snap ring from oil pump driven sprocket. Remove input shaft, oil pump drive sprocket, chain and driven sprocket out of transmission.

8) Make sure oil pump drive sprocket bearing and race are removed from transmission housing. *See Fig. 11.* Place transmission on wood block. Measure clearance between case and front clutch tip for reassembly reference.

9) Remove front clutch (clutch "1") and bearings by grasping shaft and pulling out front clutch. Be careful of bearings and races on both sides of assembly. Withdraw front planetary gear and output shaft as an assembly. Remove thrust race and then remove rear clutch (clutch "2") assembly. *See Fig. 12.*

Fig. 12: *Removing Transmission Output Shaft and Components*

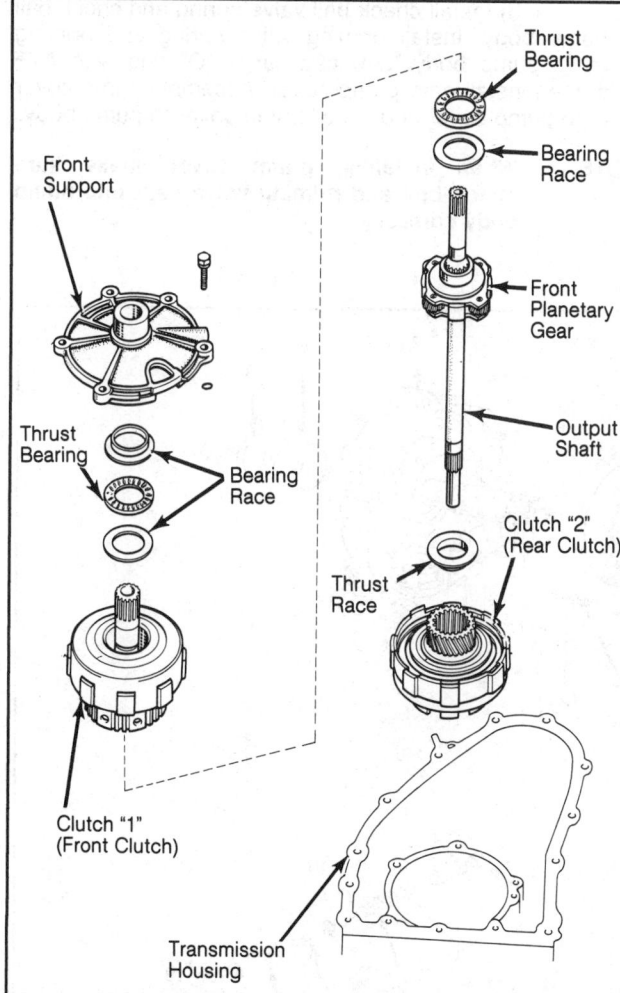

10) Remove center support bolts. Pull sun gear, center support and brake "1" (one-way) out of transmission as an assembly. Remove snap ring, then lift out brake "2" (one-way). Remove planetary gear and thrust bearing. *See Fig. 13.*

11) With rear planetary gear and thrust bearing removed, measure clearance of brake "3". *See Fig. 14.* Standard clearance is .395-.445" (10.04-11.30 mm). Note

brake "3" clearance measurement for reassembly reference.

Fig. 13: *Removing Center Support, Brakes and Planetary Gears from Transmission*

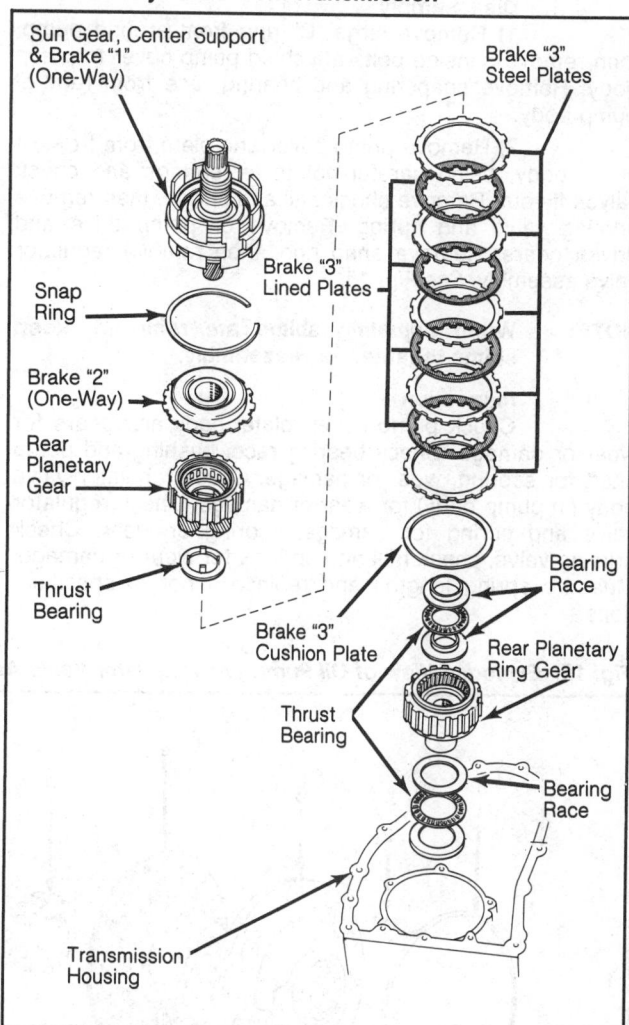

Fig. 14: *Measuring Brake "3" Clearance*

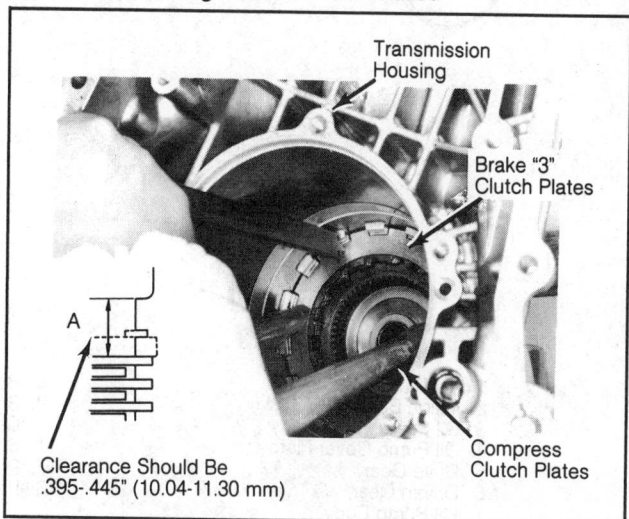

TOYOTA MODEL A-55 (Cont.)

COMPONENT DISASSEMBLY & REASSEMBLY

OIL PUMP AND REGULATOR VALVE

Disassembly

1) Remove large "O" ring from around pump, then remove 3 inside bolts attaching pump cover to pump body. Remove snap ring and bearing race from rear of pump body.

2) Remove pump cover and plate from front of pump body, being careful not to let springs and check valves fly out. Remove check ball and spring, then remove priming valve and spring. Remove oil pump drive and driven gears. Remove snap ring, then remove regulator valve assembly. *See Fig. 15.*

NOTE: **When adjusting shims are removed, keep shims together for reassembly.**

Inspection

Check pump cover, plate, body and gears for wear or damage. Check bearing race, bushing and pump shaft for scoring, wear or damage. Check regulator valve body (in pump body) for wear or damage. Check regulator valve and spring for damage, scoring or wear. Check priming valve, check ball and springs for wear or damage. Measure spring lengths and replace if not to specifications.

OIL PUMP SPRING FREE LENGTH

Application	In. (mm)
Regulator Spring	2.126 (54.0)
Check Ball Spring	1.032 (26.2)
Priming Valve	.756 (19.2)

Reassembly

1) Install oil pump driven and drive gears to pump body. Using a feeler gauge, measure clearance between a straightedge (layed across pump body) and pump gears. Clearance should be .0008-.002" (.02-.05 mm). Measure clearance between driven gear and pump body.

2) Clearance should be .0028-.0060" (.07-.15 mm). Next, measure clearance between driven gear tooth and crescent in pump body. Clearance should be .0043-.0055" (.11-.14 mm). *See Fig. 16.* If clearances are not to specifications, replace oil pump.

3) Install check ball valve spring and check ball to pump body. Install priming valve spring and priming valve to pump body. Lubricate large "O" ring with ATF fluid, then install onto pump cover. Assemble pump cover plate to pump cover and install pump cover to pump body.

NOTE: **When installing pump cover, make sure check ball and priming valve seat into pump body correctly.**

Fig. 15: Exploded View of Oil Pump and Regulator Valve Assembly

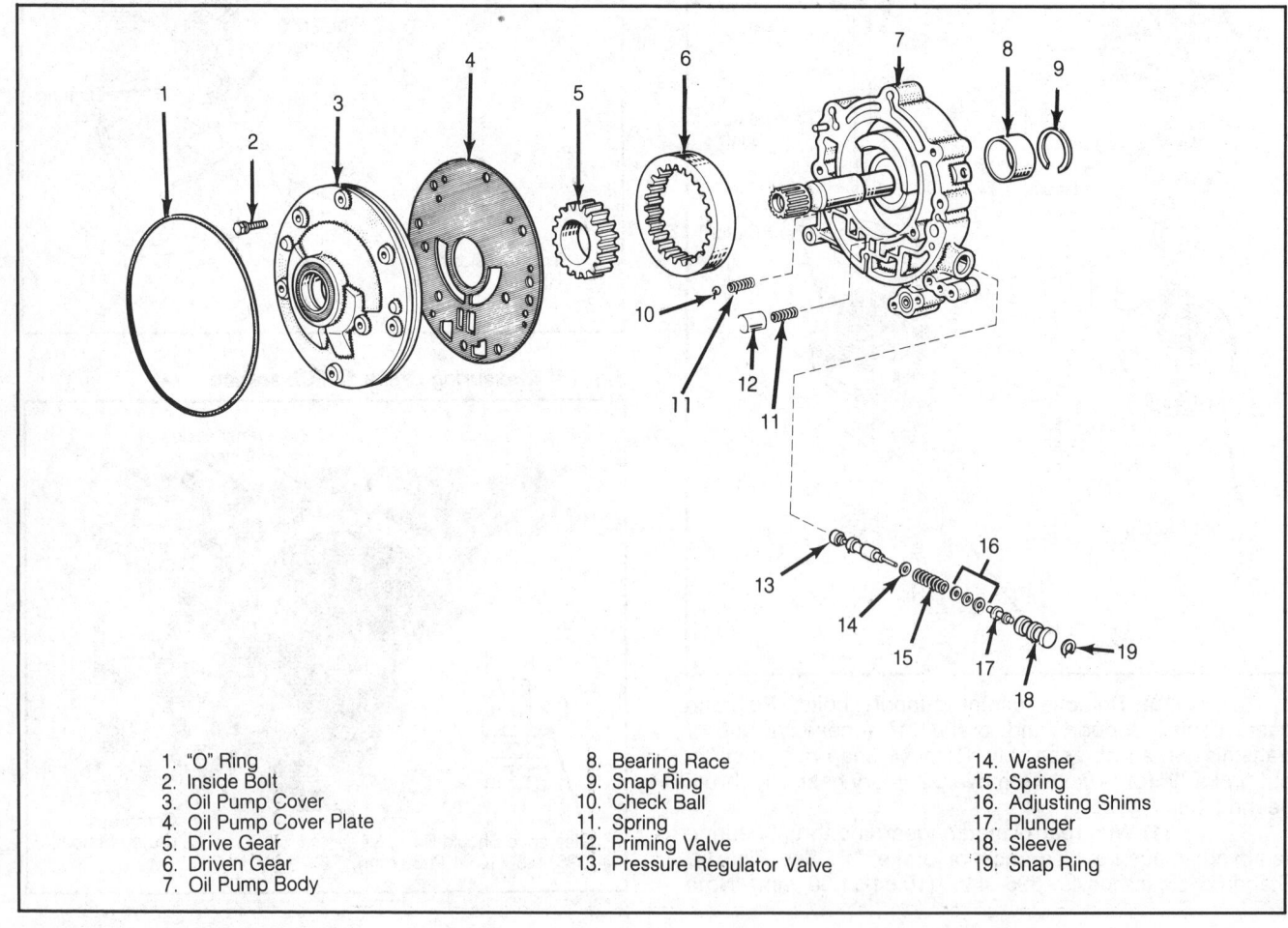

1. "O" Ring	8. Bearing Race	14. Washer
2. Inside Bolt	9. Snap Ring	15. Spring
3. Oil Pump Cover	10. Check Ball	16. Adjusting Shims
4. Oil Pump Cover Plate	11. Spring	17. Plunger
5. Drive Gear	12. Priming Valve	18. Sleeve
6. Driven Gear	13. Pressure Regulator Valve	19. Snap Ring
7. Oil Pump Body		

TOYOTA MODEL A-55 (Cont.)

4) Temporarily install and tighten (by hand) inside bolts to retain pump cover in place. Check rotation of pump drive gear. Install pressure regulator valve, washer and spring to pump body. Assemble same number of adjusting shims as removed to plunger, then install plunger to spring in pump body. Install sleeve and snap ring.

Fig. 16: Measuring Oil Pump Gear Clearance

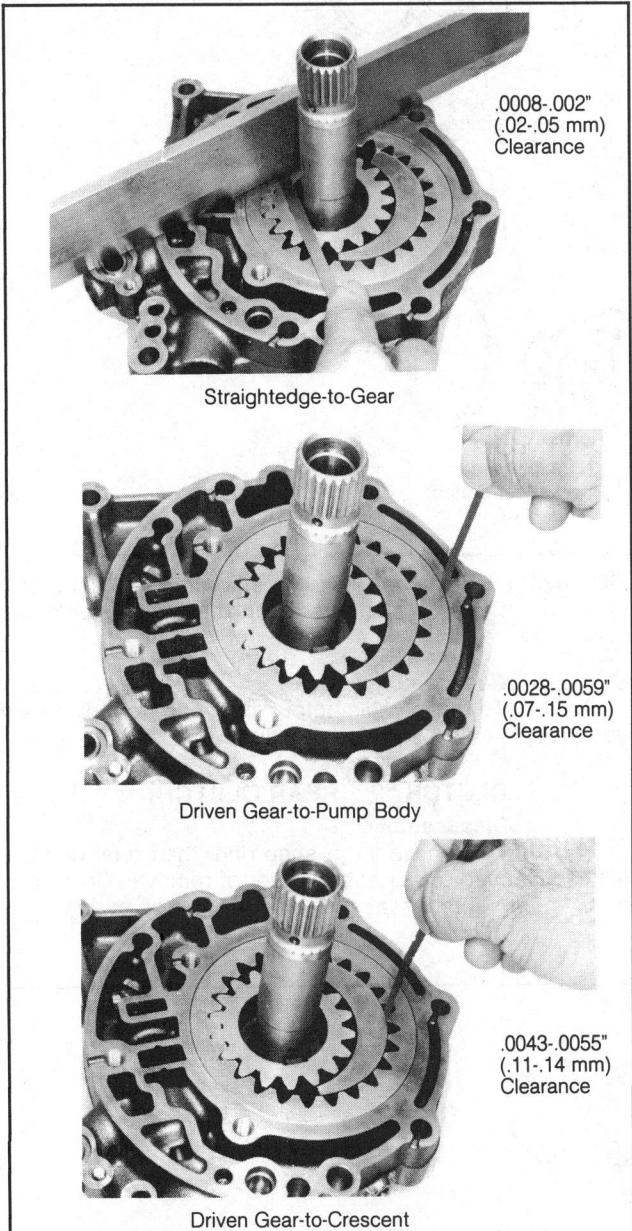

.0008-.002"
(.02-.05 mm)
Clearance

Straightedge-to-Gear

.0028-.0059"
(.07-.15 mm)
Clearance

Driven Gear-to-Pump Body

.0043-.0055"
(.11-.14 mm)
Clearance

Driven Gear-to-Crescent

INPUT SHAFT, GEARS AND CHAIN
Disassembly
Check input shaft, drive and driven gears for wear or damage. Remove snap ring, roller bearing and thrust bearing from input shaft driven gear. Check components for wear, scoring or damage. Check input shaft-drive gear rear thrust bearing and race for wear or damage. Inspect chain for wear or damage. Check input shaft oil seal rings for wear or damage.

Reassembly
Replace any components found worn or damaged. Replace oil seal rings if worn or damaged. Install thrust bearing and roller bearing into input shaft driven gear and install snap ring. Install thrust bearing and roller bearing to input shaft drive gear and install snap ring. Place thrust bearing and race to rear of input shaft.

FRONT SUPPORT
Disassembly
Check mating surfaces of front support for wear or damage. Check oil seal rings on support shaft and replace if worn or damaged. Check front support shaft bushing for wear or damage.
Reassembly
Install new oil seal rings if they were worn or damaged. Install new small "O" ring to front support.

NOTE: **Oil seal ring ends are interlocking. Make sure rings fit together correctly.**

CLUTCH "1" (FRONT CLUTCH)
Disassembly
1) Remove thrust bearing and race from front side of race. Note position of races. Remove large snap ring from front clutch drum. Remove front and rear clutch hub by lifting out together. Remove thrust bearings and races. Note position of races.
2) Remove clutch plate and disc. Remove thin snap ring. Remove remaining clutch plates and discs. Place compressor tool (SST09350-20013) on spring retainer and compress springs with a press. Using a screwdriver, remove snap ring. Remove spring retainer and all springs.
3) Slide front clutch onto front support. Apply compressed air to front support to remove piston. Remove front clutch from front support. See Fig. 17.

NOTE: **Do NOT allow discs to dry out. Prepare new discs by soaking at least 2 hours in ATF.**

Inspection
Inspect front clutch piston. Check that check ball is free by shaking piston. Check that valve does not leak by applying low-pressure compressed air.

Reassembly
1) Install new "O" rings on piston. Install piston in front clutch drum. Press housing with cup side up (check ball down). Be careful not to damage "O" rings.
2) Install 20 piston return springs, spring retainer and snap ring into place. Compress return springs on spring retainer with compressor (SST09350-20013) and arbor. Install snap ring with a screwdriver.
3) Using low-pressure compressed air, blow all excess ATF from discs. For measurement of clutch pack, install all plates and discs (temporarily without thinner snap ring). Install in following order: Cushion plate, plate, disc, plate, disc, plate.
4) Measure completely around circumference of front clutch. Standard clearance is .0138-.0539" (.35-1.37 mm). If not, use thicker snap ring. Remove snap ring, rear clutch hub and 1 plate and disc to allow installation of inner snap ring. Install inner race and needle bearing.
5) Press into place. Face lip of race toward front of clutch body. Install planetary ring gear, aligning disc lugs with hub teeth. Make sure hub meshes with all

Automatic Transmissions

TOYOTA MODEL A-55 (Cont.)

Fig. 17: Exploded View of Clutch "1" (Front Clutch)

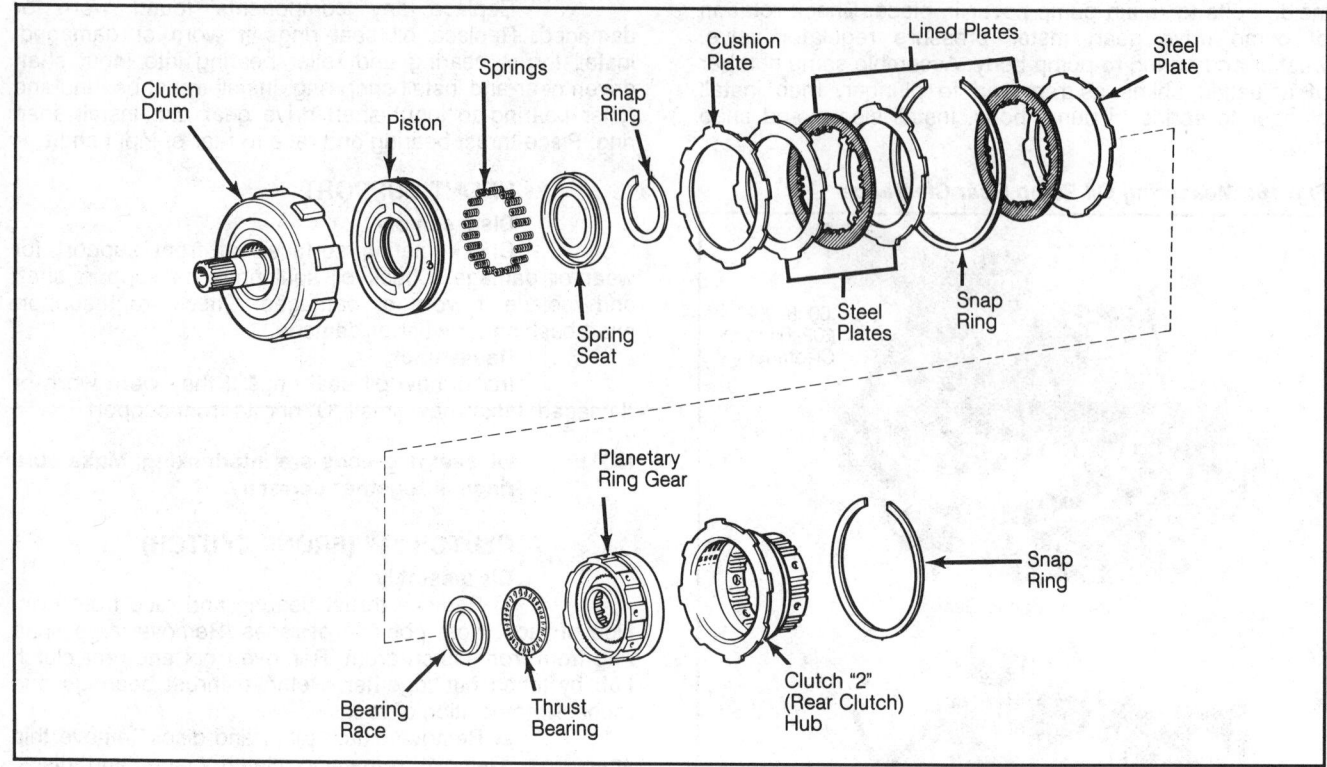

discs and is fully inserted. Install rear clutch drum and outer snap ring. Check that snap ring ends are not aligned with cutouts.

OUTPUT SHAFT & FRONT PLANETARY GEAR
Disassembly
   1) Remove thrust bearing and race from front side of planetary gear. Remove planetary gear snap ring. Pull planetary gear off output shaft. Check output shaft for wear or damage.
   2) Check planetary gear for wear or damage. Check planetary gear thrust play. Thrust play should be

.008-.020" (.2-.5 mm). Check planetary thrust bearing and race for wear or damage. Replace components as necessary.

Reassembly
   To reassemble output shaft and front planetary gear, reverse disassembly procedure.

CLUTCH "2" (REAR CLUTCH)
Disassembly
   1) Remove large snap ring, then remove steel plates and lined plates noting order of removal. Compress piston return spring seat and remove small snap ring.

Fig. 18: Exploded View of Clutch "2" (Rear Clutch)

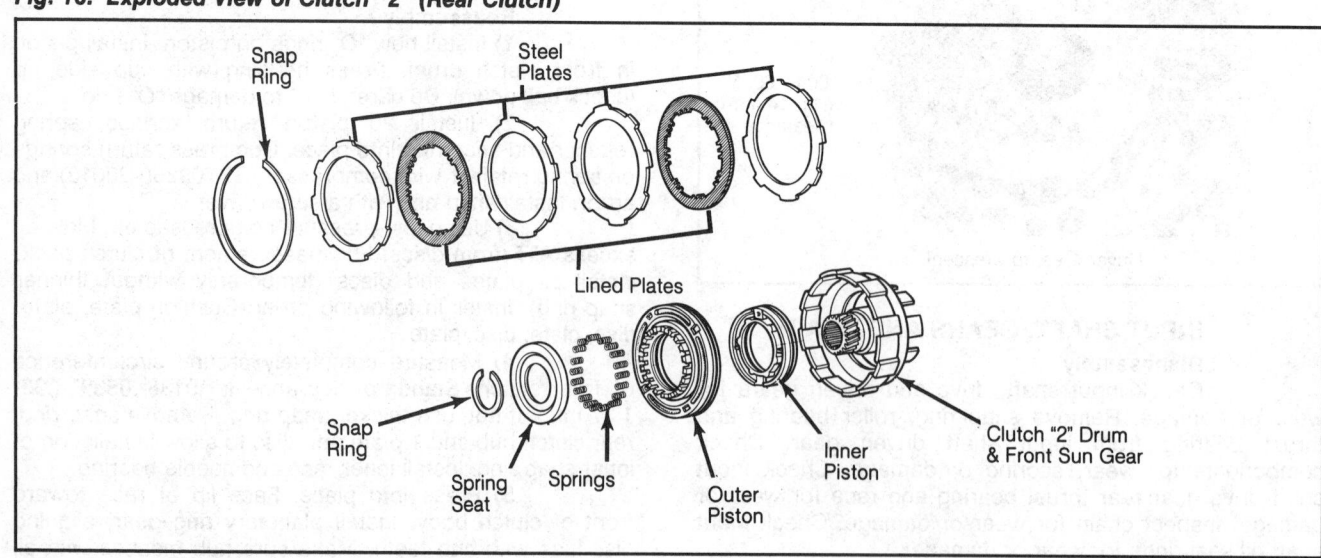

TOYOTA MODEL A-55 (Cont.)

2) Slowly remove pressure on spring seat, then remove spring seat with all return springs. Remove inner piston, then remove outer piston. *See Fig. 18.*

3) If pistons are difficult to remove, place clutch drum into center support. Using air pressure applied to inner piston port, blow out inner piston. Move air pressure to outer piston port and remove outer piston. *See Fig. 19.*

Fig. 19: *Removing Inner and Outer Pistons of Clutch "2" with Compressed Air*

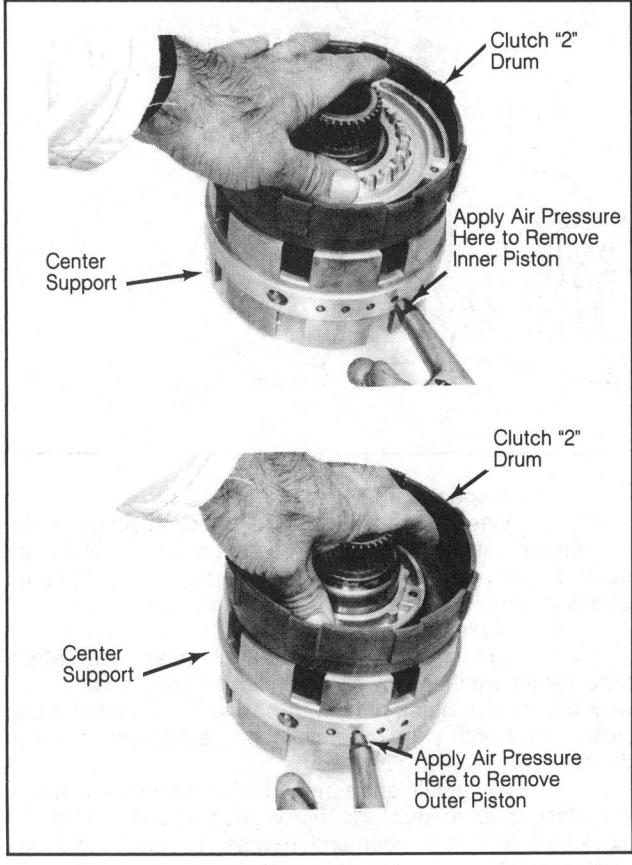

Inspection

1) Check clutch drum, sun gear, spring retainer and piston for wear or damage. Make sure seal ring contacting surface and snap ring groove areas are not damaged. Shake outer piston to make sure check ball has movement. Apply air to check ball orifice. No air should leak by.

2) Check inner piston in same manner as outer. Check return springs for a free length of 1.138" (28.9 mm), outside coil diameter of .276" (7.0 mm) and for 12 coils. Check steel plates and lined plates for burning, excessive wear or other damage.

Reassembly

1) Install new "O" rings to inner and outer pistons (lubricate "O" rings before installation). Lubricate pistons and install into clutch drum. Make sure spring seats in pistons are facing out of drum. With springs installed to pistons, install spring seat and compress to install snap ring. Make sure snap ring is seated properly before releasing spring compressor.

2) Install plates to clutch drum in this order: steel plate, lined plate, 2 steel plates, lined plate and

cushion plate. Make sure round edge of cushion plate faces into drum. Install snap ring.

3) Install clutch "2" into center support and apply air pressure to center support. *See Fig. 20.* Measure piston stroke. Measurement should be .035-.059" (.9-1.5 mm) with 56 psi (4 kg/cm²) air pressure applied.

Fig. 20: *Checking Clutch "2" Piston Stroke*

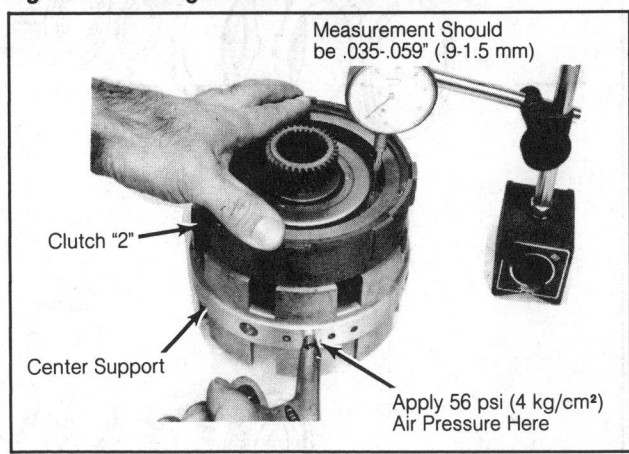

CENTER SUPPORT AND COMPONENTS

Disassembly

1) Withdraw sun gear from center support. Remove front one-way clutch from center support. Remove large snap ring holding brake "1" plates, then remove steel plate, lined plate and cushion plate.

2) Compress spring retainer of brake "1". Remove small snap ring and slowly release compressor. Remove springs, then apply air pressure to remove piston. Remove No. 1 piston "O" rings.

3) Turn center support over and remove large snap ring, steel plates and lined plates for brake "2". Using a spring compressor, compress spring seat of brake "2" and remove small snap ring. Slowly release pressure and remove spring seat with springs.

4) Apply air pressure to center support brake "2" pressure port to remove piston. Remove No. 2 piston "O" rings. Remove 3 oil seal rings from center support. Remove one-way clutch assembly and oil seal rings from sun gear.

Inspection

1) Check all components for wear or damage. Check center support oil seal rings and grooves for wear or damage. Check brake "1" and brake "2" springs for a free length of .635" (16.1 mm), coil outside diameter of .276" (7.0 mm) and for 6 coils.

2) Check front one-way clutch by inserting sun gear into clutch and checking for rotation. From sun gear tooth end, sun gear should rotate counterclockwise but lock up in clockwise rotation. Check oil seal rings on sun gear. Replace components as necessary.

Reassembly

1) Install new "O" rings and one-way clutch assembly on sun gear. Install new oil seal rings on center support. Install new "O" rings on brake pistons and lubricate with ATF fluid. Install brake "1" piston into center support by pressing in with cup side up, being careful not to damage "O" rings.

2) Rotate by hand to make sure it is seated correctly. Place springs on piston and position spring

Automatic Transmissions

TOYOTA MODEL A-55 (Cont.)

Fig. 21: Exploded View of Center Support, Brake "1", Brake "2", Sun Gear and Front One-Way Clutch

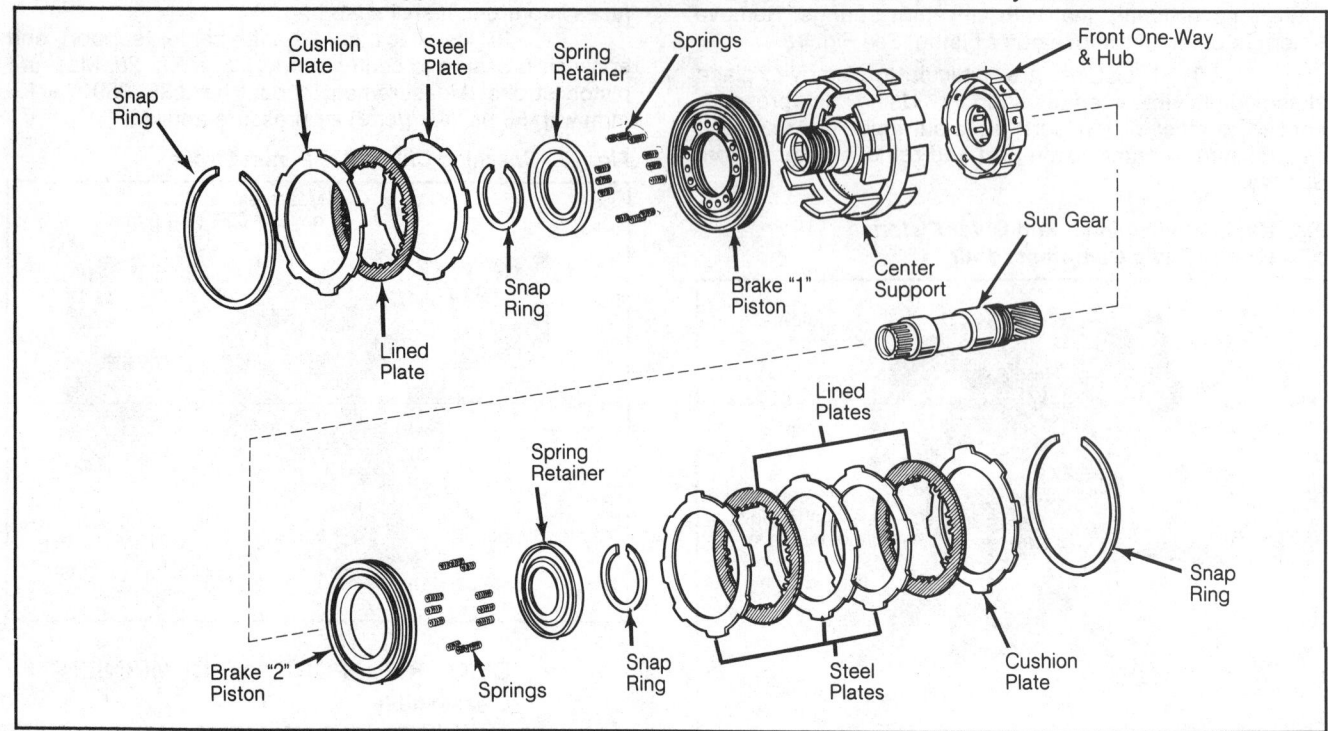

retainer with snap ring in place. Compress spring retainer and install small snap ring. Install new "O" rings on center support and piston.

   3) Turn center support over and install brake "2" piston, springs and retainer in the same manner as brake "1". Turn center support over and install No. 1 brake "1" plates, disc and flange. Use low pressue compressed air to blow all excess ATF from discs. *See Fig. 21 for steel plate and lined plate installation sequence.*

   4) With large snap rings installed to brake plates, measure piston stroke of brake piston. Make sure snap ring ends are not aligned with cutouts. Brake "1" piston stroke should be .026-.051" (.65-1.3 mm) with 57-114 psi (4-8 kg/cm²) air pressure applied.

   5) Turn center support over and install No. 2 brake piston plate, discs and flange in the same manner as No. 1. Using low pressure compressed air, blow all excess ATF from discs. Install snap ring to center support. Make sure snap ring is not aligned with cutouts.

   6) Brake "2" piston stroke should be .037-.068" (.93-1.7 mm) with 57-114 psi (4-8 kg/cm²) air pressure applied. If stroke exceeds the limit, clutch pack is probably worn. If stroke is less than the limit, parts may be misassembled or there is excess ATF on discs.

   7) Install sun gear to center support. Align No. 2 brake disc flukes. Mesh brake hub with discs, twisting and jiggling hub as required. Check rotation of gear to confirm correct installation of front one-way clutch.

REAR ONE-WAY CLUTCH AND PLANETARY GEAR

Disassembly

   Remove thrust washer from rear of planetary gear. Remove brake reaction plate from front of planetary gear. Remove snap ring, one-way clutch and thrust washer from planetary gear. *See Fig. 22.*

Inspection

   Check one-way clutch, brake reaction plate, and thrust washers for wear or damage. Check planetary gears for smooth rotation and any damage to gear teeth. Check all thrust bearings for damage or wear.

Reassembly

   1) Install thrust washer in planetary gear. Make sure thrust washer slot fits into slot in gear. Install one-way clutch into outer race with spring cage facing front. Rollers on clutch should be inclined in a counterclockwise direction.

   2) Install snap ring. Install reaction plate to planetary gear to test. Planetary gear must rotate freely clockwise and lock counterclockwise. If clutch does not work correctly, it must be replaced.

Fig. 22: Exploded View of Rear One-Way Clutch and Planetary Gear

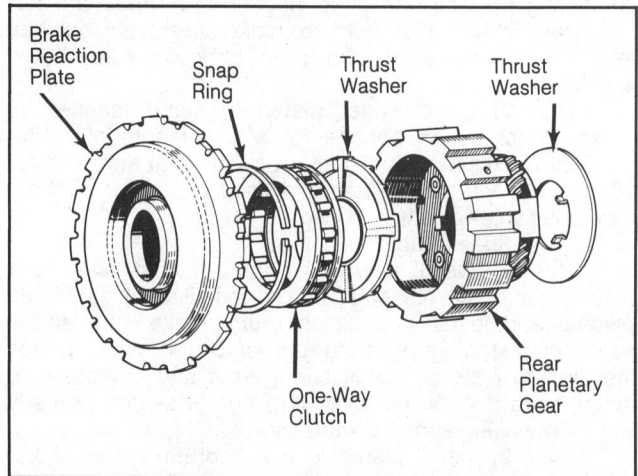

TOYOTA MODEL A-55 (Cont.)

BRAKE "3" PISTON
Disassembly

Compress spring retainer. Remove small snap ring. Slowly release spring compressor and remove spring retainer and springs. Place shop towels on top of piston and ease piston out slowly while applying air pressure to brake "3" pressure port. *See Fig. 23.*

Fig. 23: Removing Brake "3" Piston with Air Pressure

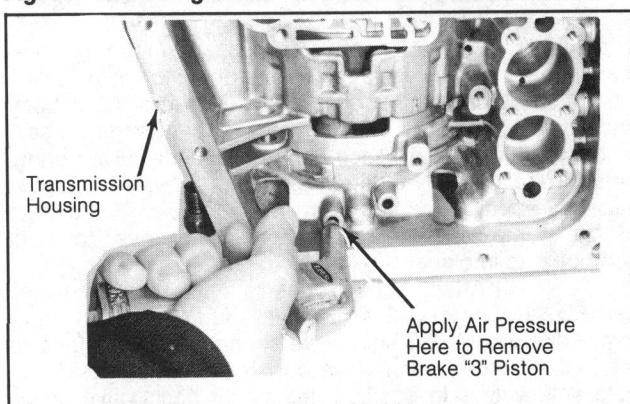

Inspection

Check piston, spring retainer, snap ring and transmission housing (piston area) for wear or damage. Check bushing in transmission housing for wear or damage. Check piston springs for a free length of 1.03" (26.2 mm).

Reassembly

1) Install a new "O" ring to piston and reaction sleeve and install piston to transmission housing. Make sure lip on piston mates with notch in transmission housing (this notch is wider than other notches). Install

springs and spring seat, then compress spring seat and install snap ring. *See Fig. 25.*

2) Check steel plates and lined plates of brake "3". Install cushion plate (concave side down toward transmission housing). Install brake plates, starting with a steel plate and alternating with lined plates until all plates are installed.

Fig. 25: Exploded View of Brake "3"

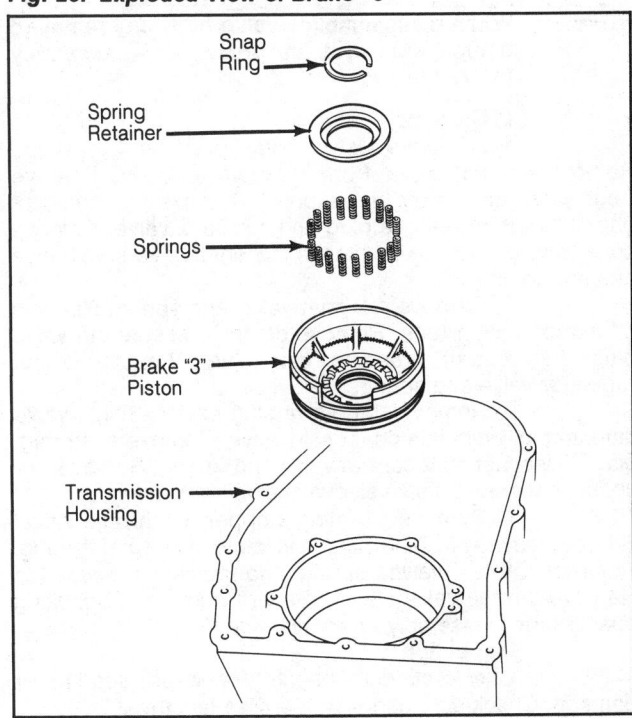

Fig. 24: Exploded View of Throttle Body and Components

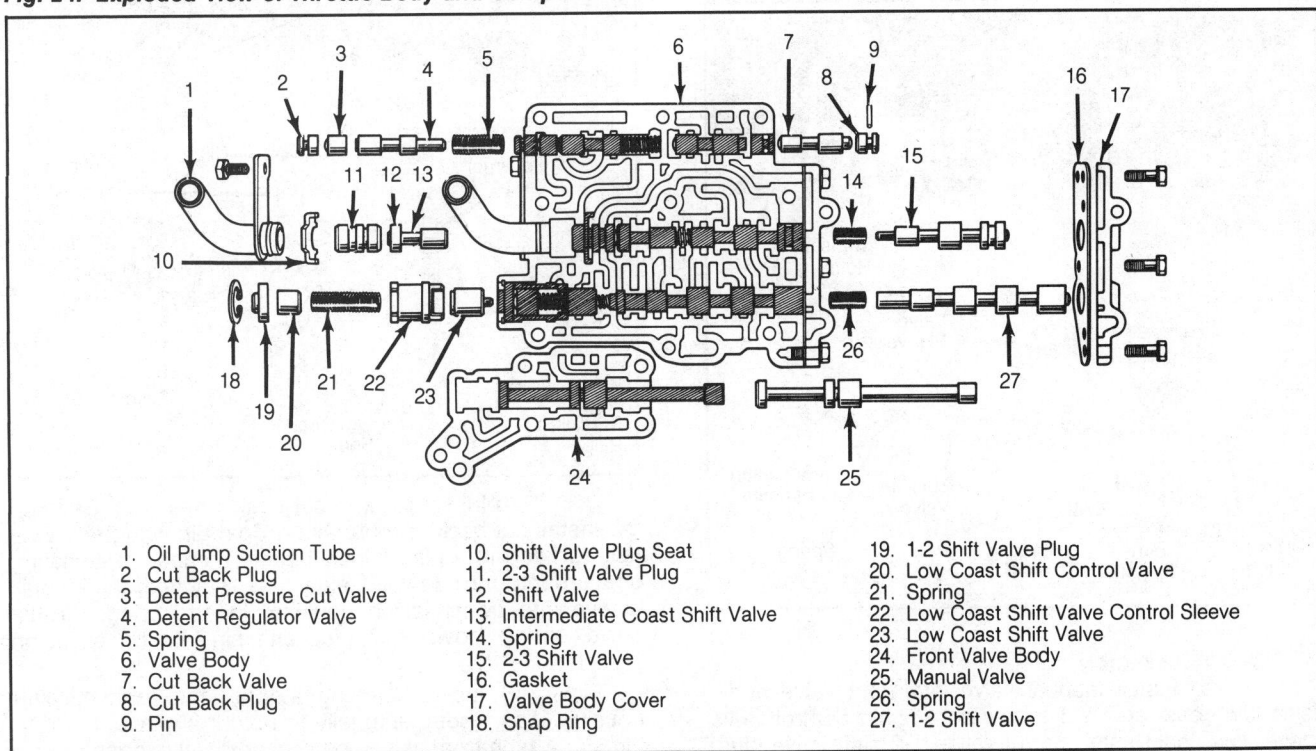

1. Oil Pump Suction Tube	10. Shift Valve Plug Seat	19. 1-2 Shift Valve Plug
2. Cut Back Plug	11. 2-3 Shift Valve Plug	20. Low Coast Shift Control Valve
3. Detent Pressure Cut Valve	12. Shift Valve	21. Spring
4. Detent Regulator Valve	13. Intermediate Coast Shift Valve	22. Low Coast Shift Valve Control Sleeve
5. Spring	14. Spring	23. Low Coast Shift Valve
6. Valve Body	15. 2-3 Shift Valve	24. Front Valve Body
7. Cut Back Valve	16. Gasket	25. Manual Valve
8. Cut Back Plug	17. Valve Body Cover	26. Spring
9. Pin	18. Snap Ring	27. 1-2 Shift Valve

TOYOTA MODEL A-55 (Cont.)

3) Measure brake "3" clearance. Refer to *Fig. 14* and to Transmission Disassembly for measuring procedures. Clearance should be .395-.445" (10.04-11.30 mm). If clearance is not to specifications, recheck plates for excessive wear or a damaged cushion plate. Replace components as necessary.

VALVE BODY

NOTE: When disassembling valve body, lay removed components out in order for reassembly reference.

Disassembly

1) Remove valve body plate and gaskets. Remove manual valve from front valve body. Remove front valve body from valve body. Remove pin from cut back plug, then remove plug and cut back valve. Remove cover and gasket, then remove 2-3 shift valve seat, valve and spring.

2) Remove 1-2 shift valve and spring. Remove oil pump suction tube. Remove detent pressure cut valve plug then detent pressure cut valve. Remove detent regulator valve and spring.

3) Remove shift valve plug seat, 2-3 shift valve plug and intermediate coast shift valve. Remove snap ring, plug, low coast shift control valve and spring. Remove low coast shift control valve sleeve and valve. *See Fig. 24.*

4) Remove vibrating stopper for throttle valve. Remove downshift plug pin, then remove downshift plug. Remove throttle valve, spring and adjusting spacer(s). Remove throttle valve sleeve. Record number of adjusting spacers for reassembly reference. *See Fig. 26.*

Inspection

Check all components for wear, scoring or damage. Check springs for proper free length.

Fig. 26: *Exploded View of Throttle Valve*

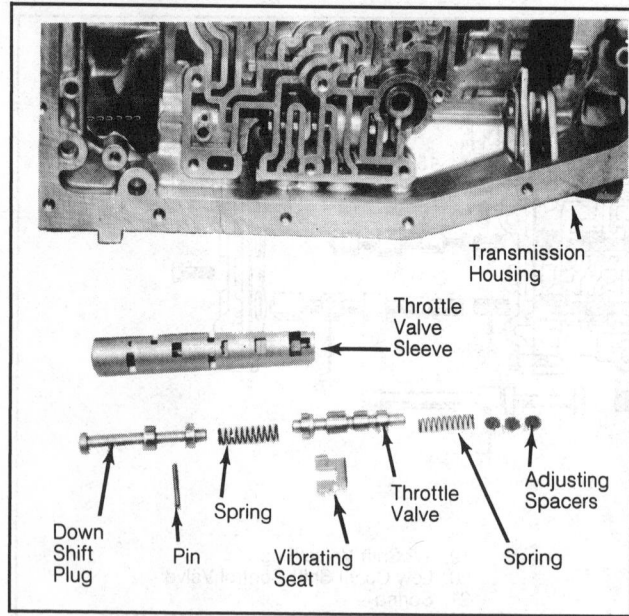

Reassembly

1) Install manual valve into front valve body. Insert low coast shift valve, low coast shift control valve sleeve, low coast shift control valve, 1-2 shift valve plug,

VALVE BODY SPRING FREE LENGTH

Application	In. (mm)
1-2 Shift Valve Spring	1.024 (26.0)
Low-Coast Valve Spring	1.437 (36.5)
2-3 Shift Valve Spring	.870 (22.1)
Detent Regulator Valve Spring	1.038 (22.4)
Throttle Valve Spring (Front)	1.194 (30.3)
Throttle Valve Spring (Rear)	1.083 (27.5)

and snap ring to valve body. *See Fig. 24.* Insert intermediate coast shift valve with small end down to valve body.

2) Insert 2-3 shift valve plug into valve body and hold in place with shift valve plug seat (tangs on seat face into valve body). Place detent regulator valve spring, detent regulator valve, detent pressure cut valve and plug into valve body. Plug has a groove cut into it. Place edge of oil pump suction tube into this groove to hold components in place.

3) Attach suction tube to valve body with bolt. *See Fig. 24.* Insert 1-2 shift valve spring, 1-2 shift valve (small end down), 2-3 shift valve spring and 2-3 shift valve into valve body. Attach valve body cover, with gasket, to hold shift valves in position. Install cut back valve (small end down) and plug into valve body.

Fig. 27: *Exploded View of Governor Valve Assembly*

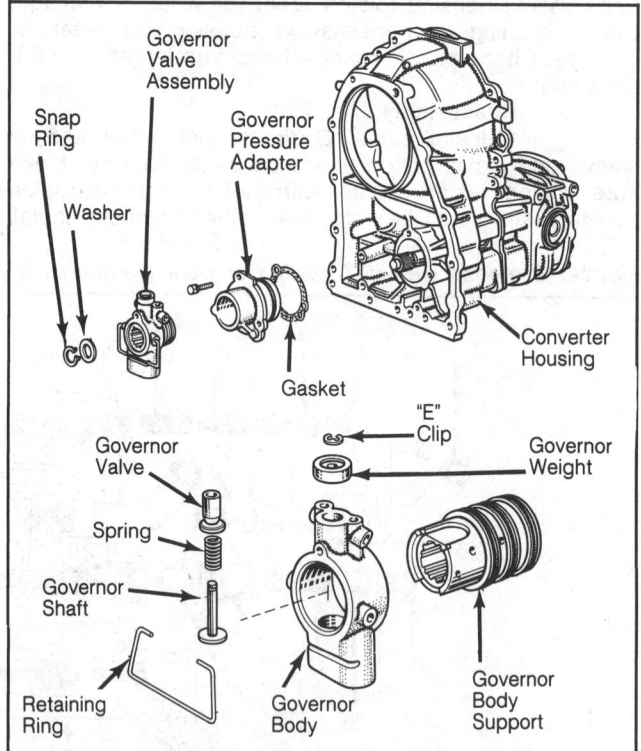

4) Insert pin into cut back valve plug. *See Fig. 24.* Install cut back valve retainer. Coat pin with petroleum jelly to keep it in place. Install same number of adjusting spacers into throttle valve sleeve as removed, then install sleeve into transmission housing. Insert spring, throttle valve, spring, down shift plug and pin into transmission housing.

5) Insert vibrating stopper into transmission housing. Apply petroleum jelly to hold it in place. *Refer to Fig. 26.* Attach front valve body cover to valve body.

TOYOTA MODEL A-55 (Cont.)

GOVERNOR VALVE

Disassembly

Remove snap ring and washer. Remove governor body support. Pry up retaining ring slightly with a screwdriver and pull out governor body with support. Compress spring by pushing up on the shaft and down on the weight. Remove "E" clip with screwdriver. Lift off governor weight. Remove governor valve by sliding it through bore. *See Fig. 27.*

Inspection

Check all governor components for wear or damage. Check governor body support oil seal rings for wear or damage. Check governor spring for free length of .728" (18.5 mm). Clean oil strainer and check for wear or damage.

Reassembly

To reassemble governor, reverse disassembly procedure. Replace oil seal. Make sure retaining ring holes in governor body support are aligned with holes in governor body. When installing "O" ring and drive pinion, coat with multi-purpose grease.

TRANSMISSION REASSEMBLY

1) Install drive plate, with spacers, to crankshaft. Install front spacer, .127" (3.2 mm) thick, with beveled edge facing drive plate, then install drive plate. Install rear spacer, .056" (1.4 mm) thick, with cupped edge facing converter.

2) Install thrust bearing and races, then install rear planetary ring gear to transmission housing. Install cushion plate and steel and lined plates to transmission housing. Install thrust bearing by coating race with petroleum jelly and sticking to ring gear.

3) Align notch and tab of thrust washer and planetary gear, coat thrust washer with petroleum jelly and stick to planetary gear. Align disc flukes. Install rear planetary gear and thrust plate.

4) Make sure planetary ring gear is fully seated, then measure brake "3" clearance. *Refer to Fig. 14.* Clearance should be .395-.445" (10.04-11.30 mm).

5) Install thrust washer, planetary gear, brake reaction plate, snap ring and center support to transmission housing. Refer to *Fig. 13* for plate installation sequence and *Fig. 28* for thrust bearing and bearing race installation.

6) Install center support bolts, make sure oil holes in center support are aligned with oil holes in transmission housing and tighten center support bolts. After center support bolt installation, make sure planetary sun gear is easy to turn in a clockwise direction and hard to turn in a counterclockwise direction.

7) Install clutch "2", bearing race and output shaft to transmission housing. *Refer to Fig. 12.* Install a thrust bearing and race over output shaft. Align the flukes of the rear clutch discs and mesh them with the front clutch hub. Install front clutch assembly into case (over output shaft).

8) After clutch "1" installation, lay a straightedge across clutch drum and transmission housing. Measure distance from straightedge to clutch drum. Distance should be the same as distance measured during disassembly. Standard distance is .024-.063" (.6-1.6 mm).

9) Install thrust bearing and race to clutch "1" shaft. Insert bearing race into front support. Install "O" ring

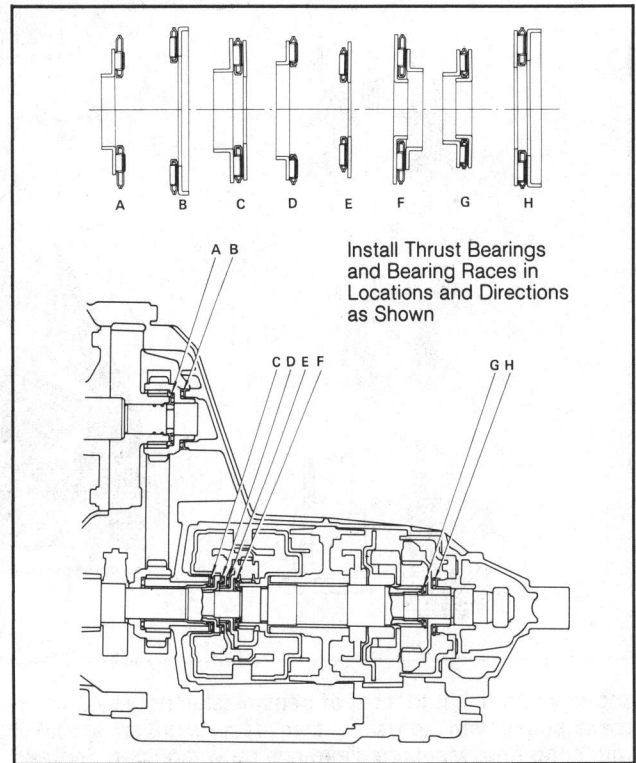

Fig. 28: Installation of Thrust Bearings and Bearing Races

Install Thrust Bearings and Bearing Races in Locations and Directions as Shown

to transmission housing. *See Fig. 29.* Coat thrust washer with petroleum jelly and set into front support with lip side to front support.

10) Install front support to transmission housing. Make sure there is no clearance between surfaces of support and case when pressing down. If there is clearance, front support is not correctly installed. Make sure there is thrust play on input shaft and tighten bolts diagonally a little at a time.

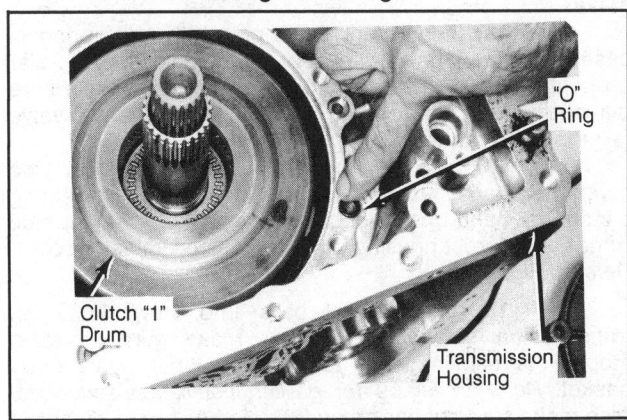

Fig. 29: Installation of "O" Ring in Transmission Housing Oil Passage

11) After front support installation, check clutch "1" shaft for ease of rotation and that end play is .0094-.0378" (.24-.96 mm). Check output shaft for ease of rotation and that end play is .012-.060" (.31-1.53 mm).

12) Place transmission so valve body side is down and install bearing race, thrust bearing, input shaft

Fig. 30: Installation of Oil Tubes and Pipes to Front of Transmission Housing

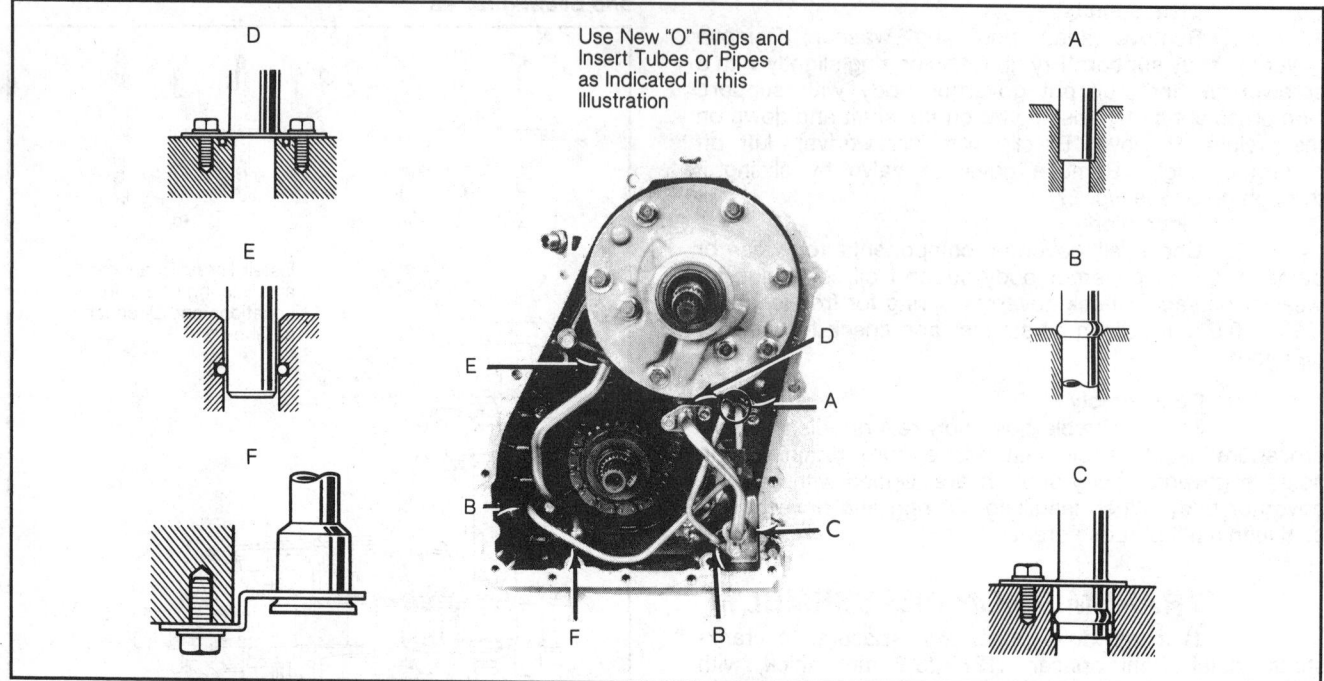

Use New "O" Rings and Insert Tubes or Pipes as Indicated in this Illustration

and drive sprocket to front of transmission housing. Install chain and driven sprocket, then secure driven sprocket with snap ring. Measure clearance between snap ring and driven sprocket. Clearance should be .0043-.027" (.11-.69 mm).

13) Install bearing race to input shaft, then install oil pump over input shaft. *Refer to Fig. 11.* Install throttle pressure tube, then install reverse line pressure tube to front of transmission housing. Using new "O" rings, install oil pump delivery tube and oil pump suction to front of transmission housing. *See Fig. 30.*

14) Assemble new collar to manual valve lever. Install manual valve lever. While holding detent ball with plate, install manual valve shaft. Drive in slotted spring pin (always use new pin). After assembly, turn spacer 90° and stake.

15) Install park pawl, pivot pin and spring in case. Install park pawl bracket on case, making sure collar on control rod is toward front of transmission. Make sure planetary gear output shaft is locked when manual valve lever is in "P" range.

16) Turn transmission over so valve body side is up. Install accumulator springs and pistons, fully seating pistons by hand. Install accumulator gasket (straight side of gasket nearest housing), then install accumulator cover. *Refer to Fig. 9.*

17) Install steel balls into valve body on transmission side. *See Fig. 31.* Make sure vibrating stopper is still in place and install upper valve body gasket. *Refer to Fig. 9 for gasket installation sequence.* Also make sure cut back plug lock pin has not fallen out.

18) Install valve body plate, lower gasket and valve body. When installing valve body, make sure oil pump suction pipe is fully seated in transmission housing. Install oil strainer and gasket to valve body.

19) Attach rod to manual valve lever and to manual valve (in front valve body), then install front valve

body to transmission housing. Install front valve body cover and gasket. Place a waved washer, then a plain washer on throttle lever shaft.

20) Insert throttle lever shaft into transmission, then install a plain washer, throttle lever, washers and nut. Check throttle lever thrust clearance. If clearance is greater than .020" (.5 mm), install additional washers to outside of lever. Install oil pressure tubes. *See Fig. 32.* Install oil pan and gasket.

21) Place transmission housing-to-converter housing gasket on transmission housing (coated with sealant). Install new "O" rings into transmission housing-

Fig. 31: Installation Locations of Valve Body Steel Balls

TOYOTA MODEL A-55 (Cont.)

Fig. 32: Intallation of Oil Pressure Tubes

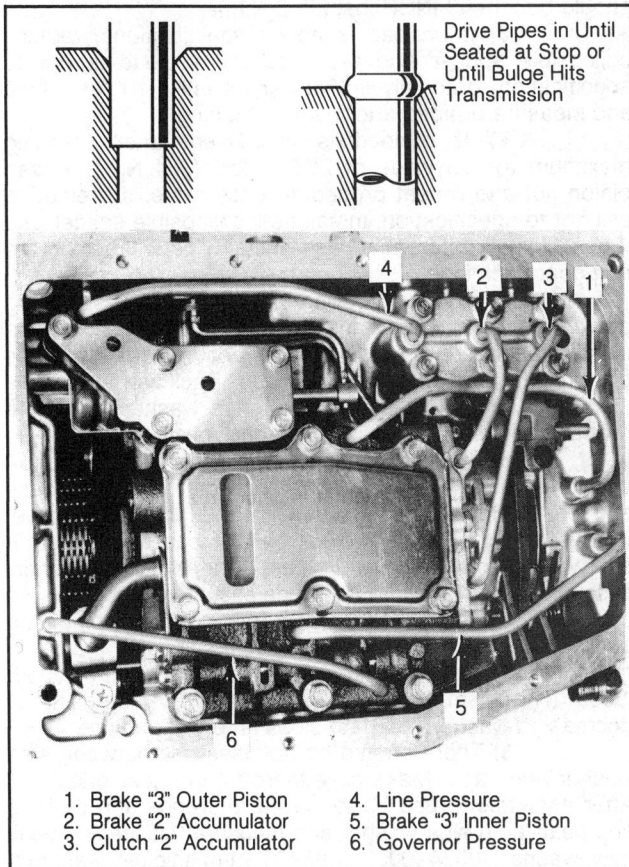

Drive Pipes in Until Seated at Stop or Until Bulge Hits Transmission

1. Brake "3" Outer Piston
2. Brake "2" Accumulator
3. Clutch "2" Accumulator
4. Line Pressure
5. Brake "3" Inner Piston
6. Governor Pressure

to-converter housing oil passages. Attach converter housing-to-transmission housing. *Refer to Fig. 7.*

22) Install output shaft sleeve with speedometer drive gear and balls to transmission output shaft. Secure sleeve with snap ring. Install extension housing and gasket to transmission housing. Attach transmission rear mount to rear of transmission housing.

Fig. 33: Aligning Neutral Start Switch

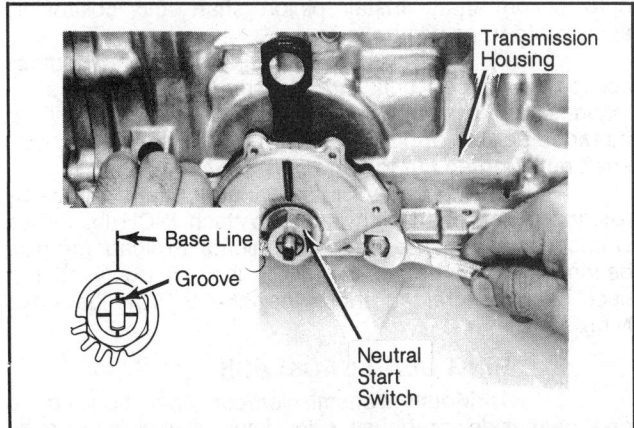

Transmission Housing

Base Line

Groove

Neutral Start Switch

23) Install speedometer driven gear, neutral start switch, oil filler tube and control rod to transmission. When installing neutral start switch, align switch shaft groove to neutral base line. *See Fig. 33.* Install torque converter.

FINAL DRIVE

DIFFERENTIAL ASSEMBLY

Disassembly

1) Remove differential from transaxle. Mount differential carrier on support stand and remove differential cover. Set it so ring gear faces in a horizontal position. Measure and record ring gear backlash, ring gear runout and check tooth contact pattern.

2) If runout is more than .0028" (.07 mm), a new ring gear is needed. Install INCH lb. torque wrench and measure pinion shaft bearing preload for reassembly reference. Preload should be 5.2-8.7 INCH lbs. (.6-1.0 N.m). Remove oil seals from differential carrier.

3) Remove and mark side bearing caps, races and side bearing washers. Mark for reassembly reference. Remove side washer on ring gear teeth side. Remove differential case and bearing outer race. Remove snap ring from governor body and pressure adapter.

4) Remove governor body. Wrap spline with tape and remove governor pressure adapter. Loosen staked portion of pinion shaft nut. Remove pinion shaft nut. While removing nut, turn pinion shaft clockwise with collar (SST09556-16020). Press out drive pinion.

Fig. 34: Measuring Ring Gear Backlash

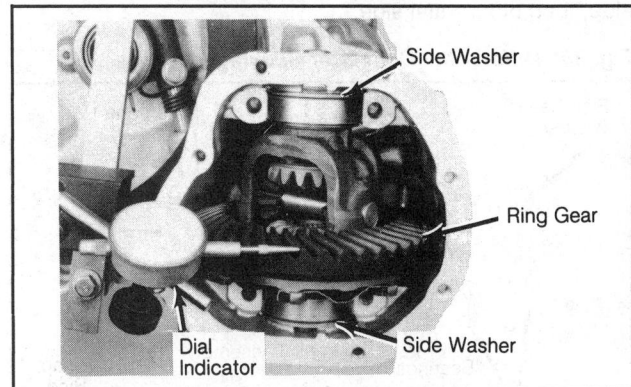

Side Washer

Ring Gear

Dial Indicator

Side Washer

Inspection

1) Inspect drive pinion bearings and outer races. If necessary to replace them, remove rear bearing from drive pinion with puller (SST09950-20014). Install plate washer selected according to Gear Tooth Contact Pattern test. Install new bearing with driver (SST09608-20011) and press.

2) Using a hammer and brass bar, remove outer races by tapping on notched portion. Install new races with installer (SST09608-30011 for front, SST09608-30021 for rear) and driver.

3) Inspect side bearings and outer race. If necessary to replace, remove bearings with puller. Install new bearings with a press. Inspect pinion and side gears. Measure side gear backlash while holding pinion gear toward case. Standard backlash is .0016-.0094" (.04-.24 mm).

NOTE: Differential case has indentations for insertion of puller jaws to ease side bearing removal.

4) If necessary, replace ring gear, differential pinions and side gears by lifting lock plates and removing side bolts. Draw alignment mark on ring gear and case.

TOYOTA MODEL A-55 (Cont.)

Using a brass bar and hammer, tap on ring gear to separate it from differential case.

5) Using a punch, tap out straight pin toward ring gear installation surface. Remove and check pinion shaft, pinion gears, side gears and thrust washers. Install side gears, washers, pinion gears, washers, pinion gears and shaft. Measure side gear backlash while holding pinion gear toward case.

6) Standard backlash is .0016-.0094" (.04-.24 mm). If backlash is not to specification, use different thickness thrust washer. Using a hammer and punch, drive straight pin through case and hole in pinion shaft. Stake pin and differential case.

7) Clean contact surface of differential case. Heat ring gear to 194-230°F (90-110°C) in an oil bath. Quickly install ring gear to differential case. Do NOT heat gear to more than 230°F (110°C). Coat ring gear set bolts with gear oil.

8) Coat lock plates and set bolts. Tighten set bolts uniformly, a little at a time, to specification. Stake lock plate. Stake one claw flush with flat surface of nut. For claw contacting protruding postion of nut, stake only half on tightening side.

9) Inspect governor pressure adapter seal. If necessary to replace, use a press and 29 mm socket to remove oil seal. Press in new seal first on transmission side, then differential side.

Fig. 35: Differential/Converter Housing

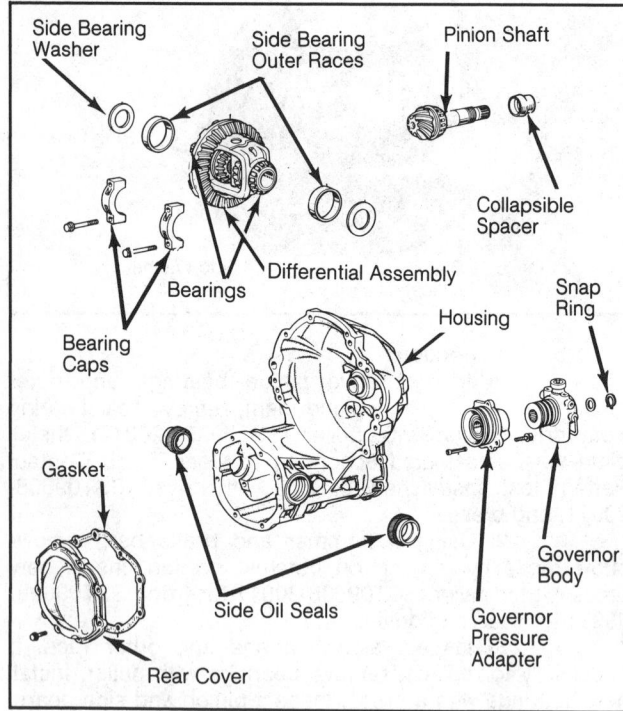

Reassembly

1) Install new spacer to drive pinion and install drive pinion to differential case. Using installer and press, temporarily press in bearing until threaded portion is protruding .12" (3 mm). Apply gear oil to threaded portion of drive pinion.

2) Tighten nut and apply gear oil to bearings. Snug down bearing by turning drive pinion several times. Measure drive pinion preload. For new bearing, it should

be 4.3-8.7 INCH lbs. (.5-1.0 N.m). For used bearings, it should be 2.6-4.3 INCH lbs. (.3-.5 N.m).

3) If preload is above specifications, replace collapsible spacer and test again. If preload is not to specification, gradually tighten pinion nut 5-10° at a time and measure preload after each tightening.

4) If preload is insufficient after reaching maximum torque value of 267 ft. lbs. (364 N.m), loosen pinion nut and repeat procedure once more. If preload is still not to specification, install new collapsible spacer and repeat. Install differential case. Install side washer on the ring gear back side.

5) Make sure ring gear has backlash. Snug down washer and bearings by tapping ring gear with a plastic hammer. Hold side bearing boss on teeth surface of ring gear and measure backlash. Backlash should be .0039" (.10 mm). Select a ring gear washer to create proper backlash.

6) Select a ring gear side washer of a thickness to eliminate any clearance between outer race and case. Remove side washers and differential case. Install side washer into lower part of case. Place other side washer onto differential case, and install differential case with outer race into transaxle case.

7) Snug washer and bearing by tapping ring gear with a plastic hammer. Using a dial indicator, measure ring gear backlash. Backlash should be .0039-.0059" (.10-.15 mm). Adjust if necessary by increasing or decreasing washers on both sides an equal amount.

8) There should be no clearance between side washer and case. Make sure there is ring gear backlash. After adjustment, use backlash as reference and remove ring gear teeth side washer and measure thickness. Install new washer .0024-.0035" (.06-.09 mm) thicker than that removed.

9) Washer should be able to be pushed in 2/3 of the way by finger. Using a plastic hammer, tap in side washer. Recheck ring gear backlash. Install side bearing caps and tighten bolts.

PINION BEARING PRELOAD

1) Measure and record thickness of pinion shim with micrometer and install shim on pinion shaft. Press on new front bearing. Slide new collapsible spacer onto pinion shaft. Install pinion shaft and collapsible spacer into transaxle housing.

2) Press in rear bearing (do not smash collapsible spacer) until threaded portion of pinion shaft extends .12" (3 mm) above rear bearing surface. Coat threaded portion of pinion shaft with oil, then install pinion shaft nut. Tighten nut to 108 ft. lbs. (147 N.m).

3) Apply gear oil to bearings. Seat bearings by rotating pinion shaft with socket. Attach INCH lb. torque wrench and measure bearing preload. Preload for new bearings should be 4.3-8.7 INCH lbs. (.5-1.0 N.m). For used bearings preload should be 2.6-4.3 INCH lbs. (.3-.5 N.m).

RING GEAR BACKLASH

1) Mount transmission/converter housing so ring gear side of housing is down. Install outer side bearing races. Insert lower differential side bearing washer, then install differential case into housing. Tap differential into position with plastic hammer.

NOTE: Do not interchange side bearings.

TOYOTA MODEL A-55 (Cont.)

2) Mount dial indicator. Hold upper side bearing outer race against side bearing and measure ring gear backlash. Backlash should be .0039-.0059" (.10-.15 mm). Select and install a washer which will eliminate any clearance between outer race and housing.

3) Recheck ring gear backlash. Remove differential side bearing races and washer. Measure thickness of washers with micrometer, divide by 2 and select appropriate shims of equal thickness for each side of differential assembly.

4) Side bearing washers are available in the following thicknesses: .103-.129" (2.62-3.28 mm) in .001" (.03 mm) increments. Backlash will change about .0008" (.02 mm) with .001" (.03 mm) alteration of side bearing washers.

5) Reinstall differential assembly, side bearing outer races and washers. Measure ring gear runout. If not to specification, increase or decrease washer thickness until specification is obtained. Ring gear runout should be .0028" (.07 mm).

6) After adjusting ring gear backlash, install side bearing caps and tighten bolts. Do not interchange bearing caps. Mount dial indicator on pinion nut and measure total ring and pinion bearing preload. Preload should be 2.6-4.3 INCH lbs. (.3-.5 N.m) PLUS amount of pinion bearing preload.

GEAR TOOTH CONTACT PATTERN

NOTE: Final adjustments to differential are made with results from gear tooth contact pattern. See Gear Tooth Contact Pattern Article in back of book.

1) If excessive heel or toe contact is evident, readjust pinion shaft depth. Pinion depth is adjusted by installing thinner shim (excessive toe contact) or thicker shim (excessive heel contact).

2) Changing pinion washer thickness by .0039" (.10 mm) will change center of tooth contact by 1/8 of total contact width. Pinion washers are available in thicknesses ranging from .0591" (1.50 mm) to .0768" (1.95 mm) in .0012" (.03 mm) increments.

3) Too much flank or face contact reveals incorrect ring gear backlash. Flank contact can be changed by installing thicker side bearing washers (adjust backlash closer to high side of specification). Face contact can be changed by installing thinner side bearing washers (adjust backlash closer to low side of specification).

4) Backlash will change about .008" (.02 mm) with a .0012" (.03 mm) change in side washer. Make sure to increase or decrease both side washers in equal amounts. After adjusting pinion depth as indicated by gear tooth contact pattern, recheck ring gear backlash.

5) Stake pinion nut and reinstall rear cover and gasket. Install differential side bearing oil seals with installer (SST09223-46011). Seal should extend .331-.354" (8.4-9.0 mm) from housing.

TIGHTENING SPECIFICATIONS

Application	Ft. Lbs. (N.m)
Axle Shaft Nut	73-108 (99-147)
Ball Joint-to-Steering Knuckle	40-52 (54-71)
Center Support Bolts	18-20 (25-27)
Drive Plate	33-43 (45-58)
Engine Front Mount-to-Crossmember	26-39 (35-53)
Engine Rear Mount-to-Body	26-36 (35-49)
Engine-to-Converter Housing	37-57 (50-78)
Hub-to-Rotor	29-36 (39-49)
Lower Arm-to-Crossmember	51-65 (69-88)
Lower Arm-to-Strut Bar	29-39 (39-53)
Pinion Nut	109-267 (148-363)
Rear Trans. Mount-to-Ext. Hsg.	55-79 (75-107)
Ring Gear Bolts	67-75 (91-102)
Side Bearing Caps	33-39 (45-53)
Stabilizer Bracket	22-32 (30-44)
Stabilizer-to-Lower Arm	11-15 (15-20)
Strut Bar-to-Strut Bracket	55-79 (75-107)
Strut-to-Steering Knuckle	40-52 (54-71)
Transmission-to-Converter Hsg.	11-15 (15-20)

Automatic Transmissions

VOLKSWAGEN TYPE 010 3-SPEED

Jetta
Rabbit & Pickup
Scirocco

TRANSMISSION IDENTIFICATION

Transmission type may be identified by a group of numbers cast into top of case, behind case rib. One of the numbers is "010". This denotes the VW "two planetary" type transmission. Transmission model may be identified by a group of figures stamped into converter housing near governor. Figures consist of a model code (EQ) and a build date code.

Transmission used in diesel engined Jetta and Rabbit models (and some gas models) includes an "E-mode" option. Models equipped with this transmission can be identified by an "E" position between "N" and "D" on the shift console.

NOTE: **All references to "Rabbit" include Pickup and Convertible.**

DESCRIPTION

Transaxle assembly consists of 2 main units: Automatic transmission and final drive assembly. The transmission housing contains 2 planetary gear sets, 2 multiple-disc clutches, 1 brake band and servo, 1 multiple-disc brake, a one-way clutch, and a hydralic control system. The final drive housing contains torque converter, governor for transmission, three-gear type ring and pinion assembly, and differential unit.

Transmissions with E-mode operation are designed to improve fuel economy. With selector lever in "E" position, transmission is disengaged from differential whenever accelerator pedal is released. In any other selector lever position, transmission operates the same as the conventional model.

LUBRICATION & ADJUSTMENT

See the appropriate article in AUTOMATIC TRANSMISSION SERVICING Section.

SERVICE (IN VEHICLE)

AXLE SHAFTS

See SERVICE (IN VEHICLE) in Volkswagen Jetta, Pickup, Rabbit & Scirocco 4 & 5-Speed Manual Transaxle article.

TROUBLE SHOOTING

NO MOVEMENT
In Any Gear
Low fluid level. Manual lever disconnected from manual valve. Torque converter disconnected from

Fig. 1: Cross-Sectional View of Volkswagen Type 010 Automatic Transmission Assembly

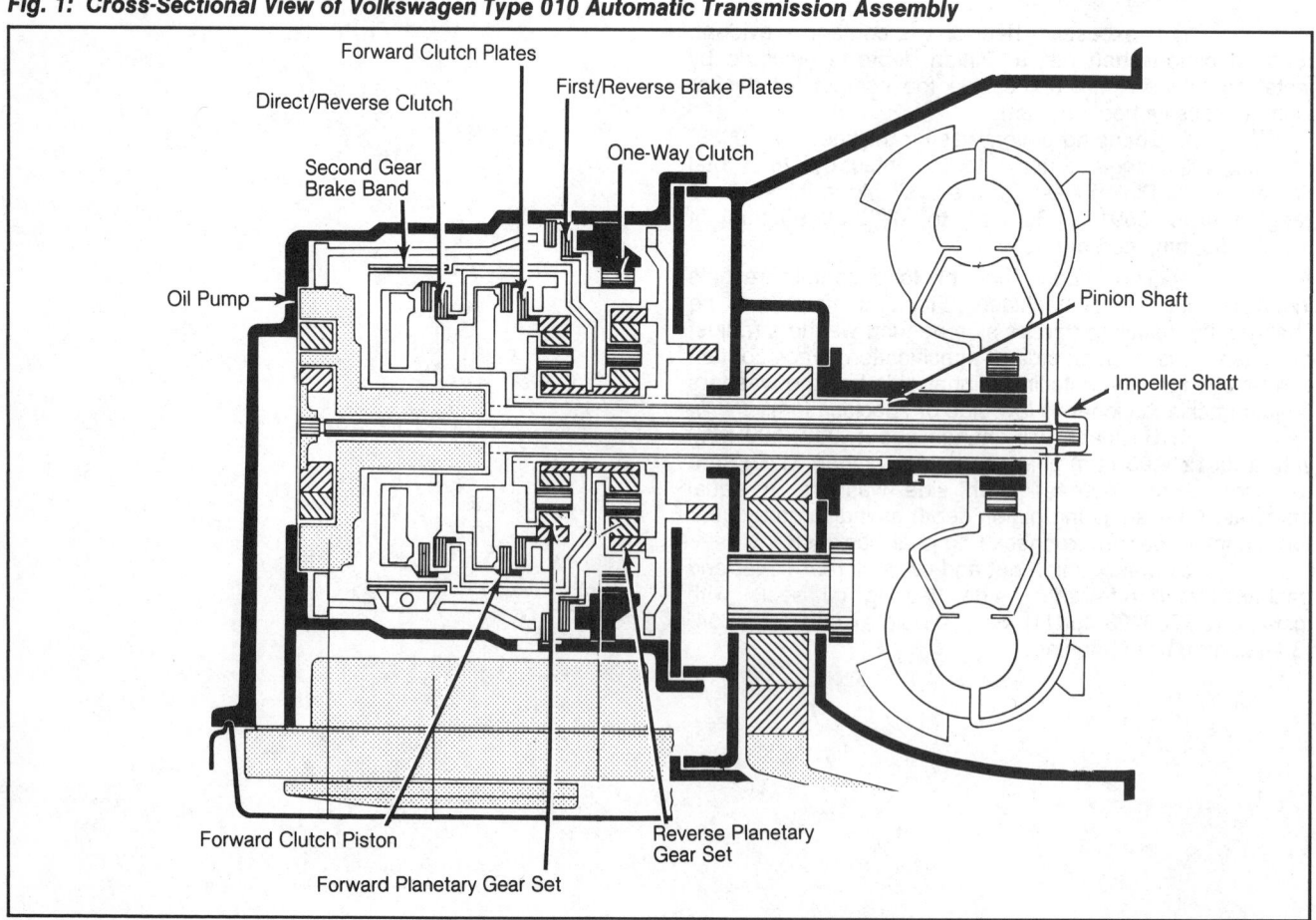

Forward Clutch Plates

Direct/Reverse Clutch

First/Reverse Brake Plates

Second Gear Brake Band

One-Way Clutch

Oil Pump

Pinion Shaft

Impeller Shaft

Forward Clutch Piston

Reverse Planetary Gear Set

Forward Planetary Gear Set

VOLKSWAGEN TYPE 010 3-SPEED (Cont.)

drive plate. Main pressure valve sticking. Oil pump drive plate or shaft defective.

In Forward Gears
Forward clutch internal damage (worn plate, spring broken, seals leaking, etc.)

In First Gear in "D" or "2"
One-way clutch not holding. Forward clutch internal damage.

In First Gear in "1"
First/reverse brake plates worn or burnt.

In Second Gear
Second gear brake band out of adjustment or burnt, or servo defective.

In Third Gear
Direct/reverse clutch internal damage (worn plates, seals leaking, etc.)

In Reverse
Check first/reverse brake plate for wear or burned linings. Direct/reverse clutch internal damage. Forward clutch seized in applied position.

NO UPSHIFT

Into Second Gear
Governor drive defective. Governor dirty or improperly assembled. Accumulator cover plate loose. Valve body dirty. 1-2 shift valve sticking.

Into Third Gear
Governor dirty. Valve body dirty. 2-3 shift valve sticking. Sealing balls missing from transfer plate.

NO DOWNSHIFTS
Governor or valve body dirty. Check for sticking valves in valve body.

DELAYED ENGAGEMENT ON UPSHIFTS

1-2
Fluid level too low. Valve body dirty. Second gear brake band out of adjustment or burnt. Second gear servo faulty.

2-3
Fluid level too low. Valve body dirty. Second gear brake band out of adjustment or burnt. Second gear servo faulty. Gears damaged. Direct/reverse clutch plates worn or burnt. Direct/reverse clutch improperly assembled.

SHIFT SPEEDS FAULTY
Governor or valve body dirty, damaged, or improperly installed. Gasket or "O" ring between transmission and final drive leaking.

INCORRECT OPERATING PRESSURES
Oil pump defective. Leakage in hydraulic circuit. Control valve sticking.

IMPROPER E-MODE OPERATION
If transmission fails to disengage from engine during closed throttle conditions with shift lever in "E", check accelerator cable or shift lever cable adjustment. Declutching valve in valve body sticking.

TESTING

ROAD TEST
1) Before road testing, be certain that fluid level and condition, and control linkage adjustments have been checked and corrected as necessary. During test, transmission should upshift and downshift at approximately the speeds shown in *Shift Speed Specifications* chart. All shifts may vary somewhat due to production tolerances or tire size. The important factor is the quality of the shifts. All shifts should be smooth, responsive, and with no slippage or engine speed runaway.

2) Slippage or engine runaway in any gear usually indicates clutch, band, or brake problems. The slipping unit in a particular gear can usually be identified by noting transmission operation in other selector positions and comparing which internal units are applied in those positions. *See Clutch and Band Application Chart.*

3) This process of elimination can be used to detect any unit which slips, and to confirm proper operation of good units. However, the actual cause of the malfunction usually cannot be easily decided. Practically any condition can be caused by leaking hydraulic circuits or sticking valves. Therefore, unless an obvious condition exists, do not disassemble transmission until hydraulic pressure tests have been made.

CLUTCH AND BAND APPLICATION CHART (ELEMENTS IN USE)

Selector Lever Position	Forward Clutch	Direct/Reverse Clutch	First/Reverse Brake	Second Gear Band	One Way Clutch
D — DRIVE					
First Gear	X				X
Second Gear	X			X	
Third Gear	X	X			
2 — INTERMEDIATE					
First Gear	X				X
Second Gear	X			X	
1 — LOW	X		X		
R — REVERSE		X	X		

NEUTRAL OR PARK — All clutches, brake and band released and/or ineffective.

VOLKSWAGEN TYPE 010 3-SPEED (Cont.)

SHIFT SPEED SPECIFICATIONS

Application	Shift Points (MPH)	
	Full Throttle	Kickdown
With E-Mode		
1-2 Upshift	21-24	35-37
2-3 Upshift	50-61	61-62
3-2 Downshift	33-45	56-58
2-1 Downshift	16-19	30-33
All Others		
1-2 Upshift	20-29	33-37
2-3 Upshift	48-61	64-67
3-2 Downshift	35-48	60-63
2-1 Downshift	14-16	28-31

HYDRAULIC PRESSURE TEST

Connect a pressure gauge to main pressure test point on case (adjacent to servo cover). With tramsission at normal operating temperature, place selector lever in "D", run engine to 35 MPH, release throttle and read pressure on gauge. Run engine at full throttle with vehicle speed above 25 MPH and note pressure with transmission in "D".

With vehicle at rest, place selector lever in "R" position and note reading on pressure gauge. Pressures in each part of test should be as shown in *Main Pressures* chart.

If pressures obtained do not match those shown in chart, refer to *Incorrect Operating Pressures* in *Trouble Shooting* section.

Fig. 2: View of Transmission Case Showing Pressure Test Connection

Attach Pressure Gauge Here

MAIN PRESSURES

Application	psi (kg/cm²)
"D"@Idle [1]	41-44 (2.9-3.0)
"D"@Full Throttle [1]	83-86 (5.8-5.9)
"R"@Idle [2]	
Model EQ Before 17 07 0	100-109 (7.0-7.6)
All Other Models	129-145 (9.0-10.0)

[1] — Test should be performed on a dynamameter whenever possible. Full throttle test above 30 MPH.

[2] — Vehicle stationary.

STALL SPEED TEST

Testing Precautions

When making test, do not hold throttle open any longer than the time it takes to read tachometer. Maximum stall speed test time is 20 seconds. If engine speed exceeds limits shown in *Stall Speed Specifications* table, release accelerator immediately as clutch or band slippage is indicated.

Testing Procedure

With engine at normal operating temperature, connect a tachometer to engine. Start engine and set parking and service brakes. Place selector lever in "D". Depress accelerator briefly to full throttle and note maximum RPM obtained. Repeat test with selector lever in "1" position. Engine speed should be within limits shown in table.

NOTE: Normal stall speed will drop about 125 RPM per 3200 feet altitude (4000 feet with E-Mode). Also, stall speed will drop slightly at high ambient temperature.

STALL SPEED SPECIFICATIONS

Application	Stall RPM
With E-Mode	2555-2805
All Others	
1.5L Engine	2250-2500
1.6L Engine	2100-2350
1.7L Engine	2200-2500

Test Results

1) If stall speed is too high in "D", but OK in "1", one-way clutch is defective. If stall speed is too high in both ranges, forward clutch is faulty.

2) If stall speed is about 200 RPM below normal, check engine operation (ignition timing, fuel injection, compression). If stall speed is about 400 RPM too low, stator one-way clutch in torque converter is probably defective, and converter should be replaced.

REMOVAL & INSTALLATION

See the appropriate article in *AUTOMATIC TRANSMISSION REMOVAL* Section.

TORQUE CONVERTER

NOTE: Torque converter is a sealed unit and cannot be disassembled for service.

BUSHING REPLACEMENT

1) Check bushing for wear using an inside micrometer. Wear limit of bushing is 1.348" (34.25 mm), and maximum allowable out-of-round is .001" (.03 mm).

2) To replace bushing, use a bushing puller (US 691 and adapter US 4452) to withdraw bushing from converter hub. Press new bushing into place with bushing driver.

VOLKSWAGEN TYPE 010 3-SPEED (Cont.)

Fig. 3: Removing Torque Converter Bushing

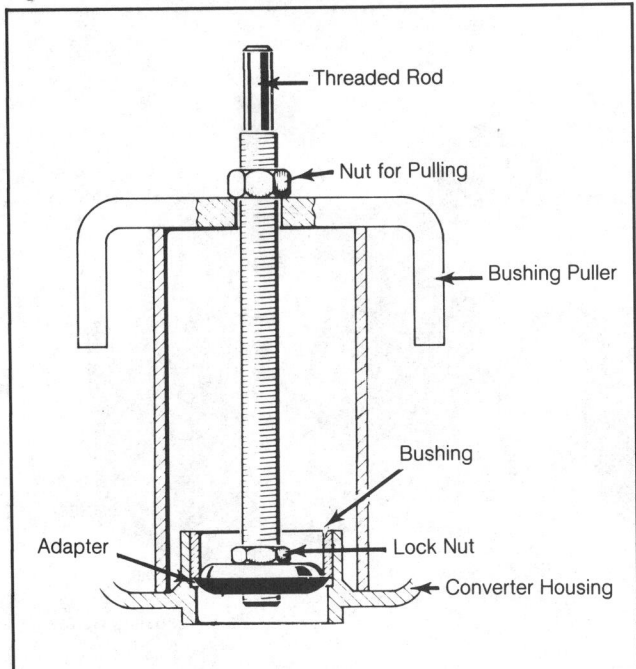

TRANSMISSION DISASSEMBLY

1) Withdraw torque converter from final drive housing. Remove governor cover and gasket, then pull governor from final drive housing using a clockwise twisting motion to disengage governor drive gear from gear on transmission annulus gear.

2) Remove nuts from transmission-to-final drive studs and separate transmission from final drive. Withdraw pump shaft and impeller shaft from transmission. Final drive disassembly and reassembly procedures are covered at end of article.

3) Remove screws retaining separation plate in transmission case, then withdraw plate and gasket. Remove governor drive gear/ring gear assembly from case. Withdraw needle bearing and thrust washer from top of reverse (front) planetary gear set.

4) Remove large snap ring retaining one-way clutch assembly in case. Fabricate 2 hooks from 3/16" welding rod and use hooks to lift one-way clutch assembly from case.

5) Grasp reverse (front) planetary gear set and pull from case along with its thrust washer. Remove first/reverse brake plates and wave washer from assembly, then withdraw sun gear and driving shell (with thrust washer) and forward (rear) planetary gear set.

Fig. 4: Bottom View of Transmission Case Showing Kickdown and Selector Linkage

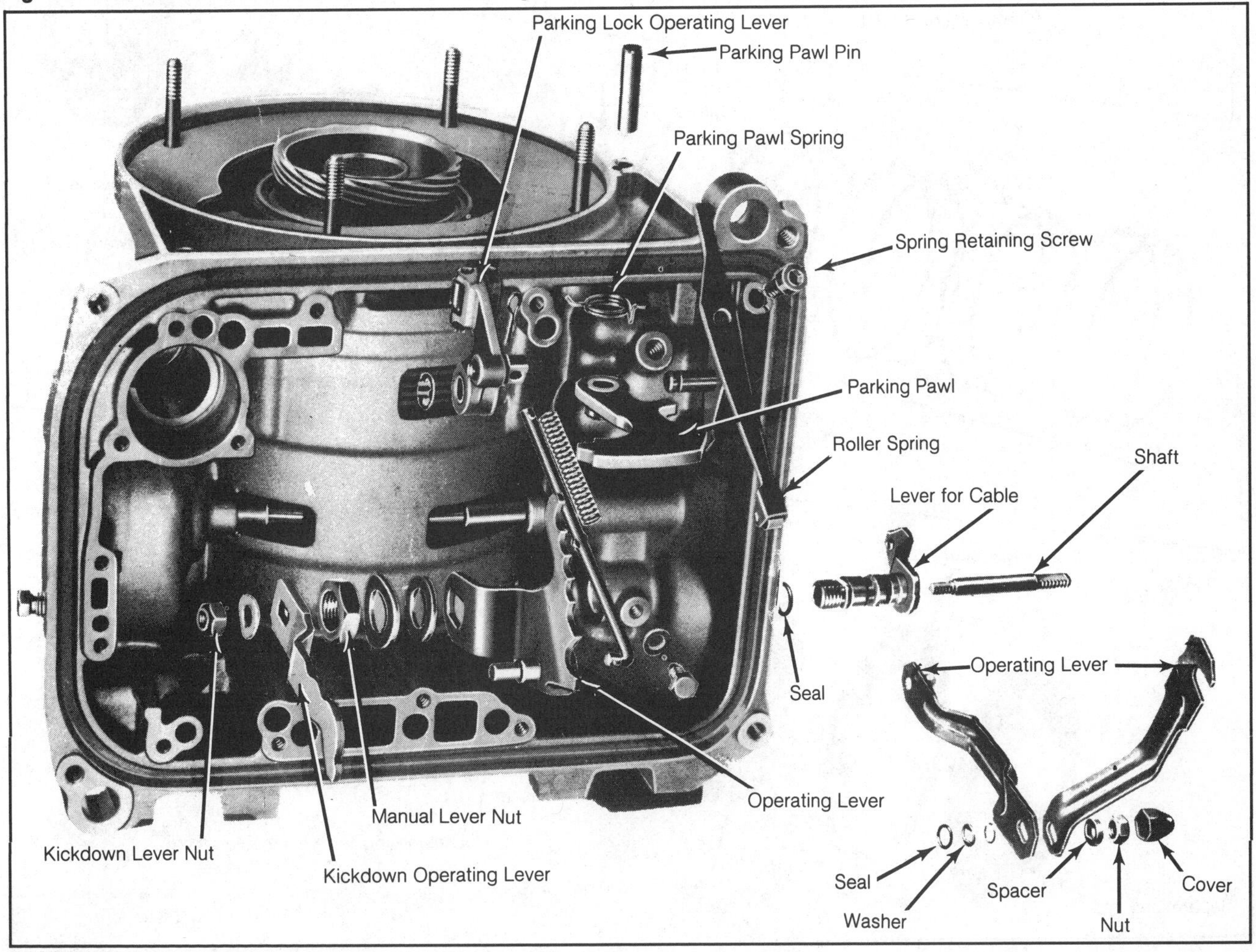

Automatic Transmissions

VOLKSWAGEN TYPE 010 3-SPEED (Cont.)

Fig. 5: Exploded View of Automatic Transmission Assembly

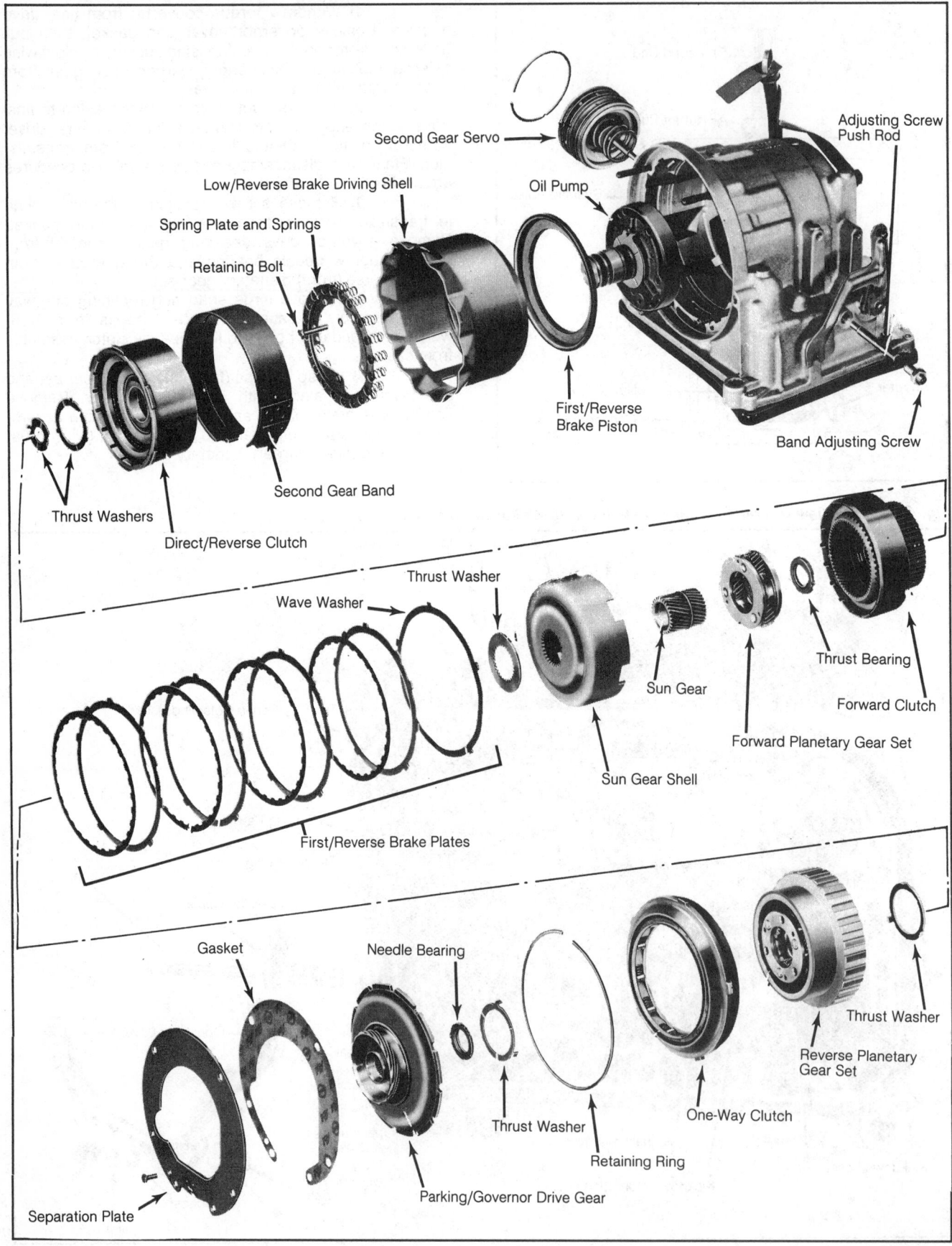

VOLKSWAGEN TYPE 010 3-SPEED (Cont.)

Fig. 6: Removing One-Way Clutch from Case

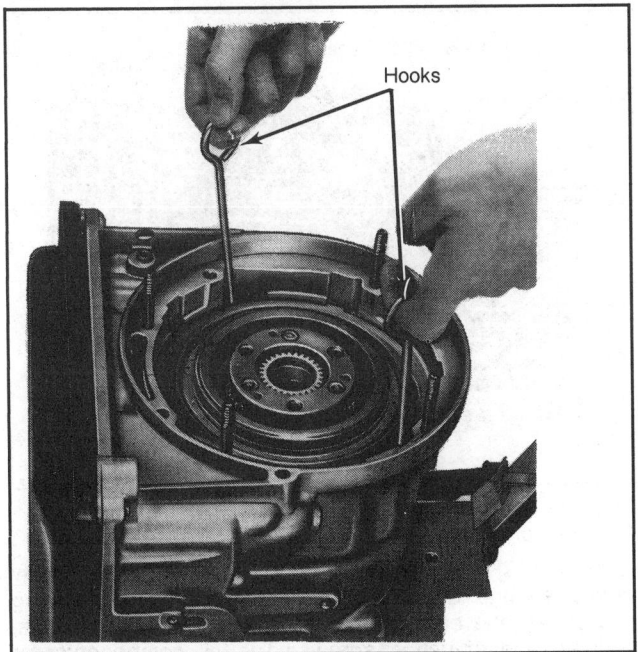

Hooks

Use 2 fabricated hooks to lift assembly out of case.

6) Slide forward clutch out of assembly. Remove the 2 forward clutch-to-direct/reverse clutch thrust washers, then withdraw direct/reverse clutch from case.

7) Push second gear servo assembly down into transmission case and remove retaining snap ring. Withdraw servo assembly (cover, piston, and spring) from case. On opposite side of case, loosen second gear band adjusting screw. From inside case, withdraw second gear band.

8) Remove bolts from first/reverse brake spring plate. Withdraw spring plate and springs, then pull driving shell, brake piston, and oil pump from case.

9) Position transmission case on bench with oil pan facing upward. Remove pan bolts and withdraw pan and gasket. Remove oil strainer screws from valve body. Remove 11 hex-head bolts from valve body and lift

valve body from case. Use care not to lose manual valve. Withdraw accumulator spring and piston from case. If necessary for parts replacement, disassemble kickdown and selector linkage using *Fig. 4* as a guide.

COMPONENT DISASSEMBLY & REASSEMBLY

OIL PUMP ASSEMBLY

Disassembly
Remove metal sealing rings, thrust washer, thrust bearing and second thrust washer from front of pump housing. Hold cover plate tight against housing (plate is under spring tension), remove cover plate screws and remove cover plate. Remove check ball and spring. Withdraw pump drive plate, mark pump gears for reassembly reference and remove gears.

Inspection
Wash all parts in solvent and air dry. Check parts for wear, scoring, chipped teeth or any other damage. Replace parts as necessary.

Reassembly
1) Coat pump gears with transmission fluid and install into pump housing, aligning marks made at disassembly. Position drive plate on top of inner gear and check ball and spring in housing. Place cover plate over rear of assembly. Compress spring and check ball taking care not to displace them, then install and tighten cover-to-housing screws.

2) Install thrust bearing and washers with lugs on inside washer toward bearing. Install sealing rings with ends locked together. To check for proper oil pump operation, insert pump shaft into oil pump and rotate gears. Pump assembly should rotate freely, with no sticking or binding.

VALVE BODY ASSEMBLY

Disassembly
1) Remove oil strainer-to-valve body retaining screws. Remove strainer cover, strainer and gasket. Remove transfer plate-to-main valve body screws (23 with E-mode, 19 all others). Remove transfer and separator

Fig. 7: Exploded View of Oil Pump Assembly

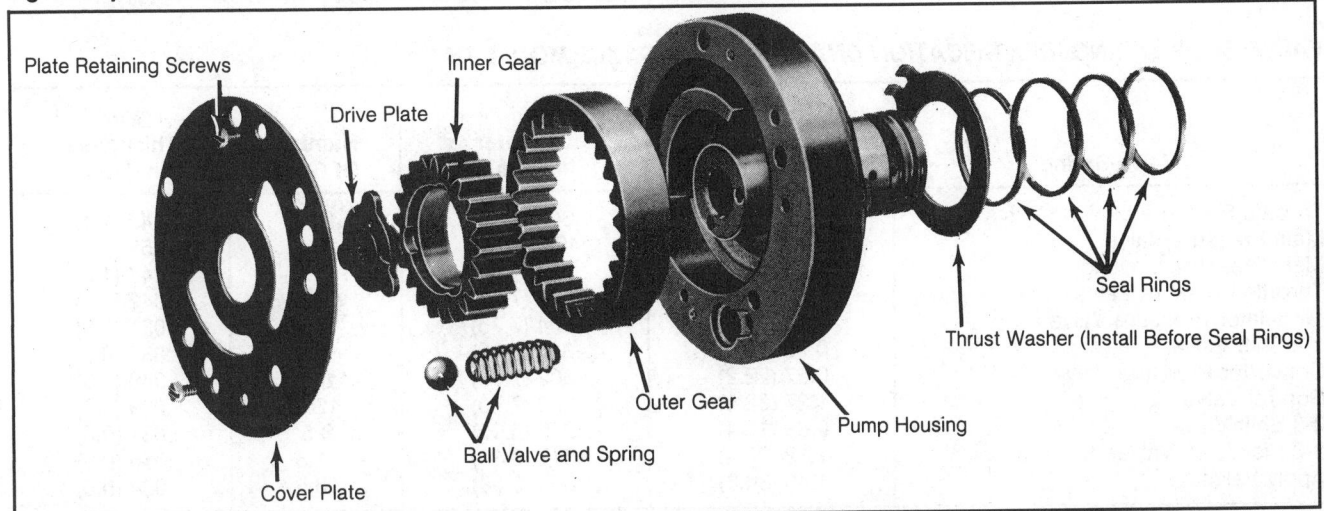

Plate Retaining Screws

Inner Gear

Drive Plate

Seal Rings

Thrust Washer (Install Before Seal Rings)

Outer Gear

Pump Housing

Ball Valve and Spring

Cover Plate

VOLKSWAGEN TYPE 010 3-SPEED (Cont.)

plates from main body. Remove check balls from main body. *See Fig. 9.*

Fig. 8: Exploded View of Oil Pan,
Oil Strainer and Valve Body Assemble

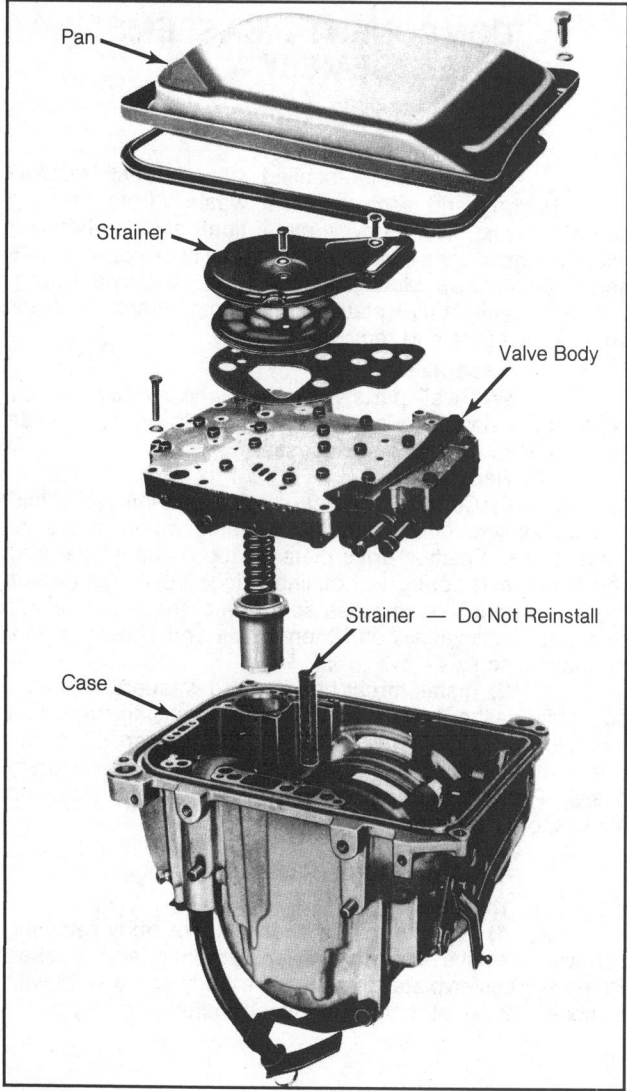

Pan

Strainer

Valve Body

Strainer — Do Not Reinstall

Case

Fig. 9: Location of Check Balls in Valve Body

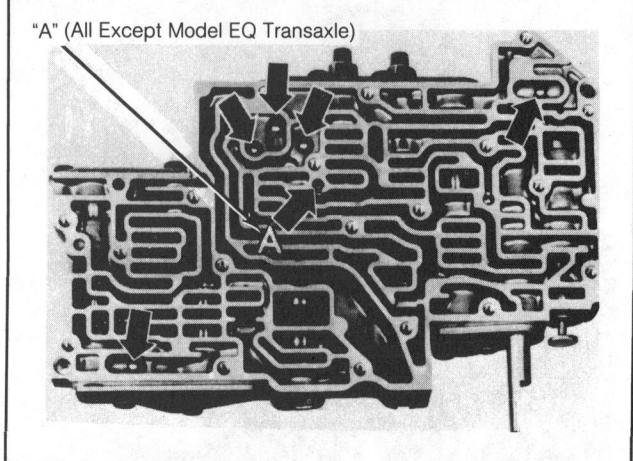

"A" (All Except Model EQ Transaxle)

A

Diameter of check ball "A" is .12" (3 mm).
All others are .24" (6 mm).

2) Remove rear end plate and withdraw valves, springs, and adjusting screws. Remove remaining end plates one at a time and withdraw all valves, plugs, springs, and adjusting screws. Tag all components, or arrange in relationship to valve body, to ensure correct reassembly.

NOTE: Do not alter settings of adjusting screws.

Inspection

1) Wash all parts in solvent and air dry only (do not use fluffy rags, etc.). Check all parts for burrs and scores; replace assembly if damage is found.

2) When valves are clean and lubricated with fluid, they should fall of their own weight in respective bore; if not, check for valve or bore damage.

3) Check all springs for damage and collapsed coils. Take care not to disturb settings of adjusting screws; pressures affected by these screws can only be measured and adjusted accurately on a test stand.

4) If transmission was disassembled due to failure to shift into 3rd gear, trouble may be caused by a missing sealing ball in transfer plate. *See Fig. 10.* If any ball is missing, use following procedure to install replacement balls.

VALVE BODY SPRING IDENTIFICATION CHART — TRANSAXLE MODEL TB

Valve Spring	Length In. (mm)	Diameter In. (mm) [1]	Number Of Coils	Wire Thickness In. (mm)
Throttle Pressure Limiting Valve	1.49 (37.9)	.302 (7.70)	14.5	.042 (1.1)
Main Pressure Valve	2.72 (69.2)	.468 (11.90)	16.5	.055 (1.4)
Main Pressure Limiting Valve	1.08 (27.5)	.229 (7.60)	12.5	.047 (1.2)
Throttle Pressure Valve	1.73 (44.0)	.304 (7.75)	16.5	.042 (1.1)
Modulator Pressure Valve	1.13 (28.6)	.304 (7.75)	11.5	.031 (0.8)
1-2 Shift Valve	0.78 (19.9)	.317 (8.10)	6.5	.035 (0.9)
Converter Pressure Valve	0.87 (22.2)	.302 (7.70)	8.5	.049 (1.3)
Control Valve	1.27 (32.4)	.302 (7.70)	12.5	.039 (1.0)
2-3 Shift Valve	0.69 (17.4)	.273 (6.95)	8.5	.031 (0.8)
3-2 Kickdown Valve	1.12 (28.4)	.317 (8.10)	11.5	.035 (0.9)
Apply Valve	1.43 (36.3)	.354 (9.00)	10.5	.024 (0.6)

[1] — Inner diameter of coils, within tolerance of ±.012" (.3 mm).

VOLKSWAGEN TYPE 010 3-SPEED (Cont.)

VALVE BODY SPRING IDENTIFICATION CHART — ALL MODELS WITH E-MODE

Valve Spring	Length In. (mm)	Diameter In. (mm) [1]	Number Of Coils	Wire Thickness In. (mm)
Throttle Pressure Limiting Valve	1.49 (37.9)	.303 (7.70)	14.5	.043 (1.1)
Main Pressure Valve	2.95 (75.0)	.468 (11.90)	16.5	.059 (1.5)
Main Pressure Limiting Valve	1.08 (27.5)	.299 (7.60)	12.5	.047 (1.2)
Throttle Pressure Valve	1.73 (44.0)	.305 (7.75)	16.5	.043 (1.1)
Modulator Pressure Valve	1.13 (28.6)	.305 (7.75)	11.5	.031 (0.8)
1-2 Shift Valve	0.78 (19.9)	.319 (8.10)	6.5	.035 (0.9)
Converter Pressure Valve	0.87 (22.2)	.303 (7.70)	8.5	.049 (1.3)
Control Valve	1.28 (32.4)	.303 (7.70)	12.5	.039 (1.0)
2-3 Shift Valve	0.69 (17.4)	.274 (6.95)	8.5	.031 (0.8)
3-2 Kickdown Valve	1.12 (28.4)	.319 (8.10)	11.5	.035 (0.9)
Apply Valve	0.68 (17.2)	.137 (3.50)	15.5	.019 (0.5)

[1] — Inner diameter of coils, within tolerance of ± .012" (.3 mm).

VALVE BODY SPRING IDENTIFICATION CHART — TRANSAXLE MODEL EQ

Valve Spring	Length In. (mm)	Diameter In. (mm) [1]	Number Of Coils	Wire Thickness In. (mm)
Throttle Pressure Limiting Valve	1.39 (35.3)	.302 (7.70)	14.5	.043 (1.1)
Main Pressure Valve				
Before Transaxle No. 23 07 9	2.82 (71.6)	.468 (11.90)	16.5	.059 (1.5)
As of Transaxle No. 23 07 9	3.03 (77.0)	.468 (11.90)	16.5	.059 (1.5)
Main Pressure Limiting Valve	1.28 (32.4)	.302 (7.70)	11.0	.047 (1.2)
Throttle Pressure Valve	1.71 (43.4)	.305 (7.75)	16.0	.049 (1.3)
Modulator Pressure Valve				
Before Transaxle No. 11 09 8	0.74 (18.7)	.208 (5.30)	12.0	.027 (0.7)
As of Transaxle No. 11 09 8 [2]	1.13 (28.6)	.305 (7.75)	11.5	.031 (0.8)
1-2 Shift Valve				
Standard	0.78 (19.9)	.319 (8.10)	6.5	.035 (0.9)
Alternative	1.02 (26.0)	.323 (8.20)	9.5	.031 (0.8)
Converter Pressure Valve				
Standard	1.28 (32.4)	.303 (7.70)	12.5	.039 (1.0)
Alternative	0.87 (22.2)	.303 (7.70)	8.5	.049 (1.3)
Control Valve	1.28 (32.4)	.303 (7.70)	12.5	.039 (1.0)
2-3 Shift Valve				
Standard	0.78 (19.9)	.319 (8.10)	6.5	.035 (0.9)
Alternative	1.02 (26.0)	.323 (8.20)	9.5	.031 (0.8)
3-2 Kickdown Valve	1.12 (28.4)	.319 (8.10)	11.5	.035 (0.9)
Apply Valve	1.12 (28.4)	.319 (8.10)	11.5	.035 (0.9)

[1] — Inner diameter of coils, within tolerance of ± .012" (.3 mm).
[2] — Valve diameter changed from .315" (8.0 mm) to .433" (11.0 mm).

Fig. 10: Installing Transfer Plate Sealing Ball

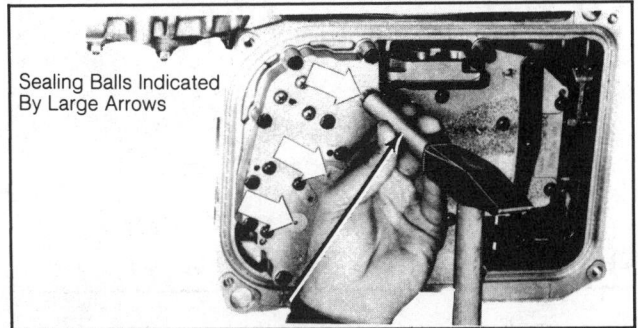

Sealing Balls Indicated By Large Arrows

Large arrows indicate sealing ball positions.

5) To install new sealing ball, stick .118" (3 mm) diameter ball to end of 8 mm punch with small amount of grease. Drive ball flush into hole of transfer plate.

Reassembly

Lubricate all parts with transmission fluid. Install valve trains into proper valve body bores in reverse order of removal. Make sure all parts slide freely in bores. Make sure check balls are installed in proper body passages. *See Fig. 9.* Install transfer plate-to-main body screws and tighten from center outward. DO NOT overtighten.

Automatic Transmissions

VOLKSWAGEN TYPE 010 3-SPEED (Cont.)

Fig. 11: Exploded View of Main Valve Body

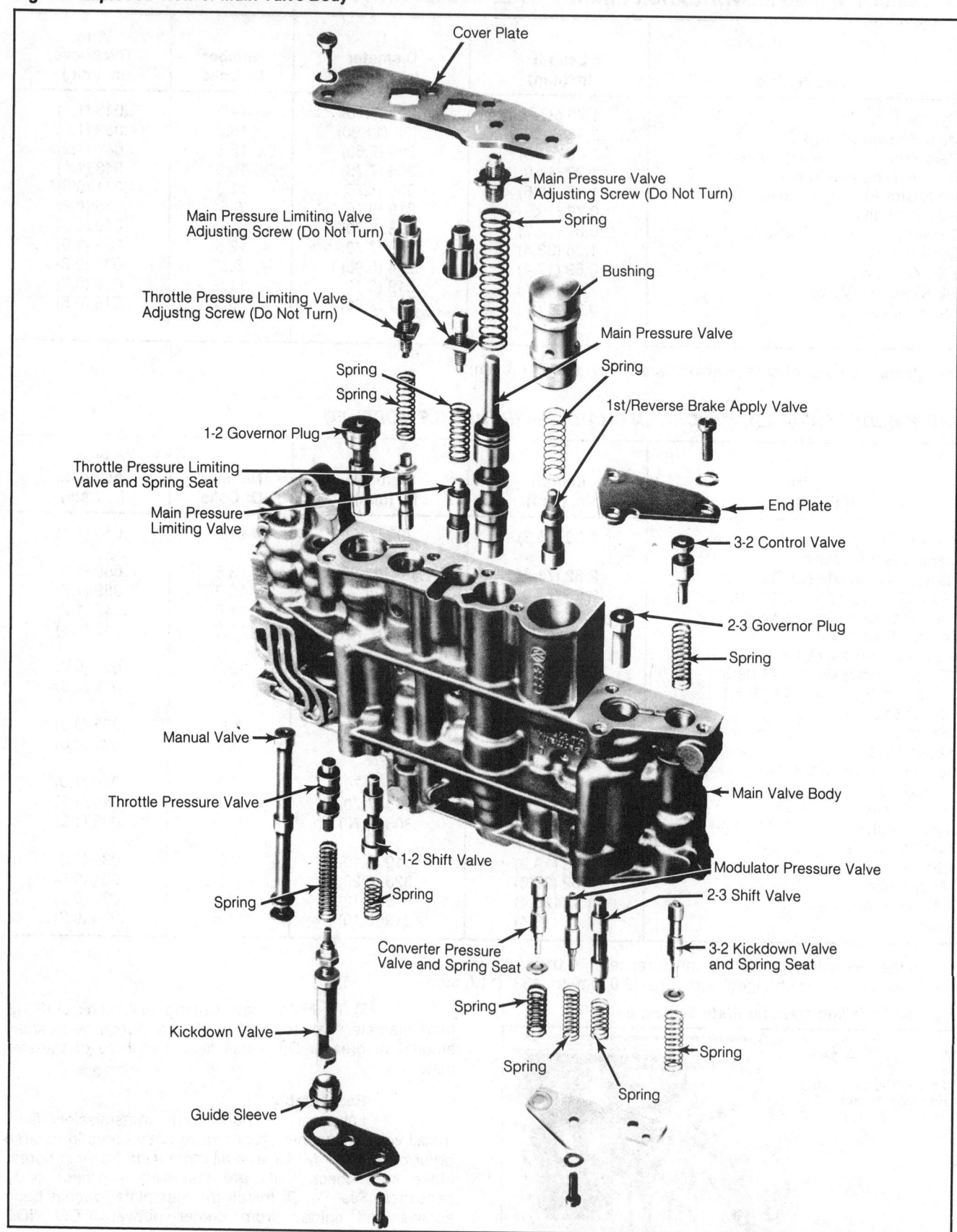

All models except with E-mode.

VOLKSWAGEN TYPE 010 3-SPEED (Cont.)

Fig. 12: _Exploded View of Main Valve Body_

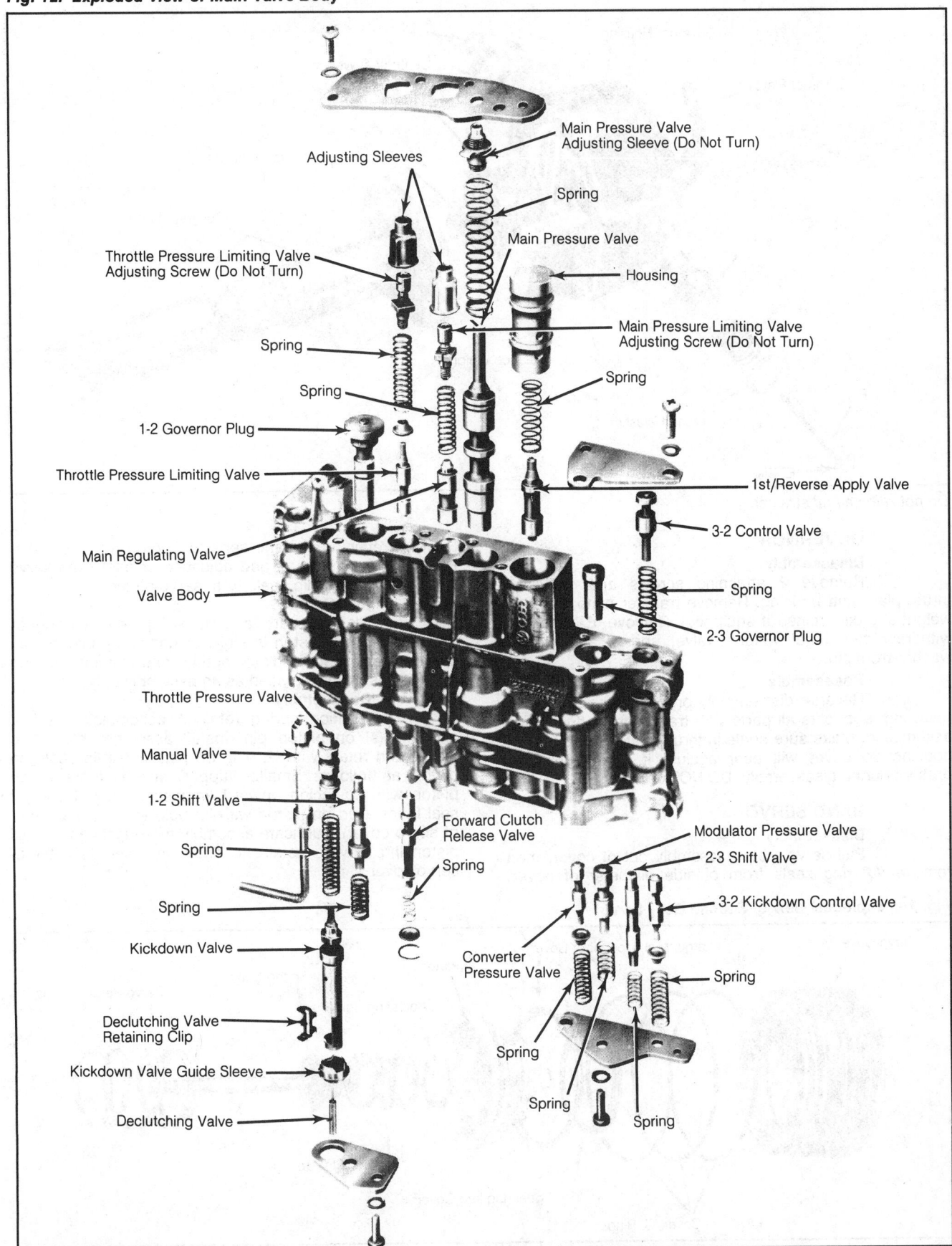

Main Pressure Valve Adjusting Sleeve (Do Not Turn)

Adjusting Sleeves

Spring

Main Pressure Valve

Throttle Pressure Limiting Valve Adjusting Screw (Do Not Turn)

Housing

Main Pressure Limiting Valve Adjusting Screw (Do Not Turn)

Spring

Spring

Spring

1-2 Governor Plug

1st/Reverse Apply Valve

Throttle Pressure Limiting Valve

3-2 Control Valve

Main Regulating Valve

Spring

Valve Body

2-3 Governor Plug

Throttle Pressure Valve

Manual Valve

1-2 Shift Valve

Forward Clutch Release Valve

Modulator Pressure Valve

Spring

2-3 Shift Valve

Spring

3-2 Kickdown Control Valve

Spring

Spring

Kickdown Valve

Converter Pressure Valve

Spring

Declutching Valve Retaining Clip

Spring

Kickdown Valve Guide Sleeve

Spring

Declutching Valve

Spring

All with E-mode.

Fig. 13: Exploded View of Governor Assembly

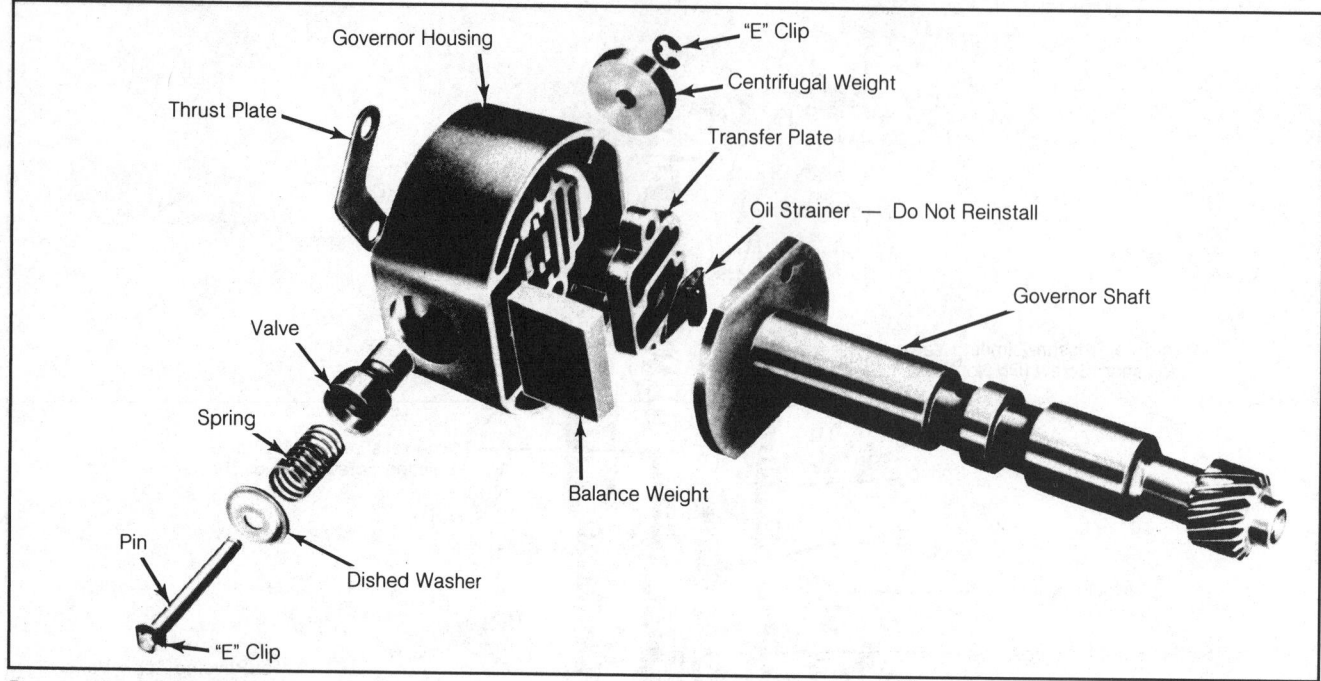

Do not reinstall oil strainer.

GOVERNOR
Disassembly
Remove 2 attaching screws and withdraw thrust plate and housing. Remove transfer plate, balance weight and oil strainer (if equipped). Remove "E" clips and withdraw centrifugal weight, valve, spring, and dished washer from pin.

Reassembly
Reverse disassembly procedure and note the following: Lubricate all parts with transmission fluid when assembling. Make sure angle in thrust plate is in center of housing so cover will bear against it. If strainer was present during disassembly, DO NOT reinstall.

BAND SERVO
Disassembly
Pull servo piston assembly out of cover, then remove "O" ring seals from outside diameter of cover.

Remove retaining clip and separate piston pin, accumulator spring, spring seat, and adjusting shim(s) from servo piston. Withdraw 2 lip seals from servo piston.

Inspection
Clean all parts and check for wear, scoring, or other damage. If piston is worn or damaged, piston, pin, spring retainer, accumulator spring, and shim(s) must be replaced as unit is serviced as an assembly only.

Reassembly
Position spring retainer, accumulator spring, and shim(s) on piston pin. Install assembly into servo piston and retain with "E" clip on pin. Install lip seals on piston as follows: Smaller (upper) seal is installed on piston with lip facing upward (into servo cover). Larger seal is installed on piston with lip pointed downward (out of servo cover). Lubricate assembly thoroughly and install piston into cover. Install "O" rings on outer diameter of servo cover.

Fig. 14: Exploded View of Second Gear Servo

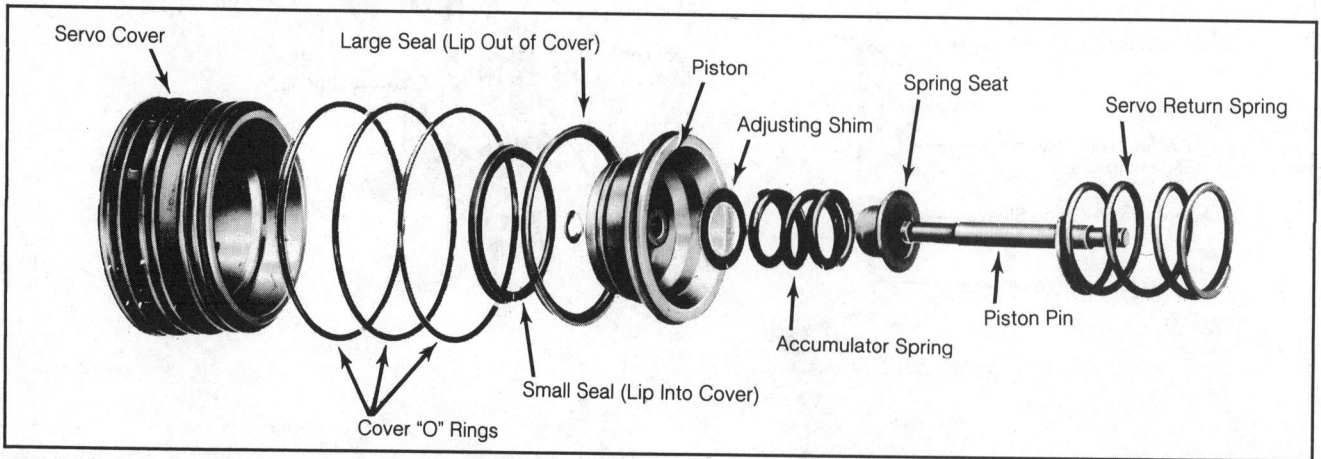

VOLKSWAGEN TYPE 010 3-SPEED (Cont.)

Fig. 15: Exploded View of Direct/Reverse Clutch

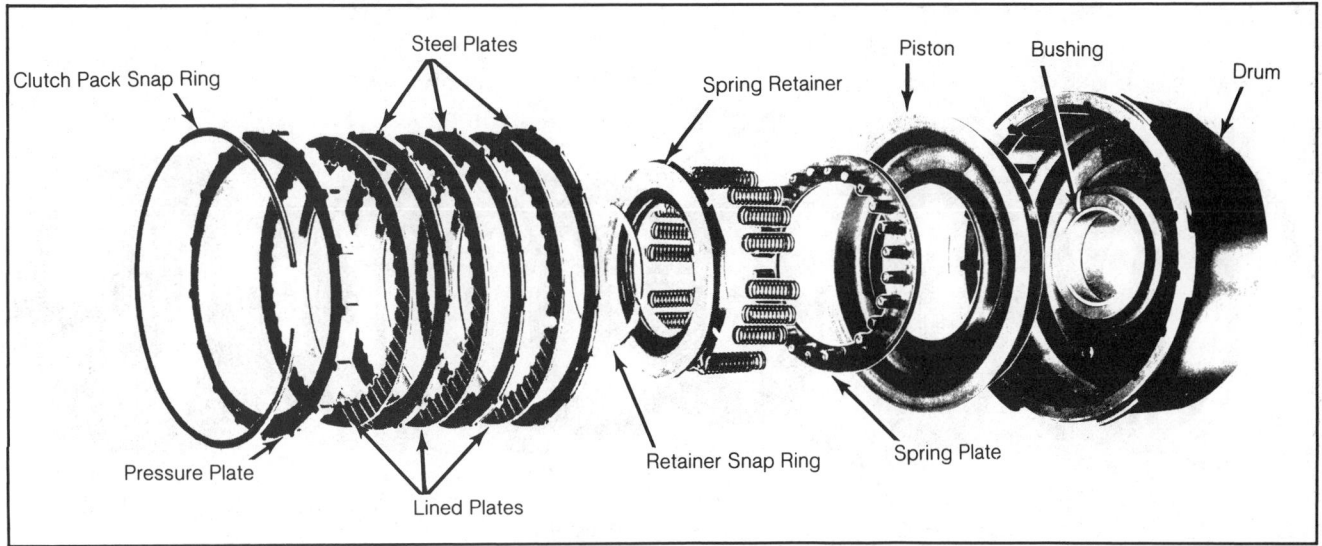

DIRECT/REVERSE CLUTCH

Disassembly

1) Remove clutch pack retaining snap ring from drum. Remove pressure plate, lined and steel clutch plates. Place clutch drum in press, apply downward pressure to piston spring retainer and remove retaining snap ring. Release press.

2) Remove spring retainer, piston springs and clutch piston. Remove seals from clutch piston and drum. If necessary, place clutch drum in press and drive bushing out of clutch drum with driver (US 1099).

Inspection

1) Clean all parts in solvent and dry with compressed air. Check piston and drum for scoring or other damage. Inspect steel plates for wear and burn marks. Replace if worn or blue.

2) Check lined plates for wear, cracking or chipping. Replace any damaged plates. Inspect check ball in clutch drum for freedom of operation and proper sealing. Check piston return springs for distortion or collapsed coils. Replace any damaged parts.

Reassembly

1) If removed, use a press and bushing driver (VW 433) to install clutch drum hub bushing until it is .067"

Fig. 16: Measuring Direct/Reverse Clutch Clearance

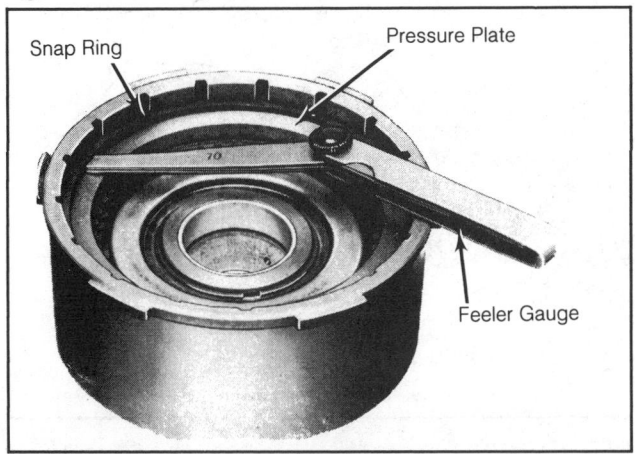

Clearance should be .081-.098" (2.05-2.55 mm).

(1.7 mm) below hub lip. Install new seals on clutch drum and on piston. Seal lips must face downward into drum. Completely lubricate piston assembly with ATF and install in drum.

2) Position piston return springs on top of piston. Place retainer on top of springs, compress assembly and install retaining snap ring. Lubricate all clutch plates with ATF. Any new plates must be soaked in clean ATF for at least 15 minutes prior to installation.

3) Install 1 steel plate (external splines), then 1 lined plate (internal splines) into drum. Continue alternating steel and lined plates until all clutch plates are installed. Install pressure plate and clutch pack retaining snap ring.

DIRECT/REVERSE CLUTCH PLATE CHART

Application	Steel Plates	Lined Plates
All Models	3	3

4) Using a feeler gauge, measure clearance between clutch pack retaining snap ring and pressure plate. Clearance should be .081-.098" (2.05-2.50 mm).

5) If clearance is incorrect, remove clutch pack snap ring and replace it with a snap ring of correct thickness to bring clearance within specifications. Snap rings are avaiable in various thicknesses from .059" (1.5 mm) to .098" (2.5 mm). Recheck clearance after installing replacement snap ring.

FORWARD CLUTCH

Disassembly

1) Remove waved snap ring from clutch drum (flat snap ring with E-mode). Remove pressure plate, lined and steel clutch plates, planetary ring gear and thrust plate. On all models except with E-mode, remove flat snap ring, diaphragm spring and clutch piston.

2) On models with E-mode, remove spring washer and spring. Use press to compress spring plate and remove small snap ring. Slowly release pressure on spring plate. Remove plate. Remove spring retaining ring and spring assembly. Remove spring support ring and piston.

Fig. 17: Exploded View of Forward Clutch

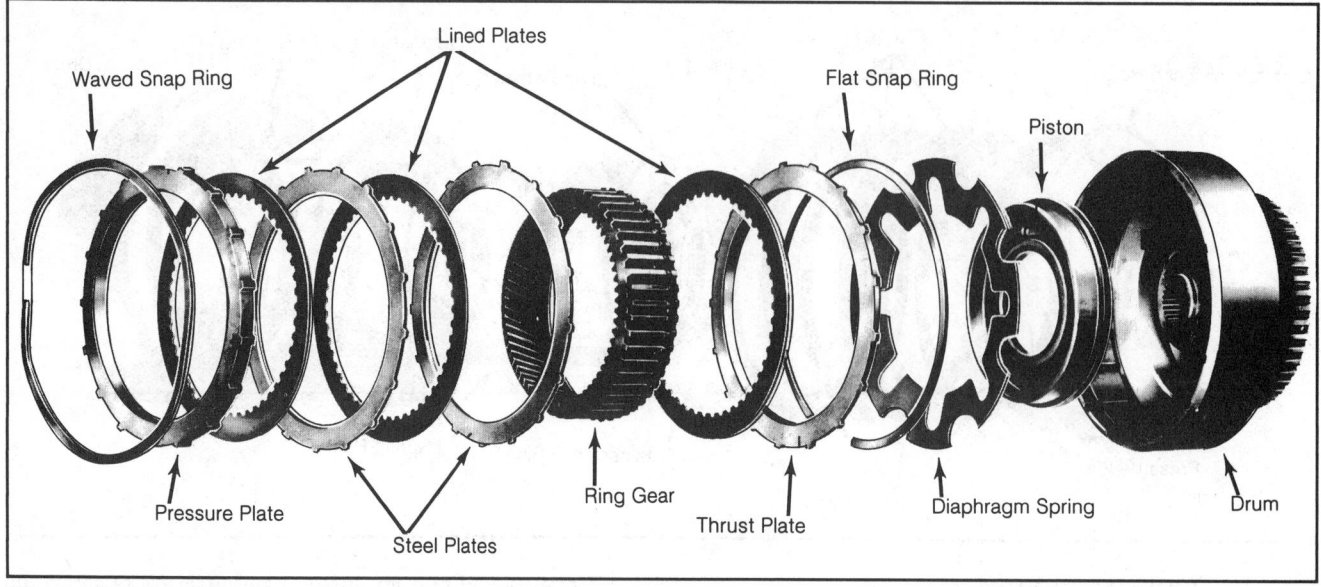

All models except with E-mode.

Inspection
Use inspection procedures given for direct/reverse clutch. In addition, check planetary ring gear inner and outer splines for wear, scoring or other damage. Replace as needed.

Reassembly
1) Coat clutch piston with transmission fluid and install into drum. On all models except with E-mode, position diaphragm spring in drum with convex side towards bottom of drum. Install flat retaining snap ring.

NOTE: **With snap ring installed, diaphragm spring should be lightly tensioned. If not, replace spring.**

2) On models with E-mode, install spring support ring, spring retaining ring and spring assembly, and spring plate. Retaining ring and springs must be installed with small diameter end of springs up (towards spring plate).

3) Compress spring plate and install small snap ring. Install spring and spring washer. Ensure that spring and washer are installed with convex side down (into drum).

4) On all models, lubricate with transmission fluid and install thrust plate and 1 lined plate in clutch drum. Thrust plate must be installed with convex side down (into drum).

5) Install planetary ring gear into assembly, engaging inner splines of lined plate. When installed, lined plate should be under retaining edge on outer splines of ring gear.

6) After soaking in ATF, install remaining clutch plates, starting with 1 steel plate and alternating lined and steel plates until all clutch plates are installed. Install pressure plate and snap ring.

FORWARD CLUTCH PLATE CHART

Application	Steel Plates	Lined Plates
With E-Mode	3	4
All Others	2	3

Fig. 18: Exploded View of Forward Clutch

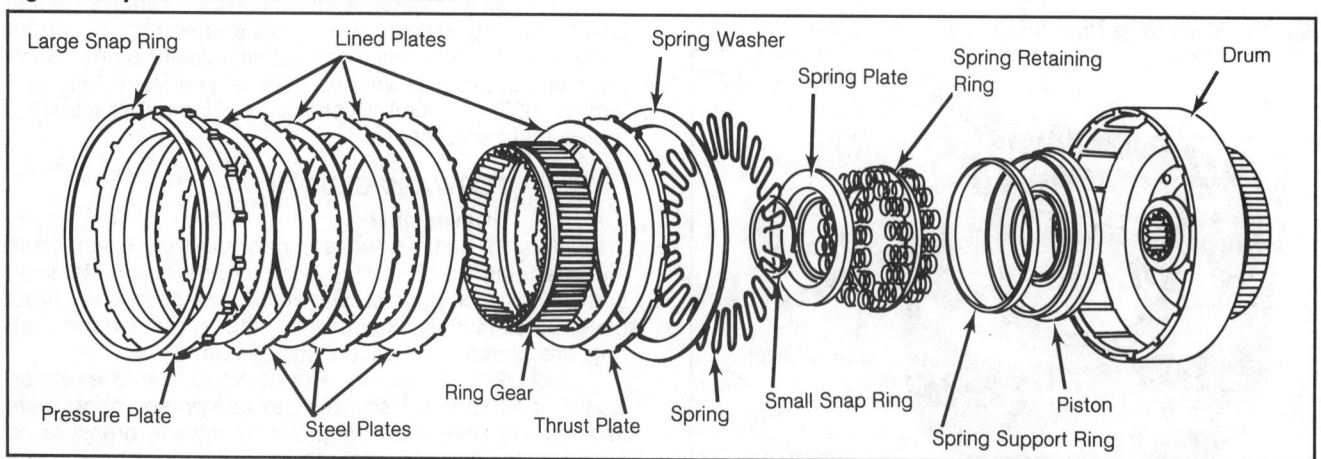

All models with E-mode transaxle.

VOLKSWAGEN TYPE 010 3-SPEED (Cont.)

7) Position dial indicator on assembly with indicator pointer resting on pressure plate. Zero indicator. Pull up on planetary ring gear and note reading on dial. End play of assembly should be .020-.035" (.5-.9 mm).

8) If end play is incorrect, replace pressure plate (large snap ring on models with E-mode) with selective plate (snap ring) of required thickness to bring play to proper specifications.

9) Pressure plates are available in thicknesses of 2.36" (6.0 mm) to .299" (7.6 mm) in increments of .016" (.40 mm). Snap rings for models with E-mode are available in various thicknesses between .059" (1.5 mm) and .138" (3.5 mm).

Fig. 19: Measuring Forward Clutch End Play

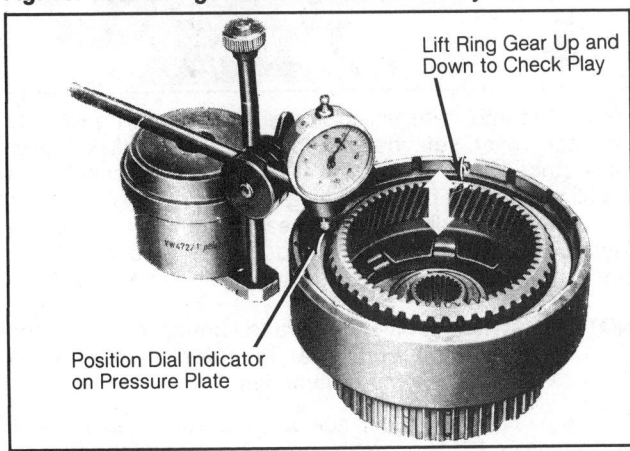

End play should be .020-.035" (0.5-0.9 mm).

ONE-WAY CLUTCH

Disassembly

Remove upper retaining ring from assembly. Remove roller cage, rollers and springs. Remove lower

Fig. 20: Exploded View of One-Way Clutch

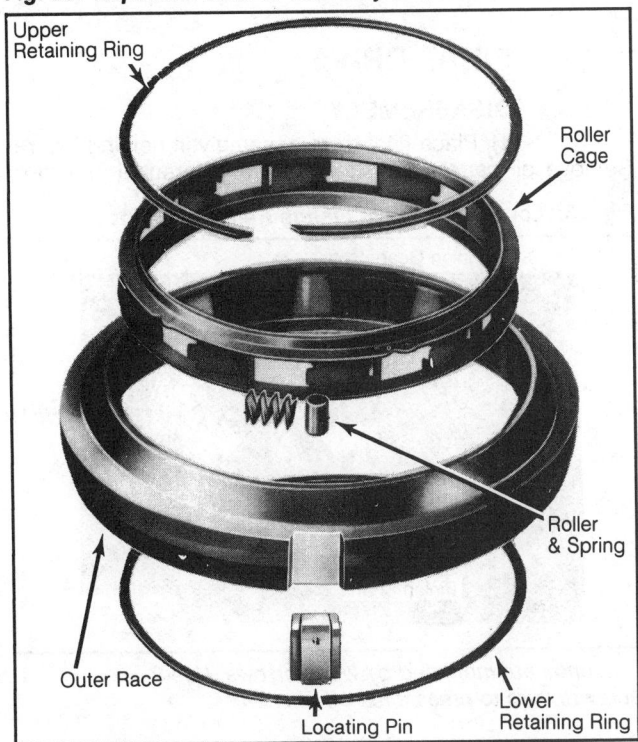

retaining ring from outer race. Inspect all parts for wear, scoring, or other damage and replace as needed.

Reassembly

1) Install lower snap ring in groove of outer race. If necessary, heat outer race to 300° F (150° C), then place roller cage into race with 2 pair of pliers.

Fig. 21: Correct Roller Cage Installation In One-Way Clutch Outer Race

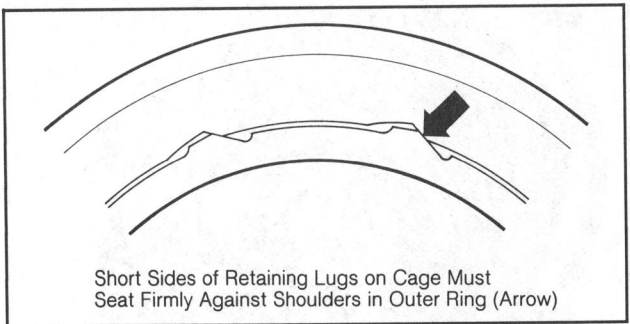

Short Sides of Retaining Lugs on Cage Must Seat Firmly Against Shoulders in Outer Ring (Arrow)

NOTE: The heat from outer race will transfer quickly to roller cage, causing cage to stick inside race. If cage is not correctly positioned against lower snap ring, DO NOT attempt to press it into position after cage has stuck. Carefully knock cage out of race and repeat procedure again after race has cooled down.

2) Install upper snap ring. Install rollers and springs into cage. Be sure that guide lug on springs (if so equipped) is pointed toward roller. See Fig. 22.

Fig. 22: Roller and Spring Installation in One-Way Clutch

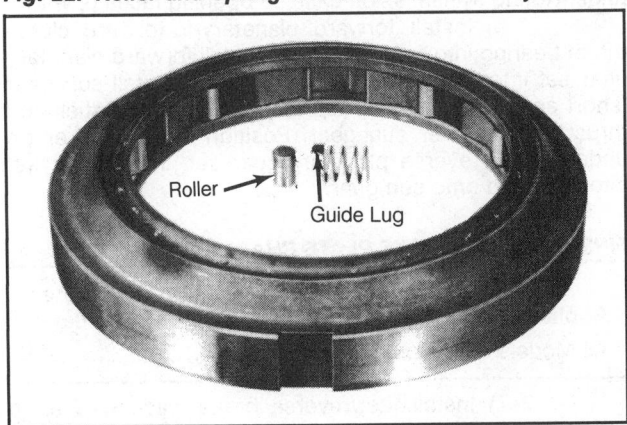

Assemble guide lug on spring over roller as shown.

TRANSMISSION REASSEMBLY

1) Coat first/reverse brake piston with transmission fluid and install in oil pump housing. Insert pump housing into transmission case (thin rib of pump pointing upward). Install first/reverse driving shell into case so that tab of shell engages upper groove in transmission case. See Fig. 23.

2) Position low/reverse brake piston return springs on spring plate. Insert assembly into case with springs downward, then install and tighten retaining bolts. Position second gear band in transmission case. Install second gear servo in case, making sure piston pin engages band end inside case. Install servo-to-case snap ring.

3) On opposite side of case, install band adjusting screw push rod. Be sure rod engages band end inside case. Install adjusting screw just enough to hold band in place.

Fig. 23: *Installing First/Reverse Driving Shell*

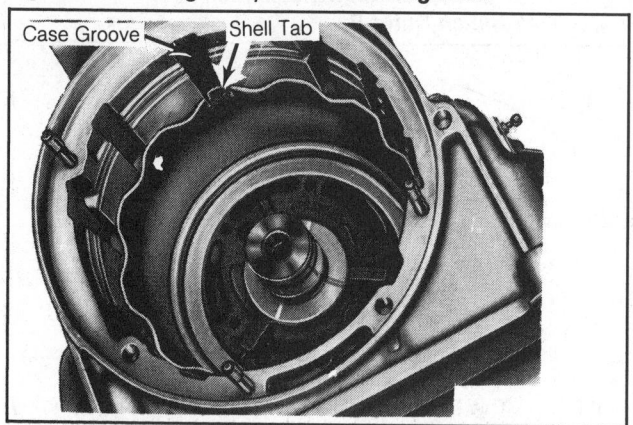

When installed, shell tab must engage with case groove.

4) Coat forward clutch-to-direct/reverse clutch thrust washers with petroleum jelly and position on rear end of forward clutch. Install forward clutch into direct/reverse clutch. Make sure that splines on forward clutch drum fully engage splines on direct/reverse clutch lined plates.

5) With transmission case opening angled downward, install assembled clutch units in case and over neck of oil pump. Use care not to damage pump seal rings. Rotate transmission case so opening faces upward.

6) Install forward planetary-to-forward clutch thrust bearing into forward clutch. Install forward planetary gear set into ring gear in forward clutch. Install sun gear (short end first) into gear set, then install driving shell and thrust washer over sun gear. Position thrust washer on underside of reverse planetary gear set. Install gear set into case and onto sun gear.

FIRST/REVERSE BRAKE PLATE CHART

Application	Steel Plates	Lined Plates
All Models	4	4

7) Install first/reverse brake wave washer in case. Install lined and steel plates in case alternately, starting with a steel plate. If any new lined plates are used, they must be soaked in transmission fluid for at least 15 minutes prior to installation.

8) Install one-way clutch assembly into transmission case. Push clutch downward while rotating reverse planetary gear set to fully engage parts. With all parts engaged, install one-way clutch-to-case retaining snap ring.

NOTE: **With one-way clutch installed, it should not be possible to rotate reverse planetary gear set counterclockwise.**

9) Position needle bearing and thrust washer on rear side of governor drive gear/ring gear assembly.

Fig. 24: *Installing One-Way Clutch Snap Ring*

Parts Are Installed Properly if Groove For One-Way Clutch Snap Ring is Exposed

Install unit into transmission case, fully engaging reverse planetary gear set. Install separation plate gasket over case studs. Place separation plate on top of gasket, then install and tighten plate retaining screws.

10) Adjust second gear brake band as follows: Tighten band adjusting screw to 84 INCH lbs. (9.5 N.m). Back off screw 1 3/4 to 2 turns and tighten lock nut.

NOTE: **When adjusting brake band, transmission must be horizontal in order to keep band from slipping or jamming.**

11) If case linkage was disassembled, reinstall in case using *Fig. 4* as an assembly guide. Install new seal on accumulator piston (lip pointing toward case). Install piston and spring into case.

12) Install valve body assembly, making sure manual valve engages manual lever and kickdown valve engages kickdown lever. Install valve body-to-case bolts and tighten from center outward. Install oil pan with new gasket.

FINAL DRIVE

DISASSEMBLY

1) Place final drive assembly in holding fixture. Remove oil pan and gasket. Rotate differential assembly

Fig. 25: *Location of Drive Flange Retaining Clips*

Clip ends are indicated by white arrows. Use 2 screwdrivers to press clips off of shaft.

VOLKSWAGEN TYPE 010 3-SPEED (Cont.)

in case until differential pinion gear opening appears. Use 2 screwdrivers to remove 2 clips retaining axle drive flanges in differential.

Fig. 26: Removing Differential Side Bearing Adjusting Ring

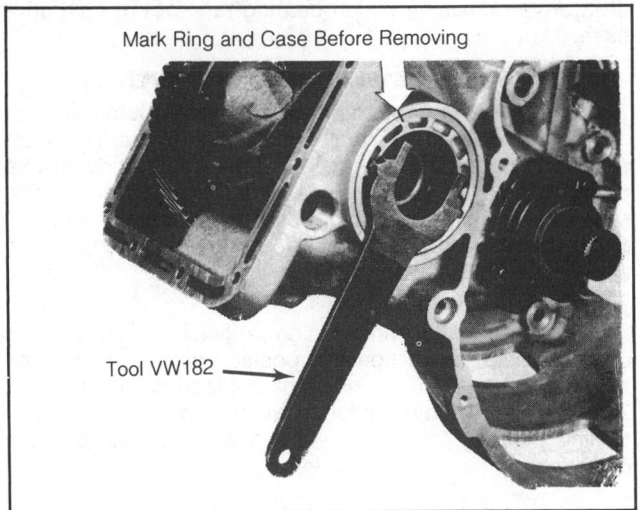

Mark Ring and Case Before Removing

Tool VW182

2) Pull axle drive flanges out of assembly, turning slightly to prevent catching on differential side gear thrust washers. Remove retaining bolt and withdraw speedometer driven gear assembly straight out of case.

3) If bearings are to be reused, scribe a match mark on differential side bearing adjusting ring and case for reassembly reference. Remove lock clip from adjusting ring and screw ring out of case. On opposite side of case, remove nuts and withdraw the other differential side bearing retainer (cover). Grasp differential and ring gear assembly and remove from final drive case.

4) Inside converter housing area of final drive case, mark relationship of intermediate gear shaft and case with scribe. Remove lock clip from intermediate gear shaft and screw shaft out of case. From inside case, remove intermediate gear and bearings.

5) Remove bolts retaining stator support to converter housing area of case, then withdraw support and pinion shaft assembly from case.

6) To disassemble differential assembly, remove 2 differential pinion shaft retaining rings and drive shaft from case with drift. Move differential pinion gears around to case openings. Remove pinion gears and thrust washers. Remove differential side gears and thrust washers.

Fig. 27: Exploded View of Differential and Related Parts in Final Drive Case

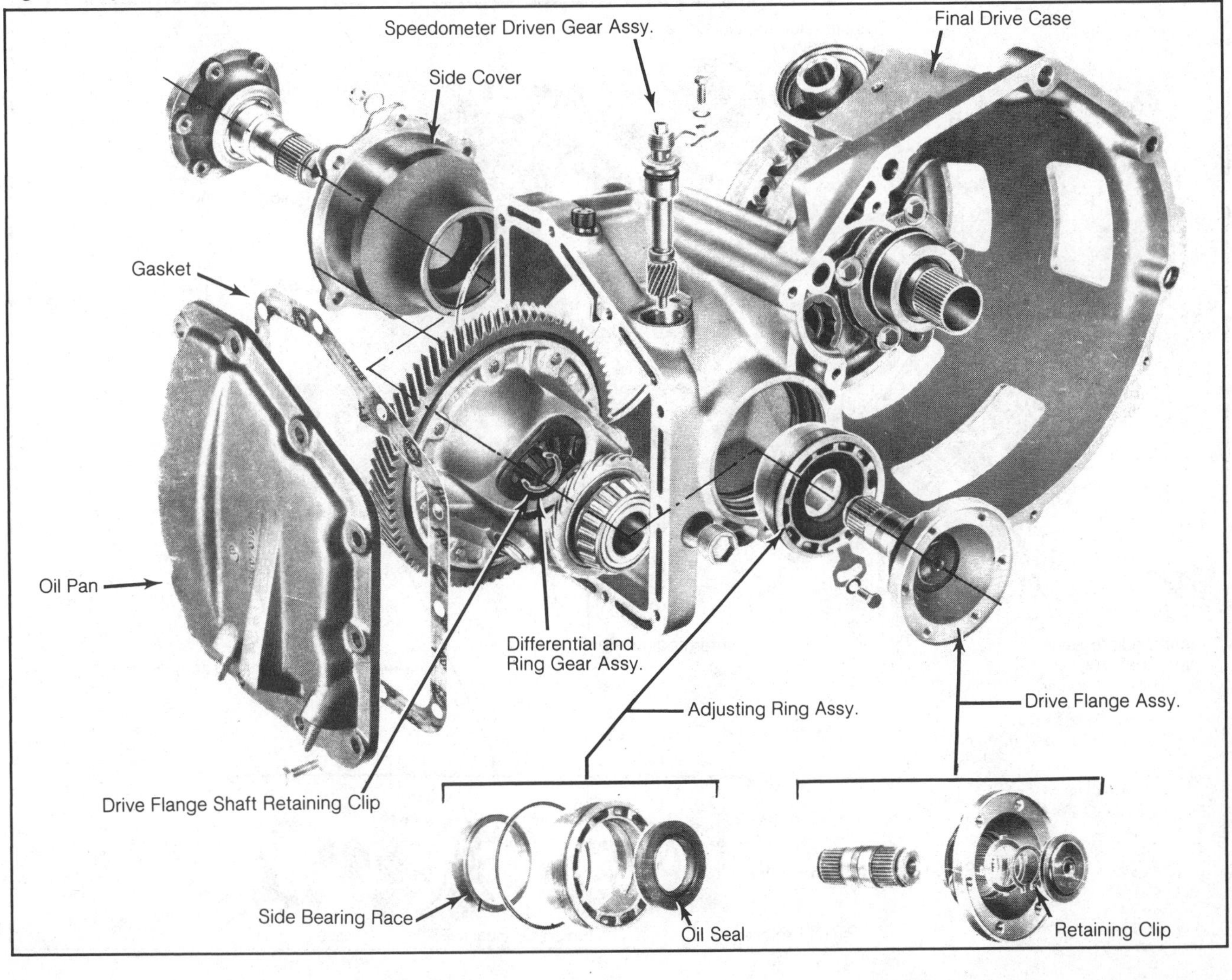

Speedometer Driven Gear Assy.

Final Drive Case

Side Cover

Gasket

Oil Pan

Differential and Ring Gear Assy.

Drive Flange Shaft Retaining Clip

Adjusting Ring Assy.

Drive Flange Assy.

Side Bearing Race

Oil Seal

Retaining Clip

Automatic Transmissions

VOLKSWAGEN TYPE 010 3-SPEED (Cont.)

Fig. 28: Removing Intermediate Gear Shaft

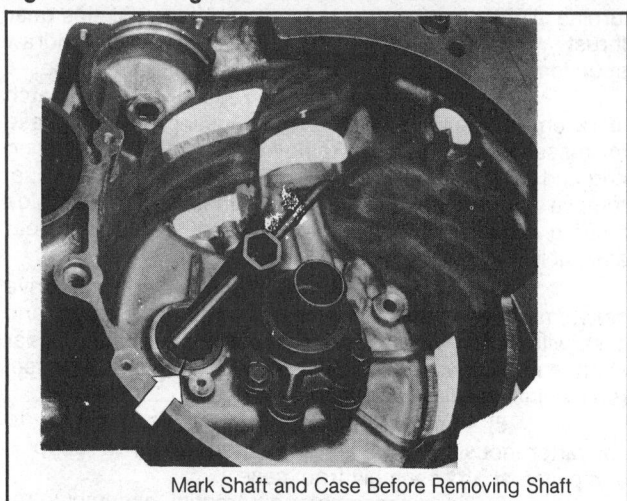

Mark Shaft and Case Before Removing Shaft

7) Remove ring gear attaching bolts. Separate ring gear from case with press. If required, withdraw differential side bearings and speedometer drive gear from case using a press, then withdraw bearing races from adjusting ring and side cover.

8) If replacement of pinion bearings or pinion shaft is required, proceed as follows: Place pinion assembly in press. With press plates positioned under bearings, drive bearings from pinion shaft. Place stator support in press and drive out pinion bearing race along with preload shim and pinion oil seal. Using a hammer and drift, drive remaining pinion bearing race out of final drive case.

REASSEMBLY & ADJUSTMENT

Pinion Reassembly & Preload Adjustment

1) If pinion gear and/or pinion bearings were replaced, lubricate bearings with final drive lubricant and press onto pinion shaft. Using a drift, install pinion bearing race into final drive housing. Temporarily install remaining pinion bearing race (without adjusting shim) into stator support. Install pinion assembly into final drive case, tightening stator support bolts securely.

2) With transmission attaching face of final drive housing facing upward, position a dial indicator on housing with button of indicator contacting pinion shaft. Zero indicator. Move pinion shaft up and down (without turning) noting maximum end play reading on dial indicator.

Fig. 29: Exploded View of Intermediate Gear and Pinion Gear Assemblies in Final Drive Case

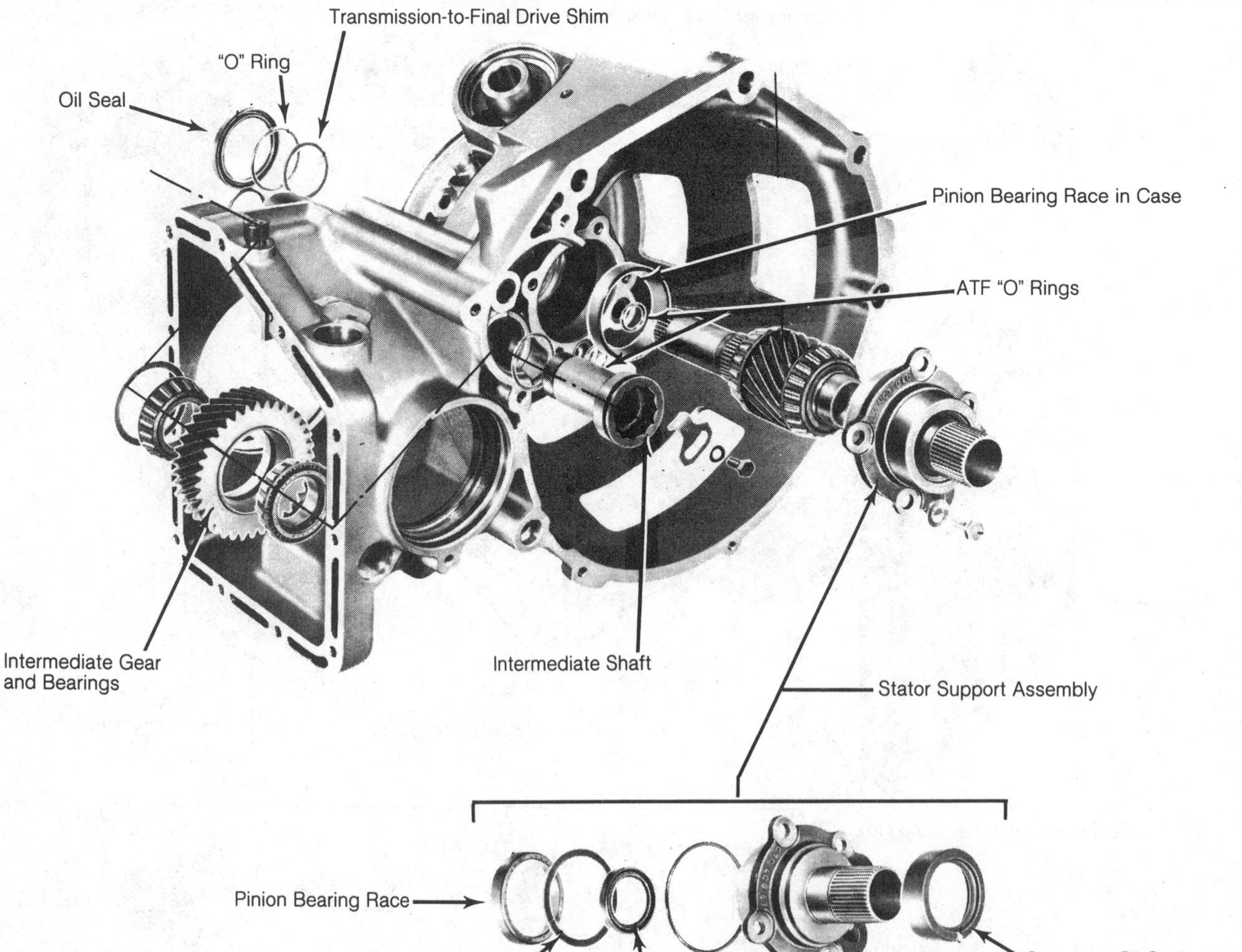

VOLKSWAGEN TYPE 010 3-SPEED (Cont.)

3) To determine proper pinion preload shim usage (to be installed under bearing race in stator support), add .008" (.2 mm) to end play reading. Preload shim thickness should be equal to this amount. Pinion preload shims are available in thicknesses of .039" (1.0 mm) to .087" (2.2 mm) in increments of .002" (.05 mm). If exact size shim is not available, use shim size closest to ideal thickness.

Fig. 30: Using Dial Indicator to Determine Pinion Preload Shim Thickness

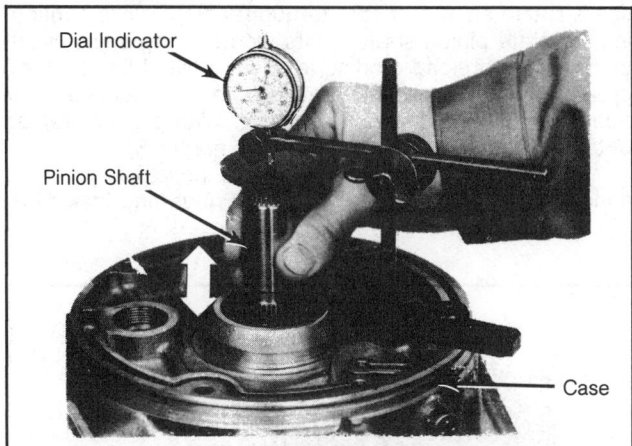

Move pinion shaft up and down. Add .008" (.2 mm) to highest value to determine preload shim thickness.

4) Remove pinion assembly from final drive case and press bearing race out of stator support. Install pinion oil seal into support. Install preload shim determined in steps **2)** and **3)**. Position bearing race in support and press into place.

5) Install converter oil seal on front side of support, then install sealing "O" ring on rear side. Install new transmission fluid passage "O" rings in final drive case, at stator support attaching face.

6) Thoroughly coat pinion bearings with final drive lubricant and position pinion assembly in final drive case. Install stator support and tighten retaining bolts. Attach torque wrench to pinion shaft. Turn shaft with wrench and note torque reading for future reference.

Fig. 31: Checking Pinion Bearing Preload

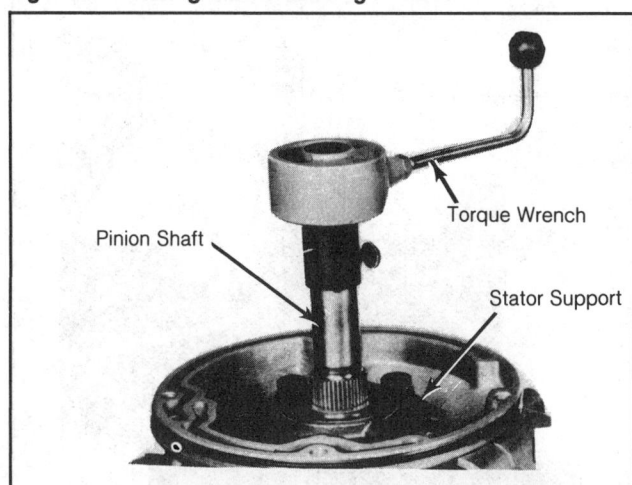

Check reading on torque wrench while rotating shaft.

NOTE: Torque reading is basis for intermediate shaft and differential assembly preload adjustments. Reading must be noted before any further assembly steps are taken.

Intermediate Gear Reassembly & Preload Adjustment

1) If intermediate gear and bearings were replaced, coat bearings with final drive lubricant and install in intermediate gear. Position gear assembly into final drive case, insert intermediate shaft and tighten shaft slightly. Attach torque wrench to pinion shaft. Rotate shaft and note preload reading on wrench.

2) While continuing to rotate pinion shaft, turn intermediate shaft left or right until preload reading on wrench is about 13 INCH lbs. (1.4 N.m) higher than reading obtained in step **6)** of *Pinion Reassembly and Preload Adjustment*. With proper preload obtained, install and tighten shaft lock plate bolt.

Differential Reassembly & Preload Adjustment

1) Lubricate differential side gears and thrust washers with final drive lubricant and position in differential case. Coat differential pinion gears and thrust washers with lubricant. Place gears and washers onto side gears through opening in differential case. Rotate gears into alignment with differential pinion shaft bores in case.

NOTE: Pinion gears must be exactly opposite one another in order to install pinion shaft.

2) Install differential pinion shaft into differential case and through pinion gears. Install pinion shaft retaining clips. If removed, press differential side bearings and speedometer drive gear onto differential case.

Fig. 32: Exploded View of Differential and Ring Gear Assembly

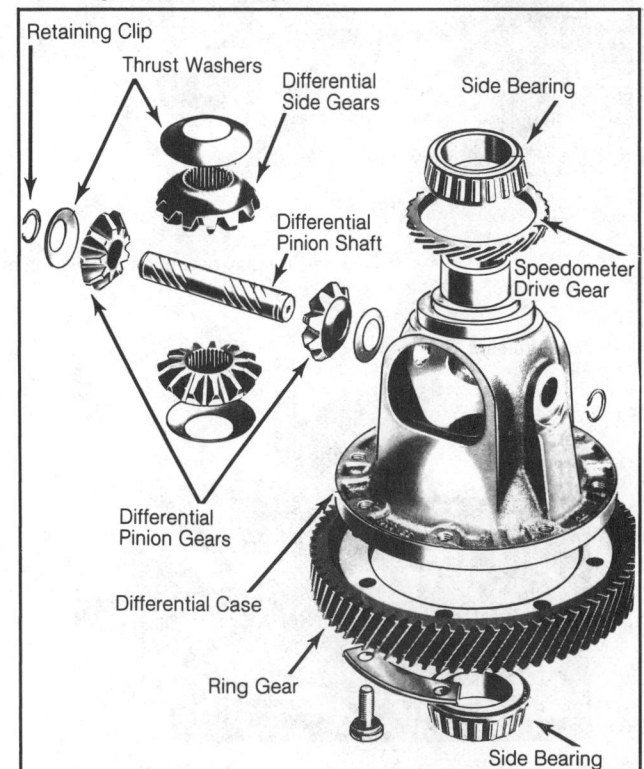

Automatic Transmissions

VOLKSWAGEN TYPE 010 3-SPEED (Cont.)

3) If ring gear is being replaced, install guide pins into differential case bolt hole. Heat ring gear in hot oil to about 212° F (100° C). Using pins to guide ring gear into place, install gear on case. Install and tighten attaching bolts.

4) If differential case, pinion gears, side gears, thrust washers, or axle drive flange shafts are replaced, drive flange shaft retaining rings must be selected. Two sizes of retaining rings are available. To determine which rings to use, go to step **5)**. If parts listed are being reused, go to step **6)**.

5) To select drive flange shaft retaining rings, install each flange shaft into differential case and bottom against differential pinion shaft. While holding side gear against differential case, attempt to install the thicker of the 2 available snap rings. If ring jams at sides and cannot be installed, thinner retaining ring must be used when drive flanges are installed.

6) Install side bearing races and new oil seals in adjusting ring and side cover (if removed). Install new sealing "O" rings on ring and cover. Thoroughly coat ring gear and side bearings with final drive lubricant, position differential assembly in final drive case and engage with intermediate gear.

7) Install side cover to engage with side bearing, then install and tighten cover retaining nuts. Screw side bearing adjusting ring into case and over side bearing so differential is firmly supported.

8) With torque wrench attached to pinion shaft, rotate shaft and note torque reading. While continuing to rotate pinion shaft, rotate side bearing adjuster left or right until preload reading is about 6 INCH lbs. (.7 N.m) greater than last reading obtained in *Intermediate Gear Reassembly and Preload Adjustment.* With proper preload obtained, install and tighten adjusting ring lock.

9) If disassembled, install drive flanges onto flange shafts and secure with spring rings and lock clips.

Fig. 33: *Measuring Transmission-to-Final Drive End Play*

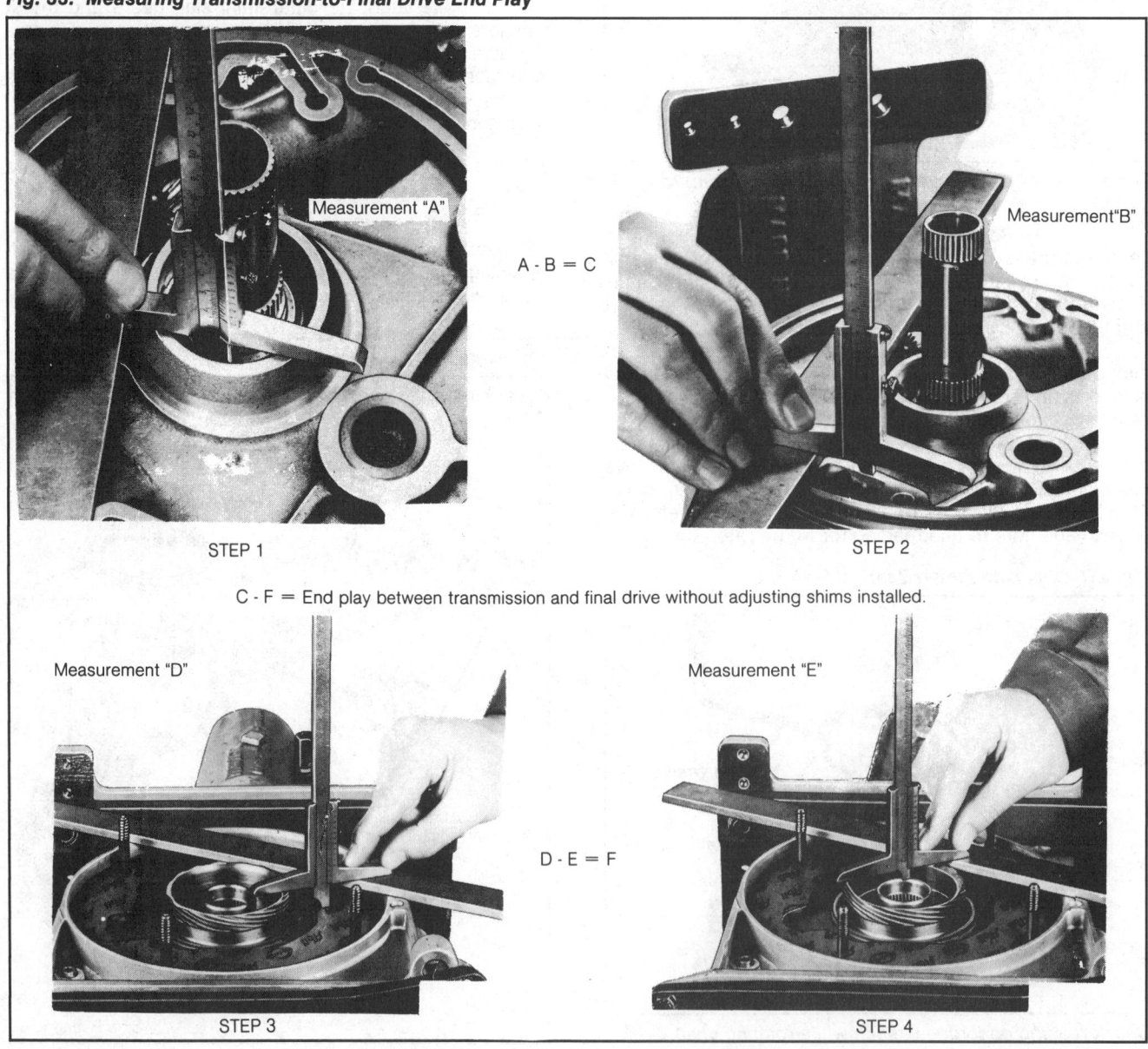

Measurement "A"

A - B = C

Measurement "B"

STEP 1

STEP 2

C - F = End play between transmission and final drive without adjusting shims installed.

Measurement "D"

Measurement "E"

D - E = F

STEP 3

STEP 4

VOLKSWAGEN TYPE 010 3-SPEED (Cont.)

Install end caps into flange shafts, then install shafts into final drive case, securing with retaining clips selected in step **5)**. Install oil pan with new gasket.

Final Assembly of Transaxle

1) Measure play between final drive and transmission: Place a straightedge on transmission attaching face of final drive housing. Using a depth gauge, measure distance from top surface of straightedge to surface of pinion bearing inner race. This is measurement "A".

2) Measure distance from top surface of straightedge to face of final drive housing. This is measurement "B". Subtract "B" from "A" to obtain "C". Record for future reference.

3) Place a new gasket on transmission separation plate. Position straightedge on transmission case and measure distance from top surface of straightedge to gasket surface. This is measurement "D".

4) Measure distance from top surface of straightedge down to inner shoulder of governor drive gear. This is measurement "E". Subtract "E" from "D" to obtain "F" and record.

5) Subtract "F" from "C". This amount is end play (without shims) between final drive and transmission. Refer to *End Play Shim Chart* to determine shim pack thickness required. Shims are available in thicknesses of .016" (.4 mm) and .047" (1.2 mm). Combine shims as required to obtain correct total thickness.

6) Install selected shim(s) into final drive case, on top of pinion bearing inner race. Next, install sealing "O" ring and final drive-to-transmission oil seal into pinion cavity of final drive housing. Install impeller shaft and pump shaft fully into transmission.

7) Position a new "O" ring seal on final drive case, then mate final drive and transmission cases. Install final drive-to-transmission case nuts and tighten. Place new "O" ring seals on governor, governor cover, and speedometer driven gear assembly. Install in case. Install torque converter on stator support to complete assembly.

END PLAY SHIM CHART

If End Play Is In.(mm)	Install Shim Pack In. (mm)
.009-.033 (0.23-0.84)	None
.034-.049 (0.85-1.24)	.016 (0.4)
.050-.065 (1.25-1.64)	.032 (0.8)
.066-.080 (1.65-2.04)	.048 (1.2)
.081-.096 (2.05-2.44)	.064 (1.6)
.097-.112 (2.45-2.84)	.080 (2.0)
.113-.128 (2.85-3.24)	.096 (2.4)
.129-.143 (3.25-3.64)	.112 (2.8)
.144-.153 (3.65-3.88)	.128 (3.2)

TIGHTENING SPECIFICATIONS

Application	Ft. Lbs. (N.m)
Transmission	
Locknut On 2nd Gear Brake Band Adjusting Screw	14 (20)
Pan-to-Transmission Case	14 (20)
Transaxle-to-Engine	40 (56)
Converter-to-Drive Plate	22 (31)
Converter Cover Plate-to-Bell Housing	11 (15)
Starter-to-Bell Housing	22 (31)
Constant Velocity Joint-to-Drive Flange	32 (45)
Transmission Case-to-Final Drive Housing	22 (31)
Manual Valve-to-Shaft Nut	14 (20)
Kickdown Valve-to-Shaft Nut	11 (15)
Final Drive	
Side Bearing Cover	22 (31)
Cover-to-Final Drive Housing	36 (50)
Ring Gear	50 (70)

	INCH lbs. (N.m)
Transmission	
Valve Body-to-Case	35 (3.9)
Strainer-to-Valve Body	26 (2.9)
Pump-to-Case	35 (3.9)

Automatic Transmissions

VOLKSWAGEN VANAGON

TRANSAXLE IDENTIFICATION

Transmission portion of transaxle assembly may be identified by a group of numbers stamped into top of transmission case. One of the numbers is "090". This denotes the Volkswagen "2-planetary" type transmission. Final drive portion of transaxle assembly is identified by a group of figures stamped into final drive housing near governor assembly. These figures consist of a 2 letter model code and a build date code.

DESCRIPTION

Transaxle assembly consists of two main units: Automatic transmission and final drive assembly. The transmission housing contains two planetary gear sets, two multi-disc clutches, one brake band and servo, one multiple-disc brake, a one-way clutch, and a hydraulic control system. The final drive housing contains the torque converter, governor assembly for transmission, ring and pinion gear, and the differential assembly.

LUBRICATION & ADJUSTMENT

See the appropriate article in AUTOMATIC TRANSMISSION SERVICING Section.

SERVICE (IN-VEHICLE)

For Axle Drive Shaft, Constant Velocity (CV) Joint, and Rear Wheel Bearing Housing removal and installation see the appropriate article in MANUAL TRANSMISSIONS Section.

TROUBLE SHOOTING

NO MOVEMENT

In Any Gear

Low fluid level. Manual lever not connected to manual valve. Torque converter disconnected from drive plate. Main pressure valve sticking. Oil pump drive plate and/or shaft defective.

In Forward Gears

Forward clutch internal damage (worn plates, broken diaphragm spring, seals leaking, etc.). Forward planetary gear set damaged.

In First Gear in "D" or "2"

One-way clutch not holding. Forward clutch internal damage.

In First Gear in "1"

1st/Reverse brake plates worn or burnt.

In Second Gear

2nd gear brake band out of adjustment, or burnt, or servo defective.

In Reverse

1st/Reverse brake plates damaged, worn or burnt. Direct/Reverse clutch internal damage. Forward clutch seized in applied position.

NO UPSHIFTS

Into Second Gear

Governor drive defective. Governor dirty or improperly assembled. Accumulator cover plate loose. Valve body dirty. 1-2 shift valve sticking. 2nd gear brake band burnt or worn.

Into Third Gear

Governor or valve body dirty. 2-3 shift valve sticking. Oil pump bolts loose.

Fig. 1: Volkswagen Vanagon Automatic Transaxle Assembly

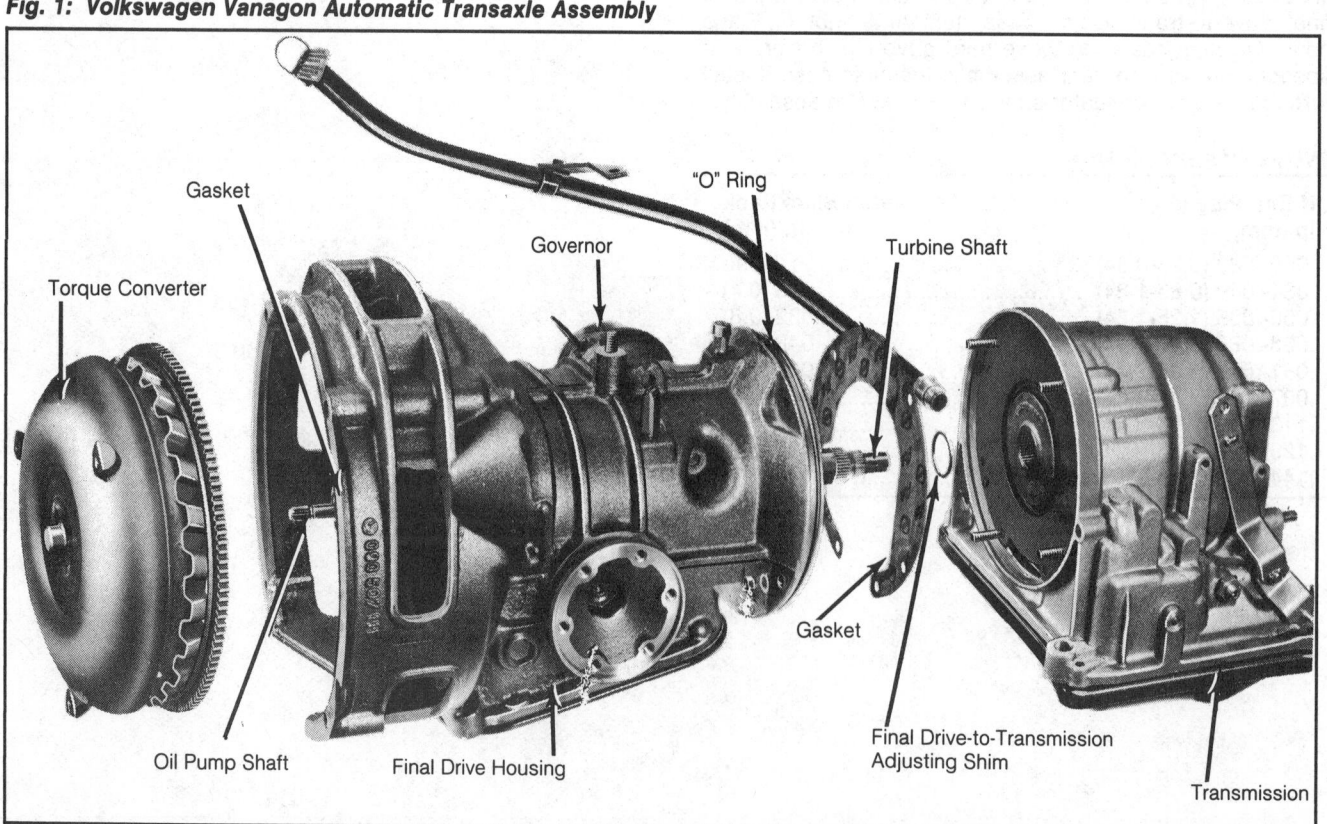

Gasket

"O" Ring

Governor

Turbine Shaft

Torque Converter

Oil Pump Shaft

Final Drive Housing

Gasket

Final Drive-to-Transmission Adjusting Shim

Transmission

VOLKSWAGEN VANAGON (Cont.)

NO DOWNSHIFTS

Into Second Gear
Governor dirty. 2-3 shift valve sticking.

Into First Gear
Governor dirty. 1-2 shift valve sticking.

DELAYED ENGAGEMENT ON UPSHIFTS

1-2 Upshift
Low fluid level. Dirty valve body. 2nd gear brake band worn, burnt or out of adjustment. 2nd gear servo defective.

2-3 Upshift
Low fluid level. Dirty valve body. 2nd gear brake band worn, burnt or out of adjustment. 2nd gear servo defective. Direct/Reverse clutch plates worn or burnt. Wrong Direct/Reverse clutch installed.

ERRATIC DRIVE

Low fluid level. Bushing in one-way clutch support and turbine shaft worn. Oil filter dirty.

INCORRECT SHIFT SPEEDS

Governor dirty. Valve body dirty. Planetary gears or separation plate gasket damaged.

TESTING

ROAD TEST

1) Before road testing, be certain that fluid level and condition, and control linkage adjustments have been checked and corrected as necessary. During the test, transmission should upshift and downshift at approximately the speeds shown in *Shift Speeds* chart. All shifts may vary somewhat due to production tolerances or tire size. The important factor is the quality of the shifts. All shifts should be smooth, responsive, and with no slippage or engine speed runaway.

2) Slippage or engine runaway in any gear usually indicates clutch, band or brake problems. The slipping unit in a particular gear can usually be identified by noting transmission operation in other selector positions and comparing which internal units are applied in those positions. *See Clutch and Band Application Chart.*

3) This process of elimination can be used to detect any unit which slips, and to confirm proper operation of good units. However, the actual cause of the malfunction usually cannot be easily determined. Most conditions can be caused by leaking hydraulic circuits or sticking valves. Therefore, unless an obvious condition exists, do not disassemble transmission until a hydraulic pressure test has been made.

SHIFT SPEED SPECIFICATIONS

Application	Shift Points (MPH)	
	Full Throttle	Kickdown
1-2 Upshift	16-22	30-32
2-3 Upshift	37-47	55-56
3-2 Downshift	27-37	52-53
2-1 Downshift	11-12	27-29

HYDRAULIC PRESSURE TEST

1) Connect a pressure gauge to main pressure test point on case (adjacent to servo cover). Bring

Fig. 2: View of Transmission Case Showing Main Pressure Test Point

Arrow Indicates Pressure Connection

CLUTCH AND BAND APPLICATION CHART (ELEMENTS IN USE)

Selector Lever Position	Forward Clutch	Direct-Reverse Clutch	First-Reverse Brake	Second Gear Band	One-Way Clutch
D — DRIVE					
First Gear	X				X
Second Gear	X			X	
Third Gear	X	X			
2 — INTERMEDIATE					
First Gear	X				X
Second Gear	X			X	
1 — LOW (First)	X		X		
R — REVERSE		X	X		

NEUTRAL OR PARK — All clutches, brakes, and bands released and/or ineffective.

transmission to normal operating temperature and place selector lever in "D". Accelerate to about 30 MPH, release throttle completely and read pressure on gauge.

NOTE: **This test, as well as full throttle test performed next, should be carried out on a dynamometer when possible.**

      2) Next, run engine at full throttle with vehicle speed above 25 MPH, and again note pressure reading in "D".

      3) Finally, with vehicle at a standstill, place selector lever in "R" position, and note reading on pressure gauge.

      4) Pressures obtained in each phase of test should be approximately as shown in *Main Pressure* chart. If not, disassemble and clean valve body and check especially for sticking valves.

MAIN PRESSURE SPECIFICATIONS

Application	psi (kg/cm^2)
"D" at Idle [1]	41-43 (2.9-3.0)
"D" at Full Throttle	83-85 (5.9-6.0)
"R" at Idle [2]	129-138 (9.1-9.7)

[1] — Engine speed at about 30 MPH, throttle released.
[2] — With vehicle stationary.

STALL SPEED

Testing Precautions

      When making test, do not hold throttle open any longer than the time it takes to read tachometer. Maximum stall speed test time is 5 seconds. If repetition is necessary, wait at least 20 seconds between tests. If engine speed exceeds limits shown in *Stall Speeds* table, release accelerator immediately as clutch or band slippage is indicated.

Testing Procedure

      With engine at normal operating temperature, connect a tachometer. Start engine and set parking and service brakes. Place selector lever in "D". Depress accelerator briefly to full throttle and note maximum RPM obtained. Engine speed should be within limits shown in *Stall Speeds* table.

NOTE: **Normal stall speed will drop approximately 125 RPM per 3200 feet altitude. Also, stall speed will drop slightly at high ambient temperatures.**

STALL SPEED SPECIFICATIONS

Application	Stall RPM
All Models	1950-2250

Stall Test Results

      1) If stall speed is higher than specified, forward clutch or 1st gear one-way clutch is slipping. If stall speed in "D" is too high, repeat stall test in "1". If RPM is within specifications, one-way clutch for 1st gear is defective.

      2) If stall speed is approximately 200 RPM below specifications, engine performance may be unsatisfactory. If stall speed is approximately 400 RPM below specifications, torque converter stator one-way clutch is defective and complete converter should be replaced.

REMOVAL & INSTALLATION

      See the appropriate article in AUTOMATIC TRANSMISSION REMOVAL Section.

TORQUE CONVERTER

NOTE: **The torque converter is a sealed unit and cannot be disassembled for service. However, the bushing in converter hub may be replaced as follows:**

BUSHING REPLACEMENT

      1) Check bushing wear using an inside micrometer. Wear limit of bushing is 1.348" (34.25 mm), and maximum allowable out-of-round is .001" (.03 mm).

      2) To replace bushing, use a bushing puller to withdraw bushing from converter hub. Press new bushing into place until it is fully seated in hub.

TRANSMISSION DISASSEMBLY

NOTE: **To separate transaxle units, withdraw torque converter from final drive housing and remove oil pump shaft from center of turbine shaft. Disconnect oil filler pipe. Remove attaching nuts from transmission studs that attach final drive to transmission, then separate final drive unit from transmission case. Withdraw turbine shaft from final drive assembly pinion shaft. For final drive disassembly and reassembly, see Final Drive information at rear of this article.**

Fig. 3: Removing First Gear One-Way Clutch Assembly Retaining Snap Ring

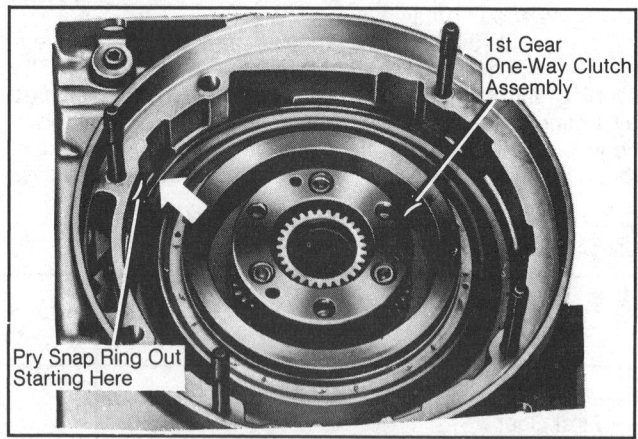

      1) Mount transmission assembly in a work stand. Remove separation plate attaching screws and lift plate and gasket from transmission case. Remove forward annulus gear and 2 thrust washers behind it from case.

      2) Using a screwdriver, carefully pry large snap ring retaining 1st gear one-way clutch assembly from case. Lift out one-way clutch, 1st/Reverse gear brake plates, and reverse planetary gear set as a unit.

      3) Remove thrust washers, then lift the following components from case as an assembly: Sun gear, driving shell, forward planetary gear set, and forward clutch assembly.

VOLKSWAGEN VANAGON (Cont.)

Fig. 4: Removing Brake Band Servo Assembly

Top Cover

Tap cover until cover and piston pop out under spring pressure.

4) Remove 2nd gear brake band servo cover snap ring. Then using a rubber mallet, tap cover until cover and piston assembly pop out under spring tension.

5) Loosen 2nd gear brake band adjusting screw lock nut and remove lock nut and screw, then withdraw push rod for adjusting screw.

6) Lift out remaining planetary gear set components that are housed in 1st/Reverse gear brake shell. Remove bolt from 1st/Reverse brake spring plate, withdraw spring plate and springs, then pull driving shell, brake piston, and oil pump from case.

7) Invert transmission so that oil pan is facing up. Remove attaching bolts and lift off pan and gasket.

Remove screws from oil strainer and separate strainer from valve body.

8) Remove the valve body attaching bolts and lift valve body assembly from case using care not to drop manual valve. Remove attaching screws from accumulator cover plate, then remove cover, spring and accumulator piston. If necessary for parts replacement, disassemble kickdown and selector linkage using *Fig. 5* as a disassembly guide.

COMPONENT DISASSEMBLY & REASSEMBLY

OIL PUMP ASSEMBLY

CAUTION: Oil pump cover is under spring tension.

Disassembly

1) Remove pump cover attaching screws and separate cover from housing. Remove check ball and spring, then lift out inner and outer pump gears along with drive plate.

2) Using needlenose pliers, unhoook oil seal ring ends and carefully remove seal rings from pump housing. Remove thrust washer from pump housing.

Inspection

Wash all parts in kerosene and blow out oil passages with compressed air. Inspect all parts for wear, scoring, chipped teeth, and any other damage. Replace parts as necessary.

Fig. 5: Bottom View of Transmission Case Showing Kickdown and Selector Linkage

Parking Pawl Pin

"E" Clip

Parking Lock Operating Lever

Roller Spring

Spring Retaining Bolt

Parking Pawl

Kickdown Lever

Parking Pawl Spring

Support Ring

"O" Ring

Lever Shaft

Manual Lever

"O" Ring

Operating Lever Rod & Spring

Kickdown Lever Nut

Manual Lever Nut

Kickdown Operating Lever

Manual Operating Lever

NOTE: From Transmission Number 22050, Operating Lever is Stamped Steel with Pressed in Bushings and Rollers. Operating Rod and Spring Cannot be Disassembled, Rod and Spring are Attached to Operating Lever with an "E" Clip.

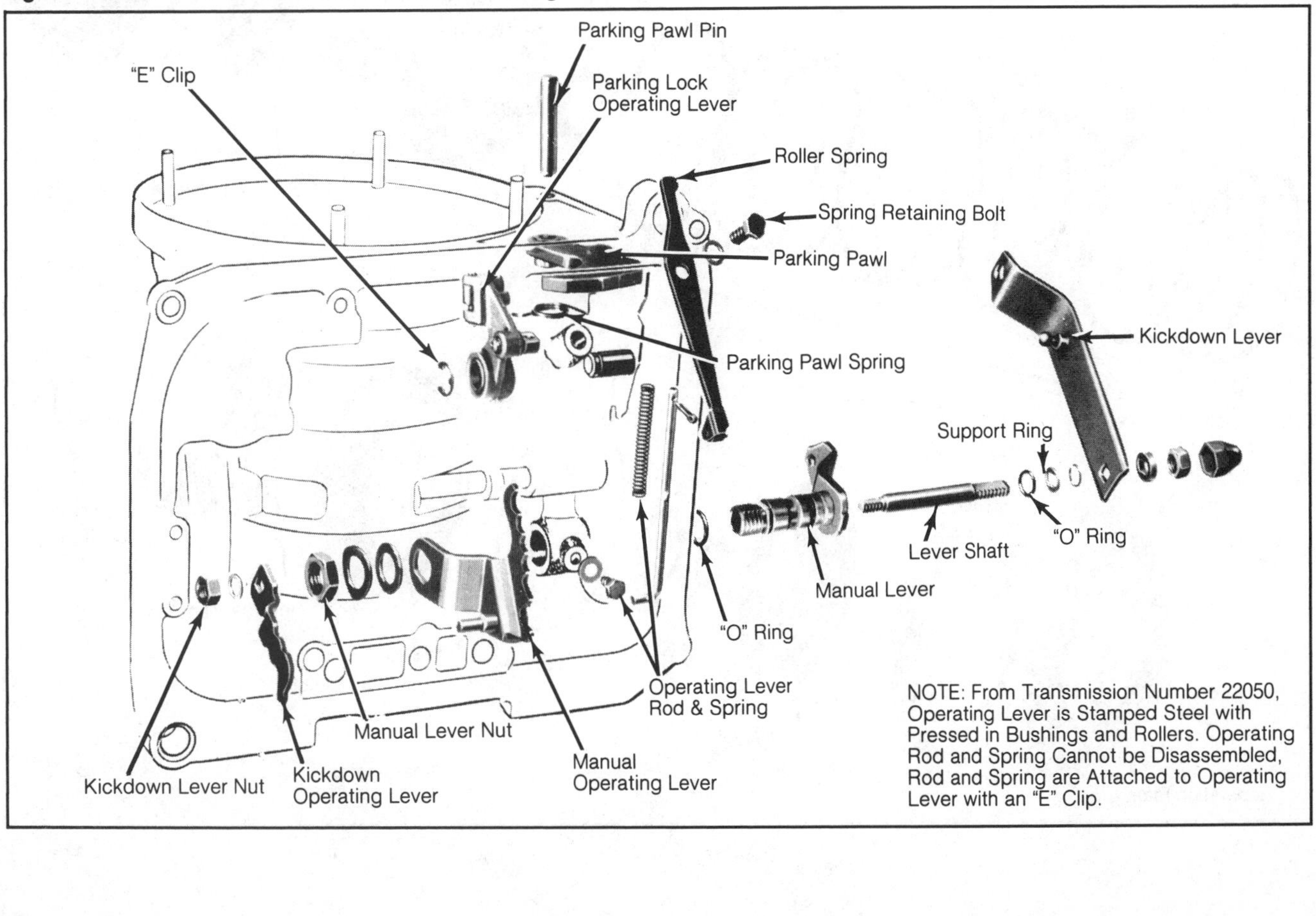

Automatic Transmissions
VOLKSWAGEN VANAGON (Cont.)

Fig. 6: Exploded View Showing Major Components of Transmission Assembly

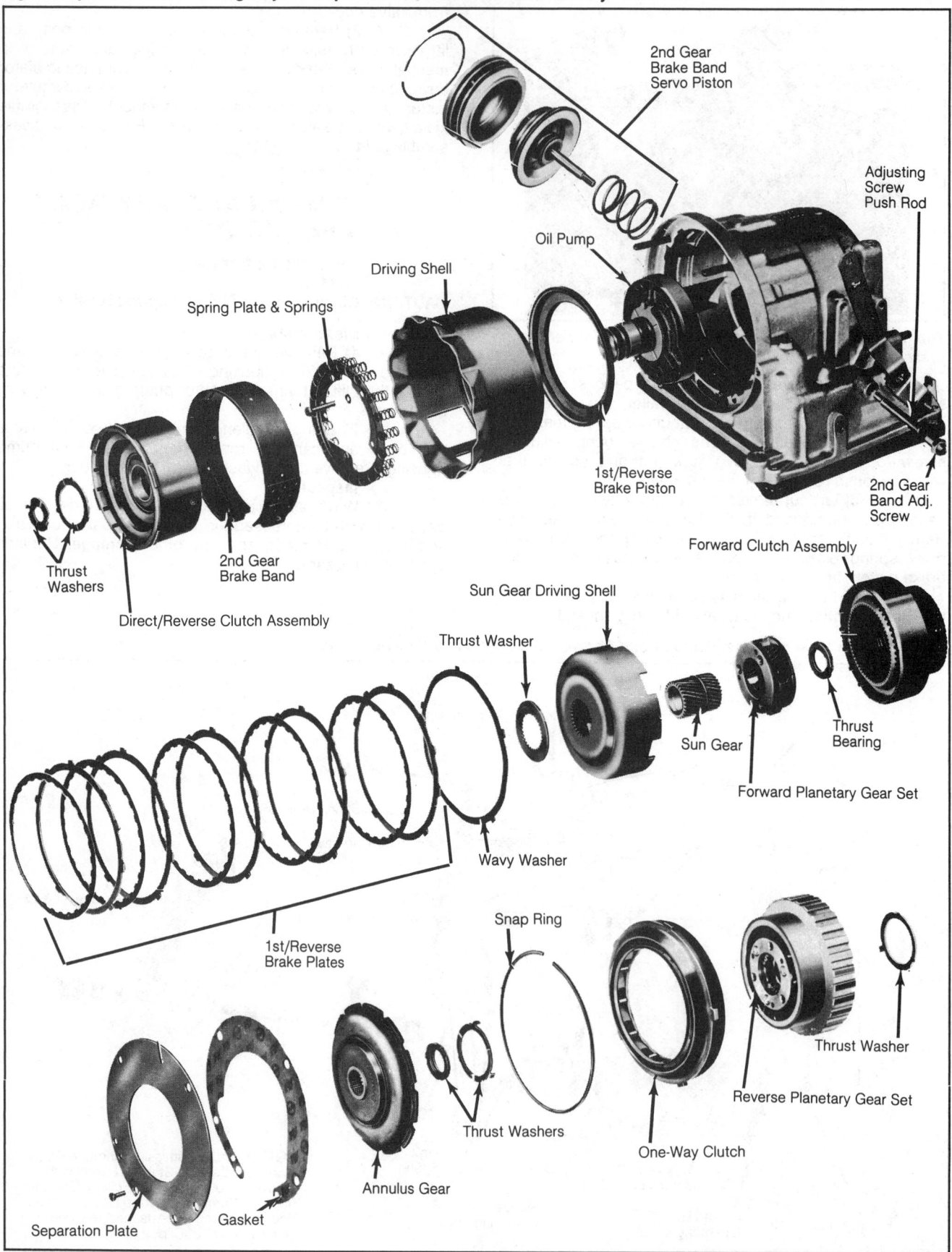

Fig. 7: Exploded View of Oil Pump Assembly

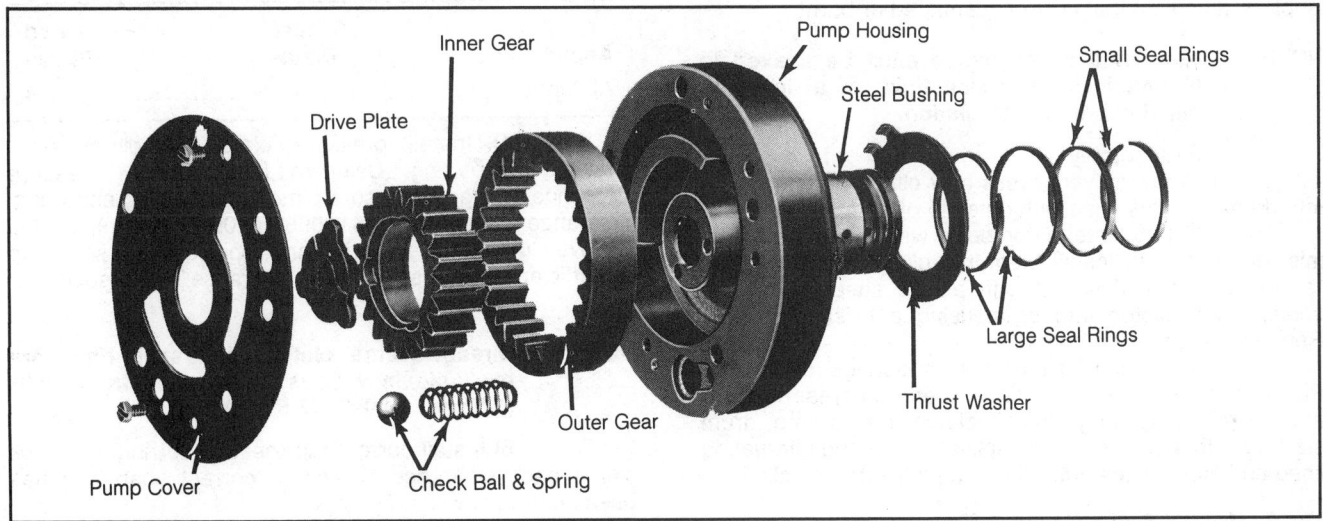

NOTE: If either of the pump gears, the pump housing or cover are damaged, then entire oil pump assembly must be replaced. The drive plate, oil seal rings, and thrust washers can be replaced individually.

Reassembly

1) Install thrust washer on pump housing. Carefully install first the large oil seal rings and then the small seal rings onto pump housing, ensuring that ring ends hook correctly.

2) Lubricate all parts with automatic transmission fluid. Install inner and outer pump gears into housing, then install drive plate with extended hub inserted into pump housing shaft opening. Install check ball and spring into housing. Align cover with housing, then install and tighten attaching screws.

NOTE: After pump has been reassembled, insert pump shaft into pump and ensure that gears rotate freely and smoothly. Gear rotation should also be checked after oil pump is installed into transmission case.

DIRECT/REVERSE CLUTCH

Disassembly

1) Using a screwdriver, pry clutch pack retaining snap ring from clutch drum. Withdraw clutch pressure plate, lined clutch plates and steel clutch plates from drum.

2) Place clutch drum in a press, apply downward pressure to piston spring retainer and remove snap ring. Release press and remove spring retainer. Using a twisting motion, remove piston with return springs from drum. Remove piston seals and springs from piston.

3) If necessary for replacement, place clutch drum in a press and drive bushing from drum hub using a driver.

Inspection

1) Inspect friction surfaces of piston and drum for wear or damage. Check clutch drum ball valve for free movement. Inspect piston springs for wear or collapsed coils and replace as necessary.

2) Inspect steel (external splines) clutch plates. If plates are scored or have radial grooves, they must be replaced. Plates that are only discolored can be reused.

Fig. 8: Exploded View of Direct/Reverse Clutch Assembly

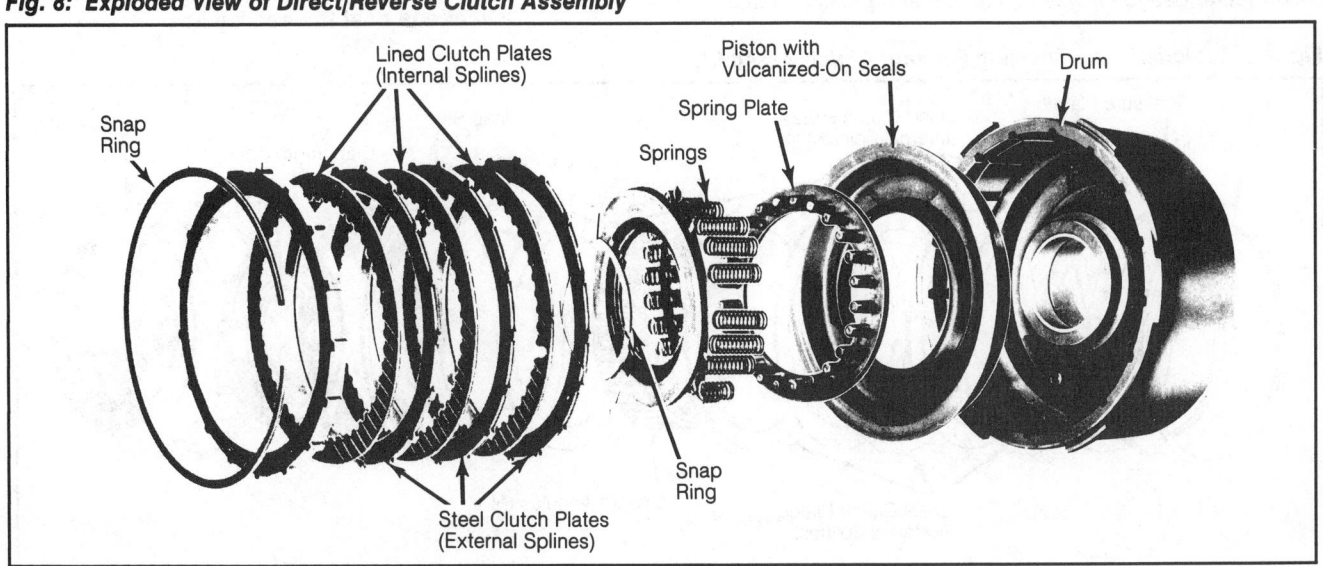

VOLKSWAGEN VANAGON (Cont.)

3) Inspect lined (internal splines) clutch plates. Replace any plate that is worn, damaged or burnt.

NOTE: New lined clutch plates must be soaked in automatic transmission fluid for at least 15 minutes prior to installation.

Reassembly

1) If removed, press new clutch drum bushing into drum until it is flush with outer lip of hub.

2) Lubricate piston seals with automatic transmission fluid, then install them into clutch drum with lips facing into drum. Using a stiff plastic sheet to protect seals, install piston into drum using a twisting motion. Remove plastic sheet from drum.

3) Position piston return springs on piston. Place spring retainer on springs, then compress retainer and install snap ring. Install clutch plates into drum starting with a steel (external splines) plate and alternating lined and steel plates until all clutch plates are installed.

Fig. 9: Using a Feeler Gauge to Measure Direct/Reverse Clutch Pack Clearance

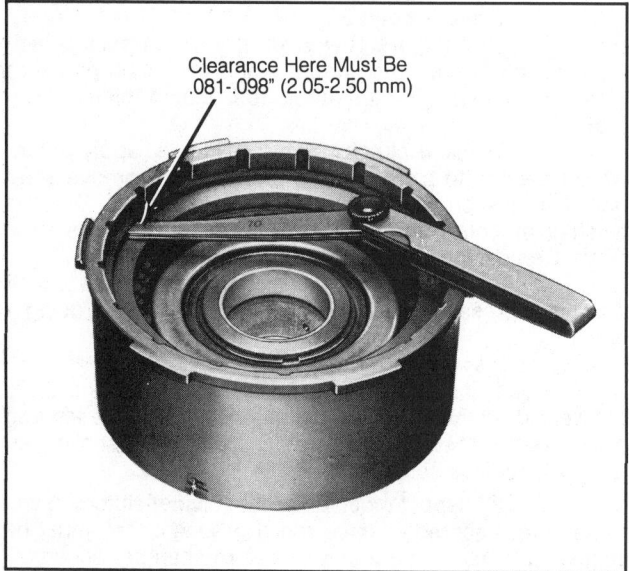

Insert feeler gauge between snap ring and pressure plate.

DIRECT/REVERSE CLUTCH PLATE CHART

Application	Steel Plates	Lined Plates
All Models	4	4

4) Install pressure plate and clutch pack retaining snap ring. Using a feeler gauge, measure clearance between pressure plate and retaining snap ring. Clearance should be .081-.098" (2.05-2.50 mm); if not, remove clutch pack snap ring and replace with a snap ring of sufficient thickness to bring clearance within specifications.

NOTE: Direct/Reverse clutch pack snap rings are available in various thicknesses from .059" (1.5 mm) to .098" (2.5 mm).

5) Install correct thickness snap ring. Recheck clutch pack clearance to ensure correct snap ring has been installed.

FORWARD CLUTCH

Disassembly

1) Using a screwdriver, pry clutch pack retaining snap ring from clutch drum. Then withdraw pressure plate, forward annulus gear, lined and steel clutch plates, and thrust plate.

2) Carefully pry out diaphragm spring snap ring. Remove diaphragm spring. Lift out piston.

NOTE: It may be necessary to force piston from clutch drum using compressed air.

Inspection

1) Inspect clutch drum for scoring, wear, or other damage. Check clutch drum ball valve for free movement and ensure that drilling is clear.

2) Inspect diaphragm spring and piston for damage. Also, place diaphragm spring onto piston and ensure that top of spring reaches to at least the lower edge of snap ring groove; if not, replace spring.

NOTE: The forward clutch piston sealing lips are vulcanized to the piston. Replace the piston if there is damage to the sealing lips or if there is leakage past the sealing lips.

Fig. 10: Exploded View Showing Forward Clutch Assembly

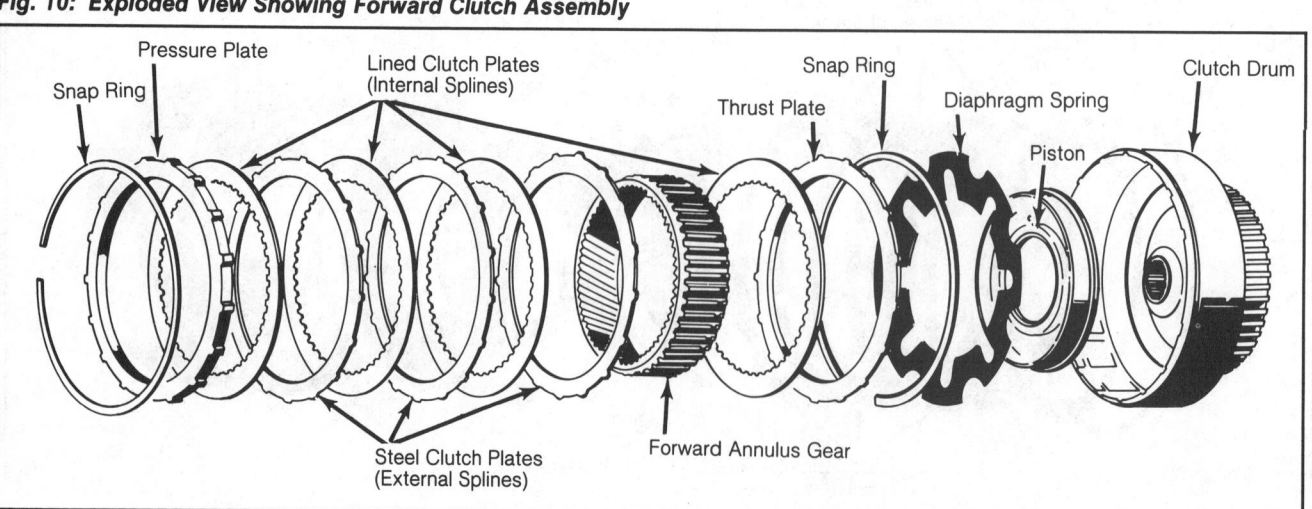

VOLKSWAGEN VANAGON (Cont.)

3) Use Direct/Reverse clutch inspection procedures to inspect the lined and steel clutch plates.

NOTE: If new lined (internal splines) clutch plates are to be installed, they must be soaked in automatic transmission fluid for at least 15 minutes prior to installation.

Reassembly

1) Lubricate piston sealing lips with automatic transmission fluid, then install piston into drum using a twisting motion. Install diaphragm spring, with convex side toward piston, into clutch drum. Install retaining snap ring.

NOTE: With snap ring installed, diaphragm spring should be lightly tensioned; if not, replace spring.

2) Install thrust plate into drum. If one side of thrust plate is chamfered, install chamfered side toward diaphragm spring.

3) Install one lined (internal splines) clutch plate into drum, then install annulus gear so that short splines beneath its retaining ridge are engaged in the lined clutch plate. Install remaining clutch plates starting with a steel (external splines) plate and alternating lined and steel clutch plates until all plates have been installed.

FORWARD CLUTCH PLATE CHART

Application	Steel Plates	Lined Plates
All Models	3	4

4) Install pressure plate and retaining snap ring into clutch drum. Next, position a dial indicator on clutch assembly so that indicator tip contacts pressure plate, then zero dial face.

5) Measure forward clutch end play by moving annulus gear up and down so that dial indicator will show play between pressure plate and snap ring.

6) Forward clutch end play should be .020-.035" (.50-.90 mm). If not, replace pressure plate with one of sufficient thickness to bring end play within specifications. After correct pressure plate is installed, recheck end play.

Fig. 11: Using a Dial Indicator to Measure Forward Clutch End Play

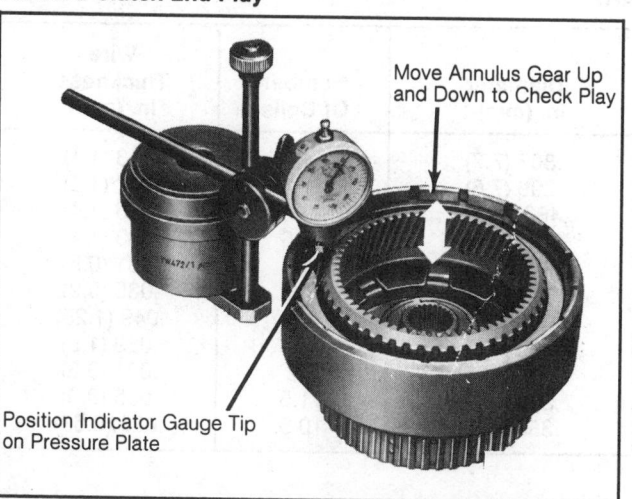

Move Annulus Gear Up and Down to Check Play

Position Indicator Gauge Tip on Pressure Plate

NOTE: Forward clutch pressure plates are available in thicknesses of .236" (6.0 mm) to .299" (7.6 mm) in increments of .016" (.4 mm).

FIRST GEAR ONE-WAY CLUTCH
Disassembly

Remove one-way clutch rollers and springs. Remove snap rings. Using a plastic mallet, carefully drive roller cage out of outer race.

Inspection

Inspect all parts for wear scoring, or other damage and replace as necessary.

NOTE: One-way clutch has been modified and now has a retaining key to hold ring from turning in transmission housing. Previously, 5 protruding lugs served this purpose. New type clutch cannot be installed in transmission with old type clutch.

Fig. 12: Modified One-Way Clutch and Retaining Ring

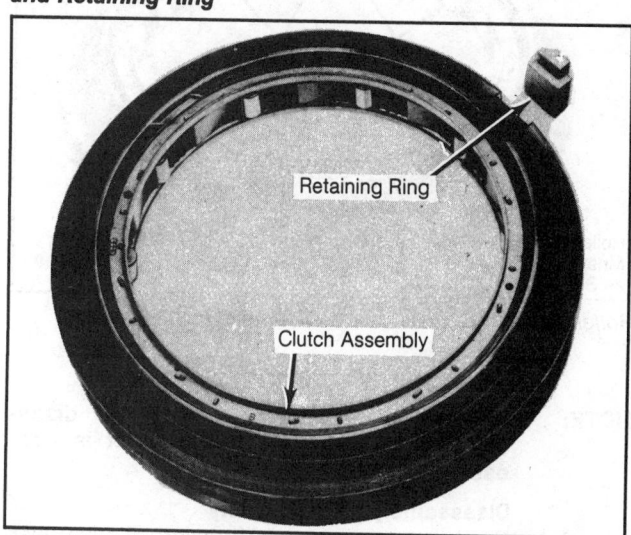

Retaining Ring

Clutch Assembly

Fig. 13: Exploded View of First Gear One-Way Clutch Assembly

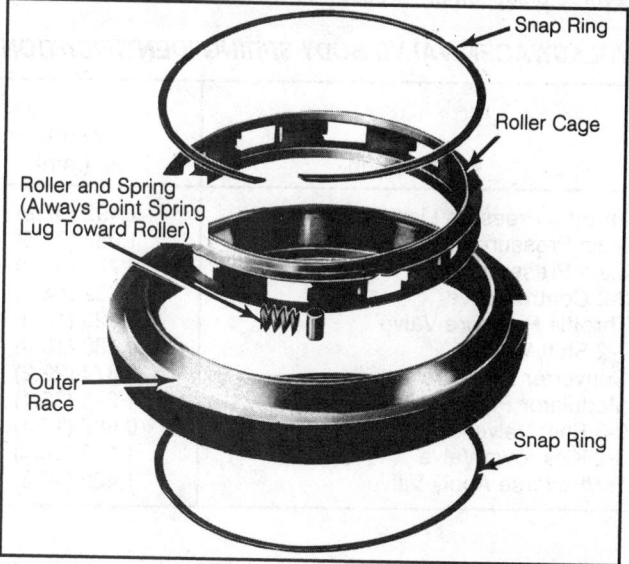

Snap Ring

Roller Cage

Roller and Spring (Always Point Spring Lug Toward Roller)

Outer Race

Snap Ring

Automatic Transmissions

VOLKSWAGEN VANAGON (Cont.)

Reassembly

1) Install lower snap ring in groove of outer race. If necessary, heat outer race to 300°F (150°C), then place roller cage into race using 2 pair of pliers.

NOTE: The heat from outer race will transfer quickly to roller cage, causing cage to stick inside race. If cage is not correctly positioned against lower snap ring inside race, DO NOT attempt to press it into position after cage has stuck. Carefully knock cage out of outer race and repeat procedure again after race has cooled down.

2) Install upper snap ring. Install rollers and springs into cage as shown in *Fig. 14.*

Fig. 14: View of One-Way Clutch Assembly Showing Correct Roller and Spring Installation

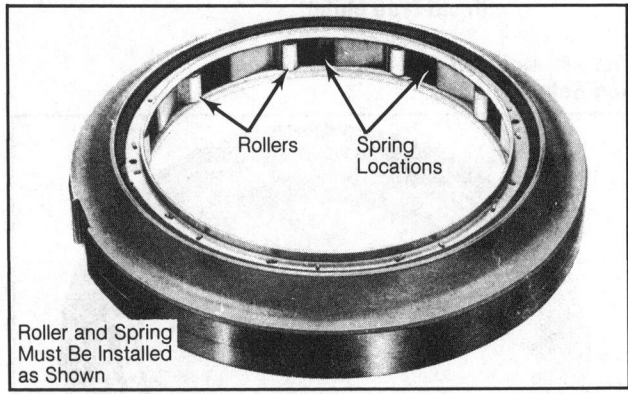

Roller and spring must be installed as shown.

REVERSE ANNULUS GEAR

NOTE: Reverse annulus gear should be disassembled only if parts replacement is necessary.

Disassembly & Reassembly

Remove snap ring and lift governor drive gear out of parking gear. Inspect parking lock notches on parking gear and replace worn part. To reassemble, reverse disassembly procedure.

Fig. 15: Disassembled View of Reverse Annulus Gear

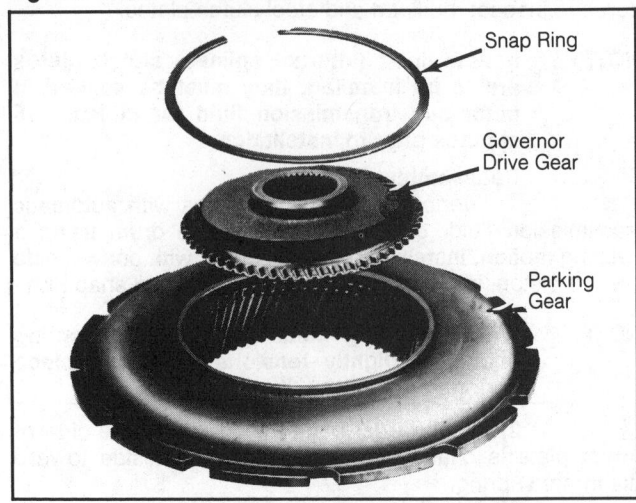

VALVE BODY ASSEMBLY

NOTE: As valve body components are removed from each valve bore, place individual parts in correct order in relative position to valve body to simplify reassembly.

Disassembly

1) Remove transfer plate-to-valve body attaching screws. Lift transfer plate and separator plate from main valve body. Remove .24" (6 mm) check balls (5) and .12" (3 mm) check ball (1) from valve body. *See Fig. 17.*

CAUTION: DO NOT alter setting of adjusting screws when removing from valve body.

2) Remove rear end cover plate and withdraw valves, springs and adjusting screws. Remove remaining end plates, one at a time, and withdraw all valves, plugs, springs and adjusting screws. Tag all parts for reassembly reference.

Inspection

1) Wash all parts in clean kerosene and dry them with compressed air only (do not use fluffy rags, etc.). Check all parts for burrs and scores; replace assembly if damage is found.

VOLKSWAGEN VALVE BODY SPRING IDENTIFICATION CHART

Valve Spring	Length In. (mm)	Diameter In. (mm) [1]	Number Of Coils	Wire Thickness In. (mm)
Throttle Pressure Limiting Valve	1.492 (37.9)	.303 (7.7)	14.5	.043 (1.1)
Main Pressure Limiting Valve	1.083 (27.5)	.299 (7.6)	12.5	.047 (1.2)
Main Pressure Valve	2.724 (69.2)	.469 (11.9)	16.5	.055 (1.4)
3-2 Control Valve	1.732 (44.0)	.305 (7.75)	16.5	.043 (1.1)
Throttle Pressure Valve	1.126 (19.9)	.305 (7.75)	11.5	.031 (0.8)
1-2 Shift Valve	0.783 (19.9)	.319 (8.1)	6.5	.035 (0.9)
Converter Pressure Valve	0.874 (22.2)	.303 (7.7)	8.5	.049 (1.25)
Modulator Pressure Valve	1.276 (32.4)	.303 (7.7)	12.5	.039 (1.0)
2-3 Shift Valve	0.685 (17.4)	.274 (6.95)	8.5	.031 (0.8)
3-2 Kickdown Valve	1.118 (28.4)	.319 (8.1)	11.5	.035 (0.9)
1st/Reverse Apply Valve	1.429 (46.3)	.354 (9.0)	10.5	.025 (0.63)

[1] — Inner diameter of coils should be within a tolerance of ± .012" (.3 mm).

VOLKSWAGEN VANAGON (Cont.)

Fig. 16: Exploded View Showing Removal of Strainers and Valve Body Assembly

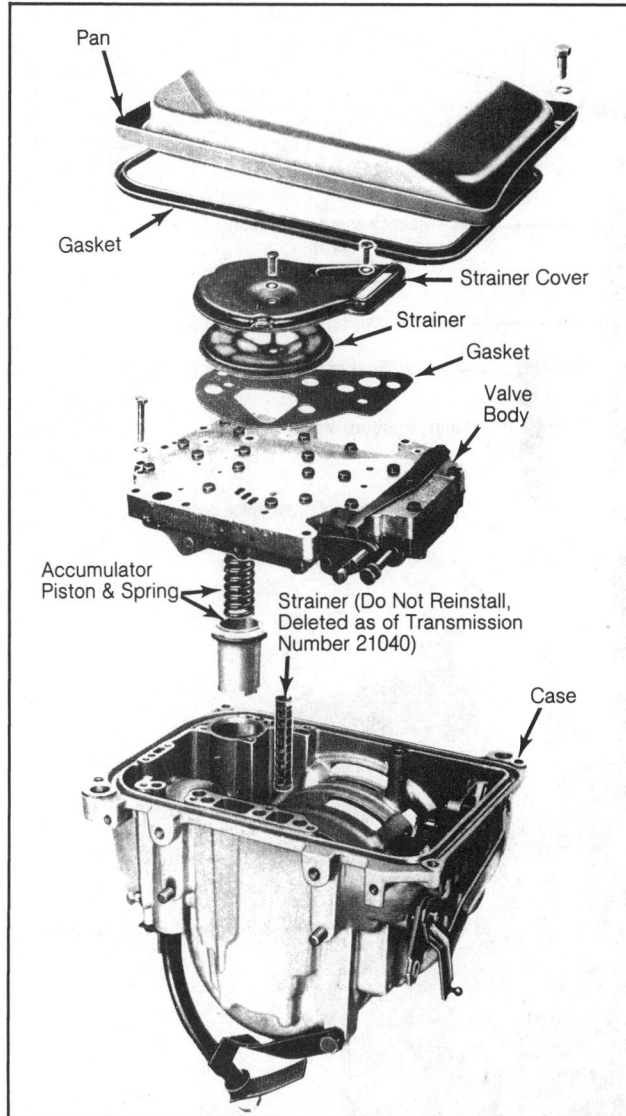

reverse order of disassembly. When tightening end plate attaching screws, be careful not to overtighten them as this could easily strip the threads or distort the valve body enough to cause a valve to stick.

Fig. 17: View of Main Valve Body Showing Check Ball Locations

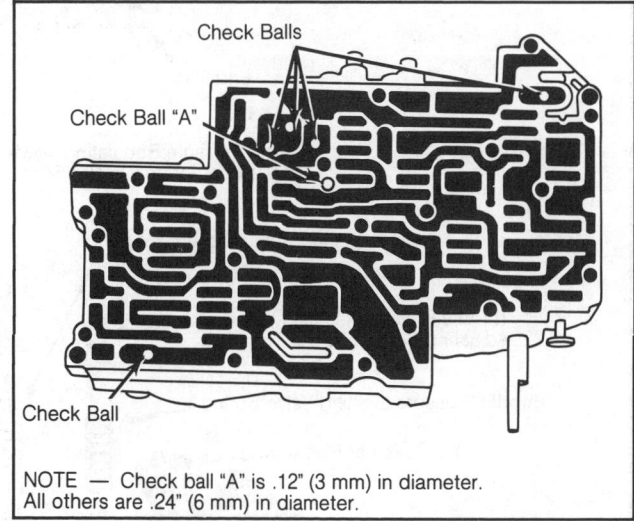

NOTE — Check ball "A" is .12" (3 mm) in diameter. All others are .24" (6 mm) in diameter.

2) Ensure all check balls are installed in proper valve body passages. Install transfer plate-to-main valve body screws and tighten from center outward, taking care not to overtighten.

NOTE: **Two collar-type screws are used for attaching roller assembly to body, 3 galvanized screws are for accumulator cover plate, and the remaining 17 screws are used for transfer plate-to-main body attachment.**

Fig. 18: View of Valve Body Installed

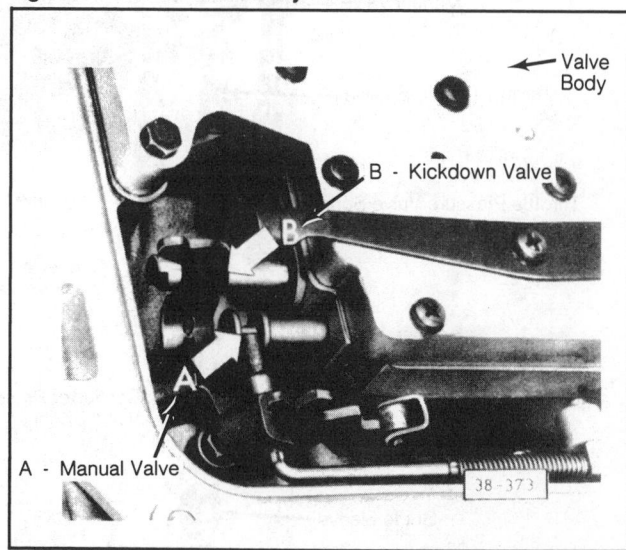

Arrows show relation of operating levers to manual control valves.

2) When valves are clean and lubricated with fluid, they should fall freely of their own weight in respective bore; if not, check for valve or bore damage.

3) Check all valve body springs for damage or collapsed coils.

CAUTION: **Several valve body springs have similar dimensions; however, they must not be interchanged as they have different tolerances. See Valve Body Spring Identification table.**

4) Take care not to disturb settings of adjusting screws; pressures affected by these screws can only be measured and adjusted accurately on a test stand.

Reassembly

1) Lubricate all parts with automatic transmission fluid and install into proper valve body bores, in

Automatic Transmissions
VOLKSWAGEN VANAGON (Cont.)

Fig. 19: Exploded View Showing Main Body Assembly Valve Trains

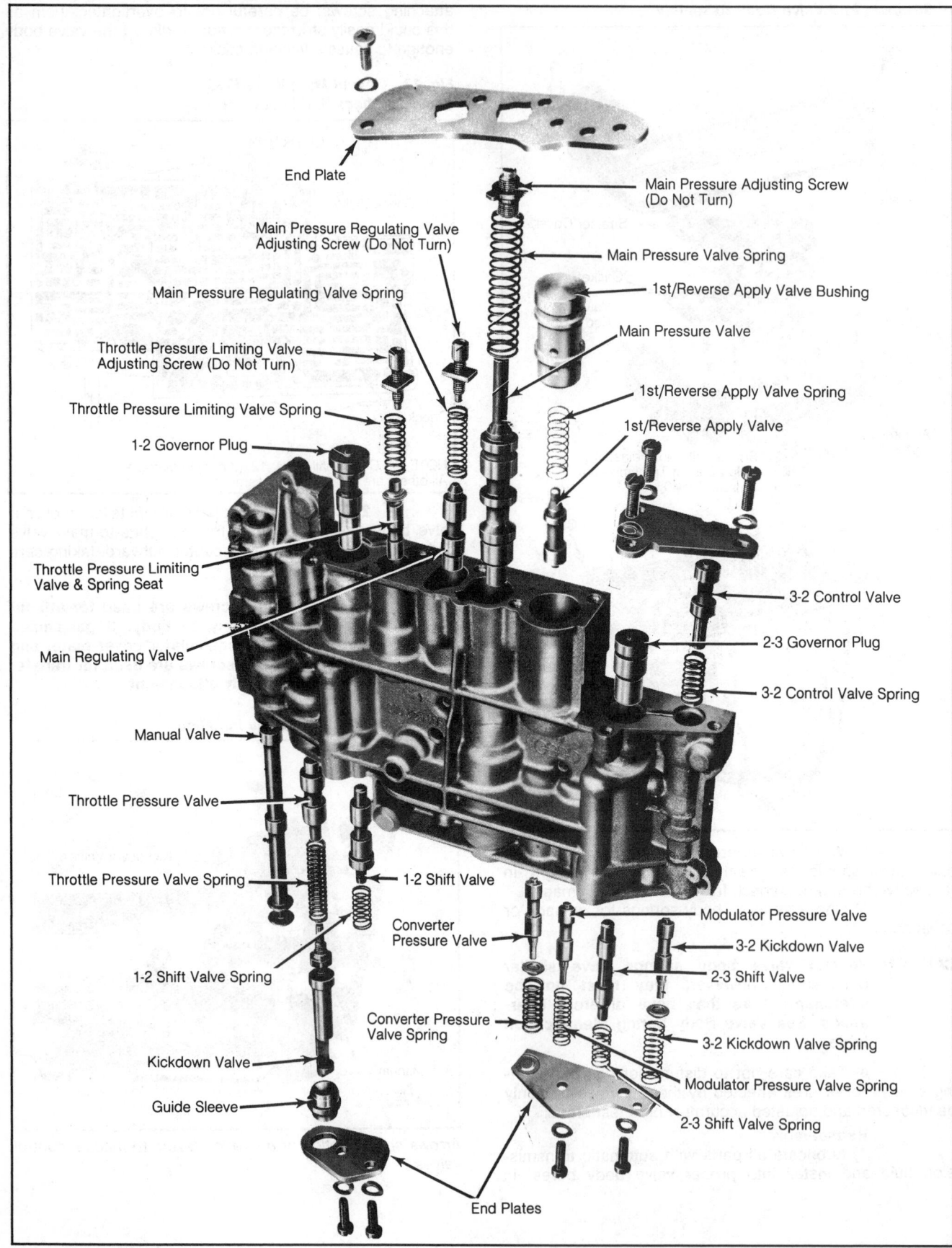

End Plate

Main Pressure Adjusting Screw (Do Not Turn)

Main Pressure Regulating Valve Adjusting Screw (Do Not Turn)

Main Pressure Valve Spring

Main Pressure Regulating Valve Spring

1st/Reverse Apply Valve Bushing

Throttle Pressure Limiting Valve Adjusting Screw (Do Not Turn)

Main Pressure Valve

Throttle Pressure Limiting Valve Spring

1st/Reverse Apply Valve Spring

1-2 Governor Plug

1st/Reverse Apply Valve

Throttle Pressure Limiting Valve & Spring Seat

3-2 Control Valve

Main Regulating Valve

2-3 Governor Plug

3-2 Control Valve Spring

Manual Valve

Throttle Pressure Valve

Throttle Pressure Valve Spring

1-2 Shift Valve

Converter Pressure Valve

Modulator Pressure Valve

3-2 Kickdown Valve

2-3 Shift Valve

1-2 Shift Valve Spring

Converter Pressure Valve Spring

3-2 Kickdown Valve Spring

Kickdown Valve

Modulator Pressure Valve Spring

Guide Sleeve

2-3 Shift Valve Spring

End Plates

VOLKSWAGEN VANAGON (Cont.)

Fig. 20: Exploded View Showing Components of Governor Assembly

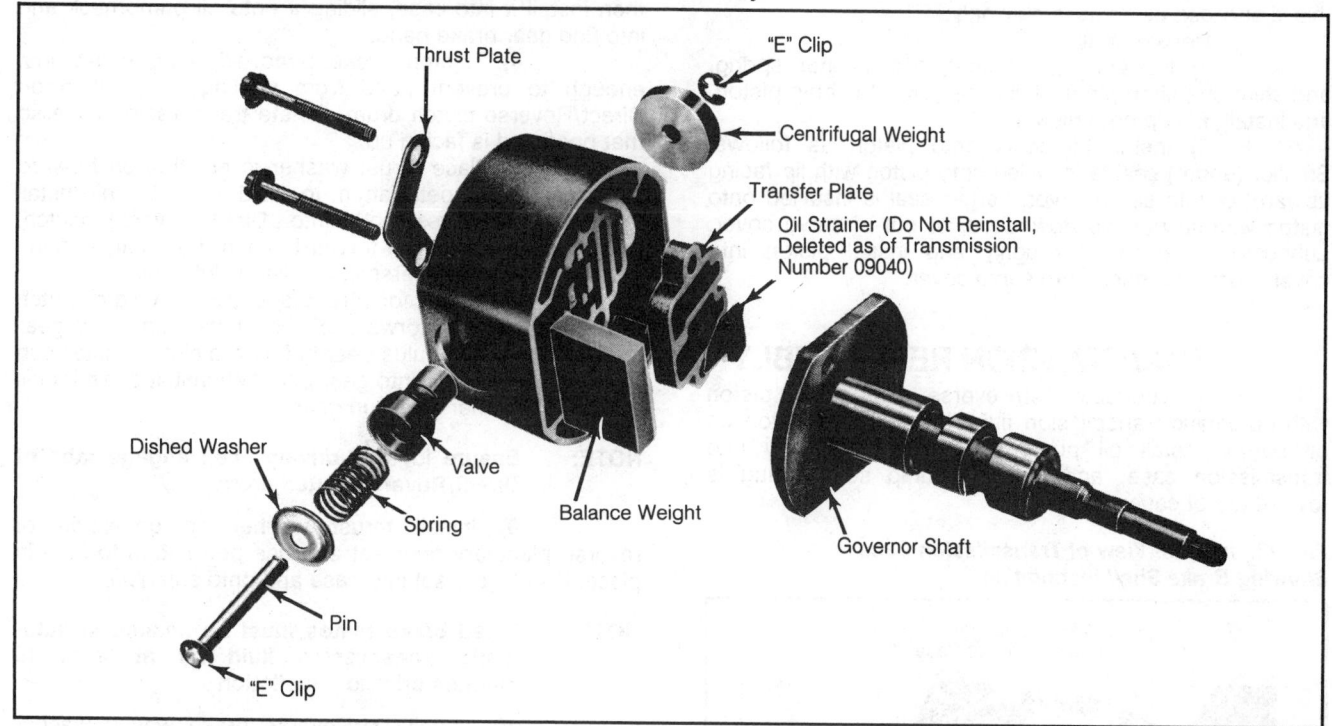

GOVERNOR ASSEMBLY

NOTE: **The governor is mounted in the final drive housing.**

Removal

Remove attaching bolts and washers and remove governor cover and "O" ring from final drive housing. Withdraw governor from housing using a clockwise twisting motion that will allow governor drive gear to disengage drive pinion gear.

Disassembly

Remove 2 attaching screws and withdraw thrust plate and governor housing. Remove transfer plate, balance weight, and if equipped, oil strainer. Remove "E" clips and withdraw centrifugal weight, valve, spring, and dished washer from pin.

Reassembly

Reverse disassembly procedure to assemble. Do not reinstall oil strainer in governor. Make sure angle in thrust plate is in center of housing so cover will bear against it.

Installation

Reverse removal procedure and note the following: Prior to installation, check governor oil seal and needle bearing in final drive case for damage and wear, and replace if necessary. After installation, rotate governor to engage drive gear.

BAND SERVO

Disassembly

Pull servo piston assembly out of cover, then remove "O" ring seals from outside diameter of cover. Remove retaining "E" clip and separate piston pin, accumulator spring, spring seat, and adjusting shim from servo piston. Withdraw 2 lip seals from piston.

Inspection

Clean all parts and check for wear, scoring, or other damage. If replacement of piston is necessary, pin,

Fig. 21: Disassembled View of Servo Assembly

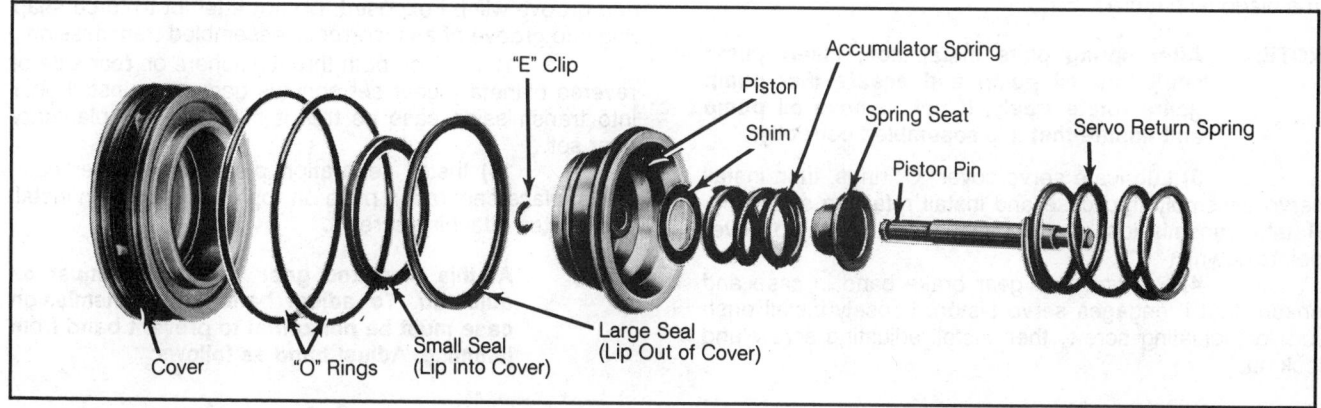

VOLKSWAGEN VANAGON (Cont.)

spring, spring seat, and shim must also be replaced as this is serviced as an assembly only.

Reassembly

1) Position spring seat, accumulator spring, and shim on piston pin, install assembly into servo piston, and install "E" clip onto piston.

2) Install lip seals onto piston as follows: Smaller (upper) seal is installed onto piston with lip facing upward, or into servo cover. Larger seal is installed onto piston with lip pointed downward, or out of servo cover. Lubricate assembly thoroughly and install piston into cover. Install "O" rings onto servo cover.

TRANSMISSION REASSEMBLY

1) Lubricate 1st/Reverse gear brake piston with automatic transmission fluid. Install brake piston on oil pump. Install oil pump and piston assembly into transmission case, and position pump so that lug is toward top of case.

Fig. 22: Internal View of Transmission Case Showing Brake Shell Installation

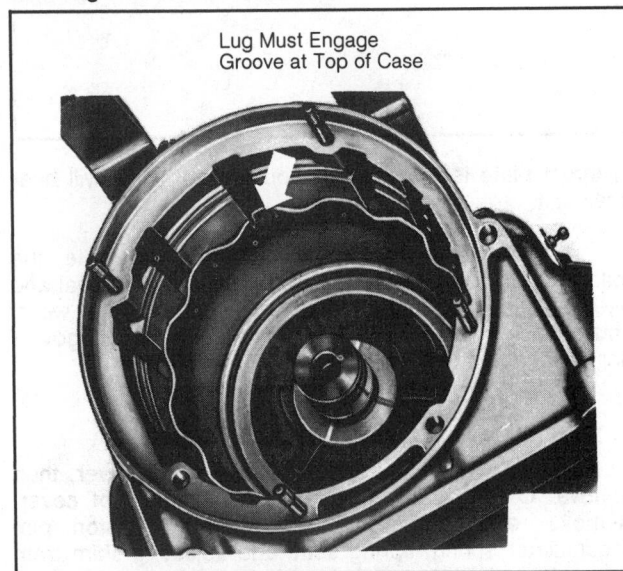

Lug Must Engage
Groove at Top of Case

2) Install 1st/Reverse gear brake shell into case so that lug engages in groove at top of case. Position 1st/Reverse brake piston return springs on spring plate, insert plate into case with springs downward, then install attaching bolts and tighten to specified torque in a diagonal pattern.

NOTE: **After spring plate installation, insert pump shaft into oil pump and ensure that pump gears rotate freely; if not, remove oil pump and ensure that it is assembled correctly.**

3) Lubricate servo cover "O" rings, then install servo assembly into case and install retaining snap ring. Rotate transmission on work stand so that servo cover points down.

4) Position 2nd gear brake band in case and ensure that it engages servo piston. Loosely install push rod for adjusting screw, then install adjusting screw and lock nut.

5) Lubricate Direct/Reverse clutch assembly, then install it into case, sliding it onto oil pump neck and into 2nd gear brake band.

6) Tighten brake band adjusting screw just enough to prevent band from shifting its position on Direct/Reverse clutch drum. Rotate transmission case so that open end is facing up.

7) Place thrust washer in position on forward clutch and use petrolatum to hold it in place. Install forward clutch assembly into Direct/Reverse clutch, making sure splines on forward clutch drum fully engage splines on Direct/Reverse clutch lined clutch plates.

8) Install forward planetary-to-forward clutch thrust washer into forward clutch. Install planetary gear set into forward annulus gear in forward clutch. Install sun gear (short end first) into gear set, then install driving shell and thrust washer over sun gear.

NOTE: **Ensure lugs of driving shell engage tabs of Direct/Reverse clutch drum.**

9) Install thrust washer on underside of reverse planetary gear set and use petrolatum to hold in place. Install gear set into case and onto sun gear.

NOTE: **Lined brake plates must be soaked in automatic transmission fluid for at least 15 minutes prior to installation**

10) Install 1st/Reverse brake waved washer into case. Install 1st/Reverse brake plates into case starting with a steel (external splines) plate and alternating lined (internal splines) plates and steel plates until all brake plates are installed.

FIRST/REVERSE BRAKE PLATE CHART

Application	Steel Plates	Lined Plates
All Models	5	5

11) Install 1st gear one-way clutch assembly into transmission case, then push clutch downward while rotating reverse planetary gear set to fully engage parts.

NOTE: **With one-way clutch installed, it should not be possible to rotate reverse planetary gear set counterclockwise due to the locking action of the one-way clutch.**

12) Install one-way clutch-to-case snap ring. If all parts are correctly installed, the one-way clutch snap ring groove will be exposed. Do not attempt to force snap ring into groove of an incorrectly assembled transmission.

13 Position both thrust washers on rear side of reverse planetary gear set annulus gear, then install gear into transmission case so that it fully engages planetary gear set.

14) Install separation plate gasket over case studs, place separation plate on top of gasket, then install and tighten attaching screws.

NOTE: **At this time 2nd gear brake band must be adjusted. To adjust band, the transmission case must be horizontal to prevent band from jamming. Adjust band as follows:**

VOLKSWAGEN VANAGON (Cont.)

Fig. 23: Checking for Correct Parts Installation

Parts are Installed Correctly if Groove for One-Way Clutch Snap Ring is Exposed

15) Tighten brake band adjusting screw to 84 INCH lbs. (9.5 N.m). Loosen screw. Retighten again to 43 INCH lbs. (5.0 N.m). Back off adjusting screw 2 1/2 turns and tighten adjusting screw lock nut.

16) If case linkage was disassembled, reassemble in case using *Fig. 5* as an assembly guide.

17) Install a new seal on accumulator piston (lip pointing toward case), and install piston and spring into case. Install valve body assembly into case, making sure manual valve engages manual lever, and that kickdown valve engages kickdown lever. Install valve body-to-case attaching bolts and tighten from center outward.

NOTE: **Do not use sealer on oil pan gasket, as any surplus sealer may find its way into transmission fluid and cause control valves to stick.**

18) Position a new oil pan gasket on transmission case. Install oil pan and tighten attaching bolts.

FINAL DRIVE

DISASSEMBLY

NOTE: **Measure pinion shaft turning torque BEFORE disassembly. See Pinion Depth and Bearing Preload adjustment for checking procedure.**

1) Remove retaining bolts from center of axle drive flange shafts and pull drive flanges from final drive housing. Mark position of each side bearing adjusting ring on ring and housing, then measure screw-in depth of each ring in housing using a micrometer. Record measurements for reassembly reference.

2) Remove final drive pan bolts and pan, then remove side bearing adjusting ring lock plates. While supporting differential, unscrew side bearing adjusting rings, move differential to right side of case, tilt upward, and remove from final drive housing.

3) If necessary for replacement, use a hook type puller and remove oil seal from each side bearing adjusting ring.

4) If differential side bearings are to be replaced, use a drift and drive bearing outer race from each adjusting ring.

5) Loosen ring gear attaching bolts, tap on bolts with a soft hammer to break loose ring gear, then remove ring gear from differential case.

6) If side bearings require replacement, pull from case using a puller. Using a screwdriver, pry differential housing cover from housing. Drive out pinion gear shaft, then withdraw differential pinion gears and thrust washers, side gears and thrust washers, and nuts for drive flange shaft retaining bolts.

Fig. 24: Removing Pinion Bearing Outer Race from Final Drive Housing

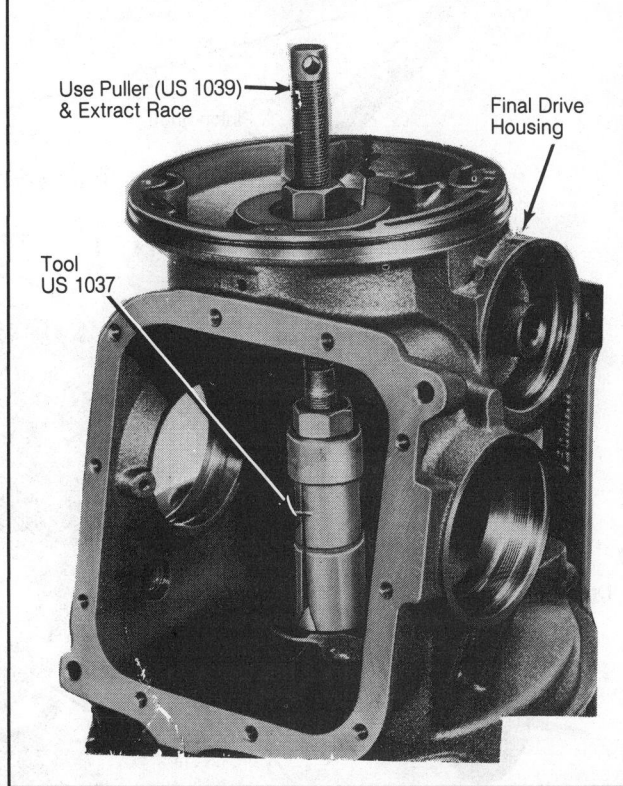

Use Puller (US 1039) & Extract Race

Final Drive Housing

Tool US 1037

7) Remove pinion shaft cover from final drive housing. Withdraw pinion shaft from final drive housing.

8) If necessary for replacement, use a press and press pinion oil seals out of pinion cover. If pinion shaft bearings are to be replaced, press bearing outer race from pinion cover.

9) Use a hook type puller and remove pinion oil seal from final drive housing. Remove other pinion shaft bearing outer race from final drive housing using a puller (US 1039 and US 1037) as shown in *Fig. 24*.

10) If necessary for replacement, use a press (with press plates to support bearing) and press bearings, shims and oil seal bushing from pinion shaft.

11) Use pullers to extract torque converter oil seal and governor oil seal from final drive housing.

Fig. 25: Exploded View Showing Main Components of Final Drive Assembly

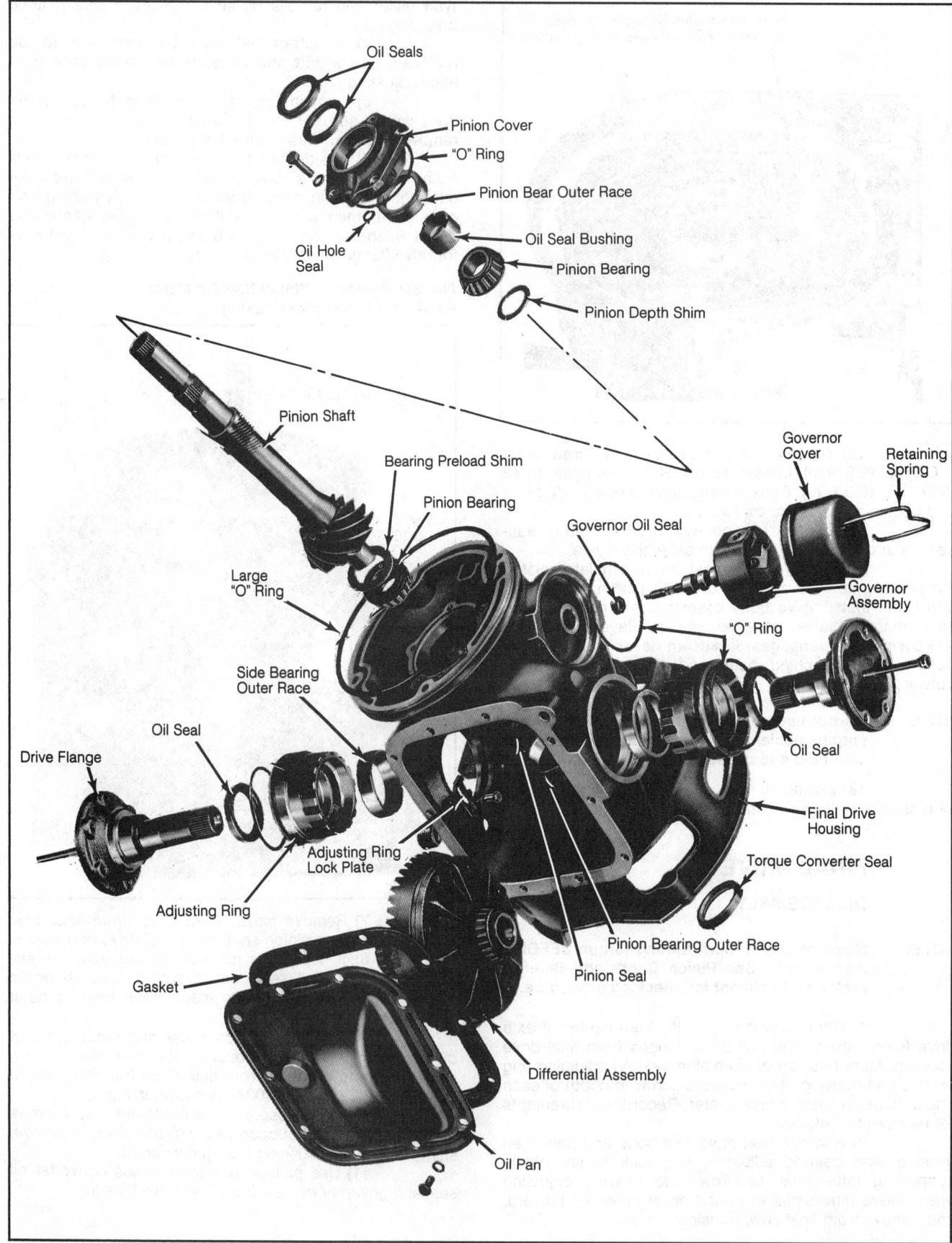

Fig. 26: Exploded View of Differential Assembly

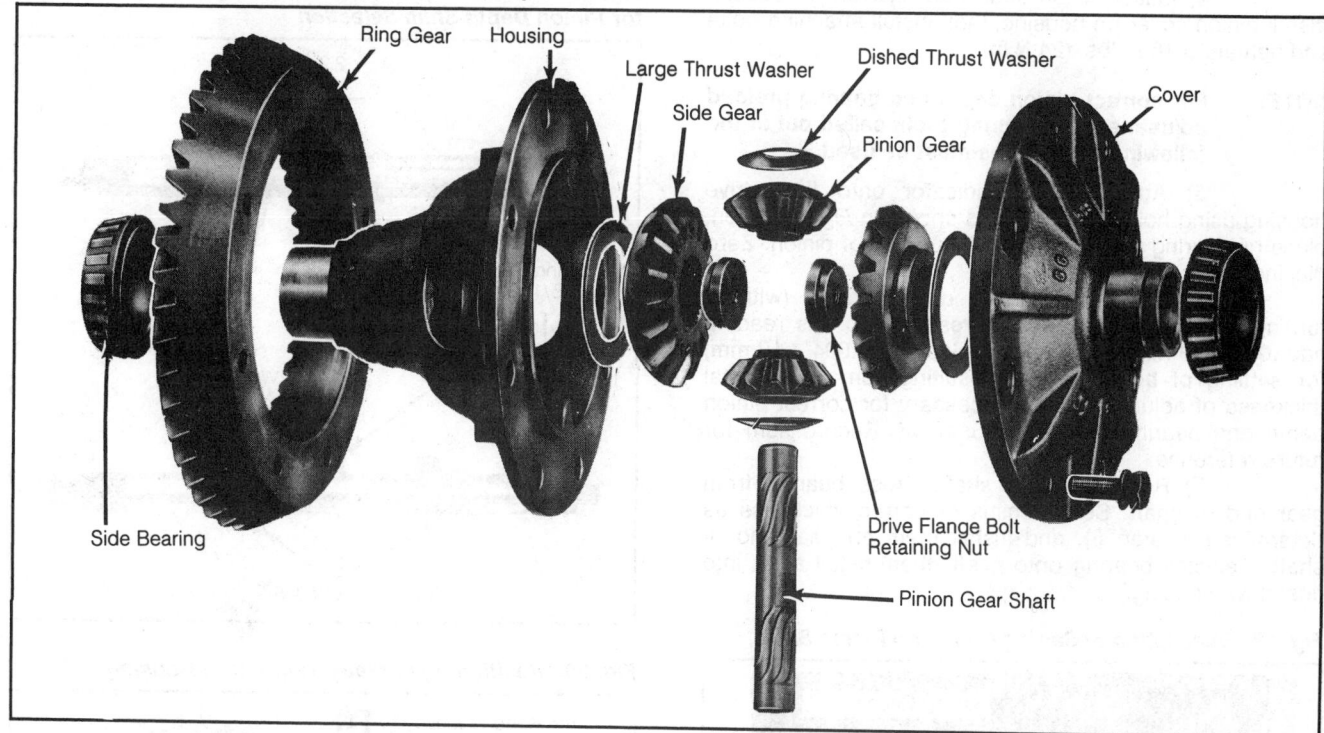

REASSEMBLY & ADJUSTMENTS

Differential Assembly

1) Inspect all thrust surfaces on differential housing, cover, ring gear, pinion gear shaft and thrust washers. Replace all worn parts. Inspect gear teeth for burrs, or excessive wear and replace as necessary.

NOTE: If ring gear requires replacement, pinion shaft must also be replaced as they are a matched set.

2) Position differential side gears, large thrust washers, dished washers, drive flange retaining bolt nuts and pinion gears in differential housing. Align pinion gear holes with pinion shaft holes in housing, then drive pinion gear shaft through gears.

NOTE: If differential pinion gear shaft does not fit tightly, replace it with a new shaft.

3) Heat ring gear in hot oil to approximately 212°F (100°C). Place differential cover on housing. Install ring gear on housing, then install attaching bolts through cover and into ring gear. Tighten attaching bolts to specified torque.

4) If differential side bearings were removed, heat them in oil and press them onto differential housing and cover. Press side bearing outer races into position in side bearing adjusting rings.

Pinion Depth and Bearing Preload

1) If original parts are reinstalled, use the same thickness pinion depth and bearing preload adjusting shims as were removed. If a new ring and pinion gear set is installed, new adjusting shims must be selected.

2) Press new pinion shaft bearing outer races into final drive housing and pinion cover until they are fully seated. Install new pinion oil seal into final drive case. Install new oil seal into final drive side of pinion cover with

Fig. 27: Measuring Pinion Shaft Play to Determine Total Pinion Adjusting Shim Thickness

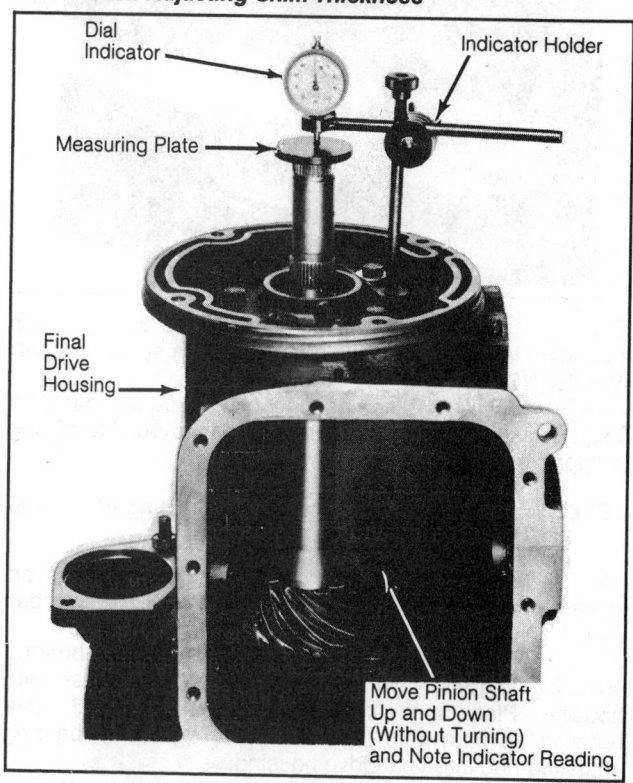

open side of seal towards final drive housing, then install a new oil seal into transmission side of pinion cover with open side towards transmission.

3) Heat pinion shaft bearings to 212°F (100°C) in hot oil. Install both bearings (without shims) onto pinion shaft until they are seated.

VOLKSWAGEN VANAGON (Cont.)

4) Install pinion shaft into final drive housing. Install pinion cover on housing, then install attaching bolts and tighten to 18 ft. lbs. (24 N.m).

NOTE: **For correct pinion depth and bearing preload adjustment, measuring tools called out in the following procedures must be used.**

5) Attach a dial indicator onto final drive housing using holder (VW 387) as shown in *Fig. 27*. Then, place measuring plate (VW 385/17) on end of pinion. Zero dial indicator without preload.

6) Move pinion shaft up and down (without turning) and note dial indicator reading. To this reading add .004" (.10 mm) for bearing preload and .004" (.10 mm) for settling of bearings. The resulting sum is the total thickness of adjusting shims necessary for correct pinion depth and bearing preload adjustment. Record sum for future reference.

7) Remove pinion shaft. Press bearing from gear end of shaft. Select shims of correct thickness as determined in step **6)**, and install them on gear end of shaft. Reinstall bearing onto shaft, then install shaft into final drive housing.

Fig. 28: Installation of Setting Gauge on Pinion Shaft

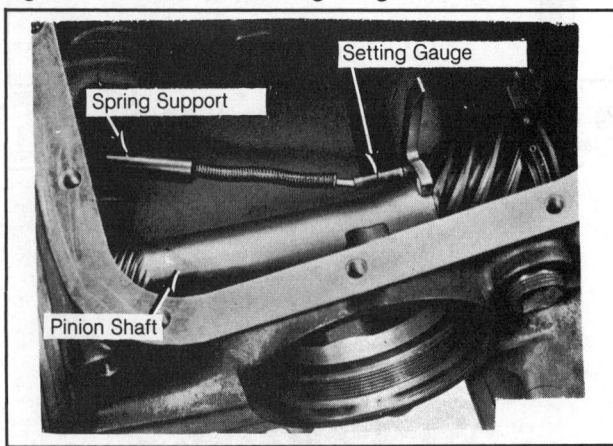

8) Install setting gauge (VW 385/22) on pinion as shown in *Fig. 28*, and hold in place with spring support (VW 385/19).

9) Adjust setting ring on measuring bar (VW 385/1), until distance from center of bar to outside of ring is approximately 2.9" (74 mm).

NOTE: **Refer to Fig. 29 for the assembling of tools to measuring bar.**

10) Slide centering discs (VW 385/2) on measuring bar. Screw measuring pin (VW 385/14) into bar with .118" (3 mm) extension (VW 385/20).

11) Screw left side differential side bearing adjusting ring into final drive housing until it is flush with housing. Place measuring bar assembly in final drive housing as shown in *Fig. 30*. Install right side bearing adjusting ring into final drive housing.

12) Turn knob on end of measuring bar to move centering discs outward until bar can just barely be turned by hand. Attach a dial indicator to measuring bar. Place setting block (VW 385/21) on measuring bar as shown in *Fig. 30*, then zero dial indicator without preload. Remove setting block.

Fig. 29: Assembling Special Measuring Tools for Pinion Depth Shim Selection

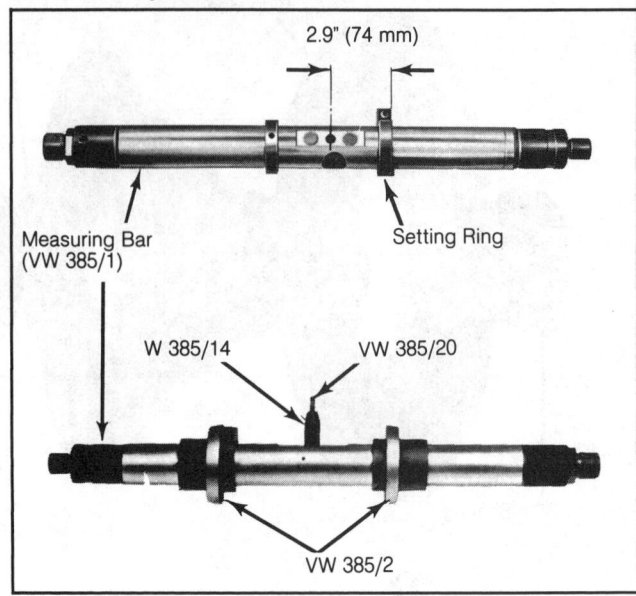

Fig. 30: Positioning of Measuring Bar in Housing

13) Rotate measuring bar until measuring pin rests against setting gauge on pinion face, then rotate bar back and forth over center. Read and record maximum dial indicator reading.

14) Add the dial indicator reading just obtained to the deviation number stamped in ring gear *(Fig. 31)*. The resulting sum is thickness of pinion depth adjusting shim to use at reassembly.

NOTE: **The ring gear deviation number is in hundredth millimeters.**

15) Next, subtract the thickness of pinion depth shim just selected from the total pinion adjusting shim thickness obtained in step **6)**. The remainder is thickness of pinion bearing preload shim to use at reassembly.

NOTE: **Pinion depth and bearing preload shims are available in thicknesses from .043" (1.1 mm) to .075" (1.9 mm) in increments of .001" (.025 mm). Also, shim thickness should be measured at several points on shim prior to installation to ensure correct thickness shims are being installed.**

VOLKSWAGEN VANAGON (Cont.)

Fig. 31: Location of Deviation Number on Ring Gear

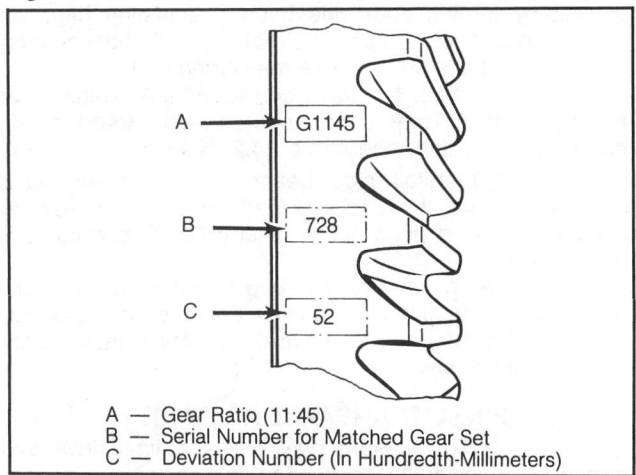

A — Gear Ratio (11:45)
B — Serial Number for Matched Gear Set
C — Deviation Number (In Hundredth-Millimeters)

16) Remove measuring tools and pinion shaft from final drive housing. Press bearings from pinion shaft. Install the selected pinion bearing preload shim onto gear end of pinion shaft, then press bearing back onto shaft. Place the selected pinion depth shim on opposite end of shaft, then press remaining bearing onto shaft along with pinion oil seal bushing.

17) Install pinion shaft into final drive housing and lubricate bearings with hypoid gear oil. Reinstall measuring bar into housing and zero dial indicator with .04" (1.0 mm) preload.

18) Recheck pinion depth and bearing preload adjustment. If correct shims have been installed, dial indicator reading should be equal to the ring gear deviation number with a tolerance of ± .0016" (.04 mm). Remove measuring bar and side bearing adjusting rings.

Fig. 32: Adjusting Ring Settings for Side Bearing Preload Adjustment

Screw in Left Ring 5 Teeth

Unscrew Right Ring 2 1/2 Teeth

19) Finally, attach a torque wrench to pinion shaft and check pinion shaft turning torque. Turning torque should be at least 12.4 INCH lbs. (1.4 N.m).

NOTE: Turning torque value given is for new bearings only. If used bearings are installed, turning torque should be measured piror to final drive disassembly. When assembled correctly, turning torque with used bearings should be approximately 1.7-3.5 INCH lbs. (.2-.4 N.m) greater than it was prior to disassembly.

Side Bearing Preload & Ring Gear Backlash

1) With pinion shaft correctly adjusted, install differential assembly into final drive housing. Coat "O" rings and threads of side bearing adjusting rings with multi-purpose grease and coat side bearings with hypoid gear oil.

2) Install both adjusting rings into final drive housing until they are flush with housing. Next, adjust right side (ring gear end) adjusting ring in until ring gear meshes with pinion shaft gear with no backlash, then screw left ring in and preload slightly so that side bearings have no play.

3) From this position, unscrew right adjusting ring 2 1/2 teeth, then screw in left adjusting ring 5 teeth. This should correctly set side bearing preload and ring gear backlash.

4) To check ring gear backlash, rotate pinion shaft several times in both directions to settle bearings. Install locking sleeve (VW 521/4) with slotted sleeve (VW 521/7) in differential and secure with nut. See Fig. 33.

5) Adjust length of backlash measuring bar (VW 388) to 3.15" (80 mm). Attach correctly adjusted measuring bar to locking sleeve.

Fig. 33: Installation of Backlash Measuring Bar on Locking Sleeve

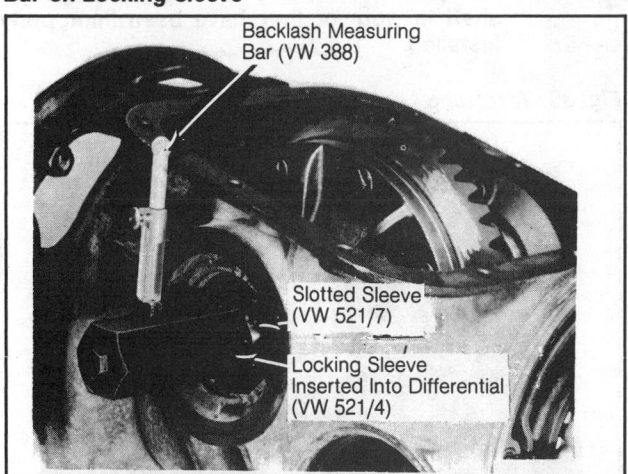

Backlash Measuring Bar (VW 388)

Slotted Sleeve (VW 521/7)

Locking Sleeve Inserted Into Differential (VW 521/4)

NOTE: Refer to Fig. 34 for positioning of ring gear backlash measuring tools.

6) Install dial indicator with .24" (6 mm) flat end extension (VW 382/10) in indicator holder (VW 387). Bolt holder to final drive housing so that indicator is located at a right angle to backlash measuring bar.

7) Turn ring gear (via pinion shaft) until measuring bar contacts dial indicator gauge pin, then turn

VOLKSWAGEN VANAGON (Cont.)

Fig. 34: Positioning of Ring Gear Backlash Measuring Tools

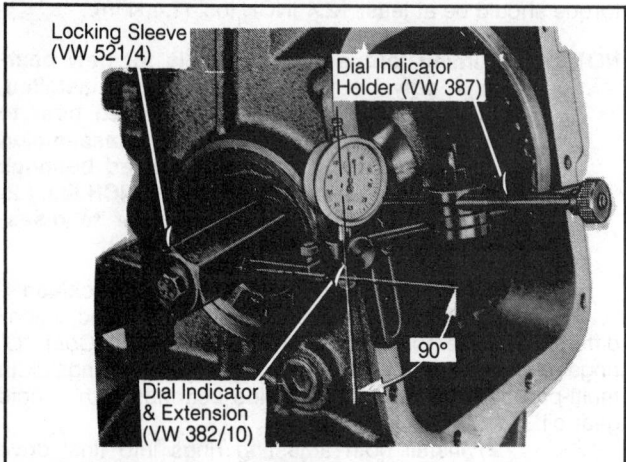

Indicator must be at right angle to measuring bar.

ring gear further until indicator shows .04" (1 mm) preload. Attach locking clamp (VW 386) to pinion shaft as shown in *Fig. 35*, then tighten clamp screw to lock pinion shaft.

8) Turn ring gear away from dial indicator until it is stopped by the locked pinion shaft, then zero dial indicator. Next, turn ring gear towards indicator until it is again stopped by pinion shaft. Read and record indicator reading. This reading is the ring gear backlash.

9) Repeat backlash measurement procedure at three other points 90° apart around ring gear. Add the four measurements together, then divide the total by four. The resulting sum is the average ring gear backlash, which should be .006-.010" (.15-.25 mm).

NOTE: **The individual backlash measurements should not vary from each other by more than .002" (.05 mm); if they do, ring gear or pinion shaft is worn or they have been improperly installed.**

Fig. 35: Attaching Locking Clamp to Pinion Shaft

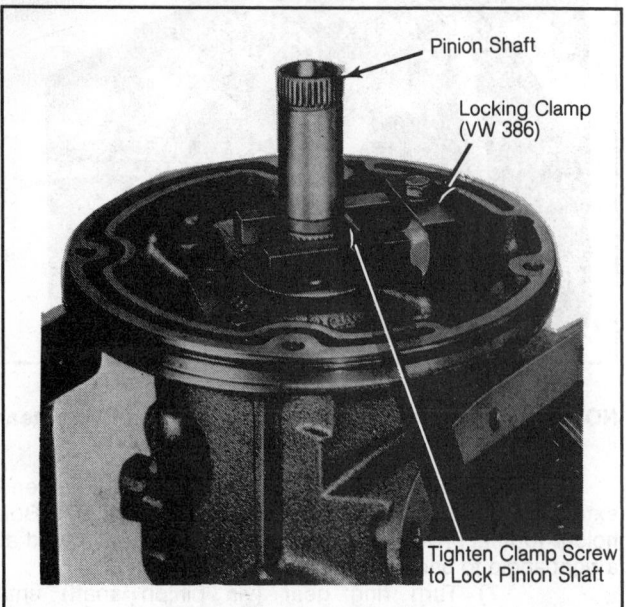

10) If backlash is not within specifications, correct by turning both side bearing adjusting rings an equal amount in opposite directions so that bearing preload is not altered. Remove measuring tools.

11) With backlash correct, check pinion shaft turning torque. Total pinion shaft turning torque, with differential installed, should be 14.2 INCH lbs. (1.6 N.m).

12) Install side bearing adjusting ring lock plates and tighten bolts to specified torque. Install new oil seals in adjusting rings. Install final drive oil pan using a new gasket.

13) Install a new torque converter oil seal into final drive housing. Install a new governor oil seal into housing with lip pointing toward governor, then install governor assembly.

FINAL TRANSAXLE ASSEMBLY

1) To measure play between final drive and transmission, place a straightedge on transmission attaching face of final drive housing, and using a depth gauge, measure distance from top surface of straightedge down to edge of pinion shaft oil seal bushing.

2) Next, measure distance from top surface of straightedge to face of final drive housing. Subtract this second measurement from first measurement obtained in step **1)** and note for future reference.

3) Place a new gasket on transmission separation plate, position straightedge on transmission case, and measure distance from top surface of straightedge down to gasket surface. Next, measure distance from top of straightedge down to shim surface on shoulder of annulus gear flange. Subtract this measurement from first measurement obtained in this step and record for future reference.

4) Subtract the last measurement obtained in step **3)** from last measurement obtained in step **2)**. Remainder is end play (without shims) between final drive and transmission. Select proper end play shim(s) to use by finding applicable end play reading in first column of *End Play Shim Chart*, and obtaining shim thickness noted in second column.

NOTE: **Transmission-to-final drive end play adjusting shims are available in thicknesses of .016" (.4 mm) and .047" (1.2 mm). Combine shim thicknesses to obtain total thickness required.**

END PLAY SHIM SELECTION CHART

If End Play Is In. (mm)	Install This Shim In. (mm)
.009-.033 (.23-.84)	None
.034-.049 (.85-1.24)	.016 (.4)
.050-.065 (1.25-1.64)	.032 (.8)
.066-.080 (1.65-2.04)	.048 (1.2)
.081-.096 (2.05-2.44)	.064 (1.6)
.097-.112 (2.45-2.84)	.080 (2.0)
.113-.128 (2.85-3.24)	.096 (2.4)
.129-.143 (3.25-3.64)	.112 (2.8)
.144-.153 (3.65-3.88)	.128 (3.2)

5) Install selected shim(s) into final drive case, on top of pinion shaft oil seal bushing. Next, lubricate and install sealing "O" ring into groove on transmission end of final drive housing.

SECTION 7

IMPORT MANUAL TRANSMISSIONS

NOTE: ALSO SEE GENERAL INDEX.

Manual Transmissions

AUDI 4000 4-SPEED

DESCRIPTION

Transaxle is a 4-speed fully synchronized unit with independent front suspension. Transmission has helical cut gears which are in constant mesh with the exception of reverse gear.

Mainshaft is carried at front end by a needle bearing in final drive housing and at rear by a ball bearing in transmission case. Countershaft incorporates axle drive pinion gear and is carried by a straight roller bearing at pinion gear end and by a ball bearing in transmission case.

Pinion gear drive depth is controlled by a spacing shim at transmission end of countershaft. Differential assembly is carried by taper roller bearings located in final drive housing and final drive housing side plate.

Shims located behind outer roller bearing races control backlash and preload of differential assembly bearings. Axle drive flanges press into differential assembly and are retained by bolts.

LUBRICATION & ADJUSTMENT

See the appropriate article in MANUAL TRANS-MISSION SERVICING Section.

SERVICE (IN-VEHICLE)

AXLE DRIVE SHAFTS

NOTE: **Vehicle weight must be resting on wheels to remove axle shaft nut.**

Removal

1) Loosen axle shaft nut. Raise and support vehicle. Remove axle nut and wheel. Disconnect and remove exhaust pipe from exhaust manifold and transaxle bracket on right side of engine. Remove Allen bolts connecting inner constant velocity (CV) joint to differential case drive flange.

2) Mark position of both ball joint flanges on the control arms. Remove ball joint from control arm and pull pivot mounting outward while removing drive shaft. Press drive shaft out of hub and guide past transaxle.

NOTE: **Axle drive shafts should be disassembled ONLY to replace defective rubber boots. If boots are replaced, check all components for wear or damage and replace as complete assembly.**

Disassembly

1) On inner CV joint, remove circlip from axle shaft and drive protective cap from CV joint. Place axle shaft in holder (VW402) and press CV joint from shaft with adapter (VW408a), supporting hub to prevent damage. Pivot hub and cage assembly out of inner joint, then push out and remove balls. Align ball hub grooves with cage and remove hub.

NOTE: **Inner CV joint and ball hub are matched sets. DO NOT interchange with outer joint. Also, balls of CV joints cannot be interchanged between CV joints.**

Fig. 2: Removing Inner CV Joint Ball Hub

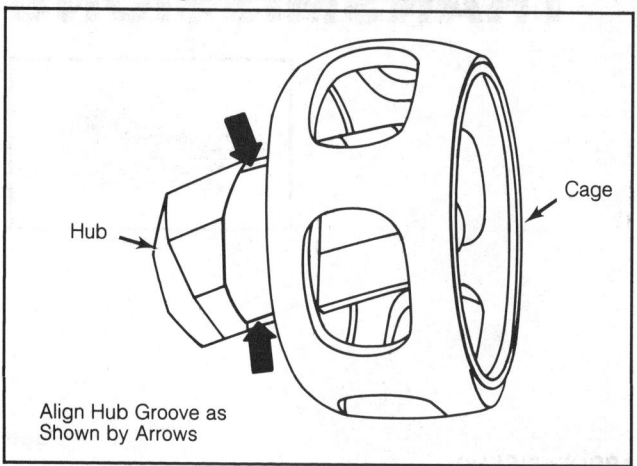

Align Hub Groove as Shown by Arrows

2) Remove and discard inner boot clamp and boot. On outer CV joint, spread circlip inside ball hub and drive CV joint off axle shaft with brass drift; tap on hub. Mark position of ball hub and outer joint, then tilt cage and remove each ball.

Fig. 1: Exploded View of Axle Shaft Assembly

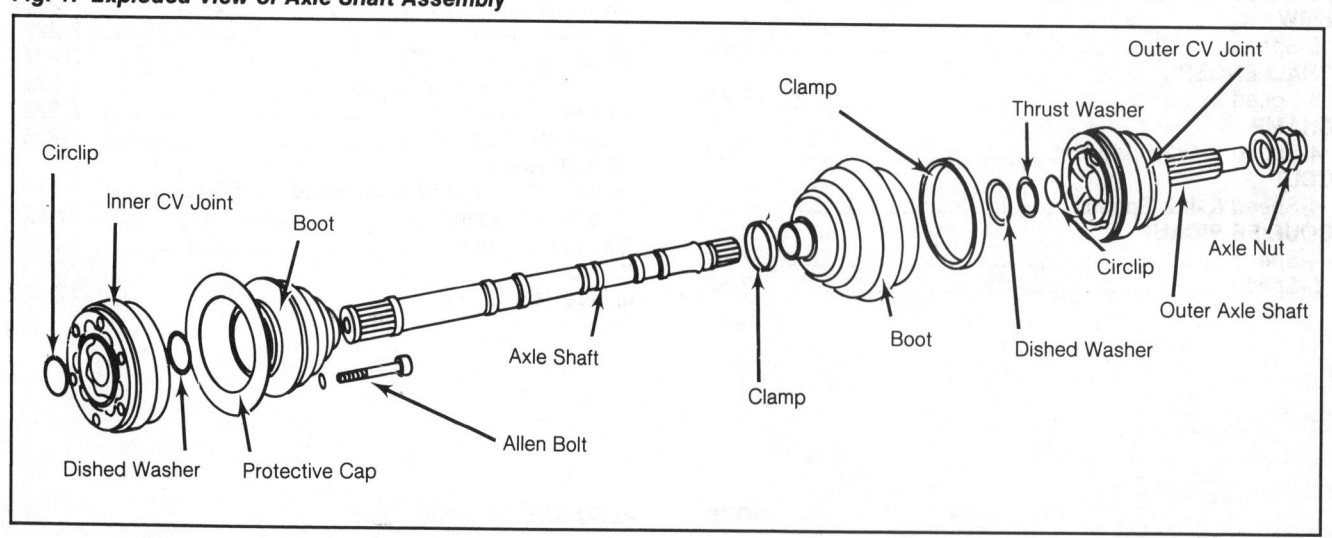

AUDI 4000 4-SPEED (Cont.)

3) Align cage perpendicular to joint. Align 2 large openings of cage with raised portions of joint and remove cage and hub. Position 1 retainer of hub in large opening and remove hub by tilting outward. Remove and discard outer boot and clamp.

Reassembly

1) To reassemble CV joints, reverse disassembly procedure and note the following: Lubricate joints with 3 ozs. (90 g) of molybdenum disulphide grease. After inserting balls into inner CV joint hub and cage, insert hub and cage into joint perpendicularly.

2) Chamfer of ball hub splines must face larger diameter of joint. Then rotate ball and cage into position and ensure CV joint wide ball groove and narrow hub groove are on same side of joint. *See Fig. 3.* Joint is correctly assembled if hub can move over shaft splines by hand.

Fig. 3: Installing Ball Hub and Cage in Inner CV Joint

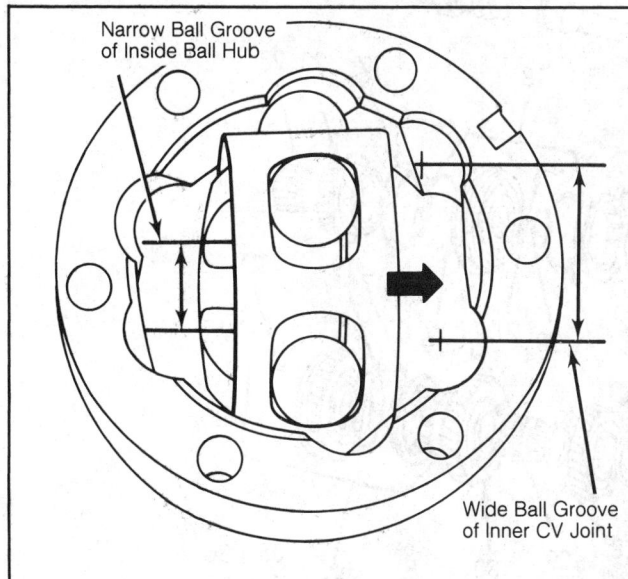

3) Outer CV joint alignment marks must match after reassembly. Replace dust boots and clamps. Install CV joints onto drive axle shaft with inside ball hub chamfer facing shaft.

4) Outer CV joint must be assembled with dished washer concave side facing thrust washer and convex side of thrust washer facing CV joint. *See Fig. 4.*

5) Inner CV joint must be assembled with dished washer concave side facing CV joint when installed

Fig. 4: Cutaway View of Outer CV Joint Showing Installation of Dished and Thrust Washers

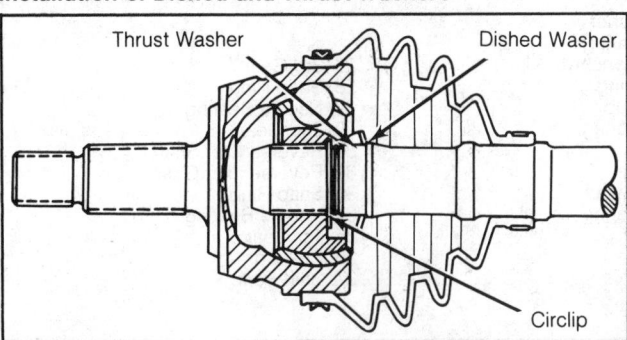

on shaft. Install boot clamps with open end facing opposite direction of normal rotation. Always use new circlips to retain CV joints on shafts.

Installation

To install, reverse removal procedure and note the following: After installing right shaft, align ball joint with mark made at removal and tighten nuts. Check camber setting and adjust if necessary.

FRONT WHEEL BEARINGS

Removal

1) With vehicle supported and drive axle shafts removed, remove stabilizer bar clamps. Remove caliper mounting bolts and hang caliper from frame with wire; DO NOT disconnect hydraulic line. Remove brake disc and ball joint bolt. Press off tie rod and remove ball joint from hub.

2) Support suspension strut with jack and remove upper strut retaining nuts from inside engine compartment. Remove strut assembly from vehicle and mount in holding fixture.

3) Press out wheel hub with hub remover (VW295 & 295a). Remove circlips from both sides of bearing housing and press out bearing (toward outboard end of housing). Remove inner wheel bearing race from hub.

NOTE: **Wheel bearing must be replaced. Removal procedure destroys wheel bearing for reuse.**

Fig. 5: Exploded View of Front Suspension Strut Assembly

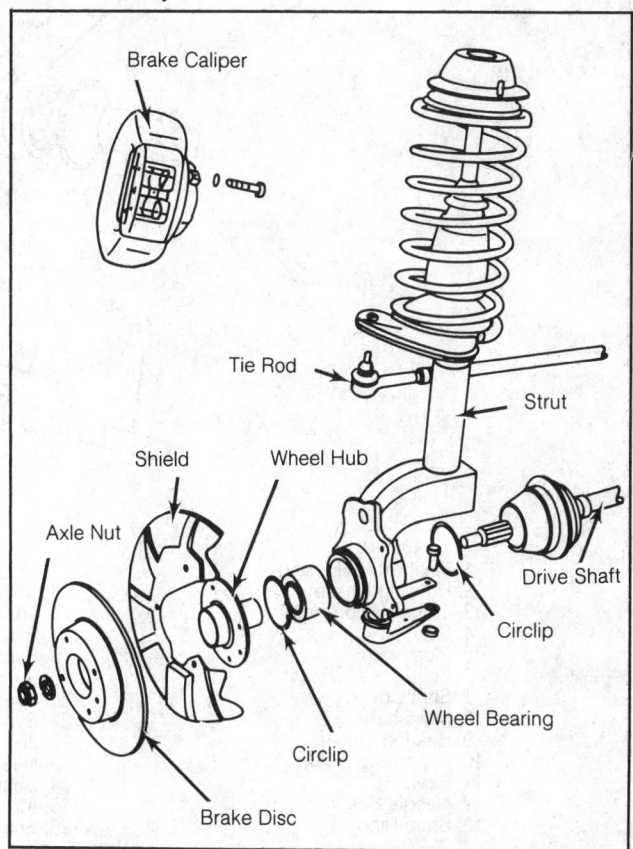

Manual Transmissions
AUDI 4000 4-SPEED (Cont.)

Fig. 6: Exploded View of Audi/Volkswagen 4-Speed Transaxle Assembly

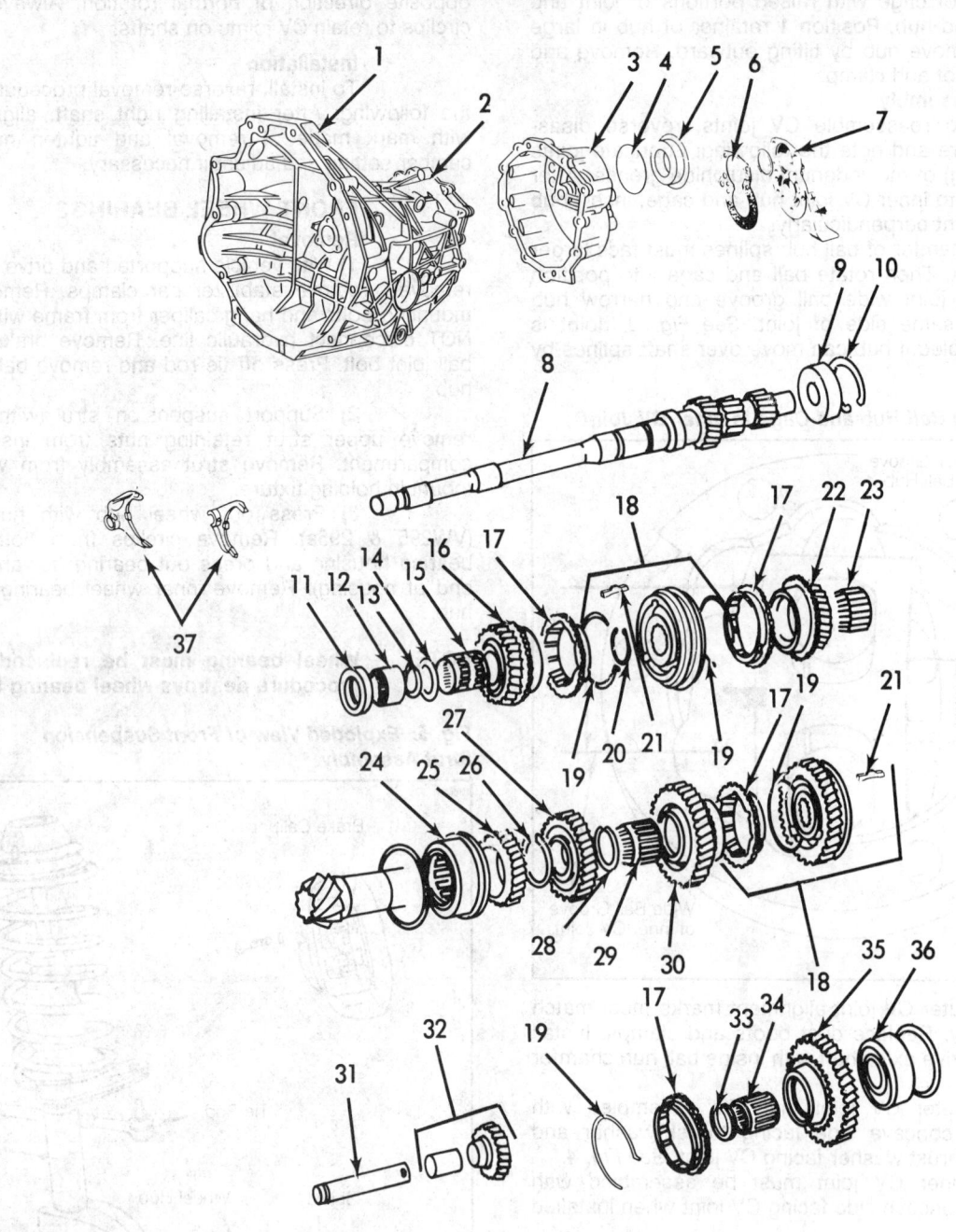

1. Final Drive Housing	14. Thrust Washer	
2. Housing Gasket	15. Needle Bearing	
3. Transmission Housing	16. 4th Gear Synchro	27. 3rd Gear
4. Seal	17. Blocking Ring	28. Snap Ring
5. Plug	18. Synchro Hub	29. Needle Bearing
6. Shift Cover Gasket	19. Synchro Spring	30. 2nd Gear
7. Shift Cover	20. Snap Ring	31. Reverse Idler Shaft
8. Mainshaft	21. Synchro Key	32. Reverse Idler Gear
9. Bearing	22. 3rd Gear Synchro	33. Snap Ring
10. Snap Ring	23. Needle Bearing	34. Needle Bearing
11. Seal	24. Bearing	35. 1st Gear
12. Needle Bearing	25. 4th Gear	36. Bearing
13. Snap Ring	26. Trap Ring	37. Shift Fork

AUDI 4000 4-SPEED (Cont.)

Installation

To install, reverse removal procedure and note the following: Offset portion of stabilizer bar must be installed facing downward.

INNER DRIVE FLANGE OIL SEALS
Removal

Disconnect inner CV joint from drive flange and support drive axle out of the way. Insert a long drift punch into 1 drive flange hole to prevent drive flange movement, then remove drive flange retaining bolt. Place drip pan under transaxle housing and pull out drive flange. Pry out oil seal.

Installation

Lightly lubricate seal lips and fully seat seal with driver (30-212). Install drive flange and tighten drive flange retaining bolt. Install drive axle and tighten bolts. Check and add lubricant to transaxle, if required.

TRANSAXLE REMOVAL & INSTALLATION

See the appropriate article in MANUAL TRANS-MISSION REMOVAL Section.

TRANSAXLE DISASSEMBLY

1) Remove drive flange attaching bolt. Remove drive flanges as previously outlined. Remove final drive cover bolts and pry off final drive cover. Remove differential.

2) Mount transaxle in a work fixture and drain fluid. Remove shift housing, gasket and shim from transaxle case. Retain shim and gasket for future use in determining shift housing position.

3) Measure drive pinion depth using gauge tool (VW385/1). To assemble tool, adjust sliding set ring until it is about 2" (50 mm) from center of bar. Assemble remainder of tool. See Fig. 13. With master gauge on end of plunger, set dial indicator to .157" (4 mm) for preload.

4) Zero dial indicator by removing master gauge (VW385/23). Place end plate (VW385/17) onto end of drive pinion. Install gauge tool into housing and install final drive cover with bearing race. Tighten cover bolts to specification. Adjust centering ring outward until tool can just be turned by hand.

5) Rotate tool by hand until maximum dial indicator deflection is reached and note measurement. This measurement is the production deviation from nominal pinion depth. Record measurement for future use in case deviation is not marked on gear set.

6) Carefully pull 3rd/4th gear selector rod away from transmission housing until interlock can be removed. Remove interlock and push rod back into neutral position. Lock shafts by engaging 1st and reverse shift rails.

7) Install mainshaft support bar (VW30-211) and tighten bolt until it touches mainshaft. Remove circlip and thrust washer from mainshaft. Remove mainshaft bearing with puller (330-207). Remove transmission housing attaching bolts. Remove transmission housing from final drive housing. Drive out dowel pins.

NOTE: DO NOT drop magnet from rear of final drive cover.

COMPONENT DISASSEMBLY & REASSEMBLY

SHIFT HOUSING ASSEMBLY

NOTE: Shift housing shim and gasket thickness will have to be determined if any of the following items are replaced: Mainshaft ball bearing, pinion shaft ball bearing, transmission case or shift housing.

Disassembly

Pull selector shaft from shift housing. Using arbor press and tool (VW418a), press transmission rear mount from shift housing. With a drift, drive out inner bushing. Pry oil seal from nose of shift housing. Using tool (VW439), press outer bushing from nose of shift housing.

Reassembly

1) Using tool (32-102), drive outer bushing into nose of shift housing until flush. Using same tool, install oil seal in same manner. Turn housing end for end and drive inner bushing in until flush with same tool.

2) Install new rear mount onto nose of housing using press and tool (VW455). Slide selector shaft into housing assuring that spring presses inner shift lever in direction of 3rd and 4th gear selector shaft.

3) Mount a dial indicator on measuring tool (VW382/7), then zero dial indicator with .12" (3 mm) preload. Measure distance between mainshaft bearing and gear carrier housing (Dimension "A" in Fig. 7).

4) Measure distance between pinion bearing and gear carrier housing (Dimension "B" in Fig. 7). Then

Fig. 7: Cutaway View Showing the Various Dimensions for Gearshift Housing Shim and Gasket Selections

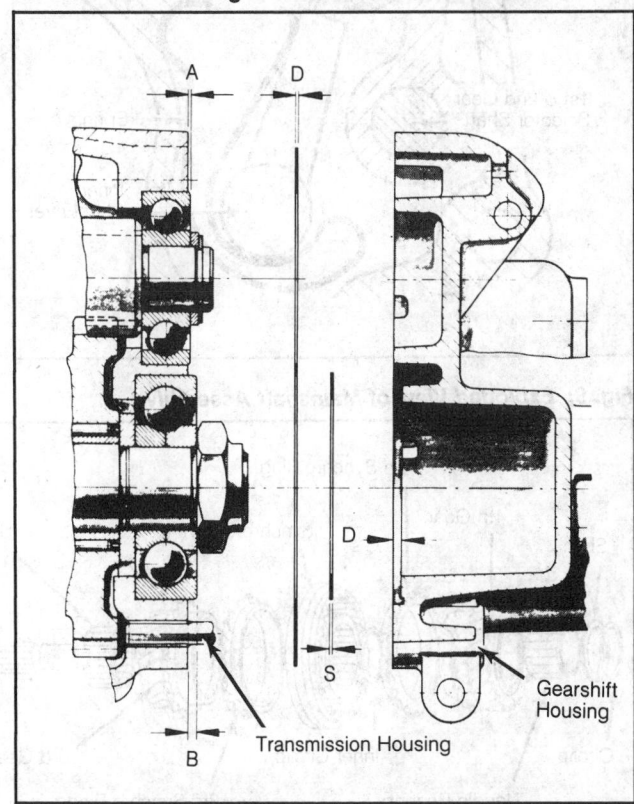

Transmission Housing

Gearshift Housing

Manual Transmissions

AUDI 4000 4-SPEED (Cont.)

measure distance between end face of gearshift housing and shim contact surface in gearshift housing (*Dimension "C" in Fig. 7*).

5) To compute shim thickness (*Dimension "S" in Fig. 7*), add dimension "A" to dimension "C", then subtract dimension "B" from this total. Use only 1 shim and always use shim closest to required value.

NOTE: **Gearshift housing shims are available in thicknesses from .018" (.45 mm) to .030" (.75 mm) in increments of .002" (.05 mm). Use shims with code letter "A" which are flat on one side.**

6) To determine housing gasket thickness (*Dimension "D" in Fig. 7*), measure projection of mainshaft bearing (*Dimension "A" in Fig. 7*). If dimension "A" is .008-.010" (.20-.25 mm), use a gasket .012" (.30 mm) thick or if "A" is .011-.013" (.28-.33 mm), use a gasket .016" (.41 mm) thick.

Fig. 8: Shift Housing Inner Shift Lever Spring Installation Position

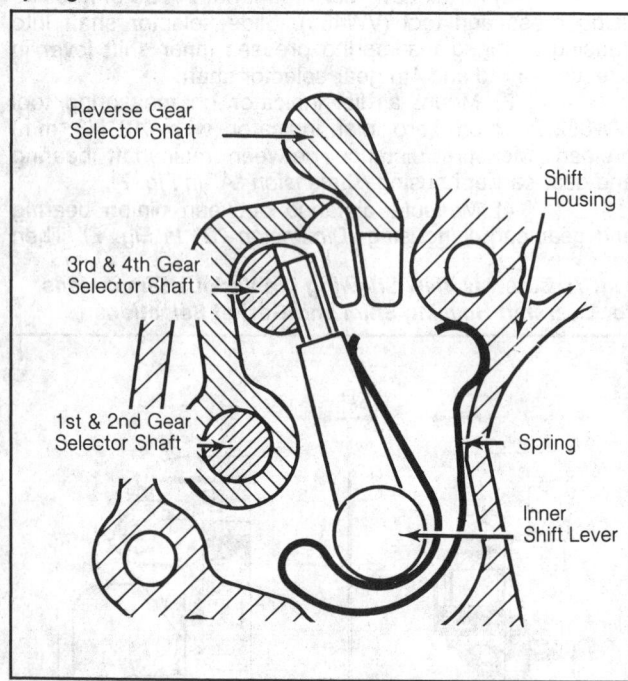

Reverse Gear Selector Shaft

Shift Housing

3rd & 4th Gear Selector Shaft

1st & 2nd Gear Selector Shaft

Spring

Inner Shift Lever

TRANSMISSION HOUSING ASSEMBLY
Disassembly

1) Mount transmission housing in soft-jawed vise. Support selector rod with a hammer to prevent damage to selector rod bore, then drive out 3rd/4th shift fork roll pin. Remove 3rd/4th shift fork and mainshaft while pulling 3rd/4th shift rail out rear of transmission housing.

2) Unscrew reverse lever bolt from top of transmission case. Remove reverse lever, shift fork and shift rail pin from transmission housing. Working from inside transmission case, drive reverse idler shaft out rear of housing and lift out reverse idler gear.

3) Drive out 1st/2nd shift dog roll pin, then remove shift dog from shift rail. Remove pinion shaft nut. Remove housing from vise and press pinion shaft out of bearing, tapping on 1st/2nd shift rail to prevent binding during shaft and rail removal.

NOTE: **If transaxle is being reassembled without replacing parts, readjustment of pinion depth is not necessary. However, if transaxle case, transmission housing, pinion bearing, 1st gear needle bearing or ring and pinion gear set are replaced, pinion depth MUST be checked and shim replaced if required. See Drive Pinion Depth in this article.**

Reassembly

1) Using a press and arbor (VW426), press in pinion shaft and pinion bearing race with 1st/2nd shift fork and rail properly engaged. Install reverse gear and press in reverse shaft. Insert reverse shift rail, roll pin and relay lever. Install reverse lever bolt with washer and push relay lever in toward case.

2) Turn lever bolt until it aligns with relay lever hole. Back off bolt until starting thread engages with threaded hole in lever. Tighten bolt to 25 ft. lbs. (34 N.m). Select reverse gear position several times. If lever and reverse gear do not move easily through full range of movement, repeat adjustment of reverse relay lever.

3) Place 1st/2nd shift dog on shift rail and install roll pin. Install mainshaft and 3rd/4th shift fork into case. Place selector rod in neutral position and install 3rd/4th roll pin.

Fig. 9: Exploded View of Mainshaft Assembly

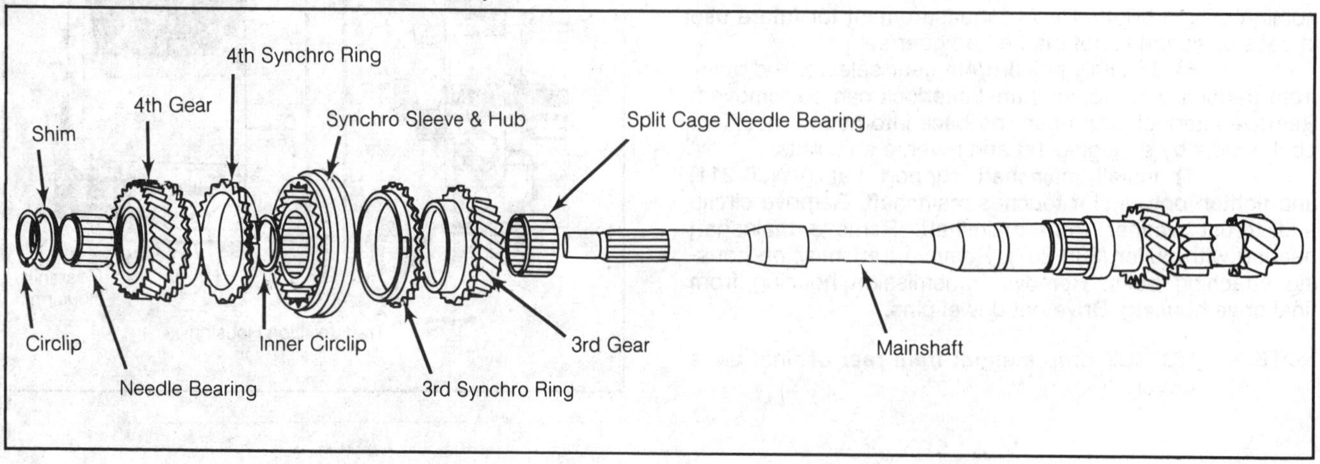

Shim

4th Gear

4th Synchro Ring

Synchro Sleeve & Hub

Split Cage Needle Bearing

Circlip

Needle Bearing

Inner Circlip

3rd Synchro Ring

3rd Gear

Mainshaft

AUDI 4000 4-SPEED (Cont.)

NOTE: If mainshaft bearing was replaced with a new bearing, shift housing gasket and shim thickness must be calculated. See Shift Housing Assembly.

4) Engage 3rd/4th shift fork with synchro sleeve on mainshaft (wider shoulder of shift fork facing 4th gear). Slide mainshaft and shift fork into transmission housing. Insert 3rd/4th shift rail through shift fork and install spring pin. Pull 3rd/4th shift rail out rear of transmission far enough to install lock pin. Install shim washer and circlip on transmission end of mainshaft.

5) Engage 1st and reverse gears and tighten pinion shaft nut to specifications. Check that shift rods work correctly and that forks are properly engaged prior to assembling gear case to transaxle case.

MAINSHAFT ASSEMBLY

Disassembly

Remove circlip and shim from mainshaft. Slide 4th gear and needle bearing from shaft. Remove inner circlip and press off 3rd/4th synchro assembly and 3rd gear from mainshaft. Remove split cage needle roller for 3rd gear.

Reassembly

1) Engage synchro inserts into synchro hub and install synchro sleeve over hub. Install synchro spring with bend end in synchro insert. Install spring on opposite side of hub with bend staggered 120°. Press synchro rings onto 3rd and 4th gears by hand and measure clearance between ring and gear. Clearance should be .053-.075" (1.35-1.90 mm) with wear limit of .020" (.50 mm).

2) Lubricate and install 3rd gear split cage needle roller on mainshaft. Place 3rd gear on mainshaft and press on synchro assembly with hub chamfer facing 3rd gear. Install inner circlip and press synchro hub back against circlip.

3) Slide needle bearing and 4th gear on mainshaft. Install shim and circlip. Using a feeler gauge, measure clearance between shim and 4th gear. Clearance should be .004-.016" (.10-.40 mm). Shim as necessary, staying on low side of range.

NOTE: Mainshaft and shims have corresponding flats. Shims are available in thicknesses of .136" (3.45 mm), .140" (3.55 mm), and .144" (3.65 mm).

PINION SHAFT ASSEMBLY

Disassembly

Using a gear puller, pull inner pinion bearing race, pinion depth shim (S_3) and 1st gear from pinion shaft. Next, pull 2nd gear and synchro assembly. Remove circlip from shaft and pull off 3rd gear. Press off 4th gear and remove roller bearing from pinion shaft.

NOTE: Prior to reassembly, drive pinion shaft, 3rd gear and 4th gear must be absolutely free of oil and grease. These gears are heated to approximately 250°F (120°C) prior to being pressed onto pinion shaft.

Reassembly

1) Slide roller bearing onto shaft. Press 4th gear onto shaft using plate (VW402). Press 3rd gear onto shaft and measure clearance between edge of circlip groove and face of 3rd gear with a feeler gauge. If clearance is less than .063" (1.6 mm), use a circlip which is .059" (1.5 mm) thick. If it is greater than .063" (1.6 mm), use a circlip which is .063" (1.6 mm) thick.

2) Assemble synchro hub and sleeve so that hub cutouts match grooved tooth of sleeve splines. Hub teeth have a groove cut on front face of hub. This groove must face 1st gear. Install synchro spring with bend end in synchro insert.

3) Install spring on opposite side of hub with bend end staggered 120°. Press synchronizer rings onto 1st/2nd gears by hand and measure clearance between ring and gear. Clearance should be .043-.067" (1.1-1.7 mm) with a wear limit of .020" (.50 mm).

NOTE: Synchronizer ring for 1st gear has 110° tooth angle and is identified by 3 teeth missing around circumference. This synchronizer ring MUST be installed for 1st gear ONLY. If ring is damaged, replace with standard synchronizer ring. Special ring is not available as replacement part.

4) Place 2nd gear, needle bearing and synchro ring on pinion shaft. Align cutouts in synchro ring with synchro inserts and press on synchro hub assembly. Install 1st gear, spacing collar, needle bearing, pinion depth shim (S_3) and press on inner pinion bearing race.

Fig. 10: Exploded View of Pinion Shaft Assembly

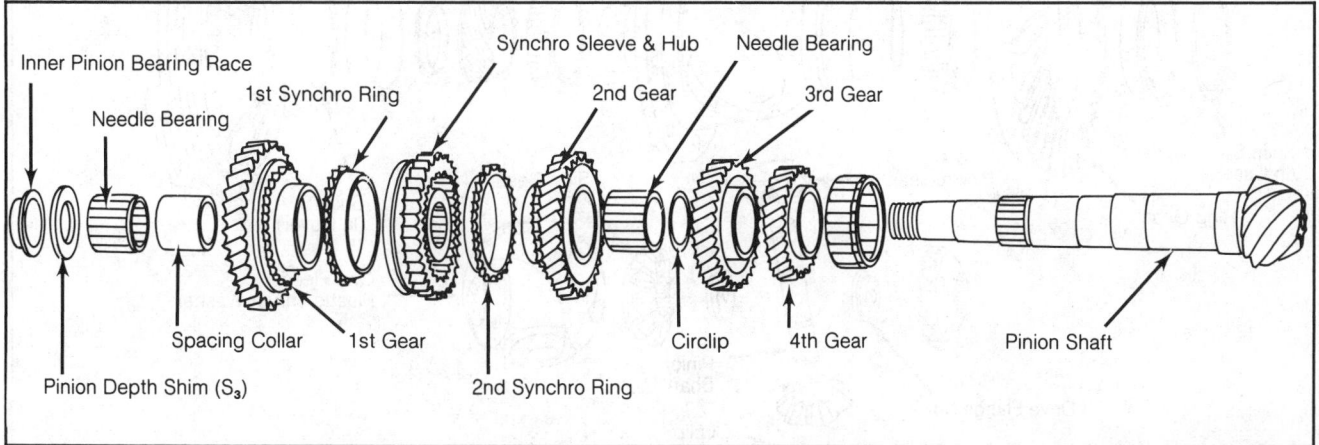

AUDI 4000 4-SPEED (Cont.)

NOTE: If pinion bearing or spacing collar were replaced, pinion shim (S_3) thickness must be calculated. See Drive Pinion Depth in this article.

FINAL DRIVE HOUSING
Disassembly
1) Remove clutch release bearing guide sleeve. Using tool (VW681), pry out mainshaft oil seal. Working from transmission side of final drive housing, insert drift tools (VW431 & VW439) and drive mainshaft sleeve out clutch side of housing.

2) Working from clutch side of housing, insert tools (VW431 & VW439) and drive mainshaft needle bearing out transmission side of housing.

3) From hole located in side cover flange, remove dowel pin retaining pinion roller bearing outer race. Using tools (VW295 & 30-205), drive bearing race out clutch side of final drive housing.

Reassembly
1) With grooved side of bearing race facing transmission and dowel pin hole aligned with hole in housing, drive bearing race into housing using tools (VW295 & 30-205).

2) Install dowel pin which retains bearing race. Dowel pin will project .012" (.3 mm) above side cover flange when properly engaged with hole in roller bearing race.

3) From clutch side of housing, drive in mainshaft sleeve and oil seal. From transmission side of housing, drive in mainshaft needle bearing using tools (VW295 & VW295a).

DIFFERENTIAL ASSEMBLY
Disassembly
1) Using a puller and adapter (VW295a), pull off side bearings. Remove speedometer drive gear and

bushing with bearing. Remove ring gear attaching bolts and tap ring gear off differential housing.

NOTE: Ring gear and pinion must be replaced as matched set.

2) Remove pinion shaft circlips and drive out pinion shaft. Rotate differential side gears with aid of drive flanges to housing opening and remove pinion gears. Remove drive flanges, drive flange nuts, side gears and thrust washer.

NOTE: If differential housing is stamped with one-piece plastic thrust washer symbol, ONLY that thrust washer can be installed.

Reassembly
1) Coat thrust washer and gears with transmission fluid and install thrust washer in housing. Place side gears and drive flange nuts into differential housing. Install pinion gears. Rotate drive flange to align pinion shaft and insert pinion shaft. Install pinion shaft circlips.

2) Heat ring gear to 212°F (100°C) and place on differential housing. Center with drift, then install and tighten bolts. Heat side bearings to same temperature and press onto differential.

3) Place speedometer gear and bushing on differential. Insert a .06" (1.4 mm) thick shim in bushing. Press bushing, shim and drive gear on as a unit, then remove shim.

NOTE: Shim assures correct alignment of drive gear and bushing as they are pressed on.

Fig. 11: Exploded View of Differential Assembly

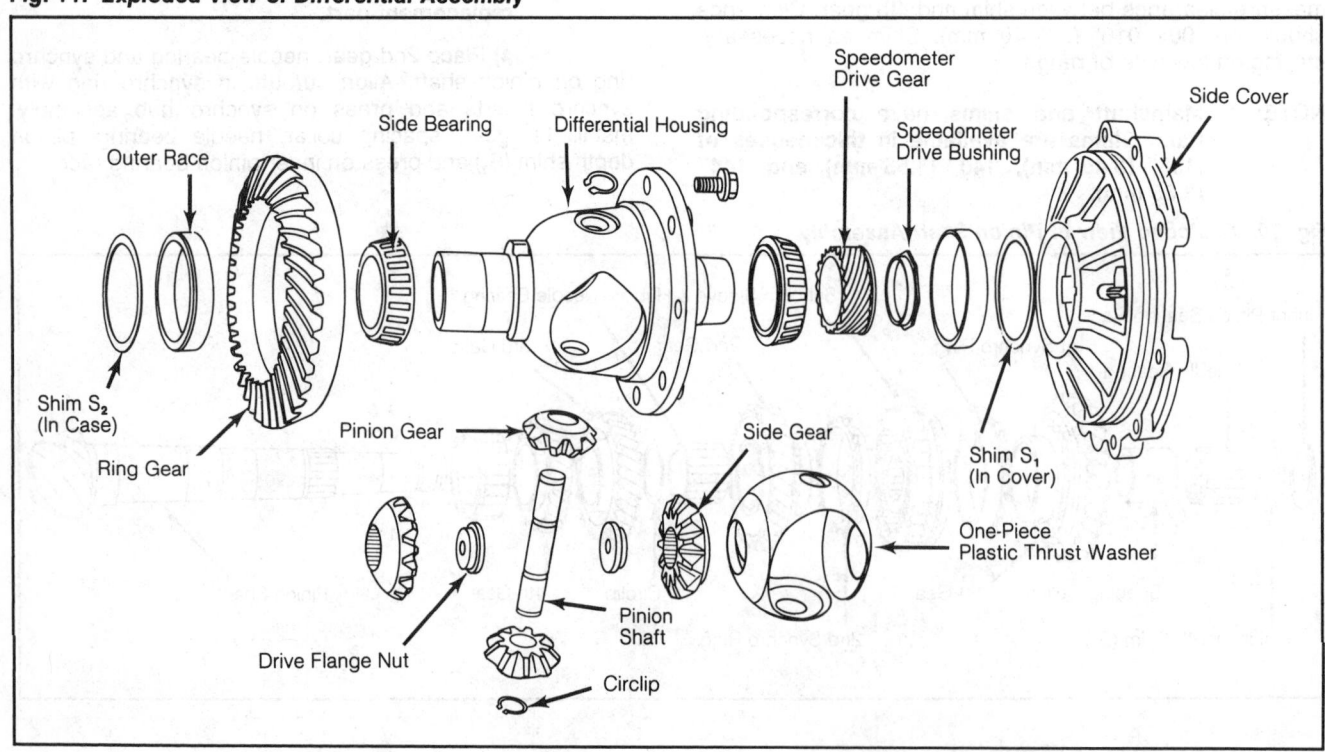

AUDI 4000 4-SPEED (Cont.)

TRANSAXLE REASSEMBLY & ADJUSTMENTS

DRIVE PINION DEPTH

1) Install pinion gear with a standard .157" (4 mm) shim. Place pinion in transmission case and torque pinion nut to 14-22 ft. lbs. (19-30 N.m). With 4 nuts, mount transmission housing to final drive housing. Mount tensioner tool (VW297/8) on rear of transmission. *See Fig. 12.* Place a 36 mm socket over pinion nut and lock in place with knurled screw.

Fig. 12: Installation of Tensioner Tool on Transmission Housing

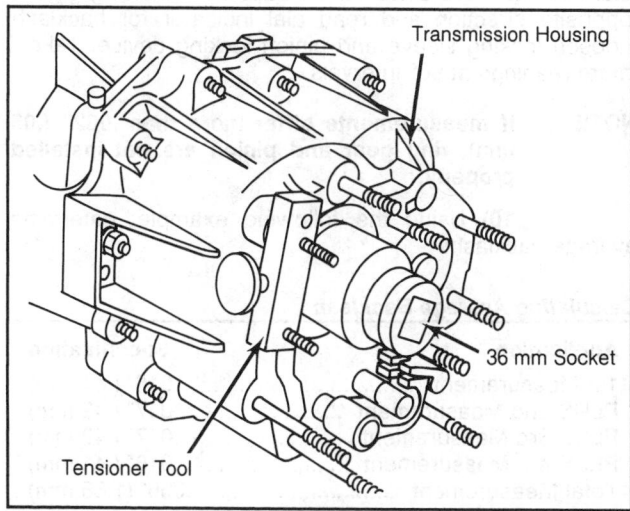

NOTE: **If assembly was originally equipped with gasket between final drive and transmission housing, gasket must be present when making measurement. Before starting measurement, be sure ball bearing is pressed in fully.**

2) Assemble measuring bar (VW385/1) and position sliding set ring until it is approximately 2" (50 mm) from center of bar. Complete assembly of measuring bar. *See Fig. 13.* Install dial indicator and set dial indicator to .157" (4 mm) preload. Zero gauge by removing master gauge (VW385/23).

Fig. 13: Assembling Pinion Depth Measuring Tool

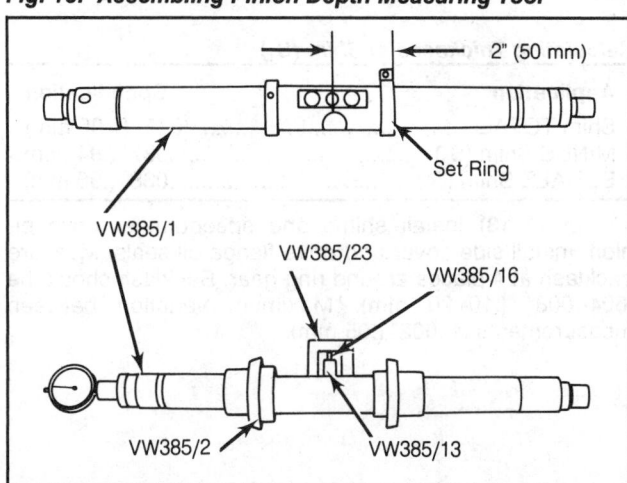

3) Turn adjusting knob on measuring bar to move setting ring back to stop. Place end plate (VW385/17) on end of drive pinion and install measuring bar in housing. Install final drive cover together with bearing outer race and tighten cover bolts to specifications. Adjust centering ring outward until measuring bar can just be turned by hand. *See Fig. 14.*

Fig. 14: Sectional View Showing Installation of Measuring Tools Used to Obtain Pinion Depth Reading

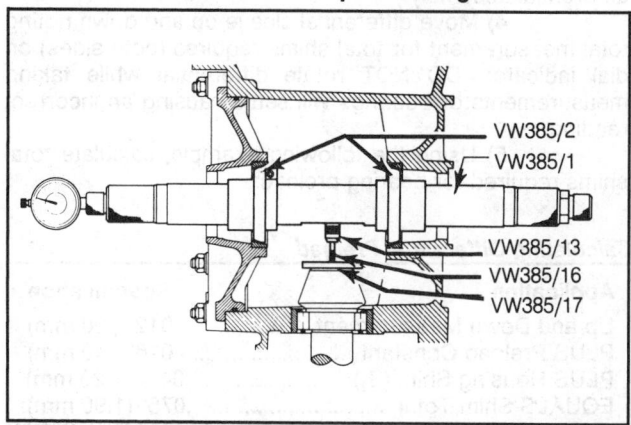

4) Rotate measuring bar until maximum dial indicator deflection is reached and note measurement. This measurement (minus .978" or 2 mm) for preload) is the amount of additional shim thickness needed to set pinion at desired depth. Determine production deviation, marked in hundredths of a millimeter on service gearsets, or measured at disassembly on production gearsets.

Typical Pinion Depth Shim (S_3) Calculations ($S_3 = e - r + x$)

Application	Specification
Dial Indicator Deflection (e) [1]	.035" (.90 mm)
MINUS Production Deviation (r)	.018" (.45 mm)
PLUS Standard Pinion Test Shim (x) ...	.157" (4.0 mm)
EQUALS Pinion Depth Shim (S_3)	.174" (4.45 mm)

[1] — MINUS .078" (2 mm) preload factor.

5) Disassemble measuring tools and remove pinion shaft. Remove pinion depth shim from pinion shaft and install NEW shim of appropriate thickness. Install pinion with correct shim installed and check reading with dial indicator. With correct shim installed, reading should be production deviation ±.0015" (.04 mm).

NOTE: **In this sample calculation, 2 shims must be used to obtain correct clearance. Install thinner shim between thicker shim and inner bearing race. Shims are available in thicknesses of .150" (3.8 mm) to .205" (5.2 mm) in addition to thin shim of .006" (.15 mm).**

BACKLASH & SIDE BEARING PRELOAD

1) Remove differential oil seals and outer roller bearing races from final drive housing and side cover. Remove bearing shims (S_1 and S_2) from behind bearing races. Place a .047" (1.2 mm) shim (S_2) in final drive housing and press bearing race in housing using tools (VW295 and 30-205). Press bearing race in side cover without shim (S_1).

AUDI 4000 4-SPEED (Cont.)

2) With open side of final drive housing facing up, install differential assembly (without speedometer drive gear) so ring gear teeth are facing down. Install final drive cover and attaching bolts. Tighten bolts to specifications in a diagonal sequence.

3) Place end disc (VW385/17) on flange end of differential assembly. Install a dial indicator so foot will rest on end disc with a .039" (1.0 mm) preload. On bottom side of transaxle, install locking sleeve (VW521/4) into differential assembly.

4) Move differential sleeve up and down noting total measurement for total shims required (both sides) on dial indicator. DO NOT rotate differential while taking measurements or bearings will settle causing an incorrect reading.

5) Using the following example, calculate total shims required for bearing preload:

Calculating Differential Preload

Application	Specification
Up and Down Measurement	.012" (.30 mm)
PLUS Preload Constant	.016" (.40 mm)
PLUS Housing Shim (S_2)	.047" (1.20 mm)
EQUALS Shim Total	.075" (1.90 mm)

6) Remove side cover and press out bearing race. Install shim (S_1) which is a total of preload constant plus measured value for a total of .028" (.70 mm). Reinstall bearing race and side cover.

Fig. 15: Cutaway View of Final Drive Housing Showing Backlash Measuring Tool Installation

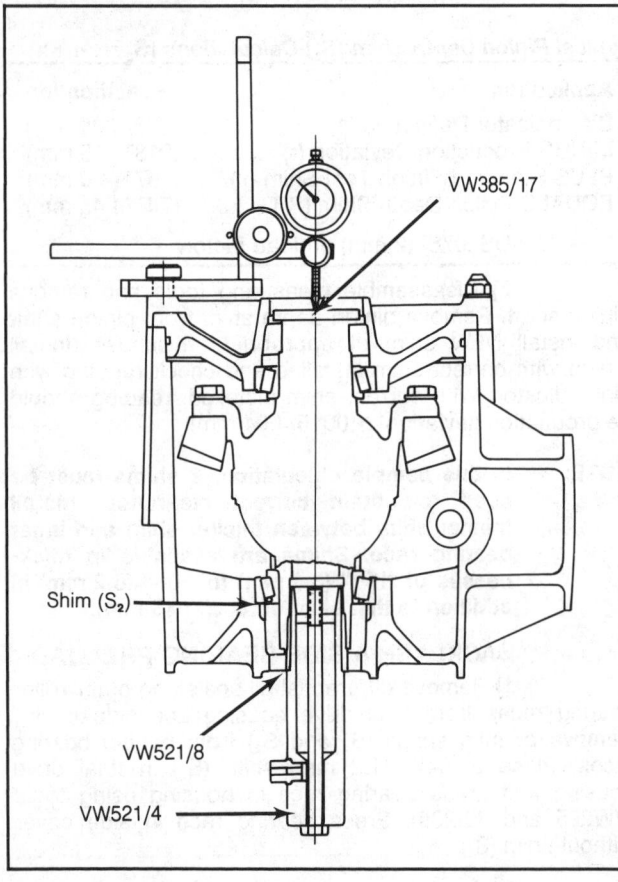

VW385/17

Shim (S_2)

VW521/8

VW521/4

NOTE: Differential rotating torque must be at least 23 INCH lbs. (2.6 N.m) with new roller bearings.

7) Install transmission housing and pinion shaft to final drive housing. Ensure .047" (1.2 mm) shim is installed on housing side. Screw measuring bar (VW388) into locking sleeve (VW521/4).

8) Mount dial indicator extension onto measuring bar so extension extends 2.8" (71 mm) above measuring bar. Mount dial indicator with contact foot touching tip of extension.

9) With pinion shaft locked as previously described, rotate ring gear as far as it will turn and zero dial indicator. *See Drive Pinion Depth.* Rotate ring gear in opposite direction and read dial indicator for backlash. Loosen locking sleeve and pinion locking device. Take 3 more readings at 90° intervals.

NOTE: If measurements differ more than .002" (.06 mm), ring gear and pinion are not installed properly.

10) Using the following example, determine average backlash:

Calculating Average Backlash

Application	Specification
1st Measurement	.016" (.41 mm)
PLUS 2nd Measurement	.017" (.42 mm)
PLUS 3rd Measurement	.017" (.42 mm)
PLUS 4th Measurement	.016" (.41 mm)
Total Measurement	.066" (1.66 mm)
Total Divided By 4 EQUALS Average Backlash	.016" (.41 mm)

11) Determine thickness of shim (S_2) located in final drive housing in following manner:

Calculating Thickness of Shim (S_2)

Application	Specification
Shim Inserted	.047" (1.20 mm)
MINUS Average Backlash	.016" (.41 mm)
PLUS Lift Constant	.006" (.15 mm)
EQUALS Shim (S_2)	.037" (.94 mm)

12) Determine thickness of shim (S_1) located in side cover in following manner:

Calculating Thickness of Shim (S_1)

Application	Specification
Shim TOTAL	.075" (1.90 mm)
MINUS Shim (S_2)	.037" (.94 mm)
EQUALS Shim (S_1)	.038" (.96 mm)

13) Install shims and speedometer drive pinion. Install side cover and drive flange oil seals. Measure backlash at 4 places around ring gear. Backlash should be .004-.008" (.10-.20 mm). Maximum variation between measurements is .002" (.05 mm).

AUDI 4000 4-SPEED (Cont.)

NOTE: Shims are available in thicknesses of .006" (.15 mm) to .047" (1.2 mm) in increments of .004" (.10 mm) above .008" (.20 mm). Given backlash figure is only valid for new ring and pinion. If old ring and pinion are reused, backlash should be restored as accurately as possible to old figure measured prior to disassembly.

TRANSAXLE REASSEMBLY

1) Using sealing compound, slide transmission assembly into final drive housing and tighten attaching nuts.

NOTE: Transmissions are mounted using a gasket WITHOUT sealing compound. Method used in production (sealing compound or gasket) must always be used for reassembly.

2) Having previously determined gasket and shim thickness, place gasket on transmission studs and shim in shift housing. Start shift housing onto transmission studs far enough to hold housing.

3) Slide and rotate selector shaft until it correctly engages shift rails in transmission case. Push shift housing up to transmission case and tighten attaching nuts.

4) Place differentail assembly into final drive housing with speedometer drive pinion facing side cover. Use new side cover "O" ring and install side cover, tightening bolts diagonally. Install speedometer drive gear and drive flanges.

5) Flange shaft bolts must be cleaned and coated with locking compound prior to installing and tightening.

TIGHTENING SPECIFICATIONS

Application	Ft. Lbs. (N.m)
Inner Drive Flange Bolt	14 (19)
Engine-to-Transaxle	40 (54)
Inner Drive Flange-to-CV Joint	25 (34)
Ball Joint-to-Control Arm	47 (64)
Axle Nut	167 (226)
Transmission Hsg.-to-Final Drive Hsg.	14 (19)
Shift Hsg.-to-Transmission Hsg.	14 (19)
Final Drive Cover	18 (24)
Pinion Shaft Nut	72 (98)
Reverse Lever Bolt	25 (34)
Ring Gear Bolts	
With Lock Washer	40 (54)
Without Lock Washer	50 (68)

Manual Transmissions

AUDI 4000 & VOLKSWAGEN QUANTUM 5-SPEED

DESCRIPTION

This transaxle is a 5-speed unit, fully synchronized in all forward gears. The mainshaft and pinion shaft are supported by roller bearings housed in the gear carrier. The final drive housing contains the clutch housing, clutch release mechanism as well as a ring and pinion gear differential.

The differential drive pinion shaft also serves as the countershaft for the transmission. Fifth gear is housed in the rear cover and all others are contained in the gear carrier.

LUBRICATION & ADJUSTMENT

See the appropriate article in MANUAL TRANS-MISSION SERVICING Section.

SERVICE (IN-VEHICLE)

AXLE DRIVE SHAFTS

NOTE: Vehicle weight must be resting on wheels to remove axle shaft nut.

Removal

1) Loosen axle shaft nut. Raise and support vehicle. Remove axle nut and wheel. Disconnect and remove exhaust pipe from exhaust manifold and transaxle bracket on right side of engine. Remove Allen bolts connecting inner constant velocity (CV) joint to differential case drive flange.

2) Mark position of both ball joint flanges on control arms. Remove ball joint from control arm and pull pivot mounting outward while removing drive shaft. Press drive shaft out of hub and guide past transaxle.

NOTE: Axle drive shafts should be disassembled ONLY to replace defective boots. If boots are replaced, check all components for damage or wear and replace as a complete assembly if necessary.

Disassembly

1) On inner CV joint, remove circlip from axle shaft and drive protective cap from CV joint. Place axle shaft in holder (VW402) and press CV joint from shaft with adapter (VW408a), supporting hub to prevent damage.

Pivot hub and cage assembly out of inner joint, then push out and remove balls. Align ball hub grooves with cage and remove hub.

Fig. 2: Removing Inner CV Joint Ball Hub

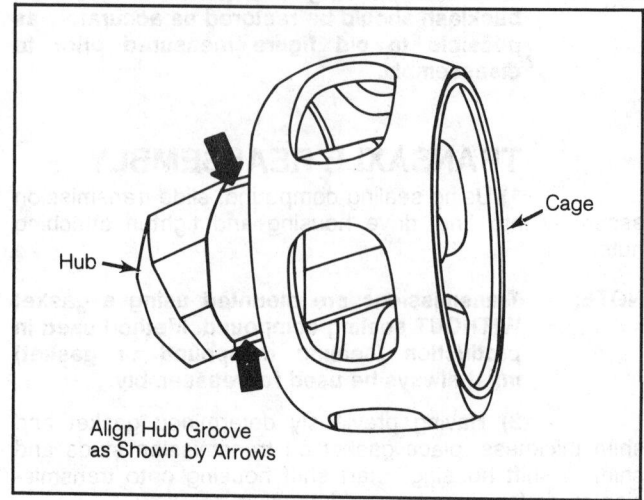

Hub
Cage
Align Hub Groove as Shown by Arrows

NOTE: Inner CV joint and ball hub are matched sets. DO NOT interchange with outer joint. Also, balls of CV joints cannot be interchanged between CV joints.

2) Remove and discard inner clamp and boot. On outer CV joint, spread circlip inside ball hub and drive CV joint off of axle shaft with brass drift by tapping on hub. Mark position of ball hub and outer joint, then tilt cage and remove each ball.

3) Align cage perpendicular to joint. Align 2 large openings in cage with raised portions of joint and remove cage and hub. Position 1 retainer of hub in large opening of cage and remove hub by tilting outward. Remove and discard outer boot and clamp.

Reassembly

1) To reassemble CV joints, reverse disassembly procedure and note the following: Lubricate joints with 3 ozs. of molybdenum disulphide grease. Chamfer of ball hub splines must face larger diameter of joint. When rotating ball and cage into joint, ensure that wide ball groove and narrow hub groove are on same side of joint. See Fig. 4.

Fig. 1: Exploded View of Audi/Volkswagen 5-Speed Transaxle

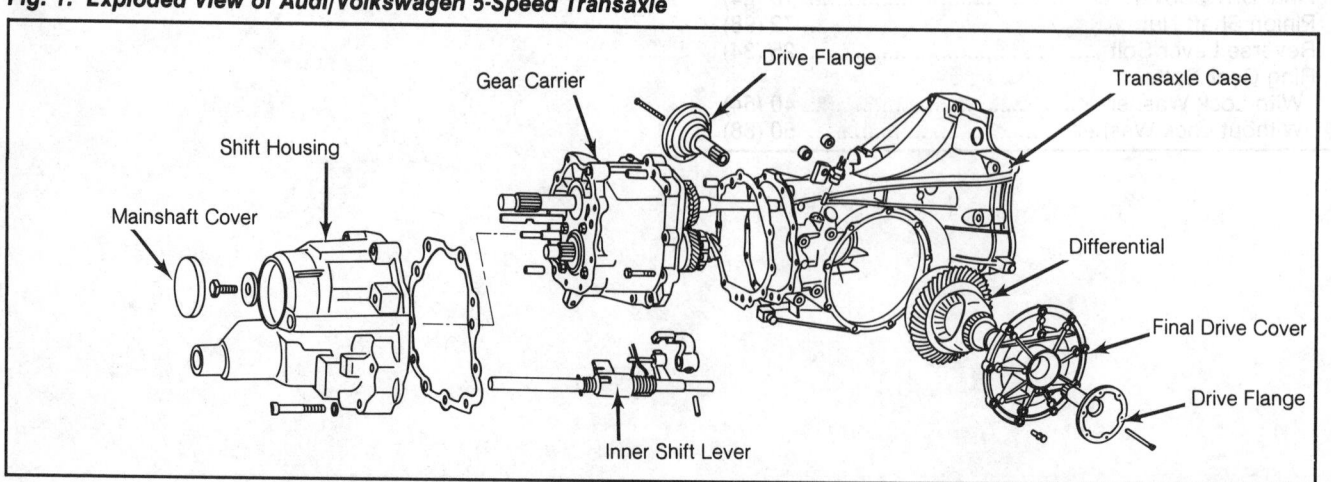

Gear Carrier
Drive Flange
Transaxle Case
Shift Housing
Mainshaft Cover
Differential
Final Drive Cover
Drive Flange
Inner Shift Lever

AUDI 4000 & VOLKSWAGEN QUANTUM 5-SPEED (Cont.)

Fig. 3: Exploded View of Axle Drive Shaft

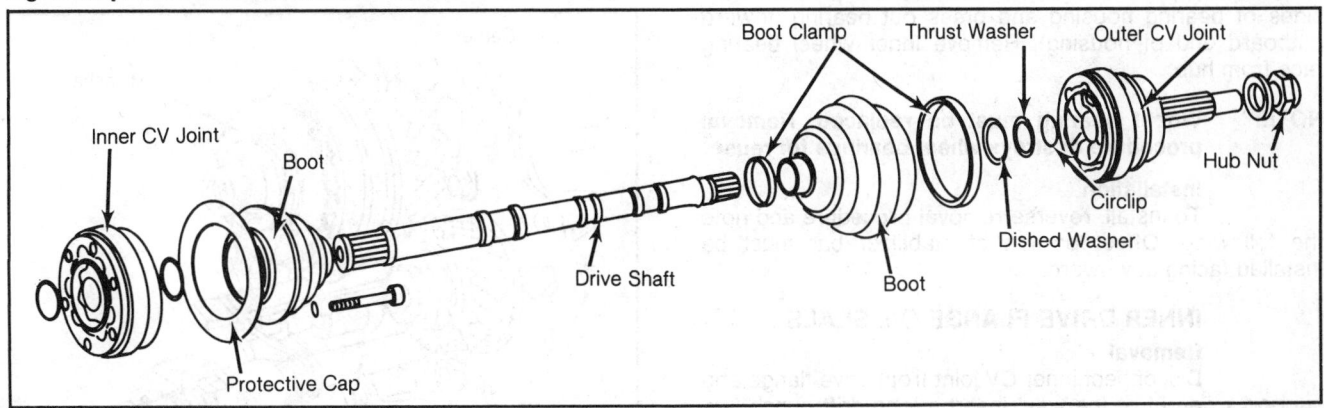

Fig. 4: Installing Ball Hub and Cage in Inner CV Joint

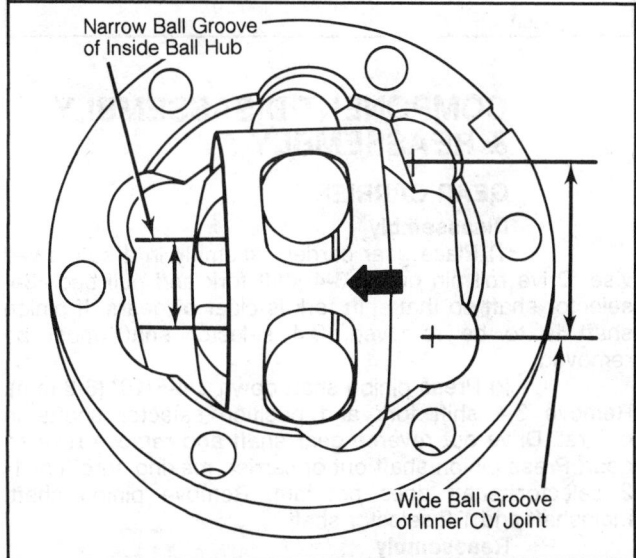

2) Outer CV joint alignment marks must align after reassembly. Inside ball hub chamfer faces axle shaft on both joints. Concave side of dished washer faces CV joint on both joints and convex side of thrust washer faces CV joint on outer joint. Always use new circlips to retain CV joints on shafts. Open end of boot clamps should face opposite direction of normal rotation of shaft. *See Fig. 5.*

Fig. 5: Cutaway View of Outer CV Joint Showing Installation of Dished and Thrust Washers

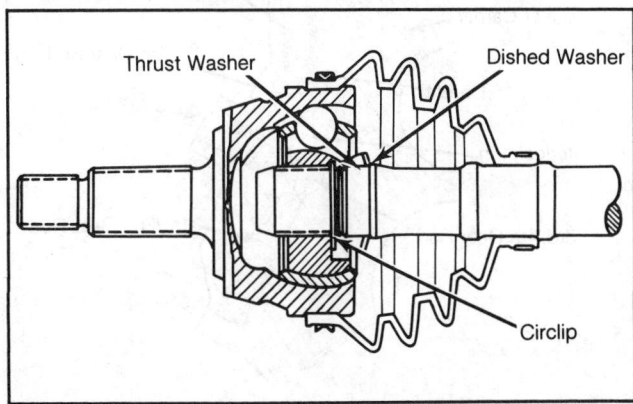

Installation

To install, reverse removal procedure and note the following: After installing axle shafts, align ball joint flanges with marks made at disassembly and tighten nuts. Check camber setting and adjust as necessary.

FRONT WHEEL BEARINGS

Removal

1) With vehicle supported and axle drive shafts removed, remove stabilizer bar clamps. Remove caliper mounting bolts and hang caliper from frame with wire. DO NOT disconnect hydraulic line or allow caliper to hang by hydraulic line. Remove brake disc and ball joint bolt. Press off tie rod and remove ball joint from hub.

Fig. 6: Exploded View of Front Suspension Strut Assembly

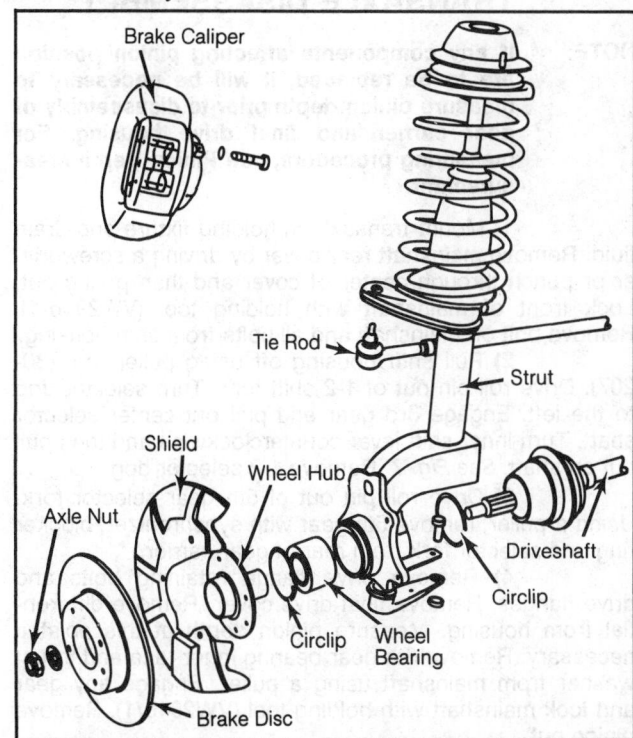

2) Support suspension strut with jack and remove upper strut retaining nuts from inside engine compartment. Remove strut assembly from vehicle and place in holding fixture. Press out wheel hub with hub

AUDI 4000 & VOLKSWAGEN QUANTUM 5-SPEED (Cont.)

removal tool (VW295 & 295a). Remove circlips from both sides of bearing housing and press out bearing (toward outboard end of housing). Remove inner wheel bearing race from hub.

NOTE: **Wheel bearing must be replaced. Removal procedure destroys wheel bearings for reuse.**

Installation

To install, reverse removal procedure and note the following: Offset portion of stabilizer bar must be installed facing downward.

INNER DRIVE FLANGE OIL SEALS

Removal

Disconnect inner CV joint from drive flange and support axle out of the way. Insert a long drift punch into one drive flange hole to prevent rotation, then remove drive flange bolt. Place drip pan under transaxle and pull out drive flange. Pry out oil seal.

Installation

Lightly lubricate seal lips and fully seat seal with driver (30-212). Install drive flange and tighten drive flange retaining bolt. Install drive axle and tighten bolts. Check and add lubricant to transaxle if necessary.

TRANSAXLE REMOVAL & INSTALLATION

See the appropriate article in MANUAL TRANSMISSION REMOVAL Section.

TRANSAXLE DISASSEMBLY

NOTE: **If any components affecting pinion position are to be replaced, it will be necessary to measure pinion depth prior to disassembly of gear carrier and final drive housing. For measuring procedure, see Pinion Depth Measurement.**

1) Mount transaxle in holding fixture and drain fluid. Remove mainshaft rear cover by driving a screwdriver or punch through center of cover and then prying out. Lock front of mainshaft with holding tool (VW294b/1). Remove bolt on mainshaft and all bolts from shift housing.

2) Pull shift housing off using puller tool (30-207). Drive roll pin out of 1-2 shift fork. Turn selector dog to the left. Engage 3rd gear and pull out center selector shaft. Turn inner shift lever counterclockwise and then pull out on shaft. See Fig. 7. Remove 1-2 selector dog.

3) Drive roll pin out of 5th gear selector fork. Using a puller, remove 5th gear with synchronizer, blocker ring and selector fork from rear of gear carrier.

4) Remove drive flange retaining bolts and drive flanges. Remove final drive cover. Remove differential from housing. Measure pinion depth at this point if necessary. Remove 5th gear bearing inner race and thrust washer from mainshaft using a puller. Engage any gear and lock mainshaft with holding tool (VW294b/1). Remove pinion nut.

5) Remove 5th gear from pinion shaft. Shift gear train into neutral. Remove gear carrier-to-final drive housing bolts and dowel pins. Pull complete gear carrier assembly off of final drive housing.

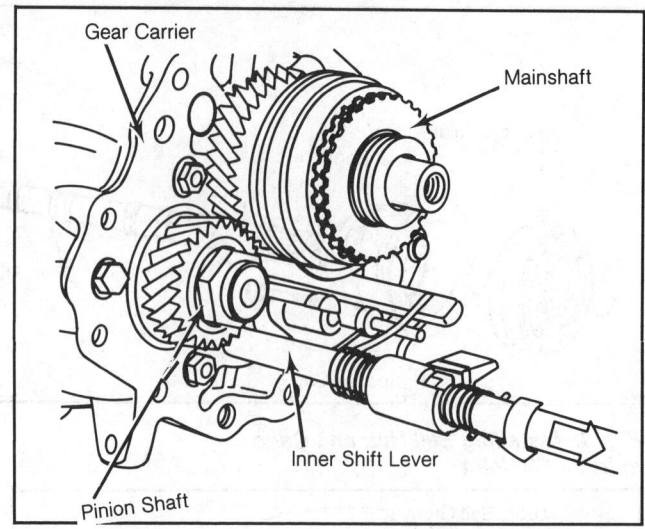

Fig. 7: Inner Shift Lever Removal

COMPONENT DISASSEMBLY & REASSEMBLY

GEAR CARRIER

Disassembly

1) Place gear carrier assembly in a soft-jawed vise. Drive roll pin out of 3-4 shift fork and pull back 3-4 selector shaft so that shift fork is clear of gears. If pinion shaft is to be removed, 3-4 selector shaft must be removed.

2) Press pinion shaft down 1/4-5/16" (6-8 mm). Remove 3-4 shift fork and position selector shafts in neutral. Drive out reverse gear shaft and remove reverse gear. Press pinion shaft out of carrier, making sure that 1-2 selector shaft does not jam. Remove pinion shaft, mainshaft and 1-2 selector shaft.

Reassembly

1) Check to make sure that all interlock plungers and detents are in proper position. See Fig. 8. Position 1-2 shift fork with selector shaft onto pinion shaft. Mesh pinion shaft gear teeth with mainshaft gear teeth. Install assembled gear shafts into gear carrier.

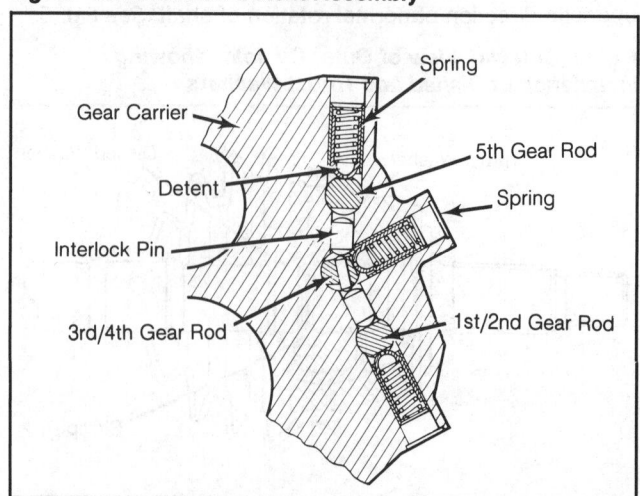

Fig. 8: Selector Rod Detent Assembly

AUDI 4000 & VOLKSWAGEN QUANTUM 5-SPEED (Cont.)

Fig. 9: *Exploded View of Mainshaft Assembly*

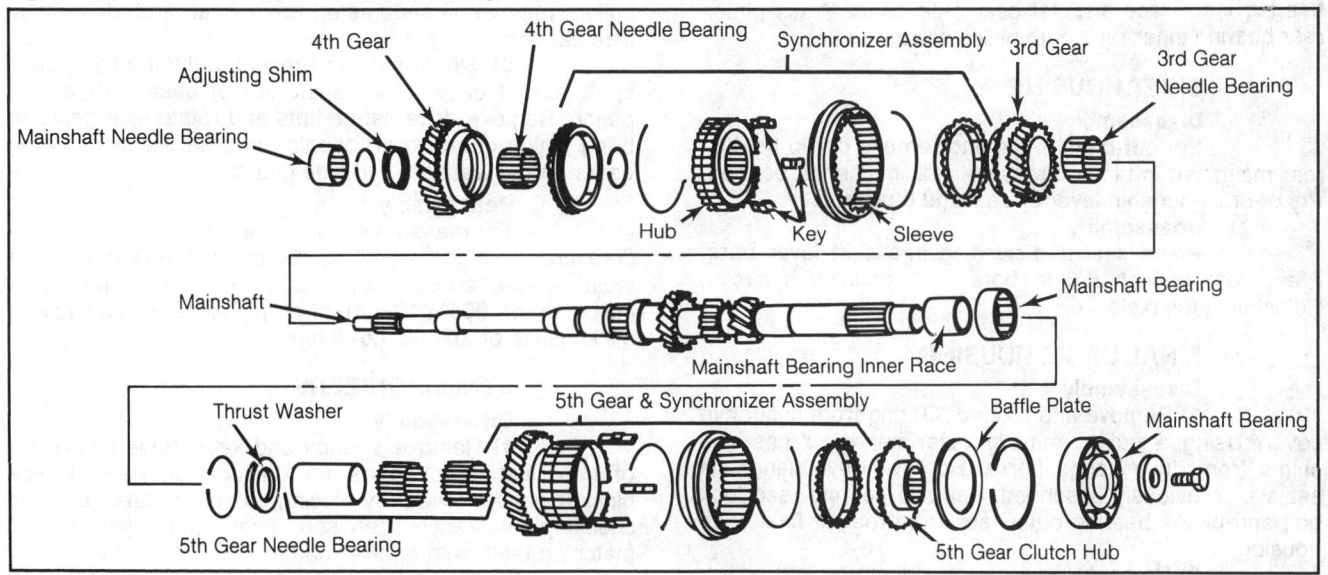

2) Install reverse gear and shaft. Position selector shafts in neutral. Install 3-4 selector shaft with small interlock pin and secure with roll pin at 3-4 shift fork.

3) Press inner bearing race onto pinion shaft. Install mainshaft thrust washer. Heat 5th gear inner bearing race to 250°F (121°C) and install onto mainshaft. Heat 5th gear to 250°F (121°C) and install onto mainshaft.

4) Install 5th gear and synchronizer assembly with blocker ring onto mainshaft. Heat synchronizer clutch hub to 250°F (121°C) and install on to mainshaft.

MAINSHAFT
Disassembly
1) Remove circlip from end of mainshaft. Remove shim, 4th gear, needle bearing and blocker ring. Remove and discard circlip holding 3-4 synchronizer onto shaft. Press 3-4 synchronizer hub and sleeve off of shaft.

2) Remove 3rd gear and needle bearing. Press mainshaft bearing inner race off rear of mainshaft. Remove circlip retaining mainshaft bearing outer race to gear carrier. Press outer race out of carrier. Drive mainshaft needle bearing out of final drive housing.

Reassembly
Check all bearings for damage or excessive wear. To reassemble, reverse disassembly procedure and note the following: End play measured between 4th gear and shim should be .004-.016" (.10-.40 mm). If end play is not within specifications, adjust by changing shim thickness. Shims are available in the following sizes: .137" (3.47 mm), .141" (3.57 mm) and .145" (3.67 mm).

PINION SHAFT
Disassembly
Engage 2nd gear. Press pinion rear bearing inner race and 1st gear off of shaft. Press 1-2 synchronizer hub with sleeve and 2nd gear off of pinion shaft. Press 3rd gear off shaft and then remove circlip retaining 4th gear. Press 4th gear off of shaft and then remove pinion front bearing inner race.

Reassembly
1) Ensure that pinion shaft is free of all traces of grease and oil. Reinstall front bearing onto pinion shaft. Heat 4th gear to 250°F (121°C) and install onto pinion shaft until fully seated. Retain 4th gear with a selective fit snap ring. Snap ring should be a tight fit. Snap rings are available in sizes from .0925" (2.35 mm) to .0972" (2.47 mm).

2) Press 3rd gear onto shaft and retain with a selective fit snap ring. Snap rings are available in thicknesses of .060-.063" (1.5-1.6 mm). Install 2nd gear, blocker ring and 1-2 synchronizer onto shaft. Groove on

Fig. 10: *Exploded View of Pinion Shaft Assembly*

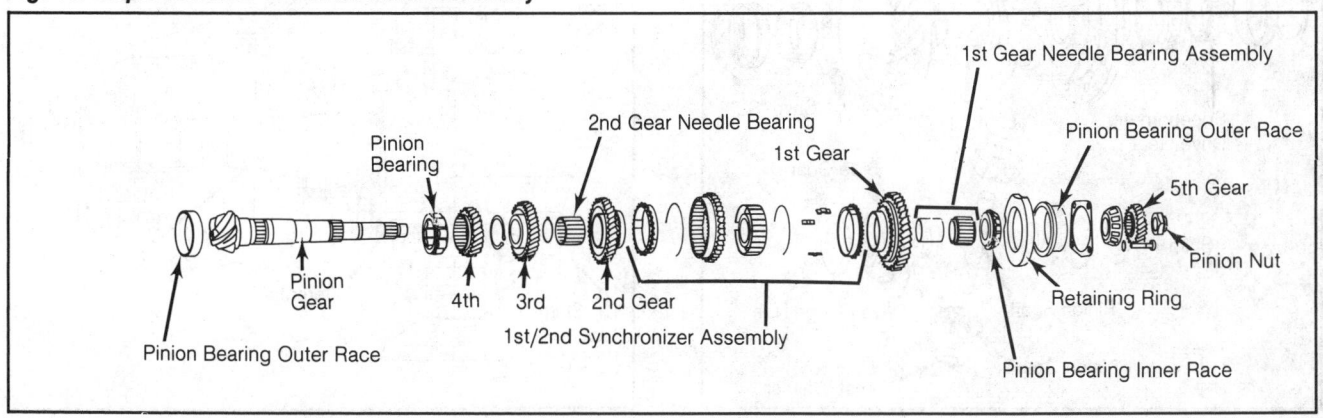

AUDI 4000 & VOLKSWAGEN QUANTUM 5-SPEED (Cont.)

edge of synchronizer hub faces 1st gear. Press 1st gear bearing inner race and 1st gear onto shaft. Press pinion rear bearing inner race onto pinion shaft.

SHIFT HOUSING
Disassembly
Pry out baffle plate and remove circlip holding rear mainshaft in place. Press out rear mainshaft bearing. Pry or drive out shift lever oil seal and bushing.

Reassembly
Press seal and bushing into shift lever bore. Press rear mainshaft into bore and retain with circlip. Reinstall baffle plate.

FINAL DRIVE HOUSING
Disassembly
1) Remove and discard "O" ring from final drive cover. Using a puller, remove outer bearing races and shims from drive flange bores. Remove drive flange oil seals as previously described. Remove bearing race lock bolt and pinion bearing outer race from rear of final drive housing.

2) Remove speedometer drive gear and adapter from housing. Remove clutch release bearing, clutch release shaft with bushings and clutch release bearing guide sleeve with mainshaft oil seal from front of housing.

Reassembly
1) Inspect all bearings for damage or excessive wear. Replace seals as necessary. Reinstall new mainshaft oil seal after filling lips of seal with multipurpose grease. Reinstall clutch release bearing guide sleeve, but do not lubricate.

2) Coat moving parts of clutch release shaft with molybdenum disulphide grease and reinstall along with release bearing. Replace mainshaft needle bearing and pinion bearing outer race into rear of housing. Secure pinion bearing outer race with lock bolt.

DIFFERENTIAL
Disassembly
1) Place differential, with ring gear facing down, in a soft-jawed vise. Remove ring gear bolts and

drive ring gear off of differential with a drift punch. Using a puller, remove speedometer drive gear and differential side bearings.

2) Drive roll pin securing differential pinion shaft out of case. Drive shaft out of case with a drift punch. Remove drive flange nuts and rotate side gears to bring pinion gears to an opening in case. Remove pinion gears, thrust washers and side gears.

Reassembly
To reassemble, reverse disassembly procedure and note the following: Differential side gear shim must be selected so that gears turn freely by hand with a maximum of .004" (.10 mm) of play. Shims are available in thicknesses of .02-.03" (.5-.8 mm).

SYNCHRONIZERS
Disassembly
1) Remove springs and keys. Slide sleeve off of hub. Inspect all parts for damage or wear. Check blocker rings for wear by placing on appropriate gear and checking clearance between gear and synchronizer matching teeth with a feeler gauge.

2) Clearance should be at least .020" (.5 mm). If clearance is not within specifications, replace blocker ring.

Reassembly
Slide sleeve over hub and insert keys. Install springs with open ends 120° offset. On 1-2 synchronizer, groove on edge of hub faces 1st gear. On 3-4 synchronizer, groove on edge of hub faces 4th gear.

TRANSAXLE REASSEMBLY & ADJUSTMENTS

SIDE BEARING PRELOAD MEASUREMENT
1) Remove drive flange oil seals, differential bearing outer races and preload shims. Reinstall side bearing outer races without shims. With pinion gear and gear carrier removed, install differential and ring gear (without speedometer drive gear) into final drive housing. Install final drive cover and tighten bolts in a diagonal sequence.

Fig. 11: Exploded View of Differential Assembly

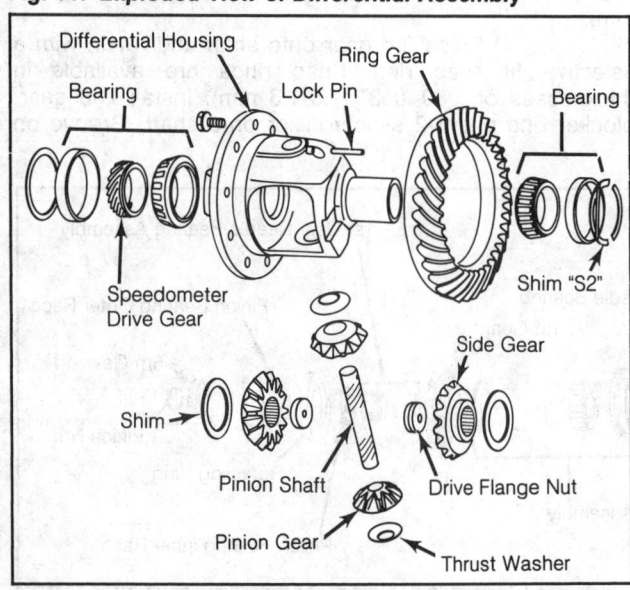

Fig. 12: Final Drive Adjustment Locations

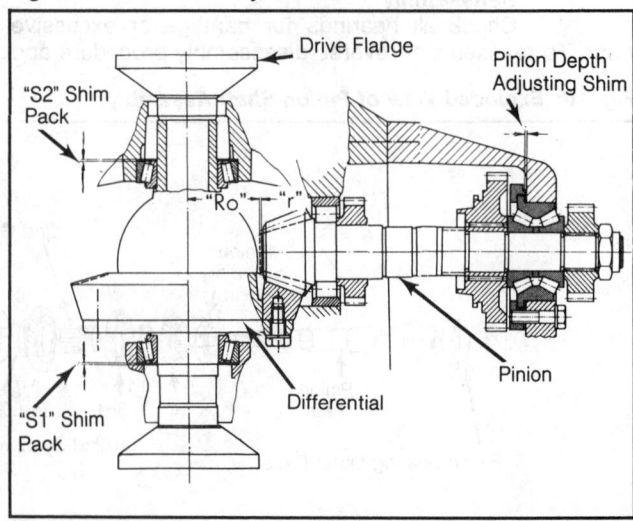

AUDI 4000 & VOLKSWAGEN QUANTUM 5-SPEED (Cont.)

2) Place an end plate (VW385/17) on cover end of differential. Assemble a dial indicator to read differential end play. Move differential up and down. Note dial indicator reading.

3) Add dial indicator reading to a preload constant of .0197" (.50 mm) on 5-cylinder models and .0157" (.40 mm) on 4-cylinder models to obtain total differential side bearing shim thickness. Temporarily install entire shim pack behind side bearing outer race on "S2" side of differential. See Fig. 12.

4) Check rotational torque of differential using an INCH lb. torque wrench together with adapters (VW521/8 & VW521/4). Torque should be at least 23 INCH lbs. (2.5 N.m) for new bearings and 2.7 INCH lbs. (.30 N.m) for used bearings. Remove final drive cover and differential.

PINION DEPTH MEASUREMENT

NOTE: Production (factory) gearsets are not marked with a pinion depth deviation specification. If any parts affecting pinion depth (final drive housing, rear pinion bearings, gear carrier and/or 1st gear needle bearing are to be replaced), pinion depth must be measured prior to disassembly of transaxle and gear carrier.

1) Assemble measuring bar. Slide setting ring about 2" (50 mm) from center of bar. Set master gauge (VW385/30) to "Ro" or 2.22" (56.40 mm) for 5-cylinder models and 1.99" (50.70 mm) for 4-cylinder models and place on measuring bar. Preload dial indicator travel by .079" (2 mm) and then zero dial face. Move setting ring back to stop. See Fig. 13.

2) Place end plate on end of pinion gear and install measuring bar in housing. Install final drive cover together with bearing outer race and tighten bolts. Adjust center ring outward until measuring bar can just be turned by hand.

Fig. 13: Measuring Bar Assembly & Adjustment

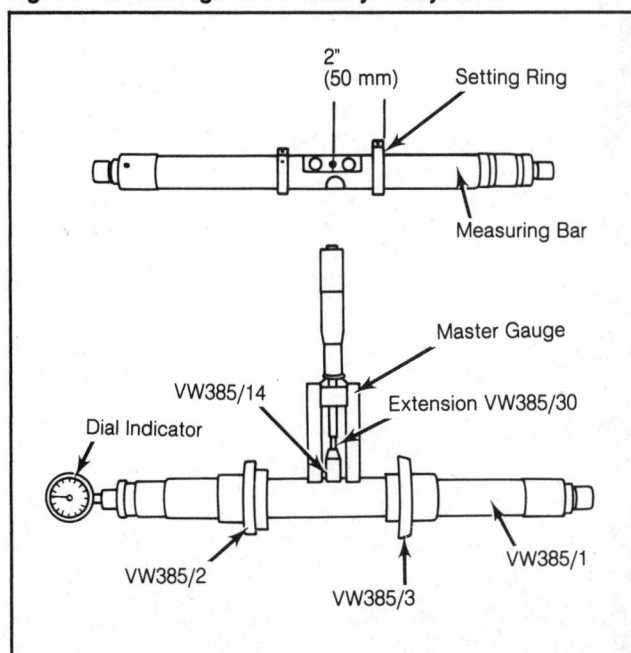

CAUTION: Dial indicator extension must contact pinion measuring plate and remain in contact with plate until measurement is completed. Otherwise dial indicator extension may push measuring plate off of pinion face when measuring bar is turned. Do not strike final drive cover when installing, as this may upset dial indicator reading.

3) Turn measuring bar back and forth slightly until maximum dial indicator reading is reached. This reading, when taken prior to gear carrier removal, is "r" or deviation from nominal pinion depth. Pinion depth deviation, when added to nominal pinion depth ("Ro") included in gauge travel in step 1), results in actual pinion depth ("R").

4) When this reading is taken during reassembly, pinion depth shim(s) should not be in place. Deviation from nominal pinion depth ("r"), whether marked on side of new service gear or measured at disassembly, should be subtracted from dial indicator reading to provide shim thickness necessary for reassembly. Remove final drive cover and measuring bar.

PINION DEPTH ADJUSTMENT

NOTE: This procedure may be carried out by installing mainshaft together with shift forks and selector shafts at the same time as pinion shaft as described in Gear Carrier Reassembly. However, if it becomes necessary to remove pinion shaft to add or subtract shim thickness, the extra components involved will complicate the procedure.

1) Press pinion rear bearing outer race into gear carrier together with correct pinion depth shim selected previously. Install race retaining ring and bolts. Install preassembled pinion shaft into gear carrier. Press pinion rear bearing inner race onto rear of pinion shaft.

2) Place gear carrier assembly in soft-jawed vise. Install spacer (VW472/2) in place of pinion shaft 5th gear. Install and tighten pinion nut to specifications. Install gear carrier onto final drive housing and secure with 4 bolts. Recheck pinion depth measurement and correct as necessary.

RING GEAR BACKLASH ADJUSTMENT

1) With entire side bearing shim pack installed behind outer bearing race of "S2" side of differential, install differential and side cover into housing. Install fully assembled gear carrier with correct pinion depth shim onto final drive housing. Lock pinion shaft with holding tool (VW381/11). Attach dial indicator to differential. See Fig. 14.

2) Turn ring gear to stop and zero dial indicator. Turn ring gear back and note backlash. Loosen locking bolts and rotate ring gear 90°. Retighten locking bolts and repeat procedure 3 more times at equally spaced points around the ring gear. Add all 4 dial indicator readings together and divide total by 4 to obtain average backlash.

3) Subtract average backlash from total side bearing shim pack thickness determined during Side Bearing Preload Measurement and add .006" (.15 mm) to the result to obtain "S2" shim pack thickness. Subtract

AUDI 4000 & VOLKSWAGEN QUANTUM 5-SPEED (Cont.)

Fig. 14: Backlash Measurement

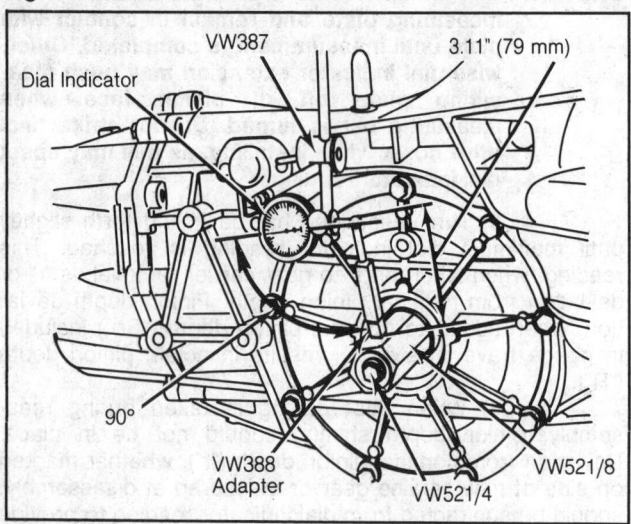

"S2" shim pack thickness from total thickness to obtain "S1" thickness. Install shims in appropriate location. *See Fig. 12.* Recheck backlash and correct as necessary.

TRANSAXLE REASSEMBLY

1) Lightly coat sealing face on final drive housing with sealing compound. Install new gasket and dowel pins. Attach gear carrier housing to final drive housing and install bolts. Engage any gear and lock mainshaft with holding tool (VW294b/1). Install and tighten pinion nut to specifications.

2) Install selector dog for 1st/2nd gear and shift transaxle into 3rd gear (pull out selector shaft). Install inner shift lever selector, placing ends of spring on 3-4 gear shaft and supporting selector dog against selector shaft. Position all selector shafts in neutral.

3) Align selector dog for 1st/2nd gear selector shaft and drive in roll pin. Install new gasket between gear carrier and shift housings. Press on shift housing and install bolts. Install new mainshaft cover.

TIGHTENING SPECIFICATIONS

Application	Ft. Lbs. (N.m)
Axle Shaft Hub Nut	167 (226)
Inner CV Joint Bolts	25 (34)
Drive Flange Retaining Bolt	18 (24)
Transaxle-to-Engine Bolts	40 (54)
Shift Housing-to-Gear Carrier Bolts	18 (24)
Gear Carrier-to-Final Drive Housing Bolts	18 (24)
Final Drive Cover Bolts	18 (24)
Mainshaft Bearing Retainer Bolt	33 (45)
Pinion Nut	72 (98)
Pinion Bearing Outer Race Retainer	18 (24)
Reverse Lever Bolt	25 (34)
Ring Gear Bolts	51 (69)

AUDI 5000, PORSCHE 924 & 944 5-SPEED

DESCRIPTION

The transaxles installed in Audi 5000, Porsche 924 and 944 models are mechanically identical with the exception of a reverse gear synchronizer added to the 5000 models. The transmission portion of the transaxle is a 5-speed unit, fully synchronized in all forward gears with helical cut, constant mesh gears.

The final drive section of the transaxle consists of a drive pinion, which shares a common shaft with the transmission, a ring gear and a 2 pinion differential. The 924 and 944 models have a driveshaft tube, attached to the transaxle bell housing, which extends forward to the clutch housing at the rear of the engine.

LUBRICATION & ADJUSTMENT

See the appropriate article in MANUAL TRANS-MISSION SERVICING Section.

SERVICE (IN VEHICLE)

AXLE DRIVE SHAFTS

NOTE: Axle drive shafts should only be disassembled to replace defective rubber boots. If boots are being replaced, inspect all parts for damage or wear and replace as a complete assembly if necessary.

Removal (5000)

Loosen axle shaft nut. Raise and support vehicle. Remove wheels and any shields or guards that may interfere with axle shaft removal. Remove bolts connecting inner constant velocity (CV) joint to transaxle drive flange. Press driveshaft out of hub and guide past transaxle. Remove locking compound from shaft splines.

Removal (924 & 944)

Raise and support vehicle. Remove bolts attaching inner CV joint to transaxle drive flange. Remove bolts attaching outer CV joint to wheel shaft. Remove axle drive shaft from vehicle.

Disassembly (All Models)

1) On inner CV joint, remove circlip and drive protective cap off of CV joint. Press drive shaft out of inner CV joint. To remove outer CV joints on 924 and 944 models, repeat procedure used for inner CV joints.

2) To remove outer CV joints on 5000 models, cut clamps off of boot and discard. Slide boot away from joint and remove circlip from inside of joint. Drive CV joint off of shaft with a soft-faced hammer or copper drift by striking inner hub.

3) Tilt cage and hub out of CV joint to remove balls and disassemble joint. See Fig. 2, 3 and 4. Inspect parts for abnormal wear or damage. Parts cannot be interchanged between joints. DO NOT mix parts. If any part of joint is damaged, replacement of entire CV joint is necessary.

Fig. 2: Removing Inner CV Joint Ball Hub

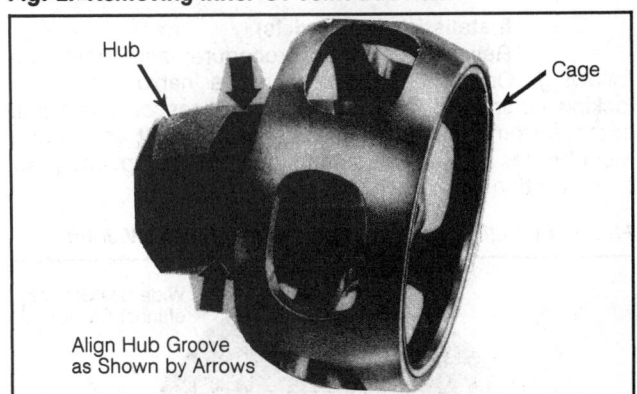

Hub

Cage

Align Hub Groove as Shown by Arrows

Fig. 1: Exploded View of Audi-Porsche 5-Speed Transaxle Assembly

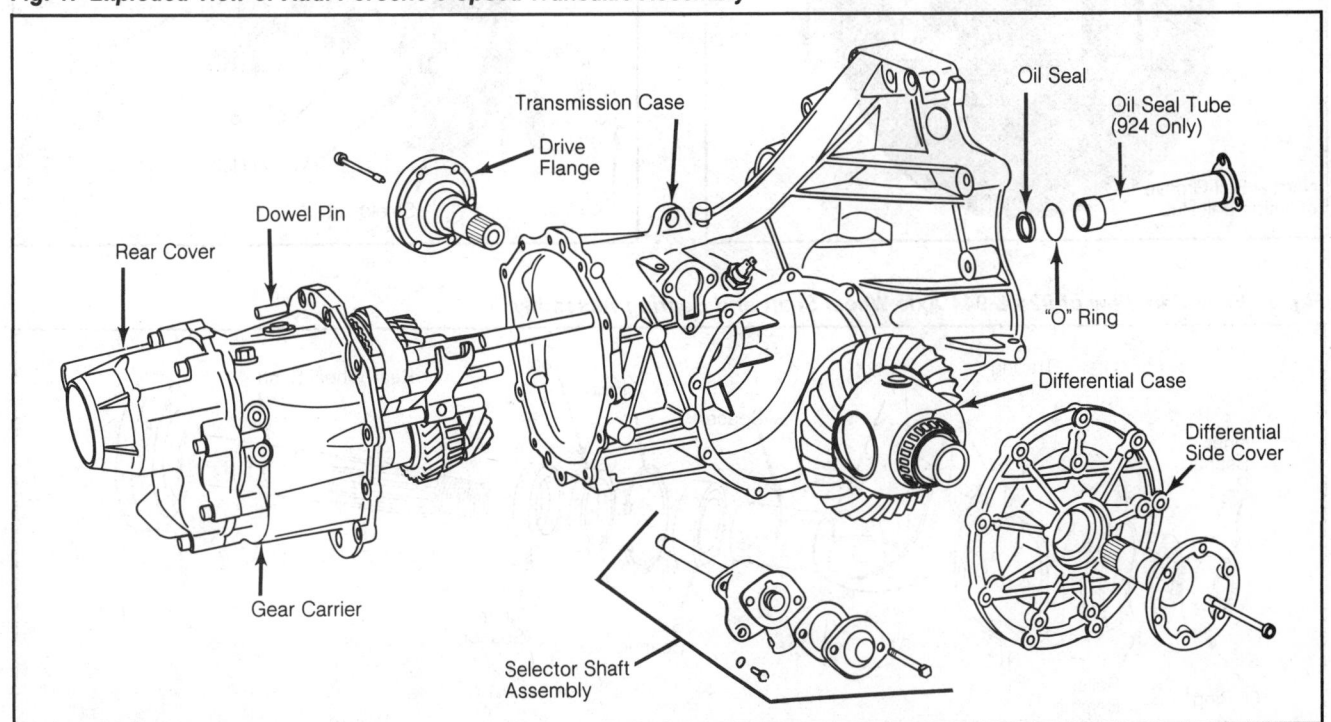

Transmission Case

Drive Flange

Oil Seal

Oil Seal Tube (924 Only)

Dowel Pin

Rear Cover

"O" Ring

Differential Case

Differential Side Cover

Gear Carrier

Selector Shaft Assembly

Manual Transmissions

AUDI 5000, PORSCHE 924 & 944 5-SPEED (Cont.)

Reassembly (All Models)

Reverse disassembly procedure and note the following: Pack each side of CV joints with 1.6 oz. of molybdenum disulfide grease.

Fig. 3: Removing Outer CV Joint Ball Hub

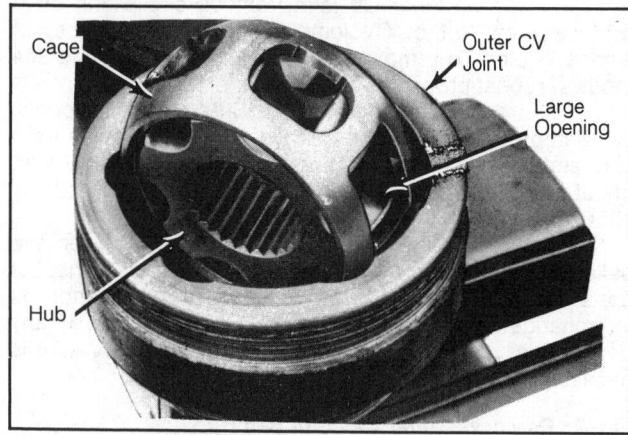

Installation (All Models)

Reverse removal procedure and note the following: On 5000 models, apply a narrow bead of locking compound to outer end of splines on shaft that extends from outer CV joint. Splines on shaft and in hub must be free of oil, grease and old locking compound prior to installation of shaft.

Fig. 4: Installing Ball Hub and Cage in Inner CV Joint

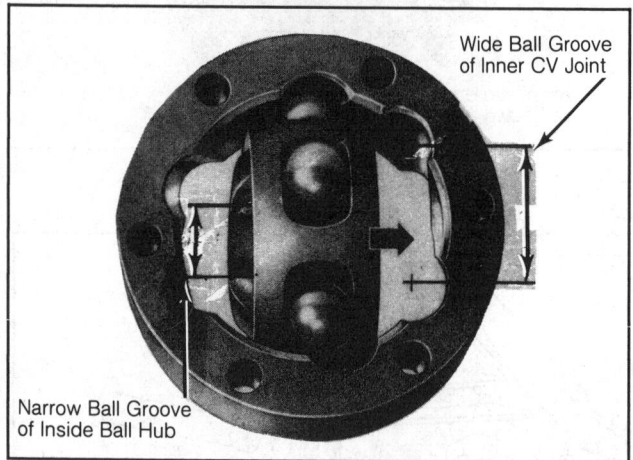

FRONT WHEEL BEARINGS (5000 ONLY)

Removal

1) With vehicle supported and drive axle shafts removed, remove stabilizer bar clamps. Remove caliper mounting bolts and hang caliper from frame with wire; DO NOT disconnect hydraulic line. Remove brake disc and ball joint bolt. Press off tie rod and remove ball joint from knuckle.

2) Support suspension strut with jack and remove 3 strut retaining nuts from inside engine compartment. Remove strut assembly from vehicle and mount in holding fixture (VW401 & VW402). Press out wheel hub with hub remover (VW295 & VW295a). Remove circlips from both sides of bearing housing and press out bearing (toward outboard end of housing). Remove inner wheel bearing race from hub. See Fig. 6.

Fig. 6: Exploded View of 5000 Front Suspension Strut Assembly

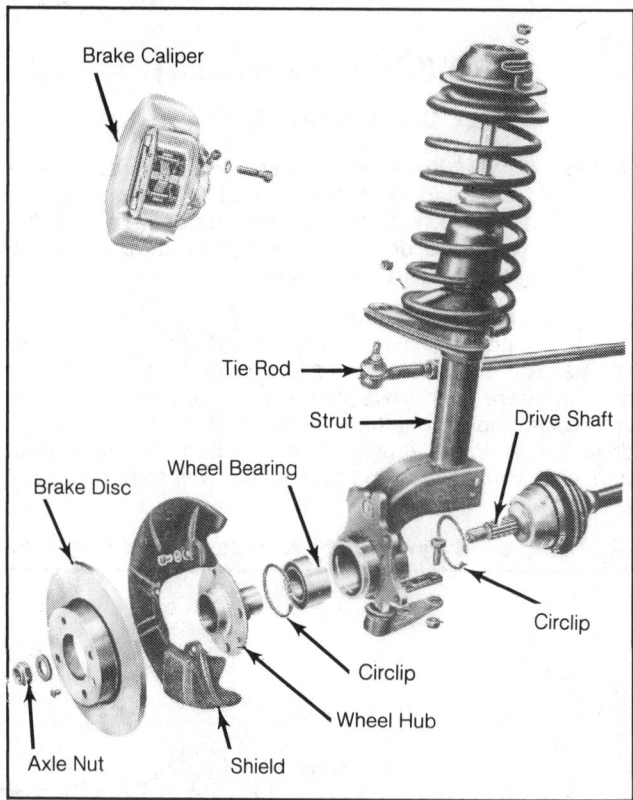

Fig. 5: Exploded View of 924 & 944 Axle Wheel Shaft and Bearing Assembly

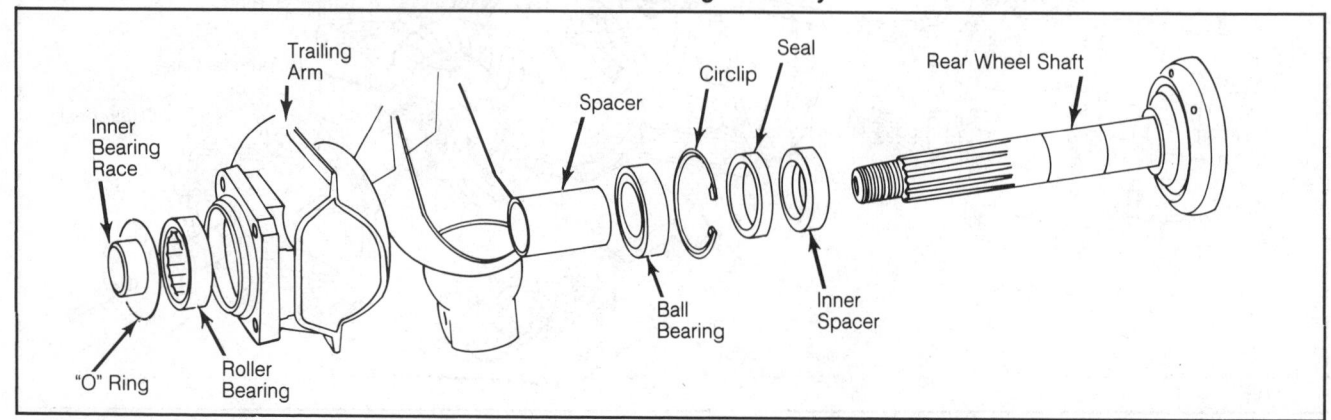

AUDI 5000, PORSCHE 924 & 944 5-SPEED (Cont.)

Fig. 7: Exploded View of Typical Axle Drive Shaft

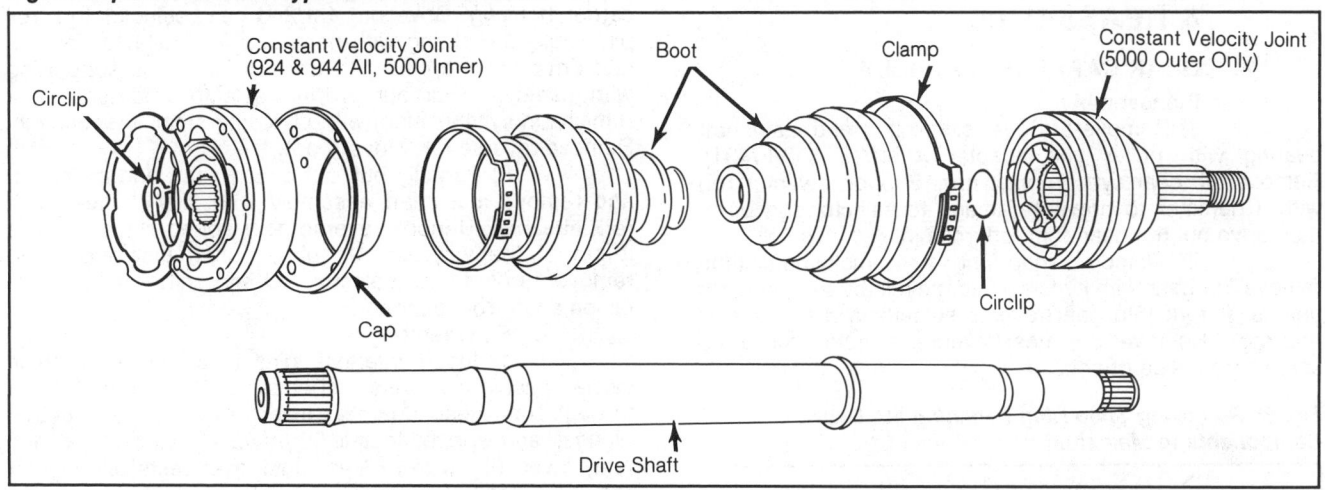

NOTE: **Wheel bearing must be replaced. Removal procedure destroys wheel bearing for reuse.**

Installation
To install, reverse removal procedure.

REAR WHEEL BEARINGS (924 & 944 ONLY)
Removal
Remove brake drum and wheel. Disconnect drive shaft from axle flange. Press shaft from housing with double arm puller. Pry seal out of housing, remove circlip and drive grooved ball bearing and roller bearing out with soft drift.

Installation
Press grooved ball bearing in inner end of housing and replace circlip. Put spacer in housing and drive roller bearing in place (flanged side facing out). Install seal in inboard side of housing. Place outer spacer on shaft and press in along with inner bearing race, using castellated nut and driver. See Fig. 5.

DRIVE FLANGE OIL SEALS
NOTE: **On some models, removal of certain guards may be necessary to provide access to oil seals.**

Removal
Disconnect inner CV joint from drive flange and support drive axle out of the way. Insert a long drift punch in 1 drive flange hole to prevent drive flange movement, then remove drive flange retaining bolt. Place a drip pan under transmission housing and pull out drive flange. Pry out oil seal.

Installation
Lightly lubricate seal lips and fully seat seal with a seal installer. Install drive flange and tighten drive flange retaining bolt. Install axle drive shafts and tighten bolts. Check and add lubricant to transaxle if necessary.

TRANSAXLE REMOVAL & INSTALLATION
See the appropriate article in MANUAL TRANSMISSION REMOVAL Section.

TRANSAXLE DISASSEMBLY
1) Mount transaxle in a holding fixture and drain oil. Remove selector shaft. On 924 models, loosen bolts securing mainshaft oil seal tube. Place seal protector (9113) over mainshaft splines. Pry tube loose with an offset screwdriver. Remove tube and remove seal from tube.

2) On all models, remove transaxle case-to-gear carrier bolts, drive out dowel pins and separate gear carrier from transaxle case. On all models except 924, remove input shaft front oil seal. On 944 models, remove input shaft front needle bearing from transmission case using a puller.

3) Mount gear carrier in soft-jawed vise with rear cover facing up. Remove cap from end of rear cover by driving a screwdriver into center of cap and prying up. Remove bolt from end of mainshaft.

Fig. 8: Removing Rear Cover from Gear Carrier

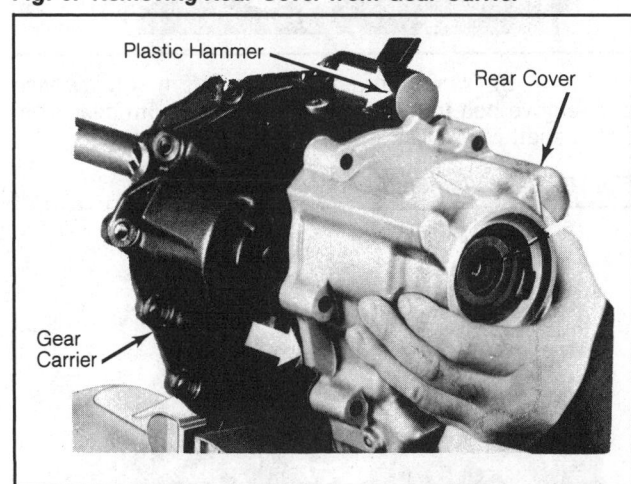

4) Reposition gear carrier in vise, clamping lower portion of gear carrier. Remove cover attaching bolts and drive cover from gear carrier with plastic hammer. Remove mainshaft inner bearing race.

5) Remove drive flange retaining bolt and drive flange. Remove final drive cover attaching bolts and pry cover from housing using 2 screwdrivers. DO NOT lose magnet on rear of final drive cover. Remove differential assembly.

Manual Transmissions

AUDI 5000, PORSCHE 924 & 944 5-SPEED (Cont.)

COMPONENT DISASSEMBLY & REASSEMBLY

GEAR CARRIER ASSEMBLY

Disassembly

1) Remove 5th gear clutch hub and mainshaft bearing with puller and adapter (US1078 & VW431). Remove 5th gear synchronizer ring. Support selector rod with a hammer to prevent damage to selector rod bore, then drive out 5th gear shift fork roll pin.

2) Remove snap ring from mainshaft, then remove 5th gear with synchro hub, needle bearing and 5th gear shift fork (5th gear/reverse selector rod remains in housing). Remove 5th gear/reverse selector rod stop screws from side of housing.

Fig. 9: Removing Snap Ring Retaining 5th Gear Components to Mainshaft

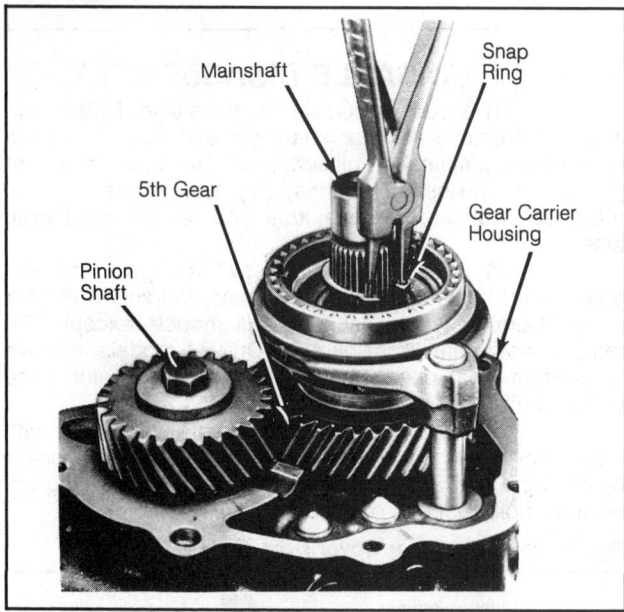

3) Clamp 4th gear/pinion shaft in soft-jaw vise and remove bolt from pinion shaft. Remove 5th gear from pinion shaft with puller, then remove adjusting shim.

Fig. 10: Removing Shift Fork Roll Pins

4) Reposition gear carrier in vise by clamping carrier housing. Drive out 1st/2nd gear selector fork roll pin, while supporting with hammer. Turn selector fork up and drive out 3rd/4th shift fork roll pin, while supporting with hammer. Pull out 3rd/4th selector rod (shift fork remains in synchro hub) without losing small interlock pin. Remove reverse relay lever boot.

5) Partially pull out pinion shaft and mainshaft and remove mainshaft assembly with 3rd/4th gear shift fork attached. Unhook reverse gear spring clip and move it out of the way. Lift up pinion shaft just enough to remove 1st/2nd gear selector rod and shift fork. Remove pinion shaft from gear carrier.

Reassembly

1) Insert interlock pins in correct position in carrier case bore. Insert springs and plungers for 1st through 4th gear detents. Insert reverse gear detent plunger and spring. Install 5th/reverse selector rod and relay lever. Press relay lever until lever rests on selector rod and in groove of reverse gear. *See Fig. 11.*

Fig. 11: Reverse Relay Lever Adjustment

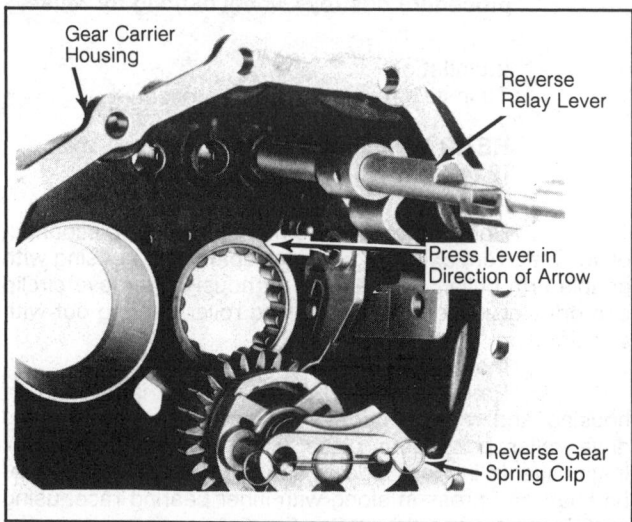

NOTE: **Reverse relay lever bolt and threaded bushing of lever must be in line.**

2) Tighten adjusting screw against stop on threaded bushing. Press relay lever against screw and loosen screw until tip of threads can be heard to engage in threaded bushing. Tighten screw to 25 ft. lbs. (34 N.m). Engage reverse gear several times and check that relay lever moves easily in all positions. Relay lever should be centered over reverse gear detent.

3) Engage pinion shaft with reverse gear and partially insert pinion shaft into gear carrier. Install 1st-2nd gear shift fork and selector rod, then press pinion shaft into housing. Push 3rd/4th gear shift fork onto 5th/reverse gear selector rod.

4) Press off mainshaft inner bearing race, then partially install mainshaft into housing. Insert 3rd/4th gear shift fork into clutch sleeve and press mainshaft into housing until fully seated. Move selector rods into neutral position and check for proper position of interlock pins.

5) Install 3rd/4th gear shift rod and insert small interlock pin (coated with grease). Secure 3rd/4th and 1st/2nd gear shift forks and selector rods with roll pins. Install selector rod stop screws into carrier housing using new gaskets.

AUDI 5000, PORSCHE 924 & 944 5-SPEED (Cont.)

6) Position gear carrier assembly in a soft-jawed vise, with jaws clamped on 4th gear of pinion shaft. Using a depth gauge, measure dimension "A" as shown in *Fig. 12* to determine correct 5th gear adjusting shim to install. Select correct 5th gear adjusting shim using the following table:

NOTE: See Fig. 12 for Dimension "A" measurement.

PINION SHAFT 5TH GEAR ADJUSTING SHIM CHART

If "A" Is In. (mm)	Use this Shim In. (mm)
.331-.339 (8.4-8.6)	.043 (1.1)
.343-.350 (8.7-8.9)	.055 (1.4)
.354-.362 (9.0-9.2)	.067 (1.7)
.366-.374 (9.3-9.5)	.079 (2.0)
.378-.386 (9.6-9.8)	.091 (2.3)

Fig. 12: 5th Gear Pinion Shaft Adjusting Shim Selection

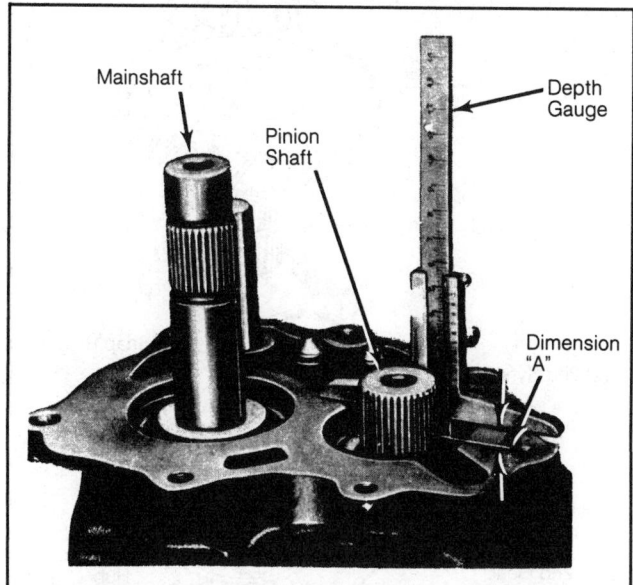

Measure Depth at "A" and Convert to Shim Size Using Chart

7) Install selected 5th gear adjusting shim, then heat 5th gear to 250°F (120°C) and slide onto pinion shaft until seated. Install washer and bolt on end of pinion shaft and tighten bolt. Collar of washer must face pinion head.

8) Clamp mainshaft in soft-jawed vise so that mainshaft and pinion shaft are vertical. Heat mainshaft bearing inner race to 250°F (120°C) and slide it onto mainshaft until seated.

9) Install 5th gear with synchronizer hub, needle bearing and shift rod onto mainshaft. Install shift fork roll pin into fork and selector rod. Select a snap ring that will provide a maximum mainshaft end play of .002" (.05 mm), then install snap ring into mainshaft groove.

NOTE: Mainshaft snap rings are available in following thicknesses: .050" (1.35 mm), .055" (1.40 mm) and .060" (1.45 mm).

10) Install 5th gear synchronizer ring. Heat 5th gear clutch hub to 250°F (120°C) and install it on mainshaft until fully seated. Drive on mainshaft bearing

inner race, then install guide sleeve and new gasket on gear carrier housing. Install rear cover on carrier housing.

11) Heat other half of mainshaft bearing inner race and drive onto mainshaft. Install washer and bolt on end of mainshaft and tighten bolt. Install and tighten rear cover mounting bolts. Install new rear cover cap.

MAINSHAFT ASSEMBLY
Disassembly

Remove snap ring from end of shaft. Remove 4th gear thrust washer, 4th gear, 4th gear needle bearings, synchronizer ring and snap ring. Using a press, press off 3rd gear, synchronizer ring, 3rd/4th gear synchro assembly and 3rd gear needle bearing.

Reassembly

1) Inspect all components for wear or damage and replace as necessary. Install 3rd gear needle bearing onto mainshaft. Place synchro assembly, 3rd gear synchro ring and 3rd gear in correct relationship atop each other.

NOTE: Turn synchronizer ring so grooves are in line with hollow keys. Also, groove on synchronizer hub or wide collar must face 4th gear.

2) Press mainshaft into 3rd gear and synchronizer assembly. To determine correct snap ring to install, use a feeler gauge to measure 3rd/4th gear synchronizer hub end play as shown in *Fig. 13*. Install a snap ring that will allow an end play of 0-.002" (0-0.5 mm).

NOTE: Snap rings for 3rd/4th synchronizer hub end play adjustments are available in the following thicknesses: .059" (1.59 mm), .061" (1.56 mm) and .064" (1.62 mm).

Fig. 13: Checking 3rd/4th Gear Synchronizer Hub End Play

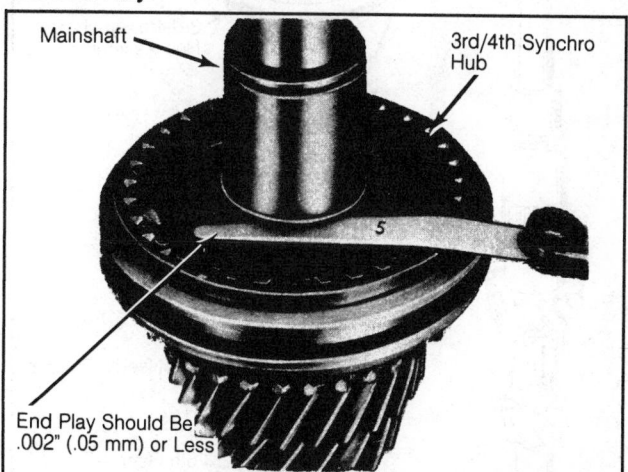

3) Install synchronizer ring on 4th gear side of synchronizer hub, then install 4th gear needle bearing, 4th gear, thrust washer and snap ring. Measure clearance between thrust washer and snap ring. Clearance should be .008-.013" (.20-.35 mm). If not, correct by installing a different thickness snap ring.

NOTE: Snap rings for 4th gear end play adjustment are available in the following thicknesses: .065" (1.65 mm), .067" (1.70 mm) and .069" (1.75 mm).

Manual Transmissions

AUDI 5000, PORSCHE 924 & 944 5-SPEED (Cont.)

PINION SHAFT

Disassembly

1) Mount pinion shaft assembly into a holding fixture. Using a press, remove small inner bearing and 1st gear by pressing from shaft.

2) Remove 1st gear needle bearing and synchro ring. Remove snap ring, then press off 1st/2nd gear synchro hub assembly, 2nd gear synchro ring and 2nd gear.

3) Remove 2nd gear needle bearing, snap ring, then press off 3rd gear. Remove circlip, then remove 4th gear snap ring and press off 4th gear and large bearing from shaft.

Fig. 14: Exploded View of Mainshaft Assembly

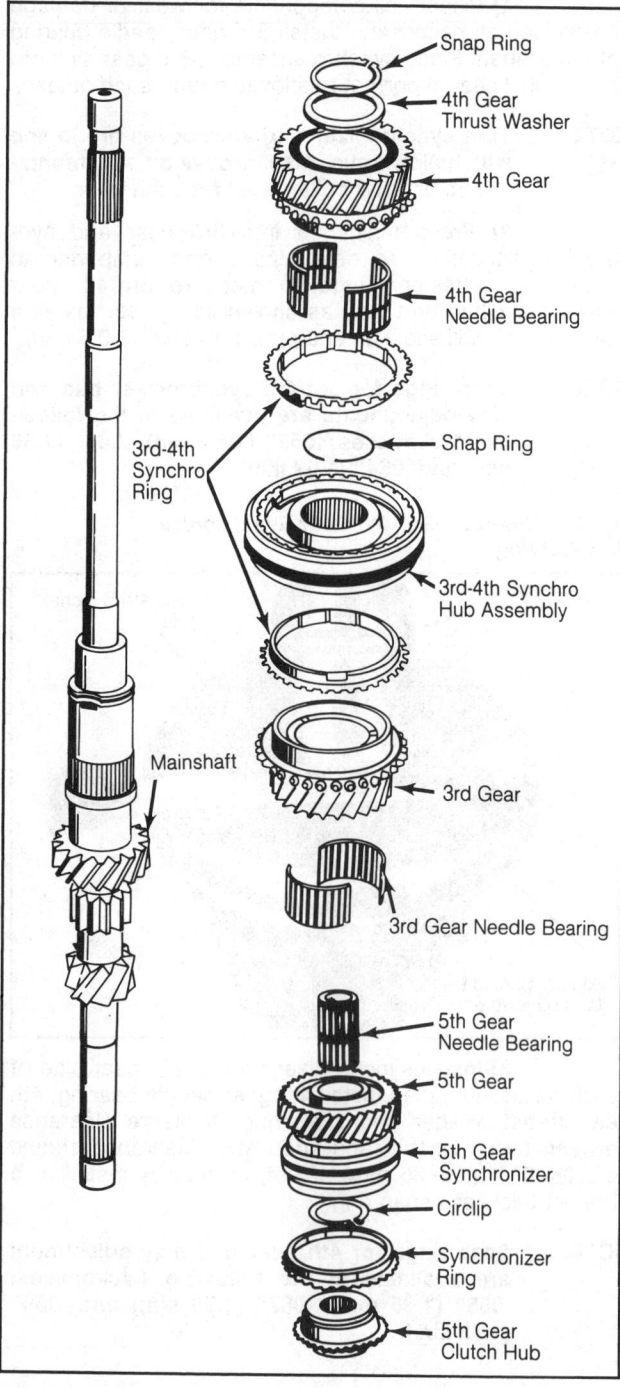

- Snap Ring
- 4th Gear Thrust Washer
- 4th Gear
- 4th Gear Needle Bearing
- 3rd-4th Synchro Ring
- Snap Ring
- 3rd-4th Synchro Hub Assembly
- Mainshaft
- 3rd Gear
- 3rd Gear Needle Bearing
- 5th Gear Needle Bearing
- 5th Gear
- 5th Gear Synchronizer
- Circlip
- Synchronizer Ring
- 5th Gear Clutch Hub

Reassembly

1) Ensure all gears and shaft are oil-free and replace any damaged or defective parts. Press large bearing onto pinion shaft. Heat 4th gear to 250°F (120°C), slide gear onto pinion shaft (shoulder facing 3rd gear) and press until fully seated.

Fig. 15: Exploded View of Pinion Shaft Assembly

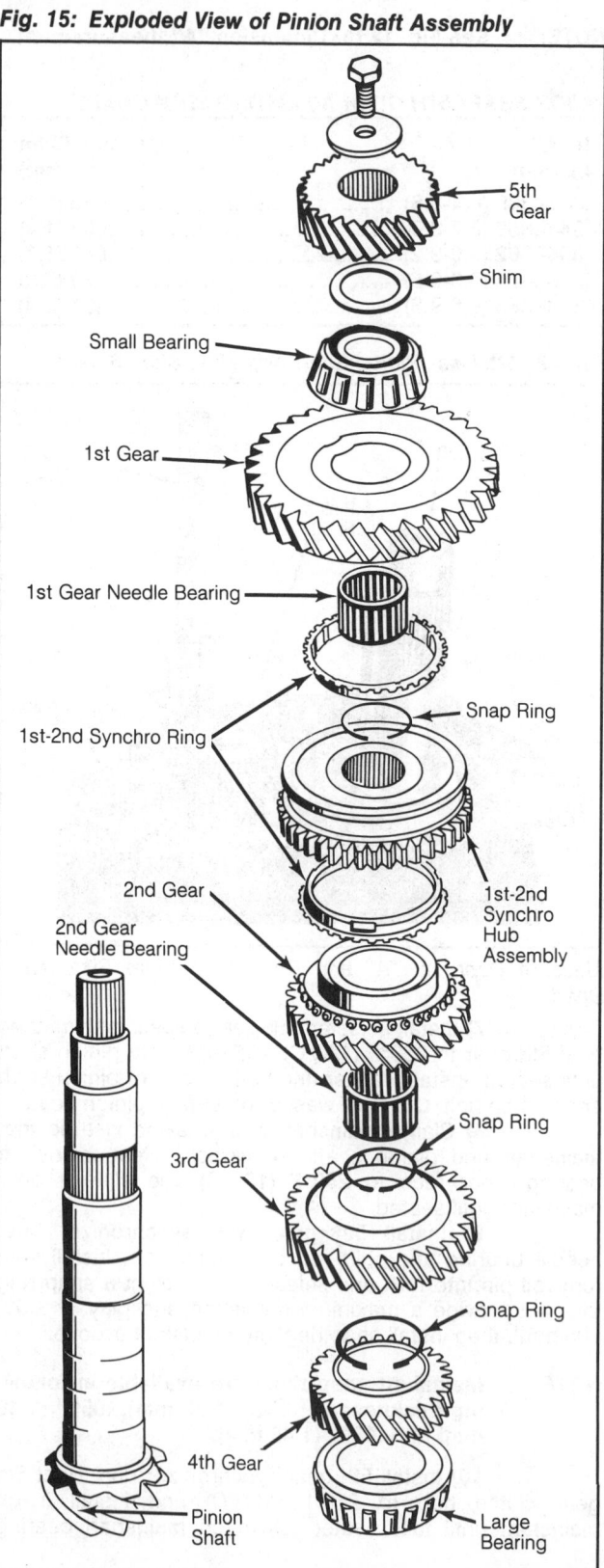

- 5th Gear
- Shim
- Small Bearing
- 1st Gear
- 1st Gear Needle Bearing
- 1st-2nd Synchro Ring
- Snap Ring
- 1st-2nd Synchro Hub Assembly
- 2nd Gear
- 2nd Gear Needle Bearing
- Snap Ring
- 3rd Gear
- Snap Ring
- 4th Gear
- Pinion Shaft
- Large Bearing

AUDI 5000, PORSCHE 924 & 944 5-SPEED (Cont.)

NOTE: After approximately 3 minutes, press 4th gear onto shaft again to ensure correct adjustment of end play. After 4th gear has cooled, continue reassembly procedure.

2) Measure 4th gear end play with a feeler gauge and adjust end play to not more than .0008" (.02 mm) with correct snap ring. Snap rings are available in sizes ranging from .088" (2.24 mm) to .094" (2.40 mm) in .0008" (.02 mm) increments.

3) Install a .094" (2.4 mm) snap ring into second snap ring groove of pinion shaft. Heat 3rd gear to 250°F (120°C) and slide gear onto shaft with shoulder toward 2nd gear.

4) Press gear onto shaft until seated against snap ring, then install retaining snap ring. Using a feeler gauge, measure 3rd gear end play as shown in *Fig. 16*. End play should be 0-.002" (0-.05 mm). If not, install a different retaining snap ring.

NOTE: Snap rings for 3rd gear end play adjustment are available in the following thicknesses: .065" (1.65 mm), .067" (1.70 mm) and .069" (1.75 mm).

Fig. 16: Checking 3rd Gear End Play

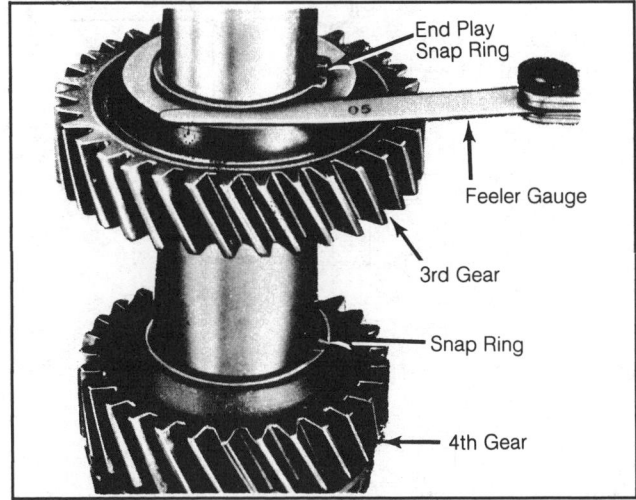

5) Oil 2nd gear needle bearing and install on shaft. Place 2nd gear, 2nd gear synchro ring and synchro hub assembly atop one another. Press all components onto pinion shaft. Measure synchronizer hub assembly end play with a feeler gauge. End play should be 0-.0016" (0-.04 mm). Adjust end play with a snap ring.

NOTE: Snap rings for 1st/2nd synchronizer hub adjustment are available in the following thicknesses: .059" (1.50 mm), .061" (1.55 mm) and .063" (1.60 mm).

6) Install remaining synchronizer ring onto hub. Oil and install 1st gear needle bearing, then slide 1st gear onto pinion shaft. Press pinion shaft small bearing onto shaft until fully seated.

SYNCHRONIZER ASSEMBLIES
Disassembly
Remove snap ring and separate synchronizer hub from sleeve. Use care not to lose or damage synchronizer keys and springs.

Inspection
Check all parts for wear or damage. Using a feeler gauge, check synchronizer rings for wear as shown in *Fig. 17*. Clearance "A" should be .039-.075" (1.0-1.9 mm) for 5th gear synchro or .039-.067" (1.0-1.7 mm) for all others.

Fig. 17: Checking Synchronizer Rings for Wear

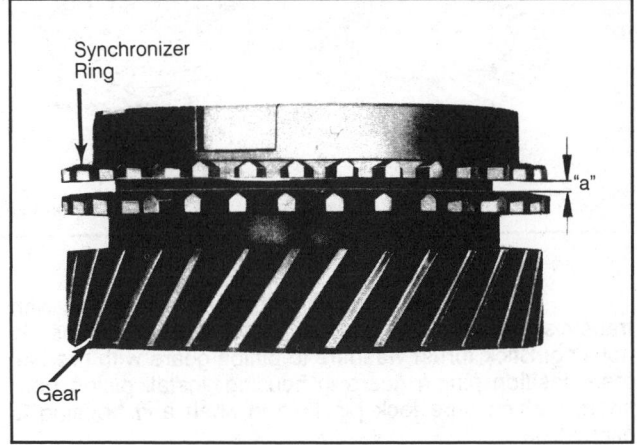

Reassembly
Reverse disassembly procedure and use *Fig. 18* as an assembly guide. Install springs with ends 120° offset. Bent end of spring must engage hollow synchro key.

Fig. 18: Assembled View of Synchronizer Assembly

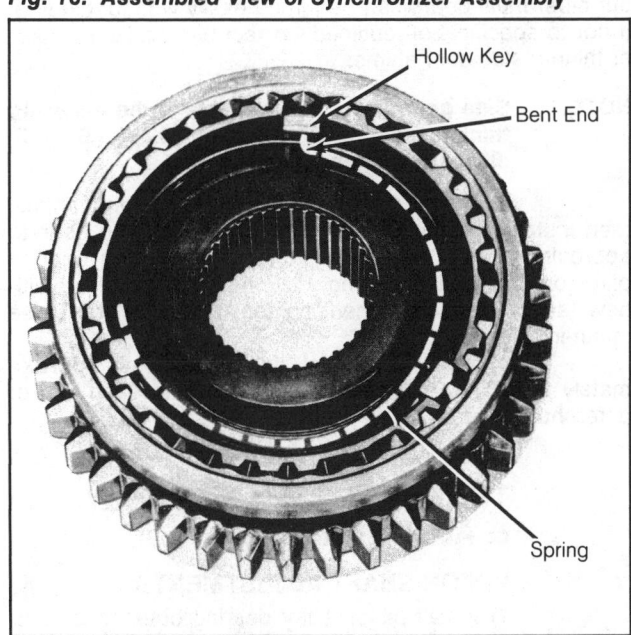

DIFFERENTIAL
Disassembly
1) Place differential assembly in soft-jawed vise. Remove ring gear bolts and ring gear. Using a puller, remove differential side bearings.

2) Drive out pinion shaft lock pin with a punch. Then drive out pinion shaft with a punch. Rotate differential gear set and remove pinion gears, side gears, shims, thrust washers and drive flange nuts through opening in differential housing.

Fig. 19: *Exploded View of Differential Assembly*

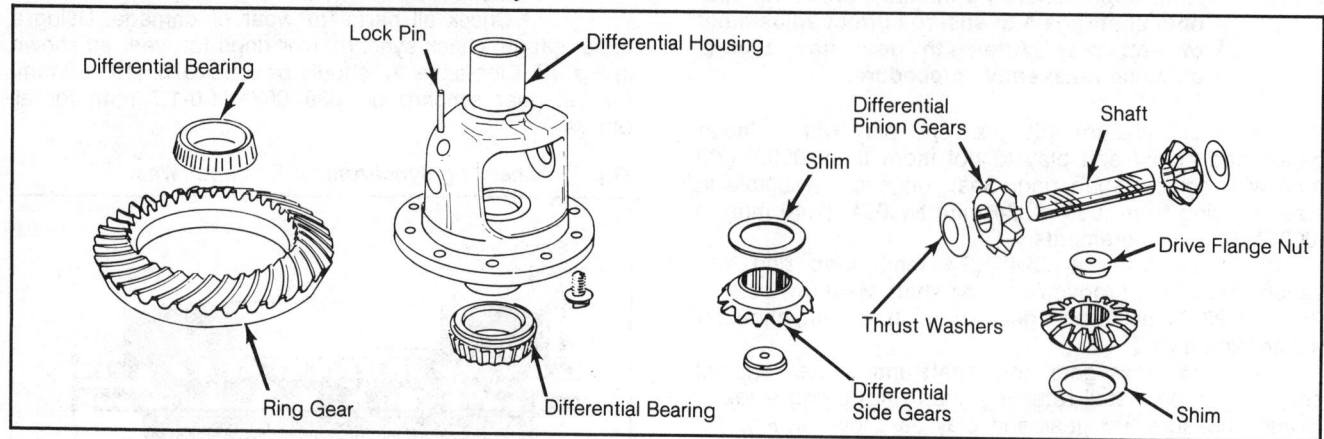

Reassembly

1) Lubricate pinion gears and side gears with transmission oil. Position side gears with shims in housing. Stick thrust washers to pinion gears with grease, then position pinion gears in housing. Install pinion gear shaft, making sure lock pin hole in shaft and housing is aligned.

CAUTION: Side gears, pinion gears, shims and thrust washers must not be interchanged.

2) Check pinion and side gear adjustment by pushing pinion gears outward and check play of side gears. Adjustment is correct if no play can be felt by hand, but differential gears can be turned easily without binding. If not to specification outlined, correct by installing thicker or thinner side gear shims.

NOTE: **Side gear shims are available in the following thicknesses: .020" (.5 mm), .024" (.6 mm), .028" (.7 mm) and .032" (.8 mm).**

3) Install correct side gear adjusting shims, then install pinion gear shaft lock pin. Heat ring gear to approximately 250°F (120°C), then position ring gear in place on differential housing. Pull ring gear into place with new attaching bolts, then tighten bolts in crosswise manner.

4) Heat differential side bearings to approximately 212°F (100°C), then press them onto each end of differential housing.

TRANSAXLE REASSEMBLY & ADJUSTMENTS

PINION SHAFT ADJUSTMENTS

1) Install pinion shaft bearing outer races into final drive housing and gear carrier WITHOUT shims. Install assembled gear carrier to final drive housing and tighten attaching bolts.

2) Place magnetic measuring plate (VW385/17) onto rear end of pinion shaft, then mount a dial indicator to gear carrier as shown in *Fig. 20*. Zero dial indicator with .039" (1 mm) preload. Move pinion shaft up and down (without turning shaft) and record indicator reading.

CAUTION: Turning pinion shaft during measurement will cause bearings to settle, giving an inaccurate reading.

Fig. 20: *Measuring Pinion Shaft End Play to Determine Total Pinion Adjusting Shim Thickness*

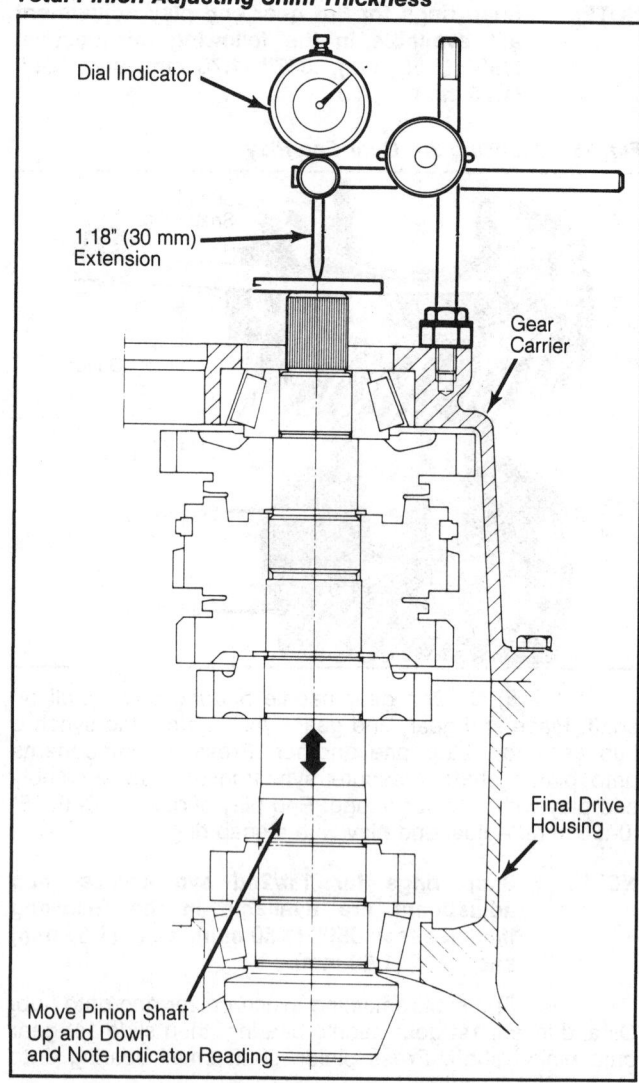

3) Remove gear carrier from final drive housing. To determine total thickness of shims necessary to obtain correct pinion depth and bearing preload, add constant preload value of .012" (.30 mm) to dial indicator reading just obtained. Resulting sum is total thickness of required shims.

AUDI 5000, PORSCHE 924 & 944 5-SPEED (Cont.)

5) Adjust clamping ring on measuring bar (VW385/1) so dimension "a" in *Fig. 21* is 2" (50 mm). Next, assemble the following measuring tools onto measuring bar as shown in *Fig. 21:* Dial Indicator, Centering Discs (VW385/2 and 3), Measuring Pin (VW385/14), Measuring Pin Extension (VW385/15), and Setting Gauge (VW385/27). With all tools assembled to bar, zero dial indicator with .039" (1 mm) preload and remove setting gauge (VW385/27).

NOTE: Move clamping ring back to stop.

Fig. 21: Assembling Measuring Tools for Pinion Depth Shim Selection

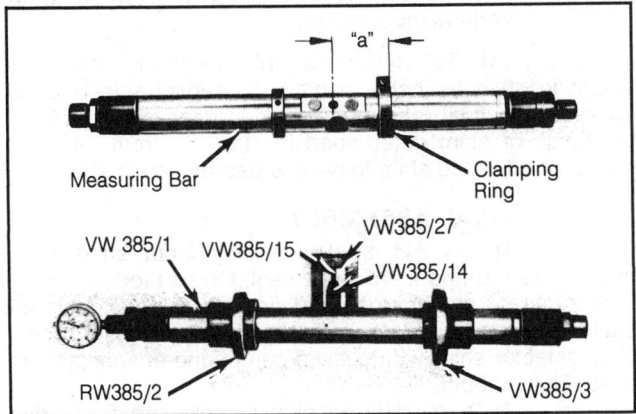

6) Place magnetic measuring plate (VW385/17) on end of pinion shaft. Install assembled measuring bar into final drive housing with centering disc (VW385/2) facing final drive cover. Install final drive cover and secure with 4 bolts.

7) Turn knob on end of measuring bar to move clamping ring and the other centering disc (VW385/3) outward, until bar can just barely be turned by hand.

8) Rotate measuring bar until measuring pin extension rests squarely against magnetic plate on pinion shaft. Then rotate bar back and forth over center. Read and record maximum dial indicator reading.

9) To determine correct pinion depth adjusting shim(s) to install behind bearing outer race in gear carrier, add the deviation number stamped on ring gear to the dial indicator reading obtained in step **8)**.

NOTE: Deviation number stamped on ring gear is in hundredth millimeters. A marking of 25 would be .25 mm.

10) To determine thickness of shim to install under pinion bearing outer race in final drive housing, subtract thickness of pinion depth shim determined in step **9)** from total pinion shim thickness obtained in step **3)**.

NOTE: Shims for outer race installed in gear carrier are available in thicknesses of .008" (.20 mm) to .045" (1.15 mm) in various increments. Shims for outer bearing race in final drive housing are available in thicknesses of .009" (.24 mm) to .056" (1.41 mm) in various increments.

11) Remove measuring bar assembly from final drive housing. Separate gear carrier from final drive housing. Remove pinion shaft bearing outer race from gear carrier and final drive housing, then install selected shims with outer race back into carrier and housing.

12) Install gear carrier to final drive and tighten attaching bolts. To check adjustment, reinstall measuring bar assembly and recheck measurements. If correct shims have been installed, dial indicator reading (counterclockwise) should be the ring gear deviation number with a tolerance of ± .0016" (.04 mm).

13) To check pinion bearing preload, lubricate pinion bearings with transmission oil, then check pinion shaft turning torque with a torque wrench. Pinion shaft turning torque with NEW bearings installed should be 17-34 INCH lbs. (2-3.8 N.m). Turning torque with USED bearings installed should be 2.5-5.0 INCH lbs. (0.3-0.6 N.m). *See Fig. 22.*

Fig. 22: Checking Pinion Shaft Turning Torque

14) If turning torque is not within specifications, sufficient shim thickness for bearing preload and bearing settling has not been allowed.

RING GEAR ADJUSTMENTS

1) Remove gear carrier from final drive housing. Remove differential oil seals and side bearing outer races from final drive housing and take out shims. Reinstall side bearing outer races WITHOUT shims. Install differential assembly into final drive housing. Install final drive cover and tighten attaching bolts in a diagonal pattern to 18 ft. lbs. (24 N.m).

NOTE: Differential assembly is installed with ring gear side facing final drive cover.

Fig. 23: Measuring Differential Bearing Preload

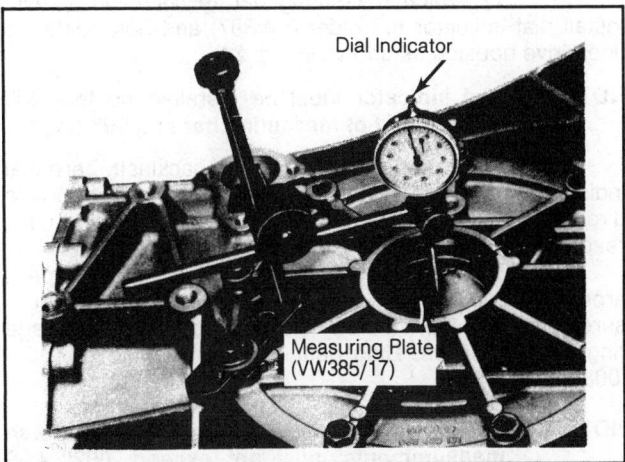

Manual Transmissions

AUDI 5000, PORSCHE 924 & 944 5-SPEED (Cont.)

2) Position magnetic measuring plate (VW385/17) and dial indicator as shown in *Fig. 23*, then zero dial indicator with .039" (1 mm) preload. Move differential assembly up and down and note dial indicator reading.

CAUTION: Do not rotate differential while taking measurement as bearings will settle and make measurement inaccurate.

3) To the dial indicator reading obtained in step **2)**, add the constant preload value of .020" (.50 mm). Resulting sum is thickness of shims necessary for correct differential bearing preload.

4) Remove measuring tools and final drive housing cover. Remove differential side bearing outer race from cover, then reinstall race with a shim of the thickness obtained in step **3)** behind it. Reinstall final drive housing cover.

5) Lubricate differential side bearings with transmission oil, then connect an INCH lb. torque wrench to differential and check turning torque. Differential turning torque with new side bearings should be 22 INCH lbs. (2.5 N.m).

NOTE: It is not necessary to measure differential turning torque when used bearings are reinstalled.

6) Insert clamping sleeve (VW521/4) with slotted sleeve (VW521/8) into differential and secure with nut. Adjust length of backlash measuring bar (VW388) until dimension "A" in *Fig. 24* in 3.11" (79 mm).

Fig. 24: Position of Ring Gear Backlash Measuring Tools

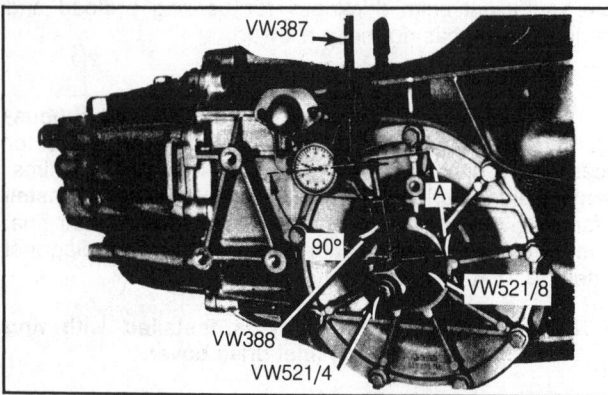

7) Attach measuring bar to clamping sleeve. Install dial indicator in holder (VW387) and bolt holder to final drive housing as shown in *Fig. 24*.

NOTE: Dial indicator must be installed so foot will contact end of measuring bar at a 90° angle.

8) Turn ring gear to take up backlash. Zero dial indicator and clamp in holder. Turn ring gear in opposite direction until it is stopped and note indicator reading. This reading is ring gear backlash.

9) Check ring gear at 4 locations (90° apart) around circumference of ring gear. Add the 4 measurements together, then divide by 4 to find the average ring gear backlash. Ring gear backlash should be .004-.008" (.10-.20 mm).

NOTE: Difference between the 4 ring gear backlash measurements must not exceed .002" (.06

mm). **If measurements differ more than this, ring gear is incorrectly installed or final drive housing is damaged.**

10) To determine thickness of shim to install behind differential bearing outer race in final drive housing cover (opposite ring gear side), subtract the average ring gear backlash from the total shim thickness obtained in step **3)**. To this value add the constant preload value of .006" (.15 mm). Resulting sum is the thickness of ring gear adjusting shim to install in final drive housing cover.

NOTE: Ring gear adjusting shims for final drive housing cover are available in thicknesses from .006" (.15 mm) to .047" (1.2 mm) in various increments.

11) To determine thickness of ring gear adjusting shim to install behind differential side bearing outer race in final drive housing (ring gear side), subtract thickness of shim determined in step **10)** from the total ring gear adjusting shim thickness determined in step **3)**.

FINAL ASSEMBLY

1) On 944 models, install input shaft front needle bearing and input shaft seal. On all models, lightly coat joints of gear carrier and final drive housings with sealing compound. Mate units together and tighten bolts. Coat selector shaft with sealing compound and install into case. Tighten bolts.

2) Place differential assembly into final drive housing. Install differential cover magnet at the bottom. Install both drive axle flanges and tighten bolts.

3) On 5000 models, install speedometer driven gear and adapter. Install input shaft seal. Install clutch release shaft, spring and bearing assembly into clutch housing. Lubricate release shaft with multi-purpose grease.

4) On 924 models, install mainshaft seal in tube with seal driver (9119). Install seal protector (9113) over mainshaft and install seal tube, with new "O" ring onto mainshaft. Install shifter adapter (9155/1) and check operation of transmission in all gears.

TIGHTENING SPECIFICATIONS

Application	Ft. Lbs. (N.m)
Axle Shaft Nut	
924 (Rear)	253 (343)
944 (Rear 1st Step)	275 (373)
944 (Rear 2nd Step)	326 (442)
5000 (Front)	202 (274)
CV Joint Bolts	30 (41)
Gear Carrier-to-Final Drive Housing	18 (24)
Drive Flange Bolts	18 (24)
Final Drive Cover	18 (24)
Mainshaft End Bolt	36 (49)
5th Gear End Bolt	36 (49)
Reverse Relay Lever Bolt	25 (34)
Ring Gear Bolts	72 (98)
Upper Strut Retaining Nuts (5000)	18 (24)
Transaxle-to-Engine (5000)	40 (54)
Oil Seal Tube (924)	12 (16)
Central Tube-to-Transaxle (924 & 944)	
10 mm Bolts	30 (41)
12 mm Bolts	61 (83)
Central Tube-to-Clutch Housing (924 & 944)	30 (41)

BMW 5-SPEED

320i, 528e, 633CSi, 733i

DESCRIPTION

This 5-speed transmission is fully synchronized with constant mesh helical cut gears in forward speeds, and uses non-synchronized helical cut reverse gears. Shifting is accomplished through 3 shift rails and forks. Transmission case is a 3-piece design.

NOTE: **This article is general to cover all models; minor variations in construction may exist between models.**

LUBRICATION & ADJUSTMENT

See the appropriate article in MANUAL TRANS-MISSION SERVICING Section.

TROUBLE SHOOTING

HARD SHIFTING

Check clutch adjustment, or check gears, shafts, bearings or synchronizers for wear or damage.

SLIPS OUT OF GEAR

Check for worn or damaged interlock, bearings or gears.

NOISE IN TRANSMISSION

Ensure noise is from transmission and not clutch. Check for proper transmission lubricant level. Check for worn or damaged bearings or gears.

REMOVAL & INSTALLATION

See the appropriate article in MANUAL TRANS-MISSION REMOVAL Section.

TRANSMISSION DISASSEMBLY

TRANSMISSION CASE

1) Remove crossmember and exhaust support bracket. Secure transmission in holding device and drain oil. Remove guide sleeve, cover, spring and locking pin from upper right front of housing. Unscrew back-up light switch.

2) Drive out pins and remove bolts and hex-head screw on rear housing. Remove front bearing race, snap ring and washer. Using a puller, remove front housing.

3) Remove rear lock plate. Using a clamping tool, hold output flange and unscrew collar nut. Remove output flange and cover, making note of shims. Drive out 2 pins on rear cover and remove bolt. Engage 2nd gear and, using pullers, remove rear housing.

SHIFT CONTROL ASSEMBLY

1) Remove bolts in top and side of transmission case. Remove clamp from end of lower selector rod. Pull selector rod towards rear and remove operating lever. Drive out selector arm pin and pull selector rod towards rear. Remove selector arm.

2) Push 5th-Reverse shift rod towards rear enough to expose fork. Drive out pin and remove fork with sliding sleeve. Turn selector rod until slot faces upward and remove by pulling towards rear.

Fig. 1: Exploded View of BMW 5-Speed Transmission Case Components

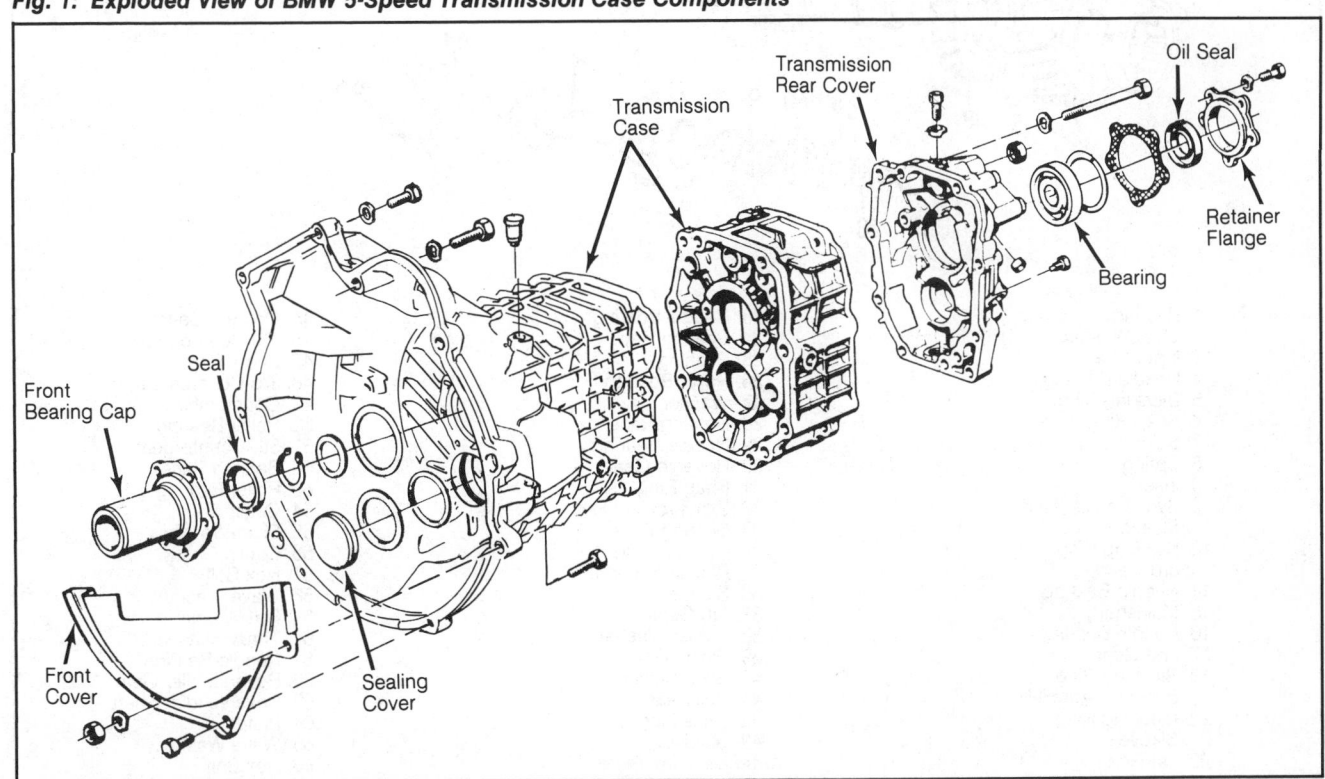

Manual Transmissions
BMW 5-SPEED (Cont.)

Fig. 2: Exploded View of BMW 5-Speed Transmission Gears and Shafts

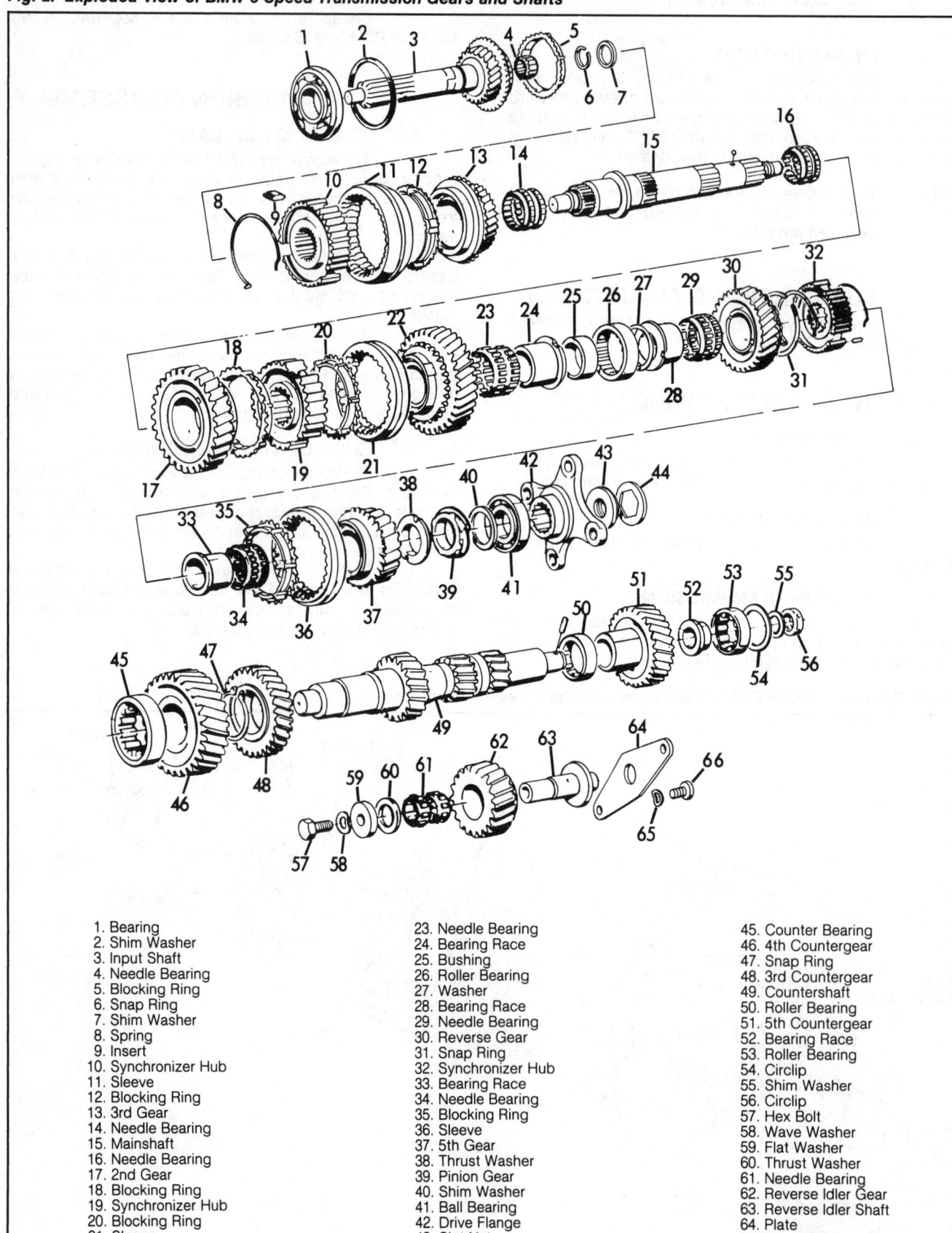

1. Bearing	23. Needle Bearing	45. Counter Bearing
2. Shim Washer	24. Bearing Race	46. 4th Countergear
3. Input Shaft	25. Bushing	47. Snap Ring
4. Needle Bearing	26. Roller Bearing	48. 3rd Countergear
5. Blocking Ring	27. Washer	49. Countershaft
6. Snap Ring	28. Bearing Race	50. Roller Bearing
7. Shim Washer	29. Needle Bearing	51. 5th Countergear
8. Spring	30. Reverse Gear	52. Bearing Race
9. Insert	31. Snap Ring	53. Roller Bearing
10. Synchronizer Hub	32. Synchronizer Hub	54. Circlip
11. Sleeve	33. Bearing Race	55. Shim Washer
12. Blocking Ring	34. Needle Bearing	56. Circlip
13. 3rd Gear	35. Blocking Ring	57. Hex Bolt
14. Needle Bearing	36. Sleeve	58. Wave Washer
15. Mainshaft	37. 5th Gear	59. Flat Washer
16. Needle Bearing	38. Thrust Washer	60. Thrust Washer
17. 2nd Gear	39. Pinion Gear	61. Needle Bearing
18. Blocking Ring	40. Shim Washer	62. Reverse Idler Gear
19. Synchronizer Hub	41. Ball Bearing	63. Reverse Idler Shaft
20. Blocking Ring	42. Drive Flange	64. Plate
21. Sleeve	43. Slot Nut	65. Wave Washer
22. 1st Gear	44. Securing Plate	66. Hex Bolt

BMW 5-SPEED (Cont.)

NOTE: Take care not to lose detent balls when performing the following procedures.

3) Remove pins in driving dog and 1st-2nd shift fork. Remove driving dog. Engage 3rd gear. Remove pin from 3rd-4th shift fork by driving out between gap in sliding sleeve tooth and opening in 3rd gear. Remove 1st-2nd and 3rd-4th shift forks.

Fig. 3: Exploded View of Shift Rods and Forks

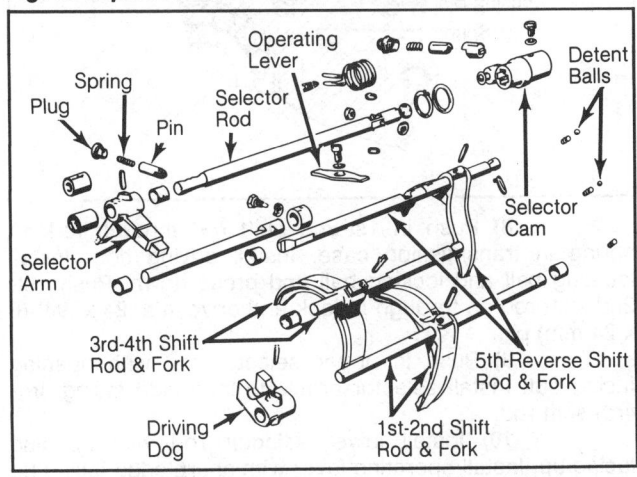

TRANSMISSION GEAR ASSEMBLIES

1) Remove pin and spacer from 5th countergear, making note of shims. Using a puller, remove 5th countergear from countershaft.

2) Remove 5th gear, synchronizer blocking ring and needle bearing from mainshaft. Using a puller, remove synchro hub from shaft.

3) Using pullers, remove reverse gear and needle bearing from mainshaft. Removal of needle bearing inner race requires the use of bearing removal tool (23-1-060 and 33-1-301) on some models. Remove mainshaft and countershaft from transmission case.

COMPONENT DISASSEMBLY & REASSEMBLY

MAINSHAFT

Disassembly
Pull input shaft, synchronizer blocking ring and needle bearing off mainshaft. Remove snap ring and slide synchronizer hub, sleeve, blocking ring and 3rd gear with

Fig. 4: Checking Measurement for Mainshaft Shim Thickness

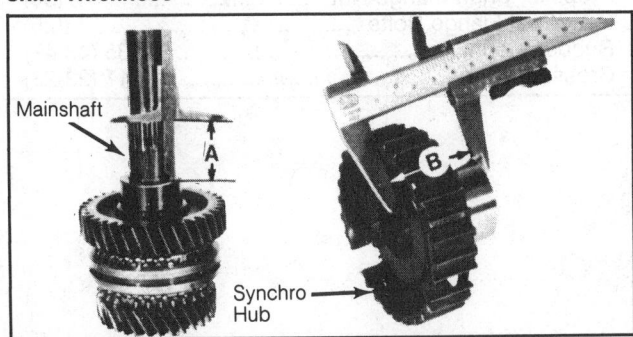

needle bearing off front of mainshaft. Place mainshaft in a holder and press mainshaft from remaining gear assemblies.

Reassembly
Reverse disassembly procedure making note to measure distance "A" of mainshaft collar to inner bearing race on gear assembly and distance "B" of reverse synchronizer hub to bearing bushing. *See Fig. 4.* If "A" and "B" are not equal, subtract one from the other and install shim of appropriate (measurement difference) thickness.

SYNCHRONIZER ASSEMBLIES

Disassembly
Remove blocking ring, then push hub from sleeve. Separate inserts and insert springs from hub.

Inspection
Check all parts for wear or damage. Blocking rings must be replaced if tapered clutch surface is pitted or excessively worn. Place each synchronizer ring into position on its respective gear, then, using a feeler gauge, measure clearance between ring and gear. If clearance is less than .040" (1 mm), replace synchronizer ring.

Fig. 5: Synchronizer Spring and Insert Installation

Fig. 6: Synchronizer Sleeve Installation

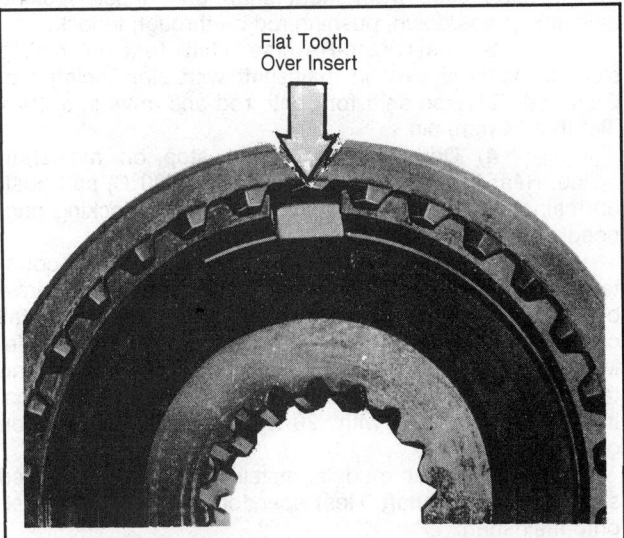

Reassembly
Stagger hooks on insert springs in notches in hub. Install inserts and push sleeve over hub. Install blocking ring on hub and install synchronizer on mating gear.

COUNTERSHAFT

Disassembly

Pull bearing off front of countershaft, then press off 4th gear. Remove snap ring and press off 3rd gear. Remove rear circlips making note of shims. Pull outer bearing off rear of countershaft, then press off 5th gear. Pull off inner bearing.

Inspection

Check shaft and gears for wear or damage. Lightly polish any scoring from shaft surfaces.

Reassembly

Reverse disassembly procedure by heating gears to 250-300°F (120-150°C) and then pressing gears into position.

REVERSE IDLER GEAR & SHAFT

Disassembly

Remove end plate. Unscrew hex bolt while holding shaft at front. Remove bolt and washers. Install a bolt in tapped bore and push out assembly towards rear. Separate needle bearing and gear from shaft.

Inspection

Inspect components for wear or damage and replace if necessary.

Reassembly

Reverse disassembly procedure using Loctite (or equivalent) on holding bolt.

TRANSMISSION REASSEMBLY

GEAR & SHAFT CONTROL ASSEMBLIES

1) Install mainshaft and countershaft assemblies in intermediate transmission case. Install appropriate shim, heat bearing race to about 175°F (80°C) and push onto mainshaft. Press needle bearing and reverse gear onto mainshaft. Slide 5th gear synchronizer assembly onto mainshaft.

2) Push 5th-Reverse shift rod up to spring in transmission case from input shaft end. Insert locking balls and press down, pushing rod on through to lock.

3) Insert 5th-Reverse shift fork in sliding sleeve. Install sleeve on mainshaft with pins facing out. Guide 5th-Reverse shift fork onto rod and drive in a .24 x .94" (6 x 24 mm) pin.

4) Drive sleeve against stop on mainshaft spline. Heat bearing race to about 175°F (80°C) and push on mainshaft to sleeve. Install synchronizer blocking ring, needle bearing and 5th gear onto mainshaft.

5) Install inner roller bearing and 5th countergear on countershaft. Using appropriate driver, drive bearing race onto countershaft. On 320i models, install circlip and insert a .2" (5 mm) mandrel in bore hole. Measure distance between spacer and bearing race and take up countershaft end play with appropriate shims. Install locking circlip with .20 x 1" (5 x 26 mm) pin on countershaft.

6) On all models, install washer with bevelled side out on mainshaft. Heat speedometer gear and push onto mainshaft.

7) Install 1st-2nd and 3rd-4th shift forks. Push in 3rd-4th shift rod through shift fork to spring. Insert locating ball and locking ball and press down. Push 3rd-4th shift rod on through to lock making sure that opening on shift rod faces 5th-Reverse shift rod. Drive in a .24 x .94" (6 x 24 mm) pin.

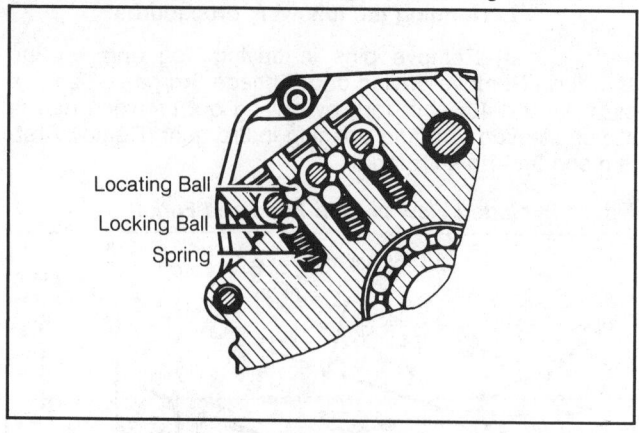

Fig. 7: Arrangement of Locating and Locking Balls

Locating Ball
Locking Ball
Spring

8) Push in 1st-2nd shift rod through fork to spring in transmission case. Install driving dog. Install locating ball and locking ball and press down. Push 1st-2nd shift rod on through to lock and drive in a .24 x .94" (6 x 24 mm) pin.

9) Push in upper selector rod with opening facing out. Install selector arm with long side facing 3rd-4rth shift rod.

10) Install lower selector rod with opening facing up. Install operating lever with sharp edge facing up and push in rod.

11) Install bolt in top of transmission case with Loctite (or equivalent) making sure that center engages bore of operating lever. Test operating lever for ease of movement. Push clamp onto lower selector rod with bevelled side facing shift fork.

12) Install bolt in side of transmission case with Loctite (or equivalent) making sure that center engages groove in lower selector rod. Hold 4 rollers on selector rod with grease.

TRANSMISSION CASE

Thoroughly clean all sealing surfaces, coat with Loctite (or equivalent and reverse disassembly procedure.

TIGHTENING SPECIFICATIONS

Application	Ft. Lbs. (N.m)
Transmission-to-Engine or Clutch Hsg.	
8 mm Bolts	18-19 (24-26)
10 mm Bolts	35-37 (47-50)
12 mm Bolts	54-60 (72-80)
Transmission Cover Plate Bolts	
(Front & Rear)	18 (24)
Propeller Shaft Flange Nut	72 (98)
Rear Seal Flange Bolts	7 (9.5)
Rubber Mount	32-35 (43-47)
Crossmember	16-17 (22-23)

CHAMP & COLT 4 & 4x2-SPEED

DESCRIPTION

Two types of transaxle assemblies are used, the KM 160 and KM 165. Both types are fully synchronized and incorporate an input shaft, intermediate shaft and output shaft. The major difference is that the KM 165 has a high and low gear on the input shaft which allows 2 speed ranges that can be selected. The differential assembly consists of a differential drive gear in mesh with output shaft gear, side gears and pinion gears.

LUBRICATION & ADJUSTMENT

See the appropriate article in MANUAL TRANS-MISSION SERVICING Section.

SERVICE (IN VEHICLE)

AXLE SHAFTS

Removal

1) Remove front wheel dust cap and loosen lock nut. Raise vehicle and remove tires and undercover

Fig. 1: Sectional View of Transaxle Assembly

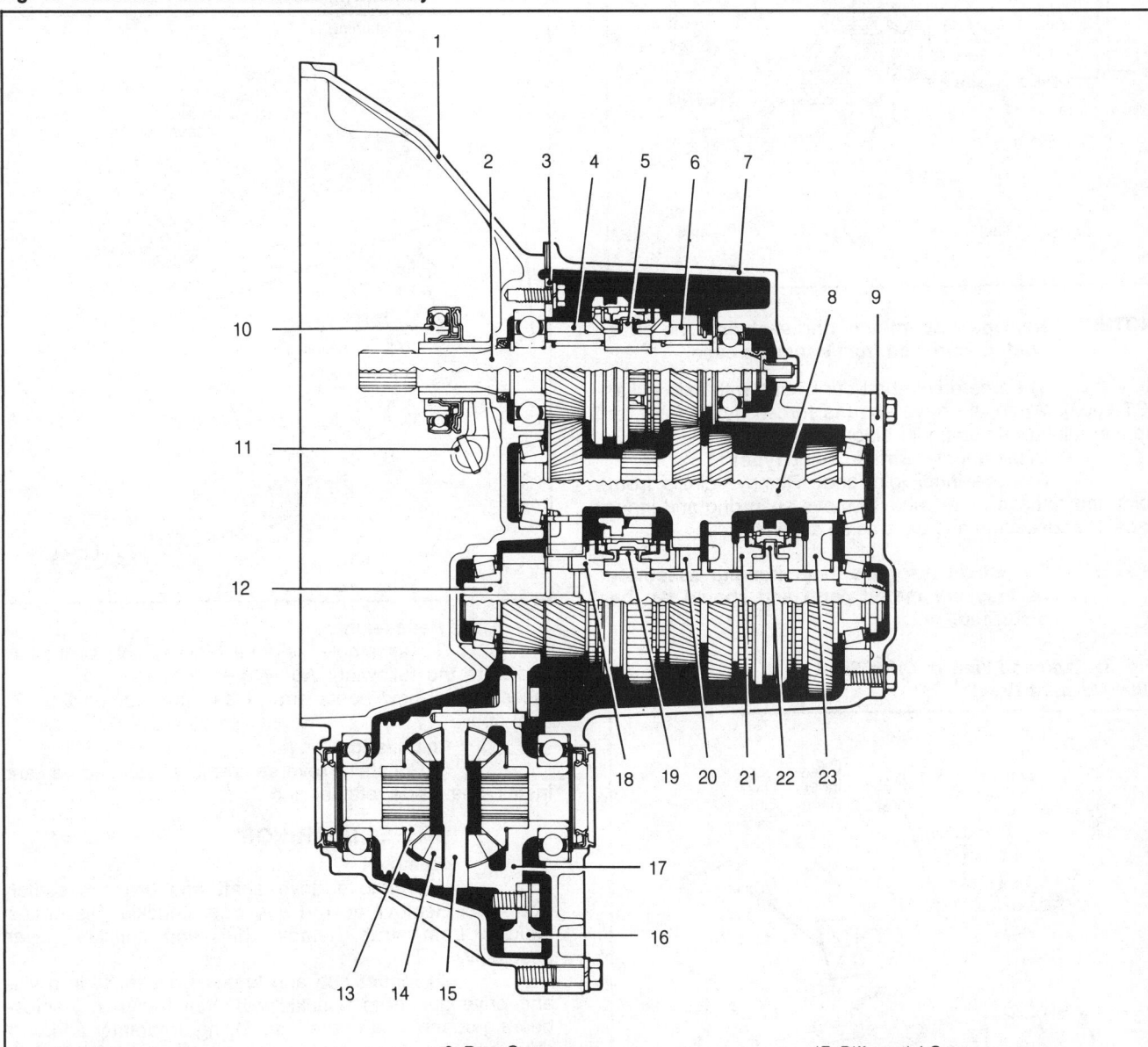

1. Clutch Housing
2. Input Shaft
3. Bearing Retainer
4. Input Low Gear (KM 165 Only)
5. Synchro Assembly (KM 165 Only)
6. Input High Gear (KM 165 Only)
7. Transaxle Case
8. Intermediate Gear
9. Rear Cover
10. Clutch Release Bearing
11. Clutch Release Fork
12. Output Shaft
13. Differential Side Gear
14. Differential Pinion
15. Pinion Shaft
16. Differential Drive Gear
17. Differential Case
18. 4th Speed Gear
19. 3rd-4th Synchronizer Assembly
20. 3rd Gear
21. 2nd Gear
22. 1st-2nd Synchronizer Assembly
23. 1st Gear

CHAMP & COLT 4 & 4x2-SPEED (Cont.)

panel. Remove lower ball joint and strut from lower control arm. Drain transaxle fluid.

2) Insert pry bar between transaxle case and Double Offset Joint (D.O.J.) or Tripod Joint (T.J.). Apply pressure to the tool handle and force axle shaft from transaxle.

Fig. 2: View of Drive Axle Removal

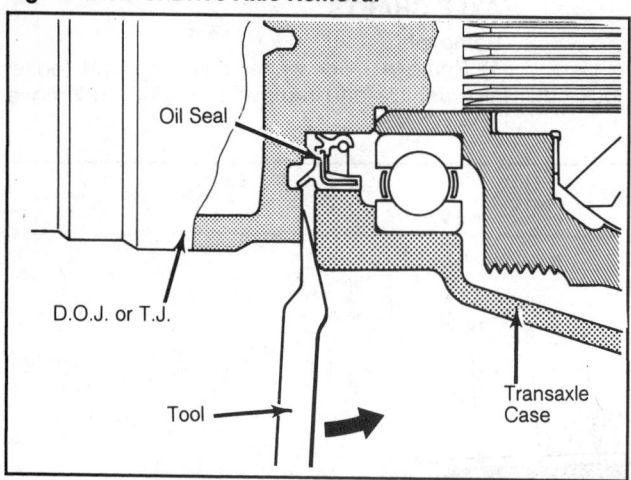

NOTE: Replace side retainer ring each time the drive shaft is removed from transaxle case.

3) Force drive shaft out of hub with axle puller (CT-1003). When the drive shaft is forced out, do not let spacer fall out of hub (inner side).

Disassembly (Birfield Joint Type)
Remove inner joint boot. Remove circlip from joint and remove outer race. Remove snap ring and inner race. Remove cage and balls as an assembly.

NOTE: Do not disassemble inner bearing assembly as they are mated parts and should not be disturbed.

Fig. 3: Exploded View of Drive Shaft (Birfield Joint Type)

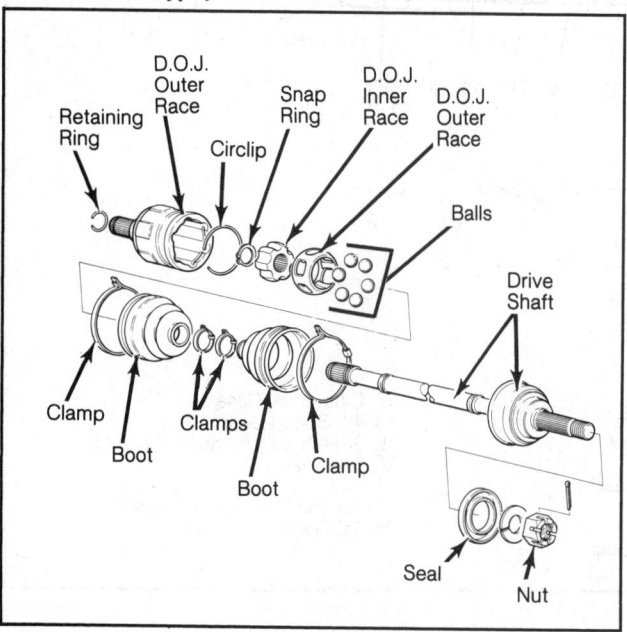

Reassembly
To assemble, reverse disassembly procedure and note the following: Apply grease to inner and outer races. Install CV joint assembly on shaft with chamfered edge of inner race facing outer edge of shaft. Install new boots and place boot clamps 3.5" (90 mm) apart.

Disassembly (Tripod-Rzeppa Joint Type)
Remove inner joint boots. Pull drive shaft out from inner case. Remove snap ring and take out spider assembly. Clean, but do not disassemble, spider assembly. Remove remaining boots.

Fig. 4: Exploded View of Drive Shaft (Tripod-Rzeppa Joint Type)

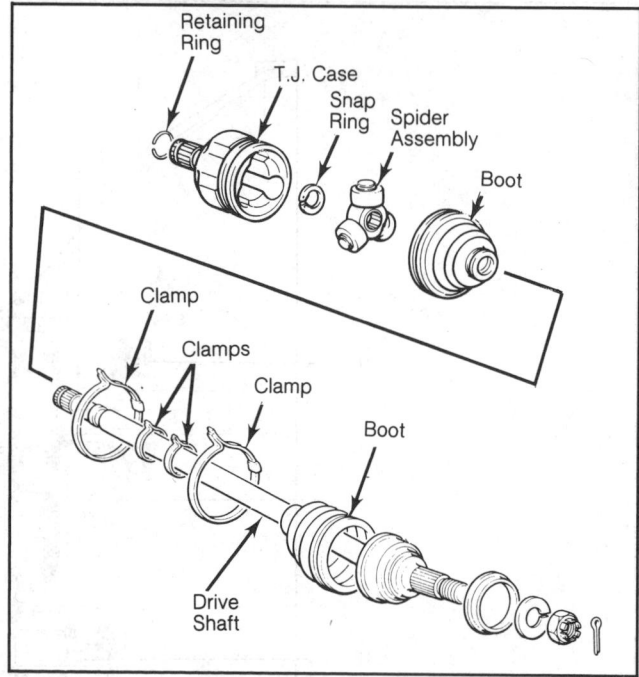

Reassembly
To assemble, reverse disassembly procedure and note the following: Apply grease to inner and outer races. Install new boots and place boot clamps 3.0" (75 mm) apart.

Installation
To install, reverse removal procedure and install a new side retainer ring.

WHEEL BEARINGS
Removal
1) Remove drive shaft and brake assembly from hub. Remove tie rod end from knuckle. Disconnect knuckle from strut. Remove hub and knuckle as an assembly.

2) Mount hub and knuckle assembly in a vise and drive hub from knuckle with soft hammer. Remove bearing spacer and brake disc. Using a hammer and drift, drive out inner and outer bearing races.

Installation
1) Drive outer races of inner and outer bearings into knuckle. Install spacer selection gauge (MB990959) and dial indicator into hub assembly. Tighten nuts "A" and "B" finger tight. See Fig. 5.

2) Tighten nut "B" so gauge face contacts inside bearing inner race. Tighten nut "A" about 5 turns. Rotate gauge 10 times to seat the bearing. Zero dial indicator.

CHAMP & COLT 4 & 4x2-SPEED (Cont.)

Fig. 5: Exploded View of Transaxle Gear Components

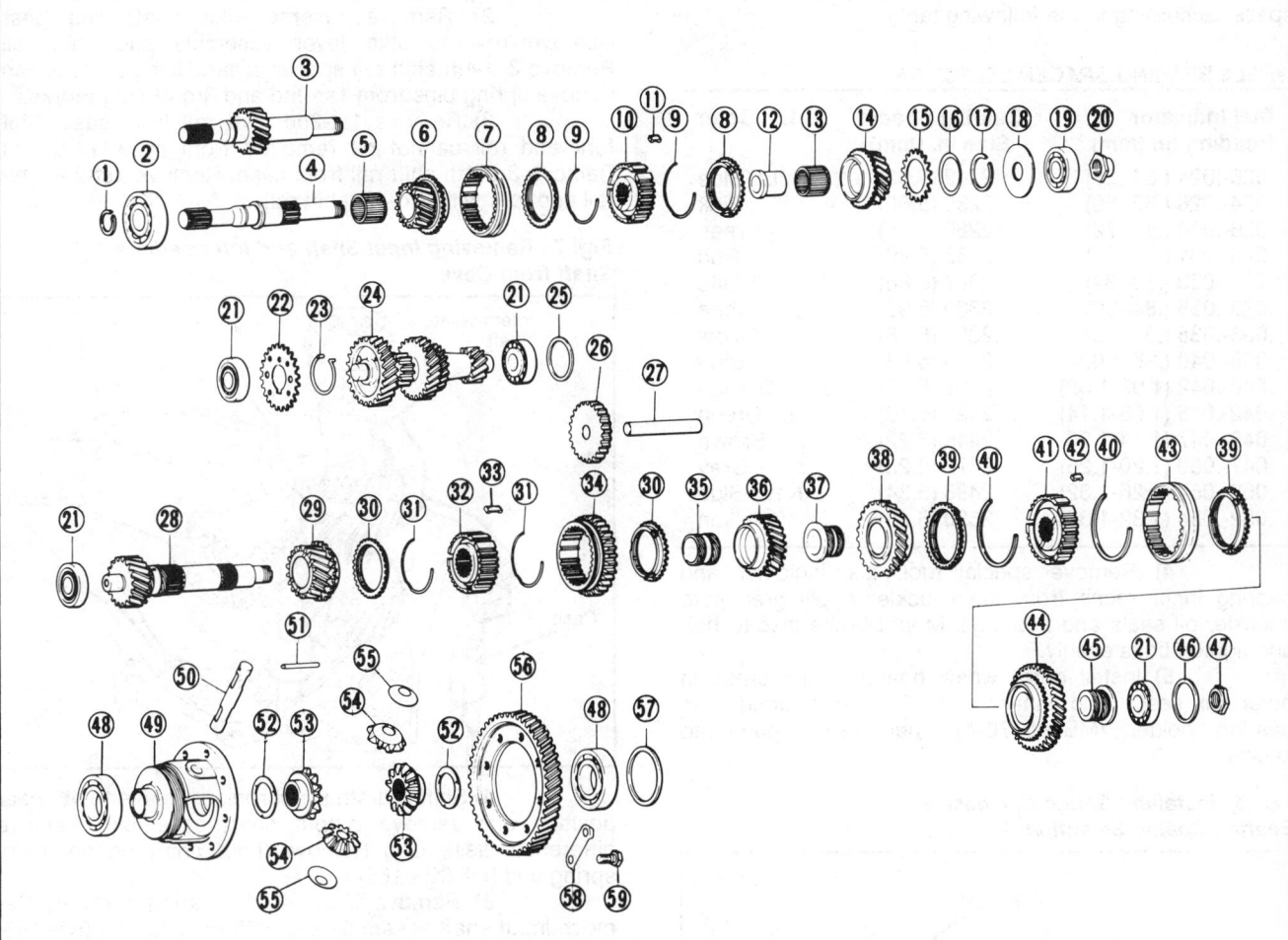

1. Snap Ring	22. Sub-Gear	43. Sleeve
2. Bearing	23. Spring	44. 1st Gear
3. Input Shaft [1]	24. Intermediate Gear	45. Sleeve
4. Input Shaft [2]	25. Spacer	46. Spacer
5. Bearing [2]	26. Reverse Idler Gear	47. Lock Nut
6. Input Low Gear [2]	27. Idler Gear Shaft	48. Bearing
7. Sleeve [2]	28. Output Shaft	49. Differential Case
8. Synchronizer Ring [2]	29. 4th Gear	50. Pinion Shaft
9. Synchronizer Spring [2]	30. Synchronizer Ring	51. Lock Pin
10. Synchronizer Hub [2]	31. Spring	52. Spacer
11. Synchronizer Key [2]	32. Synchronizer Hub	53. Differential Side Gear
12. Sleeve [2]	33. Synchronizer Key	54. Differential Pinion
13. Bearing [2]	34. Synchronizer Sleeve	55. Washer
14. Input High Gear [2]	35. Sleeve	56. Differential Drive Gear
15. Sub-Gear	36. 3rd Gear	57. Spacer
16. Spacer	37. Sleeve	58. Lock Washer
17. Snap Ring	38. 2nd Gear	59. Bolt
18. Spacer	39. Synchronizer Ring	
19. Bearing	40. Spring	[1]. KM 160 Only.
20. Lock Nut	41. Synchronizer Hub	[2]. KM 165 Only.
21. Bearing	42. Synchronizer Key	

CHAMP & COLT 4 & 4x2-SPEED (Cont.)

3) Loosen nut "B" until pointer of dial indicator stops, and read dial indicator. Select proper size bearing spacer according to the following table.

WHEEL BEARING SPACER SELECTION

Dial Indicator Reading In. (mm)	Bearing Spacer Size In. (mm)	I.D. Color
.020-.024 (.54-.60)	.2212 (5.62)	Lt. Blue
.024-.026 (.60-.66)	.2236 (5.68)	Pink
.026-.028 (.66-.72)	.2260 (5.74)	Green
.028-.031 (.72-.78)	.2283 (5.80)	Red
.031-.033 (.78-.84)	.2307 (5.86)	White
.033-.035 (.84-.90)	.2330 (5.92)	None
.035-.038 (.90-.96)	.2354 (5.98)	Yellow
.038-.040 (.96-1.02)	.2378 (6.04)	Blue
.040-.042 (1.02-1.08)	.2402 (6.10)	Orange
.042-.045 (1.08-1.14)	.2425 (6.16)	Lt. Green
.045-.047 (1.14-1.20)	.2449 (6.22)	Brown
.047-.050 (1.20-1.26)	.2472 (6.28)	Gray
.050-.052 (1.26-1.32)	.2496 (6.34)	Navy Blue
.052-.054 (1.32-1.38)	.2520 (6.40)	Vermilion

4) Remove special tool, dial indicator and bearing inner races from the knuckle. Apply grease to knuckle, oil seals and bearings. Mount brake disc to hub and tighten bolts evenly.

5) Install outer wheel bearing, then press in outer oil seal. Hold inner race of outer bearing with bearing holder (MB990776-A), then press hub into knuckle.

Fig. 6: Installing Gauge to Measure Bearing Spacer Selection

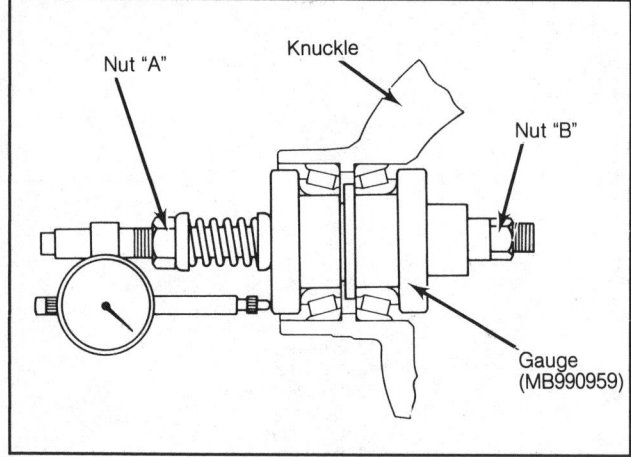

TRANSAXLE REMOVAL & INSTALLATION

See the appropriate article in MANUAL TRANSMISSION SERVICING Section.

TRANSAXLE DISASSEMBLY

1) Remove clutch cable bracket and transaxle mounting bracket. Remove backup light switch. Remove steel balls from case. Remove rear cover and remove spacers from bearings. Remove transaxle case. Place shift rails in neutral, remove plugs from side of case and remove springs and 3 steel balls.

2) Remove reverse idler shaft and gear. Remove reverse shift lever assembly and shift rail. Remove 3rd-4th shift rail spacer collar. Using a flat punch, remove spring pins from 1st-2nd and 3rd-4th shift forks.

3) Remove 1st-2nd shift rail from case. Shift fork and rail cannot be removed from case as a unit. Remove 3rd-4th shift rail from case. Remove 1st-2nd shift rail and fork with 3rd-4th shift rail.

Fig. 7: Removing Input Shaft and Intermediate Shaft from Case

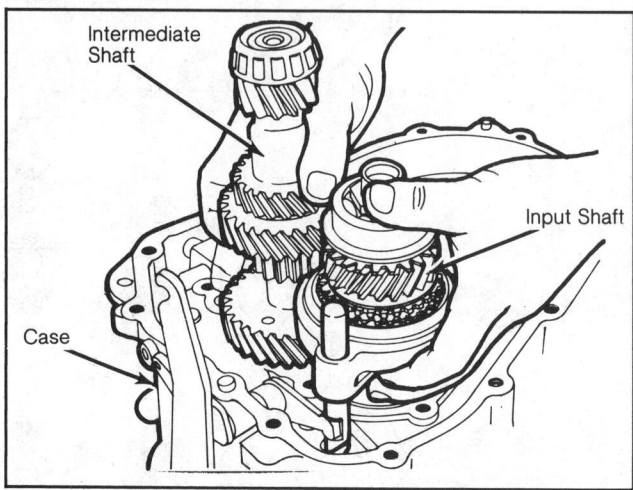

4) Shift 3rd-4th synchronizer sleeve to 4th gear position and remove output shaft assembly. Remove differential assembly. Remove input shaft poppet plug, spring and ball (KM 165).

5) Remove input shaft bearing retainer. Remove input shaft assembly and shift rail and fork (KM 165) with intermediate shaft. Remove shift shaft spring retainer.

6) Pull out shift shaft spring pin with pliers, then remove shift shaft through case hole. When shift shaft is removed, place finger over control finger hole to prevent poppet ball from falling out. Remove control finger, springs, spacer, poppet spring and ball.

7) Remove selector finger lock pin, selector shaft and selector finger (KM 165). Place identification mark on bearing outer race and remove bearing. Outer race MUST be installed in original position. Remove speedometer driven gear assembly.

COMPONENT DISASSEMBLY & REASSEMBLY

INPUT SHAFT

Disassembly (KM 160)

Remove snap ring from front bearing. Use tool and press off bearing. Remove staking from lock nut on rear of shaft. Remove lock nut and bearing from rear of shaft.

Inspection

Check splines for damage and wear. Check oil seal area for damage or wear.

NOTE: **Bearing must be replaced. Removal destroys bearing beyond serviceability.**

CHAMP & COLT 4 & 4x2-SPEED (Cont.)

Reassembly

1) Using tool, press front bearing onto input shaft and install snap ring. Snap rings are available in 3 sizes, use the thickest one that will fit.

2) Install sub-gear onto input shaft in the following order: Install sub-gear onto high gear and apply oil to entire surface. Install cone spring in direction shown in *Fig. 9*

3) Install new snap ring. Install spacer on rear of shaft with stepped side facing rear of bearing. Install bearing onto shaft with tool. Install lock nut and tighten. Stake lock nut only at the notch on shaft. *See Fig. 8.*

NOTE: **The shaft rear end will interfere with the breather if deformed by staking, resulting in breakage.**

Fig. 8: Staking Input Shaft Lock Nut

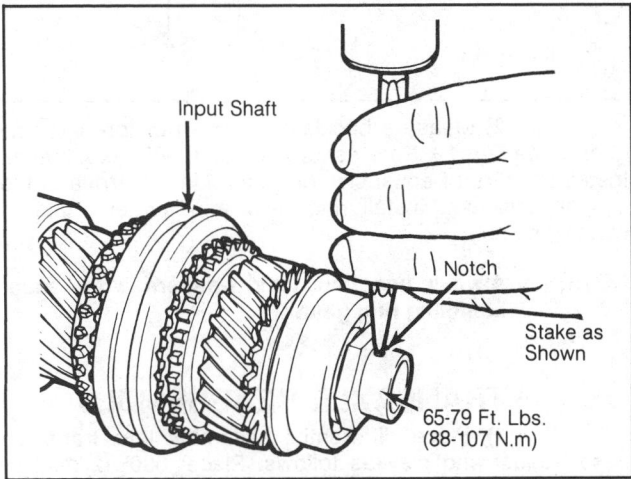

Disassembly (KM 165)

Remove front bearing snap ring. Use puller and remove bearing. Remove staking at rear lock nut and remove lock nut. Support low gear between press plates and press input shaft from gears.

Inspection

Check splines for wear or damage. Check oil seal fitting area for damage or wear. Check gear bearing surface for wear or scoring.

Reassembly

1) Using tool, press front bearing onto input shaft and install snap ring. Snap rings are available in 3 sizes; use the thickest one that will fit.

2) Install synchronizer assembly onto input shaft. Install sub-gear onto input shaft in the following

Fig. 9: View of Correct Sub-Gear Installation

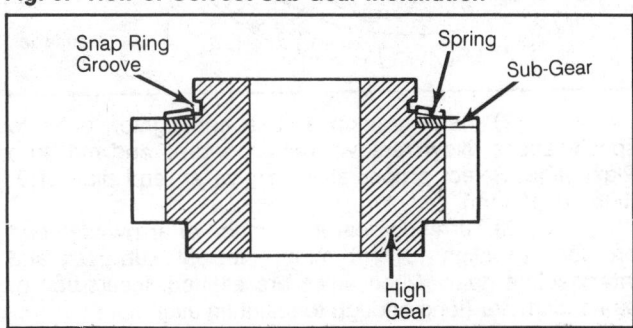

order: Install sub-gear onto high gear and apply oil to entire surface. Install cone spring in direction shown in *Fig. 9*. Install new snap ring.

3) Install low gear and needle bearing onto shaft. Install synchronizer ring and synchronizer assembly on shaft and check for proper operation.

4) Install high gear and bearing onto shaft. Install spacer with stepped side facing rear bearing and install bearing. Install rear nut and tighten. Stake nut.

INTERMEDIATE SHAFT
Disassembly

Use puller and remove front bearing from shaft. Remove sub-gear and spring. Remove rear bearing using same puller as used on front.

Inspection

Inspect gears for wear or damage. Replace any defective parts as required.

Fig. 10: View of Sub-Gear Installation

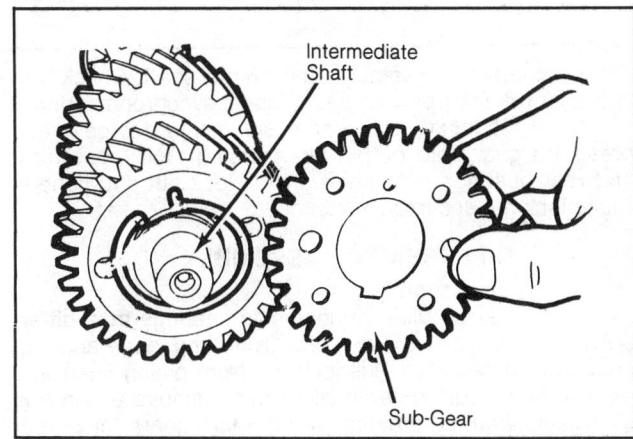

Reassembly

Install sub-gear spring in position on intermediate shaft. *See Fig. 10.* Install sub-gear onto shaft. Press on new bearings with tool. Replace outer bearing races.

OUTPUT SHAFT
Disassembly

Remove staking on rear nut and remove lock nut from shaft. Use puller and remove front and rear bearing. Remove 1st gear, 1st-2nd synchronizer assembly and 2nd gear. Remove 2nd gear sleeve, 3rd gear, sleeve, 3rd-4th synchronizer and 4th gear.

Inspection

Check output shaft for wear or damage. Check gear wear areas for scoring or excessive wear.

Reassembly

1) Assemble synchronizer assemblies as shown in *Fig. 11.* Install 4th gear onto output shaft. Install synchronizer ring. Use tool and press 3rd-4th synchronizer assembly onto shaft. Check 4th gear for smooth rotation on output shaft.

NOTE: **Oil all moving parts with sufficient oil during reassembly.**

2) Install synchronizer ring onto output shaft. Install 3rd gear onto output shaft. Install 2nd gear bushing onto output shaft. Check that 3rd gear rotates freely on shaft. Install 2nd gear. Install synchronizer ring. Install 1st-

CHAMP & COLT 4 & 4x2-SPEED (Cont.)

Fig. 11: View of Synchronizers in Proper Assembled Order

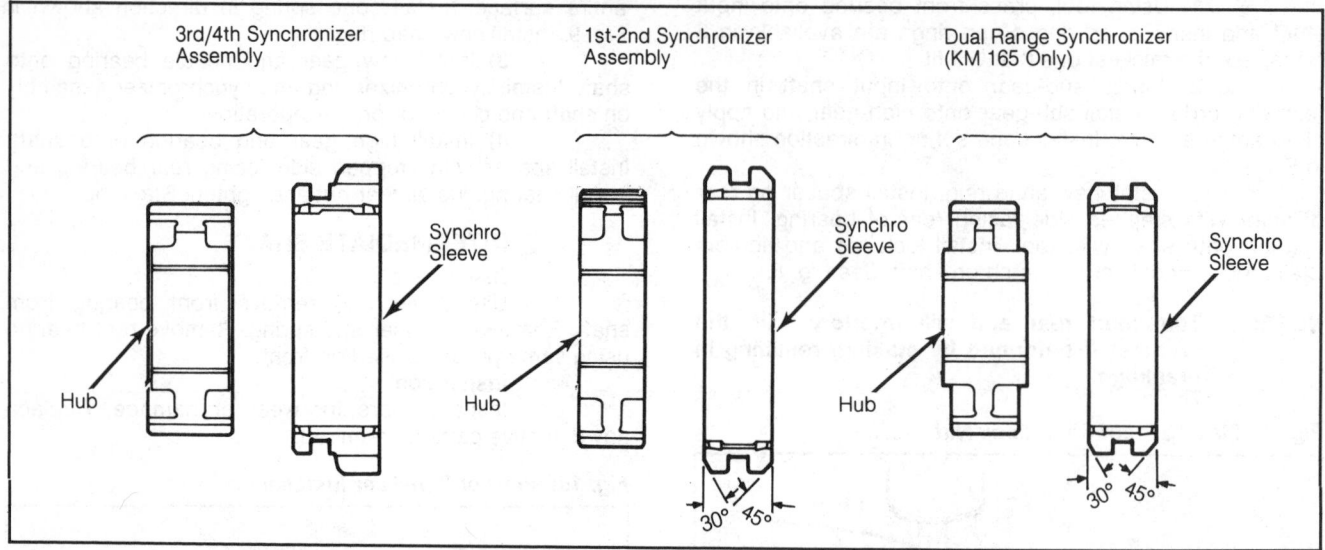

2nd synchronizer assembly onto output shaft. Check that 2nd gear rotates freely on shaft. Install synchronizer ring.

3) Install 1st gear bushing into 1st gear and press 1st gear onto output shaft. Using tool, press front and rear bearings onto shaft. Install lock nut and tighten. Stake lock nut securely.

DIFFERENTIAL ASSEMBLY
Disassembly
Using puller, remove side bearings from differential assembly. Remove bolts from ring gear and tap gear from differential. Pull lock pin from pinion shaft and remove shaft from differential carrier. Remove pinion and side gears from differential carrier. Mark gears for proper installation.

Inspection
Check splines for damage or wear. Check gears for chipped or worn teeth.
Reassembly
1) Press bearings onto both ends of differential carrier. Place spacers on the back side of side gears and place gears into differential carrier. Place washers behind pinion gears and install pinion gears meshing with side gears at the same time. Install pinion shaft.

Fig. 12: Checking Pinion and Side Gear Backlash

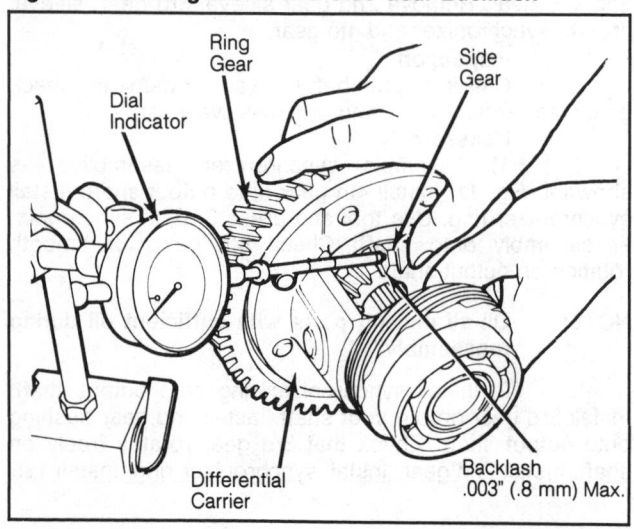

2) Measure backlash between pinion and side gears. *See Fig. 12.* Backlash should be 0.003" (0.076 mm). Install spacers of equal size on both sides to arrive at the proper backlash. Install ring gear and tighten bolts to specifications.

NOTE: Always use new lock washers when reassembling ring gear.

TRANSAXLE REASSEMBLY
1) Place differential assembly into transaxle case. Adjust end play as follows: Place .080" (2 mm) of Plastigage on bearing surface as shown in *Fig. 13.*

Fig. 13: Measuring Differential Play

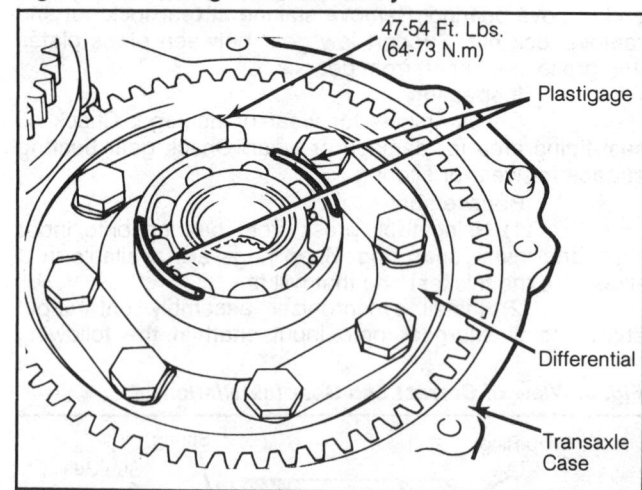

2) Install transaxle case and tighten bolts to specifications. Now remove transaxle case and measure Plastigage. Select proper shim to give an end play of 0-.006" (0-.15 mm).

3) Turn sub-gear in direction of arrow stamped on gear to align .31" (8 mm) holes of sub-gear and intermediate gear. When holes are aligned, insert bolt of same diameter (long enough to maintain alignment).

CHAMP & COLT 4 & 4x2-SPEED (Cont.)

4) Mesh input and intermediate shaft together and place into transaxle case. On KM 165 transaxle, install shift detent and spring and tighten end plug. On all transaxles, install input bearing retainer. Pull out the sub-gear aligning bolt and install output shaft.

5) Install 1st-2nd and 3rd-4th shift rail into case. Install shift forks and install spring pins. Install reverse shift rail. Install detents and springs (spring with white marking is for reverse shift rail).

6) Install reverse gear, shaft and fork. Measure distance "A". See Fig. 14. Specified distance should be 1.44-1.53" (36.6-39.0 mm). Replace reverse shift lever if not within specifications.

Fig. 14: Measuring Reverse Idler Gear

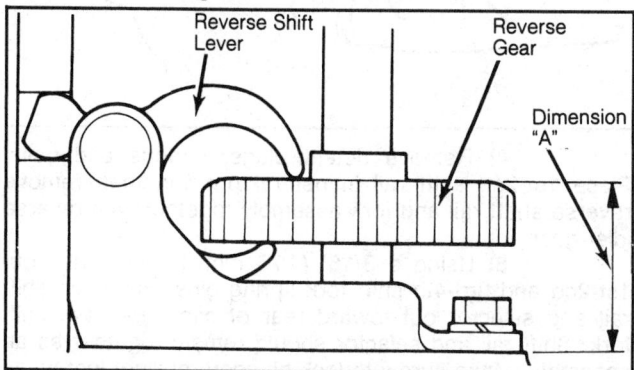

7) Install clutch housing gasket in place on transaxle. Place shims for differential bearing in case with grease. Install clutch housing to transaxle case. Install bolts and tighten to specifications.

8) Install intermediate and output shaft bearing races in case and press them into place by hand. Install spacer of proper thickness (a little thinner than dimension "H" in Fig. 15.)

Fig. 15: Measuring End Play Spacer installation

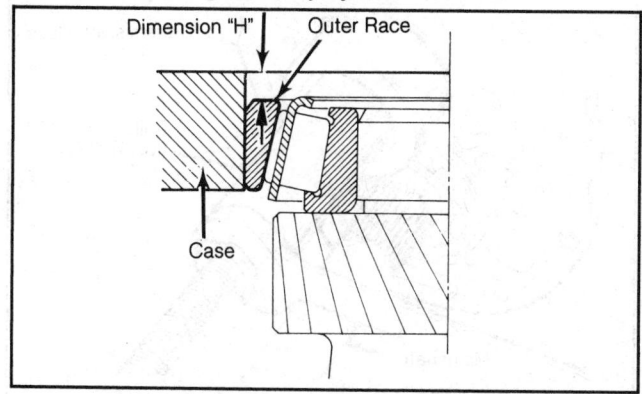

9) Place straightedge as shown in Fig. 16. and turn spacer with finger. If spacer turns lightly, replace spacer with one .0012" (.03 mm) thicker and turn in same manner. Repeat until a spacer is selected that brings straightedge-to-spacer clearance closest to zero.

Fig. 16: Adjusting End Play

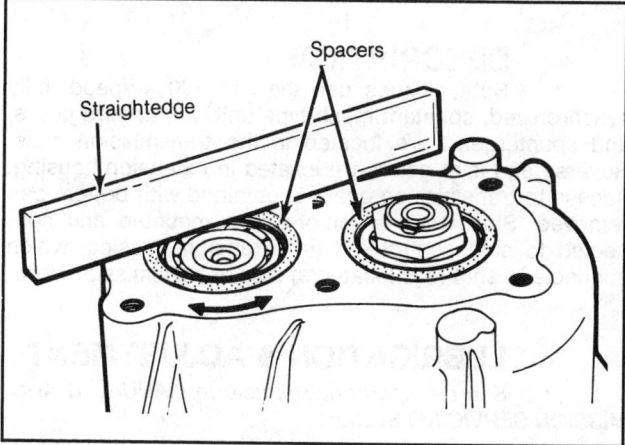

Place straightedge on one spacer at a time.

NOTE: Specified end play of intermediate shaft is .0020" (.05 mm) loose, while that of output shaft is .0010" (.025 mm) tight to .0010" (.025 mm) loose. Therefore, a spacer installed on outer race of output shaft may be .0012 (.03 mm) thicker. Spacers are available in sizes of .0724-.1055" (1.84-2.68 mm).

10) Place selected spacers on outer races. Apply sealant to transaxle case surface of rear cover. Install cover and tighten bolts.

TRANSAXLE SPECIFICATIONS

Application	In. (mm)
Synchronizer Ring-to-Gear	.032 (.8) Max.
Shift Lever-to-Rail	.002-.008 (.05-.20)
Ring Gear-to-Drive Shaft Spline	.002-.007 (.05-.18)
Ring Gear-to-Case	.001-.003 (.03-.08)
Pinion Gear-to-Side Gear Backlash	0-.003 (0-.08)
Differential Case End Play	0-.006 (0-.15)

TIGHTENING SPECIFICATIONS

Application	Ft. Lbs. (N.m)
Rear Cover	14-16 (19-22)
Engine-to-Transaxle	
Bolt with Washer	22-25 (30-34)
All Others	32-39 (43-53)
Clutch Housing-to-Transaxle	26-30 (35-41)
Input Shaft Lock Nut	65-79 (88-107)
Output Shaft Lock Nut	65-79 (88-107)
Ring Gear Bolts	47-54 (64-73)

CHRYSLER CORP. IMPORTS 4-SPEED

Arrow Pickup, Ram-50 Pickup

DESCRIPTION

Both pickups use the KM 130 4-speed, fully synchronized, constant mesh-type unit. All forward gears, and countergear, are located in the transmission case. Reverse and idler gears are located in extension housing. Access to transmission gears is obtained with bottom pan removed. Shift lever is remote floor mounted and connected to shift control rod (in extension housing) which connects to shift rails located at rear of transmission case.

LUBRICATION & ADJUSTMENT

See the appropriate article in MANUAL TRANS-MISSION SERVICING Section.

TROUBLE SHOOTING

DIFFICULTY MESHING GEARS

Malfunction of gearshift lever or control shaft. Synchro rings or gear coned surfaces worn or excessive play. Synchro shift keys worn or damaged.

JUMPS OUT OF GEAR

Shifting forks worn or detent springs broken. Mainshaft or mainshaft support bearings worn or damaged. Clearance between synchro hub and sleeve excessive. Gears or gear bushings worn. Countergear worn.

NOISE IN TRANSMISSION

Lubrication oil incorrect or insufficient. Gears or bearings worn. Mainshaft spline worn or damaged.

REMOVAL & INSTALLATION

See the appropriate article in MANUAL TRANS-MISSION REMOVAL Section.

TRANSMISSION DISASSEMBLY

NOTE: Transmission case and extension housing are made of aluminum and care should be exercised when handling machined surfaces.

1) Before proceeding with disassembly, clean exterior of transmission case. In clutch housing, use a 3/16" (4.76 mm) punch to drive out spring pin in clutch shaft. Remove clutch shaft from clutch housing and remove release fork, felt packing and return springs.

2) From extension housing, remove speedometer locking plate and then remove speedometer driven gear assembly. Remove back-up light switch and transmission switch.

CAUTION: When switch is removed, take care not to lose ball.

3) Remove extension housing attaching bolts. Rotate control lever to left and hold while pulling extension housing off to the rear. Remove bottom pan from transmission case.

Fig. 1: Removing Spring Pin from Clutch Cross Shaft

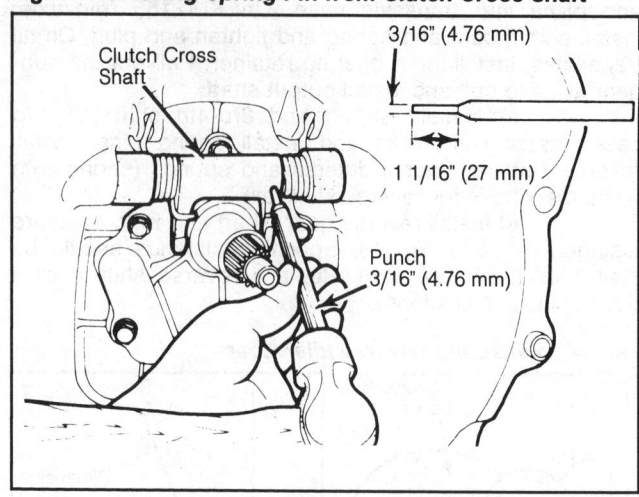

4) Remove detent plugs, springs and balls. Place 1st-2nd shift rail in neutral position then remove reverse shaft rail and fork assembly together with reverse idler gear.

5) Using a 3/16" (4.76 mm) punch, drive out 1st-2nd and 3rd-4th shift fork spring pins. Pull each shift rail and selector out toward rear of case. Remove shift fork. Shift rail and selector should remain together as an assembly. Make sure interlock plungers are not lost when removing shafts.

6) Remove snap ring from rear of countergear. Remove counter reverse gear and spacer. Remove mainshaft lock nut and reverse gear from mainshaft. Remove retaining screws and then bearing retainer. Remove front bearing retainer.

Fig. 2: Removing Countergear Rear Bearing from Transmission Case

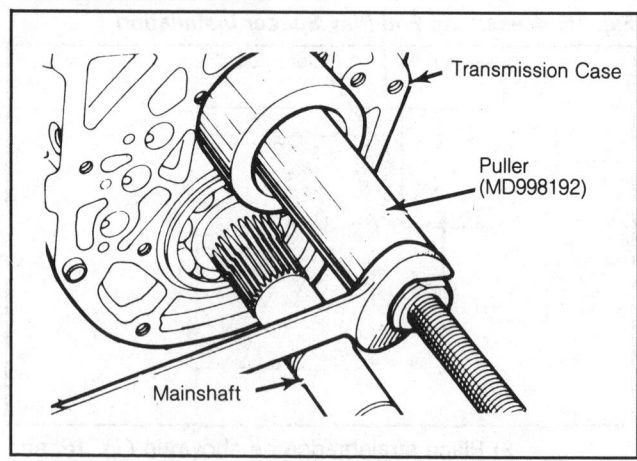

7) Press countergear rearward and remove snap ring. Use bearing puller and remove countergear rear bearing. Remove snap ring from front of countergear bearing, then remove bearing with bearing puller. Remove countergear from transmission case.

8) Pull input shaft pinion from front of transmission case. Remove snap rings from input shaft pinion then remove bearing with gear puller. Remove mainshaft bearing snap ring and then bearing. Remove mainshaft from transmission case.

CHRYSLER CORP. IMPORTS 4-SPEED (Cont.)

Fig. 3: Removing Mainshaft Assembly from Transmission Case

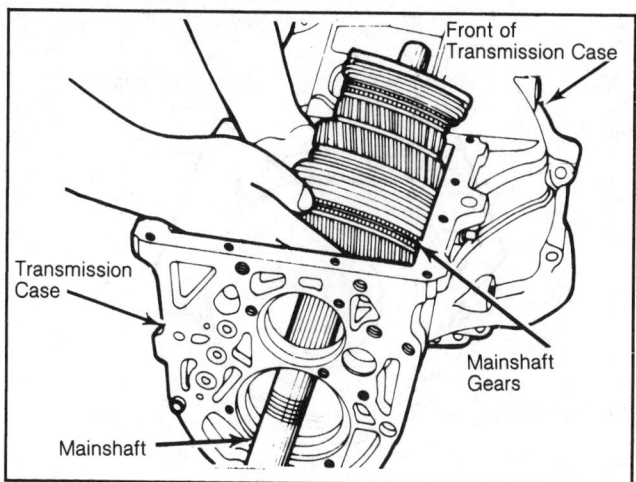

3) Check synchro ring to gear clearance on all synchro rings. *See Fig. 4.* If the clearance is not .032" (.8 mm) replace synchro ring. With hub and sleeve assembled, check that sleeve slides smoothly and that there is not excessive looseness. If either part is defective, replace both synchro sleeve and hub as an assembly.

4) Check synchro pieces for wear and damage, especially the projecting part. Check synchro springs for deterioration and breakage. Check countergear for wear or chipped teeth.

5) Check reverse idler gear and shaft for wear or damage. Check shift forks, rail and selector for wear or damage. Check clearance between shift fork and fork grove on synchro sleeve and gear. Clearance should be .006-.014" (.15-.35 mm) for overdrive and reverse and .004-.012" (.1-.3 mm) for all others. Check detent ball slots for wear. Check clearance between selector and lever. Clearance should be .004-.012" (.1-.3 mm).

6) Check detent balls and springs for damage or breakage. Check shift rails, control lever and forks for wear, damage or breakage. If any parts do not meet above specifications, they must be replaced.

Reassembly

1) Assemble both synchro assemblies, making sure components are positioned correctly. *See Fig. 6.*

2) Install needle bearing, 3rd gear, synchro ring and 3rd-4th synchro assembly onto front of mainshaft.

NOTE: **Make sure synchro rings and assemblies are installed in same position that they were removed from.**

3) Select snap ring of proper size so 3rd-4th synchro hub end play is 0-.003" (0-.08 mm). *See 3rd-4th Synchronizer Hub End Play chart.*

COMPONENT DISASSEMBLY & REASSEMBLY

MAINSHAFT

Disassembly

1) Pull 1st gear, 1st-2nd synchro and 2nd gear toward rear of mainshaft. Remove snap ring from forward end of mainshaft, then remove 3rd-4th synchro and 3rd gear.

2) Using a 3/16" (4.76 mm) punch, remove pin locking the gear shifter. Remove control shaft assembly. Press gear shifter forward and pull lock pin off, being careful not to bend control shaft.

Inspection

1) Check transmission case and extension housing for cracks and damage. Check mainshaft for worn or damaged gear area, bearing surfaces and splines. Check spacers and bearings for wear or damage. Check all bearings for smooth rolling action. Replace parts as necessary.

2) Check all gears for damaged, worn or chipped teeth. Check inside diameter for wear or damage. Check all synchro assemblies for worn or damaged teeth, cone surface, internal surface and rings.

Fig. 4: Checking Synchro Ring-to-Gear Clearance

3RD-4TH SYNCHRONIZER HUB END PLAY CHART

Application (Color)	Thickness In. (mm)
No Color	.085 (2.16)
Yellow	.087 (2.21)
Green	.090 (2.29)
White	.093 (2.36)

Fig. 5: Using a Feeler Gauge to Check 3rd Gear End Play

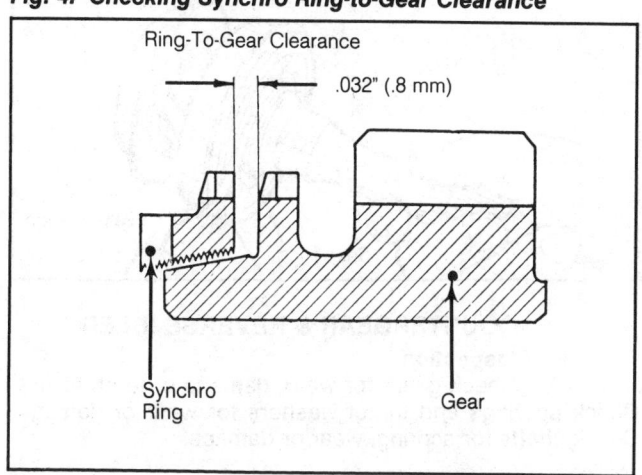

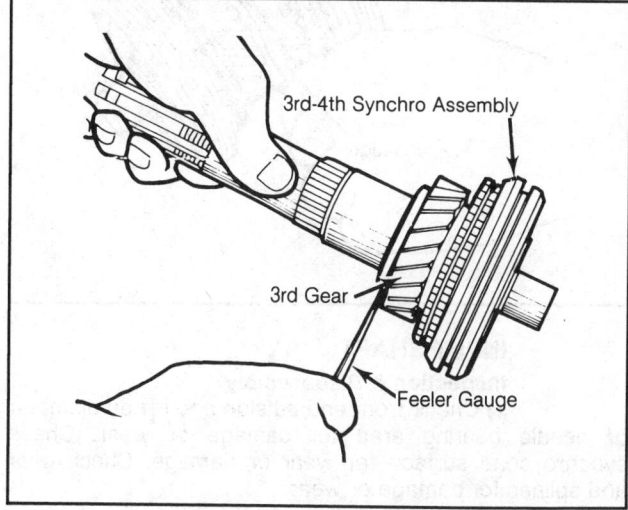

Manual Transmissions

CHRYSLER CORP. IMPORTS 4-SPEED (Cont.)

Fig. 6: Correct Position and Assembly of Synchronizer Assembly Components

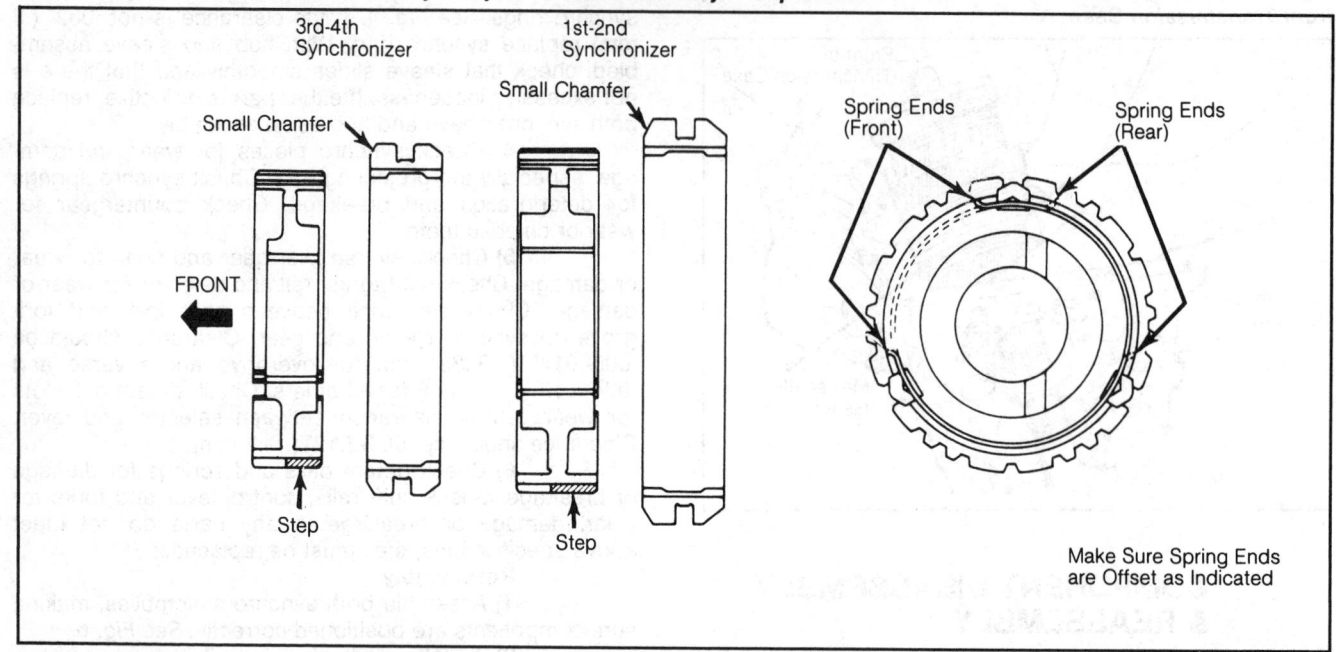

4) Check 3rd gear end play using a feeler gauge. Specified end play is .002-.008" (.04-.20 mm). See Fig. 5. If end play is not to specifications, check cone part of 3rd gear and coned part of 3rd-4th synchro assembly for wear. Replace components as necessary.

5) Install needle bearing, 2nd gear, synchro assembly, bearing sleeve, needle bearing, 1st gear and bearing spacer onto rear of mainshaft. Press bearing spacer forward and check end play of 2nd and 1st gears. End play should be .002-.008" (.04-.20 mm). See Fig. 7.

Fig. 7: Checking 1st-2nd Gear End Play

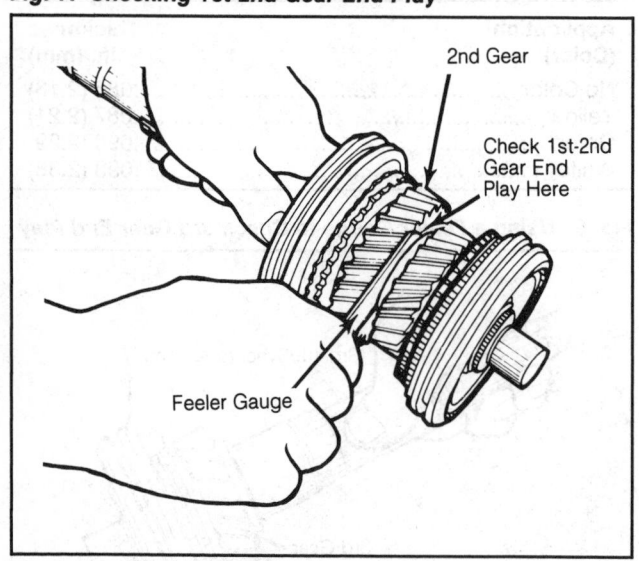

INPUT SHAFT

Inspection & Disassembly

1) Check front end outside and inside diameter of needle bearing area for damage or wear. Check synchro cone surface for wear or damage. Check gear and splines for damage or wear.

2) Rotate input shaft ball bearing and check for noise or roughness. If necessary to replace bearing, use bearing puller (MD-998056). Check coned surface of gear for wear or damage.

Reassembly

To install input shaft ball bearing, use bearing installer (MD-998029). Then install selective fit snap ring to obtain clearance between snap ring and bearing of 0-.002" (0-.05 mm). See Input Shaft Snap Ring Chart.

INPUT SHAFT SNAP RING SIZES

Application (Color)	Thickness In. (mm)
White	.091 (2.30)
No Color	.092 (2.35)
Red	.094 (2.40)
Blue	.096 (2.45)
Yellow	.098 (2.50)

Fig. 8: Checking Input Shaft Bearing End Play

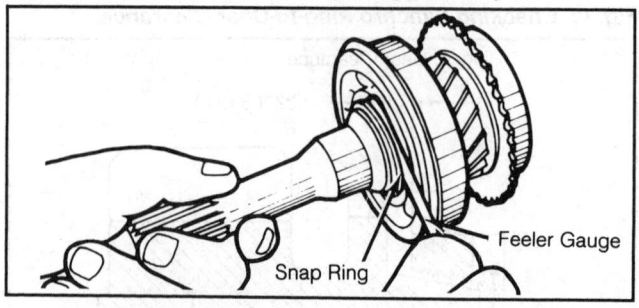

COUNTERGEAR & REVERSE IDLER

Inspection

Check gears for wear, damage or tooth failure. Check bearings and thrust washers for wear or damage. Check shafts for scoring, wear or damage.

CHRYSLER CORP. IMPORTS 4-SPEED (Cont.)

Fig. 9: Exploded View of Chrysler Corp. KM130 4-Speed Transmission

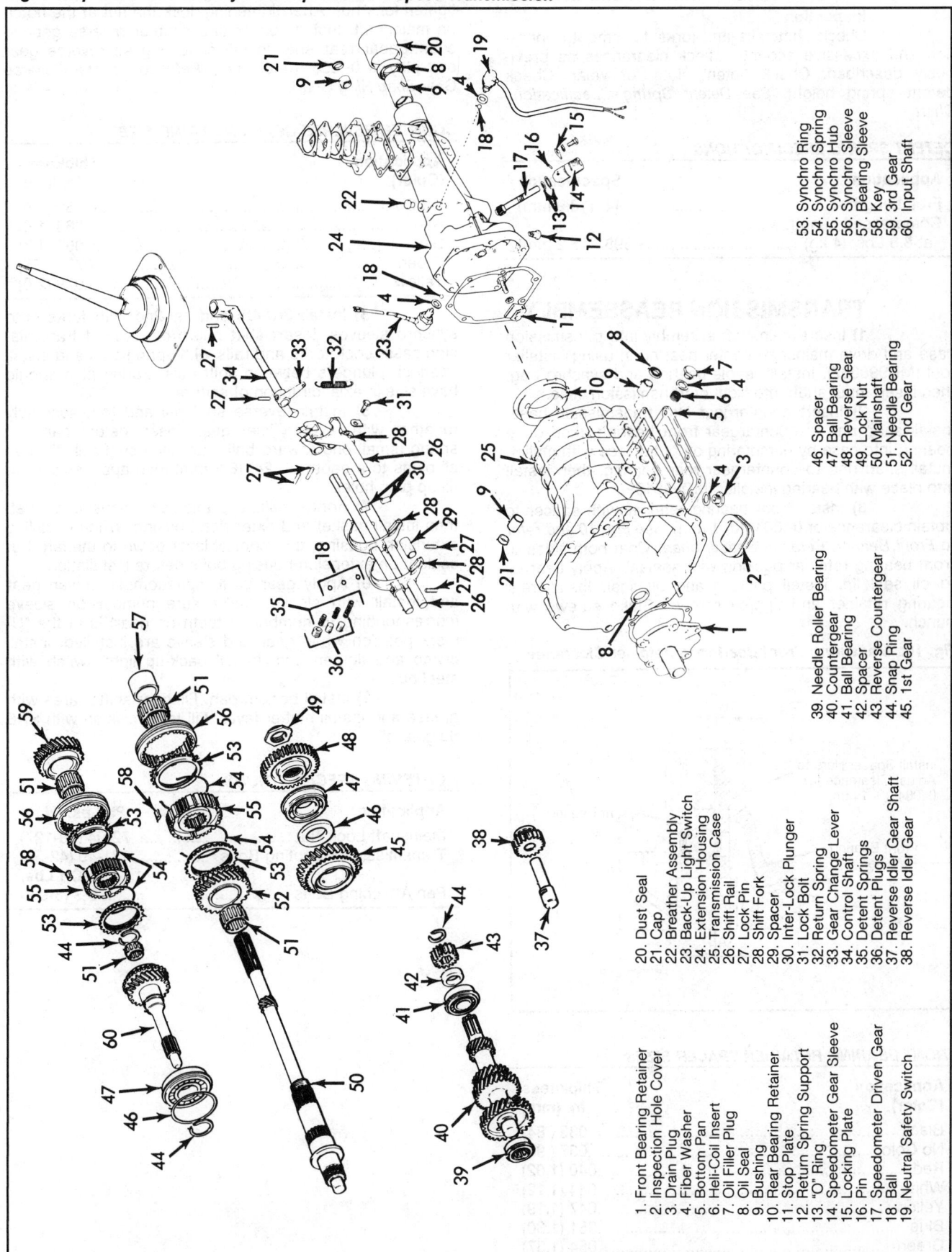

1. Front Bearing Retainer
2. Inspection Hole Cover
3. Drain Plug
4. Fiber Washer
5. Bottom Pan
6. Heli-Coil Insert
7. Oil Filler Plug
8. Oil Seal
9. Bushing
10. Rear Bearing Retainer
11. Return Spring Support
12. "O" Ring
13. Speedometer Gear Sleeve
14. Locking Plate
15. Pin
16. Speedometer Driven Gear
17. Ball
18. Neutral Safety Switch
19.

20. Dust Seal
21. Cap
22. Breather Assembly
23. Back-Up Light Switch
24. Extension Housing
25. Transmission Case
26. Shift Rail
27. Lock Pin
28. Shift Fork
29. Spacer
30. Inter-Lock Plunger
31. Lock Bolt
32. Return Spring
33. Gear Change Lever
34. Control Shaft
35. Detent Springs
36. Detent Plugs
37. Reverse Idler Gear Shaft
38. Reverse Idler Gear

39. Needle Roller Bearing
40. Countergear
41. Ball Bearing
42. Spacer
43. Reverse Countergear
44. Snap Ring
45. 1st Gear

46. Spacer
47. Ball Bearing
48. Reverse Gear
49. Lock Nut
50. Mainshaft
51. Needle Bearing
52. 2nd Gear

53. Synchro Ring
54. Synchro Spring
55. Synchro Hub
56. Synchro Sleeve
57. Bearing Sleeve
58. Key
59. 3rd Gear
60. Input Shaft

CHRYSLER CORP. IMPORTS 4-SPEED (Cont.)

SHIFTING MECHANISM & COMPONENTS
Inspection

Check shift rails and forks for smooth operation and excessive scoring. Check clearances as previously described. Check detent slots for wear. Check detent spring height. *See Detent Spring Specifications Chart.*

DETENT SPRING SPECIFICATIONS

Application	Specification
Free Length	.744" (18.9 mm)
Compressed Length at 8.8 Lbs. (4 kg)	.598" (15.2 mm)

TRANSMISSION REASSEMBLY

1) Insert mainshaft assembly into transmission case and drive mainshaft center bearing in using installer tool (MD998067). Install needle bearing and synchro ring, then insert input shaft into front of transmission case.

2) Insert countergear into transmission case. Install snap ring to countergear front bearing, then drive bearing into case by hammering on outer race with mallet. Install snap ring to countergear rear bearing, then install into place with bearing installer (MD998199).

3) Install front bearing retainer with spacer to obtain clearance of 0-.004" (0-.1 mm). *See Fig. 10 and refer to Front Bearing Retainer Spacer chart.* Coat both sides of front bearing retainer packing with sealant. Apply gear oil to oil seal lip. Install packing and oil seal. Install rear bearing retainer and tighten screws. Stake screws with punch.

Fig. 10: *Measuring Front Bearing-to-Retainer Clearance*

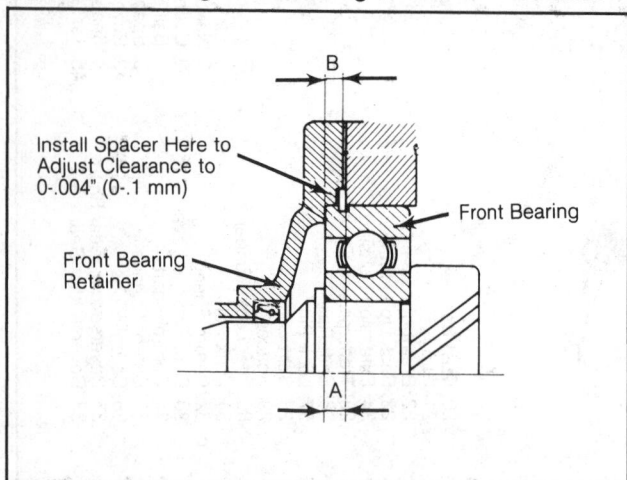

FRONT BEARING RETAINER SPACER SIZES

Application (Color)	Thickness In. (mm)
Black	.033 (.84)
No Color	.037 (.94)
Red	.040 (1.02)
White	.044 (1.12)
Yellow	.047 (1.19)
Blue	.051 (1.30)
Green	.054 (1.37)

4) Install reverse gear onto mainshaft and tighten lock nut. After tightening, lock the nut at the notch on mainshaft. Install spacer and counter reverse gear to countergear rear end. Install snap ring so reverse gear end play is 0-.003" (0-.07 mm). *Refer to Counter Reverse Gear Snap Ring Chart.*

COUNTER REVERSE GEAR SNAP RING SIZES

Application (Color)	Thickness In. (mm)
No Color	.059 (1.5)
Red	.063 (1.6)
Blue	.067 (1.7)
Green	.073 (1.85)
Yellow	.079 (2.0)

5) Install 3rd-4th and 1st-2nd shift forks onto synchro sleeves. Insert shift rails from rear of transmission case. Lock forks and rails with spring pins and install interlock plungers between shift rails. Spring pins should have slits in axial direction of shift rail.

6) Install reverse shift rail and fork assembly together with reverse idler gear. Insert detent ball and spring (small end toward ball) into each shift rail. Tighten all plugs to a depth of .24" (6.1 mm) then apply sealant to fill up plug holes.

7) Apply sealant to extension housing gasket, then install gasket and extension housing. When installing extension housing, turn control lever down to the left. Put sealant on extension housing bolts before installation.

8) Apply gear oil to speedometer driven gear and install with sleeve. Make sure number on sleeve (corresponding to number of teeth on gear) is in the "U" mark position when gear and sleeve are installed. Install clamp and tighten bolt. Install back-up light switch with steel ball.

9) Install bottom pan. Fill gear shifter area with grease and install shifter lever. Fill transmission with SAE 80 gear oil.

TIGHTENING SPECIFICATIONS

Application	Ft. Lbs. (N.m)
Mainshaft Lock Nut	72-94 (98-127)
Transmission Mounting Bolts	31-40 (42-54)
	INCH Lbs.
Pan Attaching Bolts	6-7 (8-9.5)

CHRYSLER CORP. IMPORTS 5-SPEED

**Arrow Pickup, Challenger,
Ram-50 Pickup, Sapporo**

DESCRIPTION

The models KM145 (Ram-50 4WD) and KM 132 (all others) transmissions are 5-speed fully synchronized type with constant mesh in all forward gears. Forward gears are helical type. Reverse gear is a non-synchronized spur type.

First through 3rd gears are located in transmission case, 4th gear is direct, 5th and reverse gears are located in the extension housing. Shift lever assembly is located on the top rear portion of the extension housing.

LUBRICATION & ADJUSTMENT

See the appropriate article in MANUAL TRANSMISSION SERVICING Section.

TROUBLE SHOOTING

DIFFICULTY MESHING GEARS

Malfunction of gearshift lever or control shaft. Synchro rings or gear coned surfaces worn or excessive play. Synchro shift keys worn or damaged.

JUMPS OUT OF GEAR

Shifting forks worn or detent springs broken. Mainshaft or mainshaft support bearings worn or damaged. Clearance between synchro hub and sleeve excessive. Gears or gear bushings worn. Countergear worn.

NOISE IN TRANSMISSION

Lubricating oil incorrect or insufficient. Gears or bearings worn. Mainshaft spline worn or damaged.

REMOVAL & INSTALLATION

See the appropriate article in MANUAL TRANSMISSION REMOVAL Section.

TRANSMISSION DISASSEMBLY

1) On 4WD, remove transfer case assembly. See the appropriate article in TRANSFER CASE Section. On all models, remove return clip, then clutch release bearing and carrier. Using a 3/16" (4.76 mm) punch, drive roll pin from clutch release shaft. See Fig. 1. Remove shaft, felt, return spring(s) and clutch release arm. Remove bottom pan from transmission case. Remove back-up light switch and steel ball.

2) Remove extension housing bolts. Unscrew plug of neutral return plunger "B". See Fig. 11. Move shifter down to the left. See Fig. 2. Slide extension housing from transmission case and mainshaft. Remove snap ring and withdraw speedometer drive gear. Remove other snap ring and pull ball bearing from rear of mainshaft.

3) Unscrew the 3 detent plugs, remove 3 springs and 3 balls. Using a 3/16" (4.76 mm) punch, drive 3rd-4th and 1st-2nd roll pins from shift forks. Pull each shift rail toward rear of transmission until shift forks can be removed. Take out interlock plunger.

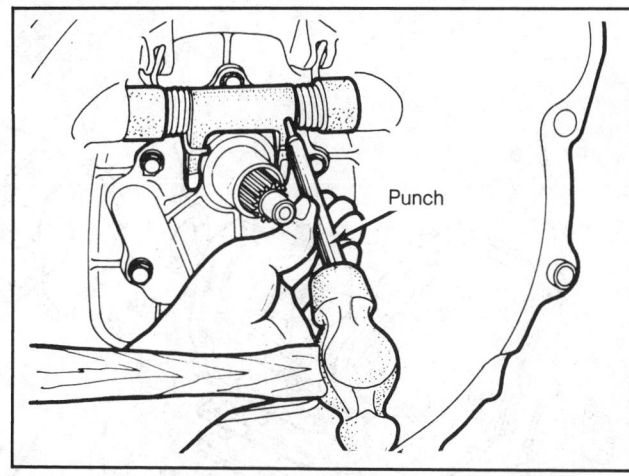

Fig. 1: Removing Roll Pin from Clutch Release Shaft

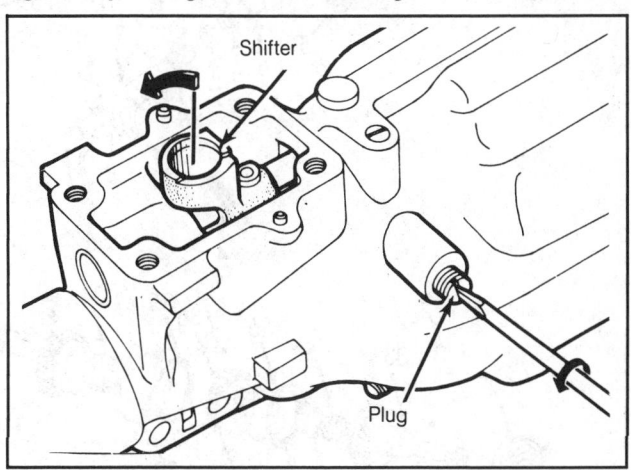

Fig. 2: Separating Extension Housing from Transmission

4) Using a 3/16" (4.76 mm) punch, drive out 5th-reverse roll pin, then remove shift rails and fork. See Fig. 3.

5) Bend back the lock washer. Engage 2nd and reverse gears to lock mainshaft and countergear while removing lock nuts from countergear and mainshaft.

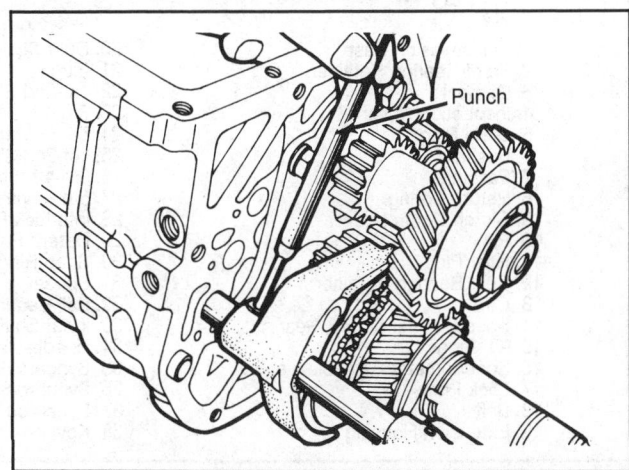

Fig. 3: Driving Out 5th-Reverse Roll Pin

Manual Transmissions

CHRYSLER CORP. IMPORTS 5-SPEED (Cont.)

Fig. 4: *Exploded View of Chrysler Corp. KM132 5-Speed Transmission Assembly*

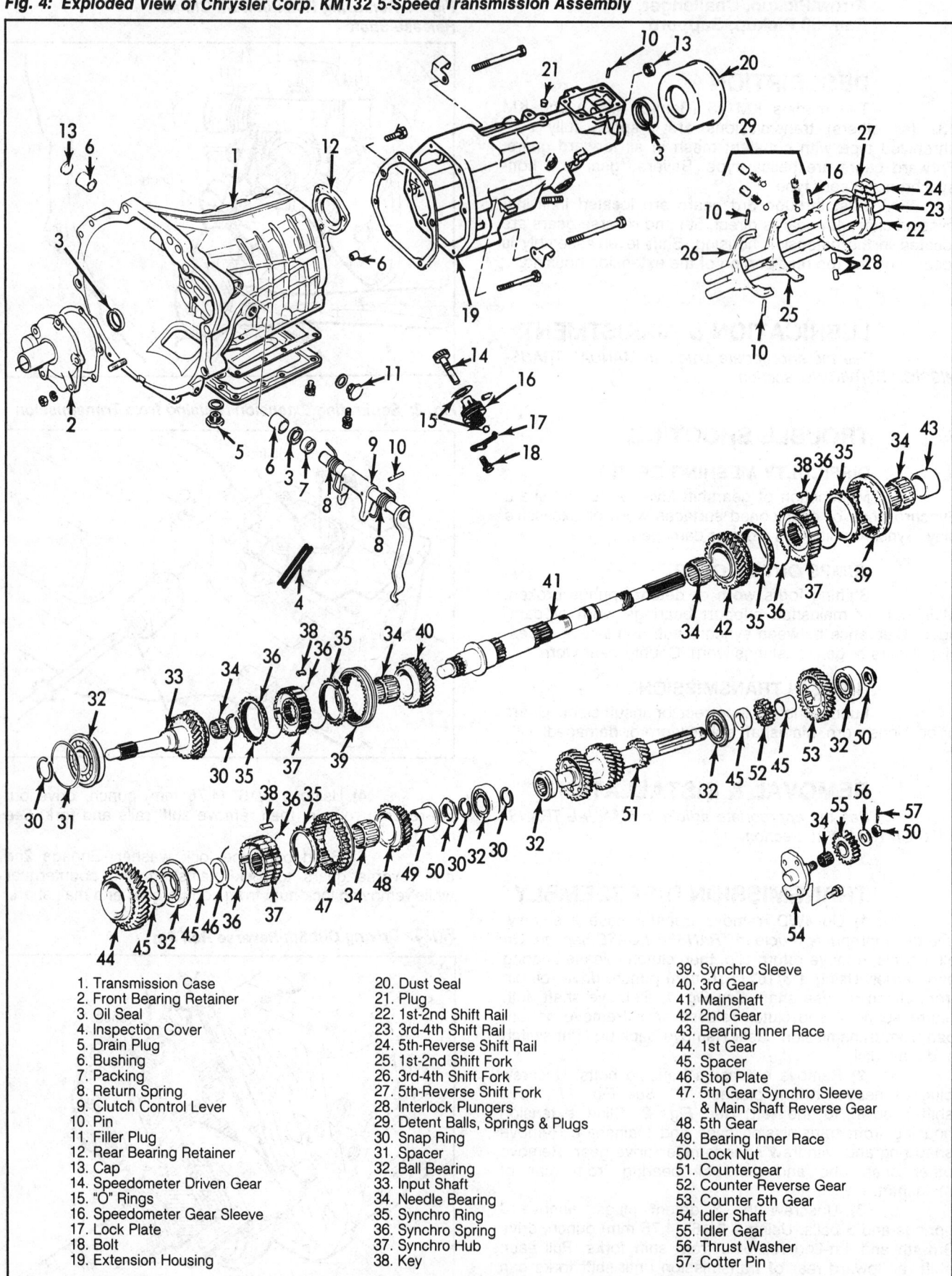

1. Transmission Case	20. Dust Seal	39. Synchro Sleeve
2. Front Bearing Retainer	21. Plug	40. 3rd Gear
3. Oil Seal	22. 1st-2nd Shift Rail	41. Mainshaft
4. Inspection Cover	23. 3rd-4th Shift Rail	42. 2nd Gear
5. Drain Plug	24. 5th-Reverse Shift Rail	43. Bearing Inner Race
6. Bushing	25. 1st-2nd Shift Fork	44. 1st Gear
7. Packing	26. 3rd-4th Shift Fork	45. Spacer
8. Return Spring	27. 5th-Reverse Shift Fork	46. Stop Plate
9. Clutch Control Lever	28. Interlock Plungers	47. 5th Gear Synchro Sleeve
10. Pin	29. Detent Balls, Springs & Plugs	& Main Shaft Reverse Gear
11. Filler Plug	30. Snap Ring	48. 5th Gear
12. Rear Bearing Retainer	31. Spacer	49. Bearing Inner Race
13. Cap	32. Ball Bearing	50. Lock Nut
14. Speedometer Driven Gear	33. Input Shaft	51. Countergear
15. "O" Rings	34. Needle Bearing	52. Counter Reverse Gear
16. Speedometer Gear Sleeve	35. Synchro Ring	53. Counter 5th Gear
17. Lock Plate	36. Synchro Traping	54. Idler Shaft
18. Bolt	37. Synchro Hub	55. Idler Gear
19. Extension Housing	38. Key	56. Thrust Washer
		57. Cotter Pin

CHRYSLER CORP. IMPORTS 5-SPEED (Cont.)

Fig. 5: Pulling 5th Gear and Bearing from Countergear

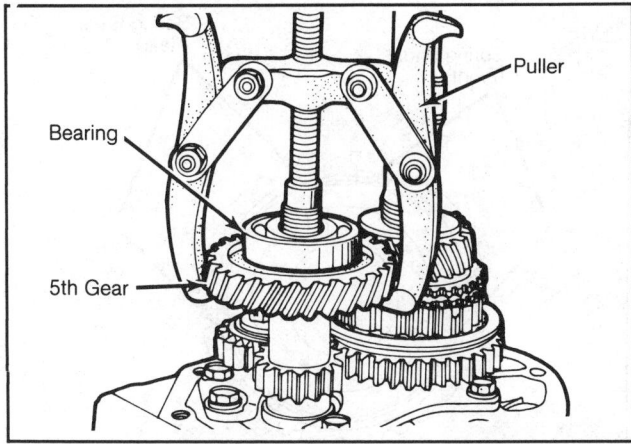

6) Using a puller, remove countergear 5th gear and ball bearing. *See Fig. 5.* Remove spacer and reverse gear from countergear.

7) Remove 5th gear, sleeve, synchronizer assembly and spacer from mainshaft. Pull cotter pin from reverse idler shaft. Unscrew castle nut and remove thrust washer, reverse gear and needle bearing. Working from inside case, use a punch to drive reverse idler shaft from case. *See Fig. 6.*

Fig. 6: Driving Reverse Idler Shaft from Transmission Case

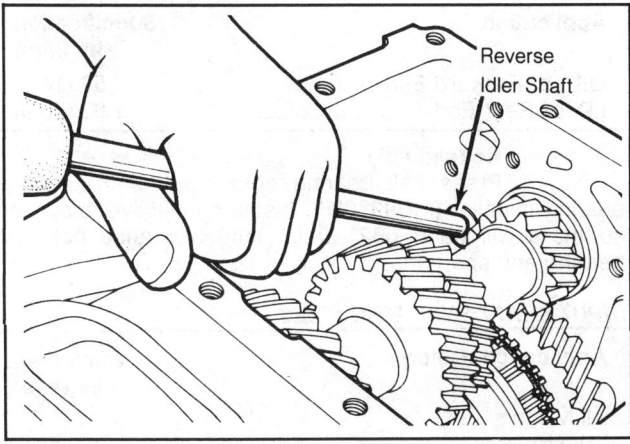

8) Remove front bearing retainer. With countergear pressed rearward, remove bearing snap ring.

Fig. 7: Pulling Mainshaft Bearing from Transmission Case

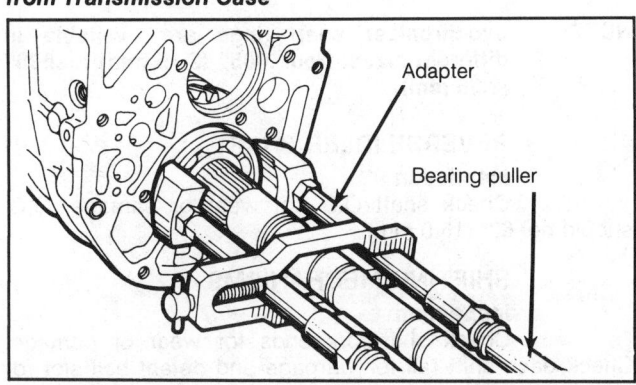

Using a bearing puller (MD998192), remove rear countergear bearing. Repeating the above procedure, remove front countergear bearing and lift countergear from case.

9) Pull input shaft/pinion gear assembly from front of case. Remove large snap ring from bearing and small snap ring from input shaft. Using a bearing puller (MD998056), pull bearing off input shaft.

10) Remove mainshaft bearing snap ring and pull bearing from case and shaft, then remove mainshaft assembly from case. *See Fig. 7.*

COMPONENT DISASSEMBLY & REASSEMBLY

MAINSHAFT

Disassembly (2WD)

Slide 1st gear, 1st-2nd synchronizer and 2nd gear off rear of mainshaft. Remove snap ring from forward end of mainshaft. Slide 3rd-4th synchronizer and 3rd gear from mainshaft.

Disassembly (4WD)

Remove snap ring from front of mainshaft. Remove 3-4 synchronizer, synchro ring, 3rd gear and needle bearing. Remove bearing spacer, 1st gear and needle bearing rearward from mainshaft. Support 2nd gear on press and push mainshaft end to remove 1st speed gear bearing, sleeve, 1-2 synchronizer assembly, 2nd gear and needle bearing.

Inspection

1) Clean and inspect mainshaft and gear assemblies as follows: Check mainshaft O.D. and splines for wear or damage. Check gear teeth for wear or damage. Check I.D. of gear. Inspect synchronizer cone surface for wear or damage.

TRANSMISSION GEAR STANDARD DIMENSIONS

Application	Specification In. (mm)
All Models	
1st & 2nd Gear I.D.	1.89 (48.0)
3rd & 5th Gear I.D.	1.58 (40.1)
Reverse Idler Gear I. D.	.79 (20.1)
Countergear Forward O.D.	.98 (25.0)

2) On synchronizer rings, check gear teeth and cone I.D. for wear and damage. Place ring on mating gear and measure dimension "A" as shown in *Fig. 8.* Standard value is .059" (1.5 mm) and maximum wear limit is .031" (.8 mm). With hub and sleeve assembled, check for excessive clearance and see if the parts slide smoothly.

Fig. 8: Measuring Synchronizer Ring-to-Gear Clearance

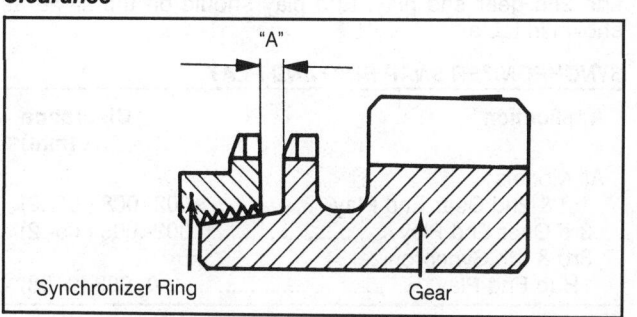

CHRYSLER CORP. IMPORTS 5-SPEED (Cont.)

Fig. 9: *Synchronizer Assembly and Spring Location*

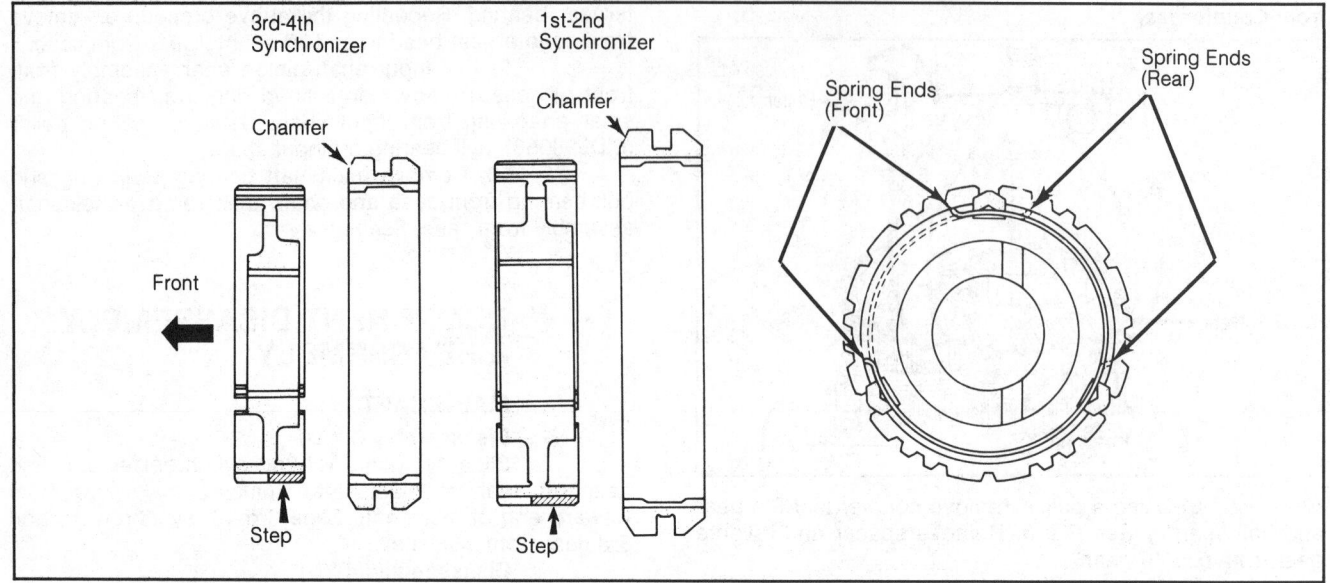

NOTE: If sleeve or hub need replacing, always replace them as an assembly. Check shift fork groove in sleeve for wear.

Reassembly

1) Assemble 1st-2nd and 3rd-4th synchronizers as shown in *Fig. 9*. Place the needle bearing, 3rd gear, synchronizer ring and 3rd-4th synchronizer assembly on front of mainshaft. Check gear end play. End play should be as specified in table. *See Synchronizer Snap Ring End Play chart*.

Fig. 10: *Measuring Synchronizer Hub End Play*

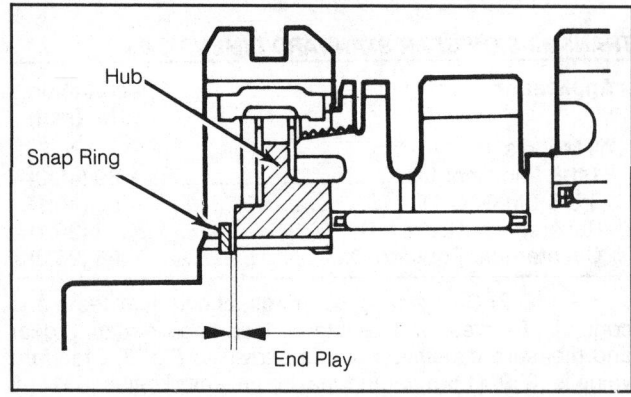

2) Place the needle bearing, 2nd gear, synchronizer assembly, bearing sleeve, needle bearing, 1st gear and bearing spacer on mainshaft from the rear end. Pressing forward with the bearing spacer, measure 1st and 2nd gear end play. End play should be the same as shown in table.

SYNCHRONIZER SNAP RING END PLAY

Application	Clearance In. (mm)
All Models	
1st & 2nd Gear End Play	.002-.008 (.05-.2)
3rd Gear End Play	.002-.008 (.05-.2)
3rd & 4th Synchronizer Hub End Play	0-.003 (0-.08)

INPUT SHAFT/PINION GEAR
Inspection

Check O.D. of forward end and I.D. of rear end of input shaft. Inspect tapered synchronizer surface, gear teeth and clutch disc splines for wear or damage.

INPUT SHAFT STANDARD DIMENSIONS

Application	Specification In. (mm)
O.D. of Forward End	.59 (14.9)
I.D. of Rear End	1.02 (25.9)

Reassembly

Press ball bearing onto input shaft using a bearing installer (MD998029). Install a selective snap ring so there will be 0-.002" (0-.06 mm) clearance between bearing and snap ring.

INPUT SHAFT SNAP RING SIZES

Application (Color)	Thickness In. (mm)
All Models	
White	.091 (2.31)
No Color	.092 (2.34)
Red	.094 (2.39)
Blue	.096 (2.44)
Yellow	.098 (2.49)

NOTE: Synchronizer snap rings are available in different sizes, from .085" (2.15 mm) to .093" (2.36 mm).

REVERSE IDLER SHAFT
Inspection

Check shaft O.D. for wear or damage. O.D. should be .63" (16.0 mm).

SHIFTING MECHANISMS
Inspection

Check shift fork ends for wear or damage. Check each shift rail for warpage and detent ball slot for

CHRYSLER CORP. IMPORTS 5-SPEED (Cont.)

wear. Check forward end of control finger and shift lug groove for wear.

SHIFT MECHANISM STANDARD DIMENSIONS

Application	Specification In. (mm)
Shift Fork, Sleeve Groove	.197 (5.00)
Shift Fork-to-Sleeve	.004-.012 (.1-.3)
Shift Fork-to-Sleeve (5th Gear)	.006-.014 (.15-.36)
Warpage of Shift Rail	.0016 (.04) Max.
Control Finger-to-Shift Lug	.004-.012 (.1-.3)
Detent Spring Length	.744 (18.90)

EXTENSION HOUSING
Disassembly
1) Remove locking plate, then speedometer driven gear. Remove all three screw plugs, springs, neutral return plungers ("A" and "B") and detent ball from housing. See Fig. 11.

2) Press gear shifter all the way forward in housing. Using a 3/16" (4.76 mm) punch, drive roll pin from shifter. Separate shifter and control shaft by pulling shaft out front of housing.

Inspection
Inspect forward end of neutral return plunger and detent ball slot for wear. Check neutral return springs and detent spring for collapsing or beakage. Length of neutral return springs is 1.64" (41.6 mm) and detent spring is 1.09" (27.7 mm).

Fig. 11: Removing Neutral Return Plungers from Extension Housing

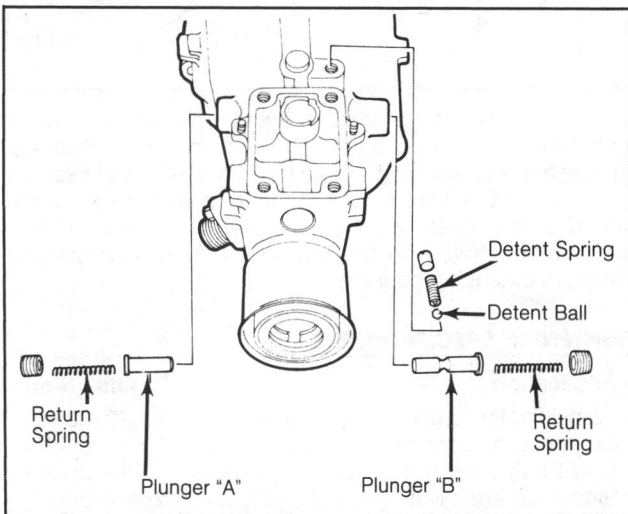

Reassembly
See Transmission Reassembly for extension housing reassembly.

TRANSMISSION REASSEMBLY

NOTE: Replace all gaskets, seals and roll pins with new ones. Oil all rolling or sliding parts and grease seal lips before reassembly.

1) Place mainshaft assembly into transmission case. Using a bearing installer, drive middle mainshaft bearing onto mainshaft and into case while holding front

of mainshaft by hand. Install needle bearing and synchronizer, then slide input shaft/pinion gear assembly into transmission case with needle bearing engaging end of mainshaft.

2) Position countergear into case. Install respective snap rings on front needle bearing and rear ball bearing. Drive needle bearing and ball bearing into case. Install front bearing retainer with a bearing spacer which will give a clearance of 0-.004" (0-.1 mm) at dimension "C" See Fig. 12. Apply a sealer to both sides of gasket.

FRONT BEARING RETAINER SPACER SIZES

Application (Color)	Thickness In. (mm)
All Models	
Black	.033 (.84)
No Color	.037 (.94)
Red	.040 (1.0)
White	.044 (1.1)
Yellow	.047 (1.2)
Blue	.051 (1.3)
Green	.054 (1.4)

3) Install rear bearing retainer. Place reverse idler shaft into position and install bolts to act as guides. Using a large drift, drive reverse idler shaft into case.

Fig. 12: Retainer-to-Bearing Clearance Measurement

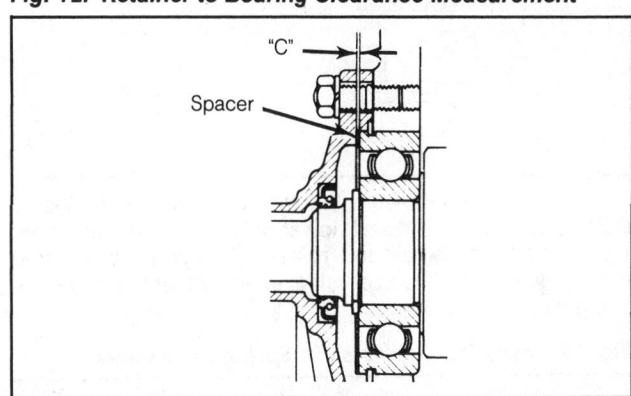

4) Install needle bearing, reverse idler gear and thrust washer with ground side facing gear. Install and tighten castle nut.

Fig. 13: Using a Feeler Gauge to Check Reverse Idler Gear End Play

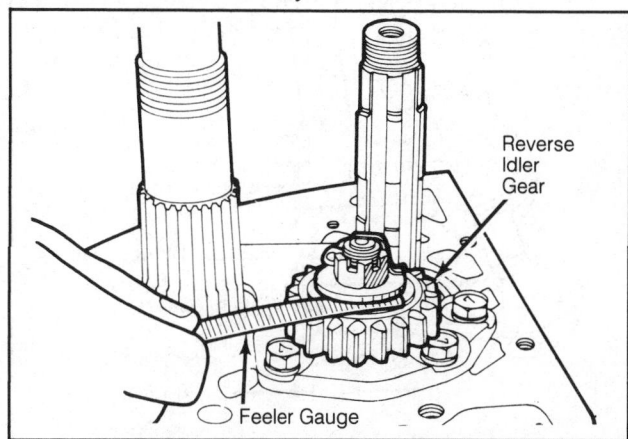

CHRYSLER CORP. IMPORTS 5-SPEED (Cont.)

5) Check to see that end play between washer and gear is .005-011" (.12-.28 mm). Then install cotter pin in castle nut. *See Fig. 13.*

6) Assemble 5th gear synchronizer. *See Fig. 14.* Install spacer, stop plate, synchronizer ring and 5th gear on mainshaft.

7) Install and tighten lock nut, staking it at a notch in mainshaft. End play measured between 5th gear and lock nut should be .004-.010" (.10-.25 mm).

8) Install spacer and 5th countergear ball bearing. Tighten lock nut and stake into notch at rear end of countergear. Engage 1st-2nd and 3rd-4th shift forks in their respective synchronizer sleeves.

Fig. 14: 5th Gear Synchronizer Assembly

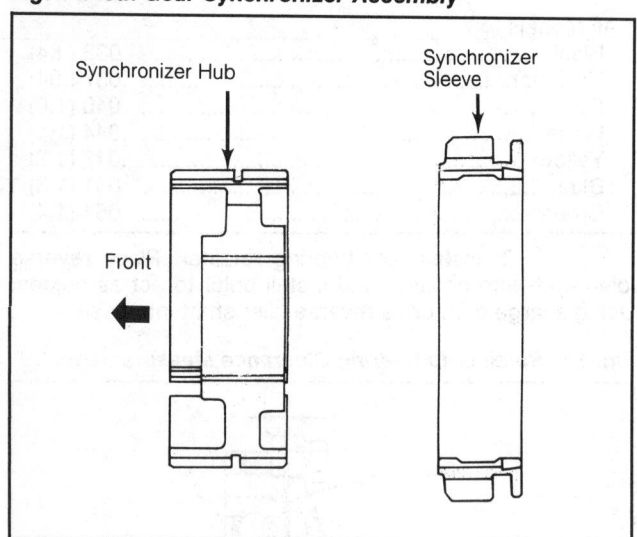

9) Slide lower shift rail into position and install shift fork roll pin. Install lower interlock plunger. Next install middle shift rail and roll pin. Position 5th-Reverse shift fork in synchronizer sleeve. Install upper interlock plunger.

Fig. 15: Installing Detent Balls, Springs and Plugs

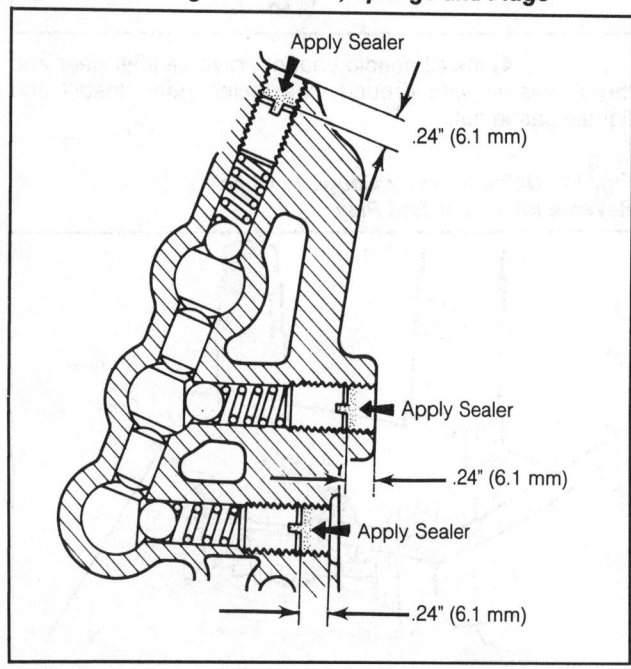

10) Slide upper shift rail into position and install shift fork roll pin. Install all 3 detent balls and springs with small end of spring facing ball. Screw detent plugs approximately .24" (6.1 mm) into case and apply sealer to head of plugs. *See Fig. 15.*

11) Install snap ring in forward groove of mainshaft. Install bearing retaining snap ring. Install speedometer gear snap ring and speedometer gear. Finally install snap ring.

12) Apply sealer to both sides of extension housing gasket and position on housing. While holding shifter fully to the left, slide housing onto mainshaft. Make sure forward end of control finger is snugly fitted in slot of shift lug. Apply sealer to threads of attaching bolts and tighten bolts.

13) Install neutral return plungers "A" and "B", springs and plugs. Then install detent ball, spring and plug. Screw all plugs flush with housing and apply sealer to head of plugs. *See Fig. 16.*

Fig. 16: Installing Neutral Return Plungers

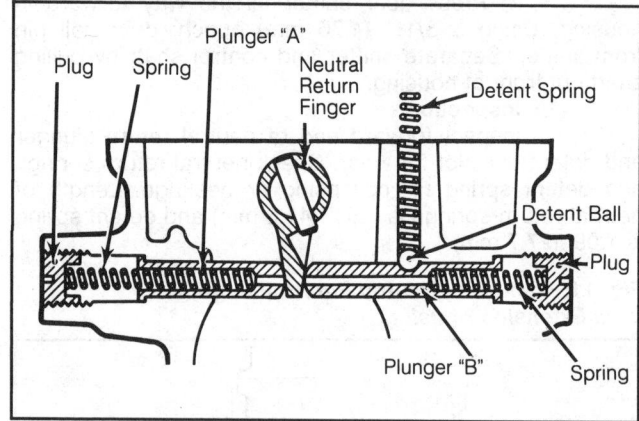

14) Using sealer, install speedometer drive lock plate. Place steel ball in position and screw back-up light switch into housing. Install bottom pan and gasket.

15) Install stopper bracket assembly to extension housing cover, making sure reverse resistance plate is smoothly moved on bracket. Install extension housing cover on extension housing.

TIGHTENING SPECIFICATIONS

Application	Ft. Lbs. (N.m)
Transmission Case-to-Engine Bolts	22-30 (30-41)
Countergear Lock Nut	50-72 (68-98)
Idler Shaft Lock Nut	15-43 (20-58)
Mainshaft Lock Nut	72-94 (98-128)

COURIER 4-SPEED

DESCRIPTION

A 4-speed synchromesh type transmission is standard on Courier models. All forward gears are selective synchromesh type, reverse gear is sliding mesh type.

Shift mechanism is floor type built into the extension housing. Transmission case consists of 2 mating halves bolted together with removable extension and clutch housing.

LUBRICATION & ADJUSTMENT

See the appropriate article in MANUAL TRANS-MISSION SERVICING Section.

REMOVAL & INSTALLATION

See the appropriate article in MANUAL TRANS-MISSION REMOVAL Section.

TRANSMISSION DISASSEMBLY

NOTE: Transmission can be disassembled without disassembling most of the sub-assemblies.

1) Remove clutch release bearing return spring and slide bearing off clutch housing. Remove clutch lever and boot from clutch housing. Remove clutch housing retaining bolts and separate from transmission housing. Remove gasket and input shaft bearing thrust washer.

2) Position transmission on bench with left side down. Remove extension housing retaining bolts. Position control lever in neutral and press to left or downward as far as possible and slide extension housing off transmission.

3) Remove all nuts, bolts, and washers connecting case halves. Lift right case half off left case half. Lift countershaft assembly out. Remove input and output shafts as an assembly by rolling out from under shift forks. Separate input and output shafts after removal.

4) To remove reverse idler, push center shift rail forward as far as possible. This will allow clearance to rotate reverse shifter as idler is removed. Remove set screw and slide out reverse idler shaft.

COMPONENT DISASSEMBLY & REASSEMBLY

INPUT SHAFT
Disassembly

Remove roller bearing assembly from inside input shaft bearing pocket. Remove bearing snap ring. Install a support (T71P-4621-B) under bearing so that bearing inner race is supported and press bearing off shaft. Inspect all components for wear or damage.

Reassembly

Place input shaft bearing on shaft and press into position using a support (T62F-4621-A). Install snap ring and roller bearing assembly.

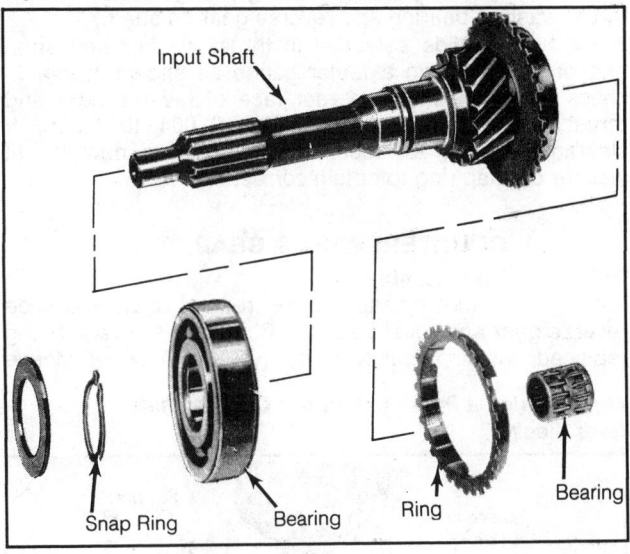

Fig. 1: *Exploded View of Input Shaft Assembly*

OUTPUT SHAFT
Disassembly

1) Remove snap ring at front of output shaft. Slide off 3rd and 4th gear synchronizer, synchronizer ring and 3rd gear. Mark synchronizer hub to ensure it is installed in same direction if not previously marked.

2) Remove rear snap ring and slide off speedometer gear and drive ball. Remove front speedometer gear snap ring. Remove next snap ring (selective fit type) and thrust washer.

3) Slide off reverse gear, output shaft bearing, 1st gear, 1st gear bushing, 1st and 2nd synchronizer and 2nd gear. Note that oil groove on synchronizer faces forward. Inspect all components for wear or damage and replace as necessary.

Reassembly

1) Install 3rd gear, 3rd gear synchronizer ring, and 3rd and 4th synchronizer hub on front of shaft. Note marks on hub made during disassembly and install front snap ring. Slide 2nd gear and synchronizer ring on shaft.

2) Install 1st and 2nd speed synchronizer and ring on shaft, making sure oil groove in hub faces forward.

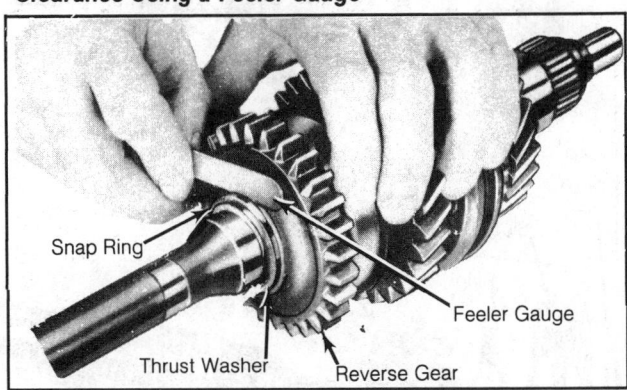

Fig. 2: *Checking Reverse Gear-to-Snap Ring Clearance Using a Feeler Gauge*

COURIER 4-SPEED (Cont.)

Install 1st speed synchronizer ring, 1st gear and sleeve, thrust washer, bearing and reverse gear on shaft.

3) Slide selective fit thrust washer and snap ring on shaft. Using a feeler gauge as shown in *Fig. 2*, check clearance between rear face of reverse gear and thrust washer. Clearance should be 0-.004" (0-.1 mm). If clearance is not to specification, install a new thrust washer or snap ring to obtain correct clearance.

COUNTERSHAFT & GEAR
Disassembly
Remove snap ring on rear of shaft and slide reverse gear and roller bearing off shaft. If sleeve is being replaced, install a support tool (OTC-950) under sleeve

Fig. 3: Using a Press to Remove Countershaft Gear Sleeve

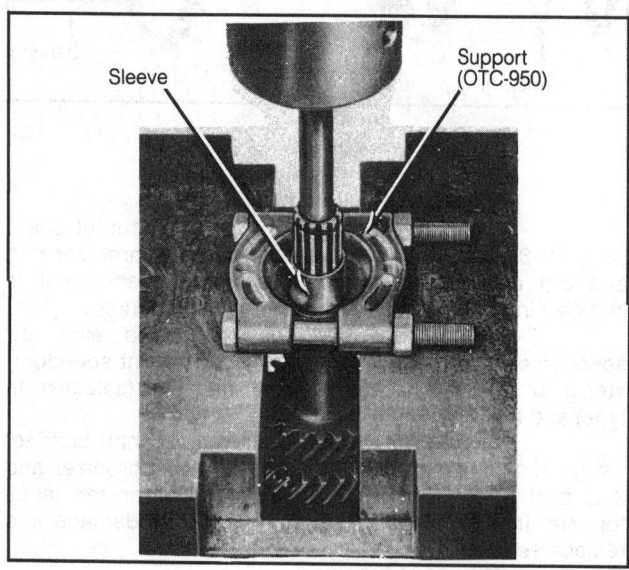

against shaft. Place shaft and tool in a press and press off sleeve. To remove front bearing, remove snap ring and press off bearing using a support (T71P-4621-B) under bearing.

Reassembly
Press sleeve back into position using a support. Install roller bearing and reverse gear on shaft and install snap ring. Press ball bearing on front of shaft using a support (T72J-7025) and install snap ring.

SHIFT RAILS

NOTE: All components of detent assemblies should be installed in original position. Mark or identify all components for reassembly.

Disassembly
Remove each spring cap (one at a time) and withdraw spring, ball and adjusting plate. Now move to next spring cap to avoid mixing of components. Remove interlock plug and remove interlock pins. Remove shift fork attaching screws and withdraw shift forks and rails from case.

Reassembly
1) Place shift fork in case and slide in 1st and 2nd gear shift rail through fork and case. Install 2 pilot shift rails (T27J-7280) in case. Use alignment pin part of tool to align holes in pilot shift rail and 1st and 2nd gear shift rail. Rotate case up on edge and drop interlock pin into position. Remove pilot shift rail from 3rd and 4th gear shift rail bore in case.

2) Position 3rd and 4th gear shift fork in case and slide shift rail (with over-travel washer if required) into case. Use alignment pin part of tool to align holes in pilot shift rail and 3rd and 4th gear shift rail. Rotate case up on edge and drop interlock pin into position.

3) Remove remaining pilot shift rail and install reverse shift rail and fork. Use alignment pin part of tool to align holes in pilot shift rail and reverse gear shift rail.

Fig. 4: Exploded View of Output Shaft Assembly

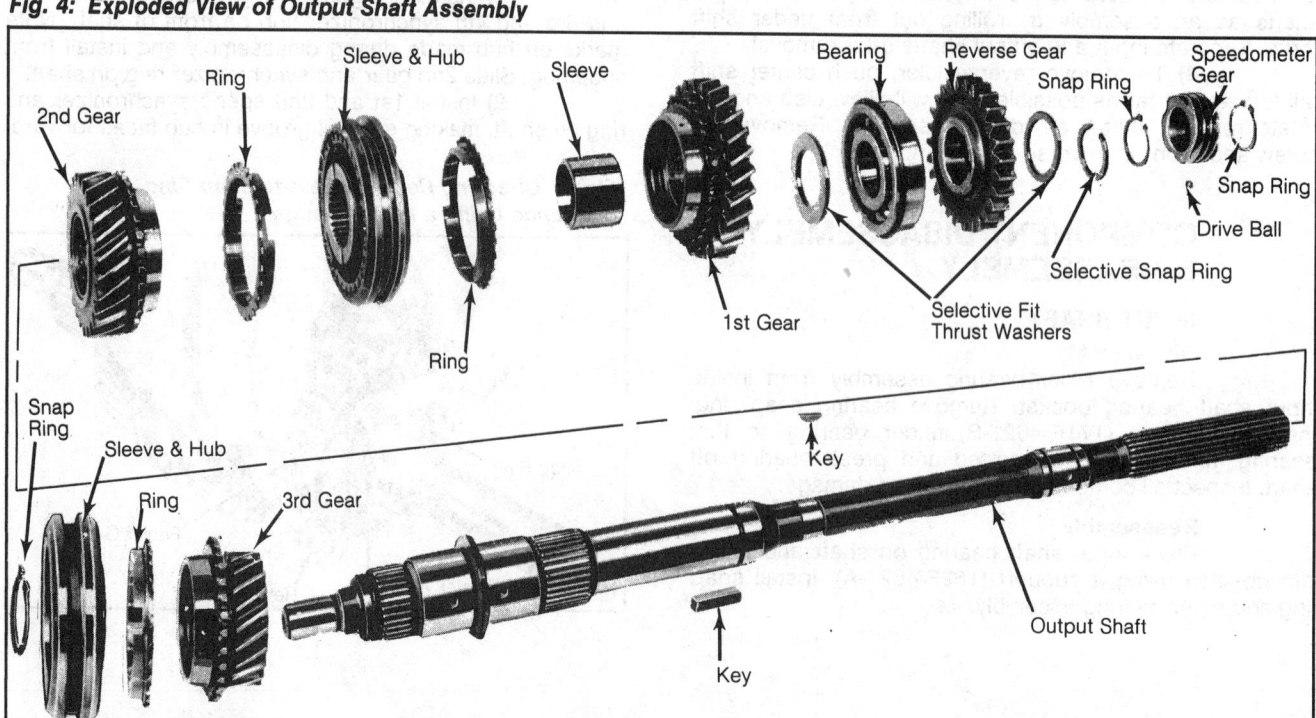

COURIER 4-SPEED (Cont.)

Raise case on edge and drop in interlock pin. Install interlock bore plugs and tighten to specification.

    4) Align shift forks on rails. Install lock bolts and tighten to specifications. Place case on bench with open side down. Install each detent ball, spring, adjusting plate shim (if equipped), and plug. Make sure detent assemblies are installed in original hole. Tighten detent plugs to specifications. Lubricate all shift rail components before assembling transmission.

EXTENSION HOUSING

Disassembly

    Place housing on right side and remove speedometer gear and back-up light switch with the friction spring loaded piece. Place housing upright and remove lock bolt securing cupped control lever end to control lever rod. Remove control lever end from rod, slide rod from housing.

Fig. 5: Exploded View of Extension Housing

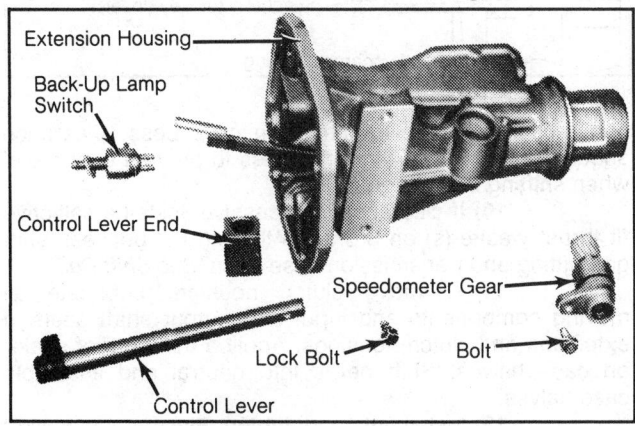

Reassembly

    Slide control lever rod into housing. Install rod end and lock bolt. Tighten bolt to specification. Install friction piece and back-up lamp. Lubricate speedometer gear housing seal and install speedometer gear.

SHIFT TOWER & LEVER

Disassembly

    Remove three bolts securing shift lever to tower. Remove lever and components.

Fig. 6: Exploded View of Countershaft Gear Assembly

Fig. 7: Exploded View of Shift Tower and Lever

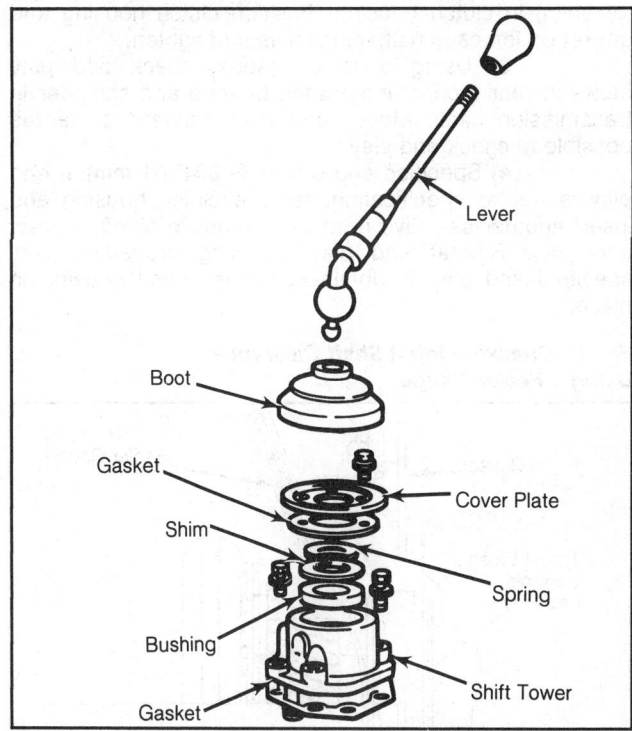

Reassembly

    If shift lever was loose in tower before disassembly, increase pressure on socket by adjusting washer thickness. To reassemble shift tower and lever, reverse disassembly procedure.

TRANSMISSION REASSEMBLY

    1) Make sure all components are clean, including mating surfaces on case halves. Position reverse idler gear in case and insert shaft. Install lock screw and tighten to specification. Insert input shaft roller bearing assembly in bearing pocket. Place shift forks in neutral.

    2) Connect input shaft and output shaft and position in case. Place countershaft assembly in case, making sure that dowel hole in roller bearing is aligned with dowel in case. Gear train will rotate freely when

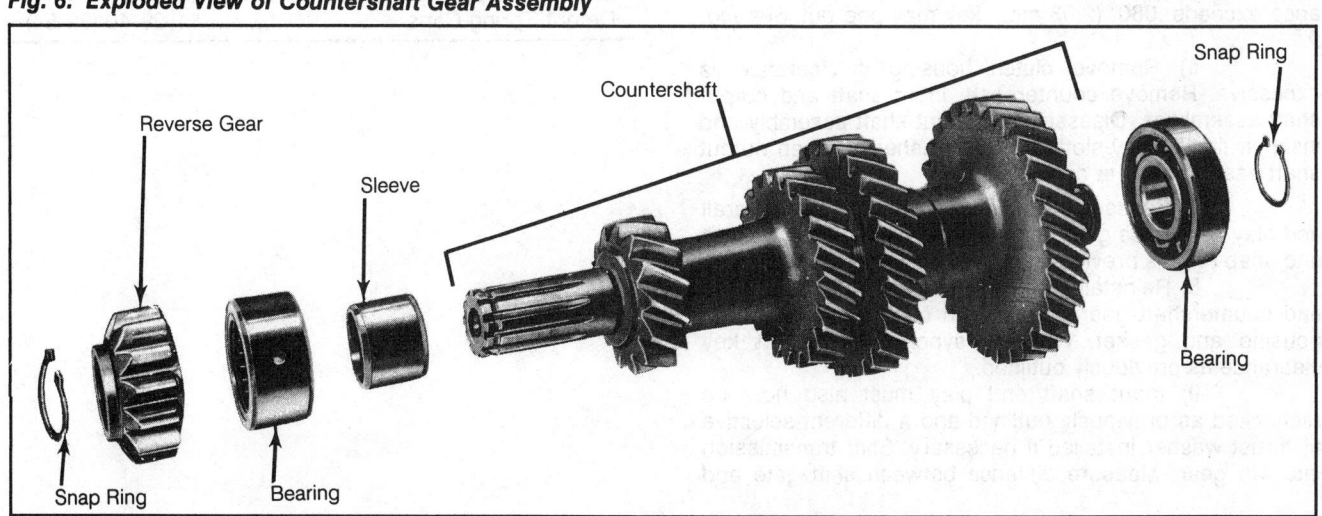

COURIER 4-SPEED (Cont.)

dowel is correctly aligned. Place input shaft thrust washer (or shim) in clutch housing. Position clutch housing and gasket on left case half. Install nuts and tighten.

3) Using a feeler gauge, check end play between rear face of input shaft bearing and shoulder in transmission case. Move input shaft forward as far as possible to check end play.

4) Specified end play is 0-.004" (.1 mm). If end play is not to specification, remove clutch housing and insert another selective fit thrust washer to obtain correct end play. Repeat end play checking procedure until specified end play is obtained. Leave clutch housing in place.

Fig. 8: Checking Input Shaft Clearance Using a Feeler Gauge

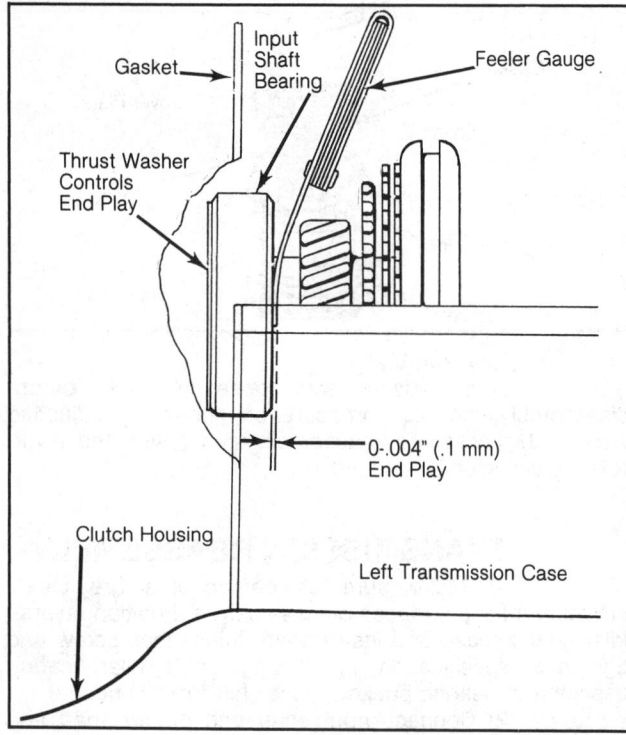

5) Shift transmission into 3rd gear. Using a feeler gauge, check clearance between synchronizer insert and the exposed edge of synchronizer ring. Specified clearance is .030-.080" (.76-2.03 mm). If clearance exceeds .080" (2.03 mm), key may pop out. *See Fig. 9.*

6) Remove clutch housing if clearance is excessive. Remove countershaft, input shaft and output shaft assemblies. Disassemble output shaft assembly and insert a thicker key-slotted thrust washer between output shaft bearing and 1st gear.

7) Reassemble output shaft and adjust overall end play at reverse gear using a selective fit thrust washer and snap ring as previously outlined. *See Output Shaft.*

8) Reinstall input and output shaft assemblies and countershaft gear assembly in case. Reinstall clutch housing and gasket. Recheck synchronizer insert key clearance as previously outlined.

9) Input shaft end play must also now be rechecked as previously outlined and a different selective fit thrust washer installed if necessary. Shift transmission into 4th gear. Measure distance between shift gate and

Fig. 9: View Showing Synchronizer Insert Clearance

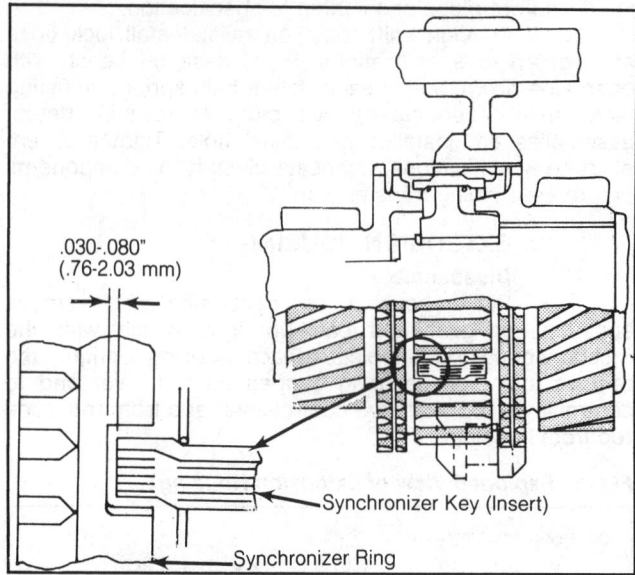

end of shift rail and transmission case boss. Clearance should be 0-.028" (0-.74 mm) or less to prevent over-travel when shifting into 4th gear.

10) If clearance is excessive, install a selective fit thrust washer(s) on 3rd and 4th shift rail between shift gate fitting and transmission case boss. *See Shift Rails.*

11) Remove clutch housing. Lubricate all moving components and input and output shaft seals in extension and clutch housings. Apply a thin coat of sealer on case halves. Shift gears into neutral and assemble case halves.

12) Install nuts and tighten. Place a new gasket on case and install extension housing. Install and tighten nuts. Place clutch housing and gasket on case, then install and tighten nuts. Install clutch release lever, bearing and components in clutch housing.

TIGHTENING SPECIFICATIONS

Application	Ft. Lbs. (N.m)
Case Half Nuts (To Bolt)	12-17 (16-23)
Case Half Nuts (To Stud)	23-34 (31-46)
Clutch Housing-to-Case	41-60 (56-81)
Extension Housing-to-Case	23-34 (31-46)
Detent Spring Caps	29-40 (39-54)

COURIER 5-SPEED

DESCRIPTION

The 5-speed transmission is fully synchronized in all gears except reverse, which is constant mesh. All forward gears are helical type for quiet running. Reverse gear and reverse idler gear are spur type.

The transmission case is of light metal and consists of removable clutch and extension housings. Gear shifting is of direct control, floor shift type, built into the extension housing.

LUBRICATION & ADJUSTMENT

See the appropriate article in MANUAL TRANSMISSION SERVICING Section.

REMOVAL & INSTALLATION

See the appropriate article in MANUAL TRANSMISSION REMOVAL Section.

TRANSMISSION DISASSEMBLY

1) Remove nuts attaching clutch housing to transmission case and remove clutch housing and gasket. Remove drain plug and drain transmission. Clean metal filings from drain plug magnet (if necessary) then reinstall drain plug.

2) Place transmission in holder. Put transmission in neutral, then remove 4 attaching bolts holding gearshift retainer to extension housing and remove gearshift lever retainer and gasket. Remove speedometer lock plate and driven gear assembly from extension housing.

3) Remove 7 nuts attaching extension housing to transmission case. Raise control lever to left and slide toward rear of transmission, then slide extension housing off mainshaft.

NOTE: Be careful not to damage oil seal.

Fig. 1: Removing Extension Housing

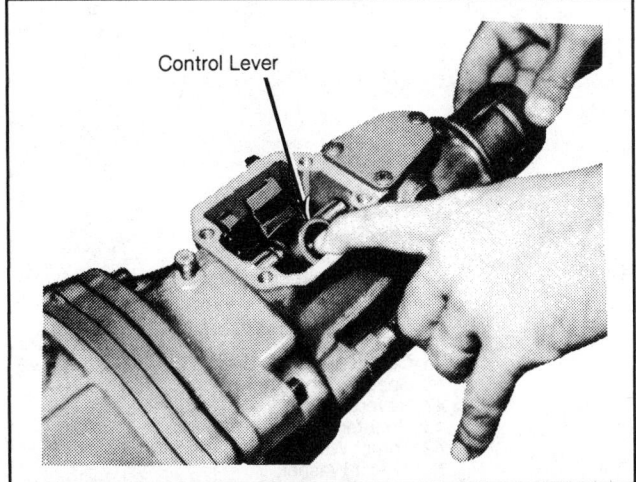

Control Lever

4) Remove spring cap bolts, spring and friction piece from extension housing. Remove bolt attaching gearshift control lever end to control lever, then remove control lever end, key and control lever. Remove back-up light switch from extension housing.

5) Remove snap ring securing speedometer drive gear to mainshaft, slide drive gear off mainshaft, and remove lock ball and snap ring.

6) Unscrew bolts securing transmission case cover, then remove cover and gasket. Mark shifter rails (for later reassembly) then remove bolts attaching shift rod ends and remove ends from shift rods.

Fig. 2: Removing Control Lever End

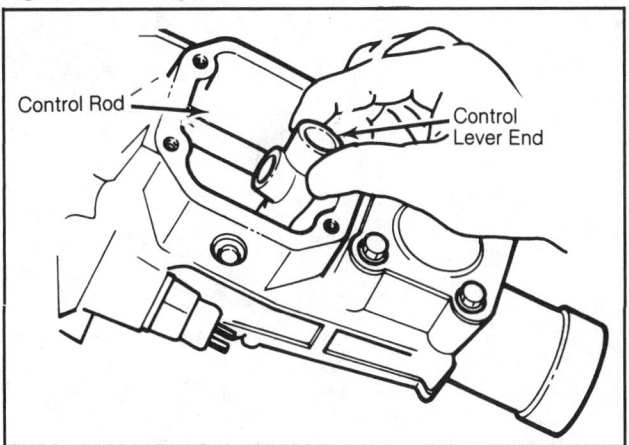

Control Rod

Control Lever End

7) Carefully pry bearing housing from transmission case with screwdriver, then slide housing off mainshaft. Remove snap ring and washer retaining mainshaft rear bearing to mainshaft, then press main bearing from case.

Fig. 3: Removing Mainshaft Rear Bearing

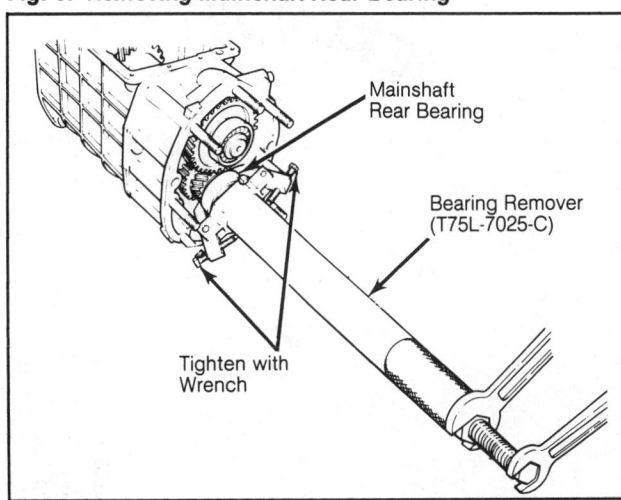

Mainshaft Rear Bearing

Bearing Remover (T75L-7025-C)

Tighten with Wrench

8) Remove snap ring and washer from rear end of countershaft and press countershaft bearing from case.

9) Remove 5th gear and spacer from rear of countershaft. Remove center housing attaching bolts. *See Fig. 5.* If necessary, tap housing with plastic hammer and remove center housing.

10) Remove 3 spring cap bolts, detent springs and detent balls from transmission case. Remove nuts attaching covers on side of transmission case and remove covers and gaskets.

11) Remove attaching bolt from 5th-reverse shift fork and slide shaft out of transmission case. Remove attaching bolts from 1st-2nd and 3rd-4th shift forks and slide shafts from rear of case.

Manual Transmissions

COURIER 5-SPEED (Cont.)

Fig. 4: Exploded View of Courier 5-Speed Transmission Showing Shafts and Gears

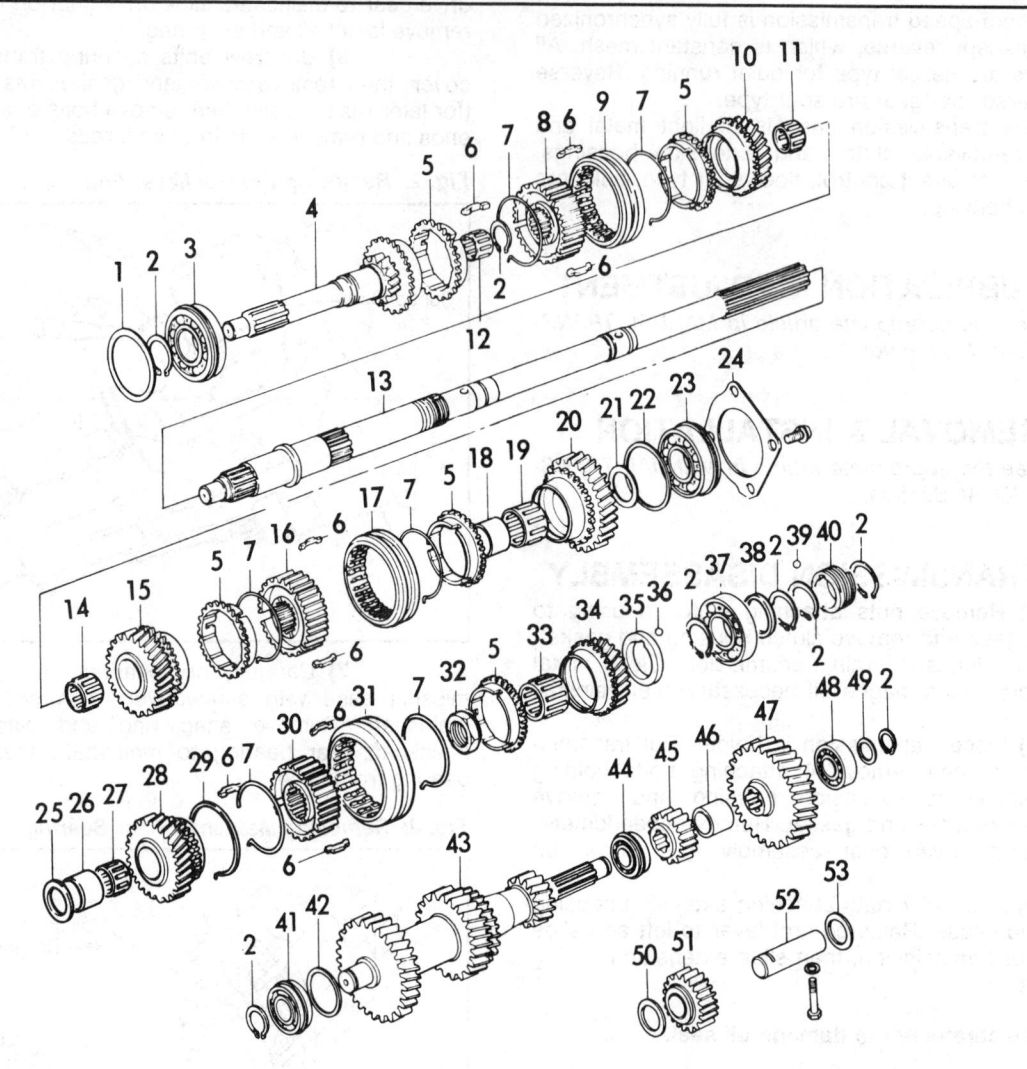

1. Shim	19. Needle Bearing	37. Mainshaft Rear Bearing
2. Snap Ring	20. 1st Gear	38. Thrust Washer
3. Main Driveshaft Bearing	21. Thrust Washer	39. Lock Ball
4. Input Shaft	22. Shim	40. Speedometer Drive Gear
5. Synchronizer Ring	23. Mainshaft Front Bearing	41. Countershaft Front Bearing
6. Synchronizer Key	24. Bearing Cover	42. Shim
7. Synchronizer Key Spring	25. Thrust Washer	43. Countershaft
8. 3rd-4th Clutch Hub	26. Bearing Inner Race	44. Countershaft Center Bearing
9. Clutch Sleeve	27. Needle Bearing	45. Counter Reverse Gear
10. 3rd Gear	28. Reverse Gear	46. Spacer
11. Needle Bearing	29. Stop Ring	47. Reverse Gear
12. Needle Bearing	30. 5th-Reverse Clutch Hub	48. Countershaft Rear Bearing
13. Mainshaft	31. Clutch Sleeve	49. Thrust Washer
14. Needle Bearing	32. Mainshaft Lock Nut	50. Thrust Washer
15. 2nd Gear	33. Needle Bearing	51. Reverse Idler Gear
16. 1st-2nd Clutch Hub	34. 5th Gear	52. Idler Gear Shaft
17. Clutch Sleeve	35. Thrust Washer	53. Thrust Washer
18. Bearing Inner Race	36. Lock Ball	

COURIER 5-SPEED (Cont.)

Fig. 5: Removing Countershaft Rear Bearing

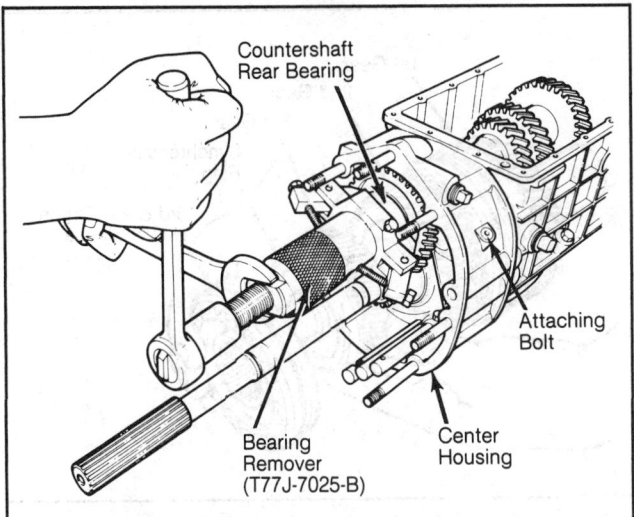

Countershaft Rear Bearing

Attaching Bolt

Center Housing

Bearing Remover (T77J-7025-B)

12) Remove snap ring securing 5th gear to mainshaft. Remove thrust washer, 5th gear, lock ball and needle bearing from rear of mainshaft.

Fig. 6: 1st-2nd and 3rd-4th Shift Fork Attaching Bolt Locations

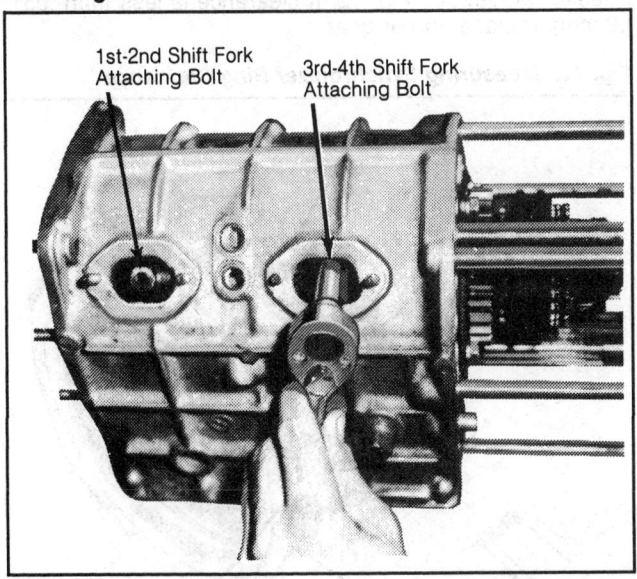

1st-2nd Shift Fork Attaching Bolt

3rd-4th Shift Fork Attaching Bolt

13) Engage 2nd gear and counter reverse gear to lock mainshaft. Straighten staked part of lock nut, remove lock nut and slide reverse gear and clutch hub assembly off mainshaft.

14) Slide spacer and counter reverse gear off rear of countershaft. Remove reverse idler gear with idler gear shaft from transmission case.

15) Remove key and spacer from mainshaft. Install synchronizer ring holder (T77J-7025-E), between 4th gear synchronizer ring and synchromesh gear on mainshaft. See Fig. 7.

16) Secure ring holder with 2 bottom cover attaching bolts. Remove snap ring securing countershaft front bearing to front end of countershaft.

17) Press countershaft front bearing from case. Remove adjusting shim(s) from countershaft front

bearing bore. Remove bolts attaching bearing cover to transmission case, then remove bearing cover.

Fig. 7: Installing Synchronizer Ring Holder

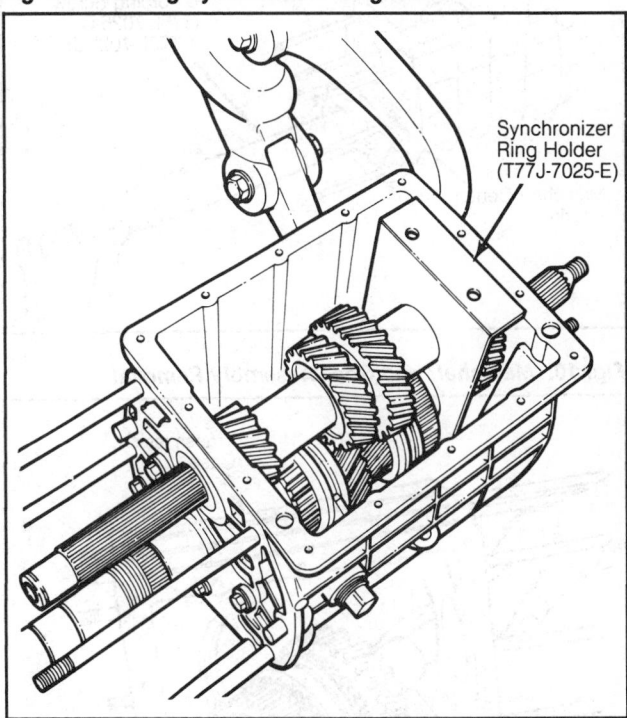

Synchronizer Ring Holder (T77J-7025-E)

18) Press countershaft center bearing from case. Remove snap ring and adjusting shims retaining mainshaft front bearing. With special synchronizer ring holder still in place, press out mainshaft front bearing and center bearing.

Fig. 8: Removing Mainshaft Front Bearing

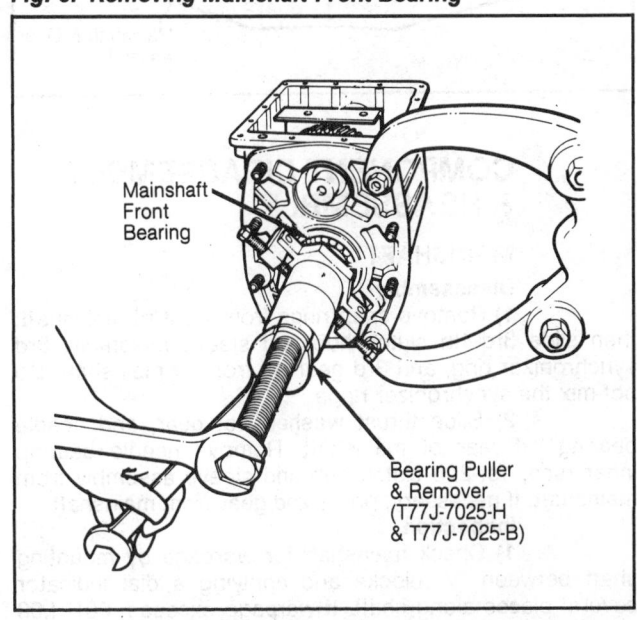

Mainshaft Front Bearing

Bearing Puller & Remover (T77J-7025-H & T77J-7025-B)

19) Remove mainshaft and gear assembly from transmission case. See Fig. 10. Remove 1st-2nd and 3rd-4th shift fork from case. Remove shift inter-lock pins from case.

Manual Transmissions

COURIER 5-SPEED (Cont.)

Fig. 9: Removing Mainshaft Center Bearing

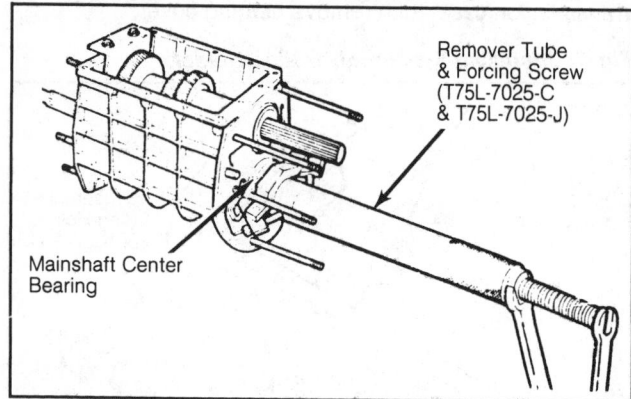

Fig. 10: Mainshaft and Gear Assembly Removal

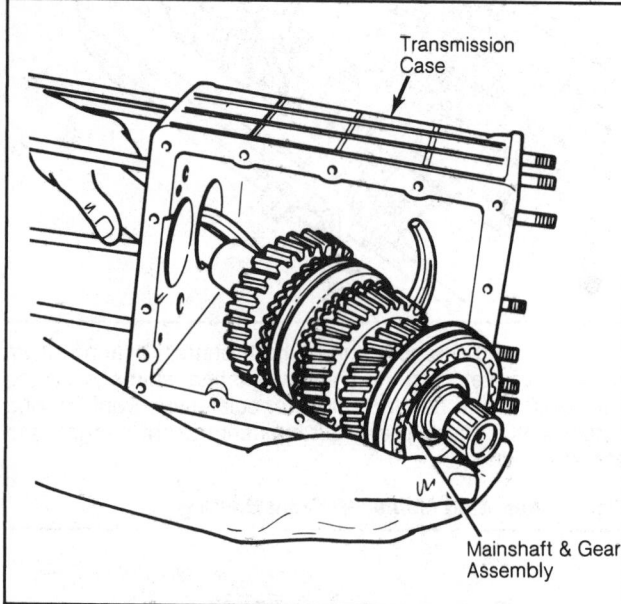

Fig. 11: Mainshaft Disassembly

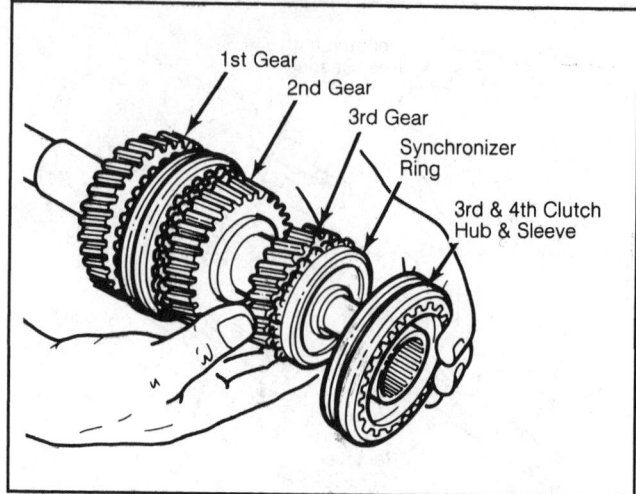

3) Check bearings for wear and make sure they rotate smoothly. Check for worn, broken or missing teeth on all gears. Replace if necessary.

4) Check gear teeth on synchronizer rings. Inspect rings for wear by fitting the ring evenly to cone and measuring the clearance between the side faces with a feeler gauge. See Fig. 12. If clearance is less than .031" (.8 mm), replace ring or gear.

Fig. 12: Measuring Synchronizer Ring Clearance

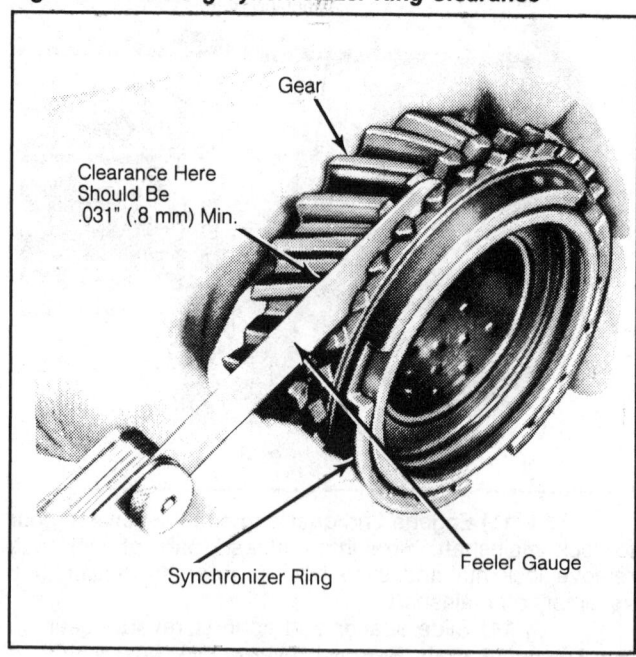

5) Inspect contact between inner surface of ring and cone surface of gear. If contact is poor, correct by applying a lapping compound to surfaces and lap until proper fit is obtained.

6) Using a feeler gauge, check and ensure that clearance between shift fork shaft and control lever is less than .031" (.8 mm). See Fig. 13. Check that clearance between shift forks and clutch sleeve is less than .020" (.5 mm). See Fig. 14. If clearances exceed specifications, replace parts as necessary.

COMPONENT DISASSEMBLY & REASSEMBLY

MAINSHAFT

Disassembly

1) Remove snap rings from front of mainshaft, then slide 3rd-4th clutch hub and sleeve assembly, 3rd synchronizer ring, and 3rd gear off front of mainshaft. Do not mix the synchronizer rings.

2) Slide thrust washer, 1st gear, and needle bearing off rear of mainshaft. Remove needle bearing inner race, 1st-2nd clutch hub and sleeve assembly from mainshaft. If necessary, press 2nd gear from mainshaft.

Inspection

1) Check mainshaft for warpage by mounting shaft between "V" blocks and applying a dial indicator several places along shaft. If warpage exceeds .001" (.03 mm) replace shaft.

2) Clean bearings by rotating in solvent until all lubricant is removed. Dry with compressed air. Do not allow bearing to rotate while drying.

COURIER 5-SPEED (Cont.)

Fig. 13: *Measuring Shift Fork-to-Control Lever Clearance*

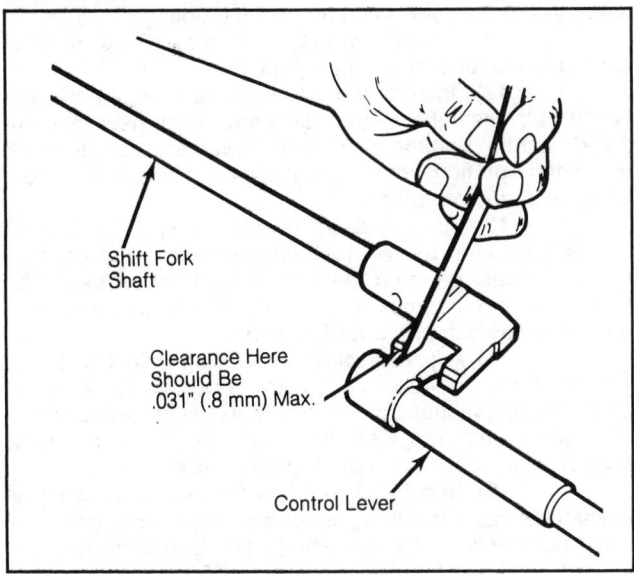

Shift Fork Shaft

Clearance Here Should Be .031" (.8 mm) Max.

Control Lever

Fig. 14: *Measuring Shift Fork-to-Sleeve Clearance*

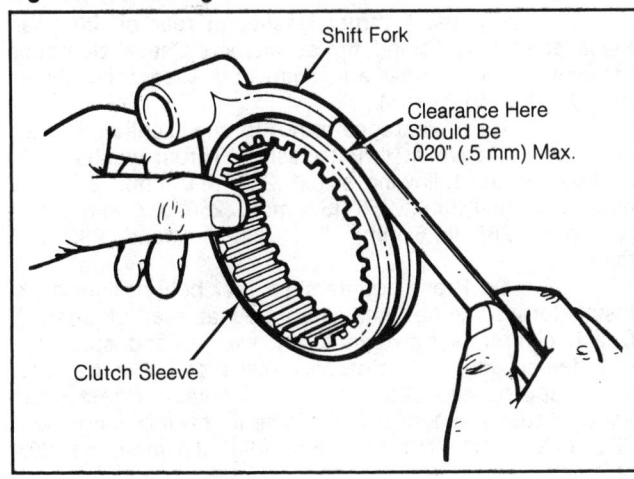

Shift Fork

Clearance Here Should Be .020" (.5 mm) Max.

Clutch Sleeve

Reassembly

1) Assemble 1st-2nd clutch hub to sleeve. Place the 3 synchronizer keys into clutch hub key slots and install key springs. *See Fig. 15.*

Fig. 15: *Synchronizer Key Location*

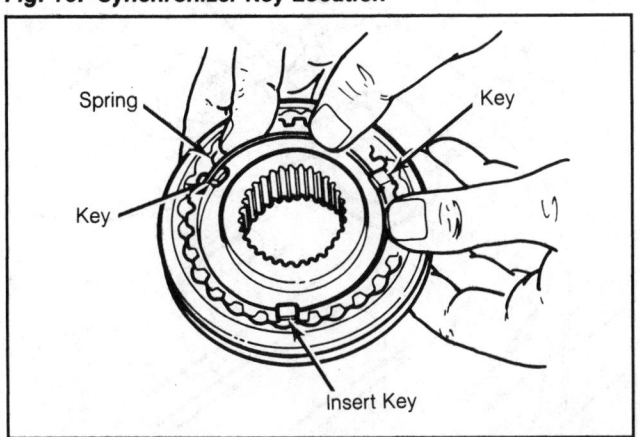

Spring

Key

Key

Insert Key

NOTE: The open end of the key springs should be kept 120° apart in order to keep spring tension on each key uniform.

2) Assemble 3rd-4th and 5th synchronizer assembly in the same manner as 1st-2nd. Place synchronizer ring on 2nd gear and slide unit onto mainshaft with synchronizer ring toward rear of shaft.

3) Press 1st gear needle bearing inner race and 1st-2nd clutch hub/sleeve assembly onto mainshaft with clutch hub oil grooves toward front of mainshaft.

NOTE: Make sure the 3 synchronizer keys engage the notches in second synchronizer ring.

4) Place synchronizer ring on 3rd gear and slide unit onto front of mainshaft with synchronizer ring toward front.

5) Install 3rd-4th clutch hub and sleeve assembly onto front mainshaft, making sure the 3 synchronizer keys engage the notches in the synchronizer ring. *See Fig. 16.*

Fig. 16: *Exploded View of Synchromesh Assembly*

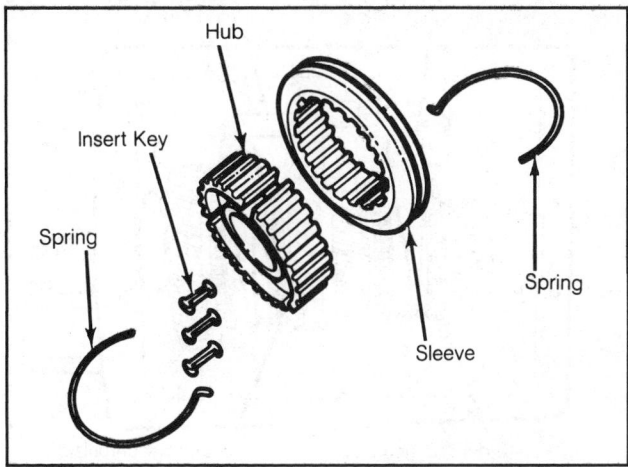

Hub

Insert Key

Spring

Spring

Sleeve

NOTE: The direction of the 3rd-4th clutch hub and sleeve assembly should be as shown in Fig. 17.

Fig. 17: *Clutch and Hub Locating Direction*

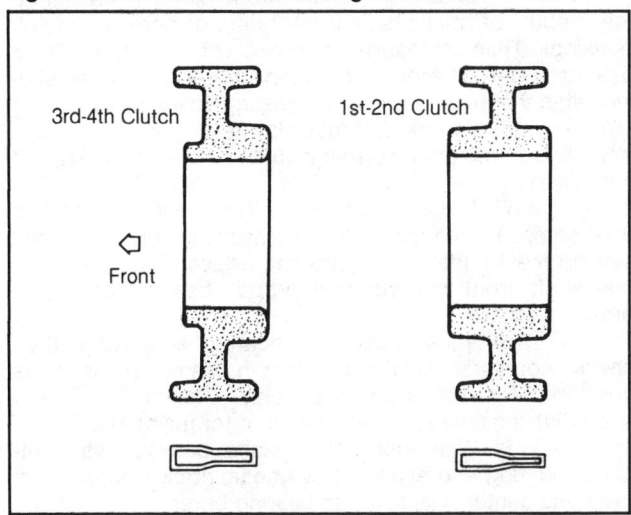

3rd-4th Clutch

1st-2nd Clutch

Front

COURIER 5-SPEED (Cont.)

6) Install snap ring on front of mainshaft, then slide 1st gear needle bearing onto mainshaft.

7) Place synchronizer ring on 1st gear. Slide unit onto mainshaft with synchronizer ring facing front of shaft. Rotate 1st gear as necessary to engage notches in the synchronizer ring with the synchronizer keys. Install original thrust washer on mainshaft.

TRANSMISSION REASSEMBLY

1) Make sure all components are clean and properly lubricated. install mainshaft and gear assembly in case, then place needle bearing on front end of mainshaft.

2) Place synchronizer ring on input shaft, then install input shaft on front end of mainshaft, making sure the 3 synchronizer keys in the 3rd-4th synchromesh unit engage the notches in the synchronizer ring.

3) Place the 1st-2nd and 3rd-4th shift fork in groove of clutch hub and sleeve assembly. *See Fig. 18.*

Fig. 18: *Installing Shift Forks*

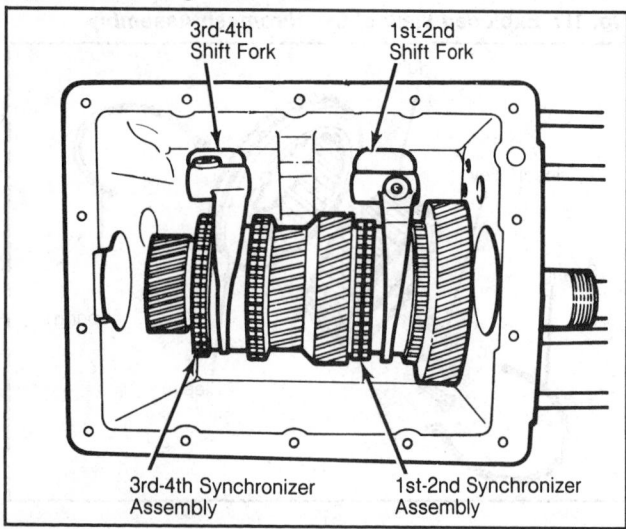

4) Press inner race of countershaft center bearing onto countershaft, then position countershaft gear in case, making sure countershaft gears engage each gear of mainshaft assembly.

5) Check mainshaft thrust play by measuring the depth of mainshaft front bearing bore in clutch housing. Then measure thickness of mainshaft front bearing. The difference between the 2 measurements indicates the thickness of the adjusting shims needed.

6) Standard thrust play is 0-.004" (0-.1 mm). Adjusting shims are available in .004" (.1 mm) and .012" (.3 mm) sizes.

7) Install synchronizer ring tool (as used in disassembly), between 4th synchronizer ring and the synchromesh gear on mainshaft. Place mainshaft and mainshaft front bearing into proper bearing bore and press into place.

8) Install mainshaft bearing snap ring, then check countershaft thrust play in same manner as described for mainshaft thrust play. Standard end play and adjusting shims are same as that for mainshaft.

9) With tool still in place between 4th synchronizer ring and synchromesh gear, press countershaft front and center bearings into bearing bores.

10) Secure countershaft front bearing with snap ring then remove ring holder tool. Install bearing cover to transmission case and tighten bolts.

11) Install reverse idler gear. Slide reverse gear and spacer onto countershaft.

12) Install spacer, key, reverse gear, and clutch hub assembly onto mainshaft. Install new lock nut (hand tight). Engage 2nd and reverse gear to lock mainshaft rotation, then tighten lock nut to specification. Stake lock nut into place.

13) Place 2nd-3rd clutch sleeve in third gear. Check clearance between synchronizer key and edge of ring with feeler gauge. Clearance should not exceed .079" (2.0 mm). If clearance does exceed this amount, synchronizer key can pop out of position.

14) Adjust clearance by using select fit thrust washer fitted between mainshaft front bearing and 1st gear. Thrust washers are available in the following sizes: .098" (2.5 mm), .118" (3.0 mm) and .138" (3.5 mm). After correcting clearance, bend tab of lock washer.

15) Install needle bearing and lock ball on mainshaft. Position 5th synchronizer ring on 5th gear and slide assembly onto mainshaft with synchronizer ring toward front of mainshaft. Rotate 5th gear as necessary to engage notches in synchronizer ring with synchronizer keys.

16) Install thrust washer at rear of 5th gear. Place snap ring behind thrust washer. Check clearance between thrust washer and snap ring. Clearance should be .004-.012" (.1-.3 mm).

17) If clearance is not to specification, correct by using selective fit thrust washer. Thrust washers are available in the following sizes: .236" (6.0 mm), .244" (6.2 mm), .252" (6.4 mm), .256" (6.5 mm), .260" (6.6 mm), .264" (6.7 mm), .268" (6.8 mm), .276" (7.0 mm) and .283" (7.2 mm).

18) Press countershaft rear bearing into case. Install thrust washer and snap ring at rear of bearing. Check clearance between thrust washer and snap ring with feeler gauge. If clearance exceeds .004" (.1 mm), select appropriate thrust washer to obtain correct clearance. Thrust washers are available in the following sizes: .075" (1.92 mm), .079" (2.0 mm), .083" (2.1 mm) and .087" (2.2 mm).

Fig. 19: *Measuring Countershaft Rear Bearing End Play*

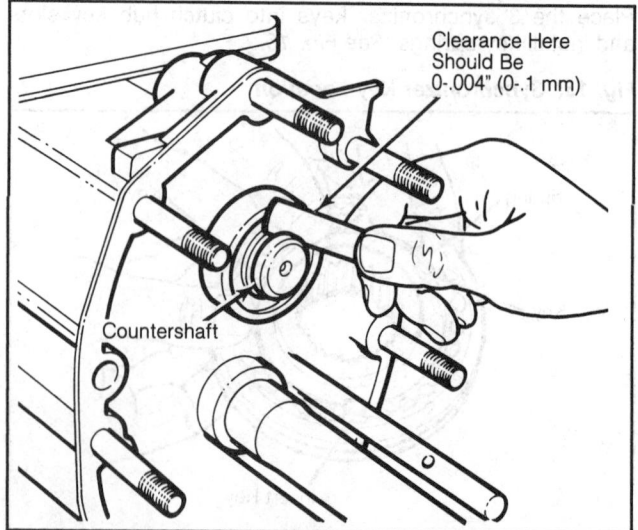

COURIER 5-SPEED (Cont.)

19) Repeat the procedure for rear main bearing. Clearance between thrust washer and snap ring on rear bearing is 0-.006" (0-.15 mm). Thrust washers are available in the following sizes: .079" (2.00 mm), .085" (2.15 mm) and .091" (2.30 mm).

20) Slide 1st-2nd, 3rd-4th, and 5th-reverse shift fork shafts into case from rear. Lock shift forks on shafts with lock nuts. Install 3 detent balls and springs in case and screw in spring cap bolts. Install inter-lock pin in transmission case.

21) Install 2 covers and gaskets on side of transmission, then tighten attaching bolts. Apply a thin coat of sealer to contacting surfaces of center housing and transmission case. Position center housing on case.

22) Align reverse idler gear shaft boss with center housing attaching bolt boss. Install and tighten center housing attaching bolt. Install countershaft 5th gear onto countershaft. Make sure "F" mark on gear is toward front of shaft. *See Fig. 20.*

Fig. 20: Countershaft 5th Gear Identification Mark Location

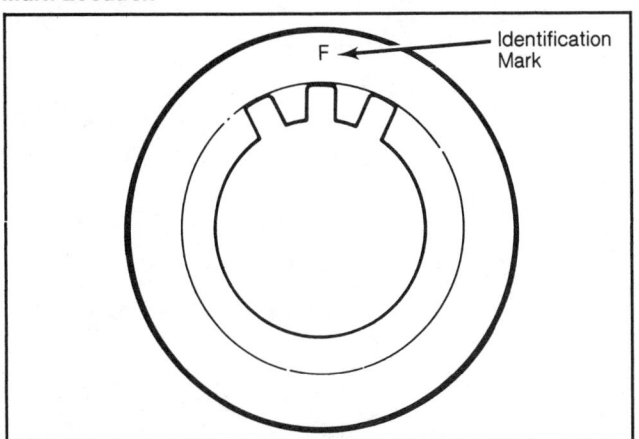

Fig. 21: Exploded View of Transmission Case

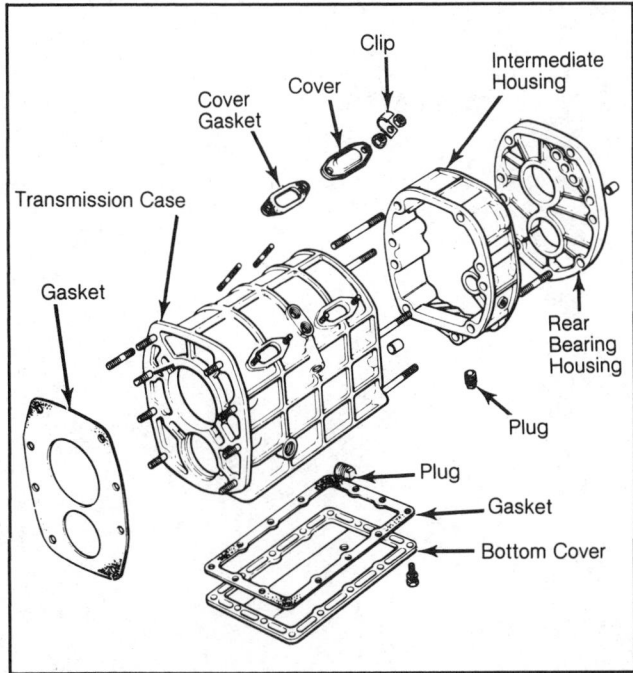

23) Apply thin coat of sealer to contacting surfaces of bearing housing and center housing. Position housing on studs of center housing. Install shift fork shaft ends onto proper shift fork shafts (note marks made during disassembly). Tighten bolts. Install snap ring, lock ball, speedometer drive gear and snap ring on mainshaft.

Fig. 22: Installing Shift Shaft Fork Ends

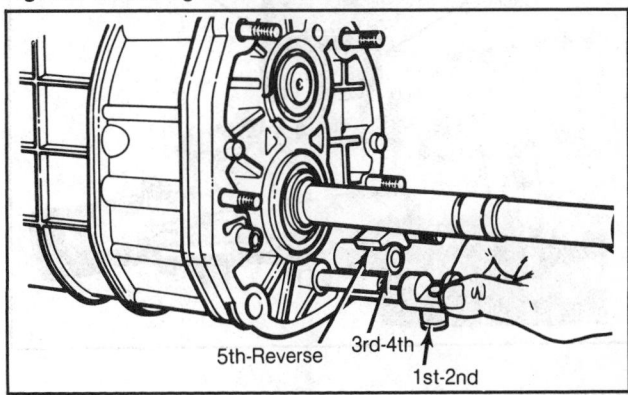

24) Insert gearshift control lever through holes from front side of extension housing. Install Woodruff key, then install control lever end on control lever, and secure with bolt.

25) Place spring and friction piece in extension housing and tighten spring cap bolt. Apply a thin coat of sealer to contacting surfaces of bearing housing and extension housing. Place gearshift control lever as far to left as possible and install extension housing on studs. Tighten attaching nuts.

Fig. 23: Disassembled View of Speedometer Driven Gear Assembly

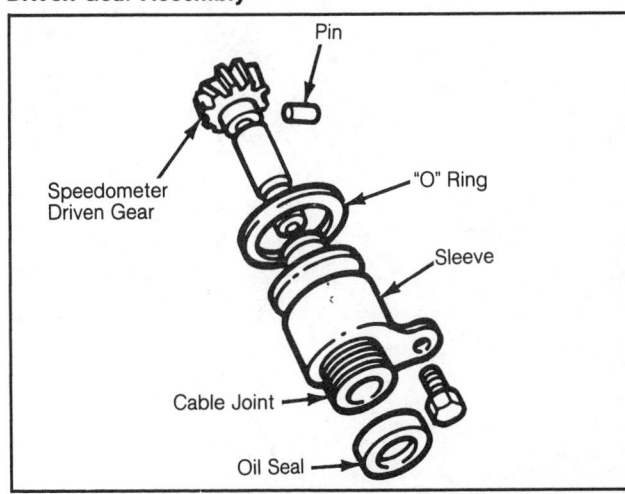

26) Insert speedometer driven gear assembly into extension housing and secure with bolt. Install gearshift lever retainer and gasket on extension housing, then tighten attaching bolts.

27) Check input shaft bearing clearance by measuring depth of bearing bore in clutch housing and measuring bearing thickness. The difference between the measurements indicated the required shim thickness. Standard clearance is 0-.004" (0-.1 mm). If a shim is needed to obtain correct clearance, the following sizes are available: .004" (.1 mm) and .012" (.3 mm).

25) Install clutch housing on transmission. Install back-up light switch.

Fig. 24: *Installing Gearshift Lever Retainer*

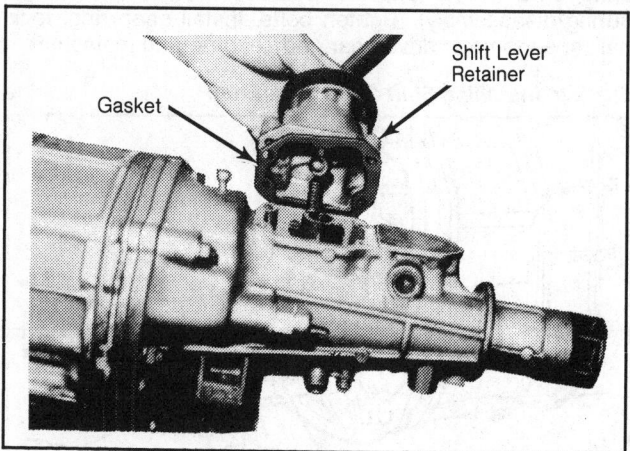

Gasket — Shift Lever Retainer

TIGHTENING SPECIFICATIONS

Application	Ft. Lbs. (N.m)
Detent Spring Plugs	29-40 (39-54)
Mainshaft Nut	116-173 (157-234)
Shift Rod End-to-Shift Rod Bolt	20-25 (27-34)
Transmission-to-Clutch Housing	41-60 (56-81)

DATSUN/NISSAN MAXIMA, PICKUP, 200SX & 280ZX 5-SPEED

DESCRIPTION

The FS5W71B transmission is fully synchronized with constant mesh gears. All forward gears are helical type. The 5th gear (overdrive gear) rides freely on mainshaft. The countershaft 5th gear is fitted to countershaft by splines. The 5th gear synchronizer system is also on rear of mainshaft. Placing control lever in 5th gear position will bring reverse and 5th gear coupling sleeve on mainshaft into mesh with countershaft gear. The reverse and 5th synchronizer hub is fitted to mainshaft by splines. The main components of transmission are: Transmission case, adapter plate and rear extension housing.

LUBRICATION & ADJUSTMENT

See the appropriate article in MANUAL TRANS-MISSION SERVICING Section.

REMOVAL & INSTALLATION

See the appropriate article in MANUAL TRANS-MISSION REMOVAL Section.

TRANSMISSION DISASSEMBLY

1) Drain oil, remove dust cover and release bearing. Remove "E" clip, shifter return plug, spring and plunger from extension housing. Remove back-up light switch, speedometer driven gear and front cover. Remove countershaft front bearing shim. Remove input shaft bearing snap ring.

2) Turn shifter control fully to left and remove rear extension, using a standard puller. Separate transmission case from adapter plate, using a soft hammer.

COMPONENT DISASSEMBLY & REASSEMBLY

GEAR ASSEMBLY

Disassembly

1) Drive out retaining pins from fork rods, using a pin punch. Remove 3 check ball plugs and drive out fork rods from adapter plate, by tapping lightly on front of rods.

2) With gears engaged, remove countershaft front bearing, using a puller. Remove countergear snap ring and remove counterdrive gear and input shaft assembly.

3) Before disassembling mainshaft, measure gear backlash. *Refer to Gear End Play Chart for measurement limits.* Record gear end play measurements for reassembly reference.

GEAR END PLAY MEASUREMENTS

Application	In. (mm)
1st Gear	.011-.013 (.27-.34)
2nd Gear	.005-.008 (.12-.19)
3rd Gear	.005-.015 (.12-.37)
5th Gear	.004-.007 (.10-.17)
Reverse Gear	.002-.020 (.05-.50)

4) Remove snap ring and thrust washer from mainshaft. Remove 3rd and 4th synchronizer assembly. Remove 3rd gear. Remove snap ring and speedometer gear and bearing from rear of mainshaft.

5) Release staking on countershaft and mainshaft nuts, and loosen nuts. Remove countershaft nut. Using puller, remove countershaft 5th gear and bearing. Remove counter reverse idler gear and spacer. Remove countershaft (by tapping lightly at the rear end).

6) Remove reverse idler gear snap ring and reverse idler gear. Remove snap ring on mainshaft bearing. Remove mainshaft end bearing with a puller, (KV 32101330).

7) Remove mainshaft nut, thrust washer, mainshaft reverse gear, overdrive synchronizer and overdrive gear. Remove mainshaft gear assembly and countershaft.

NOTE: **Countershaft and mainshaft nuts should be discarded and replaced with new nuts.**

Inspection

1) Wash all parts in a cleaning solvent and check for wear, damage or other faulty conditions.

2) Check transmission case and extension housing for cracks, or other faulty conditions. If rear extension housing bushing is worn or cracked, replace extension housing and bushing as an assembly.

3) Check synchro assemblies for wear. Place synchro ring on gear cone as far as it will go. Measure gap between gear and synchro ring. If clearance is less than .031" (.8 mm) on 1st-4th gears or .020" (.5 mm) on 5th gear, replace synchro ring.

Fig. 1: Exploded View of Shift Control Components

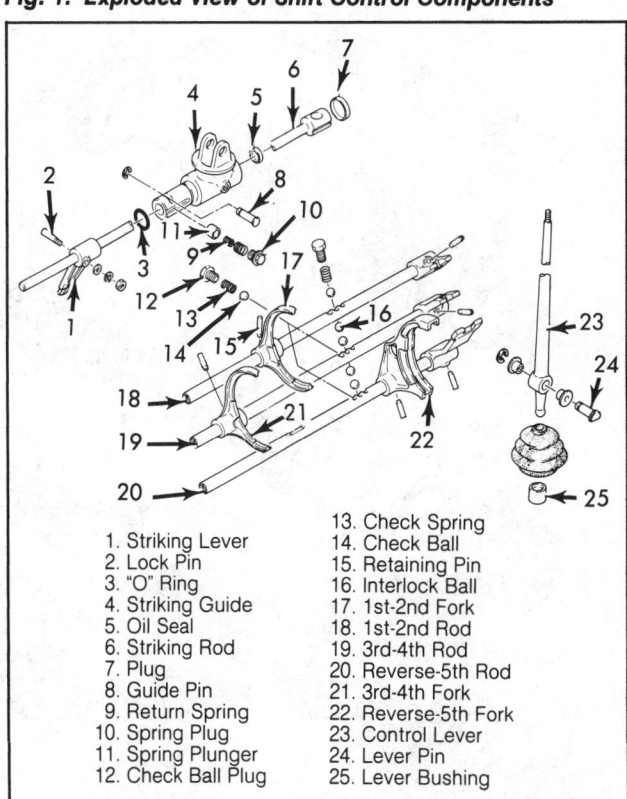

1. Striking Lever
2. Lock Pin
3. "O" Ring
4. Striking Guide
5. Oil Seal
6. Striking Rod
7. Plug
8. Guide Pin
9. Return Spring
10. Spring Plug
11. Spring Plunger
12. Check Ball Plug
13. Check Spring
14. Check Ball
15. Retaining Pin
16. Interlock Ball
17. 1st-2nd Fork
18. 1st-2nd Rod
19. 3rd-4th Rod
20. Reverse-5th Rod
21. 3rd-4th Fork
22. Reverse-5th Fork
23. Control Lever
24. Lever Pin
25. Lever Bushing

7-64

Manual Transmissions
DATSUN/NISSAN MAXIMA, PICKUP, 200SX & 280ZX
5-SPEED (Cont.)

Fig. 2: Exploded View of FS5W71B 5-Speed Transmission Assembly

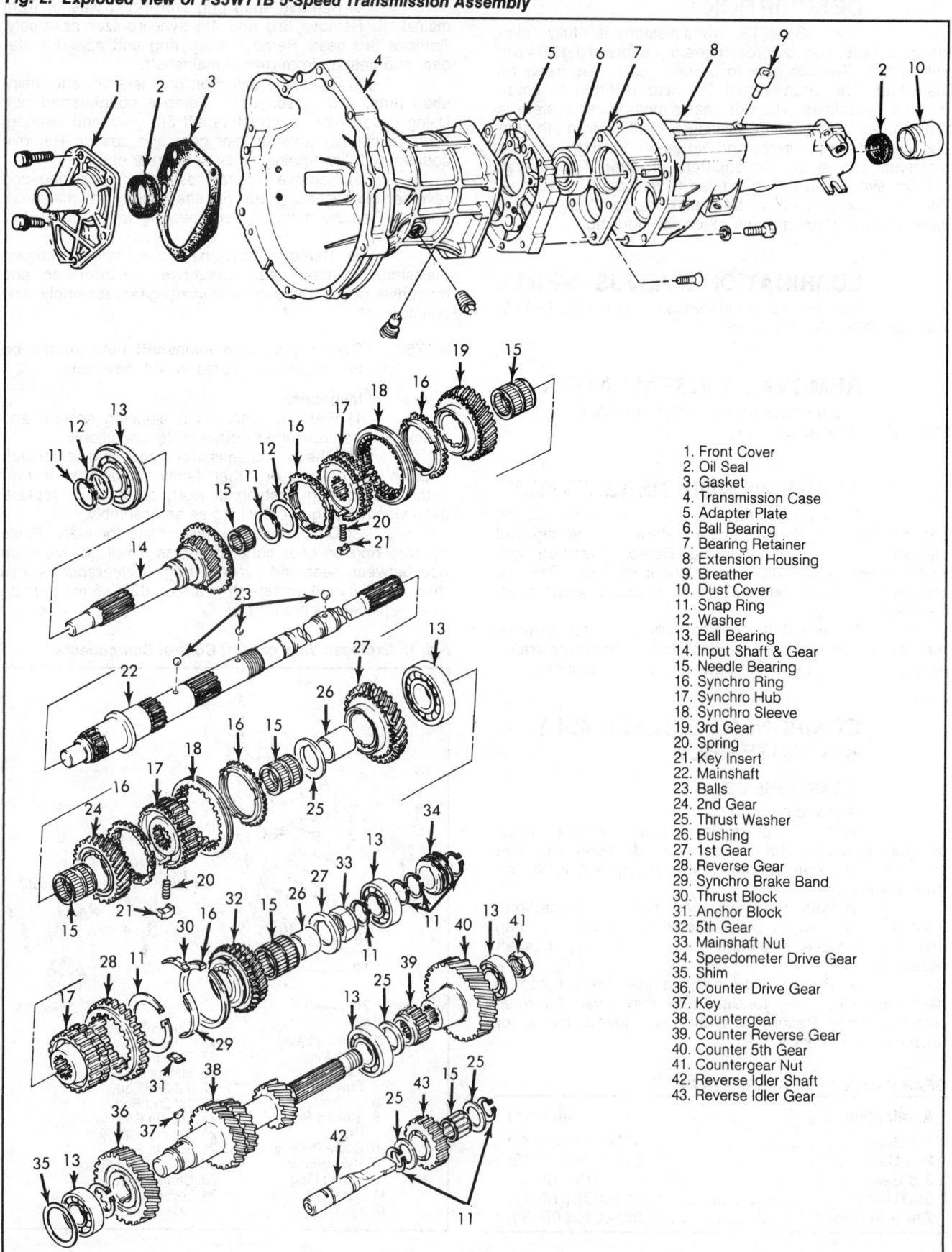

1. Front Cover
2. Oil Seal
3. Gasket
4. Transmission Case
5. Adapter Plate
6. Ball Bearing
7. Bearing Retainer
8. Extension Housing
9. Breather
10. Dust Cover
11. Snap Ring
12. Washer
13. Ball Bearing
14. Input Shaft & Gear
15. Needle Bearing
16. Synchro Ring
17. Synchro Hub
18. Synchro Sleeve
19. 3rd Gear
20. Spring
21. Key Insert
22. Mainshaft
23. Balls
24. 2nd Gear
25. Thrust Washer
26. Bushing
27. 1st Gear
28. Reverse Gear
29. Synchro Brake Band
30. Thrust Block
31. Anchor Block
32. 5th Gear
33. Mainshaft Nut
34. Speedometer Drive Gear
35. Shim
36. Counter Drive Gear
37. Key
38. Countergear
39. Counter Reverse Gear
40. Counter 5th Gear
41. Countergear Nut
42. Reverse Idler Shaft
43. Reverse Idler Gear

DATSUN/NISSAN MAXIMA, PICKUP, 200SX & 280ZX 5-SPEED (Cont.)

Fig. 3: Component Installation (on Mainshaft)

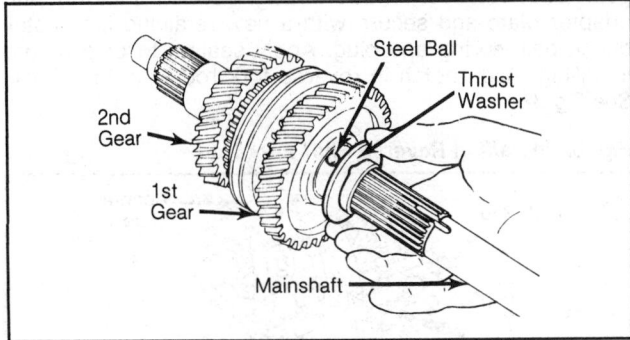

Reassembly

1) Install idle shaft and gear to adapter plate and mount in press. Press main and countershaft bearings into adapter plate.

2) Install 2nd gear needle bearing, 2nd gear synchro ring, 1st and 2nd gear synchro assembly, 1st gear synchro ring, 1st gear bushing, 1st gear, steel ball and thrust washer on mainshaft. *See Fig. 3.*

3) Place adapter plate on transmission press stand (KV31100401). *See Fig. 4.* Install mainshaft assembly to adapter plate. Make sure that bearing is placed squarely against shaft and press into place.

Fig. 4: Installing Mainshaft Assembly

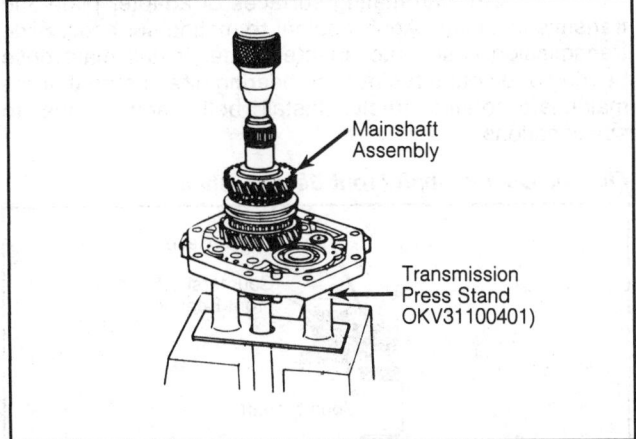

4) Install new Woodruff keys in grooves in countershaft and tap lightly until seated. Place adapter plate assembly and mainshaft assembly so that countershaft rear bearing rests on transmission press stand. Install countershaft into adapter plate.

5) Install 3rd gear needle bearing, mainshaft 3rd gear, synchro ring and 3rd and 4th gear synchro assembly on front of mainshaft. Install thrust washer and secure with a snap ring of the proper thickness. Snap rings are available in the following thicknesses: .055" (1.4 mm), .059" (1.5 mm) and .063" (1.6 mm).

6) Using transmission adapter plate (ST 23860000), press input shaft bearing onto input shaft, making sure that snap ring groove on shaft clears bearing. Place input bearing spacer on input shaft bearing and secure bearing with a snap ring that will eliminate end play. *See Main Drive Bearing Snap Ring Chart.*

MAIN DRIVE BEARING SNAP RINGS

No.	Thickness In. (mm)
1	.0680 (1.73)
2	.0709 (1.80)
3	.0736 (1.87)
4	.0764 (1.94)
5	.0791 (2.01)
6	.0819 (2.08)

Fig. 5: Installing Countershaft Front Bearing

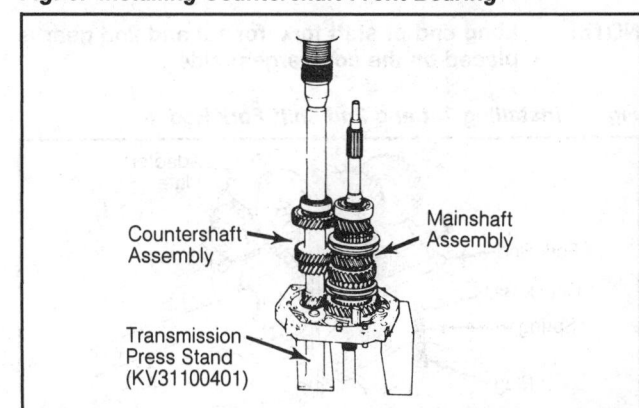

Fig. 6: Exploded View of Overdrive Gear Assembly

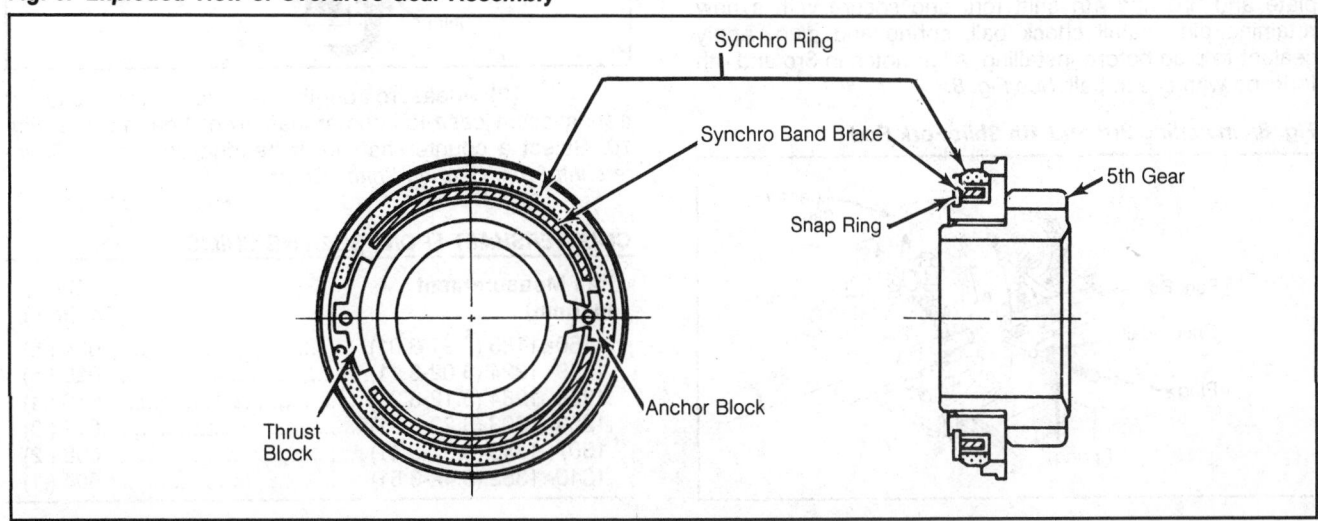

7-66

Manual Transmissions
DATSUN/NISSAN MAXIMA, PICKUP, 200SX & 280ZX
5-SPEED (Cont.)

7) On Maxima Diesel vehicles only, install washer on countershaft. Install torsional damper-to-counter drive gear. Insert coil spring end in .20" (5 mm) hole in sub gear. Insert other spring end into .20" (5 mm) hole in counter drive gear. Rotate sub gear 2 teeth counterclockwise and engage with input shaft gear.

8) On all models, mesh and install countershaft gear and input shaft, onto transmission shaft assemblies. *See Fig. 5.* Press countershaft front bearing onto countershaft.

9) Place adapter plate in a vise. Position synchronizer ring, band brake, thrust block and anchor block on overdrive clutch gear. Install circlip. *See Fig. 6.* Install snap ring, spacer, needle bearing, reverse idler gear, spacer and snap ring.

10) Install 5th and reverse synchronizer assembly, 5th gear, steel ball and thrust washer on the rear of mainshaft. Install counter reverse gear, counter 5th gear, bearing and new countershaft nut. Tighten mainshaft and countershaft nuts and stake to shafts.

11) Check each gears end play and adjust if necessary. *Refer to Gear End Play Chart for measurement limits.*

12) Install 1st and 2nd, 3rd and 4th shift forks into grooves on coupling sleeves. Slide 1st and 2nd fork rod through adapter plate and 1st and 2nd shifter fork. *See Fig. 7.* Secure rod to shift fork with a new retaining pin. Install check ball, check spring and plug. Apply sealant to plug before installing. Align notch in 1st and 2nd fork rod with check ball.

NOTE: Long end of shift fork, for 1st and 2nd gear is placed on the countergear side.

Fig. 7: Installing 1st and 2nd Shift Fork Rod

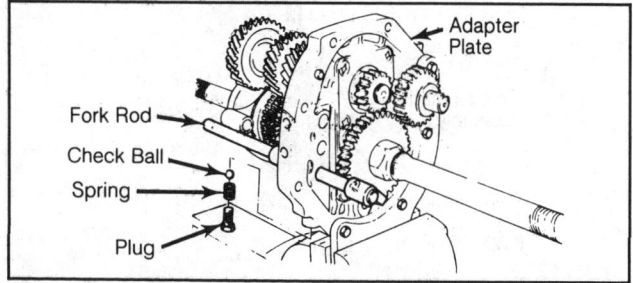

13) Slide 3rd and 4th fork rod through adapter plate and 3rd and 4th shift fork and secure with a new retaining pin. Install check ball, spring and plug. Apply sealant to plug before installing. Align notch in 3rd and 4th fork rod with check ball. *See Fig. 8.*

Fig. 8: Installing 3rd and 4th Shift Fork Rod

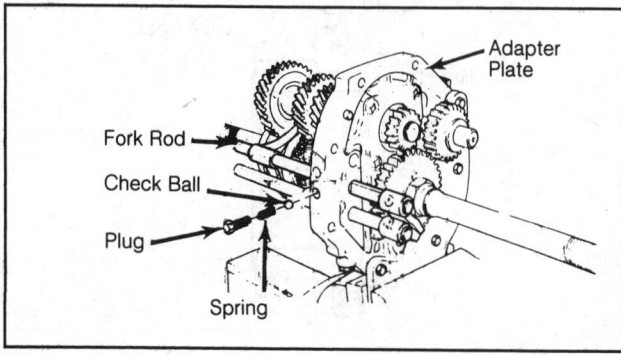

14) Place reverse shift fork in reverse idler gear. Slide reverse fork rod through reverse shift fork and adapter plate and secure with a new retaining pin. Install check ball, spring and plug. Apply sealant to plug before installing. Align notch in reverse fork rod with check ball. *See Fig. 9.*

Fig. 9: Installing Reverse Shift Fork Rod

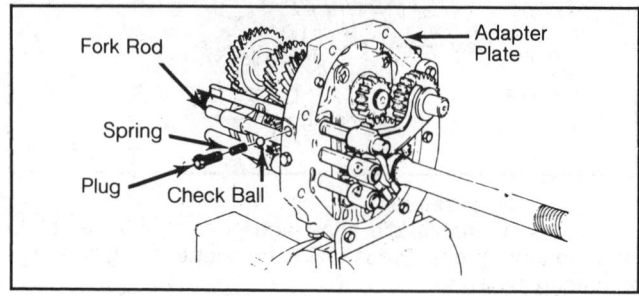

TRANSMISSION REASSEMBLY

1) Clean mating surfaces of extension and adapter plate, and apply sealant to mating surfaces. With fork rods in neutral position and shifter control fully to the left, gradually slide extension onto adapter plate. Make sure that gear change cross lever engages with fork rod bracket.

2) Clean mating surfaces of adapter plate and transmission case. Apply sealant to mating surfaces. Slide transmission case onto adapter plate. Install main drive bearing and countershaft front bearing. Make sure that the mainshaft rotates freely. Install bolts and torque to specifications.

Fig. 10: Countershaft Front Bearing Shim

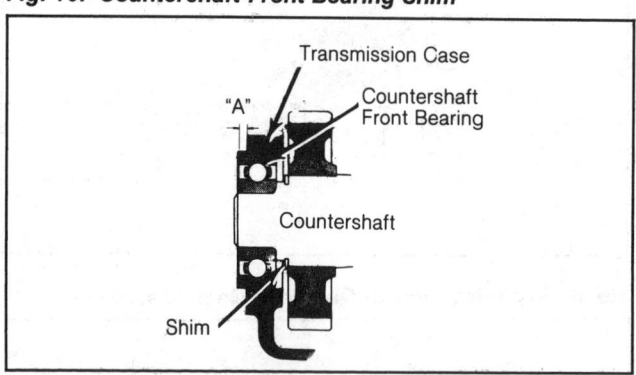

3) Measure depth "A" from front end of transmission case-to-countershaft front bearing. *See Fig. 10.* Select a countershaft front bearing shim from *Countershaft Front Bearing Shims Chart.*

COUNTERSHAFT FRONT BEARING SHIMS

"A" Measurement In. (mm)	Shims In. (mm)
.1150-.1185 (2.91-3.01)	.024 (.6)
.1189-.1224 (3.02-3.11)	.020 (.5)
.1228-.1264 (3.12-3.21)	.016 (.4)
.1268-.1303 (3.22-3.31)	.012 (.3)
.1307-.1343 (3.32-3.41)	.008 (.2)
.1346-.1382 (3.42-3.51)	.004 (.1)

DATSUN/NISSAN MAXIMA, PICKUP, 200SX & 280ZX
5-SPEED (Cont.)

4) Apply grease to shim to retain it on countershaft front bearing. Install front cover to transmission case. Apply grease to reverse select return plunger and install in rear extension. Install speedometer pinion assembly on rear extension. Apply grease to release bearing. Temporarily install control lever and shift control lever. Shift transmission through all gears to ensure correct operation.

TIGHTENING SPECIFICATIONS

Application	Ft. Lbs. (N.m)
Bearing Retainer-to-Adapter	12-17 (16-25)
Countergear Nut	72-94 (98-128)
Mainshaft Nut	101-123 (137-167)

Manual Transmissions

DATSUN/NISSAN SENTRA, STANZA & 310 4 & 5-SPEED

DESCRIPTION

The Datsun manual transaxle assembly contains the clutch, transmission and final drive (differential). Transmission is a 4-speed or 5-speed unit, fully synchronized in all forward gears. All forward gears are helically cut and in constant mesh.

Final drive is directly coupled to transmission and housed in transmission case. Transmission and final drive are lubricated from a common oil supply. Constant velocity (CV) joints are used on both ends of drive axle shafts.

LUBRICATION & ADJUSTMENT

See the appropriate article in MANUAL TRANS-MISSION SERVICING Section.

SERVICE (IN-VEHICLE)

WHEEL BEARINGS

Removal (Sentra & Stanza)

1) Raise and support vehicle. Remove wheel and tire. Remove brake caliper. Pry cotter pin out of hub. Loosen, but do not remove, wheel hub nut from drive shaft while holding wheel hub against rotation. Remove tie-rod end from steering knuckle.

2) Remove lower ball joint and discard nut. Drain gear oil and remove drive shaft. Do not damage oil seal when removing axle shaft. If axle shaft oil seals in transaxle are suspected of leakage, they may be replaced at this time. Insert a shaft into each side of differential to prevent side gears from falling into differential case.

3) Remove knuckle attaching bolts. Remove hub, knuckle and drive shaft as a unit. Remove hub nut and withdraw axle shaft from hub. Separate wheel hub and knuckle using a slide hammer puller. Remove bolts securing hub to rotor.

4) Remove spacer and inner race of outboard wheel bearing from hub using a puller. Remove and discard outboard grease seal. Remove and discard inboard grease seal. Remove outer races of both inboard and outboard wheel bearings from knuckle using a puller.

Installation (Sentra & Stanza)

To install, reverse removal procedure and note the following:

1) When knuckle is replaced, a new spacer must be selected. Install both outer races into knuckle and measure the distance between the 2 races. Subtract .0035" (.09 mm) from this distance to obtain shim thickness. Shims are available in thicknesses from .2918" (7.410 mm) to .3319" (8.430 mm) in increments of .0023" (.060 mm).

2) After tightening hub nut to specifications, force required to turn wheel hub after assembly should be 3-10 lbs. (1.4-4.9 kg). If proper bearing preload cannot be obtained or if play still exists, spacer must be replaced with one of larger or smaller dimension.

Removal (310)

1) Raise and support front of vehicle. Remove wheel. Disconnect brake line from caliper, plug line and remove caliper assembly.

Fig. 1: Sentra & Stanza Steering Knuckle Assembly

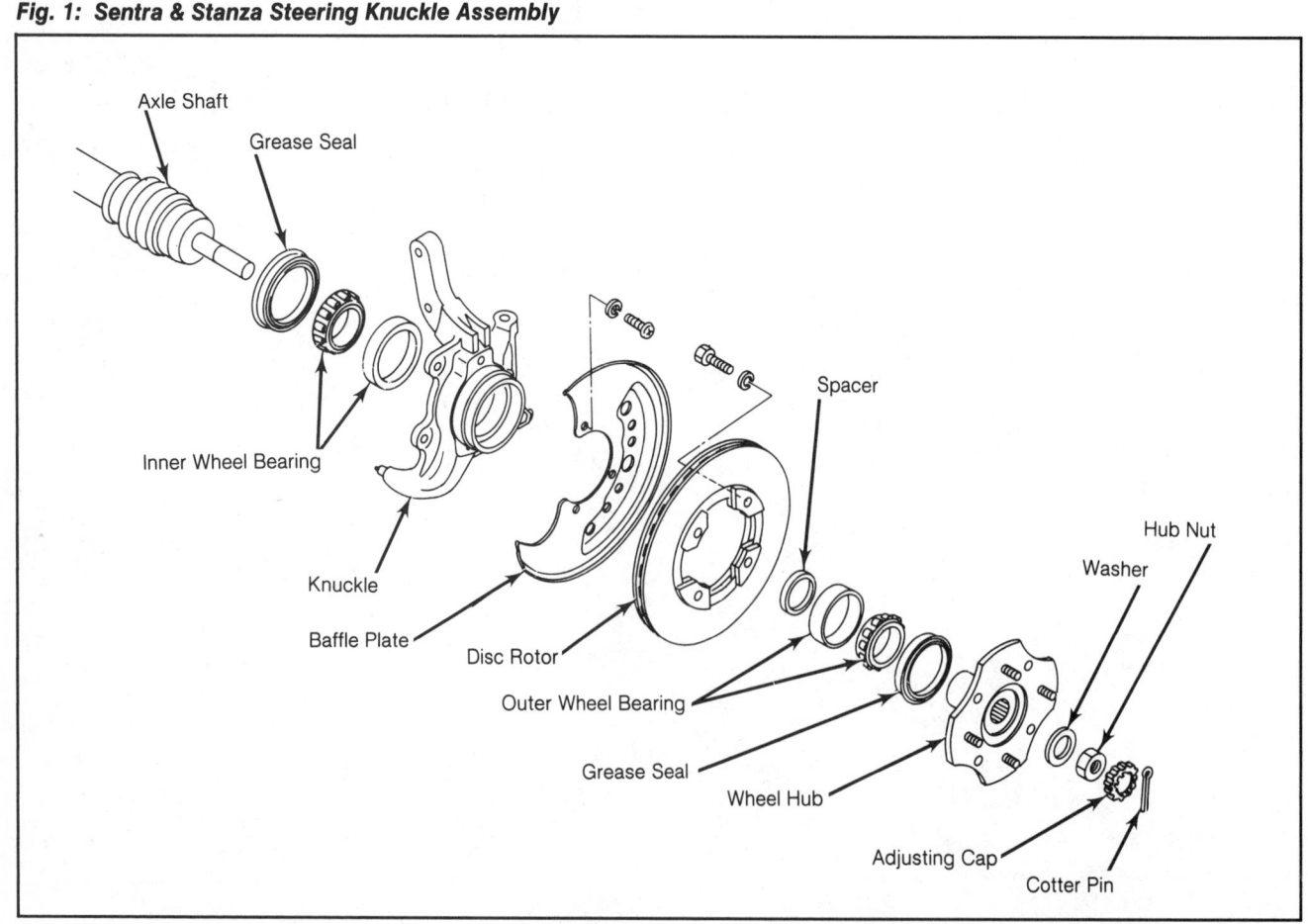

DATSUN/NISSAN SENTRA, STANZA & 310 4 & 5-SPEED (Cont.)

Fig. 2: Sentra & Stanza Wheel Bearing Installation

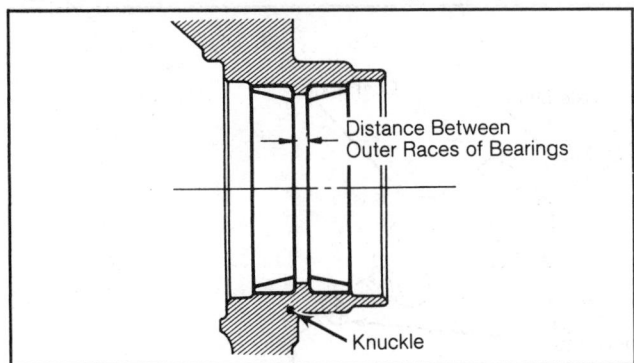

2) Remove cotter pin, nut and washer from axle shaft. Using puller, remove stub axle and brake rotor from axle shaft as an assembly. Remove output flange-to-axle shaft attaching bolts and remove axle shaft assembly from vehicle. If axle shaft oil seals in transaxle are suspected of leakage they may be replaced at this time.

3) Remove cotter pin and ball joint stud nut. Using ball joint driver and hammer, drive ball joint out of steering knuckle. Remove 4 bolts securing knuckle to strut and remove knuckle from vehicle.

4) Remove bolts attaching rotor to stub axle and press stub axle out of rotor. Using press or bearing puller, remove outer bearing and seal from stub axle. Use a hammer and brass drift to drive outer and inner bearing races out of knuckle.

Fig. 3: Exploded View of Datsun/Nissan 310 Steering Knuckle and Stub Axle Assembly

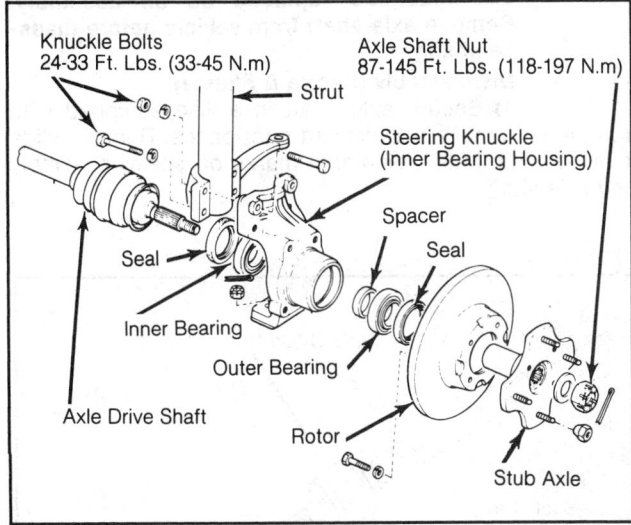

Installation (310)

1) Using installer tools, press or drive inner and outer bearing races into steering knuckle.

2) It is now necessary to determine required thickness of bearing spacer. Place outer bearing on base (KV40100700-3) and place steering knuckle over it so bearing seats in outer race. Then, slide inner bearing over dummy shaft (KV40100700-1), and place shaft bearing in knuckle with end of shaft in outer bearing in inner race.

3) Slide weight (KV40100700-2) over dummy shaft and down onto knuckle. Turn knuckle back and forth to seat bearing. Assemble dial indicator with contact button resting on top of dummy shaft, and set indicator to zero. Pull upward on shaft until it reaches end of travel, rotate it 1 revolution and record maximum deflection of indicator needle.

Fig. 4: Determining Required Spacer Thickness

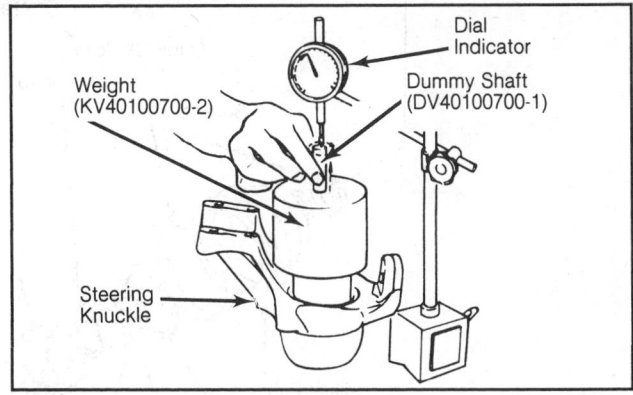

This applies to 310 models only.

4) To determine required spacer thickness, add recorded dial indicator reading to metric thickness dimension stamped on side of flange on end of dummy shaft.

5) Select required spacer. Spacers are available in 18 sizes, ranging from .291-.293" (7.38-7.44 mm) to .331-.333" (8.40-8.46 mm) in .002" (.06 mm) increments. For size identification, spacers are numbered "05" (smallest) through "22" (largest).

6) Pack grease seals and bearings with bearing grease. Install outer grease seal and press outer bearing onto stub axle. Install rotor on stub axle. Place knuckle in position on stub axle, install spacer and press inner bearing onto stub axle and knuckle assembly until it just bottoms. Install inner seal.

7) Clamp axle shaft in a vise with splined end up. Set stub axle and knuckle on shaft and align splines. Using a soft hammer, tap on stub axle until washer and nut can be installed. Tighten nut to specification.

8) Spin assembly in both directions to check for free rotation. Check bearing preload at hub nut. If end play is present or preload is less than specification, install smaller spacer. If preload is greater than specification, install larger spacer.

9) To install knuckle on vehicle, reverse removal procedures and bleed brake system.

AXLE SHAFTS

Removal & Installation (Sentra & Stanza)
See Wheel Bearing Removal and Installation procedures.

Removal (310)

1) Raise and support front of vehicle. Remove wheel. Remove cotter pin, nut and washer from axle shaft. Remove output flange-to-axle shaft attaching bolts and place shaft on steering rack.

2) Using puller, force axle shaft out of stub axle and knuckle assembly. Remove shaft from vehicle. If axle shaft oil seals in transaxle are suspected of leakage they may be replaced at this time.

CAUTION: Take care not to damage grease seals when removing or installing axle shaft.

DATSUN/NISSAN SENTRA, STANZA & 310 4 & 5-SPEED (Cont.)

Fig. 5: Sentra & Stanza Axle Shaft Components

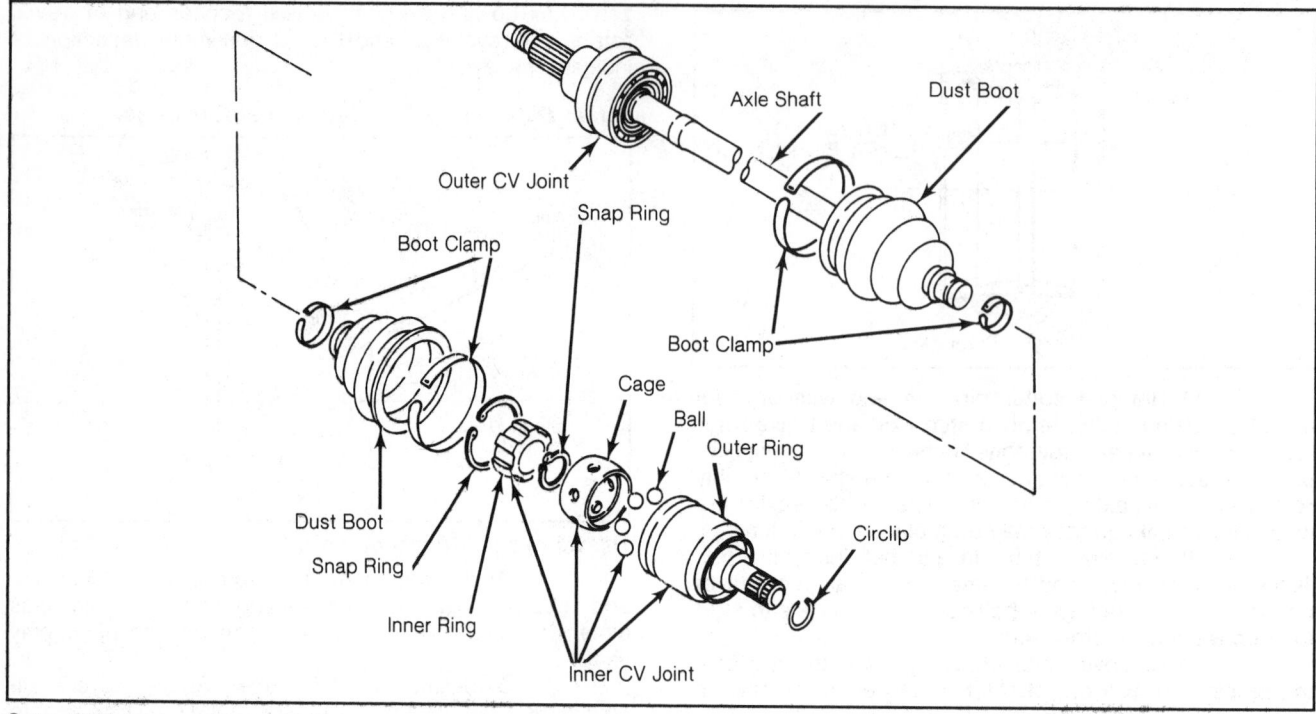

Outer CV joint is not serviceable.

Installation (310)

Insert splined end of axle shaft into stub axle and knuckle and align splines. If necessary, lightly hammer on flanged end of shaft until threads are exposed. Install washer and tighten shaft nut to specification. Check bearing preload at nut. If not as specified, adjust as described in *Wheel Bearings — Installation* in this article. Install output flange-to-axle shaft attaching bolts.

NOTE: **Install "O" rings between output flange and axle shaft before connecting.**

CONSTANT VELOCITY (CV) JOINTS

NOTE: **Inner CV joint can be disassembled and serviced, outer CV joint is non-serviceable and must be replaced as an assembly. Remove axle shaft from vehicle before disassembling.**

Disassembly (Sentra & Stanza)

1) Secure axle shaft in a vise equipped with soft jaws. Remove and discard boot bands. Remove slide joint housing. Make alignment marks on spider assembly and axle shaft.

Fig. 6: Datsun/Nissan 310 Axle Shaft

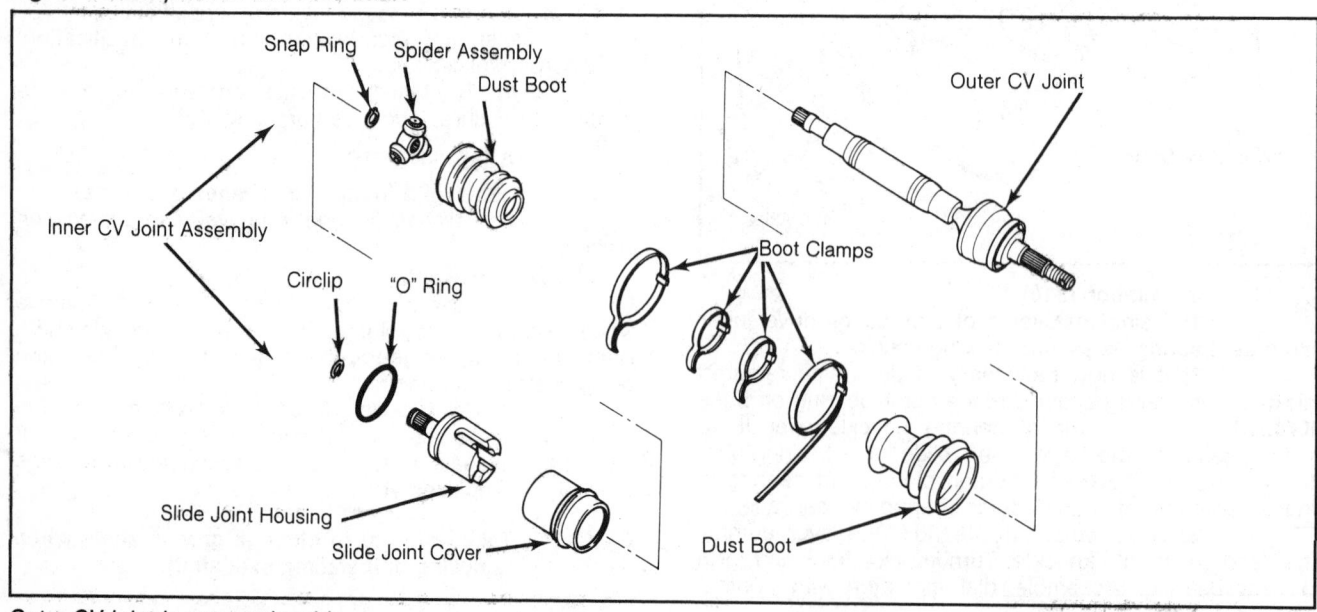

Outer CV joint is not serviceable.

DATSUN/NISSAN SENTRA, STANZA & 310 4 & 5-SPEED (Cont.)

2) Remove and discard snap ring from end of axle shaft and press shaft out of spider assembly. Remove boot and boot band from shaft. Remove and discard slide joint cover by cutting edge of cover and then bending cover off of joint. Remove and discard "O" ring.

Fig. 7: Sentra & Stanza CV Joint Disassembly

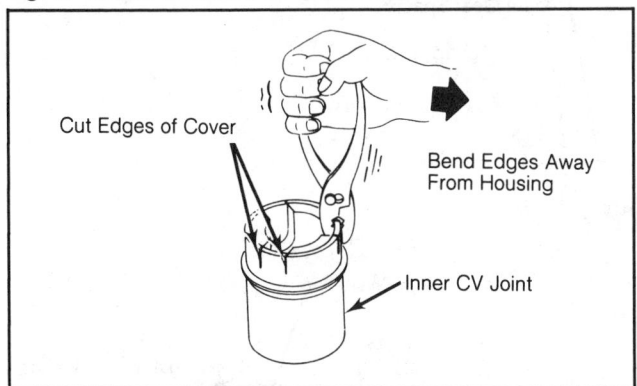

Reassembly (Sentra & Stanza)
1) Apply a coat of grease to a new "O" ring. Install "O" ring onto slide housing. Install a new cover onto housing and bend over top edge of cover around entire circumference of housing. Apply sealant to bent over edge of cover.

2) Slide boot and a new small boot band onto shaft. Secure axle shaft in a vise equipped with soft jaws. With chamfered side of spider facing shaft, match up alignment marks and install spider onto shaft.

3) Install new snap ring onto shaft with round side of snap ring facing spider assembly. Pack joint with 6.35 oz. (180 g) of grease. Install new large boot band onto boot. Set boot length to 4.17" (106 mm) and allow air pressure to equalize between inside and outside of boot. Install new small boot clamp onto boot.

Disassembly (310)
Place axle shaft in a soft-jawed vise. Cut large clamp off of inner boot and slide boot back on shaft. Remove large snap ring and slide outer race off of shaft. Remove balls from cage. Turn cage 1/2 turn and slide off of inner race. Remove small snap ring and tap inner race off of shaft.

Reassembly (310)
To reassemble, reverse disassembly procedure and note the following: Repack CV joint with grease and install new clamp on boot.

TRANSAXLE REMOVAL & INSTALLATION

See the appropriate article in MANUAL TRANS-MISSION REMOVAL Section.

Fig. 8: Exploded View of Transaxle Case Assembly

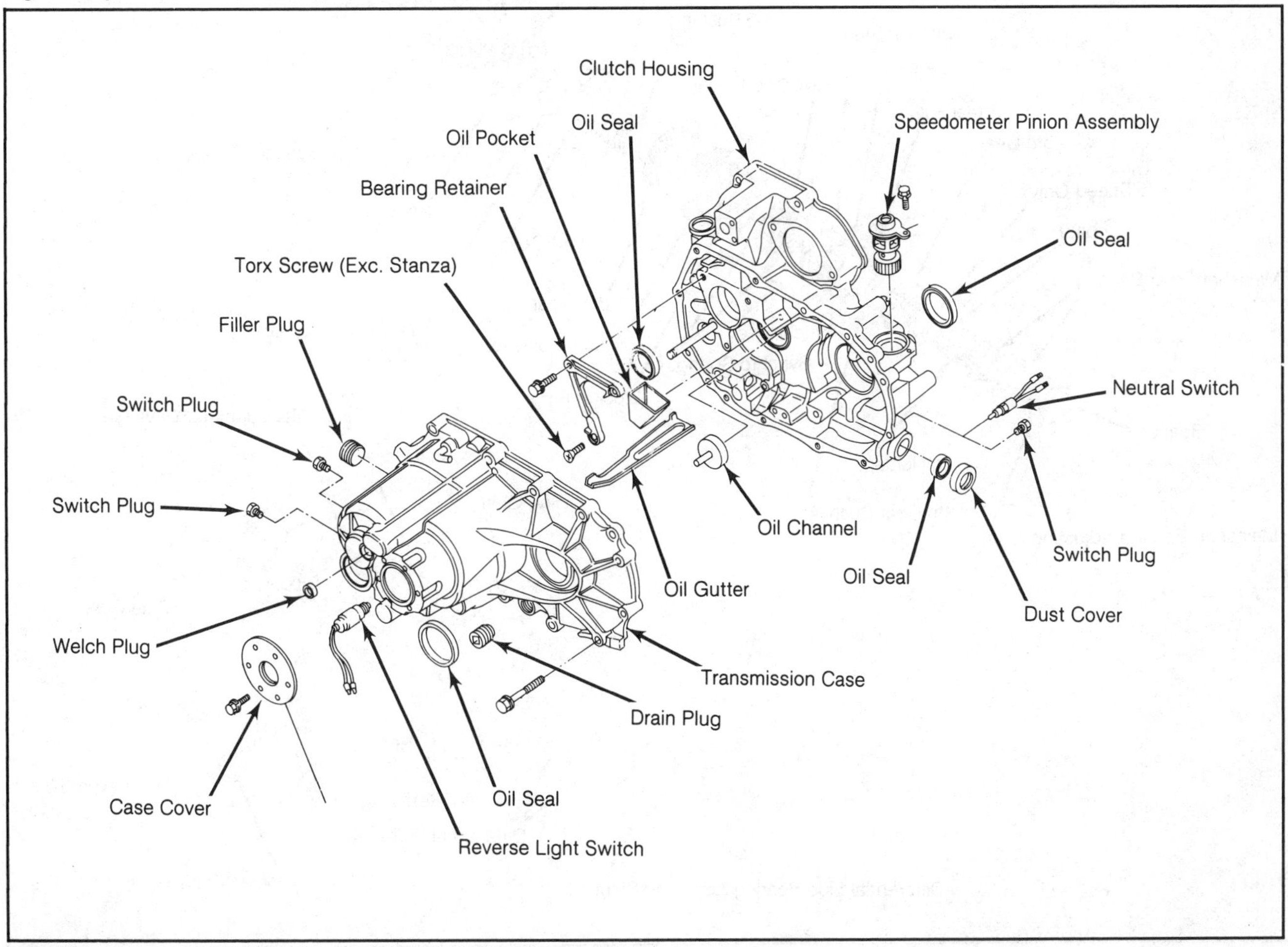

Sentra and 310 shown; Stanza uses different bearing retainer.

Manual Transmissions

DATSUN/NISSAN SENTRA, STANZA & 310 4 & 5-SPEED (Cont.)

Fig. 9: Exploded View of Transaxle Gears

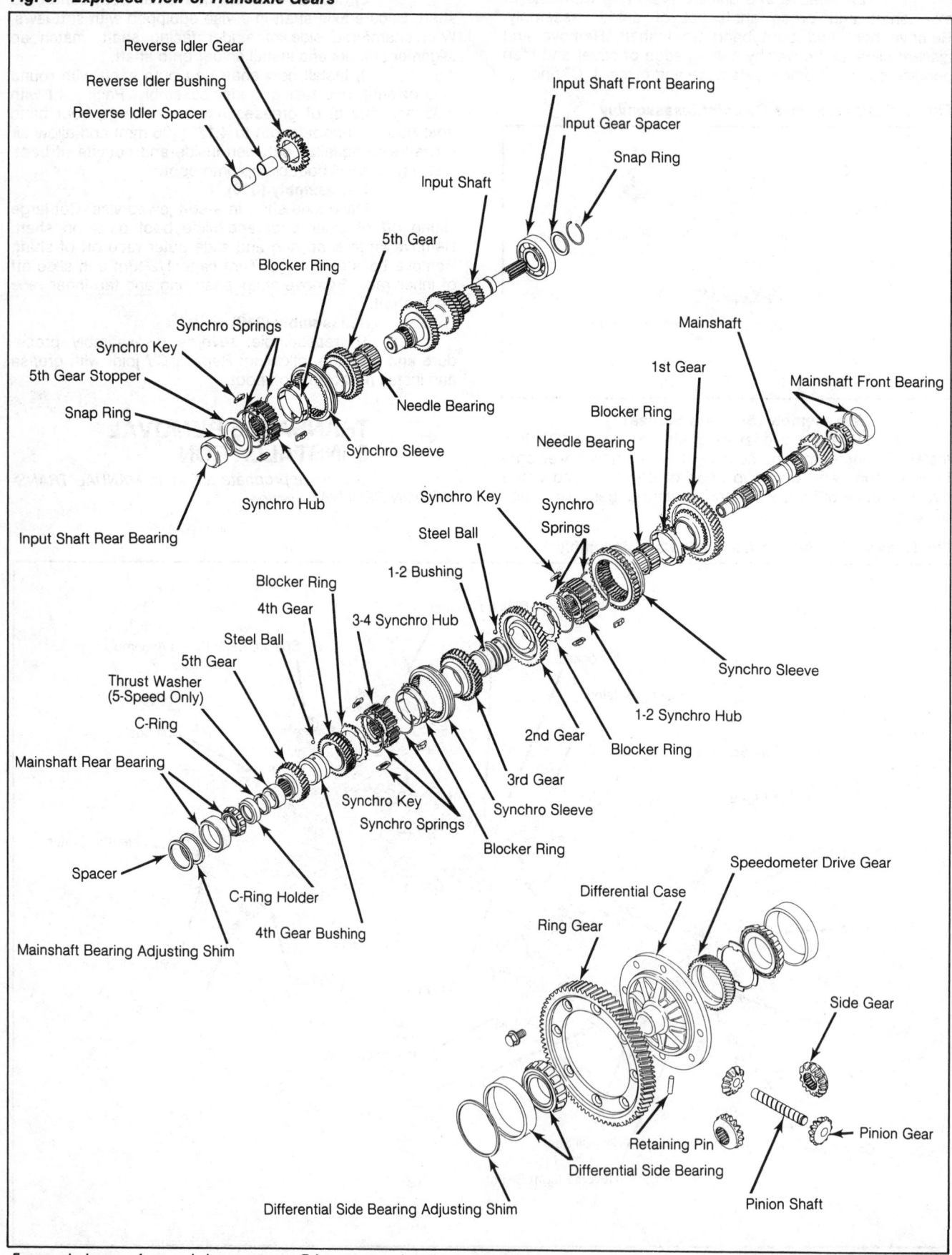

5-speed shown; 4-speed does not use 5th gear or related components.

DATSUN/NISSAN SENTRA, STANZA & 310 4 & 5-SPEED (Cont.)

TRANSAXLE DISASSEMBLY & REASSEMBLY

TRANSAXLE CASE
Disassembly
1) Wipe dirt and grease off of transaxle. Drain oil from transaxle case. Remove transmission case attaching bolts. Using a plastic hammer, tap the transmission case to dislodge it from the clutch housing.

2) Remove transmission case from clutch housing by lifting (and slightly tilting on 5-speed transaxles) away from clutch housing. Remove back-up light switch and oil gutter from transmission case.

3) Remove input shaft rear bearing. Remove case cover and mainshaft bearing adjusting shim and spacer. Remove mainshaft rear bearing outer race and differential side bearing outer race.

4) Clean transmission case and inspect for cracks or cavities. Check all gasket surfaces for nicks, projections or excess sealant. Replace any seals suspected of leakage.

Reassembly
1) Press differential side bearing and mainshaft rear bearing outer races into transmission case. Install input shaft needle bearing. Apply sealer to input shaft access welch plug and install plug into case. Install oil gutter.

2) Apply sealer to back-up light switch and install in transmission case. If transmission case is replaced, adjust differential side bearing and mainshaft rotary frictional force by selecting proper shims.

3) Before installing a new transmission case, determine appropriate thickness of differential side bearing adjusting shim with both main and input shafts removed from case. See Adjustments — Differential in this article.

4) After properly adjusting the bearings, clean mating surface of transmission case and clutch housing and apply sealant to clutch housing. When applying sealant, apply an even, continuous coat to prevent leakage.

5) Assemble transmission case onto clutch housing noting that 1 of the 12 attaching bolts is longer than the others. Install case cover with convex side facing out.

6) Measure gear rotary frictional force and make sure that gear moves smoothly and without binding. See Adjustments in this article. Make sure that gears shift smoothly. Apply sealant to drain plug and install in transmission case.

CLUTCH HOUSING
Disassembly
1) Wipe dirt and grease off of outside of transaxle. Drain oil. Remove transmission case. Remove reverse idler spacer and shift fork shaft. Remove 5th, 3rd and 4th shift forks without dropping shifter caps.

2) Remove control bracket with 1st and 2nd shift fork. On 5-speed transaxles, be careful not to lose detent ball, spring or shift caps.

3) On Sentra and 310 models, remove the 3 screws securing bearing retainer to clutch housing. One of the screws is a torx-head screw and requires the use of an offset torx-bit screwdriver for removal. Do not remove reverse idler shaft from clutch housing.

4) Turn clutch housing so that bottom side faces down. Lightly tap on engine side of input shaft with a plastic hammer to dislodge shaft from housing. Remove mainshaft and input shaft as an assembly.

5) When removing gearshafts, pull straight away from housing to avoid breaking plastic oil channel. Also, make sure that differential does not fall out when gearshafts are removed and that input shaft oil seal is not damaged by input shaft splines. Remove reverse idler gear and differential.

Fig. 10: Exploded View of Shift Mechanism

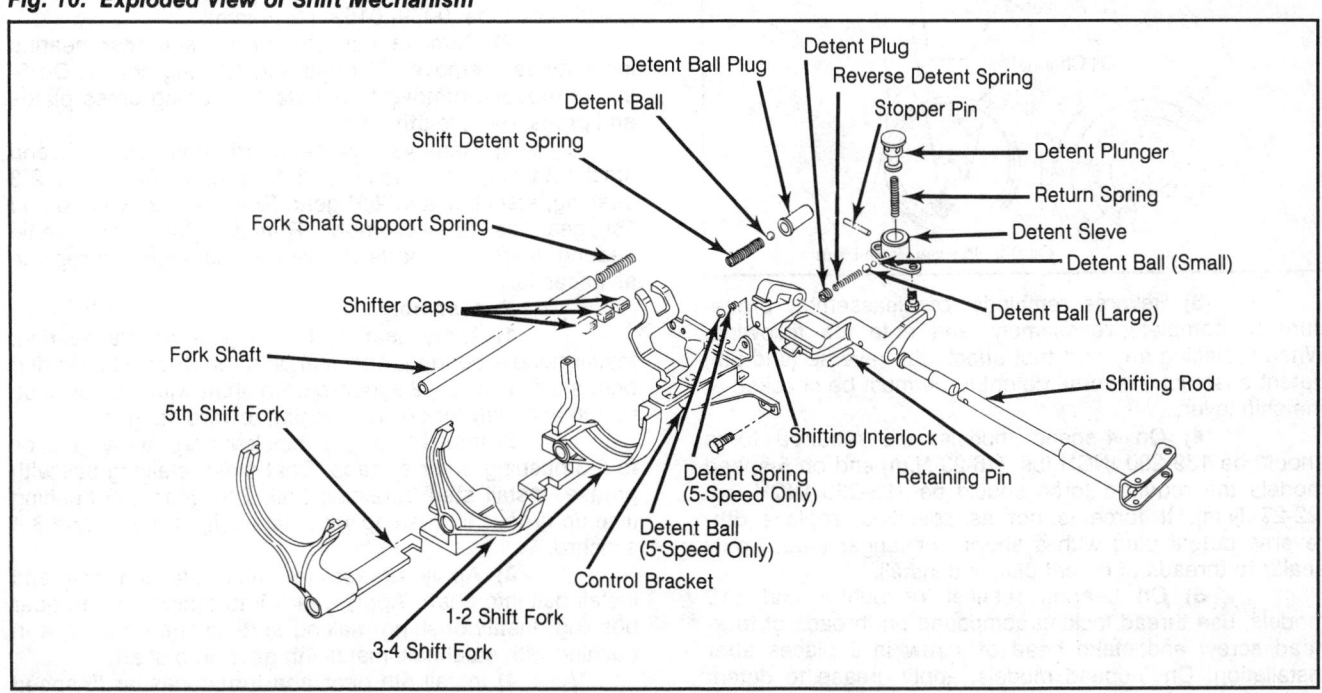

Stanza and 310 shown; Sentra similar.

DATSUN/NISSAN SENTRA, STANZA & 310 4 & 5-SPEED (Cont.)

6) On Stanza models, remove mainshaft and differential. When removing mainshaft, pull straight out from housing to avoid damaging plastic oil channel.

7) Remove input shaft bearing retainer bolts. Turn clutch housing so that bottom side faces down. Lightly tap on engine side of input shaft with a plastic hammer to dislodge shaft from housing.

8) Remove input shaft together with bearing retainer and reverse idler gear. Make sure that input shaft oil seal is not damaged by input shaft splines. Do not remove reverse idler shaft from housing.

9) On all models, remove oil pocket, shift detent ball, detent springs and detent ball plug. Drive roll pin out of shifting rod. Remove shifting rod, shifting lever and shifting interlock. Tape edges of shifting rod to prevent seal from being damaged when rod is removed.

10) Remove reverse and 5th detent plug, detent balls and detent spring. Remove 5th and reverse detent assembly. Remove clutch control shaft, release bearing and clutch lever.

11) Remove mainshaft bearing outer race and differential side bearing outer race. Remove oil channel. Clean clutch housing and check for cracks or cavities. Check mating surfaces of clutch housing for nicks, projections or excess sealer. Replace any seals suspected of leakage.

Reassembly

1) Install a new oil channel making sure that channel oil groove faces housing oil pocket. Install mainshaft bearing outer race and differential side bearing outer race.

2) Install clutch control shaft, clutch release bearing and clutch lever. Install oil pocket and make sure that oil flows from oil pocket to oil channel.

Fig. 11: Checking Lubrication Passage

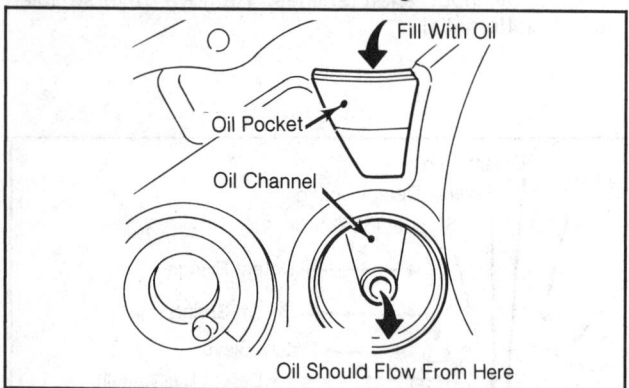

3) Reverse remainder of disassembly procedure to complete reassembly, and note the following: When replacing any part that affects the reverse (and 5th) detent assembly, reverse detent force must be checked at the shift lever.

4) On 4-speed models, the required force should be 139-200 INCH lbs. (16-23 N.m) and on 5-speed models the required force should be 195-239 INCH lbs. (22-27 N.m). If force is not as specified, replace 5th-reverse detent plug with a shorter or longer plug. Apply sealer to threads of detent plug and install.

5) On bearing retainer of Sentra and 310 models, use thread locking compound on threads of torxhead screw and stake head of screw in 2 places after installation. On 5-speed models, apply grease to detent ball, then install detent ball and spring in shifting interlock.

6) Apply grease onto shifter caps prior to installing control bracket. Apply grease to support spring to prevent spring from falling. Install spring and fork shaft into housing. Measure gear rotary frictional force and ensure that gears move smoothly and without binding. *See Adjustments in this article.*

COMPONENT DISASSEMBLY & REASSEMBLY

INPUT SHAFT

Disassembly

1) With input shaft removed from transaxle, remove snap ring and spacer from front of input shaft and pull front bearing off of shaft. Measure 5th input gear end play.

2) End play should be .0071-.0161" (.18-.41 mm). Remove snap ring and 5th gear stopper. Remove 5th gear synchro and 5th gear. Inspect all parts for wear or damage. Replace as necessary.

Reassembly

1) Install 5th gear and 5th gear synchronizer onto shaft. Install 5th gear stopper onto shaft. Select and install proper thickness snap ring to obtain snap ring groove clearance of 0-.004" (0-.1 mm).

2) Check 5th gear end play. If end play is not within .0071-.0161" (.18-.41 mm), recheck all parts for wear or damage and replace as necessary. Install bearing retainer on Stanza models only. Install input shaft front bearing with a press.

3) Install input shaft spacer. Select and install proper thickness snap ring to obtain snap ring groove clearance of 0-.004" (0-.1 mm).

MAINSHAFT

Disassembly

1) With mainshaft removed from transaxle, measure end play of gears. End play at 1st gear should be .0071-.0122" (.18-.31 mm). End play at 2nd, 3rd and 4th gears should be .0079-.0157" (.2-.4 mm).

2) Remove mainshaft front and rear bearing inner races. Remove "C" rings and "C" ring holder. On 5-speed models, remove thrust washer. Using press plates and press, remove 5th gear.

3) Remove 4th gear, 4th gear bushing and steel retaining ball. Remove 3-4 synchro, 3rd gear, 2-3 bushing, steel ball and 2nd gear. Remove 1-2 synchro and 1st gear as an assembly. Remove 1st gear needle bearing. Inspect all parts for wear or damage and replace as necessary.

Reassembly

1) Apply gear oil to 1st gear needle bearing. Install needle bearing, 1st gear and 1st gear blocker ring onto shaft. Install 1-2 synchro onto shaft with shallow side of hub and shift fork groove facing toward 1st gear.

2) Install 2nd gear blocker ring. Apply gear oil to 2-3 bushing outer surface. Coat steel retaining ball with grease. Install steel retaining ball, 2nd gear, 2-3 bushing (line up groove in bushing with steel ball), 3rd gear and 3-4 synchro.

3) Apply grease to steel retaining ball and install ball into shaft. Apply gear oil to outside of 4th gear bushing. Install bushing making sure to line up groove in bushing with steel ball. Install 4th gear onto shaft.

4) Install 5th gear and thrust washer (5-speed only). Select and install proper thickness "C" ring to obtain

DATSUN/NISSAN SENTRA, STANZA & 310 4 & 5-SPEED (Cont.)

shaft groove clearance of 0-.004" (0-.1 mm). Install mainshaft front and rear bearing inner races.

5) Measure end play of gears. End play at 1st gear should be .0071-.0122" (.18-.31 mm). End play at 2nd, 3rd and 4th gears should be .0079-.0157" (.2-.4 mm). If end play is not as specified, recheck all parts for wear or damage and replace as necessary.

SYNCHRONIZERS
Disassembly
Remove springs and keys from synchro assembly. Slide sleeve off of hub. Inspect all parts for damage or wear and replace as necessary. Blocker ring to gear clearance should be no less than .028" (.7 mm).

Reassembly
To reassemble, reverse disassembly procedure and note the following: Make sure that open portion of springs are offset.

DIFFERENTIAL
Disassembly
1) With differential removed from transaxle, take out ring gear retaining bolts. Remove ring gear from differential. Using a punch, drive out pinion shaft retaining pin.

2) Remove pinion shaft from differential. Remove differential pinion gears and side gears. Using press plates and a press, remove differential side bearings.

3) Remove speedometer drive gear and stop ring from differential. Check all parts for wear or damage and replace as necessary.

Reassembly
1) Install speedometer drive gear and stop ring. Press on differential side bearings. Install differential pinion gears and pinion shaft into differential. Install pinion shaft retaining pin flush with differential case. Install side gears directly opposite each other against pinion gears.

2) Simultaneously rotate side gears into their proper position in differential case. Measure side gear clearance using a shaft inserted into side gear and a dial indicator.

3) With shaft positioned against back of side gear and dial indicator tip on end of shaft, move side gear up and down and note measurement. Perform measurement on both side gears.

4) Clearance should be no more than .020" (.5 mm). If clearance exceeds specification, replace pinion gears, side gears and case as a set. Apply thread locking compound to ring gear bolts and install ring gear.

ADJUSTMENTS

MAINSHAFT
Apply gear oil to mainshaft rear bearing outer race. Install outer race and spacer. Using a depth gauge, measure distance from case surface to spacer. Add .008" (.2 mm) to measurement to obtain correct shim thickness. Install proper shim between bearing outer race and spacer. Install cover and tighten bolts to specifications.

DIFFERENTIAL
1) Ensure that differential side bearing rotary frictional force is within specifications. Shift into 4th gear

Fig. 12: Mainshaft Preload Adjustment

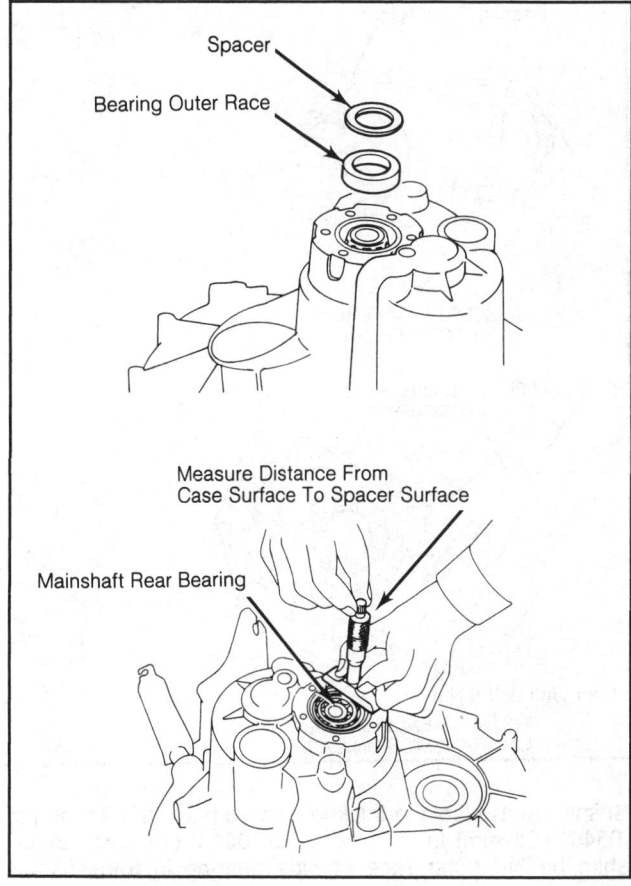

and turn input shaft at least 10 times to seat bearings. Insert wrench adapter (KV38105900) into differential through axle shaft hole.

2) Connect a torque wrench to wrench adapter. Measure the force required to rotate differential assembly. Required force should be 65-95 INCH lbs. (7.5-11 N.m). Fluctuations in required force should be no more 9 INCH lbs. (1 N.m). If specifications are not met, change differential side bearing shim thickness to obtain desired result.

3) If the differential, side bearings, clutch housing, or transmission case have been replaced, the housing must be measured for a new differential side bearing shim. Clean mating surfaces of clutch housing and transmission case with solvent.

4) Install differential assembly and side bearing outer race into clutch housing. Hold bearing in place and turn differential several turns to seat bearings. Attach measuring plate (KV38105810) to clutch housing and side bearing.

5) Using a depth gauge, measure distance from upper surface of side bearing outer race to surface of measuring plate. Subtract .9449" (24 mm) from measured distance to obtain bearing height. Attach measuring plate to surface of transmission case and measure distance from bottom of side bearing outer race bore to surface of measuring plate. Subtract .9449" (24 mm) from measured distance to obtain bore depth.

6) To obtain shim thickness, subtract bearing height from bore depth and add .012" (.3 mm) to the result.

DATSUN/NISSAN SENTRA, STANZA & 310 4 & 5-SPEED (Cont.)

Fig. 13: Differential Side Bearing Preload Adjustment

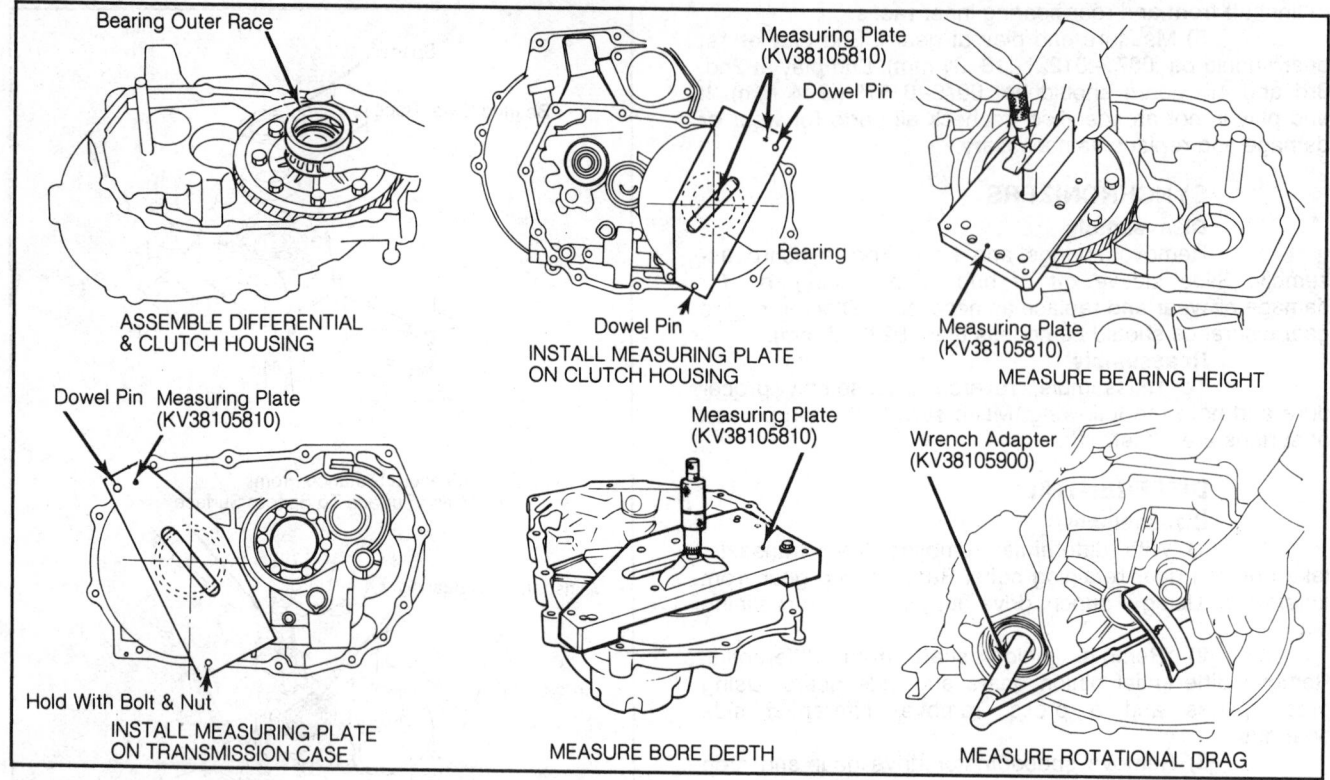

Shims are available in thicknesses from .0173" (.44 mm) to .0346" (.88 mm) in increments of .0016" (.04 mm). Install shim behind outer race of side bearing in transmission case. With differential in place, assemble transmission case onto clutch housing.

7) Insert wrench adapter (KV38105900) into differential through axle shaft hole. Connect a torque wrench to wrench adapter. Rotate differential at least 10 times to seat bearings. Measure the force required to rotate differential assembly.

8) With input shaft and mainshaft removed, required force should be 43-65 INCH lbs. (5-7.5 N.m). Fluctuations in required force should be no more 9 INCH lbs. (1 N.m). If specifications are not met, change differential side bearing shim thickness to obtain desired result. After obtaining correct preload, separate transmission case from clutch housing and install remainder of transaxle.

TIGHTENING SPECIFICATIONS

Application	Ft. Lbs. (N.m)
Clutch Hsg.-to-Trans. Case	12-15 (16-21)
Bearing Retainer-to-Clutch Hsg.	12-15 (16-21)
5th-Rev. Detent Plug	14-18 (19-25)
Ring Gear Bolts	54-65 (74-88)
Filler Plug	18-25 (25-34)
Drain Plug	18-25 (25-34)
Back-Up Light Switch	14-22 (20-29)
Neutral Switch	14-22 (20-29)
Switch Plug	11-14 (15-20)
Transaxle-to-Engine	12-15 (16-21)
	INCH Lbs. (N.m)
Speedometer Gear	32-44 (4-5)
Trans. Case Cover Bolts	55-73 (6-8)
Control Brkt.-to-Clutch Hsg.	55-73 (6-8)
5th-Rev. Detent Assy.	55-73 (6-8)

DATSUN/NISSAN 210 & PICKUP 4-SPEED

TRANSMISSION IDENTIFICATION

A center support-type transmission is used in both vehicles. F4W56A transmission is used on 210 models equipped with 1.2L engine only. F4W60L transmission is used on 210 models equipped with the 1.5L engines. F4W71B transmission is used on Pickup models. All transmissions may be identified by a serial number stamped on a pad located on top of clutch housing.

DESCRIPTION

Transmissions are 4-speed, fully synchronized, constant mesh-type units, using helical type gears in all forward ranges, and sliding mesh spur type gears in reverse range. Transmission consists of 3 main parts: Transmission case with integral clutch housing, adapter plate (center support) to which all gears and shafts are installed, and an extension housing. Adapter plate supports mainshaft, countergear, idler shaft, and 3 shift rods, and is bolted at front to transmission case and at rear to extension housing by means of through bolts.

LUBRICATION & ADJUSTMENT

See the appropriate article in MANUAL TRANSMISSION SERVICING Section.

TROUBLE SHOOTING

Hard Shifting

With hard shifting, check clutch adjustment first. If clutch adjustment is correct, check for worn gears, shaft, bearing, and/or sliding part. Also check for damaged synchronizer.

Slips Out of Gear

Check for worn or damaged interlock plunger, check ball, check ball spring, fork rod ball groove, bearing, and gear. Check motor mounts.

Noisy Operation

Make sure noise is from transmission and not clutch. If transmission is noisy, check for correct level and type of lubricant. Check for oil leaks and clogged breather cap. Check for worn or damaged bearings, bushings, and gears.

Fig. 1: Removal of Front Cover on F4W56A and F4W60L Transmissions

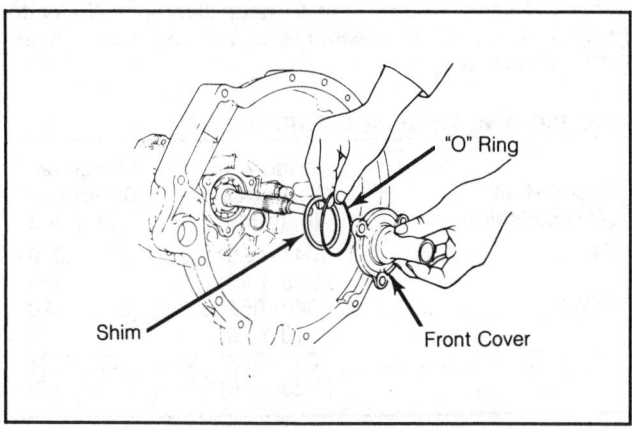

REMOVAL & INSTALLATION

See the appropriate article in AUTOMATIC TRANSMISSION REMOVAL Section.

TRANSMISSION DISASSEMBLY

1) Drain oil and remove release bearing and lever. Remove back-up light and high gear switches. Remove speedometer driven gear and sleeve. Remove nut or "C" ring and stopper pin bolt from extension housing. Remove plug, return spring, reverse check spring and plunger from extension housing.

2) Remove front cover, "O" ring, adjusting shim and bearing snap ring (if equipped) from front of transmission case. Remove extension housing bolts. Turn striking lever clockwise on F4W56A and F4W60L transmissions or counterclockwise on F4W71B transmission, and remove extension housing.

NOTE: **On F4W71B transmission, make sure that countergear thrust washer is removed after front cover is removed.**

3) Remove adapter plate from transmission case by tapping on transmission case with a mallet. On F4W56A and F4W60L transmissions, remove countergear thrust washer.

Fig. 2: Removal of Front Cover on F4W71B Transmission

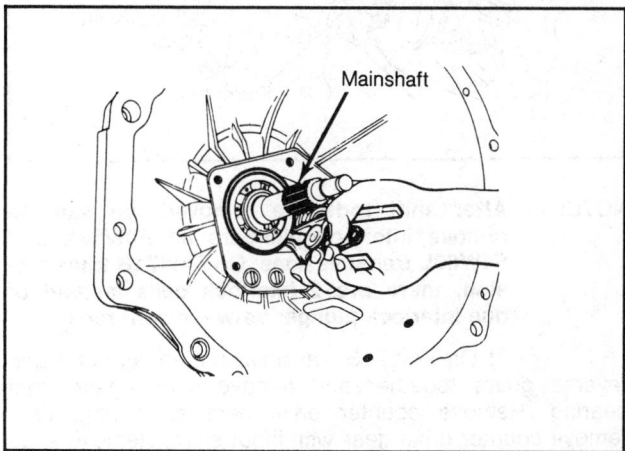

COMPONENT DISASSEMBLY & REASSEMBLY

GEAR ASSEMBLY

NOTE: **During disassembly, check gear end play. For specifications, see Gear End Play Chart.**

Disassembly

1) Mount adapter plate in a holding fixture. Remove detent plugs, springs and balls. On F4W56A transmission, detent ball and spring for reverse shift rod is removed after shift rod is removed.

2) Drive out retaining pins attaching shift forks to shift rods. On F4W56A and F4W60L transmissions, remove reverse shift fork and reverse idler gear. On all transmissions, remove shift forks and drive out shift rods.

DATSUN/NISSAN 210 & PICKUP 4-SPEED (Cont.)

GEAR END PLAY

Application	Clearance In. (mm)
F4W56A	
1st Gear	.006-.010 (.15-.25)
2nd Gear	.006-.010 (.15-.25)
3rd Gear	.004-.012 (.10-.30)
F4W60L	
1st Gear	.006-.010 (.15-.25)
2nd Gear	.012-.016 (.30-.40)
3rd Gear	.006-.014 (.15-.35)
F4W71B	
1st Gear	.011-.013 (.27-.34)
2nd Gear	.005-.007 (.13-.19)
3rd Gear	.005-.015 (.13-.37)

Fig. 3: Checking Gear End Play with a Feeler Gauge

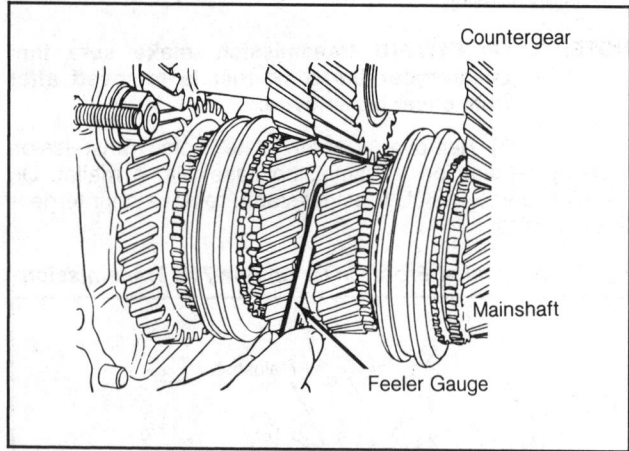

NOTE: **After shift rods are removed, be sure to remove interlock plungers on F4W56A and F4W60L transmissions. On F4W71B transmission, there are 2 interlock balls instead of one interlock plunger between shift rods.**

3) On F4W71B transmission, engage 2nd and reverse gears together and remove countergear front bearing. Remove counter drive gear snap ring, then remove counter drive gear with input shaft. Remove snap ring from mainshaft, 3rd-4th synchro assembly and 3rd gear. Release staking on mainshaft nut and remove nut with thrust washer and reverse gear.

Fig. 4: Removing Mainshaft from Adapter Plate

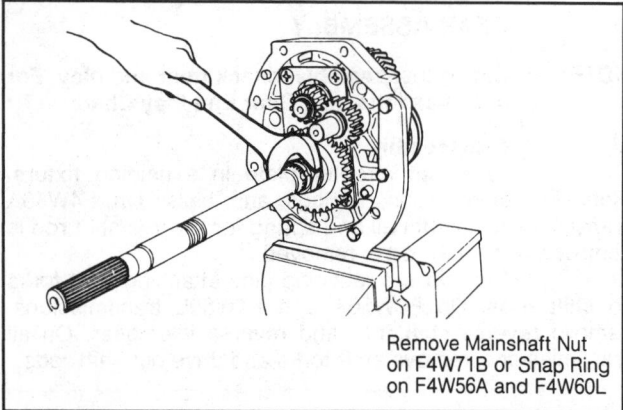

Remove Mainshaft Nut on F4W71B or Snap Ring on F4W56A and F4W60L

4) On F4W56A and F4W60L transmissions, remove reverse gear snap ring from mainshaft and remove thrust washer with reverse gear. On F4W60L transmission, remove bearing retainer. On all transmissions, remove mainshaft and countergear together by lightly tapping on rear of mainshaft while holding onto mainshaft and countergear.

5) On F4W60L transmission, remove snap ring from mainshaft. On F4W56A transmission, remove needle bearing, thrust washer and steel ball. On F4W56A and F4W60L transmissions, remove 3rd-4th synchro assembly, 3rd gear and needle bearing from front of mainshaft.

6) On all transmissions, remove thrust washer, 1st gear, needle bearing, bushing, 1st-2nd synchro assembly, 2nd gear and needle bearing from mainshaft. Remove snap ring, thrust washer and ball bearing from input shaft.

NOTE: **Be sure not to lose pilot needle bearing in end of input shaft.**

7) On F4W56A and F4W60L transmissions, remove needle bearing and thrust washer from front of countergear. Remove snap ring, counter reverse gear and ball bearing from rear of countergear.

8) On F4W71B transmission, remove snap ring, counter reverse gear and ball bearing from rear of countergear. Remove bearing retainer plate, then remove idler shaft from adapter plate. On F4W56A and F4W60L transmissions, remove idler shaft snap ring then tap idler shaft from adapter plate.

Inspection

1) Wash all components in solvent. Check transmission case and extension housing for cracks or damage. If extension housing bushing is worn or damaged, replace extension housing and bushing as an assembly.

NOTE: **Do not wash or soak oil seal in cleaning solvent.**

2) Check all bearings for smooth operation and for signs of wear or damage, and replace as necessary. Check all gears for wear or damage. Check shafts for wear, damage or bending. Replace components as necessary.

3) Check gear end play, condition of gears, condition of thrust washers and bushings. Replace components as necessary.

4) Check synchro assemblies for wear or damage. Check synchro ring to gear clearance. *Refer to Synchro Ring-to-Gear Clearance chart.* Replace components as necessary.

SYNCHRO RING-TO-GEAR CLEARANCE

Application (Transmission)	Standard Clearance In. (mm)	Minimum Clearance In. (mm)
F4W56A	.041-.055 (1.05-1.40)	.020 (.5)
F4W60L	.043-.055 (1.10-1.40)	.020 (.5)
F4W71B	.047-.063 (1.20-1.60)	.031 (.8)

DATSUN/NISSAN 210 & PICKUP 4-SPEED (Cont.)

Fig. 5: *Exploded View of Datsun 4-Speed Transmission Gear Assembly*

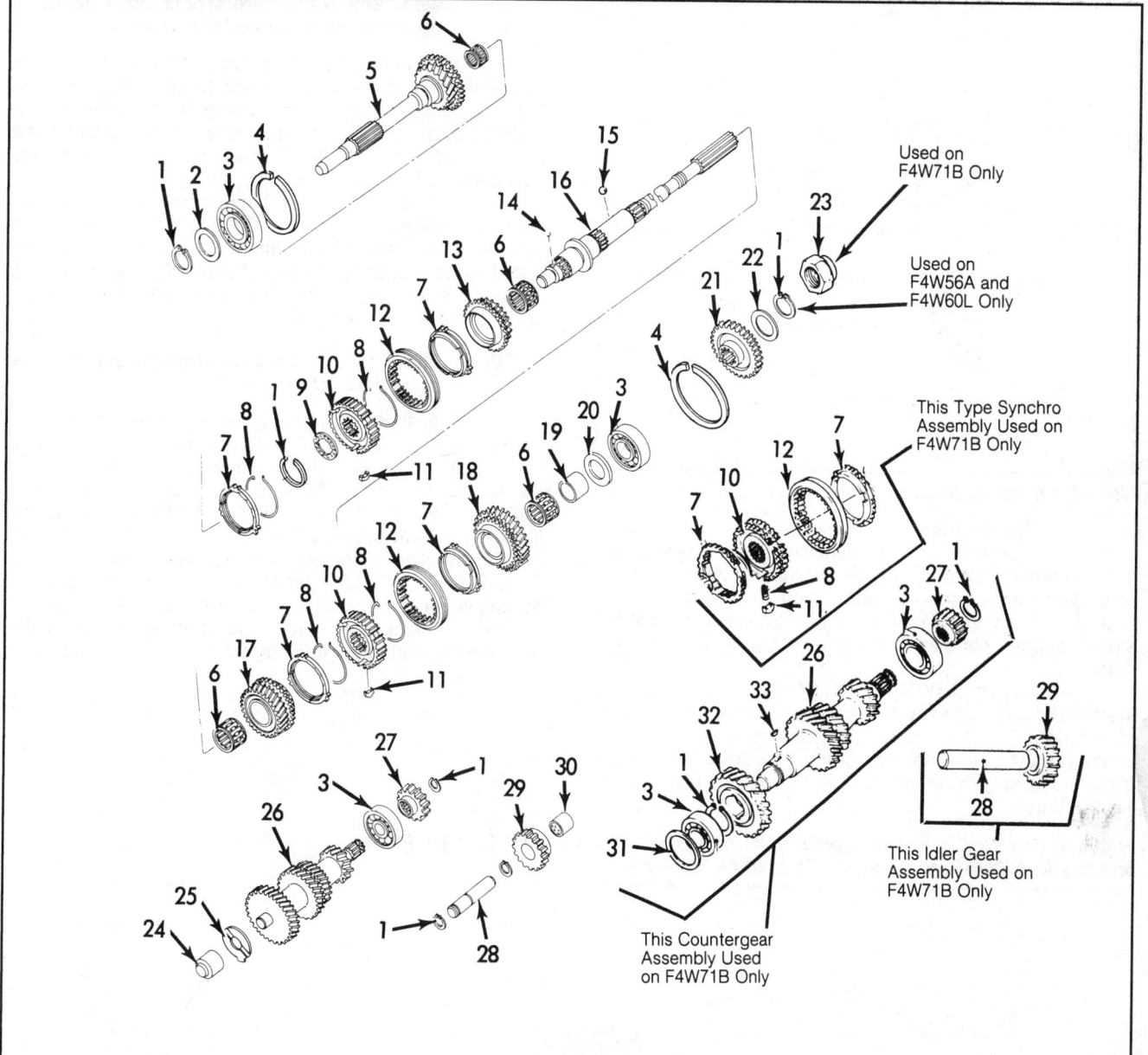

Used on
F4W71B Only

Used on
F4W56A and
F4W60L Only

This Type Synchro
Assembly Used on
F4W71B Only

This Idler Gear
Assembly Used on
F4W71B Only

This Countergear
Assembly Used
on F4W71B Only

1. Snap Ring
2. Shim
3. Ball Bearing
4. Large Snap Ring (F4W60L Only)
5. Input Shaft
6. Needle Bearing
7. Synchro Ring
8. Synchro Spring
9. Thrust Washer
10. Synchro Hub
11. Key

12. Synchro Sleeve
13. 3rd Gear
14. Ball (F4W56A)
15. Ball (F4W71B)
16. Mainshaft
17. 2nd Gear
18. 1st Gear
19. Bushing
20. Thrust Washer
21. Reverse Gear
22. Concave Thrust Washer

23. Mainshaft Nut (F4W71B Only)
24. Bearing
25. Thrust Washer
26. Countergear
27. Counter Reverse Gear
28. Idler Shaft
29. Idler Gear
30. Bushing
31. Countergear Shim
32. Counter Drive Gear
33. Woodruff Key

DATSUN/NISSAN 210 & PICKUP 4-SPEED (Cont.)

Fig. 6: Synchro Ring-to-Gear Clearance

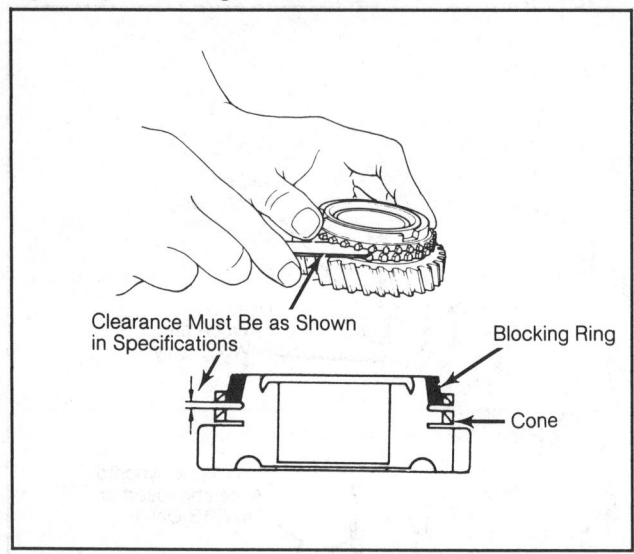

Clearance Must Be as Shown in Specifications

Blocking Ring

Cone

Use a feeler gauge to check clearance.

Reassembly

1) On F4W71B transmission, install new dowel pin in adapter plate so that pin protrudes .295" (7.5 mm) from each side of adapter plate. Install mainshaft bearing to adapter plate then install oil gutter. Bend gutter on front side of adapter plate and expand it on rear side of adapter plate.

2) On F4W56A and F4W60L transmissions, install idler shaft to adapter plate, then install snap ring to idler shaft. On all transmissions, assemble synchronizer assemblies by placing synchronizer sleeve onto hub. Install keys to grooves in hub, then install springs to hold keys in place.

NOTE: Do not hook front and rear ends of spring to same key. Make sure synchronizer assembly operates correctly and smoothly.

3) Install needle bearing, 2nd gear, 1st-2nd synchronizer assembly (with synchronizer ring), 1st gear bushing, needle bearing and 1st gear to mainshaft. On F4W56A and F4W60L transmissions, install thrust washer to mainshaft. On F4W71B transmission, install steel ball (lubricated) then thrust washer to mainshaft.

4) On F4W71B transmission, install adapter plate to holding fixture (KV31100401). Install mainshaft to adapter plate. Install Woodruff key to countergear, then install countergear to mainshaft. Install needle bearing, 3rd gear, 3rd-4th synchronizer assembly (with synchronizer ring) to front of mainshaft.

NOTE: Make sure short protrusion of synchronizer hub faces forward.

5) Install thrust washer and snap ring to front of mainshaft. Select snap ring that will minimize clearance. Snap rings for F4W71B transmission are available in 3 sizes: .055" (1.4 mm), .059" (1.5 mm) and .063" (1.6 mm).

6) On F4W56A and F4W60L transmissions, install mainshaft bearing. Install needle bearing, 3rd gear, 3rd-4th synchro assembly (with synchro ring) to front of mainshaft. On F4W56A transmission, install steel ball and thrust washer (lubricated) to front of mainshaft. On F4W60L transmission, install snap ring to mainshaft that eliminates clearance. *Refer to Mainshaft Front Snap Ring chart.*

Fig. 7: Cross Section of Positions of Shift Rods, Forks, Check Balls, Springs, Plugs and Interlock Plungers in Adapter Plate of All Transmissions

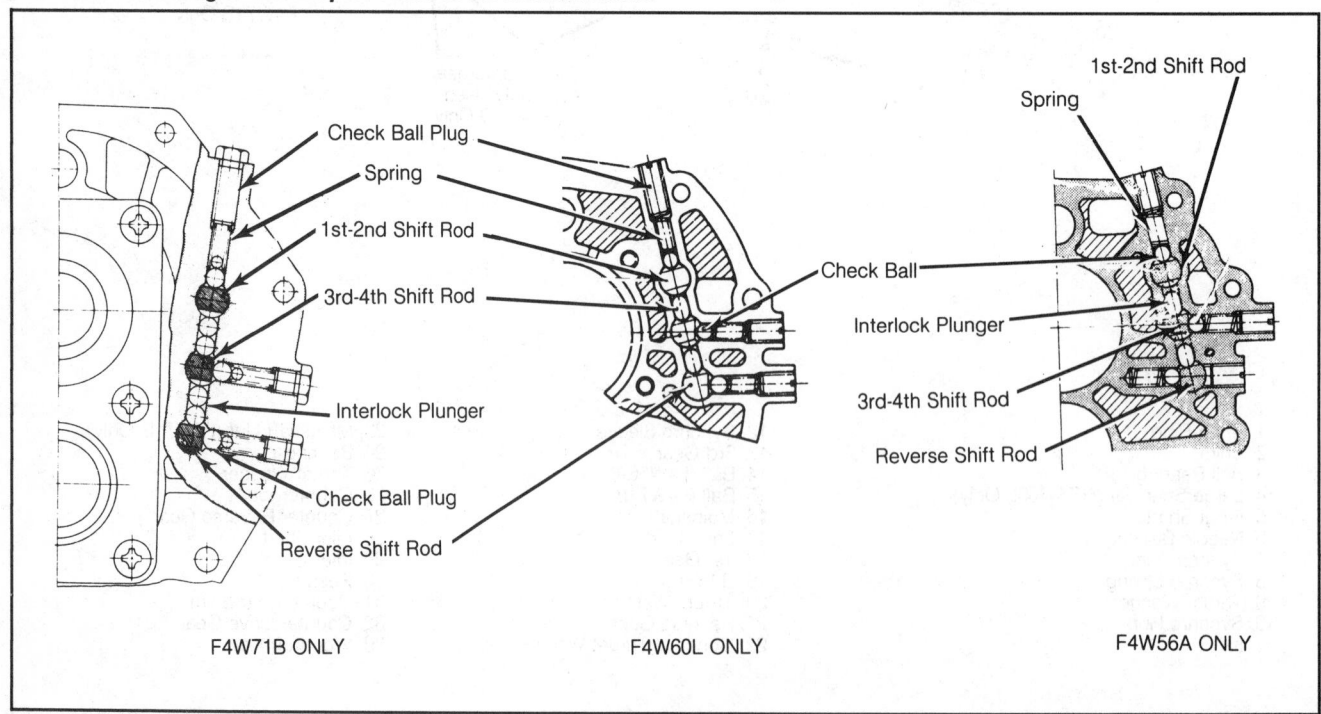

Check Ball Plug

Spring

1st-2nd Shift Rod

3rd-4th Shift Rod

Interlock Plunger

Check Ball Plug

Reverse Shift Rod

1st-2nd Shift Rod

Spring

Check Ball

Interlock Plunger

3rd-4th Shift Rod

Reverse Shift Rod

F4W71B ONLY

F4W60L ONLY

F4W56A ONLY

DATSUN/NISSAN 210 & PICKUP 4-SPEED (Cont.)

MAINSHAFT FRONT SNAP RINGS

Snap Ring No.	Thickness In. (mm)
1	.061-.063 (1.55-1.60)
2	.063-.065 (1.60-1.65)
3	.065-.067 (1.65-1.70)

7) On F4W71B transmission, install 3rd-4th front synchronizer ring to synchronizer assembly. Apply gear oil to input shaft pilot bearing and install to mainshaft. Install input shaft with countergear to mainshaft and adapter plate. Install mainshaft drive gear to mainshaft. Make sure that inner diameter of gear that protrudes faces toward rear.

8) Install counter drive gear to countergear and install snap ring that will minimize clearance. Snap rings are available in .055" (1.4 mm), .059" (1.5 mm) and .063" (1.6 mm) sizes. Install countergear front bearing.

9) Install reverse gear to mainshaft, then plain washer and mainshaft nut. Tighten mainshaft nut temporarily. Install counter reverse gear and snap ring that will minimize clearance. Snap rings are available in .055" (1.4 mm), .059" (1.5 mm), .063" (1.6 mm) and .067" (1.7 mm) sizes. Install idler gear, engage 2nd and reverse gears and tighten mainshaft nut. Stake nut after tightening.

10) On F4W56A transmission, install bearing onto input shaft, making sure bearing clears snap ring groove. Install thrust washer (concave side facing bearing) then install snap ring, making sure snap ring fits into groove.

11) On F4W60L transmission, install bearing onto input shaft, making sure snap ring groove is clear. Install bearing spacer and install snap ring that eliminates end play. *Refer to Input Shaft Bearing Snap Rings chart.*

INPUT SHAFT BEARING SNAP RINGS

Snap Ring No.	Thickness In. (mm)
1	.053-.055 (1.34-1.40)
2	.055-.057 (1.40-1.46)
3	.057-.060 (1.46-1.52)
4	.060-.062 (1.52-1.58)
5	.062-.065 (1.58-1.64)
6	.065-.067 (1.64-1.70)
7	.067-.069 (1.70-1.76)

12) On F4W56A and F4W60L transmissions, install bearing to rear of countergear. Install original thrust washer to countergear and install into transmission case. Using special countergear height gauge (ST23050000) and a feeler gauge, check clearance between countergear rear bearing and height gauge. End play should be 0-.008" (0-.2 mm) on F4W56A transmission or .004-.008" (.1-.2 mm) on F4W60L transmission. *See Fig. 8.*

13) If clearance is not to specifications, select thrust washer thickness to obtain specified clearance. Thrust washers are available in 8 different sizes, ranging from .087-.089" (2.20-2.25 mm) up to .100-.102" (2.55-2.60 mm) in .002" (.05 mm) increments.

14) With correct thrust washer selected, remove countergear from transmission case. Install counter reverse gear to countergear and install snap ring to countergear groove.

15) Install synchronizer ring to input shaft and install input shaft to mainshaft. Be sure that pilot bearing is in place before input shaft installation. Assemble mainshaft and countergear together and install them to adapter plate. Use a puller to pull mainshaft into adapter plate. Tapping mainshaft and countergear with a mallet will aid in installation.

NOTE: **Be sure to hold gear assemblies from dropping during installation.**

16) Make sure that snap ring groove on mainshaft rear bearing clears adapter plate. Install snap ring to mainshaft rear bearing, then install bearing retainer and screws. Stake screws after installation. Install reverse gear and thrust washer to rear of mainshaft, then install snap ring. Make sure concave side of thrust washer faces reverse gear.

17) On all transmissions, install 1st-2nd and 3rd-4th shift forks to synchronizer assemblies. Install 1st-2nd shift rod to adapter plate and place in neutral position. Install interlock plunger in adapter plate. Install 3rd-4th shift rod, place in neutral position and install interlock plunger.

NOTE: **On F4W71B transmission, there are 2 interlock balls instead of 1 interlock plunger.**

18) Install reverse shift rod, fork and idler gear to adapter plate. Install check balls, springs and plugs to adapter plate. Apply sealant to plugs after installation. Install new retaining pins to all shift forks. Apply gear oil to all sliding surfaces and make sure all components operate properly.

19) On all transmissions, make sure all mating surfaces are cleaned, then apply sealant to mating surfaces. On F4W56A and F4W60L transmissions, install countergear thrust washer selected. Apply grease to thrust washer before installation. Slide transmission case onto adapter plate by tapping with mallet.

20) Install mainshaft bearing and countergear needle bearing. Make sure mainshaft rotates freely, then install snap ring to input shaft bearing.

21) On F4W56A and F4W60L transmissions, select front cover shim by measuring distance from front of transmission case (where front cover bolts) to input shaft bearing. Refer to *Front Cover Shim chart* for shim thickness. *See Fig. 10.* On F4W71B transmission, select countergear front bearing shim by measuring distance from front bearing to transmission case and selecting shim thickness from *Countergear Front Shim chart. See Fig. 11.*

Fig. 8: Determining Countergear Shim Thickness on F4W56A and F4W60L Transmissions

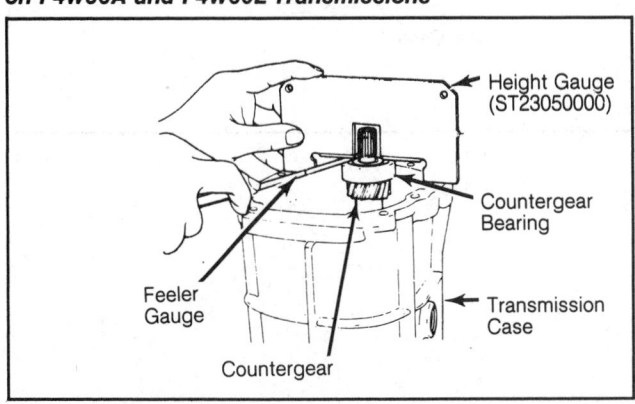

Manual Transmissions
DATSUN/NISSAN 210 & PICKUP 4-SPEED (Cont.)

Fig. 9: Exploded View of Shift Rods and Forks

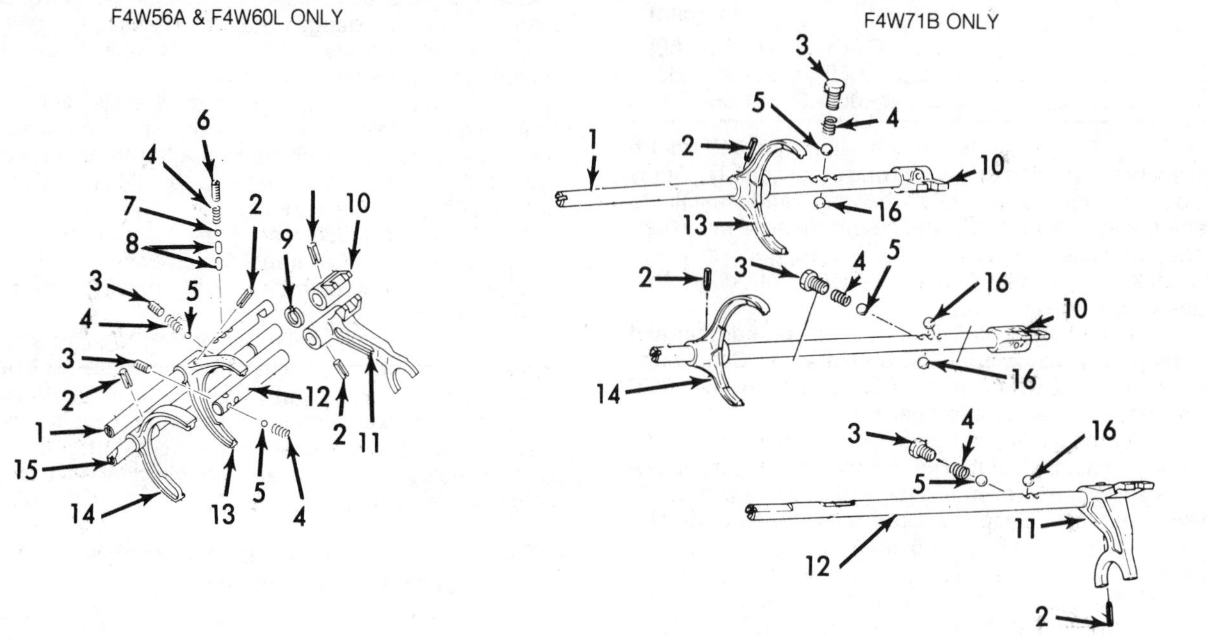

F4W56A & F4W60L ONLY

F4W71B ONLY

1. 1st-2nd Shift Rod
2. Retaining Pin
3. Check Ball Plug
4. Spring
5. Check Ball
6. Interlock Plunger Plug
7. Ball
8. Interlock Plungers
9. Stopper Ring
10. Shift Rod Bracket
11. Reverse Shift Fork
12. Reverse Fhift Rod
13. 1st-2nd Shift Fork
14. 3rd-4th Shift Fork
15. 3rd-4th Shift Rod
16. Interlock Ball

Fig. 10: Determining Front Bearing Shim Thickness

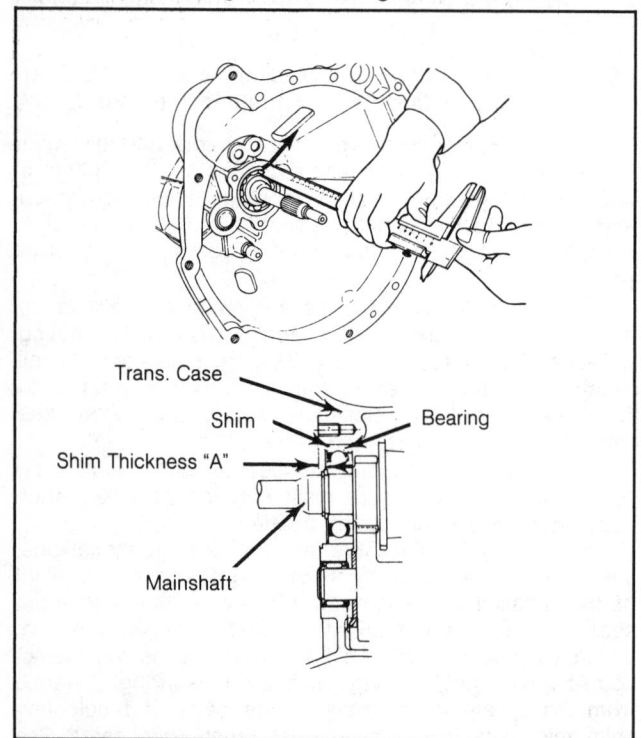

Trans. Case

Shim   Bearing

Shim Thickness "A"

Mainshaft

On F4W56A and F4W60L transmissions

Fig. 11: Determining Countergear Shim Thickness (On F4W71B Transmission)

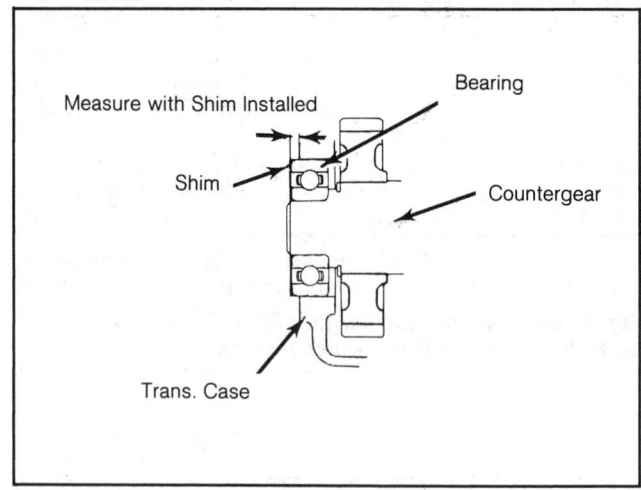

Measure with Shim Installed   Bearing

Shim   Countergear

Trans. Case

DATSUN/NISSAN 210 & PICKUP 4-SPEED (Cont.)

FRONT COVER SHIMS

Application Shim	Thickness In. (mm)
F4W56A	
1	.203-.207 (5.16-5.25)
2	.207-.211 (5.25-5.35)
3	.211-.215 (5.36-5.45)
F4W60L	
1	.238-.240 (6.05-6.10)
2	.240-.242 (6.10-6.15)
3	.242-.244 (6.15-6.20)
4	.244-.246 (6.20-6.25)
5	.246-.248 (6.25-6.30)
6	.248-.250 (6 30-6.35)
7	.250-.252 (6.35-6.40)

COUNTERGEAR THRUST WASHER

Application Shim	Thickness In. (mm)
F4W60L	
1	2.20-2.25 (.0866-.0886)
2	2.25-2.30 (.0886-.0906)
3	2.30-2.35 (.0906-.0925)
4	2.35-2.40 (.0925-.0945)
5	2.40-2.45 (.0945-.0965)
6	2.45-2.50 (.0965-.0984)
7	2.50-2.55 (.0984-.1004)
8	2.55-2.60 (.1004-.1024)
F4W56A	
1	2.30-2.35 (.0906-.0925)
2	2.35-2.40 (.0925-.0945)
3	2.40-2.45 (.0945-.0965)
4	2.45-2.50 (.0965-.0984)
5	2.50-2.55 (.0984-.1004)
6	2.55-2.60 (.1004-.1024)

Fig. 12: Exploded View of Transmission Case Components

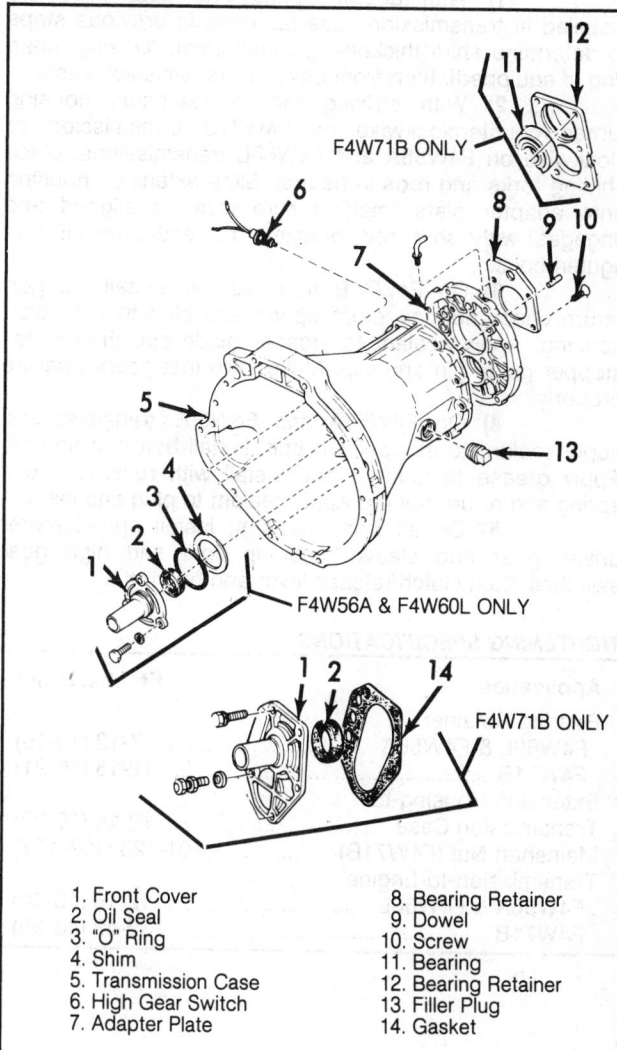

F4W71B ONLY

F4W56A & F4W60L ONLY

F4W71B ONLY

1. Front Cover
2. Oil Seal
3. "O" Ring
4. Shim
5. Transmission Case
6. High Gear Switch
7. Adapter Plate
8. Bearing Retainer
9. Dowel
10. Screw
11. Bearing
12. Bearing Retainer
13. Filler Plug
14. Gasket

Fig. 13: Exploded View of Extension Housing Components

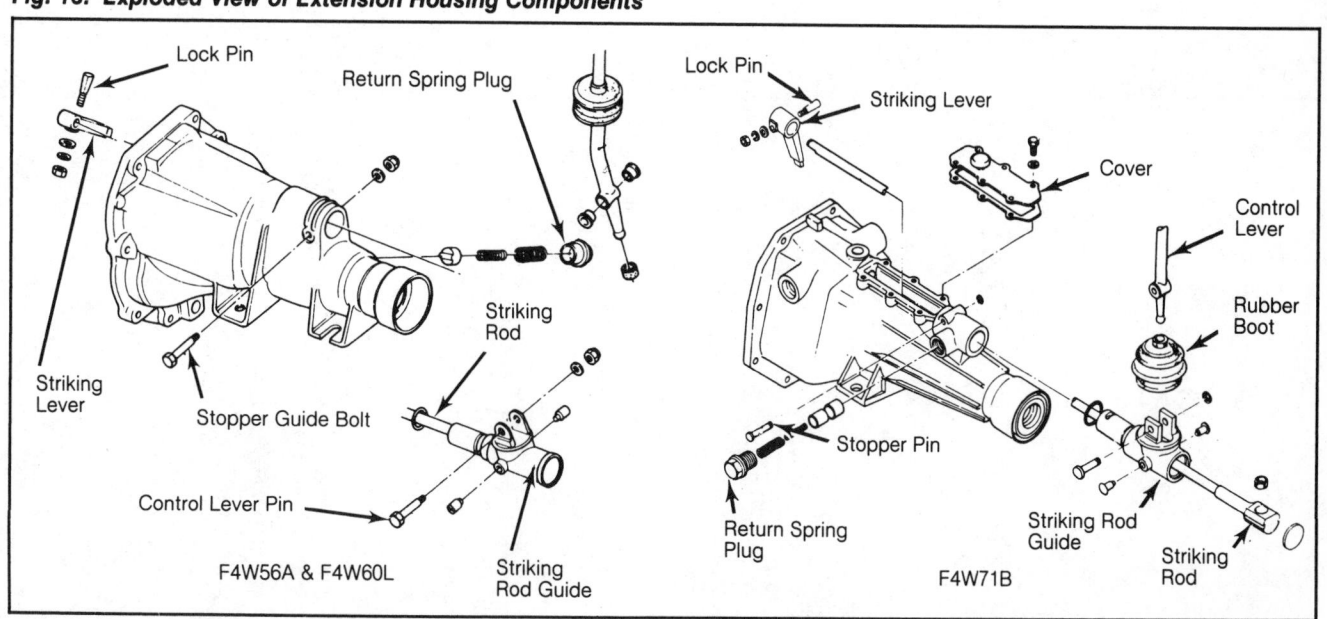

Lock Pin

Return Spring Plug

Striking Rod

Striking Lever

Stopper Guide Bolt

Control Lever Pin

Striking Rod Guide

F4W56A & F4W60L

Lock Pin

Striking Lever

Cover

Control Lever

Rubber Boot

Return Spring Plug

Stopper Pin

Striking Rod Guide

Striking Rod

F4W71B

Manual Transmissions

DATSUN/NISSAN 210 & PICKUP 4-SPEED (Cont.)

TRANSMISSION REASSEMBLY

1) With adapter plate and gear assembly installed in transmission case (as done in previous steps to determine shim thickness), install shim, "O" ring, snap ring (if equipped), then front cover to transmission case.

2) With striking rod in extension housing turned counterclockwise on F4W71B transmission or clockwise on F4W56A and F4W60L transmissions, place shifting forks and rods in neutral. Slide extension housing onto adapter plate, making sure lever is aligned and engages with shift rod brackets correctly. Install and tighten bolts.

3) On F4W71B transmission, install plunger, return check spring, return spring and plug to extension housing. Apply sealant to stopper guide pin, then install stopper guide pin and clip. Make sure that gears operate properly.

4) On F4W56A and F4W60L transmissions, apply sealant to stopper pin bolt, install bolt and tighten. Apply grease to plunger and install with reverse check spring and return spring. Apply sealant to plug and install.

5) On all transmissions, install speedometer driven gear and sleeve, back-up light and high gear switches, then clutch release lever and bearing.

TIGHTENING SPECIFICATIONS

Application	Ft. Lbs. (N.m)
Bearing Retainer	
F4W60L & F4W56A	7-12 (10-16)
F4W71B	12-15 (16-21)
Extension Housing-to-	
Transmission Case	12-16 (16-22)
Mainshaft Nut (F4W71B)	101-123 (137-177)
Transmission-to-Engine	
F4W56A & F4W60L	12-16 (16-22)
F4W71B	32-43 (43-58)

DATSUN/NISSAN 210 5-SPEED

DESCRIPTION

The Datsun FS5W60A transmission is a 5-speed, fully synchronized, constant mesh unit that uses helical type gears on 1st through 5th speeds. Reverse gear is sliding mesh, spur type gear. Transmission assembly consists of three main parts: Transmission case, adapter plate and extension housing. The adapter plate supports the mainshaft, countergear, idler shaft and fork rods. Adapter plate is bolted to rear of transmission case, extension housing is bolted to adapter plate and transmission case.

LUBRICATION & ADJUSTMENT

See the appropriate article in MANUAL TRANS-MISSION SERVICING Section.

REMOVAL & INSTALLATION

See the appropriate article in MANUAL TRANS-MISSION REMOVAL Section.

TRANSMISSION DISASSEMBLY

1) Drain oil, remove dust cover and release bearing. Remove back-up switch, neutral switch, speedometer driven gear and front cover.

2) Remove nut and stopper pin bolt from extension housing. Remove return spring plug, spring and plunger from extension housing. Remove reverse check sleeve assembly. Remove "O" ring, spacer and snap ring from front of input shaft. See Fig. 1.

Fig. 1: Removing Snap Ring from Input Shaft

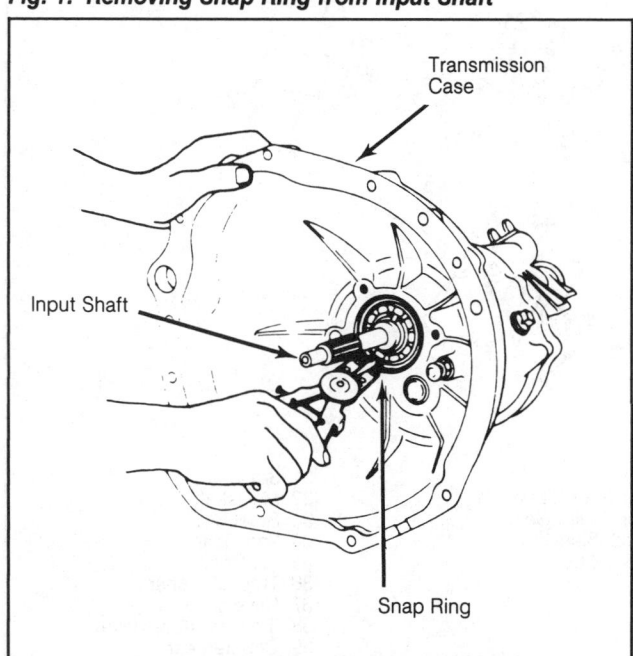

3) Remove extension housing with puller. Separate transmission case from adapter plate by tapping on transmission case with mallet while holding onto rear of mainshaft. Install adapter plate to a holding fixture and remove thrust washer from countergear. See Fig. 2.

Fig. 2: Removing Transmission Case from Adapter Plate

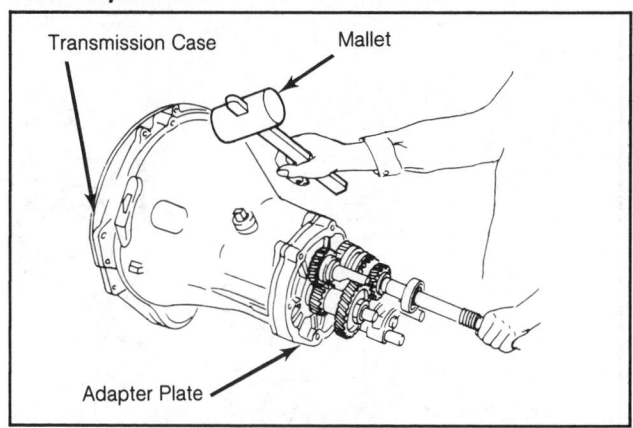

COMPONENT DISASSEMBLY & REASSEMBLY

GEAR ASSEMBLY

NOTE: Check gear clearance and end play before disassembly. See Inspection.

1) Drive out retaining pins from shift rods, using a punch. Remove 3 check ball plugs, and drive out shift rods from adapter plate (by tapping lightly on front ends of shift rods). Remove shift forks.

NOTE: Be careful not to lose the 3 detent balls and 2 interlock plungers.

2) Remove snap ring from mainshaft end bearing, then remove bearing with a puller. Remove other end bearing snap ring. Engage 1st and reverse gears at the same time, then loosen staking on countergear nut. Remove countergear nut. See Fig. 4.

Fig. 4: Loosening Staking on Countergear Nut

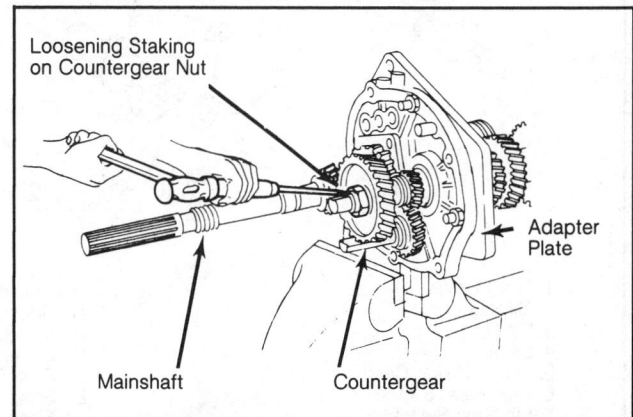

3) Remove small snap ring, large snap ring holder and large snap ring from mainshaft. Remove 5th gear and bearing from mainshaft with counter 5th gear.

4) Remove snap ring and 5th-Reverse synchro assembly. Remove reverse gear with needle bearing from mainshaft and reverse gear from countergear at the same time.

Manual Transmissions
DATSUN/NISSAN 210 5-SPEED (Cont.)

Fig. 3: Exploded View of Datsun FS5W60A 5-Speed Transmission Assembly

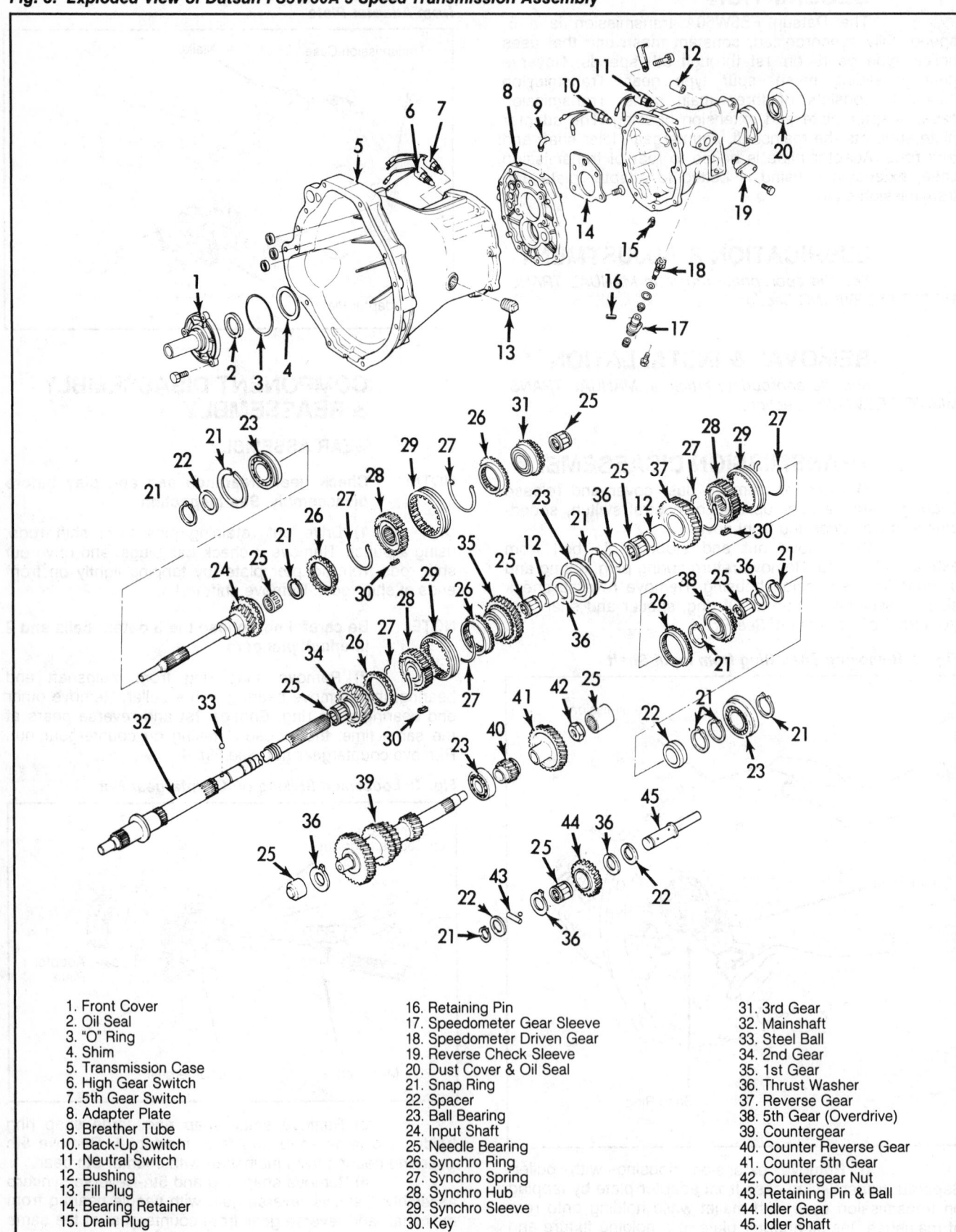

1. Front Cover	16. Retaining Pin	31. 3rd Gear
2. Oil Seal	17. Speedometer Gear Sleeve	32. Mainshaft
3. "O" Ring	18. Speedometer Driven Gear	33. Steel Ball
4. Shim	19. Reverse Check Sleeve	34. 2nd Gear
5. Transmission Case	20. Dust Cover & Oil Seal	35. 1st Gear
6. High Gear Switch	21. Snap Ring	36. Thrust Washer
7. 5th Gear Switch	22. Spacer	37. Reverse Gear
8. Adapter Plate	23. Ball Bearing	38. 5th Gear (Overdrive)
9. Breather Tube	24. Input Shaft	39. Countergear
10. Back-Up Switch	25. Needle Bearing	40. Counter Reverse Gear
11. Neutral Switch	26. Synchro Ring	41. Counter 5th Gear
12. Bushing	27. Synchro Spring	42. Countergear Nut
13. Fill Plug	28. Synchro Hub	43. Retaining Pin & Ball
14. Bearing Retainer	29. Synchro Sleeve	44. Idler Gear
15. Drain Plug	30. Key	45. Idler Shaft

DATSUN/NISSAN 210 5-SPEED (Cont.)

5) Remove thrust washer from countergear. Remove bearing retainer screws from adapter plate, then remove retainer plate. Remove mainshaft rear bearing snap ring. Drive mainshaft, with countergear, out of adapter plate by tapping on end of mainshaft with a mallet. *See Fig. 5.*

NOTE: Be careful to hold both the mainshaft and countergear from falling when removing from adapter plate.

Fig. 5: Removing Mainshaft and Countergear from Adapter Plate

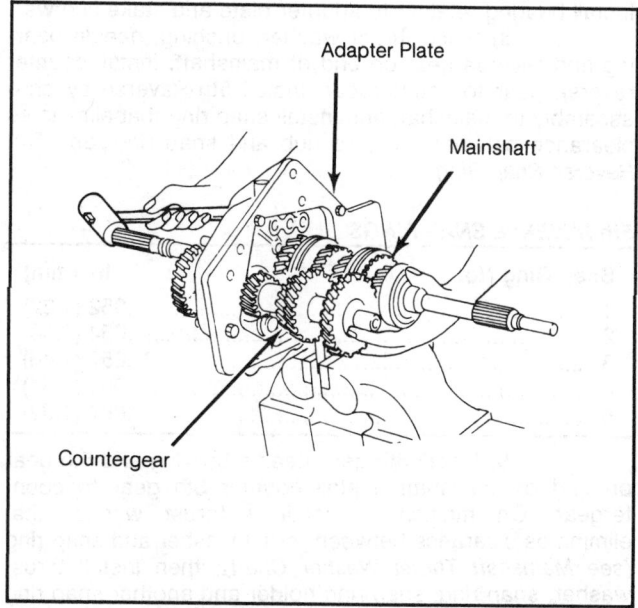

6) Remove idler shaft snap ring and spacer. Tap idler shaft out of adapter plate just enough so that retaining pin can be driven out of idler shaft. Remove retaining pin, then remove idler shaft from adapter plate. Remove thrust washers, spacer, idler gear and needle bearing from idler shaft.

7) From front of mainshaft, remove snap ring. Then remove synchro assembly, 3rd gear and needle bearing. Pull mainshaft bearing from mainshaft rear end.

8) Remove thrust washer, 1st gear, needle bearing, bushing, synchro assembly, 2nd gear and needle bearing together. On input shaft, remove snap ring, spacer and bearing. On countergear, press bearing off.

Inspection

1) Wash all parts in a cleaning solvent and check for wear, damage or other faulty conditions

NOTE: Do not clean, wash or soak oil seals in solvent.

2) Check transmission case and rear extension for cracks, distortion or other faulty conditions. If rear extension bushing is worn or cracked, replace extension housing and bushing as an assembly.

3) If bearing race or ball surfaces are worn, rough or out-of-round, replace bearings. Replace needle bearing and taper roller bearing if worn or damaged.

4) Check gears for wear, chips or cracks. Measure gear end play on all gears. *Refer to Fig. 6 and see Gear End Play Chart* for specifications.

Fig. 6: Checking Gear End Play

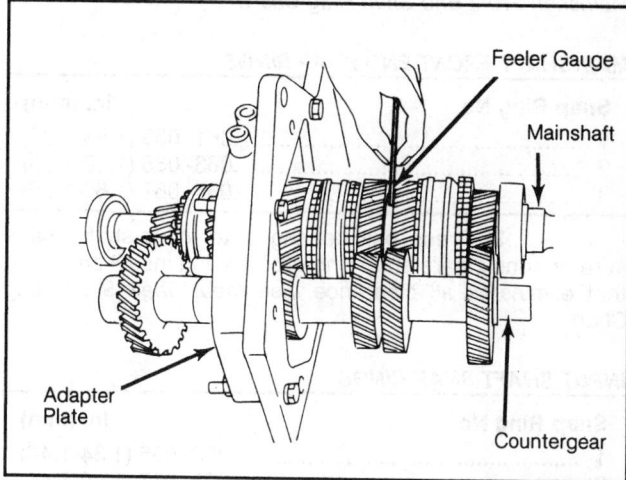

GEAR END PLAY

Application	In. (mm)
1st Gear	.006-.010 (.15-.25)
2nd Gear	.012-.016 (.30-.40)
3rd Gear	.006-.014 (.15-.35)
5th Gear	.012-.016 (.30-.40)
Reverse Gear	.012-.022 (.30-.55)
Countergear	.004-.008 (.10-.20)
Idler Gear	0-.008 (0-.20)

5) Check mainshaft for binding, cracks or wear. Check synchro rings for cracks, wear or damage. Replace as necessary. Check synchro ring to gear clearance. Clearance should be .043-.055" (1.1-1.4 mm). *See Fig. 7.*

Fig. 7: Checking Synchro Ring to Gear Clearance

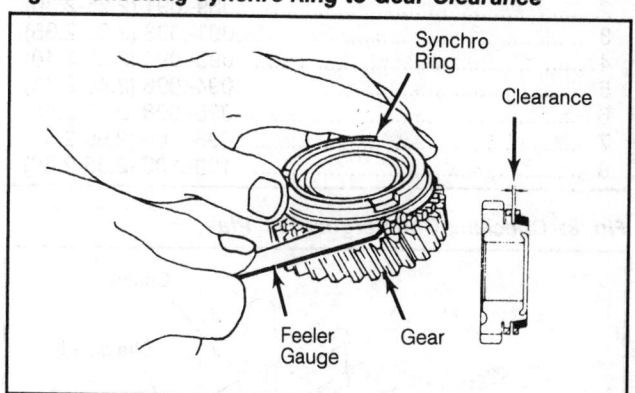

6) Replace oil seal if sealing lip is deformed, cracked or spring is out of position. Check oil seal lip contact face on shaft; if necessary, replace seal and shaft as a set.

Reassembly

1) Install needle bearing, 2nd gear, 1st-2nd synchro assembly, bushing, needle bearing, 1st gear and thrust washer onto mainshaft. Press roller bearing onto mainshaft.

2) Place needle bearing, 3rd gear, 3rd-4th synchro assembly to front end of mainshaft. Place a snap ring on front of mainshaft that will allow a minimum of clearance between synchro hub and snap ring. *See Mainshaft Front End Snap Ring Chart.*

MAINSHAFT FRONT END SNAP RINGS

Snap Ring No.	In. (mm)
1	.061-.063 (1.55-1.60)
2	.063-.065 (1.60-1.65)
3	.065-.067 (1.65-1.70)

3) Press ball bearing onto input shaft (make sure bearing clears snap ring groove) and install snap ring that eliminates all clearance. *See Input Shaft Snap Ring Chart.*

INPUT SHAFT SNAP RINGS

Snap Ring No.	In. (mm)
1	.053-.055 (1.34-1.40)
2	.055-.057 (1.40-1.46)
3	.057-.060 (1.46-1.52)
4	.060-.062 (1.52-1.58)
5	.062-.065 (1.58-1.64)
6	.065-.067 (1.64-1.70)
7	.067-.069 (1.70-1.76)

4) Install countergear and thrust washer into transmission case. Select thrust washer by placing a straightedge across rear of transmission case and use a feeler gauge to measure clearance between countergear and straightedge. *See Fig. 8.* With thrust washer in place, end play should be .004-.008" (.1-.2 mm). *See Countergear Thrust Washer Chart.*

COUNTERGEAR THRUST WASHERS

Thrust Washer No.	In. (mm)
1	.087-.089 (2.20-2.25)
2	.089-.091 (2.25-2.30)
3	.091-.093 (2.30-2.35)
4	.093-.094 (2.35-2.40)
5	.094-.096 (2.40-2.45)
6	.096-.098 (2.45-2.50)
7	.098-.100 (2.50-2.55)
8	.100-.102 (2.55-2.60)

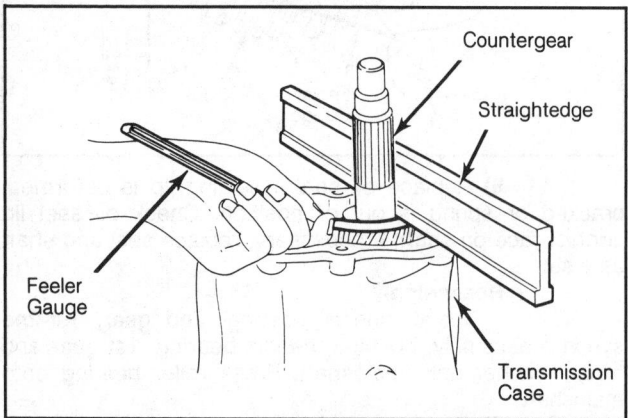

Fig. 8: Checking Countergear End Play

5) After selecting appropriate thrust washer, remove countergear from transmission case. Assemble idler shaft by installing thrust washers, needle bearing,

idler gear and thrust washer. Insert new retaining pin to idler shaft. Install idler shaft into adapter plate. Install thrust washer and fit a snap ring so that a minimum of clearance exists.

6) Install synchro ring to input shaft and install input shaft to front of mainshaft (make sure pilot bearing is installed in input shaft before installing to mainshaft). Combine mainshaft assembly with countergear and install both into adapter plate.

7) Use a puller to pull mainshaft into adapter plate. Make sure snap ring groove, in mainshaft, clears adapter plate. Install snap ring on mainshaft. Snap rings are available in .043" (1.1 mm) and .047" (1.2 mm) sizes. Install bearing retainer to adapter plate and stake screws.

8) Place thrust washer, bushing, needle bearing and reverse gear on end of mainshaft. Install counter reverse gear to countergear. Install 5th-Reverse synchro assembly to mainshaft and install snap ring that eliminates clearance between synchro hub and snap ring. *See 5th-Reverse Snap Ring Chart.*

5th-REVERSE SNAP RINGS

Snap Ring No.	In. (mm)
1	.052 (1.32)
2	.054 (1.38)
3	.057 (1.46)
4	.061 (1.54)
5	.064 (1.62)

9) Install 5th gear needle bearing and 5th gear on end of mainshaft. Install counter 5th gear to countergear. On mainshaft, install a thrust washer that eliminates clearance between thrust washer and snap ring *(see Mainshaft Thrust Washer Chart)*, then install thrust washer, snap ring, snap ring holder and another snap ring to mainshaft.

MAINSHAFT THRUST WASHERS

Thrust Washer No.	In. (mm)
1	.310 (7.87)
2	.313 (7.94)
3	.315 (8.01)
4	.318 (8.08)
5	.321 (8.15)
6	.324 (8.22)

10) Engage 1st and reverse gears at the same time, then tighten countergear nut. Stake countergear nut. Measure gear end play and make sure that it is to specifications. Install a .045" (1.15 mm) snap ring to front end of mainshaft end bearing. Install mainshaft end bearing to mainshaft.

11) Install a thick snap ring onto mainshaft that eliminates play between bearing and snap ring. Snap rings are available in 2 sizes, .045" (1.15 mm) and .047" (1.2 mm).

12) Install 5th-Reverse shift rod into its shift fork and install in adapter plate. Place 5th-Reverse shift fork in neutral and install interlock plunger in adapter plate. Install 3rd-4th shift rod into 5th-Reverse fork and install new snap ring to 3rd-4th shift rod.

13) Install 3rd-4th shift rod to adapter plate and its shift fork. Place 3rd-4th shift rod in neutral, install interlock plunger to adapter plate. Install 1st-2nd shift rod

DATSUN/NISSAN 210 5-SPEED (Cont.)

to its shift fork and install in adapter plate. Secure shift forks and shift rods with new retaining pins. *Refer to Fig. 9.*

Fig. 9: Shift Rod and Shift Fork Installation

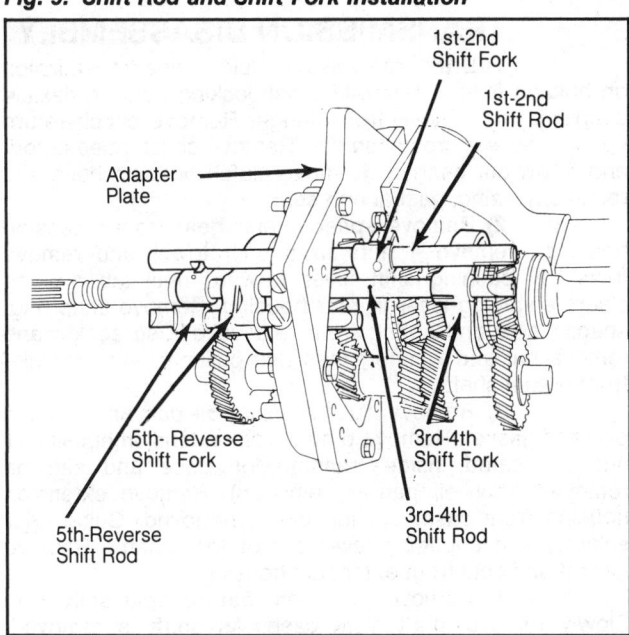

NOTE: Be sure to install interlock plunger when installing adjacent shift rods to adapter plate. Properly align 3rd-4th shift fork with groove in synchro sleeve. Also align 1st-2nd and 5th-Reverse shift forks with synchro sleeve before installing.

14) Install detent balls, springs and plugs. Apply sealer to plugs before installation. *See Fig. 10.* Apply gear oil to sliding surfaces and make sure all shift forks, rods and gears operate properly.

Fig. 10: Interlock Plungers, Detent Balls, Springs and Plug Installation

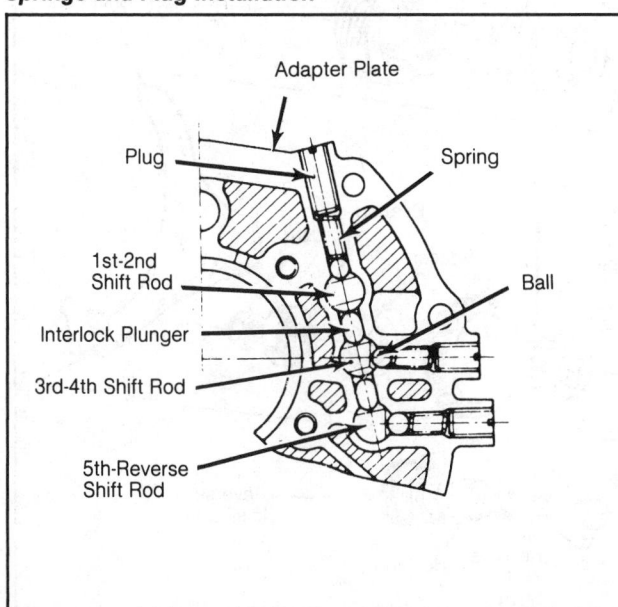

TRANSMISSION REASSEMBLY

1) Clean mating surfaces of adapter plate and transmission case. Apply sealant to cleaned surfaces. Install countergear thrust washer selected previously. Apply grease to sliding surface of thrust washer. Install adapter plate to transmission case, lightly tapping with mallet. Install input shaft bearing snap ring.

2) Clean mating surfaces of adapter plate and extension housing. Apply sealant to cleaned surfaces. Place striking rod in neutral, turn striking guide clockwise, then set striking lever and shift arm.

3) Align shift arm pin with groove in shift rod and install extension housing to adapter plate. Install bolts and tighten. Grease plunger and install it in extension housing. Install return spring and plug.

4) Select front cover shim by measuring distance from front end of transmission case to input shaft bearing outer race. *See Fig. 11.* Select shim that will give an end play of .219-.220" (5.55-5.59 mm). *Refer to Front Cover Shim Chart.* Install front cover to transmission case.

FRONT COVER SHIMS

Shim No.	Measurement A In. (mm)	Shim Thickness In. (mm)
1	.238-.240 (6.05-6.10)	.020 (.50)
2	.240-.242 (6.10-6.15)	.022 (.55)
3	.242-.244 (6.15-6.20)	.024 (.60)
4	.244-.246 (6.20-6.25)	.026 (.65)
5	.246-.248 (6.25-6.30)	.028 (.70)
6	.248-.250 (6.30-6.35)	.030 (.75)
7	.250-.252 (6.35-6.40)	.032 (.80)

Fig. 11: Measuring Front Cover for Shim Selection

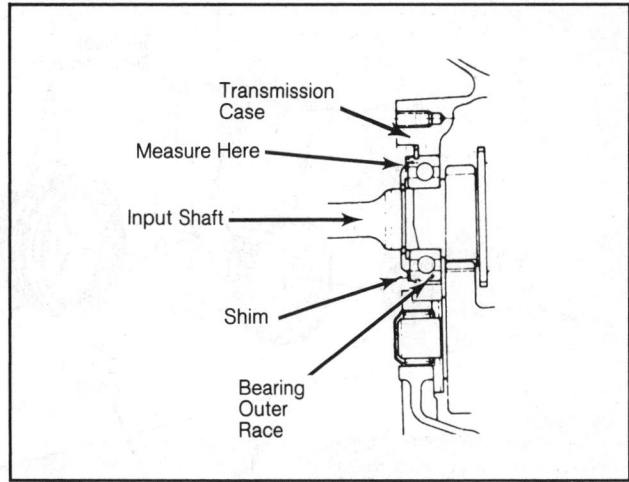

TIGHTENING SPECIFICATIONS

Application	Ft. Lbs (N.m)
Transmission Case-to-Engine	12-16 (16-22)
Countergear Nut	36-43 (50-60)
Front Cover	7-12 (10-16)
Extension Housing	12-16 (16-22)

Manual Transmissions

FIAT SPIDER 2000 5-SPEED

DESCRIPTION

Transmission is a 5-speed fully synchronized constant mesh type. Forward gears are helical cut and are in constant mesh with corresponding gears on countershaft. The transmission case is in 4 parts, clutch housing, main case, rear housing and shift tower. The rear housing contains the 5th and reverse gears. The main housing has an oil pan which can be removed for inspection of inner housing and gear components.

LUBRICATION & ADJUSTMENT

See the appropriate article in MANUAL TRANS-MISSION SERVICING Section.

TROUBLE SHOOTING

HARD SHIFTING

Improperly adjusted clutch. Weakened synchro insert spring. Face of synchro ring in contact with insert, worn. Cones on synchro ring and gear worn or not in proper contact.

SLIPS OUT OF GEAR

Bearings worn or defective. Excessive play between gears and collars. Play in clutch hub and sliding sleeve. Shift arm worn. Lock ball spring weak or broken.

TRANSMISSION NOISY

Low or incorrect lubricant. Gears or bearings worn or damaged. Worn gears or collars. Worn clutch hub or mainshaft splines. Incorrectly meshed gears.

REMOVAL & INSTALLATION

See the appropriate article in MANUAL TRANS-MISSION REMOVAL Section.

TRANSMISSION DISASSEMBLY

1) Drain transmission fluid. Place transmission on holding fixture. Remove 3 self-locking nuts on flexible coupling and remove from flange. Remove clutch return spring and rear crossmember. Remove clutch release fork and throw-out bearing. Remove clutch housing bolts and remove housing, gasket and seal.

2) Remove speedometer gear from extension housing. Remove 4 nuts from shift tower and remove tower by pushing shift lever forward until tab on dog clears engaging lever in rear housing. Remove snap ring, spacer, seal and spring from rear yoke. Use socket and remove nut and washer, then use puller to remove yoke from output shaft.

3) Remove 10 nuts from oil pan and remove pan and gasket. Remove 6 nuts from extension housing (1 nut is located inside transmission case and can be removed after oil pan is removed). Remove extension housing from case, as housing is removed. Guide gear selector and engaging lever out of fork shafts. Remove gasket and seal from extension housing.

4) Remove bolt from 5th-Reverse shift fork. Slowly remove shaft from case. As shaft is removed, detent ball will drop into case. Lock transmission in 2 gears. Loosen nut and bolt on ends of countershaft. Remove cover on side of case. Remove detent springs and balls. Remove bolt from 3rd-4th shift fork and slowly remove shaft from case. Remove detent dowels from

Fig. 1: View Showing 5th-Reverse Gear Components

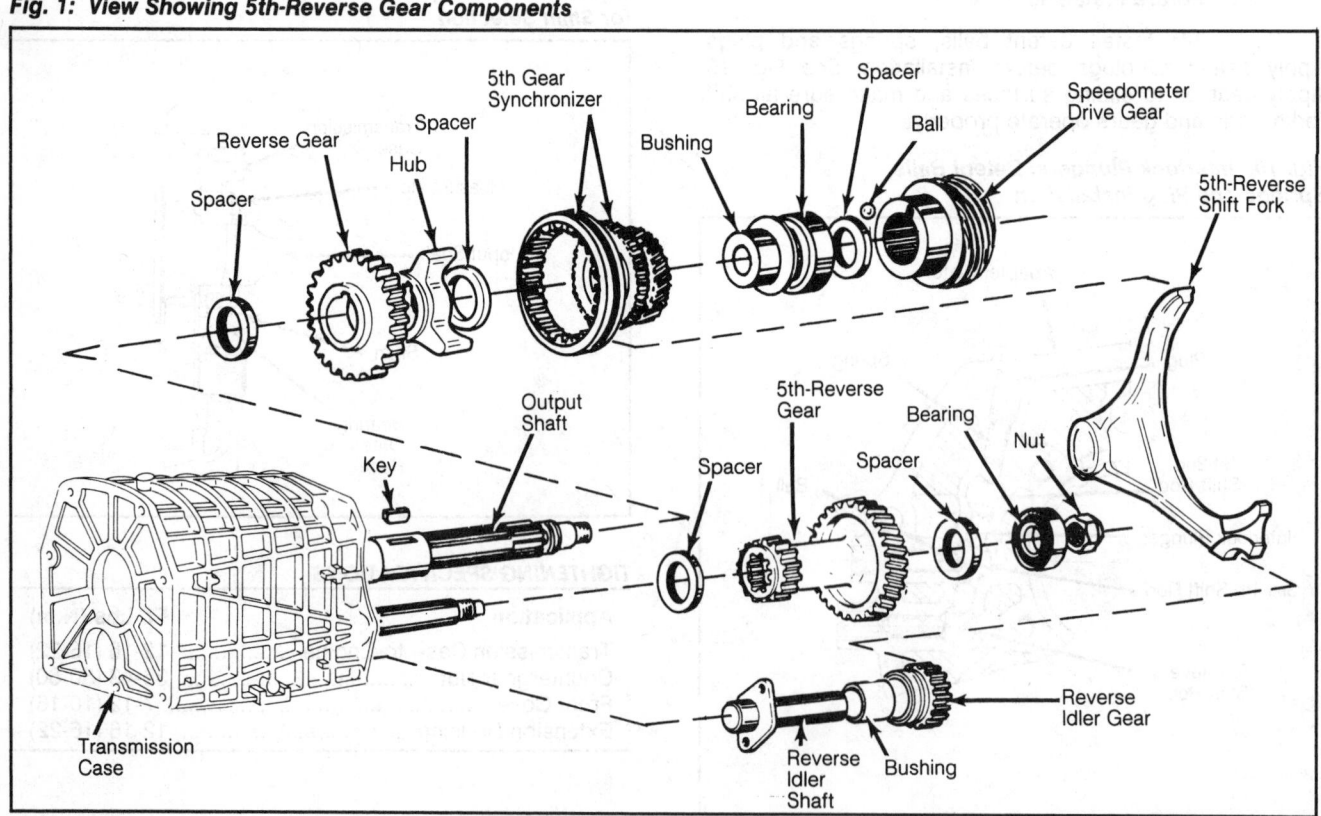

FIAT SPIDER 2000 5-SPEED (Cont.)

case. Remove 1st-2nd shift fork bolt. Remove shaft from case.

5) Remove speedometer drive gear, ball, spacer and bearing from output shaft. Remove nut, bearing and spacer from countershaft. Use a plastic hammer and tap 5th-reverse gear from countershaft, along with reverse sliding gear from its shaft. Remove spacer, bushing, shift fork and 5th gear synchronizer assembly from output shaft. Remove spacer, hub and reverse gear from output shaft.

6) Remove bolt, washer and lock washer from front of countershaft. Using a plastic mallet, tap on front of countershaft until front bearing can be removed from case, then tap on rear bearing until it is free of case. Remove countershaft from case. Remove 3rd-4th shift fork and 1st-2nd shift fork. Remove 3 screws from rear bearing retainer, remove retainer and bearing. Remove mainshaft rearward and out of case. Pull input shaft from front of case.

COMPONENT DISASSEMBLY & REASSEMBLY

MAINSHAFT

Disassembly

1) Remove 3rd gear synchronizer sleeve. From rear of mainshaft, remove bushing, 1st gear, 1st-2nd synchronizer assembly and 2nd gear. Place mainshaft in press with plates positioned under shoulder of shaft. Position sleeve tool (A.70159) over shaft and apply pressure to compress spring washer. Remove snap ring, spring washer and synchronizer hub from mainshaft and 3rd gear assembly.

NOTE: Do not support mainshaft assembly on 3rd gear when compressing spring washer.

2) Position sleeve tool (A.70159) on 3rd gear assembly and apply pressure to compress spring. Remove snap ring, synchronizer, spring and spring retainer from gear. Remove 3rd gear from mainshaft. Remove synchronizer sleeve from 5th gear assembly. Remove and discard snap ring. Using tool (A.70166), remove synchromesh ring. Remove springs, lock and stop from 5th gear.

NOTE: Disassembly and reassembly procedures for 1st-2nd gear assemblies are same as 3rd gear except 3rd gear is assembled on mainshaft.

Inspection

Check mainshaft for straightness. Maximum runout should not exceed .001" (.05 mm). Check splines for damage, remove burrs and nicks with file or emery cloth. Check bearing surfaces for nicks or burrs. Check gears for chipped teeth. Check synchronizer crown teeth for flatness, check sleeves for nicks or burrs. Check 1st gear-to-bushing clearance. It should be .002-.004" (.05-.10 mm). Replace if worn. Check 2nd-3rd gear-to-mainshaft clearance. Clearance should be .002-.004" (.05-.10 mm). Replace if worn.

Reassembly

1) Lightly coat all parts with oil. Install ONLY 3rd gear on mainshaft. On 1st, 2nd and 3rd gear assemblies, install spring retainer on gear with cup side facing away from gear. Install spring and synchronizer with small end of synchronizer facing away from gear.

2) Using sleeve tool (A.70159), compress spring assembly and install snap ring. Make sure synchronizer sleeve can be moved along gear and springs

Fig. 3: Exploded View of Synchronizer Assemblies

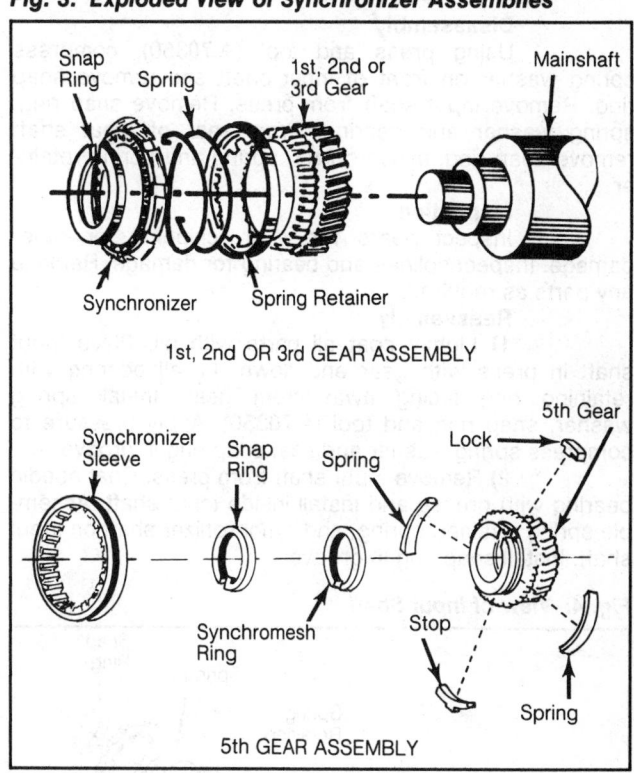

1st, 2nd OR 3rd GEAR ASSEMBLY

5th GEAR ASSEMBLY

Fig. 2: Exploded View of Mainshaft Assembly

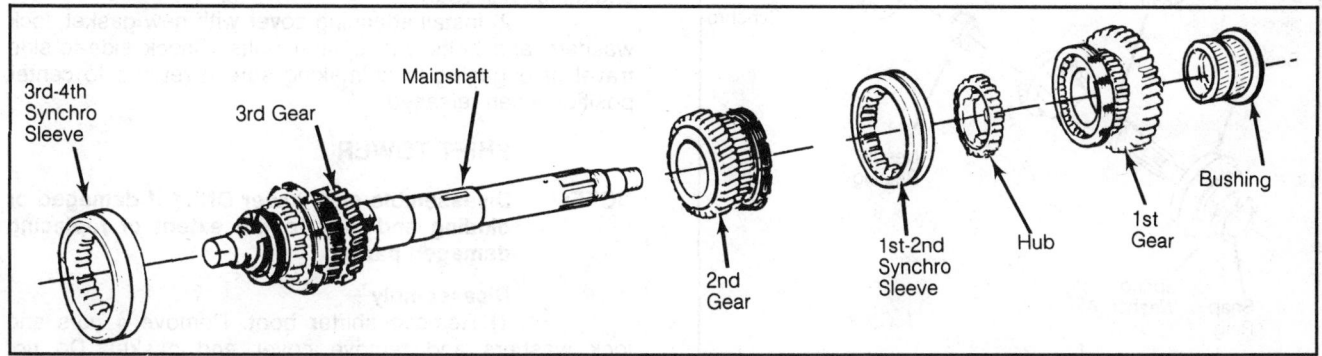

FIAT SPIDER 2000 5-SPEED (Cont.)

back when released. Place 5th gear with gear side down on bench. Install lock into slot in gear. Install stop and 2 springs.

3) Carefully spread synchromesh ring and install around assembled parts so open end is positioned over stop. Using tool (A.70166), install new snap ring with dog end installed in slot of gear. Install synchronizer sleeve. Place mainshaft in press with plates positioned under shoulder of shaft.

4) Install synchronizer hub, spring washer and snap ring. Position sleeve tool (A.70159) over shaft and apply pressure to compress spring washer, then seat snap ring in groove. Remove mainshaft assembly from press.

5) Install 2nd gear assembly, synchronizer sleeve and hub, 1st gear assembly and bushing on output end of mainshaft. Carefully assemble all parts making sure synchronizer sleeve straddles synchronizers on 1st and 2nd gear assemblies. Install synchronizer sleeve on 3rd gear assembly.

INPUT SHAFT

Disassembly

Using press and tool (A.70350), compress spring washer on front of input shaft and remove snap ring. Remove input shaft from press. Remove snap ring, spring washer and bearing. From rear of input shaft remove snap ring, synchronizer, spring and spring retainer.

Inspection

Inspect gears for wear, chipping, or other damage. Inspect splines and bearing for damage. Replace any parts as required.

Reassembly

1) Lightly coat all parts with oil. Place input shaft in press with gear end down. Install bearing with retaining ring facing away from gear. Install spring washer, snap ring and tool (A.70350). Apply pressure to compress spring washer and seat snap ring in groove.

2) Remove input shaft from press. Coat needle bearing with grease and install inside input shaft. Assemble spring retainer, spring, and synchronizer shaft on input shaft. Install snap ring in groove.

Fig. 4: View of Input Shaft

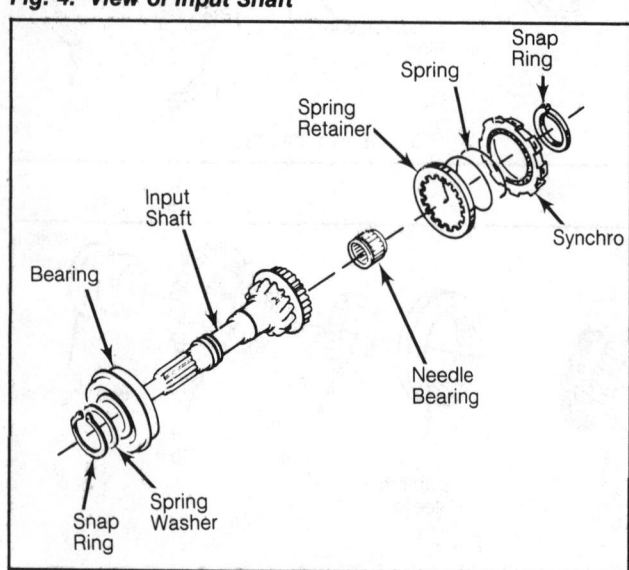

ENGAGING LEVER

NOTE: **Disassemble engaging lever ONLY if damaged or binding.**

Disassembly

1) Remove 2 bolts and lock washers and remove attaching cover and gasket. Slowly slide engaging lever rod out side of rear housing.

2) As rod is withdrawn, carefully remove spring, spring retainer, engaging lever, spring and thrust washer. Remove thrust washer from rear housing.

Inspection

Check engaging rod lever for straightness, excessive wear and/or damage. Check that dog is not bent or damaged. Replace if worn, damaged or bent. Check all springs for tension and/or wear. Replace as required.

Fig. 5: Exploded View of Engaging Lever Assembly

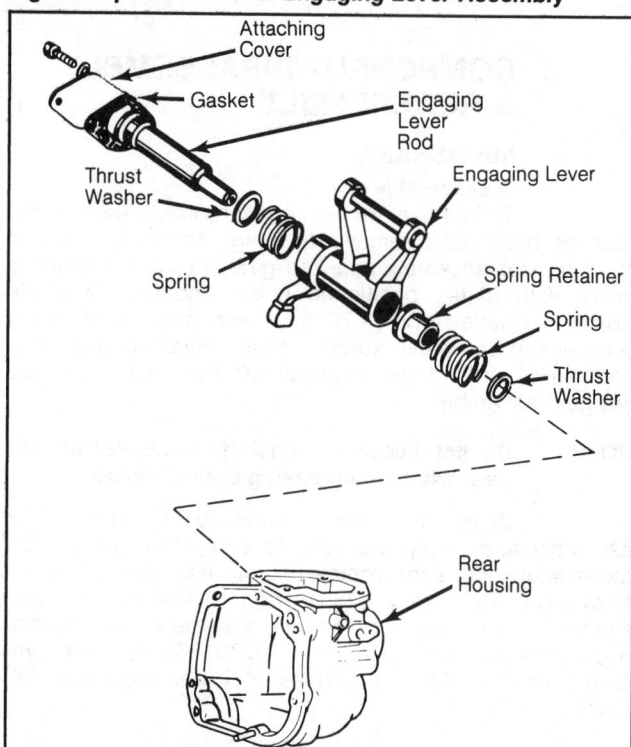

Reassembly

1) Install thrust washer in rear housing. Slowly install engaging lever rod and assemble thrust washer, spring, engaging lever, spring retainer and spring on engaging lever rod.

2) Install attaching cover with new gasket, lock washers and bolts and tighten bolts. Check side-to-side travel of engaging lever making sure it returns to center position when released.

SHIFT TOWER

NOTE: **Disassemble shift tower ONLY if damaged or binding and only to the extent of replacing damaged parts.**

Disassembly

1) Remove shifter boot. Remove 4 nuts and lock washers and remove cover and gasket. Do not

FIAT SPIDER 2000 5-SPEED (Cont.)

remove reverse lockout screw or lock nut unless damaged. Remove 3 nuts and lock washers and remove bearing cover.

2) Remove nut and washer from bearing and remove bearing, socket cover, cover and spring. Lift shift lever from shift tower and remove spring clip. Remove bolt and lock washer and slide shift shaft out rear of shift tower, then remove dog. Remove bearing cap and bearing only if worn or damaged.

Fig. 6: Exploded View of Shift Tower Assembly

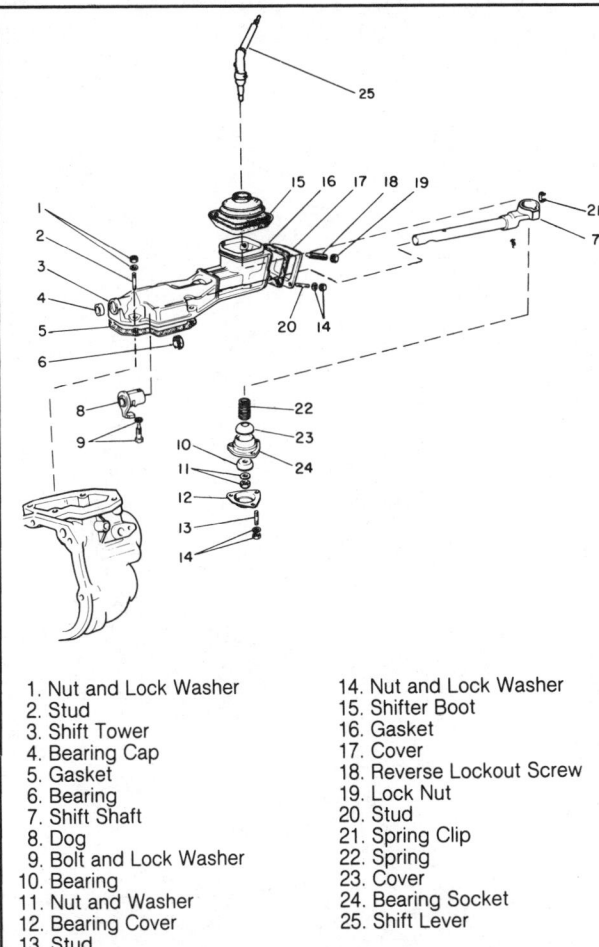

1. Nut and Lock Washer	14. Nut and Lock Washer
2. Stud	15. Shifter Boot
3. Shift Tower	16. Gasket
4. Bearing Cap	17. Cover
5. Gasket	18. Reverse Lockout Screw
6. Bearing	19. Lock Nut
7. Shift Shaft	20. Stud
8. Dog	21. Spring Clip
9. Bolt and Lock Washer	22. Spring
10. Bearing	23. Cover
11. Nut and Washer	24. Bearing Socket
12. Bearing Cover	25. Shift Lever
13. Stud	

Inspection

Check all parts for excessive wear and/or damage. Check that shifter shaft is not bent. Check for free movement without binding or excessive play. Replace parts as required.

Reassembly

1) Install bearing and bearing cap if removed. Install shifter shaft into shift tower and into dog. Install lock washer and bolt and tighten bolt. Install spring clip on shifter shaft and install shift lever.

2) Install spring, cover, socket cover, bearing, washer and nut and tighten nut. Install bearing cover, 3 lock washers and nuts and tighten nuts. If reverse lockout screw was removed, install screw and lock nut in shift tower.

3) Adjust by placing shift lever in 5th-Reverse gate position. Screw in reverse lockout screw until it contacts shift lever. Back screw out 3 turns and tighten

lock nut. Install cover with new gasket. Install 4 lock washers and nuts. Tighten nuts. Install shifter boot.

TRANSMISSION REASSEMBLY

1) Insert mainshaft into case. Make sure there is a bearing in input shaft end, then install shaft into case. Place output shaft rear bearing into position, install bearing retainer and fasten with 3 screws. Tighten screws with impact driver. Check for free movement of input and output shaft. Check operation of synchro assemblies.

2) Install 1st-2nd and 3rd-4th shift forks in their respective position on mainshaft. Install countershaft into case. Install end bearings, washer and bolt on front of countershaft and tighten.

3) Install reverse idler shaft on case and tighten screws with impact driver. Place spacer and key on output shaft. Slide reverse gear, hub and spacer on output shaft. Install spacer on countershaft.

4) Partially slide 5th-reverse gear assembly on countershaft and 5th gear on output shaft. Place 5th-reverse shift fork on its respective sleeve. Slide gears into position on shafts, tap on 5th-reverse gear until it is fully seated on countershaft.

Fig. 7: Exploded View of Yoke Assembly

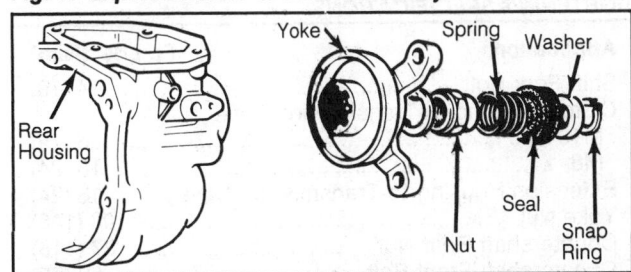

5) Place spacer, bearing and nut on rear of countershaft. Finger tighten the nut. Place bushing, bearing, spacer, ball and speedometer drive gear on rear of output shaft. Install 1st-2nd shift shaft into case. Install bolt and tighten. Install long detent dowel. Install 3rd-4th shift shaft and detent into case. Install and tighten bolt.

6) Install 2 detent balls and springs for shift shafts. Install side cover. Lock transmission gears and tighten countershaft front bolt. Tighten rear countershaft nut. Install 5th-reverse shift shaft. Install bolt and tighten.

7) Install new seal in extension housing. Place new extension housing gasket in place on transmission. Move selector lever rearward and guide gear selector lever into shift shafts as housing is mated to transmission. Install and tighten bolts.

8) Coat rear output splines with grease and install yoke. Install washer and nut. Tighten nut. Install spring, seal, spacer and snap ring on rear of output shaft. Coat seal with grease.

9) Install new shift tower gasket on extension housing. Move shift lever forward and place shift tower on extension housing. Move shift lever rearward to engage dog on engaging lever. Install washers and nuts. Tighten nuts.

10) Install new clutch housing gasket and seal. Coat spring washer with grease and install on input shaft. Install bolts and tighten. Install release fork, throw-out bearing and return spring. Refill transmission with SAE 90 gear oil to proper fluid level.

Fig. 8: Installing Shift Tower Assembly

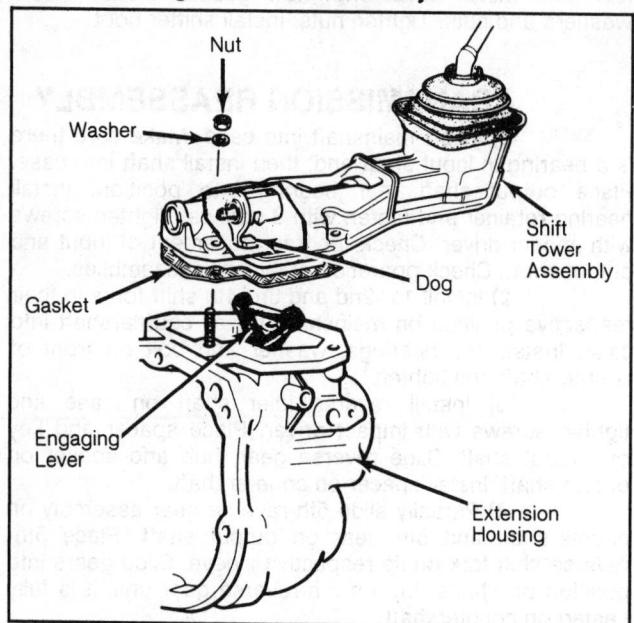

TIGHTENING SPECIFICATIONS

Application	Ft. Lbs. (N.m)
Shift Fork Bolt	14 (19)
Clutch Housing-to-Transmission Case	
M10	36 (49)
M8	18 (24)
Extension Housing-to-Transmission Case	18 (24)
Yoke Nut	108 (146)
Countershaft Rear Nut	87 (118)
Countershaft Front Bolt	69 (95)
Detent Cover Bolt	18 (24)
Dog-to-Selector Shaft Bolt	14 (19)
Gear Lever Support Bolt	14 (19)
Shift Lever Lower Locking Nut	11 (15)

FIAT X1/9 5-SPEED

DESCRIPTION

Transmission and final drive are incorporated in a single case. All forward gears are synchromesh type. High gear is indirect. Helical gears are used for all forward speeds. Access to transaxle internals is provided by a 2 piece case. Final drive is helical gear type and the only adjustment required is side bearing preload, which is accomplished through the use of shims.

LUBRICATION & ADJUSTMENT

See the appropriate article in MANUAL TRANS-MISSION SERVICING Section.

SERVICE (IN-VEHICLE)

AXLE SHAFTS

Removal & Disassembly

Raise vehicle and remove wheel. Remove and discard 6 Allen head bolts from each CV joint at each end of shaft. Remove shaft complete with CV joints. Remove large clamps retaining boots onto CV joints. Remove snap rings from each end of shaft. Slide CV joints off of shaft.

Reassembly & Installation

Slide CV joints onto shaft, making sure that reference groove on outside diameter of CV joint is toward the end of shaft. Install snap ring on end of shaft. Grease CV joint socket and boot with not more than 3.2 oz. (100 g) of grease. Slide boot over CV joint and secure with clamp. Reverse removal procedure to install shafts in vehicle.

Fig. 1: Cutaway View of Axle Shaft Assembly

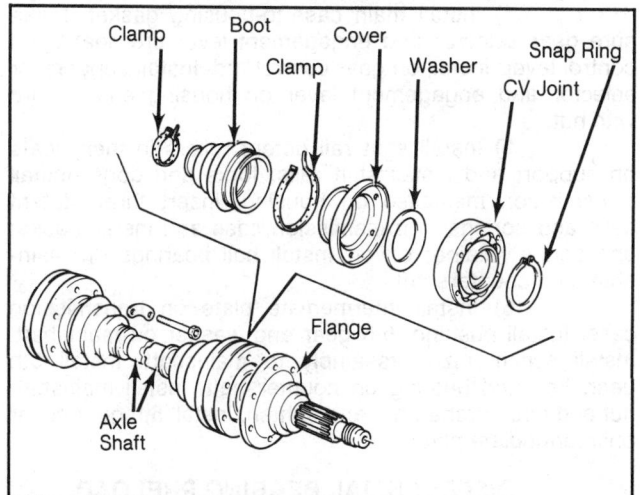

WHEEL BEARINGS

NOTE: Bearings, ring nuts and seals must be replaced with new parts if removed from support housing.

Removal

Remove stub shaft from support housing. Remove support housing from vehicle. Remove thrust ring. Place housing in press and using driver, press hub out of support housing. Remove outer race of bearing from hub with a 3-jaw puller. Smooth out staking on hub

bearing ring nut and unscrew nut with octagonal wrench (A.57149). Remove bearing from support housing using tool (A.74377).

Installation

Using a new bearing and new seals, reverse removal procedure to install.

TRANSAXLE REMOVAL & INSTALLATION

See the appropriate article in MANUAL TRANS-MISSION REMOVAL Section.

Fig. 2: Exploded View of Transaxle Housing Assembly

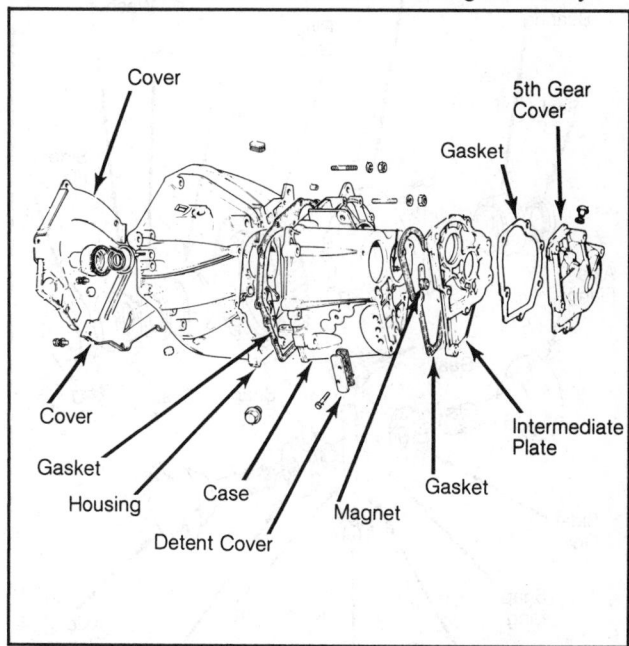

TRANSAXLE DISASSEMBLY

1) Mount transaxle in a support fixture and drain fluid. Remove screws securing oil boots. Remove axle drive flanges. Remove back-up light switch. Remove 5th gear cover.

2) Hold countershaft and mainshaft from turning, then remove countershaft and mainshaft nuts (do not reuse these nuts upon reassembly). Remove shift fork, synchro sleeve and synchro hub from mainshaft. Remove 5th gears from countershaft and mainshaft.

3) Remove 5th gear inner bearing race from mainshaft. Remove intermediate plate from transaxle case. Remove snap rings from mainshaft and countershaft bearings. Remove detent cover, gasket, balls and springs. Remove nuts attaching housing to main case and lift housing off of studs.

4) Remove mainshaft and countershaft bearings using a puller. Remove screws retaining shift forks and dogs to rails. Remove rails, forks and dogs from their seats in housing. Remove gear selector engagement lever support. Remove case-to-housing gasket.

5) Remove reverse idler shaft retaining plate nut and remove plate and shaft. Remove countershaft, mainshaft and differential assemblies. Remove retaining lever, then remove gearshift control rod.

Manual Transmissions

FIAT X1/9 5-SPEED (Cont.)

COMPONENT DISASSEMBLY & REASSEMBLY

DIFFERENTIAL ASSEMBLY

Disassembly

Remove 8 ring gear bolts. Using a puller, remove differential bearings and speedometer drive gear. Remove pinion shaft roll pin. Drive pinion shaft out of case. Remove side gears and pinion gears.

Fig. 3: Exploded View of Differential Assembly

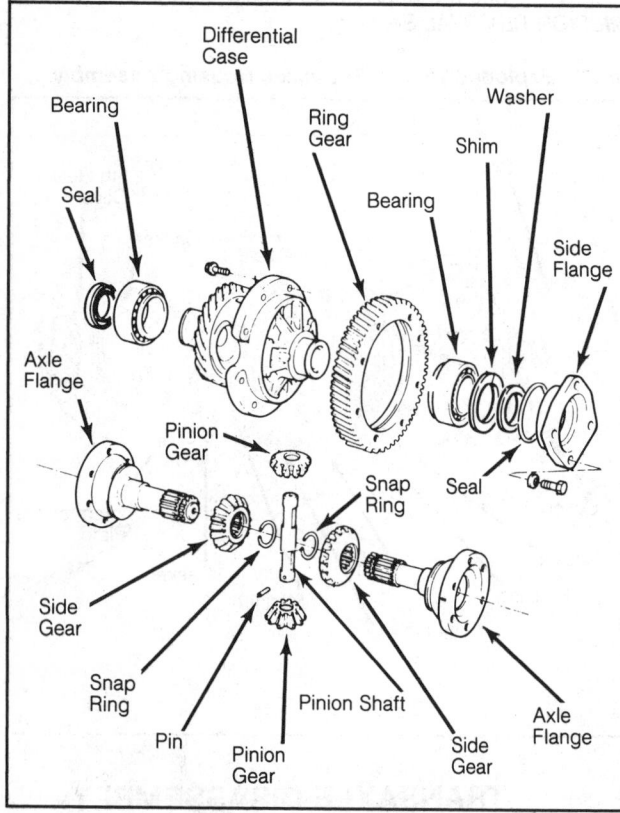

Reassembly

1) Carefully inspect all parts for wear or damage. Install side gears in case directly opposite each other, seated in their counterbores. Install pinion gear in mesh with side gears.

2) Carefully rotate assembly so that pinion gear is directly opposite large opening in case and place 2nd pinion gear in mesh. Insert pinion shaft through pinion gears and line up hole in shaft with hole in case. Insert pinion shaft retaining pin.

3) Using a driver, install differential bearings and speedometer drive gear. Install lock plate and pinion gear on case with 8 bolts.

TRANSAXLE REASSEMBLY & ADJUSTMENT

TRANSAXLE REASSEMBLY

1) Install mainshaft bearing and outer bearing ring for differential in housing. Install gearshift control rod in housing, complete with spring, gaskets, cover and boot. Install control lever on end of rod. Install differential case assembly in housing.

2) Check mainshaft runout, using a dial indicator, by placing shaft on centers and rotating by hand. Maximum runout is .001" (.03 mm). Check clearance between bushings and mainshaft gears, this clearance should be .001-.003" (.03-.08 mm). Install mainshaft and countershaft in housing. Check backlash between mainshaft and countershaft gears. Standard backlash is .004-.008" (.10-.20 mm).

Fig. 4: Exploded View of Countershaft Assembly

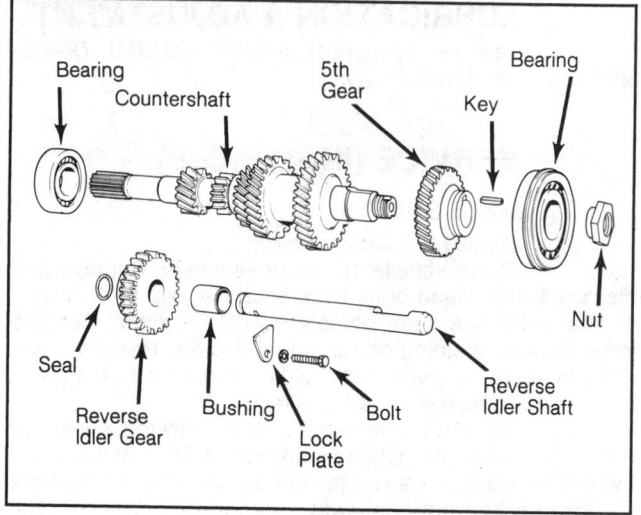

3) Check that clearance between reverse idler shaft and reverse idler gear bushing is .003-.006" (.08-.15 mm). Install reverse idler gear assembly with gasket in housing. Secure shaft with plate and bolt.

4) Install main case-to-housing gasket. Make sure gear selector and engagement lever are seated on control lever; install on gear control rod. Install support for selector and engagement lever on housing and secure with nut.

5) Install shift rail detent rollers in their seats on support and install shift rails, forks and dogs. Install transmission maincase on housing. Insert three detent balls and springs in transmission case and install gasket and spring retainer cover. Install ball bearings on mainshaft and countershaft.

6) Install intermediate plate on transmission case. Install bushing, 5th gear and washer on mainshaft. Install synchronizer assembly to mainshaft. Install 5th gear, key and bearing on countershaft. Install mainshaft nut and countershaft nut and tighten. Install 5th gear cover on intermediate plate.

DIFFERENTIAL BEARING PRELOAD ADJUSTMENT

1) Settle bearings by applying an axial load of about 770 lbs. (350 kg) to bearings. Set fixture A.95655 with dial indicator on sealing cover mounting surface and zero dial indicator on outer ring of bearing.

2) Without changing indicator, place fixture on sealing cover with indicator tip on cover and case mating surface. To determine necessary shim thickness, ADD .003" (.08 mm) to value on dial indicator. Select shim as close as possible to this value.

3) If fixture A.95655 is not available, place outer ring of carrier bearing in its seat and place shims on top of bearing. Place retaining flange on shims. Using

FIAT X1/9 5-SPEED (Cont.)

Fig. 5: Exploded View of Fiat 5-Speed Transaxle Mainshaft Assembly

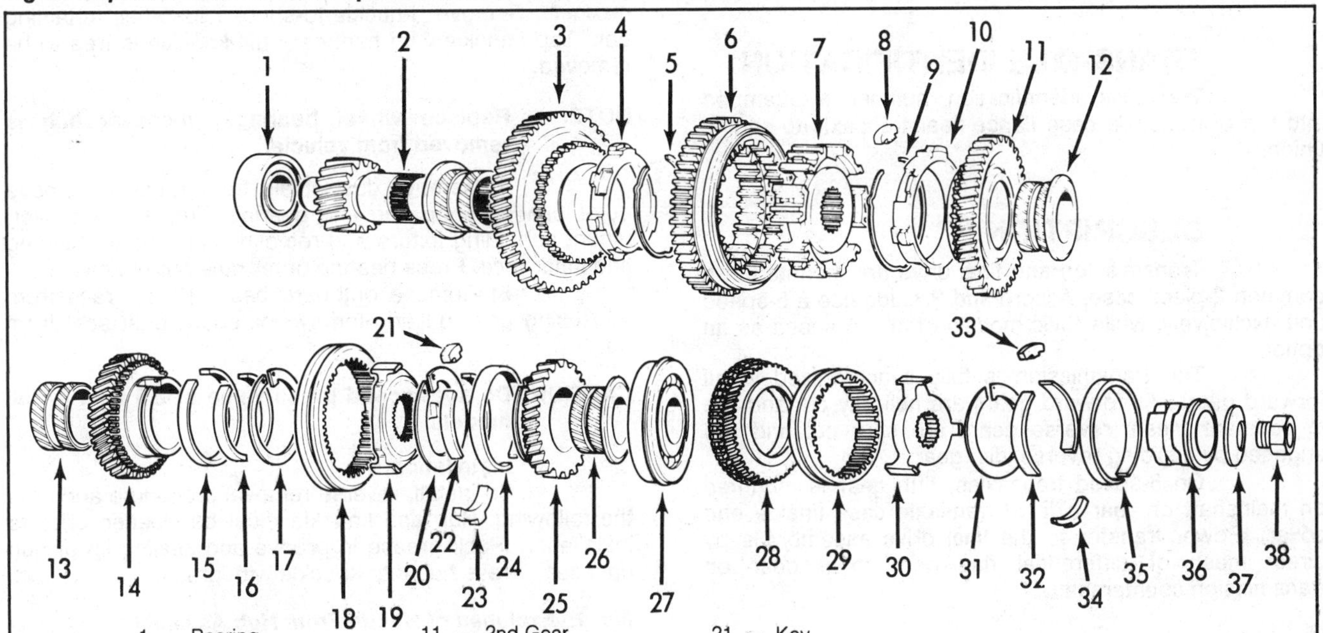

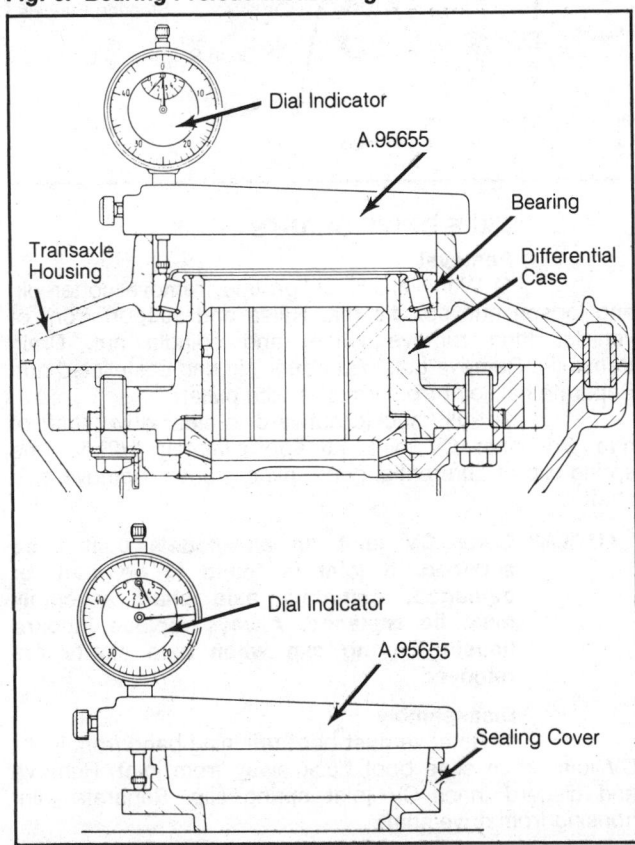

1 — Bearing	11 — 2nd Gear
2 — Mainshaft	12 — Bushing
3 — 1st Gear	13 — Bushing
4 — Synchronizer	14 — 3rd Gear
5 — Spring	15 — Synchronizer
6 — Reverse Gear	16 — Spring
7 — Hub	17 — Snap Ring
8 — Key	18 — Sleeve
9 — Spring	19 — Hub
10 — Synchronizer	20 — Snap Ring

21 — Key	31 — Snap Ring
22 — Spring	32 — Spring
23 — Key	33 — Pad
24 — Synchronizer	34 — Pad
25 — 4th Gear	35 — Synchronizer
26 — Bushing	36 — Bushing
27 — Bearing	37 — Washer
28 — 5th Gear	38 — Mainshaft Nut
29 — Sleeve	
30 — Hub	

Fig. 6: Bearing Preload Measuring Tool

If dial indicator adapter is not available, use a feeler gauge.

feeler gauge, measure clearance between flange and transaxle housing.

4) If clearance is not .003-.005" (.08-.13 mm), add or remove shims to obtain this value. Install 2 nuts on studs through flange and tighten nuts. Rotate gear train 1 full turn to set bearings, loosen nuts and check clearance again. If not to specifications, reshim.

FINAL ASSEMBLY

Install shim for bearing preload calculated above and install cover. Install clutch release lever and sliding sleeve. Install axle shafts into transaxle and lock oil seal boot cover with nuts, then tie axle shafts to prevent them from falling out.

TIGHTENING SPECIFICATIONS

Application	Ft. Lbs. (N.m)
CV Joint-to-Hub Nut	101 (137)
Countershaft Nut	87 (118)
Transaxle-to-Engine Bolts	58 (79)
Differential Case Bolts	36 (49)
5th Gear Cover	18 (24)
Final Drive Cover	18 (24)
Mainshaft Nut	87 (118)
Ring Gear Bolts	65 (88)
Transaxle-to-Clutch Housing	18 (24)
Transaxle Housing Nuts	18 (24)

HONDA 4 & 5-SPEED

Accord, Civic, Prelude

TRANSAXLE IDENTIFICATION

Transaxle identification number is stamped into top of transaxle case flange near transaxle-to-engine union.

DESCRIPTION

Transmission and final drive are mounted in a common 2-piece case. Accord and Prelude use a 5-speed unit exclusively, while Civic models offer a 5-speed as an option.

The transmission is fully synchronized in all forward gears. All forward gears are helically cut and are in constant mesh; reverse gears are spur cut and are engaged by a sliding reverse idler gear.

On 5-speed transaxles, fifth gear is mounted on mainshaft on rear side of transaxle case (inside end cover). Power transfer to the final drive assembly is by direct mesh of differential ring gear to a gear on transmission countershaft.

LUBRICATION & ADJUSTMENT

See the appropriate article in MANUAL TRANS-MISSION SERVICING Section.

TROUBLE SHOOTING

HARSH SHIFTS OR NOISY LOW GEAR OPERATION

Idle speed too high. Clutch not fully releasing.

SLIPS OUT OF GEAR

Synchronizer teeth worn. Interlock mechanism damaged. Weak interlock spring. Shift linkage out of adjustment.

TRANSMISSION NOISY

Worn or damaged gear teeth or bearings. Improperly adjusted clutch. Oil soaked or damaged clutch.

REVERSE GEAR ENGAGEMENT DURING FORWARD GEAR CHANGE

Check for a weak or damaged reverse inter-lock mechanism.

SERVICE (IN-VEHICLE)

WHEEL BEARINGS
Removal

1) With vehicle on ground, remove cotter pin and loosen hub spindle nut. Raise and support front of vehicle, then remove wheel and spindle nut. Remove caliper mounting bolts and support caliper out of way with wire. DO NOT disconnect hydraulic line.

2) Remove disc retaining screw, then install 2 8x1.25x12 bolts in disc. Turn each bolt 2 turns at a time to force disc from hub evenly. Remove ball joint cotter pin and castellated nut, then separate ball joint from knuckle.

3) Remove tie rod end from knuckle in similar manner. Remove knuckle-to-shock absorber retaining bolt. Tap knuckle with hammer until knuckle is free to be removed.

NOTE: **Replace wheel bearings whenever hub is removed from vehicle.**

4) Remove dust shield from knuckle. Remove outer bearing snap ring and bearing. Turn knuckle over, mount in holding fixture and remove seal, inboard bearing and inner race. Press bearing outer race out of knuckle.

5) Remove outboard bearing inner race from hub using gear puller. Remove outboard dust seal from hub.

CAUTION: **Do not exceed press value of 2.5 tons for all models.**

Installation

To install, reverse removal procedure and note the following: Hub and knuckle must be cleaned prior to installation. Pack grease in groove and sealing lip of hub dust seal. Press hub into knuckle with press.

Fig. 1: Exploded of Honda Front Hub Assembly

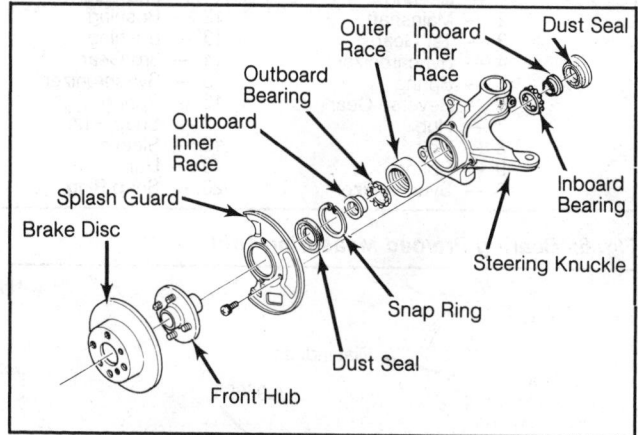

AXLE DRIVE SHAFTS
Removal

1) With vehicle on ground, remove cotter pin and loosen hub spindle nut. Raise and support front of vehicle, then remove wheel and spindle nut. Drain transaxle. Remove ball joint cotter pin and castellated nut. Separate ball joint from knuckle with puller.

2) Pull knuckle outward to clear drive shaft of hub. Pry inner CV joint out approximately 1/2" to free spring clip of differential gear spline groove. Remove axle shaft.

CAUTION: **Outer CV joint on all models cannot be serviced. If joint is found to be worn or damaged, complete axle shaft assembly must be replaced. Always replace inboard housing spring clip when axle shafts are removed.**

Disassembly

1) Remove dust boot retaining band from inner CV joint, then slide boot back away from joint. Remove and discard inner CV joint spring clip. Separate joint housing from drive shaft.

Manual Transmissions
HONDA 4 & 5-SPEED (Cont.)

Fig. 2: Exploded View of Honda 5-Speed Manual Transmission Assembly

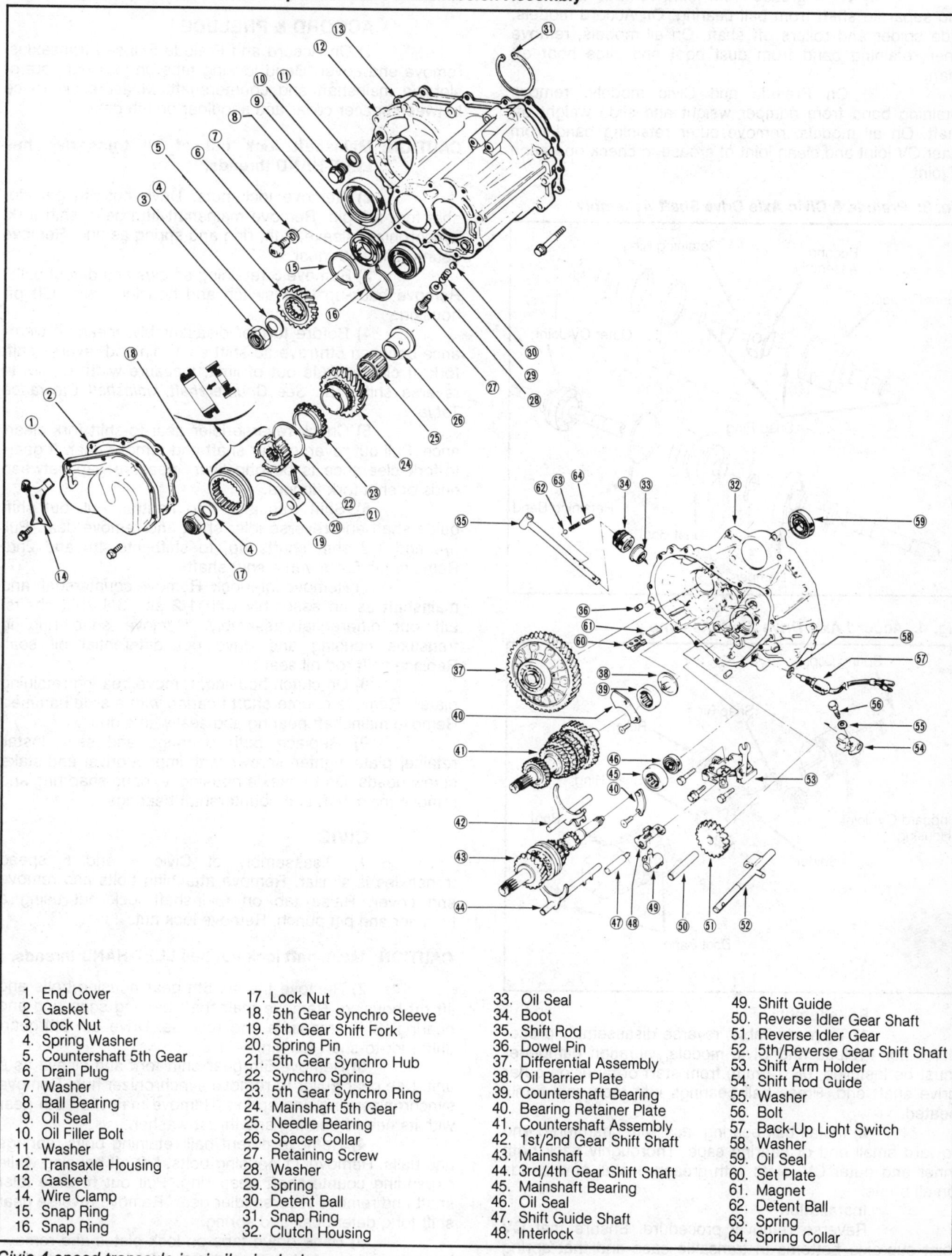

1. End Cover	17. Lock Nut	33. Oil Seal	49. Shift Guide
2. Gasket	18. 5th Gear Synchro Sleeve	34. Boot	50. Reverse Idler Gear Shaft
3. Lock Nut	19. 5th Gear Shift Fork	35. Shift Rod	51. Reverse Idler Gear
4. Spring Washer	20. Spring Pin	36. Dowel Pin	52. 5th/Reverse Gear Shift Shaft
5. Countershaft 5th Gear	21. 5th Gear Synchro Hub	37. Differential Assembly	53. Shift Arm Holder
6. Drain Plug	22. Synchro Spring	38. Oil Barrier Plate	54. Shift Rod Guide
7. Washer	23. 5th Gear Synchro Ring	39. Countershaft Bearing	55. Washer
8. Ball Bearing	24. Mainshaft 5th Gear	40. Bearing Retainer Plate	56. Bolt
9. Oil Seal	25. Needle Bearing	41. Countershaft Assembly	57. Back-Up Light Switch
10. Oil Filler Bolt	26. Spacer Collar	42. 1st/2nd Gear Shift Shaft	58. Washer
11. Washer	27. Retaining Screw	43. Mainshaft	59. Oil Seal
12. Transaxle Housing	28. Washer	44. 3rd/4th Gear Shift Shaft	60. Set Plate
13. Gasket	29. Spring	45. Mainshaft Bearing	61. Magnet
14. Wire Clamp	30. Detent Ball	46. Oil Seal	62. Detent Ball
15. Snap Ring	31. Snap Ring	47. Shift Guide Shaft	63. Spring
16. Snap Ring	32. Clutch Housing	48. Interlock	64. Spring Collar

Civic 4-speed transaxle is similar in design.

Manual Transmissions

HONDA 4 & 5-SPEED (Cont.)

2) Wipe grease from joint, remove snap ring and separate shaft from ball bearing. On Accord models, slide spider and rollers off shaft. On all models, remove inner retaining band from dust boot and slide boot off shaft.

3) On Prelude and Civic models, remove retaining band from damper weight and slide weight off shaft. On all models, remove outer retaining band from outer CV joint and clean joint of grease to check operation of joint.

Fig. 3: Prelude & Civic Axle Drive Shaft Assembly

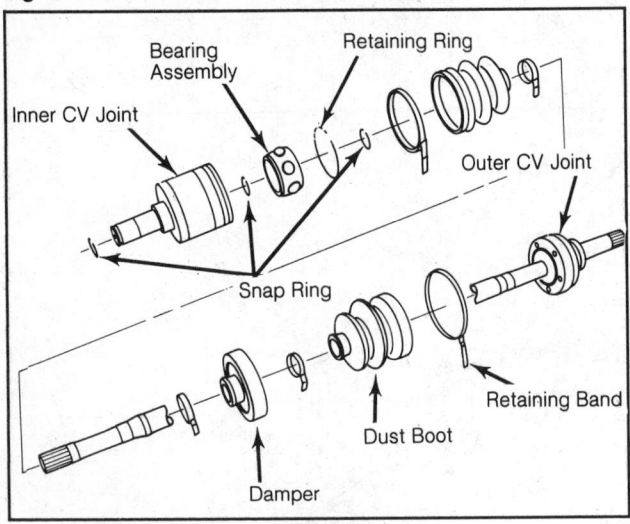

Fig. 4: Accord Axle Drive Shaft Assembly

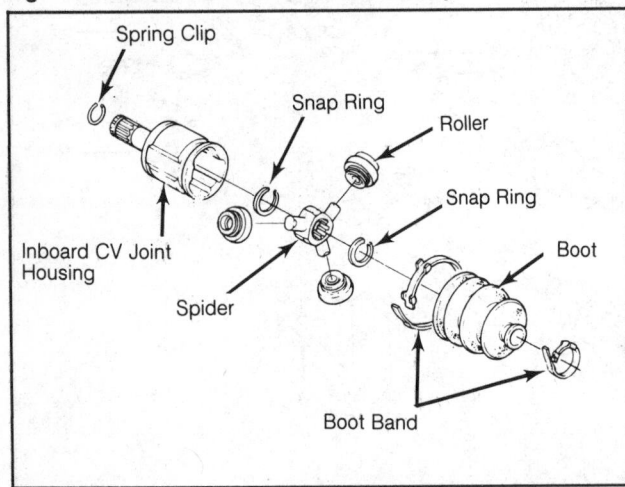

Reassembly

1) To reassemble, reverse disassembly procedure. For Prelude and Civic models, vibration dampener must be installed .08" (2 mm) from start of taper on outer drive shaft end. Press ball bearings into race until firmly seated.

2) Install ball bearing race with chamfered end toward small end of bearing cage. Thoroughly pack both inner and outer CV joints with grease. Install new bands on all boots.

Installation

Reverse removal procedure. Ensure that CV joint sub-axle bottoms in transaxle case and that spring clip holds axle securely in transaxle.

TRANSAXLE DISASSEMBLY

ACCORD & PRELUDE

1) On Accord and Prelude 5-speed transaxles, remove end cover. Bend locking tabs on lock nuts out of slots in mainshaft and countershaft. Measure clearance between spacer collar and shoulder on 5th gear.

CAUTION: Mainshaft lock nut of all transaxles has LEFT-HAND threads.

2) Remove lock nuts. Drive out 5th gear-to-shift fork roll pin. Remove mainshaft fifth gear, shift fork, synchronizer sleeve, hub, ring and spring as unit. Remove countershaft 5th gear.

3) Remove 3 retaining screws and detent balls. Remove back-up light switch and housing bolts. Lift off housing.

4) Before further disassembly, measure clearance between 5th/reverse shift shaft pin and reverse shift fork. If clearance is out of limit, measure width of slot in reverse shift fork. *See Countershaft/Mainshaft Clearance Table.*

5) Check reverse idler gear-to-shift fork clearance. Pull out reverse idler shaft and remove gear. If gear-to-fork clearance is beyond limit, measure gap between ends of shift fork fingers.

6) Shift transaxle into neutral. Pull out shift guide shaft and reverse idler shaft and remove gear. Pull 3/4 and 1/2 shift shafts up, to shift into 4th and 2nd. Remove the 5th/reverse shift shaft.

7) Remove interlock. Remove countershaft and mainshaft as an assembly with 1/2 and 3/4 shift shafts. Lift out differential assembly. Remove snap ring in transaxle housing and drive out differential oil seal. Replace shift rod oil seal.

8) On clutch housing, remove bearing retaining plates. Remove countershaft bearing with a slide hammer. Remove mainshaft bearing and seal with a drift.

9) Replace both bearings and seal. Install retainer plate, tighten screws with impact driver and stake screw heads. On transaxle housing, expand snap ring and remove mainshaft and countershaft bearings.

CIVIC

1) Disassembly of Civic 4 and 5 speed transaxles is similar. Remove attaching bolts and remove end cover. Raise tab on mainshaft lock nut using a hammer and pin punch. Remove lock nut.

CAUTION: Mainshaft lock nut has LEFT-HAND threads.

2) Remove the six 5th gear housing bolts and lift off housing. Remove mainshaft bearing snap ring and bearing. Shift transaxle into reverse. Drive out 5th/gear-shift fork-to-shaft roll pin.

3) Remove 5th gear shift fork and sleeve as a unit. Use gear puller to remove synchronizer hub. Remove synchronizer ring and spring. Remove mainshaft 5th gear with its needle bearing and thrust washer.

4) Remove detent ball retaining bolts, springs and balls. Remove 11 housing bolts. Lift off housing while expanding countershaft snap ring. Pull out reverse idler shaft and remove reverse idler gear. Remove reverse gear shift fork, detent ball and spring.

5) Bend down tabs on lock plates and remove bolts from shift forks. Remove the 5th/reverse, 1st/2nd

HONDA 4 & 5-SPEED (Cont.)

and 3rd/4th shift shafts. Shift synchronizer into 2nd position and remove the 1st/2nd shift fork. Lift out countershaft and mainshaft as an assembly.

6) Lift out differential assembly. Remove snap ring and drive out differential seal. Remove shift arm holder and selector arm. Drive out seals in clutch and transaxle housings. Replace shift rod oil seal.

7) On clutch housing, remove bearing retainer plate. Use slide hammer to remove countershaft bearing. Replace bearing. Install retainer plate, tighten screws with impact driver and stake screw heads. Remove mainshaft bearing and seal using a drift and hammer.

Fig. 5: Exploded View of 5th Gear Components

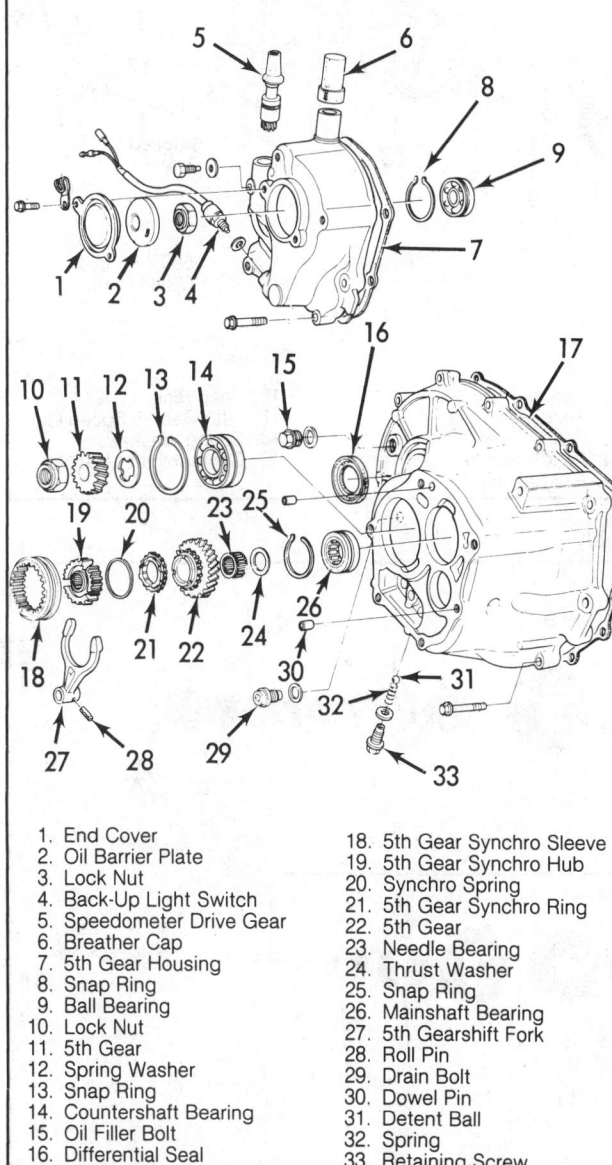

1. End Cover	18. 5th Gear Synchro Sleeve
2. Oil Barrier Plate	19. 5th Gear Synchro Hub
3. Lock Nut	20. Synchro Spring
4. Back-Up Light Switch	21. 5th Gear Synchro Ring
5. Speedometer Drive Gear	22. 5th Gear
6. Breather Cap	23. Needle Bearing
7. 5th Gear Housing	24. Thrust Washer
8. Snap Ring	25. Snap Ring
9. Ball Bearing	26. Mainshaft Bearing
10. Lock Nut	27. 5th Gearshift Fork
11. 5th Gear	28. Roll Pin
12. Spring Washer	29. Drain Bolt
13. Snap Ring	30. Dowel Pin
14. Countershaft Bearing	31. Detent Ball
15. Oil Filler Bolt	32. Spring
16. Differential Seal	33. Retaining Screw
17. Transaxle Housing	

Civic model is shown; Accord and Prelude are similar.

COMPONENT DISASSEMBLY & REASSEMBLY

NOTE: **Measure mainshaft and countershaft clearances before disassembly. If clearances are within specifications, disassembly of shafts is unnecessary. Check clearances with all bearings and 5th gear components installed. Lock nuts must be tightened to specifications.**

COUNTERSHAFT

Disassembly (All Models)

Remove lock nut and washer. Using a puller, remove ball bearing. With illustration as a guide, remove remaining parts from countershaft.

Inspection

1) Inspect all parts for wear or damage and replace as necessary. Also, place synchronizer hubs on countershaft and slide them back and forth and ensure they slide freely.

2) Measure countershaft runout. Check oil passages for restrictions. Measure diameter of Civic countershaft at points "A" and "B". *See Fig. 6.* Wear limit for diameter "A" is 1.179" (29.94 mm) and limit for diameter "B" is 1.257" (31.93 mm).

3) On Accord and Prelude, measure diameter of countershaft at points "A", "B" and "C". *See Fig. 7.* The diameter wear limits are as follows: "A"-1.297" (32.95 mm), "B"-1.336" (33.93 mm), "C"-.981" (24.93 mm).

4) Also on Accord and Prelude, measure 2nd gear thickness. Standard value is 1.198-1.200" (30.42-30.47 mm). Replace if worn beyond 1.192" (30.3 mm).

5) On Accord and Prelude models, replace worn out thrust washers. They are available in 4 sizes from .116-.120" (3.02-3.04 mm) in increments of .001" (.025 mm).

6) On Civic models, replacement spacer collars are available in 3 sizes from .074-.076" (1.89-1.92 mm). Thrust washers are available in 4 sizes from 1.103-1.104" (28.01-28.04 mm) in increments of .001" (.025 mm).

Reassembly

1) Reverse disassembly procedures, using illustrations as a guide. Synchronizer sleeve has 3 sets of longer teeth spaced 120° apart that must be matched with deeper grooves in hub. Coat all parts with oil before reassembling.

2) After reassembly on Civic models, torque countershaft lock nut to 65 ft. lbs. (88 N.m). Loosen and retighten to same torque. If clearances are in tolerance, stake shoulder on lock nut with center punch.

3) On Accord and Prelude models, reassemble mainshaft and countershaft and recheck all clearances. If they are correct, disassemble 5th gear components and install bearings in housing.

Manual Transmissions
HONDA 4 & 5-SPEED (Cont.)

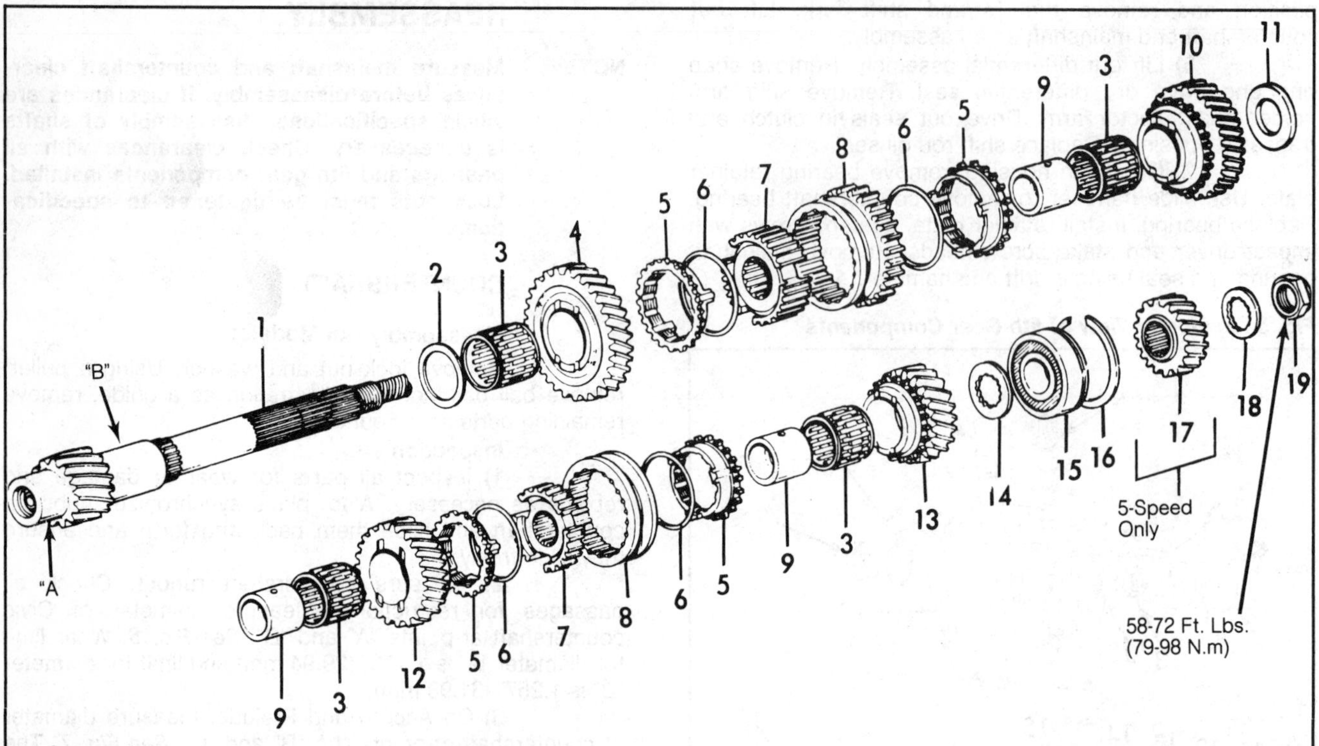

Fig. 6: Exploded View of Civic Countershaft Assembly

Fig. 7: Exploded View of Accord and Prelude Countershaft Assembly

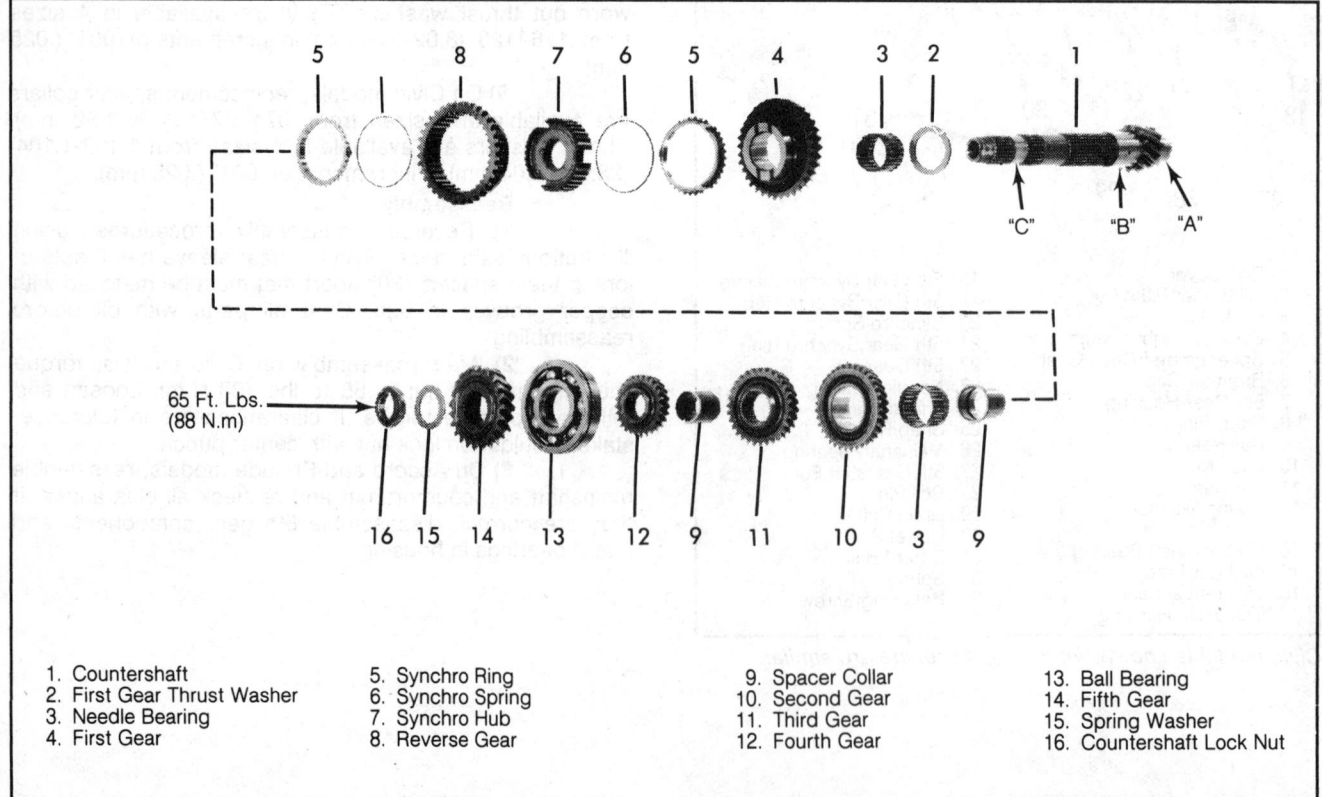

Fig. 6 Legend:

1. Countershaft
2. First Gear Thrust Washer
3. Needle Bearing
4. First Gear
5. Synchro Ring
6. Synchro Spring
7. Synchro Hub
8. Synchro Sleeve
9. Spacer Collar
10. Second Gear
11. Spacer Plate
12. Third Gear
13. Fourth Gear
14. Fourth Gear Thrust Washer
15. Ball Bearing
16. Snap Ring
17. Fifth Gear (5-Speed Only)
18. Spring Washer
19. Countershaft Lock Nut

5-Speed Only

58-72 Ft. Lbs. (79-98 N.m)

Fig. 7 Legend:

1. Countershaft
2. First Gear Thrust Washer
3. Needle Bearing
4. First Gear
5. Synchro Ring
6. Synchro Spring
7. Synchro Hub
8. Reverse Gear
9. Spacer Collar
10. Second Gear
11. Third Gear
12. Fourth Gear
13. Ball Bearing
14. Fifth Gear
15. Spring Washer
16. Countershaft Lock Nut

65 Ft. Lbs. (88 N.m)

HONDA 4 & 5-SPEED (Cont.)

COUNTERSHAFT/MAINSHAFT CLEARANCE TABLE (CIVIC)

Application	Specification In. (mm)
Countershaft	
Runout	.002 (.05) Max.
1st Gear-to-Thrust Washer	
Standard	.001-.003 (.03-.08)
Limit	.007 (.18)
2nd Gear-to-Spacer Plate	
Standard	.002-.005 (.05-.12)
Limit	.007 (.18)
3rd Gear Shoulder-to-Spacer Plate	
Standard	.002-.005 (.05-.12)
Limit	.007 (.18)
4th Gear Shoulder-to-Thrust Washer	
Standard	.002-.005 (.05-.12)
Limit	.007 (.18)
5th Gear-to-Thrust Washer	.002-.015 (.05-.38)
Gear-to-Synchro Ring	
Standard	.033-.043 (.85-1.1)
Limit	.016 (.4)
Shift Fork-to-Synchro Ring	
Standard	.02-.03 (.5-.7)
Limit	.04 (1.0)
Shift Fork Finger Thickness [1]	
Standard	.25-.26 (6.4-6.5)
Limit	.24 (6.0)
5th Gear Shift Fork Finger Thickness	
Standard	.21-.22 (5.4-5.5)
Limit	.20 (5.0)

[1] - 1st/2nd, 3rd/4th and reverse gear shift forks.

MAINSHAFT/COUNTERSHAFT CLEARANCE TABLE (ACCORD & PRELUDE)

Application	Specification In. (mm)
Countershaft	
Runout	.004 (.10) Max.
1st Gear-to-Thrust Washer	.001-.003 (.03-.08)
2nd-to-3rd Gear Shoulder	
Standard	.0012-.004 (.03-.1)
Limit	.007 (.18)
2nd Gear Thickness	
Standard	1.198-1.200 (30.42-30.47)
Limit	1.192 (30.3)
Gear-to-Sychro Ring	
Standard	.033-.043 (.85-1.10)
Limit	.016 (.4)
Shift Fork-to-Synchro Ring	
Standard	.014-.026 (.35-.65)
Limit	.039 (1.0)
Synchro Groove Width	.26-.270 (6.75-6.85)
3rd/4th Shift Shaft-to-Shift Guide	
Standard	.008-.02 (.2-.5)
Limit	.03 (.8)

MAINSHAFT

Disassembly (All Models)

If mainshaft requires disassembly, remove lock nut and washer. Using a puller, remove bearing from mainshaft of Civic. Using appropriate illustration as a guide, remove remaining parts from mainshaft.

Inspection

1) Inspect mainshaft for wear or damage to teeth, splines and bearing journals, and replace complete mainshaft if necessary. Using appropriate table, measure clearance listed and replace defective parts.

2) With mainshaft completely disassembled, measure runout through 2 revolutions. If specification is exceeded or oil passages are plugged, replace shaft.

3) On Accord and Prelude, measure mainshaft diameter at points "A", "B" and "C". See Fig. 8. On Civic, measure mainshaft diameter at points "A" and "B" on 5-speed and point "A" on 4-speed. See Fig. 9.

4) Check clearances against Mainshaft Diameter Table. Replace mainshaft if worn beyond limits.

5) On Accord and Prelude models, measure 3rd and 4th gear and replace if thickness is less than 1.15" (29.3 mm). Replace 5th gear if thickness is less than 1.055" (26.8 mm).

MAINSHAFT DIAMETER TABLE

Application	Dimension In. (mm)
Civic	
4-Speed	
"A"	
Standard	.8656-.8661 (21.987-22.000)
Limit	.8634 (21.930)
5-Speed	
"A"	
Standard	.9837-.9843 (24.987-25.000)
Limit	.981 (24.930)
"B"	
Standard	.8653-.8661 (21.987-22.000)
Limit	.863 (21.930)
Accord & Prelude	
5-Speed	
"A"	
Standard	1.0238-1.0243 (26.044-26.017)
Limit	1.022 (25.95)
"B"	
Standard	1.2592-1.2598 (31.984-32.000)
Limit	1.257 (31.93)
"C"	
Standard	.9835-.9840 (24.980-24.993)
Limit	.98 (24.93)

Fig. 8: Measuring Accord & Prelude Mainshaft Diameter

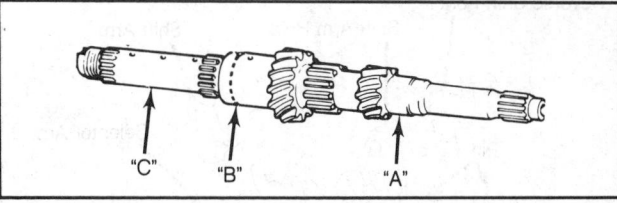

Fig. 9: Measuring Civic Mainshaft Diameter

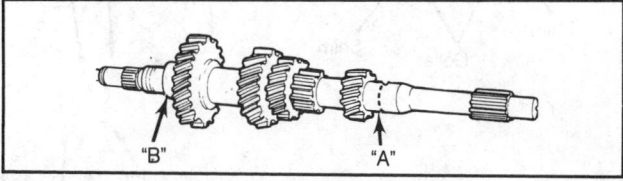

Measure only diameter "A" on 4-speeds.

Manual Transmissions

HONDA 4 & 5-SPEED (Cont.)

Reassembly

1) Reverse disassembly procedure and note the following: Coat all parts with oil before reassembly and ensure correct thickness spacer collars and thrust washers are installed (if used).

2) On all mainshafts, clearances must be rechecked after assembly. Make sure lock nut is tightened to specification.

SHIFT ARM HOLDER
Disassembly (Civic)

Using an impact driver, remove holder plate attaching screws. Slide interlock bar from assembly. Pull shift arm shaft out and catch detent ball and spring when they drop from shift arm. Lift shift arm, spring seats and springs from holder.

Fig. 10: Exploded View of Civic Shift Arm Holder

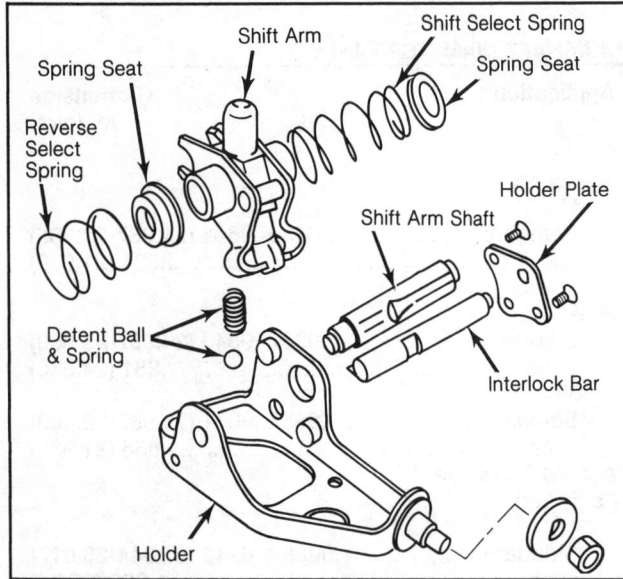

After assembly, check shift arm for free movement.

Reassembly

1) Position shift arm, spring seats and springs into holder. Invert assembly and install detent ball and

Fig. 11: Exploded View of Accord & Prelude Shift Arm Holder

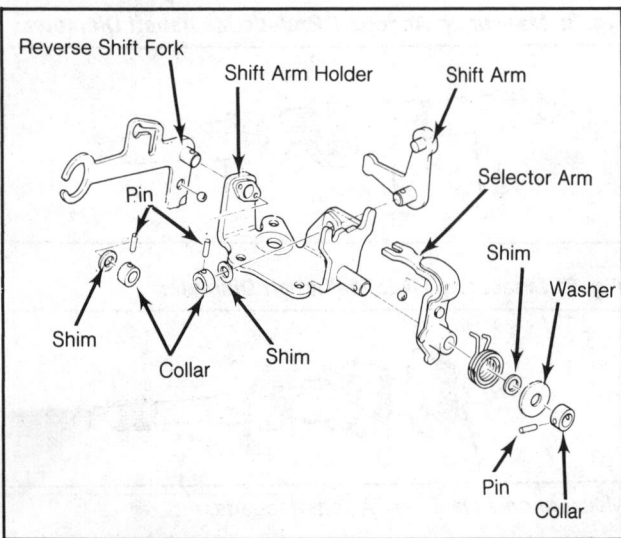

spring into bore in shift arm, then hold ball and spring in place and insert shift shaft through arm, seats, and springs.

2) Install interlock bar. Install holder plate and tighten attaching screws, then stake screws in place with a center punch.

Inspection (Accord & Prelude)

1) Before removing shift arm holder from transaxle housing, measure the clearances between collar and shim on shaft of selector arm. Also check shift arm-to-shift guide clearance and selector arm-to-interlock clearance.

2) Compare values to those listed in *Shift Arm Holder Specifications Table*. Selector arm shims are available in 5 thicknesses in increments of .008" (.2 mm) ranging from .031" (.8 mm) to .063" (1.6 mm).

3) Remove shift arm holder and shift rod. Check shift arm-to-shift rod guide clearance. If worn beyond limit, measure width of slot in shift rod guide. Replace shift rod if slot is wider than standard.

4) Check selector arm-to-shift rod guide clearance. If not within limits, measure width of tab on selector arm. Replace arm if tab is narrower than standard.

Disassembly

Using an impact driver, remove holder plate attaching screws. Drive out retaining pins, then remove reverse fork, shift arm and selector arm from holder. Measure clearances shown in chart. If any specification is exceeded, replace part showing greatest wear.

Reassembly

To reassemble, reverse disassembly procedure and note the following: If collar-to-shim clearances are not correct, select new shim for reassembly.

SHIFT ARM HOLDER SPECIFICATIONS (ACCORD & PRELUDE)

Application	Specification In. (mm)
Collar-to-Shim Clearance (All)	.0004-.008 (.01-.20)
Shift Arm-to-Shift Rod Guide	
Standard	.004-.012 (.1-.3)
Limit	.024 (.60)
Shift Guide Slot Width	.311-.315 (7.9-8.0)
Selector Arm-to-Shift Rod Guide	
Standard	.002-.01 (.05-.25)
Limit	.02 (.5)
Selector Arm Tab Width	.469-.472 (11.9-12.0)
Shift Arm-to-Shift Rod Guide	
Standard	.002-.010 (.05-.35)
Limit	.03 (.8)
Shift Guide Slot Width	.46-.47 (11.8-12.0)
Selector Arm-to-Interlock	
Standard	.002-.01 (.05-.25)
Limit	.03 (.7)
Selector Arm Finger	
End Gap	.396-.400 (10.05-10.15)

DIFFERENTIAL

CAUTION: Ring gear bolts have LEFT HAND threads.

Disassembly

Using a puller, pull bearings from differential housing. Remove attaching bolts and lift ring gear from differential. Using a pin punch, remove pinion gear shaft

HONDA 4 & 5-SPEED (Cont.)

retaining pin. Remove pinion shaft, pinion gears, side gears and thrust washers from housing.

Reassembly

1) Reverse disassembly procedure and note the following: Coat all parts with Molykote before reassembly. After reassembly, place differential assembly on blocks and install drive axle shaft.

2) Using a dial indicator, check pinion gear-to-side gear backlash. Measure at edge of teeth. Backlash should be .002-.006" (.05-.15 mm) for all models. If backlash exceeds limit, disassemble differential and select new thrust washers of different thickness.

3) Thrust washers must be of equal thickness. Thrust washers are available from .028" (.7 mm) to .039" (1.0 mm) in increments of .1 mm.

Fig. 12: Exploded View of Differential Assembly

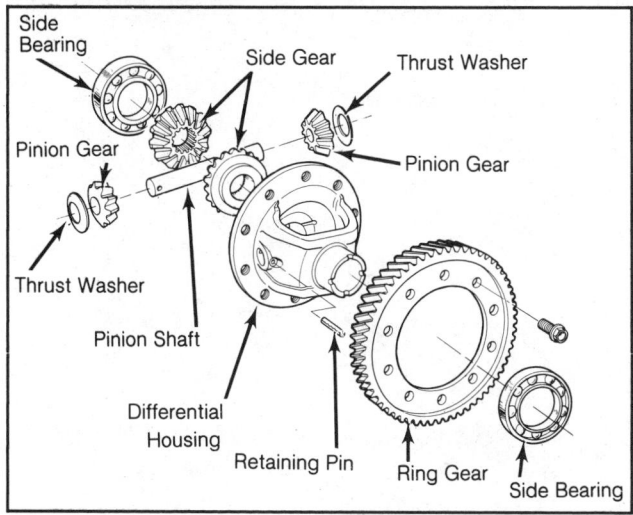

TRANSAXLE REASSEMBLY & ADJUSTMENT

DIFFERENTIAL BEARING PRELOAD

1) Install differential bearing retaining snap ring into position in clutch housing, but do not install oil seals at this time. Install differential assembly into place in clutch housing using hammer to ensure it is seated.

2) Install all transaxle gear assemblies in clutch housing. *See Transaxle Reassembly.* Install gasket and transaxle housing to clutch housing. Install all attaching bolts and tighten to specification in sequence. *See Fig. 13.*

NOTE: If transaxle housing, differential carrier or differential bearings were replaced, the differential side clearance must be measured.

3) Use hammer and driver to bottom differential assembly in transaxle housing. Using a feeler gauge, measure clearance between snap ring and outer race of bearing in clutch housing.

4) Clearance should not exceed .006" (.15 mm). If thickness is not within specification, select a new snap ring of appropriate thickness. Install differential seals.

NOTE: Snap rings for Civic are available in thicknesses from .096" (2.45 mm) to .116" (2.95

Fig. 13: Tightening Transaxle Housing Bolts

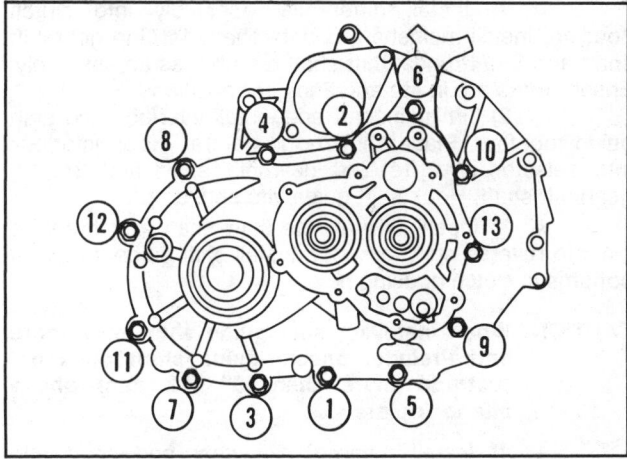

Torque bolts in 3 steps.

mm) in .004" (0.1 mm) increments. For Accord and Prelude models, snap rings are available in thicknesses from .098" (2.50 mm) to .114" (2.90 mm) in increments of .004" (.1 mm).

TRANSAXLE REASSEMBLY

Civic

1) Install differential assembly into clutch housing. Install shift arm holder onto clutch housing and tighten attaching bolts to specifications. Mesh mainshaft gears with countershaft gears, then install both assemblies into clutch housing.

2) Shift into 2nd gear. Install 1st/2nd gear shift fork on synchronizer sleeve. Rotate into place so that lugs on back of fork fit over shift arm. Install 3rd/4th shift fork shaft into 3rd/4th shift fork. Install shift fork and hook shift guide to shift arm.

3) Install 1st/2nd shift shaft. Hook reverse (5th/reverse on 5-speed) shift guide to shift arm and install shift shaft.

4) On 5-speed models, install spring and detent ball in hole in clutch housing. Ensure reverse shift fork is aligned with detent ball.

5) On all models, install reverse shift fork with special washer and nut. Install reverse idler gear and shaft. Install lock plates and bolts on shift shafts and bend tabs.

6) Install transaxle housing and gasket while expanding countershaft bearing snap ring. Tighten housing bolts in sequence from center of housing to outer edge. *See Fig. 13.* Install 3 detent balls, washers, springs and retaining screws.

7) On 5-speed models, install all 5th gear components in reverse order of assembly. Install synchronizer sleeve with chamfered surface facing end cover and synchronizer hub with high side facing 5th gear.

8) On all models, install housing cover bearing in housing with part number facing end cover. Install housing cover. Install mainshaft lock nut and tighten to specification. Loosen and retorque to same specification.

9) Stake shoulder on lock nut. Install oil barrier with plate tang aligned with housing groove. Install end cover. Install differential seals.

Manual Transmissions

HONDA 4 & 5-SPEED (Cont.)

Accord & Prelude

1) Install differential assembly into clutch housing. Install mainshaft, countershaft, 1st/2nd gearshift shaft and 3rd/4th gearshift shaft together as an assembly. Ensure forks are in 4th and 2nd gear positions.

2) Lift mainshaft and install interlock and shift guide together. Place shift rod in neutral. Hook interlock into selector arm, 1st/2nd gearshift shaft and 3rd/4th gearshift shaft. Hook shift guide into shift arm.

3) Install 5th/reverse shift shaft and hook its pin into reverse shift fork slot. Install shift guide so that it bottoms in clutch housing hole.

CAUTION: When installing shift guide shaft on Accord and Prelude, ensure guide shaft does not protrude more than .5" (12 mm) above interlock plate.

4) Install reverse idler gear and shaft and back-up light switch. Shift transaxle into 3rd gear and install transaxle gasket and housing. Shift guide shaft must seat in blind hole in transaxle housing. Tighten bolts in sequence starting from center outward. *See Fig. 13.*

5) Install 3 detent balls, washers and retaining screws. Install 5th gear with high side facing down. Install spring washer with dished side facing 5th gear.

6) Install remainder of 5th gear components in reverse order of removal. Install spring washer with spring washer facing synchronizer hub. Shift transmission into reverse. Tighten mainshaft and countershaft lock nuts to specifications.

7) Loosen and retighten to same specification. Stake shoulders on lock nuts into slots in mainshaft and countershaft. Install end cover. Install differential oil seals.

TIGHTENING SPECIFICATIONS

Application	Ft. Lbs. (N.m)
Hub Spindle Nut	108 (150)
Lower Ball Joint	25 (34)
Cover-to-Transaxle	10 (14)
Transaxle Hsg.-to-Clutch Hsg.	20 (27)
Mainshaft Lock Nut	
Accord & Prelude	66 (90)
Civic (4 & 5 Speed)	41 (58)
Countershaft Lock Nut	65 (88)
Ring Gear Attaching Bolts	
Accord & Prelude	75 (103)
Civic	74 (100)

ISUZU & LUV 4-SPEED

Isuzu I-Mark, P'UP; LUV Pickup

DESCRIPTION

Transmission is a floor shifted, fully synchronized 4-speed unit with block ring type synchronizers and a sliding mesh type reverse. The unit consists of a case with integral clutch housing, center support, rear extension, and gears. A shifter cover, located on top of rear extension housing, contains the transmission control mechanism. The case, center support and rear extension case are aluminum alloy to reduce weight.

LUBRICATION & ADJUSTMENT

See the appropriate article in MANUAL TRANS-MISSION SERVICING Section.

TROUBLE SHOOTING

HARD SHIFTING

Improperly adjusted clutch. Weakened insert spring. Face of blocker ring, in contact with insert, worn. Cones on blocker ring and gear worn or not in proper contact.

SLIPS OUT OF GEAR

Bearings worn or defective. Excessive play between gears and collars. Play in clutch hub and sliding sleeve. Shift arm worn. Lock ball spring weak or broken.

TRANSMISSION NOISY

Low or incorrect lubricant. Gears or bearings worn or damaged. Worn collars. Worn clutch hub or mainshaft splines. Incorrectly meshed gears.

REMOVAL & INSTALLATION

See the appropriate article in MANUAL TRANS-MISSION REMOVAL Section.

Fig. 1: Removing Throw-Out Bearing & Clutch Fork

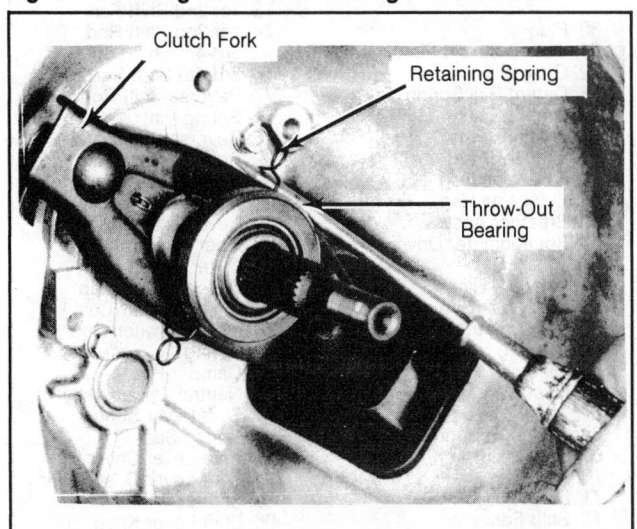

TRANSMISSION DISASSEMBLY

1) Disconnect retaining springs from throw-out bearing and remove bearing, dust cover and clutch fork. Remove 4 front bearing retainer bolts and remove retainer, gasket and spring washer.

2) Remove speedometer gear attaching bolt and take out speedometer driven gear assembly. Unscrew shifter cover bolts and remove cover and gasket.

3) Remove back-up light switch and CRS switch (if equipped). Remove rear extension attaching bolts, then remove extension and gasket.

4) Remove thrust washers and reverse idler gear from reverse idler gear shaft, then remove snap rings, speedometer drive gear and key from mainshaft.

5) Drive out roll pin from reverse shifter fork and remove shifter fork and reverse gear. Remove snap ring from outer edge of input shaft bearing. Slide off center support assembly from transmission case. Drive out roll pins from 3rd-4th and 1st-2nd shift forks.

Fig. 2: Removing Reverse Gear

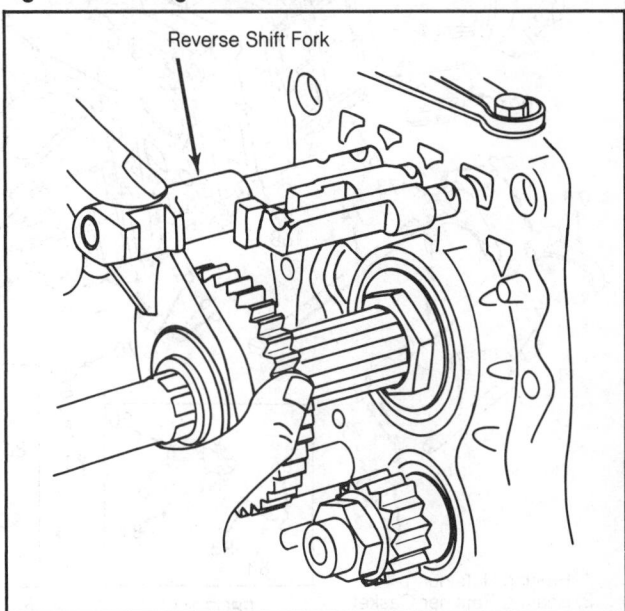

Reverse Shift Fork

NOTE: Be careful not to damage shift forks when removing roll pins.

6) Remove detent spring plate, springs and balls from center support. Slide out 1st-2nd and 3rd-4th shift rods and remove shift forks. Remove reverse shift rod through front of case as it is fitted with detent interlock pins located between shifter rods in center support.

7) Move both synchros rearward to lock mainshaft. It may be necessary to tap synchros with hammer handle to engage them both. Straighten tab on lock washer and remove lock nut and washer from mainshaft.

8) Remove locking nut, washer, countergear reverse gear and collar from rear of countergear. Remove countergear bearing snap ring by expanding snap ring and tapping on front face of center support. Remove mainshaft rear bearing snap ring and remove center support.

Manual Transmissions
ISUZU & LUV 4-SPEED (Cont.)

Fig. 3: Exploded View of LUV 4-Speed Transmission Assembly

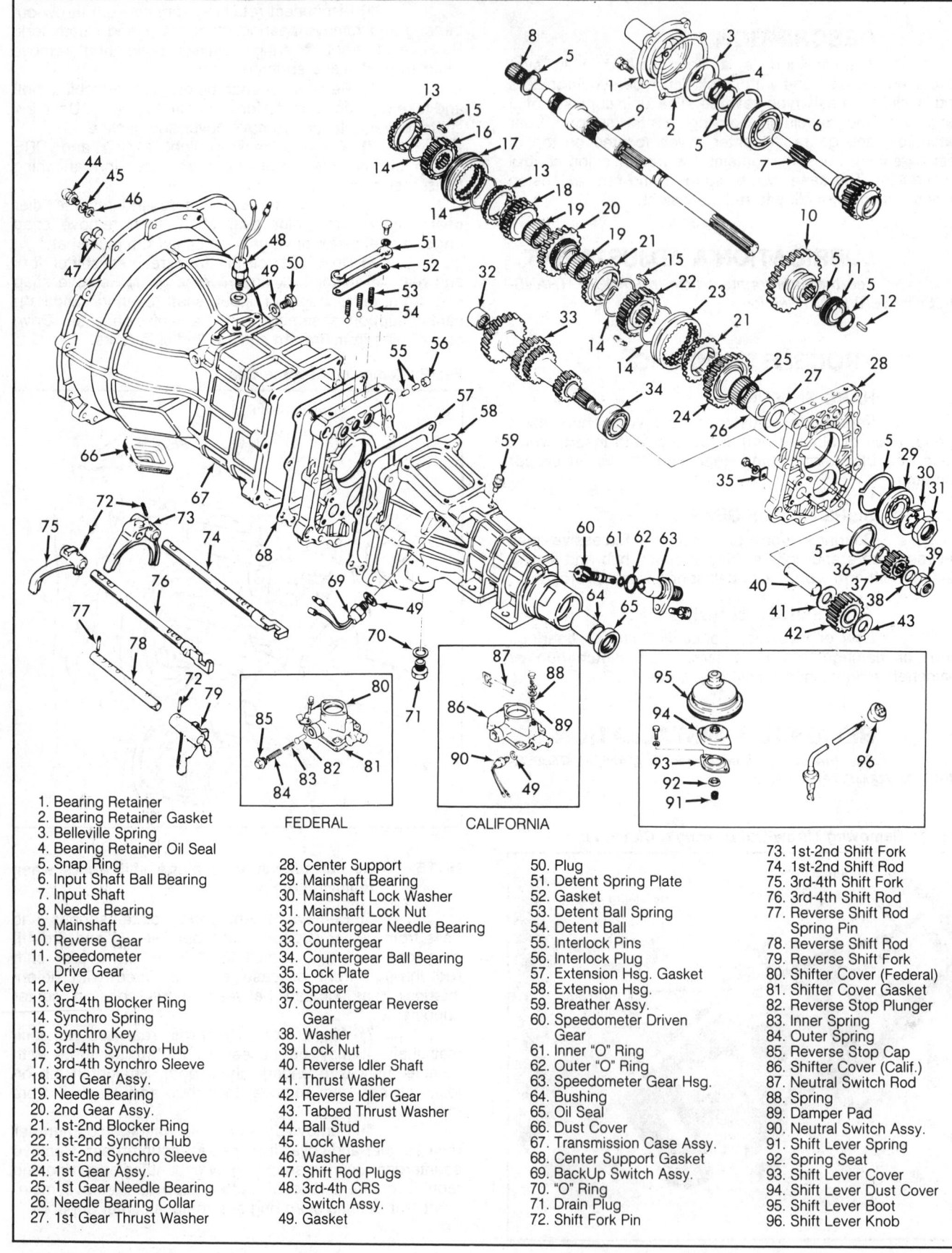

FEDERAL   CALIFORNIA

1. Bearing Retainer
2. Bearing Retainer Gasket
3. Belleville Spring
4. Bearing Retainer Oil Seal
5. Snap Ring
6. Input Shaft Ball Bearing
7. Input Shaft
8. Needle Bearing
9. Mainshaft
10. Reverse Gear
11. Speedometer
    Drive Gear
12. Key
13. 3rd-4th Blocker Ring
14. Synchro Spring
15. Synchro Key
16. 3rd-4th Synchro Hub
17. 3rd-4th Synchro Sleeve
18. 3rd Gear Assy.
19. Needle Bearing
20. 2nd Gear Assy.
21. 1st-2nd Blocker Ring
22. 1st-2nd Synchro Hub
23. 1st-2nd Synchro Sleeve
24. 1st Gear Assy.
25. 1st Gear Needle Bearing
26. Needle Bearing Collar
27. 1st Gear Thrust Washer

28. Center Support
29. Mainshaft Bearing
30. Mainshaft Lock Washer
31. Mainshaft Lock Nut
32. Countergear Needle Bearing
33. Countergear
34. Countergear Ball Bearing
35. Lock Plate
36. Spacer
37. Countergear Reverse
    Gear
38. Washer
39. Lock Nut
40. Reverse Idler Shaft
41. Thrust Washer
42. Reverse Idler Gear
43. Tabbed Thrust Washer
44. Ball Stud
45. Lock Washer
46. Washer
47. Shift Rod Plugs
48. 3rd-4th CRS
    Switch Assy.
49. Gasket

50. Plug
51. Detent Spring Plate
52. Gasket
53. Detent Ball Spring
54. Detent Ball
55. Interlock Pins
56. Interlock Plug
57. Extension Hsg. Gasket
58. Extension Hsg.
59. Breather Assy.
60. Speedometer Driven
    Gear
61. Inner "O" Ring
62. Outer "O" Ring
63. Speedometer Gear Hsg.
64. Bushing
65. Oil Seal
66. Dust Cover
67. Transmission Case Assy.
68. Center Support Gasket
69. BackUp Switch Assy.
70. "O" Ring
71. Drain Plug
72. Shift Fork Pin

73. 1st-2nd Shift Fork
74. 1st-2nd Shift Rod
75. 3rd-4th Shift Fork
76. 3rd-4th Shift Rod
77. Reverse Shift Rod
    Spring Pin
78. Reverse Shift Rod
79. Reverse Shift Fork
80. Shifter Cover (Federal)
81. Shifter Cover Gasket
82. Reverse Stop Plunger
83. Inner Spring
84. Outer Spring
85. Reverse Stop Cap
86. Shifter Cover (Calif.)
87. Neutral Switch Rod
88. Spring
89. Damper Pad
90. Neutral Switch Assy.
91. Shift Lever Spring
92. Spring Seat
93. Shift Lever Cover
94. Shift Lever Dust Cover
95. Shift Lever Boot
96. Shift Lever Knob

ISUZU & LUV 4-SPEED (Cont.)

Fig. 4: Removing Center Support from Transmission Case

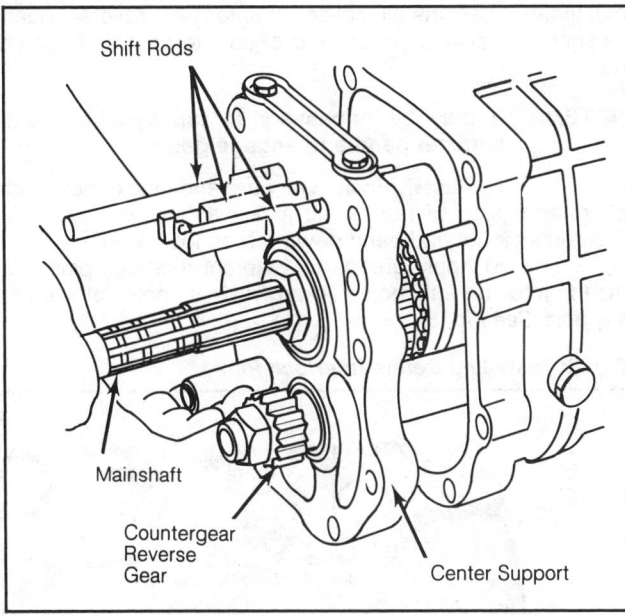

COMPONENT DISASSEMBLY & REASSEMBLY

MAINSHAFT

Disassembly

1) Separate input shaft, needle bearing and blocker ring from mainshaft. Using adapter plate tool (J-22912) and an arbor press, remove rear bearing from mainshaft. Remove thrust washer, 1st gear, needle bearing, collar and blocker ring.

2) Remove 1st-2nd synchro assembly. Remove 2nd gear, blocker ring and needle bearing. Remove snap ring, 3rd-4th synchro assembly and blocker ring. Remove 3rd gear and needle bearings. Remove snap ring from input shaft and press bearing off shaft. Using adapter plate tool (J-22912) and an arbor press, remove countergear bearing from countergear.

Fig. 5: Mainshaft Components

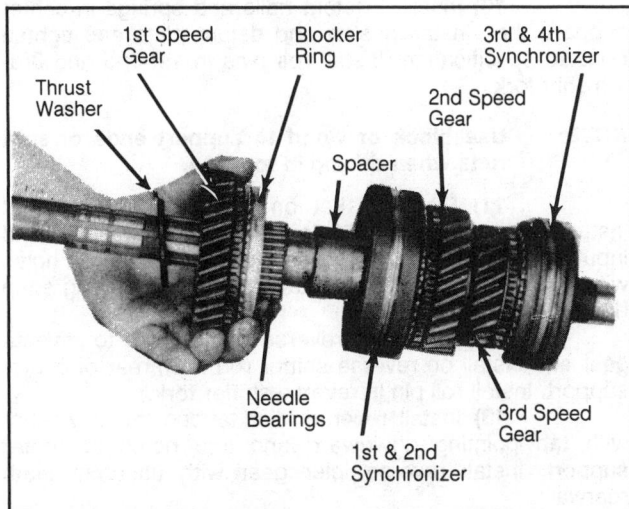

Inspection

1) Check mainshaft for wear, scoring or excessive runout. Maximum mainshaft runout is .002" (.05 mm). Check all gear teeth and splines for wear and/or damage. Check all bearings for smooth operation.

2) Check synchronizer assemblies for wear by holding blocker ring against cone section of gear and measuring clearance. If clearance exceeds .032" (.8 mm), replace blocker ring. Measure inside diameter of 1st, 2nd and 3rd gears. Measurements should be 1.773-1.776" (45.0-45.1 mm) for 1st gear; 1.615-1.619" (41.0-41.1 mm) for 2nd and 3rd gear.

3) Measure inside diameter of 1st gear and outside diameter of collar. If clearance exceeds .0197" (.5 mm), replace gear. Measure outside diameter of reverse idler gear shaft and inside diameter of gear bushing. Shaft diameter should be .866" (22 mm). If clearance between shaft and bushing exceeds .006" (.15 mm), replace bushing. Measure clearance between synchronizer hub splines and mainshaft splines in normal direction of rotation.

4) If clearance exceeds .008" (.2 mm), replace synchro-clutch hub. Check grooves in shift arms and blocks for wear and/or distortion. If thickness of shift arm pad is less than .256" (6.5 mm) for 3rd-4th shift arm and .276" (7.0 mm) for all other shift arms, replace as required.

Fig. 6: Measuring Blocker Ring Clearance

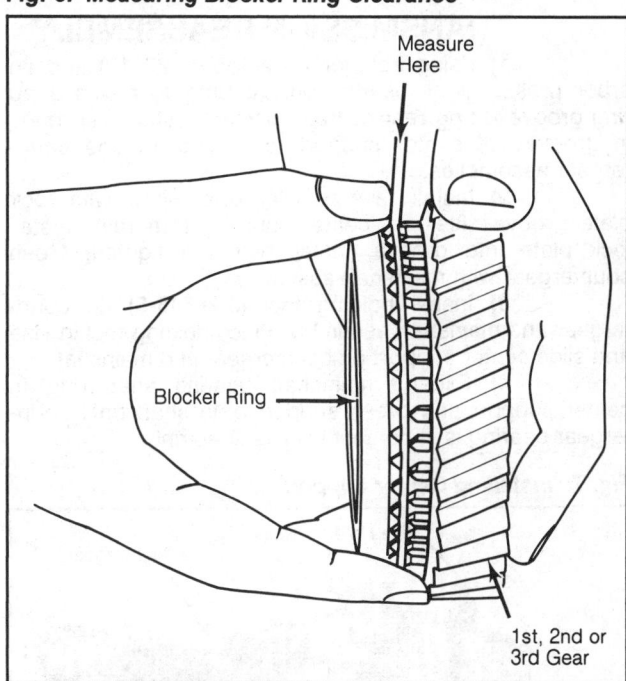

5) Check shift rod detent springs for weakening and/or damage. Measure spring free length. If less than 1.083" (27.5 mm) for all forward gears, or 1.051" (26.7 mm) for reverse gear, replace springs as required.

Reassembly

1) Hold front of mainshaft upward. Install 3rd gear with tapered side facing front of mainshaft and install needle bearing. Install blocker ring with teeth upward. Install synchro hub with heavy boss toward face of sleeve with small chamfer on outer edge.

2) Place keys into key grooves and position synchro springs into hole inside face of hub. Make sure

ISUZU & LUV 4-SPEED (Cont.)

hub and sleeve slide smoothly. Install 3rd-4th synchro assembly on mainshaft with face of sleeve with small chamfer on outer edge facing rearward. Install snap ring.

3) Hold rear of mainshaft upward. Install 2nd gear and needle bearing with taper surface of gear facing rearward on mainshaft. Install blocker ring with teeth downward. Install 1st-2nd synchro assembly with small chamfer on sleeve facing front of mainshaft. Install synchro hub with chamfer on inner edge toward face of sleeve with large chamfer on outer edge.

4) Place keys into key grooves and position synchro springs into hole in either side face of hub. Make sure hub and sleeve slide smoothly. Install blocker ring with teeth rearward. Install collar, needle bearing and 1st gear with tapered side of gear facing front of mainshaft.

5) Install 1st gear thrust washer with grooved side facing 1st gear on mainshaft. Place rear bearing on mainshaft with snap ring groove facing front of mainshaft. Press bearing onto shaft using adapter plate tool (J-22912) and an arbor press. Place input shaft bearing on input shaft with snap ring groove facing front of input shaft.

6) Press bearing onto shaft using adapter plate tool (J-22912) and an arbor press. Install snap ring on input shaft bearing and install needle bearing, blocker ring and input shaft assembly to front of mainshaft.

TRANSMISSION REASSEMBLY

1) Using adapter plate tool (J-22912) and an arbor press, install bearing onto countergear with snap ring groove facing rear of transmission. Install snap rings in grooves of center support for mainshaft and countergear assemblies.

2) Install reverse idler gear shaft with lock plate groove side into center support from rear. Install lock plate into groove, install bolt and tighten. Mesh countergear with mainshaft assembly.

3) Install holding tool (J-26545-5) on countergear and mainshaft assembly. Place holding tool in vise and slide center support on countergear and mainshaft.

4) Expand mainshaft bearing snap ring in center support and press support onto shaft until countergear bearing is in contact with its snap ring.

Fig. 7: Installing Center Support

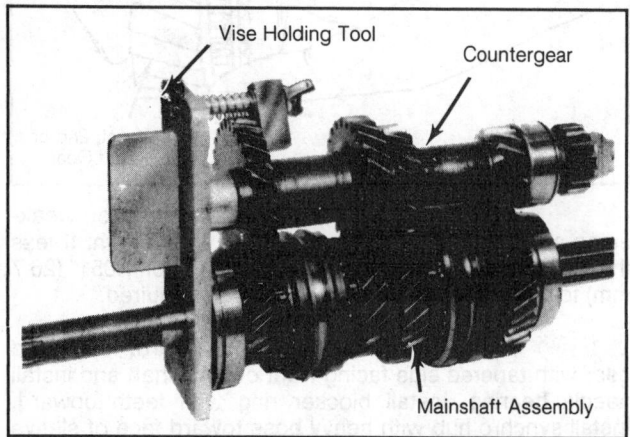

5) Expand countergear bearing snap ring and press center support further until the mainshaft and countergear snap rings snap into their grooves.

6) Remove holding tool from countergear and mainshaft assembly. Slide both synchros rearward to lock mainshaft, then install collar, countergear reverse gear, washer and locking nut on rear of countergear and tighten nut.

NOTE: **It may be necessary to tap synchros with hammer handle to engage gears.**

7) Install lock washer and lock nut with chamfered side of nut facing lock washer on mainshaft. Tighten lock nut and bend down tab on lock washer.

8) Apply grease to 2 detent interlock pins and insert into detent holes from middle hole of center support. See Fig. 8.

Fig. 8: Installing Detent Interlock Pins

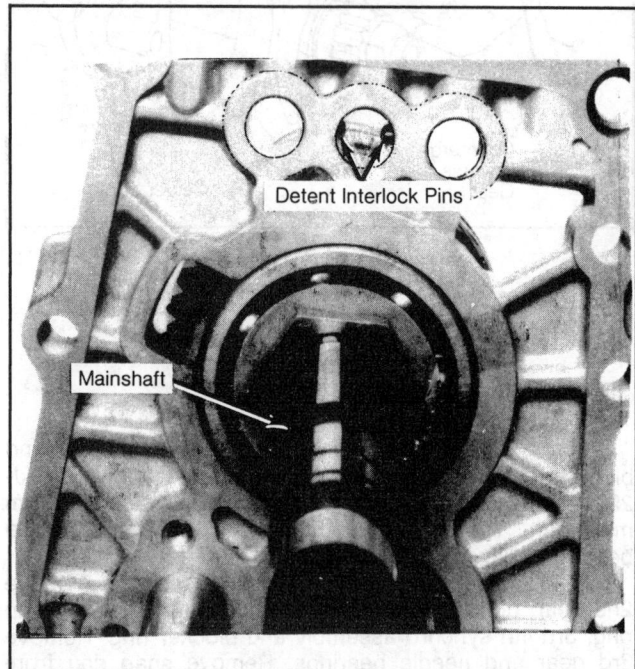

9) Place shift forks into position on synchronizer grooves then install 1st-2nd and 3rd-4th shifter rods through holes in center support and shift forks from front side of center support.

10) Insert 3 detent balls and springs in center support, then install gasket and detent plate and tighten bolts to specification. Install roll pins in 1st-2nd and 3rd-4th shift fork.

NOTE: **Use block of wood to support ends of shift rods when driving in roll pins.**

11) Place gasket on transmission case and install center support with mainshaft, countergear and input shaft assembly, making sure to align dowel pin holes with dowel pins correctly. Install input shaft bearing snap ring.

12) Assemble reverse shifter fork to reverse gear and install on reverse shifter rod from rear of center support. Install roll pin in reverse shifter fork.

13) Install reverse idler tabbed thrust washer with tab pointing downward and into notch in center support. Install reverse idler gear with undercut teeth rearward.

Fig. 9: *Installing Reverse Idler Gear*

Thrust Washer
Tab

14) Install speedometer drive gear snap ring and Woodruff key on mainshaft, then install speedometer drive gear on shaft, aligning gear with key. Install snap ring.

15) Coat outer reverse idler thrust washer with grease and install in extension housing with tab pointing downward into notch in housing. Check gear backlash. It should not exceed .016" (.4 mm) for all gears. If not, replace gears as required.

16) Place gasket on center support and install extension housing. Make sure to align dowel pin correctly. Install and tighten bolts. Install back-up light and CRS (Federal models) switches.

17) Install gasket and gear shift cover on extension housing and tighten bolts to specification, then install speedometer driven gear to rear extension and tighten bolt.

18) Install spring washer on shaft, with dished face toward input shaft gear bearing. Install input shaft bearing retainer gasket and retainer. Tighten bolts.

NOTE: The 2 shorter bolts are used on countergear front bearing side of bearing retainer.

19) Install dust cover, clutch fork and throw-out bearing with retaining springs. Install drain plug and refill transmission with correct fluid.

TIGHTENING SPECIFICATIONS

Application	Ft. Lbs. (N.m)
Countergear Lock Nut	108 (146)
Mainshaft Lock Nut	94 (127)
Detent Plate Bolts	14 (19)
Extension Housing-to-Center Support Bolts	27 (37)
Shift Cover Bolts	14 (19)
Input Shaft Bearing Retainer	14 (19)

Manual Transmissions

ISUZU & LUV 4-SPEED WITH INTEGRAL TRANSFER CASE

Isuzu P'UP (4WD), LUV Pickup (4WD)

DESCRIPTION

Transmission is a floor shifted, fully synchronized 4-speed unit with block ring type synchronizers and a sliding mesh type reverse. This unit consists of a transmission case with integral clutch housing, center support, transfer case with transfer side case and gears. A shifter cover, located on top of transfer case, contains the transmission control mechanism. Another shifter cover located on the transfer side case contains the range and four wheel drive shifting mechanism.

LUBRICATION & ADJUSTMENT

See the appropriate article in MANUAL TRANS-MISSION SERVICING Section.

TROUBLE SHOOTING

HARD SHIFTING

Improperly adjusted clutch. Weakened insert spring. Face of blocker ring, in contact with insert, worn. Cones on blocker ring and gear worn or not in proper contact.

SLIPS OUT OF GEAR

Bearings worn or defective. Excessive play between gears and collars. Play in clutch hub and sliding sleeve. Shift arm worn. Lock ball spring weak or broken.

TRANSMISSION NOISY

Low or incorrect lubricant. Gears or bearings worn or damaged. Worn gears or collars. Worn clutch hub or mainshaft splines. Incorrectly meshed gears.

REMOVAL & INSTALLATION

See the appropriate article in MANUAL TRANS-MISSION REMOVAL Section.

TRANSMISSION DISASSEMBLY

1) Remove retainer springs, throw-out bearing and clutch fork. Remove 4 bolts holding bearing retainer-to-transmission case and remove bearing retainer, gasket and spring washer. Remove speedometer gear bolt, bushing and driven gear assembly.

2) Remove back-up light and coasting richer switch (Federal models) switches. Remove snap ring from input shaft bearing. Remove 8 bolts holding transfer case, center support and transmission case together. Separate transmission case from center support and transfer case.

3) Remove pin from reverse shifter fork. Remove 4 bolts attaching transfer countershaft lock plate, remove lock plate and shim. Remove center support from transfer case.

4) Drive pins out from 3rd-4th and 1st-2nd shift forks. Remove detent spring plate from center support, remove detent springs and balls. Remove 1st-2nd and 3rd-4th shift rods from center support and remove shift forks. Remove reverse shifter rod rearward.

NOTE: When shifter rods are removed, be careful not to lose detent interlock pins. Pins are located between shifter rods in center support.

5) Move both synchronizers rearward to prevent mainshaft from turning. Remove mainshaft lock nut with spacer. Remove transfer clutch hub, transfer input gear, roller bearing, collar, thrust washer, shim and reverse gear from rear of mainshaft.

6) Remove countergear lock nut, washer and collar from rear of countergear. Remove countergear snap ring by inserting snap ring pliers into hole in center support. Tap on front of center support while expanding snap ring. Remove center support while expanding mainshaft rear bearing snap ring.

COMPONENT DISASSEMBLY & REASSEMBLY

MAINSHAFT

Disassembly

1) Separate input shaft gear, needle bearing and blocker ring from mainshaft assembly. Using bearing removal tool (J-22912) and an arbor press, remove rear bearing from mainshaft.

2) Remove thrust washer, 1st gear, needle bearing, collar and blocker ring. Remove 1st-2nd gear synchronizer assembly.

3) Remove 2nd gear, blocker ring and needle bearing. Remove snap ring, 3rd-4th synchronizer assembly and blocker ring. Remove 3rd gear and needle bearings.

4) Remove snap ring from input shaft gear and remove bearing using an arbor press. Remove countershaft reverse gear and countergear bearing using bearing removal tool (J-22912) and an arbor press.

Inspection

1) Check mainshaft for wear, scoring or warpage. Maximum permissable warpage of mainshaft is .002" (.05 mm). Check all gear teeth and splines for wear or damage. Check all bearings for smooth operation.

2) Check synchronizer assemblies for wear by holding blocker ring against cone section of gear and measure clearance. If clearance is less than .032" (.8 mm), replace blocker ring. Measure clearance between synchronizer clutch hub splines and mainshaft splines in normal direction of rotation.

3) If clearance exceeds .008" (.2 mm), replace synchronizer clutch hub. Check grooves in shift arms and blocks for wear and/or damage. If thickness of shift arm pads is less than .256" (6.5 mm) for 3rd-4th shift arm, .276" (7.0 mm) for 1st-2nd and reverse shift arm and .236" (6.0 mm) for transfer range and 4WD shift arm, replace shift arms as required.

4) Check shift rod detent springs for weakening and/or distortion. Measure spring free length. If less than 1.083" (27.5 mm) for all forward gears, 1.051" (26.7 mm) for reverse and 1.615" (41.0 mm) for transfer range and 4WD, replace springs as required.

5) Measure outside diameter of reverse idler gear shaft and inside diameter of reverse gear bushing. Shaft diameter is 1.379" (35.0 mm). If more than .008" (.2 mm) clearance, replace bushing.

ISUZU & LUV 4-SPEED WITH INTEGRAL TRANSFER CASE (Cont.)

Fig. 1: *Exploded View Showing LUV 4-Speed Transmission Case & Transfer Case with Shifting Mechanism*

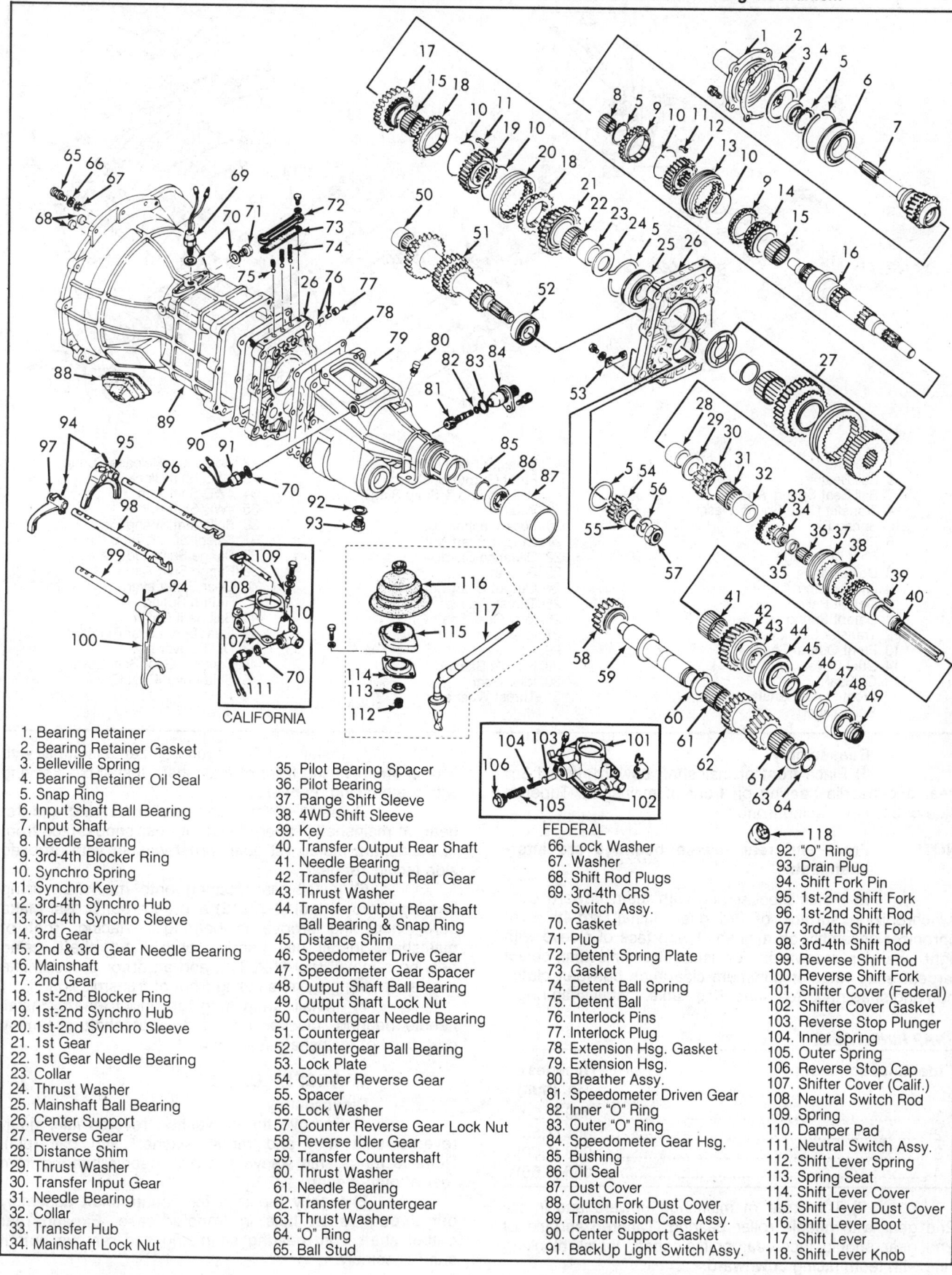

1. Bearing Retainer
2. Bearing Retainer Gasket
3. Belleville Spring
4. Bearing Retainer Oil Seal
5. Snap Ring
6. Input Shaft Ball Bearing
7. Input Shaft
8. Needle Bearing
9. 3rd-4th Blocker Ring
10. Synchro Spring
11. Synchro Key
12. 3rd-4th Synchro Hub
13. 3rd-4th Synchro Sleeve
14. 3rd Gear
15. 2nd & 3rd Gear Needle Bearing
16. Mainshaft
17. 2nd Gear
18. 1st-2nd Blocker Ring
19. 1st-2nd Synchro Hub
20. 1st-2nd Synchro Sleeve
21. 1st Gear
22. 1st Gear Needle Bearing
23. Collar
24. Thrust Washer
25. Mainshaft Ball Bearing
26. Center Support
27. Reverse Gear
28. Distance Shim
29. Thrust Washer
30. Transfer Input Gear
31. Needle Bearing
32. Collar
33. Transfer Hub
34. Mainshaft Lock Nut

35. Pilot Bearing Spacer
36. Pilot Bearing
37. Range Shift Sleeve
38. 4WD Shift Sleeve
39. Key
40. Transfer Output Rear Shaft
41. Needle Bearing
42. Transfer Output Rear Gear
43. Thrust Washer
44. Transfer Output Rear Shaft
   Ball Bearing & Snap Ring
45. Distance Shim
46. Speedometer Drive Gear
47. Speedometer Gear Spacer
48. Output Shaft Ball Bearing
49. Output Shaft Lock Nut
50. Countergear Needle Bearing
51. Countergear
52. Countergear Ball Bearing
53. Lock Plate
54. Counter Reverse Gear
55. Spacer
56. Lock Washer
57. Counter Reverse Gear Lock Nut
58. Reverse Idler Gear
59. Transfer Countershaft
60. Thrust Washer
61. Needle Bearing
62. Transfer Countergear
63. Thrust Washer
64. "O" Ring
65. Ball Stud

CALIFORNIA

FEDERAL

66. Lock Washer
67. Washer
68. Shift Rod Plugs
69. 3rd-4th CRS
   Switch Assy.
70. Gasket
71. Plug
72. Detent Spring Plate
73. Gasket
74. Detent Ball Spring
75. Detent Ball
76. Interlock Pins
77. Interlock Plug
78. Extension Hsg. Gasket
79. Extension Hsg.
80. Breather Assy.
81. Speedometer Driven Gear
82. Inner "O" Ring
83. Outer "O" Ring
84. Speedometer Gear Hsg.
85. Bushing
86. Oil Seal
87. Dust Cover
88. Clutch Fork Dust Cover
89. Transmission Case Assy.
90. Center Support Gasket
91. BackUp Light Switch Assy.

92. "O" Ring
93. Drain Plug
94. Shift Fork Pin
95. 1st-2nd Shift Fork
96. 1st-2nd Shift Rod
97. 3rd-4th Shift Fork
98. 3rd-4th Shift Rod
99. Reverse Shift Rod
100. Reverse Shift Fork
101. Shifter Cover (Federal)
102. Shifter Cover Gasket
103. Reverse Stop Plunger
104. Inner Spring
105. Outer Spring
106. Reverse Stop Cap
107. Shifter Cover (Calif.)
108. Neutral Switch Rod
109. Spring
110. Damper Pad
111. Neutral Switch Assy.
112. Shift Lever Spring
113. Spring Seat
114. Shift Lever Cover
115. Shift Lever Dust Cover
116. Shift Lever Boot
117. Shift Lever
118. Shift Lever Knob

Manual Transmissions

ISUZU & LUV 4-SPEED WITH INTEGRAL TRANSFER CASE (Cont.)

Fig. 2: *Exploded View Showing LUV 4-Speed Transmission Side Case Gears and Shift Mechanism*

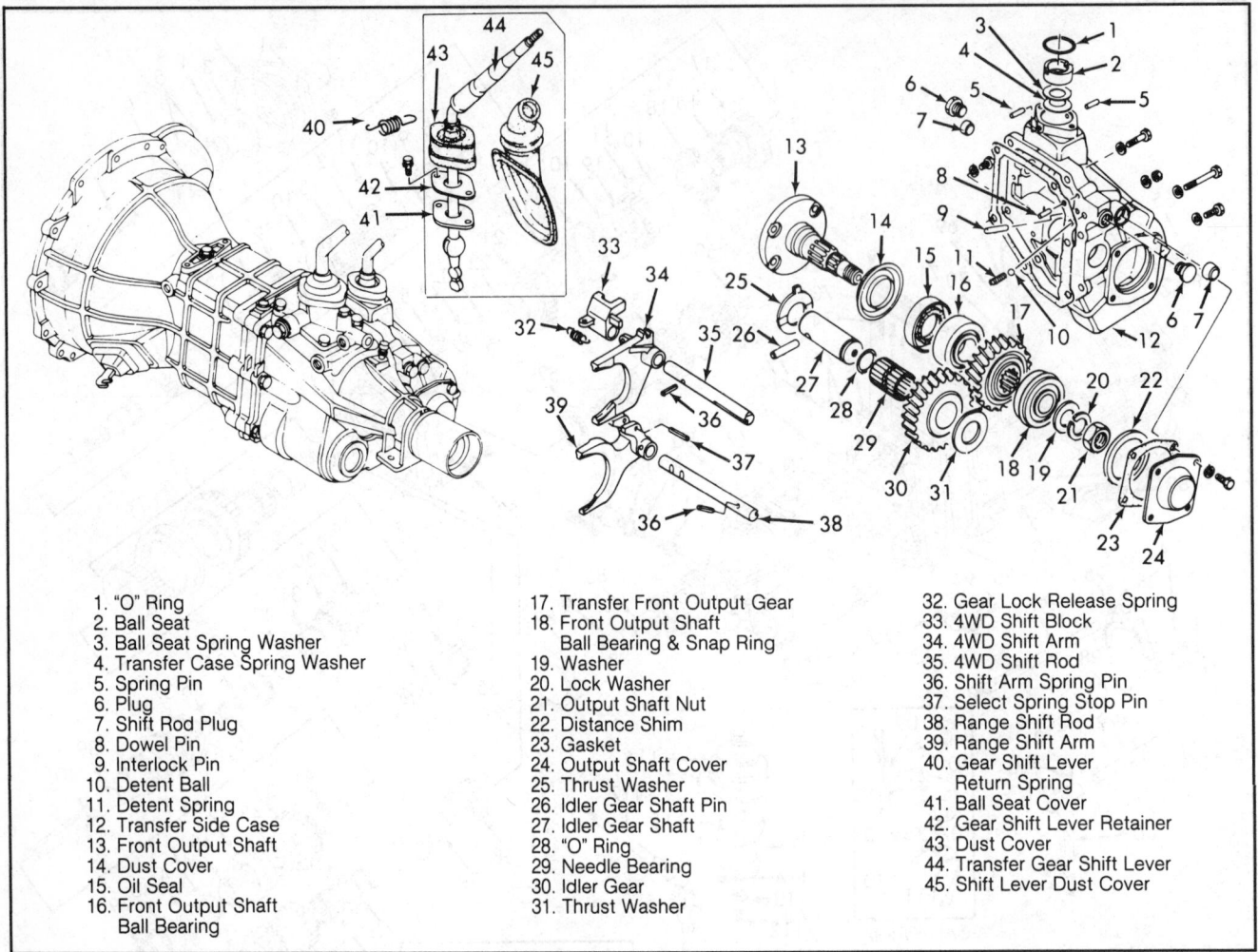

1. "O" Ring
2. Ball Seat
3. Ball Seat Spring Washer
4. Transfer Case Spring Washer
5. Spring Pin
6. Plug
7. Shift Rod Plug
8. Dowel Pin
9. Interlock Pin
10. Detent Ball
11. Detent Spring
12. Transfer Side Case
13. Front Output Shaft
14. Dust Cover
15. Oil Seal
16. Front Output Shaft
   Ball Bearing

17. Transfer Front Output Gear
18. Front Output Shaft
   Ball Bearing & Snap Ring
19. Washer
20. Lock Washer
21. Output Shaft Nut
22. Distance Shim
23. Gasket
24. Output Shaft Cover
25. Thrust Washer
26. Idler Gear Shaft Pin
27. Idler Gear Shaft
28. "O" Ring
29. Needle Bearing
30. Idler Gear
31. Thrust Washer

32. Gear Lock Release Spring
33. 4WD Shift Block
34. 4WD Shift Arm
35. 4WD Shift Rod
36. Shift Arm Spring Pin
37. Select Spring Stop Pin
38. Range Shift Rod
39. Range Shift Arm
40. Gear Shift Lever
   Return Spring
41. Ball Seat Cover
42. Gear Shift Lever Retainer
43. Dust Cover
44. Transfer Gear Shift Lever
45. Shift Lever Dust Cover

Reassembly

1) Place front of mainshaft upward, install 3rd gear and needle bearing on front of mainshaft. Tapered side of 3rd gear facing front.

NOTE: **Front and rear needle bearings are interchangeable.**

2) Install blocker ring with teeth upward over synchronizing surface of 3rd gear. Install 3rd-4th synchronizer assembly on mainshaft with face of sleeve with light chamfer rearward. For Isuzu transmission, select largest snap ring for minimum clearance between clutch hub and snap ring. *See Snap Ring Table.* Install snap ring.

SNAP RING TABLE

Identification mark	Thickness In. (mm)
1	.059 (1.50)
2	.061 (1.55)
3	.063 (1.60)
4	.065 (1.65)

3) Turn rear of mainshaft upward and install 2nd gear with needle roller bearing. Tapered surface of 2nd gear should face rear of mainshaft. Install blocking ring with teeth facing downward.

4) Install 1st-2nd synchronizer assembly with light chamfer facing front of mainshaft. Install blocker ring with teeth facing rearward.

5) Install collar, needle roller bearing and 1st gear on mainshaft. Tapered side of gear should face front of mainshaft. Install 1st gear thrust washer with grooved side facing 1st gear.

6) Install rear bearing onto mainshaft using bearing removal tool (J-22912) and an arbor press. Make sure snap ring groove in bearing is facing front of mainshaft. Install ball bearing onto input shaft, using bearing removal tool (J-22912) and an arbor press. Make sure snap ring groove is facing front of transmission.

7) Install snap ring on input shaft. Install needle bearing, blocker ring and input shaft assembly onto front of mainshaft assembly.

TRANSFER CASE

Disassembly

1) Remove thrust washer, reverse idler gear, reverse shift arm and thrust washer with ball (pin). Remove range shift sleeve and pilot needle bearing from rear of output shaft.

2) Lightly tap transfer countershaft assembly out through shaft hole in transfer case. Expand rear output shaft front bearing snap ring and remove output shaft assembly.

ISUZU & LUV 4-SPEED WITH INTEGRAL TRANSFER CASE (Cont.)

3) Remove "O" ring, thrust washer, countergear, needle roller bearing and thrust washer from transfer countershaft.

Fig. 3: Alignment of Transfer Countershaft in Transfer Case

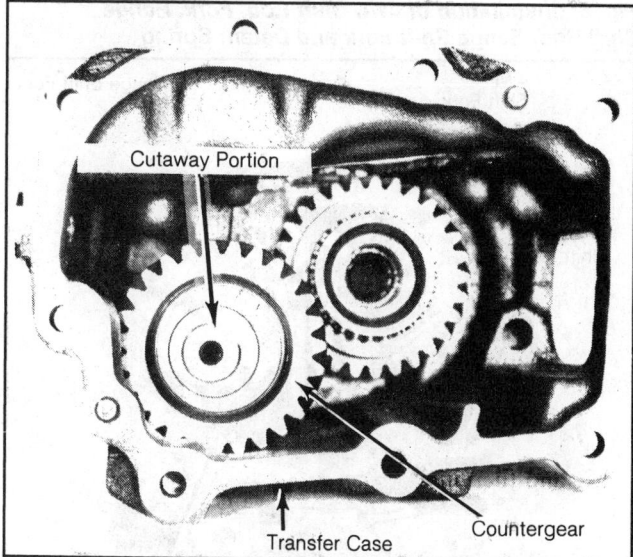

4) Remove rear output shaft nut, press rear bearing off output shaft using press. Remove spacer, speedometer drive gear and key from distance piece on output shaft.

5) Press output shaft front bearing with thrust washer and rear output gear from output shaft. Remove output gear needle roller bearing and 4 wheel drive shift sleeve from output shaft.

Inspection

1) Check output shaft for wear or scoring. Check splines for damage. Light scoring or damage can be corrected with an oil stone, otherwise replace shaft.

2) Measure outside diameter of reverse idler shaft. Measure inside diameter of idler gear bushing. If difference between the 2 measurements (clearance) is more than .008" (.2 mm), replace bushing.

Reassembly

1) If removed, install new oil seal to transfer case and output shaft front bearing snap ring to transfer case.

2) Install 4 wheel drive shift sleeve, with heavy chamfered side toward output gear, on rear of output shaft. Install needle roller bearing, output gear and thrust washer on output shafts. Make sure grooved side of thrust washer faces output gear.

3) Press output shaft front bearing onto output shaft, making sure snap ring groove is turned rearward. Install shim, with grooved side toward front bearing, speedometer drive gear key, drive gear and spacer to output shaft.

4) Press output shaft rear bearing, with sealed face facing rearward, on output shaft. Install output shaft nut and tighten. Stake nut to groove in shaft.

5) Apply grease to needle roller bearings and both faces of thrust washers. Install thrust washer on countershaft by aligning finger on washer with cutaway portion of shaft. Install needle roller bearing, countergear, needle roller bearing, thrust washer and "O" ring to transfer countergear.

NOTE: Thrust washer oil grooves should face countergear.

6) Install output shaft assembly into transfer case by expanding front bearing snap ring into transfer case groove far enough so front bearing can be inserted. Allow snap ring to engage bearing groove.

7) Install transfer countershaft assembly into transfer case. Make sure cutaway portion at front end of countershaft is positioned correctly. The finger on thrust washer, on rear of shaft, should be aligned with groove in transfer case. *See Fig. 3 and Fig. 4.*

8) Grease output shaft pilot bearing, and install bearing and range shift sleeve on output shaft. Make sure end of sleeve with heavy chamfering is toward front of transfer case.

9) Install thrust washer with ball (pin), reverse idler gear and reverse shift arm. Install idler gear so that shift arm fitting groove is turned toward rear of transfer case. Install thrust washer.

Fig. 4: Alignment of Thrust Washer on Transfer Countershaft in Transfer Case

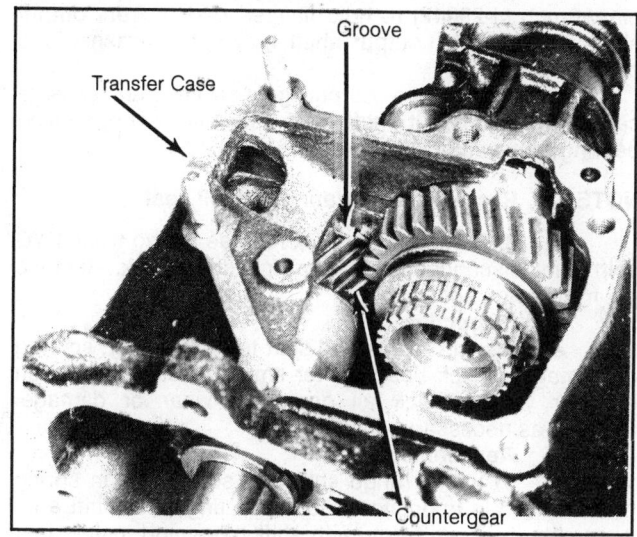

TRANSFER SIDE CASE

Disassembly

1) Remove range shift rod detent spring, detent ball and plug from each shift rod. Remove spring pin from 4WD shift arm.

2) Hold range shift rod in high position and, at the same time, drive out 4 wheel drive shift rod from rear side. Plug will come out at the same time.

3) Remove shift arm and shift block. Remove detent ball, spring and interlock spring from transfer side case.

NOTE: Detent ball may pop out as shift rod is removed, be careful not to lose ball.

4) Remove spring pin from range shift arm and remove range shift rod with plug through front side. Remove shift arm and dowel pin from idler shaft.

5) Remove idler shaft by inserting a bolt (M8x1.25) into threaded hole and pulling idler shaft out. Remove thrust washers, idler gear and needle roller bearing.

ISUZU & LUV 4-SPEED WITH INTEGRAL TRANSFER CASE (Cont.)

Fig. 5: Assembling 4WD Shift Arm with Shift Block

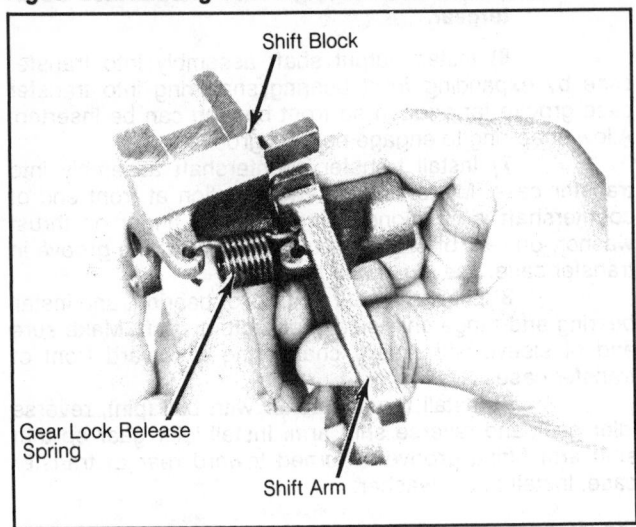

6) Remove output shaft cover and shim. Use a pin wrench (J-29042) to hold flanged part of front output shaft from turning, output shaft nut, spring washer and plain washer.

7) Remove output gear from transfer side case. Remove output shaft front and rear bearings using bearing removal tools (J-8092 and J-29040).

NOTE: Remove front bearing with oil seal.

8) Remove gear lock release spring from 4WD shift arm, disconnect shift arm and shift block. Remove pin from range shift arm.

Inspection
Inspect shafts and shift forks for wear, scoring or damage. Check bearings for smoothness of operation and for wear. Check all gears for wear or damage. Replace as necessary.

Reassembly
1) Install range shift arm so that slit in spring pin is turned in opposite direction as fingers of shift arm. Assemble 4WD shift arm with shift block and install gear lock release spring. See Fig. 5.

2) Using installer tools (J-8092 and J-29040), drive front output shaft rear bearing into transfer side case until it contacts snap ring. Install output gear.

3) Using installer tools, drive output shaft front bearing into transfer side case until it contacts output gear. Install output shaft oil seal.

4) Install output shaft, plain washer, spring washer and output shaft nut. Use pin wrench to hold shaft from turning and tighten output shaft nut. Install shim in transfer side case, output shaft cover and tighten bolts.

5) Apply grease to both sides of idler gear thrust washer and install with grooved face toward gear. Make sure tab on washer aligns with notch in case. Grease idler gear needle bearing and install bearings on gear. Make sure heavier bossed end is turned toward front. Install idler shaft.

6) Install dowel pin into transfer side case. Dowel should protrude .355-.433" (9-11 mm). Install range shift arm and shift rod, then install spring pin to hold in place.

7) Install interlock pin, 4WD shift rod detent spring and detent ball into case. Hold range shift rod in

high range, 4WD shift arm and shift block with shift rod into transfer side case. Insert spring pin to secure parts.

8) Install shift rod plugs and screw type plugs. Install range shift rod detent ball and spring into position. See Fig. 6.

Fig. 6: Installation of 4WD Shift Rod, Fork, Range Shift Rod, Range Shift Fork and Detent Spring

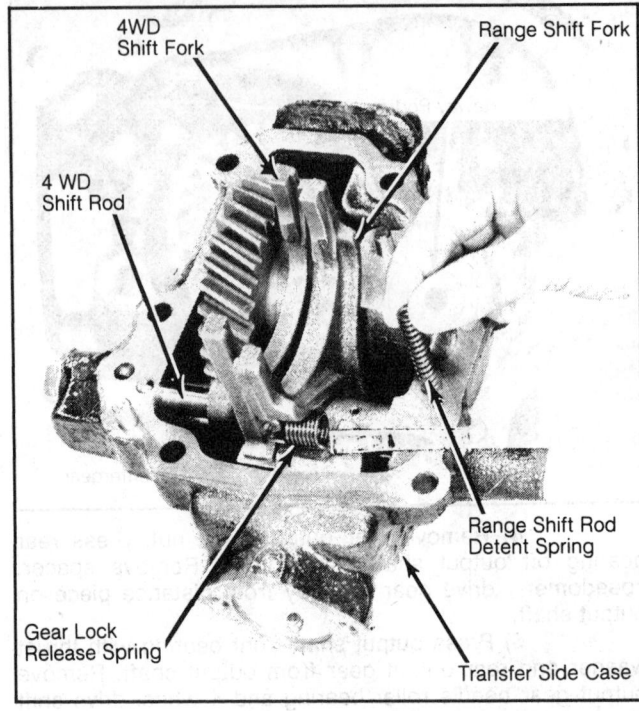

TRANSMISSION REASSEMBLY

1) If removed, install countershaft reverse gear and countergear ball bearing with snap ring groove facing rear of transmission. Use adapter (J-22912) and press to install bearing. If removed, install snap rings in countergear and mainshaft snap ring grooves of center support.

2) Mesh gears of mainshaft and countergear together and install on a holding fixture (J-26545-5). Install holding fixture in a vise, then install center support. While installing center support, expand mainshaft snap ring and press center support onto mainshaft and countergear until countergear bearing hits its snap ring.

3) Expand countergear snap ring and press center support further until both snap rings fit into grooves. Remove holding fixture from mainshaft and countergear. Move both synchronizers rearward to prevent mainshaft from turning.

4) Install collar, washer and nut. Tighten nut to 80 ft. lbs. (110 N.m.) at rear of countergear. Install reverse gear shim on mainshaft with under cut teeth facing rearward.

5) Install transfer input gear thrust washer on mainshaft with grooved side facing input gear. Install collar, needle bearing and input gear on mainshaft. Input gear should be installed with teeth facing rearward.

6) Install transfer clutch hub on mainshaft with grooved side facing input gear. Install lock nut on

ISUZU & LUV 4-SPEED WITH INTEGRAL TRANSFER CASE (Cont.)

mainshaft and tighten. Caulk lock nut. Install spacer to mainshaft.

7) Apply grease to 2 interlock pins and insert into detent holes from middle hole of center support. Install 1st-2nd shifter fork and 3rd-4th shifter fork into grooves in synchronizer assembly.

8) Install 3rd-4th shifter rod from rear of center support through middle hole. Then install into 1st-2nd and 3rd-4th shifter forks. Align spring pin hole in shifter fork with hole in shifter rod.

NOTE: The 3rd-4th shifter rod can be identified by 2 detent grooves on side of rod.

9) Install 1st-2nd shifter rod from rear of center support, through 1st-2nd shifter fork and align hole in rod to hole in shifter fork. Install reverse shifter rod from rear of center support. Install 2 spring pins in 1st-2nd, 3rd-4th and reverse shifter forks.

NOTE: When installing spring pins, make sure shifter rod is supported, by round bar against end of shifter rod.

10) Install detent balls, detent spring, gasket and retainer on top of center support. Place transfer case upright and on wooden blocks. Apply a thin coat of grease to end of reverse shift rod, mainshaft and transfer countershaft.

11) Install center support and gasket into transfer case, making sure the following parts are installed together in the following order: reverse shift rod-to-reverse shift arm, mainshaft-to-output shaft, transfer countershaft-to-countershaft hole fitting, input gear-to-transfer countergear is engaged, range shift sleeve-to-clutch hub is engaged and dowel pins fit into dowel pin holes. *See Fig. 7.*

Fig. 7: Installation of Center Support to Transfer Case

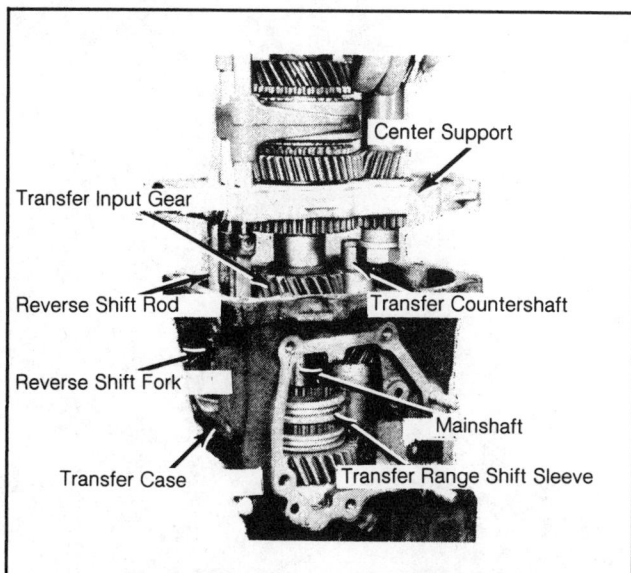

12) Install spring pin in reverse shifter fork. Tighten 4 bolts attaching center support-to-transfer case evenly. Measure how much transfer countershaft protrudes from center support. Select distance shim so thrust clearance will be .004-.014" (.10-.35 mm). *See Fig. 8.*

Fig. 8: Measuring Transfer Countershaft for Distance Shim Selection

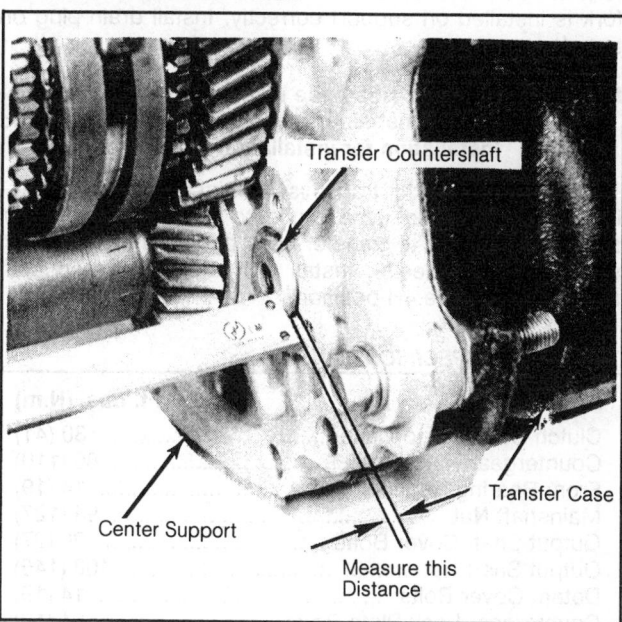

TRANSFER COUNTERGEAR DISTANCE SHIMS

Countergear Measurement	Shim Thickness	Color Code
.106-.114" (2.7-2.9 mm)	.118" (3.0 mm)	Red
.114-.122" (2.9-3.1 mm)	.126" (3.2 mm)	Orange
.122-.130" (3.1-3.3 mm)	.134" (3.4 mm)	No Color
.130-.138" (3.3-3.5 mm)	.142" (3.6 mm)	Green
.138-.142" (3.5-3.6 mm)	.150" (3.8 mm)	Blue

13) Remove bolts attaching center support to transfer case, next install transfer countergear shim selected and lock plate. Install transmission case and gasket to transfer case and center support. Make sure dowel pin and dowel pin hole are aligned. Tighten the 8 bolts.

14) Install back-up light switch and coasting richer switch (CRS) if equipped. Install speedometer driven gear to rear of transfer case.

NOTE: To prevent damage to "O" ring when installing, coat "O" ring with oil.

15) Install front bearing retainer seal. Install snap ring to input shaft bearing. Apply grease to bearing retainer spring washer and install in bearing retainer.

NOTE: Install spring washer so dished face is toward bearing outer race.

16) Install bearing retainer to front of transmission case. Apply sealer to threads of bolt installed in lower left corner of retainer, then install other 3 bolts and tighten.

17) Install ball stud to transmission case. Install dust boot, clutch fork and throw-out bearing. Install

ISUZU & LUV 4-SPEED WITH INTEGRAL TRANSFER CASE (Cont.)

retaining springs. Apply grease to input shaft splines, shift fork support and shift block. Make sure hook on clutch fork is installed on support correctly. Install drain plug on transfer case.

NOTE: **Transfer side case is installed after transmission is installed in vehicle. See Removal and Installation for installation of transmission.**

18) With transmission installed in vehicle, install transfer side case studs to transmission. Install transfer side case to transfer case by aligning grooves in shift arms and sleeve. Install with shift arms and shift sleeves held in the 4H position.

TIGHTENING SPECIFICATIONS

Application	Ft. Lbs. (N.m)
Clutch Ball Stud-to-Case	30 (41)
Countergear Nut	80 (110)
Front Bearing Retainer Bolts	14 (19)
Mainshaft Nut	94 (127)
Output Shaft Cover Bolts	20 (27)
Output Shaft Nut	108 (146)
Detent Cover Bolts	14 (19)
Countergear Lock Plate Bolts	14 (19)
Shifter Cover Bolts	14 (19)
Shift Rod Plugs	36 (49)
Speedometer Hsg. Retainer Bolt	14 (19)
Transfer Case-to-Transmission Case Bolts	27 (37)

ISUZU & LUV 5-SPEED

Isuzu I-Mark, P'UP, LUV Pickup

DESCRIPTION

Five speed fully synchronized unit with blocker ring synchronizers and a constant mesh reverse gear. First through fourth gears are housed within the case. Reverse and fifth gears are contained in the extension housing. The input/output shaft and the countershaft are supported by 3 ball bearings. The bearings are located in the front wall of the case, the center support and the extension housing. All gear teeth are helical cut.

LUBRICATION & ADJUSTMENT

See the appropriate article in AUTOMATIC TRANSMISSION SERVICING Section.

TROUBLE SHOOTING

HARD SHIFTING

Improperly adjusted clutch. Synchronizers worn or broken. Shift shafts or forks worn.

SLIPS OUT OF GEAR

Shift shafts and/or bearings worn. Drive gear retainer broken or loose. Excessive play in synchronizers.

TRANSMISSION NOISY

Low or incorrect lubricant. Gears or bearings worn or damaged. Worn clutch hub or mainshaft splines. Incorrectly meshed gears.

REMOVAL & INSTALLATION

See the appropriate article in MANUAL TRANSMISSION REMOVAL Section.

TRANSMISSION DISASSEMBLY

1) Remove plug and drain transmission. Remove release bearing and fork assembly. Remove input shaft bearing retainer and Belleville spring. See Fig. 3.

2) Remove speedometer driven gear, retainer and back-up light switch. Remove shift lever quadrant and coasting fuel cut switch. Remove extension housing from transmission case.

Fig. 1: Cutaway View of Isuzu & LUV 5-Speed Transmission

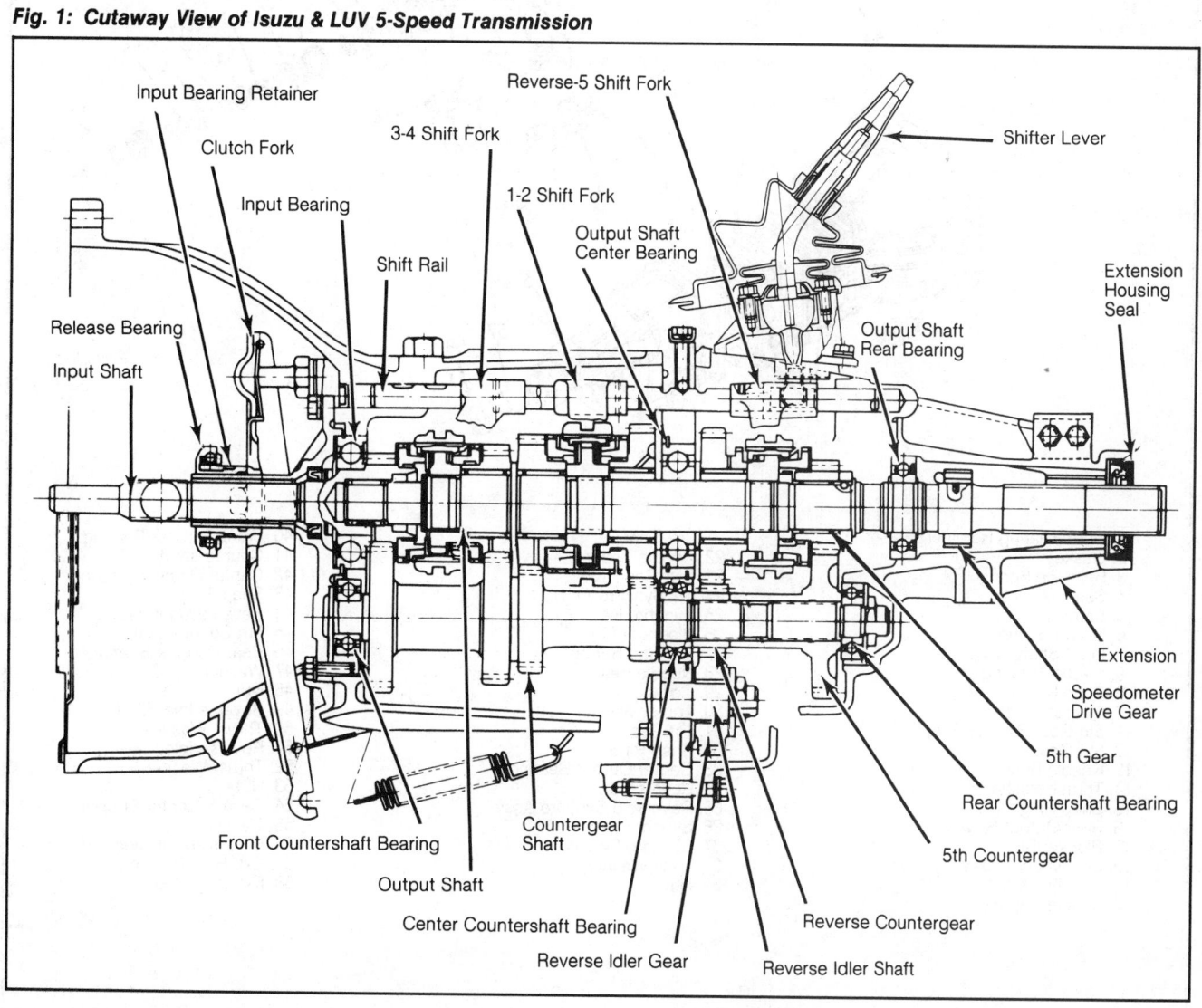

Manual Transmissions

ISUZU & LUV 5-SPEED (Cont.)

Fig. 2: Exploded View of Isuzu & LUV 5-Speed Transmission

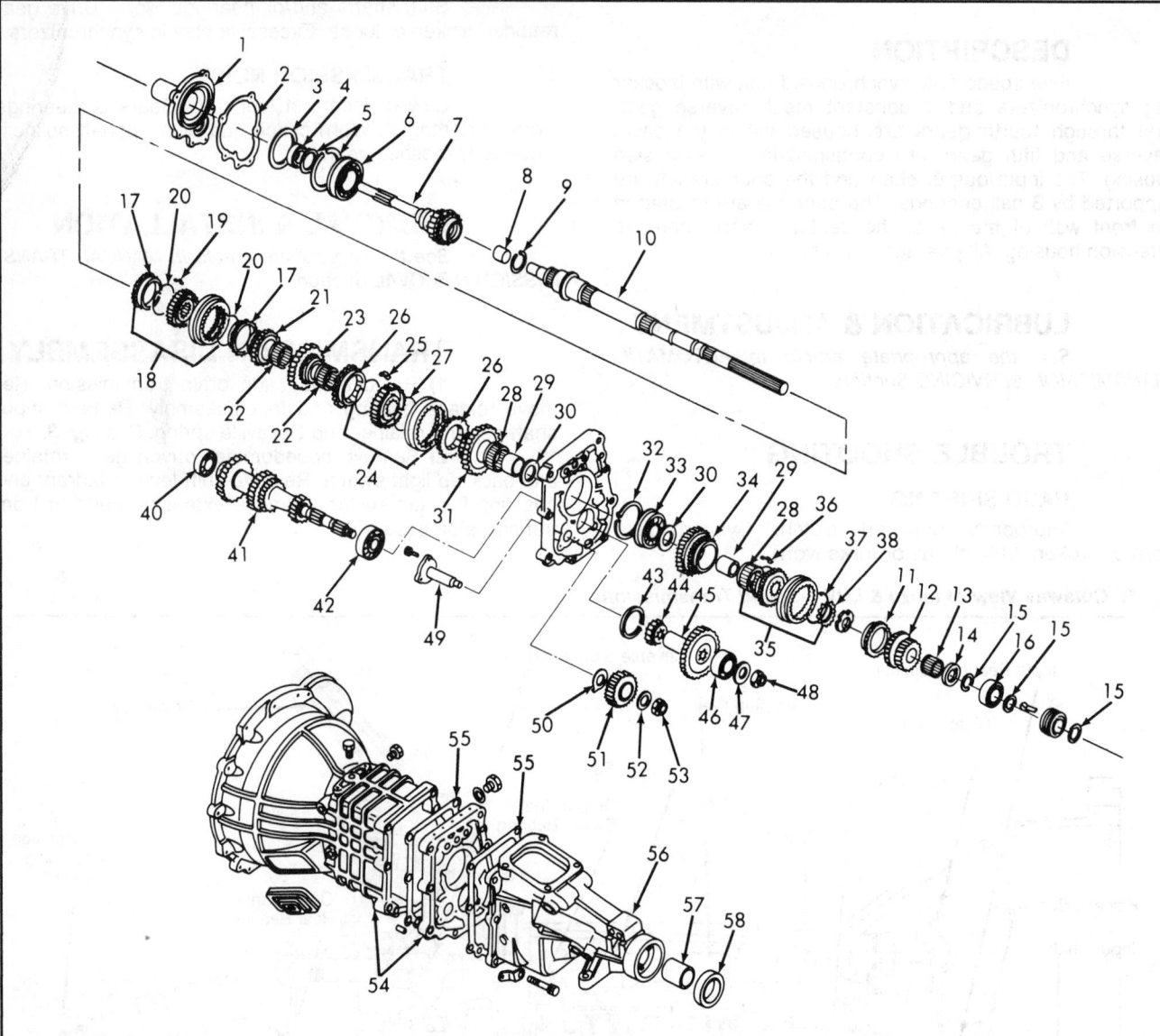

1. Input Bearing Retainer
2. Gasket
3. Belleville Spring
4. Seal
5. Snap Ring
6. Input Bearing
7. Input Shaft
8. Needle Bearing
9. Snap Ring
10. Output Shaft
11. 5th Gear Blocker Ring
12. 5th Gear
13. Needle Bearing
14. Thrust Washer
15. Snap Ring
16. Rear Output Bearing
17. Blocker Ring
18. 3-4 Synchro Assy.
19. Synchro Key
20. Synchro Spring

21. 3rd Gear
22. Needle Bearing
23. 2nd Gear
24. 1-2 Synchro Assy.
25. Synchro Key
26. Blocker Ring
27. Synchro Spring
28. Needle Bearing
29. Collar
30. Thrust Washer
31. 1st Gear
32. Snap Ring
33. Center Output Bearing
34. Reverse Gear
35. Reverse-5 Synchro Assy.
36. Synchro Key
37. Synchro Spring
38. Lock Washer
39. Nut

40. Front Counter Bearing
41. Countershaft
42. Center Counter Bearing
43. Snap Ring
44. Reverse Countergear
45. 5th Countergear
46. Rear Counter Bearing
47. Washer
48. Nut
49. Reverse Idler Shaft
50. Thrust Washer
51. Reverse Idler Gear
52. Thrust Washer
53. Nut
54. Case & Center Support
55. Gasket
56. Extension Housing
57. Ext. Hsg. Bushing
58. Ext. Hsg. Seal

ISUZU & LUV 5-SPEED (Cont.)

3) Remove speedometer drive gear, snap rings, spacer and bearing. Remove snap ring from main shaft, thrust washer and lock ball. Remove outer snap ring from input shaft bearing. Remove center support from case with all gears attached.

4) Using a punch, drive pins out of shift forks, making sure to support ends of shift shafts. Remove detent spring plate, springs and detent balls. Remove shift shafts from center support. Remove shift forks from synchronizer sleeves. Remove interlock pins. *See Fig. 4.*

Fig. 3: Input Bearing Retainer Assembly

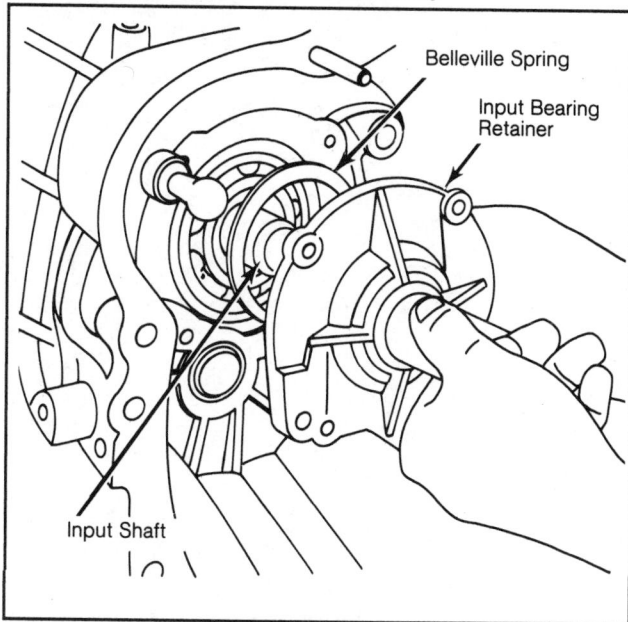

Dished side of spring faces rearward.

5) Engage 1st and 3rd gears to prevent rotation of countershaft. Install holding fixture (J-29768) onto front of gear assembly. Remove nut from rear of countershaft. Using a puller, remove rear countershaft bearing and 5th gear.

Fig. 4: Exploded View of Shift Shaft Assembly

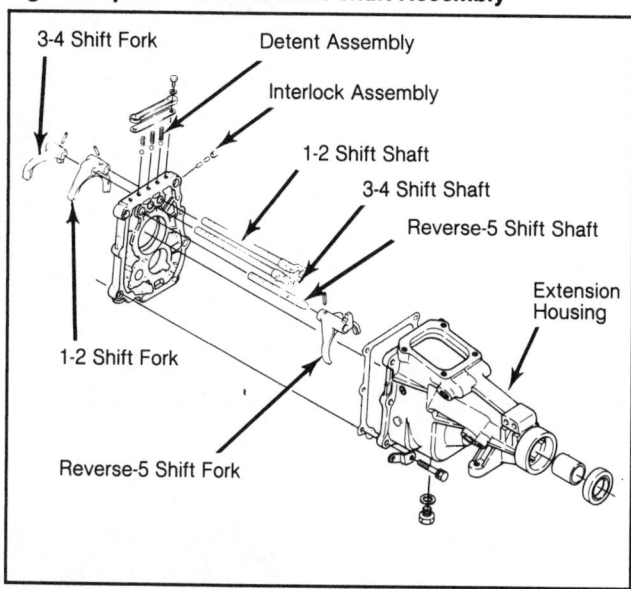

6) Remove 5th gear, needle bearings and blocker ring from output shaft. Remove thrust washers, reverse idler gear and retaining nut from reverse idler shaft.

7) Bend locking retainer back and remove mainshaft nut. Remove retainer and reverse-5th synchronizer assembly. Remove reverse gear, collar, needle bearings and thrust washer from rear of output shaft. Remove reverse gear from countershaft. Remove holding fixture.

8) Return synchronizers to neutral position. Expand countergear center bearing snap ring. Gently tap on front of center support to remove countershaft. Expand output shaft center bearing snap ring. Remove output shaft from center support. Remove input shaft, needle bearings and 4th gear blocker ring from output shaft.

COMPONENT DISASSEMBLY & REASSEMBLY

OUTPUT SHAFT

Disassembly

1) Using a press, remove output shaft center bearing. Remove thrust washer, 1st gear, needle bearings and spacer. Remove 1-2 synchronizer, 2nd gear and needle bearings.

2) Remove snap ring from front of output shaft. Remove 3-4 synchronizer and 3rd gear blocker ring. Remove 3rd gear and needle bearings.

Inspection

Check all parts for excessive wear or damage. Check bearings and synchronizers for rough operation. Replace damaged parts as necessary.

Reassembly

1) Install 3rd gear onto front of output shaft. Synchronizer cone faces forward. Install 3rd needle bearings. Install 3-4 synchronizer with chamfered end forward. Retain synchronizer with selective fit snap ring. Snap ring size should be selected to minimize end play.

2) Install 2nd gear and needle bearings on rear of shaft. Coned end of 2nd gear faces rearward. Install 1-2 synchronizer on rear of shaft with chamfered end facing rearward.

3) Install spacer, needle bearings and 1st gear on rear of shaft. Coned end of 1st gear faces forward. Install 1st gear thrust washer with slots facing gear. Press center bearing onto shaft. Groove on bearing faces front of transmission.

INPUT SHAFT

Disassembly

Remove snap ring from front of shaft. Press bearing off of shaft.

Reassembly

Press bearing onto shaft, so bearing groove faces toward front of transmission. Install snap ring.

COUNTERSHAFT

Disassembly & Reassembly

Countershaft bearings are removed and installed using a bearing separator and press. Groove on center bearing faces rearward.

Manual Transmissions

ISUZU & LUV 5-SPEED (Cont.)

OIL SEALS

Removal & Installation

Remove seals by prying with a screwdriver or small chisel. Coat outside of new extension housing seal with sealer (Permatex No. 2 or equivalent). Install seals with seal driver (Ext. Hsg. J-26508; Input J-26540).

TRANSMISSION REASSEMBLY

1) If removed, install center support snap rings and reverse idler shaft. Install input shaft onto front of output shaft. Engage countershaft with input and output shaft gears. Install gear assembly into holding fixture (J-29768).

2) Install center support onto gear assembly. Expand center support snap rings. Position center support and seat snap rings into bearing grooves. Engage 1st and 3rd gears to prevent countershaft rotation.

3) Install reverse countergear. Install reverse thrust washer with oil groove facing rearward. Install reverse gear with needle bearing and collar assembly onto rear of output shaft. Install reverse-5th synchronizer. Recessed side of synchronizer hub faces rearward.

4) Install locking retainer and nut onto rear of output shaft. Chamfered side of nut faces forward. Tighten to 94 ft. lbs. (127 N.m), then bend down retainer to lock nut in place.

5) Install reverse idler gear and thrust washers onto idler shaft. Flange on side thrust washer is fitted to stopper on center support. Install new self-locking nut on idler shaft.

6) Install 5th gear with blocker ring and needle bearing onto output shaft. Install 5th countergear, bearing and new self-locking nut onto countershaft. Remove assembly from holding fixture. Shift synchronizers to neutral position.

7) Grease interlock pins and install in center support. Install shift forks onto synchronizer sleeves. Insert shift shafts through center support and shift forks. Install detent balls and springs in center support, then install gasket and detent plate.

8) Support shift shafts and replace shift fork retaining pins. Place a new gasket on rear of transmission case. Install center support and gear assembly into case. Do not apply load to mainshaft rear end.

9) Install outer snap ring on input shaft bearing. Install lock ball, thrust washer and snap ring onto rear of output shaft. Check clearance between 5th gear and thrust washer with a feeler gauge. Clearance should be .004-.012" (.10-.30 mm). Adjust clearance as necessary with selective thickness thrust washers. Do not bend or distort thrust washer snap ring.

10) Install speedometer drive gear front snap ring, ball bearing and spacer. Align lug in speedometer drive gear with groove and install on shaft, then install rear snap ring.

11) Install gasket on rear of center support. Install extension housing. Install gasket and shift lever quadrant on extension housing. Install speedometer driven gear and back-up light switch.

12) Install belleville washer with dished side to drive gear bearing. Install gasket and input bearing retainer into front of transmission. Seal lower 3 retainer bolts with sealer (Permatex No. 2 or equivalent). Install release bearing and fork assembly.

TIGHTENING SPECIFICATIONS

Application	Ft. Lbs. (N.m)
Input Shaft Bearing Retainer Bolts	14 (19)
Shift Box Bolts	14 (19)
Reverse Idler Shaft Bolts	14 (19)
Extension Housing Bolts	27 (37)
Countergear Nut	80 (108)
Reverse Idler Gear-to-Shaft	80 (108)
Output Shaft Nut	94 (127)

MAZDA GLC 4 & 5-SPEED

DESCRIPTION

Transaxle combines a 4 or 5-speed transmission, a differential and a clutch housing into an integral drivetrain. This unit is designed for a transverse engine, front wheel drive vehicle. All gear assemblies are supported by tapered roller bearings with preload being adjusted by shims. Helical cut gears are used throughout, so adjustment of gear tooth contact is not necessary.

LUBRICATION & ADJUSTMENT

See the appropriate article in MANUAL TRANSMISSION SERVICING Section.

SERVICE (IN-VEHICLE)

AXLE DRIVE SHAFTS

Removal

1) Raise and support vehicle. Drain transaxle fluid. Remove wheels and axle hub cap. Loosen drive shaft lock nut. Remove lower ball joint nut and swing lower control arm away from steering knuckle.

2) Separate the drive shaft from the transaxle by pulling out firmly but slowly on steering knuckle. Pull drive shaft out of steering knuckle and lower away from vehicle.

Disassembly

1) Remove boot retaining band from inner CV joint. Remove circlip from outer ring of inner CV joint. Separate outer ring from spider and drive shaft.

2) Remove snap ring retaining spider to drive shaft. Slide spider off of shaft and pry balls out of cage with a screwdriver. Turn spider slightly and remove from inner cage.

Reassembly

1) Reverse disassembly procedure and note the following: Outer CV joint cannot be serviced. Do not remove ring located on inner end of drive shaft splines unless replacement is necessary.

2) Use tape on splines when installing boots to prevent damage. Vibration dampener on right side drive shaft should be 14.45" (367 mm) from outer end of outer CV joint.

Fig. 1: Exploded View of Mazda GLC Transaxle Assembly

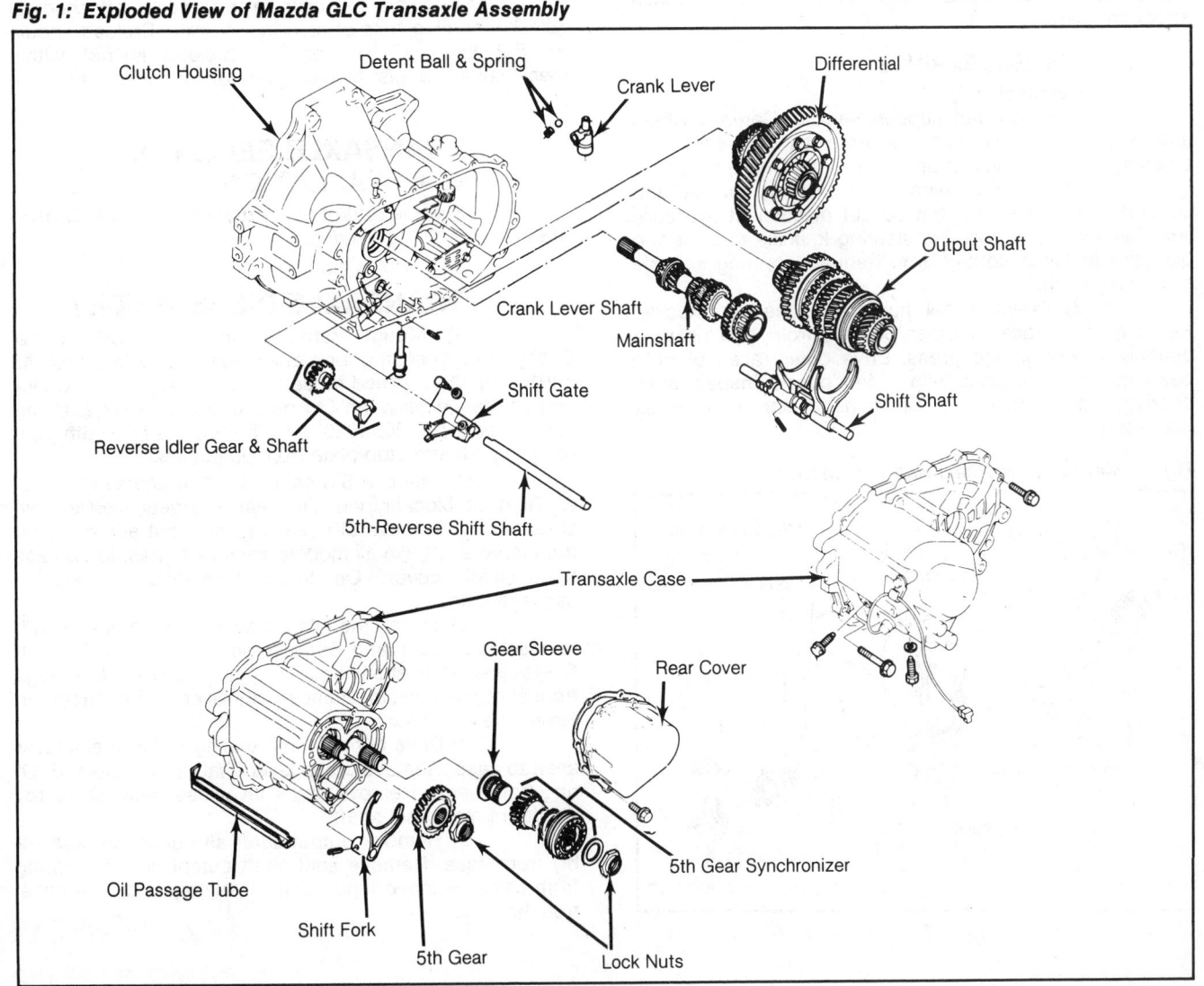

Manual Transmissions
MAZDA GLC 4 & 5-SPEED (Cont.)

Fig. 2: Exploded View of Axle Drive Shaft

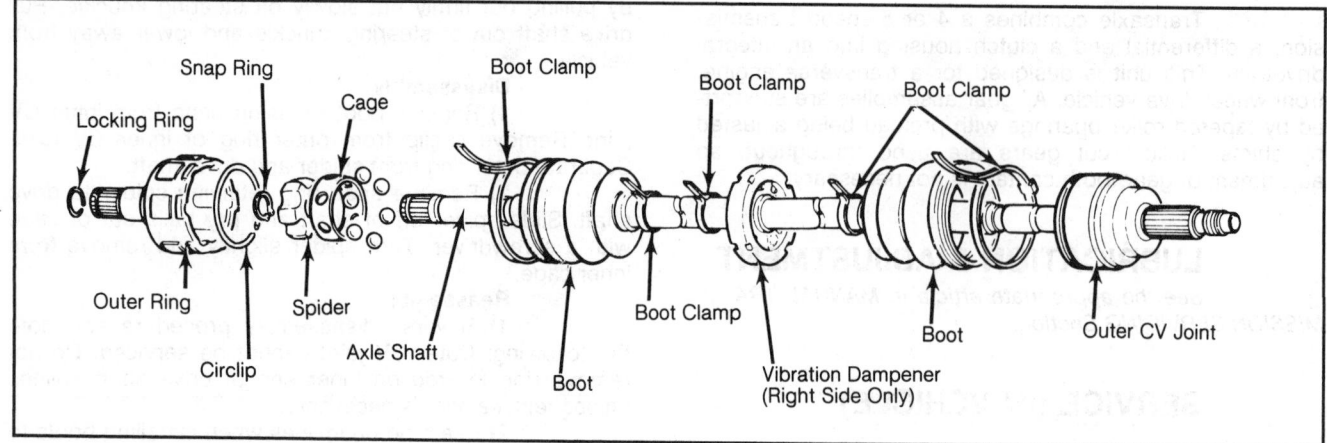

Installation

1) Reverse removal procedure and note the following: Check the seals at both ends of the drive shaft and replace prior to installation if necessary.

2) Lubricate the transaxle seal lip with ATF and the wheel hub seal lip with grease before installing drive shaft. Stake the drive shaft nut in place with a blunt punch after tightening.

WHEEL BEARINGS
Removal

1) Raise and support vehicle. Remove wheel and drive shaft lock nut. Separate tie rod end from steering knuckle. Remove brake line support clip at strut.

2) Remove caliper from steering knuckle and support out of the way, but do not disconnect hydraulic line. Remove bolts securing steering knuckle to strut and ball joint to lower control arm. Remove steering knuckle from drive shaft.

3) Press wheel hub from steering knuckle. Remove inner race of outer bearing from hub using a bearing separator and press. Drive outer races of both bearings out of knuckle with a drift punch. Inspect seal, bearings, bore and hub for damage and replace as necessary.

Fig. 3: Mazda Front Wheel Hub Assembly

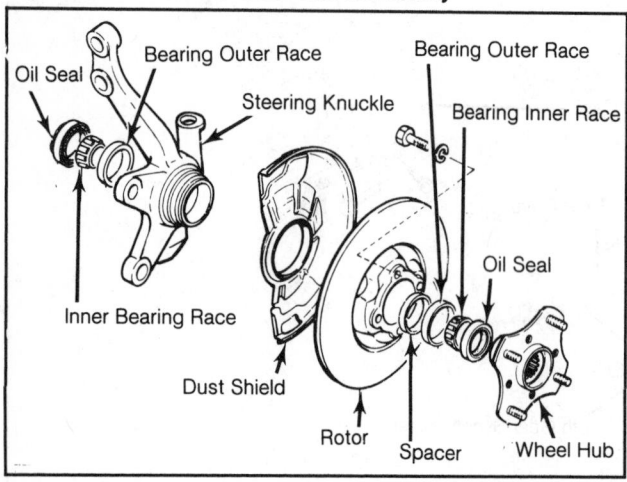

Installation

1) Reverse removal procedure and note the following: Bearing preload must be checked using the spacer selector tool (49 B001 727). Use the original spacer for measurement.

2) Tighten spacer selector to 145 ft. lbs. (197 N.m). Measure preload with a pull scale attached to caliper mounting hole of steering knuckle. Preload should be .5-2 lbs. (.23-.91 kgs). If preload is not within specifications, adjust by changing spacer thickness.

TRANSAXLE REMOVAL & INSTALLATION

See the appropriate article in MANUAL TRANS-MISSION REMOVAL Section.

TRANSAXLE DISASSEMBLY

1) Mount transaxle in a support fixture. Engage any gear and lock mainshaft with holder tool (49 F401 440). On 5-speed models, remove rear cover. Check end clearance between 5th gear and gear sleeve. Clearance should be .006-.020" (.14-.5 mm). Remove 5th gear retaining nut and stop plate from output shaft.

2) Remove 5th gear shift fork and synchronizer. Remove blocker ring, 5th gear and gear sleeve from output shaft. Remove 5th gear retaining nut and 5th gear from input shaft. On all models, remove transmission case from clutch cover. On 5-speed models, remove oil passage tube.

3) On all models, remove reverse idler shaft, reverse idler gear and 5th-reverse shift fork bolt. Wrap 5th-reverse shift shaft with a rag and turn to disengage from shift mechanism. Remove 5th-reverse shift shaft and 5th-reverse shift fork.

4) Drive out roll pin retaining shifter crank lever shaft to case. Remove crank lever shaft from case and "O" ring from shaft. Remove crank lever assembly. Drive roll pin out of main shift shaft.

5) Remove output shaft and gear fork assembly from case. Remove shift shaft detent ball and spring from case. Remove input shaft assembly and differential from housing.

MAZDA GLC 4 & 5-SPEED (Cont.)

Fig. 4: Exploded View of Transaxle Case and Related Components

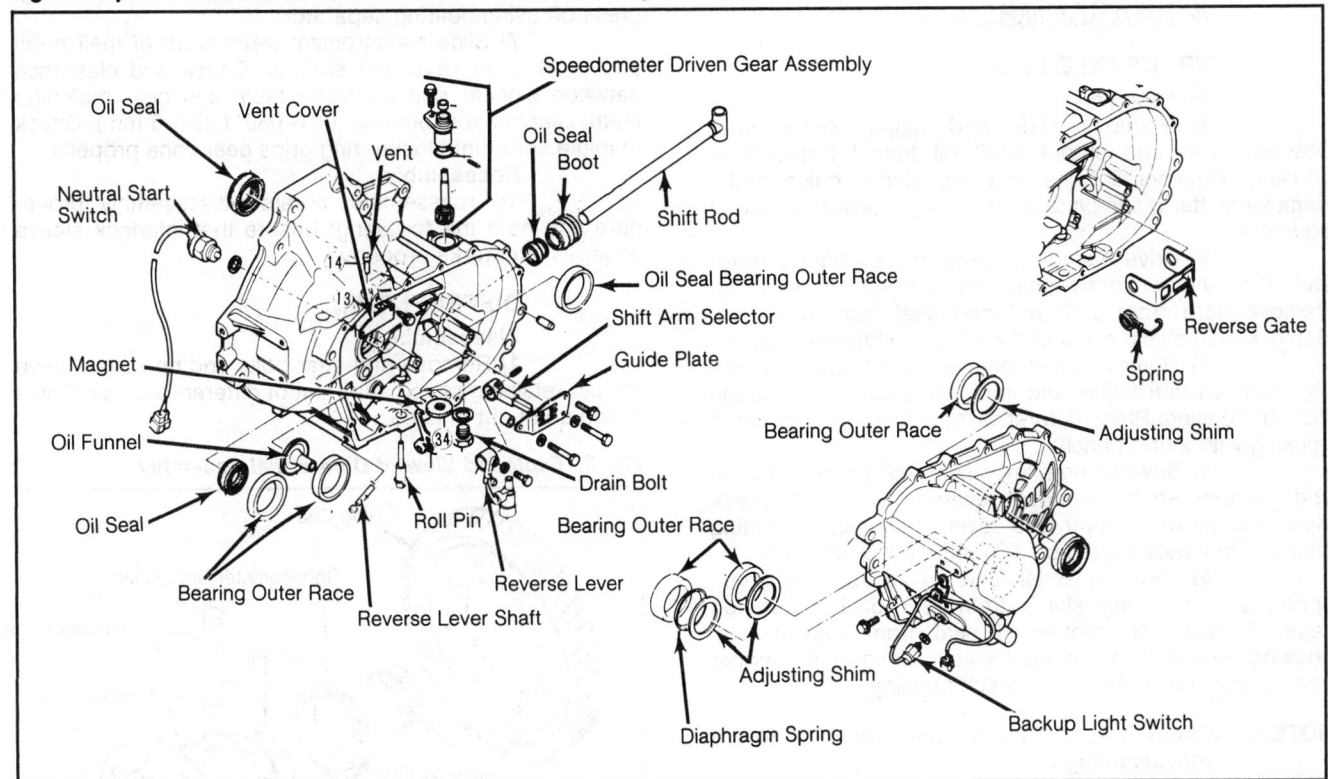

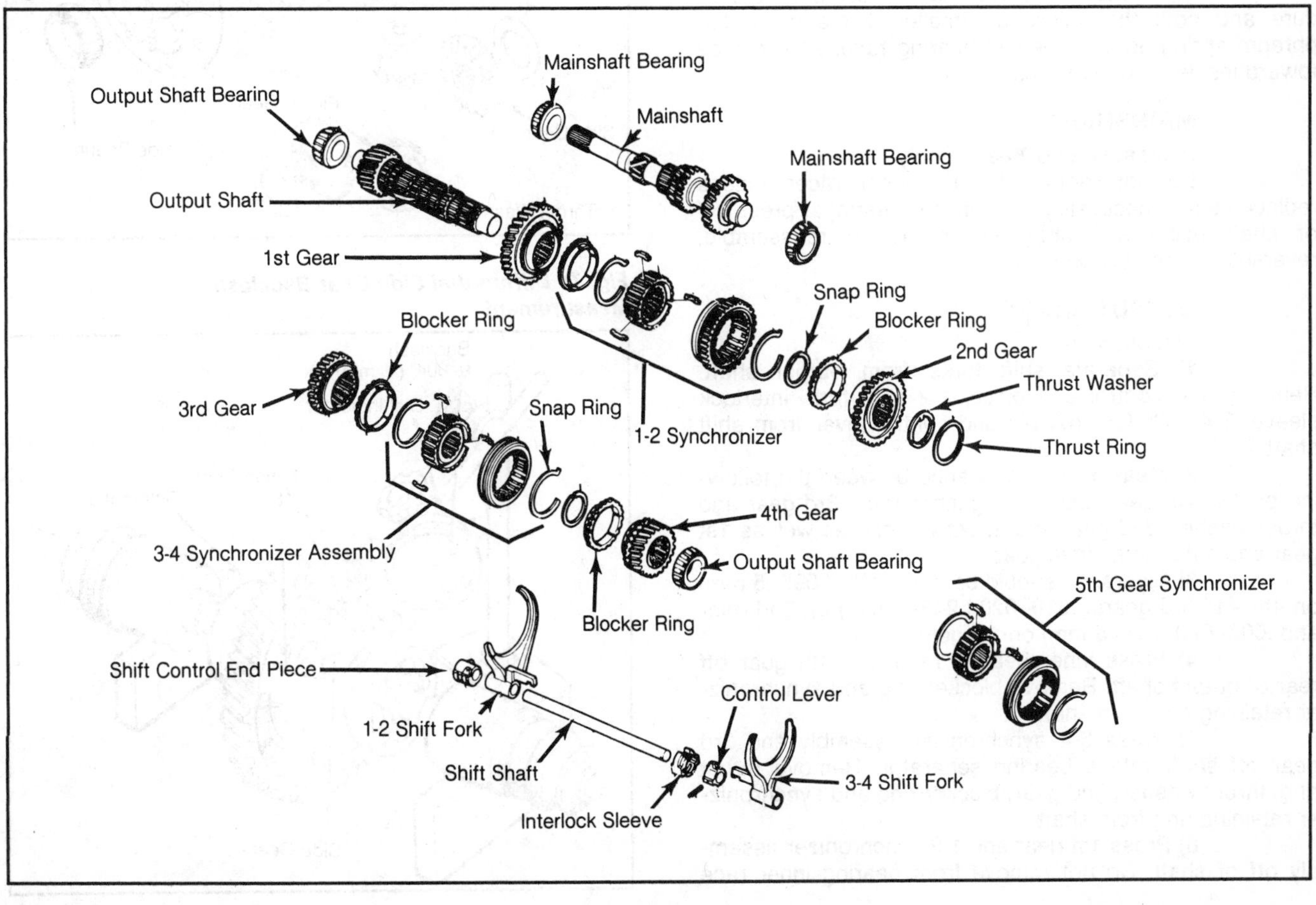

Fig. 5: Exploded View of Transaxle Gear Shafts

COMPONENT DISASSEMBLY & REASSEMBLY

TRANSAXLE CASE
Disassembly

1) Remove main and output shaft outer bearing races and output shaft oil funnel from clutch housing. Remove 3 bolts retaining shifter guide plate. Remove shifter guide plate and reverse gate with spring, if equipped.

2) Drive out roll pin retaining selector arm-to-shift rod and withdraw shift rod from clutch housing. Remove boot from shift rod and seal from rod bore. Remove vent shield and vent from top of clutch housing.

3) Remove speedometer driven gear assembly. Remove differential and input shaft oil seals through front of housing. Press differential side bearing race out of housing with a drift punch.

4) Drive reverse lever shaft roll pin out of case and remove shaft. Remove reverse lever and check clearance between lever and reverse idler gear shifting sleeve. Clearance should be .004-.020" (.095-.500 mm).

5) Remove outer bearing races, diaphragm spring and adjusting shims from rear of transmission case. Remove differential oil seal from transmission housing. Remove backup light switch, drain plug, magnet and neutral start switch from clutch housing.

NOTE: Check and adjust bearing preload before reassembling case.

Reassembly

To reassemble, reverse disassembly procedure and note the following: Smaller diameter of diaphragm spring, located behind bearing race, should face toward inside of transaxle case.

MAINSHAFT
Disassembly & Reassembly

Do not remove bearing inner races unless replacement is necessary. To remove bearings, press off of shaft using a bearing separator. To reassemble, reverse disassembly procedure.

OUTPUT SHAFT
Disassembly

1) Separate shift forks from output shaft. Remove shift control end piece, 1-2 shift fork, interlock sleeve, 3-4 shift fork roll pin and control lever from shift shaft.

2) Measure end clearance between the following points: 4th gear and bearing inner race, 3rd gear and thrust washer, 2nd gear and thrust washer, as well as 1st gear and differential drive gear.

3) Clearance should be .004-.020" (.095-.5 mm) on 4th and 3rd gears, .010-.020 (.245-.5 mm) on 2nd gear and .006-.020" (.14-.5 mm) on 1st gear.

4) Press inner bearing race and 4th gear off rear of output shaft. Remove blocker ring and synchronizer retaining ring from shaft.

5) Press 3-4 synchronizer assembly and 3rd gear off shaft with a bearing separator. Remove thrust ring, thrust washer, 2nd gear, blocker ring and synchronizer retaining ring from shaft.

6) Press 1st gear and 1-2 synchronizer assembly off of shaft. Do not remove front bearing inner race

unless replacement is necessary. To remove bearing, press off using bearing separator.

7) Slide synchronizer sleeves off of their hubs and remove all keys and springs. Check end clearance between blocker ring matching teeth and gear matching teeth. Clearance should be .031-.059" (.79-1.5 mm). Check to make sure that blocker ring grips gear cone properly.

Reassembly

To reassemble, reverse disassembly procedure and note the following: Ensure that interlock sleeve engages shift forks properly.

DIFFERENTIAL
Disassembly

1) Remove ring gear bolts and ring gear. Drive roll pin retaining pinion shaft out of differential case. Press pinion shaft out of case.

Fig. 6: Exploded View of Differential Assembly

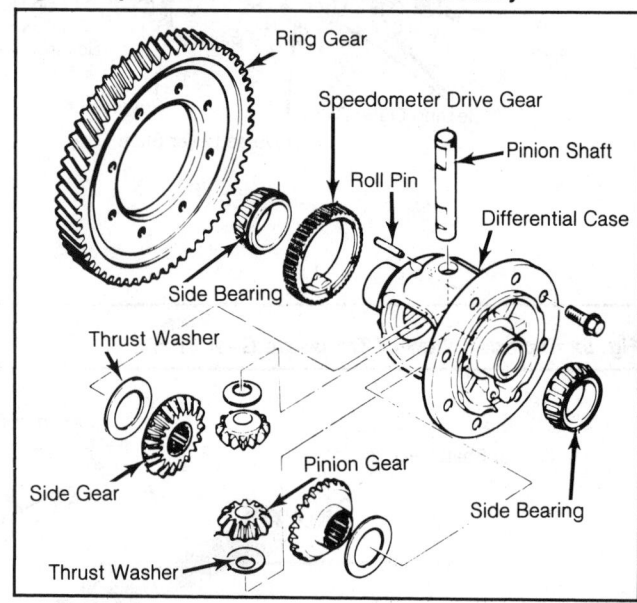

Fig. 7: Differential Side Gear Backlash Measurement

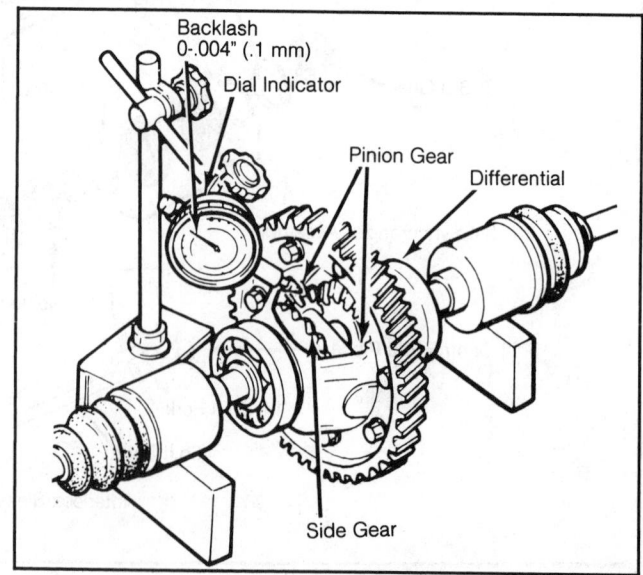

MAZDA GLC 4 & 5-SPEED (Cont.)

Fig. 8: Bearing Preload Adjustment Procedure

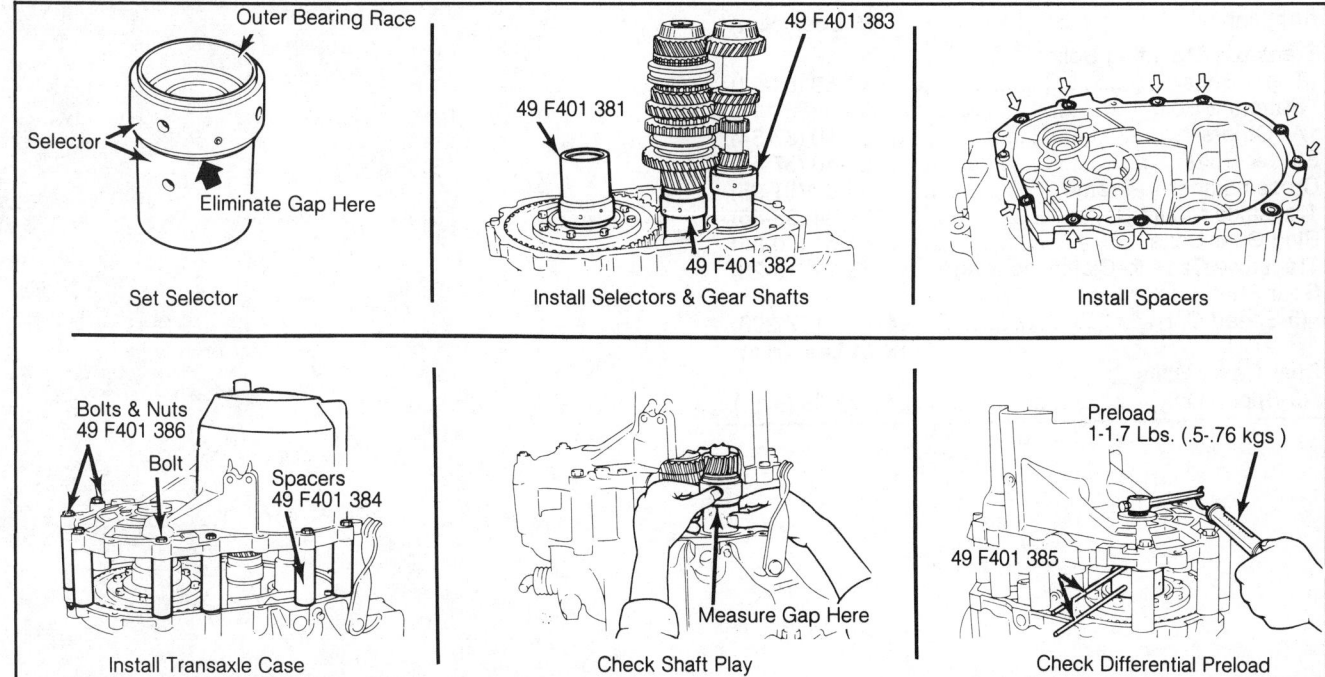

Outer Bearing Race / Selector / Eliminate Gap Here — **Set Selector**	49 F401 381 / 49 F401 383 / 49 F401 382 — **Install Selectors & Gear Shafts**	**Install Spacers**
Bolts & Nuts 49 F401 386 / Bolt / Spacers 49 F401 384 — **Install Transaxle Case**	Measure Gap Here — **Check Shaft Play**	Preload 1-1.7 Lbs. (.5-.76 kgs) / 49 F401 385 — **Check Differential Preload**

2) Rotate side gears to bring pinion gears and thrust washers to an opening in case. Remove pinion gears, side gears and thrust washers from case. Press differential side bearings and speedometer drive gear off of case.

Reassembly

To reassemble, reverse removal procedure and note the following: Pinion gear to side gear backlash must be checked using a dial indicator. Backlash should be 0-.004" (0-.1 mm). Adjust backlash by changing the thickness of the side gear thrust washer.

TRANSAXLE REASSEMBLY & ADJUSTMENT

BEARING PRELOAD

1) Remove differential side oil seals and rear side bearing outer race. Remove side bearing adjusting shim. Remove outer races of both shaft bearings from transaxle housing.

2) Remove adjusting shims and diaphragm spring. Reinstall shaft bearing races without shims or spring. Remove outer races of both shaft gears from clutch housing.

3) Insert rear differential race and front shaft races into shim selector tools (49 401 383 for mainshaft, 49 F401 382 for output shaft and 49 F401 381 for differential).

4) Adjust all 3 selector tools to minimum height. Place clutch housing on bench or support fixture with clutch housing flange facing down. Install differential in case.

5) Place selector tools for mainshaft and output shaft into proper bearing bore and install both gear shafts. Install differential selector tool on top of differential. Install transaxle case and secure with 10 spacers and bolts (49 F401 384 & 386). Tighten bolts.

6) Using turning bars (49 F401 385), rotate collars of tools until fully expanded. Turn collars of the 2 gear shaft tools to bring them back to collapsed position.

7) Expand collars as far as possible by hand and measure gap around entire circumference of tools. Subtract thickness of diaphragm spring .04" (1 mm) from tool reading on mainshaft.

8) Select a shim equal to or the next size larger than result of step 4) for each shaft. Shims are available in sizes from .008" (.2 mm) to .022" (.55 mm) in increments of .002" (.05 mm).

9) Install preload adapter shaft and attachment arm (49 FT01 515 & 49 01080 510A) into the differential. Attach a pull scale to hole in end of arm.

10) Adjust tool collars until 1-1.7 lbs. (.5-.76 kgs) are required to turn differential. Measure gap around entire circumference of tool.

11) Round gap measurement off to next larger shim size. No more than 3 shims should be used to make up required thickness. Shims are available in the sizes from .004" (.10 mm) to .036" (.90 mm) in increments of .004" (.10 mm).

TRANSAXLE REASSEMBLY

1) Reverse disassembly procedure and note the following: Install selected shim packs behind the appropriate bearing races. Recessed side of 5th gear synchronizer faces 5th gear.

2) Recheck differential preload with transaxle assembled. Using input shaft holder and pull scale, check mainshaft preload.

3) Force required to rotate mainshaft should be .88-1.54 lbs. (.40-.70 kgs). Check operation of shift mechanism to ensure proper engagement of all gears.

TIGHTENING SPECIFICATIONS

Application	Ft. Lbs. (N.m)
Transaxle Mounting Bolts	
Top 4 Bolts	47-69 (64-94)
Bottom 2 Bolts	65-86 (88-117)
All Others	27-40 (37-54)
Starter Bolts	27-40 (37-54)
Crossmember-to-Frame	45-63 (61-85)
Transaxle Mount Bolts	24-34 (33-46)
Ring Gear Bolts	51-61 (70-85)
Transaxle Case-to-Clutch Housing	13-19 (18-26)
Gear Shaft Lock Nuts	
(5-Speed Only)	94-152 (127-206)
	INCH Lbs. (N.m)
Rear Cover Bolts	
(5-Speed Only)	72-96 (8-11)

MAZDA RWD 4 & 5-SPEED

B2000 Pickup
GLC (Wagon)
RX7
626

DESCRIPTION

The 4 and 5-speed transmissions are fully synchronized in all forward gears. Synchronizers are of blocker type and provide for smooth gear engagement. Gear selection is accomplished by direct control from floor mounted shift lever. On all models, clutch housing is integral with transmission case. The center support plate is mounted between transmission case and extension housing on 4-speed models, and between transmission case and intermediate housing on 5-speed models and is also the main gear support.

LUBRICATION & ADJUSTMENT

See the appropriate article in MANUAL TRANS-MISSION SERVICING Section.

TROUBLE SHOOTING

HARD SHIFTING

Improperly adjusted clutch. Weakened synchronizer insert spring. Face of synchronizer ring, in contact with insert, worn. Cones on synchronizer ring and gear worn or not in proper contact.

SLIPS OUT OF GEAR

Bearings worn or defective. Excessive play between gears and collars. Play in clutch hub and sliding sleeve. Shift arm worn. Lock ball spring weak or broken.

TRANSMISSION NOISY

Low or incorrect lubricant. Gears or bearings worn or damaged. Worn gears or collars. Worn clutch hub or mainshaft splines. Incorrectly meshed gears.

REMOVAL & INSTALLATION

See the appropriate article in MANUAL TRANS-MISSION REMOVAL Section.

TRANSMISSION DISASSEMBLY

1) Clean exterior of transmission assembly. On GLC models, remove clutch cross-shaft bolt, cross-shaft, release lever, spring and throw-out bearing. On all other models, remove dust cover, throw-out bearing and clutch release fork. Remove front cover bolts (or nuts) and remove front cover, shim, gasket and oil seal.

2) Remove gearshift lever retainer and gasket from extension housing. Remove extension housing bolts and slide extension housing off mainshaft with control lever positioned to the left as far as possible. Remove control lever end attaching bolt and remove control lever end and control rod from housing.

3) Remove speedometer driven gear assembly, back-up light switch and overdrive switch from extension housing. Remove top switch from transmission

case. On 4-speed models, remove speedometer drive gear snap ring from mainshaft and slide drive gear off mainshaft. Remove lock ball.

Fig. 1: Exploded View of Front Bearing Cover and Input Shaft Assembly

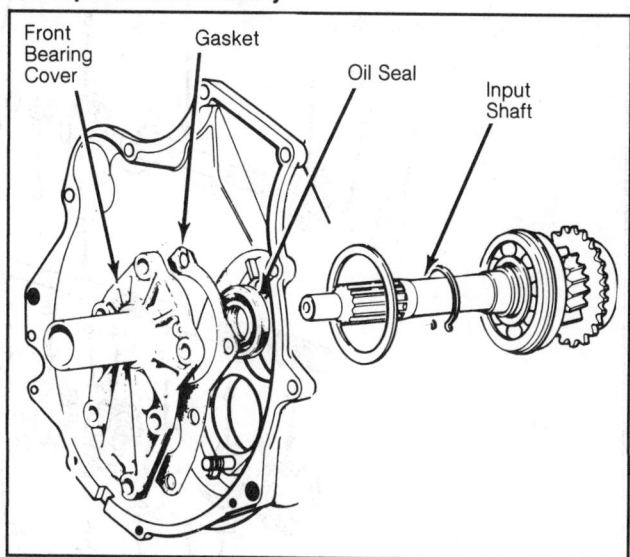

Front Bearing Cover
Gasket
Oil Seal
Input Shaft

GLC (Wagon) model shown; other models similiar.

4) On all models, remove snap ring from input shaft and countershaft. Separate transmission case from bearing plate/intermediate housing using push tool (49 0305 430) or by tapping input shaft with plastic faced hammer. Remove input shaft bearing from transmission case. Using bearing puller tool (49 0710 520), remove countershaft front bearing from countershaft.

5) On 5-speed models, remove speedometer drive gear snap ring from mainshaft and slide drive gear off mainshaft. Remove lock ball and drive gear positioning snap ring. On 4-speed models, remove 3 spring cap bolts and remove springs and shift locking balls.

6) On 5-speed models, remove shift rod end attaching bolts and remove shift rod ends. Separate bearing plate from intermediate housing by lightly tapping housing with plastic faced hammer.

7) On 4-speed models, remove reverse shift rod, shift fork assembly and reverse gear from bearing plate. Remove shift fork set screws. Remove shift rods and forks by pushing shift rods rearward through shift forks and bearing plate. Remove reverse shift rod locking ball, spring and interlock pins from bearing plate.

8) On 5-speed models, remove 3 spring cap bolts and remove springs and shift locking balls. Remove 3 shift rod snap rings. Remove shift fork attaching bolts, shift fork rods and shift forks. Remove lock ball, spring and interlock pins.

NOTE: On 5-speed, be careful not to lose lock ball when removing 5th-Reverse shift rod.

9) On 4-speed models, straighten lock washer tab and secure mainshaft with holding tool (49 0259 440) and loosen lock nut using wrench. Remove reverse gear and key from mainshaft. Remove countershaft snap ring and counter reverse gear.

10) Remove bearing cover and reverse idler gear shaft from bearing plate. Using plastic faced

Manual Transmissions
MAZDA RWD 4 & 5-SPEED (Cont.)

Fig. 2: Exploded View of Mazda 4 and 5-Speed Transmission Gears and Shafts

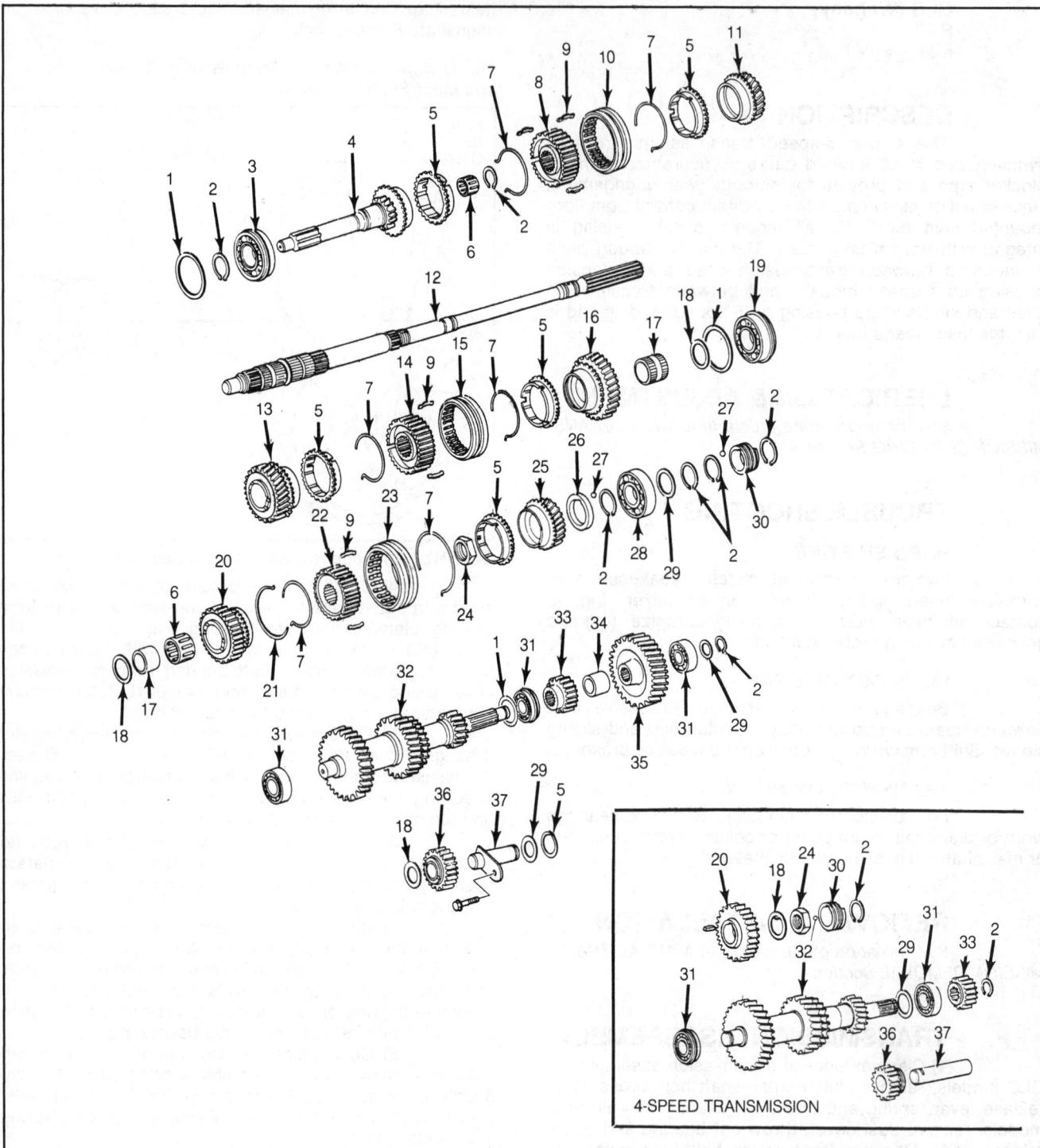

4-SPEED TRANSMISSION

1. Adjusting Shim	11. 3rd Gear	21. Retaining Ring	31. Bearing
2. Snap Ring	12. Mainshaft	22. 5th & Reverse Clutch Hub	32. Countershaft
3. Bearing	13. 2nd Gear	23. Hub Sleeve	33. Counter Reverse Gear
4. Input Shaft	14. 1st & 2nd Clutch Hub	24. Lock Nut	34. Spacer
5. Synchro Ring	15. Hub Sleeve	25. 5th Gear	35. Counter 5th Gear
6. Bearing	16. 1st Gear	26. Thrust Washer	36. Reverse Idler Gear
7. Synchro Key Spring	17. Gear Sleeve	27. Locking Ball	37. Idler Gear Shaft
8. 3rd & 4th Clutch Hub	18. Thrust Washer	28. Bearing	
9. Synchro Key	19. Bearing	29. Adjusting Washer	
10. Hub Sleeve	20. Reverse Gear	30. Speedometer Drive Gear	

MAZDA RWD 4 & 5-SPEED (Cont.)

hammer, tap rear end of mainshaft and countershaft assemblies and remove from bearing plate, being careful not to damage shafts. Remove bearings from bearing plate.

11) On 5-speed models, remove mainshaft and countershaft snap rings and adjusting washers. Remove rear bearings using bearing removal tool (49 0839 425C).

12) From rear of mainshaft, remove snap ring, thrust washer, lock ball, 5th gear, synchronizer ring, counter 5th gear and spacer. Engage clutch sleeves into 1st and reverse gear to lock mainshaft assembly. Mount bearing plate in vise. Remove lock nut caulking using a chisel.

13) Remove and discard lock nut using wrench. Remove 5th-Reverse clutch hub assembly, reverse gear, needle bearing, inner race, thrust washer, counter reverse gear, snap ring, thrust washers and reverse idler gear.

14) Using plastic faced hammer, tap rear end of mainshaft and countershaft assemblies and remove from bearing plate. Remove bearing cover and bearings from bearing plate.

COMPONENT DISASSEMBLY & REASSEMBLY

MAINSHAFT

Disassembly

1) On 4-speed models, remove thrust washer, 1st gear, sleeve and synchronizer ring from mainshaft. Remove snap ring from front of mainshaft. Using arbor press, remove 3rd-4th clutch hub and sleeve assembly, synchronizer ring and 3rd gear from front of mainshaft.

2) Reposition mainshaft in press and remove 1st-2nd clutch hub and sleeve assembly, synchronizer ring and 2nd gear from rear of mainshaft.

3) On 5-speed models, remove snap ring from front of mainshaft. Remove 3rd-4th synchronizer hub assembly, synchronizer ring, 3rd gear, thrust washer, synchronizer ring, 1st gear, needle bearing, inner race, 1st-2nd synchronizer hub assembly, synchronizer ring and 2nd gear.

Fig. 3: Removing Reverse and Counter Reverse Gear Assemblies

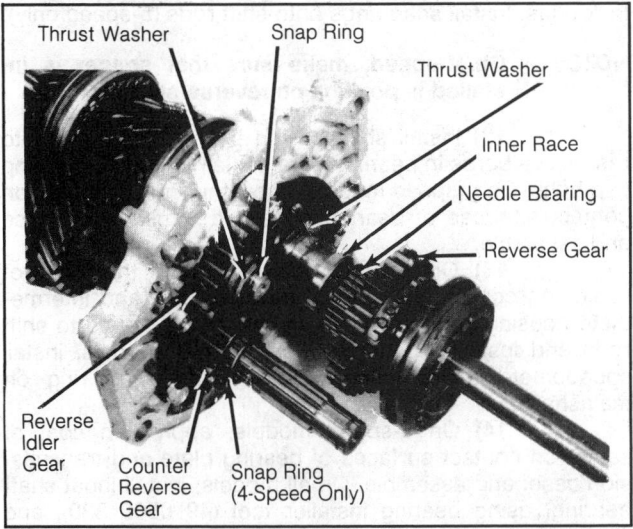

Mainshaft Inspection

Inspect mainshaft for runout by positioning a dial indicator along the shaft in several places. If runout exceeds .0012" (.03 mm), straighten shaft using press or replace. Inspect all other surfaces and splines for wear and/or damage.

Synchronizer Inspection

1) Inspect unit for worn or damaged parts. Install synchronizer ring evenly to gear cone and measure clearance between side faces of ring and gear with feeler gauge. If clearance is less than .031" (0.8 mm), replace synchronizer ring or gear.

2) Inspect contact between ring and gear using machinist blue on cone surface of gear. If contact pattern is poor, correct by lapping surfaces together or by replacing ring or gear. Check synchronizer key spring for tension. Ensure that clutch sleeve slides easily on clutch hub. Check clearance between shift fork and clutch using feeler gauge. Clearance limit is .020" (0.5 mm).

Fig. 4: Checking Synchronizer Ring Clearance with Feeler Gauge

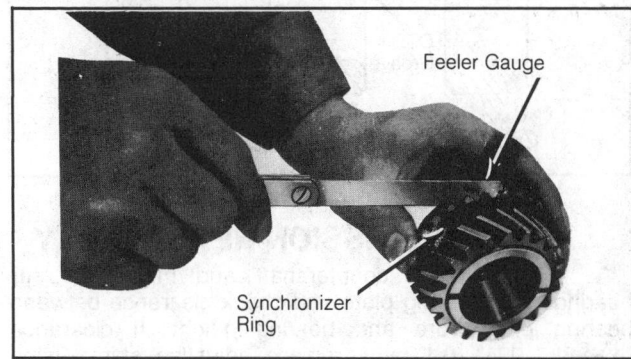

Bearing Housing Inspection

Place a straightedge across the bearing housing. Measure clearance between straightedge and each bearing, using a feeler gauge. Clearance should be 0-.002" (0-.05 mm). If clearance is not within limits, install correct shim. See Fig. 5.

Fig. 5: Checking Bearing Housing Clearances

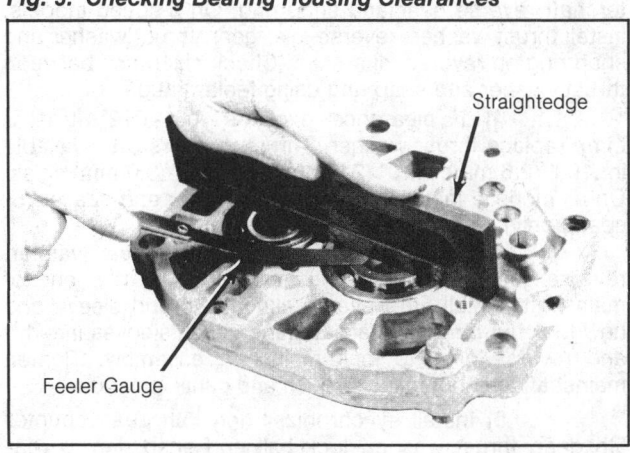

Reassembly

1) On 4-speed models, from rear of mainshaft, install 2nd gear, synchronizer ring, 1st-2nd clutch hub and sleeve assembly using arbor press.

MAZDA RWD 4 & 5-SPEED (Cont.)

2) Reposition mainshaft in press and install 3rd gear, synchronizer ring, 3rd-4th clutch hub and sleeve assembly. Install snap ring on front of mainshaft and install synchronizer ring, sleeve, 1st gear and thrust washer.

3) On 5-speed models, install 2nd gear, synchronizer ring, 1st-2nd clutch hub assembly, inner race, needle bearing, 1st gear, synchronizer ring, thrust washer, 3rd gear, synchronizer ring and 3rd-4th clutch hub assembly. Install snap on front of mainshaft. On all models, install input shaft with needle bearing onto mainshaft.

Fig. 6: *Synchronizer Position on Mainshaft*

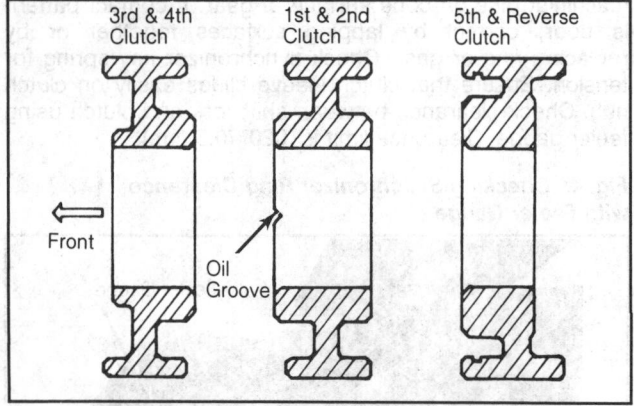

Fig. 7: Assembled View of Reverse Shift Fork and Shift Rod Assemblies

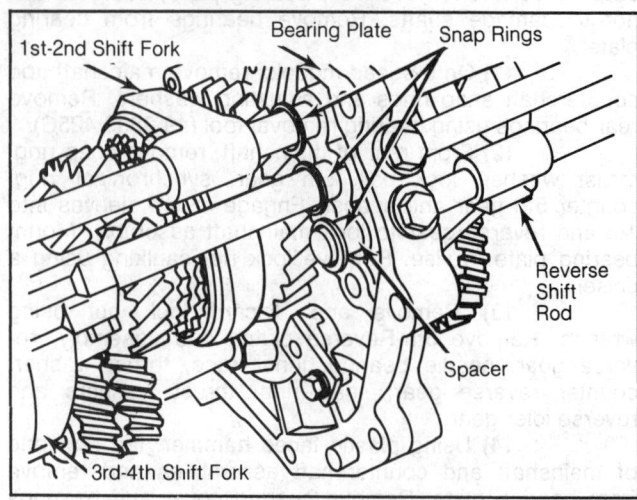

Thrust washers are available in .252" (6.4 mm), .256" (6.5 mm), .260" (6.6 mm), and .264" (6.7 mm) sizes. Install mainshaft rear bearing using wrench tool (49 1243 465A).

8) Install bearing, adjusting washer and snap ring. Check clearance between mainshaft adjusting washer and snap ring using feeler gauge. If clearance exceeds .004" (0.1 mm), replace adjusting washer. Adjusting washers are available in .075" (1.9 mm), .079" (2.0 mm), .083" (2.1 mm) and .087" (2.2 mm) sizes.

9) Install countershaft rear bearing using bearing installer tool (49 0500 330). Install countershaft thrust washer and snap ring. Check clearance between thrust washer and snap ring using feeler gauge. If clearance exceeds .004" (0.1 mm), replace thrust washer. Thrust washers are available in .079" (2.0), .083" (2.1 mm), .087" (2.2 mm), .091" (2.3 mm) and .094" (2.4 mm) sizes.

10) On all models, install reverse shift spring and locking ball into bearing plate. Push ball down using screwdriver and install reverse shift rod, shift fork and reverse idler gear (4-speed only) at same time. Install washer and snap ring (5-speed only).

11) Install 1st-2nd and 3rd-4th shift forks onto clutch sleeves. Using guide tools (49 0862 350 & 49 0187 451A), install each shift fork rod and interlock pin. Align bolt holes in both shift forks and rods. Install and tighten lock bolts. Install snap rings onto shift rods (5-speed only).

NOTE: **On 4-speed, make sure that spacer is installed in position on reverse shift fork rod.**

TRANSMISSION REASSEMBLY

1) Install countershaft and mainshaft rear bearings into bearing plate and check clearance between bearing plate bore and bearing height. If clearance exceeds .004" (0.1 mm), replace adjusting shim. Using arbor press, install countershaft and mainshaft assembly into bearing plate.

2) Install bearing cover and reverse idler gear shaft. On 4-speed models, install reverse gear with key onto mainshaft and chamfer on teeth of gear facing rearward. Secure mainshaft with holding tool (49 0259 440) and install and tighten lock nut using wrench.

3) Bend over lock washer tab. Install countershaft reverse gear and snap ring. On 5-speed models, install thrust washer, reverse idler gear, thrust washer and snap ring on reverse idler shaft. Check clearance between thrust washer and snap ring using feeler gauge.

4) If clearance exceeds .004-.012" (0.1-0.3 mm), replace thrust washer. Thrust washers are available in .106" (2.6 mm), .110" (2.8 mm) and .118" (3.0 mm) sizes. On all models, install counter reverse gear and spacer (5-speed only) on countershaft.

5) On 5-speed models, install thrust washer, reverse gear, needle bearing and sleeve on rear end of mainshaft. Install 5th-Reverse clutch hub and sleeve and new lock nut on mainshaft. Engage clutch sleeves into 1st and reverse gear to lock mainshaft assembly. Tighten mainshaft lock nut using wrench and caulk lock nut.

6) Install synchronizer ring, 5th gear, counter 5th gear, thrust washer, lock ball and snap ring to rear end of mainshaft.

7) Check clearance between 5th gear thrust washer and snap ring using feeler gauge. If clearance exceeds .004-.012" (0.1-0.3 mm), replace thrust washer.

12) Install shift locking balls and springs into respective bores in bearing plate. Install and tighten spring cap bolts. On 4-speed models, apply thin coat of sealer on contact surfaces of bearing plate and transmission case and assemble.

13) On 5-speed models, apply thin coat of sealer on contact surfaces of bearing plate and intermediate housing and assemble. Install shift rod ends to shift rods and install and tighten bolts. On all models, install speedometer drive gear, lock ball and snap ring on mainshaft.

14) On 5-speed models, apply thin coat of sealer on contact surfaces of bearing plate and transmission case, and assemble. On all models, install input shaft bearing, using bearing installer tool (49 0500 330), and

MAZDA RWD 4 & 5-SPEED (Cont.)

install snap ring. Install countershaft front bearing, using bearing installer tool (49 0180 321A).

15) Install speedometer driven gear assembly, lock plate and bolt into extension housing and tighten bolt. Install control lever through holes from front side of extension housing. Install control lever end, control lever and tighten bolt. Install back-up light switch, top switch and overdrive switch.

Fig. 8: View of Front Case Showing Front Bearing End Play Shim Location

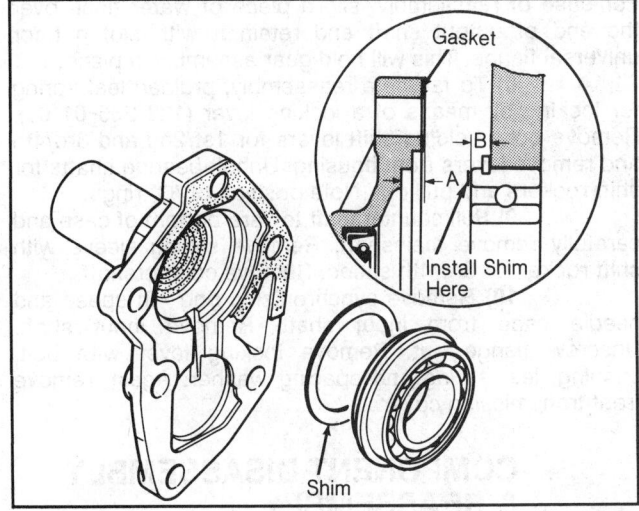

16) Apply thin coat of sealer on contact surfaces of bearing plate/intermediate housing and extension housing and assemble with control lever positioned to the left as far as possible. Install and tighten bolts, making sure control rod operates properly. Install gearshift lever retainer and gasket to extension housing.

17) Lubricate lip of oil seal inside front cover and install front cover to transmission case. Check clearance between bearing outer race and front cover using feeler gauge. If clearance exceeds .004" (0.1 mm), replace adjusting shim. Adjusting shims are available in .006" (1.5 mm) and .012" (.30 mm) sizes.

18) On GLC models, install throw-out bearing, spring, release lever, cross-shaft and cross-shaft bolt and tighten bolt. On all other models, install throw-out bearing, clutch release fork and dust cover.

TIGHTENING SPECIFICATIONS

Application	Ft. Lbs. (N.m)
Mainshaft Lock Nut	
4-Speed	116-174 (157-237)
5-Speed	94-152 (128-207)
Control Lever End Bolt	20-25 (27-34)

	INCH Lbs. (N.m)
Shift Fork Bolts	108-144 (12-16)
Spring Cap Bolts	84-132 (10-15)
Interlock Pin Plug	84-132 (10-15)
Shift Rod End Bolts	72-108 (8-12)

Fig. 9: Exploded View of 4-Speed Transmission Shift Control Linkage

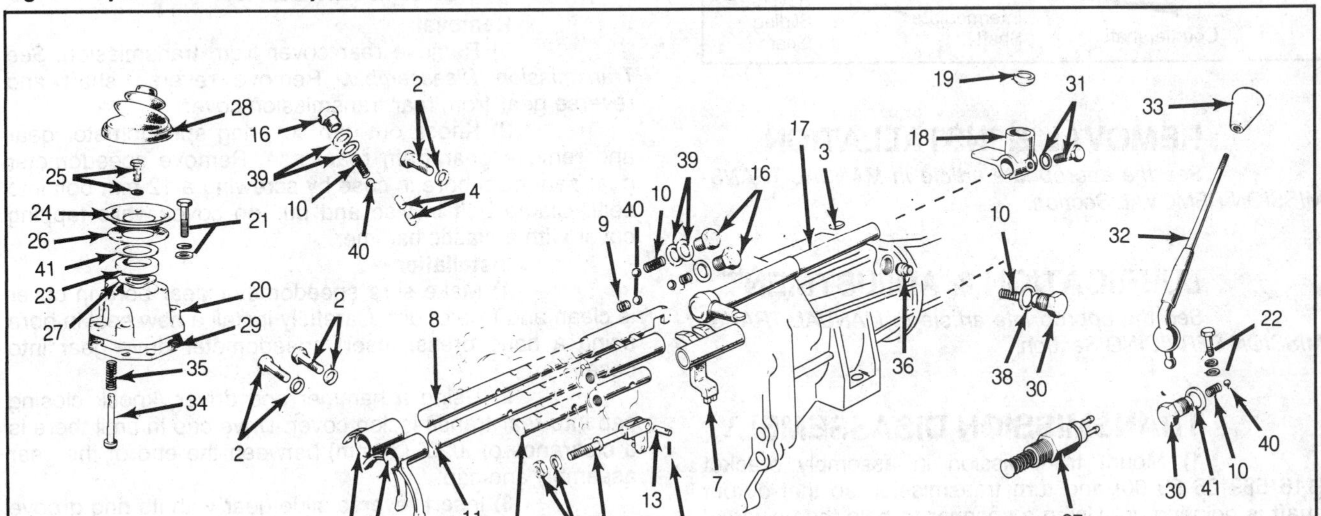

1. Nut & Lock Washer
2. Bolt & Spring Washer
3. Key
4. Interlock Pin
5. 1st-2nd Shift Fork
6. 3rd-4th Shift Fork
7. Reverse Shift Fork
8. Shift Rod
9. Spring
10. Spring
11. Shift Rod
12. Shift Lever
13. Pin
14. Pin
15. Reverse Shift Rod
16. Plug
17. Control Lever
18. Control Rod End
19. Spring Seat
20. Shifter Housing
21. Retaining Bolt & Washer
22. Bolt & Washer
23. Bushing
24. Cover Plate
25. Bolt & Spring Washer
26. Gasket
27. Wave Washer
28. Dust Boot
29. Gasket
30. Spring Cap
31. Lock Bolt
32. Shift Lever
33. Knob
34. Select Lock Spindle
35. Spring
36. Detent
37. Back-Up Light Switch
38. Washer
39. Washer
40. Detent Ball
41. Shim

5-speed shift control linkage similar.

MERCEDES-BENZ 4-SPEED

240D

DESCRIPTION

Transmisson model 716.210 (GL68/20A) is a fully synchronized, 4-speed unit with a sliding gear reverse gear. The transmission housing and clutch housing are a one-piece light alloy casting. This casting has a network of ribs and cavities to provide strength and to reduce noise characteristics. To save weight and provide a compact housing, the center distance between the mainshaft and the counter shaft has been reduced from 76 mm to 68 mm.

Fig. 1: Sectional View of Mercedes-Benz 4-Speed Transmission

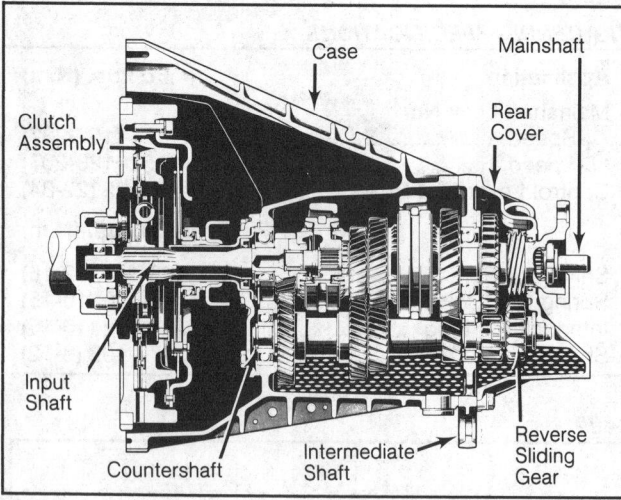

REMOVAL & INSTALLATION

See the appropriate article in MANUAL TRANS-MISSION REMOVAL Section.

LUBRICATION & ADJUSTMENT

See the appropriate article in MANUAL TRANS-MISSION SERVICING Section.

TRANSMISSION DISASSEMBLY

1) Mount transmission in assembly bracket (116 589 05 59 00) and turn transmission so that output shaft is pointing up. Using a spanner to hold the universal flange, remove the nut securing flange to output shaft.

2) Remove universal flange, use puller if necessary. Unscrew detent cage and remove from housing with gasket. Loosen screws for shift levers 1st/2nd and 3rd/4th speed.

3) Remove front transmission cover. Remove snap ring from front of countershaft. Shift transmission into two gears at once. Using puller (123 589 10 33 00) remove countershaft front bearing.

4) Remove snap ring on input shaft. Using puller (123 589 11 33 00) remove ball bearing from input shaft. Take care to notice thickness and position of compensating washers on bearing. Replace transmission front cover with two bolts to keep input shaft from falling out.

5) Remove rear transmission cover. Remove speedometer drive gear and reverse gear from mainshaft. Remove snap ring retaining reverse counter gear and remove gear.

6) Remove retainer for rear mainshaft bearing. Install two bolts to hold intermediate plate to transmission case. Use puller (123 589 10 33 00) to remove output shaft bearing. Notice thickness and position of compensating washers on bearing.

7) Remove bolts and intermediate plate. Using a mandrel, press roller sleeve out of intermediate plate. For ease of reassembly, slip a piece of water hose over the end of output shaft and retain it with slot nut for universal flange. This will hold gear assembly in place.

8) To facilitate reassembly, preload leaf spring for locking by means of a locking lever (123 265 01 08). Remove bolts holding shift levers for 1st/2nd and 3rd/4th and remove levers from housing. Unbolt bearing shafts for shift rockers and pull out. Note position of "O" rings.

9) Pull countershaft toward bottom of case and carefully remove mainshaft. Remove sliding sleeve with shift rocker for 3rd/4th speed. Remove countershaft.

10) Remove synchronizing ring 4th speed and needle cage from input shaft. Remove input shaft. Unscrew flange nut. Remove locking lever with bolt, bushing, leaf spring and spacing washer. Again, remove front transmission cover.

COMPONENT DISASSEMBLY & REASSEMBLY

SPEEDOMETER GEAR
Removal

1) Remove rear cover from transmission. See Transmission Disassembly. Remove reverse shaft and reverse gear from rear transmission cover.

2) Knock out cap covering speedometer gear and remove gear from rear case. Remove speedometer gear seal from bore in case by screwing a 12 mm bolt into seal. Clamp bolt in vise and pull on cover while tapping cover with a plastic hammer.

Installation

1) Make sure speedometer gear bore in cover is clean and free of dirt. Carefully install a new seal in bore using a hand press. Insert speedometer drive gear into case.

2) Using a hammer and driver, knock closing cap into rear transmission cover. Drive cap in until there is a clearance of .020" (.5 mm) between the end of the gear assembly and cap.

3) Insert reverse slide gear with its ring groove into rear of transmission cover. Make sure that the shift bolt of the reverse speed lever enters the ring groove.

4) Slip reverse shaft into reverse slide gear and rear transmission cover so that the cutout on shaft is in alignment with locating bore in cover. Check shaft for anit-torsion lock.

MAINSHAFT
Removal

1) Sliding sleeve, shift rocker and shift fork for 3rd and 4th gear must be removed separately from transmission. Turn shift rocker for 3rd/4th gear by 90° and remove together with shift fork from sliding sleeve from 3rd/4th gear. Remove shift fork from shift rocker.

MERCEDES-BENZ 4-SPEED (Cont.)

Fig. 2: *Locating Compensating Washers in Mercedes-Benz 4-Speed Transmission*

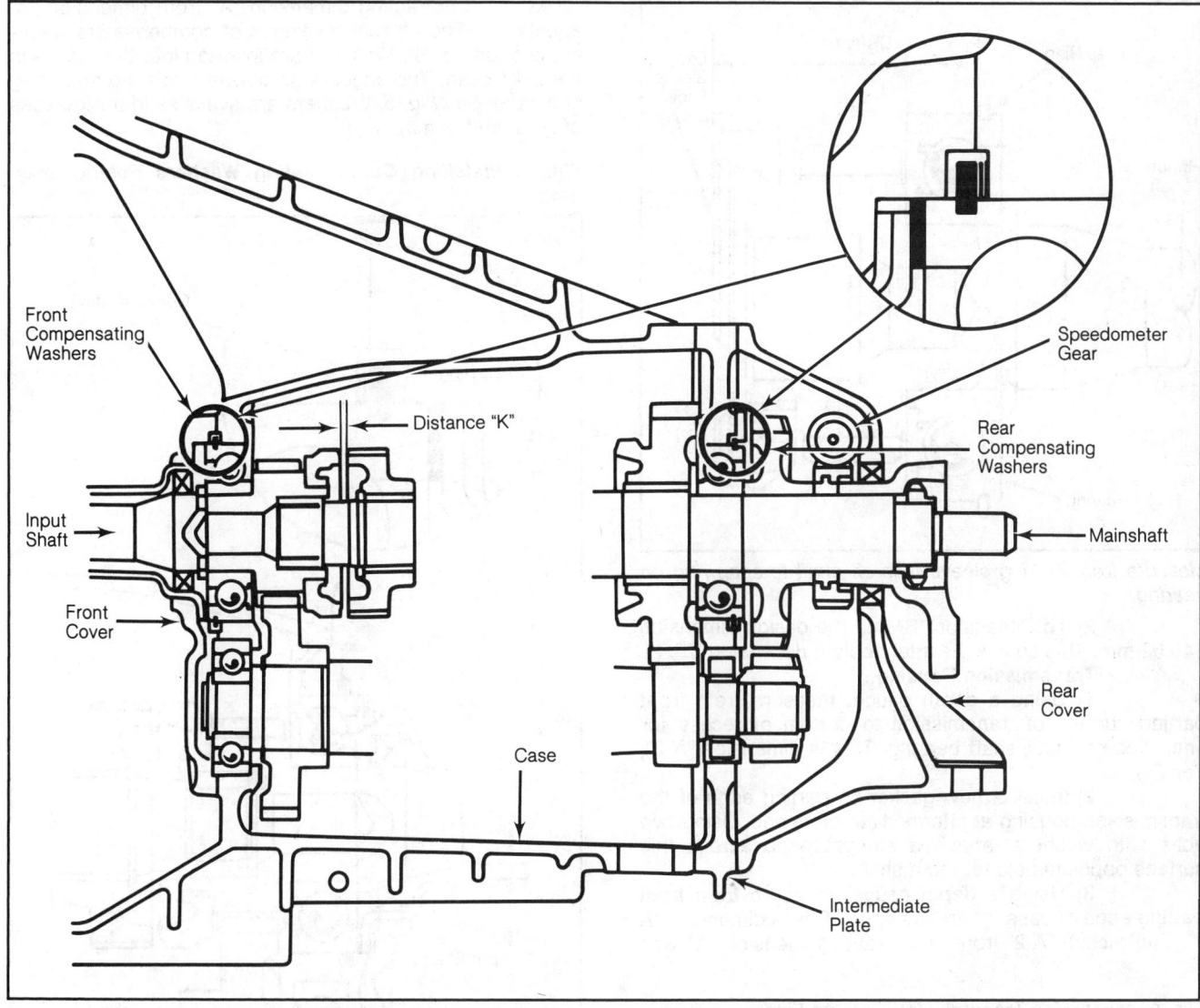

Transmission is measured to provide distance "K" between input and main shafts.

2) Clamp mainshaft carefully in vise. Remove snap ring from front of mainshaft. Remove synchornizing body for 3rd and 4th gears. Push synchronizing ring from 3rd gear. Remove 3rd gear and needle cage.

3) Turn mainshaft around and clamp into vise. Remove thrust washer. Remove 1st gear with synchronizer ring and needle cage. Remove synchronizing ring from 1st gear.

4) Turn shift rocker 90° and remove it together with shift fork. Separate shift fork and rocker. Remove sliding sleeve from synchronizer body. Remove snap ring from synchronizing body for 1st and 2nd gears.

5) Remove synchronizing body for 1st and 2nd gear. Remove synchronizing ring from 2nd gear. Remove 2nd gear and needle sleeve.

Inspection
Check all parts for wear. In particular, check roller sleeve of counter shaft rear for damage and quiet running. Check synchronizing rings for wear by inserting ring into sliding sleeve. Measure the distance in height between the sleeve and the ring at three different places. If the ring is set back more than .039" (1 mm), replace ring.

Reassembly
Reassembly is the reverse of disassembly procedure. Make sure all parts are lubricated before they are assembled.

MEASURING TRANSMISSION
Measuring of transmission should be done very carefully. Dimensions for required distance "K" between input shaft and mainshaft are determined by measuring transmission housing, input shaft, mainshaft, intermediate plate and ball bearings. *See Fig. 2.* This dimension is adjusted by the use of compensating washers placed near ball bearings on the input shaft and at the intermediate plate. After transmission is assembled, clearance does not need to be rechecked.

FRONT WASHER SELECTION
Input Shaft
1) With bearing and snap rings installed on input shaft and bearing, measure from locking sleeve face of input shaft to snap ring mounted on input shaft bearing. *See Fig. 3.* This dimension is "B".

Manual Transmissons

MERCEDES-BENZ 4-SPEED (Cont.)

Fig. 3: Measuring Input Shaft Distance

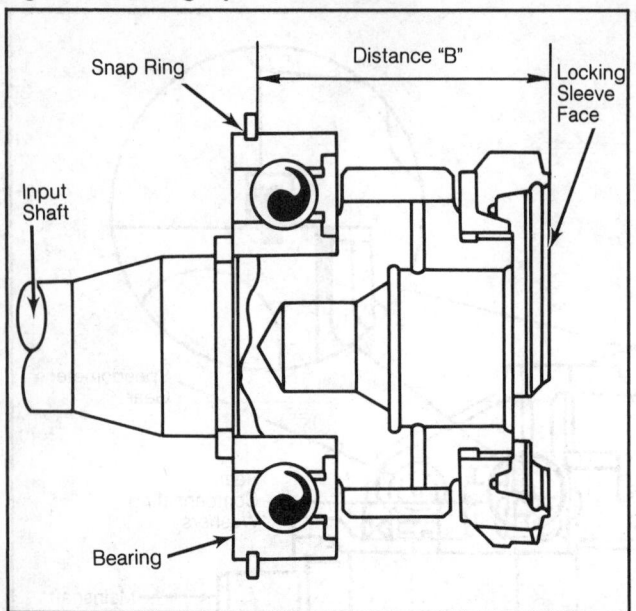

Measure from locking sleeve face on shaft to snap ring on bearing.

2) To Dimension "B" add the design dimension 140.02 mm. This sum is the intermediate dimension "Z".

Transmission Housing

1) Using a depth gauge, measure from front parting surface of transmission to bottom of recess for snap ring on input shaft bearing. This is dimension "A 2". *See Fig. 4.*

2) Install a new gasket on parting edge of the transmission housing at intermediate plate end. Using two bolts with washers, attach a straight edge across this surface opposite hole for input shaft.

3) Using a depth gauge, measure from front parting edge of case to straight edge. This is dimension "A 1". Subtracting "A 2" from "A 1" leaves dimension "A". *See Fig. 4.*

Fig. 4: Measuring Transmission Case to Find Dimension "A"

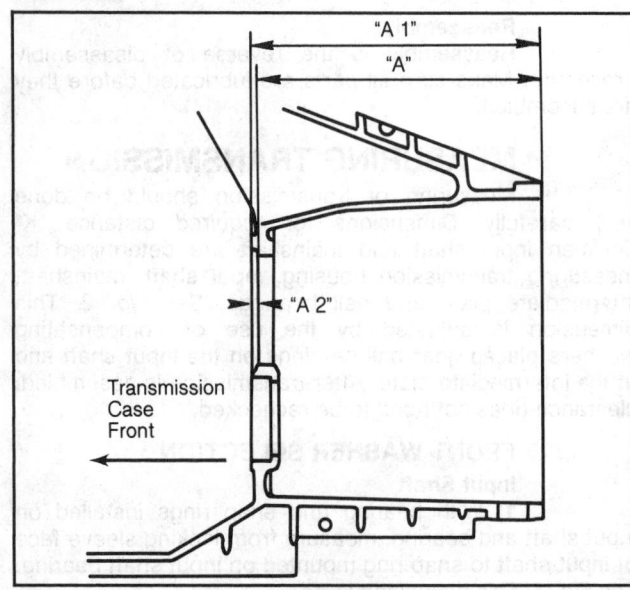

Subtract measurement "A 2" from "A 1".

Washer Selection

Subtracting dimension "A" from dimension "Z" equals "S". The correct thickness of compensating washers is equal to "S". Washers are inserted into the recess in the front case. The spacers go between bearing snap ring and case. *See Fig. 5.* Washers are available in thicknesses of .1, .2 and .3 mm.

Fig. 5: Installing Compensating Washers Behind Snap Ring

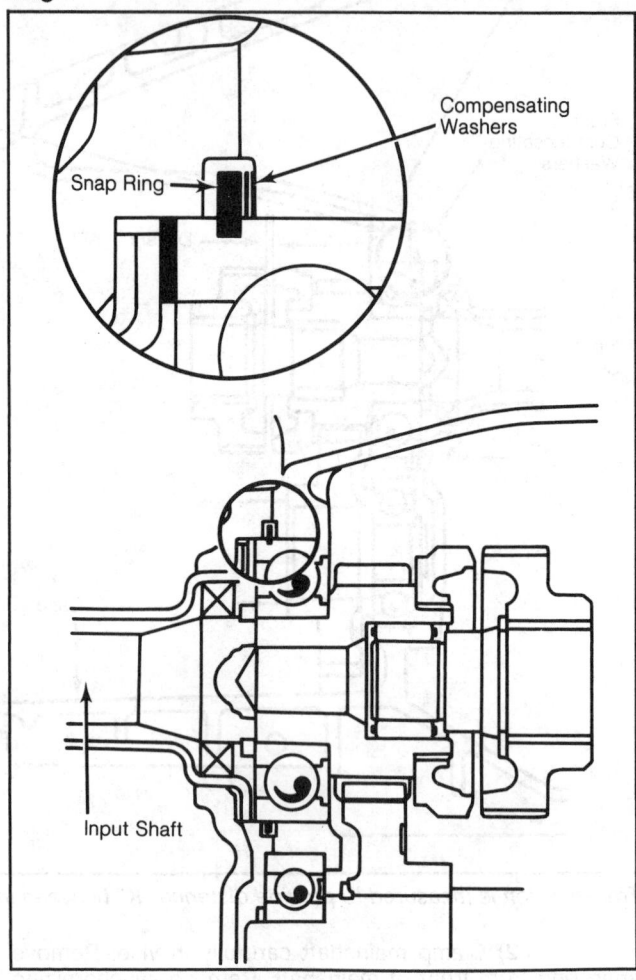

Fig. 6: Measuring Mainshaft

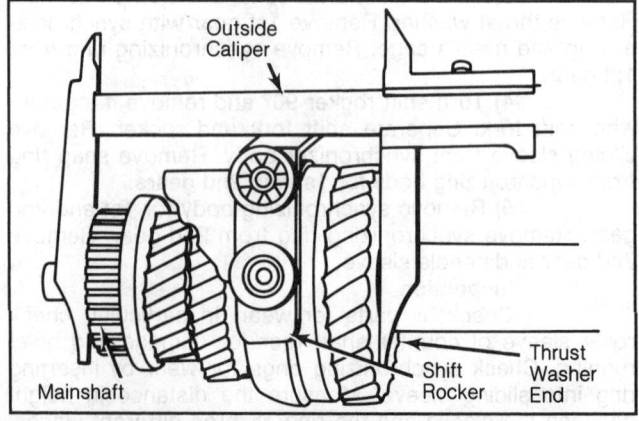

Use outside caliper and measure from thrust washer to synchronizing body for 3rd/4th gear.

MERCEDES-BENZ 4-SPEED (Cont.)

REAR WASHER SELECTION
Mainshaft

Using an outside caliper, measure mainshaft from synchronizing body for 3rd/4th gear and thrust washer on outside of 1st gear. *See Fig. 6.* This dimension is "C". *See Fig. 7.*

Fig. 7: Locating Dimension "C" on Mainshaft

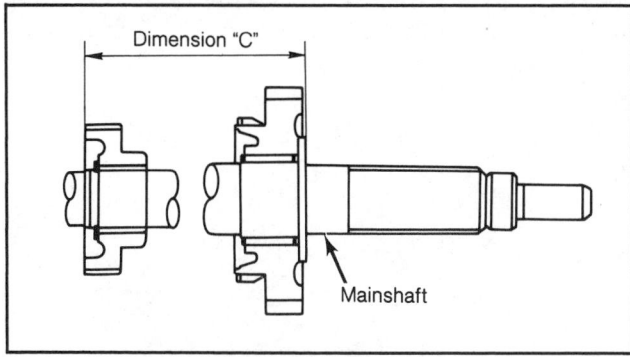

Mainshaft Bearing

Using a depth gauge, measure from the thrust washer side of the bearing to the snap ring. *See Fig. 8.* This dimension is "D". Adding dimension "C" and "D" equals "Z 1", this is the rear intermediate dimension.

Fig. 8: Measuring Mainshaft Bearing

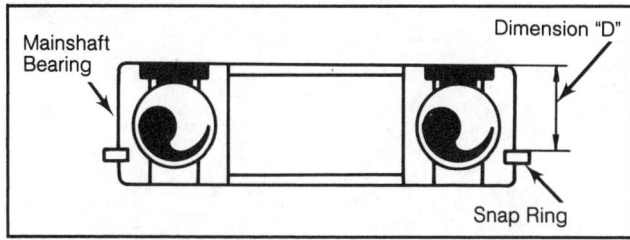

Intermediate Plate

1) Place intermediate plate on a straight edge with the recess for the snap ring facing up. Using a depth gauge, measure from the bearing retainer mating surface to the bottom of the recess.

2) Measure from the bearing retainer mating surface to the straightedge. Subtract the smaller dimension from the larger. This will provide dimension "E".

3) Add to dimension "E" the design dimension of 138.52 mm. This provides dimension "Z 2". Subtract dimension "Z 2" from "Z 1". This will provide dimension "S". Dimension "S" is the thickness of the compensating washers used at the intermediate plate bearing.

4) Place compensating washers on side of the snap ring that faces the recess in the intermediate plate. *See Fig. 9.* Washers are available in .1, .2 and .3 mm thicknesses.

TRANSMISSION REASSEMBLY

1) Install locking lever for reverse gear with bolt, bushing, leaf spring and spacing washer. Tighten new flange nut.

2) Using a mandrel, knock input shaft with bearing and compensating washers into transmission housing. Insert needle cage into input shaft. Press synchronizing ring of 4th gear on input shaft until annular spring enters groove of input shaft.

Fig. 9: Installing Compensating Washers on Rear Bearing

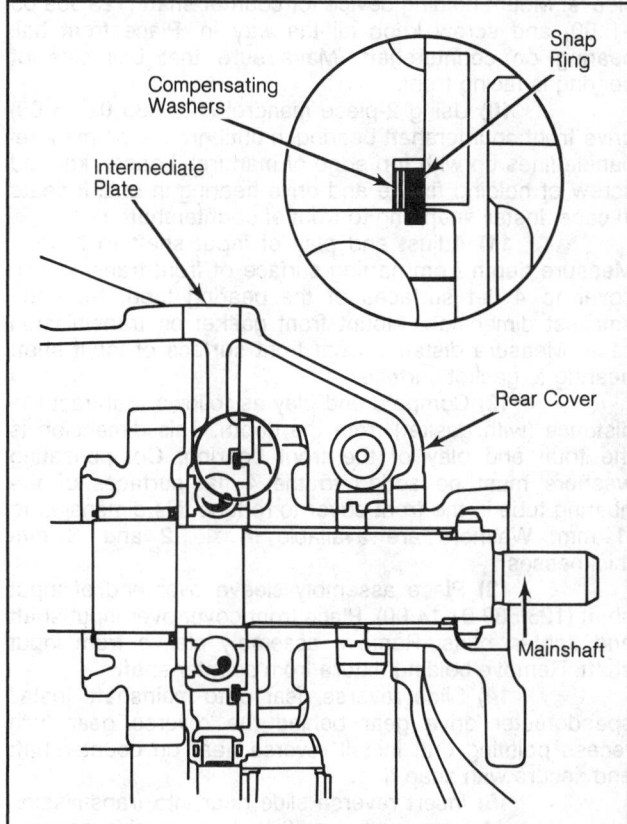

Washers are between bearing snap ring and intermediate plate.

3) Position sliding sleeve for 3rd/4th gear with fork and shift rocker on synchronizing ring and input shaft. Make sure that groove in sliding sleeve points toward 3rd gear.

4) Install bearing shaft for 3rd/4th gear shift rocker and tighten. Take care when mounting new "O" ring in housing around shaft. Install shift lever for 3rd/4th gear. Teeth on shift lever must engage teeth on shift rocker. Coat shift lever bolt with Loctite 242 and tighten.

5) Carefully insert countershaft into transmission housing. Tension leaf spring with locking lever (123 265 01 08). Pull countershaft toward bottom of case. Carefully install mainshaft with shift rocker for 1st/2nd gear in case and input shaft.

6) Install bearing shaft for 1st/2nd gear shift rocker and tighten. Take care when installing new "O" ring in housing and around shaft. Install shift lever for 1st/2nd gear. Teeth on shift lever must engage teeth on shift rocker. Coat shift lever bolt with Loctite 242 and tighten.

7) Remove locking lever from leaf spring. Remove hose from mainshaft. Place new gasket on parting surface at rear of transmission case. Place assembly sleeve on countershaft (123 589 00 14 00 or 123 589 02 14 00). Let locking lever for reverse gear rest against case.

8) With bearings installed in intermediate plate, install plate on rear of transmission and press it onto mainshaft with pressing tool (123 589 03 43 00). Make sure to fit reverse gear lever through plate. To prevent plate from canting during assembly, tap it with a plastic hammer while using pressing tool.

Manual Transmissons

MERCEDES-BENZ 4-SPEED (Cont.)

9) Remove pressing tool and installation sleeve. Mount holding device for counter shaft (123 589 05 31 00) and screw knob all the way in. Place front ball bearing on countershaft. Make sure that ball side of bearing is facing front.

10) Using 2-piece mandrel (123 589 02 15 00) drive front countershaft bearing in until groove on mandrel handle lines up with top edge of mandrel. Loosen knurled screw of holding fixture and drive bearing in until it seats in case. Install snap ring to front of countershaft.

11) Adjust end play of input shaft to .1 mm. Measure depth from parting surface of front transmission cover to 4 flat surfaces of the bearing tube. Note the smallest dimension. Mount front gasket on transmission case. Measure distance from front surface of input shaft bearing to gasket surface.

12) Compute end play as follows: Subtract the distance (with gasket) from the depth. This dimension is the total end play of the front bearing. Compensating washers must be added to the 4 flat surfaces of the bearing tube in the front cover to reduce this dimension to .1 mm. Washers are available in .1, .2 and .3 mm thicknesses.

13) Place assembly sleeve over end of input shaft (123 589 01 14 00). Place front cover over input shaft and tighten bolts. Remove assembly sleeve from input shaft. Remove holding fixture from counter shaft.

14) Slide reverse gear onto mainshaft. Install speedometer drive gear behind the reverse gear with recess pointing out. Install reverse gear on countershaft and secure with snap ring.

15) Insert reverse slide gear into transmission rear cover. Make sure that shift bolt enters ring gear on groove. Insert reverse shaft into slide gear in such a manner that the cut out on the shaft is in alignment with locating bore in cover. Check shaft for anti-torsion lock.

16) Set locking lever for reverse gear so that it comes to rest at the lower end of recess. Mount rear cover on transmission. Make sure the reverse gear shaft does not fall out. Install cover screws and tighten.

17) Grease universal flange on running surface of seal and mount flange on mainshaft. Install new nut, tighten and stake in place. Insert detent cage with gasket into transmission case. Make sure that one ball is pointing downward. Tighten detent cage screws. Fill transmission with lubricant.

TIGHTENING SPECIFICATIONS

Application	Ft. Lbs.
Clamping Nut on Driveshaft	22-30 (30-40)
Drain & Fill Plug	52 (70)
Driveshaft Intermediate Bearing Screws	18 (25)
Slot Nut for Universal Flange	118 (160)
Front Cover Bolts	15 (20)
Nut for Shift Lever	18 (25)
Screws for Holding Ring	11 (15)
Reverse Flange Locking Nut	15 (20)
Reverse Gear Shift Lever	18 (25)
Rear Cover Bolts	12 (16)

	INCH Lbs.
Screws for Shift Rocker Shafts	72 (8)
Screws for Detent Cage	72 (8)
Shift Bracket-to-Tunnel	53 (6)
Guide Pin-to-Shift Bracket	84 (10)

PEUGEOT 4 & 5-SPEED

DESCRIPTION

The 4 and 5-speed transmissions have a split aluminum case. Access to gear assembly is with one half of the case removed. All forward gears are of the helical type which provide for quiet operation. All forward gears are also synchronized for smooth gear engagement. Shift linkage is floor mounted with external linkage.

On 4-speed transmissions, reverse gears are located in the extension housing. On 5-speed transmissions, reverse and 5th gears are located in the extension housing.

LUBRICATION & ADJUSTMENT

See the appropriate article in MANUAL TRANS-MISSION SERVICING Section.

TROUBLE SHOOTING

HARD SHIFTING

Improperly adjusted clutch. Excessive input shaft end play. Face of synchro hub in contact with cone, worn. Synchro cones worn, damaged, distorted or not in proper contact.

SLIPS OUT OF GEAR

Bearings worn or defective. Excessive play between gears and synchro cage. Play in synchro hub. Shift arm worn. Lock ball spring weak or broken. Lock ball missing.

TRANSMISSION NOISY

Low or incorrect lubricant. Gears or bearings worn or damaged. Worn gears or synchro cage. Exces-sive input shaft end play. Worn synchro hub or splines. Incorrectly meshed gears.

TRANSMISSION REMOVAL & INSTALLATION

See the appropriate article in MANUAL TRANS-MISSION REMOVAL Section.

TRANSMISSION DISASSEMBLY

1) Place transmission on holding fixture with right side away from fixture (left side bolts to fixture). From extension housing, remove speedometer driven gear set screw and gear. Place shift control levers in neutral position.

2) On 4-speed, remove extension housing bolts. Remove extension housing, tapping with plastic mallet if necessary.

3) On 5-speed, turn transmission so extension housing is facing up. Remove extension housing bolts. Remove large plug on rear of housing and replace with extractor body (V1 of tool set 8.0314).

4) Insert extractor bolt (V2 of tool set 8.0314) into extractor body. To remove extension housing, turn bolt and tap sides of housing with plastic mallet.

5) Remove snap ring from mainshaft. Using a puller, remove 5th driven gear and speedometer drive gear. Remove 5th-reverse countergear shaft adjusting shim and washer. Lift off 5th drive gear. Remove snap ring from mainshaft.

6) Mark position of 5th-reverse synchro sleeve to its hub for reassembly reference. Engage 5th gear. Mount holding plate (8.0314W) over 5th gear selector fork shaft and attach plate to housing with 2 bolts. Drive out

Fig. 1: Sectional View of Peugeot 4-Speed Transmission

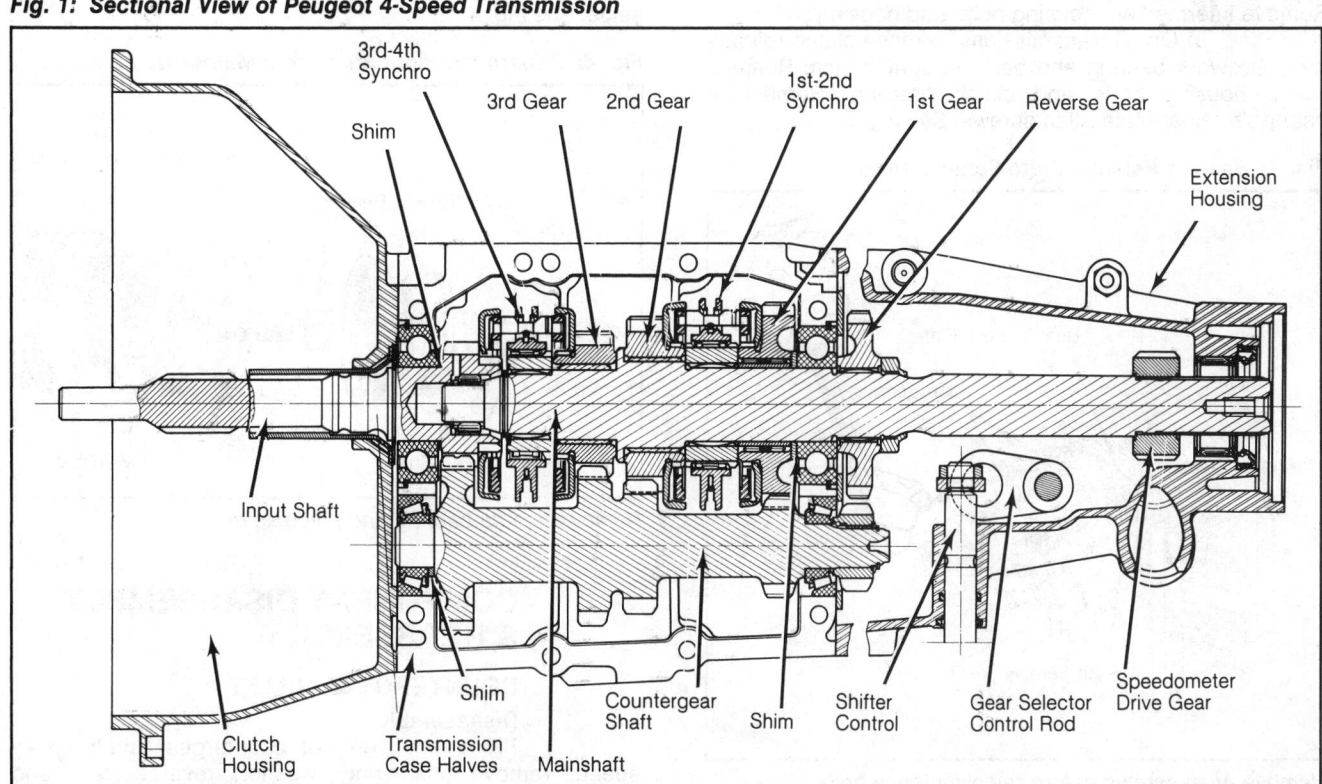

Fig. 2: *Sectional View of Peugeot 5-Speed Transmission*

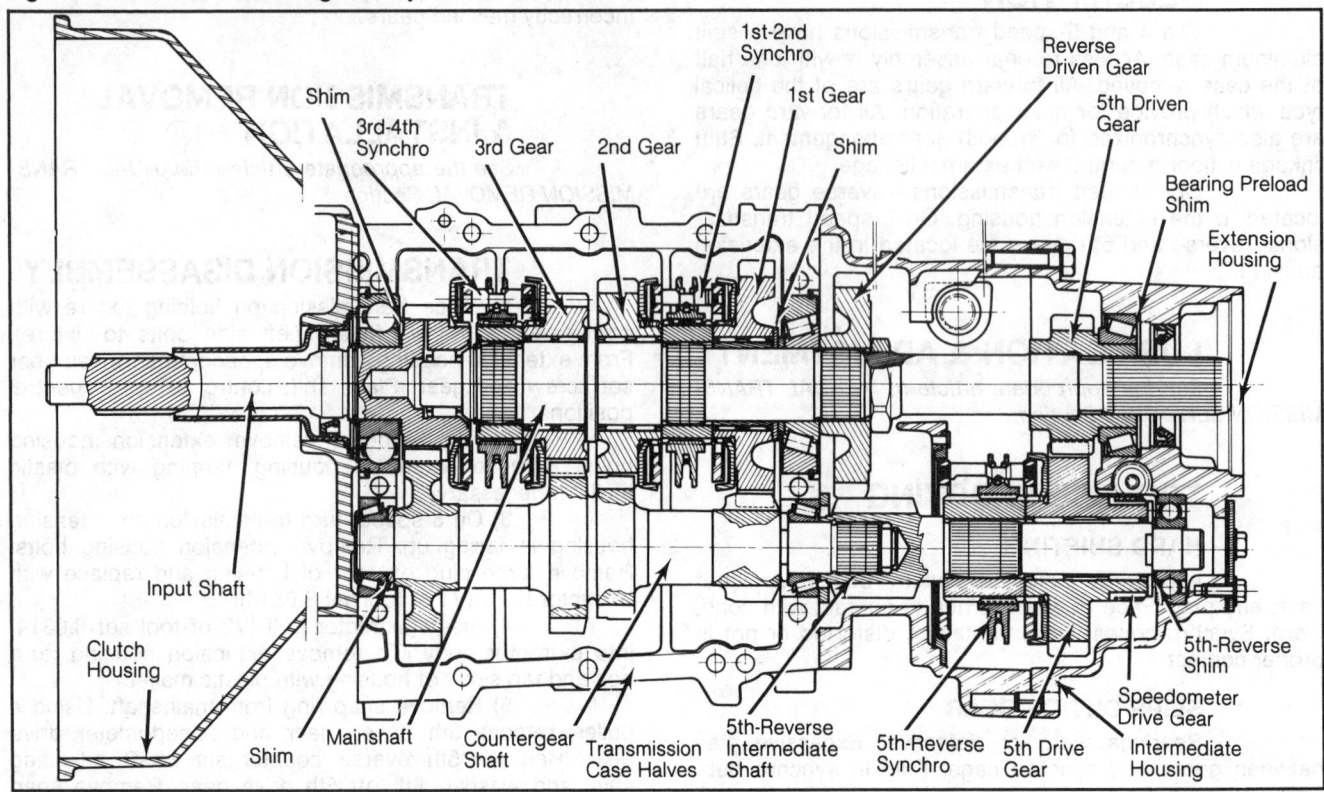

5th-reverse fork roll pin without damaging face of housing. Remove holding plate.

7) Return transmission to neutral position. Remove 5th-reverse selector fork and collar and synchronizer hub. Lift 5th-reverse intermediate shaft from housing. Disengage selector fork fingers from shift rail. Remove intermediate housing bolts and housing.

8) On all transmissions, remove clutch release fork, throwout bearing and back-up light switch. Remove clutch housing bolts and clutch housing. Remove 4 bearing retainer plate Allen screws. *See Fig. 3.*

Fig. 3: *Bearing Retainer Plate Screw Removal*

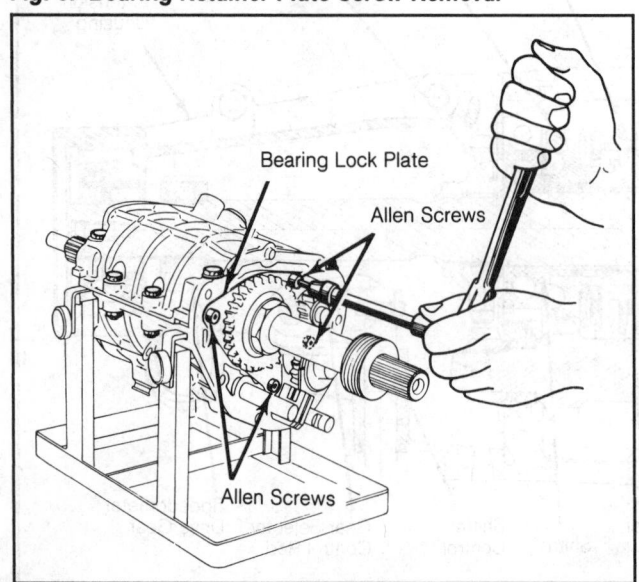

Remove Allen screws before removing case bolts.

9) Turn holding fixture until right side of case is facing up. Remove right side transmission case bolts and case half. Lift and remove entire gear assembly. Mark and remove countergear shaft end bearings. Slide synchronizer sleeve on mainshaft into 3rd gear position. Separate input shaft from mainshaft and place needle bearing aside. *See Fig. 4.*

Fig. 4: *Separating Input Shaft from Mainshaft*

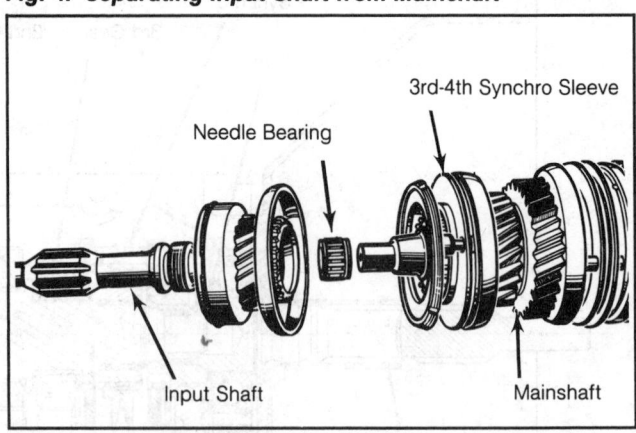

Remove needle bearing and place aside.

COMPONENT DISASSEMBLY & REASSEMBLY

COUNTERGEAR SHAFT
Disassembly
From small end of countergear shaft on 4-speed, remove snap ring, washer, reverse gear and

PEUGEOT 4 & 5-SPEED (Cont.)

bearing outer race. On all models, use a press and adapter plates to remove front and rear bearings. Set adjusting shim (located under rear bearing) aside.

Fig. 5: 4-Speed Countergear Shaft Disassembly

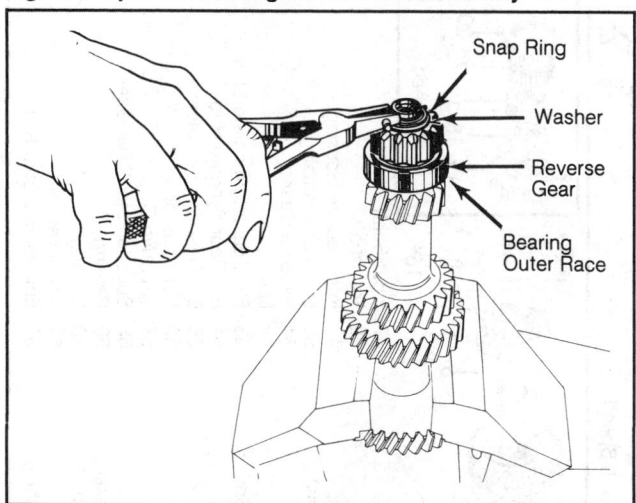

Inspection & Reassembly

Clean all parts in solvent and blow dry with compressed air. To reassemble, reverse disassembly procedure and note the following: DO NOT install adjusting shim at this time.

MAINSHAFT
Disassembly

1) Mark position of 3rd-4th speed synchro sleeve to its hub for reassembly reference. Remove synchro sleeve. Place mainshaft in vise, rear end down. Remove snap ring and washer from 3rd-4th synchro hub. While holding mainshaft reverse gear, use spanner wrench (8.0310P) to loosen mainshaft rear lock nut.

Fig. 6: Removing 3rd-4th Synchronizer Hub and Nut from Mainshaft

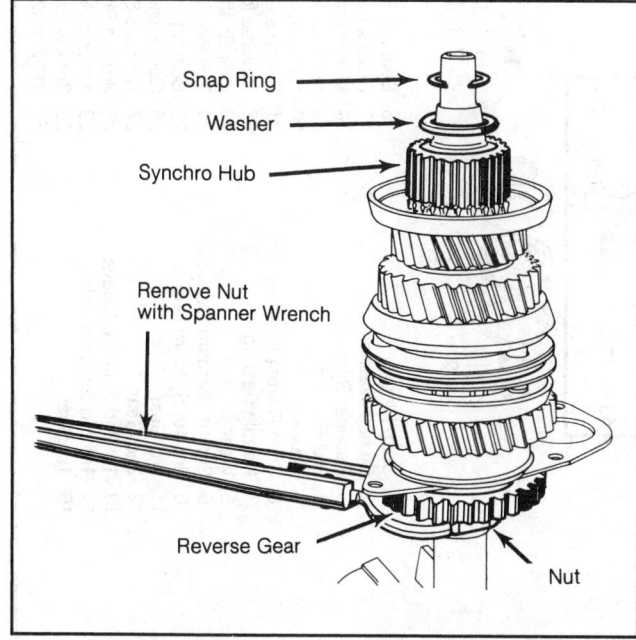

Hold mainshaft reverse gear and remove lock nut.

2) Using a press with adapter plates placed beneath outer edge of 3rd gear, press off synchronizer hub and 3rd gear. Position mainshaft upside down with input shaft end facing down.

3) Place safety plate (8.0310K) between press and mainshaft. Press on mainshaft until bearing is released. On 4-speed, continue pressing until speedometer drive gear is released.

4) Remove safety plate and press. Remove the following components from mainshaft and arrange in order of removal (facing right direction): Speedometer drive gear (4-speed only), lock nut, reverse gear, retainer plate, bearing, adjusting shim, 1st gear, bushing, needle bearings, 1st-2nd synchro (without separating hub from sleeve), needle bearings and 2nd gear.

Fig. 7: Mainshaft Rear Components

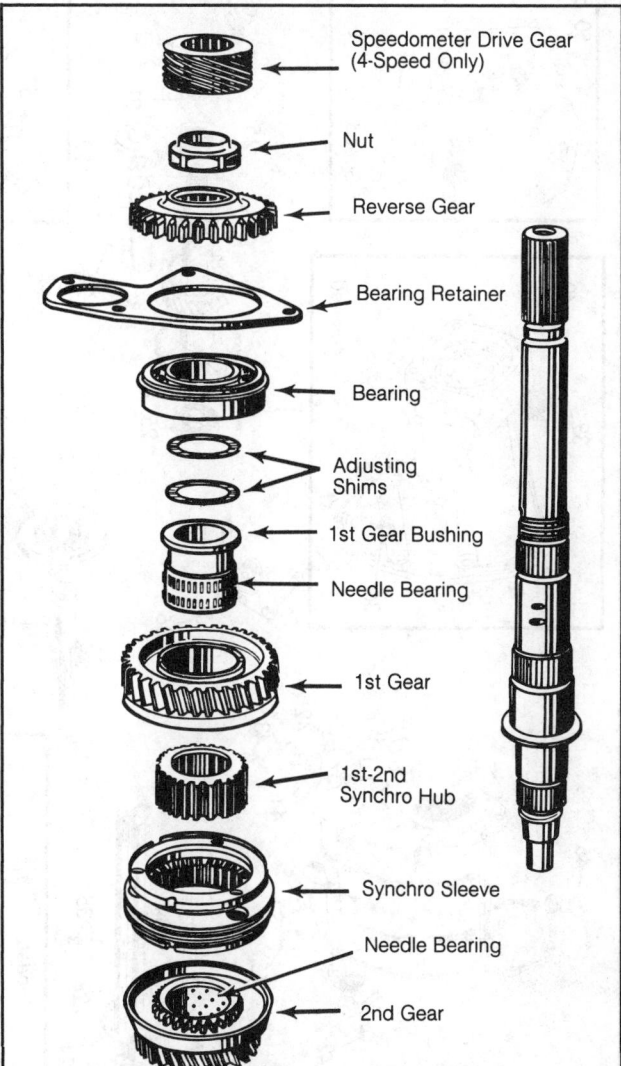

Note position and direction of components.

Inspection & Reassembly

Clean all parts in solvent and blow dry with compressed air. Inspect all parts for wear or damage and replace necessary components. To reassemble, reverse disassembly procedure and align marks scribed during disassembly. If mainshaft, gears or synchronizers are replaced, install a new .13" (3.3 mm) adjusting shim. If none of the above parts are replaced, install original shim.

Manual Transmissions
PEUGEOT 4 & 5-SPEED (Cont.)

Fig. 8: *Exploded View of Peugeot 4 and 5-Speed Transmissions*

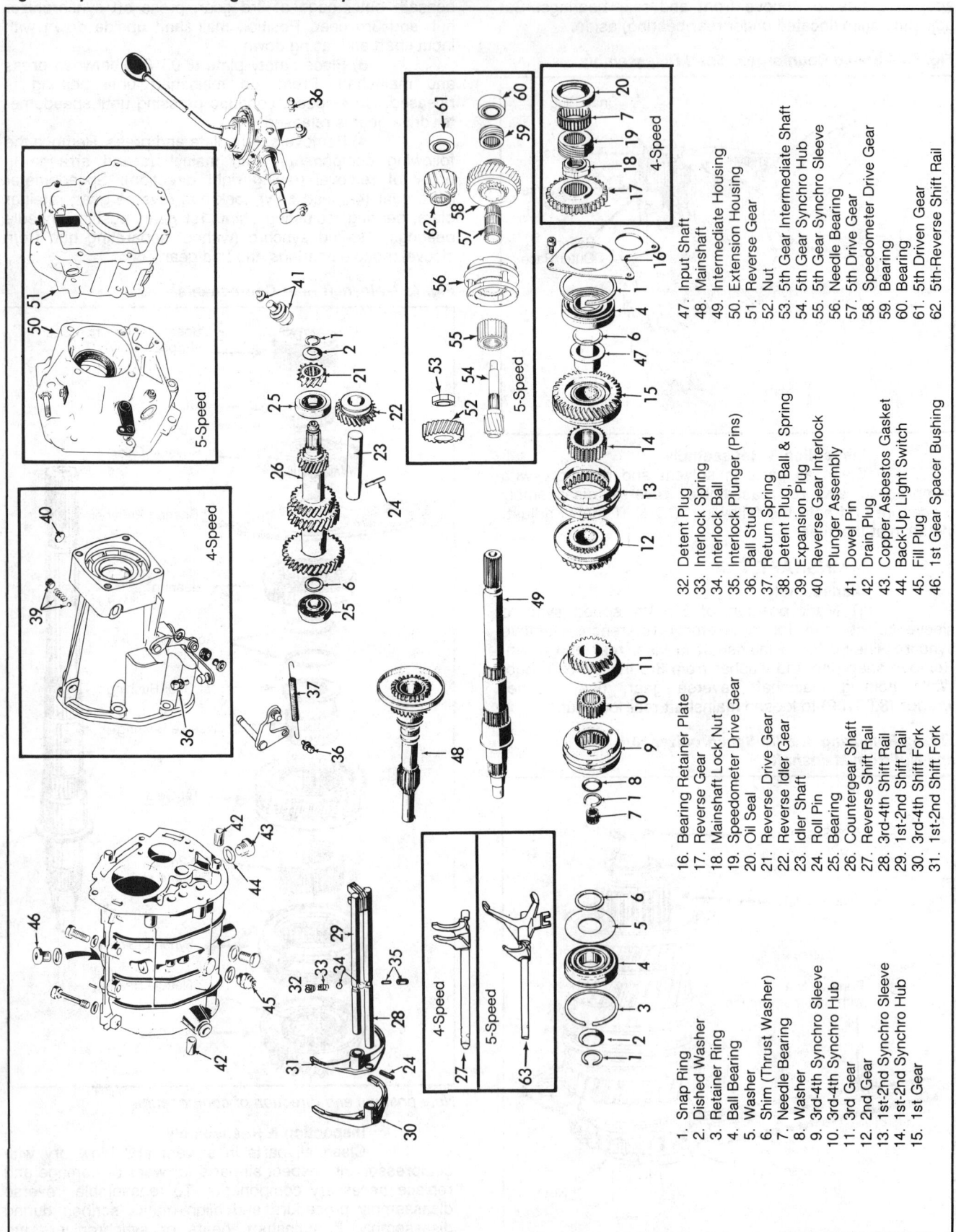

1. Snap Ring
2. Dished Washer
3. Retainer Ring
4. Ball Bearing
5. Washer
6. Shim (Thrust Washer)
7. Needle Bearing
8. Washer
9. 3rd-4th Synchro Sleeve
10. 3rd-4th Synchro Hub
11. 3rd Gear
12. 2nd Gear
13. 1st-2nd Synchro Sleeve
14. 1st-2nd Synchro Hub
15. 1st Gear
16. Bearing Retainer Plate
17. Reverse Gear
18. Mainshaft Lock Nut
19. Speedometer Drive Gear
20. Oil Seal
21. Reverse Drive Gear
22. Reverse Idler Gear
23. Idler Shaft
24. Roll Pin
25. Bearing
26. Countergear Shaft
27. Reverse Shift Rail
28. 3rd-4th Shift Rail
29. 1st-2nd Shift Rail
30. 3rd-4th Shift Fork
31. 1st-2nd Shift Fork
32. Detent Plug
33. Interlock Spring
34. Interlock Ball
35. Interlock Plunger (Pins)
36. Ball Stud
37. Return Spring
38. Detent Plug, Ball & Spring
39. Expansion Plug
40. Reverse Gear Interlock Plunger Assembly
41. Dowel Pin
42. Drain Plug
43. Copper Asbestos Gasket
44. Back-Up Light Switch
45. Fill Plug
46. 1st Gear Spacer Bushing
47. Input Shaft
48. Mainshaft
49. Intermediate Housing
50. Extension Housing
51. Reverse Gear
52. Nut
53. 5th Gear Intermediate Shaft
54. 5th Gear Synchro Hub
55. 5th Gear Synchro Sleeve
56. Needle Bearing
57. 5th Drive Gear
58. Speedometer Drive Gear
59. Bearing
60. Bearing
61. 5th Driven Gear
62. 5th-Reverse Shift Rail

PEUGEOT 4 & 5-SPEED (Cont.)

INPUT SHAFT

NOTE: Shafts which have oil slingers are identified by grooves in front of the bearing.

Disassembly

If necessary to replace bearing, remove snap ring and press off old bearing. When bearing is removed, pay particular attention to thickness of shims for reassembly reference. Also note position of oil slinger, if equipped.

Inspection & Reassembly

Inspect all parts for wear or damage. Check bearing by rotating by hand and check for noise or roughness. To reassemble, reverse disassembly procedure. If the input shaft, 3rd-4th synchronizer or 3rd-4th shift shaft have been replaced, install a .20" (.50 mm) adjusting shim (.14"/.50 mm on shafts with oil slinger). If none of the above parts are replaced, install original shim.

INTERMEDIATE SHAFT (5-SPEED ONLY)

Disassembly

If necessary to replace bearing or speedometer drive gear, use a universal bearing puller and adapter. Pull off bearing and speedometer drive gear.

Inspection & Reassembly

Inspect parts for wear or damage. Check bearing by rotating by hand and check for noise or roughness. To reassemble, reverse disassembly procedure and note the following: Undercut side of speedometer drive gear faces away from bearing.

SHIFTING MECHANISMS

Disassembly

1) Place 1st-2nd shift rail in 2nd gear position and remove pin in 1st-2nd gear shift fork. With pin removed, move shift rail back to neutral position. Shift 3rd-4th shift rail into 4th gear position and remove pin in shift fork. Return shift rail to neutral position.

Fig. 9: Removing Pins from Shift Forks

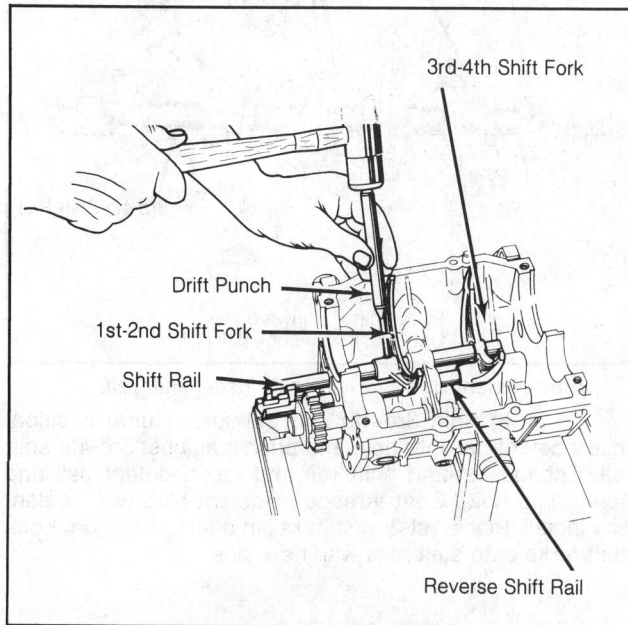

Use a drift punch to drive out roll pins.

2) Turn transmission case so it is on its side and remove detent plug. *See Fig. 10.* Remove shift rail for 1st-2nd gear and 3rd-4th gears. As shift rails are removed, catch detent ball and spring. Remove and set aside lockout needle for 3rd-4th shift rail.

Fig. 10: Removing Detent Plug

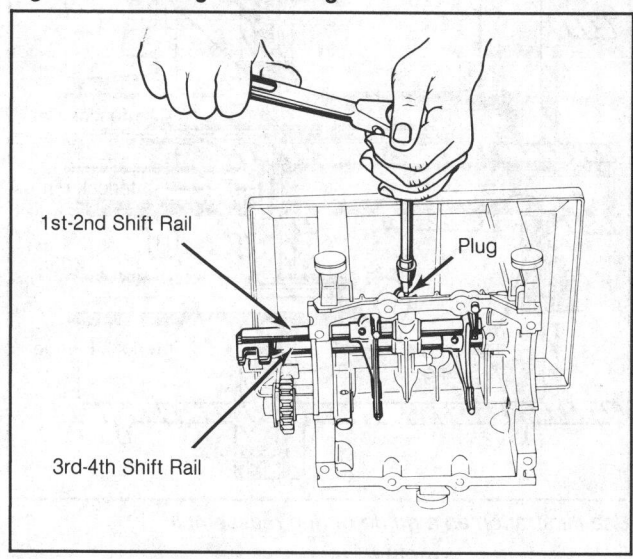

Catch detent ball and spring if they pop out.

3) Remove reverse (5th-reverse on 5-speed) detent plug, spring and ball from side of case. Remove reverse shift fork with idler gear. Using a punch, drive out reverse idler shaft pin. Remove shaft by pushing it toward outside of case. Using a long punch, push interlock balls and plunger out of case.

Fig. 11: Removing Interlock Balls and Plunger

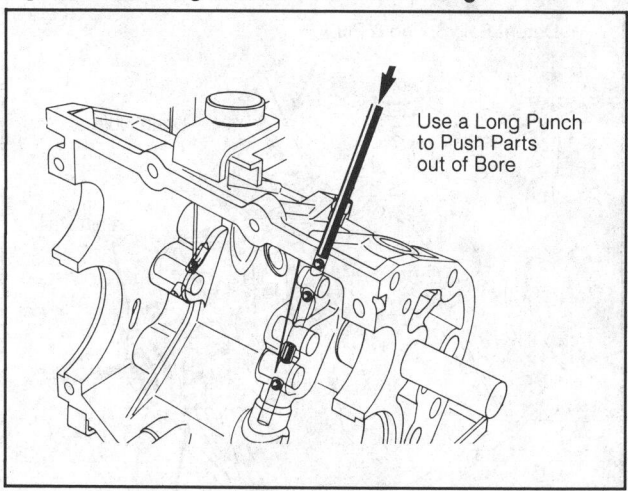

Make sure all balls and plungers are removed.

Inspection

Check neutral ball lock for positive locking action by moving selector lever in both directions. Also check that neutral ball lock plug is flush with case. If ball lock is inoperative, remove plug and inspect ball and spring. Clean all parts in solvent and blow dry with compressed air. Inspect all parts for wear or damage and replace necessary components. When installing plugs into case, use sealant.

Manual Transmissions
PEUGEOT 4 & 5-SPEED (Cont.)

Fig. 12: Detent and Interlock Positions

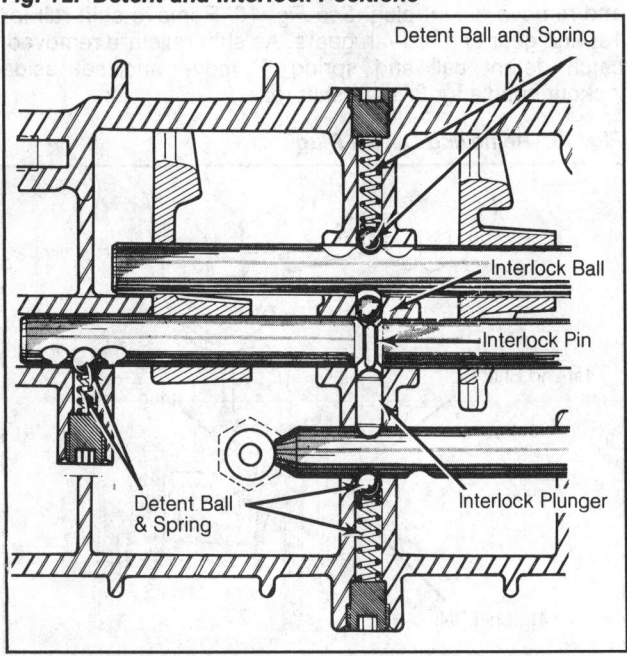

Use illustration as a guide during reassembly.

Reassembly

1) Install reverse idler gear shaft and use new straight pin to hold shaft in position. Position shift fork on reverse idler gear with beveled edge of gear facing transmission case. Install reverse shift rail into hole while positioning reverse idler gear on its shaft. Insert detent ball and spring. Use sealer on detent plug threads and install plug into reverse detent hole.

Fig. 13: Installing Reverse Idler Gear & Detent Assembly

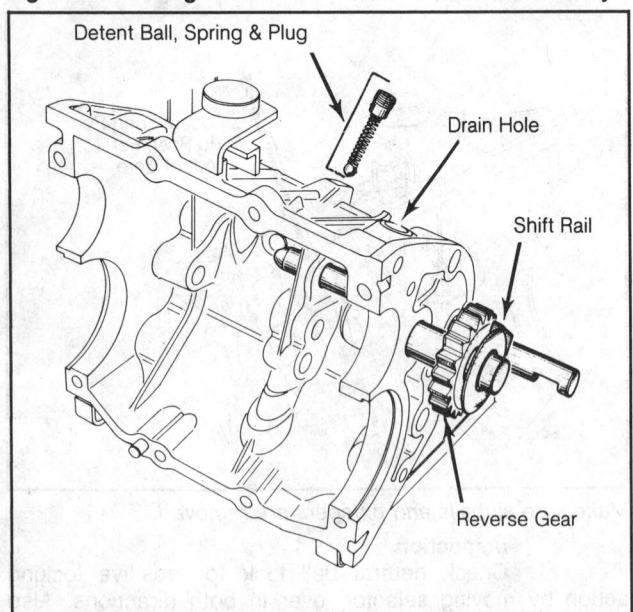

Install shift rail and gear at the same time.

2) Position reverse shift rail in neutral position. Flip case over to other side. Install 3rd-4th-reverse interlock plunger in case and seat it against reverse shift rail. Grease and install interlock pin into 3rd-4th shift rail.

Fig. 14: Interlock Plunger Position in Case Half

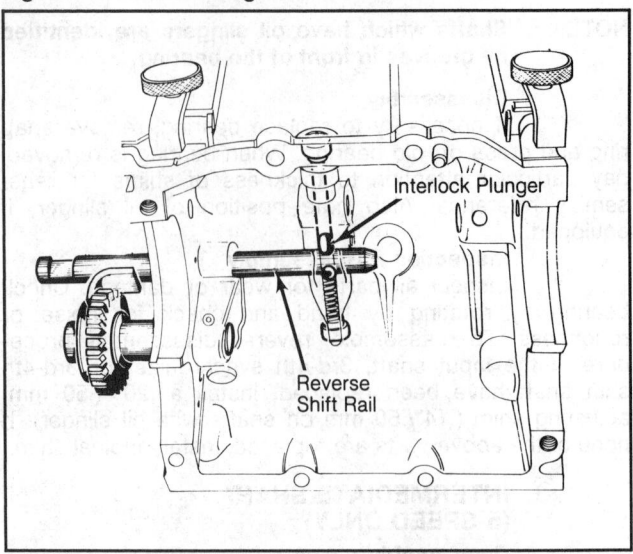

Plunger should seat against reverse shift rail.

3) Turn case and install 1st-2nd shift fork (larger of 2) and 3rd-4th shift fork in transmission case. Insert 3rd-4th shift rail into case, through both shift forks, until shaft is flush with edge of detent hole.

4) Insert 1 detent spring and ball into detent hole. Use drift punch to compress spring and ball assembly. Slide shift rail forward until punch can be released and ball will not jump out of hole.

Fig. 15: Installing 3rd-4th Shift Rail and Fork

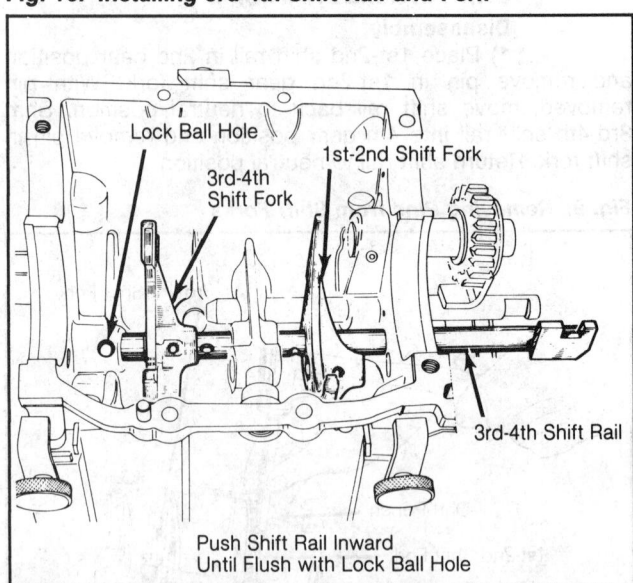

Compress detent ball and spring to install shift rail.

5) Shift 3rd-4th shift rail into neutral position. Insert detent ball into hole and push it against 3rd-4th shift rail. Engage 1st-2nd shift rail and insert detent ball and spring into hole. Coat threads of detent plug with sealant and install. Place 1st-2nd shift rail in neutral position. Lock shift forks onto shift rails with new pins.

PEUGEOT 4 & 5-SPEED (Cont.)

Fig. 16: Completed Shifting Mechanism Installation

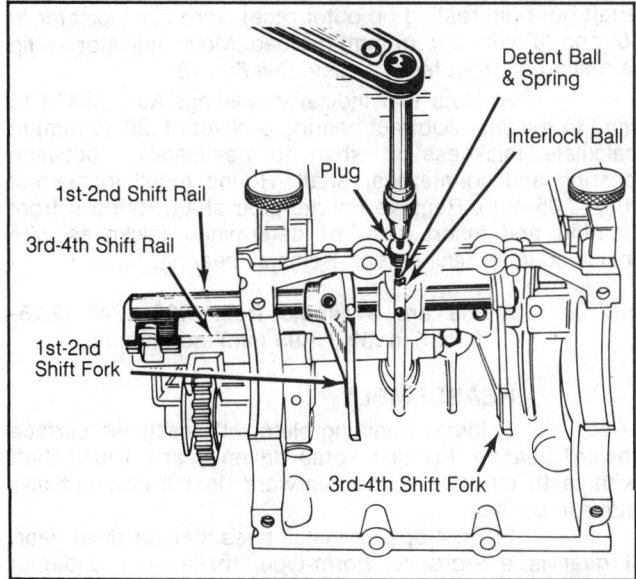

Detent Ball & Spring

Interlock Ball

Plug

1st-2nd Shift Rail

3rd-4th Shift Rail

1st-2nd Shift Fork

3rd-4th Shift Fork

Note position of shift rails, forks and lockout components.

CLUTCH HOUSING
Disassembly
If equipped with oil seal, carefully pry out seal without damaging case. Remove throwout bearing guide snap ring and press out guide. Transmissions which use an oil slinger on input shaft do not use an oil seal.

Inspection
Mount a dial indicator and measure runout of front and rear mating surfaces of housing. If runout exceeds .004" (.10 mm), replace clutch housing. Inspect all mating surfaces for wear or damage.

Reassembly
Lightly coat bearing face of throwout bearing guide with grease (Molykote or equivalent). Press in guide with slot (if equipped) facing housing openings and install snap ring. On models with oil seal, DO NOT install seal at this time.

INTERMEDIATE HOUSING (5-SPEED ONLY)
Disassembly
Using a punch, drive out each roll pin. Compress shift rail spring and remove 4 bushings. Remove shift rail. Separate components and set aside. Remove and discard "O" ring from hole.

Inspection & Reassembly
Inspect all components and mating surfaces of housing for wear, damage and warpage. Lubricate bushings. Install new "O" ring in hole. Insert the shift rail into case while positioning shift fork, spring and bushings on rail. Install roll pins so that splits face opposite directions (1 should face to right; the other to left).

TRANSMISSION ADJUSTMENT & REASSEMBLY

ADJUSTMENTS
Centering Synchronizers (Except 4th Gear)
NOTE: This adjustment is made by changing size of shim located under mainshaft bearing.

1) Install needle bearing inside input shaft. Assemble input shaft to mainshaft (without reverse driven gear and nut). Install mainshaft assembly in transmission case. Install clutch housing. Install and tighten Allen screws in retainer plate. Place all synchronizers in neutral position.

2) Spread synchronizers apart between sleeve and hub. Insert gauge (8.0314X) between each synchronizer sleeve and hub without forcing. *See Fig. 17.* If the gauge fits easily between all 3 points, retain original shim. If gauge does not easily fit between all 3 points, perform the following adjustments to determine new shim size.

Fig. 17: Synchronizer Centering Adjustment (Except 4th Gear)

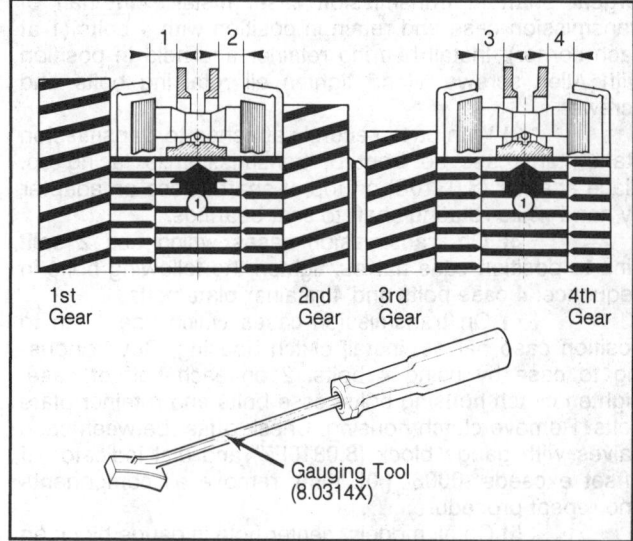

1st Gear   2nd Gear   3rd Gear   4th Gear

Gauging Tool (8.0314X)

Do not force gauge between synchronizers.

3) If the gauge does not easily fit between points 1 and/or 3 of *Fig. 17*, insert gauge and feeler gauge at point 2. Insert feeler gauge of various thicknesses to determine amount of change. Reduce shim thickness by this amount.

4) If the gauge does not easily fit at point 2 of *Fig. 17*, measure clearance at points 1 and 3. Increase shim thickness by the smaller of the readings.

NOTE: Shims are available in sizes .094-.134" (2.4-3.4 mm) for transmissions without shouldered 1st gear spacer. Shims for shouldered applications are .0098", .0118", .0138", .0157" and .0236" (.25, .30, .35, .40 and .60 mm).

Centering 4th Gear Synchronizer

NOTE: This adjustment is made by changing the size of the shims located under input shaft bearing.

1) Spread 4th gear synchronizer apart and insert gauge without forcing. If gauge slides in freely, measure the excess clearance. If clearance is .039" (1 mm) or less, retain original shims. If clearance exceeds .039" (1 mm), increase shims to equal thickness of original shim plus measured excess.

2) If the gauge does not fit, remove mainshaft, input shaft and clutch housing. Separate input shaft from

PEUGEOT 4 & 5-SPEED (Cont.)

mainshaft and remove shims. Reinstall components and measure and record clearance at 4th gear synchronizer. On transmissions equipped with an oil slinger, leave slinger on shaft at all times.

3) Remove components, disassemble input shaft and install shims of thickness equal to measured clearance. Reinstall all components and recheck clearance. Remove all components after final check.

NOTE: Shims are available from .006-.020" (.15-.50 mm) in .002" (.05 mm) increments. Use as few shims as possible to reach desired thickness.

Bearing Preload (Countergear Shaft)

1) Remove clutch housing and install countergear shaft in transmission case. Install right half of transmission case and retain in position with 4 bolts (1 at each corner). Install bearing retainer and hold in position with Allen screws. Hand tighten all retaining bolts and screws.

2) With case securely attached to transmission stand, turn case so front of transmission is facing up. Place adapter (8.0310S) on top of shaft. Press on adapter by hand while rotating shaft to seat bearings.

3) On transmission cases which use 2 split pins to position case halves, tighten the following bolts in sequence: 4 case bolts and 4 retainer plate bolts.

4) On transmission cases which use 1 pin to position case halves, install clutch housing. Retain housing to case by using 4 bolts, 2 on each half of case. Tighten clutch housing bolts, case bolts and retainer plate bolts. Remove clutch housing. Check offset between case halves with gauge block (8.0310FZ) and dial indicator. If offset exceeds .0008" (.02 mm), remove all components and repeat procedure.

5) On all models, center hole in gauge block on countergear shaft. Install dial indicator so indicator tip rests against bearing outer race surface. Rotate indicator through 1 complete revolution. Warpage between case halves MUST not exceed .0008" (.02 mm).

6) If specification is exceeded, align bearing race by inserting arbor (8.0310S) and tapping with a plastic mallet. After aligning outer bearing race, check that drag is not added to shaft and recheck warpage. To reduce drag, loosen and retighten 2 front case bolts.

Fig. 18: Measuring Countergear Shaft Bearing Preload

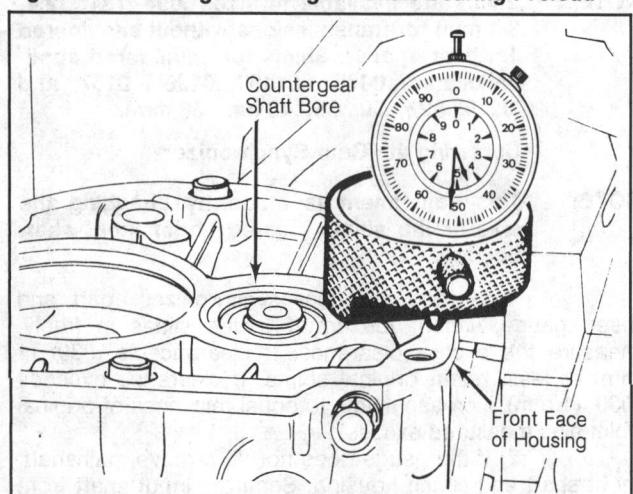

Zero dial indicator with .20" (5 mm) preload.

7) With dial indicator in place on countergear shaft bore (tip resting on outer race), zero dial indicator at "5" and "0" with .20" (5 mm) preload. Move indicator so tip is resting on front face of case. *See Fig. 18.*

8) Note dial indicator reading. Add .004" (.10 mm) to reading. Subtract bearing preload of .20" (5 mm) to calculate thickness of shim to be installed between bearing and countergear shaft. Round result to nearest .002" (.05 mm). Remove countergear shaft. Remove front bearing and insert shim of determined thickness with inside chamfer facing gear. Reinstall bearing.

NOTE: Shims are available from .089-.134" (2.25-3.40 mm) in .002" (.05 mm) increments.

REASSEMBLY

1) Install retaining plate with machined surface toward bearing. Install reverse driven gear on mainshaft with teeth chamfer facing rearward. Install new nut and stake in position.

2) On 4-speed, install speedometer drive gear. If gear is a 9-groove worm-type, make sure undercut faces toward rear.

3) On all transmissions, install needle bearing inside input shaft and assemble input shaft and mainshaft. Place 3rd-4th synchronizer in neutral position. Install outer races onto outer bearings of countergear shaft. Mesh countergear shaft with mainshaft and input shaft.

4) With teeth of shaft assemblies meshed and while holding assembly together in this manner, install assembly into transmission case. *See Fig. 19.* Make sure shift forks engage with synchro sleeves. Apply a thin coat of sealer to faces of case halves.

Fig. 19: Installing Shafts into Transmission Case

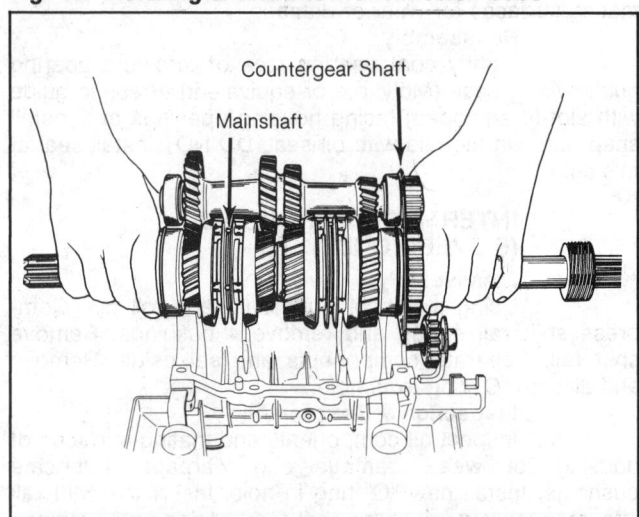

Make sure shift forks engage synchro sleeves.

5) With countergear and mainshaft installed, assemble 2 halves of transmission case together. Make sure positioning dowels are in place. Install new prelubricated input shaft oil seal. Using a seal protector, install clutch housing with small amount of sealant on rear face of clutch housing.

6) Tighten case half bolts. Rotate input shaft to seat bearings. Tighten retainer plate bolts. Loosen 4 bearing bolts and tap case half while turning input shaft. Tighten 4 bearing bolts.

PEUGEOT 4 & 5-SPEED (Cont.)

7) On transmissions which use 1 dowel pin for positioning, rotate case so clutch housing faces down. Using a dial indicator, measure to determine if case halves are aligned with one another. If case half alignment varies more than .0008" (.02 mm), loosen case half bolts and try to align case halves. Retighten bolts.

Fig. 20: Measuring Case Half Alignment

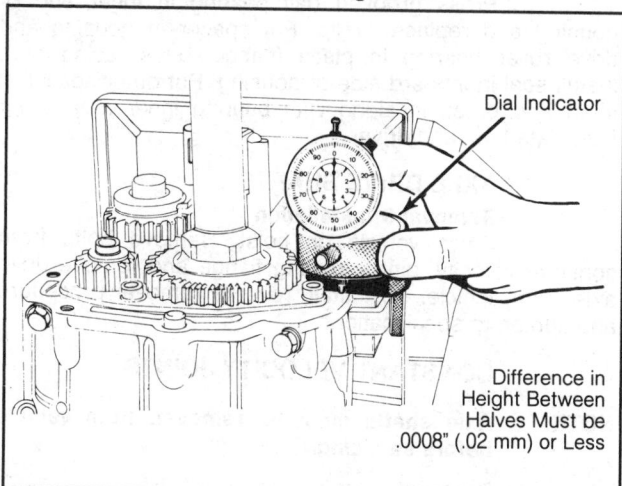

Dial Indicator

Difference in
Height Between
Halves Must be
.0008" (.02 mm) or Less

Measure alignment on cases which are positioned with only 1 dowel pin.

8) On 4-speed, lubricate needle bearing and apply thin coat of sealant on gasket surfaces of case and extension housing. Install extension housing while engaging selector fingers in fork shaft gates. Install and tighten all bolts. Install speedometer driven gear, and "O" ring. Tighten set screw with lock nut.

9) On 5-speed, apply a thin coat of sealant on gasket surfaces of case and intermediate housing. Install intermediate housing dowels. Install housing while engaging selector fingers in fork shaft gates. Tighten bolts and nuts.

10) Install 5th-reverse intermediate shaft and synchronizer. Position synchro so mark made during disassembly is visible (if new, so circular groove on face points toward reverse).

11) Place 5th-reverse selector shaft in 5th gear. At the same time, install 5th-reverse synchro sleeve and fork, aligning reference marks made during disassembly. Install retainer (8.0314W) on case housing and install new roll pin in 5th-reverse shift fork. Remove retainer and place assembly in neutral.

12) Install 5th drive gear, needle bearing and spacer. Make sure lugs on spacer are properly aligned. Install extension housing without bearing. Mount dial indicator and holder on extension housing with indicator tip resting on countergear shaft shoulder (not on spacer). Zero dial indicator with .236" (6 mm) preload.

13) Remove extension housing and press bearings into housing. Place gauge block (8.0314G) under countergear shaft bearing. Mount dial indicator on extension housing with indicator tip resting on gauge block and note reading.

14) Subtract preload amount of .236" (6 mm). From the difference, subtract .002" (.05 mm). Roundoff reading to nearest .002" (.05 mm) and install this size shim on 5th-reverse shaft. Remove dial indicator and gauge block.

Fig. 21: Countergear Shaft Shim Measurement

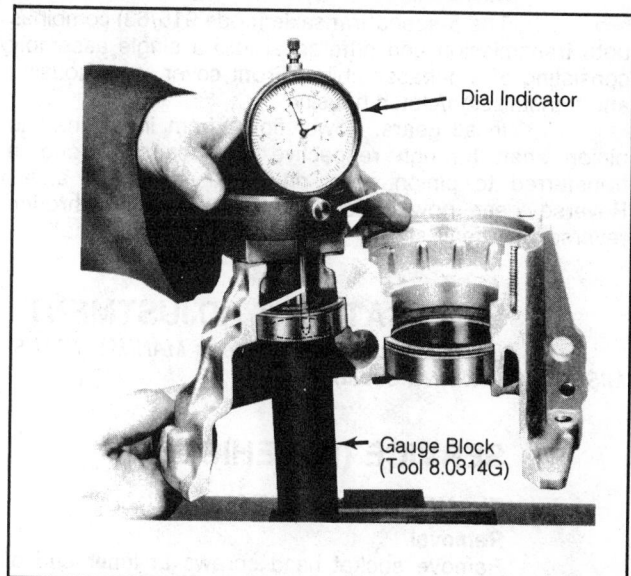

Dial Indicator

Gauge Block
(Tool 8.0314G)

Place indicator tip on gauge block.

15) Install snap ring in mainshaft groove. Lubricate machined surface of mainshaft and press 5th driven gear and speedometer drive onto mainshaft using bushing (8.0310Y) and installing wrenches (8.0310P & 8.0314).

16) Install new snap ring to retain 5th driven gear and speedometer drive gear. Using bearing driver (8.0314Y), install lubricated extension housing seal until driver contacts housing surface.

17) Install 2 locating dowel pins in extension housing and coat housing mating surfaces with sealant. Install extension housing while engaging selector finger with selector fork shaft gate. Tap housing just above 5th-reverse intermediate shaft with a mallet and tighten bolts.

18) Install plug and new "O" ring in extension housing. Install speedometer driven gear with 2 new "O" rings. Retain speedometer driven gear with set screw.

19) On both transmissions, pack dust boot in clutch housing with grease. Apply grease (Molykote or equivalent) onto throwout bearing guide. Install clutch fork with retaining spring behind dust boot. Place pushrod inside rubber protector on outside of clutch housing and install throwout bearing. Install back-up light switch.

TIGHTENING SPECIFICATIONS

Application	Ft. Lbs. (N.m)
Mainshaft Lock Nut	40 (54)
Clutch Housing-to-Trans. Case	20 (27)
Case Half Bolts	
4 Bearing Bolts	11 (15)
All Others	7.25 (9.8)
Retainer Plate	7.25 (9.8)
Extension Housing-to-Trans. Case	11 (15)
Propeller Shaft Hsg.-to-Extension Hsg.	44 (60)
Inter. Hsg.-to-Trans. (5-Speed)	
Nuts	13 (18)
Bolts	11 (15)

Manual Transmissions
PORSCHE 911SC 5-SPEED

DESCRIPTION

The 5-speed transaxle (code 915/63) combines both transmission and differential into a single assembly consisting of 3 subassemblies: Front cover, gear housing and transmission/clutch housing.

In all gears, power flows from input shaft to pinion shaft through respective gear pairs. Torque is transferred to pinion gear, ring gear and drive axles. Reverse gear power flows from input shaft through reverse idler gear, sliding gear and then to pinion shaft.

LUBRICATION & ADJUSTMENT

See the appropriate article in MANUAL TRANS-MISSION SERVICING Section.

SERVICE (IN-VEHICLE)

FLANGED SHAFT SEAL

Removal

Remove socket head screws at inner end of shaft, then disconnect and support axle drive shaft. Remove inner flange bolt while holding flange from turning by inserting punch in drive flange bolt hole. Remove flange and pull out seal with tool (VW 681).

Installation

Fill cavity between sealing and dust lips with multi-purpose grease and drive seal in place with tool (VW 195). Replace flange and drive shaft and tighten to specifications.

REAR WHEEL BEARINGS

Removal

With brake calipers off and drive shaft disconnected at axle flange, press shaft from housing, remove circlip and drive grooved ball bearing and roller bearing out with soft drift.

Installation

Press grooved ball bearing in inner end of housing and replace circlip. Put spacer in housing and drive roller bearing in place (flanged side facing out). Install seal in inboard side of housing. Put outer spacer in shaft and press in along with bearing inner race using castellated nut and driver.

AXLE DRIVE SHAFTS

Removal & Installation

Raise vehicle on hoist. Remove bolts from constant velocity joint-to-mating flange and remove drive axle from vehicle. To install, reverse removal procedure and tighten to specifications.

CONSTANT VELOCITY JOINTS

NOTE: **Axle shafts must be removed from vehicle before servicing.**

Removal

Clamp axle shaft in a vise with soft jaws. Remove boot clamp and push boot to center of axle. Remove circlip from axle shaft, press joint from axle shaft using special tools VW 401 and VW 408.

Fig. 1: Exploded View of 911SC 5-Speed Transaxle

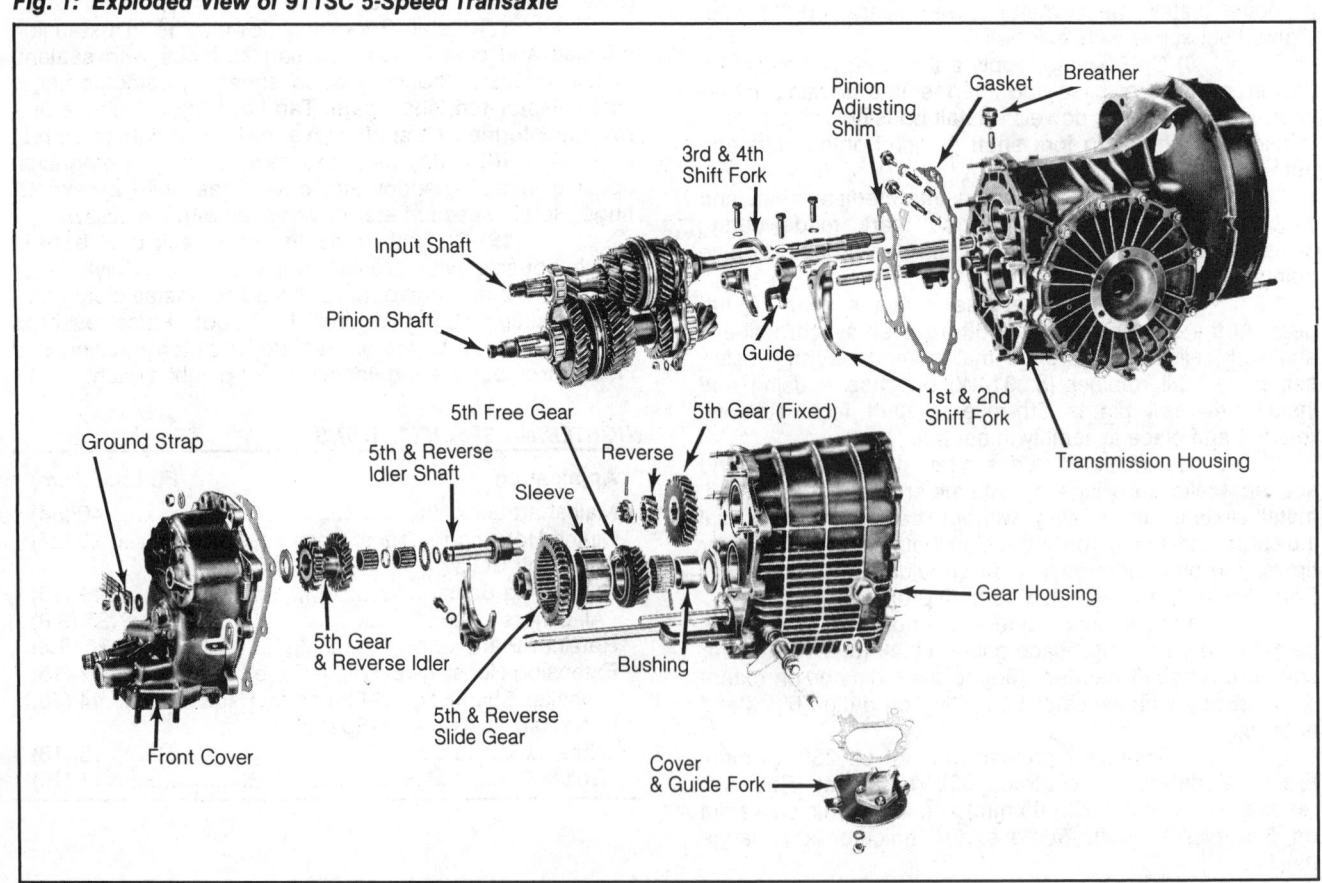

PORSCHE 911SC 5-SPEED (Cont.)

Fig. 2: Exploded View of Rear Axle Shaft Assembly

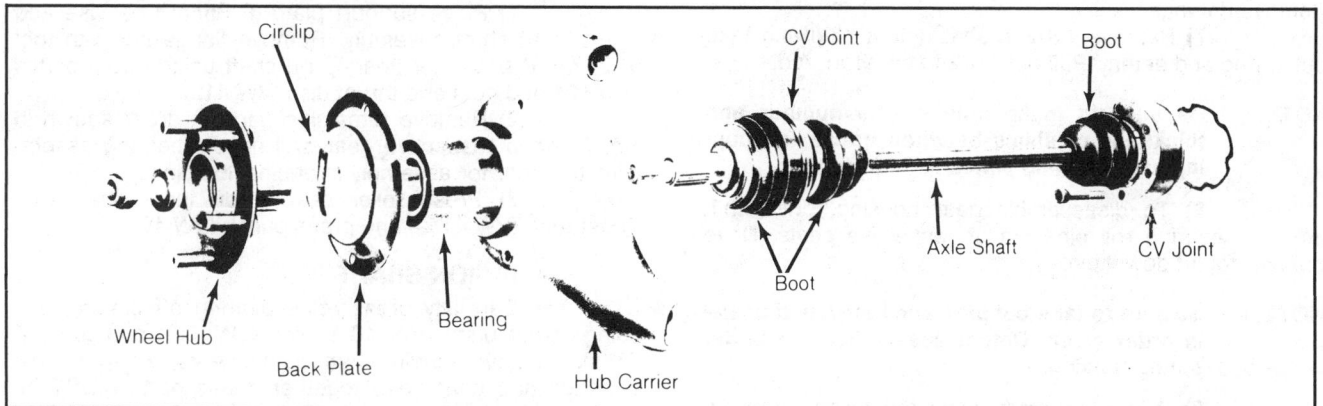

Disassembly

Swing ball and ball cage from joint and press out in direction of arrow. *See Fig. 3.* Tilt ball hub out of ball cage via ball groove. *See Fig. 4.* Clean all parts in a cleaning solvent and blow dry. Inspect for wear and damage.

Fig. 3: Ball Hub and Ball Cage Removal

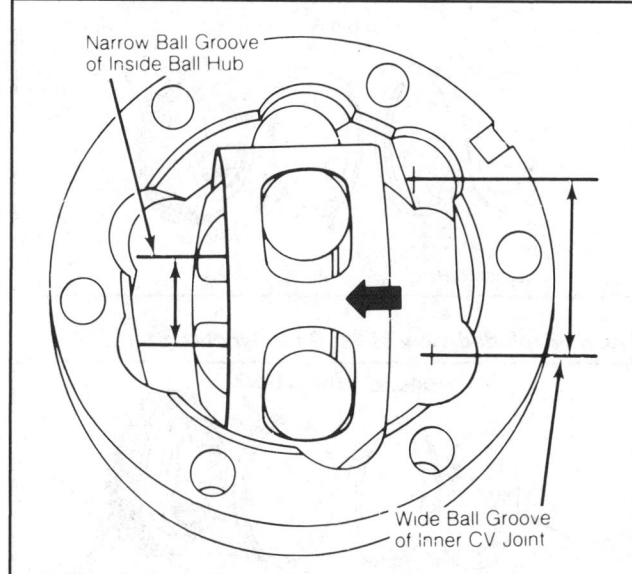

Fig. 4: Removal of Ball Hub from Cage

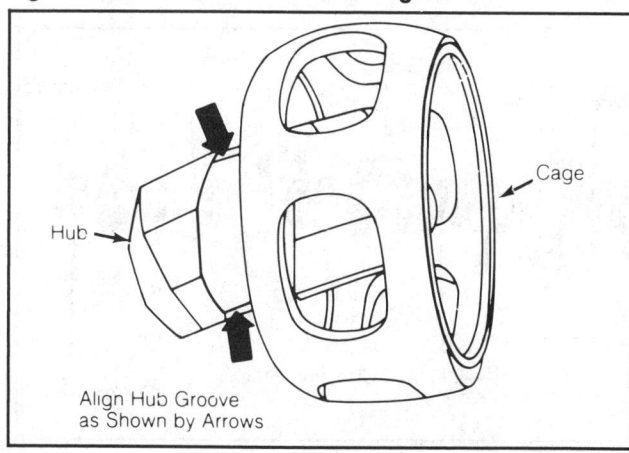

NOTE: Ball hub and joint are paired. Do not mix parts. The 6 balls are also mated together and cannot be mixed with others.

Reassembly

Place ball hub in ball cage. Press balls into cage. Install hub with cage and balls into joint and swing into assembled position. Check for smooth operation.

Installation

Reverse removal procedure and note the following: Install a new gasket on flange cover. Pack joint with molybdenum grease.

TRANSAXLE REMOVAL & INSTALLATION

See the appropriate article in *MANUAL TRANSMISSION SERVICING* Section.

TRANSAXLE DISASSEMBLY

GEAR HOUSING

1) Separate engine and transaxle assembly. Mount assembly on stand and lock input shaft in place with special tool (P 37a). Engage 5th gear.

2) Drain lubricant. Remove transaxle front cover. Remove castle nut from input shaft. Remove flange nut from pinion shaft.

3) Identify needle bearing of 5th speed free gear to aid in reassembly. When assembling transmission, needle bearings, gears and other matched parts must be replaced in original positions. Remove guide fork cover and gasket.

4) Remove gear housing nuts (12). Remove housing and selector fork rod (5th and reverse) and fork rod and shaft. It may be necessary to tap gently with mallet to remove assembly from studs.

NOTE: Shift fork rod for 5th and reverse must be in NEUTRAL position. If not, housing will jam.

5) Remove 3rd/4th gear detent plug. Take out spring and detent. Remove bolt from 1st/2nd gear selector fork. Spread clamp with screwdriver. Remove input and pinion shaft retaining plates.

6) Remove input and pinion shaft assemblies from case. Shift fork rod for 3rd and 4th gear and shift

Manual Transmissions
PORSCHE 911SC 5-SPEED (Cont.)

fork for 1st and 2nd gear should come out with assembly. Remove detent.

7) Remove 1st/2nd shift detent plug and take out spring and detent. Pull out 1st/2nd shift fork rod.

NOTE: **Be sure to make note of the number and thickness of shims between transaxle housing and retaining plates for reassembly.**

8) To disassemble gear housing, drive shift detents securing roll pins out of respective seats. Drive out half-round dowel pin.

NOTE: **Be sure to take out pins and half-round dowel in order given. Detent assemblies are under spring tension.**

9) If bearing outer races are to be removed, special tool (US 8050 or equivalent) must be used. Gear housing must be heated to about 250°F (120°C) to drive out races.

INPUT SHAFT

1) Place support plate (P 355a) in a vise and insert input shaft assembly. Remove flange nut with tool (P 252a). Press roller bearing off shaft using thrust plates (VW 401 and 402) and thrust disc (VW 412).

2) Remove remaining parts in order shown in *Fig. 6*. Keep respective gear and needle bearing assemblies together for assembly in original locations.

3) Press roller bearing off input shaft with thrust tube (VW 415a) and press punch (VW 407).

PINION SHAFT

Carefully press roller bearing off pinion shaft using thrust plate (VW 401), disc (VW 412) and tube (P 255a). Remove pinion shaft components. Keep needle bearings and gear pairs together; these parts MUST be installed in original position. Remove speedometer drive gear.

SYNCHRONIZERS

Remove clip from gear. Disassemble as shown in *Figs. 7 and 8*. Check all parts for wear or damage and replace as necessary.

Fig. 5: *Exploded View of Gear Housing*

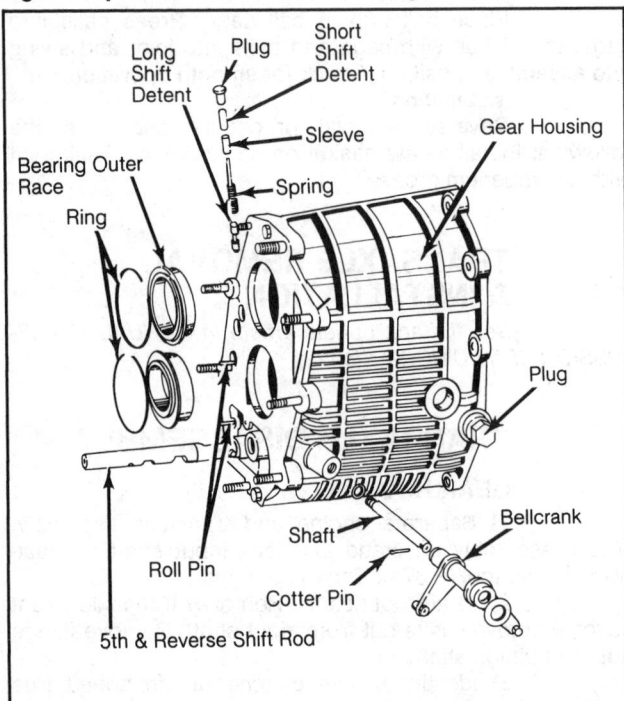

Fig. 7: *Exploded View of 2nd Gear Synchronizer*

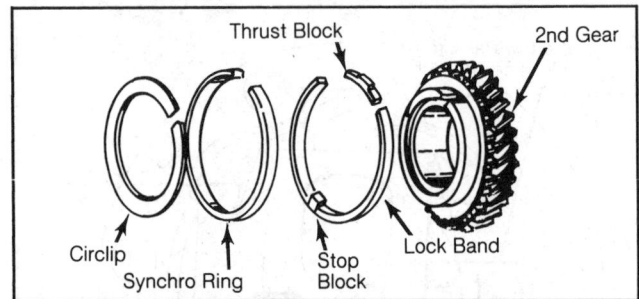

Fig. 8: *Exploded View of 1st Gear Synchronizer*

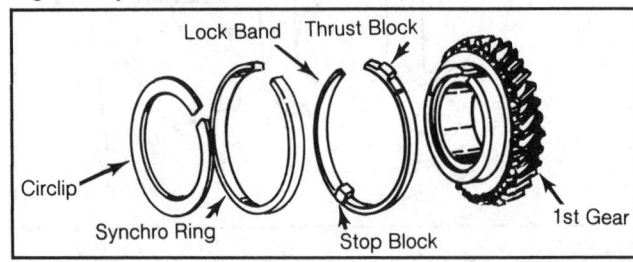

Fig. 6: *Exploded View of Input Shaft Assembly*

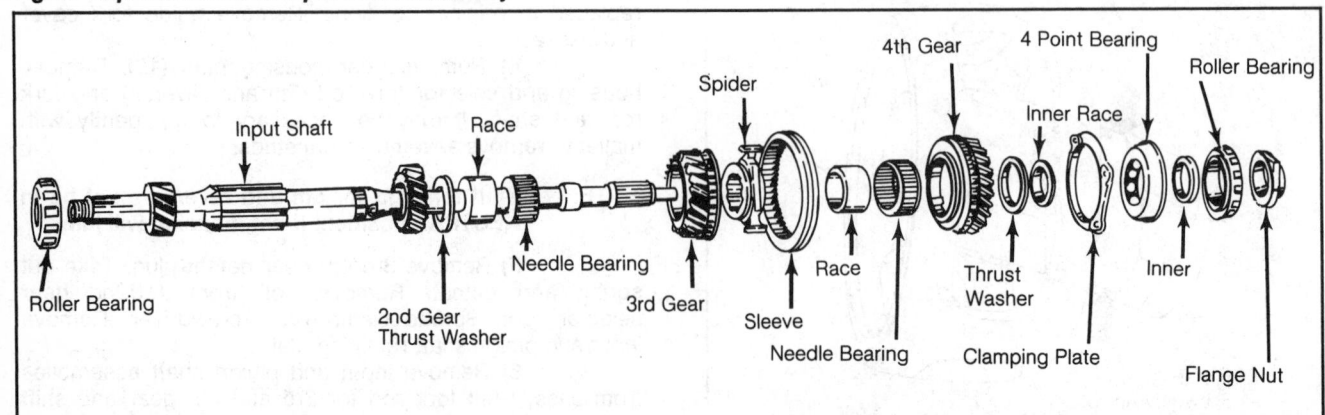

Fig. 9: *Exploded View of Pinion Shaft Assembly*

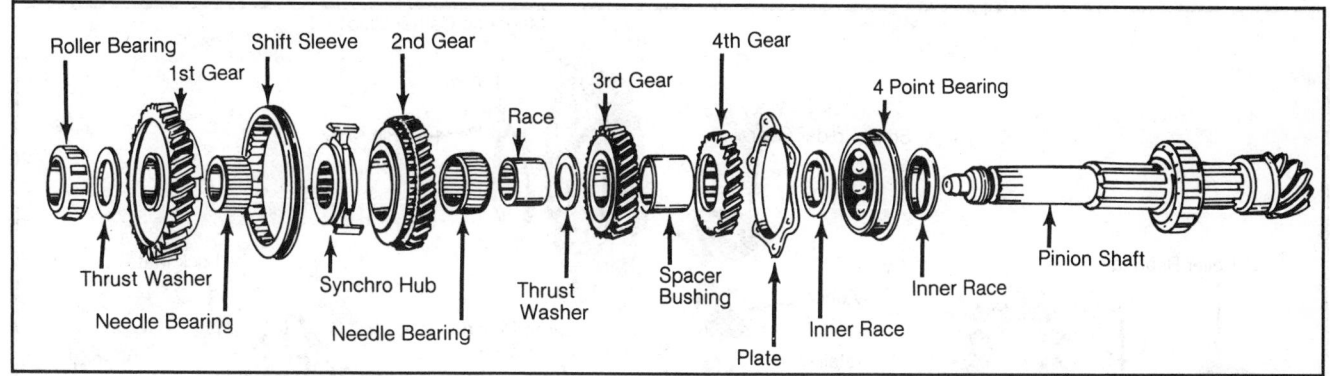

FRONT COVER

Remove parts as shown in *Fig. 10*. If speedometer gear shaft bushing is to be removed, heat front cover to about 250°F (120°C). Pull out bushing. If necessary, bushing may be carefully drilled out. Clean cover and check for cracks or damage. Replace parts as necessary.

FINAL DRIVE (DIFFERENTIAL)

1) Remove expansion bolt from center of flange. Withdraw flange shaft. Drive seals and outer bearing races out of final drive housing and side cover with drift.

2) Drive roll pin from differential pinion shaft, then drive pinion shaft out and remove anchor piece. Remove tapered roller bearing with puller and thrust piece (P 263). Puller arms must fit through openings in magnetic carrier disc to remove bearing from side opposite ring gear.

3) Do not interchange spacer washers and shims. Right and left side must be kept separate and

Fig. 10: *Exploded View of Front Cover Assembly*

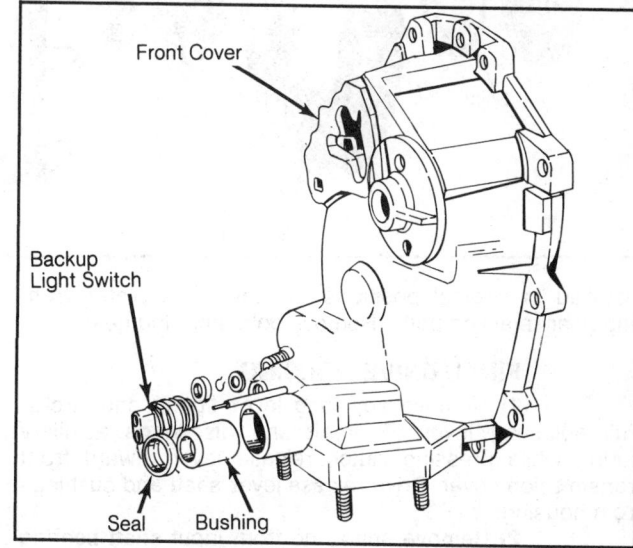

Fig. 11: *Exploded View of Final Drive and Housing*

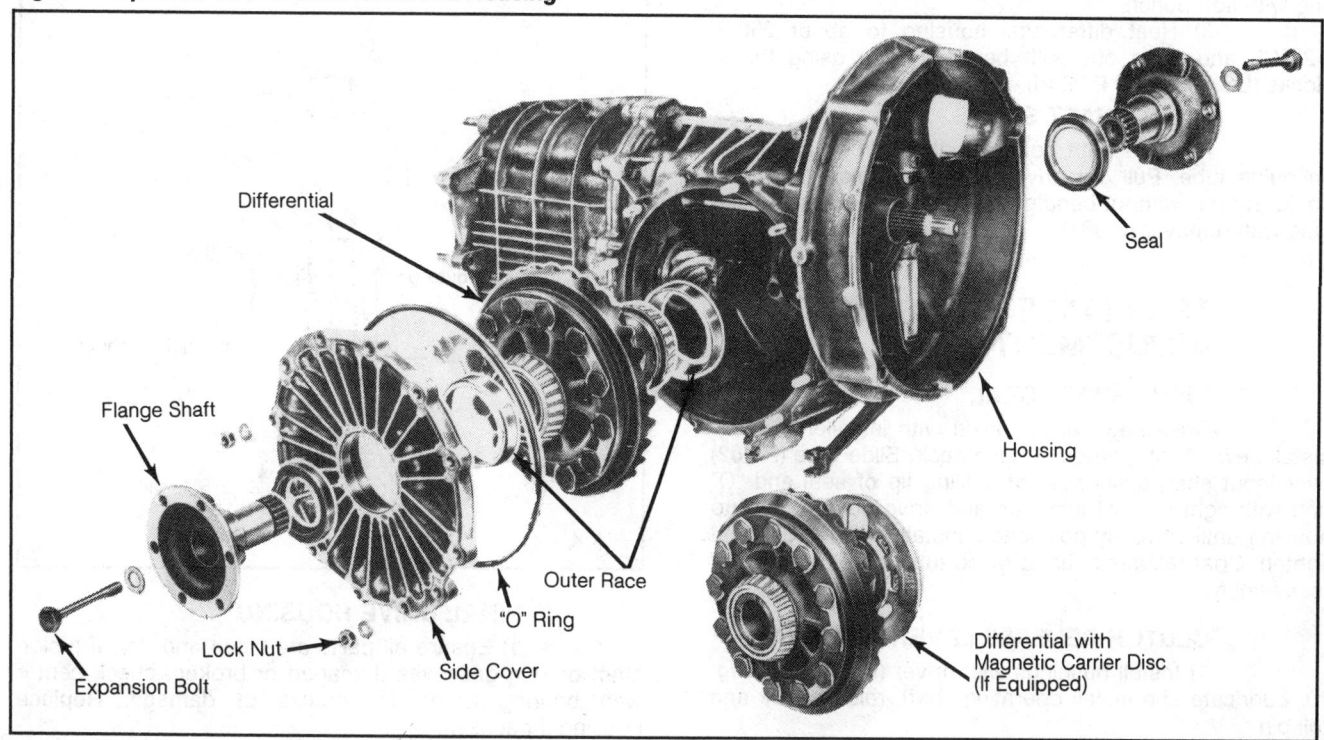

Manual Transmissions

PORSCHE 911SC 5-SPEED (Cont.)

Fig. 12: *Exploded View of Ring Gear and Carrier Assembly*

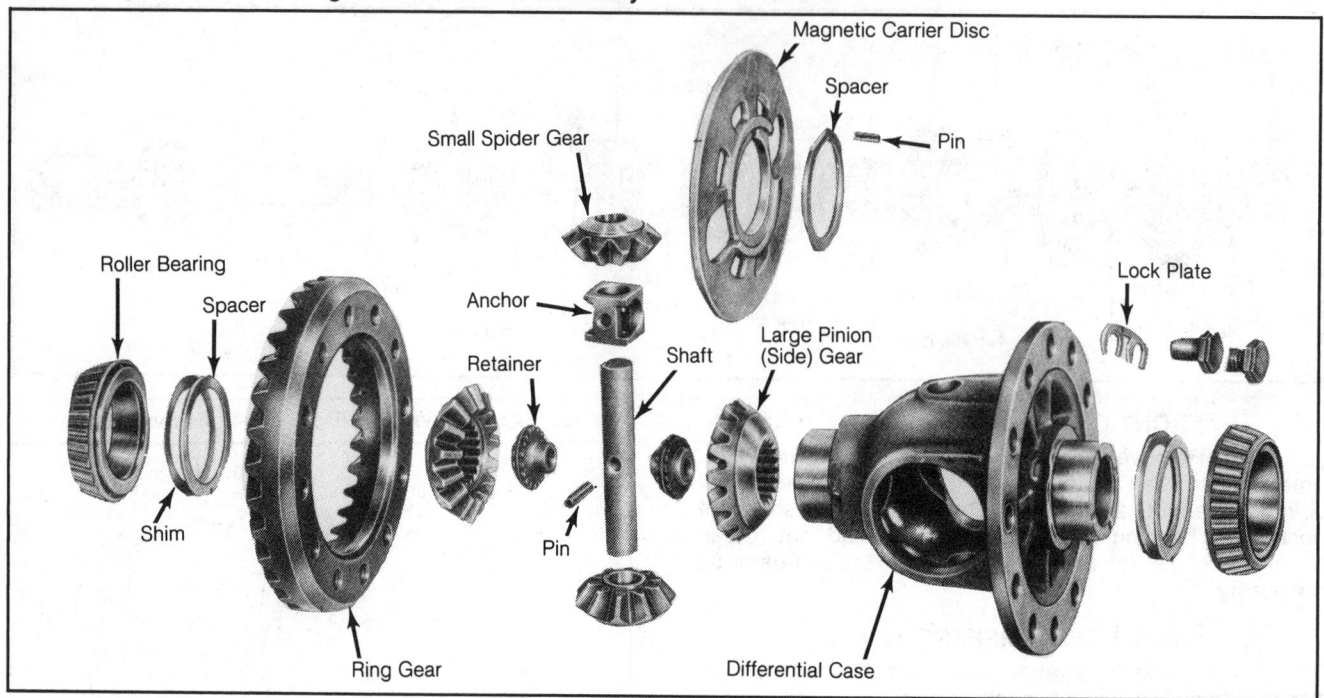

installed in original positions. Remove lock plates from ring gear retaining bolts. Remove bolts and ring gear.

FINAL DRIVE HOUSING

1) Remove adjusting lever spring and circlip. Pull adjusting lever off shaft and disengage auxiliary spring while pressing clutch release lever toward front transmission cover. Drive release lever shaft and bushings from housing.

2) Remove snap ring from input shaft bearing race. Bearing must first be driven slightly away from snap ring with soft punch.

3) Heat differential housing to about 250°F (120°C), and drive out both bearing races using thrust blocks (US 8050 and P 254d).

INPUT SHAFT SEAL

Remove both countersunk Phillips head bolts on guide tube. Pull out drive shaft seal guide tube with hook and bar without bending tube lip. Remove seal from tube with remover (P 381).

TRANSAXLE REASSEMBLY & ADJUSTMENT

INPUT SHAFT SEAL

Drive new seal in guide with installer (P 381). Install new "O" ring on guide tube neck. Slide tube (P 382) over input shaft splines. Coat sealing lip of seal and "O" ring with light coat of lubricant and drive guide tube into housing until correctly positioned. Install Phillips bolts and tighten. Coat release bearing guide tube with lubricant for reassembly.

CLUTCH RELEASE LEVER AND SHAFT

1) Install bushings with driver (P 375). *See Fig. 13.* Lubricate and install operating shaft, release fork and roll pin.

2) Install release lever on shaft along with spring and adjusting screw. Secure in place with pin. Snap auxiliary spring past dead point to stop pin in order to pre-tension against lever.

NOTE: **Do not install adjusting lever until after transaxle assembly has been installed in vehicle.**

Fig. 13: *Clutch Lever Shaft Bushing Installation and Location*

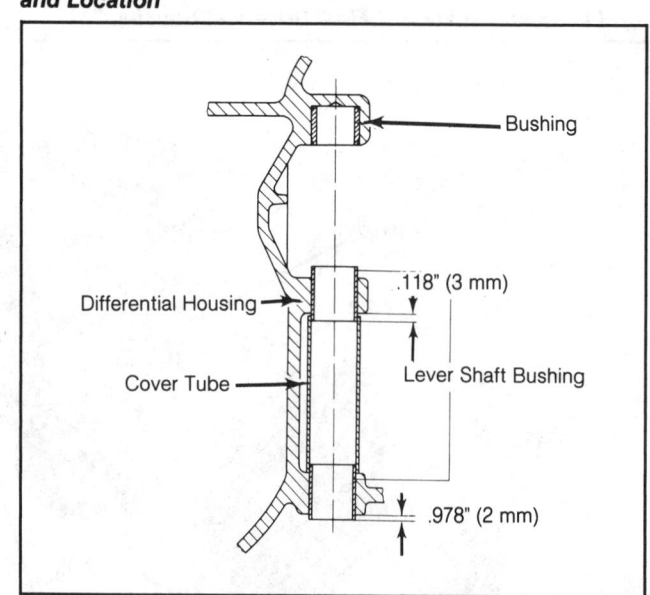

FINAL DRIVE HOUSING

1) Ensure all parts are clean and dry. If pinion shaft or ring gear was damaged or broken, check center web bearing bores for cracks or damage. Replace housing if necessary.

PORSCHE 911SC 5-SPEED (Cont.)

NOTE: Do not clean pressure-cast housings in corrosive liquids as magnesium alloy will be damaged. Cleaned pressure-cast housings must be treated with seasonal corrosion preservatives of bitumen or wax base such as TECTYL.

2) Install snap ring securing input shaft bearing race into groove in housing. Heat housing to about 250°F (120°C). Drive both bearing outer races into place with tool (US 8050 or equivalent).

3) Install breather vent in housing and torque. Hole in hex head must face toward transmission front cover.

FINAL DRIVE (DIFFERENTIAL)

1) Slide lock plates into bolt head grooves. Pinch open ends together with pliers to firmly hold plates to bolts. Bolt ring gear to carrier. Secure bolts by bending plate tab down over corner of bolt head.

2) Coat thrust surfaces of differential pinion and spider gear with Molykote or other lubricant. Insert large pinion side gears through oval shaped opening in housing.

3) Insert flange shafts to center pinions. Insert small spider gears through housing opening and position opposite each other so that bores align with bores in housing.

4) Install threaded retainers with lock rings into large side gears. Slide anchor between threaded retainers.

CAUTION: Differential pinion shaft must be positioned so pinion shaft hole aligns with hole in anchor.

5) Hold anchor in place and drive in pinion shaft. Install bearing shims and spacer washers in CORRECT ORIGINAL locations on differential housing. Install anchor pin.

6) Install tapered roller bearing using thrust plate (P 264). When replacing magnetic carrier disc, tapered roller preload does not have to be checked if same shims are reused.

NOTE: If only differential has been replaced, proceed to RING GEAR & PINION ADJUSTMENT. If transmission gears have been removed and disassembled, proceed to correct assembly steps for remainder of transmission, then proceed to adjustment.

SYNCHRONIZERS

1) Place synchro ring on clutch carrier; rough ring surfaces face shift sleeve. Insert thrust block, stop block and lock band(s).

NOTE: First gear synchro ring has only 1 lock band. Also, 1st gear synchro ring is identified by a groove on both sides.

2) Single lock band must be inserted with recess facing outward to accommodate small stop block. Stop block is directly opposite longer thrust block on 2nd gear synchro. Small stop block for 1st gear synchro is slightly offset and is bevelled on one side only. Install circlip after lock band, stop and thrust blocks are installed.

Fig. 14: Second Gear Synchronizer

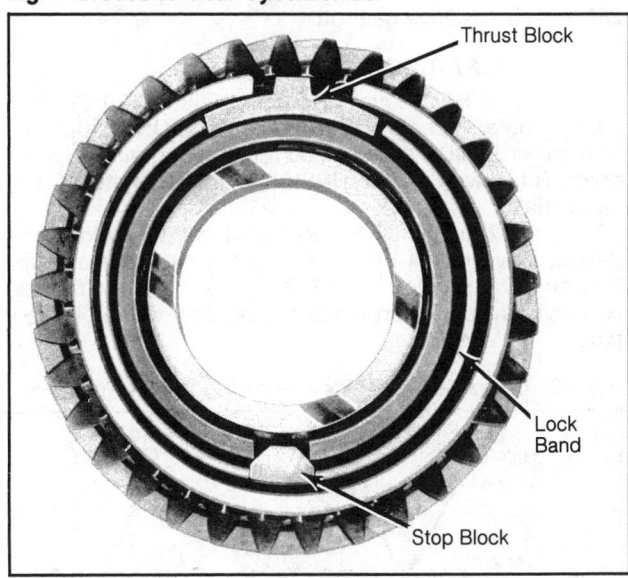

3) Maximum clearance between selector fork and shifting sleeve of 1st through 5th gear is .02" (.5 mm). Free diameter of synchronizer rings should be as shown in table.

SYNCHRONIZER RING FREE DIAMETER

Gear	In. (mm)
1st	3.43 (87.1)
2nd	3.47 (88.1)
3rd, 4th & 5th	3.07 (78.0)

INPUT SHAFT

1) Ensure all parts are dry and that there is not oil between contact surfaces. Press roller bearing on input shaft with thrust disc (VW 412) and thrust tube (VW 416b).

2) Install parts in order shown in *Fig. 6.* Be sure that needle bearings are installed with the same gears they were removed with.

3) Press roller bearing on end of input shaft with thrust plate (VW 401) and punch (VW 407). Torque flange nut to correct specification. Peen flange nut in place with punch.

4) Measure input shaft runout. Maximum allowable runout is .004" (.1 mm). If runout does not exceed .012" (.3 mm), it is possible to carefully straighten shaft with press and "V" blocks.

PINION SHAFT

1) All parts must be dry and free of oil. Pinion shaft and ring gear are marked with paired numbers. Check that these numbers match before assembly. Press roller bearing on pinion shaft with press punch (VW 407) and tube (VW 415a).

2) Bearing must be installed so ring of 2-part bearing cage faces gears. Assemble parts on shaft as shown in *Fig. 7.* Press on final roller bearing with thrust disc (VW 412) and sleeve (VW 244b).

NOTE: Asymmetrical pointed teeth of 1st/2nd synchro operating sleeve must face toward 1st gear wheel.

Manual Transmissions

PORSCHE 911SC 5-SPEED (Cont.)

3) Heat speedometer drive gear to about 250°F (120°C). Drive gear on.

GEAR HOUSING

1) Heat housing to about 250°F (120°C). Drive bearing outer races in position with tool (US 8050). Race with larger INSIDE diameter corresponds to pinion (lower) shaft. Race with smaller INSIDE diameter matches with input shaft.

2) Install 5th/reverse shift rod. Insert long shift detent. Drive in roll pin. Install spring and sleeve. Apply tension with special tool (P 366) and drive in roll pin. Release tension. Insert pin and short shift detent. Drive in plug.

Fig. 15: Cross-Sectional View Showing Detent Positions

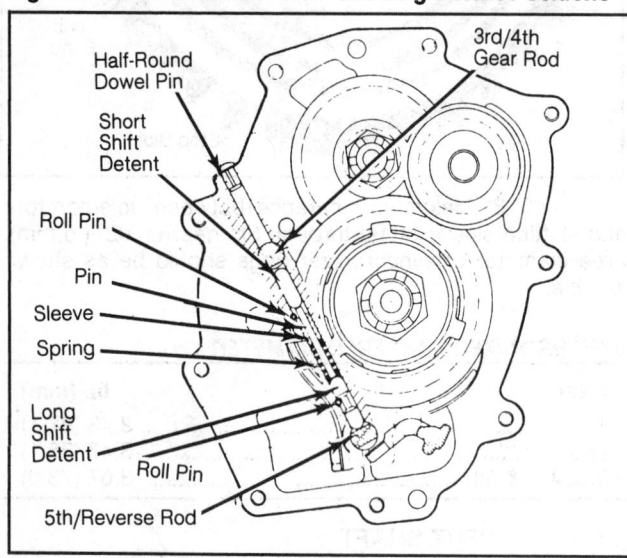

INPUT & PINION ASSEMBLY-TO-HOUSING

1) Install same number and thickness of shims on transmission housing studs as noted during disassembly. Also determined by adjusting the pinion. Insert 1st/2nd gear selector fork rod.

2) If removed. insert 1st/2nd gear shift detent and spring. Tighten bolt. Install pinion shaft with 1st/2nd gear selector fork so that pinion rests lightly in bearing race of transmission/differential housing. Slightly open selector fork clamping piece to prevent fork from binding on fork rod.

3) Insert input shaft and press into place with pinion shaft assembly. Tighten clamping plate nuts to specification.

4) Lightly tighten 1st/2nd gear selector fork bolt. Insert detent from top. Unscrew 3rd/4th gear selector fork and clamping piece bolts. Push fork and clamping piece back. Install selector fork and rod.

5) Lightly tighten fork and clamp bolts. If not already done, insert detent with spring and tighten plug. Adjust selector forks at this time. *See Selector (Shifting) Fork Adjustment in this article.*

6) Install housing gasket on studs. Install gear housing with 5th/reverse gear selector fork rod and shaft. Tighten correctly. Push fork rod in ball sleeve and selector shaft into shift pawl guides. Install guide fork cover, gasket and tighten.

7) Install idler gear shaft turning shaft until pin in housing stops rotation. Install reverse gear and start castle nut on threads. Install thrust washer for 5th (free) gear. Install 5th (free) gear needle bearing.

8) Install guide sleeve for 5th/reverse gear and start flange nut on threads. Install thrust needle bearing cage, idler gear with needle bearing cages, intermediate piece and thrust washer on idler shaft.

9) Slide 5th gear and reverse sliding gear with fork onto guide sleeve and selector fork rod. Open clamping piece on fork slightly for easier assembly. Lightly tighten selector fork bolt.

10) Apply light coat of oil to "O" ring and install. Use tool (P 37a) to block input shaft and engage 5th gear. Tighten input and pinion shaft nuts to specification.

11) Adjust 5th/reverse gear selector fork. *See Selector (Shifting) Fork Adjustment in this article.* Secure castle nut with roll pin. Secure flange nut by peening. Install backup light switch actuator pin with recessed end facing switch.

RING GEAR & PINION ADJUSTMENT

CAUTION: Unit must be assembled correctly. Front cover should not be installed at this time. Parts should be clean and dry.

Fig. 16: Ring and Pinion Identification

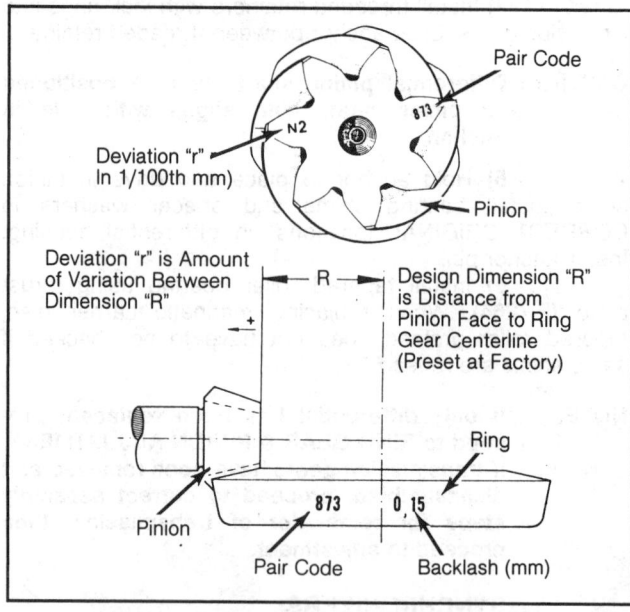

1) Deviation "r" must be added to design dimension "R" to obtain adjusting dimension. Attach input and pinion shafts, without shims, to final drive housing with clamping plates.

2) Tighten flange nut on input shaft to proper specification before taking measurements. Install special plate (P 260a). Assemble 5th speed gears with synchro hub and shifting sleeve. Engage 5th gear. Block input shaft with special holder (P 37a). Tighten flange nut to specification.

3) Move adjustable collar of universal setting gauge (VW 385) to 2.047" (52 mm) from center of contact plunger hole and tighten in position. Assemble gauge

PORSCHE 911SC 5-SPEED (Cont.)

blocks (VW 385/4) on gauge shaft and screw contact plunger (VW 385/53) into place. Using knurled knob on opposite end of shaft from dial indicator, turn adjustable collar back to stop.

4) Adjust dial indicator to 0 with a .039" (1 mm) preload using master gauge (VW 385/52). This sets design dimension "R" of 2.61" (66.3 mm). Place magnetic setting pad (VW 385/17) on pinion face and insert setting gauge in gear housing with knurled adjusting knob on side toward housing cover. Dial indicator extension must be oriented toward setting pad.

5) Install side cover without "O" ring and tighten nuts evenly to specified torque. Turn knurled knob to adjust gauge block against bearing race until gauge shaft can just be turned by hand. Note maximum clockwise deflection of dial indicator (when extension is perpendicular to pad on pinion shaft end). Use the following example to determine shim thickness:

SAMPLE PINION DEPTH SHIM CALCULATION

Calculation	In. (mm)
Design value (R) set in indicator	2.610 (66.30)
Minus indicator reading	.011 (.28)
Equals distance to pinion shaft face	2.599 (66.02)
Adjustment value (R+r)	2.618 (66.50)
Minus distance to pinion shaft face	2.599 (66.02)
Equals SHIM THICKNESS	.019 (.48)

6) Shims are available in thicknesses of .004" (.10 mm), .006" (.15 mm) and .008" (.20 mm). Any combination of shims up to .020" (.50 mm) may be used.

7) After installing correct shims, recheck adjustment value. Deviation of .001" (.03 mm) is allowable. No gear tooth contact pattern check is required.

8) To determine ring gear spacer thickness, proceed as follows: Side bearing outer races must be fully seated in housing and side cover. Install .138" (3.5 mm) spacer (S1) on ring gear side beneath side bearing. Install a .118" (3.0 mm) spacer (S2) on opposite side beneath other bearing.

9) Place differential with side bearings in housing. Install side cover with oil seal. DO NOT install side cover gasket at this time. Do not tighten.

10) Lightly tighten side cover with 2 nuts opposite each other to preload side bearings. Measure clearance between cover and housing with feeler gauge. Clearance should be about .006" (.15 mm) if bearings are correctly preloaded.

11) Replace spacer (S1) until correct clearance is obtained. Now tighten side cover to correct torque with all nuts (12). Install washer from tool (P 357) on U-axle flange. Slightly tighten expansion bolt.

12) Be sure pinion shaft is disengaged and side cover oil seal is removed to obtain accurate torque reading when rotating differential. Using an INCH lb. torque wrench, measure drag of assembled differential. Drag for SKF type bearings should be 22-30 INCH lbs. (2.5-3.0 N.m). Drag for FAG type bearings should be 40-65 INCH lbs. (4.0-6.5 N.m).

13) If differential drag is not within specifications, replace spacer washer and recheck. Remove differential and pull off both side bearings.

14) DO NOT interchange spacer washers after removal. Measure thickness of both spacers with microm-eter. Add these measurements to obtain total spacer thickness for ring gear adjustment.

NOTE: **In order to check backlash correctly, spacer (S1) should be .004" (.1 mm) thinner than 1/2 the sum of spacers (S1) and (S2). Spacer (S2) should be .004" (.1 mm) thicker than 1/2 the total thickness of (S1) and (S2).**

RING GEAR BACKLASH

1) Install gear cluster with shims determined during pinion shaft adjustment. Be sure to tighten pinion shaft flange nut if not already done.

2) Install differential with side bearings and correct shims (S1) and (S2). Install side cover with oil seal. Lubricate oil seal lip.

CAUTION: **Be sure that some side clearance exists between housing and side cover, as cover nuts are being tightened. Do not allow pinion to jam.**

3) Tighten side cover nuts to specifications. Block pinion shaft with holder (P 259a).

4) Place washer from tool (P 357) onto axle flange. Mount dial indicator with sensor (P 259b). Attach dial indicator over axle flange. Be sure dial indicator has a slight preload.

5) Move dial indicator holder back and forth. Read backlash on dial. Rotate ring gear about 90° and measure backlash again. Readings must not vary by more than .002" (.05 mm). Backlash tolerance is .0047" (.12 mm) to .007" (.18 mm). Compare reading with desired backlash recorded on ring gear.

6) Replace spacers (S1) and (S2) as necessary to obtain correct backlash. Use special tools (P 263 & 264b).

CAUTION: **Exchange spacers, but do not change TOTAL spacer thickness.**

7) When adjustment is completed, remove all special tools from housing. Install differential and gasket, and torque side cover to specifications.

SELECTOR (SHIFTING) FORK ADJUSTMENT

1) Input shaft flange nut must be correctly torqued. Install mounting plate (P 260a). Install 5th gear synchro hub and reverse sliding gear.

2) Block input shaft with tool (P 37a). Engage 5th gear. Tighten input shaft flange nut. Turn 1st/2nd gear selector fork rod LEFT (in driving direction) to stop.

3) Turn fork rod slightly back until unmachined flat inner surface is nearly vertical. Do not turn past middle point or back to right stop.

4) Position 1st/2nd gear selector fork so that shift sleeve is exactly in middle between synchronizing rings. Tighten bolt to proper specification. Adjust 3rd/4th gear fork in same way.

5) Position 3rd/4th gear shift guide even with selector fork. Be sure there is .08-.12" (2-3 mm) clearance between 3rd/4th shift guide and 1st/2nd shift guide. They must not touch. Check ease of shifting and readjust as necessary.

6) Adjust 5th/reverse gear fork as follows: Push idler gear on shaft against 5th (fixed) gear. Adjust

Manual Transmissions

PORSCHE 911SC 5-SPEED (Cont.)

idler gear and sliding gear to obtain a clearance of .040" (1 mm) in NEUTRAL position.

7) Press idler gear gently in direction of travel. There should be no play between shift fork and sliding gear groove.

FRONT COVER

Heat cover to about 250°F (120°C) and drive gear shift bushing in place. Drive shift rod seal on with mandrel (P 369). Install new gasket and tighten front cover nuts to specification.

TIGHTENING SPECIFICATIONS

Application	Ft. Lbs. (N.m)
Side & Front Cover Nuts	18 (24)
Guide Fork Cover Nuts	18 (24)
Input Shaft Flange Nut	120 (163)
Input Shaft Castle Nut	95 (129)
Retaining Plate & Trans.	
Support Attachment	15 (20)
Pinion Shaft Flange Nut	180 (244)
Starter Nut	35 (47)
Ring Gear Bolts	
Standard Differential	84 (115)
Positive Traction Differentials	
Grade 11.9 Bolts	105 (142)
Grade 12.9 Bolts	112 (152)

PORSCHE 924 TURBO 5-SPEED

DESCRIPTION

The Porsche 924 Turbo is equipped with a manual transaxle (type 016/Y) with a 5-speed transmission mounted in front of the final drive. Engine and transaxle are connected by a strong central tube which also houses the propeller shaft and supports the gearshift lever.

Flanges at each end of central tube attach to clutch housing and transaxle. Propeller shaft is splined to clutch disc at the front and is connected to transmission mainshaft at the rear by a coupling. Access to this coupling is through an inspection hole in rear of central tube.

A hypoid ring and pinion differential assembly drives double-jointed rear axle drive shafts. Complete drive train is mounted to unitized body by 2 front engine mounts and 2 rear transaxle mounts.

NOTE: The term "Transaxle" in this article refers to the rear axle transmission/differential assembly. The central tube and bell housings may be referred to as the "Transaxle tube". Axle drive shafts include the flexible couplings. Rear wheel axle shaft indicates the driven axle shaft mounted in the trailing arms of the rear wheel suspension.

LUBRICATION & ADJUSTMENT

See the appropriate article in MANUAL TRANS-MISSION SERVICING SECTION.

SERVICE (IN-VEHICLE)

FLANGED SHAFT SEAL
Removal

Remove socket head screws at inner end of shaft, then disconnect and support axle drive shaft. Remove inner flange bolt while holding flange from turning by inserting punch in drive flange bolt hole. Remove flange and pull out seal with tool (VW681).

Installation

Fill cavity between sealing and dust lips with multi-purpose grease and drive seal into place with seal driver (VW195). Replace flange and drive shaft. Tighten all axle bolts to specification.

REAR WHEEL BEARINGS
Removal

With brake drum off and drive shaft disconnected at axle flange, press shaft from housing with double arm puller. Pry seal out of housing, remove circlip and drive grooved ball bearing and roller bearing out with soft drift.

Installation

Press grooved ball bearing into inner end of housing and replace circlip. Put spacer in housing and drive roller bearing in place (flanged side facing out). Install seal in inboard side of housing. Put outer spacer on shaft and press in along with inner bearing race using a castellated nut and driver. See Fig. 2.

Fig. 1: Exploded View of Porsche 924 Turbo 5-Speed Transaxle Assembly

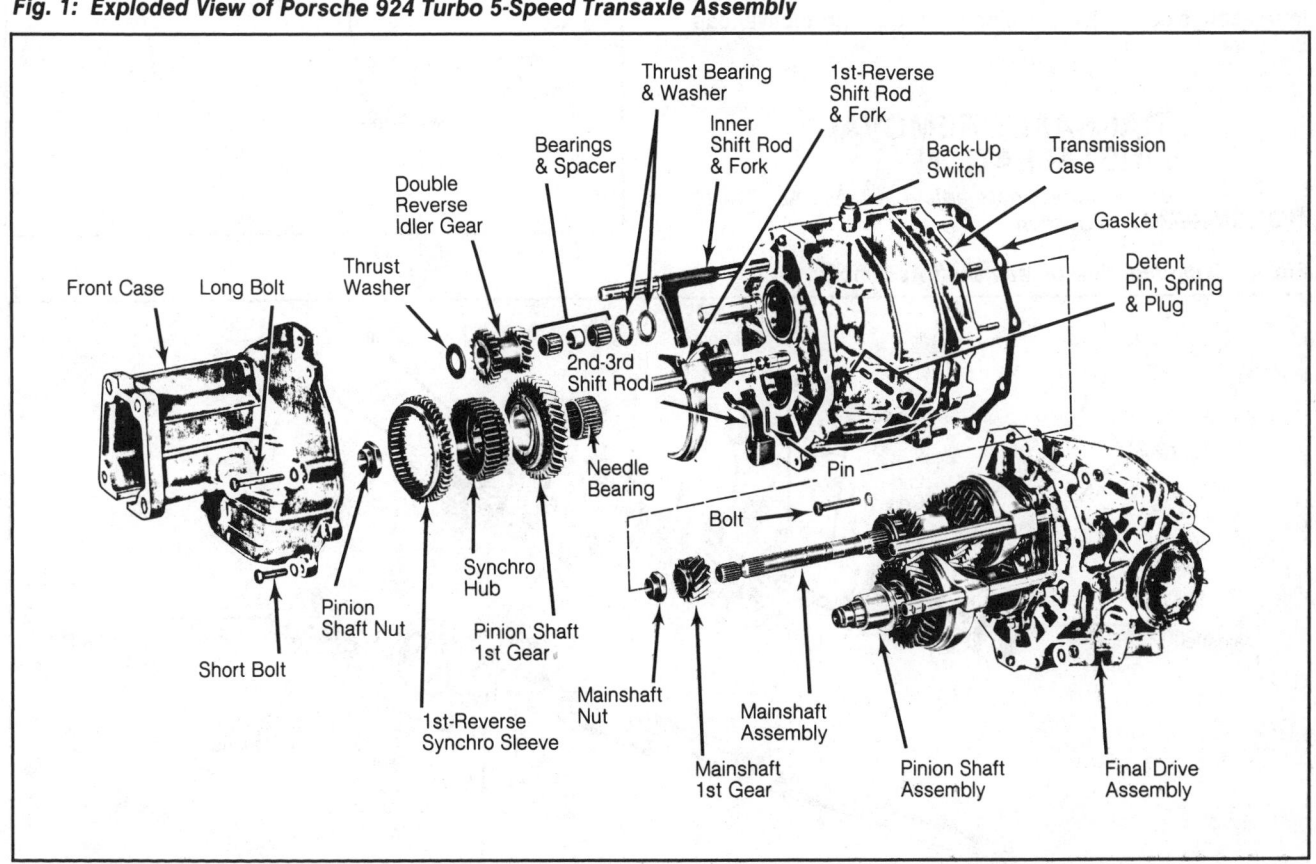

Manual Transmissions
PORSCHE 924 TURBO 5-SPEED (Cont.)

Fig. 2: *Exploded View of Drive Axle Shaft and Wheel Bearing*

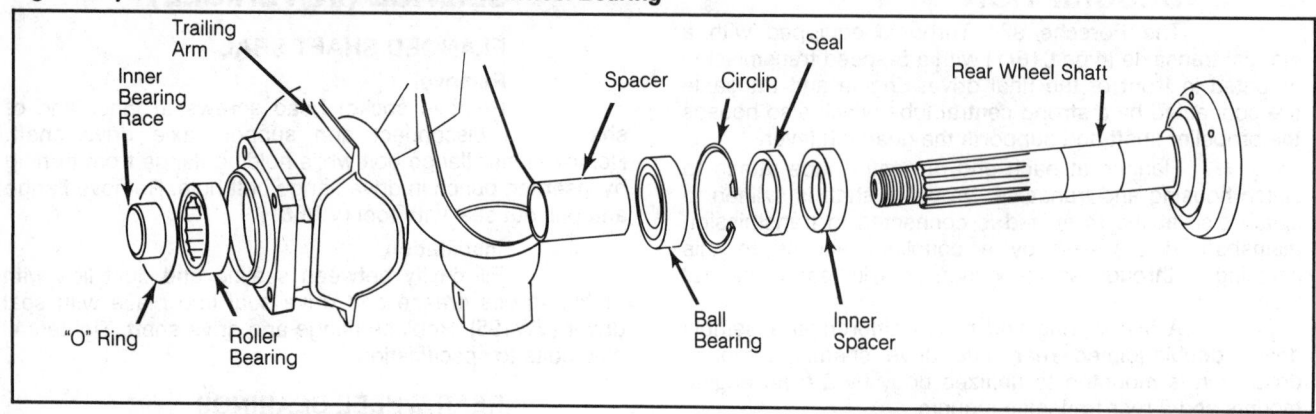

AXLE DRIVE SHAFT
Disassembly
Assure boot and CV joint areas are clean, then remove clamp holding boot on shaft. Drive protective cap off CV joint and remove circlip from end of axle. Press CV joint from shaft. Disassemble and inspect CV joint.

NOTE: Ball hubs and joints are matched sets. DO NOT interchange any balls, hubs or joints between CV joints.

Reassembly
Coat all parts with lubricant and assemble joint. Check for smooth operation throughout entire range of travel. Press CV joint assembly on axle splines with chambered side facing in toward the bearing collar. Pack about 1.6 oz. (45 grams) of molybdenum disulfide grease into each side of joint. Reinstall circlip, protective cap, boot and clamp.

TRANSAXLE REMOVAL & INSTALLATION
See the appropriate article in MANUAL TRANSMISSION REMOVAL Section.

Fig. 3: *Exploded View of Constant Velocity Joint*

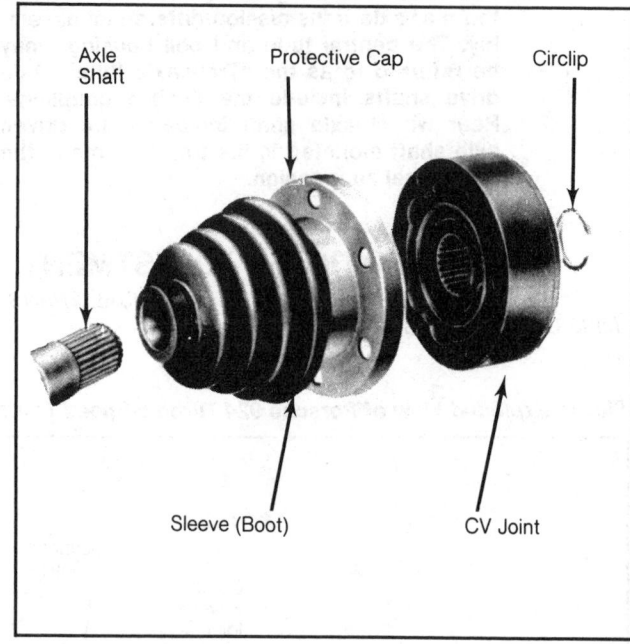

Fig. 4: *Exploded View of Mainshaft Assembly*

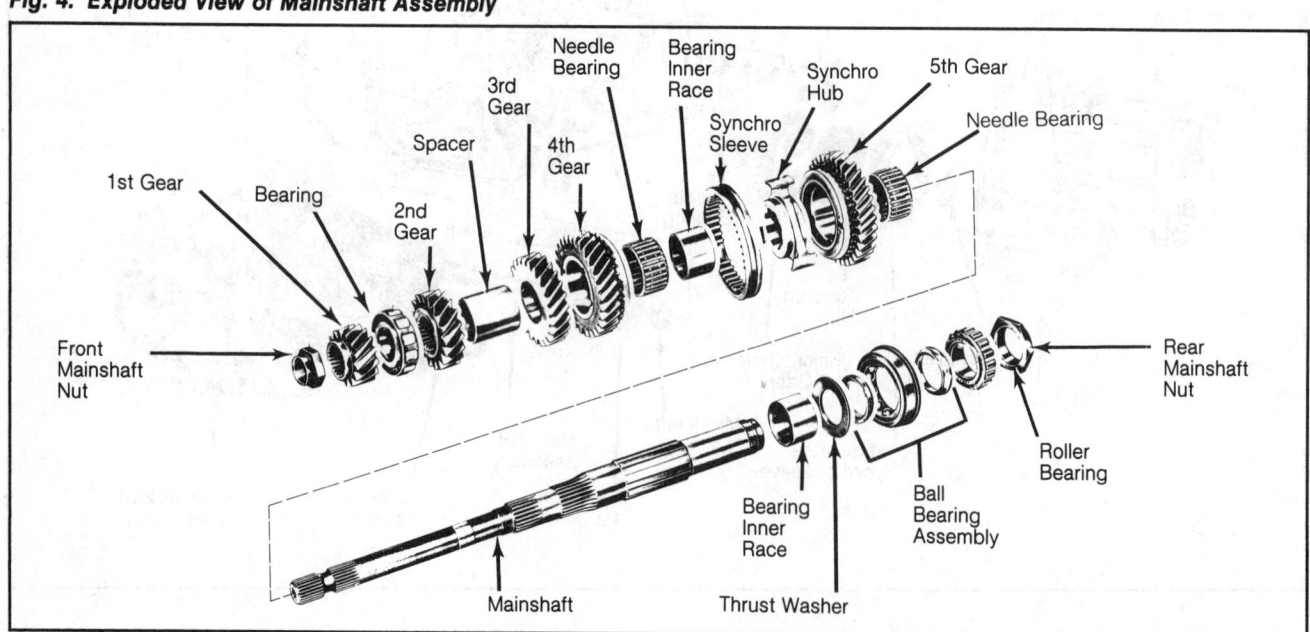

PORSCHE 924 TURBO 5-SPEED (Cont.)

Fig. 5: Exploded View of Pinion Shaft Assembly

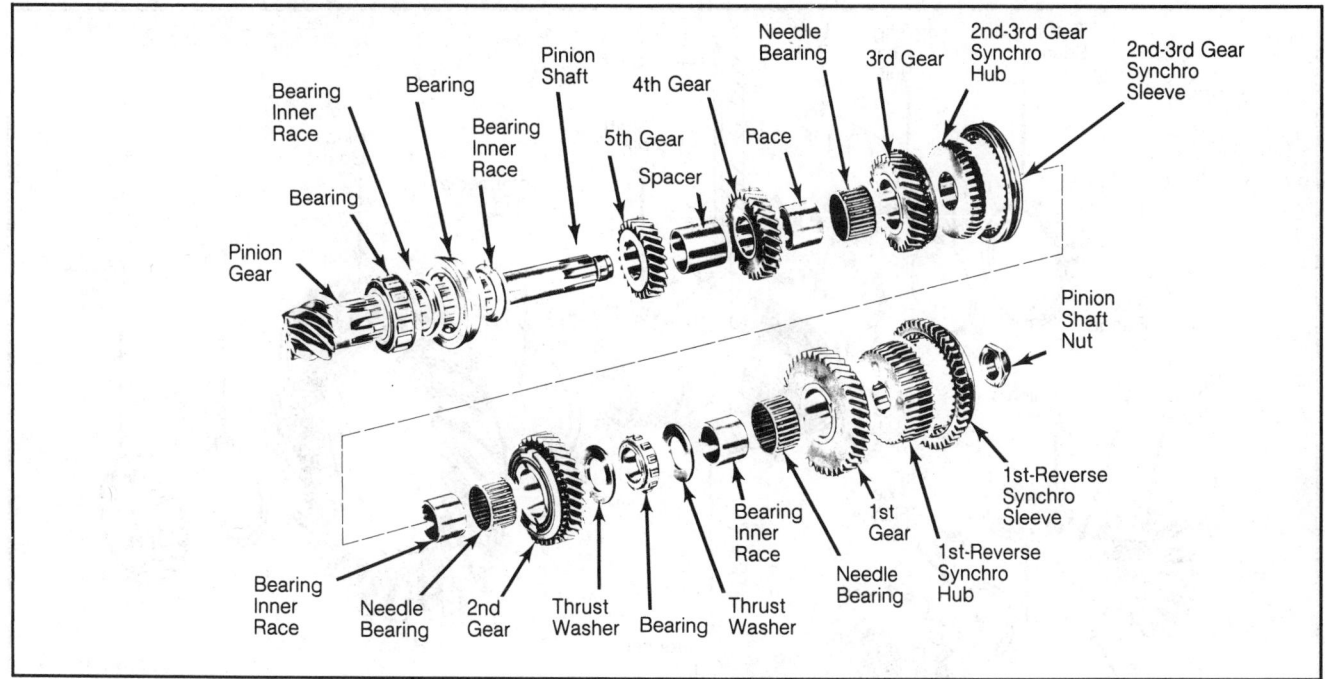

TRANSAXLE DISASSEMBLY

TRANSMISSION CASE DISASSEMBLY

1) Remove bolt attaching shifting rod to transaxle shift rod. From central tube access hole, remove bolt from sleeve connecting propeller shaft to mainshaft. Remove bolts attaching central tube to transaxle. Mount transaxle assembly in holder. Drain oil.

2) Remove bolts attaching front case to transmission case and remove front case. Engage 1st and 5th gears, then remove pinion shaft nut. Remove thrust washer, double reverse idler gear, bearings, spacer, thrust bearing and thrust washer from idler shaft.

3) Remove detent plug, spring and pin from case. Remove inner shift rod and fork. Remove back-up light switch and pin. With 1st and 5th gears still engaged, remove mainshaft nut.

4) Drive spring pins from 2nd-3rd operating lever and remove 2nd-3rd operating lever from rod. Remove 1st-reverse shift fork retaining pins and fork. Remove 1st-reverse synchro sleeve, synchro hub and pinion shaft 1st gear.

Fig. 6: Exploded View of Porsche 924 Turbo 5-Speed Final Drive Housing Assembly

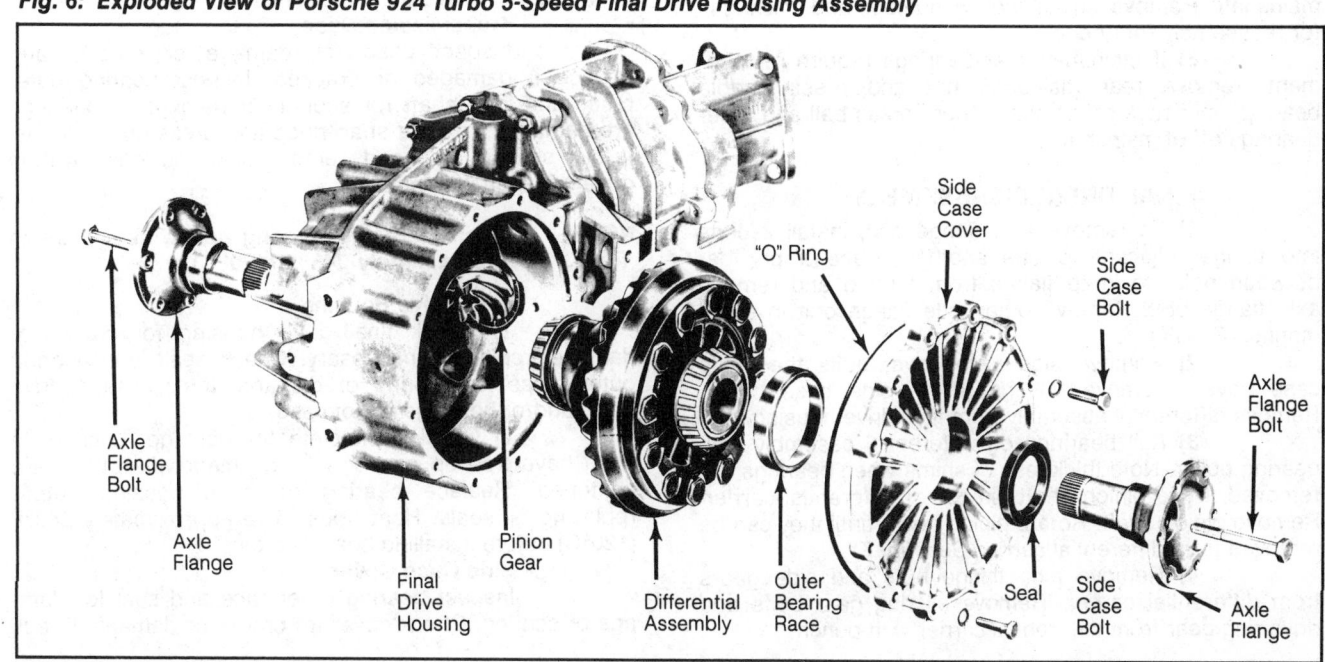

Manual Transmissions
PORSCHE 924 TURBO 5-SPEED (Cont.)

Fig. 7: Exploded View of Differential Assembly

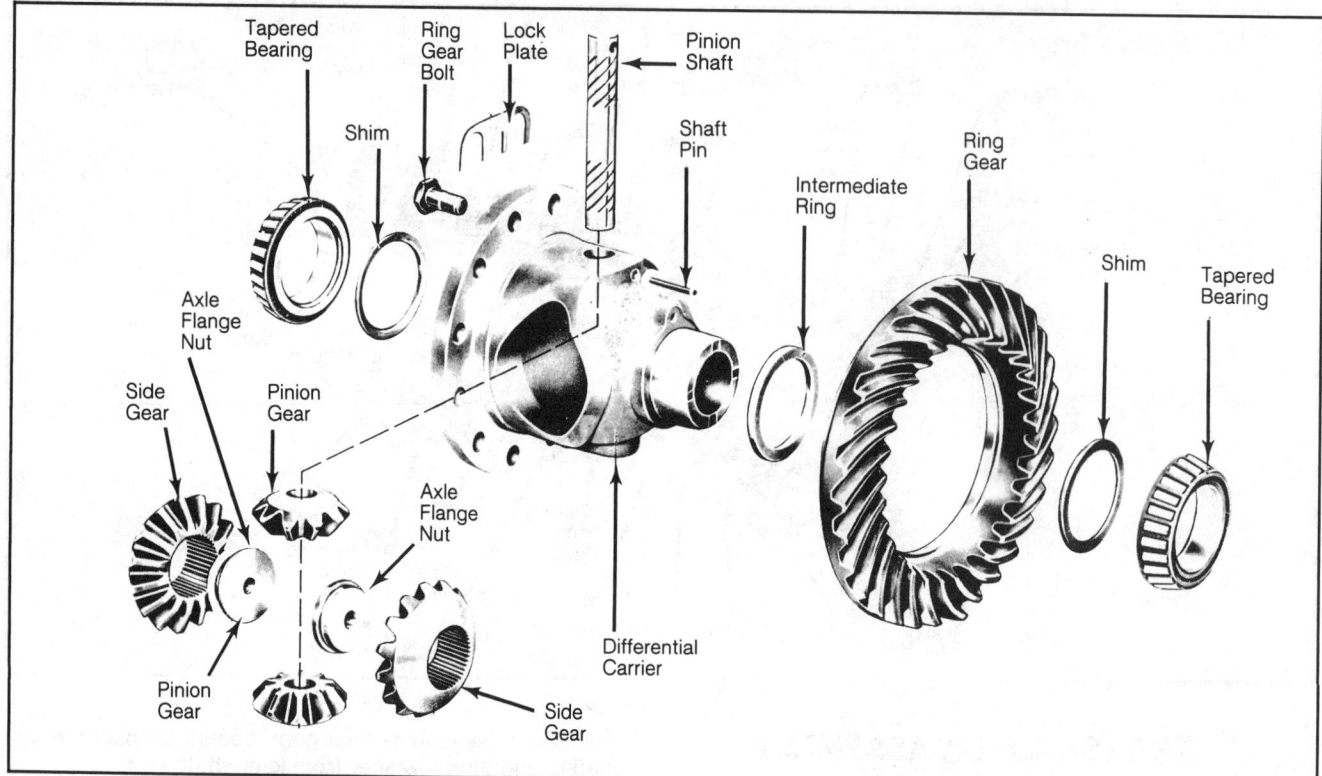

5) Separate transmission case from final drive housing. Using a gear puller, remove 2nd gear, roller bearing and 1st gear from mainshaft. Remove spacer from mainshaft.

6) From pinion shaft, remove bearings and 2nd gear making sure 2nd-3rd synchro parts are not loose. Remove 4th gear, 3rd gear and guide sleeve from pinion.

7) From mainshaft, remove spacer, 3rd gear, 4th gear, bearing, synchro assembly, 5th gear and bearing. Remove clamping plate nuts, pinion shaft and mainshaft. Remove shims, noting number and thickness for reassembly reference.

8) If mainshaft rear bearings require replacement, remove rear mainshaft nut and press needle bearing inner race off of shaft. Then, press ball and roller bearings off of mainshaft.

FINAL DRIVE DISASSEMBLY

1) To remove axle flange bolt, install 2 bolts into flange adjacent to one another. Place a pry bar between bolts to keep flange from turning and remove axle flange bolt. Remove other axle flange bolt in same manner. See Fig. 6.

2) Remove side case cover bolts then side case cover. Remove "O" ring from side case cover. Remove differential assembly from final drive housing.

3) Pull bearings off differential assembly with bearing puller. Note thickness of shims when bearings are removed. Drive pinion shaft pin out of differential carrier. Remove pinion shaft. Rotate pinion gears until they can be removed from differential carrier. See Fig. 7.

4) Remove axle flange nuts and side gears from differential carrier. Remove all ring gear bolts and drive ring gear from differential carrier with punch.

COMPONENT INSPECTION & REPAIR

TRANSAXLE HOUSINGS, CASES & COVERS

Front Cover

Inspect cover for damage or cracks. Inspect shift rod seal and guide bushing for damage or wear and replace as necessary. Inspect mainshaft seal for damage or wear and replace as necessary.

Transmission Case

Inspect case for damage or cracks, and replace if damaged or cracked. Inspect bearing outer races and idler shaft for scoring or damage. If bearings are damaged, remove snap rings and press out bearings. If idler shaft is damaged, remove plug and lock pin then drive out shaft with punch.

NOTE: When replacing bearing races, heat case to approximately 248°F (120°C).

Final Drive Housing

1) Check final drive housing for cracks or damage, replace if necessary. Check seals and bearing outer races for scoring or damage. If necessary, drive seals and/or bearings out of case.

2) Check lock plate for damage. Lock plate must have free up and down movement when bolts are tightened. Replace bearing races in housing before replacing oil seals. Heat housing to approximately 248°F (120°C) before installing bearing races.

Side Case Cover

Inspect bearing outer race and seal for damage or scoring. Check cover for cracks or damage. Check

PORSCHE 924 TURBO 5-SPEED (Cont.)

large "O" ring for damage. If necessary, drive out bearing race and oil seal. Remove "O" ring. When replacing bearing outer races, heat side case cover to 248°F (120°C), then press bearing races into side case cover. Replace "O" ring if necessary.

MAINSHAFT & PINION SHAFT

Check all gears for wear, damage or chipping. Check needle bearings and roller bearings for smooth operation, scoring and damage. Check synchro sleeves and hubs for wear or damage. Check pinion shaft and mainshaft for wear, scoring or damage. Replace components as necessary.

IDLER GEAR

Check double reverse idler gear for chipped or worn teeth. Check bearings for smooth operation or scoring. Check thrust bearing and thrust washer for wear, scoring and damage. Replace any components necessary.

SHIFT FORKS & SHAFTS

Check shift forks for wear, damage or cracks. Check shift rods for scoring. Check operation of shift forks on shift rods. If operation is not smooth, replace components as necessary.

DIFFERENTIAL ASSEMBLY

Check axle flanges for damage to splines, scoring on shaft, or cracks and damage to flange. Check ring gear, side gears and pinion gears for chips, cracks, wear or damage. Check pinion shaft for wear or scoring. Check differential carrier for damage or cracks. Replace any components necessary.

TRANSAXLE REASSEMBLY & ADJUSTMENT

PINION GEAR DEPTH

1) Before pinion gear depth can be set, bearings must be installed on mainshaft and pinion shaft, mainshaft and pinion shaft installed in final drive housing, then clamping plate installed.

NOTE: Only adjust pinion gear if final drive housing, large pinion bearing or pinion and ring gear were replaced.

2) Heat 5th gear needle bearing inner race to approximately 248°F (120°C) and press on mainshaft. Install thrust washer with ground side toward inner race. Install inner race roller bearing and roller bearing to mainshaft. Heat inner races to 248°F (120°C) before installation. Heat roller bearing to 248°F (120°C) and press on mainshaft. Install rear mainshaft nut and tighten.

3) Heat pinion shaft roller bearing and ball bearing inner races to 248°F (120°C). Then, install roller bearing, ball bearing inner race, ball bearing and other ball bearing inner race on pinion shaft.

4) Install both shafts to final drive housing. Install clamping plate (without any shims) and tighten nuts.

5) Slide special tube tool (9173) over pinion shaft, then install pinion shaft nut and tighten. On special measuring bar (VW 385/1), move adjusting ring so outside edge of ring is approximately 2.047" (52 mm) from center hole of machined flat surface.

6) Slide centering rings (VW 385/4) onto measuring bar. Install measuring plunger (VW 385/14) to center hole of measuring bar (machined flat surface), then install dial indicator with a .118" (3 mm) range and .55" (14 mm) extension (VW 385/53) on end of measuring bar. See Fig. 8.

Fig. 8: Special Tool Setup for Measuring Pinion Gear Depth

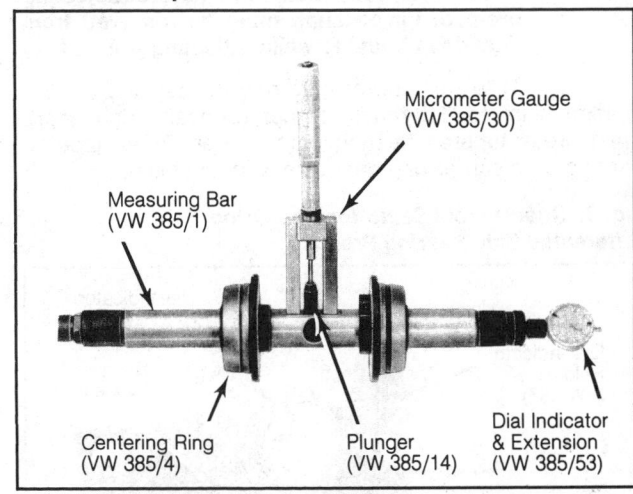

7) Set micrometer gauge (VW 385/30) to read distance of 2.610" (66.3 mm) plus deviation measurement stamped on end of pinion shaft.

NOTE: **There are 2 numbers stamped on end of pinion shaft. One is a 3-digit number which is a matching code for the ring gear. The other number consists of a letter followed by 2 digits. The digits represent the deviation measurement in hundredths of millimeters. For example, N18 would represent a deviation of .18 mm (.007"). This deviation is added to the standard distance of 2.610" (66.3 mm).**

8) With micrometer set to specifications, place over plunger on measuring bar. Adjust dial indicator to zero with a .040" (1 mm) preload. Place a magnetic disc (VW 385/17) onto end of pinion shaft.

9) Install measuring bar into final drive housing so that plunger on bar is in contact with the magnetic disc on end of pinion shaft. Install side case cover (without "O" ring) using only 4 bolts. Use bolts to pull cover into place (using a hammer may knock magnetic disc off pinion shaft).

10) Pull measuring bar until centering ring is engaged with side case cover. Rotate measuring bar slowly, watch dial indicator. When dial indicator reaches maximum deflection, note reading. This reading, added to the .040" (1 mm) preload is the shim thickness to be installed between pinion shaft bearing and clamping plate.

NOTE: **Dial indicator deflection must always be in a clockwise direction, with an indicator reading of between .040"-.080" (1-2 mm).**

11) Remove pinion shaft nut, special tube tool and clamping plate. Install determined shims then reinstall checking tools and recheck measurement. Measurement

PORSCHE 924 TURBO 5-SPEED (Cont.)

must be set distance 2.610" (66.3 mm) plus deviation marked on pinion shaft end. Maximum deviation of pinion depth is plus or minus .001" (.03 mm).

DIFFERENTIAL SIDE BEARING PRELOAD

NOTE: **Differential assembly must be assembled (without tapered bearings) before adjusting preload. Pinion shaft must be removed from final drive housing while adjusting preload.**

    1) Install intermediate ring spacer and a .197" (5 mm) shim to differential carrier (opposite ring gear). Then press tapered bearing onto carrier. Press tapered bearing onto carrier ring gear side without shims.

Fig. 9: Special Tool Setup for Measuring Differential Side Bearing Preload

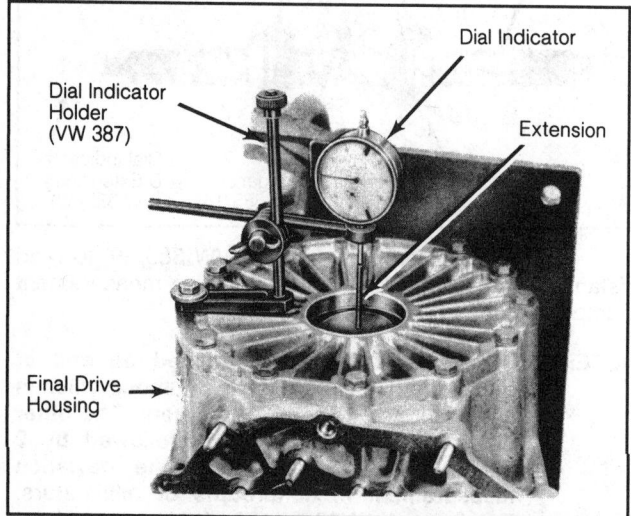

    2) Install differential assembly into final drive housing. Turn differential to seat tapered bearings. Install side case cover. Install all side case cover bolts and tighten. Place magnetic disc (VW 385/17) on collar of differential.

    3) Install dial indicator holder (VW 387) with dial indicator and extension rod to side case cover (use 1 case cover bolt). Zero dial indicator, then preload indicator to .080" (2 mm). *See Fig. 9.*

    4) Move differential assembly up and down in final drive housing and note maximum dial indicator needle deflection. To this measured value (from dial indicator), add a constant value (preload) of .012" (.3 mm). Then add the already installed .197" (5 mm) shim to get total shim thickness.

NOTE: **When selecting shim thickness from measured values, always round measurements off to the nearest .05 mm (.002"). For example, if measured value is 1.17 mm (.046"), rounded off value is 1.15 mm (.045").**

    5) Remove dial indicator and holder, side case cover and differential assembly. Remove both tapered bearings and install shims to both sides of differential assembly in the following manner:
- Divide total shim thickness value by 2.
- Add .004" (.1 mm) to one divided shim value.
- Subtract .004" (.1 mm) from other divided shim value.

NOTE: **Example: A total shim value of .258" (6.55 mm) would yield one shim pack of .133" (3.375 mm) and another shim pack of .125" (3.175 mm).**

    6) Install selected shim packs to differential assembly then press tapered bearings onto differential assembly.

DIFFERENTIAL RING GEAR BACKLASH

    1) Install pinion shaft, mainshaft, shims and clamping plate to final drive housing. Install differential assembly into final drive housing.

NOTE: **When tightening bolts on side case cover and pinion shaft nut, check that ring gear has some backlash at all times. If ring gear binds up, remove differential assembly and move tapered bearing shims so some backlash will remain in ring gear.**

    2) Install side case cover and tighten bolts.

NOTE: **Pinion gear must be held stationary while checking backlash. One way would be to install 1st-5th gears on pinion, 1st gear on mainshaft, idler double reverse gear on idler shaft, shift rods and forks, synchro sleeve and hub to final drive housing, then lock 1st and 5th gears together.**

    3) Install pinion shaft nut and tighten. Install adjustable lever (VW 388) to clamping arbor (VW 521/4). Adjust lever length from large hexagon surface to upper surface of ball to 3.268" (83 mm).

    4) Install clamping arbor with sleeve (9145) in differential assembly and clamp tight. Turn differential in both directions several times to seat tapered roller bearings.

    5) Install dial indicator holder (VW 387), with dial indicator and extension so that dial indicator axis is perpendicular to lever. *See Fig. 10.* Turn differential against stop carefully with clamping arbor (VW 521/4) and set dial indicator to zero with a .080" (2 mm) preload.

Fig. 10: Special Tool Setup for Measuring Ring Gear Backlash

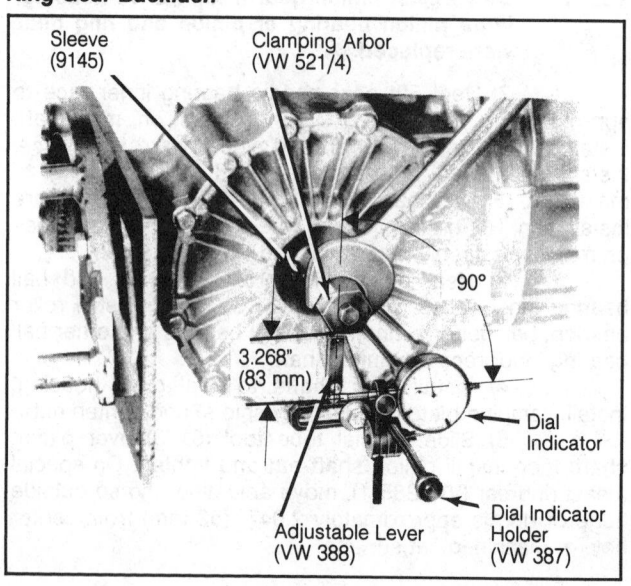

PORSCHE 924 TURBO 5-SPEED (Cont.)

6) Turn ring gear back and read amount of backlash. Note this value. Repeat this check every 90° ring gear rotation. Ring gear backlash specification is inscribed on ring gear.

7) If backlash is not to specifications, remove differential assembly, remove tapered bearings and move shim from one side to other until backlash is to specifications. Backlash specification is plus or minus .002" (.05 mm).

TRANSAXLE REASSEMBLY

NOTE: Heat all parts which require press fit to 248°F (120°C) before installation.

1) Install mainshaft and pinion shaft to final drive housing. Install same thickness shims that were removed or install shims determined in adjustment procedure. Install clamping plate and nuts and tighten.

2) On pinion shaft, install 5th gear and spacer. On mainshaft, install thrust washer, bearing inner race, needle bearing, 5th gear, synchro hub and sleeve with shift fork and rod. bearing inner race, needle bearing, 4th gear and 3rd gear. Install spacer, 2nd gear and bearing.

3) On pinion shaft, install 4th gear, bearing inner race, needle bearing, 3rd gear and 2nd-3rd synchro hub and sleeve with shift fork and rod. Then install bearing inner race, needle bearing, 2nd gear, thrust washer, bearing, thrust washer and bearing inner race.

4) Install transmission case and gasket to final drive housing. On idler shaft, install thrust washer, thrust bearing, needle bearing, spacer, needle bearing, double reverse gear and thrust washer.

5) On pinion shaft, install needle bearing, 1st gear, 1st-reverse synchro hub and sleeve with 1st-reverse shift fork and rod. Install 2nd-3rd operating lever onto 2nd-3rd shift rod and install spring pins in lever.

6) Install inner shift rod and fork to transmission case, fixed to 1st-reverse shift rod. On mainshaft, install 1st gear. Engage 1st and 5th gears, then install mainshaft nut and pinion shaft nut. Tighten pinion shaft nut, then mainshaft nut. Stake nuts to shafts.

7) Install detent pin, spring and plug to case. Install backup switch pin and switch to transmission case. With all components installed, check operation of all components. Install front case to transmission case.

TIGHTENING SPECIFICATIONS

Application	Ft. Lbs. (N.m)
Axle Flange Bolt	35 (47)
Axle Shaft Bolt	30 (41)
Central Tube-to-Clutch Housing	30 (41)
Clamping Plate Nuts	17 (23)
Central Tube-to-Front Case	61 (82)
Front Case to-Transmission Case	17 (23)
Mainshaft Nut	
Front	125 (169)
Rear	165 (224)
Pinion Shaft Nut	150 (203)
Ring Gear Bolts	112 (152)
Side Case Cover Bolts	17 (23)
Transaxle Mount Bolts	30 (41)
Transmission Case-to-Final Drive	17 (23)

Manual Transmissions

PORSCHE 928 5-SPEED

DESCRIPTION

The Porsche 928 is equipped with a manual transmission (type G28.05) which has 5 speeds. Engine and transaxle are connected by a rigid central tube which also houses the propeller shaft and supports the gear shift lever. Bell housings on each end of this tube attach to the engine and transaxle.

The propeller shaft is splined to the clutch disc at the front and is connected to the transmission mainshaft at the rear by a coupling. Access to this coupling is through an inspection hole in the rear bell housing.

A hypoid ring and pinion differential assembly drives joint rear axle drive shafts. The whole assembly is mounted to the unitized body by 2 front engine mounts and 2 rear transmission mounts.

NOTE: **The term "Transaxle" in this article refers to the rear axle transmission/differential assembly. The central tube and bell housings may be referred to as the "transaxle tube". Axle drive shafts include the flexible couplings. Rear wheel axle shaft indicates the driven axle shaft mounted in the trailing arms of the rear wheel suspension.**

LUBRICATION & ADJUSTMENT

See the appropriate article in MANUAL TRANS-MISSION SERVICING Section.

SERVICE (IN-VEHICLE)

FLANGED SHAFT SEAL
Removal

Remove socket head screws at inner end of shaft, then disconnect and support axle drive shaft. Remove inner flange bolt while holding flange from turning by inserting punch in drive flange bolt hole. Remove flange and pull out seal with tool (VW 681).

Installation

Fill cavity between sealing and dust lips with multi-purpose grease and drive seal in place with tool (VW 195). Replace flange and drive shaft and tighten to specifications.

REAR WHEEL BEARINGS
Removal

With brake calipers off and drive shaft disconnected at axle flange, press shaft from housing, remove circlip and drive grooved ball bearing and roller bearing out with soft drift.

Installation

Press grooved ball bearing in inner end of housing and replace circlip. Put spacer in housing and drive roller bearing in place (flanged side facing out). Install seal in inboard side of housing. Put outer spacer in shaft and press in along with bearing inner race using castellated nut and driver.

Fig. 1: Cross-Section of Porsche 928 Manual Transaxle Assembly

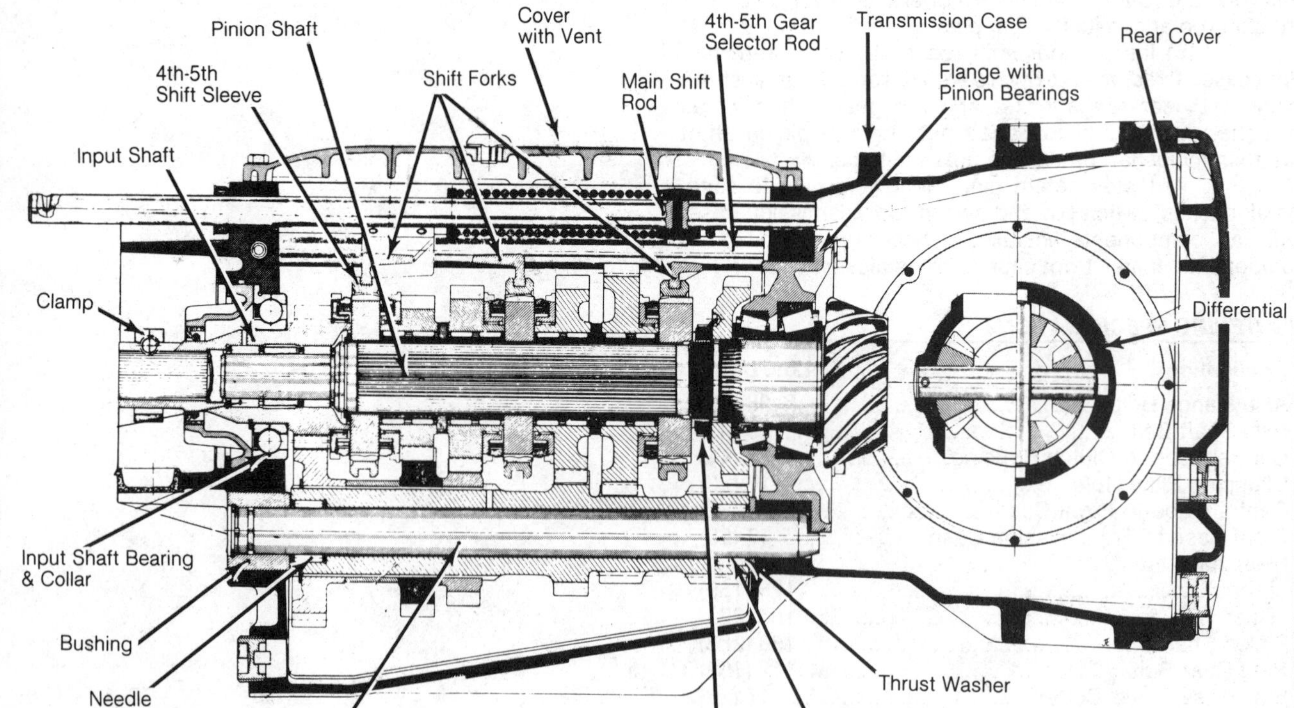

Fig. 2: Exploded View of Rear Axle Shaft Assembly

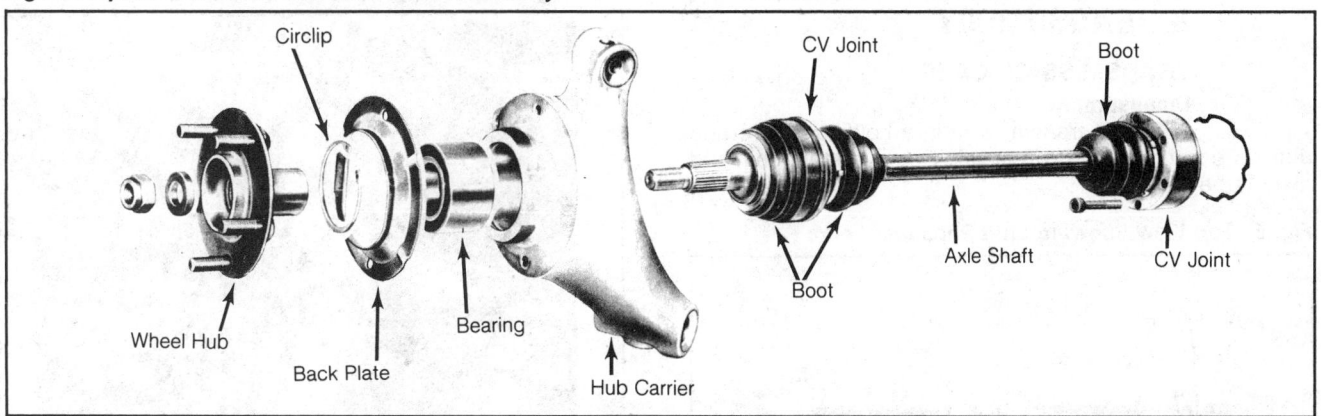

AXLE DRIVE SHAFTS
Removal & Installation
Raise vehicle on hoist. Remove bolts from constant velocity joint-to-mating flange and remove drive axle from vehicle. To install, reverse removal procedure and tighten to specifications.

CONSTANT VELOCITY JOINTS
NOTE: Axle shafts must be removed from vehicle before servicing.

Removal
Clamp axle shaft in a vise with soft jaws. Remove boot clamp and push boot to center of axle. Remove circlip from axle shaft, press joint from axle shaft using special tools VW 401 and VW 408.

Disassembly
Swing ball and ball cage from joint and press out in direction of arrow. *See Fig. 3.* Tilt ball hub out of ball cage via ball groove. *See Fig. 4.* Clean all parts in a cleaning solvent and blow dry. Inspect for wear and damage.

NOTE: Ball hub and joint are paired. Do not mix parts. The 6 balls are also mated together and cannot be mixed with others.

Fig. 3: Ball Hub and Ball Cage Removal

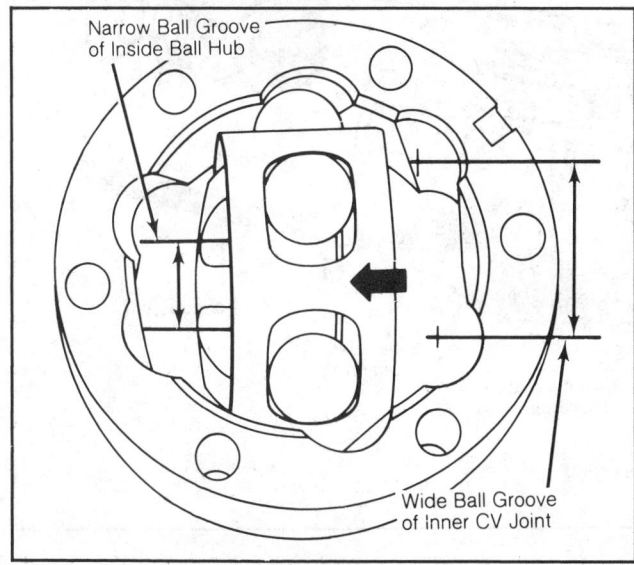

Fig. 4: Removal of Ball Hub from Cage

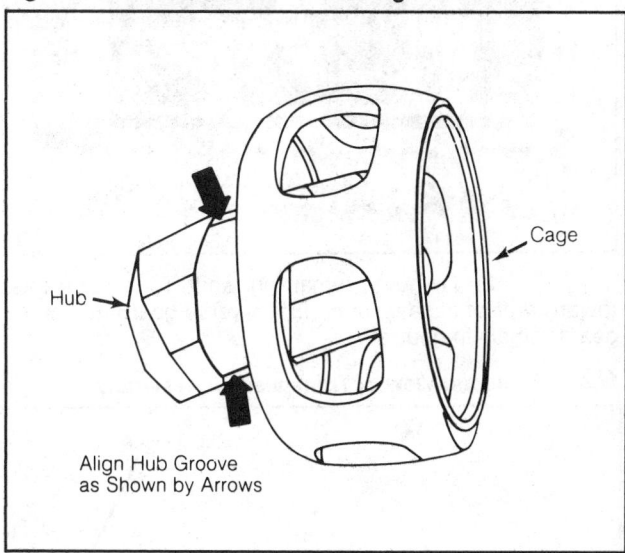

Reassembly
Place ball hub in ball cage. Press balls into cage. Install hub with cage and balls into joint and swing into assembled position. Check for smooth operation.

Installation
Reverse removal procedure and note the following: Install a new gasket on flange cover. Pack joint with molybdenum grease.

TRANSAXLE REMOVAL & INSTALLATION
See the appropriate article in MANUAL TRANS-MISSION REMOVAL Section.

TRANSAXLE DISASSEMBLY
1) Mount transaxle in holding fixture and drain oil. Remove drive axle flanges. Remove selector shaft cap bolts, cap and spring.

2) Remove shift finger and shift fork pins. Slide selector shaft in as far as possible. Remove end plate mounting bolts and separate gear case from transaxle housing. Remove differential cover bolts and differential assembly.

Manual Transmissions

PORSCHE 928 5-SPEED (Cont.)

COMPONENT DISASSEMBLY & REASSEMBLY

TRANSMISSION CASE

Disassembly

1) Mount transmission in a holding fixture and remove end cover and top cover. Remove main shift rod toward the rear.

Fig. 5: Top View Showing Shift Rods and Forks

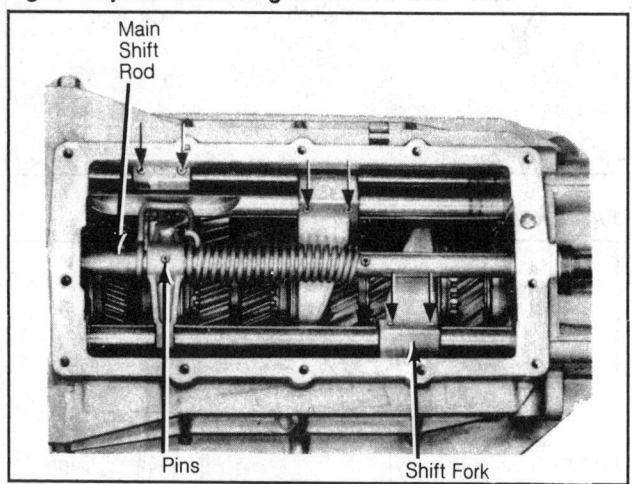

2) Remove remaining shift rods and forks toward rear of case insuring that reverse gear and 1st-2nd gears remain in neutral.

Fig. 6: View Showing Input Shaft Removal

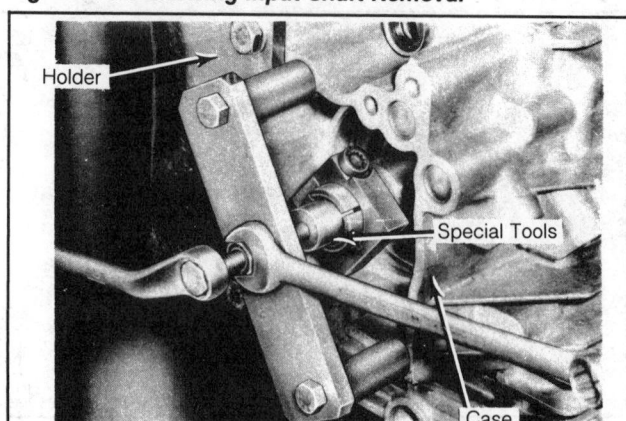

3) Remove the input shaft using special tools (9140 and 9148) and pulling shaft from the case.

4) Remove pinion shaft assembly using removal tools (9148 and P263) to press out assembly. Drive out reverse idler gear shaft, then remove reverse idler gear assembly.

NOTE: Transmission and differential case (transaxle) repairs include replacement of seals and bearing races. Case temperature should be at least 300°F (150°C) when installing bearing races. Press load should be maintained for about 2 minutes until case and bearing race have reached the same temperature.

Fig. 7: Exploded View of Transmission Assembly

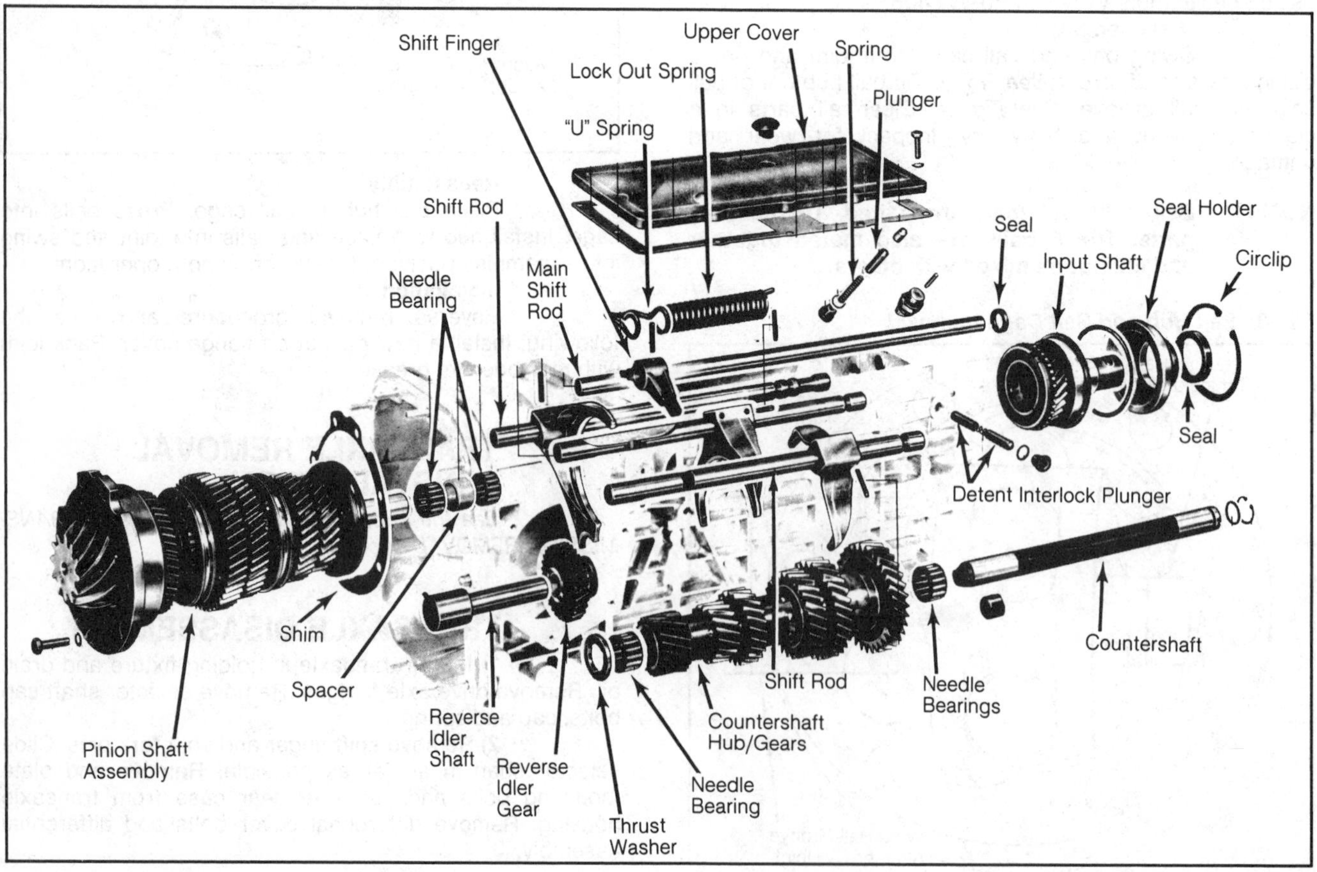

PORSCHE 928 5-SPEED (Cont.)

Fig. 8: *View Showing Pinion Shaft Removal*

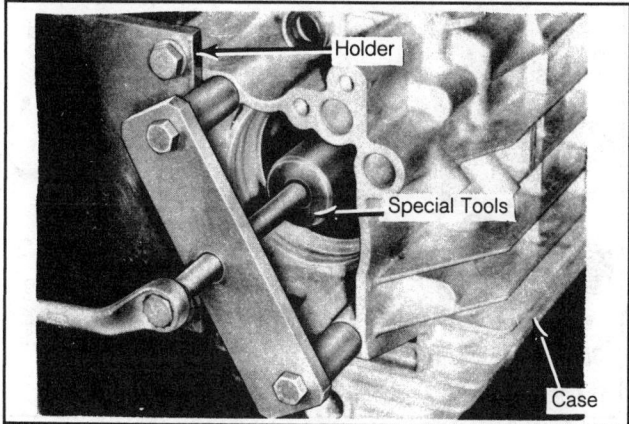

Reassembly

1) Place input shaft in case. Using mandrel, drive input shaft into ball bearing up to the stop. Work alternately over outer race to insure shaft is to the stop.

2) Attach installer (9144) to pinion bearing cover. Fabricate 2 centering pins and install as shown in

Fig. 9: *Drive Points for Input Shaft Installation*

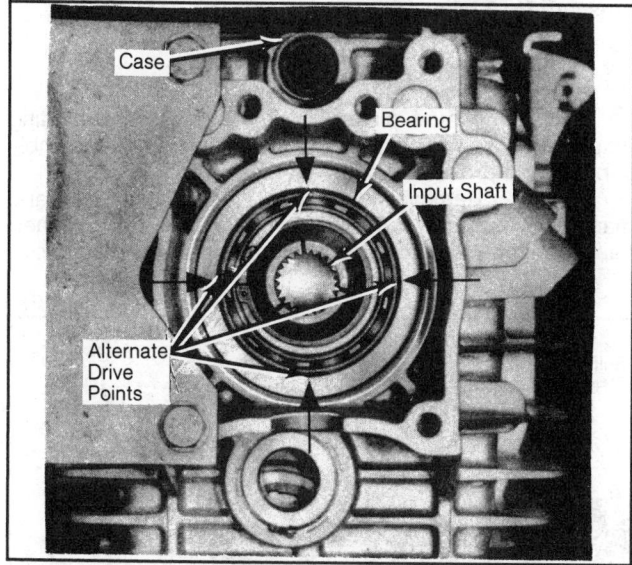

Fig. 10: *Using Special Tool and Centering Pins for Pinion Shaft Installation*

Fig. 10. Using centering pins as guides, install pinion shaft into case. Check that clearance between input shaft and 4th-5th speed hub on pinion shaft is .008-.012" (.2-.3 mm).

3) Install shift rods with shift forks and shift interlock components. Install main shift rod with shift finger. Install relaxed lock out spring so that one end rests on "U" spring and the other end of roll pin faces up.

Fig. 11: *Measuring Clearance Between Input Shaft and 4th-5th Speed Hub*

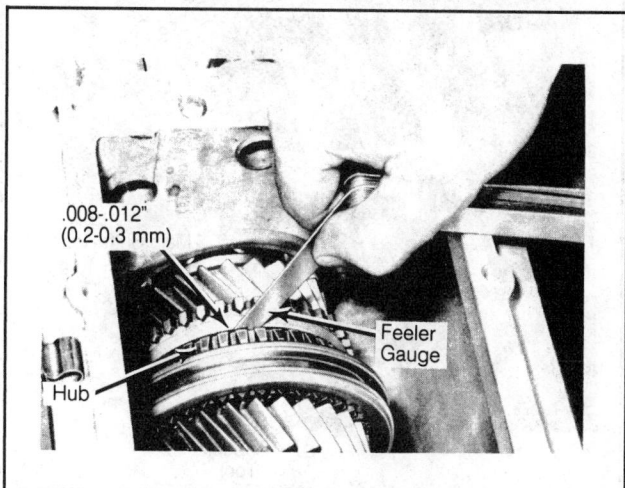

4) Using special tool (9155), turn main shift rod until shift finger pin can be installed. In this position, the lock out spring will be under tension and depression for set screw in main shift rod faces left.

Fig. 12: *Sectional View of Shift Rods and Interlock Components*

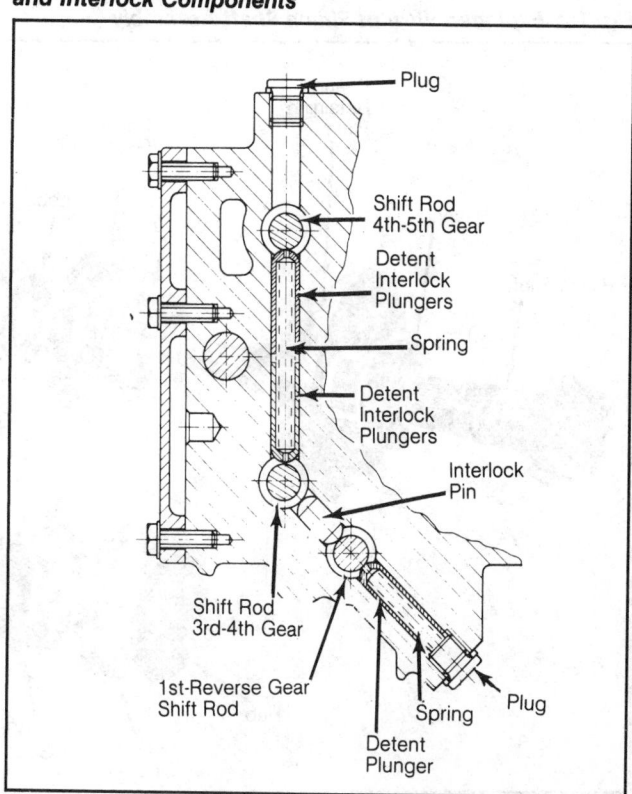

Manual Transmissions
PORSCHE 928 5-SPEED (Cont.)

Fig. 13: View Showing Main Shift Rod Alignment

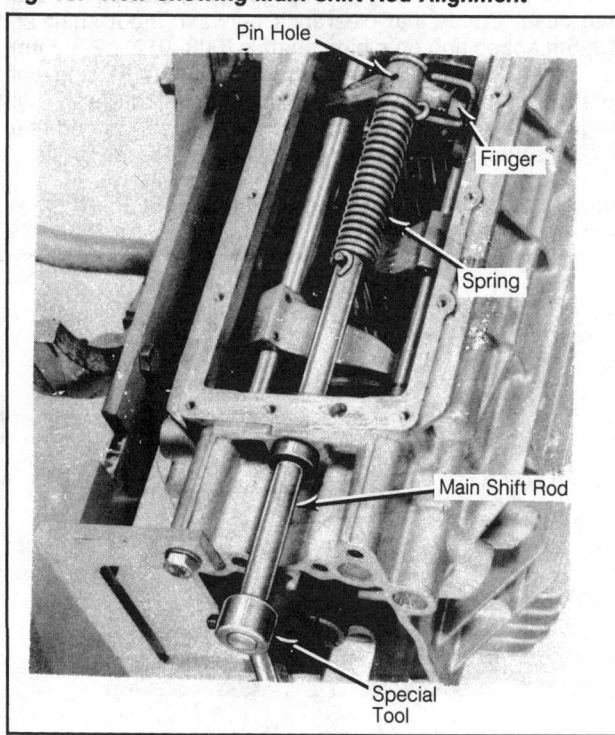

Fig. 14: Exploded View of Input Shaft Assembly

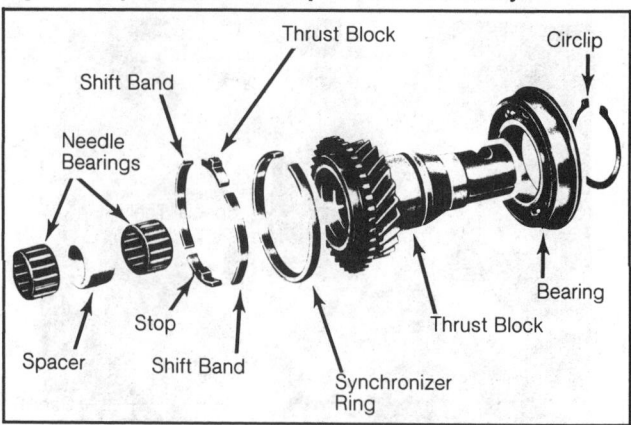

NOTE: **All parts must be clean and free of grease before reassembly.**

Reassembly

Install both needle bearings into shaft bore with spacer between bearings. Install shift band and thrust block. Install synchronizer ring. Heat ball bearing to 212°F (100°C) and press bearing onto shaft until tight. Hold pressure for 2 minutes until bearing cools. Install circlip.

INPUT SHAFT
Disassembly

Place shaft assembly in press. Using arbor (VW 457), press off ball bearing. Remove synchronizer ring, shift band and thrust block. Remove 2 needle bearings and spacer from inside shaft.

PINION SHAFT
Disassembly

1) Mount pinion shaft assembly in a holding fixture and remove circlip and shim. Place shaft assembly in press and press off shift sleeve and hub.

2) Remove needle bearing and inner race and mark for reassembly. Remove 4th gear, thrust washer, needle bearing and inner race and mark for reassembly.

Fig. 15: Exploded View of Pinion Shaft Assembly

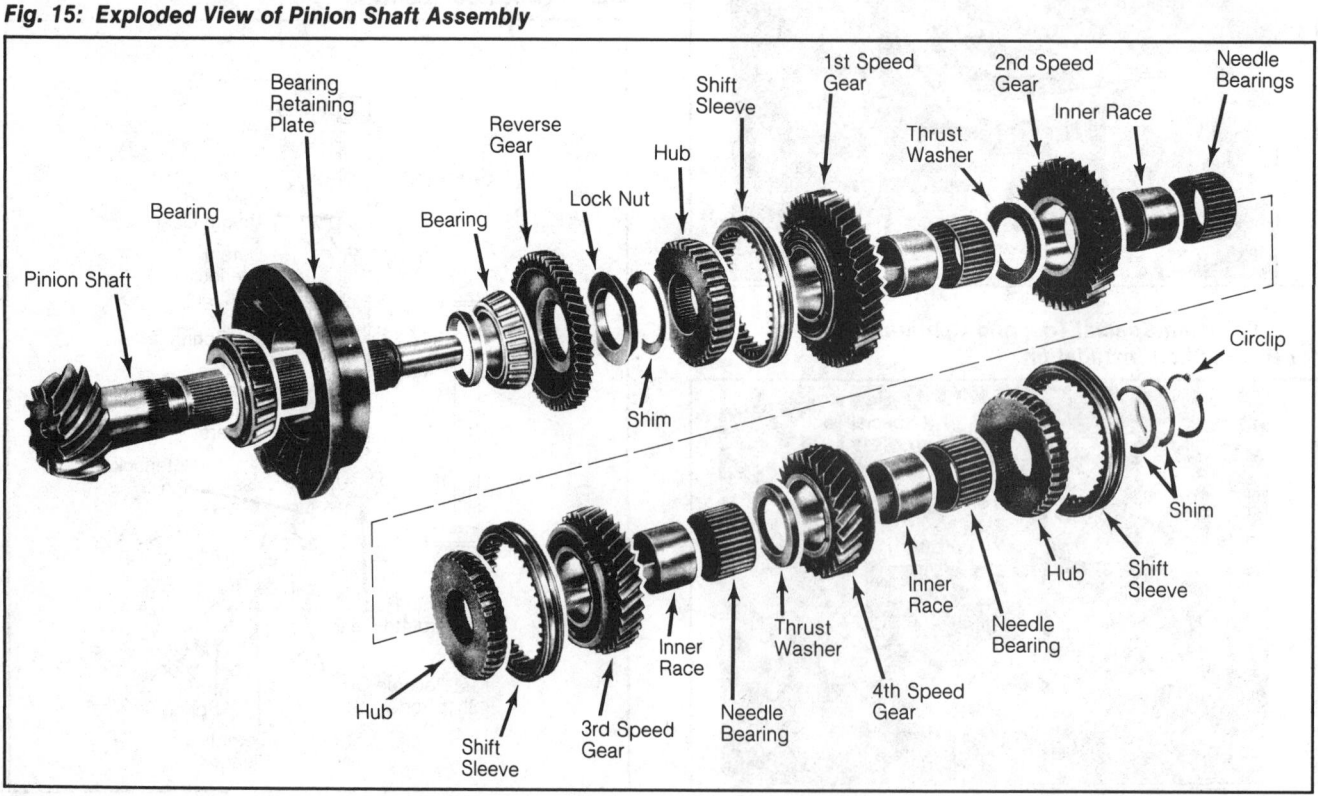

PORSCHE 928 5-SPEED (Cont.)

3) Remove 3rd gear, shift sleeve and hub. Remove needle bearing and inner race and mark for reassembly. Remove 2nd gear, thrust washer, needle bearing and inner race and mark for reassembly.

4) Remove 1st gear, shift sleeve and hub, shim and lock nut, then remove reverse gear. Press off tapered roller bearing with bearing retaining plate as a unit. Using arbor (US 1103), press off tapered roller bearing.

NOTE: It is imperative that all parts are free of grease and fingerprints during assembly unless otherwise specified. Large taper bearings and inner races must be heated to 212°F (100°C) prior to installation. Hold until temperature has balanced itself.

Reassembly

1) Press tapered roller bearing onto shaft. Press bearing retaining plate complete with tapered roller bearing and shim onto shaft. Install reverse gear with cavity facing lock nut. Install lock nut, then tighten to specifications and stake in place. See Fig. 16.

Fig. 16: *Installation of Retainer Plate Assembly on Pinion Shaft with Lock Nut Staking Point Indicated*

2) To determine thickness of shim "X" in *Fig. 17*, measure and record distance from end of pinion shaft head to lock nut (dimension "A" in *Fig. 17*) with a caliper. Shim thickness is equal to dimension "A" plus deviation "r" (stamped on pinion head) subtracted from design specification of 4.28" (108.7 mm).

Fig. 17: *Cross-Sectional View Showing Point Designations for Calculation of Shim "X" Thickness*

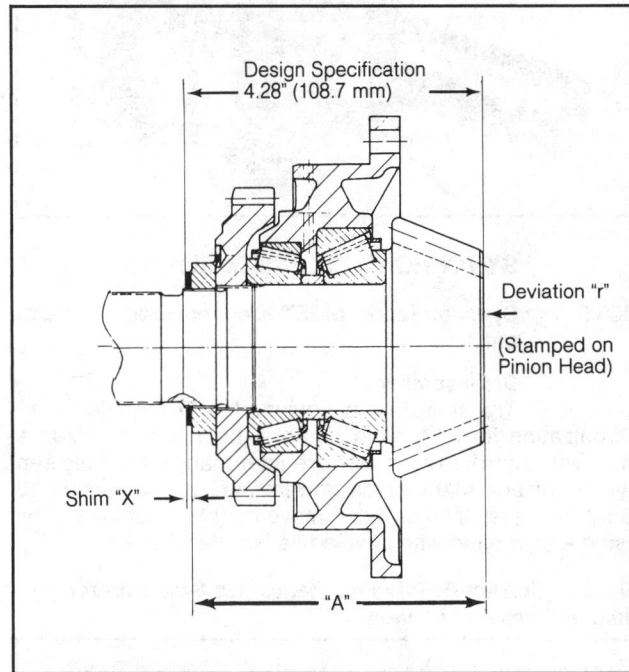

3) Install selected shim, hub and sleeve making sure flat surface on side flank faces 1st gear. Install 1st gear and check synchronization. Install needle bearings and inner races marked for 2nd, 3rd and 4th gears.

4) Check synchronization. Install needle bearing and inner race, hub and sleeve, shim and circlip. Install a shim between hub and circlip to eliminate all end play. See Fig. 19.

Fig. 18: *Sectional View of Synchronizer Rings*

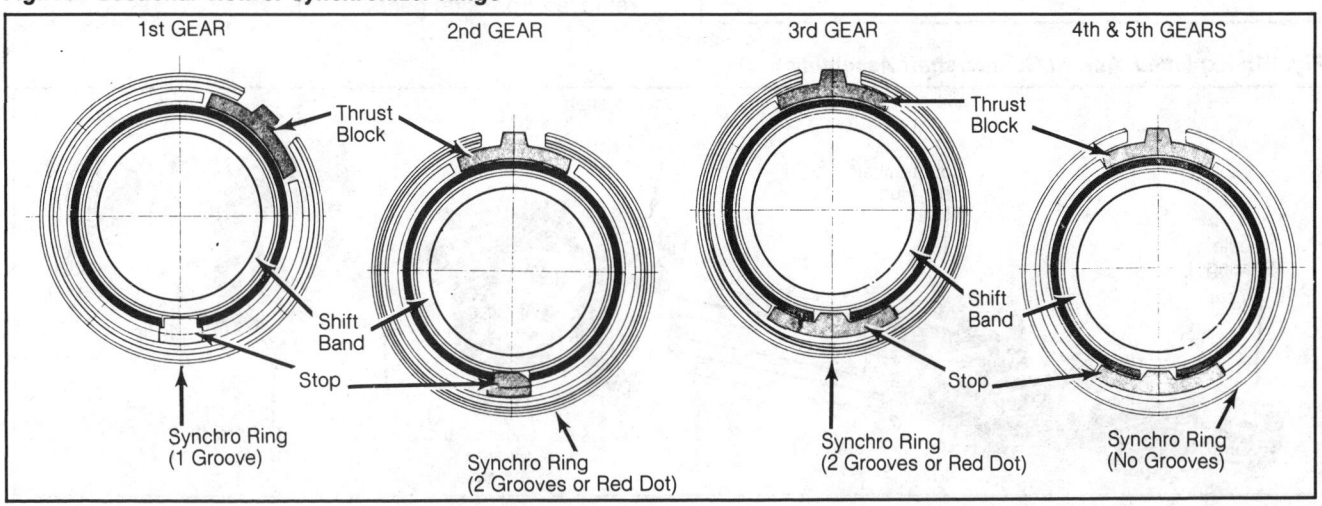

Manual Transmissions

PORSCHE 928 5-SPEED (Cont.)

Fig. 19: Selecting Gear Set End Shim

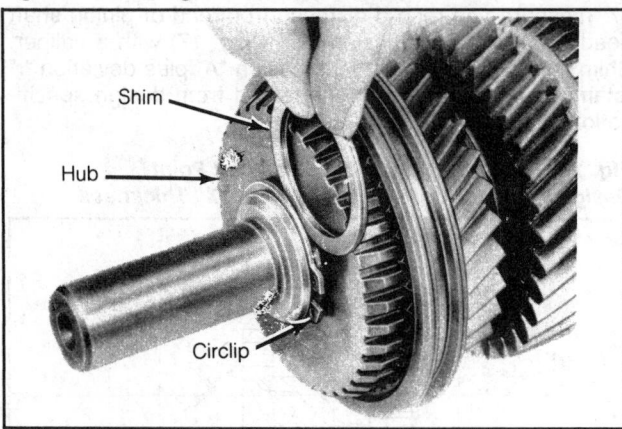

Shim

Hub

Circlip

SYNCHRONIZER ASSEMBLIES

NOTE: **Synchronizers MUST be replaced in pairs only.**

Disassembly

Transmission is equipped with modified synchronization for all forward speeds. Each synchronizer is different, therefore no parts are interchangeable between synchronizers. Mark synchronizers before disassembly to facilitate reassembly. Axial movement is eliminated by using a shift band with beveled flanks. *See Fig. 18.*

Fig. 20: Correct Position for Measuring Synchronizer Ring at Thickest Location

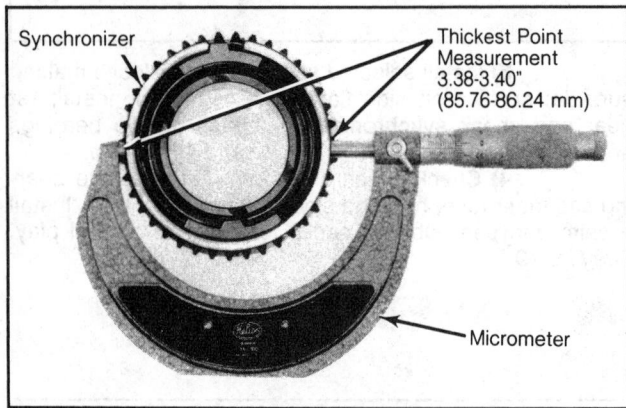

Synchronizer

Thickest Point Measurement 3.38-3.40" (85.76-86.24 mm)

Micrometer

Inspection

Clean and dry all parts. Check for chipped teeth or any other irregularity. Using a micrometer, check all synchronizer rings at the thickest point. Measurement should read 3.38-3.40" (85.76-86.24 mm).

Reassembly

To reassemble, reverse disassembly procedure, insuring that correct parts for particular synchronizer are used.

NOTE: **When reassembling 1st gear, short side of shift band must be to right of thrust block. When reassembling 2nd gear, bevelled side of stop must face to right as seen from top view.**

COUNTERSHAFT

Disassembly

Remove circlip and needle bearing. Place countershaft assembly in a press. Using support rail (VW 457) and arbor (VW 407), press off countershaft drive gear and spacer. Remove countershaft 4th speed and 3rd speed gears. Remove end needle bearing.

Inspection

Clean and dry all parts. Check for chips, burrs or any irregularities.

NOTE: **When replacement of a gear is required, replace in pairs only.**

Reassembly

To reassemble, heat gears to 212°F (100°C) and reverse disassembly procedure making note of the following: Place 3rd gear onto shaft so small shoulder faces stop. Place 4th gear onto shaft so large shoulder faces 3rd gear. Place countershaft gear onto shaft so large shoulder faces spacer. *See Fig. 21.*

DIFFERENTIAL

Disassembly

1) Place differential assembly in vise fitted with jaw protectors. Remove ring gear bolts and drive ring gear off housing. Remove bearings (if required) using a double arm puller.

2) Remove pinion shaft lock pin, then remove pinion shaft, pinion gears, side gear drive flange nuts and side gears. Note location and thickness of any shims removed from side gears.

Fig. 21: Exploded View of Countershaft Assembly

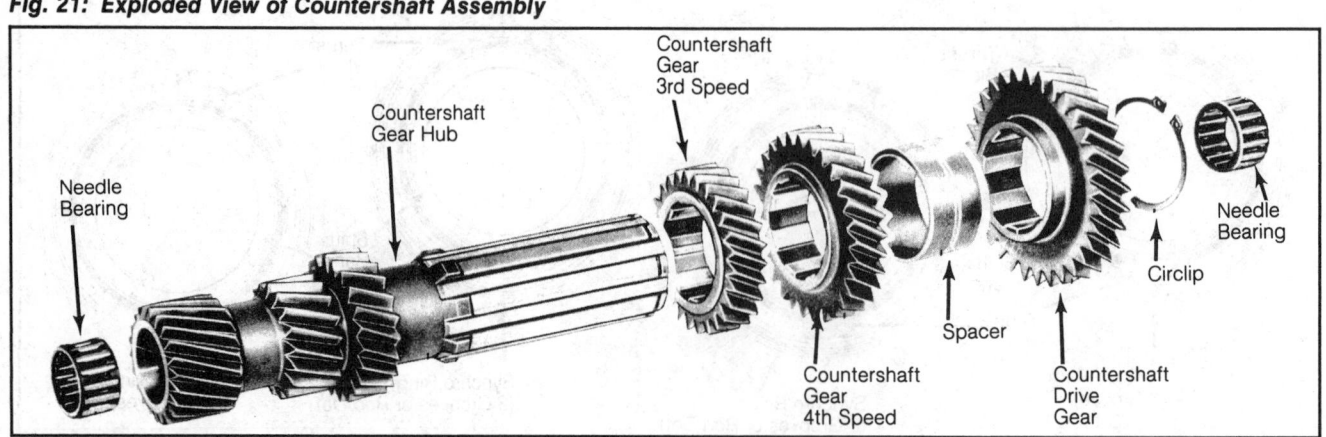

Needle Bearing

Countershaft Gear Hub

Countershaft Gear 3rd Speed

Countershaft Gear 4th Speed

Spacer

Countershaft Drive Gear

Circlip

Needle Bearing

PORSCHE 928 5-SPEED (Cont.)

Reassembly

1) Heat ring gear to about 212°F (100°C) and place on differential using centering pins to align bolt holes. Install new retaining bolts and tighten to specifications in an alternating sequence. Slide lock plate into bolt head groove, bend ends together, then bend lock plate ends down over side of bolt head.

2) Place correct shims under large gears and insert in case. Hold small gear thrust washers in place with grease and install small gears. Align gear and washer holes with bore and insert shaft. Position correctly and lock in position with lock pin.

3) If bearings were removed, heat inner bearing race to 212°F (100°C) and press on case.

Fig. 22: Exploded View of Differential Assembly

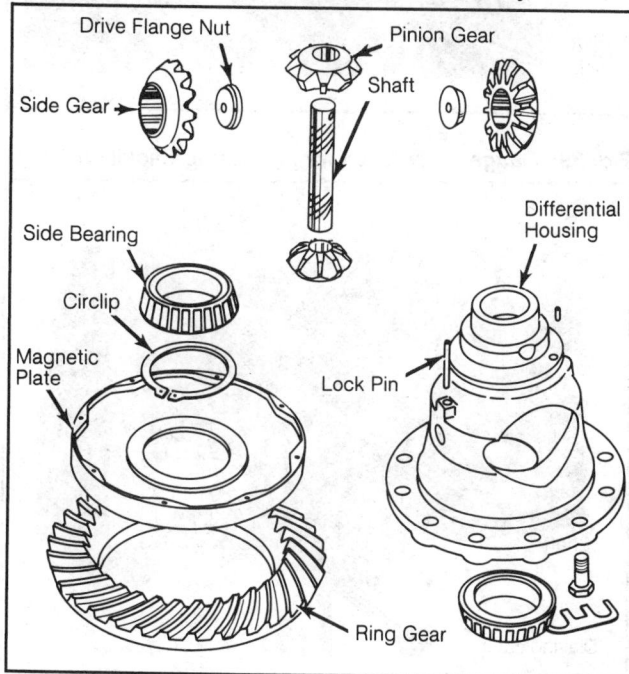

Fig. 23: Location of Stamped Codes and Specifications of Pinion and Ring Gears

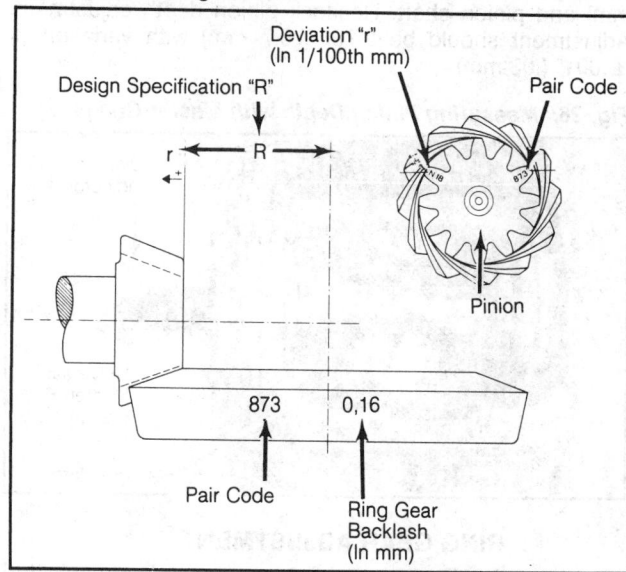

adjusting ring of universal master gauge (VW 385/1) at 2.36" (60 mm) from gauge center point. *See Fig. 24.*

Fig. 24: Universal Master Measuring Gauge

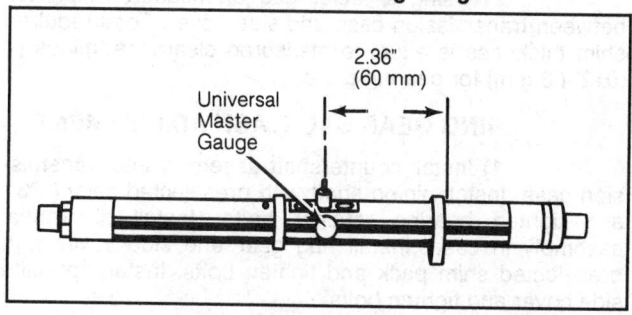

3) Install centering discs (VW 385/4) onto master gauge and attach gauge plunger (VW 385/14) with dial indicator extension. *See Fig. 25.* Install opposite side cover without "O" ring and secure with 2 bolts.

Fig. 25: Universal Master Measuring Gauge with Dial Indicator Attached

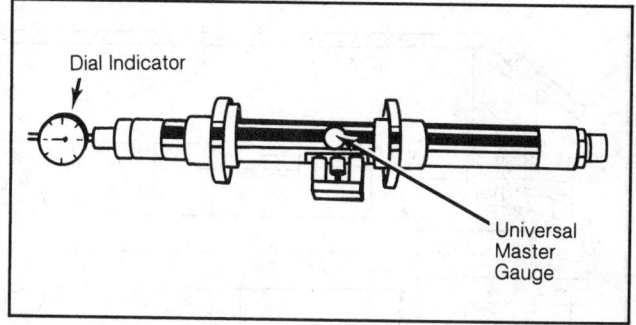

4) Install master gauge and set dial indicator at zero with .004" (1 mm) preload. Install gauge plate on pinion head. Carefully turn universal gauge until dial gauge extension is perpendicular to face of pinion head. At this time dial gauge needle will reach reversal point (highest point). Read and record dial gauge. *See Fig. 26.*

TRANSAXLE REASSEMBLY & ADJUSTMENT

NOTE: Differential assembly must be adjusted ONLY when repairs to assembly require replacement parts. Adjust ring gear if transmission case, side cover, pinion bearing and retaining plate, pinion and ring gear set, differential housing or differential bearings are replaced. Adjust pinion gear if transmission case, pinion bearing and retaining plate or pinion and ring gear set are replaced.

PINION GEAR ADJUSTMENT

1) Pinion depth adjustment is calculated by adding design specification "R", which equals 2.78" (70.7 mm), to deviation "r" stamped on pinion gear face. *See Fig. 23.* Pinion depth is adjusted by shims "S3". *See Fig. 27.*

2) Install input shaft. Install pinion without shim(s) and tighten bearing retaining plate bolts. Install 1 side cover without "O" ring and secure with 2 bolts. Set

Manual Transmissions

PORSCHE 928 5-SPEED (Cont.)

5) Remove master gauge and pinion shaft. Install calculated shim rounded off to nearest .002" (.05 mm) and pinion shaft. Recheck pinion depth adjustment. Adjustment should be 2.78" (70.7 mm) with variation of ±.001" (.03 mm).

Fig. 26: *Measuring Pinion Depth with Master Gauge*

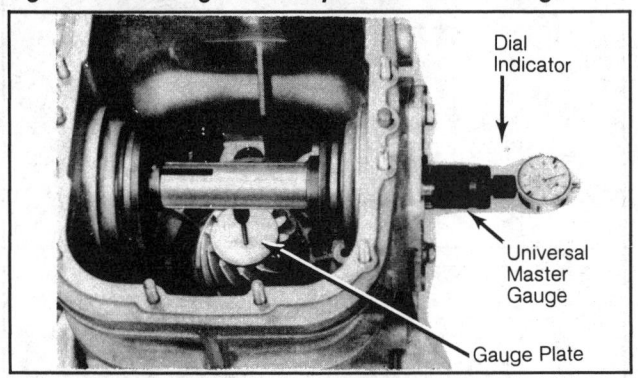

RING GEAR ADJUSTMENT

1) Remove pinion gear and preselected shim(s). Install differential assembly in case. Install ring gear end side cover without shims and tighten bolts. Carefully install opposite side cover.

2) Using a feeler gauge, measure clearance between transmission case and side cover. Total required shim thickness is equal to measured clearance, minus (-) .012" (.3 mm) for bearing preload.

RING GEAR BACKLASH ADJUSTMENT

1) Install countershaft assembly into transmission case. Install pinion shaft with preselected shim ("S3") and tighten bearing retainer bolts. Install differential assembly in case. Install ring gear end side cover with preselected shim pack and tighten bolts. Install opposite side cover and tighten bolts.

2) Turn differential in both directions several times to seat bearings. Mount dial indicator with support (VW 388) and set adjustable lever at 3.15" (80 mm). *See Fig. 29.*

Fig. 28: *Measuring Shim Thickness Between Side Cover and Transmission Case*

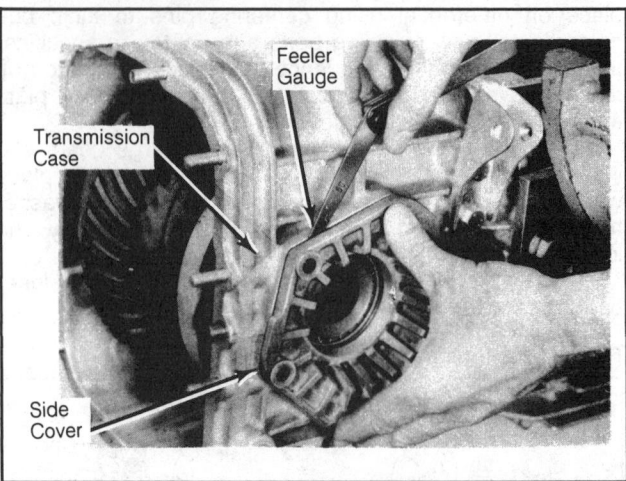

Fig. 29: *Gauge Installation for Measuring Backlash*

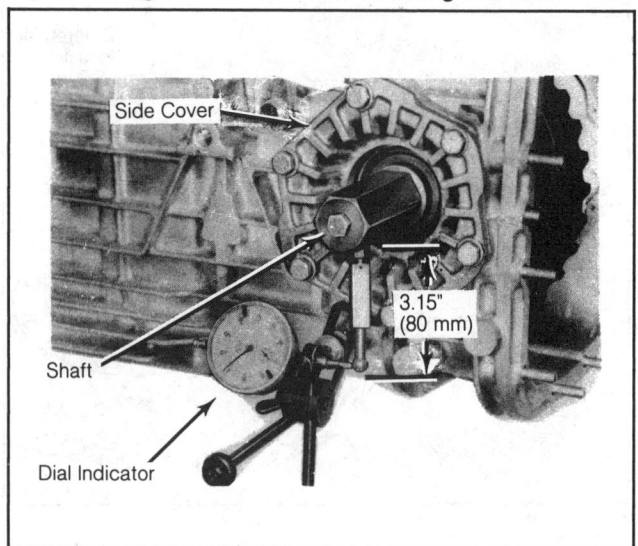

Fig. 27: *Sectional View Showing Location of Pinion and Ring Gear Adjusting Shims*

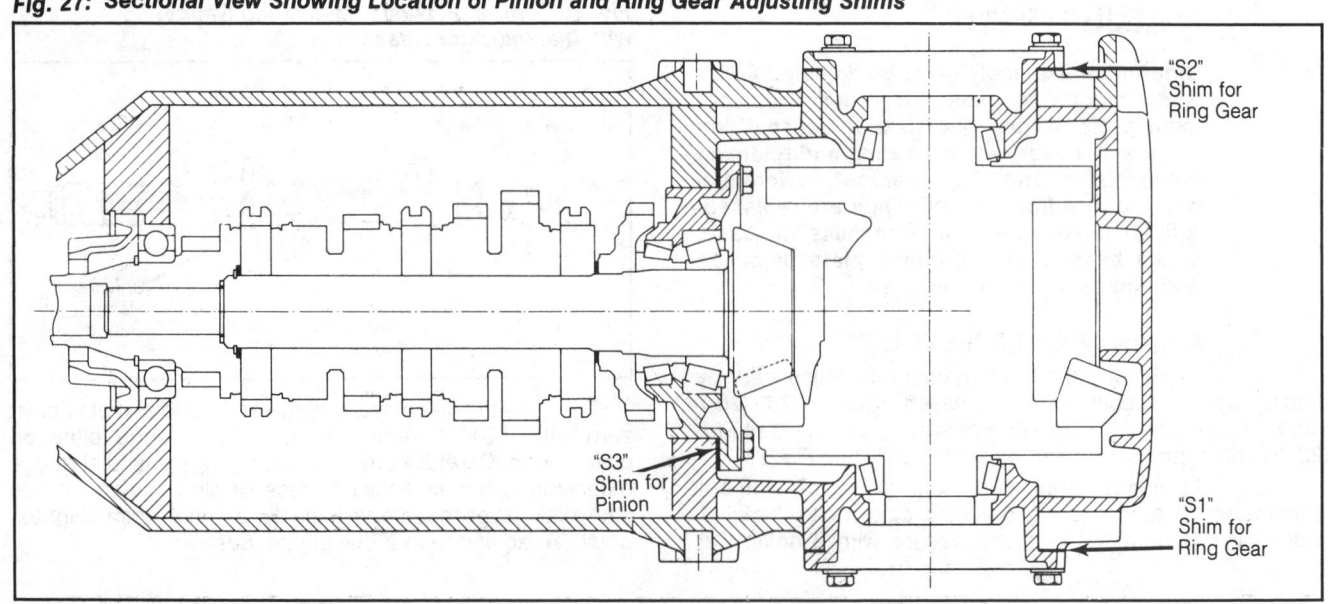

PORSCHE 928 5-SPEED (Cont.)

Fig. 30: Installation of Fabricated Tool on Reverse Gear to Hold Pinion Gear Assembly in Position

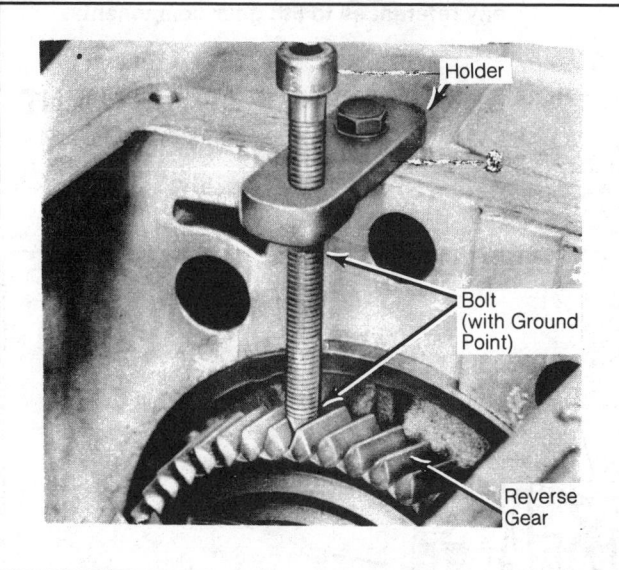

3) Engage 5th and reverse gears. Hold pinion gear assembly with a locally fabricated tool on reverse gear. *See Fig. 30.* Turn ring gear to stop by hand and set dial indicator at zero. Turn ring gear back and record amount of backlash. Backlash should be equal to that stamped on ring gear.

NOTE: When shift rods are installed, the engagement of 2 gears will require removal of detent plunger for 1st and reverse gear shift rod.

4) To determine thickness of shim "S1", subtract measured backlash from shim total, then add specified backlash (stamped on ring gear). Multiply results by .66 (lift constant).

5) Final figure equals thickness of shim "S1" (ring gear side shim). Calculate thickness of shim "S2" by subtracting shim "S1" thickness from total shim thickness.

6) Remove side covers and divide shims to give correct shim "S1" and "S2" thicknesses. Install shift rods and forks into case. Install side covers and shims and tighten bolts.

7) Measure backlash again. If not within specifications, change shims "S1" and "S2" until specified backlash is obtained. Check backlash 4 times by turning ring gear 90° each time. The 4 measurements must not deviate from each other by more than .002" (.05 mm).

TIGHTENING SPECIFICATIONS

Application	Ft. Lbs. (N.m)
Central Tube-to-Transaxle	40 (54)
Pinion Retaining Nut	202 (280)
Pinion Retaining Plate-to-Case	25 (34)
Ring Gear Retaining Bolts	120 (163)
Side Cover Bolts	17 (23)
Rear Cover Bolts	17 (23)
Drive Shaft-to-Input Shaft Coupling	35 (47)
Axle Shaft Flange Bolts	30 (41)

Manual Transmissions
RENAULT FUEGO & 18i 4 & 5-SPEED

DESCRIPTION

Transaxle consists of a removable clutch housing, a split gear case and a rear cover. The rear cover houses the shift mechanism as well as 5th gear on 5-speed models. All forward gears are in constant mesh and are fully synchronized. Final drive is located in front of transmission section of transaxle.

The only difference between the 2 transaxles is the addition of 5th gear on 5-speed units.

NOTE: The following procedures are for the 5-speed transaxle. For 4-speed transaxles, disregard any references to 5th gear components.

LUBRICATION & ADJUSTMENT

See the appropriate article in MANUAL TRANS-MISSION SERVICING Section.

Fig. 1: Cutaway View of Renault 18i Manual Transaxle

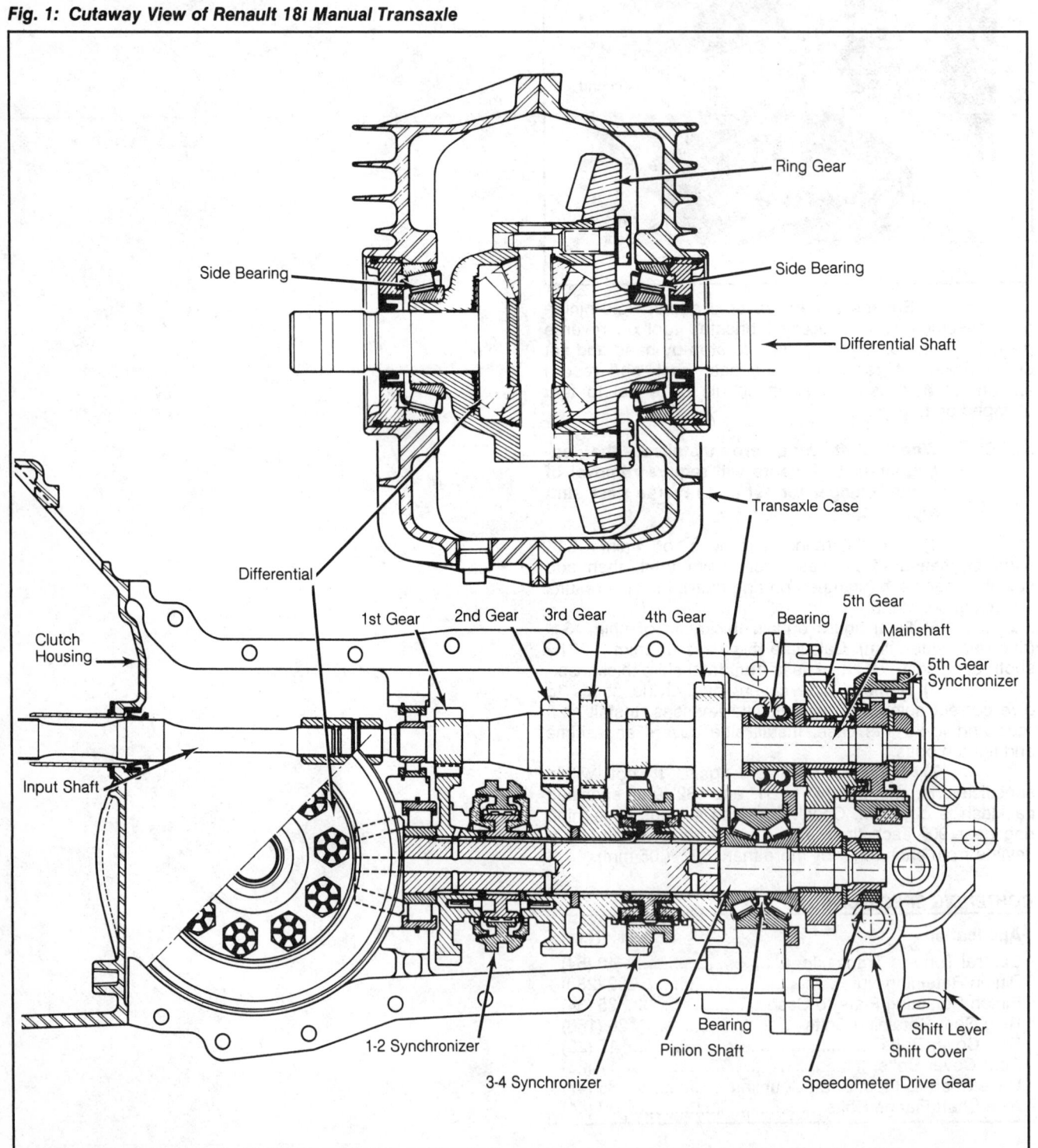

5-speed model shown here. 4-speed is similar.

RENAULT FUEGO & 18i 4 & 5-SPEED (Cont.)

SERVICE (IN-VEHICLE)

AXLE DRIVE SHAFTS

Removal

1) Raise and support vehicle. Compress control arm assembly and insert spacer (T. Av. 509-01) between lower control arm pivot shaft and bottom of shock absorber. Hold hub stationary and remove hub nut. Loosen upper ball joint nut and tie rod end nut, but do not remove.

2) Press on ball joint and tie rod end studs to loosen from steering knuckle. Remove brake caliper, but do not disconnect hydraulic line. Remove ball joint and tie rod end nuts.

3) Tilt steering knuckle outward to allow removal of drive shaft. Separate drive shaft from hub. Drive roll pin out of inner CV joint and separate drive shaft from transaxle.

Disassembly

1) Remove boot retaining collar from outer CV joint. Remove as much grease as possible from joint. Remove bell shaped stub axle from drive shaft by lifting arms of retaining starplate one at a time. Do not twist arms off of starplate. Separate stub axle from drive shaft and remove boot if necessary.

Fig. 2: Separating Retaining Starplate from Outer End of Drive Shaft

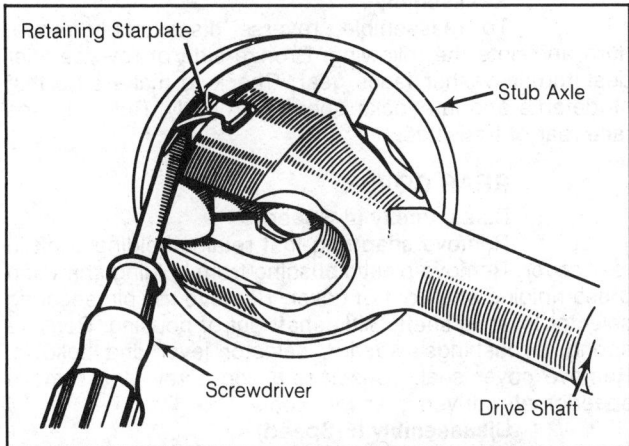

Be careful not to break off arms when removing plate.

2) Protect sealing surface of inner CV joint with tape or a plastic cap. Cut retaining collar and boot off of inner CV joint and remove as much grease as possible.

Fig. 3: Cutaway View of Inner CV Joint

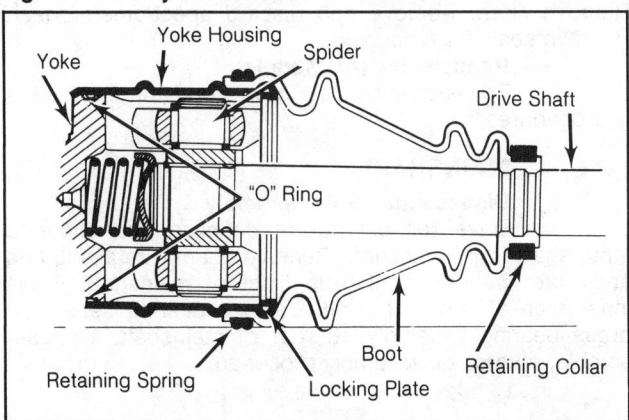

3) Bend 3 locking plate tabs out of the way and remove yoke. Do not remove rollers from their journals. If necessary, use tape to secure rollers. Using a press, remove drive shaft from inner CV joint spider.

NOTE: **Never use thinner for cleaning of any component parts.**

Reassembly

1) Install seal expander (T. Av. 537-02) over outer end of drive shaft. Place drive shaft in soft-jawed vise. Using motor oil, lubricate entire surface of tool and inside of boot. Slide boot onto end of tool and smooth out first fold of boot.

Fig. 4: Cutaway View of Outer CV Joint

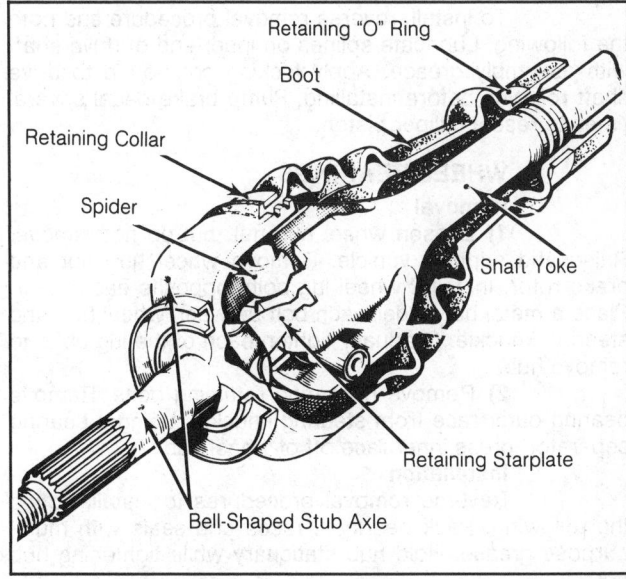

2) Move boot as close as possible toward drive shaft, then let it slide back on tool. Repeat 4 to 5 times to stretch boot, adding oil as necessary. When boot becomes easier to slide back and forth, slide it all the way into position on drive shaft. Remove tool.

3) Install spring and thrust ball joint into spider. Position roller cages in center of joint. Align retaining starplate so that each arm is between 2 roller cages. Reinstall drive shaft into bell-shaped stub axle. Fill boot and spider with about 5.25 ozs. (150 grams) of grease and secure boot with retaining rings.

4) On inner CV joint, if yoke and any other parts are replaced, proceed as follows: Lubricate drive shaft and slide on boot with retaining collar. Slide metal yoke housing onto drive shaft. Install spider onto drive shaft splines and stake in place at 3 equally spaced points around shaft.

5) Install new "O" ring onto yoke perforation. Install yoke into metal housing by tapping in until fully seated and hold with a press. Crimp end of housing that faces transaxle onto housing. Proceed to step 8).

6) If only boot or spider was replaced, proceed as follows: Lubricate drive shaft and slide on boot with retaining collar. Install spider onto drive shaft and stake in place at 3 equally spaced points around shaft. Remove tape from roller cages and engage spider with yoke.

7) Fabricate a shim from .098" (2.5 mm) flat stock measuring 1.575" (40 mm) long, .236" (6 mm) at

RENAULT FUEGO & 18i 4 & 5-SPEED (Cont.)

each end and having a 1.772" (45 mm) radius across one of the long sides. Insert this shim under each of the locking tabs on yoke while tapping tabs back into place using a drift punch.

8) To complete assembly of inner CV joint, fill yoke and boot with about 5.25 ozs. (150 grams) of grease. Position lips of boot in grooves of drive shaft and yoke housing. Place retaining collar on drive shaft end of boot. Insert a smooth round-ended rod under yoke end of boot to allow air to escape.

9) Extend or compress joint until distance from back of yoke housing (not splined coupling) to drive shaft end of boot is 6.34-6.42" (161-163 mm). Remove rod from boot. Place retaining spring around yoke end of boot being careful not to stretch spring.

Installation

To install, reverse removal procedure and note the following: Lubricate splines on inner end of drive shaft with assembly grease. Apply locking compound to drive shaft roll pins before installing. Pump brake pedal several times to reseat caliper piston.

WHEEL BEARINGS

Removal

1) Loosen wheel hub nut, but do not remove. Raise and support vehicle. Remove wheel hub nut and brake rotor. Install 2 wheel lug bolts opposite each other. Place a metal bar under each bolt between wheel hub and steering knuckle. Gradually tighten each of the lug bolts to remove hub.

2) Remove 6 bearing retaining bolts. Remove bearing outer race from steering knuckle. Using a bearing separator, press inner race off of wheel hub.

Installation

Reverse removal procedures to install, noting the following: Pack bearings, races and seals with multipurpose grease. Hold hub stationary while tightening hub nut.

TRANSAXLE REMOVAL & INSTALLATION

See the appropriate article in MANUAL TRANS-MISSION REMOVAL Section.

TRANSAXLE DISASSEMBLY

1) Drain transaxle, remove backup light switch and mount transaxle in a support fixture. Remove bell housing attaching bolts. Remove 5th gear detent screw, spring, and ball.

2) Shift transaxle into neutral and remove rear cover while turning selector lever to disengage. Engage 5th and 2nd gear. Remove 5th gear synchronizer nut and washer. Remove speedometer drive gear nut. Return shift forks to neutral.

3) Engage 3rd gear and drive roll pin out of 5th gear shift fork. Mark 5th gear synchronizer hub and sleeve for reassembly reference. Remove 5th gear synchronizer assembly and shift fork.

4) Remove 5th gear from mainshaft with needle bearing and ring. Remove speedometer drive gear, nut and washer. Remove 5th gear and bearing thrust washer from pinion shaft.

5) Remove differential nut lock stops. Remove differential nuts. Remove housing-half bolts and separate halves. Remove differential assembly. Secure outer race of pinion bearing to inner race and remove pinion shaft. Remove mainshaft.

COMPONENT DISASSEMBLY & REASSEMBLY

TRANSAXLE CASE

Disassembly

1) Return all shift forks to neutral and remove 5th gear shift shaft. Drive roll pin out of 3-4 shift fork, then remove fork and shaft. Remove detent ball, spring and interlock disc.

2) Remove reverse gear selector and shaft. Drive roll pin out of 1-2 shift fork, then remove fork and shaft. Remove detent ball and spring.

3) Remove circlip retaining reverse idler gear to shaft. Remove reverse idler gear, shaft, thrust washer, guide, detent ball and spring. Drive side bearing outer races out of case and remove adjusting nut seals.

NOTE: DO NOT reassemble case until the various adjustments of gear position and preload have been made.

Reassembly

To reassemble, reverse disassembly procedure and note the following: Bronze side of reverse idler gear thrust washer faces gear. Check to make sure that all detents and interlocks operate properly. Roll pin gaps face rear of transaxle.

REAR COVER

Disassembly (4-Speed)

Remove snap ring that retains holding shaft in rear cover. Remove plastic bushing from holding shaft and press holding shaft out of cover. Remove roll pin securing selector lever to shaft. Slide shaft out of housing. Remove spring, 2 bushings, washer, selector lever and bellows. Remove cover seal. Loosen retaining screw and remove speedometer driven gear with seal.

Disassembly (5-Speed)

1) Remove roll pins securing selector lever to shaft. Slide out selector lever shaft. Remove bushings, spring, selector lever and bellows. Remove cover seal.

2) Remove snap ring and plastic bushing from holding shaft. Press holding shaft out of rear cover. Pry open catches holding speedometer drive gear onto shaft. Remove shaft. Remove and discard speedometer gear. Remove seals from housing.

Reassembly (All Models)

To reassemble rear cover, reverse disassembly procedures.

MAINSHAFT

Disassembly & Reassembly

Drive roll pin out of coupling and separate input shaft from mainshaft. Remove bearing retaining ring and outer bearing race from front of mainshaft. Press inner race off front of shaft. Using a bearing separator, press bearing assembly off rear of mainshaft. To reassemble, reverse disassembly procedure.

RENAULT FUEGO & 18i 4 & 5-SPEED (Cont.)

Fig. 5: Exploded View of Mainshaft Assembly

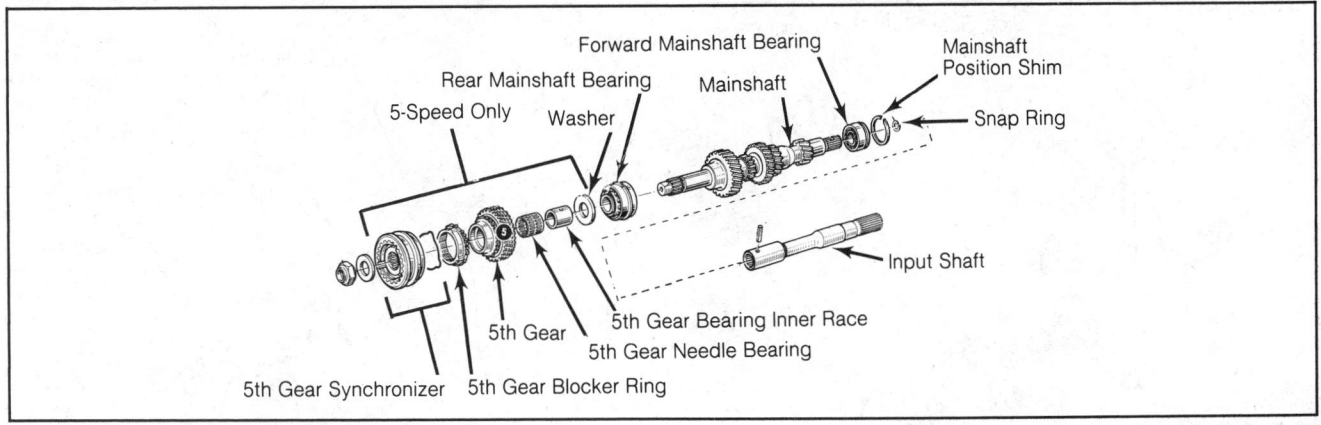

PINION SHAFT

Disassembly

1) Support shaft in a vise by clamping onto 1st gear. Remove double taper bearing, 4th gear, 4th gear blocker ring and 3-4 synchronizer sleeve with keys and springs (scribe a reference mark on hub and sleeve for reassembly).

NOTE: Observe position of synchro springs and hub offset during disassembly. Differences in pinion shaft design require that the synchronizer be assembled and installed exactly as it was removed. Also, location of 3-4 synchro snap ring and lock washer can be on either side of 3-4 synchro hub depending on snap ring groove location. Snap ring and lock washer must be installed in same position that they were removed from. The only exception is when pinion shaft is replaced with one of different design. If this is the case, reverse orientation of 3-4 synchro hub, springs, keys, lock washer and snap ring. Do not reverse orientation of 3-4 synchro sleeve.

2) Remove snap ring and lock washer (if installed). Using a bearing separator, press 3-4 synchronizer hub off of shaft. Remove snap ring and lock washer (if installed). Remove 3rd gear and 3rd gear blocker ring.

3) Remove 2nd gear lock washers, snap ring, 2nd gear, 2nd gear blocker ring, 1-2 synchronizer sleeve (scribe a reference mark on hub and sleeve for reassembly) with keys and springs, and 1-2 synchronizer hub lock washer.

4) Using a bearing separator, press 1-2 synchronizer hub off of shaft. Remove 1st gear blocker ring, lock washer, snap ring and 1st gear. Remove front bearing from pinion shaft.

Reassembly

To reassemble, reverse disassembly procedure and note the following: Snap rings and speedometer drive gear cannot be reused. Orientation of components related to the 3-4 synchro depends on snap ring groove location. After tightening the speedometer drive gear to specifications, stake the gear to the shaft.

Fig. 6: Exploded View of Pinion Shaft Assembly

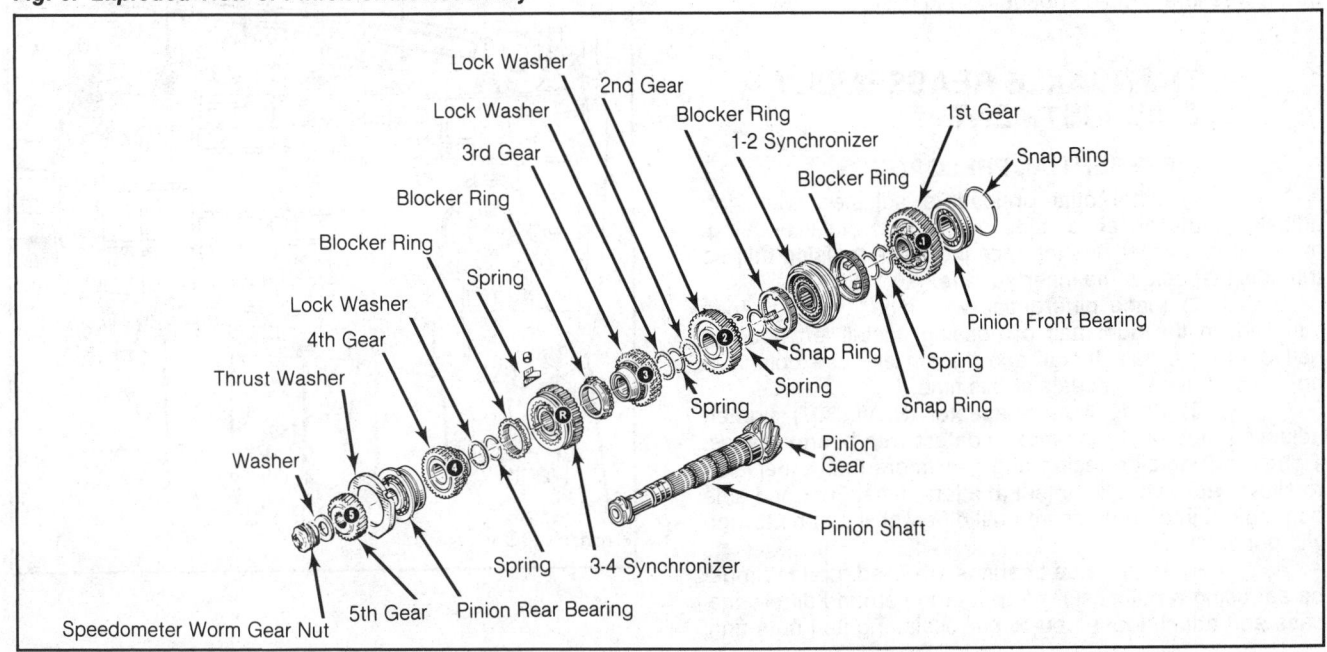

Manual Transmissions

RENAULT FUEGO & 18i 4 & 5-SPEED (Cont.)

Fig. 7: Exploded View of Differential Assembly

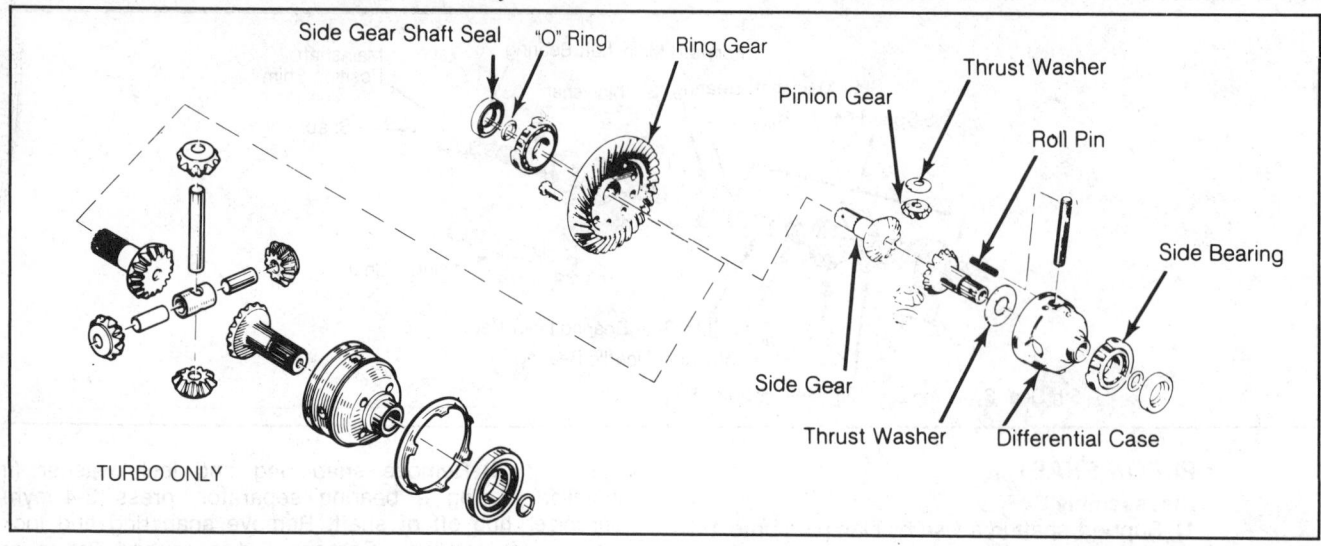

DIFFERENTIAL

Disassembly & Reassembly (Turbo Only)

Remove and discard 4 ring gear bolts. Attach a 3-jaw puller to side bearings and remove side bearings from housing. Remove and discard remainder of ring gear bolts. Remove pressed-on collar to gain access to pinion shafts. Separate ring gear from differential housing. Slide pinion shafts out of housing and remove pinion gears. To reassemble, reverse disassembly procedure.

Disassembly (All Exc. Turbo)

Remove and discard all ring gear bolts except for 2 directly opposite each other. Remove side bearings with puller. Remove and discard remainder of ring gear bolts. Drive roll pin out of pinion shaft. Remove pinion shaft, pinion gears and side gears.

Reassembly (All Exc. Turbo)

To reassemble, reverse disassembly procedure and note the following: Lubrication groove on side gear thrust washer must face gear. Use oversize thrust washer if excessive end play exists. Locking pin of pinion thrust washers should engage hole in case.

TRANSAXLE REASSEMBLY & ADJUSTMENT

DIFFERENTIAL PRELOAD

1) Differential preload is adjusted with ring adjusting nuts on either side of the differential housing. Install proper outer bearing race into each housing half so that it is just below the inner surface.

2) Place differential, with inner bearing races installed, in the right half of housing. Install left housing half onto right half. Install and tighten all case bolts. Do not install drive shaft seals at this time.

3) Using wrench adapter (B. Vi. 807), tighten adjusting nuts until they make contact with bearing races. Tighten nut on side facing ring gear more than other side to allow backlash adjustment at a later time. For used side bearings, tighten nuts down until differential can be turned without any play.

4) If new side bearings are used, preload must be set using a pull scale. Wrap a string around differential case and attach loose end to pull scale. Tighten nuts until

a force of 2-7 lbs. (1-3 kgs) is required to rotate differential. Mark position of both differential adjusting nuts on case. Remove nuts from case, separate case halves and remove differential.

TRANSAXLE REASSEMBLY

1) To reassemble, reverse disassembly procedure and note the following: Align differential adjusting nuts with reference marks made during preload adjustment procedure.

2) Before installing clutch housing, ring gear backlash must be checked and adjusted if necessary. Mount dial indicator on front of transaxle housing so that plunger squarely contacts a ring gear tooth. Lock pinion shaft in place and check backlash by rotating differential.

Fig. 8: Case Bolt Tightening Sequence

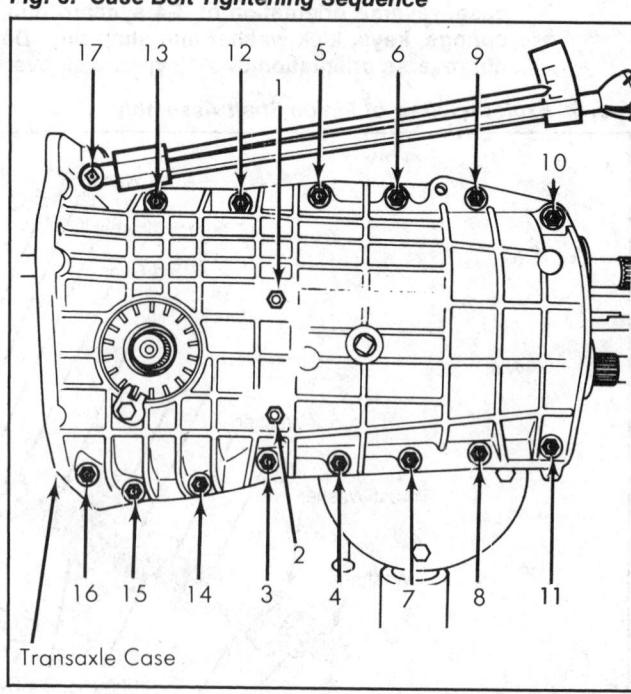

RENAULT FUEGO & 18i 4 & 5-SPEED (Cont.)

3) Adjust backlash, if necessary, by turning 1 adjusting nut in and the other adjusting nut out an equal number of turns (to maintain preload setting) to move differential in required direction. Backlash should be .005-.010" (.12-.25 mm).

4) Recheck backlash at 4 equally spaced points around ring gear. Variation between points should be minimal. If variation exceeds specification range, disassemble case and check for proper installation of bearings.

TIGHTENING SPECIFICATIONS

Application	Ft. Lbs. (N.m)
Clutch Housing-to-Transaxle	
8 mm Bolts	18 (24)
10 mm Bolts	26 (35)
Speedometer Worm Gear Nut	74-89 (100-121)
Input Shaft Nut (5-Speed Only)	74-89 (100-121)
Ring Gear Bolts	92 (125)
Wheel Hub Nut	185 (251)
	INCH Lbs. (N.m)
Case Half Bolts	
7 mm Bolts	180-228 (20-26)
8 mm Bolts	240-288 (27-33)
Rear Cover Bolts	120 (14)
Reverse Relay Lever Bolt	228 (26)
Differential Adjusting Nut Lock Bolt	216 (24)
Wheel Bearing Retaining Bolts	132 (15)

Manual Transmissions

RENAULT LE CAR 4-SPEED

DESCRIPTION

Transaxle is equipped with a 4-speed transmission which is fully synchronized in all forward gears. Transaxle houses transmission and differential with a common oil supply used to lubricate both assemblies. Final drive is a hypoid type gear. Constant velocity joints are used at each end of axle drive shafts.

LUBRICATION & ADJUSTMENT

See the appropriate article in MANUAL TRANSMISSION SERVICING section.

SERVICE (IN VEHICLE)

AXLE DRIVE SHAFTS

Removal

1) Remove stub axle nut and washer using hub locking tool (Rou. 436-01). Using ball joint extender tool (T. Av. 476), disconnect upper and lower suspension and steering arm ball joints.

2) Mount drive shaft extracting tool (T. Av. 235) on hub. Push out drive shaft far enough for lower ball joint to clear stub axle. Withdraw drive shaft. Repeat on other side.

Fig. 1: Removing Axle Drive Shaft

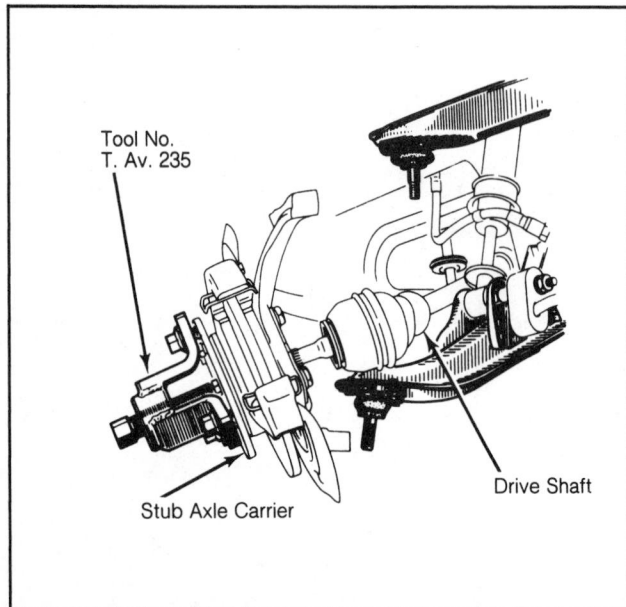

Push out drive shaft until ball joint clears stub axle.

NOTE: If components show excessive or abnormal wear, complete axle drive shaft must be replaced.

Installation

1) Coat stub axle splines with grease. Insert drive shaft into side gear and hub, and at the same time connect lower ball joint into stub axle carrier.

2) Using installation tool (T. Av. 409-01), draw drive shaft into hub splines. See Fig. 2. Using pliers, hold ball joint cone stationary and reconnect ball joints. Attach stub axle washer and nut. Tighten nut. Fill transaxle with oil.

Fig. 2: Installing Axle Drive Shaft

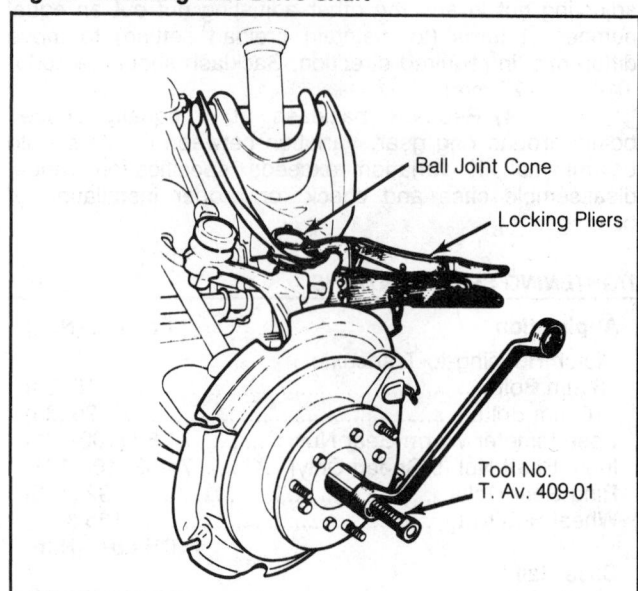

Use locking pliers to hold ball joint cone stationary while reconnecting ball joints.

WHEEL BEARINGS

Removal

Remove hub and disc assembly. Disconnect 3 ball joints using extractor (T. Av. 476). Disconnect ball joints and withdraw stub axle carrier. Using puller (B. V. 28-01), remove outer bearing. Remove bearing cover plate. Press out inner bearing.

Fig. 3: Removing Wheel Bearing

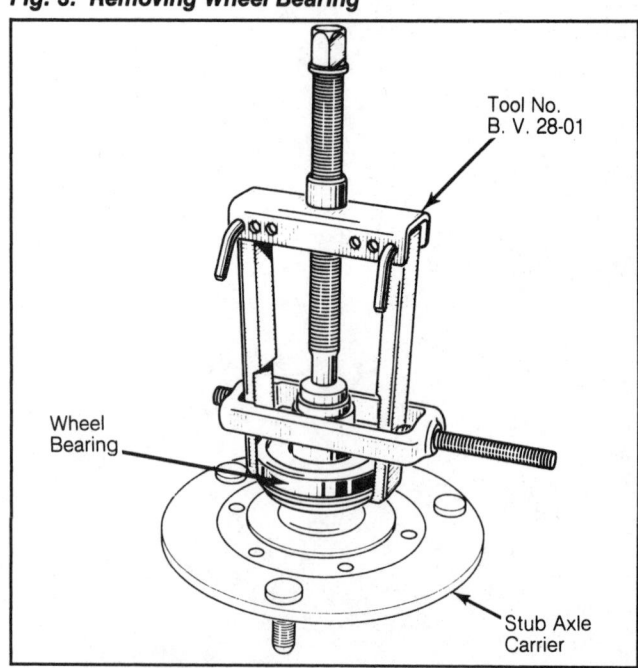

Installation

Inspect condition of bearing carrier bore for damage or wear. Reverse removal procedure to install, noting the following: Press inner bearing in. Place 1 oz. (25 g) of grease into stub axle carrier center section. Apply sealing compound and fit bearing cover plate.

RENAULT LE CAR 4-SPEED (Cont.)

TRANSAXLE REMOVAL & INSTALLATION

See the appropriate article in MANUAL TRANS-MISSION SERVICING section.

TRANSAXLE DISASSEMBLY

1) Mount transaxle onto a work stand. Remove clutch housing. Remove differential adjusting ring nuts and lock washers. Remove clutch shaft roll pin retaining spring and roll pin. Slide out clutch shaft. Remove differential.

2) Remove 12 top cover bolts and top cover. Remove springs and selector fork shaft locking balls. Remove 9 front cover bolts and front cover. Remove countershaft setting shims. Remove countershaft rear bearing retaining plate.

3) Using a punch, drive out 2 roll pins retaining reverse gear pinion shaft. Remove reverse gear selector shaft and locking disc between selector shafts. *See Fig. 4.*

4) Engage transmission gears. Unlock and remove speedometer end nut. Remove rubber washer and return transmission gears to neutral. Push final drive pinion in toward differential and remove taper roller bearing. Withdraw final drive pinion shaft.

5) Push countershaft toward differential and remove rear bearing race. Remove front bearing, countershaft, reverse gear shaft and reverse gear. Using a punch, drive out 1st-2nd and 3rd-4th shift fork roll pins. Remove shafts and selector forks.

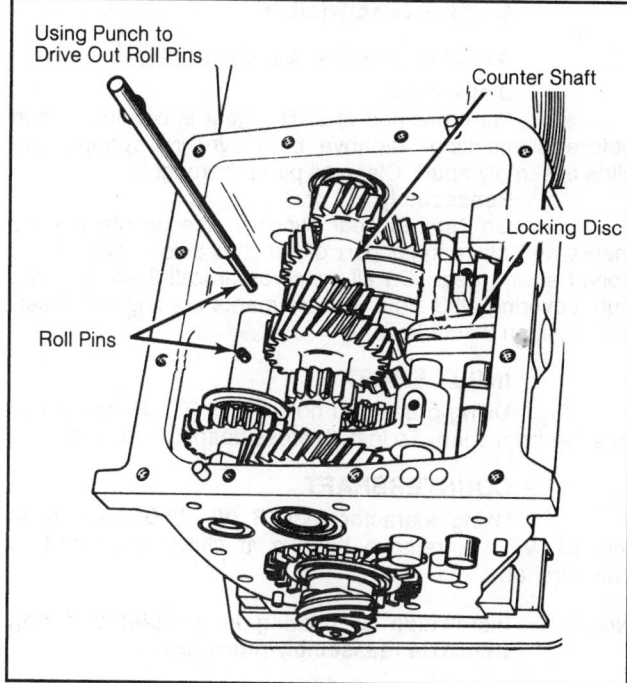

Fig. 4: Removing Reverse Gear Selector Shaft

Using Punch to Drive Out Roll Pins

Counter Shaft

Locking Disc

Roll Pins

6) Remove lock plate and mainshaft bearing adjusting nut. Remove 4th gear thrust washer. Push out countershaft front bearing race. Remove gear and synchro assembly from case.

Fig. 5: Exploded View of Renault Le Car 4-Speed Manual Transaxle

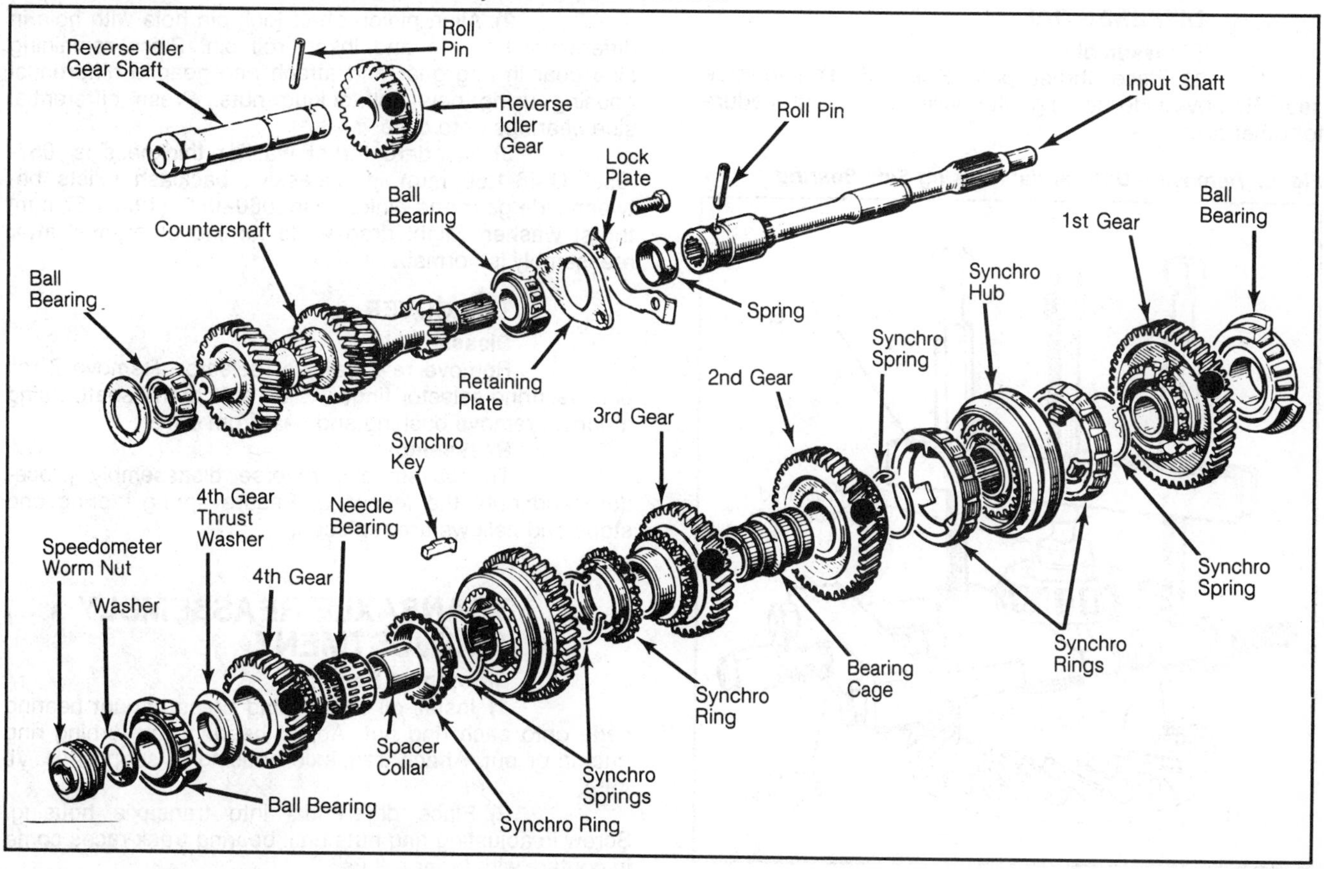

Reverse Idler Gear Shaft
Roll Pin
Reverse Idler Gear
Roll Pin
Input Shaft
Lock Plate
Ball Bearing
Ball Bearing
Countershaft
1st Gear
Synchro Hub
Ball Bearing
Ball Bearing
Spring
Synchro Spring
Retaining Plate
2nd Gear
Synchro Key
3rd Gear
Needle Bearing
Synchro Spring
Speedometer Worm Nut
4th Gear Thrust Washer
Synchro Rings
Washer
4th Gear
Synchro Ring
Bearing Cage
Synchro Rings
Spacer Collar
Synchro Springs
Ball Bearing
Synchro Ring

Manual Transmissions

RENAULT LE CAR 4-SPEED (Cont.)

COMPONENT DISASSEMBLY & REASSEMBLY

SYNCHRONIZER ASSEMBLIES

Disassembly

Mark position of sliding gear in relation to hub before dismantling. Remove both synchro springs and slide assembly apart. Clean all parts thoroughly.

Reassembly

On 1st-2nd gear synchro, line up dismantling marks and place inner part of synchro below level of 3rd speed sliding gear. On all synchros, install 2 springs into hub, covering all 3 slots. Ensure marks are aligned. Insert and position 3 shift keys.

INPUT SHAFT

Using press and holder tool (T. AR. 65), press bearing from shaft. To install, press bearing onto shaft.

COUNTERSHAFT

Using extractor tool (B. Vi. 22-01) and shell tool (B. Vi. 41), remove bearing at clutch shaft end of countershaft.

NOTE: Installation of bearing is completed during transaxle reassembly procedure.

TRANSAXLE CASE

Press pinion bearing outer race out of case. Check for cracks or damage in bearing bore. Reinstall pinion bearing outer race by pressing into case until fully seated.

DIFFERENTIAL

Disassembly

1) Place thrust pad (Rou. 15-01) into side gear. Remove side bearing with puller. Repeat procedure for other side.

Fig. 6: Removing Differential Housing Side Bearing

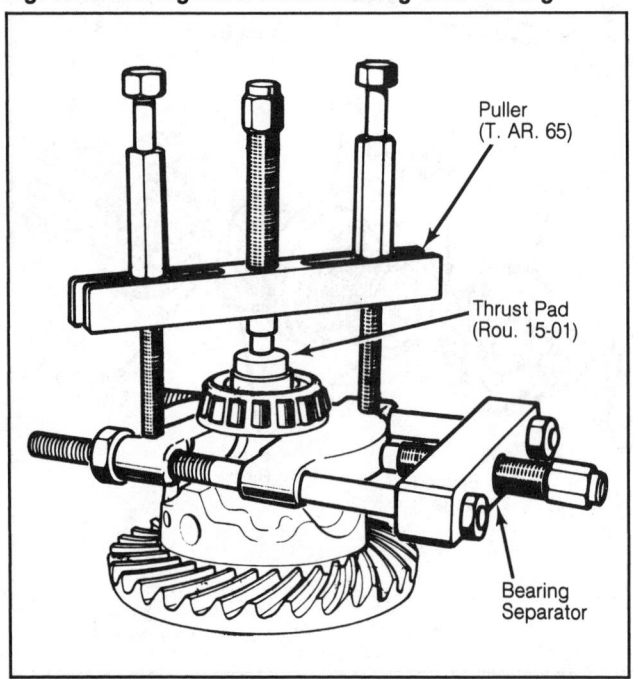

Puller (T. AR. 65)

Thrust Pad (Rou. 15-01)

Bearing Separator

2) Remove self-locking ring gear mounting bolts and discard. Drive out pinion shaft retaining pin with punch.

Inspection

Check pinion gears, side bearings and side gears for scoring or signs of excessive wear. Replace components as needed.

Reassembly

1) Lubricate all components with EP 80 oil before reassembly. Place thrust washer in differential case with oil groove facing side gear. Fit pinions and thrust washers into differential housing so that lock tabs engage hole in housing.

Fig. 7: Exploded View of Differential Assembly

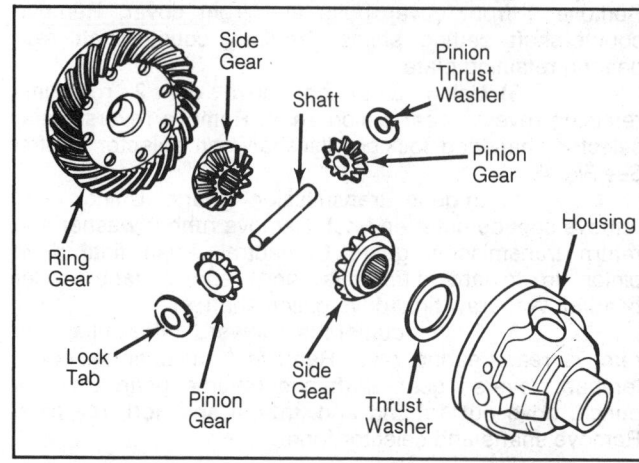

Side Gear

Shaft

Pinion Thrust Washer

Pinion Gear

Housing

Ring Gear

Lock Tab

Pinion Gear

Side Gear

Thrust Washer

Install thrust washer with oil groove toward side gear.

2) Align pinion shaft lock pin hole with hole in differential housing and insert roll pin. Place remaining side gear in ring gear and attach ring gear to differential housing using new self-locking nuts. Press differential side bearings onto case.

3) Standard thrust washer thickness is .057-.059" (1.46-1.50 mm). If excessive backlash exists between side gear and pinion, use .060-.062" (1.53-1.57 mm) thrust washer. Slight drag while turning differential after reassembly is normal.

TOP COVER

Disassembly

Remove reverse gear selector. Remove 2 roll pins securing selector finger. Slide out control shaft. Using a punch, remove bushing and seal from cover.

Reassembly

To reassemble, reverse disassembly procedure and note the following: Ensure spring, spring end stops and bellows are replaced.

TRANSAXLE REASSEMBLY & ADJUSTMENT

Differential Bearings

1) Install oil seal. Using press, mount bearing cage onto each ring nut. Adjust bearings by turning ring nuts in or out. Attach transaxle housing to support (B. Vi. 495).

2) Place differential into transaxle housing. Screw in adjusting ring nuts until bearing track races come in contact with taper rollers.

RENAULT LE CAR 4-SPEED (Cont.)

3) Differential must turn without play. If there is play, tighten ring nuts until play is eliminated. Mark position of ring nuts in relation to housing. Remove ring nuts and differential.

NOTE: **If tightening ring nuts does not remove play, install new bearings and fit through preload adjustment.**

Side Bearing Preload

1) Rotate differential several turns to seat bearings. Wrap a piece of string around differential. Attach a spring scale to string and pull. Force required to rotate differential should be 2-7 lbs. (.9-3.2 kg). Force must be consistent during rotation of differential.

Fig. 8: Checking Differential Preload

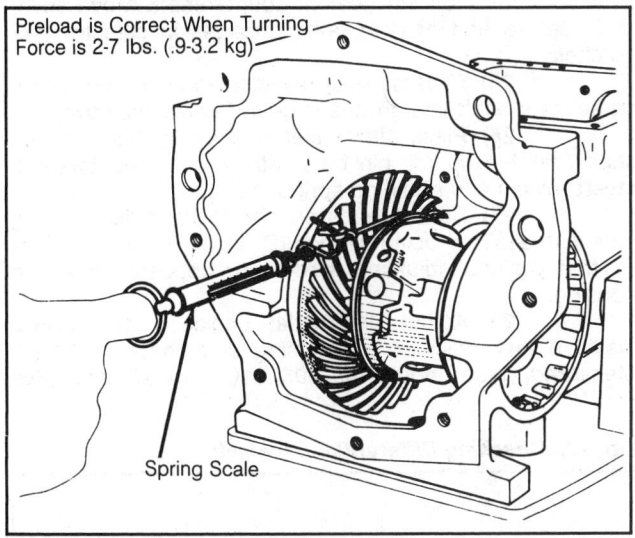

Use preload adjustment to properly seat new bearing.

2) If more force is required, carefully loosen one of the adjusting ring nuts. If it turns too freely, carefully tighten the nut. Recheck preload again. When final adjustment is obtained, mark the position of ring nuts in relation to housing. Remove ring nuts and differential.

Transaxle Casing

Using a press, install bearing outer race (under final drive pinion head) into housing.

Mainshaft Bearing Adjusting Nut

Mount tapered roller bearing outer cage into adjusting nut using a press.

TRANSAXLE REASSEMBLY

1) Place transaxle casing vertically on flat surface. Place the stack of mainshaft gears inside the casing. Do not include 4th speed driven gear at this time.

2) Insert final drive pinion and begin mounting 2 hubs. Place a 2-part block under final drive pinion. Position a piece of tube to take load of 3rd-4th hub. Mount 2 synchros. Check position of synchro rings.

3) Attach transaxle casing to support (B. Vi. 495). Ensure pinion splines mate with splines of 1st-2nd and 3rd-4th speed synchro hubs. Place 4th gear and gear ring into casing.

4) Install 2 needle roller cages and 4th gear sleeve. Position 4th gear thrust washer with large diameter facing toward gear. Screw bearing ring adjusting nut on as far as possible.

5) Place tapered roller bearing onto final drive pinion hand tight. Hold sliding gear in place with wrench (B. Vi. 499). Screw on speedometer drive pinion so tapered roller bearing is drawn into position. See Fig. 9.

Fig. 9: Installing Tapered Roller Bearing

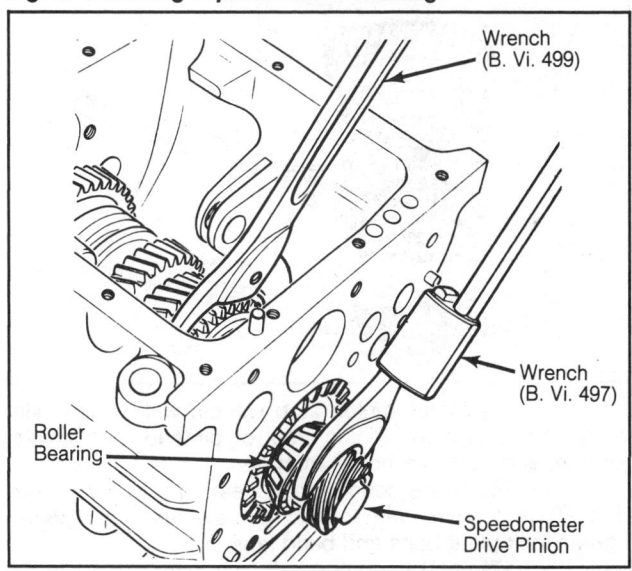

6) Remove speedometer drive pinion and insert spring washer. Replace drive pinion and tighten to 75-90 ft. lbs. (102-122 N.m) using a torque wrench fitted with adapter (B. Vi. 497). Lock into position.

7) Adjust mainshaft bearing by turning ring nut. Unscrew ring nut until outer ring touches rollers using wrench (B. Vi. 499). Bearings may be reused if there is no end play when mainshaft is turned.

8) If end play exists, continue to unscrew ring nut until end play has diminished. Lock ring nut with lock plate.

NOTE: **New bearings must be preloaded.**

9) If installing new bearings, unscrew ring nut while turning mainshaft by hand. When shaft becomes slightly hard to turn, stop unscrewing ring nut.

10) Rotate mainshaft several times to seat bearings. Tie a piece of string around 3rd-4th sliding gear groove. Attach a spring scale to string and pull. Gear should rotate under force of 1.0-3.5 lbs. (.5-1.6 kg). When correct adjustment is obtained, lock ring nut with lock plate. See Fig. 10.

11) Position 1st-2nd speed selector fork into casing. Slide selector shaft through casing bracket and into selector fork. Install roll pin with a punch.

NOTE: **Slot in roll pins must face toward differential.**

12) Position 3rd-4th speed selector fork into casing. Slide selector shaft through casing bracket and into selector fork. Install roll pin with a punch.

13) Position transaxle casing so countershaft will stand vertically, with 4th gear resting on casing wall. Use a length of tube to mount bearing on clutch shaft side.

14) Position reverse gear in transaxle casing with groove facing toward differential. Install reverse gear shaft. Secure gear to shaft with roll pin.

RENAULT LE CAR 4-SPEED (Cont.)

Fig. 10: Checking Preload on New Bearings

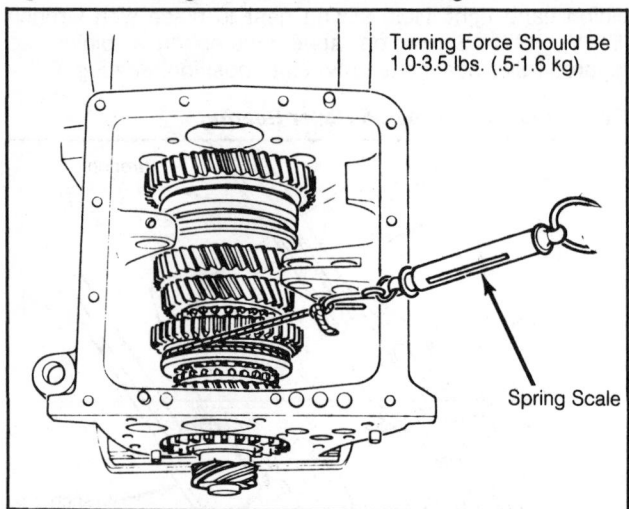

Turning Force Should Be
1.0-3.5 lbs. (.5-1.6 kg)

Spring Scale

15) Install pinion stop roll pin with roll pin slit at right angle to shaft. Pinion stop roll pin should protrude out both ends of shaft equal amounts.

16) Place countershaft bearing race over rear of shaft and cover with retaining plate and lock plate. Tighten lock plate bolts and bend tabs over.

17) Install countershaft front bearing by sliding onto shaft. Using a piece of tubing, slide outer track race on until it is flush with case.

18) Adjust countershaft bearing end play using shims. End play must be .001-.005" (.03-.13 mm). Attach a dial gauge on end of shaft and push bearing race in to obtain less play.

19) With proper amount of play obtained, place shims behind bearing track race. Last shim should extend beyond gasket face by .012" (.30 mm).

Fig. 11: Selector Lever Alignment

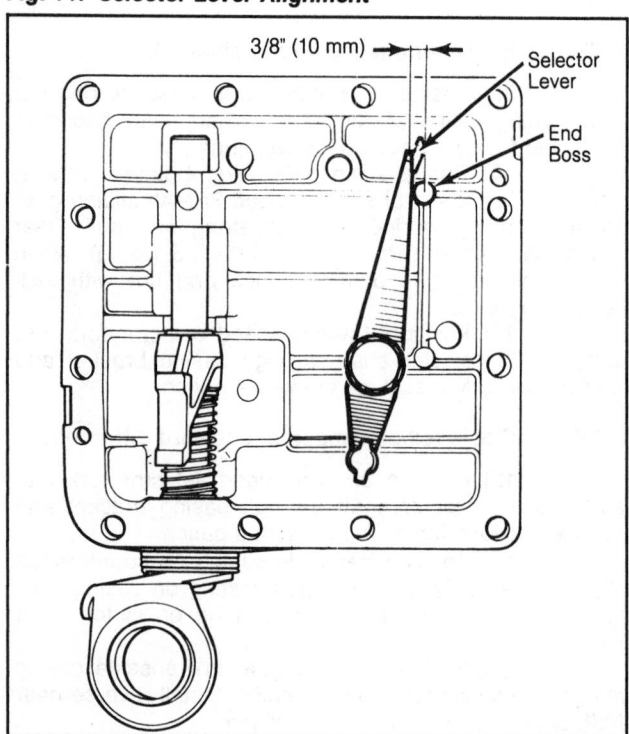

3/8" (10 mm)

Selector Lever

End Boss

20) Install locking disc between selector shaft. Drop in lock balls and their springs. Longest spring is for 1st-2nd gear shaft.

21) Install speedometer gear sleeve in place with "O" ring seal. Position speedometer driven gear, countershaft adjusting shims and gasket. Install front cover.

22) Line up top cover with cover ring and seal. Pull bellows over lever shaft and mount shaft on top cover along with spring, end stops and selector finger. Install roll pins.

23) Place reverse gear selector in position and tighten bolt. Line up selector lever with reverse gear shaft. Space end of selector lever 3/8" (10 mm) from center line of boss. See Fig. 11.

24) Position transaxle in neutral. Slide reverse gear so it rests on 4th gear of countershaft. Move cover and seal so end of gear lever engages in selector fork notches.

25) Reverse gear selector engages with notch on selector shaft and groove in gear. Secure the cover.

26) Place differential in housing. Insert clutch shaft and line up roll pin hole with hole in countershaft. Insert roll pin and retaining spring.

27) Coat threads on differential adjusting ring nuts with sealant. Using wrench (B. Vi. 494), turn ring nuts so that preload adjusting marks are opposite those on housing.

28) Adjust differential backlash as follows: Install a dial indicator on housing and check backlash. Measured value should be .005-.010" (.13-.25 mm). See Fig. 12.

Fig. 12: Checking Differential Backlash

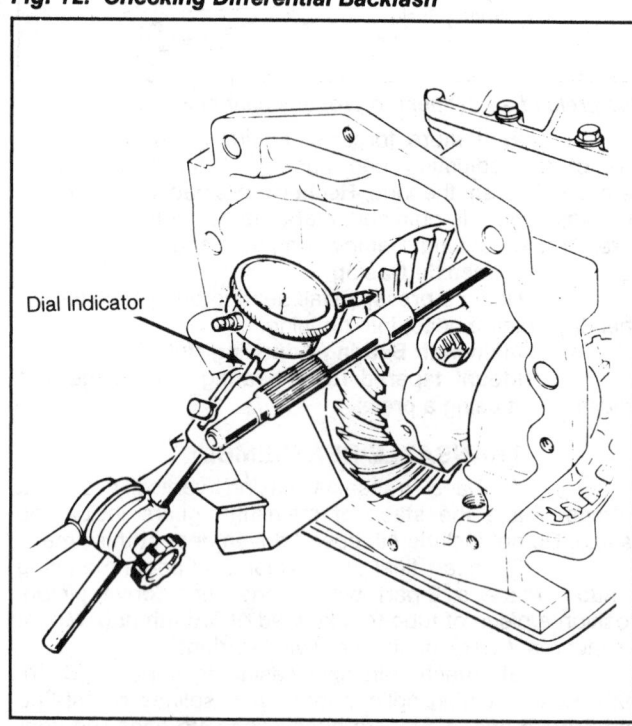

Dial Indicator

29) If backlash is excessive, loosen adjusting nut on casing side and screw in ring gear side adjusting nut the same amount. If backlash is insufficient, reverse above procedure. Lock ring gear adjusting nuts with lock plates.

RENAULT LE CAR 4-SPEED (Cont.)

30) Install oil seal on clutch housing using tube tool (B. Vi. 488), then fit clutch housing. Position housing by sliding along shaft of oil seal tool. Tighten clutch housing bolts.

TIGHTENING SPECIFICATIONS

Application	Ft. Lbs. (N.m)
Clutch Housing Bolts	30 (41)
Speedometer Drive Pinion	75-90 (102-122)
Ring Gear Bolts	65-80 (88-108)

Application	INCH Lbs. (N.m)
Top Cover Bolt	120 (14)
Front Cover Bolt	180 (20)
Mainshaft Thrust Plate Bolt	180 (20)
Differential Lock Plate Bolts	180 (20)
Reverse Gear Lever Bolt	240 (27)

Manual Transmissions

SAAB 900 4 & 5-SPEED

DESCRIPTION

The transaxle assembly is a 2-piece unit containing both transmission and final drive. Transaxle assembly is located underneath the engine and part of transmission case serves as an engine oil sump. The transmission and final drive are assembled in rear section of the transaxle and primary gear unit is housed in the front section.

All forward gears are in constant mesh while reverse gear is engaged by a sliding gear. The chain driven primary gear unit transmits engine power via the clutch to transmission. Final drive assembly consists of differential assembly, pinion shaft, and front drive axle shaft housings.

NOTE: **Throughout the production of the 5-speed transaxle, many different sizes and ratios of gears have been used. Ensure that any gears replaced are an exact match for the gears removed. Otherwise, gear noise and durability problems will result.**

LUBRICATION & ADJUSTMENT

See the appropriate article in MANUAL TRANS-MISSION SERVICING Section.

SERVICE (IN-VEHICLE)

AXLE DRIVE SHAFTS & WHEEL BEARINGS

NOTE: **Downward movement of the control arms is limited by rubber buffer inside of shock absorber. Therefore, it will be necessary either to remove shock absorber before raising vehicle or to support control arm with a jack at outer end of lower control arm.**

Removal

1) Remove hub cap, loosen hub nut and loosen wheel lugs. Raise and support vehicle. Remove wheels. Rotate brake disc to align recess in disc edge with brake pads. Disconnect parking brake cable. Remove caliper mounting bolts and hang caliper out of way with wire; DO NOT disconnect hydraulic line.

2) Remove hub and disc assembly with extractor (8996084). Remove larger clamp on inner universal joint bellows. Remove steering arm and upper ball joint with remover (8995409). Disconnect screws on lower control arm bracket. Separate inner CV joint from drive flange. Cover end of rubber bellows to prevent needle bearings from falling onto floor.

3) Grasp wheel splash guard and pull axle assembly through wheel housing to remove. Thoroughly clean axle assembly. Place steering knuckle housing in a press and press out drive shaft. Remove snap ring from bearing housing. Press out and discard bearing.

NOTE: **Axle shafts cannot be disassembled. If damaged or defective, replace as complete assembly.**

Installation

1) Press bearing into steering knuckle housing, then install snap ring. Mount axle shaft in a press and

Fig. 1: Sectional View of Saab Steering Knuckle

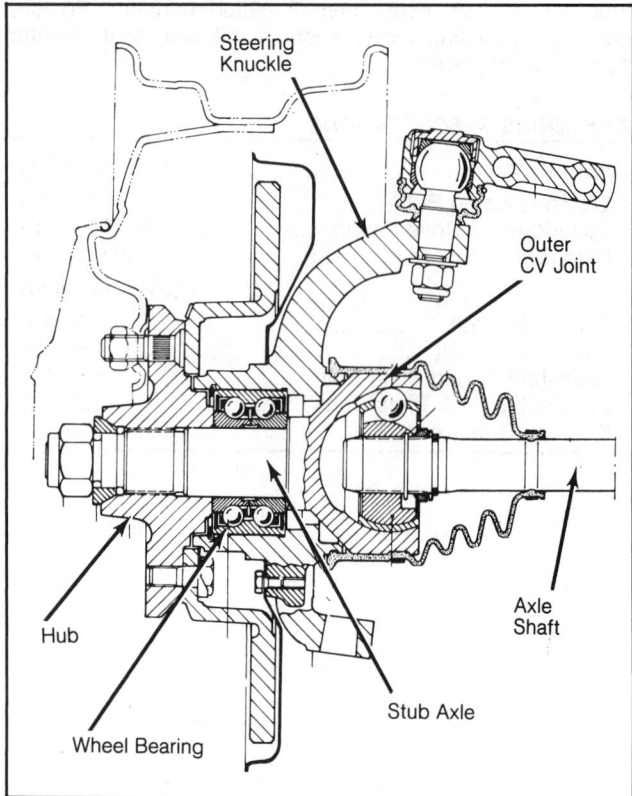

press on knuckle housing and bearing. Install inner oil seal. Press wheel hub and brake disc onto axle splines and install washer and new lock nut.

NOTE: **Do not tighten lock nut at this time.**

2) Install axle shaft through wheel housing. Mount any needle bearings which may have fallen out of inner CV joint on ends of "T" piece. Attach inner CV joint to drive flange. Install upper ball joint to steering knuckle and reinstall lower control arm bracket. Mount tie rod end to steering arm. Mount brake caliper.

3) Reinstall front wheel and lower vehicle. Tighten hub lock nut, then secure in place by peening into locking groove. Pump brake pedal several times to seat brake pads.

PRIMARY GEAR UNIT
Removal

1) Remove hood, battery, radiator, grille and radiator/headlight assembly from vehicle. Disconnect exhaust pipe from manifold. Remove rubber bellows from throttle valve housing. Remove alternator. Remove engine mount nuts, then connect a lifting device to engine so clutch end of engine will be lifted first. Remove front engine mount.

2) Raise engine until primary gear cover clears front engine beam. Remove cover. Remove chain tensioner. Remove upper and lower primary gear snap rings, and pull gears (with chains) off of housing simultaneously.

Installation

To install, reverse removal procedure and note the following: Install a new clutch shaft seal and cover gasket. Coat cover and housing mating surfaces with sealing compound.

SAAB 900 4 & 5-SPEED (Cont.)

Fig. 2: Exploded View of 4-Speed Transaxle Assembly

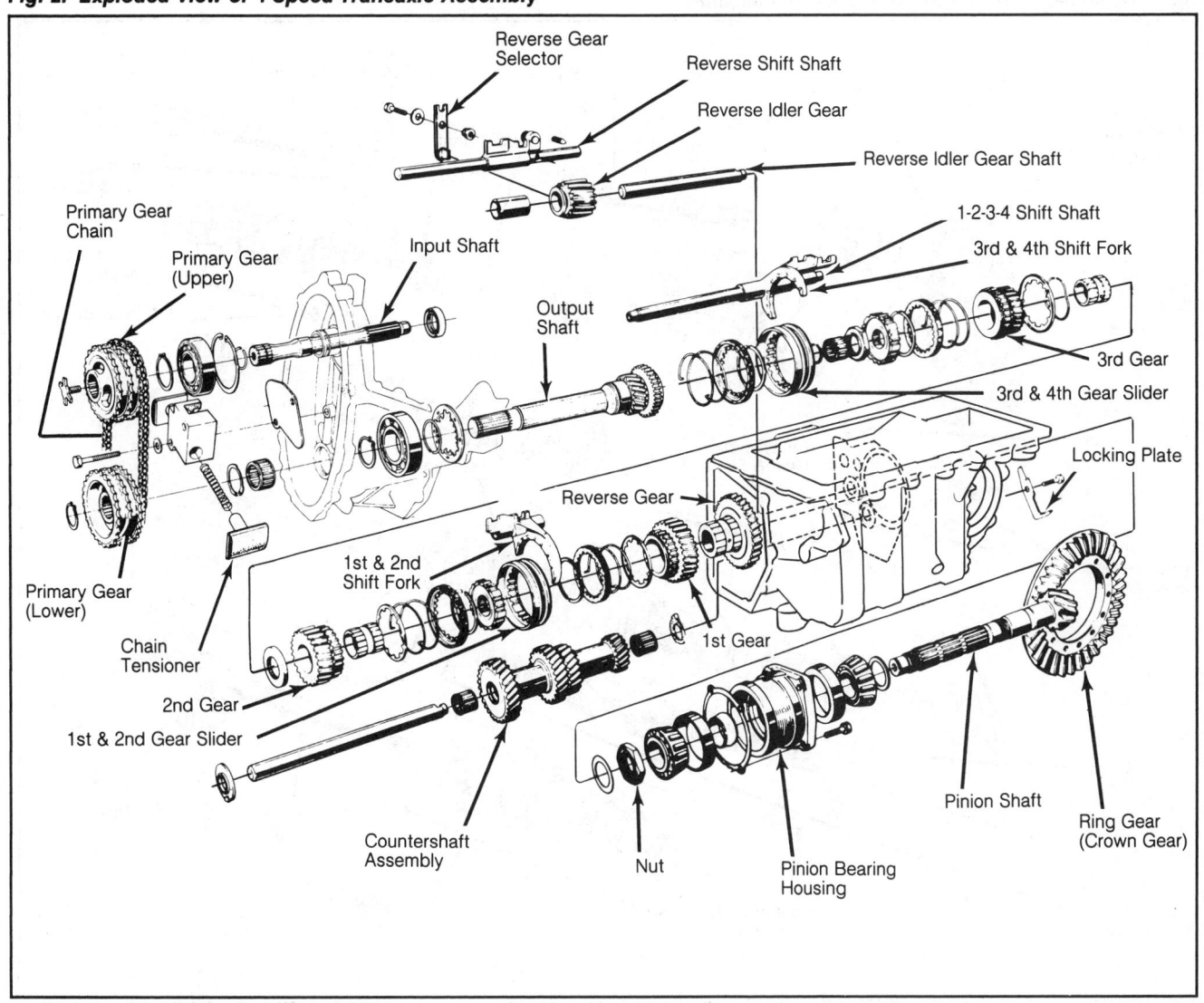

TRANSAXLE REMOVAL & INSTALLATION

See the appropriate article in MANUAL TRANS-MISSION REMOVAL Section.

TRANSAXLE DISASSEMBLY

NOTE: Prior to disassembling transmission gears, measure ring-to-pinion gear backlash and pinion depth. If ring and pinion gear set have less than 6000 miles, backlash and pinion depth can be adjusted to specifications. However, if mileage is exceeded, backlash and pinion depth must be set to that recorded prior to disassembly. See Pinion Depth Adjustment in this article.

4-SPEED

1) Mount transaxle assembly on work stand and drain transmission oil. Remove axle shaft housing attaching bolts and remove housings using a puller.

NOTE: When removing axle housings, do not lose spring and plunger located in end of inner shaft. Also, note the number and thickness of adjusting shims installed with housings.

2) Remove final drive cover. Measure ring-to-pinion gear backlash and pinion depth. Tilt differential assembly to one side and remove from case. Remove countershaft and reverse gear shaft locking plate. Remove countershaft with remove (8390049) so countershaft gear set drops down. Remove attaching bolts and separate primary gear housing from transaxle housing. Remove countershaft gear set.

3) Remove transaxle case side cover. Take out spring and ball catch for gear selector rod. Remove reverse gear shift rail retaining screw, then turn selector rod and pull out shift rail. Remove 1st/2nd and 3rd/4th gear shift rail, then lift out shift forks and 3rd gear sliding sleeve.

Manual Transmissions
SAAB 900 4 & 5-SPEED (Cont.)

Fig. 3: Exploded View of 5-Speed Transaxle Assembly

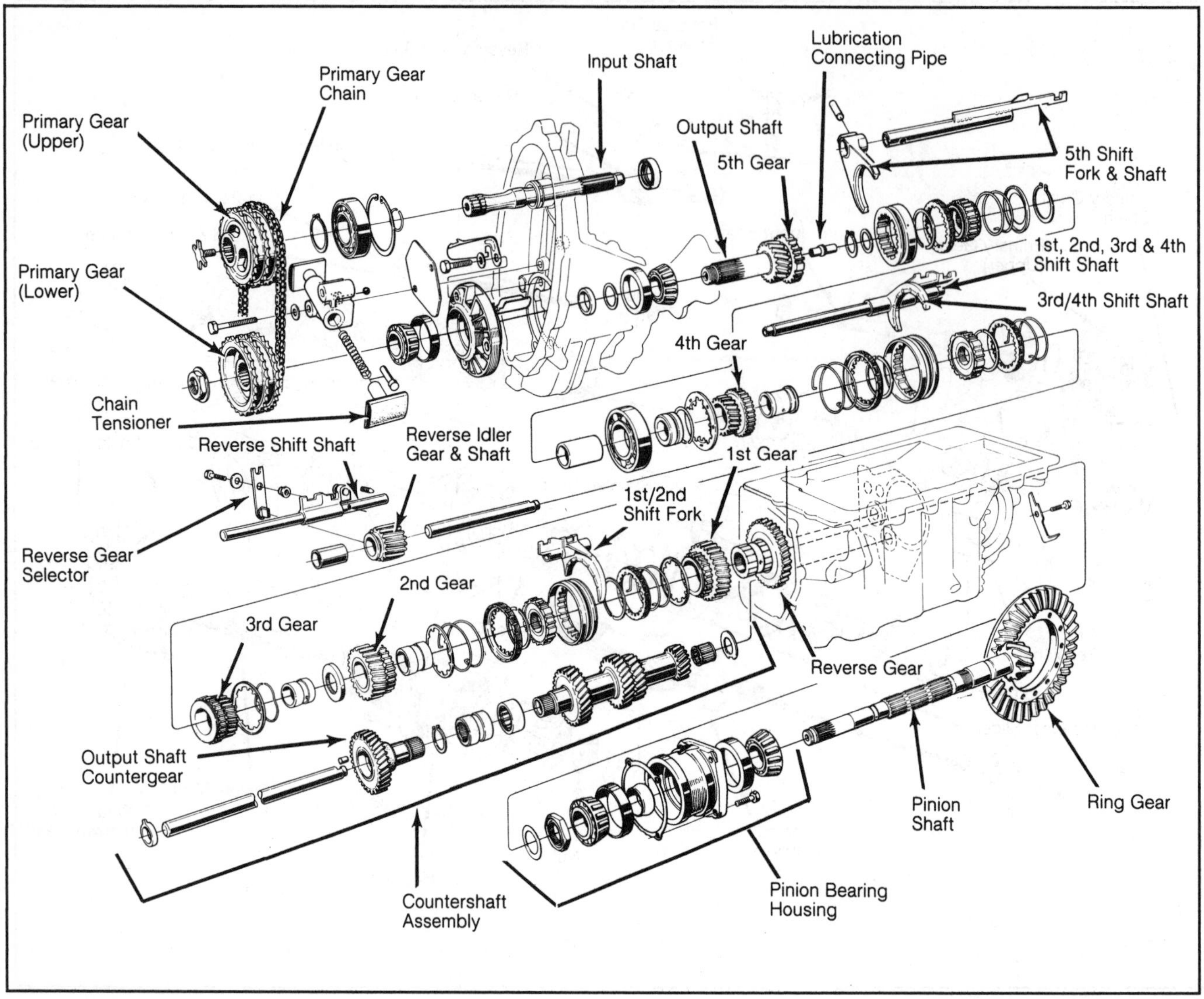

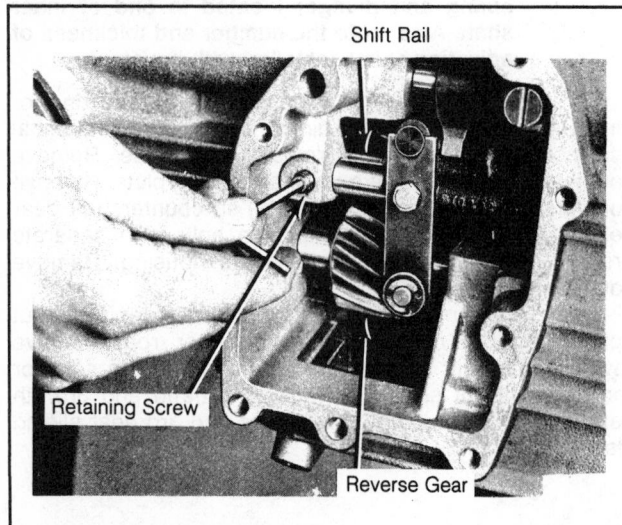

Primary Gear Chain
Input Shaft
Lubrication Connecting Pipe
Primary Gear (Upper)
Output Shaft
5th Gear
5th Shift Fork & Shaft
Primary Gear (Lower)
1st, 2nd, 3rd & 4th Shift Shaft
3rd/4th Shift Shaft
Chain Tensioner
4th Gear
Reverse Shift Shaft
Reverse Idler Gear & Shaft
1st Gear
1st/2nd Shift Fork
Reverse Gear Selector
Reverse Gear
2nd Gear
3rd Gear
Output Shaft Countergear
Pinion Shaft
Ring Gear
Countershaft Assembly
Pinion Bearing Housing

Fig. 4: Removing 4-Speed Reverse Gear Shift Rail Retaining Screw

Shift Rail

Retaining Screw

Reverse Gear

4) Pull out reverse idler gear shaft and lift out reverse idler gear. Pull out pinion shaft needle bearing, then install clamp (8790503) to lock reverse gear in place. Remove pinion shaft nut. Remove tool and lift out 3rd/4th gear synchronizer hub and 3rd gear. Remove pinion bearing housing retaining bolts and press pinion shaft from transaxle case.

5-SPEED

1) Mount transaxle assembly on a work stand and drain fluid. Remove primary gear housing front cover and side cover. Remove oil filler plug cover and final drive cover. Measure ring-to-pinion gear backlash and pinion depth. Remove axle shaft housing attaching bolts and remove housings with a puller.

NOTE: When removing axle housings, do not lose spring and plunger located in end of inner shaft. Also, note the number and thickness of adjusting shims installed with housings.

SAAB 900 4 & 5-SPEED (Cont.)

Fig. 5: Disconnecting 5-Speed Mainshaft Countergear

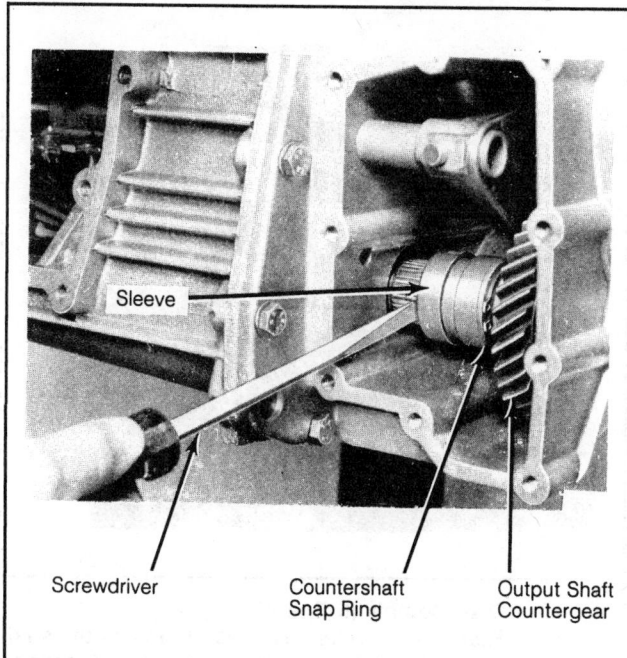

COMPONENT DISASSEMBLY & REASSEMBLY

PINION SHAFT

Disassembly

Place pinion shaft in a holding fixture, then remove pinion bearing retaining nut from shaft. Place shaft in a press and press pinion shaft and rear pinion bearing from bearing housing. Press rear bearing from shaft, then using a driver, remove pinion bearing outer races from bearing housing, then remove spacer sleeve from housing.

Fig. 6: Exploded View of Pinion Shaft Assembly

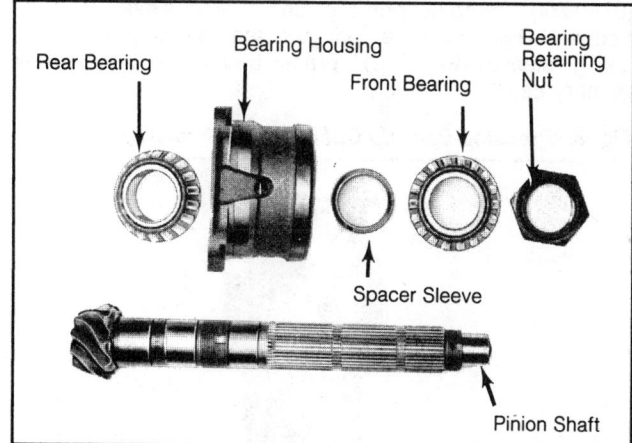

2) Tilt differential assembly to one side and remove from case. Remove reverse gear operating lever retaining bolt and lever. Engage reverse gear and 5th gear to lock transmission. Unstake output shaft tab washer (lower primary gear), then remove unit. Remove chain tensioner.

3) Remove snap ring (located behind upper primary gear). Using slide hammer (8390270) and puller (8790891), remove primary gears and chain simultaneously. Free countershaft gear from output shaft countergear by loosening snap ring and pushing sleeve against countershaft. See Fig. 5.

4) Remove countershaft and reverse idler shaft retaining plate. Using extractor (8390049), remove countershaft, then remove countershaft gear with sleeve and snap ring through side cover.

5) Remove input shaft bearing housing oil catcher bolts and oil catcher. Remove bearing housing bolts. Remove bearing housing with slide hammer and adapter (8790917).

6) Remove 5th gear selector fork locking stud and push gear selector toward housing until it stops. Remove fork and slider. Remove 5th gear synchro hub snap ring and shim(s). Remove synchro hub and spacer from pinion shaft.

7) Remove all primary gear housing retaining bolts. Drive dowels into case to separate primary gear housing from transmission housing. The 5th gear selector will remain in the housing and may be removed later.

8) Remove countershaft assembly with needle bearings and thrust washer identified for installation in original position. Remove selector shafts (from front) and selectors. Remove 1st and 2nd gear selectors with respective synchro unit. Reverse selector should be removed still attached to selector shaft. Remove selector ball and guide pin.

9) Remove reverse idler shaft and reverse idler gear. Remove 4 pinion shaft bearing housing retaining screws. Press pinion out with remover (8790909).

Reassembly

1) Lubricate bearings with transmission oil, then press bearing outer races into bearing housing. Press rear pinion bearing onto pinion shaft until it butts against stop. Place spacer sleeve onto shaft, then install housing over sleeve.

2) Place front bearing on shaft and position shaft in a press. Slowly press bearing into housing while turning housing by hand, until resistance is felt, then remove shaft from press. Coat bearing retaining nut threads with Loctite (or equivalent) and install, but do not tighten.

3) Install pinion shaft assembly in holding fixture and place in a vise. Attach spring pull gauge to housing as shown in Fig. 7.

4) Tighten retaining nut until force required to rotate housing is 10-15 lbs. (4.5-6.8 kg) for new bearings or 4.2-9.2 lbs. (1.9-4.2 kg) for used bearings. Bearings are considered "used" when they have been in use for over

Fig. 7: Checking Pinion Bearing Preload

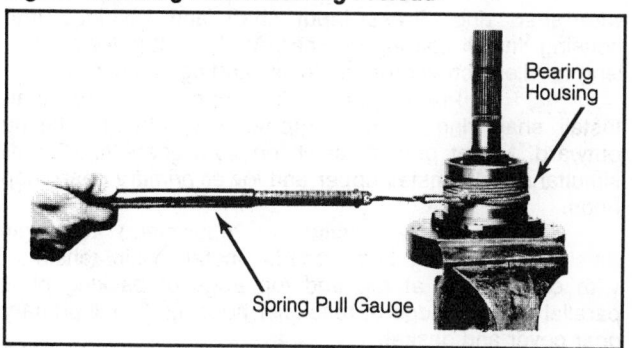

SAAB 900 4 & 5-SPEED (Cont.)

1200 miles (2000 km). When correct value is obtained, peen retaining nut with a drift to lock nut in position.

NOTE: With the retaining nut correctly tightened, pinion bearing preload is set to correct specification.

PRIMARY GEAR HOUSING
Disassembly (4-Speed)
1) Remove primary gear cover attaching bolts and separate cover from housing. Remove chain tensioner. Remove lower primary gear snap ring. Remove upper primary gear snap ring (located behind primary gear).

2) Using slide hammer (8390270) and puller (8790834), remove primary gears and chain simultaneously. Remove upper primary gear bearing snap ring. Using sleeve (8790842), press bearing out of upper primary gear.

Fig. 8: Pressing Bearing Out of Upper Primary Gear

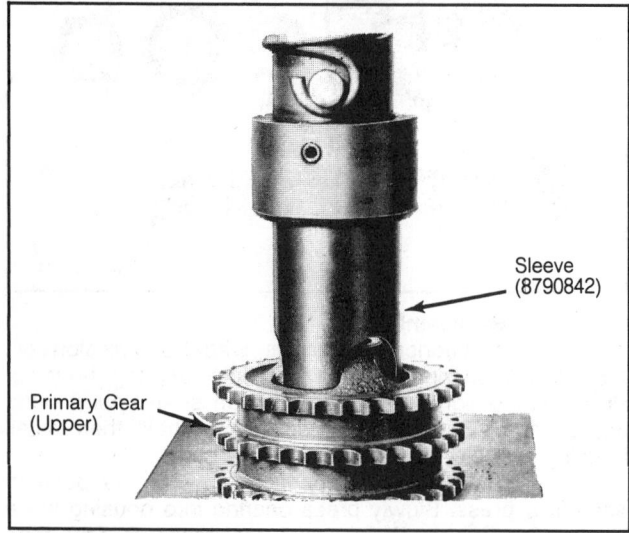

Sleeve (8790842)

Primary Gear (Upper)

3) Remove 4 Allen screws from input shaft bearing retainer and remove retainer. Press input shaft out of housing. Remove input shaft bearing snap ring and press bearing off shaft. Remove needle bearing snap ring, then remove needle bearing from housing. Pry out input shaft oil seal.

Reassembly
1) Inspect all parts for wear or damage; replace as necessary. Press in new input shaft oil seal and needle bearing (mark facing outward in housing). Install needle bearing snap ring.

2) Press bearing onto input shaft and secure with snap ring. Press input shaft and bearings into housing. Install bearing retainer. Apply Loctite (or equivalent) to Allen screw threads. Install and tighten screws.

3) Press bearing into upper primary gear. Install snap ring in outer groove with chamfer facing outward. Mount primary chain on both gears and install simultaneously. Install upper and lower primary gear snap rings.

4) Apply Loctite (or equivalent) to chain tensioner mounting bolt threads. Install chain tensioner with oil passage at top and top edge of backing plate parallel with top edge of tensioner housing. Install primary gear cover and gasket.

Fig. 9: Pressing Input Shaft and Bearing into Housing

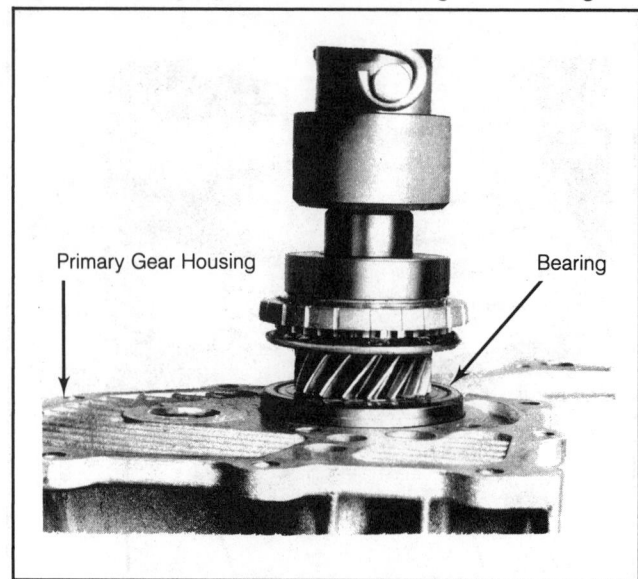

Primary Gear Housing

Bearing

Disassembly (5-Speed)
Remove 4 Allen screws from input shaft bearing retainer and remove retainer. Drive out bearing with drift (8390106) and sleeve (8390148). Remove needle bearing from primary gear case with a drift. Pry out input shaft oil seal. Remove upper primary gear snap ring. Using sleeve (8790842), press bearing out of upper primary gear.

NOTE: DO NOT remove lever control ball valve. Check that ball moves freely and securely sets on seat. Ball acts at low speeds while going down hills to prevent oil from running out of gear case into primary gear housing.

Reassembly
Inspect all parts for wear or damage; replace as necessary. Press in new input shaft oil seal and needle bearing (mark facing outward in housing). Press input shaft bearing into housing. Install bearing retainer. Apply Loctite (or equivalent) to Allen screw threads. Install and tighten screws.

OUTPUT SHAFT BEARING HOUSING (5-SPEED ONLY)
Disassembly
Remove oil catcher from bearing housing. Press output shaft out of bearing housing using support (8390098), being careful not to damage lubrication connection pipe. Retain front bearing, spacer and shims. Using support (8790636) and ring (8790933), press rear bearing off output shaft. Using a drift, knock bearing outer races out of bearing housing.

Reassembly
1) Press rear bearing onto output shaft. Press outer races into bearing housing. Install output shaft, shims, spacer and bearing into bearing housing (shims must be installed between rear bearing and spacer).

2) Lubricate bearings and press together using support (8390098) and drift (7841075). While pressing with 3 tons (2722 kg) pressure, rotate bearing housing against upper and lower bearings 40 times in each direction to seat ball bearings.

SAAB 900 4 & 5-SPEED (Cont.)

3) Install dial indicator as shown in *Fig. 10.* Maintain installation pressure and check axial play of bearing housing. Adjust axial play to 0 by inserting correct shim.

4) After installing correct shim, recheck axial play. If axial play cannot be removed with shims, replace spacer. Bearings should have no resistance to movement or play. Install oil catcher in bearing housing.

NOTE: Shims are available in .004" (.10 mm), .006" (.15 mm), .010" (.25 mm) and .020" (.50 mm) thicknesses. Spacers are available in .3181" (8.08 mm), .3185" (8.09 mm), .3189" (8.10 mm) and .3192" (8.11 mm) lengths.

SYNCHRONIZER ASSEMBLIES
Disassembly
Synchronizer rings are removed by removing snap ring which attaches ring to gear. On 5-speed transaxles, 5th gear synchronizer ring is removed by removing snap ring in front of guide ring. DO NOT remove synchronizer ring snap ring.

Reassembly
1) Install guide ring for retaining ring, then, on 3rd and 4th gears only, lock guide rings in place on gears with snap rings.

2) Install retaining spring on gear with long wire end nearest guide ring, then position other end on gear so there are 11 teeth between spring ends (5 teeth on 5th gear). Retaining spring for 1st gear is shorter and softer.

NOTE: Guide rings for 3rd and 4th gears are assembled during production and are peened into position. DO NOT peen guide rings which are supplied as replacements.

3) Install synchronizer ring onto gear so ends of spring fit into spaces between teeth. Install snap ring.

Fig. 10: *Checking Axial Play of 5-Speed Output Shaft Bearing Housing*

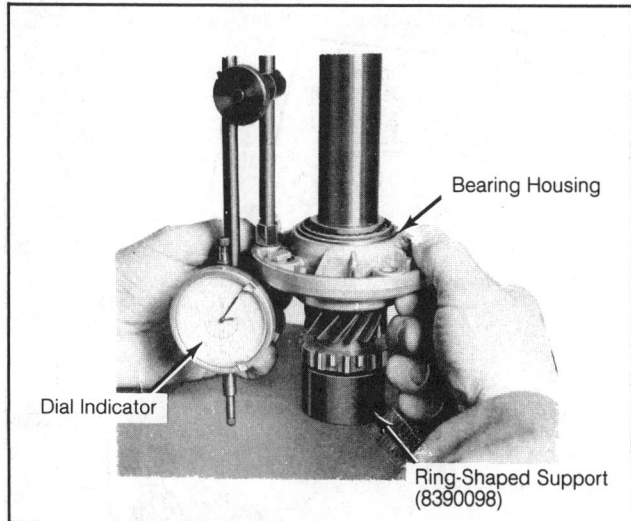

Bearing Housing

Dial Indicator

Ring-Shaped Support (8390098)

NOTE: Synchronizer ring for 2nd gear has molybdenum-coated synchronizing surface for identification.

Fig. 11: *Removing Snap Ring to Separate Synchronizer Ring from Gear (Except 5th Gear of 5-Speed)*

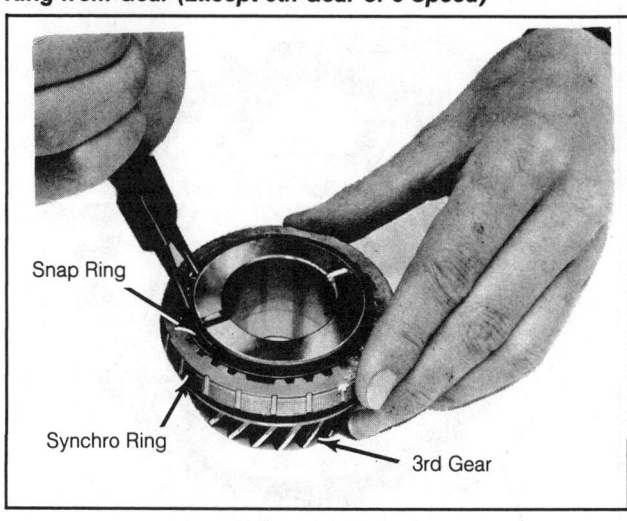

Snap Ring

Synchro Ring

3rd Gear

Fig. 12: *Exploded View of 1st/2nd Gear Synchronizer*

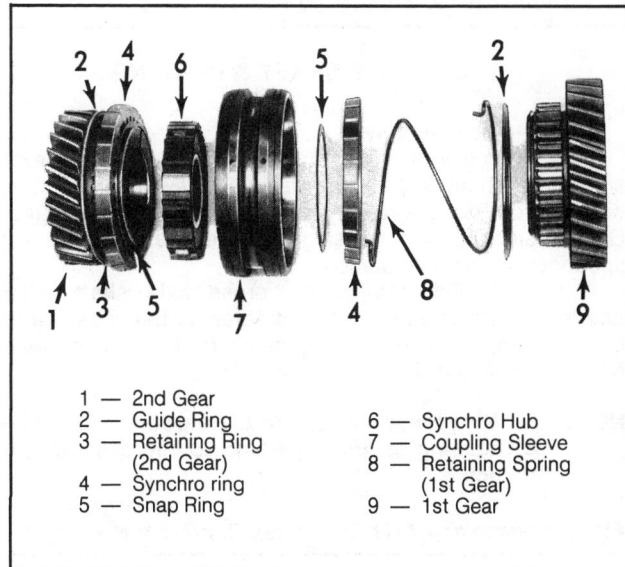

1 — 2nd Gear
2 — Guide Ring
3 — Retaining Ring (2nd Gear)
4 — Synchro ring
5 — Snap Ring
6 — Synchro Hub
7 — Coupling Sleeve
8 — Retaining Spring (1st Gear)
9 — 1st Gear

Fig. 13: *Exploded View of 3rd Gear Synchronizer*

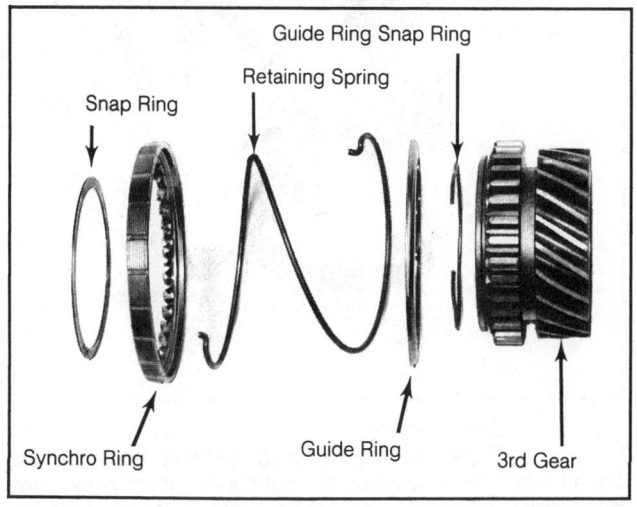

Snap Ring

Guide Ring Snap Ring

Retaining Spring

Synchro Ring

Guide Ring

3rd Gear

Fig. 14: Synchronizer Retaining Spring Installation

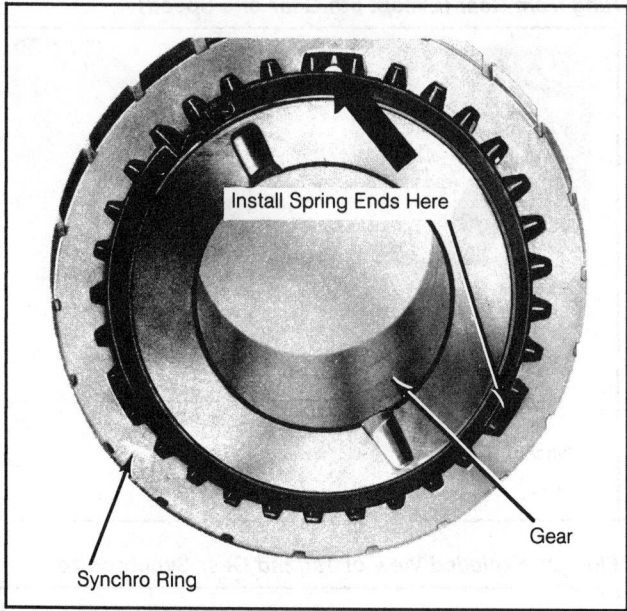

Install Spring Ends Here

Gear

Synchro Ring

INNER AXLE SHAFT & BEARING HOUSING

Disassembly

1) Remove axle shaft snap ring and press axle shaft out of bearing housing. Using a screwdriver, remove oil seal from housing taking care not to damage housing. On left side bearing housing, remove shaft and lift out speedometer drive assembly.

2) On both sides, press axle shaft roller bearings from housing. If new differential bearings are to be installed, remove bearing outer races from bearing housing using a drift.

NOTE: A washer is located between race and housing on the right side to improve lubrication.

Fig. 15: Removing Axle Shaft Snap Ring from Housing

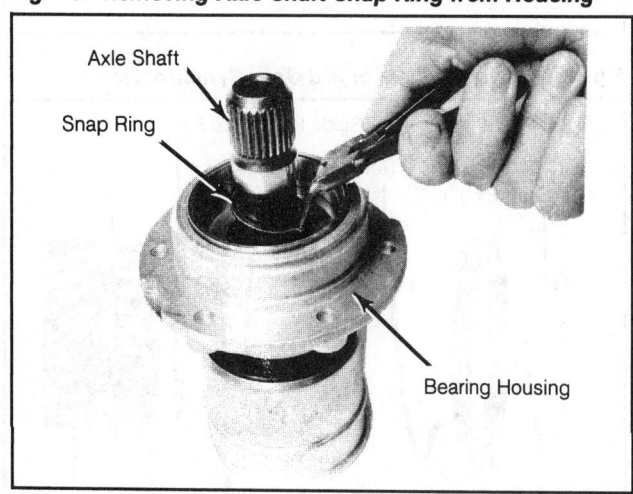

Axle Shaft

Snap Ring

Bearing Housing

Reassembly

Press new axle shaft bearing into housing. Install lubrication washer on right side, then press new differential bearing outer races into bearing housing.

Using a drift, press bearing housing oil seal into housing until it protrudes .08" (2 mm) above face of housing.

NOTE: Axle shafts will be installed during Transaxle Reassembly.

DIFFERENTIAL ASSEMBLY

Disassembly

1) If differential bearings require replacement, remove speedometer drive gear from left side and use puller to remove bearings from differential housing.

Fig. 16: Exploded View of Left Side Inner Axle Shaft and Differential Bearing Housing

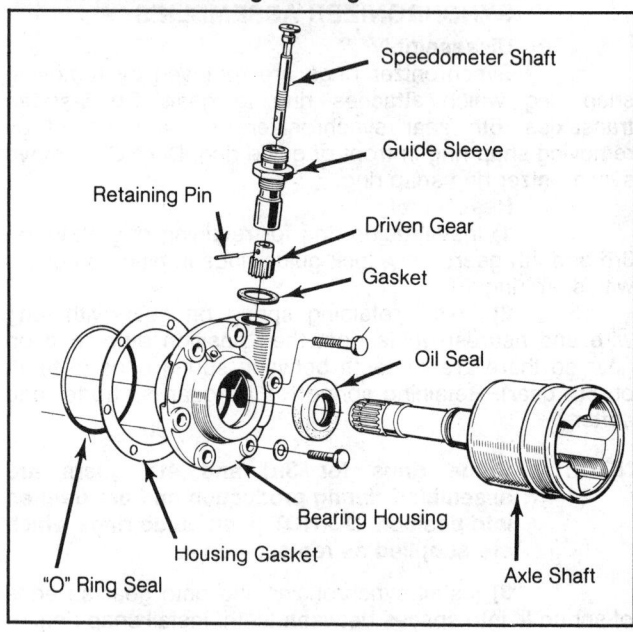

Speedometer Shaft

Guide Sleeve

Retaining Pin

Driven Gear

Gasket

Oil Seal

Bearing Housing

Housing Gasket

"O" Ring Seal

Axle Shaft

Fig. 17: Exploded View of Differential Assembly

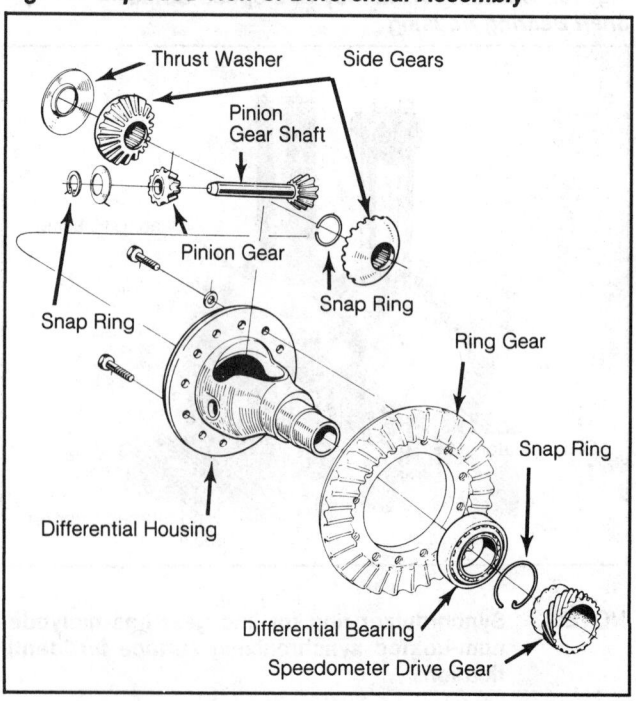

Thrust Washer

Side Gears

Pinion Gear Shaft

Snap Ring

Pinion Gear

Snap Ring

Ring Gear

Snap Ring

Differential Housing

Differential Bearing

Speedometer Drive Gear

SAAB 900 4 & 5-SPEED (Cont.)

2) Remove ring gear bolts and separate ring gear from differential. Remove snap ring, then press out pinion shaft. Remove pinion gears and side gears, thrust washers and gear springs from housing.

Reassembly

Install pinion gears and side gears, thrust washers and springs into housing. Install pinion shaft and secure with snap ring. Mount ring gear on differential housing and install attaching bolts after applying Loctite (or equivalent) to threads. If removed, press new bearings onto housing, then install speedometer drive gear.

TRANSAXLE REASSEMBLY & ADJUSTMENT

PINION DEPTH ADJUSTMENT

NOTE: **Pinion bearing preload must be correctly adjusted before adjusting pinion depth. See Pinion Shaft Reassembly. Pinion Depth Adjustment specifications (in metric) are stamped into end face of pinion shaft gear. See Fig. 18.**

1) Pinion depth must be measured using Saab measuring instrument (8390155), which consists of a measuring jig with attached dial indicator and a gauge block for calibrating dial indicator.

2) To calibrate indicator, place calibration stops of measuring tool against gauge block. Distance between stops and centerline of tool should be 2.362" (60 mm), which is equal to the distance from end face of pinion shaft gear to centerline of ring gear.

3) Ensure that dial indicator pointer is zeroed when measuring tip touches gauge block.

Fig. 18: End View of Pinion Shaft Gear Showing Pinion Depth Adjustment Specifications

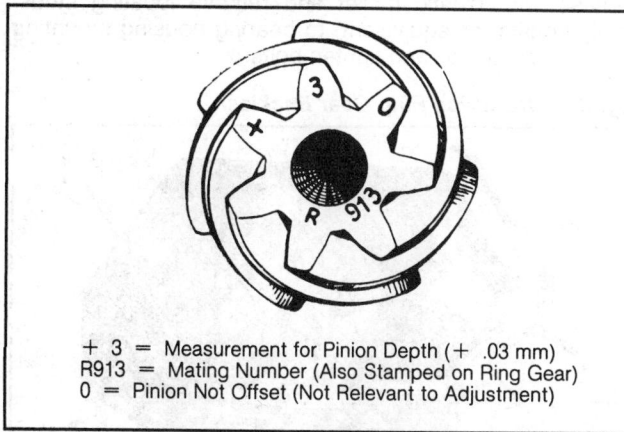

+ 3 = Measurement for Pinion Depth (+ .03 mm)
R913 = Mating Number (Also Stamped on Ring Gear)
0 = Pinion Not Offset (Not Relevant to Adjustment)

4) Install pinion shaft into transaxle case and tighten bolts. Position measuring tool in transaxle case with measuring tip applied to flat end of pinion gear. See Fig. 19. Record reading.

5) When pinion gear is correctly positioned, dial indicator should read the number (in hundredths of millimeters; plus or minus) stamped into pinion with a permitted tolerance of .002" (.05 mm). For example, if pinion is stamped -7, indicator should read a negative (-) .07 mm with a tolerance of ±.05 mm.

NOTE: **On dial indicator, clockwise movement of needle is positive, while counterclockwise movement is negative.**

Fig. 19: Positioning Measuring Tool in Transaxle Case

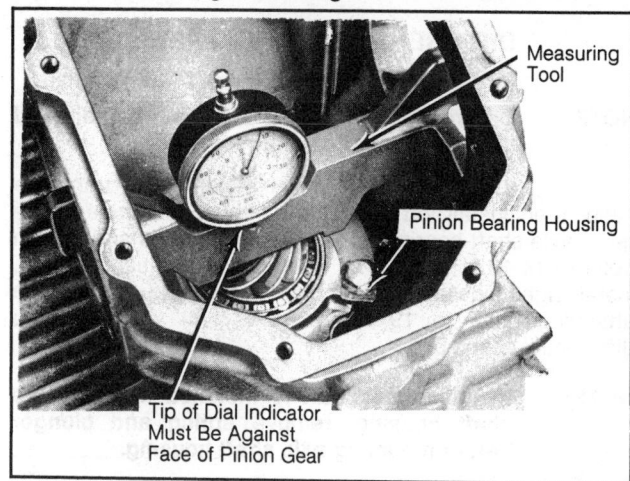

Measuring Tool

Pinion Bearing Housing

Tip of Dial Indicator Must Be Against Face of Pinion Gear

NOTE: **If ring and pinion gear set have been in use for over 6000 miles, reassemble pinion shaft to specifications recorded during disassembly.**

6) If measured pinion depth is not within specifications (stamped on pinion gear), pinion shaft must be adjusted. To adjust, remove pinion shaft from case and add or remove shims between pinion bearing housing and case as follows: If reading is higher than specifications, increase shim thickness; if reading is lower than specifications, reduce shim thickness.

Fig. 20: Sectional View Showing Position of Pinion Depth Adjusting Shims

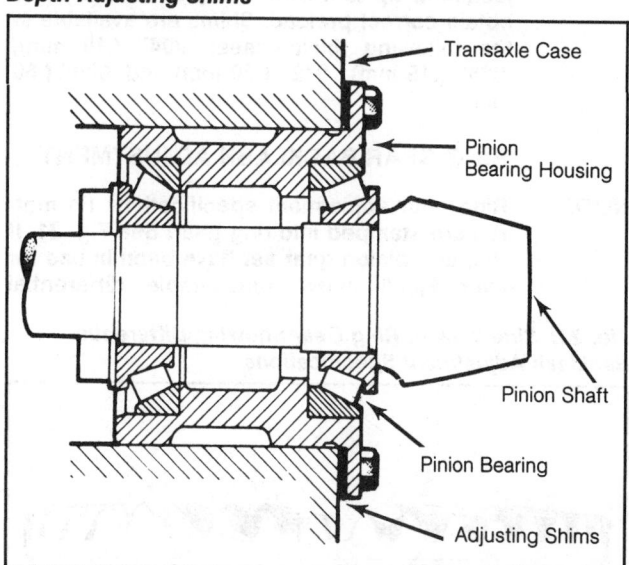

Transaxle Case

Pinion Bearing Housing

Pinion Shaft

Pinion Bearing

Adjusting Shims

7) Reduce or increase shim thickness according to difference between measured value and specified value. Before reinstalling pinion shaft assembly, differential bearing preload must be adjusted. See Differential Bearing Preload Adjustment.

SAAB 900 4 & 5-SPEED (Cont.)

NOTE: Pinion depth adjusting shims are available in the following thicknesses: .004" (.10 mm), .006" (.15 mm), .012" (.30 mm), and .020" (.50 mm).

DIFFERENTIAL BEARING PRELOAD ADJUSTMENT

NOTE: Differential bearing preload must be adjusted prior to installation of pinion shaft.

1) Position differential assembly in transaxle case, then install left side (side with speedometer drive gear) axle shaft bearing housing without shims and tighten bolts to 14-18 ft. lbs. (19-24 N.m). Oil differential bearings, install right side axle shaft bearing housing and tighten attaching bolts to 19 ft. lbs. (26 N.m) while rotating differential assembly.

NOTE: If inner axle shaft is installed in right axle shaft housing, remove spring and plunger before mounting axle shaft housing.

2) Using a feeler gauge, measure clearance between right axle housing and transaxle case at 2 points opposite each other. Compute the average of 2 measurements and select adjusting shims which equal the average. Then add an additional .008" (.2 mm) in shim thickness to obtain correct bearing preload.

3) Measure bearing preload with an INCH lb. torque wrench. Preload for new slightly oiled bearings should be 16-24 INCH lbs. (1.8-2.7 N.m). Preload for used bearings should be 7-11 INCH lbs. (.79-1.24 N.m). Bearings are considered "used" when they have been in service for more than 1200 miles.

NOTE: Right-to-left distribution of shims will be determined during Ring Gear Backlash Adjustment. Up to 4 shims may be combined to obtain correct preload. Shims are available in the following thicknesses: .004" (.10 mm), .006" (.15 mm), .012" (.30 mm) and .020" (.50 mm).

RING GEAR BACKLASH ADJUSTMENT

NOTE: Ring gear adjustment specifications (in metric) are stamped into ring gear. See Fig. 21. If ring and pinion gear set have been in use for over 6,000 miles, reassemble differential

according to specifications recorded during disassembly. Mount pinion shaft with shims in housing.

1) Place differential assembly into transaxle case. Mount left side (speedometer drive gear side) axle shaft bearing housing to transaxle case without adjusting shims and tighten attaching bolts to 14-18 ft. lbs. (19-24 N.m). Mount right side axle shaft bearing housing with the selected bearing preload adjusting shims and tighten attaching bolts to same torque as left side.

2) Mount dial indicator on transaxle case so indicator tip is touching ring gear teeth. Move ring gear back and forth and measure backlash between ring gear and pinion gear in 4 different locations. After adjustment, remove differential.

NOTE: Backlash measurements should not deviate from each other by more than .002" (.05 mm). If measurements deviate more than specified, ring gear is not properly installed. If backlash is not to specifications (stamped on ring gear), remove both axle shaft housings and move shims as necessary from right side housing to left side housing. Reinstall housings with shims and recheck backlash. If not to specifications, repeat adjustment procedure until correct backlash is obtained. DO NOT reduce total thickness of shim pack. Move shims from one side to the other.

TRANSAXLE REASSEMBLY
4-Speed

1) Install 2 locating studs (8790438) into pinion shaft bearing housing mounting holes. Install preselected pinion depth adjusting shims on bearing housing, then position pinion shaft in transaxle case, using locating studs as guides. Gently tap pinion shaft until fully seated in case with plastic mallet and remove locating studs. Apply Loctite (or equivalent) to bearing housing mounting bolt threads. Install and tighten bolts.

Fig. 22: Measuring Ring Gear Backlash

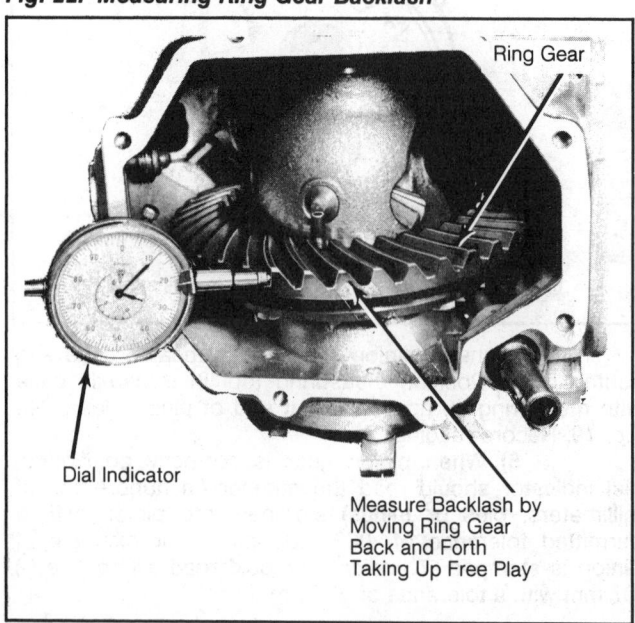

Fig. 21: Side View of Ring Gear Showing Differential Backlash Adjustment Specifications

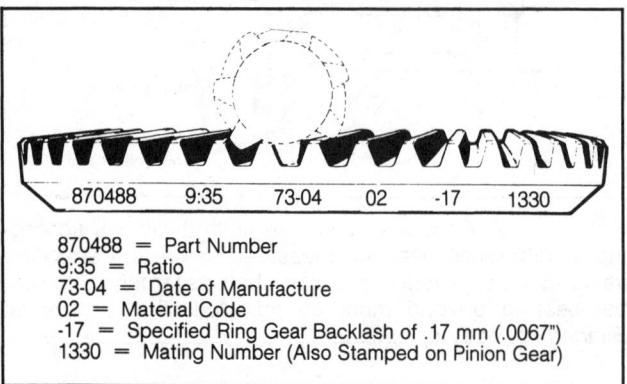

870488   9:35   73-04   02   -17   1330

870488 = Part Number
9:35 = Ratio
73-04 = Date of Manufacture
02 = Material Code
-17 = Specified Ring Gear Backlash of .17 mm (.0067")
1330 = Mating Number (Also Stamped on Pinion Gear)

SAAB 900 4 & 5-SPEED (Cont.)

2) Before installing reverse gear, measure distance from pinion bearing retaining nut to primary gear housing mounting surface on transaxle case. Distance should be 7.677-7.681" (195.0-195.1 mm). To accurately measure distance, set depth gauge to proper distance and mount on case. Measure distance between end of depth gauge and retaining nut with feeler gauge. Install shim of thickness equal to that of feeler gauge.

3) Using a micrometer, measure thickness of shim removed during disassembly. If original shim thickness equals required shim thickness, replace original shim. If not, install shim of proper thickness. Shims are available in thicknesses of .012" (.3 mm), .016" (.4 mm) and .02" (.05 mm). Install shim between retaining nut and reverse gear.

4) Install reverse gear onto pinion shaft. Fit 1st gear on reverse gear bearing sleeve. Install 1st/2nd synchronizer hub onto pinion shaft. Install 1st/2nd gear shift fork into coupling sleeve, then mount on synchronizer hub. Install 2nd gear sleeve, then mount 2nd gear on sleeve. Install 3rd gear spacer and sleeve on pinion shaft, then mount 3rd gear on sleeve.

Fig. 23: Measuring Retaining Nut-to-Mounting Surface Distance

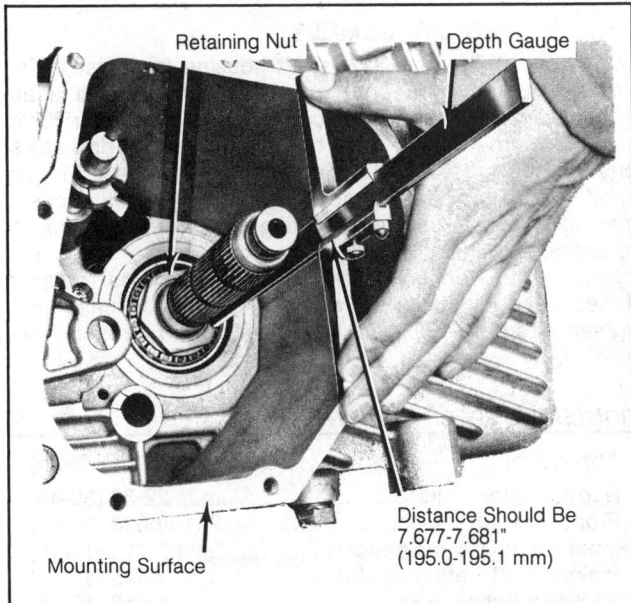

Retaining Nut   Depth Gauge

Distance Should Be 7.677-7.681" (195.0-195.1 mm)

Mounting Surface

5) Install 3rd/4th gear synchronizer hub (with 3 locking holes facing outward) onto pinion shaft. Install 3rd/4th gear shift fork into 3rd/4th gear coupling sleeve, then install on synchronizer hub. Install locking tool (8790503) to lock reverse gear. Install and tighten pinion shaft nut. Install pinion shaft needle bearing and snap ring. Remove locking tool.

6) Place transmission gears in neutral, then install shift rail for 1st/2nd and 3rd/4th gear shift forks. Turn selector rod clockwise and install reverse shift rail. Tighten stop screw. Pack countershaft gear needle bearings with grease to hold them in place, then place gear set in bottom of transaxle case.

7) Ensure countershaft gear set thrust washer is installed on primary gear housing and oil connecting tube is installed in output shaft of primary gear housing. See Fig. 24. Coat mating surface of primary gear housing with sealant. Install housing onto transaxle case and

tighten attaching bolts finger tight to prevent countergear set from jamming before countershaft is installed.

Fig. 24: Installing Oil Connecting Tube in Output Shaft

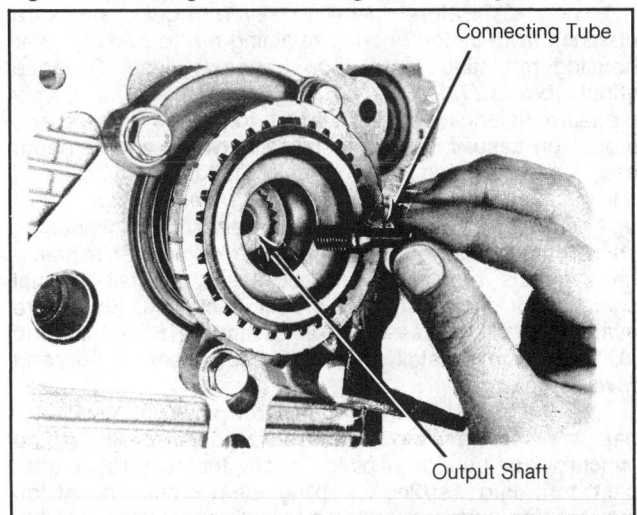

Connecting Tube

Output Shaft

8) Ease countershaft gear set into correct position. Install rear thrust washer onto gear. Insert countershaft gear shaft into gear set through bore in differential section of transaxle case. See Fig. 25. Tighten primary gear housing attaching bolts. Install reverse idler gear and shaft, making sure reverse lever is fitted into reverse idler gear groove.

Fig. 25: Installing Countershaft Assembly Shaft

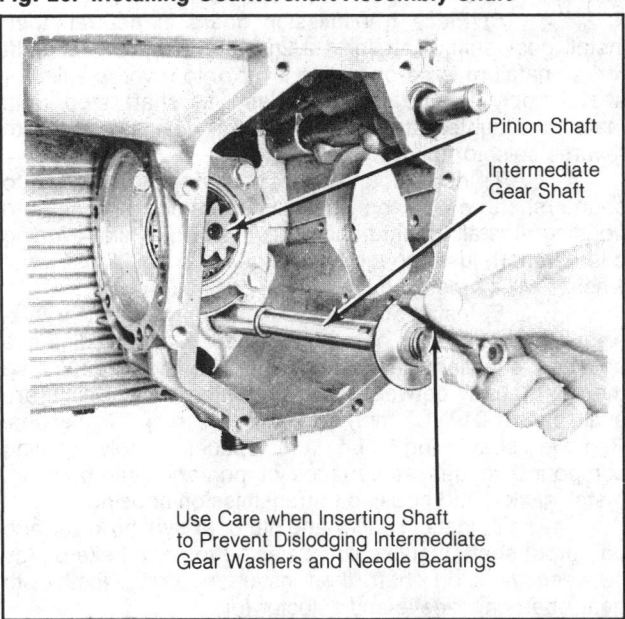

Pinion Shaft

Intermediate Gear Shaft

Use Care when Inserting Shaft to Prevent Dislodging Intermediate Gear Washers and Needle Bearings

9) Install locking plate over shaft ends. Apply Loctite (or equivalent) to attaching screw threads. Install and tighten screw. Insert spring and ball catch for gear selector rod and install transaxle case cover and gasket. Check ring gear backlash and adjust if necessary.

5-Speed

1) Install 2 locating studs (8790438) into pinion shaft bearing housing mounting holes. Install preselected pinion depth adjusting shims on bearing housing, then position pinion shaft in transaxle case, using locating

SAAB 900 4 & 5-SPEED (Cont.)

studs as guides. Gently tap pinion shaft with plastic mallet until fully seated in case, then remove locating studs. Apply Loctite (or equivalent) to bearing housing mounting bolt threads. Install and tighten bolts.

2) Before installing reverse gear, measure distance from pinion bearing retaining nut to primary gear housing mounting surface on transaxle case. Distance should be 7.677-7.681" (195.0-195.1 mm). To accurately measure distance, set depth gauge to proper distance and mount on case. Measure distance between end of depth gauge and retaining nut with feeler gauge. Install shim of thickness equal to that of feeler gauge. *See Fig. 23.*

3) Using a micrometer, measure thickness of shim removed during disassembly. If original shim thickness equals required shim thickness, reinstall original shim. If not, install shim of proper thickness. Shims are available in thicknesses of .012" (.3 mm), .016" (.4 mm) and .02" (.05 mm). Install shim between retaining nut and reverse gear.

4) Install reverse gear on pinion shaft. Fit 1st gear on bearing sleeve of reverse gear. Install 1st/2nd synchronizer hub onto pinion shaft. Insert 1st/2nd gear shift fork into 1st/2nd coupling sleeve and mount on synchronizer hub. Install 2nd gear sleeve with installer (8390148). Install 2nd gear onto sleeve. Install 3rd gear spacer and sleeve on pinion shaft, then install 3rd gear on sleeve.

5) Install 3rd/4th synchronizer hub onto pinion shaft. Install 3rd/4th gear shift fork into 3rd/4th gear coupling sleeve, then install on synchronizer hub. Install 4th gear bushing onto pinion shaft, then mount 4th gear onto bushing. Install selector shaft with double lock out guide pin.

6) Place transmission gears in neutral, then install gear shift shaft for 1st/2nd and 3rd/4th gear shift forks. Install reverse operating lever onto reverse selector shaft. Apply Loctite (or equivalent) to shaft stop bolt. Install and tighten stop bolt. Install 5th gear selector onto reverse selector shaft.

7) Install countershaft gear needle bearing into countershaft gear and install countershaft gear into housing. Install countershaft gear shaft, while aligning countershaft, just enough to hold gears in position. Thrust washer will be installed later.

8) Install 5th gear spacer, 5th gear synchronizer hub and snap ring onto pinion shaft. Measure distance between coupling sleeve and hub with feeler gauge so there is no play between parts on pinion shaft. Shims are available in .012" (.3 mm) and .016" (.4 mm) thicknesses. Remove snap ring, hub and spacer. Apply sealing compound to gasket surfaces of primary gear housing. Install gasket and housing to transmission housing.

9) Install spacer and 5th gear synchronizer hub on output shaft. Install shims selected to provide zero play between parts on shaft, then install snap ring. Install 5th gear operating sleeve and selector fork.

10) Install 3 output shaft guide pins (8790438) into lower primary gear bearing housing mounting bolt holes. Insert output shaft with bearing housing, oil catcher and oil connecting pipe installed on adapter (8790917). Mount the lower primary gear socket between the adapter and bearing housing. Insert bearing housing and output shaft assembly using slide hammer, so bearing housing is seated and output shaft meets operating sleeve.

11) Install output shaft countershaft thrust washer, coated with grease, so tab fits into recess of case. Slide output shaft countergear onto shaft and install sleeve, bearings and snap ring. Mount countershaft in case and slide gear toward thrust washer to allow alignment of gear for final installation.

12) Mount operating sleeve onto countershaft and insert snap ring into recess. Mount countergear thrust washer. Using installer (8390049), insert countergear shaft so it locks in position. Install reverse idler gear and spindle, then insert reverse idler gear shaft until it locks in position with installer (8390049).

13) Install locking plate into primary gear cover. Seal locking plate with Loctite (or equivalent), then coat threads with same sealant. Install and tighten bolts. Install upper primary gear and chain assembly. Ensure the hole for lower primary gear tab washer is facing outward. Mount chain tensioner. Coat threads of chain tensioner bolts with Loctite (or equivalent), then install and tighten bolts.

14) Lock pinion shaft by engaging reverse gear and 5th gear. Install pinion shaft nut and tighten. Bend 1 nut tab into hole provided in lower primary gear. Install reverse gear operating lever and tighten bolt. Seal bolt with Loctite (or equivalent). Install differential unit. Install selector ball and gearbox top cover gasket and cover. Install primary gear housing gasket and cover.

FINAL ASSEMBLY

1) Remove axle shaft housing from transaxle. Press axle housings onto axle shaft, then install snap rings to secure shafts in place. Install speedometer drive assembly into left axle shaft housing. Install "O" ring seals on both housings. Install spring and plunger in end of axle shaft. Install axle shaft housings onto transaxle case, making sure that correct adjusting shims are in place on each housing. Install and tighten bolts.

2) Recheck backlash adjustment and readjust if necessary. Install rear cover on transaxle case and tighten attaching bolts. Fill transaxle to correct fluid level with oil.

TIGHTENING SPECIFICATIONS

Application	Ft. Lbs. (N.m)
Hub-to-Rotor Bolts	22-36 (30-49)
Front Hub Nut	251-266 (340-361)
Input Shaft Nut (5-Speed)	67-81 (91-110)
Pinion Shaft Retaining Nut	30-45 (41-61)
All 8 mm Bolts	14-18 (19-24)
Speedometer Drive Shaft	21-36 (28-49)
Ring Gear Attaching Bolts	30-45 (41-61)
Axle Shaft Housing Bolts	14-18 (19-24)

SUBARU 4 & 5-SPEED

1600, 1800

DESCRIPTION

Transmission has 4 or 5 speeds with synchromesh in all forward gears. Both transmission and differential are mounted in the same 2-piece aluminum housing. A hypoid-type gear is used for the final drive. Gear shift linkage is incorporated in transmission cover.

Transmission and differential are lubricated from a common oil supply. Front axle drive shafts employ constant velocity joints at transaxle drive flange and axle shaft.

Four-wheel drive models have rear drive shaft which rotates with drive pinion at gear ratio of 1 to 1. Rear drive shaft is equipped with a claw clutch for 4-wheel drive shifting. Claw clutch has conventional type synchromesh system to ensure no damage to gears when shifting to 4-wheel drive while vehicle is in motion.

LUBRICATION & ADJUSTMENT

See the appropriate article in MANUAL TRANS-MISSION SERVICING Section.

TROUBLE SHOOTING

TRANSMISSION NOISE

Lubricant insufficient. Worn or chipped gears or bearings. If gear tooth surface is excessively worn, a growling sound should be apparent at high speed. When teeth are chipped, periodic knocking is audible at both high and low speeds.

DIFFERENTIAL NOISE

Lubricant insufficient. Tapered roller bearings out of adjustment. Ring and/or pinion gear out of adjustment, ring gear loose. Worn differential side gears, washers or pinion.

Fig. 1: Exploded View of Front Axle Assembly

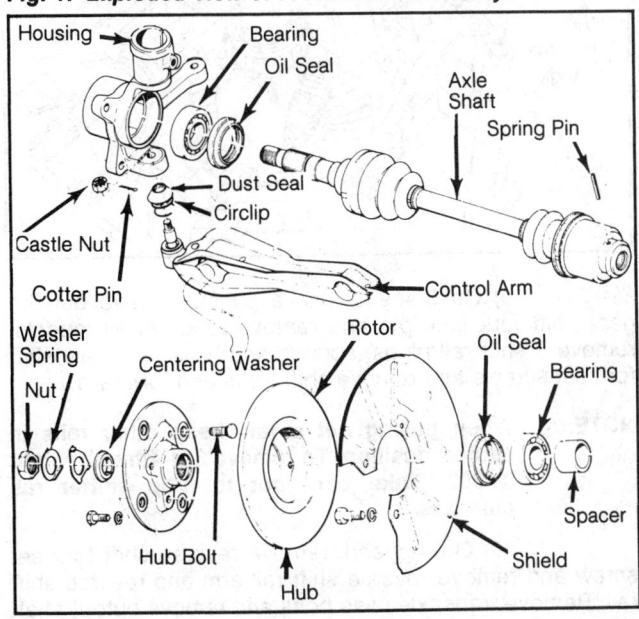

NOTE: Noise from exhaust system, tires, wheel bearings etc. is easily mistaken for differential noise. Eliminate these noises prior to disassembling differential.

HARD SHIFTING

Clutch not properly adjusted or hanging up when released. Worn, damaged or burred sleeve on gear spline or chamfered parts. Scratched bushings. Defective contact or worn synchro ring and gear cone.

SLIPS OUT OF GEAR

Loose engine mounts. Worn shifter fork or broken shifter fork rail spring. Damaged ball bearing. Excessive clearance between synchro hub and sleeve splines. Worn gears or bushings.

SERVICE (IN-VEHICLE)

WHEEL BEARINGS

Removal

1) Raise and support vehicle. Remove wheels. Disconnect parking brake linkage from caliper. Remove caliper mounting bolts and hang caliper from frame with wire. Do NOT remove hydraulic connection.

2) Remove bolts connecting shock absorber strut to housing. Remove parking brake hangar from tie rod, then remove cable bracket from housing. Straighten staked portion of axle nut and remove nut.

3) Remove tie rod ball joint and lower control arm ball joint from housing. Using a puller, remove hub and rotor assembly from axle shaft. Remove shield from housing and use a puller to remove housing from axle shaft.

Disassembly

Using brass drift and hammer, knock inner bearing from support housing. Pull out spacer and knock out outer bearing. Seals come out with bearings.

Reassembly

Use press drift and adapter to reassemble. Set bearing into adapter and press into outer side of housing until race is totally seated. Place .5 oz. bearing grease inside support housing, then insert spacer. Repeat above procedure to install outer bearing. Lubricate lips of oil seals lightly and press into position.

Installation

To install, reverse removal procedure and tighten all bolts.

AXLE DRIVE SHAFTS

Removal

1) Disconnect negative battery cable. Apply parking brake. Remove front wheel cap and cotter pin, and loosen castle nut and wheel nuts. Raise and support vehicle and remove front tires and wheels. Release parking brake. Remove parking brake cable bracket from transverse link.

2) Drive out spring pin of double offset joint. Remove disc brake assembly, disconnect tie-rod, transverse link and dampner strut. Remove axle shaft from differential spindle along with housing. Remove housing from axle shaft by using puller (921121000).

SUBARU 4 & 5-SPEED (Cont.)

Installation

To install, reverse removal procedure. Use a new retaining pin to secure inner axle shaft to drive axle. Tighten all bolts.

CONSTANT VELOCITY (CV) JOINTS
Disassembly

1) Straighten bent claw of larger end of boot on double offset joint side. Loosen band by means of screwdriver or pliers taking care not to damage boot. Remove boot band on the small end of double offset joint boot in the same manner.

2) Remove the larger end of boot on double offset joint side. Pry and remove round circlip located at the neck of outer race on double offset joint side with a screwdriver. Take out the outer race on double offset joint side from the shaft assembly.

3) Wipe off the grease and take out the balls. Move the cage to the boot side. Remove snap ring with snap ring pliers. Take out the inner race of the double offset joint.

4) Take out the cage of the double offset joint from the shaft and remove the boot from double offset joint with care not to damage it. Pull out the boot on the constant velocity joint side.

Fig. 2: Removing Outer Race and Ball Bearings

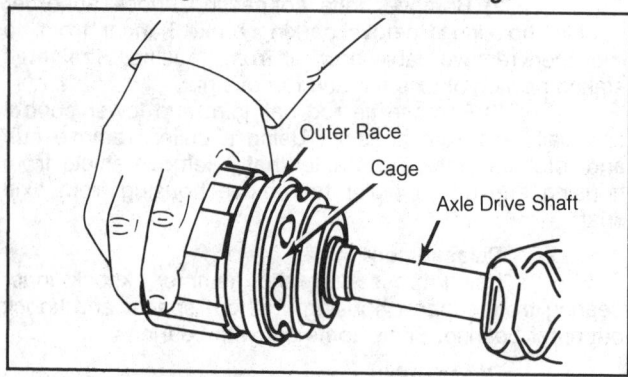

Inspection

Examine CV joint for corrosion, damage or wear. Ensure axle drive shaft does not have excessive deflection, twist or wear. Replace components as necessary.

Reassembly

To reassemble, reverse disassembly procedure. Grease constant velocity joint and double offset joint with Molylex No. 2 grease.

TRANSAXLE REMOVAL & INSTALLATION

See the appropriate article in MANUAL TRANSMISSION REMOVAL Section.

TRANSAXLE DISASSEMBLY

All Except Dual Range Models

1) Mount transaxle in work stand. Disconnect release bearing holder return springs. On 4WD single range models, remove transfer case cover and gasket.

Drive out shift fork retaining pin. Remove transfer shift rail, then remove shift fork, ball and spring.

2) Remove extension housing retaining bolts, extension housing and gasket. Lock transaxle in gear and install gear holder (498787000). Remove staking from pinion shaft lock nut and then remove lock nut. Shift gear to 1st position. Remove lock washer and transfer drive gear from pinion shaft.

3) Remove transfer case mounting bolts. Using a plastic hammer, tap transfer case off and remove gasket and shim. When removing shifter fork rail, be careful ball does not pop out of transmission case.

4) On all models, remove clutch release fork and release bearing holder. Remove transmission rear case, main case rear gasket, main shaft rear plate and back-up light clip. Remove drive pinion attaching bolts.

5) Clean spline portion of the axle drive shafts on right and left sides and wrap with vinyl tape. Separate transmission main case into right and left halves. Remove clutch cable bracket, back-up light cord clip, radio ground and oxygen sensor harness clip.

6) Remove drive pinion as shown in *Fig. 3*. Remove transmission main shaft. Remove differential. On 5-speed models, remove spring pin and 5th shifter fork. Do not mix right and left roller bearing outer races.

7) On all models, remove plugs, gaskets, springs and balls from case. Unscrew shifter fork set screws, and remove 3rd-4th and 1st-2nd shifter forks as well as shifter rails. Remove shifter set screw, reverse shifter rail arm and reverse shifter rail.

8) Remove oil seal holder lock plates, axle shaft oil seal holders and "O" rings. Remove snap ring and speedometer driven gear. Remove knock pins, reverse idler gear shaft, reverse idler gear and shifter lever.

Fig. 3: Prying Pinion Shaft Out of Case

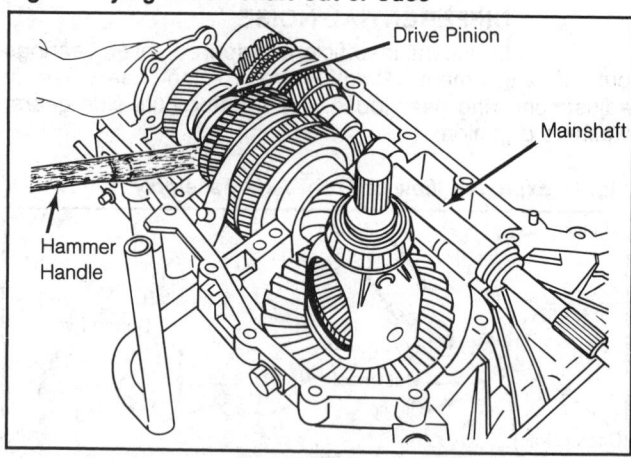

9) On 5-speed, use a punch to drive out 5th gear shift fork lock pin and remove fork. On all models, remove 3 shift rail plugs, springs and balls. Unscrew shift fork set screws and remove shift forks and fork rails.

NOTE: When pulling out a rail, keep other rails in neutral position. To remove 3rd-4th rail, rotate it 90°. Take care not to drop shifter rail plungers.

10) On 4-speed, remove reverse shift fork set screw and remove reverse shift rail arm and reverse shift rail. Remove transaxle case bolts and remove output shaft

SUBARU 4 & 5-SPEED (Cont.)

oil seal holder lock plates. Using remover (399780111), remove drive axle shaft oil seal holder and "O" ring.

11) Remove speedometer driven gear snap ring and gear. Lightly tap speedometer shaft out of case. Oil seal should come out with shaft. Remove reverse idler gear shaft retaining pins. Remove reverse idler gear shaft, idler gear and shift lever.

12) On 5-speed, remove reverse idler gear shaft retaining pins. Remove reverse idler gear shaft, idler gear and shift lever. Remove reverse shift rail outer snap ring, then remove shift rail arm and shift rail. Remove reverse shift ball, spring and plunger.

13) Remove output shaft oil seal holder. Using remover (399780111), remove drive axle shaft oil seal holder and "O" ring. Remove speedometer driven gear snap ring and gear. Lightly tap speedometer shaft out of case. Oil seal should come out with shaft.

NOTE: When removing reverse shift rail arm, ensure ball does not pop out of case.

Fig. 4: Removing Mainshaft and Differential Assembly from Transaxle Case

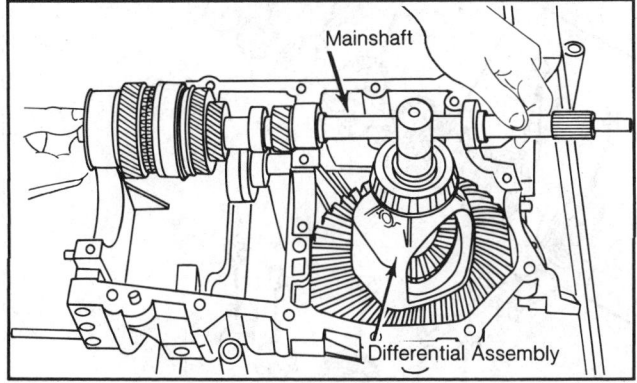

Mainshaft

Differential Assembly

Dual Range 4WD Models

1) Set transmission in stand. Remove clutch release fork and release bearing holder complete. Remove transfer case cover. Punch out the spring pin connecting high-low shifter rod to rod arm. Remove clip on transfer shifter rail with screwdriver after shifting transfer shifter rail into "4WD LO" position.

2) Pull out transfer shifter rail after shifting into "4WD HI" position. When pulling out, fix both high-low shifter arm and transfer shifter fork into "4WD HI" position in order not to interlock plunger. Be careful that ball does not fly out and drop into transfer case. Remove pin and clip on interlock rail with pliers.

3) Pull out interlock rail by turning 90°. Be careful that pin and clip on interlock rail do not fly out. Remove transfer shifter fork from transfer case, turning it in order not to interfere with high-low shifter rail. Be carefull not to loose ball and spring. Remove extension assembly.

4) Loosen front nut of rod adjusting screw connecting high-low shifter rod with ball joint assembly, and loosen rear nut (nut is left-hand threaded). Disconnect high-low shifter rod from rod arm by turning rod adjust arm screw clockwise. Disconnect rod ball joint assembly from high-low shifter center pivot by removing nut.

5) Punch out spring pin connecting high-low shifter rail to rod arm and remove rod arm. Punch out

spring pin connecting high-low shifter rail to high-low shifter arm and remove high-low shifter rail and arm. Be careful not to lose ball and plunger. Lock transmission main shaft with stopper (498787000). Release staking and remove lock nut.

6) Shift gear to 1st position to prevent shaft from turning. Remove transfer case attaching bolts. Pull out transfer case by about .040" (10 mm). Separate transfer case from main case by tapping with plastic hammer. Remove ball bearing attaching bolts at the drive pinion gear.

7) Remove input shaft holder attaching bolts. Wrap spline portions of axle shafts with vinyl tape. Separate transmission main case into left and right halves. Remove clutch cable bracket, oxygen sensor harness clip, radio ground, back-up light clips, clutch cable clamp, and stopper plate.

8) Punch out spring pin and remove high-low shift lever center pivot. Turn 90° and remove high-low shift fork. Pull countergear shaft forward until it hits on transmission main case and remove clip with screwdriver. Slide countergear washer to the rear and remove knock pin from countergear shaft.

9) Remove countergear shaft from main case being careful not to drop countergear and washers. Remove countergear from main case. Remove drive pinion as shown in *Fig. 3*. Remove transmission main shaft. Remove differential. *See Fig. 4*. Do not mix right and left roller bearing outer races.

10) Remove plugs, gaskets, springs and balls from case. Unscrew shifter fork set screws, and remove 3rd-4th and 1st-2nd shifter forks as well as shifter rails. Remove shifter set screw, reverse shifter rail arm and reverse shifter rail.

11) Remove oil seal holder lock plates, axle shaft oil seal holders and "O" rings. Remove snap ring and speedometer driven gear. Remove knock pins, reverse idler gear shaft, reverse idler gear and shifter lever.

12) Remove 3 shift rail plugs, springs and balls. Unscrew shift fork set screws and remove shift forks and fork rails. When pulling out a rail, keep other rails in neutral position. To remove 3rd-4th rail, rotate it 90°. Take care not to drop shifter rail plungers.

13) Remove reverse shift fork set screw and remove reverse shift rail arm and reverse shift rail. Remove transaxle case bolts and remove output shaft oil seal holder lock plates. Using remover (399780111), remove drive axle shaft oil seal holder and "O" ring.

14) Remove speedometer driven gear snap ring and gear. Lightly tap speedometer shaft out of case. Oil seal should come out with shaft. Remove reverse idler gear shaft retaining pins. Remove reverse idler gear shaft, idler gear and shift lever.

NOTE: When removing reverse shift rail arm, ensure ball does not pop out of case.

COMPONENT DISASSEMBLY & REASSEMBLY

MAINSHAFT

Disassembly

1) On 4WD dual range models, separate mainshaft assembly from input shaft, and remove high-low

Manual Transmissions
SUBARU 4 & 5-SPEED (Cont.)

Fig. 5: Exploded View of Transaxle Assembly Components

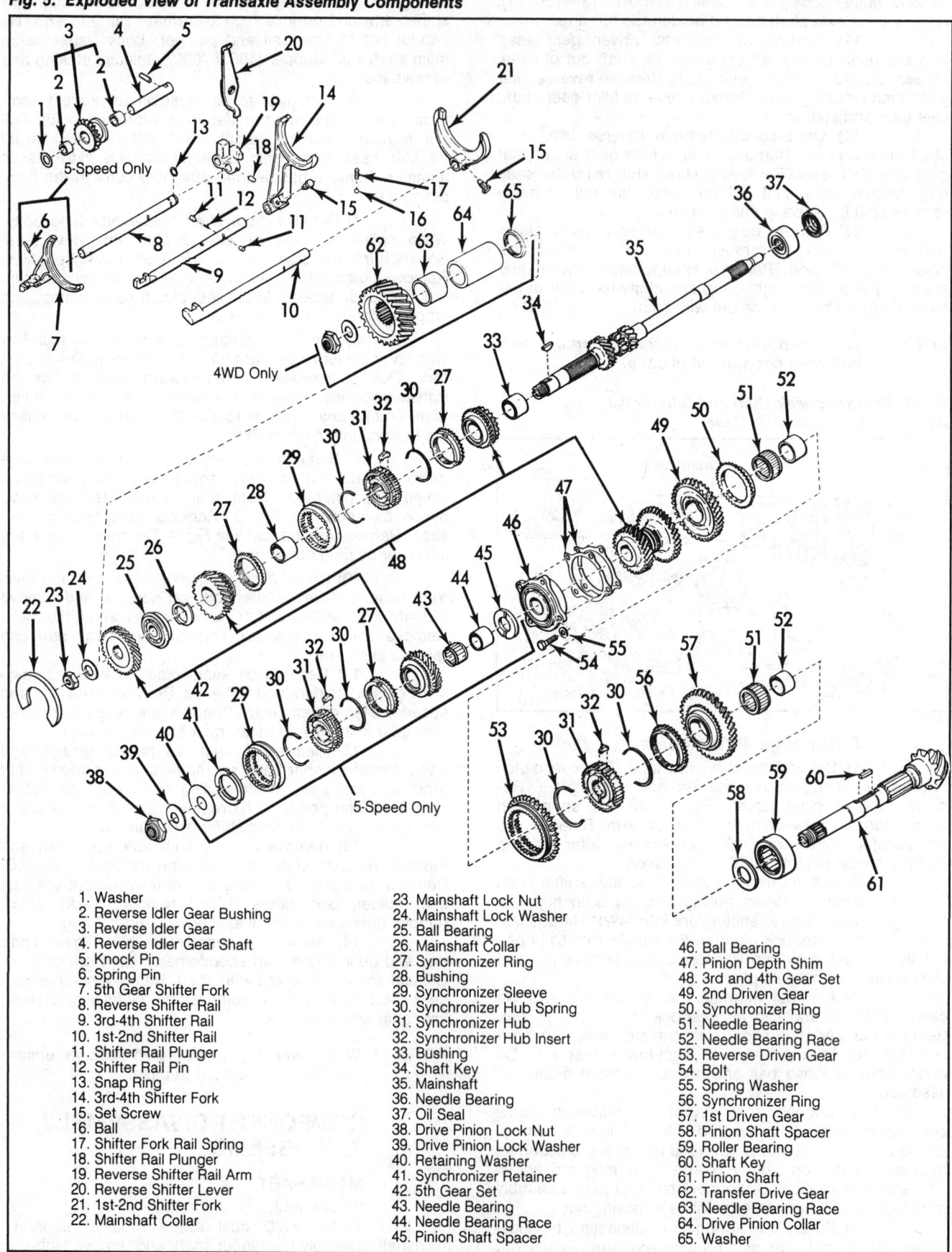

1. Washer
2. Reverse Idler Gear Bushing
3. Reverse Idler Gear
4. Reverse Idler Gear Shaft
5. Knock Pin
6. Spring Pin
7. 5th Gear Shifter Fork
8. Reverse Shifter Rail
9. 3rd-4th Shifter Rail
10. 1st-2nd Shifter Rail
11. Shifter Rail Plunger
12. Shifter Rail Pin
13. Snap Ring
14. 3rd-4th Shifter Fork
15. Set Screw
16. Ball
17. Shifter Fork Rail Spring
18. Shifter Rail Plunger
19. Reverse Shifter Rail Arm
20. Reverse Shifter Lever
21. 1st-2nd Shifter Fork
22. Mainshaft Collar

23. Mainshaft Lock Nut
24. Mainshaft Lock Washer
25. Ball Bearing
26. Mainshaft Collar
27. Synchronizer Ring
28. Bushing
29. Synchronizer Sleeve
30. Synchronizer Hub Spring
31. Synchronizer Hub
32. Synchronizer Hub Insert
33. Bushing
34. Shaft Key
35. Mainshaft
36. Needle Bearing
37. Oil Seal
38. Drive Pinion Lock Nut
39. Drive Pinion Lock Washer
40. Retaining Washer
41. Synchronizer Retainer
42. 5th Gear Set
43. Needle Bearing
44. Needle Bearing Race
45. Pinion Shaft Spacer

46. Ball Bearing
47. Pinion Depth Shim
48. 3rd and 4th Gear Set
49. 2nd Driven Gear
50. Synchronizer Ring
51. Needle Bearing
52. Needle Bearing Race
53. Reverse Driven Gear
54. Bolt
55. Spring Washer
56. Synchronizer Ring
57. 1st Driven Gear
58. Pinion Shaft Spacer
59. Roller Bearing
60. Shaft Key
61. Pinion Shaft
62. Transfer Drive Gear
63. Needle Bearing Race
64. Drive Pinion Collar
65. Washer

SUBARU 4 & 5-SPEED (Cont.)

synchronizer ring. Be careful not to drop needle bearing in input shaft. Remove snap ring with expander (899474100).

2) Remove the following parts by hand: High-low synchronizer hub with inserts, springs and sleeve, high-low synchronizer ring, input low gear, input low gear collar, needle bearing, input low gear spacer, ball and needle bearing.

3) On 5-speed models, remove lock nut staking, then remove lock nut. Using a press, remove 5th gear from shaft. Remove shaft key. On 4-speed models, remove snap ring from end of mainshaft.

NOTE: Snap ring should not be reused.

4) On all models, use press to remove ball bearing, 4th drive gear thrust plate, 4th drive gear, synchronizer hub, 4th drive gear bushing and 3rd drive gear.

NOTE: Do not remove 3rd drive gear bushing unless it is defective. If replacement is necessary, cut a groove in bushing, then press from mainshaft.

Fig. 6: Pressing Gears Off of Mainshaft

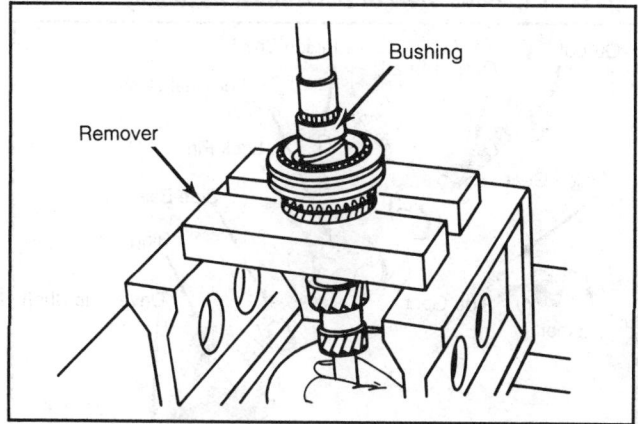

Cleaning & Inspection

Clean all parts and inspect carefully. Replace any parts which are worn or damaged. Lubricate all bearings with gear oil and spin to check for smooth and quiet operation. Replace synchro ring if ring gap is reduced to below limit .020" (.50 mm) when ring is pressed against cone. Standard clearance is .06" (1.5 mm).

Reassembly

1) If removed, install new 3rd gear bushing using press and installer (899580100) and retainer (899714110). Assemble synchro assemblies ensuring that hub spring ends are 120° apart. Note also that the shorter inserts are installed in 3rd-4th synchro and longer inserts in the 1st-2nd synchro.

2) Install 3rd drive gear and synchro assembly on mainshaft ensuring that narrower tooth width of synchro spline is on 3rd gear side. Press synchro assembly on mainshaft, if necessary.

3) Press 4th drive gear bushing onto mainshaft. Install 4th drive gear and thrust plate. Press bearing onto shaft. On 4-speed models, install 1 of 12 available snap rings on shaft to obtain 0-.002" (0-.05 mm) end play. On 5-speed models, install shaft key and press 5th drive gear onto shaft. Install lock nut, tighten and restake.

Fig. 7: Exploded View of Synchro Hub Assembly

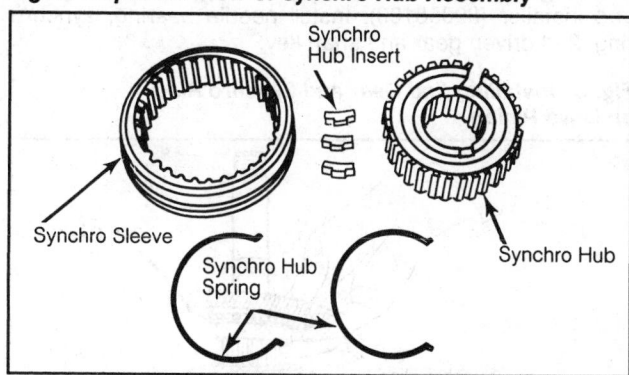

4) On 4WD single range models, install washer, drive pinion collar, transfer needle bearing race and transfer drive gear to drive pinion with press and installer (899580100). Tighten lock washer and nut. Do not stake at this time.

5) On 4WD dual range models, install 3 high-low synchronizer inserts, sleeve and 2 springs on synchronizer hub. Install springs so that relative positions of cut ends are 120° apart.

6) Install needle bearing, ball, input low gear spacer, needle bearing, input low gear collar, input low gear, high-low synchronizer ring and hub assembly previously assembled.

PINION SHAFT

Disassembly

1) Remove pinion shaft lock nut if still installed. On 5-speed models, remove lock washer, insert stopper plate, insert guide, synchro hub, 5th driven gear and needle bearing. Press 5th needle bearing race, 5th driven gear thrust plate and bearing from shaft.

2) On all models, use a press to remove 3rd-4th driven gear, rear bearing and any components between bearing and end of shaft. Remove 2nd driven gear and needle bearing.

3) Using a press, remove 1st driven gear, synchro/reverse driven gear assembly and needle bearing race. Remove shaft key and needle bearing. Use a press to remove pinion spacer and needle bearing race. Remove roller bearing.

Cleaning & Inspection

Clean all parts and inspect carefully. Replace any parts which are worn or damaged. Lubricate all bearings with engine oil and spin to check for smooth ahd quiet operation. Replace synchro ring if ring gap is reduced to below limit of .020" (.50 mm) when ring is pressed against cone. Standard clearance is .06" (1.5 mm).

Reassembly

1) Install roller bearing on drive pinion and install drive pinion thrust plate with a press and drive pinion installers (899278600, 899874100 and 899580100).

2) Install three 1st-2nd synchro inserts, reverse driven gear and 2 synchro springs on 1st-2nd synchro hub. Ensure synchro spring cut ends are 120° apart. Also check that toothed side of reverse driven gear and lower boss of synchro hub point in same direction.

3) Install needle bearing race with press and installers (899874100 and 899580100). Install needle bearing, 1st driven gear and synchro/reverse driven gear

Manual Transmissions

SUBARU 4 & 5-SPEED (Cont.)

assembly. Install 1st-2nd needle bearing race with press and installer (89958100). Install needle bearing, synchro ring, 2nd driven gear and shaft key.

Fig. 8: Installing 2nd Gear and Synchro Ring on Drive Pinion

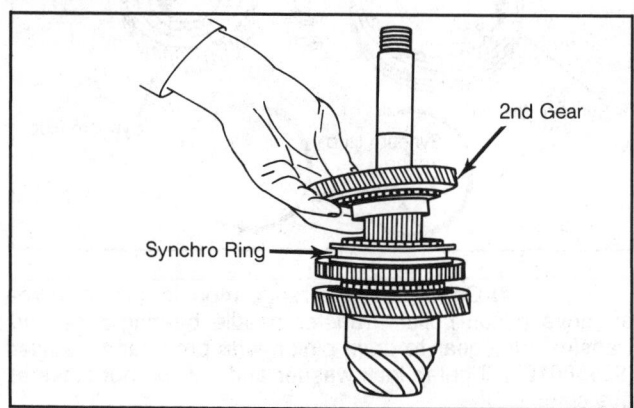

4) Install 3rd-4th driven gear using a press and installer (899580100). Install rear bearing using press and installer tool (899874100).

NOTE: If bearing slides onto shaft without being pressed on, no problem is indicated.

Fig. 9: Installing 3rd-4th Driven Gear on Drive Pinion

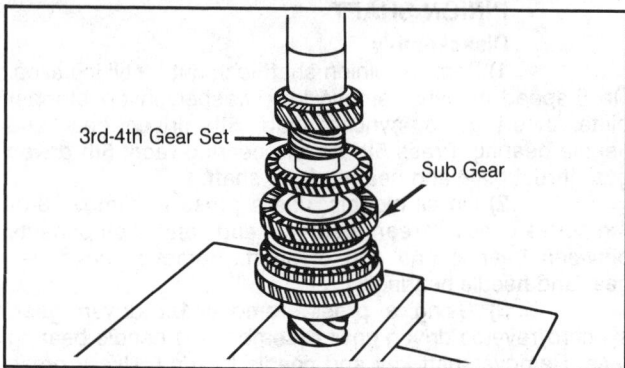

5) On 4-speed, install lock washer and tighten lock nut. On 5-speed, install thrust plate, then press needle bearing race onto shaft. Install needle bearing, 5th driven gear, synchro hub, insert guide, insert stopper plate, lock washer and lock nut. On 4WD, install washer, pinion shaft collar, rear shaft drive gear, lock washer and lock nut.

NOTE: On all models except 4WD, stake pinion shaft lock nut at this time.

DIFFERENTIAL ASSEMBLY

Disassembly

1) Remove snap rings securing drive axle shafts to differential assembly and remove shafts. Right and left shafts are not interchangeable; mark for reassembly reference. Bend back ring gear bolt locking tabs. Remove ring gear bolts and lift off ring gear.

2) Using a drift, remove pinion shaft retaining pin and pull out pinion shaft. Remove side gears, pinion gears and thrust washers. Remove side bearings with a puller.

Cleaning & Inspection

Wash and carefully inspect all parts. Replace all worn or damaged parts.

Fig. 10: Removing or Installing Pinion Shaft in Differential Case

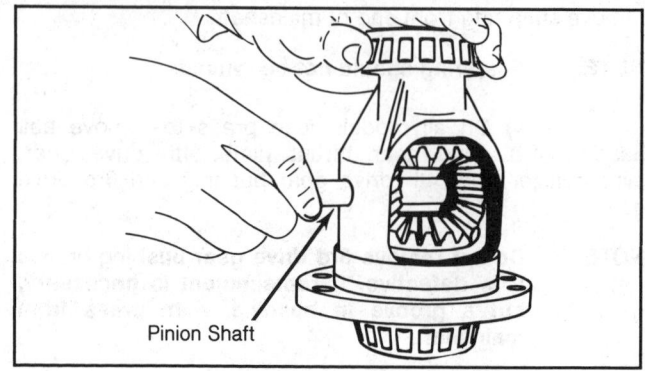

Fig. 11: Exploded View of Differential Assembly

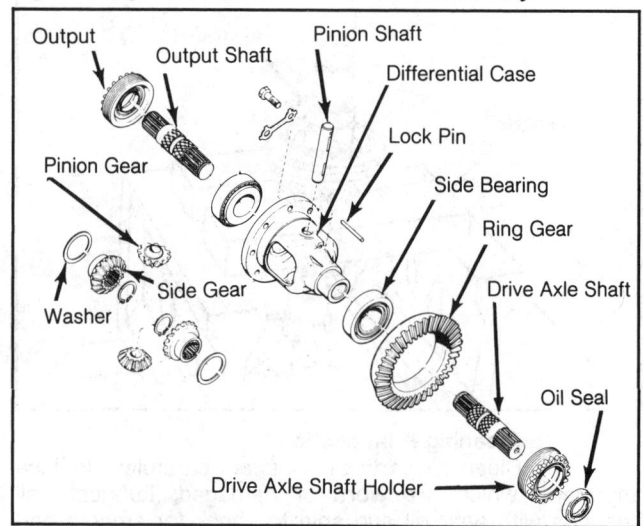

Reassembly

1) Install differential side gears, pinions and washers in differential case. Insert pinion shaft. Measure side gear and pinion backlash. Backlash should be .005-.007" (.13-.18 mm). If backlash is not correct, make adjustments by selecting a different thickness of washer.

2) Align pinion shaft with holes in case and drive lock pin from ring gear side until pin falls about .039" (1 mm) below surface. Lock pin in position by peening hole. Press side bearings onto case. Install ring gear. Install and tighten ring gear bolts, then bend locking tabs to hold bolts.

3) Install drive axle shafts and secure with snap rings. Measure clearance between pinion shaft and tip of drive axle shaft. Adjust clearance to less than .008" (.2 mm) by using thicker snap ring.

NOTE: Snap rings are available in 2 thicknesses: .039-.043" (1.0-1.1 mm) and .045-.049" (1.15-1.25 mm).

SUBARU 4 & 5-SPEED (Cont.)

Fig. 12: Pressing Differential Bearings onto Case

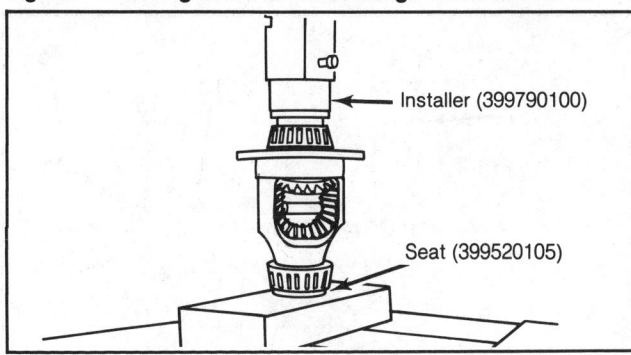

Installer (399790100)

Seat (399520105)

TRANSFER CASE (4WD MODELS ONLY)

Disassembly

Remove "O" ring from shifter arm and remove arm. Remove filler plug and gasket from transfer case. Remove reverse accent spring and ball. Remove back-up light switch and gasket. Remove plug, gasket, reverse accent shaft and spring. Using a hammer and aluminum rod, drive needle bearing out of case.

Cleaning & Inspection

Wash and carefully inspect all parts. Replace all worn or damaged parts.

Reassembly

1) Place needle bearing in bore of case with marked side toward front of case and press in until marked side is flush with case. Install snap ring to transfer case with fingers. Insert reverse return spring and reverse accent shaft, fit an aluminum adjusting gasket on plug and tighten plug.

2) Place an aluminum gasket on back-up light switch and install switch. Install ball and shifter fork rail spring in case, place aluminum washer on filler plug and tighten plug. Slide shifter arm into case and install "O" ring on arm.

EXTENSION HOUSING (4WD MODELS ONLY)

Disassembly

1) Remove snap ring from extension housing, then drive rear drive shaft from housing using a hammer and aluminum rod. Remove oil seal from rear of housing. Shift synchro into drive position. Install holder (899884100) on shaft and mount assembly in a vise.

2) Unstake lock nut and remove lock nut and lock washer. Mount shaft assembly on retainer (899714110) and press out shaft. Remove bearing, spacer collar, rear driven gear, bushing, synchro hub and spacer.

Cleaning & Inspection

Wash and carefully inspect all parts. Replace all worn or damaged parts. Pay particular attention to extension housing rear bushing. If it is excessively worn or scratched, replace it.

Reassembly

1) Assemble synchronizer sleeve on the synchronizer hub. Be sure to use sleeve without reverse taper. Press rear bearing onto shaft. Install new oil seal in rear of extension housing. Using a plastic hammer, tap rear drive shaft into extension housing. Install snap ring in groove in extension housing. Install rear drive spacer, synchro hub and sleeve assembly to rear drive shaft.

2) Using a press, install driven gear bushing to rear drive shaft. Fit transfer driven gear and 4th drive gear thrust plate to rear drive shaft. Press fit front bearing on shaft. Shift synchro sleeve into drive position, install holder on driven gear, install lock washer and tighten lock nut. Stake nut.

Fig. 13: Removing Snap Ring from Extension Housing

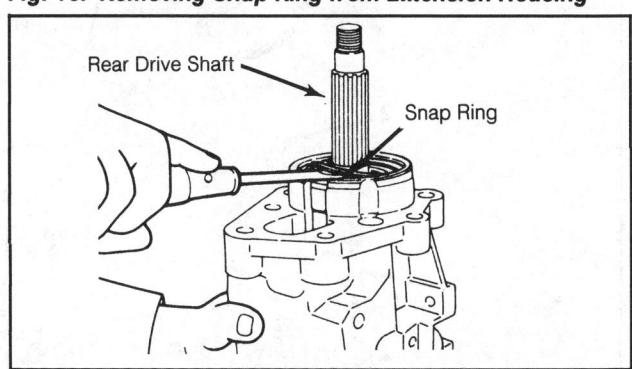

Rear Drive Shaft

Snap Ring

TRANSAXLE REASSEMBLY & ADJUSTMENT

PINION SHAFT DEPTH ADJUSTMENT

NOTE: **This adjustment must be performed using Subaru Pinion Gauge (899914100).**

1) Install pinion shaft assembly in transaxle case half (right half) with no shims between rear bearing and case. Install and tighten 2 pinion shaft retaining bolts to 22 ft. lbs. (30 N.m).

2) Place pinion gauge on its edge on a level surface, then loosen 2 setting bolts on gauge plate. Adjust gauge plate so scale indicates 0.5 when edges of plate and scale are even. Tighten bolts. Place calibrated gauge into case as shown in *Fig. 14*.

NOTE: **Ensure dowel pins of gauge are installed in dowel holes of transaxle case.**

3) Slide gauge scale along plate until it comes in contact with drive pinion, then read and record value shown on scale. The thickness of shim(s) required to obtain correct drive pinion depth is determined by adding or subtracting value stamped on end of pinion to or from gauge scale value.

Fig. 14: Measuring Pinion Shaft Depth Using Special Gauge

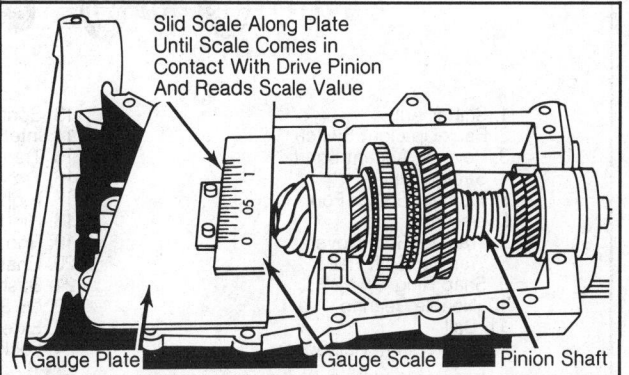

Slid Scale Along Plate Until Scale Comes in Contact With Drive Pinion And Reads Scale Value

Gauge Plate

Gauge Scale

Pinion Shaft

Manual Transmissions

SUBARU 4 & 5-SPEED (Cont.)

Fig. 15: Exploded View of 4WD Transfer Case, Extension Housing and Related Components

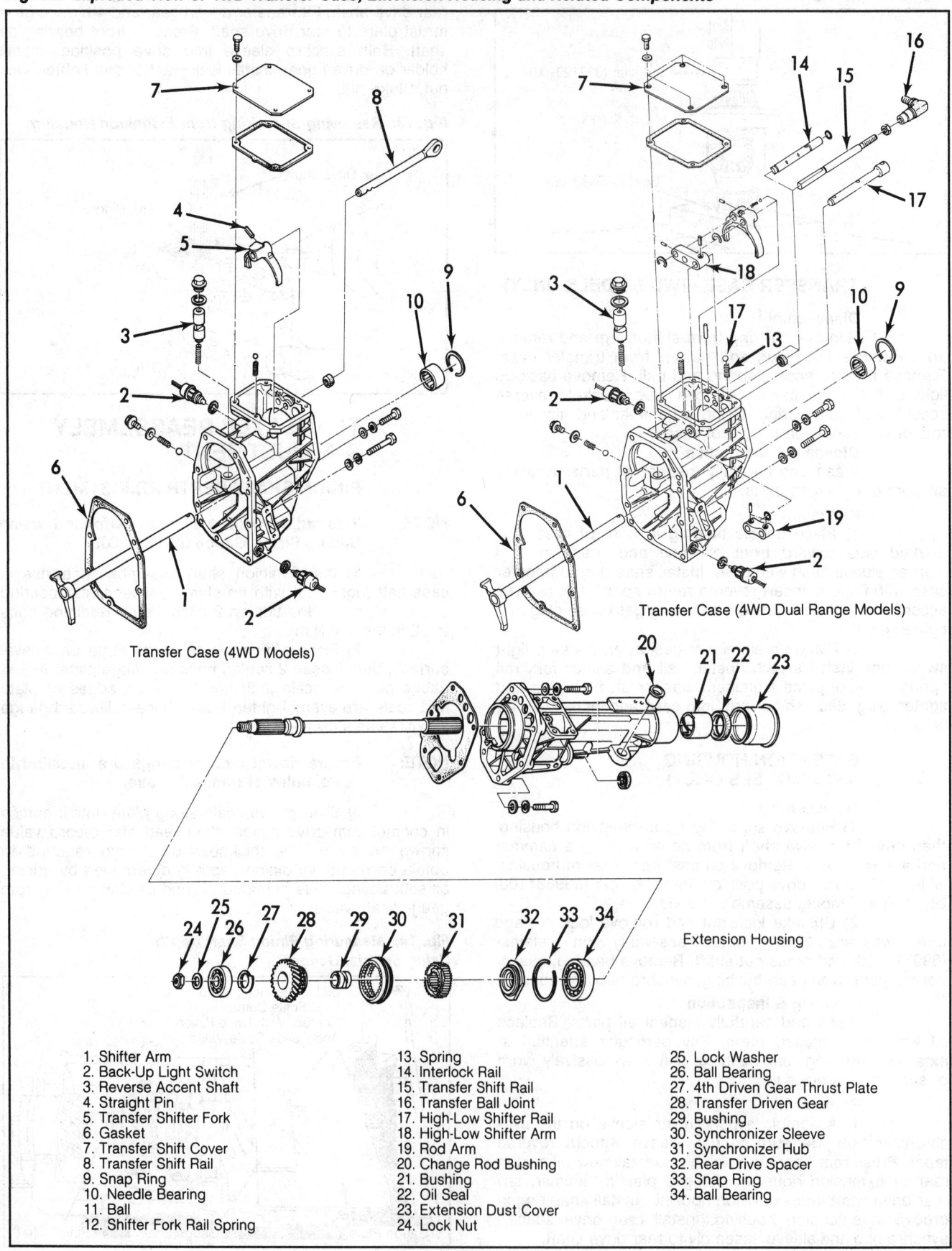

Transfer Case (4WD Models)

Transfer Case (4WD Dual Range Models)

Extension Housing

1. Shifter Arm
2. Back-Up Light Switch
3. Reverse Accent Shaft
4. Straight Pin
5. Transfer Shifter Fork
6. Gasket
7. Transfer Shift Cover
8. Transfer Shift Rail
9. Snap Ring
10. Needle Bearing
11. Ball
12. Shifter Fork Rail Spring
13. Spring
14. Interlock Rail
15. Transfer Shift Rail
16. Transfer Ball Joint
17. High-Low Shifter Rail
18. High-Low Shifter Arm
19. Rod Arm
20. Change Rod Bushing
21. Bushing
22. Oil Seal
23. Extension Dust Cover
24. Lock Nut
25. Lock Washer
26. Ball Bearing
27. 4th Driven Gear Thrust Plate
28. Transfer Driven Gear
29. Bushing
30. Synchronizer Sleeve
31. Synchronizer Hub
32. Rear Drive Spacer
33. Snap Ring
34. Ball Bearing

SUBARU 4 & 5-SPEED (Cont.)

4) Add if value stamped on pinion is prefixed by a "+"; subtract if value is prefixed by a "-". Select from 1 to 3 adjusting shims which will equal value just obtained. Remove gauge and pinion shaft from case.

NOTE: If no value is stamped on pinion, value is zero. Adjusting shim(s) will be installed during Transaxle Reassembly.

TRANSAXLE REASSEMBLY
All Except 4WD Dual Range Models
1) Press new oil seals into axle drive shaft holders. Place speedometer shaft side of transmission case in a work stand, then screw axle shaft holder (without "O" ring) into case until threads are embedded completely in case.

2) Install speedometer shaft outer snap ring and washer on shaft, then install assembly in case. Install speedometer driven gear on shaft and retain with outer snap ring. Press in new speedometer shaft oil seal.

NOTE: Install speedometer driven gear snap ring from driven gear side to avoid damaging oil seal.

3) On 5-speed, insert reverse shift arm spring and ball into reverse shift rail arm. Install reverse shift rail into case, then fit shift rail arm onto shift rail and install snap ring. Install shift fork rail spring, ball and gasket into case and tighten shift rail spring plug.

4) Install reverse idler gear and shaft. Select shift lever that will provide .06-.12" (1.5-3.0 mm) clearance between reverse idler gear and case wall when shifting reverse shift rail. Remove reverse idler gear and shaft. Install and tighten correct shift lever. Shift lever to neutral position and reinstall reverse idler gear and shaft.

5) Select washer that will provide a clearance of less than .02" (.5 mm) between washer and case wall. Remove reverse idler gear and shaft. Install washer and reinstall reverse idler assembly. Install retaining pins. Install 5th shift fork onto reverse shift rail and secure with spring pin.

6) On all other models, install reverse shift lever into case. Install reverse idler gear and shaft into case and retain with pin. Install reverse shift rail arm to end of reverse shift lever, then install reverse shift rail and tighten set screw. Install reverse shift fork rail spring, ball and gasket into case. Tighten spring plug.

7) Move reverse shift rail to reverse position and measure clearance between reverse idler gear and case. Install shift rail arm which will provide .06-.12" (1.5-

Fig. 16: Clearances Between Rails

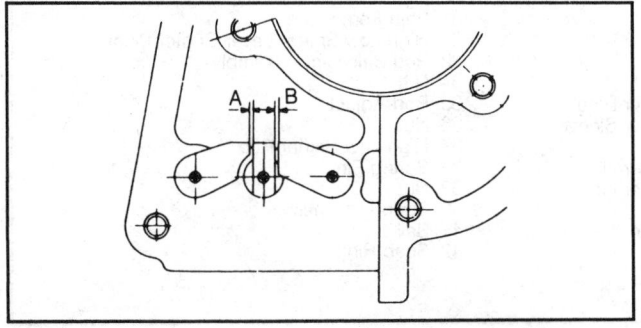

RAIL CLEARANCE VALUES

Application	In. (mm)
1600 cc Models	
"A"	.012-.063 (0.3-1.6)
"B"	.012-.063 (0.3-1.6)
1800 cc Models	
"A"	.012-.063 (0.3-1.6)
"B"	.071-.122 (1.8-3.1)

3.0 mm) clearance between gear and case. Install shift rail arm and secure with retaining pin.

8) On all models, wrap vinyl tape around splines of drive axle shafts to protect seals, then install differential in case. Install mainshaft in case, ensuring that dowel pin on case is fitted into hole in needle bearing outer race. Install shift rail pin in 3rd-4th shift rail, then install rail and 3rd-4th shift fork. Tighten set screw.

9) Install previously selected pinion depth adjusting shim(s) on pinion shaft rear bearing. If more than 1 shim is used, do not place slit ends of shims on same side. Install pinion shaft in case, ensuring that dowel pin on case is fitted into hole in rear bearing outer race.

10) Place shift rail plunger into hole in case. Install 1st-2nd shift rail and shift fork, then tighten set screw. Install shift rail balls, springs and plugs. Force mainshaft and pinion shaft toward front of case until there is no clearance between shafts and case.

Fig. 17: Transaxle Case Tightening Sequence

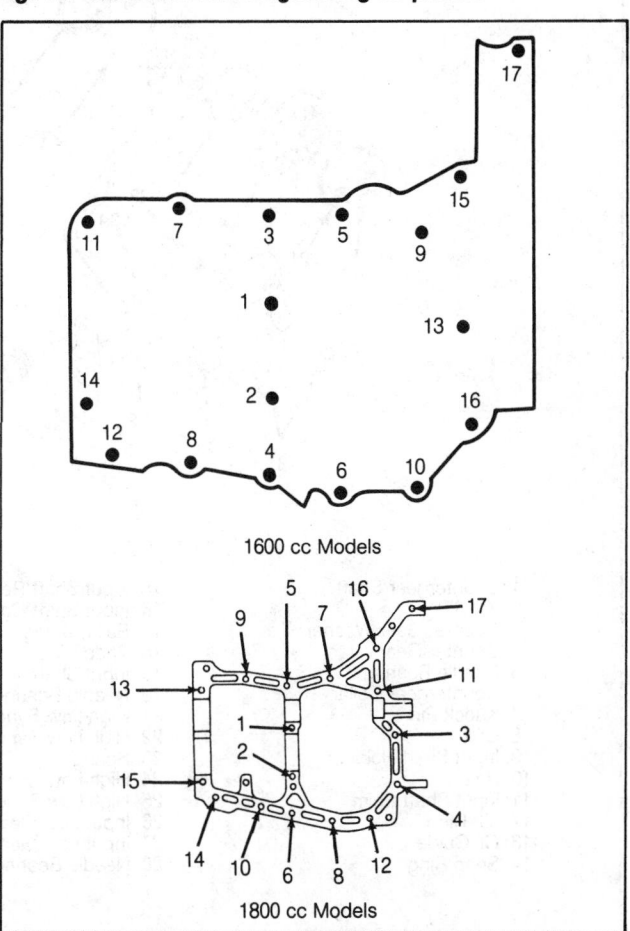

Manual Transmissions
SUBARU 4 & 5-SPEED (Cont.)

Fig. 18: Auxiliary Transmission and High-Low Shift Linkage (4WD Dual Range Models)

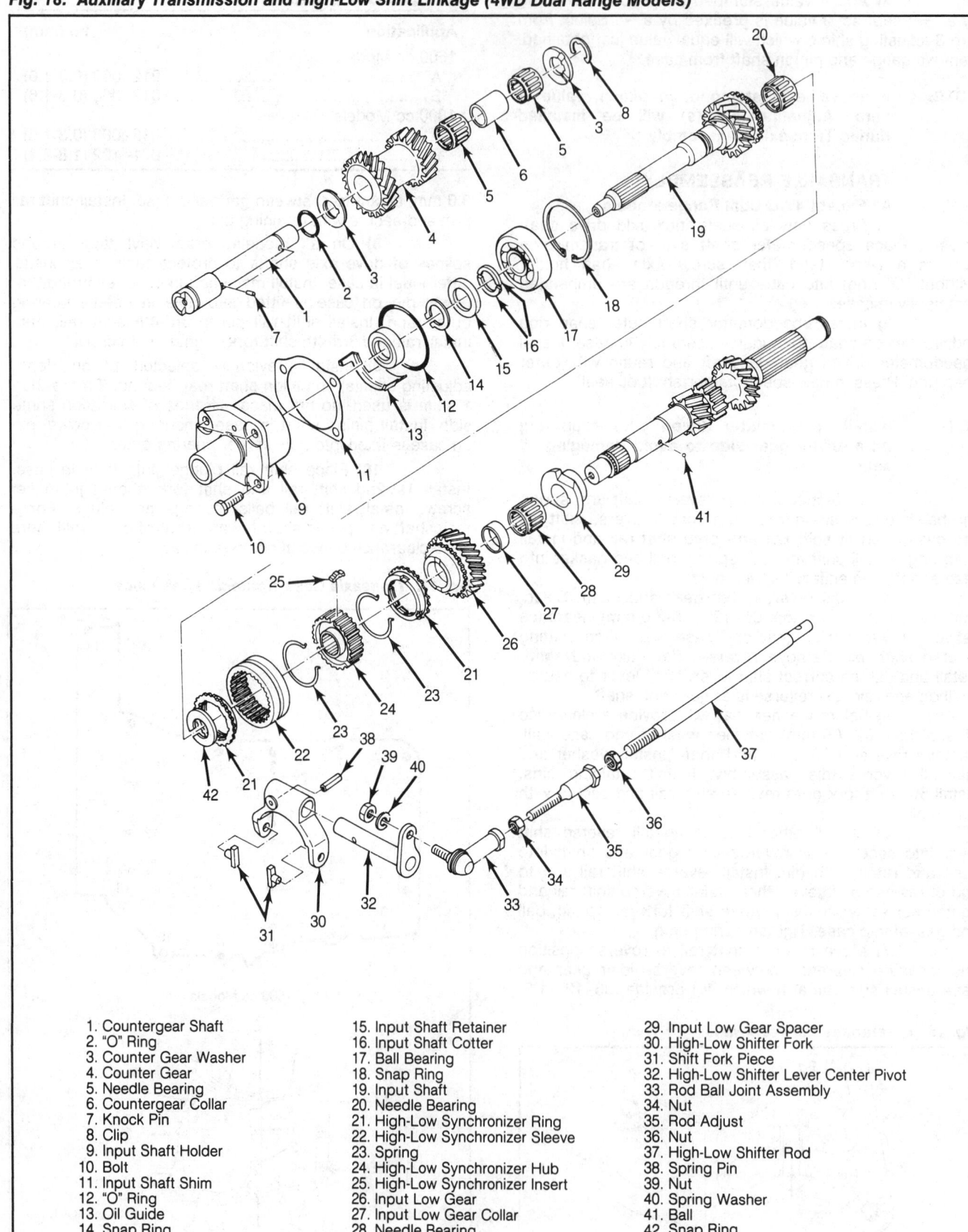

1. Countergear Shaft
2. "O" Ring
3. Counter Gear Washer
4. Counter Gear
5. Needle Bearing
6. Countergear Collar
7. Knock Pin
8. Clip
9. Input Shaft Holder
10. Bolt
11. Input Shaft Shim
12. "O" Ring
13. Oil Guide
14. Snap Ring

15. Input Shaft Retainer
16. Input Shaft Cotter
17. Ball Bearing
18. Snap Ring
19. Input Shaft
20. Needle Bearing
21. High-Low Synchronizer Ring
22. High-Low Synchronizer Sleeve
23. Spring
24. High-Low Synchronizer Hub
25. High-Low Synchronizer Insert
26. Input Low Gear
27. Input Low Gear Collar
28. Needle Bearing

29. Input Low Gear Spacer
30. High-Low Shifter Fork
31. Shift Fork Piece
32. High-Low Shifter Lever Center Pivot
33. Rod Ball Joint Assembly
34. Nut
35. Rod Adjust
36. Nut
37. High-Low Shifter Rod
38. Spring Pin
39. Nut
40. Spring Washer
41. Ball
42. Snap Ring

SUBARU 4 & 5-SPEED (Cont.)

11) Check that synchro sleeves (with rails in neutral) are centered between respective gears. Check that clearance between 5th driven gear and synchro sleeve is .41" (10.5 mm). If not, select correct shift forks (5 available) to provide this alignment.

12) Check clearance between edges of each shift rail. *See Fig. 16.* If clearance is not as listed in table, replace rail, fork and set screw. Install mainshaft oil seal. Clean mating surfaces of transaxle case halves, then apply sealant to all mating surfaces.

13) Align case halves while slightly shifting case so pinion depth shim(s) is not caught between case halves, then install and tighten attaching bolts. *See Fig. 17.* Install clutch cable bracket, back-up light cord clip, radio ground cord and oxygen sensor harness clip. Install and tighten pinion shaft retaining bolts.

Dual Range 4WD Models

1) Press new oil seals into axle drive shaft holders. Place speedometer shaft side of transmission case in a work stand, then screw axle shaft holder (without "O" ring) into case until threads are embedded completely in case.

2) Install speedometer shaft outer snap ring and washer on shaft, then install assembly in case. Install speedometer driven gear on shaft and retain with outer snap ring. Press in new speedometer shaft oil seal.

NOTE: Install speedometer driven gear snap ring from driven gear side to avoid damaging oil seal.

3) Install reverse shift lever into case. Install reverse idler gear and shaft into case and retain with pin. Install reverse shift rail arm to end of reverse shift lever, then install reverse shift rail and tighten set screw.

4) Install reverse shift fork rail spring, ball and gasket into case. Tighten spring plug. Move reverse shift rail to reverse position and measure clearance between reverse idler gear and case. Install shift rail arm which will provide .06-.12" (1.5-3.0 mm) clearance between gear and case.

5) Install shift rail arm and secure with retaining pin. Wrap vinyl tape around splines of drive axle shafts to protect seals, then install differential in case. Install "O" ring and knock pin at front side onto countergear shaft.

6) Install the following parts onto the countergear shaft when installing it into main case: 2 countergear washers, 2 needle bearings, countergear collar, knock pin and clip. Make sure the cut-out end surface of the countergear shaft does not protrude above the end surfaces of the case. *See Fig. 19.*

Fig. 19: Countergear Shaft Positioning

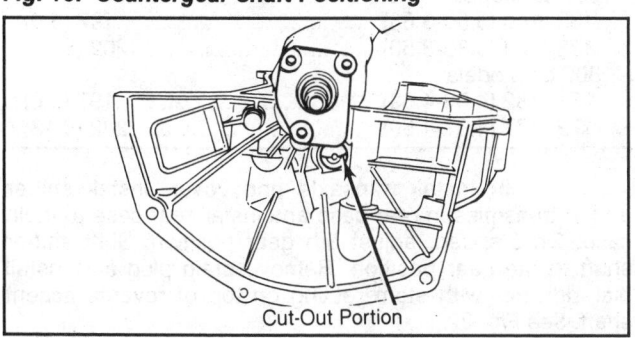

Cut-Out Portion

7) Put mainshaft assembly, needle bearing, high-low synchronizing ring and input shaft together. Shim input shaft with shim number determined by calculating measurement "D" shown in *Fig. 20.*

SHIM DETERMINATION ("D" Distance)

Shim Used	In. (mm)
No Shim	More than 1.984 (50.39)
No. 1	1.983-1.964 (50.38-49.89)
No. 2	Less than 1.96 (49.88)

Fig. 20: Adjustment of Input Shaft

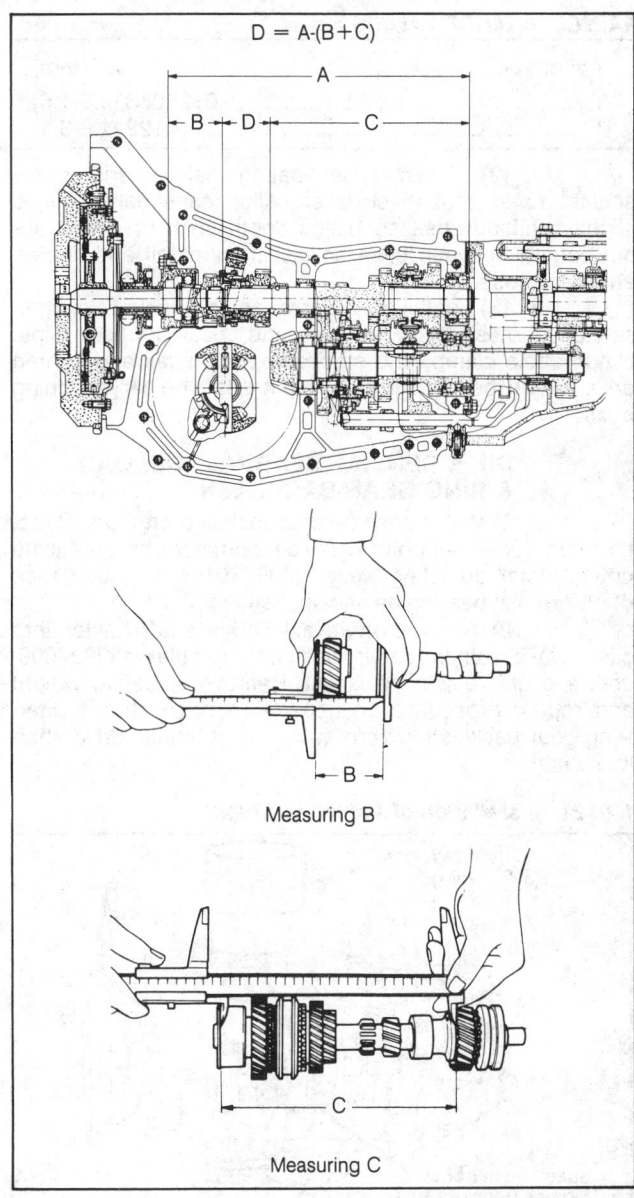

D = A-(B+C)

Measuring B

Measuring C

8) Install transmission mainshaft into case. Install high-low shifter fork with 2 high-low shifter pieces into high-low shifter sleeve. Install high-low shift lever into high-low shift fork through the case and install the pin.

9) Install the 3rd-4th shifter fork and rail with plunger and tighten set screw. Install previously selected shims and drive pinion assembly into case. Make sure the knock pin is fit to roller bearing outer race. Fit plunger to

Manual Transmissions

SUBARU 4 & 5-SPEED (Cont.)

case and install 1st-2nd shifter fork and rail. Tighten set screw.

10) Fit 3rd-4th and 1st-2nd shifter fork rail springs, balls, and gaskets into the case. Tighten the shifter rail spring plugs. Force mainshaft and pinion shaft toward front of case until there is no clearance between shafts and case.

11) Check that synchro sleeves (with rails in neutral) are centered between respective gears. Check clearance between edges of each shift rail. If clearance is not as shown in table, replace rail, fork and set screw. *See Fig. 17.*

RAIL CLEARANCE VALUES

Application	In. (mm)
"A"	.012-.063 (0.3-1.6)
"B"	.071-.122 (1.8-3.1)

12) Clean case mating halves and apply sealant to all mating surfaces. Align case halves while slightly shifting case so pinion depth shim or shims are not caught between case halves, then install and tighten attaching bolts.

13) Install the clutch cable bracket, oxygen sensor harness clip, radio ground, back-up light clips, clutch cable clamp, and stopper plate. Install and tighten drive pinion bolts. Tighten 3 input shaft holder attaching bolts.

DIFFERENTIAL BEARING PRELOAD & RING GEAR BACKLASH

1) With transaxle case installed on work stand, turn case until case half with speedometer shaft is facing down. Install adjusting weight (399780104) on outer race of differential bearing as shown. *See Fig. 21.*

2) Screw bottom axle drive shaft holder into case while rotating mainshaft with handle (499927000) until a slight resistance is felt. Remove adjusting weight and repeat procedure on upper axle drive shaft holder. Ring gear backlash is zero at this point. Install drive shaft lock plate.

Fig. 21: Installation of Adjusting Weight

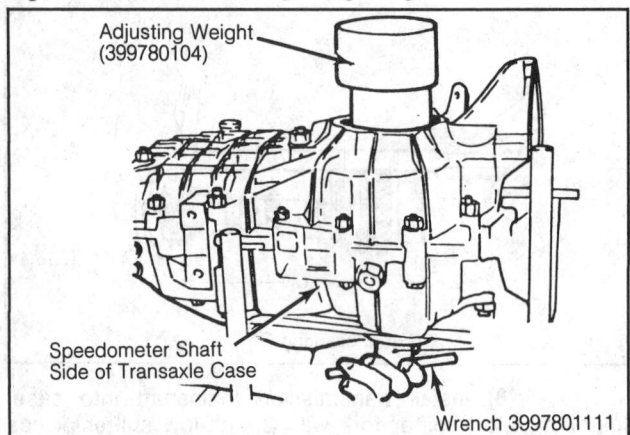

Adjusting Weight (399780104)

Speedometer Shaft Side of Transaxle Case

Wrench 3997801111

3) Loosen bottom drive shaft holder 1 1/2 notches, then screw in upper holder by the same amount to obtain ring gear backlash. Turn upper holder in an additional 1/2 to 1 notch to obtain differential bearing preload.

4) Tighten holder lock plates, then mark position of both holders for later readjustment. Turn mainshaft many times while tapping around axle shaft bearing holder lightly with a plastic hammer.

5) Install a dial indicator to transaxle case with tip of indicator inserted through transaxle drain hole and touching ring gear teeth. Measure ring gear backlash by rotating drive shafts back and forth taking up free play. If backlash does not match specification in table, repeat adjustment procedure.

RING GEAR BACKLASH

Application	In. (mm)
1600 cc Models	.004-.007 (.10-.18)
1800 cc Models	.005-.007 (.13-.18)

FINAL ASSEMBLY

All Except 4WD Dual Range

1) With differential bearing preload and ring gear backlash correctly adjusted, remove both axle drive shaft holders. Install "O" ring seal on each holder. Reinstall holders into transaxle case, making sure alignment marks on holders and case are aligned.

2) Remove tape from around axle drive shaft splines. On 4WD models, remove pinion shaft lock nut, washer and rear shaft drive gear. Select a mainshaft collar which will provide 0-.012" (0-.30 mm) clearance between mainshaft bearing and transfer case.

3) Install gasket and transfer case (with selected mainshaft collar) on transaxle and install, but do not tighten, transfer case-to-transaxle mounting nuts. Install rear shaft drive gear, washer and lock nut. Tighten lock nut and stake in 4 places. Tighten transfer case-to-transaxle mounting nuts.

4) Install new "O" ring in shift arm groove. Install gasket and extension housing on transfer case and tighten bolts. Install rear drive shift fork. Install shift rail spring and ball in transfer case, then install rear drive shift rail. Install roll pin to secure fork to rail. Install gasket and transfer case cover.

5) On all models, use depth gauge to measure the amount of ball bearing protrusion from transmission main case surface and select mainshaft collar according to table. Before measuring, lightly tap the end of the mainshaft with a plastic hammer.

MAINSHAFT COLLAR SELECTION

Bearing Protrusion In. (mm)	Collar Thickness In. (mm)
1600 cc Models	
.138-.140 (3.50-3.63)	.197 (5.0)
.133-.138 (3.38-3.50)	.202 (5.13)
1800 cc Models	
.177-.182 (4.50-4.63)	.197 (5.0)
.172-.177 (4.37-4.50)	.202 (5.13)

6) Install transaxle end cover. Install shifter arm in transmisson rear case and install rear case to main case. On 5-speed, adjust 5th gear position. Shift shifter shaft to 5th gear position. Remove drain plug and install dial indicator with stem resting on top of reverse accent shaft. *See Fig. 22.*

SUBARU 4 & 5-SPEED (Cont.)

Fig. 22: Measuring Contact Clearance for 5th Gear Positioning

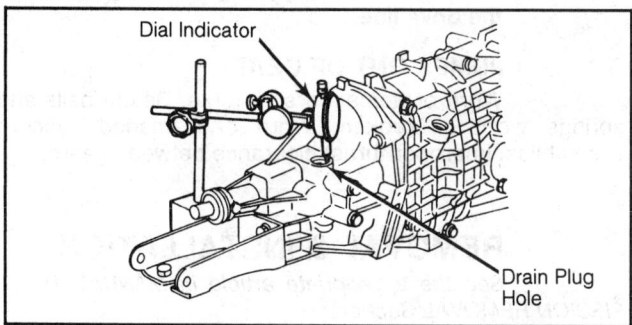

Dial Indicator

Drain Plug Hole

7) Measure clearance when shifter shaft is turned to revese side lightly. Select a reverse accent shaft so that contact clearance is within .002-.015" (.05-.40 mm). On all models, adjust gear selector as follows: Insert a rod through hole in shift arm and shift into 3rd gear.

8) Arm should move easily toward 1st-2nd gear side, but harder toward reverse side because of return spring action. Next, make adjustment to effort required to move lever to either position. Adjustment is performed by removing plug on cover and changing thickness of aluminum gasket.

9) On all except 4WD models, make adjustment so the heavy stroke (reverse side) is a little more than light side. On 4WD models, adjust strokes to take equal effort. On all models, install release bearing guide on case together with 2 release spring brackets.

10) Install clutch release fork and release bearing holder. Secure with release bearing holder spring. Install clutch release fork seal ring and spring. Fill internal groove of release bearing holder with grease.

4WD Dual Range

1) Remove lock plate, lock washer and transfer drive gear from drive pinion. Measure bearing protrusion and select proper bearing plate. Fit transfer case assembly with gasket and plate on main case and tighten bolts.

2) Transfer drive gear should be installed when clearance between main case and transfer case becomes approximately .394" (10 mm). Install lock washer and lock nut on drive pinion. When tightening, the gear should be shifted to the 1st position.

3) High-low shifter lever should be shifted to "HI" or "LO" position. After tightening nut, stake it. Install "O" ring in the side of high-low shifter rail bushing. Apply grease to plunger and fit into high-low shifter arm. Fit shifter fork rail spring and ball in transfer case, and install high-low shifter rail with high-low shifter arm.

4) Punch in straight pin into high-low shifter rail. Install extension assembly with transfer rear gasket and tighten. Before tightening, ensure that shifter arm center pivot can be shifted to any selected direction. Apply gear oil on shifter arm center pivot, and make sure oil seal fits.

5) Transfer drive and transfer driven gears should engage each other. Fit plunger, shifter fork rail spring and ball into transfer shifter fork, and install it to synchronizer sleeve. Apply gear oil to interlock rail, fit "O" ring to rail and insert rail into transfer case.

6) Punch in clip onto interlock rail groove, and insert knock pin into interlock rail hole. Install transfer ball joint assembly to transfer shifter rail. Adjust to 6.7-7.2" (171-185 mm) and tighten nut. Fit shifter fork rail spring and ball in transfer case, and install transfer shifter rail center pivot with transfer case in "4WD HI" so interlock mechanisim does not operate.

7) Fit clip onto transfer shifter rail groove. Fit nut, rod adjusting screw, nut and ball joint assembly to high-low shifter rod. Shorten linkage length by turning turnbuckle clockwise.

8) Insert rod arm into rear portion of high-low shifter rod, and punch in straight pin. Connect rod ball joint assembly with high-low shifter lever center pivot and tighten nut to the specified torque. Confirm operation by moving rod back and forth.

9) Shift transfer shifter rail into "4WD LO" position and fix high-low shifter rail by inserting stopper pin into its hole. Shift high-low shifter lever into LO position and lengthen linkage by turning turnbuckle counterclockwise while holding high-low shifter rod. Align holes of rod arm and high-low shifter rod, and punch in straight pin.

10) While holding rod ball joint assembly, turn rod adjusting screw counterclockwise and then turn back 90° clockwise at the point where ball joint movement becomes tight. Tighten rear nut, and then tighten front nut while holding rod ball joint assembly. Pull out stopper pin and confirm shift operation.

11) Install transfer case cover with gasket and tighten bolts. Insert a bar through shifter arm hole and shift gear to 3rd gear position. Shifter arm should turn lightly toward the 1st-2nd gear side and heavily toward the reverse side.

12) Remove plug on the transfer case and change the thickness of the aluminum gasket to adjust the heavy stroke (reverse side) to be the same as the light stroke. Install clutch release fork and release bearing holder by installing retainer spring into fork.

13) While pushing fork to pivot and twisting it to fit both sides, fit retainer spring onto constricted portion of pivot. Install holder and fasten with 2 clips. Install release fork seal ring.

TIGHTENING SPECIFICATIONS

Application	Ft. Lbs. (N.m)
Ball Joint Nut	25 (34)
Tie Rod Nut	22 (30)
Axle Shaft Nut	145 (197)
Drive Pinion-to-Case	22 (30)
Ring Gear-to-Differential	42-50 (57-68)
Transaxle Case Bolts	
8 mm Bolts	18 (24)
10 mm Bolts	29 (39)
Axle Shaft Holder Lock Plate	18 (24)
Drive Pinion Lock Nut	58 (79)
Transaxle Cover Bolts	16 (22)

Manual Transmissions

TOYOTA 4-SPEED — MODEL H42

Land Cruiser

DESCRIPTION

The Toyota model H42 transmission is a 4-speed unit, synchronized in all forward gears due to the use of blocker type synchronizer assemblies. All forward transmission gears are helical cut and in constant mesh. Reverse gears are spur cut type and are engaged by a sliding reverse idler gear.

NOTE: For Transfer Case service and repair procedures see appropriate article in OVERDRIVES & TRANSFER CASE Section.

LUBRICATION & ADJUSTMENT

See the appropriate article in MANUAL TRANS-MISSION SERVICING Section.

TROUBLE SHOOTING

HARD SHIFTING

Clutch not releasing. Check for proper adjustment, deformed clutch disc, seized or damaged pilot bearing. Incorrect or insufficient lubricant. Gearshift lever retainer binding or improperly lubricated. Shift forks worn or damaged. Shift shafts bent.

NOISY OPERATION

Improper or insufficient lubricant. Worn or damaged bushings, bearings and/or gears. Worn splines.

NOTE: When checking transmission for noise, ensure that it is not coming from other parts of the drive line.

JUMPS OUT OF GEAR

Worn or damaged shift forks. Detent balls and springs worn or broken. Worn or damaged synchro assemblies. Improper thrust clearance between gears.

REMOVAL & INSTALLATION

See the appropriate article in MANUAL TRANSISSION REMOVAL Section.

TRANSMISSION DISASSEMBLY

1) Remove transmission rear bearing retainer and spacer. Remove transmission shift cover assembly and side cover. Remove front bearing retainer from transmission case.

2) Remove countershaft front bearing retaining snap rings (inner and outer), then remove bearing from transmission case using a puller. Using the same procedure, remove countershaft rear bearing and thrust washer.

3) Drive input shaft assembly and bearing from case. Remove output shaft bearing snap ring, then pull bearing from transmission case with a puller.

4) Hold 1st gear tightly against the other gears to prevent gear from sliding off, then lift output shaft assembly from transmission case. See Fig. 2. Remove countershaft from case.

5) Drive reverse idler gear shaft out rear of case using care not to lose Woodruff key. Lift reverse idler

Fig. 1: Disassembled View of Land Cruiser 4-Speed Transmission Assembly

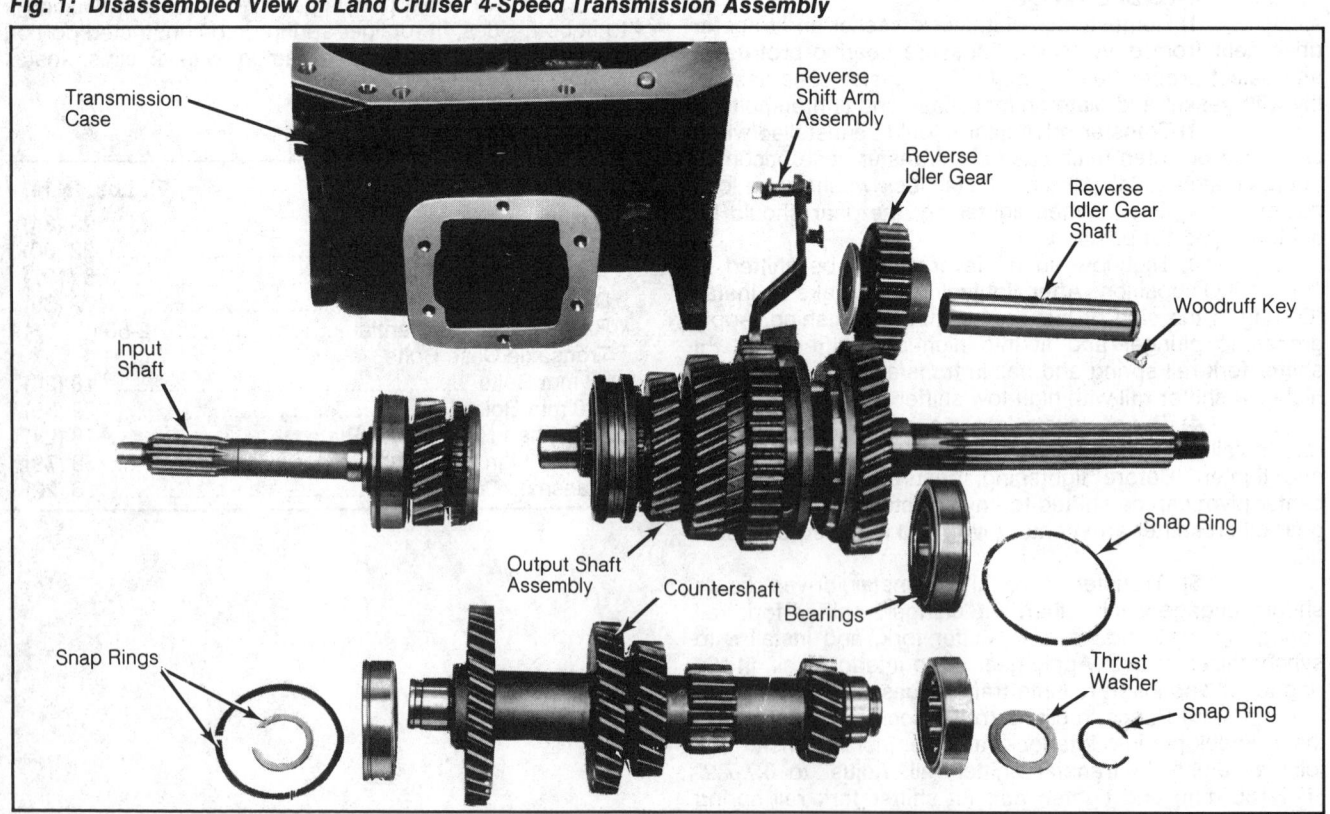

Manual Transmissions

TOYOTA 4-SPEED — MODEL H42 (Cont.)

gear from bottom of transmission case. Remove reverse shift arm assembly from case.

Fig. 2: Lifting Output Shaft Assembly from Transmission Case

Hold 1st Gear in Place when Removing Assembly

Output Shaft Assembly

COMPONENT DISASSEMBLY & REASSEMBLY

OUTPUT SHAFT ASSEMBLY

Disassembly

1) From rear of output shaft, remove 1st gear thrust washer, then slide off 1st gear and needle bearing using care not to lose pin. Slide 1st-2nd synchronizer assembly from output shaft.

2) Remove snap ring from front of output shaft, then slide off 3rd-4th synchronizer hub. Pull 3rd gear and bushing off shaft using care not to lose ball. Finally, slide 2nd gear and needle bearing off output shaft.

3) To disassemble synchronizer assembly, slide synchronizer hub sleeve from hub, then remove key springs and keys.

Inspection

1) Check output shaft surfaces for wear and damage. Inspect output shaft bushing for excessive wear and damage. Also, check bushing-to-3rd gear oil clearance (clearance between outer diameter of bushing and inner diameter of gear). Clearance should be .003-.005" (.07-.12 mm).

2) Inspect gears for wear or damage to teeth, thrust faces, inside diameter and coned surfaces. Inspect output shaft ball bearing and needle bearings for wear and damage.

3) Assemble synchronizer ring on 3rd gear and check ring-to-gear clearance as shown in *Fig. 3*. Clearance should be .031" (.8 mm). Repeat measurement for 4th gear ring.

4) Assemble 1st and 2nd gears to synchronizer assembly. Measure thickness of synchronizer ring protruding from gears as shown in *Fig. 5*. Thickness for

Fig. 3: Measuring 3rd and 4th Gear to Synchronizer Ring Clearance

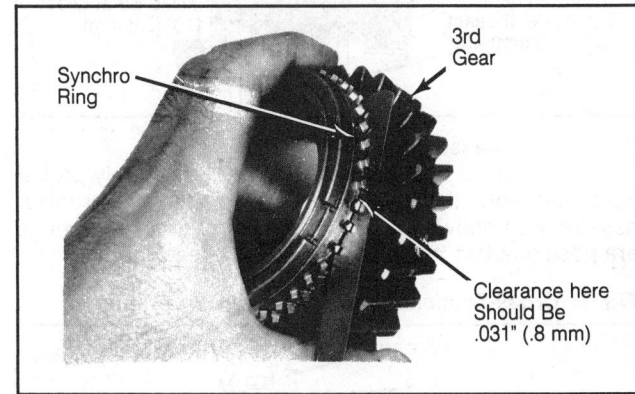

Synchro Ring

3rd Gear

Clearance here Should Be .031" (.8 mm)

Fig. 4: Exploded View Showing Output Shaft and Components

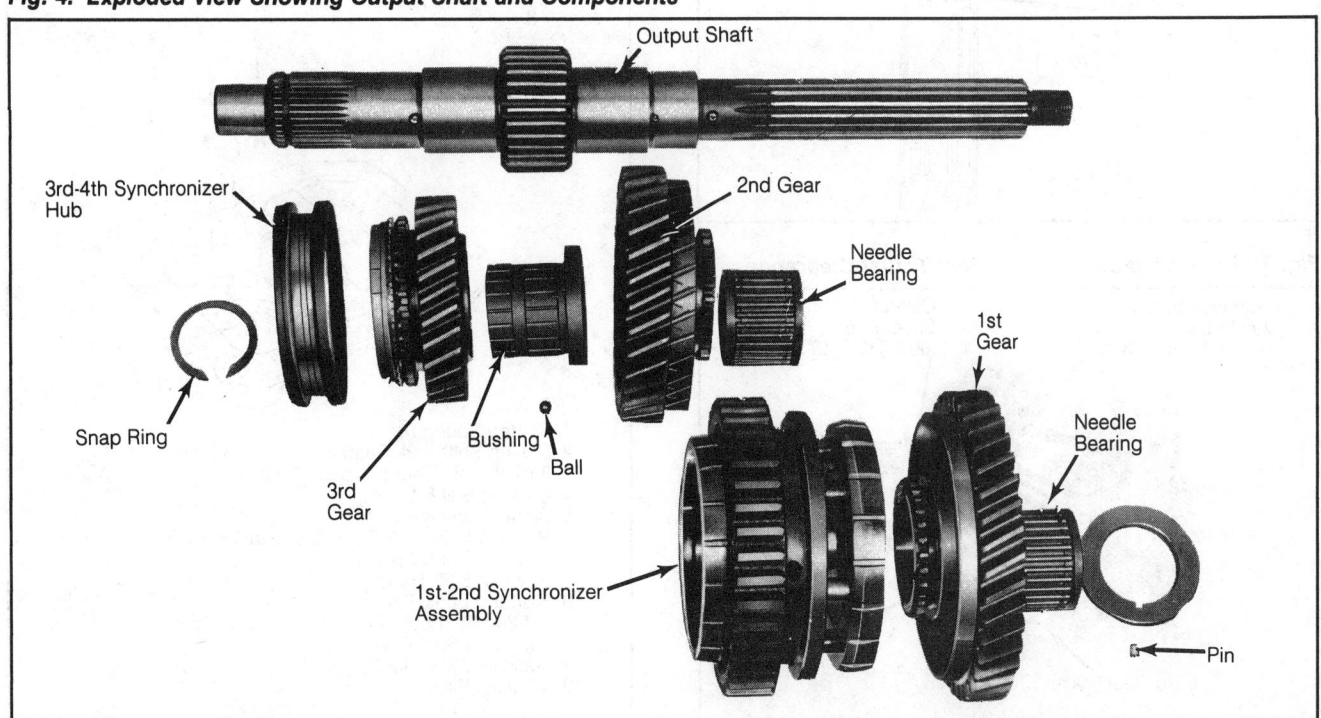

Output Shaft

3rd-4th Synchronizer Hub

2nd Gear

Needle Bearing

1st Gear

Needle Bearing

Snap Ring

Bushing

Ball

3rd Gear

1st-2nd Synchronizer Assembly

Pin

TOYOTA 4-SPEED — MODEL H42 (Cont.)

1st gear ring should be at least .110" (2.8 mm) and for 2nd gear ring at least .071" (1.8 mm).

5) Inspect splines of synchronizer hub and hub sleeve for damage and wear. Inspect the center humped part of keys for damage and wear. Inspect key springs for weakening and damage.

6) Finally, insert shift forks into their respective synchronizer hub sleeve and measure clearance between shift fork and sleeve. Clearance should be less than .032" (.8 mm).

Fig. 5: Checking 1st and 2nd Gear Synchronizer Ring Wear

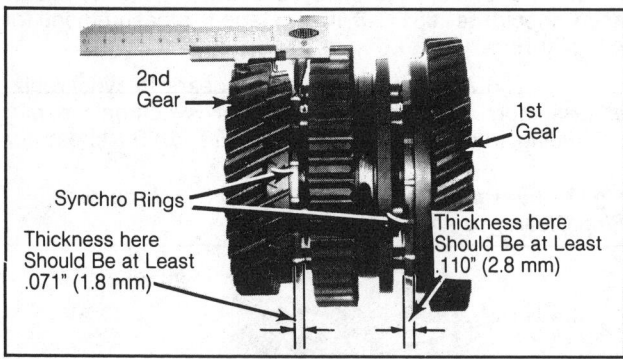

Reassembly

1) To reassemble, reverse disassembly procedure and note the following: Reassemble synchronizer assembly as shown in *Fig. 6* and ensure that key springs are positioned so that end gaps will not be in line.

Fig. 6: Cross-Sectional View of Synchro Assembly

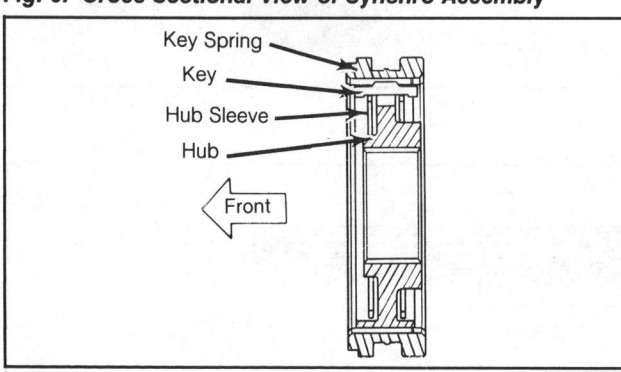

Fig. 7: Measuring 2nd and 3rd Gear Thrust Clearance

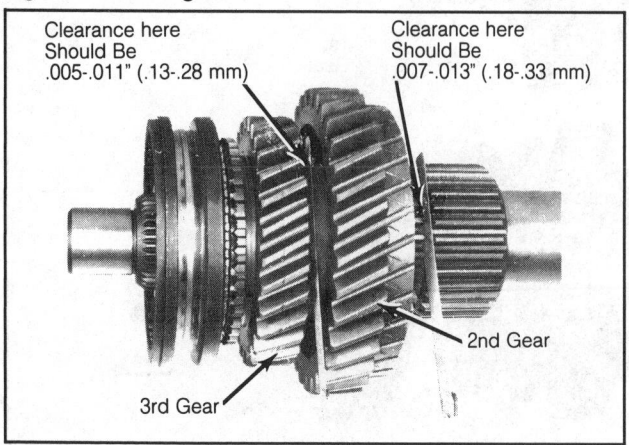

2) To install bushing on output shaft, place ball in hole of output shaft, then slide bushing onto shaft, aligning groove of bushing with ball.

3) Install thickest possible snap ring on front of output shaft that will provide a gear thrust clearance of .007-.013" (.18-.33 mm) for 2nd gear and .005-.011" (.13-.28 mm) for 3rd gear. *See Fig. 7.*

SHIFT COVER ASSEMBLY
Disassembly

1) Remove attaching bolts and lift off shift lever retainer and gasket. Move shift forks and shafts into neutral position. Invert shift cover assembly and drive out spring pin retaining 3rd-4th shift fork-to-shift fork shaft.

2) Drive out shift fork shaft together with expansion plug using a brass drift. Cover service hole with hand to prevent locking ball from flying out. Remove 3rd-4th shift fork and interlock pin. Remove locking ball and spring with magnet.

Fig. 8: Exploded View of Shift Cover Assembly

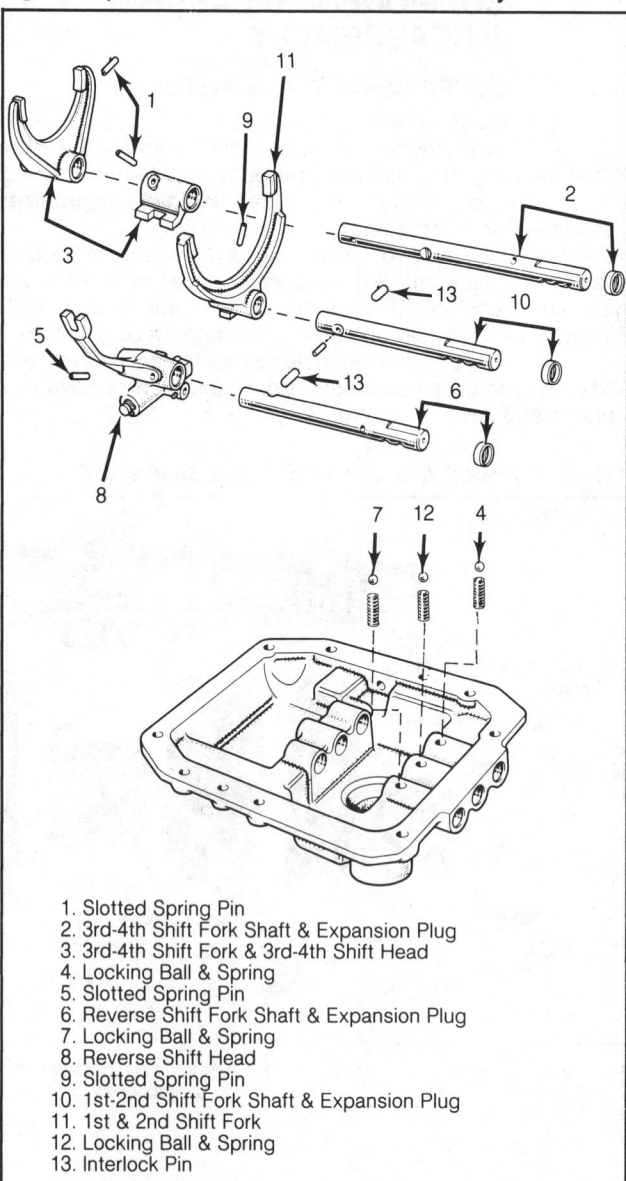

1. Slotted Spring Pin
2. 3rd-4th Shift Fork Shaft & Expansion Plug
3. 3rd-4th Shift Fork & 3rd-4th Shift Head
4. Locking Ball & Spring
5. Slotted Spring Pin
6. Reverse Shift Fork Shaft & Expansion Plug
7. Locking Ball & Spring
8. Reverse Shift Head
9. Slotted Spring Pin
10. 1st-2nd Shift Fork Shaft & Expansion Plug
11. 1st & 2nd Shift Fork
12. Locking Ball & Spring
13. Interlock Pin

TOYOTA 4-SPEED — MODEL H42 (Cont.)

3) Drive out spring pin retaining reverse shift head. Drive out shift fork shaft together with expansion plug. Cover service hole with hand. Remove 2nd locking ball and spring with magnet.

4) Drive out slotted spring pin to remove 1st-2nd shift fork. Drive out fork shaft together with expansion plug. Cover service hole with hand. Remove interlock pin from shaft using magnet. Remove 3rd locking ball and spring with magnet. Remove lock pins from case.

5) If necessary to disassemble reverse shift head, remove cotter pin and remove spring and lock ball from bore in shift head. Next, remove "C" washer and pull out reverse shift return plunger and spring.

Fig. 9: Disassembled View of Reverse Shift Head

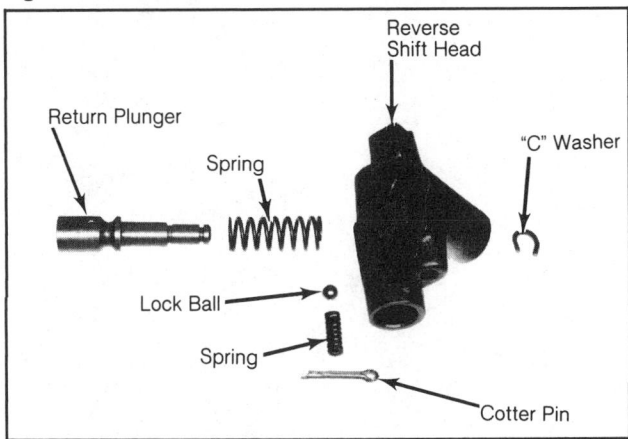

Inspection

Inspect shift fork shafts and heads for bending and wear or damage at sliding surfaces. Check shift cover bores for wear or damage. Inspect detent balls and springs for wear or damage.

Reassembly

Reverse disassembly procedure ensuring that shift forks and heads are correctly positioned before installing shift forks. Coat expansion plugs with a sealer and install in shift cover. Plugs must not be driven in more than .10" (2.5 mm) below cover surface.

INPUT SHAFT

Inspection

Inspect input shaft gear teeth, splines, coned surfaces, and bearing for damage and wear. Check inner surface of input shaft for damage and wear. Also, inspect needle bearings for wear and replace bearings as a set if necessary.

Input Shaft Bearing Replacement

Remove snap ring and press off old bearing. Press new bearing in position and select a snap ring of proper thickness to provide the minimum amount of axial play. Snap rings are available in 2 thicknesses: .130-.135" (3.31-3.42 mm) and .126-.130" (3.20-3.31 mm). Install snap ring, ensuring that it is fully seated in groove.

COUNTERSHAFT ASSEMBLY

Inspection

Inspect countergear teeth for wear and damage. Inspect front and rear bearings for wear and damage and replace if necessary. If rear bearing requires replacement, press bearing inner race from countershaft. Install new inner race on countershaft using a press.

NOTE: Make sure to position new inner race so that its flanged side will be towards front of countershaft.

REVERSE IDLER GEAR & SHAFT

Inspection

Inspect reverse idler gear, bushing and shaft for wear and damage. Also, check oil clearance between gear and shaft. Clearance should be .0063" (.16 mm). If bushing requires replacement, proceed as follows:

Reverse Idler Gear Bushing Replacement

Using press with a 24 mm socket, press bushings from gear. Using the same tools, press new bushings into the gear. Press bushings into gear until each bushing is .039" (1 mm) from gear end face.

Fig. 10: Replacing Reverse Idler Gear Bushing

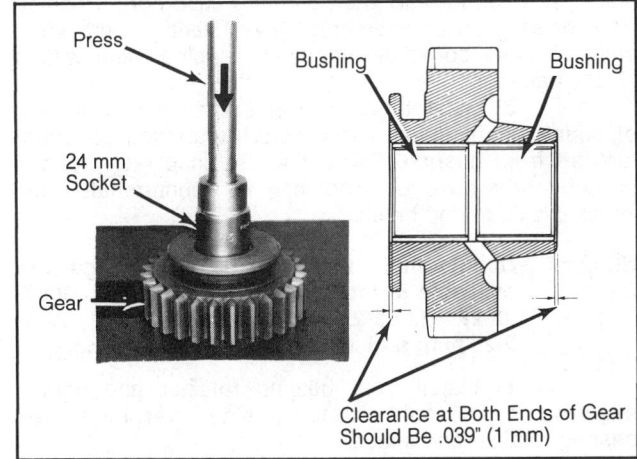

REVERSE SHIFT ARM

Inspection

Inspect shift arm shoe for damage or wear. Shoe thickness should be at least .32" (8.1 mm). Inspect shift arm at shoe mounting end and pivot mounting end for wear or damage. Check for maximum clearance of .028" (.7 mm) between shoe and reverse idler gear slot.

Fig. 11: Disassembled View of Reverse Shift Arm

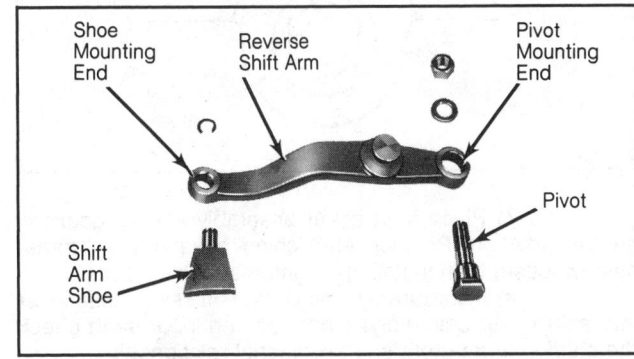

TRANSMISSION REASSEMBLY

1) Position reverse idler gear in transmission case. Install Woodruff key in reverse idler gear shaft, then install shaft into case and through gear. Install reverse shift arm assembly.

TOYOTA 4-SPEED — MODEL H42 (Cont.)

NOTE: Ensure punch mark on end of reverse shift arm pivot is positioned straight up before locking pivot nut.

2) Lay countershaft in bottom of transmission case. Install output shaft assembly into transmission case. Drive output shaft rear bearing onto shaft and into case bore until it is fully seated.

3) Install the 17 needle bearings into input shaft bore and use grease to hold them in place. Assemble synchronizer ring to synchronizer hub on input shaft. Using a plastic hammer, drive input shaft into transmission case.

NOTE: Use care not to damage synchronizer ring when installing input shaft.

4) Align countershaft with bores in case, then start rear bearing onto shaft and into case bore. Position front bearing on countershaft. Drive bearings onto shaft and into case bores by alternately tapping them with a plastic hammer.

5) Install thrust washer and snap ring on rear of countershaft. Install large (outer) snap ring on countershaft front bearing. Select thickest snap ring that will properly fit groove on front end of countershaft, then install this snap ring on shaft.

NOTE: Countershaft selective fit snap rings are available in the following thicknesses: .0807-.0827" (2.05-2.10 mm), .0846-.0866" (2.15-2.20 mm) and .0886-.0906" (2.25-2.30 mm).

6) Install front bearing retainer and tighten attaching bolts. Install transmission side cover. Install rear bearing retainer and spacer.

Fig. 12: Reverse Shift Arm Pivot Adjustment

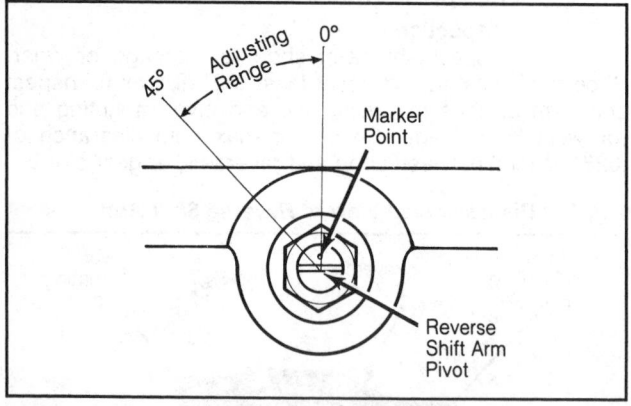

7) Place shift cover assembly and all gears in neutral position. Position shift cover assembly on transmission case, then install and tighten attaching bolts.

8) Temporarily install transmission shift lever into shift cover assembly. While rotating input shaft check the shifting and output shaft rotational relationship.

9) If abnormal noise develops while turning input shaft, correct by adjusting reverse shift arm pivot within range of 0° to 45° of marker point (punch mark). *See Fig. 12.*

TIGHTENING SPECIFICATIONS

Application	Ft. Lbs. (N.m)
Shift Cover-to-Case	22-33 (30-45)
Front Bearing Retainer-to-Case	7-12 (10-16)
Transfer Case-to-Transmission	36-58 (49-79)
Clutch Housing-to-Transmission	36-58 (49-79)
Output Shaft Rear Nut	80-101 (109-138)

TOYOTA TERCEL 4 & 5-SPEED

DESCRIPTION

Transaxle assembly consists of clutch/differential housing, intermediate plate and transmission case (4 or 5-speed) with common oil supply. The clutch/differential housing contains the clutch and differential assemblies in separate areas.

The intermediate plate mounts to rear of clutch/differential housing and allows complete removal of transmission without engine removal. Transmission case is mounted to rear of intermediate plate. Transmission case is fully synchronized in all forward gears.

Power is transmitted from input shaft, down through idler gear set to mainshaft and countershaft assemblies. Mainshaft is connected to pinion shaft by a splined sleeve connector. Pinion shaft transmits power to hypoid type differential which delivers power to axle drive shafts.

LUBRICATION & ADJUSTMENT

See the appropriate article in MANUAL TRANSMISSION SERVICING Section.

SERVICE (IN-VEHICLE)

AXLE DRIVE SHAFTS
Removal

1) Raise and support vehicle; remove tire and wheel. Depress brake pedal and loosen axle shaft nut. Remove brake caliper and suspend caliper from frame; DO NOT remove hydraulic line. Remove upper steering knuckle-to-suspension strut bolts. Push down on steering knuckle to separate knuckle from strut. Remove stabilizer bar (if equipped).

2) Remove axle shaft nut. Press axle shaft out of hub with a puller. Separate steering knuckle from strut and draw out axle drive shaft from rear of hub. Remove stiffener plate (left side only). Remove shaft from differential with remover (SST09648-16010). Install stopper (SST09563-16010) in differential case to prevent oil leakage.

Fig. 1: Exploded View of Axle Drive Shaft Assembly

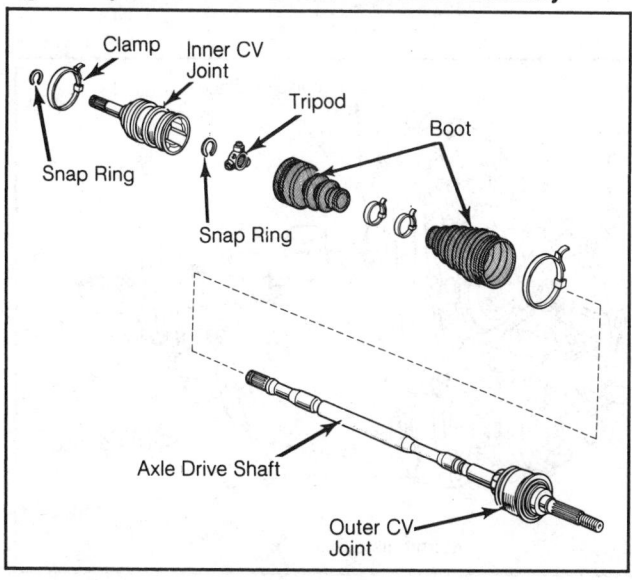

NOTE: Do not damage rubber boots of axle drive shaft. Always carry and store shaft in level position.

NOTE: Before disassembling axle drive shaft, check outer CV joint for any play. If play exists at outer CV joint, replace complete axle drive shaft assembly. Outer CV joint cannot be disassembled.

Disassembly

Draw alignment marks on inner CV joint and shaft with chalk. Remove snap ring and boot clamps. Remove inner joint from shaft. Place index marks on tripod and axle shaft. Remove snap ring and tap body of tripod to drive tripod off shaft. Remove inner CV joint boot. Remove outer CV joint boot clamps and slide boot off axle shaft.

Reassembly

1) Slide new boots onto drive axle shaft. Place clamping rings loosely over boots with open end of clamp away from direction of rotation. Do not tighten clamps at this time. Place beveled side of tripod onto shaft with beveled splines facing outer joint and align reference marks.

2) Before tapping tripod into final position, align centers of inner and outer joints. *See Fig. 2.* Tap tripod into position and install new snap ring. Pack outer CV joint with 8 ozs. (224 g) of grease (supplied with boot kit). Install outer boot and tighten clamps.

Fig. 2: Cutaway View Showing Alignment of Inner and Outer CV Joint Centers

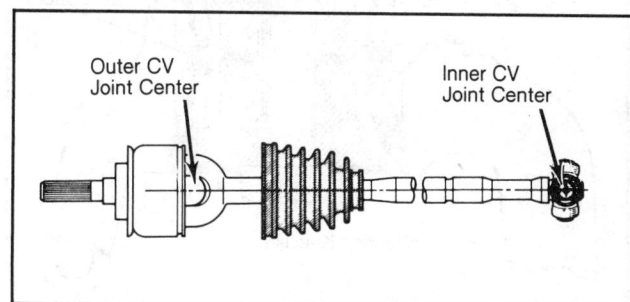

3) Pack inner CV joint with 5 ozs. (140 g) of grease (supplied with boot kit). Align reference marks made at disassembly and install inner CV joint. Install inner CV joint boot and tighten clamps. Install new snap ring on axle shaft.

NOTE: Right axle shaft is 23.07" (586 mm) long. Left shaft is 27.09" (688 mm) long. If axle shaft does not meet length specification, replace axle shaft assembly.

Installation

To install, reverse disassembly procedure and note the following: After installation of shafts, check front wheel alignment. Check boots for damage during installation. Measure the distance between drive shafts at transaxle. Distance should be less than 7.6" (194 mm).

WHEEL BEARINGS
Removal

1) Raise and support vehicle. Remove tire and wheel. Apply brakes and loosen axle shaft nut. Remove

Manual Transmissions

TOYOTA TERCEL 4 & 5-SPEED (Cont.)

brake caliper and suspend from frame with wire; DO NOT remove hydraulic line. Disconnect and remove tie rod end with remover (SST09610-20011). Disconnect and remove stabilizer bar and strut bar.

2) Place a jack and block of wood under left lower control arm and slightly lift control arm. Right side does not require lifting. Remove lower control arm-to-crossmember attaching bolt. Disconnect control arm from crossmember. Remove axle shaft nut.

3) Press axle shaft out of hub assembly with puller (SST09950-20013). Remove steering knuckle-to-suspension strut retaining bolt and separate steering knuckle from strut. Remove lower control arm from steering knuckle. Mount steering knuckle in a vise and remove dust shield, then remove inner oil seal with puller.

4) Press hub assembly out of steering knuckle with puller (SST09608-16031). Remove inner bearing and spacer from knuckle. Place reference marks on hub and disc assembly, then separate hub and disc. Place hub in vise and dislodge outer bearing from hub with hammer and chisel. Remove outer bearing with a puller. Remove scratches from hub bearing surface with oil stone.

Fig. 3: Assembled View of Wheel Bearings and Bearing Preload Adjusting Tool in Wheel Hub Assembly

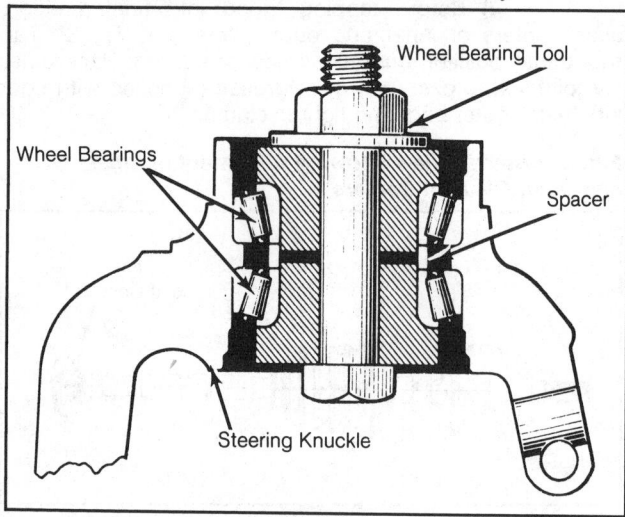

NOTE: Mark bearings for reassembly reference.

Installation

1) Place inner bearing, spacer and outer bearing onto bearing preload holder (SST09608-16040). Coat bearings and steering knuckle bores with oil. Place assembled bearings into bearing housing and tighten nut to 90 ft. lbs. (122 N.m).

2) Rotate assembly back and forth to seat bearings. Install an INCH lb. torque wrench and measure bearing preload while turning nut. Bearing preload should be 3.5-8.7 INCH lbs. (.40-.98 N.m). See Fig. 3.

NOTE: Spacers are available in 20 thicknesses ranging from .316" (8.03 mm) to .346" (8.79 mm) in .0016" (.04 mm) increments.

3) If preload is not within specifications, select and install spacer and repeat procedure. Mount hub to rotor, align marks made during removal and tighten hub-to-rotor bolts. Pack bearings and bearing housing with grease. Install outer bearing and oil seal in steering knuckle. Install preselected spacer and inner bearing in steering knuckle.

4) Place steering knuckle assembly in vise and press hub assembly into knuckle with press and arbor (SST09636-20010). Do not exceed 2205 lbs. (1000 kg) force.

5) With pressure applied, rotate steering knuckle to seat bearings. Attach spring pull scale to steering knuckle stopper and measure frictional force. Frictional force should be .8-1.7 lbs. (.4-.8 kg).

6) Increase force to 7716 lbs. (3500 kg) and turn steering knuckle to seat bearings. Attach spring pull scale to steering knuckle stopper and measure bearing preload. Preload should be .8-2.5 lbs. (.4-1.1 kg).

7) If below specification, install thinner spacer; if above specification, install thicker spacer. Install inner oil seal with installer (SST09554-22010) until seal is recessed .156" (4 mm) from end surface. Install dust shield.

8) Complete installation by reversing removal procedure and note the following: Install suspension components snugly. Lower vehicle to floor and bounce vehicle several times to settle suspension. Tighten sus-

Fig. 4: Exploded View of Tercel Transaxle Assembly

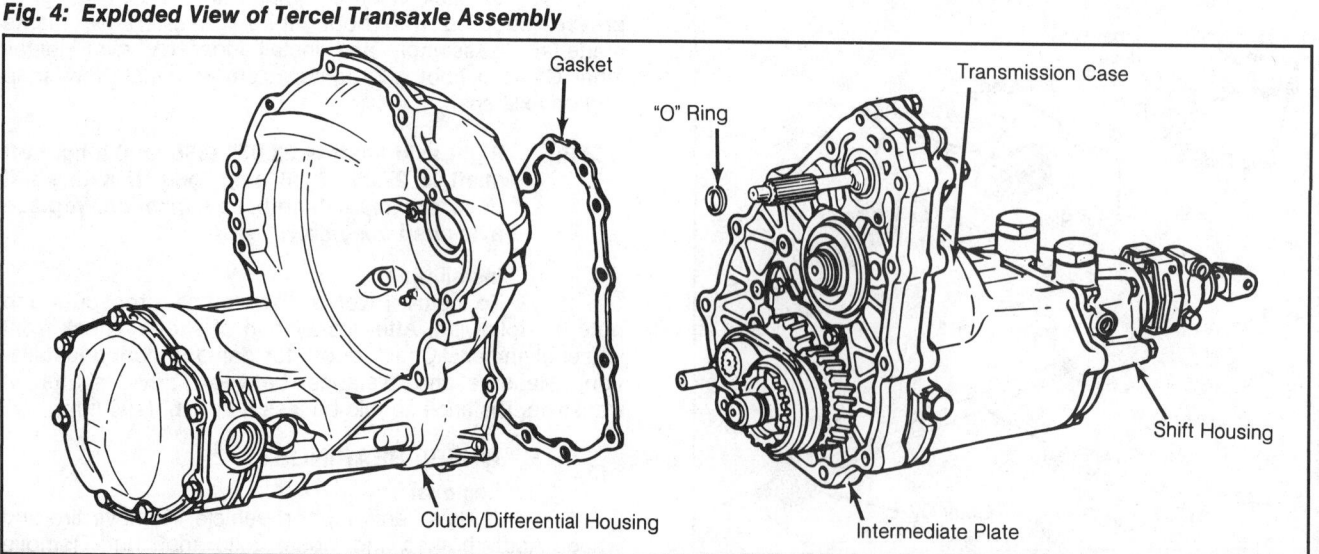

TOYOTA TERCEL 4 & 5-SPEED (Cont.)

pension components with vehicle weight resting on suspension system.

TRANSAXLE REMOVAL & INSTALLATION

See the appropriate article in MANUAL TRANS-MISSION REMOVAL Section.

TRANSAXLE DISASSEMBLY

1) Remove 9 transmission-to-clutch/differential housing bolts. Reinstall 4 bolts (8 mm) equal distance from differential side. Separate transmission from clutch/differential housing by inserting 4 bolts (10 mm) into same holes as previously installed bolts from transmission side. Tighten each 10 mm bolt a little at a time to force transmission from clutch/differential housing. Remove transmission from clutch/differential housing. See Fig. 5.

Fig. 5: Installation Position of Bolts to Separate Transmission from Clutch/Differential Housing

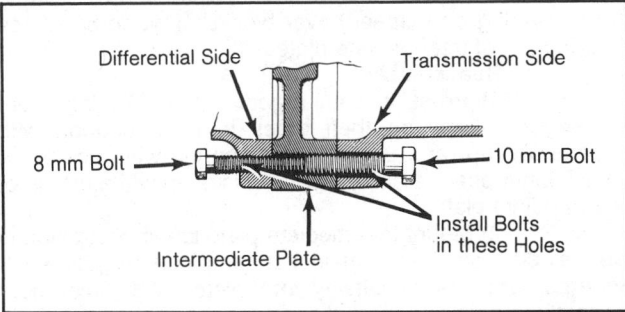

2) Remove reverse shift arm pivot from right side of transmission. Remove back-up light switch with slotted remover (SST09817-16010). Remove transmission mount brackets from shift lever housing.

3) Remove speedometer driven gear retaining bolt and extract speedometer driven gear. Remove 2 plugs from shift housing, then extract interlock springs and pins. Remove shift housing bolts and shift housing.

4) Remove speedometer drive gear snap ring, then remove speedometer drive gear and detent ball. Remove shift shaft rail head roll pins, then remove rail heads.

5) Remove 3 detent ball plugs, then extract detent springs and balls with magnet. Remove input shaft cover retaining bolts. Remove cover, gasket and input shaft from transmission case.

6) Remove countergear shaft snap ring from rear of transmission case. Tap transmission case protrusions with plastic hammer to loosen case from intermediate plate. When case is loose, tilt intermediate plate backward and remove transmission case.

COMPONENT DISASSEMBLY & REASSEMBLY

GEARSHIFT HOUSING
Disassembly
Tap lock pin from shift lever yoke with plastic hammer, then remove shift lever yoke. Extract shift lever

from rear of housing. Replace oil seal at collar with arbor (SST09304-12012).

Reassembly
To reassemble gearshift housing, reverse disassembly procedure and note the following: Ensure sliding action of shift lever is smooth and no binding is felt during shifting. Replace interlock springs and sleeves and speedometer driven gear, if defective.

Fig. 6: Exploded View of Gearshift Housing

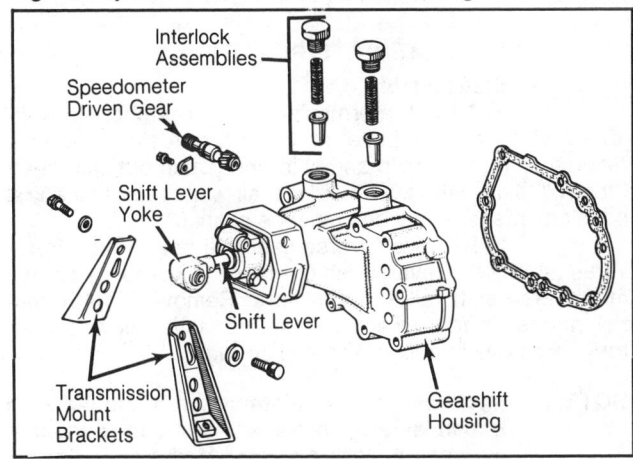

TRANSMISSION COVER
Disassembly
Remove idler gear rear bearing oil receiver, then remove bearing with remover (SST09612-10031). Remove output shaft rear bearing oil receiver, then remove bearing with remover/installer (SST09304-47010).

Fig. 7: Exploded View of Transmission Case

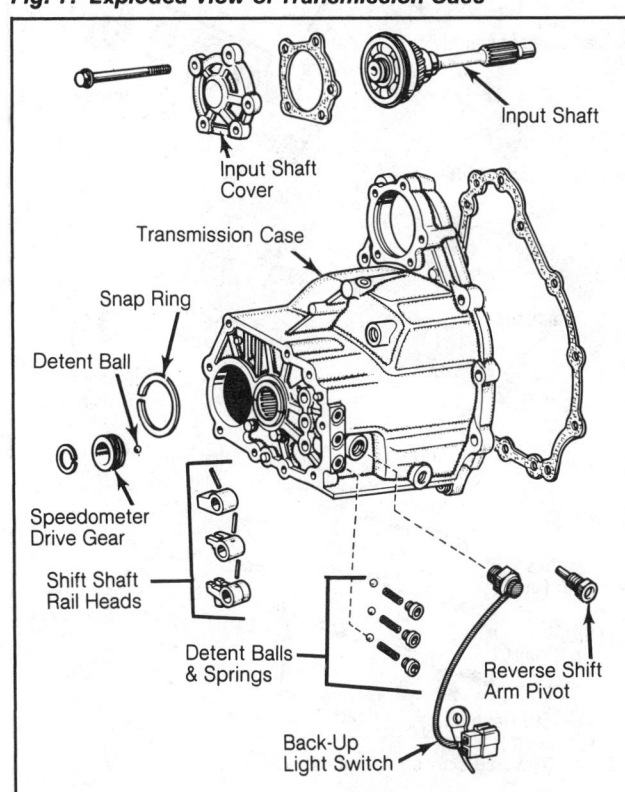

Manual Transmissions

TOYOTA TERCEL 4 & 5-SPEED (Cont.)

On 5-speed transmission, remove countergear front bearing with remover (SST09310-36021).

Reassembly

On 5-speed transmission, press in countergear front bearing with installer (SST09304-47010) until bearing is flush with end surface. On all transmissions, install output shaft rear bearing with remover/installer (SST09304-47010) and install oil receiver. Install idler gear rear bearing with installer (SST09304-47010). Install oil receiver.

INTERMEDIATE PLATE

Disassembly

1) Mount intermediate plate assembly in soft-jawed vise; secure plate at lower protrusion. Remove reverse shift arm circlip and shift arm. Drive out shift shaft fork roll pins with punch. Place all shift rails in neutral position; interlock notches must be aligned.

2) Remove reverse gearshift head from 5th/reverse shift rail (reverse shift rail of 4-speed). Remove 5th/reverse shift rail and shift fork. Remove 3rd/4th shift rail and shift fork. Remove 1st/2nd shift rail and shift forks. Remove interlock pins and springs.

NOTE: Interlock pins are identical on 4 and 5-speed transmissions; however, 5-speed transmission has 4 slotted springs and 4-speed has 3 slotted springs.

Fig. 8: Exploded View of Intermediate Plate Assembly

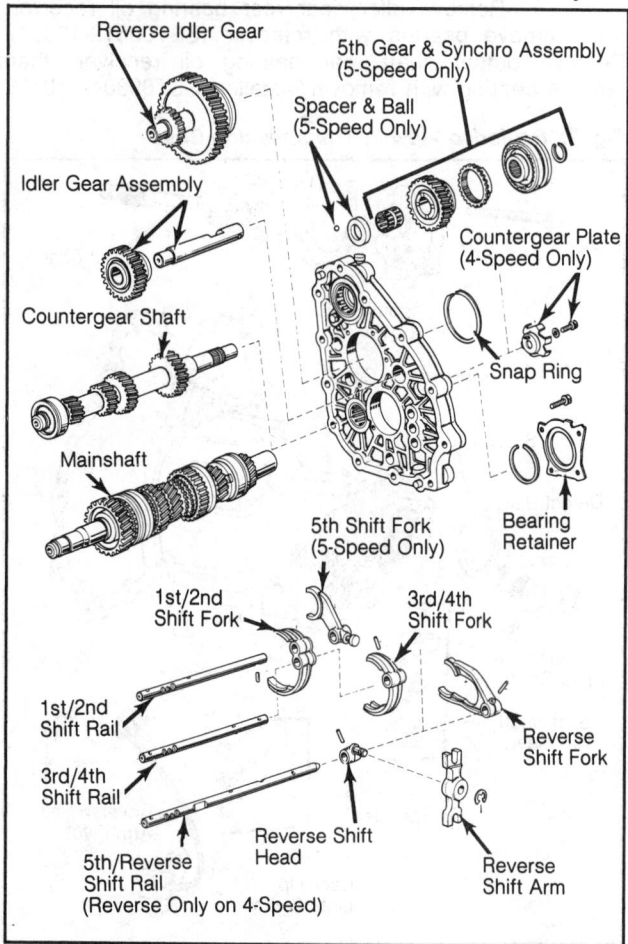

Reverse Idler Gear
5th Gear & Synchro Assembly (5-Speed Only)
Spacer & Ball (5-Speed Only)
Idler Gear Assembly
Countergear Plate (4-Speed Only)
Counntergear Shaft
Snap Ring
Mainshaft
Bearing Retainer
5th Shift Fork (5-Speed Only)
1st/2nd Shift Fork
3rd/4th Shift Fork
1st/2nd Shift Rail
3rd/4th Shift Rail
Reverse Shift Fork
Reverse Shift Head
Reverse Shift Arm
5th/Reverse Shift Rail (Reverse Only on 4-Speed)

3) On 5-speed transmission, measure 5th gear thrust clearance with a feeler gauge. Clearance should be .006-.013" (.15-.33 mm) with maximum clearance of .016" (.4 mm). Remove snap ring retaining 5th gear assembly. Then using a puller, remove 5th gear and synchro assembly. Remove 5th gear needle bearing, spacer and steel ball. Assemble 5th gear and synchro assembly and set aside.

4) On 4-speed transmission, lock transmission, then remove countergear plate retaining bolt and countergear plate. On all transmissions, remove mainshaft bearing retainer. Remove mainshaft and idler gear snap rings. Pull reverse gear shaft, idler gear and mainshaft away from intermediate plate, then remove idler gear and reverse gear shaft together.

NOTE: If mainshaft needs to be forced out of intermediate plate, use plastic hammer and support mainshaft during removal.

5) Remove countergear shaft and output shaft together. Place input shaft bearing end on block of wood. Remove oil seal and bearing lock plate, then drive input bearing out of plate. Place countergear center bearing (front bearing on 4-speed) over blocks of wood and force bearing out of intermediate plate.

Reassembly

1) Press in countergear center bearing (front bearing on 4-speed), then press in input bearing with groove (lip) upward. Secure input bearing with lock plate. Install input bearing oil seal so seal is even with surface of intermediate plate.

2) Mount intermediate plate lower protrusion in soft-jawed vise. Install mainshaft and countergear shaft together and insert halfway into plate. Align idler gear assembly with notched portion of reverse idler gear shaft. Tap idler gear assembly and reverse idler gear shaft halfway into plate and ensure idler gear does not contact mainshaft spacer.

3) Install idler gear and mainshaft snap rings. Install and tighten bearing retainer. On 4-speed, align countergear plate protrusion with cutout on countergear shaft. Install countergear plate, lock countergear shaft and tighten retaining bolt.

4) On 5-speed, align spacer groove with detent ball and install detent ball and spacer onto countershaft. Install 5th gear needle bearing, 5th gear and synchro ring. Align shifting keys with key slots in 5th gear synchro ring and press on synchro hub. Install snap ring which will provide .006-.013" (.15-.33 mm) clearance between 5th gear and intermediate plate.

NOTE: Snap rings are available in 7 sizes. Select snap ring which will reduce clearance closest to zero.

MAINSHAFT ASSEMBLY

NOTE: Before disassembling mainshaft assembly, measure thrust clearance of 1st through 4th gears. Clearance for 1st gear should be .006-.0108" (.15-.275 mm); 2nd and 3rd gears should be .006-.0098" (.15-.25 mm) and 4th gear should be .0008-.0094" (.02-.24 mm). Maximum thrust clearance for all gears is .0118" (.30 mm).

TOYOTA TERCEL 4 & 5-SPEED (Cont.)

Disassembly

1) Mount puller (SST09950-20012) in a vise and install mainshaft assembly. Remove mainshaft connecting sleeve with puller. Remove 5th gear snap ring, then pull off 5th gear with puller. Remove bearing snap ring, then pull off bearing and spacer with puller.

2) Slide off thrust bearing without dropping bearing. Slide 4th gear, synchro hub, synchro sleeve and needle bearing halves off shaft. After removing 4th gear, assemble it with synchro assembly and put aside. Remove snap ring, spacer and thrust bearing. Remove 3rd gear, synchro hub, and synchro sleeve from mainshaft with puller. Reassemble 3rd gear with synchro assembly and put aside.

3) Remove snap ring, bushing, 1st gear bearing, 1st gear and synchro sleeve. Assemble 1st gear with synchro ring and put aside. Remove detent ball with magnet, then pull off 2nd gear synchro hub, synchro sleeve and 2nd gear. Reassemble 2nd gear to synchro sleeve and put aside.

Inspection

Measure flange thickness. If thickness is less than .118" (3.0 mm), replace mainshaft assembly. Check connecting sleeve and pinion splines for wear or damage; replace defective part. Check all gears, synchro assemblies, bearings and thrust bearings for wear or damage; replace defective parts.

Fig. 9: Exploded View of Mainshaft Assembly

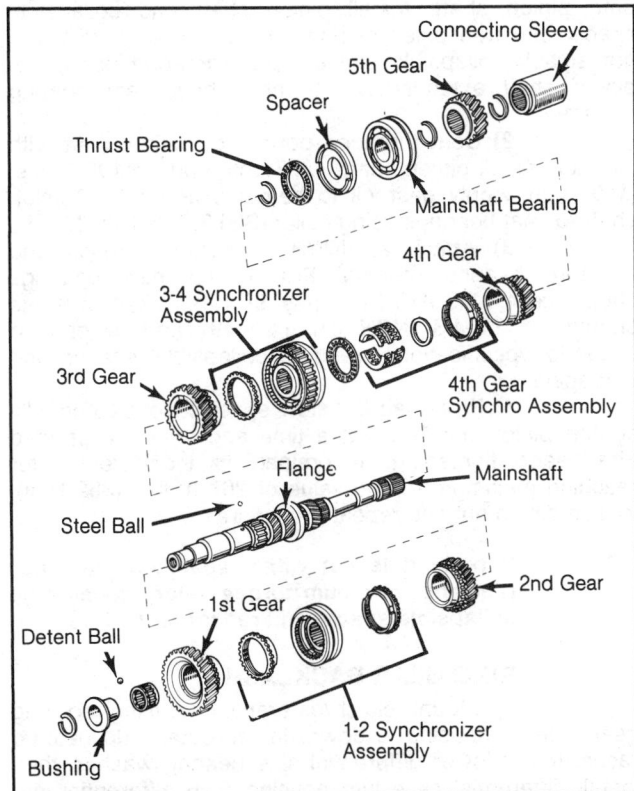

Reassembly

1) Coat mainshaft with grease. Align shifting keys of 2nd gear synchro hub with key slots in 2nd gear synchro ring and assemble synchro hub, ring and 2nd gear. Press assembly onto mainshaft. Insert detent ball.

2) Slide 1st gear synchro ring, 1st gear, bearing and bushing onto mainshaft. Align key slots of 1st

gear synchro ring with shifting keys in 2nd gear synchro hub. Groove of bushing must seat over detent ball.

3) Measure clearance for snap ring and choose a snap ring which will reduce 1st gear thrust clearance to zero. Snap rings are available in 9 thicknesses ranging from .0846-.0866" (2.15-2.20 mm) to .1004-.1024" (2.55-2.60 mm) in .002" (.05 mm) increments. Install snap ring and check thrust clearance of 1st and 2nd gear.

4) Assemble 3rd gear, synchro ring and synchro assembly with key slots of synchro ring aligned with synchro hub shifting keys. Press assembly onto mainshaft. Slide widest thrust bearing onto mainshaft. Install 4th gear needle bearing halves, synchro ring and 4th gear. Ensure key slots of 4th gear synchro ring align with shifting keys of synchro hub.

5) Install 4th gear spacer and snap ring. Coat 5th gear thrust bearing with grease and press into 5th gear spacer. Press spacer onto mainshaft with bearing facing 4th gear. Press bearing onto mainshaft with groove at the top.

6) Install a snap ring which will reduce bearing thrust clearance to zero. Measure thrust clearance of 3rd and 4th gear. Snap rings are available in 9 thicknesses ranging from .0827-.0846" (2.10-2.15 mm) to .0984-.1004" (2.50-2.55 mm) in .002" (.05 mm) increments.

7) Press 5th gear onto mainshaft and check thrust clearance. Select and install a snap ring which will reduce 5th gear thrust clearance to zero. Snap rings are available in 5 thicknesses: .0827-.0846" (2.10-2.15 mm) to .0906-.0926" (2.30-2.35 mm) in .002" (.05 mm) increments. Press mainshaft connecting sleeve onto mainshaft.

INPUT SHAFT

Disassembly

Remove input shaft bearing snap ring. Mount puller onto bearing, place puller in a vise and force input shaft out of bearing.

Reassembly

Mount input shaft bearing with snap ring groove facing rearward. Support bearing inner race with block (SST09515-20010), place a steel plate under the block and press bearing onto input shaft. Install a .0827-.0846" (2.10-2.15 mm) or .0886-.0906" (2.25-2.30 mm) thick snap ring to minimize thrust clearance.

IDLER SHAFT

Use procedure outlined for INPUT SHAFT. Snap rings are available in .0945-.0965" (2.40-2.45 mm) or .1004-.1024" (2.55-2.60 mm) thicknesses.

COUNTERSHAFT

Use procedure outlined for INPUT SHAFT. Snap rings are available in .0708-.0728" (1.80-1.85 mm) or .0768-.0787" (1.95-2.00 mm) thicknesses.

SYNCHRONIZER ASSEMBLIES

Disassembly

Mark the position of sliding gear in relation to hub before dismantling. Remove both synchro springs and slide assembly apart.

Inspection

Measure clearance between shift sleeve and corresponding shift fork. Clearance should not exceed .039" (1 mm).

TOYOTA TERCEL 4 & 5-SPEED (Cont.)

Reassembly

On 1st/2nd synchro assembly, install 3 shift keys, then mount key springs 120° apart so spring ends will not be in line. Synchro hub for 3rd/4th gear has 3 shift keys and 3 coil springs. Synchro hub for 5th gear is assembled in same manner as 1st/2nd synchro hub with a shift key retainer installed on front side of hub.

DIFFERENTIAL ASSEMBLY

Disassembly

1) Mount transaxle/clutch housing on support stand and remove differential front cover. Measure and record ring gear backlash, ring gear runout and check tooth contact pattern. Remove and mark side bearing caps and side bearing washers. Lift out differential assembly.

Fig. 10: View of Clutch/Differential Housing

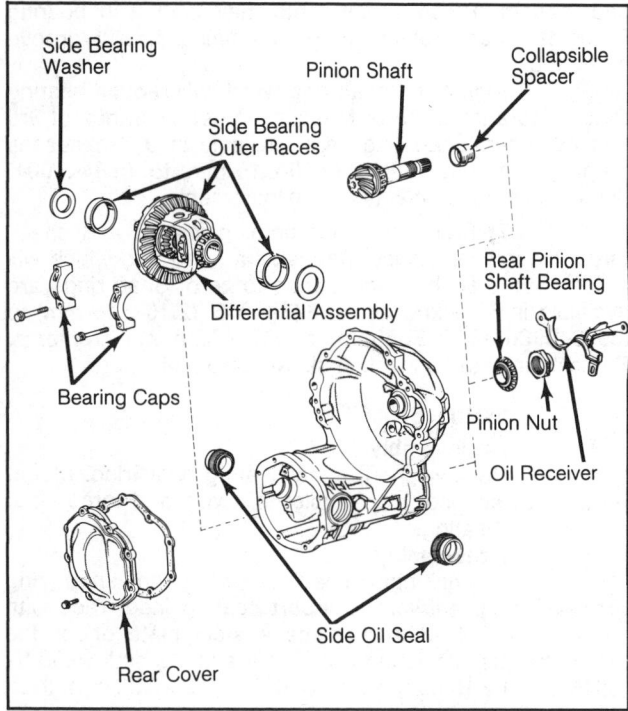

2) Remove transaxle case oil seals. Install an INCH lb. torque wrench and measure pinion shaft bearing preload for reassembly reference. Preload should be 5.2-8.7 INCH lbs. (.59-.98 N.m). Remove bearing oil reservoir. Loosen staked portion of pinion shaft nut and remove pinion shaft nut. While removing nut, turn pinion shaft clockwise with collar (SST09556-16010). Press out pinion shaft and collapsible spacer.

3) Remove pinion shaft front bearing with a puller. Remove shim and place aside for reassembly. Remove gear bearing and race. Remove differential side bearing races and mark for identification. Pull off side bearings and mark for identification.

NOTE: Differential case has indentations for insertion of puller jaws to ease side bearing removal.

4) Remove staking from ring gear bolt lock plates. Remove ring gear bolts and lock plate. Using chalk, draw alignment mark on ring gear and differential

case. Tap ring gear off differential case. Tap out differential lock pin. Remove pinion shaft, pinion gears, side gears and thrust washers.

Reassembly

1) Install thrust washers, side gears, pinion gears and pinion shaft. Hold 1 side gear and measure backlash of opposite side gear. Backlash should be .0016-.0094" (.04-.24 mm). If backlash is not to specification, disassemble differential case and install proper side gear thrust washers. Recheck backlash and install lock pin. Stake differential case.

NOTE: Side gear thrust washers are available in 6 thicknesses ranging from .059" (1.50 mm) to .069" (1.75 mm) in increments of .002" (.05 mm).

2) Heat ring gear to 212°F (100°C). Install ring gear with marks aligned. Install new lock plates. Install and tighten nuts, then stake lock plates. Press on differential side bearings.

ADJUSTMENTS

PINION BEARING PRELOAD

1) Measure and record thickness of pinion shim with micrometer and install shim on pinion shaft. Press on new front bearing. Slide new collapsible spacer onto pinion shaft. Install pinion shaft and collapsible spacer into transaxle housing. Press in rear bearing (do not smash collapsible spacer) until threaded portion of pinion shaft extends .12" (3 mm) above rear bearing surface.

2) Coat threaded portion of pinion shaft with oil, then install pinion shaft nut. Tighten nut to 108 ft. lbs. (146 N.m). Apply gear oil to bearings and rotate pinion shaft to seat bearings using collar (SST09556-16010).

3) Attach an INCH lb. torque wrench and measure bearing preload. Preload for new bearings should be 4.3-8.7 INCH lbs. (.49-.98 N.m); used bearings should be 2.6-4.3 INCH lbs. (.29-.49 N.m). If preload exceeds specifications, replace collapsible spacer and test again.

4) If preload is below specifications, gradually tighten pinion nut 5-10° at a time and measure preload after each tightening. If preload is insufficient after reaching maximum torque value of 267 ft. lbs. (362 N.m), loosen pinion nut and repeat procedure.

NOTE: If preload is not within specifications after reaching maximum torque value, install new collapsible spacer and repeat procedure.

RING GEAR BACKLASH

1) Mount clutch/differential housing so ring gear side of housing is down. Install outer side bearing races. Insert lower differential side bearing washer, then install differential case into housing. Tap differential into position with plastic hammer.

NOTE: Do not interchange side bearings.

2) Mount dial indicator. Hold upper side bearing outer race against side bearing and measure ring gear backlash. Backlash should be .0039-.0059" (.10-.15

TOYOTA TERCEL 4 & 5-SPEED (Cont.)

Fig. 11: Measuring Ring Gear Backlash

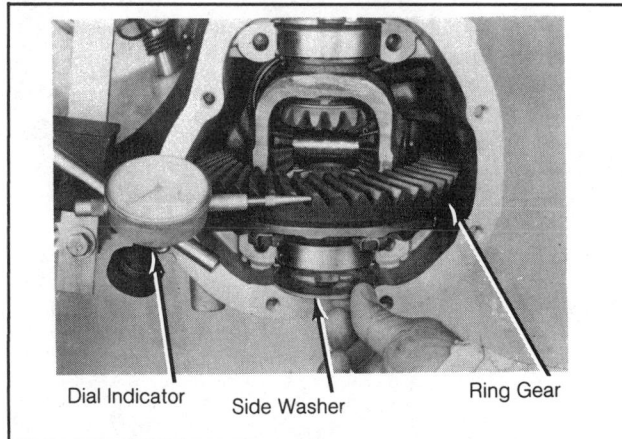

Dial Indicator   Side Washer   Ring Gear

mm). Select and install a washer which will eliminate any clearance between outer race and housing. Recheck ring gear backlash.

3) Remove differential, side bearing races and washer. Measure thickness of washers with micrometer, divide by 2 and select appropriate shims of equal thickness for each side of differential assembly.

4) Reinstall differential assembly, side bearing outer races and washers. Measure ring gear runout. If not to specification, increase or decrease washer thickness until specification is obtained.

NOTE: **Side bearing washers are available in the following thicknesses: .103-.129" (2.62-3.28 mm) in .001" (.03 mm) increments. Backlash will change about .0008" (.02 mm) with .001" (.03 mm) alteration of side bearing washers.**

5) After adjusting ring gear backlash, install side bearing caps and tighten bolts. Do not interchange bearing caps. Mount an INCH lb. torque wrench on pinion nut and measure total ring and pinion gear preload. Preload should be 2.6-4.3 INCH lbs. (.29-.49 N.m) PLUS amount of pinion bearing preload.

GEAR TOOTH CONTACT PATTERN

NOTE: **Final adjustments to differential are made with results from gear tooth contact pattern. See Gear Tooth Contact Pattern in back of book.**

1) If excessive heel or toe contact is evident, readjust pinion shaft depth. Pinion depth is adjusted by installing thinner shim (excessive toe contact) or thicker shim (excessive heel contact). Altering thickness of pinion washer .0039" (.10 mm) will change center of tooth contact 1/8 of total tooth contact.

NOTE: **Pinion washers are available in 16 thicknesses ranging from .0591" (1.50 mm) to .0768" (1.95 mm) in .0012" (.03 mm) increments.**

2) Too much flank or face contact reveals incorrect ring gear backlash. Too much flank contact can be eliminated by installing thicker side bearing washers (adjust backlash closer to high side of specification). Too much face contact can be eliminated by installing thinner side bearing washers (adjust backlash closer to low side of specification).

NOTE: **Increase or decrease both side washers in equal amounts.**

3) After adjusting pinion depth and ring gear backlash according to gear tooth contact pattern, check ring gear backlash. Stake pinion nut and reinstall rear cover and gasket. Install differential side bearing oil seals with installer (SST09223-46011) until seal protrudes .331-.354" (8.4-9.0 mm) from housing.

TRANSAXLE REASSEMBLY

1) Mount shift forks to respective synchro hubs and install shift rails. Slide reverse shift head onto rail and ensure reverse shift head hole aligns with interlock pin hole on shift rail.

2) After shift rails have been inserted into intermediate plate, insert a wire into bottom of intermediate plate (interlock pin holes). Wire should go through first 2 shift rails and be stopped by final rail; 4.7" (120 mm) from outer circumference of intermediate plate.

3) Coat interlock pins with grease and push into position with wire. After insertion of interlock pins, reinsert wire and check that it goes in 3.1" (80 mm) from end of intermediate plate. Insert 5th gear shift fork.

4) Set all shift forks in neutral position. Shift 2nd/3rd shift rail into 3rd gear position. Other rails should not move. Apply sealant to interlock pin plug and install plug. Secure shift arms to shift rails with roll pins. Install reverse shift arm and circlip.

5) Install gasket to intermediate plate and coat gasket with sealant. Mount transmission case to intermediate plate. Install countergear assembly snap ring. Insert detent balls and springs. Coat detent plug with sealant and install plug.

6) Insert reverse shift arm pivot and guide into lower portion of reverse shift arm with a screwdriver inserted from intermediate plate side. Install shift rail heads on shift rails and secure with roll pins. Install speedometer gear detent ball and drive gear. Install speedometer drive gear snap ring.

7) Install shift housing gasket and coat with sealant. Engage 3rd/4th shift head with end of shift lever inside shift housing. Mount shift housing to transmission case and tighten bolts. Insert restricting pins and springs into shift housing and tighten screws.

NOTE: **Green restrict pin must be installed at 1st/2nd shift rail and red restrict pin must be installed at 5th/reverse shift rail.**

8) Install and tighten speedometer driven gear. Install transmission mounting brackets, backup light switch and input shaft assembly. Install input shaft "O" ring on clutch housing. Mount transmission gasket and transmission case onto clutch/differential housing.

9) Turn transaxle assembly so transmission case is up, turn input shaft and tighten attaching bolts. Check operation of transmission by shifting through all gear ranges.

Manual Transmissions
TOYOTA TERCEL 4 & 5-SPEED (Cont.)

TIGHTENING SPECIFICATIONS

Application	Ft. Lbs. (N.m)
Shift Hsg.-to-Transmission Case	8-11 (11-15)
Transmission-to-Intermediate Plate	11-15 (15-20)
Transaxle Hsg.-to-Intermediate Plate	8-11 (11-15)
Clutch/Differential Hsg.-to-Engine	37-57 (50-77)
Mainshaft Rear Bearing Retainer	8-11 (11-15)
Input Shaft Bearing Retainer	8-11 (11-15)
Countergear Plate (4-Speed)	8-11 (11-15)
Restrict Pin Plugs	27-32 (37-43)
Ring Gear Bolts	67-75 (91-102)
Pinion Nut	109-267 (148-362)
Side Bearing Caps	33-39 (45-53)
Differential Front Cover	8-11 (11-15)
Axle Shaft Nut	73-108 (99-146)
Hub-to-Rotor Bolts	29-36 (39-49)
Strut-to-Steering Knuckle	40-52 (54-71)
Lower Arm-to-Strut Bar	29-39 (39-53)
Ball Joint-to-Steering Knuckle	40-52 (54-71)
Lower Arm-to-Crossmember	51-65 (69-88)
Strut Bar-to-Strut Bracket	55-79 (75-107)
Stabilizer-to-Lower Arm	11-15 (15-20)
Stabilizer Bracket	22-32 (30-43)
Engine Front Mount-to-Crossmember	26-39 (35-53)

TOYOTA 5-SPEED TRANSMISSION — MODEL K51

Starlet

DESCRIPTION

The 5-speed transmission is fully synchronized in all forward gears. Synchronizers are of the blocker type. Gear selection is accomplished by direct control through floor mounted shift lever. Clutch housing is integral with transmission case.

LUBRICATION & ADJUSTMENT

See the appropriate article in MANUAL TRANS-MISSION SERVICING Section.

TROUBLE SHOOTING

HARD SHIFTING

Improperly adjusted clutch. Worn face of synchronizer ring in contact with insert. Cones on synchronizer ring and gear not in proper contact.

TRANSMISSION SLIPS OUT OF GEAR

Bearings worn or defective. Excessive play between gears and collars. Play in clutch hub and sliding sleeve. Shift fork worn. Lock ball spring weak or broken.

TRANSMISSION NOISY

Low or incorrect lubricant. Gears or bearings worn or damaged. Worn clutch hub or mainshaft splines. Incorrectly meshed gears.

REMOVAL & INSTALLATION

See the appropriate article in MANUAL TRANS-MISSION REMOVAL Section.

TRANSMISSION DISASSEMBLY

1) Clean exterior of transmission. Remove back-up light switch. Remove clutch release bearing, release fork, boot and spring. Remove speedometer driven gear, transmission oil pan and shift lever retainer. Remove countergear thrust washer.

2) Measure extension housing thrust clearance for reassembly reference. Move extension housing to oil pan side and remove. Use care not to scratch rear oil seal of extension housing with splines on rear of output shaft.

3) Remove countergear rear thrust washer. Remove snap rings, speedometer drive gear, 5th gear shift arm bracket, shift arm and No. 3 shift fork. Remove snap ring, shifting key retainer, and No. 3 clutch hub and sleeve. Remove synchronizer ring and 5th gear using care not to damage case.

Fig. 1: *Exploded View of Transmission Gears and Shafts*

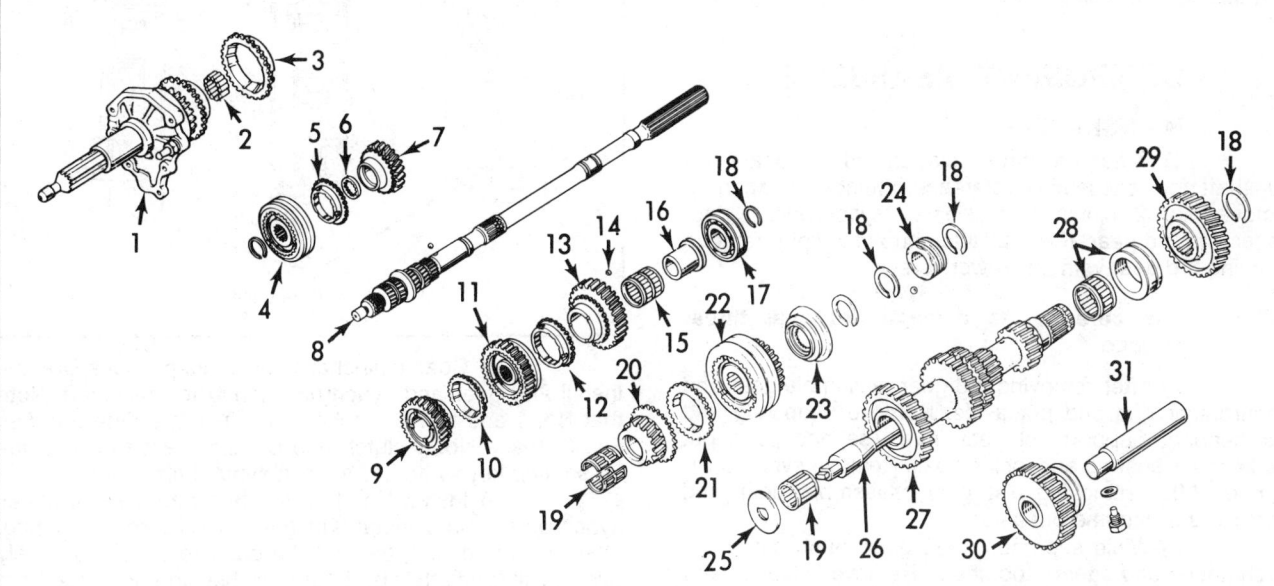

1. Input Shaft & Front Bearing Retainer	11. No. 1 Clutch & Hub	21. Synchronizer Ring
2. Needle Roller Bearing	12. Synchronizer Ring	22. No. 3 Clutch Hub & Sleeve
3. Synchronizer Ring	13. 1st Gear	23. Shifting Key Retainer
4. No. 2 Clutch Hub & Sleeve	14. Locking Ball	24. Speedometer Drive Gear
5. Synchronizer Ring	15. Needle Roller Bearing	25. Thrust Washer
6. Spacer	16. Bushing	26. Countershaft
7. 3rd Gear	17. Rear Bearing	27. Countergear
8. Mainshaft	18. Snap Ring	28. Countergear Rear Bearing
9. 2nd Gear	19. Needle Roller Bearing	29. Counter 5th Gear
10. Synchronizer Ring	20. 5th Gear	30. Reverse Idler Gear
		31. Idler Gear Shaft

TOYOTA 5-SPEED TRANSMISSION. MODEL K51 (Cont.)

4) Measure thrust clearance. Clearance should be .0079-.0118" (.20-.30 mm). Remove needle roller bearing, snap ring and counter 5th gear. Remove countergear rear bearing. Remove reverse idler gear and shaft. Remove countergear, shaft, needle roller bearing and washer.

5) Remove locking ball and springs. Using a pin punch, drive out slotted spring pins. Set each shift fork shaft to the neutral position and pull out. Shift the No. 1 clutch hub sleeve into 2nd gear and remove the shift fork from the case.

Fig. 2: Set Each Shift Fork Shaft to Neutral Position & Pull Out

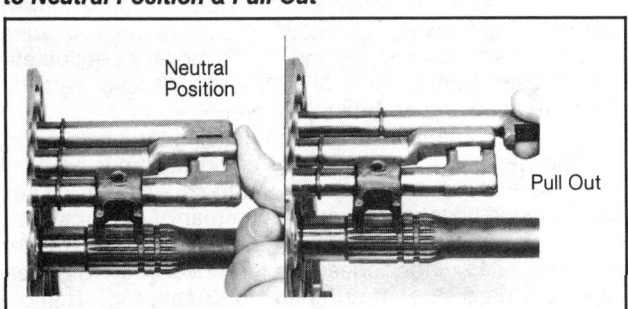

6) Remove interlock pin, input shaft and front bearing retainer. After removing input shaft, assemble it to the synchronizer ring gear and set aside. Remove outer bearing from case. Remove synchronizer ring and mainshaft through front side of case.

COMPONENT DISASSEMBLY

MAINSHAFT

1) Measure thrust clearances of gears on mainshaft for reassembly reference. Remove snap ring. Remove No. 2 clutch hub, sleeve, synchronizer ring, spacer and 3rd gear. If No. 2 clutch hub fit is tight, remove by prying 3rd gear with 2 screwdrivers.

NOTE: Use care not to damage 3rd gear thrust surface.

2) After removing 3rd gear, assemble gear and synchronizer ring and put aside. Remove snap ring and rear bearing. Support 1st gear in a vise and push out needle roller bearing and locking ball. Remove synchronizer ring. After removing 1st gear, assemble gear and synchronizer ring and put aside.

3) While separating 2nd gear, push out No. 1 clutch hub and gear together. Remove sleeve and synchronizer ring. After removing 2nd gear, assemble gear and synchronizer ring and put aside.

INSPECTION & REPAIR

MAINSHAFT

Inspect shaft for wear or damage. Diameter wear limit is 1.252" (31.8 mm). Flange wear limit is .138" (3.5 mm). Check shaft for runout. Limit is .0024" (.06 mm).

GEARS

Inspect gears for wear or damage. Measure inside diameters. The 1st gear limit is 1.4626" (37.15 mm).

The 2nd and 3rd gear limits are 1.2657" (32.15 mm). Reverse idler gear bushing bore wear limit is .717" (18.2 mm). Shaft outside diameter limit is .705" (17.9 mm). Check synchronizer braking action by placing synchronizer ring against cone and turning while pressing. Synchronizer should stick to cone.

SHIFT FORKS

Check clearance between sleeve and shift fork. Clearance limit is .031" (.8 mm). Check sliding action of shift shafts in case.

COMPONENT REASSEMBLY

1) If oil seal needs replacement, remove oil seal with removal tool (09308-00010 if mainshaft has been removed, 09308-10010 if mainshaft has not been removed).

2) Heat the extension housing to 212°F (100°C). Remove bushing with removal tool (09307-12010). Using the same tool, drive in new bushing with oil hole positioned upward. Drive in new oil seal with driver (09325-12010).

Fig. 3: View of Synchronizer Assemblies Showing Synchronizer Ring Identification

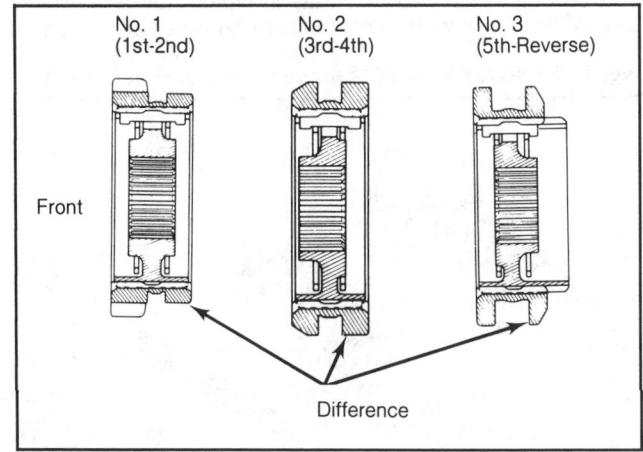

3) Coat mainshaft with multi-purpose grease. Install 2nd gear and synchronizer ring to mainshaft. Note that No. 1 and No. 2 synchronizer rings are different. *See Fig. 3.* Place No. 1 clutch hub on alignment tool and line up shifting keys with key slots in synchronizer ring.

4) Install No. 1 clutch hub and sleeve. Install synchronizer ring. Install 1st gear, needle roller bearing, bushing and locking ball. Fit the bushing groove securely over locking ball. Support 1st gear bushing so it does not separate from locking ball and press in bearing with special tool (09515-10010).

5) Select a snap ring of a thickness to reduce thrust clearance to zero. Snap rings are available in increments of .0020" (.05 mm) from .807" to .1004" (2.05 mm to 2.55 mm). Install snap ring with groove positioned toward rear. Check thrust clearances of 1st and 2nd gears.

6) Clearances should be .0071-.0110" (.18-.28 mm) for 1st gear, .0039-.0098" (.10-.25 mm) for 2nd gear. Coat mainshaft with multi-purpose grease. Line up shifting keys with key slots in synchronizer ring. Install 3rd gear, spacer, synchronizer ring, No. 2 clutch hub, sleeve and snap ring.

TOYOTA 5-SPEED TRANSMISSION. MODEL K51 (Cont.)

7) Push in No. 2 clutch hub and measure 3rd gear thrust clearance. Clearance should be .0020-.0079" (.05-.20 mm). When clearance is not within standard, select an appropriate spacer and snap ring to reduce thrust clearance to zero.

MAINSHAFT THRUST CLEARANCES

Application	In. (mm)
1st Gear	.0071-.0110 (.18-.28)
2nd Gear	.0039-.0098 (.10-.25)
3rd Gear	.0020-.0079 (.05-.20)

TRANSMISSION REASSEMBLY

1) Insert output shaft from front side of transmission case. Stand case upright and pull output shaft up. Install bearing and secure with a snap ring. Apply multi-purpose grease to needle roller bearing and assemble. Install synchronizer ring. Line up shifting keys with key slots in synchronizer ring.

Fig. 4: Shift Fork and Shaft Positioning

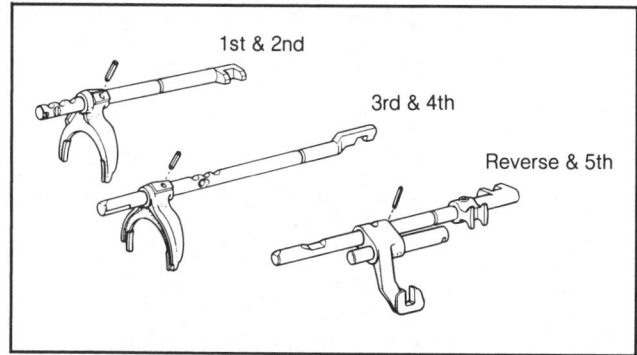

1st & 2nd
3rd & 4th
Reverse & 5th

2) Install input shaft and front bearing retainer and tighten. Shift No. 1 hub sleeve into 2nd gear. Apply multi-purpose grease to interlocking ball and assemble it to the reverse fork. Push ball in with a screwdriver until it falls into shaft groove.

3) Assemble each shaft as shown in Fig. 4. Insert shafts through forks and push them up to neutral position. Insert shaft until dummy hole on No. 1 fork end is lined up with case hole. Insert a thin screwdriver to align holes.

4) Grease interlock pins and insert each with a screwdriver. Shift No. 1, 2, and 3 shift fork shafts to neutral position. Shift No. 2 shift fork shaft to 3rd gear position. Shift fork shafts No. 1 and 2 should not move. Align pin holes in shift forks and shift fork shaft, and drive slotted spring pins to secure forks to shafts.

Fig. 5: Countershaft Protrusion

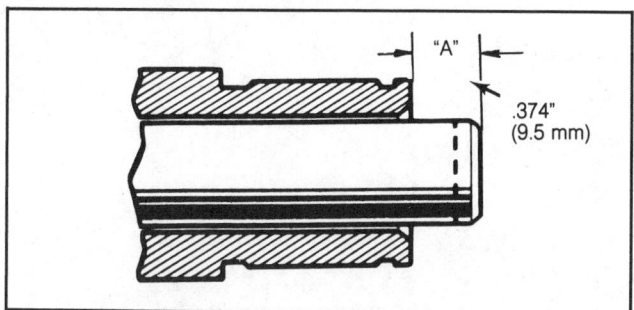

"A"
.374"
(9.5 mm)

5) Drive in No. 3 shift fork shaft pin until it is flush with reverse shift fork upper surface. Assemble together the countergear, shaft, bearing and thrust washer. Install assembly, making sure washer is installed with oil groove toward countergear side. If countershaft is properly installed, dimension "A" shown in Fig. 5 will be approximately .374" (9.5 mm).

6) Install countergear rear bearing. Install reverse idler gear and shaft. When installing reverse idler gear shaft, have shift arm engaged with hub of reverse idler gear. Assemble counter 5th gear in direction shown in Fig. 6. Install a snap ring that will allow minimum end play.

Fig. 6: Countergear Positioning

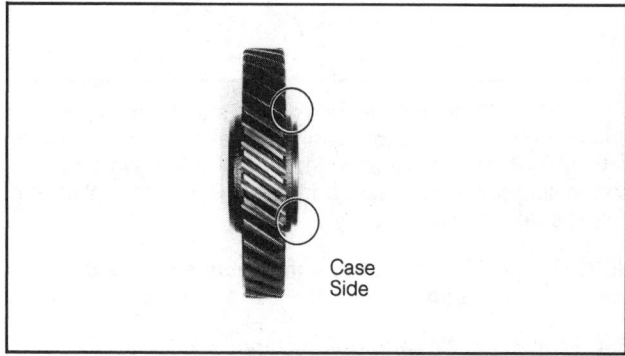

Case
Side

7) Select a thrust washer using the following procedure: Install countergear thrust washer with oil groove toward gear. Temporarily install extension housing over gasket and tighten. Measure thrust clearance. Remove extension housing and install thrust washer.

8) Install 5th gear needle roller bearing, 5th gear, synchronizer ring and No. 3 clutch hub and sleeve. Line up shifting keys with key slots in synchronizer ring. Install shifting key retainer. With retainer pressed against hub, select a thrust washer so that thrust clearance will be .008-.012" (.2-.3 mm).

9) Install snap ring. Check thrust clearance. Push up reverse idler gear until fork shaft is in position shown in Fig. 7. Install 5th gear shift arm bracket with bracket in reverse fork shaft groove, fork claw in hub sleeve and shift arm shaft in gear shift head No. 1 groove.

Fig. 7: Fork Shaft Positioning

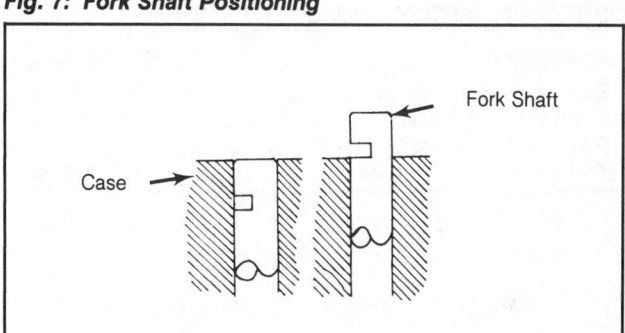

Fork Shaft
Case

10) Adjust reverse idler gear position. With gear in neutral position, turn pivot until dimension "A" in Fig. 8 is .039-.079" (1.0-2.0 mm). Adjust No. 3 clutch hub sleeve position. Shift No. 3 clutch hub sleeve into 5th gear. Turn pivot until dimension "A" shown in Fig. 9 is .039-.059" (1.0-1.5 mm).

TOYOTA 5-SPEED TRANSMISSION. MODEL K51 (Cont.)

Fig. 8: Reverse Idler Gear Clearance

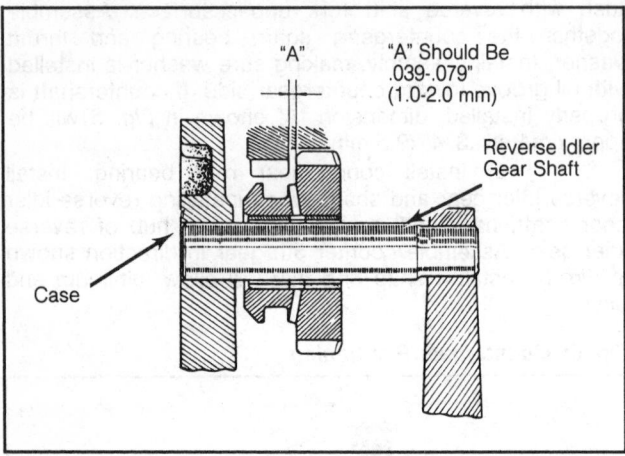

11) Install locking ball. Install speedometer drive gear and snap ring. Install countergear thrust washer with groove toward gear side. Install extension housing, connecting fork shaft slots and lever. Check that shift and select shafts move correctly.

NOTE: Take care not to damage oil seal in extension housing.

Fig. 9: Adjusting Clutch Hub Position

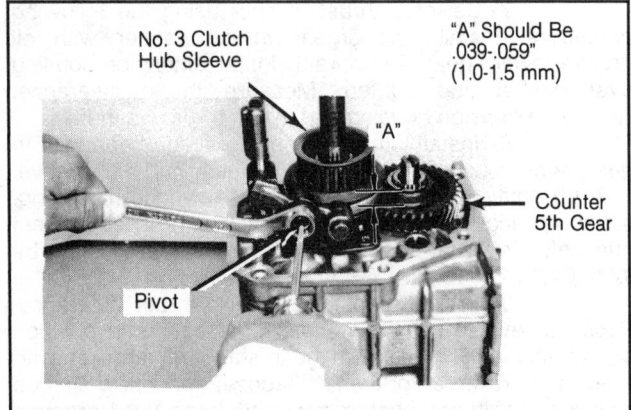

TIGHTENING SPECIFICATIONS

Application	Ft. Lbs (N.m)
Extension Housing	22-32 (30-44)
Front Bearing Retainer	11-15 (15-20)
Reverse Idler Gear Shift Arm	10-13 (14-18)
Transmission-to-Engine	37-50 (50-68)

TOYOTA 4 & 5-SPEED — MODELS L45, L48 & L52

Pickup
L45 4-Speed (4WD)
L48 4-Speed (2WD)
L52 5-Speed (4WD)

DESCRIPTION

Transmission is a 4 or 5-speed unit, fully synchronized in all forward gears due to use of blocker type synchronizer assemblies. All forward transmission gears are helical cut and are in constant mesh. Reverse gears are spur cut type and are engaged by a sliding reverse idler gear. Floor mounted shifter is linked to transmission through a control rod on side of case.

LUBRICATION & ADJUSTMENT

See the appropriate article in MANUAL TRANS-MISSION SERVICING Section.

TROUBLE SHOOTING

HARD SHIFTING OR WILL NOT SHIFT

Clutch pedal freeplay excessive. Clutch release cylinder faulty. Clutch master cylinder faulty. Clutch disc out of true, or lining greasy or broken. Splines on input shaft or clutch disc dirty or burred. Pressure plate faulty. Transmission faulty.

SLIPS OR JUMPS OUT OF GEAR

Clutch pilot bearing worn. Worn or damaged mainshaft bearings. Synchro mechanisim worn. Worn gear bushings. Shift linkage components worn or loose.

TRANSMISSION NOISE

If noise can be stopped by depressing clutch pedal, noise is in transmission or clutch. Before removing transmission, test drive to determine in which gears noise is most apparent. Make sure transmission is filled with proper lubricant.

Fig. 1: Exploded View of Toyota L45, L48 and L52 Transmission and Transfer Case

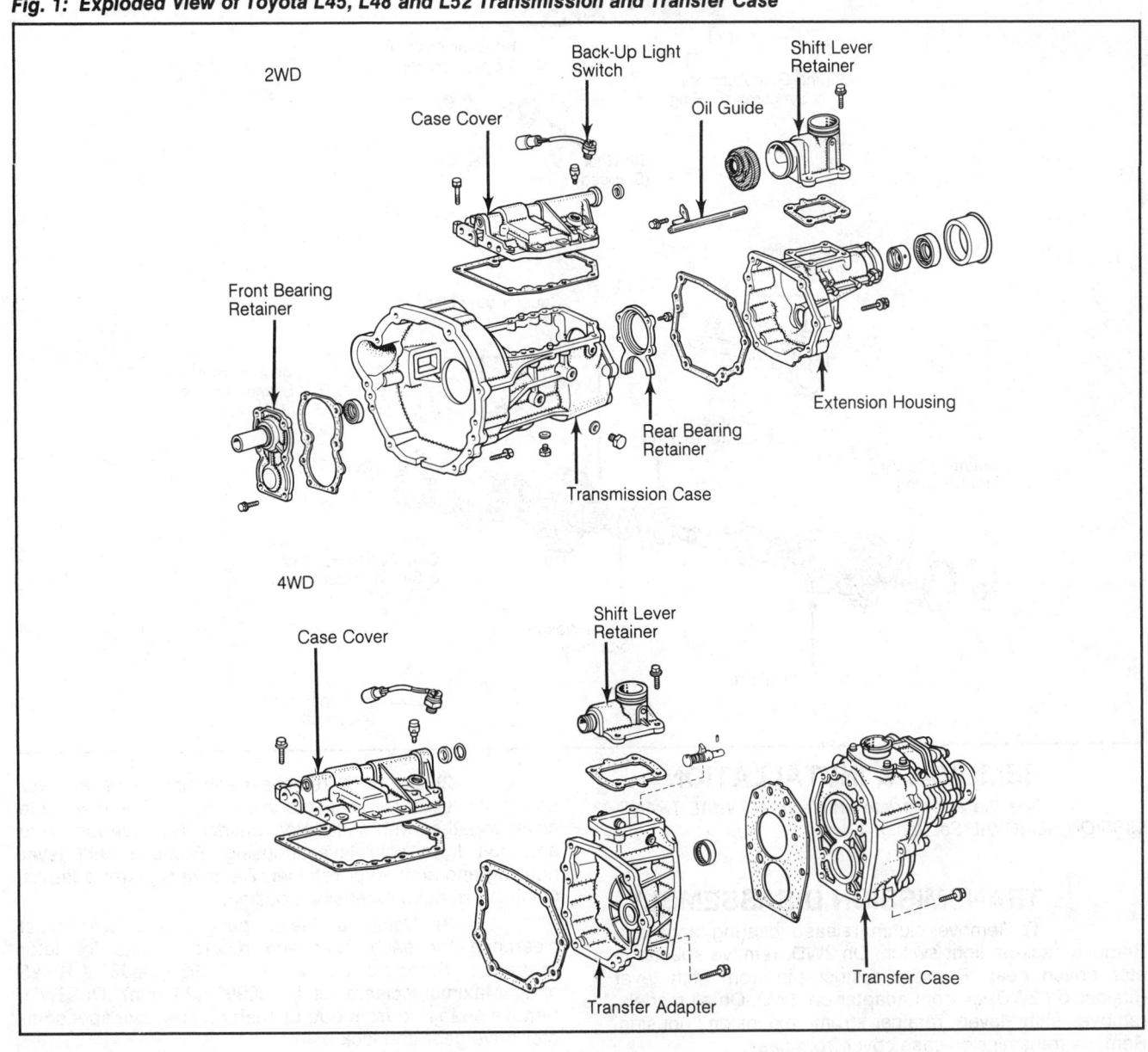

Manual Transmissions

TOYOTA 4 & 5-SPEED — MODELS L45, L48 & L52 (Cont.)

Fig. 2: Exploded View of L45, L48 and L52 4-Speed and 5-Speed Transmission Components

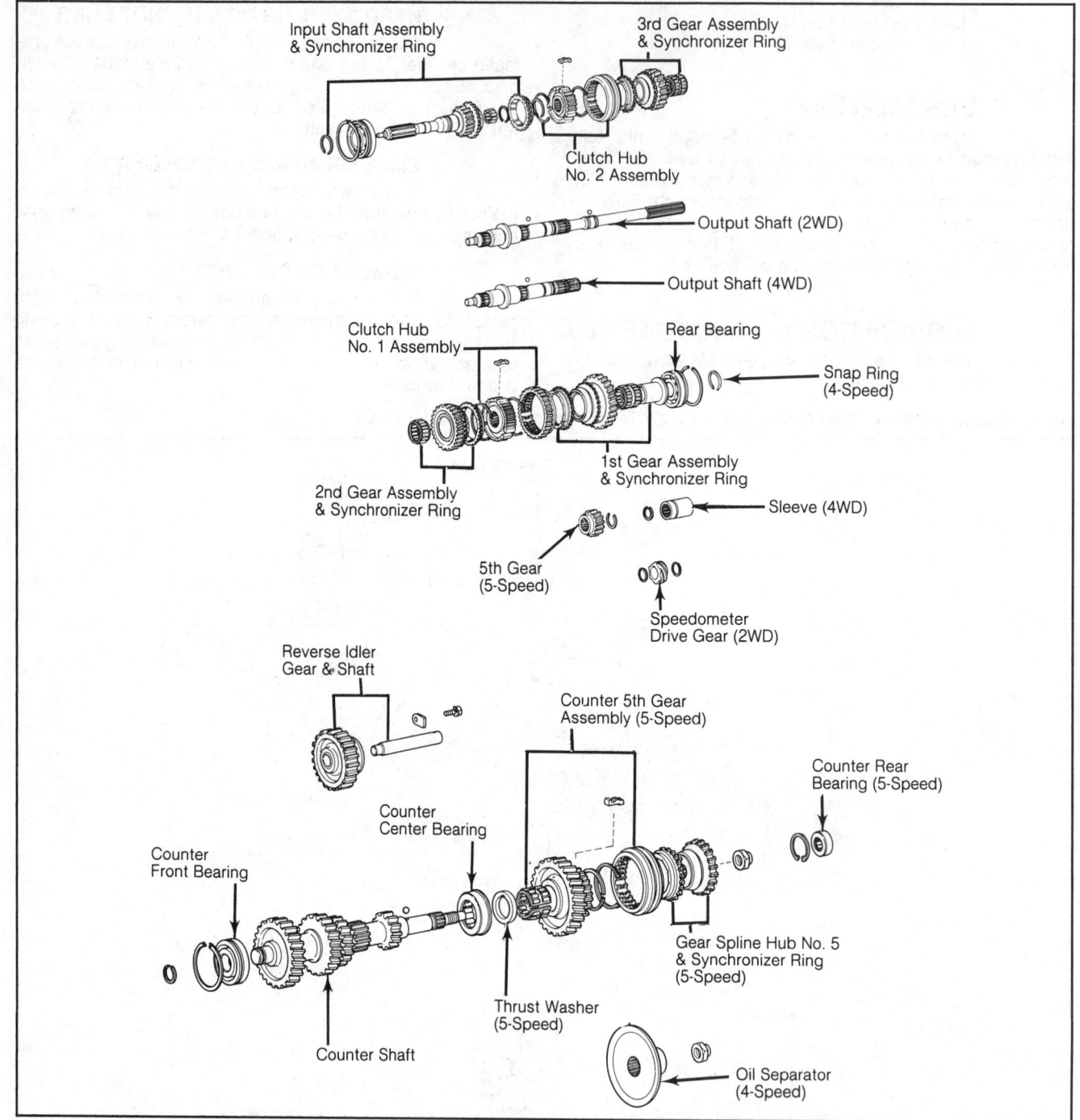

REMOVAL & INSTALLATION

See the appropriate article in MANUAL TRANS-MISSION REMOVAL Section.

TRANSMISSION DISASSEMBLY

1) Remove clutch release bearing and fork. Remove back-up light switch. On 2WD, remove speedometer driven gear. Remove restrict pin from shift lever retainer on 2WD, or from adapter on 4WD. On all models, remove shift lever retainer from extension housing. Remove transmission case cover from case.

2) On 4WD, remove transmission case cover and shift lever retainer mounting bolts. Remove case cover together with shift lever retainer. Remove lock wire and bolt from shift lever housing. Remove shift lever housing and shift lever retainer. Remove transfer adapter. On 2WD, remove extension housing.

3) Using a feeler gauge, measure thrust clearance for each gear and record results for later reference. Standard clearance is .0039-.0098" (.10-.25 mm). Maximum clearance is .0098" (.25 mm). On 2WD, remove snap ring from output shaft and remove speedometer drive gear and lock ball.

TOYOTA 4 & 5-SPEED — MODELS L45, L48 & L52 (Cont.)

Fig. 3: Exploded View of 4 and 5-Speed Shift Lever Retainer, Case Cover and Shift Components

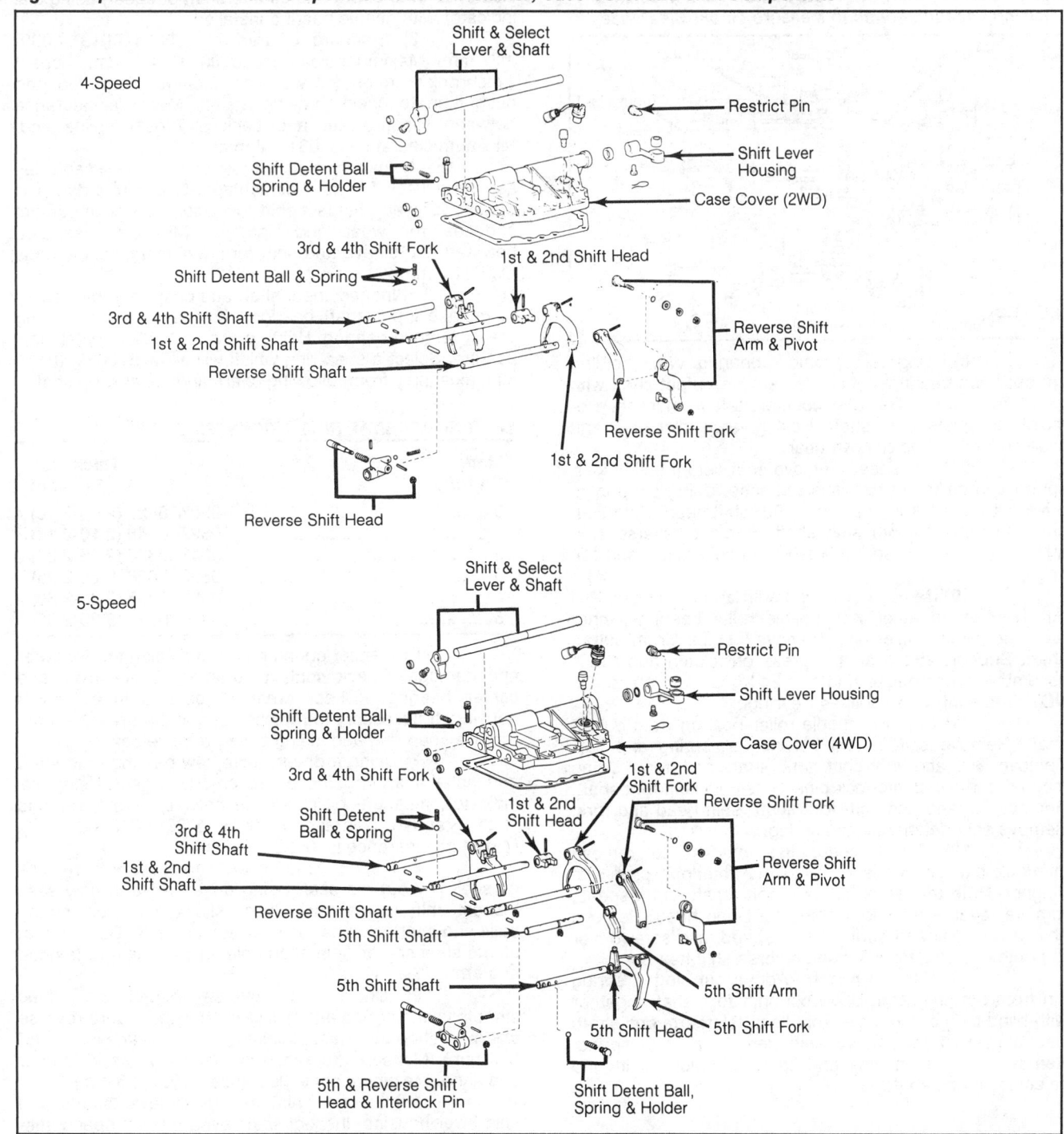

4) Remove other snap ring from groove. On 4WD, remove snap ring and using puller, remove sleeve. Remove snap ring from shaft. Engage gears, double meshing into 2nd and 3rd, but do not shift into 1st gear to avoid overshifting. On 4-speed, remove countershaft lock nut and oil separator, using hammer and chisel to loosen staked part of nut.

5) Using a socket wrench, remove lock nut. Remove oil separator from countershaft. On 5-speed, remove countershaft lock nut. Remove gear spline No. 5 hub and synchronizer ring from countershaft. Using a pin punch, drive out slotted spring pin from fork.

6) Remove shift fork, 5th gear, needle roller bearing and inner race together. Remove lock ball from countershaft. On all models, remove rear bearing retainer. On 5-speed, drive out snap ring using 2 screwdrivers. Using puller, remove 5th gear.

7) Using 2 screwdrivers, pry out center bearing from countershaft. Remove front bearing retainer. Remove 2 snap rings and countershaft front bearing. Lay countershaft on bottom of case. Remove input shaft with synchronizer ring. Remove small snap ring and large snap ring from output shaft rear bearing.

TOYOTA 4 & 5-SPEED — MODELS L45, L48 & L52 (Cont.)

Fig. 4: Cutaway View of Toyota Pickup Transmission Showing Location Points to Measure Thrust Clearance

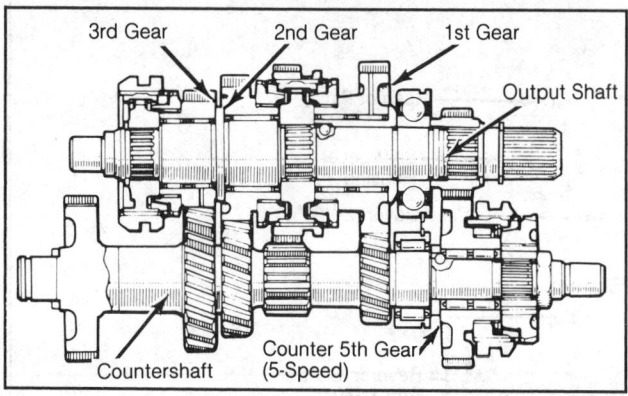

8) Using puller, remove bearing. While holding 1st gear and bearing inner race, remove output shaft with gears from case. Remove countershaft from case. Remove lock plate from shaft. Hold reverse idler gear and slide out shaft, then remove gear.

9) On 5-speed, remove shift detent ball holder, spring and ball from transmission case. Using pin punch, drive out slotted spring pin from 5th shift head. Hold shift head and pull out 5th shift shaft. Remove reverse shift arm pivot lock nut, spring washer, plate washer and "O" ring.

10) Remove pivot and shift arm from case. Pull out 1st gear together with needle roller bearings, inner race and synchronizer ring. Remove lock ball from output shaft. Support 2nd gear and press out clutch hub No. 1 assembly, synchronizer ring and 2nd gear with press. Do NOT drop shaft when splines clear hub.

11) Remove needle roller bearing from output shaft. Remove shift detent ball holder, spring and ball. Remove 3rd and 4th shift fork shaft and fork. Using magnet, remove 2 interlock pins. Small pin is in fork shaft. Remove 1st and 2nd shift fork shaft, shift head and fork. Remove shift detent ball and spring.

12) On 4-speed, use magnet to remove interlock pin. On 5-speed, remove 2 interlock pins with magnet. Note that small pin is in fork shaft. On 4-speed, remove reverse shift fork shaft, fork and head. Remove shift detent ball and spring. On 5-speed, use screwdriver to pry the "E" ring from 5th and reverse shift head.

13) Use pin punch to drive out slotted spring pin from 5th shift arm. Drive out shift fork shaft together with blind plug and remove shift head, shift arm and shaft. Use a magnet to remove shift detent ball and spring. Remove shift detent ball and spring. Remove shift and select lever and shaft.

INSPECTION

1) Inspect output shaft bearing contact surface for wear or damage. Using calipers, measure output shaft flange thickness. Minimum thickness is .193" (4.90 mm). Using dial indicator, check shaft runout. Maximum runout is .002" (.50 mm). Check gears and needle roller bearings for wear and damage.

2) Using dial indicator, measure oil clearance between gear and inner race with needle roller bearing installed. Standard clearance is .0004-.0013" (.009-.032 mm). Maximum clearance is .0013" (.032 mm). Check oil clearance of 2nd, 3rd and countershaft 5th gear, using dial indicator with needle bearing installed.

3) Standard clearance is .0004-.0013" (.009-.032 mm). Maximum clearance is .0013" (032 mm). Inspect synchronizer rings for wear or damage. Turn ring and push it in to check braking action. Measure clearance between synchronizer ring back and gear spline end. Minimum clearance is .031" (.8 mm).

4) Inspect clutch hubs, sleeves, keys and key springs. Check for wear or damage. Check rounded part of keys for wear. Inspect shift fork and hub sleeve contact surfaces for wear and damage. Measure clearance between hub sleeve and shift fork. Maximum clearance is .039" (1.0 mm).

5) Inspect input shaft and bearing. If necessary to replace input shaft bearing, remove snap ring. Using press, remove bearing. Using press and collar, install new bearing. Select a snap ring which will allow 0-.0039" (0-.10 mm) axial play from following chart, and install it on shaft.

INPUT SHAFT SNAP RING THICKNESS CHART

Mark On Ring	Thickness In. (mm)
0	.0807-.0827 (2.05-2.10)
1	.0827-.0846 (2.10-2.15)
2	.0846-.0866 (2.15-2.20)
3	.0866-.0886 (2.20-2.25)
4	.0886-.0906 (2.25-2.30)
5	.0906-.0925 (2.30-2.35)

6) Inspect countershaft and bearings for wear and damage. Check contact surfaces. Check front and center bearings. Check wear of bearing in extension housing. If necessary to replace countershaft rear bearing, remove snap ring and, using puller, remove bearing.

7) Using a driver, drive new bearing onto shaft and install snap ring. Inspect reverse idler gear. Using dial indicator, measure oil clearance between idler gear and shaft. Standard clearance is .0016-.0032" (.040-.082 mm). Maximum clearance is .0032" (.082 mm).

8) Inspect case cover. If necessary to replace oil seal, pry out old seal. Using driver, drive in new seal. Inspect shift fork shafts. Check sliding surfaces, spring balls and interlock pins for wear and damage. Be sure that shafts slide smoothly in each hole. Inspect shift fork, head and arm.

9) Check that reverse restrict pin slides smoothly with spring and ball resistance. Measure reverse shift arm shoe thickness. Minimum shoe thickness is .295" (7.5 mm). Measure clearance between reverse idler gear and shoe. Maximum shoe clearance is .024" (.6 mm).

10) Inspect shift and select lever shafts and shift lever housing. Inspect shaft lever. Inspect speedometer drive gear and driven gear. Inspect front bearing retainer. If necessary to replace oil seal, use screwdriver and pry out seal. Using driver, drive in new seal.

11) On 2WD, inspect extension housing. If necessary to replace seal, use puller and remove seal. Heat extension end to 176-212°F (80-100°C) in oil bath. Using driver, remove bushing and install new bushing. Align bushing oil hole and extension housing oil groove.

12) On 4WD, inspect transfer adapter. If necessary to replace oil seal, use screwdriver and pry out old seal. Drive in new seal. Inspect shift lever retainer. Inspect transmission case.

TOYOTA 4 & 5-SPEED — MODELS L45, L48 & L52 (Cont.)

TRANSMISSION REASSEMBLY

1) Apply gear oil to bearings, gears and shafts. On 2WD, install shift lever housing to shift and select lever shaft. Align holes of shaft and housing. Tighten bolt and secure bolt with lock wire. Apply grease to oil seal lip.

2) Align holes of shaft and lever. Tighten bolt and secure with lock wire. On 5-speed, install spring and shift detent ball in hole. Insert shaft through 5th and reverse shift head. Align shaft and 5th shift arm pin holes and drive in slotted spring pin with punch. Push in "E" ring to 5th and reverse head.

3) Install spring and shift detent ball in hole. Insert shaft through 5th-reverse shift head. Align shaft and 5th shift arm pin holes, and drive in slotted spring pin with pin punch. Using screwdriver, push in "E" ring to 5th-reverse shift head.

4) Set shaft in neutral position. Coat 2 interlock pins with multipurpose grease and push into shaft groove with a screwdriver. Install spring and shift detent ball in hole. Coat small interlock pin with multipurpose grease and install in shaft.

5) Insert shaft through 5th and reverse shift head and reverse shift fork. Align shaft and fork pin holes and drive in slotted spring pin. Using screwdriver, push in "E" ring to reverse shift fork shaft.

6) On 4-speed, install spring and shift detent ball in hole. Insert shaft through reverse shift head and arm. Align shaft, shift head and fork pin holes, and drive in slotted spring pins with punch. On all models, set shift fork shafts to neutral position. Coat interlock pin with grease. Push in interlock pin to shaft with screwdriver.

7) Install 1st and 2nd shift head, fork and shaft. First install spring and detent ball into hole. Coat small interlock pin with multipurpose grease and install it in shaft. Insert shaft through 1st and 2nd shift head and fork.

8) Align shaft, head and fork pin holes and drive in slotted spring pins with a punch. Set shift fork shafts to neutral position. Coat interlock pin with multipurpose grease. Push interlock pin into shaft groove with a screwdriver.

9) Install 2nd and 3rd shift fork and shaft, and drive slotted spring pin with a punch. Install shift detent ball, spring and holder. Apply liquid sealer to threads of holder before tightening. Apply liquid sealer to blind plugs and drive into case cover.

10) Apply multipurpose grease to output shaft and install needle roller bearings, 3rd gear and synchronizer rings on output shaft. Insert clutch hub No. 2 into hub sleeve with shifting keys. Install shifting key springs under shifting keys so that spring ends are not in line.

11) Apply multipurpose grease to output shaft and align synchronizer ring slots with shifting keys. Using a press and collar (SST09506-30011), install clutch hub No. 2. With hub on output shaft, select a snap ring which

CLUTCH HUB NO. 2 SNAP RING CHART

Mark On Ring	Thickness In. (mm)
D	.0709-.0728 (1.80-1.85)
D-1	.0728-.0748 (1.85-1.90)
E	.0748-.0768 (1.90-1.95)
E-1	.0768-.0787 (1.95-2.00)
F	.0787-.0807 (2.00-2.05)

Fig. 5: Location of Shift Lever Shafts, Forks and Interlocking Pins

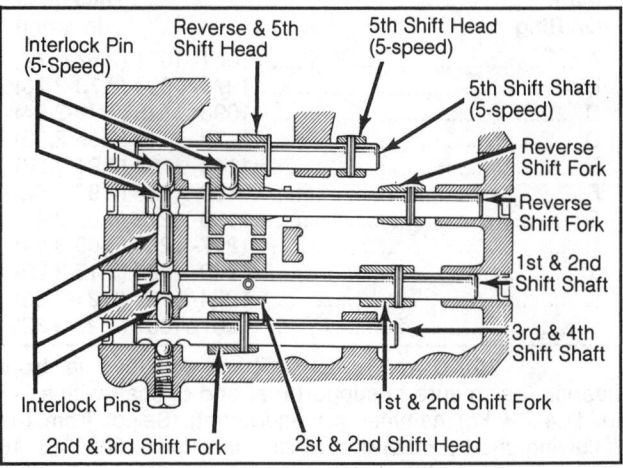

will allow 0-.0039" (0-.10 mm) axial play from following chart and install it on shaft.

12) Apply multipurpose grease to output shaft. Install needle roller bearing, 2nd gear and synchronizer ring on output shaft. Insert clutch hub No. 1 and shifting keys to reverse gear. Make sure spring ends are not in line. Grease output shaft, align synchronizer ring slots with shifting keys and press on clutch hub No. 1 (reverse gear) on output shaft.

13) Assemble 1st gear, needle bearings, inner race and synchronizer ring. Grease needle roller bearings and install bearings and 1st gear to inner race. Place synchronizer ring on 1st gear. Install inner race locking ball, align inner race slot with locking ball and install 1st gear assembly to output shaft.

14) Install reverse shift arm and pivot to transmission. Install "O" ring, plate washer, spring washer and nut to pivot. On 5-speed, install 5th shift head and shaft by inserting shift fork shaft through shift head. Align shaft and head pin holes and drive in slotted spring pin with a pin punch.

15) Install shift detent ball, spring and holder. Apply liquid sealer to holder before tightening. On all models, align reverse idler gear groove with reverse shift arm shoe. Install reverse idler gear shaft through gear. Secure shaft with lock plate. Tighten bolt.

16) Place transmission case up on its front end. Carefully install countershaft into transmission. Install output shaft into transmission, taking care not to drop off 1st gear and needle roller bearings. Support output shaft with a .39" (10 mm) piece of plate stock.

17) Install snap ring onto output shaft rear bearing. Using bearing driver, drive in bearing until it comes into contact with 1st gear needle roller bearing inner race. Remove steel plate and drive in bearing until its snap ring is flush with case end.

18) On 4-speed, select a snap ring which will allow 0-.0039" (0-.10 mm) axial play from chart, and install on shaft. On all models, install snap ring onto input shaft bearing. Coat needle roller bearing with multipurpose grease. Align synchronizer ring slots with shifting keys.

19) Using bearing driver, drive in input shaft. Install snap rings onto front and center bearings. Assemble front bearing inner race piece with its tapered side toward gear. Temporarily install front bearing to the case.

Manual Transmissions

TOYOTA 4 & 5-SPEED — MODELS L45, L48 & L52 (Cont.)

OUTPUT SHAFT REAR BEARING SNAP RING CHART

Mark On Ring	Thickness In. (mm)
A	.1051-.1071 (2.67-2.72)
B	.1075-.1094 (2.73-2.78)
C	.1098-.1118 (2.79-2.84)
D	.1122-.1141 (2.85-2.90)
E	.1146-.1165 (2.91-2.96)
F	.1169-.1189 (2.97-3.02)
G	.1193-.1213 (3.03-3.08)
H	.1217-.1236 (3.09-3.14)
J	.1240-.1260 (3.15-3.20)
K	.1264-.1283 (3.21-3.26)
L	.1287-.1307 (3.27-3.32)

20) Drive in center bearing. Drive in front bearing, being sure to support rear end of shaft with a 3-5 lb. (1.4-2.3 kg) hammer (or equivalent). Select from the following chart a snap ring which will allow 0-.0039" (0-.10 mm) axial play and install it on shaft.

COUNTERSHAFT REAR SNAP RING CHART

Mark On Ring	Thickness In. (mm)
1	.0807-.0827 (2.05-2.10)
2	.0827-.0846 (2.10-2.15)
3	.0846-.0866 (2.15-2.20)
4	.0866-.0886 (2.20-2.25)
5	.0886-.0906 (2.25-2.30)
6	.0906-.0925 (2.30-2.35)

21) Install bearing retainer with new gasket. Apply multipurpose grease to oil seal and liquid sealer to mounting bolts before tightening retainer. On 5-speed, drive 5th gear onto output shaft with long sleeve side facing toward front. Select a snap ring which will allow 0-.0039" (0-.10 mm) axial play from following chart, and install it on shaft.

5TH GEAR SNAP RING CHART

Mark On Ring	Thickness In. (mm)
A	.1051-.1071 (2.67-2.72)
B	.1075-.1094 (2.73-2.78)
C	.1098-.1118 (2.79-2.84)
D	.1122-.1141 (2.85-2.90)
E	.1146-.1165 (2.91-2.96)
F	.1169-.1189 (2.97-3.02)
G	.1193-.1213 (3.03-3.08)
H	.1217-.1236 (3.09-3.14)
J	.1240-.1260 (3.15-3.20)
K	.1264-.1283 (3.21-3.26)
L	.1287-.1307 (3.27-3.32)

22) On all models, install rear bearing retainer. On 5-speed, install clutch hub No. 3 and shifting keys to hub sleeve. Install shifting key springs under shifting keys so that spring ends are not in line. Install lock ball and thrust washer.

23) Install lubricated needle roller bearing into countershaft 5th gear. With hole in shift fork facing toward front, install countershaft 5th gear assembly together with shift fork. Align shift fork and shaft pin holes and drive in slotted spring pin. Install gear spline No. 5 with synchronizer ring slots aligned with shifting keys.

24) On all models, engage gears, double meshing into 2nd and 3rd, but do not shift into 1st gear to avoid overshifting. On 4-speed, install oil separator. On all models, tighten countershaft lock nut. Release gear double meshing to neutral position. Stake lock nut.

25) Measure thrust clearance for each gear. Standard clearance is .0039-.0098" (.10-.25 mm). Maximum clearance is .0098" (.25 mm). On 2WD, install speedometer drive gear to output shaft by installing snap ring, lock ball and drive gear, and outer snap ring.

26) On 4WD, install sleeve onto output shaft, install snap ring and drive sleeve onto output shaft. On 2WD, grease oil seal and needle roller bearing. Install extension housing with new gasket and tighten bolts. On 4WD, grease oil seal and needle roller bearing. Install transfer adapter with new gasket and tighten adapter mounting bolts.

27) On 2WD, place each shift fork, hub sleeve and reverse idler gear in neutral position. Place new gasket in position. Install transmission case cover to case. Tighten case cover mounting bolts. Install boot on shift and select lever shaft. Install transmission shift lever retainer with new gasket, apply liquid sealer to mounting bolts and tighten the retainer.

28) Install boot on shift lever retainer. On 4WD, install shift lever retainer and shift lever housing to case cover. Install shift lever housing to the shift and select lever shaft. Align the holes of the shaft and housing. Tighten bolt and secure with lock wire. Place each shift fork, hub sleeve and reverse idler gear in neutral.

29) Install transmission case cover and shift lever retainer with new gasket. Apply liquid sealer to mounting bolts and tighten the retainer. Install restrict pin to shift lever retainer on 2WD and to adapter on 4WD. Check gears rotating condition in each shift position.

30) If abnormal noise comes from reverse idler gear, adjust reverse shift arm pivot position. Correct reverse shift arm pivot position by turning pivot within 90°. Tighten lock nut. On 2WD, install speedometer driven gear and secure with lock plate and bolt.

31) On all models, install back-up light switch. Install clutch release bearing and fork. Lubricate all contact points with molybdenum disulphide lithium based grease. Insert fork into boot and install into clutch housing. Install bearing hub with 2 clips.

TIGHTENING SPECIFICATIONS

Application	Ft. Lbs. (N.m)
All Models	
Shift Lever Bolts	14-22 (19-30)
Shift Detent Ball Holder	11-15 (15-20)
Reverse Idler Gear Lock Bolt	11-15 (15-20)
Front Retainer Bolts	15-20 (20-27)
Rear Retainer Bolts	11-15 (15-20)
Countershaft Lock Nut	80-101 (109-137)
Reverse Shift Arm Bolt	14-22 (19-30)
Transmission-to-Engine	37-57 (50-78)
2WD	
Extension Housing Bolts	29-39 (39-53)
Case Cover Bolts	11-15 (15-20)
Speedometer Driven Gear	8-11 (11-15)
Engine Rear Mounting Bolts	26-36 (35-49)
Mounting Bolts-to-Extension	14-22 (19-30)
4WD	
Transfer Case Adapter	22-39 (30-53)
Shift Lever-to-Case Cover Bolts	14-22 (19-30)
Rear Support Member	55-75 (75-102)

Manual Transmissions

TOYOTA 4 & 5-SPEED — MODELS T40, T41 & T50

Corolla

TRANSMISSION IDENTIFICATION

The T40, T41 (4-Speed) and T50 (5-Speed) transmissions can be identified from other Toyota transmissions by its ribbed aluminum case; this is the only transmission currently using the split (2 piece) transmission case.

Fig. 1: Exterior View of Transmission Case

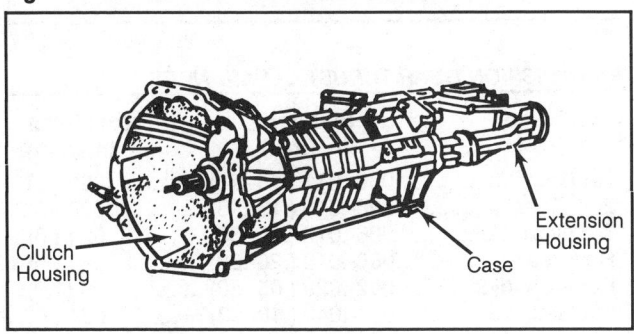

DESCRIPTION

Transmissions are 4 or 5-speed, fully synchronized units, in which all gears are helical cut and in constant mesh. Gear engagement is accomplished through use of 3 blocker-type synchronizer assemblies. Foor shift lever operates a single control rod in extension housing, which in turn is connected to shifting rails in rear of tranmission case. Access to transmission internal parts is accomplished by separating transmission case halves.

LUBRICATION & ADJUSTMENT

See the appropriate article in MANUAL TRANS-MISSION SERVICING Section.

TROUBLE SHOOTING

HARD SHIFTING

Clutch may not be operating properly. Improper contact or wear between synchro ring and gear coned surface. Shifting key may be worn or damaged.

TRANSMISSION SLIPS OUT OF GEAR

Shift fork worn or spring (for lock ball) broken. Input and output bearings worn or damaged. Clearance between synchro hub No. 2 and synchro sleeve splines is excessive. Drive gear (2nd, 3rd, 4th and 5th) worn or its bushing worn. Clearance excessive between synchro hub No. 1 and 1st-reverse gear splines. Countergear or its bearings worn.

NOISE IN TRANSMISSION

Lubricating oil incorrect or insufficient. Gears or bearings worn or damaged. Output shaft splines worn. Bushings for 2nd gear, 1st gear or idler gear worn.

REMOVAL & INSTALLATION

See the appropriate article in MANUAL TRANS-MISSION REMOVAL Section.

TRANSMISSION DISASSEMBLY

CLUTCH HOUSING

Release spring clips and remove clutch release fork and bearing. Loosen bolts evenly and remove clutch housing from transmission. Use care not to damage oil seal lip or to drop cone washers between transmission and housing.

EXTENSION HOUSING

Remove speedometer driven gear retainer bolt; take out shaft sleeve and driven gear. Remove back-up light switch. Remove 6 housing bolts. When removing extension housing, ensure that output spline does not damage rear oil seal. On T50 (5-speed), remove the reverse restrict pin by removing plug with hexagon wrench. Drive out slotted spring pin with punch and remove reverse restrict pin.

TRANSMISSION CASE

1) Remove plate holding shift fork shaft locking balls and springs. Remove balls and springs with magnet. Remove bolts holding case halves together and separate case halves by tapping on protrusion of right case half with plastic hammer. Be sure to retain locking balls between cases and countergear bearing.

Fig. 2: Using a Hammer to Separate Case Halves

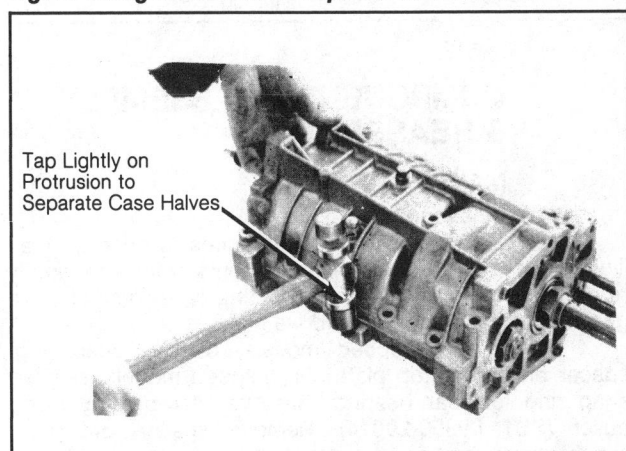

Tap Lightly on Protrusion to Separate Case Halves

2) With left half of case removed, lift mainshaft from right half of case, then lift out countergear assembly. Using pin punch, drive out pins holding shift forks to shafts. Note that pin holding No. 1 fork is driven out through hole in case. Drive out the pin in No. 2 and No. 3 shift forks. Place all shafts in neutral position and pull individually from rear of case.

TOYOTA 4 & 5-SPEED — MODELS T40, T41 & T50 (Cont.)

Fig. 3: Exploded View of T40, T41 & T50 Transmission

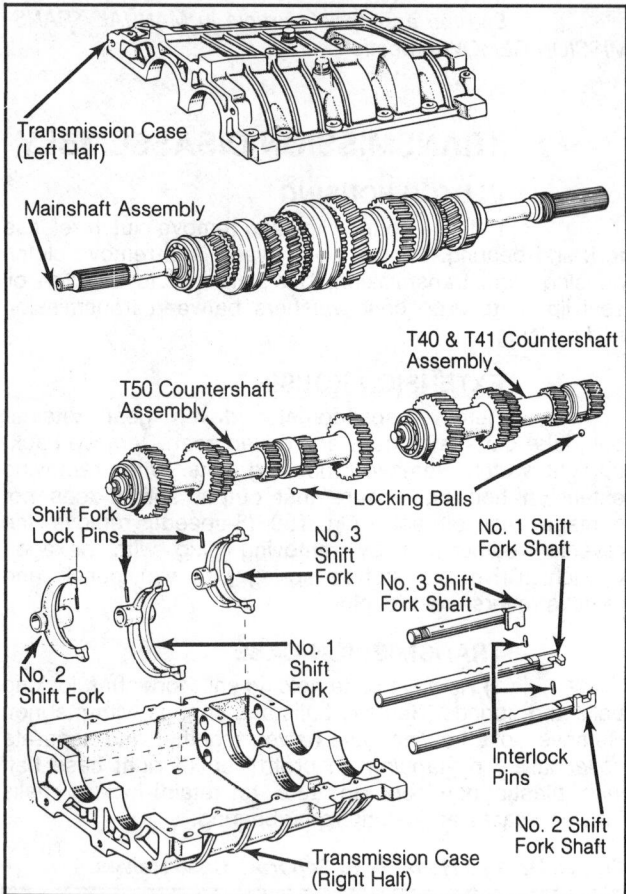

- Transmission Case (Left Half)
- Mainshaft Assembly
- T40 & T41 Countershaft Assembly
- T50 Countershaft Assembly
- Locking Balls
- Shift Fork Lock Pins
- No. 3 Shift Fork
- No. 1 Shift Fork Shaft
- No. 3 Shift Fork Shaft
- No. 1 Shift Fork
- No. 2 Shift Fork
- Interlock Pins
- No. 2 Shift Fork Shaft
- Transmission Case (Right Half)

Fig. 4: Thrust Clearance Measurement Points

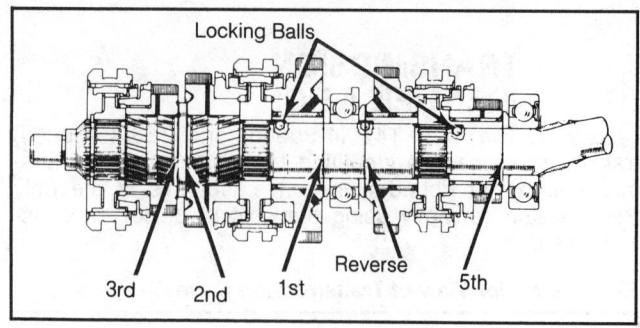

- Locking Balls
- 3rd
- 2nd
- 1st
- Reverse
- 5th

TRANSMISSION GEAR THRUST CLEARANCES

Application [1]	Standard In. (mm)	[2] Wear Limit In. (mm)
1st Gear	.006-.011 (.15-.28)	.020 (.5)
2nd Gear	.006-.010 (.15-.25)	.020 (.5)
3rd Gear	.006-.012 (.15-.30)	.024 (.6)
Reverse	.008-.013 (.20-.32)	.024 (.6)
Reverse Idler	.002-.020 (.05-.50)	.39 (1.0)
5th Gear	.004-.040 (.10-.93)	.024 (.6)

[1] — See text for measurement procedure.
[2] — This is maximum wear limit.

Inspection

1) Inspect output shaft for wear, damage or distortion. Minimum thickness of flange between 2nd and 3rd gear is .157" (4.0 mm). Minimum diameter of 2nd and

Fig. 5: Disassembled View of Mainshaft Assembly

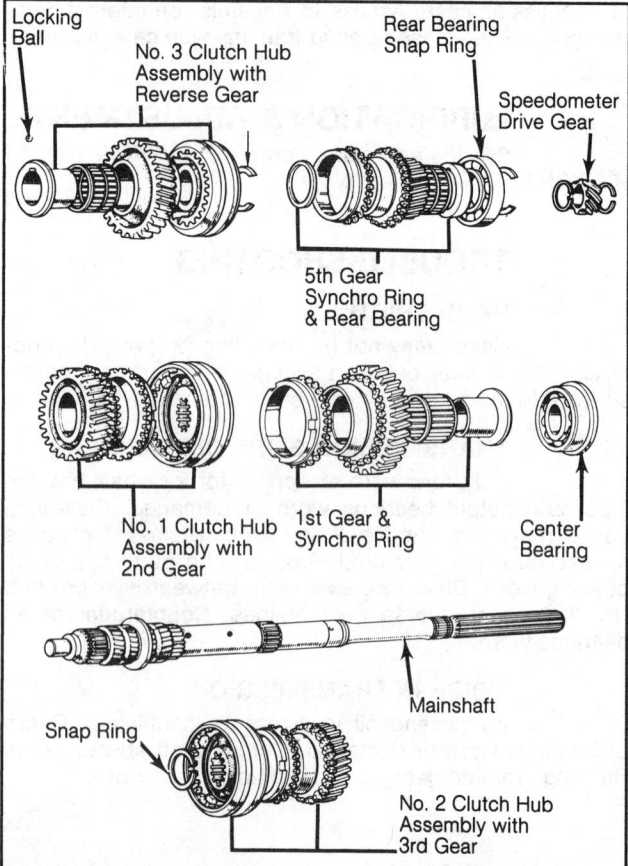

- Locking Ball
- No. 3 Clutch Hub Assembly with Reverse Gear
- Rear Bearing Snap Ring
- Speedometer Drive Gear
- 5th Gear Synchro Ring & Rear Bearing
- No. 1 Clutch Hub Assembly with 2nd Gear
- 1st Gear & Synchro Ring
- Center Bearing
- Snap Ring
- Mainshaft
- No. 2 Clutch Hub Assembly with 3rd Gear

COMPONENT DISASSEMBLY & REASSEMBLY

MAINSHAFT

Disassembly

1) Measure thrust clearances of each gear as illustrated, and record measurements for reassembly reference. Remove snap rings holding speedometer drive gear in position and remove drive gear.

2) On 4-speed models, remove snap ring, spacer and shift stop plate. On 5-speed models, remove snap ring for rear bearing. Remove rear bearing using puller (SST 09950-20014). Remove spacer, 5th gear, synchronizer ring, needle roller bearings, spacer and steel ball. Remove snap ring, then remove No. 3 clutch hub and sleeve. Remove reverse gear, needle bearing and bushing by pressing down on output shaft while supporting reverse gear with vise jaws.

3) Remove center bearing, bushing, needle bearing, 1st gear, and synchronizer ring. Remove and retain locking ball, then press output shaft from 1st gear assembly using same procedure as for reverse gear. Remove snap ring from front of shaft, then press No. 2 clutch hub and sleeve with 3rd gear and synchronizer ring from shaft.

NOTE: When pressing gear assemblies from mainshaft, support shaft with hand to prevent dropping shaft when it clears hub splines. Retain all locking balls.

TOYOTA 4 & 5-SPEED — MODELS T40, T41 & T50 (Cont.)

3rd gear journals is 1.488" (37.8 mm). Check shaft deflection at speedometer drive gear journal while rotating shaft. Maximum deflection is .002" (.06 mm).

2) Check each gear, bushing and bearing surface for wear or damage. Refer to *Gear Bearing Surface Inside Diameter Wear table* for specifications to check inside gear limits. Note that oil clearance for 1st gear is .0004-.0024" (.01-.06 mm); 2nd and 3rd gear is .0024-.004" (.06-.10 mm); 5th gear is .0004-.002" (.01-.05 mm).

3) Disassemble clutch hubs using care not to mix parts and inspect for wear or damage. Check clearance limit of .039" (1.0 mm) between shift fork and sleeve grooves. Groove maximum width is .335" (8.5 mm).

Fig. 6: Mainshaft Inspection Points

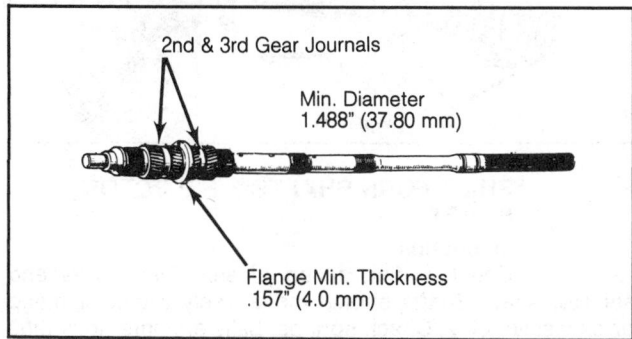

2nd & 3rd Gear Journals

Min. Diameter
1.488" (37.80 mm)

Flange Min. Thickness
.157" (4.0 mm)

4) Check synchronizer rings for wear or damage and braking effect. Ring should stick to gear cone when turned and pressed against cone. Standard clearance between synchronizer ring and gear is .039-.079" (1.0-2.0 mm). Minimum clearance is .031" (.8 mm). Replace ring and/or gear as required. Inspect shift keys and springs for wear or damage and replace if necessary.

GEAR BEARING SURFACE INSIDE DIAMETER WEAR LIMIT

Application	Specification In. (mm)
1st	1.66 (42.15)
2nd	1.50 (38.15)
3rd	1.50 (38.15)
5th	1.42 (36.15)
Reverse	1.66 (42.15)

Fig. 7: Checking Shift Fork Groove Clearance

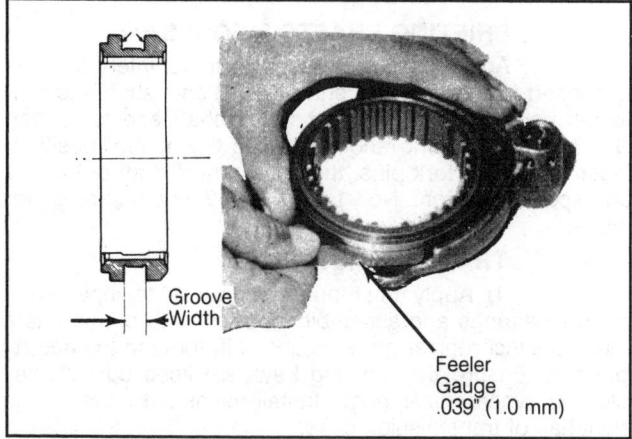

Groove Width

Feeler Gauge
.039" (1.0 mm)

Fig. 8: Synchronizer Ring Braking Check

With Synchro Ring Inserted in Gear Turn in Direction of Arrow

Reassembly

1) Assemble synchronizer assemblies individually, ensuring that key spring ends are staggered. Note location and identification of each synchronizer assembly.

Fig. 9: View Showing Synchronizer Identification

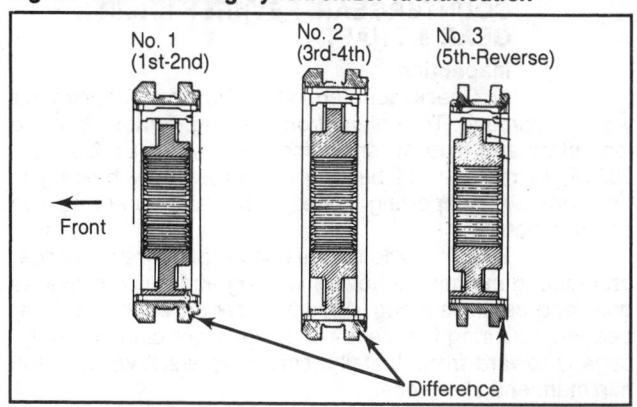

No. 1 (1st-2nd)   No. 2 (3rd-4th)   No. 3 (5th-Reverse)

Front

Difference

2) From rear of mainshaft, slide 2nd gear on shaft. With synchro No. 2 assembled, including synchro rings, slide assembly on shaft from rear. Slide on 1st gear, with coned surface facing front of shaft. Install bearing sleeve lock ball in mainshaft. Slide 1st gear roller bearing and sleeve on from rear of shaft and install them inside 1st gear.

3) Slide center support radial ball bearing directly behind 1st gear. Install bearing sleeve lock ball in shaft and install bearing and sleeve. Install reverse gear and reverse synchro hub (No. 3). On 5-speed models, install 5th gear, bushing, bearing, sleeve lock ball and rear bearing.

4) On 4-speed models, install dished washer and spacer tube with shaft lock ball. Install snap ring. Install speedometer drive gear along with drive ball and 2 snap rings. On front of shaft, install 3rd gear, synchro assembly with blocking rings, and selective retaining snap ring.

INPUT SHAFT, BEARING & RETAINER
Inspection

1) Check input shaft spline by placing input shaft into clutch disc and checking that shaft slides smoothly. Make sure there is no excessive play.

2) Check input shaft bearing by pressing on front of bearing and rotating input shaft. If there is abnormal resistance or noise, it will be necessary to replace bearing. To replace bearing, use snap ring pliers and remove front snap ring. Use press and adapter (SST

TOYOTA 4 & 5-SPEED — MODELS T40, T41 & T50 (Cont.)

09506-10010), to press off old bearing. Use adapter (SST 09316-60010) to press on new bearing. Choose a selective snap ring which will engage securely in groove and eliminate play between bearing and shaft.

INPUT SHAFT SNAP RING SPECIFICATIONS

Application	In. (mm)
T40, T41 & T50	.100-.102 (2.55-2.60)
	.098-.100 (2.50-2.55)
	.097-.098 (2.45-2.50)
	.095-.097 (2.40-2.45)
	.093-.096 (2.35-2.40)

3) Check front bearing retainer and oil seal for wear or damage. If seal shows evidence of leakage, it must be replaced. Also check mating surfaces of transmission case and clutch housing.

COUNTERGEAR, REVERSE IDLER GEAR & SHAFT

Inspection

1) Check countergear faces and bearings for wear or damage. To replace front bearing, remove bearing lock plate and take off snap ring. Use puller (SST 09950-20014) to remove old bearing and press new bearing in position by supporting inner race and pressing on countershaft.

2) To replace reverse bearing and reverse gear on 4-speed models, remove snap ring and pull off reverse gear and center bearing. Assemble center bearing to rear bearing, ensuring that center bearing larger diameter roller cage is toward front. Install a snap ring which will give the minimum end clearance.

Fig. 10: Countergear Rear Snap Ring Selection

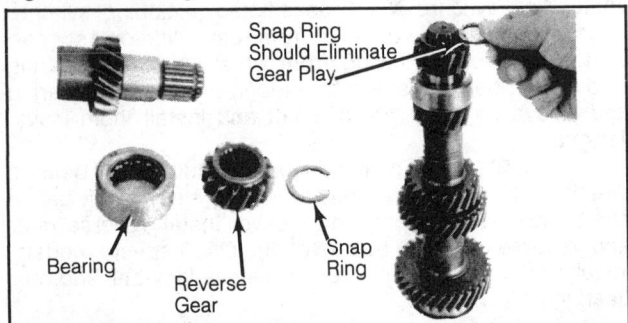

4-Speed Shown.

3) On 5-speed models, remove snap ring. Support 5th gear on steel plate to remove 5th gear and rear bearing. Press out countershaft. Remove reverse gear and center bearing. Install center bearing with larger diameter of roller cage to front, and install reverse gear. Using support for rear bearing, hold up reverse gear and press in bearing and 5th gear at same time. Install snap ring which will provide minimum end clearance.

COUNTERGEAR SHAFT SNAP RING SPECIFICATIONS

Application	In. (mm)
T40 & T41 (4-speed)	.071-.073 (1.80-1.85)
	.075-.077 (1.90-1.95)
T50 (5-speed)	.063-.065 (1.60-1.65)
	.071-.073 (1.80-1.85)
	.079-.081 (2.00-2.05)

4) Measure reverse idler thrust clearance between case and gear. Standard clearance is .002-.020" (.05-.50 mm) with a maximum limit of .039" (1.0 mm). Remove shaft and gear with thrust washers. Bushing bore wear limit is .634" (16.1 mm) and shaft diameter wear limit is .626" (15.9 mm). If installing new bushing, ensure that oil holes in bushing and gear line up.

Fig. 11: Measuring Reverse Idler Gear Thrust Clearance

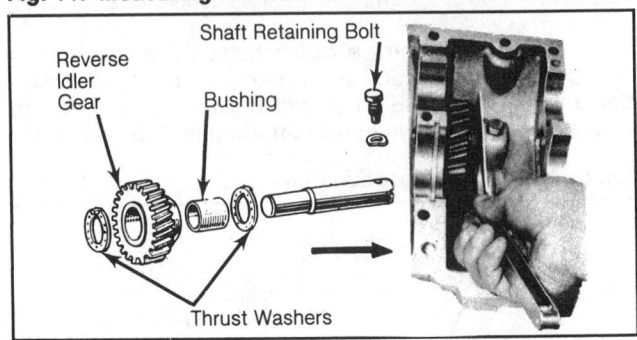

SHIFT FORK SHAFTS & SELECTOR SHAFT

Inspection

Check sliding action of shift fork shafts and selector shaft. Shafts should move freely without binding or excessive play. Check springs, balls and inter lock pins for wear and damage

EXTENSION HOUSING

Inspection

1) Inspect speedometer gear and oil seal for wear or damage. Replace inner seal and outer "O" ring as necessary. Inspect rear oil seal and bushing for wear or damage. If seal replacement is required, use puller (SST 09308-00010) to remove old oil seal and installer (SST 09325-12010) to drive in new seal.

2) To replace rear bushing, heat extension housing to 176-212°F (80-100°C) and drive out old bushing with special tool (SST 09307-12010). Ensure that oil hole is positioned at top of housing and use same tool to install new bushing to proper depth of .59" (15.0 mm) below end of extension housing. Install new seal and apply multi-purpose grease to seal lips.

TRANSMISSION REASSEMBLY

SHIFTING SHAFTS & FORKS

Apply multi-purpose grease to interlock pins and insert in case. Insert center (No. 2) shift shaft and fork to the neutral position. Insert No. 1 shaft and fork, then No. 3 shaft and fork (short shaft) to the neutral position. Install all 3 shift fork pins, then pull center shaft out to the 3rd speed position. No. 1 and No. 2 shaft should not move.

TRANSMISSION CASE

1) Apply multi-purpose grease to input shaft needle bearings and assemble input shaft to output shaft. Line up synchronizer grooves and shift forks to the neutral position. Ensure that shifting keys are lined up with key slots in synchronizer rings. Install mainshaft assembly in right half of transmission case.

2) Install countergear assembly in case and insert locking ball in case groove. Clean case joining

TOYOTA 4 & 5-SPEED — MODELS T40, T41 & T50 (Cont.)

Fig. 12: Cutaway View of Case Showing Locking Pins and Fork Shaft Installation

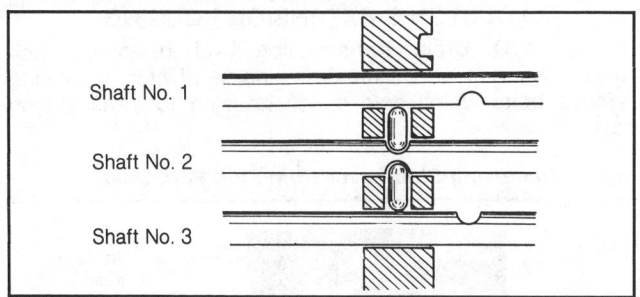

surfaces and bearing recesses. Apply liquid sealer to case joining faces and bolt threads. Install left half of case to right half and tighten bolts gradually in sequence to specifications. *See Fig. 13.*

    3) Check front end of input shaft to see that there is approximately .012" (.3 mm) play radially. Check to see that shift rods move smoothly to all gear selections.

Fig. 13: Transmission Case Bolt Tightening Sequence

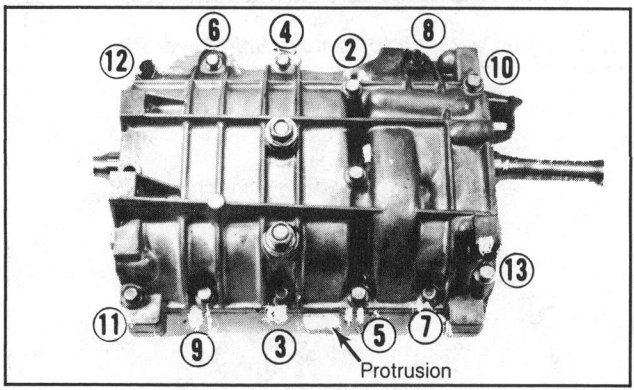

Protrusion

EXTENSION HOUSING & CLUTCH HOUSING

    1) Apply liquid sealer to both sides of gasket. Place gasket on rear of transmission housing and carefully install extension housing. Shift selector shaft should engage in No. 2 fork shaft. Install and tighten extension housing bolts.

    2) Install restrict pins (white on left and black on right) and tighten to specifications. Install shift lever retainer on extension housing. Install speedometer drive gear. Install shift rail detent balls, springs and retainer plate. Install back-up light switch.

Fig. 14: Transmission Case-to-Clutch Housing

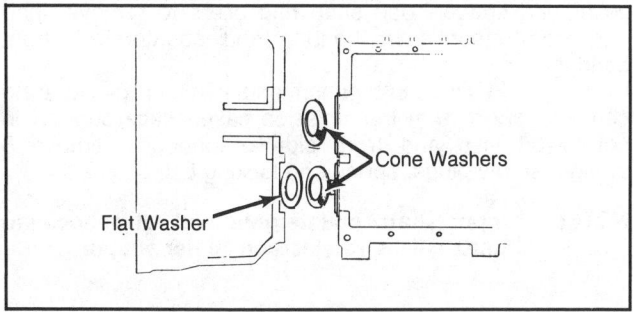

Cone and flat washer installation.

    3) Apply multi-purpose grease to oil seal lip in clutch housing and to washers. Install cone washers in recesses with dished side to rear of transmission. *See Fig. 14.* Apply liquid sealer to joining surfaces and install clutch housing on transmission.

NOTE: **When installing transmission on clutch housing, ensure that pilot shaft splines do not damage lip of oil seal.**

    4) Tighten housing bolts, to specifications, evenly in 3 or 4 steps in a criss-cross pattern. Apply multi-purpose grease to sliding surfaces and install clutch release fork and bearing.

TIGHTENING SPECIFICATIONS

Application	Ft. Lbs. (N.m)
Reverse Idler Shaft Retaining Bolt	10-13 (14-18)
Case Half Bolts	14-15 (19-20)
Extension Housing-to-Case Bolts	22-33 (30-45)
Clutch Housing-to-Case Bolts	22-33 (30-45)
Clutch Housing-to-Engine	37-50 (50-70)
Restrict Pins	27-33 (37-45)

Manual Transmissions

TOYOTA 5-SPEED — MODEL W50

Pickup (Exc. 4WD)

TRANSMISSION IDENTIFICATION

The W50 transmission utilizes a 4-piece transmission case assembly. Main components are the clutch housing, main case, intermediate plate and extension housing.

Fig. 1: Exterior View of W50 Transmission

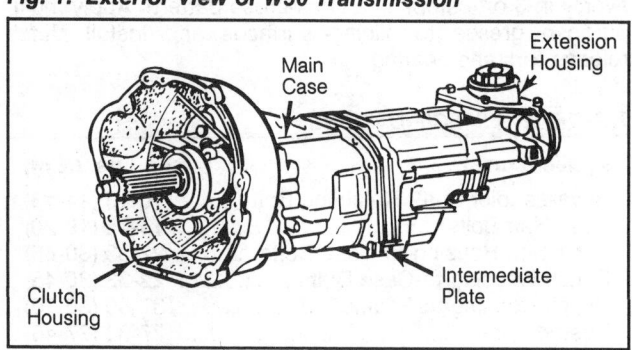

DESCRIPTION

Transmission is 5-speed, fully synchronized unit. All forward gears are helical cut and in constant mesh. Reverse gear is spur cut. Reverse and 5th gears are in constant mesh and are mounted on rear side of intermediate plate (inside extension housing). Floor shifter actuates a single control rod in extension housing operating 3 shift rails mounted in intermediate plate and main case.

LUBRICATION & ADJUSTMENT

See the appropriate article in MANUAL TRANSMISSION SERVICING Section.

TROUBLE SHOOTING

HARD SHIFTING

Clutch not disengaging properly. Bushings in cross shaft worn or damaged. Synchronizer rings making faulty contact with gear cone. Synchronizer worn or pitted.

SLIPS OUT OF GEAR

Improper meshing of gears due to shift rails being out of adjustment. Shift forks worn or ball locks broken. Excessive play in synchronizer hub No. 2, output shaft or drive gear worn. Reverse idler gear or bushing worn. Countergear, bushing or shaft worn.

TRANSMISSION NOISY

Gears or bearings worn or damaged. Insufficient or incorrect lubricant. Mainshaft splines worn or damaged. Reverse idler gear bushing worn.

REMOVAL & INSTALLATION

See the appropriate article in MANUAL TRANSMISSION REMOVAL Section.

TRANSMISSION DISASSEMBLY

CLUTCH & EXTENSION HOUSING

1) Drain transmission and remove clutch release bearing and arm. From inside of clutch housing remove bolts which hold clutch housing to transmission case.

Fig. 2: Removing Shift Lever from Shift Fork Shaft

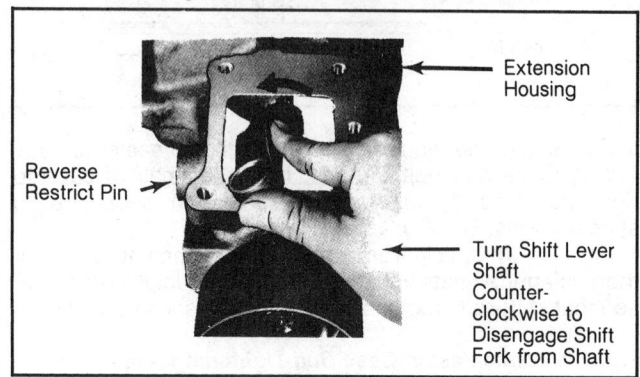

Fig. 3: Using a Punch to Remove Shift Lever Pin

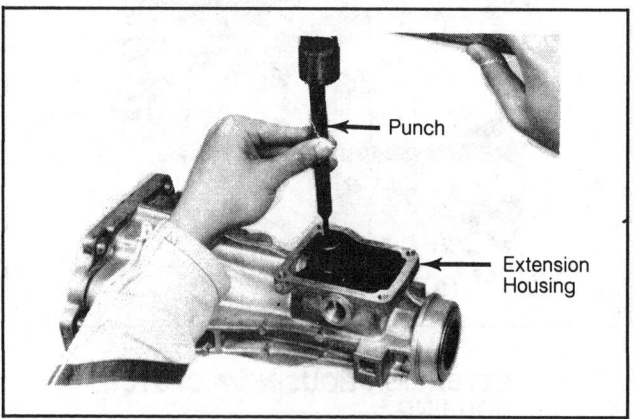

2) From the extension housing, remove speedometer driven gear and control shift lever retainer cover. From below shift lever cover, remove reverse restrict pin on side of extension housing. Remove back-up light switch (if equipped).

3) Remove bolts from extension housing, turn shift lever counterclockwise (as viewed from rear), tap housing with a plastic hammer and pull housing from case.

TRANSMISSION CASE

1) Remove front bearing retainer, countershaft cover and spacer. Use snap ring pliers to remove snap ring from input shaft bearing and countershaft front bearing.

2) Use drift punch and hammer to separate center support from transmission case. Place support in soft-jawed vise and from side of support, remove 3 straight screw plugs, spring and locking balls.

NOTE: Input shaft, countergear and all associated parts will be retained on center support.

TOYOTA 5-SPEED — MODEL W50 (Cont.)

Fig. 4: Using a Hammer and Drift to Separate Center Support from Transmission Case

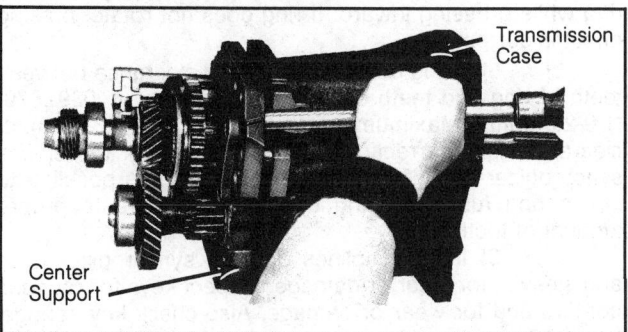

3) Use straight punch to drive out slotted pins which hold shift forks to shift fork shafts. Remove shift fork shaft from center support and remove shift forks from shafts.

NOTE: Use care not to lose 2 interlock pins and 3 interlock balls.

Fig. 5: Using a Punch to Drive Out Shift Fork Pins

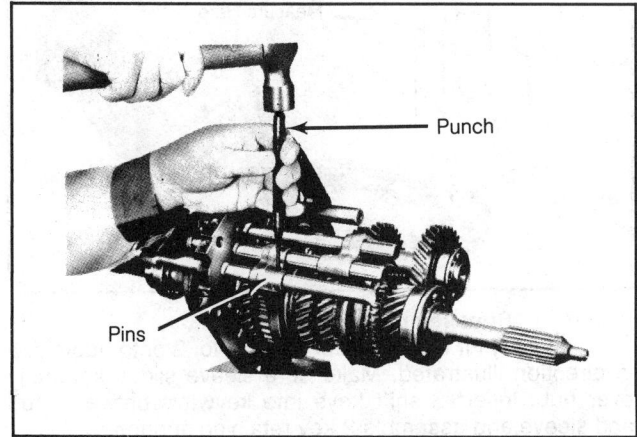

4) Remove snap ring holding speedometer drive gear on shaft. Remove speedometer gear making sure not to lose lock ball beneath gear. Use bearing puller (SST 09950-20014) to remove mainshaft rear bearing. Remove snap ring which was in front of rear bearing.

5) Remove snap ring from countershaft. Using a bearing puller, remove countergear rear bearing. Remove countershaft 5th gear and countershaft reverse gear. Remove snap ring from mainshaft and withdraw 5th gear, synchronizer ring, needle roller bearing and 5th gear bearing inner race.

CAUTION: Do not lose ball which locks 5th gear inner race.

6) Remove reverse gear and synchronizer assembly from mainshaft. Remove reverse idler gear by removing bolt and tang which retains shaft to support. Pull reverse idler shaft, gear, and spacer toward the rear.

7) Remove retainer and snap ring from mainshaft center bearing. Push countergear cylindrical roller bearing outer race toward rear and remove bearing. Remove countergear from center support. Pull input shaft and synchronizer ring from mainshaft. Withdraw mainshaft from center support.

Fig. 6: Removing 5th Gear from Mainshaft

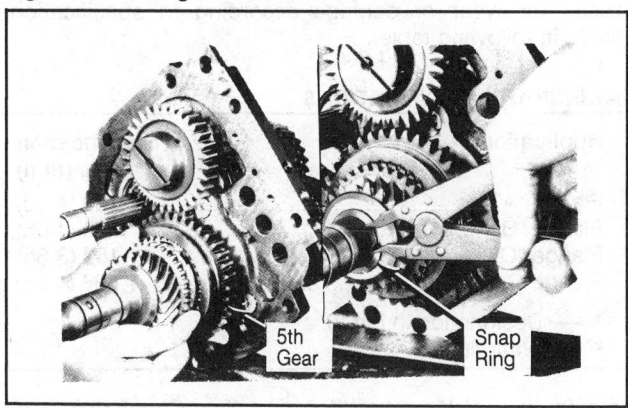

Fig. 7: Removing Countergear and Bearing from Support

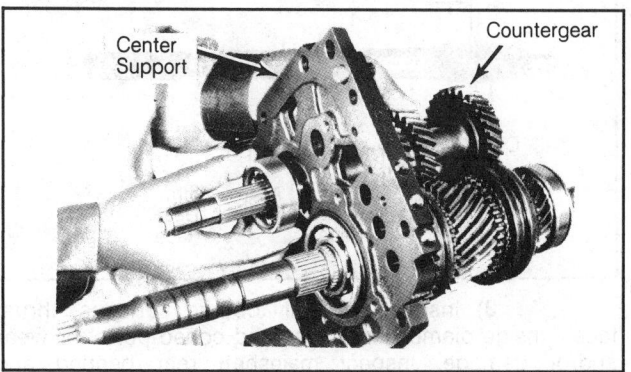

COMPONENT DISASSEMBLY & REASSEMBLY

MAINSHAFT

Disassembly

From front end of mainshaft, remove retaining snap ring and withdraw synchronizer assembly and 3rd gear. On rear end of shaft, remove bearing snap ring and, with plates positioned under 1st gear, use a press to remove bearing and 1st gear. Remove reverse gear and 1st-2nd synchronizer assembly from shaft. Remove 2nd gear and synchronizer ring.

Inspection

1) Use "V" block or shaft holding fixture to measure mainshaft runout. Runout should not exceed .002" (.05 mm). Inspect all bearing and gear installation surfaces for damage or wear. Inspect flanges and bearing inner races for wear or damage.

Fig. 8: Using a Dial Indicator to Check Shaft Runout

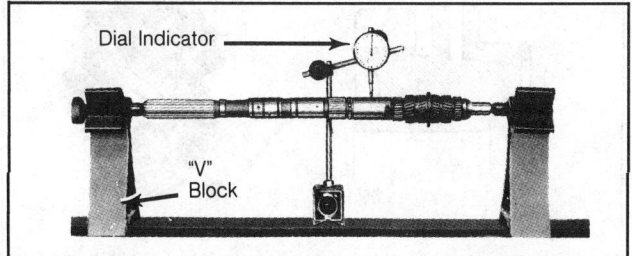

Manual Transmissions

TOYOTA 5-SPEED — MODEL W50 (Cont.)

2) Inspect mainshaft flanges and bearing inner races for wear or damage according to specifications listed in following table:

MAINSHAFT SPECIFICATIONS

Application [1]	Specification In. (mm)
Flange "A"	.189 (4.80)
Flange "B"	.179 (4.55)
Flange "C"	.152 (3.85)
Flange O.D. [2]	1.606 (40.8)

[1] — Designation in *Fig. 9*.
[2] — Wear limit.

Fig. 9: View of Mainshaft Showing Wear Check Points

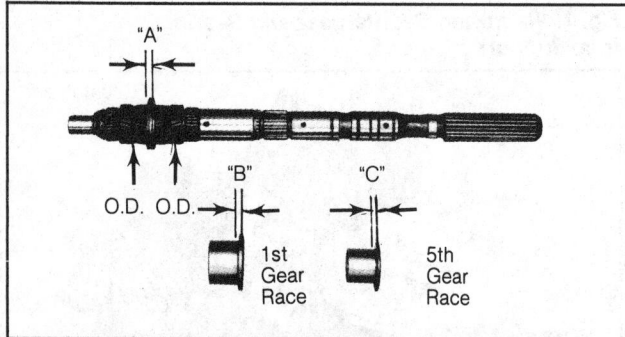

3) Inspect all gear toothed surfaces, thrust faces, inside diameter surfaces and coned parts for wear and/or damage. Inspect mainshaft rear bearing and needle roller bearing surfaces for wear, damage and following oil clearances (difference between I.D. of gear and O.D. of shaft):

GEAR OIL CLEARANCE

Application	Standard In. (mm)
1st Gear	[1] .0004-.0021 (.009-.053)
2nd & 3rd Gear	[2] .0024-.0041 (.06-.103)
5th	.0004-.0020 (.009-.051)

[1] — Maximum clearance .0024 (.60).
[2] — Maximum clearance .0059 (.15).

Fig. 10: Using a Feeler Gauge to Check Synchronizer Ring-to-Gear Clearance

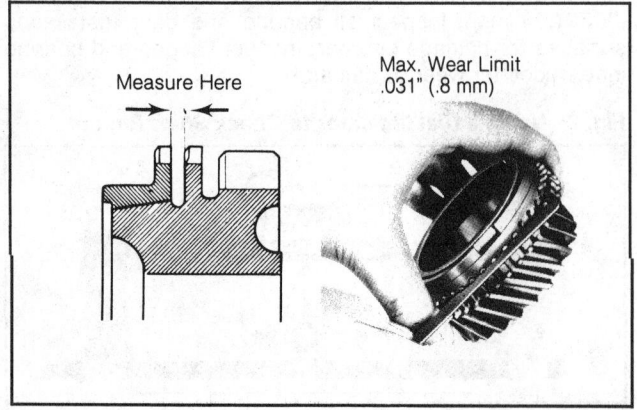

4) Check braking effect of synchronizer rings by installing ring into respective gear and trying to rotate ring while pressing inward. If ring does not rotate, braking effect is correct.

5) If ring does rotate, check clearance between teeth of ring and teeth of gear for clearance of .039-.079" (1.0-2.0 mm). Maximum wear limit is .031" (.8 mm). If clearance is incorrect, it will be necessary to replace synchronizer ring. If clearance is correct, it is possible to lap in ring (using lapping compound), to create proper amount of friction.

6) Inspect splines on both synchronizer hubs and sleeves for wear or damage. Inspect keys for rounded corners and for wear or damage. Also check key springs. Inspect contact surfaces between hub sleeves and shift forks. Clearance should be no more than .039" (1.0 mm) as measured between fork and groove, with fork held into groove.

Fig. 11: Using a Feeler Gauge to Check Shift Fork-to-Sleeve Clearance

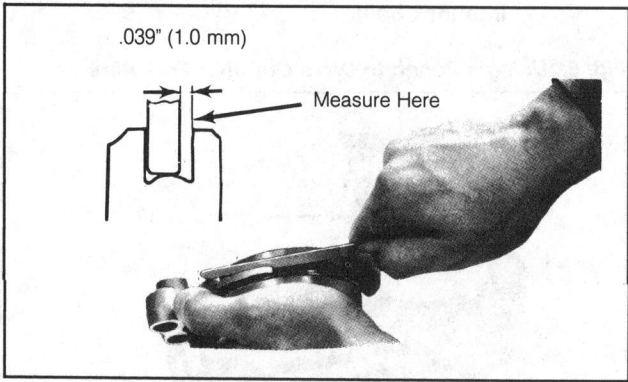

Reassembly

1) Fit synchronizer sleeve No. 2 onto hub No. 2 in direction illustrated. Make sure sleeve slides smoothly over hub. Insert 3 shift keys into keyways between hub and sleeve and assemble 2 key retaining springs.

2) Insert synchronizer assembly onto mainshaft until it rests against shaft shoulder. Use press or soft-faced hammer to seat assembly, making sure synchronizer ring slots are aligned with shifting keys. Secure hub No. 2 on shaft with snap ring. Select thickness of snap ring for 0-.002" (0-.05 mm) clearance (axial play).

Fig. 12: Cross-Sectional View of No. 2 Synchronizer

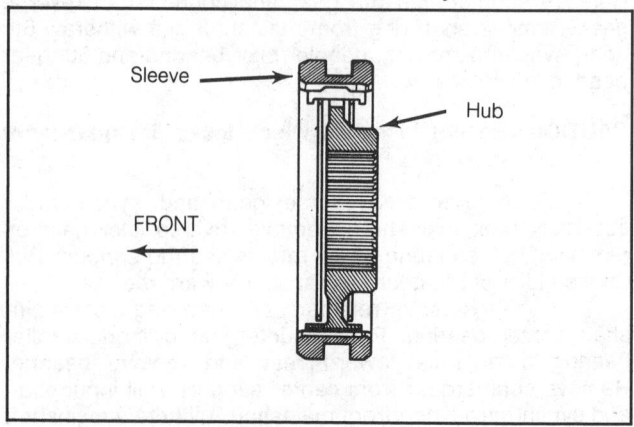

3rd and 4th Synchronizer Assembly.

TOYOTA 5-SPEED — MODEL W50 (Cont.)

SNAP RING SIZES

Mark on Snap Ring	Thickness In. (mm)
No Mark	.078-.080 (2.00-2.05)
0	.080-.082 (2.05-2.10)
1	.082-.084 (2.10-2.15)
2	.084-.086 (2.15-2.20)
3	.086-.088 (2.20-2.25)
4	.088-.090 (2.25-2.30)

3) Measure 3rd gear thrust clearance. Clearance should be .0059-.0098" (.15-.25 mm). Grease outer mainshaft surface and fit No. 2 synchronizer ring into 2nd gear and assemble onto mainshaft. Fit No. 1 synchronizer hub onto reverse gear, making sure reverse gear is assembled in correct direction and that it slides smoothly inside of gear.

4) Install 3 shift keys into keyways of hub and install 2 retaining springs. Install synchronizer assembly onto mainshaft, making sure synchronizer ring slots are aligned with shift keys, then press synchronizer assembly on until resting against mainshaft shoulder.

Fig. 13: Using a Feeler Gauge to Measure 3rd Gear Thrust Clearance

Thrust Clearance
.0059-.0098" (.15-.25 mm)

5) Measure 2nd gear thrust clearance for .0059-.0098" (.15-.25 mm). Wear limit is .0118" (.30 mm). Fit inner race lock ball into mainshaft hole and hold ball in place with heavy grease.

6) Assemble 1st gear, synchronizer ring No. 2, bearing and bearing inner race and install them as a unit onto mainshaft until inner race end face rests against hub No. 2. Make sure inner race slot is aligned with lock ball. Be sure to have synchronizer ring slots aligned with shifting keys.

Fig. 14: Cross-Sectional View of Synchronizer No. 1

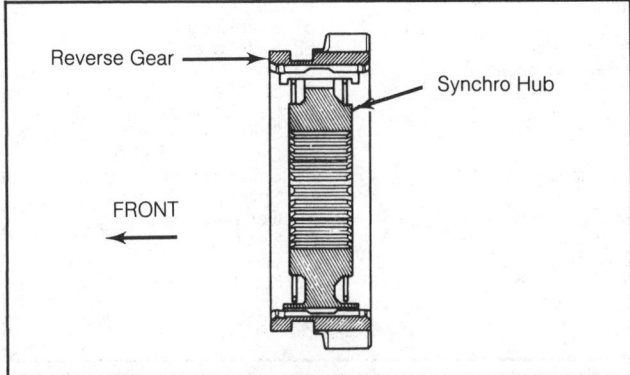

Reverse Gear

Synchro Hub

FRONT

Reverse/1st and 2nd Synchronizer Assembly.

Fig. 15: Installation of Synchronizer No. 1 and 2nd Gear Thrust Clearance Check

Thrust Clearance
.0059-.0098" (.15-.25 mm)

7) Install bearing onto mainshaft using a press. Bearing must be installed so that outer snap ring groove of bearing faces rearward. Measure thrust clearance between thrust surface of first gear and bearing. Clearance should be .0059-.0098" (.15-.25 mm). Wear limit is .0118" (.30 mm).

Fig. 16: Using a Feeler Gauge to Measure 1st Gear Thrust Clearance

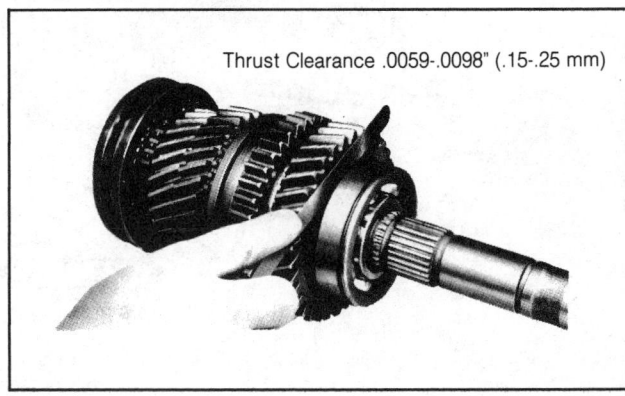

Thrust Clearance .0059-.0098" (.15-.25 mm)

INPUT SHAFT

1) Inspect gear teeth, splines and coned parts for wear or damage. Check braking effect of synchronizer ring by installing ring into gear and, while pressing inward on ring, try to turn it by hand. If ring does not turn, braking effect is correct. If ring does turn, measure clearance between ring teeth and tooth surface of gear.

2) If clearance is not .039-.079" (1.0-2.0 mm) with wear limit of .031" (.8 mm), it will be necessary to replace ring with new one. If replacing ring or when clearance is correct and ring still turns, lap ring by applying small amount of lapping compound onto coned surface of gear and turn ring (installed into gear) by hand.

3) Inspect input shaft inner surface which contacts needle roller bearings, for wear or damage. Check input shaft bearing for wear by rotating bearing and listening for noise. If necessary to replace input shaft bearing, remove snap ring and use a press. When installing new bearing, select snap ring which will allow minimum axial play, refer to table.

Manual Transmissions

TOYOTA 5-SPEED — MODEL W50 (Cont.)

Fig. 17: Exploded View of W50 5-Speed Transmission Components

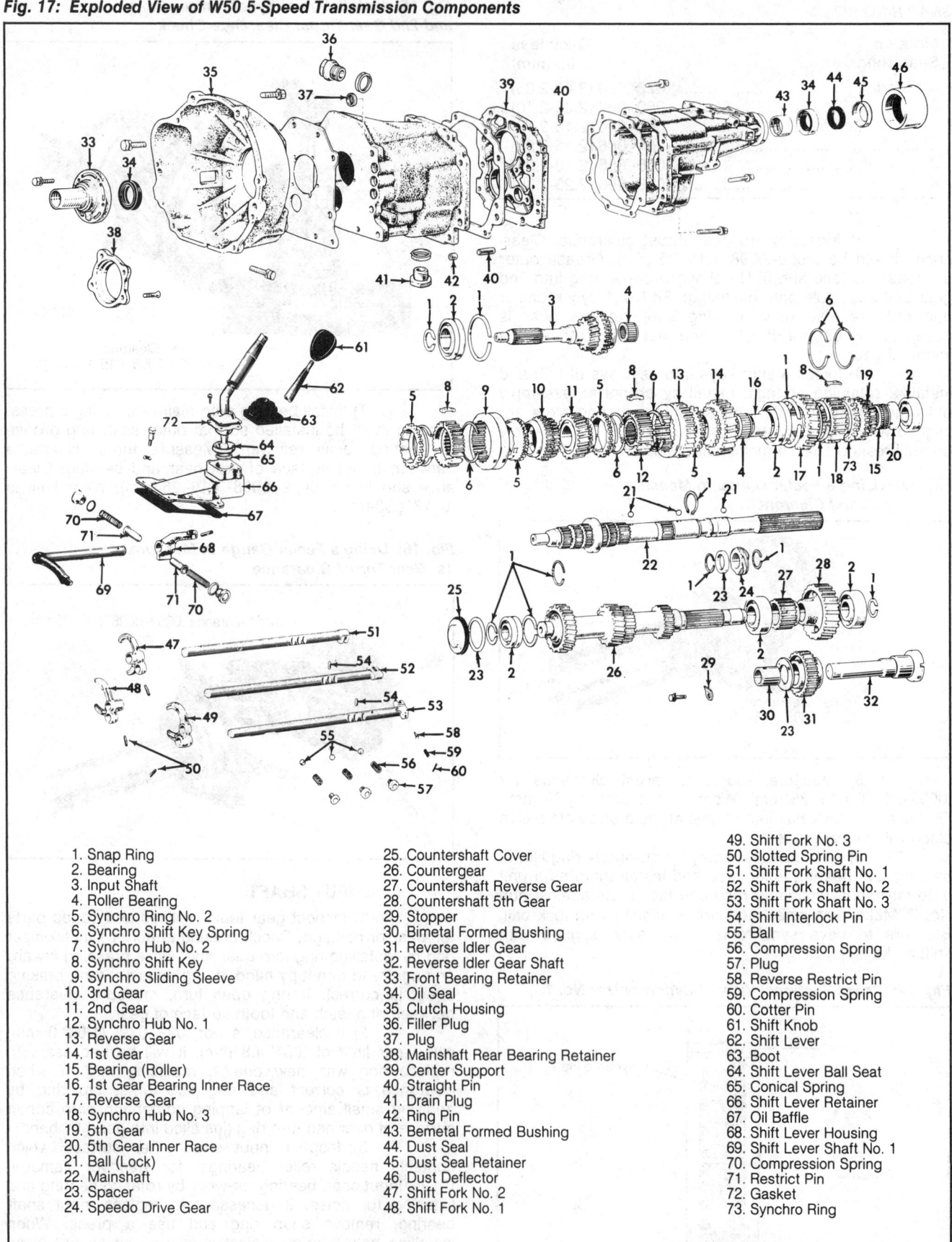

1. Snap Ring	25. Countershaft Cover	49. Shift Fork No. 3
2. Bearing	26. Countergear	50. Slotted Spring Pin
3. Input Shaft	27. Countershaft Reverse Gear	51. Shift Fork Shaft No. 1
4. Roller Bearing	28. Countershaft 5th Gear	52. Shift Fork Shaft No. 2
5. Synchro Ring No. 2	29. Stopper	53. Shift Fork Shaft No. 3
6. Synchro Shift Key Spring	30. Bimetal Formed Bushing	54. Shift Interlock Pin
7. Synchro Hub No. 2	31. Reverse Idler Gear	55. Ball
8. Synchro Shift Key	32. Reverse Idler Gear Shaft	56. Compression Spring
9. Synchro Sliding Sleeve	33. Front Bearing Retainer	57. Plug
10. 3rd Gear	34. Oil Seal	58. Reverse Restrict Pin
11. 2nd Gear	35. Clutch Housing	59. Compression Spring
12. Synchro Hub No. 1	36. Filler Plug	60. Cotter Pin
13. Reverse Gear	37. Plug	61. Shift Knob
14. 1st Gear	38. Mainshaft Rear Bearing Retainer	62. Shift Lever
15. Bearing (Roller)	39. Center Support	63. Boot
16. 1st Gear Bearing Inner Race	40. Straight Pin	64. Shift Lever Ball Seat
17. Reverse Gear	41. Drain Plug	65. Conical Spring
18. Synchro Hub No. 3	42. Ring Pin	66. Shift Lever Retainer
19. 5th Gear	43. Bemetal Formed Bushing	67. Oil Baffle
20. 5th Gear Inner Race	44. Dust Seal	68. Shift Lever Housing
21. Ball (Lock)	45. Dust Seal Retainer	69. Shift Lever Shaft No. 1
22. Mainshaft	46. Dust Deflector	70. Compression Spring
23. Spacer	47. Shift Fork No. 2	71. Restrict Pin
24. Speedo Drive Gear	48. Shift Fork No. 1	72. Gasket
		73. Synchro Ring

TOYOTA 5-SPEED — MODEL W50 (Cont.)

INPUT SHAFT SNAP RING SIZE

Mark On Snap Ring	Thickness In. (mm)
0	.080-.082 (2.05-2.10)
1	.082-.084 (2.10-2.15)
2	.084-.086 (2.15-2.20)
3	.086-.088 (2.20-2.25)
4	.088-.090 (2.25-2.30)
5	.090-.092 (2.30-2.35)

COUNTERGEAR

1) Inspect teeth of countergear for wear or damage. Inspect front bearing and rear bearing for wear or damage. Inspect roller bearing and inner race for wear or damage.

2) If necessary to replace gear bearing, remove snap ring and use bearing puller to remove bearing. To install new bearing, use adapter plate (SST 09515 10010) and a press. Install snap ring.

SHIFT COMPONENTS

Inspect sliding surfaces of shaft for wear and/or damage. Inspect springs, balls, interlock pins and reverse restrict pins for wear and/or damage. Inspect contacting surface between shift lever and restrict pins for wear and/or damage. Check springs for weakening or distortion. Replace as required.

EXTENSION HOUSING

1) Inspect oil seal lip, rear bushing and dust deflector for wear or damage. If necessary to replace oil seal, use seal puller (SST 09308 00010). To install new seal, use seal driver (SST 09325 20010). Be sure to grease new oil seal and dust seal before installing.

2) If necessary to install new bushing, remove old oil seal and heat extension housing to 212°F (100°C) in oil bath. Remove and install bushing using bushing driver (SST 09307 30010) and a press.

NOTE: Before installing new bushing, make sure oil hole of bushing is aligned with oil groove.

TRANSMISSION REASSEMBLY

TRANSMISSION CASE

1) Clamp center support in a soft-jawed vise. Grease needle bearings of input shaft and position shaft and synchronizer ring onto mainshaft. Mate countergear with mainshaft and install both onto center support simultaneously; retain both shafts with snap rings installed on rear bearings. After installing snap ring, press flush with surface of support.

2) Install mainshaft bearing retainer on rear of center support. Assemble reverse idler gear and spacer on idler shaft. Insert reverse idler assembly into support and retain with tang and lock bolt. Position reverse idler gear oil hole rearward.

3) Measure reverse idler thrust clearance between gear and shaft. Clearance should be .0059-.0098" (.15-.25 mm). Install No. 3 synchronizer hub onto reverse gear, making sure reverse gear is assembled in correct direction and that it slides smoothly. Install 3 shift keys into keyways of hub and install 2 retaining springs. Install

No. 3 synchronizer assembly onto mainshaft until resting against inner race of bearing in center support.

NOTE: If synchro hub cannot be fitted onto shaft easily, lightly tap hub using soft-faced hammer.

Fig. 18: Using a Feeler Gauge to Measure Thrust Clearance (Reverse Idler Gear)

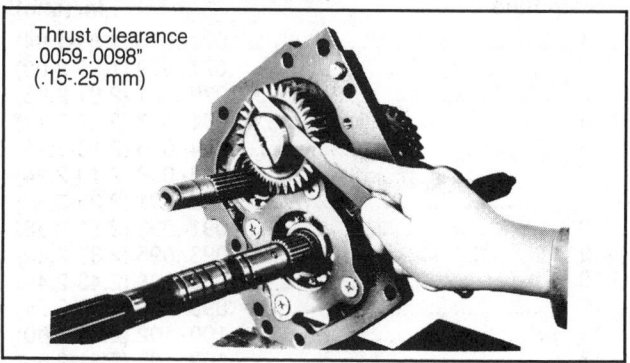

Thrust Clearance .0059-.0098" (.15-.25 mm)

Fig. 19: Cross-Sectional View of Synchronizer No. 3 (5th and Reverse Assembly)

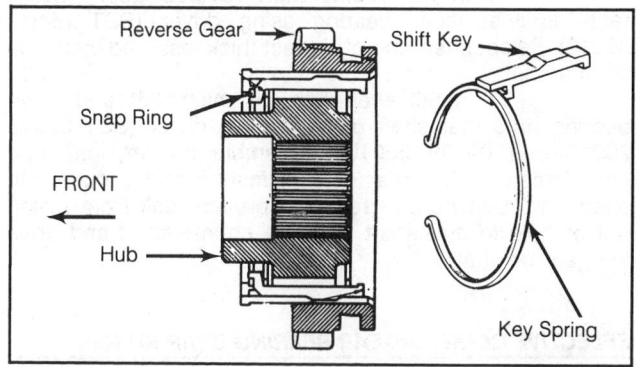

Reverse Gear — Shift Key

Snap Ring

FRONT

Hub

Key Spring

4) Install inner race lock ball into hole of mainshaft, by using heavy grease to hold ball in place. Assemble 5th gear, synchronizer ring, needle roller bearings and inner race into a set and slide this set onto mainshaft until inner race end face rests against synchronizer hub No. 3. Make sure inner race groove is aligned with lock ball and that synchronizer ring slots are aligned with shift keys.

Fig. 20: Using a Feeler Gauge to Measure 5th Gear Thrust Clearance

Thrust Clearance .0039-.0098" (.10-.25 mm)

TOYOTA 5-SPEED — MODEL W50 (Cont.)

5) Secure 5th gear set on mainshaft with snap ring which will allow minimum axial play. *See Selective 5th Gear Snap Ring Table.* Measure 5th gear thrust clearance for standard of .0039-.0098" (.10-.25 mm) and wear limit of .0118" (.30 mm).

SELECTIVE 5TH GEAR SNAP RINGS

Mark on Snap Ring	Thickness In. (mm)
1	.074-.076 (1.89-1.94)
2	.077-.079 (1.95-2.00)
3	.079-.081 (2.01-2.06)
4	.081-.083 (2.07-2.12)
5	.084-.086 (2.13-2.18)
6	.086-.088 (2.19-2.24)
7	.089-.091 (2.25-2.30)
8	.091-.093 (2.31-2.36)
9	.093-.095 (2.37-2.42)
10	.096-.098 (2.43-2.48)
11	.098-.100 (2.49-2.54)
12	.100-.102 (2.55-2.60)
13	.103-.105 (2.61-2.66)

6) Install countershaft reverse gear until it rests against inner bearing using driver (SST 09310 35010). Select snap ring of correct thickness and install on countershaft.

7) Install snap ring on mainshaft and drive bearing onto mainshaft using bearing driver (SST 09515 20010 and 09309 35010). Assemble spacer, ball and speedometer drive gear onto mainshaft and secure with snap ring. Use heavy grease to prevent ball from falling out of hole in mainshaft. Support countershaft and drive 5th gear on shaft.

SELECTIVE COUNTERGEAR BEARING SNAP RINGS

Mark on Snap Ring	Thickness In. (mm)
1	.079-.081 (2.00-2.05)
2	.071-.073 (1.80-1.85)
3	.063-.065 (1.60-1.65)
4	.055-.057 (1.40-1.45)

8) Position shift forks into place on appropriate synchronizer sleeves and make sure each synchronizer is

Fig. 21: Proper Reverse Idler Gear Position

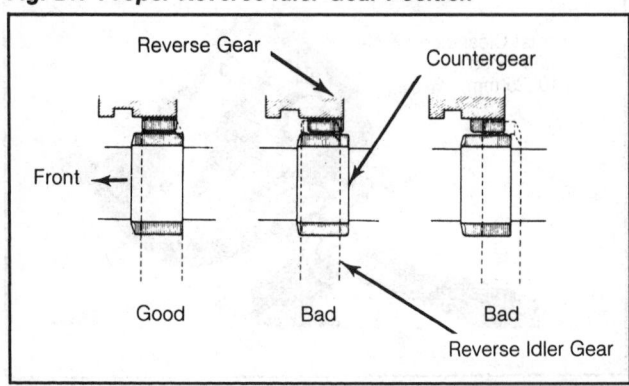

in neutral position. Install shift fork shaft, along with greased interlock pins, into bores of center support and shift forks. Install lock balls and springs into bores of support, coat plugs with sealer, and install and tighten. At this time, install new slotted spring pins into shift forks and shafts to secure assemblies.

9) Assemble transmission case as follows: With gasket in place, slide transmission case onto center support. Install snap ring for input shaft bearing and countershaft front bearing.

Fig. 22: Relationship of Shift Shafts in Case

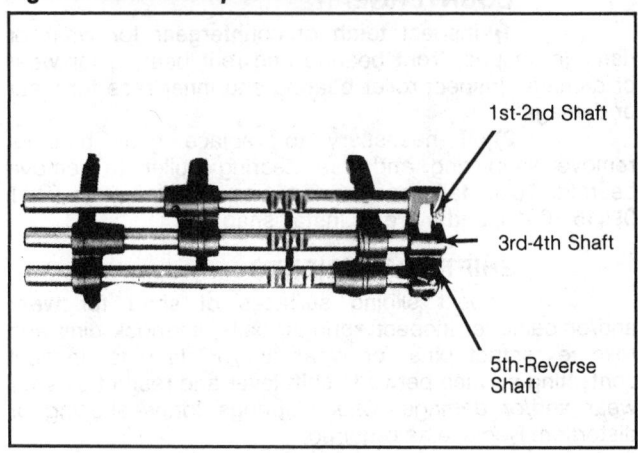

CLUTCH & EXTENSION HOUSING

1) With gasket in place, install extension housing over output shaft. With extension housing approximately .8-1.1" (20-30 mm) from center support, hold shift lever housing to the extreme left position, then rotate shift lever housing clockwise to engage shift fork shafts. If necessary, tap lightly on rear housing to bring it flush against center support. Install bolts and tighten to specifications.

2) Select countershaft front spacer by pressing firmly in on countergear and measuring depth of front bearing. Manufacturer suggests measuring this depth with dial indicator. Available spacers are listed in following table. Select the appropriate spacer and install spacer with front bearing retainer. Make sure oil return hole is aligned before tightening bearing retainer bolts.

COUNTERGEAR SPACER CHART

Clearance In. (mm)	Mark	Thickness In. (mm)
.113-.118 (2.87-2.99)	•	.077-.081 (1.95-2.05)
.118-.122 (3.00-3.10)	••	.083-.087 (2.10-2.20)
.122-.125 (3.10-3.20)	•••	.087-.093 (2.25-2.35)
.126-.123 (3.20-3.30)	••••	.095-.098 (2.40-2.50)

3) Install clutch housing onto transmission case and tighten retaining bolts. Install shift lever retainer on extension housing. Install restrict pins and springs, and secure with plugs. Install speedometer driven gear in extension housing and retain with lock plate. Install back-up light switch and drain and fill plugs into case.

TOYOTA 5-SPEED — MODEL W50 (Cont.)

Fig. 23: *Cutaway View of Front of Case Showing Countergear Clearance and Spacer Position*

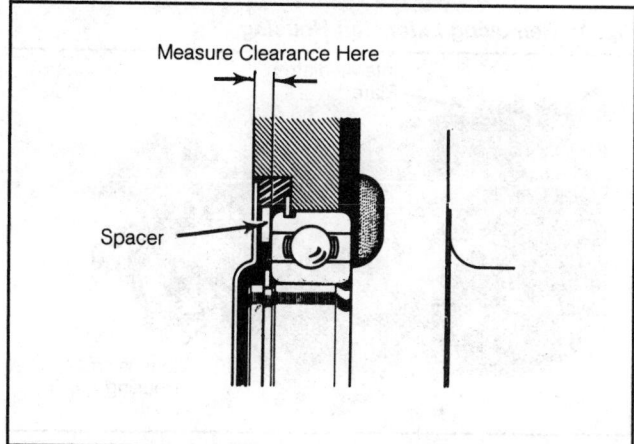

TIGHTENING SPECIFICATIONS

Application	Ft. Lbs. (N.m)
Lock Ball Plugs	14-22 (19-30)
Extension Housing Bolts	28-32 (39-44)
Reverse Pivot Lock Nut	11-15 (15-20)
Reverse Shift Arm Bracket	11-15 (15-20)
Restrict Pin Plugs	27-33 (38-45)
Clutch Housing-to-Case Bolts	37-50 (50-68)
Shift Lever Housing Bolts	11-14 (15-19)
Clutch Housing-to-Engine Bolts	37-50 (50-68)
	INCH Lbs. (N.m.)
Output Shaft Bearing Retainer	96-132 (11-15)
Front Bearing Retainer Bolts	96-120 (11-14)

Manual Transmissions

TOYOTA 5-SPEED — MODELS W55 & W58

Celica, Corona, Supra

TRANSMISSION IDENTIFICATION

The W55 and W58 transmissions use a 4-piece transmission case assembly. Main components are clutch housing, transmission case, intermediate plate and extension housing. Corona uses the W-55, Celica and Supra use the W-58.

DESCRIPTION

Transmission is a 5-speed, fully synchronized unit. All forward gears are helical cut and in constant mesh. Reverse gear is spur cut. Reverse and 5th gears are in constant mesh and are mounted on rear side of intermediate plate (inside extension housing). Floor shifter actuates a single control rod in extension housing operating 3 shift rails mounted in intermediate plate and main case.

LUBRICATION & ADJUSTMENT

See the appropriate article in MANUAL TRANS-MISSION SERVICING Section.

TROUBLE SHOOTING

HARD SHIFTING

Clutch not disengaging properly. Bushings in cross shaft worn or damaged. Synchro rings making faulty contact with gear cone. Synchro worn or pitted.

SLIPS OUT OF GEAR

Improper meshing of gears due to shift rails being out of adjustment. Shift forks worn or ball locks broken. Excessive play in synchro hub No. 2. Output shaft of drive gear worn. Reverse idler gear or its bushing is worn. Countergear or its bushing or shaft is worn.

NOISE IN TRANSMISSION

Gears or bearings worn or damaged. Insufficient or incorrect lubricant. Input shaft splines worn or damaged. Reverse idler gear bushing worn.

REMOVAL & INSTALLATION

See the appropriate article in MANUAL TRANS-MISSION REMOVAL Section.

TRANSMISSION DISASSEMBLY

CLUTCH HOUSING

Removal

Release spring clips and remove clutch release fork and bearing. Loosen bolts evenly and remove clutch housing from transmission.

EXTENSION HOUSING

Removal

Remove speedometer driven gear retainer bolt and take out shaft sleeve and driven gear. Remove 9

housing bolts and take care, when removing extension housing, that output spline does not damage rear oil seal.

Fig. 1: Removing Extension Housing

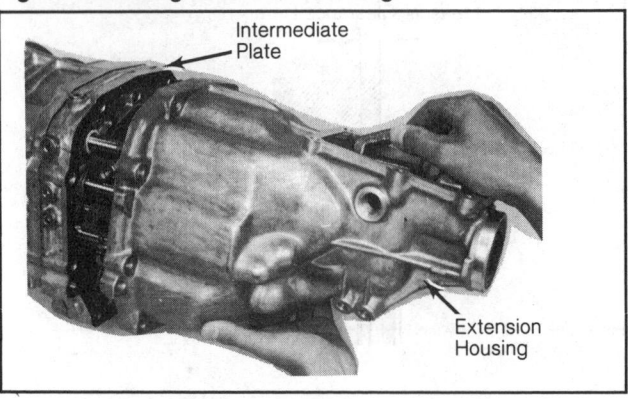

Intermediate Plate

Extension Housing

TRANSMISSION CASE

Removal

1) Remove back-up light switch wire clamp and back-up light switch. Remove 7 bolts and front bearing retainer. Using snap ring pliers, remove 2 snap rings. Separate intermediate plate from transmission case by carefully tapping transmission case with a plastic hammer. Pull transmission case from intermediate plate. Leave gasket attached to intermediate plate.

2) Mount intermediate plate in vise. Use 2 long clutch housing bolts, plate washers and nuts. Install in 2 bottom holes on intermediate plate to prevent damage on plate. Install plate washers in reverse of normal. Increase or decrease plate washers so that bolt tip and front tip surface of nut are aligned and mounted evenly in vise.

3) Remove 4 straight screw plugs with tool (SST 09313-30021). Remove 3 springs and balls. Remove shift forks and shafts by prying out lock washers of shift fork No. 1 and No. 2. Remove 2 set bolts. Using 2 drivers and hammer, tap out 2 snap rings of No. 1 and No. 2 fork shafts. Remove reverse idler gear shaft stopper.

4) Remove shift fork and shaft No. 1. Using magnet, remove interlock pin No. 1 and No. 2. Remove shift fork and shaft No. 2. Using magnet, remove interlock pin No. 3. Remove reverse idler gear and shaft. Using a pin punch and hammer, drive out No. 3 fork shaft pin. Pull out shaft fork No. 4. Remove shift fork No. 3 and reverse shift arm with pin.

5) Remove speedometer drive gear by prying both ends of clip. Measure counter 5th gear thrust clearance using feeler gauge. Standard clearance is .004-.016" (.10-.41 mm). Maximum clearance is .018" (.46 mm). Remove snap ring. Using puller (SST 09213-36010) remove counter rear bearing, spacer, 5th gear and needle bearing. Remove spacer.

NOTE: Be careful not to catch the output shaft rear bearing roller on the counter 5th gear.

6) Using 2 drivers and a hammer, tap out snap ring. Use sleeve remover (SST 09950-20014) to remove hub sleeve No. 3 assembly. Be sure to latch claw of tool onto clutch hub. Be careful not to latch it on shifting key retainer. Tap out snap ring from output shaft. Remove output shaft rear bearing and 5th gear with puller (SST 09312-20010). Remove snap ring and remove reverse gear using puller (SST 09950-20014).

TOYOTA 5-SPEED — MODEL W55 & W58 (Cont.)

7) Remove center bearing retainer using a torx-type socket. Unscrew torx screw and remove retainer. Remove bearing snap ring. Remove output shaft and countergear as a unit from intermediate plate.

COMPONENT DISASSEMBLY & REASSEMBLY

INPUT & OUTPUT SHAFTS

Disassembly

1) Remove output shaft, input shaft and countergear as a unit from intermediate plate by pulling on countergear and tapping on intermediate plate with plastic hammer. Measure each gear thrust clearance using a feeler gauge. Standard clearance between each gear is .004-.010" (.10-.25 mm). Maximum clearance is .0118" (.30 mm).

2) Remove input shaft from output shaft. Shift hub sleeve No. 1 onto 2nd gear. Remove center bearing with press. Pull off 1st gear, needle roller bearing, inner race and synchronizer ring.

3) Remove locking ball. Remove hub sleeve No. 1 assembly, 2nd gear and needle roller bearing, using a press. Remove parts as an assembly. Remove snap ring with snap ring pliers. Remove hub sleeve No. 2, synchronizer ring and 3rd gear with a press.

Inspection

1) Inspect output shaft and inner race for wear or damage. Using caliper, measure output shaft flange thickness. Minimum thickness is .221" (5.60 mm). Using calipers, measure inner race flange thickness. Minimum thickness is .185" (4.70 mm).

2) Measure 2nd gear with micrometer; minimum is 1.69" (42.85 mm). Measure 3rd gear; minimum is 1.49" (37.80 mm). Using micrometer, measure outer diameter of inner race. Minimum diameter is 1.69" (42.85 mm). Use dial indicator to check runout. Measurement should be .0024" (.06 mm).

3) Inspect output shaft rear bearing. Check bearing and outer race for wear or damage. If necessary, replace bearing and outer race. Inspect output shaft center bearing, gears and needle roller bearings for wear or damage.

Fig. 2: *Exploded View of W55 & W58 5-Speed Transmission*

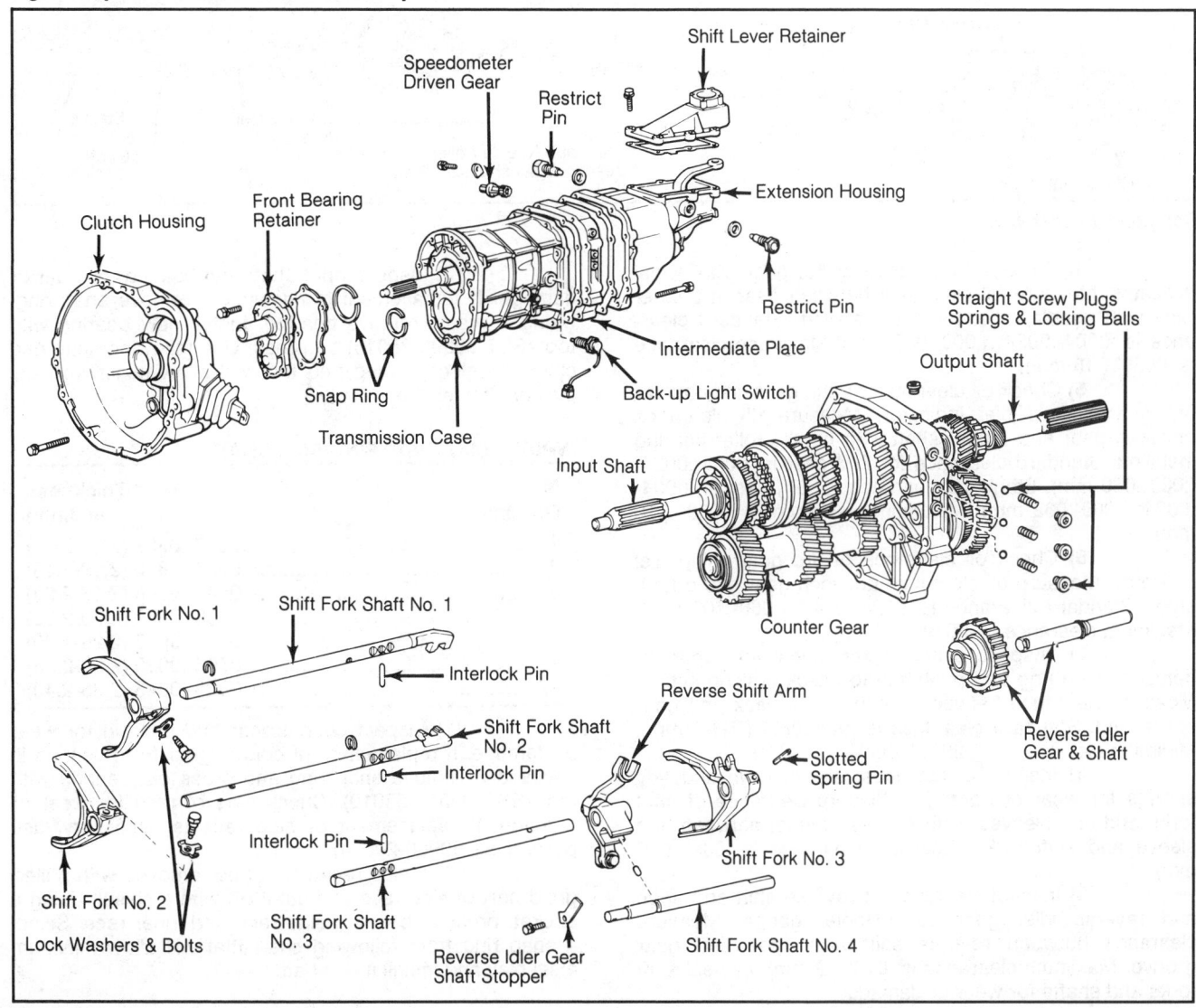

Component Assembly.

Manual Transmissions

TOYOTA 5-SPEED — MODEL W55 & W58 (Cont.)

Fig. 3: Exploded View of W55 & W58 5-Speed Transmission

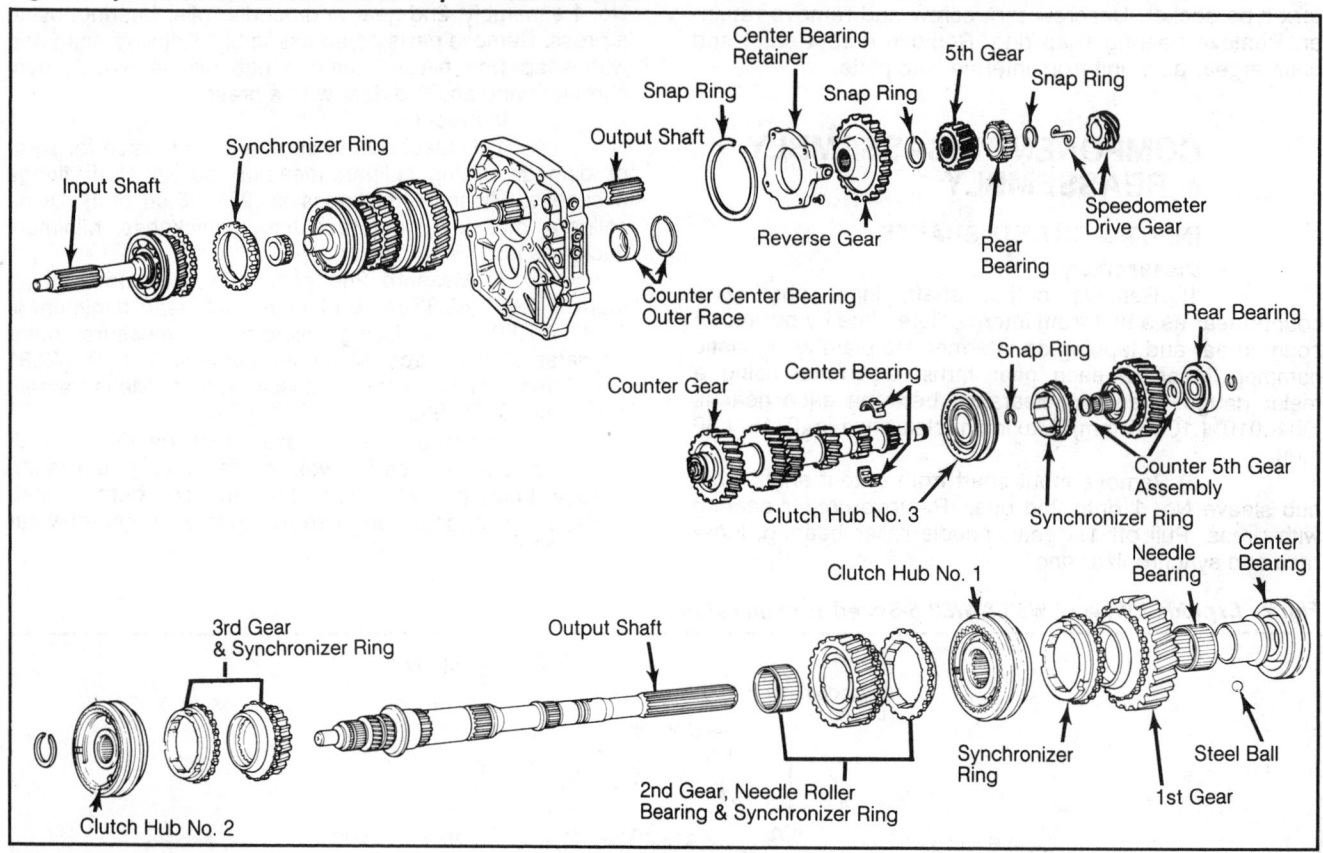

Component Assembly.

4) Check oil clearance of 1st gear with a dial indicator. Measure oil clearance between gear and inner race with needle roller bearing installed. Standard clearance is .0004-.0024" (.009-.060 mm). Maximum clearance is .0059" (.15 mm).

5) Check oil clearance of 2nd gear and counter 5th gear with a dial indicator. Measure oil clearance between gear and output shaft with needle roller bearing installed. Standard clearance for 2nd gear is .0004-.0024" (.009-.060 mm). Standard clearance for 5th gear is .0004-.0024" (.009-.062 mm). Maximum clearance is .0059" (.15 mm).

6) Check oil clearance of 3rd gear using dial indicator. Measure oil clearance between gear and output shaft. Standard clearance is .0024-.0040" (.060-.103 mm). Maximum clearance is .0079" (.20 mm).

7) Inspect synchronizer rings for wear or damage. Turn ring and push it in to check braking action. Measure clearance between synchro ring back and gear spline end. Standard clearance is .028-.067" (.7-1.7 mm). Minimum clearance is .020" (.5 mm).

8) Inspect clutch hubs, sleeve keys and key springs for wear or damage. Measure clearance of shift forks and hub sleeves, with a feeler gauge, between hub sleeve and shift fork. Maximum clearance is .039" (1.0 mm).

9) Inspect clearance of reverse shift arm shoe and reverse idler gear using feeler gauge. Measure clearance between reverse shift arm shoe and gear groove. Maximum clearance is .035" (.9 mm). Inspect shift forks and shafts for wear or damage.

10) Inspect input shaft and bearing for wear or damage. If replacement is necessary, remove snap ring. Using a press, remove bearing. Install new bearing with tool (SST 09506-35010) on press. Use following snap ring chart to select a snap ring that will allow minimum axial play and install it on shaft.

INPUT SHAFT SNAP RING SIZE CHART

Mark On Ring	Thickness In. (mm)
1	.0807-.0827 (2.05-2.10)
2	.0827-.0846 (2.10-2.15)
3	.0846-.0866 (2.15-2.20)
4	.0866-.0886 (2.20-2.25)
5	.0886-.0906 (2.25-2.30)
11	.0906-.0925 (2.30-2.35)
12	.0925-.0945 (2.35-2.40)

11) Inspect countergear and bearing for wear or damage. If replacement of countergear front bearing is necessary, remove snap ring and press out bearing with tool (SST 09555-55010). Check side of race for wear or damage. If replacement of side race is necessary, use puller (SST 09950-20014).

12) If side race cannot be removed with puller, grind part of side race and cut it off with a chisel. Using a socket, press in bearing, side race and inner race. Select a snap ring from following chart that will allow minimum axial play and install it on shaft.

TOYOTA 5-SPEED — MODEL W55 & W58 (Cont.)

COUNTERGEAR SNAP RING SIZES

Mark On Ring	Thickness In. (mm)
1	.0807-.0827 (2.05-2.10)
2	.0827-.0846 (2.10-2.15)
3	.0846-.0866 (2.15-2.20)
4	.0866-.0886 (2.20-2.25)
5	.0886-.0906 (2.25-2.30)
6	.0906-.0925 (2.30-2.35)
7	.0925-.0945 (2.35-2.40)

13) Inspect countergear rear bearing for wear or damage. Inspect idler gear and shaft. Inspect front bearing retainer. If oil seal is worn or damaged, pry out with screwdriver and install new seal with driver (SST 09608-35013).

EXTENSION HOUSING

Inspection

Inspect housing, rear oil seal and bushing for wear or damage. If oil seal replacement is necessary, use puller (SST 09308-00010 or SST 09308-10010) with output shaft installed. If rear bushing replacement is necessary, heat extension housing end to 176-212°F (80-100°C). Use tool (SST 09307-30010) to remove bushing. Use same tool to install new bushing. To drive in new oil seal, use installer (SST 09325-20010).

CLUTCH HOUSING

Inspection

Inspect release fork, bearing, clips and clutch housing for any wear or damage. Replace if necessary.

TRANSMISSION REASSEMBLY

TRANSMISSION CASE

1) Install No. 1 and No. 2 clutch hub and shifting keys to hub sleeve. Install shifting key springs under shifting keys. Install key springs so that their end gaps are not in line with each other.

2) Install 3rd gear and clutch hub No. 2 on output shaft. Apply oil to shaft. Place synchro ring on gear and align ring slots with shifting keys. Using press, install 3rd gear and clutch hub No. 2. Select a snap ring that will allow minimum axial play from following chart and install it on shaft.

OUTPUT SHAFT SNAP RING

Mark On Ring	Thickness In. (mm)
D	.0709-.0728 (1.80-1.85)
11	.0732-.0752 (1.86-1.91)
12	.0756-.0776 (1.92-1.97)
13	.0780-.0799 (1.98-2.03)
14	.0803-.0823 (2.04-2.09)
15	.0827-.0846 (2.04-2.15)

3) Measure 3rd gear thrust clearance using feeler gauge. Standard clearance is .0039-.0098" (.10-.25 mm). Maximum clearance is .0118" (.30 mm). Install clutch hub No. 1 into hub sleeve and install shifting keys. Place key springs under shifting keys. Be sure end gaps do not line up on key springs.

4) Install 2nd gear and clutch hub No. 1. Place synchronizer ring on gear and align ring slots with shifting keys. Install lubricated needle roller bearing in 2nd gear. Using press, install 2nd gear and clutch hub No. 1. Install locking ball and 1st gear assembly. Using press, install bearing on output shaft with outer race snap ring groove toward rear.

5) Measure 1st and 2nd gear thrust clearance, using feeler gauge. Standard clearance is .0039-.0098" (.10-.25 mm). Maximum clearance is .0118" (.30 mm). Install output shaft into intermediate plate. Before installing shaft, use driver (SST 0908-35013) to remove countergear center bearing outer race. Install output shaft into intermediate plate by pulling output shaft and tapping plate.

6) Install input shaft and countergear together. Using driver (SST 09316-60010), install countergear center bearing outer race. Install bearing snap ring. Be sure snap ring is flush with intermediate plate surface. Install bearing retainer with a torx-type socket. Install reverse gear using installer tool (SST 09312-20010). Install snap ring selected from the following chart.

REVERSE GEAR SNAP RING

Mark On Ring	Thickness In. (mm)
5	.0886-.0906 (2.25-2.30)
11	.0906-.0925 (2.30-2.35)
12	.0925-.0945 (2.35-2.40)
13	.0945-.0965 (2.40-2.45)
14	.0965-.0984 (2.45-2.50)
15	.0984-.1004 (2.50-2.55)
16	.1004-.1024 (2.55-2.60)
17	.1028-.1047 (2.61-2.66)
18	.1051-.1071 (2.67-2.72)
19	.1075-.1094 (2.73-2.78)
20	.1098-.1118 (2.79-2.84)
21	.1122-.1142 (2.85-2.90)
22	.1146-.1165 (2.91-2.96)
23	.1169-.1189 (2.97-3.02)

7) Install 5th gear and output shaft rear bearing using installer (SST 09312-20010). Select snap ring from following chart that will allow minimum axial play and install it on shaft.

OUTPUT SHAFT REAR BEARING SNAP RING

Mark On Ring	Thickness In. (mm)
8	.0909-.0929 (2.31-2.36)
9	.0933-.0953 (2.37-2.42)
10	.0957-.0976 (2.43-2.48)
11	.0980-.1000 (2.49-2.54)
12	.1004-.1024 (2.55-2.60)
13	.1028-.1047 (2.61-2.66)
14	.1055-.1075 (2.68-2.73)
15	.1079-.1098 (2.74-2.79)

8) Install clutch hub No. 3 and shifting key to the hub sleeve. Install shifting key springs under shifting keys. Install key springs so that their end gaps are not in line. Install shifting key retainer using (SST 09238-47012).

9) Install clutch hub No. 3 using driver (SST 09316-60010) while supporting countershaft in front with a 3-5 lb. hammer or equivalent. Select a snap ring from

Manual Transmissions

TOYOTA 5-SPEED — MODEL W55 & W58 (Cont.)

following chart that will allow minimum axial play and install it on shaft.

CLUTCH HUB NO. 3 SNAP RING

Mark On Ring	Thickness In. (mm)
2	.0811-.0831 (2.06-2.11)
3	.0835-.0854 (2.12-2.17)
4	.0858-.0878 (2.18-2.23)
5	.0882-.0902 (2.24-2.29)

10) Install bearing spacer. Apply counter 5th gear, synchronizer ring and lubricated needle roller bearings. Install 5th gear assembly with synchronizer ring slots aligned with shifting keys.

11) Using a hammer and socket wrench, drive in spacer and bearing. Support countershaft in front with 3-5 lb. hammer or equivalent. Select a snap ring from following chart that will allow minimum axial play and install it on shaft.

5th GEAR ASSEMBLY SNAP RING

Mark On Ring	Thickness In. (mm)
1	.0748-.0768 (1.90-1.95)
2	.0772-.0791 (1.96-2.01)
3	.0795-.0815 (2.02-2.07)
4	.0819-.0839 (2.08-2.13)
5	.0843-.0862 (2.14-2.19)
6	.0866-.0886 (2.20-2.25)
7	.0890-.0909 (2.26-2.31)

12) Put a clip on output shaft and install speedometer drive gear slot to clip. Slide drive gear with clip into hole. Install reverse idler gear and shaft. Insert lubricated pin into reverse shift fork No. 3 and reverse shift arm. Align shift fork No. 3 to hub sleeve No. 3 groove, put reverse shift arm into pivot of bearing retainer and install shift fork shaft No. 3 to intermediate plate.

13) Install shift fork shaft No. 4 by pushing the pin, which was inserted into reverse shift arm hole, into groove of shift fork shaft No. 3. Install shift fork shaft No. 4 to intermediate plate. Install shift fork shaft No. 4 by aligning pin hole in fork with hole in shaft. Using a pin punch, drive in slotted spring pin until it is flush with fork. Install lubricated interlock pin No. 3 into intermediate plate hole.

14) Install lubricated interlock pin No. 2 to shaft hole. Install shift fork No. 2 into groove of hub sleeve No. 2. Install fork shaft No. 2 to shift fork shaft No. 2 through intermediate plate. Install No. 2 fork shaft snap ring.

15) Install lubricated interlock pin No. 1 into intermediate plate. Install shift fork No. 1 into groove of hub sleeve No. 2. Install fork shaft No. 1 to shift fork shaft No. 1 through intermediate plate. Install No. 1 fork shaft snap ring.

16) Install shift fork set bolts with lock washers. Install 3 springs and 3 locking balls. Install 4 straight screw plugs using socket wrench. Install reverse idler gear shaft stopper and tighten bolt.

17) Remove intermediate plate from vise. Remove the nuts, bolts, plate washers and gaskets. Install transmission case to intermediate plate. Use soft hammer and tap case to install plate.

18) Install 2 bearing snap rings. Install bearing retainer with new gasket. Install and tighten bolts. Install shift lever retainer together with new gasket and tighten bolt. Install back-up light switch wire clamp. Install speedometer driven gear, lock plate and bolt.

EXTENSION HOUSING

1) Put new gasket in position on intermediate plate before installing extension housing. Push shift lever housing forward and, with it turned clockwise, push in extension housing so it is positioned 1.57-1.97" (40-50 mm) from intermidiate plate. Slighty revolve extension housing clockwise and connect select lever to shift fork shaft.

2) With shift lever housing fully turned clockwise, push in extension housing. Install restrict pins (black pin at reverse gear/5th gear side, silver on opposite side) together with a gasket and tighten pins.

CLUTCH HOUSING

Install clutch housing and tighten bolts. Install release fork and bearing. Bearing is held in place by 2 clips.

TIGHTENING SPECIFICATIONS

Application	Ft. Lbs. (N.m)
Straight Screw Plugs	14-22 (19-30)
Idler Gear Shaft Stopper	14-22 (19-30)
Front Bearing Retainer	15-21 (20-29)
Extension Housing Bolts	22-32 (30-44)
Restrict Pins	27-32 (37-44)
Shift Lever Retainer	11-15 (15-20)
Transmission-to-Engine Bolts	37-57 (50-78)
Starter Bolts	37-57 (50-78)

	INCH Lbs. (N.m)
Shift Fork Set Bolt	96-120 (11-14)
Speedometer Driven Gear Bolt	96-132 (11-15)
Release Cylinder Bolts	96-132 (11-15)

Manual Transmissions
VOLKSWAGEN JETTA, PICKUP, RABBIT & SCIROCCO
4 & 5-SPEED

DESCRIPTION

Transaxles are 4 or 5-speed, fully synchronized units, mounted transversely at the front of vehicle. Transmission gears are all helical cut and are in constant mesh with mating gears on countershaft.

Forward gear engagement is accomplished through blocker ring type synchronizer assemblies. Reverse gears are spur type and are not in constant mesh, and are engaged by a sliding type reverse idler gear.

Final drive portion of transaxle consists of a drive pinion shaft (which also carries some of the transmission gears), and a differential and ring gear assembly.

The 4-speed transmission and final drive components are carried in a common 2-piece case. The 5-speed is almost identical to the 4-speed except the 5th gear assembly is located on the end of the pinion and mainshaft in a separate housing.

Transaxle codes (020 for 4-speed, 020F for 5-speed) are stamped on lower side of transaxle case, adjacent to left axle drive flange.

LUBRICATION & ADJUSTMENT

See the appropriate article in MANUAL TRANSMISSION SERVICING Section.

SERVICE (IN VEHICLE)

AXLE DRIVE SHAFTS

NOTE: Vehicle weight must be resting on wheels to remove axle shaft nut.

Removal

Remove axle shaft nut. Raise and support vehicle; remove tire and wheel. Remove Allen bolts connecting inner constant velocity (CV) joint to differential case drive flange. Press drive shaft and guide shaft out of hub, past transaxle assembly.

NOTE: Axle drive shafts should be disassembled ONLY to replace defective rubber boots. If boots are replaced, check all components for wear or damage and replace as complete assembly.

Disassembly

1) On inner CV joint, remove circlip from axle shaft and drive protective cap from CV joint. Place axle shaft in holder (VW402) and press CV joint from shaft with adapter (VW408a), supporting hub to prevent damage.

2) Pivot hub and cage assembly out of inner joint, then push out and remove balls. Align ball hub grooves with cage and remove hub.

NOTE: Inner CV joint and ball hub are matched sets. DO NOT interchange with outer joint. Also, balls of CV joints cannot be interchanged between CV joints.

Fig. 2: Removing Inner CV Joint Ball Hub

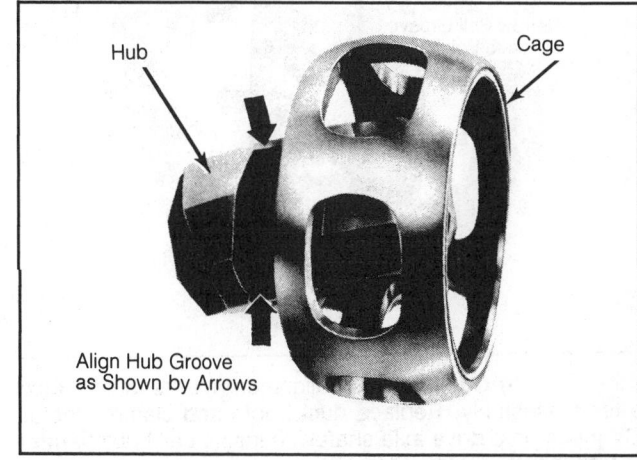

3) Remove and discard inner boot clamp and boot. On outer CV joint, spread circlip inside ball hub and drive CV joint off axle shaft with brass drift; tap on hub.

4) Mark position of ball hub and outer joint, then tilt cage and remove each ball. Align cage perpendicular to joint, align 2 large openings of cage with raised portions of joint and remove cage and hub.

5) Position 1 retainer of hub in large opening and remove hub by tilting outward. Remove and discard outer boot and clamp.

Reassembly

1) To reassemble CV joints, reverse disassembly procedure and note the following: Lubricate joints with 3 ozs. (90 g) of molybdenum disulphide grease. After

Fig. 1: Exploded View of Axle Drive Shafts

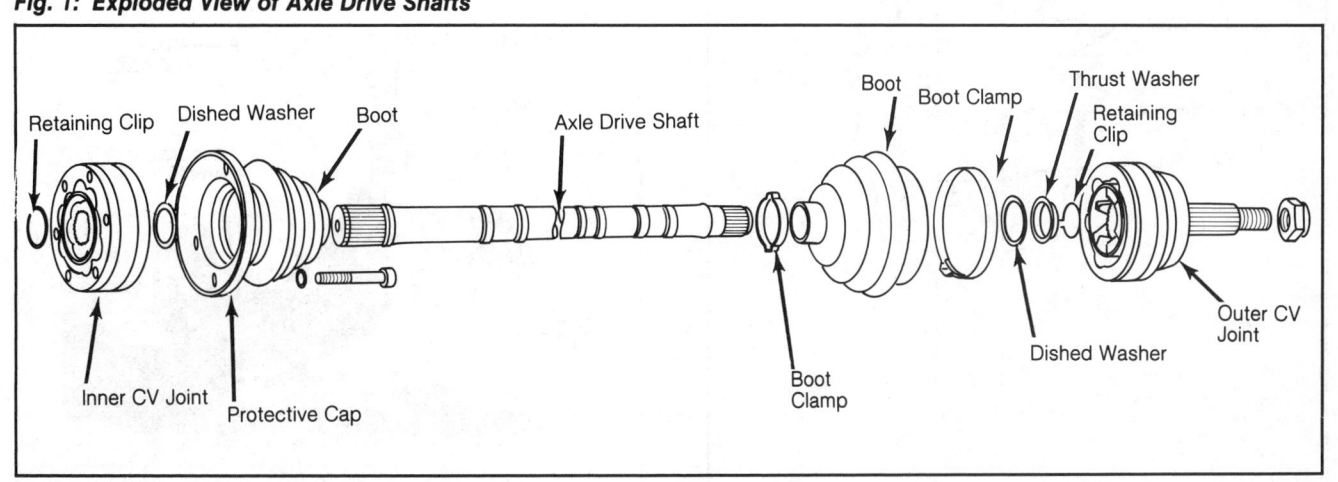

Manual Transmissions
VOLKSWAGEN JETTA, PICKUP, RABBIT & SCIROCCO
4 & 5-SPEED (Cont.)

inserting balls into inner CV joint hub and cage, insert hub and cage into joint perpendicularly.

2) Chamfer of ball hub splines must face larger diameter of joint. Then rotate ball and cage into position and ensure CV joint wide ball groove and narrow hub groove are on same side of joint. See Fig. 3. Joint is correctly assembled if hub can move over shaft splines by hand.

Fig. 3: Installing Ball Hub and Cage in Inner CV Joint

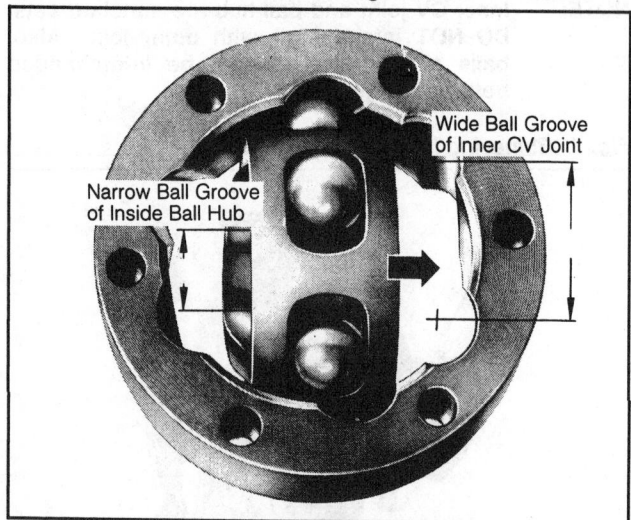

3) Outer CV joint alignment marks must match after reassembly. Replace dust boots and clamps. Install CV joints onto drive axle shaft with inside ball hub chamfer facing shaft. Outer CV joint must be assembled with dished washer concave side facing thrust washer and convex side of thrust washer facing CV joint. See Fig. 4.

Installation
To install, reverse removal procedures.

Fig. 4: Cutaway View of Outer CV Joint Showing Installation of Dished and Thrust Washers

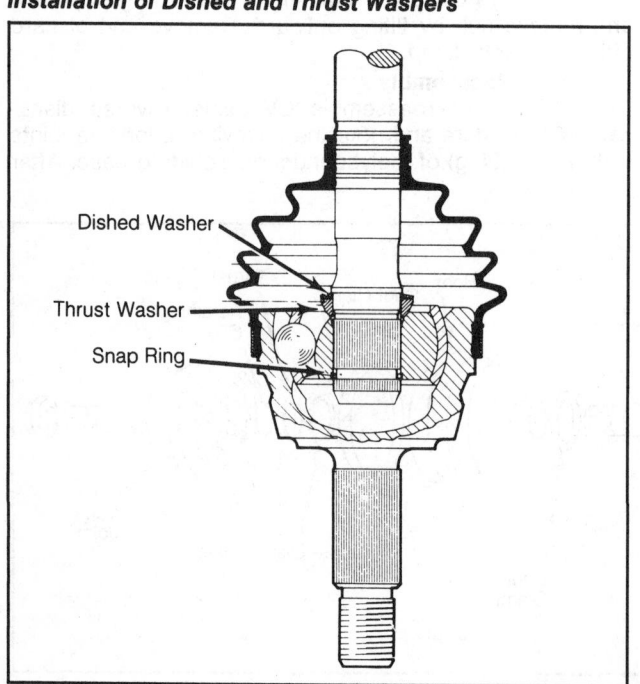

NOTE: The CV joint assembly shown in Fig. 4 is a new production assembly which may be installed on Jetta, Rabbit Convertible and Scirocco models. Former production assembly has snap ring installed closer to thrust washer. DO NOT interchange components between assemblies

FRONT WHEEL BEARINGS
Removal
1) With vehicle supported and drive axle shafts removed, remove caliper mounting bolts. Hang caliper from frame with wire; DO NOT disconnect hydraulic line. Remove brake disc.

2) Remove lower steering knuckle housing-to-ball joint retaining bolt. Remove ball joint castellated nut and cotter pin, then separate ball joint from steering knuckle.

3) Separate tie rod end from steering knuckle. Mark position of camber adjustment bolt (upper bolt securing steering knuckle to strut assembly). Remove bolts securing steering knuckle to strut assembly and remove steering knuckle.

NOTE: Camber adjustment must be checked after wheel bearing replacement. DO NOT lose camber adjustment bolt or eccentric washer.

4) Mount steering knuckle in holding fixture and press out wheel hub. Remove dust shield. Remove circlips from both sides of bearing housing and press out bearing (toward outboard end of housing) with tools shown in Fig. 5. Remove inner wheel bearing race from hub.

NOTE: Wheel bearing must be replaced. Removal procedure destroys wheel bearing for re-installation.

Fig. 5: Identification of Tools to Be Used to Replace Front Wheel Bearing

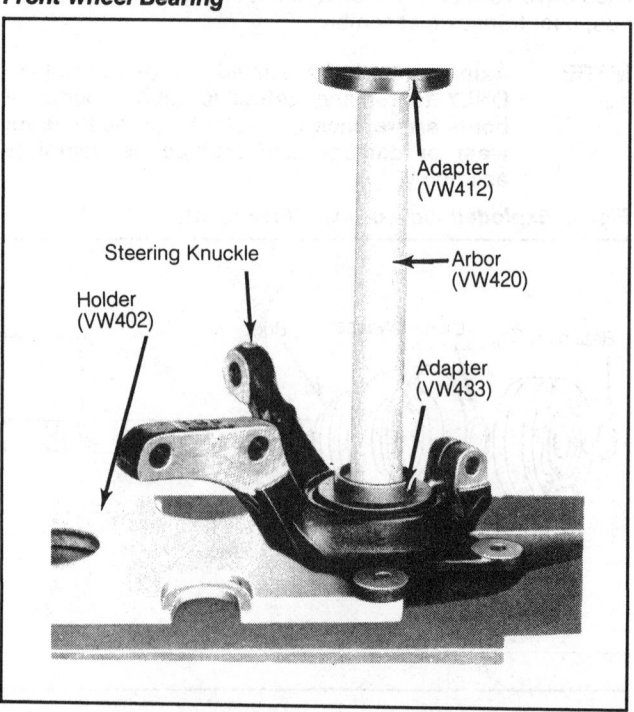

VOLKSWAGEN JETTA, PICKUP, RABBIT & SCIROCCO
4 & 5-SPEED (Cont.)

Installation

To install, reverse removal procedure and note the following: Ensure circlips are fully seated. Always replace ball joint cotter pin.

AXLE DRIVE FLANGE OIL SEALS
Removal

Disconnect axle shaft from drive flange and position out of the way. Remove cap from drive flange, then withdraw retaining snap ring and dished washer. Fasten a puller (VW391) to drive flange and pull flange from transmission. Using a seal puller (VW681), pry oil seal from housing.

Fig. 6: Using Puller to Remove Axle Drive Flange

Remove Flange with Puller after Removing Snap Ring

Installation

Drive new seal into housing with driver (US4450). Install drive flange using puller used during removal (reverse puller for installation). Place dished washer on shaft with convex side away from flange, then drive circlip in place with driver (VW30-23). Replace dust cap and install drive shaft.

Fig. 7: View of 4-Speed Transaxle Assembly

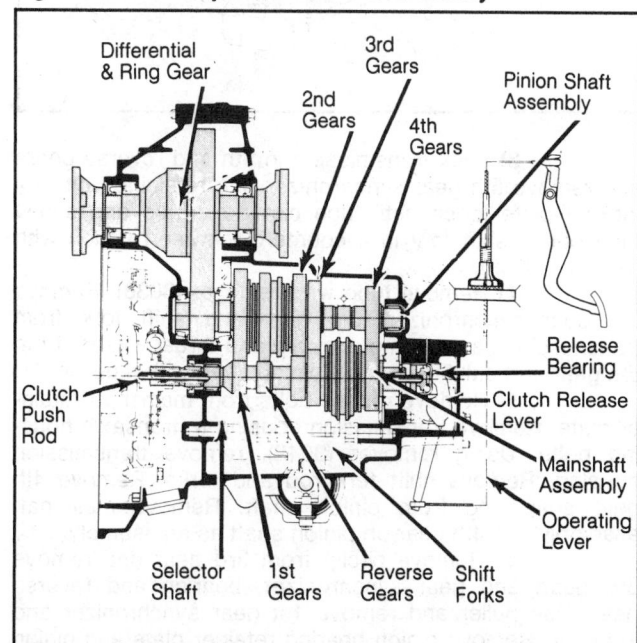

Differential & Ring Gear
3rd Gears
2nd Gears
4th Gears
Pinion Shaft Assembly
Release Bearing
Clutch Release Lever
Mainshaft Assembly
Operating Lever
Clutch Push Rod
Selector Shaft
1st Gears
Reverse Gears
Shift Forks

5-speed model is similar.

NOTE: Pack open side of seals with multi-purpose lubricant prior to installation. Check gear lube level and add as required.

TRANSAXLE REMOVAL & INSTALLATION

See the appropriate article in MANUAL TRANS-MISSION REMOVAL Section.

TRANSAXLE DISASSEMBLY

NOTE: Before disassembly, measure and record pinion depth and ring gear backlash.

4-SPEED

1) Mount transaxle in holding fixture and drain fluid. Remove clutch release push rod from center of mainshaft and withdraw from bell housing end.

2) Install support bar (30-211) across mouth of bell housing and install support block (VW 295a) between support bar and mainshaft. Tighten bolt of bar to take up clearance between bar and mainshaft. See Fig. 8.

Fig. 8: Installation of Mainshaft Support Fixture

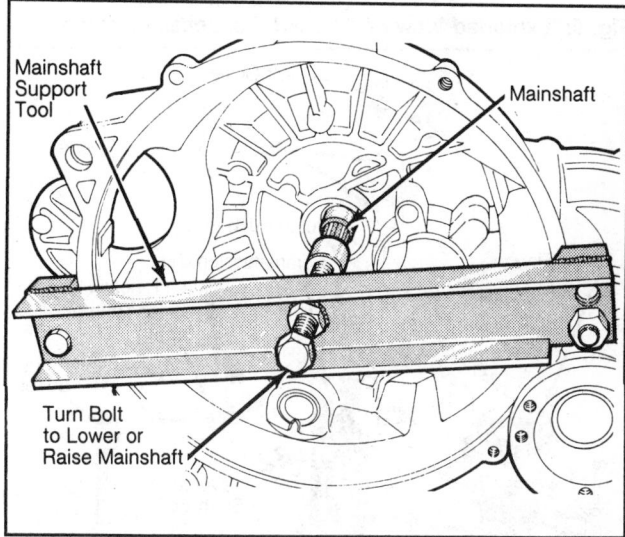

Mainshaft Support Tool
Mainshaft
Turn Bolt to Lower or Raise Mainshaft

3) Remove cap, snap ring and spring washer from drive shaft flange. Remove both drive shaft flanges with remover (VW391). Remove release bearing cover, pry circlips off release shaft.

4) Remove release shaft, clutch lever and return spring. Remove release bearing and guide sleeve. Remove 2 mainshaft bearing retaining nut plugs. Remove 3 mainshaft bearing retaining nuts. Remove reverse idler shaft bolt and backup light switch.

5) Remove selector shaft cover and lock bolt. Set shift forks in neutral position and remove selector shaft and spring with remover (US4463). Remove 2 stud nuts and 12 bolts retaining transmission case to transaxle case.

6) Install mounting plate on rear of transmission case and center remover (VW391) on mainshaft. Separate transmission case from transaxle case. Remove mainshaft bearing retaining screws that fell into case. Remove magnet from transaxle case.

Manual Transmissions

VOLKSWAGEN JETTA, PICKUP, RABBIT & SCIROCCO
4 & 5-SPEED (Cont.)

7) Remove mainshaft bearing shim. Remove 2 "E" clips from shift fork and pull shift fork shaft from housing. Swing shift forks to one side and remove reverse gear and shaft. Remove 4th gear snap ring from pinion shaft. Remove mainshaft assembly and 4th gear on pinion shaft as an assembly.

8) Remove snap ring, 3rd gear, 2nd gear, 2nd gear needle bearing and race and 2nd gear synchronizer ring. Using a puller, simultaneously remove 1st gear, 1st gear synchronizer ring, 1st-2nd gear synchronizer, 1st gear needle bearing and thrust washer. Remove pinion bearing cover bolts, remove cover and pull pinion shaft out of bore. Lift out differential unit.

NOTE: **All gears must be removed from pinion shaft before shaft and differential can be removed from case.**

5-SPEED

1) Mount transaxle in holding fixture and drain fluid. Remove clutch release push rod from center of mainshaft and withdraw from bell housing end. Install support bar (30-211) across mouth of bell housing and install support block (VW295a) between support bar and mainshaft. Tighten bolt of bar to take up clearance between bar and mainshaft. *See Fig. 8.*

Fig. 9: *Exploded View of 4-Speed Transmission Case*

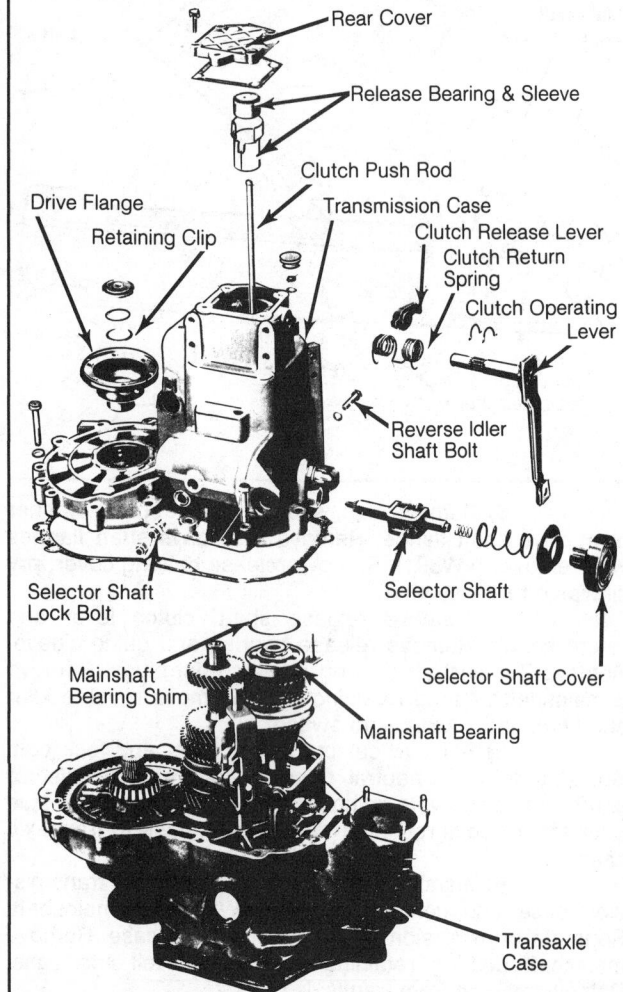

2) Remove rear housing bolts and rear housing. Remove backup light switch, 5th gear lock out and selector shaft detent. Remove selector shaft cover. Set gears in neutral position and remove selector shaft and spring. Remove cap, snap ring and spring washer from drive shaft flange. Remove both drive shaft flanges with remover (VW391).

Fig. 10: *View of 4-Speed Pinion Shaft Assembly*

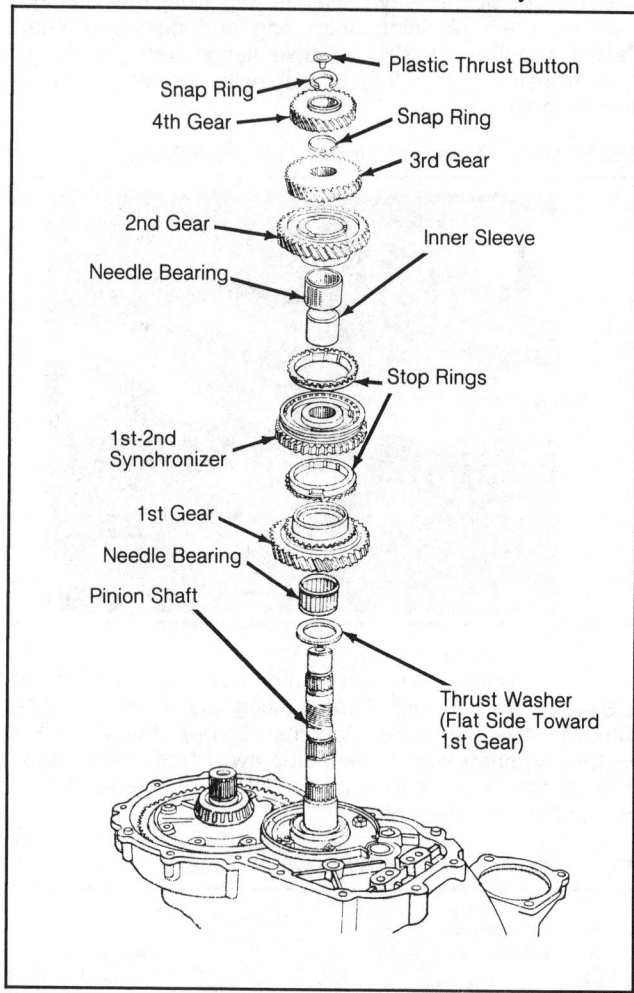

3) Lock transmission in 5th and reverse gears and remove 5th gear synchronizer hub retaining bolt. Pry locking plate loose until tube can be turned and screw tube out of shift fork in a counterclockwise rotation with remover (3059).

4) Remove tube with remover (3038). Remove 5th gear synchronizer, 5th gear and shift fork from transmission case. Remove circlip and thrust washer from 5th gear and pull 5th gear off pinion shaft with a puller.

5) Remove recess bolts from mainshaft retainer plate. Remove transmission housing-to-transaxle housing bolts. Using remover (3042), remove transmission housing. Remove shift fork rod and forks. Remove 4th gear snap ring from pinion shaft. Remove mainshaft assembly and 4th gear on pinion shaft as an assembly.

6) Remove circlip from 3rd gear and remove 3rd gear, 2nd gear synchronizer, bearing and reverse gear. Use puller and remove 1st gear synchronizer and 1st gear. Remove pinion bearing retainer plate and pinion shaft. Remove differential assembly from case.

Manual Transmissions
VOLKSWAGEN JETTA, PICKUP, RABBIT & SCIROCCO
4 & 5-SPEED (Cont.)

7-255

Fig. 11: Removing 5th Gear Synchronizer Assembly

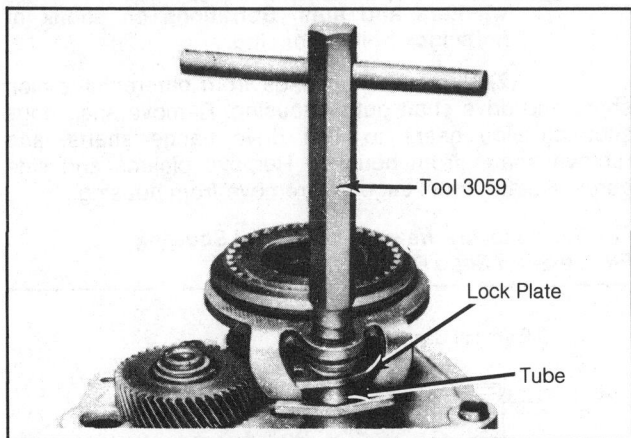

Tool 3059

Lock Plate

Tube

NOTE: Do not pull selector rod out of tube.

COMPONENT DISASSEMBLY & REASSEMBLY

MAINSHAFT

Disassembly

1) Remove mainshaft bearing with puller on 5-speed (use a press and VW402 plate for 4-speed). On all transaxles, remove 4th gear, 4th gear needle bearing and 4th gear synchro ring.

2) Remove 3rd-4th synchro assembly snap ring and simultaneously press 3rd gear and 3rd-4th synchro assembly off shaft. Remove 3rd gear needle bearing. Place reference marks on synchro hub and sleeve for reassembly reference, then push hub, shifting keys and spring out of sleeve.

Inspection

1) Check all shaft surfaces, splines, and gear teeth for wear, chipping, scoring, or other damage. Check clutch push rod bushing in mainshaft for wear or damage, and if replacement is necessary, drive out push rod bushing using a 3/8" (10 mm) rod inserted through rear of shaft.

2) Position a new bushing and oil seal on front of mainshaft, and press into shaft until flush. Assemble synchro rings on gears and check ring-to-gear clearance. Clearance for new parts should be .044-.069" (1.12-1.75 mm) for 3rd gear, .051-.075" (1.3-1.9 mm) for 4th gear. Wear limit for used parts is .020" (.5 mm).

NOTE: Replacement of any gear necessitates replacement of meshing gear, as gears are available as matched pairs only.

Reassembly

1) Position shifting keys in slots of synchronizer hub, then install hub into synchronizer sleeve, after aligning reference marks. Install key springs into assembly, making sure springs are positioned 120° offset of one another and that angled ends of springs engage hollowed-out portions of shifting keys. On 5th gear, install synchro key retainer plate.

2) Install 3rd gear needle bearing on shaft. Assemble 3rd gear, 3rd gear synchro ring and synchro assembly, ensuring notches in synchro ring engage 3 keys in synchro assembly and that splines in synchro hub face 3rd gear. Press mainshaft into assembled synchro assembly, 3rd gear and synchro ring. Install snap ring, 4th gear synchro ring, needle bearing and 4th gear. On 5-speed transmission, press bearing on mainshaft with press.

PINION SHAFT

NOTE: Gears and synchronizer assembly were removed during Transmission Disassembly, and will be installed during Transmission Reassembly. Synchronizer overhaul and bearing replacement are covered below.

Fig. 13: Exploded View of 4-Speed Pinion Shaft

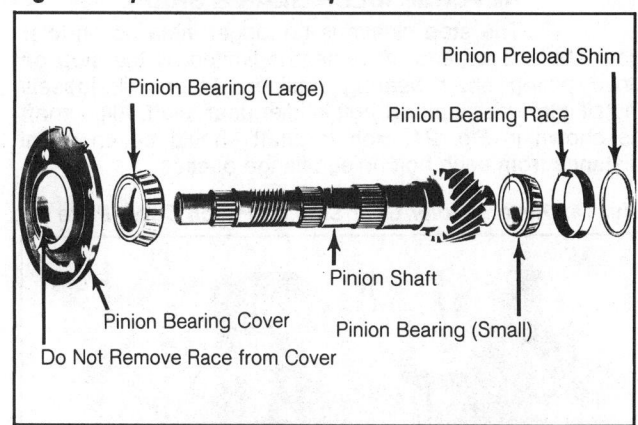

Pinion Bearing (Large)

Pinion Preload Shim

Pinion Bearing Race

Pinion Shaft

Pinion Bearing Cover

Pinion Bearing (Small)

Do Not Remove Race from Cover

Disassembly

Bearings cannot be reused after removal from pinion shaft. If bearing replacement is required, use press to remove large and small bearings from shaft. Use puller

Fig. 12: Exploded View of 4-Speed Mainshaft Assembly

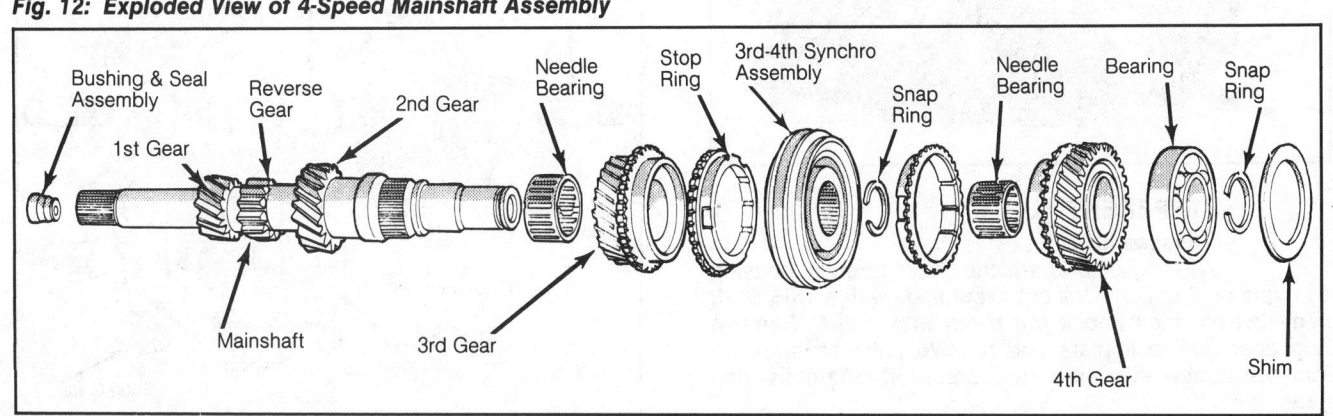

Bushing & Seal Assembly

Reverse Gear

2nd Gear

Needle Bearing

Stop Ring

3rd-4th Synchro Assembly

Snap Ring

Needle Bearing

Bearing

Snap Ring

1st Gear

Mainshaft

3rd Gear

4th Gear

Shim

Manual Transmissions
VOLKSWAGEN JETTA, PICKUP, RABBIT & SCIROCCO 4 & 5-SPEED (Cont.)

to remove small bearing outer race from case. For reassembly reference, scribe reference marks on synchro hub and operating sleeve. Then, push hub, shifting keys and springs out of sleeve.

Inspection

Check all shaft surfaces, splines and gear teeth for wear, chipping, scoring or other damage. Assemble synchro rings on gears and check ring-to-gear clearance. Clearance for new parts should be .043-.067" (1.1-1.7 mm). Wear limit for used parts is .020" (.5 mm).

NOTE: **Replacement of any gear necessitates replacement of meshing gear, as gears are available as matched pairs only.**

Reassembly

If bearings were removed from pinion shaft, heat new bearings to approximately 212°F (100°C) and install on pinion shaft with press. Install shifting keys into synchronizer hub, then install hub into synchronizer sleeve, making sure reference marks are aligned. Install shifting key springs into assembly with springs offset 120° from each other. Angled ends of springs must engage hollowed out portions of shifting keys.

NOTE: **DO NOT install pinion bearing race into case half at this time; adjustment of pinion is required and will be covered in Transmission Reassembly.**

REVERSE IDLER GEAR & SHAFT

The stop sleeve is no longer installed on idler gear shaft. Gear end movement is limited by the stop on drive pinion shaft bearing retainer. To install, loosely install idler gear support bolt in idler gear shaft. Align shaft as shown in *Fig. 21*. Bolt in shaft should be an equal distance from each bolt hole in flange of case.

Fig. 14: Reverse Idler Gear Stop on Pinion Cover Plate

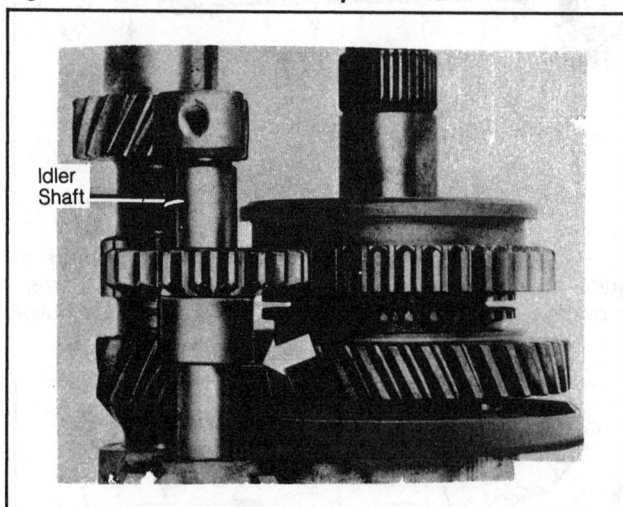

Idler
Shaft

DIFFERENTIAL
Disassembly

1) Ring gear is attached to differential housing by rivets on 5-speed. Drill out rivet heads with a 15/32" (12 mm) drill bit, then knock out rivets with a drift. Remove ring gear bolt lock plate and remove bolts on 4-speed. Place assembly in a press and press off differential ring gear.

NOTE: **Ring gear is reinstalled with special bolts, washers and nuts. Serrations on shank of bolts lock bolt in housing.**

2) Remove snap rings from differential pinion shaft, and drive shaft out of housing. Remove snap rings securing side gears to axle drive flange shafts, and remove shafts from housing. Remove pinions and side gears. Rotate thrust cage and remove from housing.

Fig. 15: Cutaway View of Differential Showing Flange Shaft Snap Ring Installation

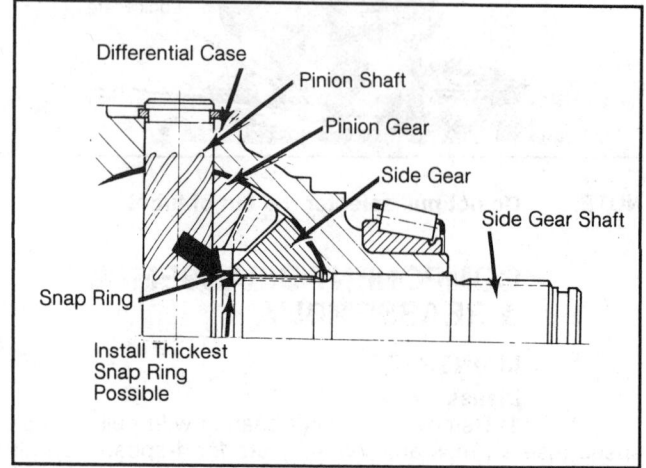

Differential Case
Pinion Shaft
Pinion Gear
Side Gear
Side Gear Shaft
Snap Ring
Install Thickest Snap Ring Possible

Reassembly

1) Insert thrust cage into differential housing. Insert pinion gears into housing and drive in pinion shaft. Install pinion shaft snap rings. Rotate thrust cage to align side gear shaft holes with side gear shaft holes of housing.

NOTE: **If bearings were removed from case, heat bearings to approximately 212°F (100°C) and use a press to drive bearings into place.**

2) Insert and position side gears so they mesh with pinion gears and are 180° apart. Rotate side gears into position inside housing. Install axle drive flange shafts, and push each shaft firmly against differential pinion shaft and install thickest snap ring possible. *See Fig. 15.*

Fig. 16: Exploded View of Differential Assembly

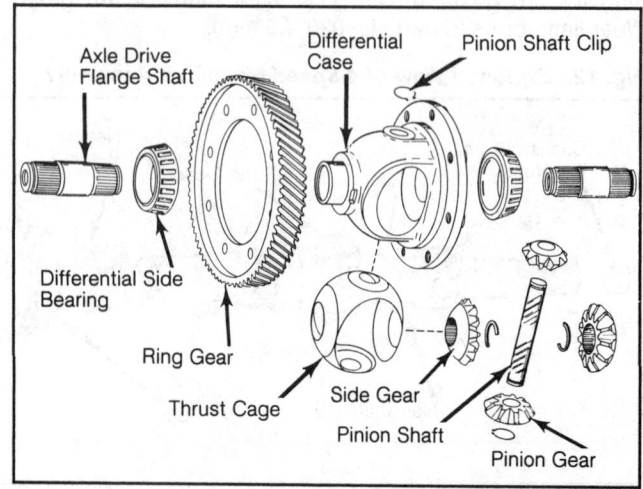

Axle Drive Flange Shaft
Differential Case
Pinion Shaft Clip
Differential Side Bearing
Ring Gear
Thrust Cage
Side Gear
Pinion Shaft
Pinion Gear

VOLKSWAGEN JETTA, PICKUP, RABBIT & SCIROCCO 4 & 5-SPEED (Cont.)

NOTE: There are two available snap rings. One is .079" (2.0 mm) thick, and the other is .091" (2.3 mm). If thicker snap ring jams sideways, install thinner snap ring.

3) Heat ring gear to about 212°F (100°C). Drive bolts into differential housing and place heated ring gear onto housing. Install washers and nuts onto ring gear bolts and tighten to 50 ft. lbs. (68 N.m).

TRANSAXLE REASSEMBLY & ADJUSTMENT

NOTE: During reassembly of transaxle, it is not always necessary to perform all adjustments described in the following procedures. If transaxle case or mainshaft have been replaced, check mainshaft adjustment. If transaxle case, pinion bearings or ring and pinion set have been replaced, adjust drive pinion. If transaxle case, differential side bearings or differential have been replaced, adjust differential. If no components were replaced during reassembly, make corresponding adjustments to conform to specifications taken prior to disassembly.

DIFFERENTIAL BEARING PRELOAD

1) If differential bearing race and shim were removed from final drive housing case half, position a .039" (1 mm) shim in bearing race bore and press in bearing race. Remove bearing race and shim from shift housing case half (if not already removed), and reinstall bearing race into housing **without shims.**

Fig. 17: Using a Dial Indicator to Measure Differential Side Play in Case

Move Differential Up and Down to Read Side Play

Dial Indicator Support

2) Install differential assembly into final drive housing case half. Position shift housing case half with gasket onto final drive housing case half and install and tighten attaching bolts. Place gauge block (VW385/17) onto axle drive flange shaft. Install dial indicator on shift housing case so button contacts gauge block. Zero dial indicator with .039" (1 mm) preload.

CAUTION: Do not rotate differential when moving up and down as this will cause an incorrect reading.

3) Move differential assembly up and down and note reading on dial indicator. Add constant preload figure of .016" (.4 mm) to dial indicator reading to obtain thickness of shim to install under shift housing case half differential bearing race.

4) Separate housings and remove differential. Press out shift housing case half differential bearing race, install shim just determined in bearing race bore, then reinstall bearing race with a press.

NOTE: Adjusting shims are available in various thicknesses from .006" (.15 mm) to .039" (1 mm). Install a combination of shims as required to make up shim pack. Thickest shim should be inserted first, with thinnest against bearing race.

5) Lubricate bearings with hypoid oil and reinstall in transaxle case. Install adapter and INCH lb. torque wrench to drive axle flange shaft and check rotating torque.

6) Rotating torque should be 11-31 INCH lbs. (1.2-3.5 N.m) for new bearings and 3 INCH lbs. (.34 N.m) for used bearings. If not within specifications, recheck bearing condition and verify proper shim thickness.

PINION BEARING PRELOAD

1) If not already removed, use a puller to withdraw pinion bearing race from final drive housing case half. Temporarily install a .025" (.65 mm) shim into bearing race bore of case half, then reinstall race using a press.

Fig. 18: Method Used to Measure Pinion Shaft End Play

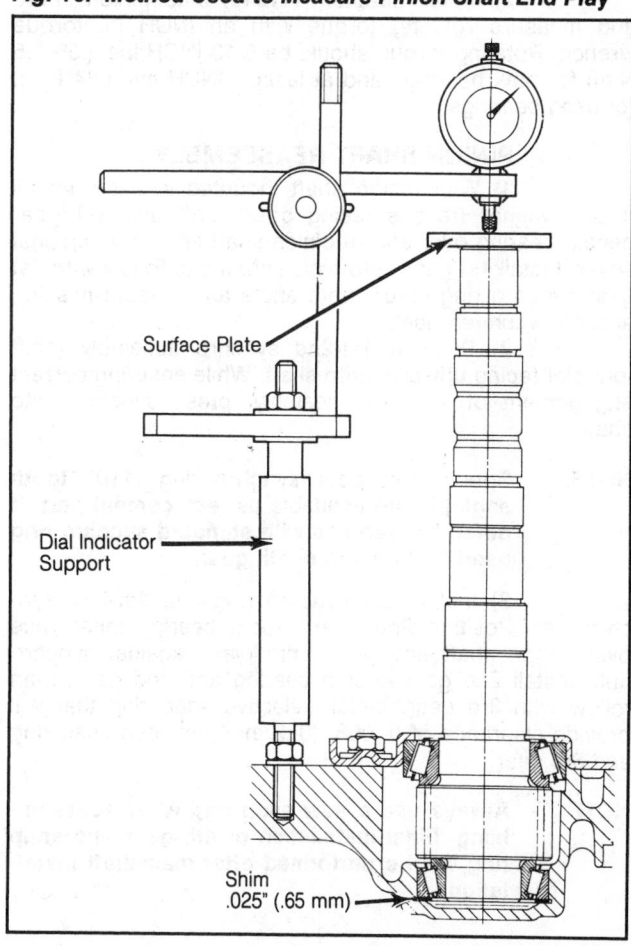

Surface Plate

Dial Indicator Support

Shim .025" (.65 mm)

7-258

Manual Transmissions
VOLKSWAGEN JETTA, PICKUP, RABBIT & SCIROCCO
4 & 5-SPEED (Cont.)

Install pinion shaft into bearing race, then install pinion bearing cover, tightening cover-to-case half bolts securely.

CAUTION: Do not rotate pinion when moving up and down as this will cause an incorrect reading.

    2) Install surface plate on top of pinion shaft. Install dial indicator and support on case half so button of indicator contacts surface plate. *See Fig. 18.* Preload dial indicator with .039" (1 mm) and zero dial face. Move pinion up and down and note maximum dial indicator reading.

    3) To dial indicator reading, add thickness of shim temporarily installed under bearing race (.025" — .65 mm), plus a constant preload figure of .008" (.2 mm). Total of 3 figures equals thickness of shims to install under pinion bearing race in case half. Remove pinion and bearing race, replace .025" (.65 mm) shim with shim pack just determined, then reinstall bearing race.

NOTE: **Adjusting shims are available in thicknesses ranging from .026" (.65 mm) to .055" (1.4 mm) in increments of .002" (.5 mm). Install a combination of shims as required to make up shim pack.**

DIFFERENTIAL & PINION INSTALLATION

    1) Place final drive housing on work bench and lubricate differential bearings with gear oil. Install differential assembly into transaxle case. Lubricate pinion bearings with gear oil and install pinion shaft. Install pinion bearing cover and tighten bearing retainer plate and transmission case-to-transaxle case attaching bolts.

    2) Install adapter (VW548) onto pinion shaft, and measure rotating torque with an INCH lb. torque wrench. Rotating torque should be 5-13 INCH lbs. (.56-1.5 N.m) for new bearings and at least 3 INCH lbs. (.34 N.m) for used bearings.

PINION SHAFT REASSEMBLY

    1) With pinion shaft mounted in case, install thrust washer (recess facing downward) and 1st gear needle bearing over end of pinion shaft and down against cover. Install 1st gear onto pinion shaft and follow with 1st gear synchro ring (110° tooth angle and 3 teeth missing around circumference).

    2) Position 1st-2nd synchro assembly (shift fork slot facing upward) onto shaft. While ensuring correct engagement of synchro assembly, press synchro onto shaft.

NOTE: **Special 1st gear synchro ring (110° tooth angle) is not available as replacement part. If defective, replace with standard synchro ring used for 2nd, 3rd or 4th gear.**

    3) Install 2nd synchro ring into 1st-2nd synchronizer. Position 2nd gear needle bearing inner race over pinion shaft and press into place against synchro hub. Install 2nd gear needle bearing and 2nd gear, then follow with 3rd gear. Install selective snap ring that will provide clearance of 0-.008" (0-.2 mm) between snap ring and 3rd gear.

NOTE: **Always use a new snap ring when reassembling. Final installation of 4th gear and snap ring will be performed after mainshaft installation.**

MAINSHAFT INSTALLATION & ADJUSTMENT
4-Speed
    1) Install mainshaft into final drive housing case half so gears of mainshaft mesh with gears of pinion gears.

NOTE: **Select a new mainshaft adjusting shim as described in the following procedure only if mainshaft or either half of transaxle case has been replaced. If no adjustment is required, install original shim in bore of shift housing case half and proceed to step 8).**

    2) Install a support bar (30-211) onto clutch housing side of final drive housing case half so adjusting bolt contacts front of mainshaft. Lift mainshaft up with adjusting bolt until a clearance of .039" (1 mm) exists between 2nd gear of pinion shaft and 3rd gear of mainshaft.

    3) Lock adjusting bolt, ensure clearance has not changed, and install dummy bearing measuring sleeve (VW549) onto mainshaft.

Fig. 19: *Measuring 4-Speed Mainshaft Installed Height*

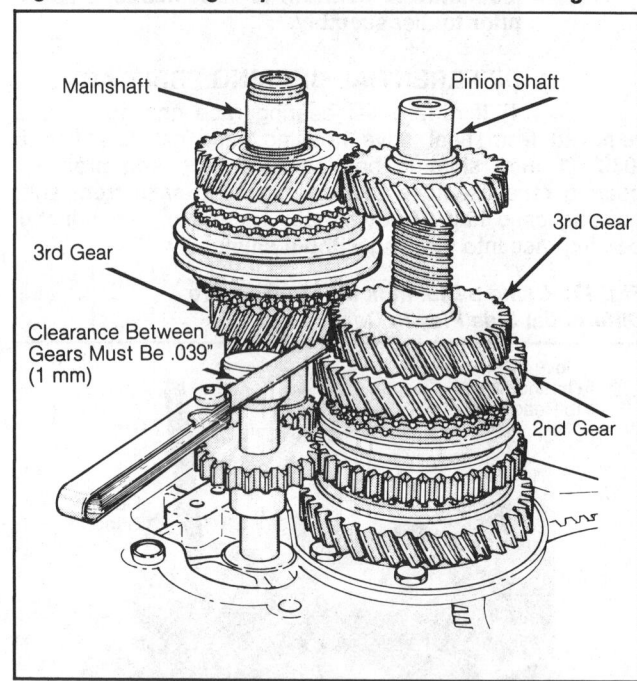

    4) Install a new gasket onto final drive case half. Install shift housing case (without mainshaft ball bearing or clamping bolts installed) onto assembly. Install and tighten 5 bolts to 14 ft. lbs. (19 N.m) to secure case halves.

    5) Install dial indicator assembly onto outside of shift housing case half. Position button of indicator against measuring sleeve tool. Zero dial indicator with .12" (.3 mm) preload.

    6) Grasp measuring sleeve and move up and down; read resulting play indicated on dial indicator. Select a shim (to be installed under bearing in shift housing case half) from table.

VOLKSWAGEN JETTA, PICKUP, RABBIT & SCIROCCO
4 & 5-SPEED (Cont.)

Fig. 20: *Measuring 4-Speed Mainshaft End Play*

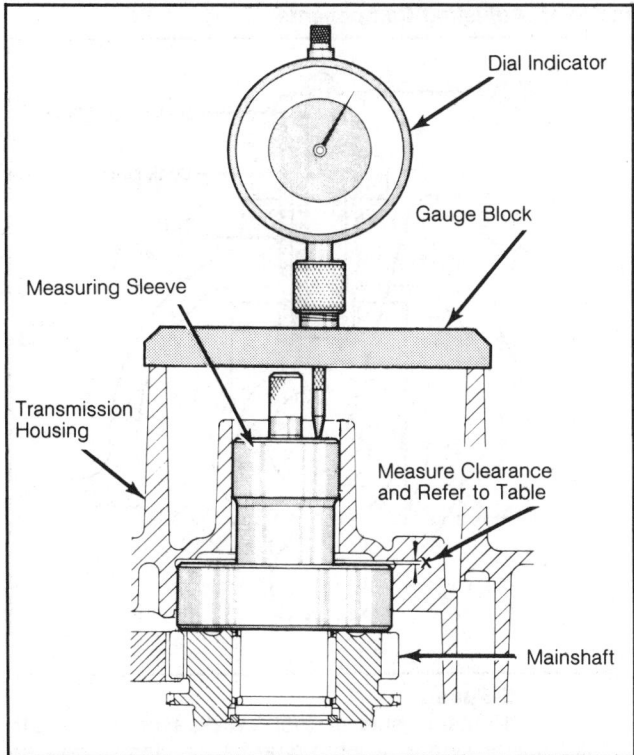

NOTE: For measurement only, install a fourth gear thrust washer between measuring sleeve and shoulder of mainshaft. The thrust washer inside diameter can be enlarged with a file to ease installation and removal from mainshaft.

Fig. 21: *Centering 4-Speed Reverse Idler Shaft in Case*

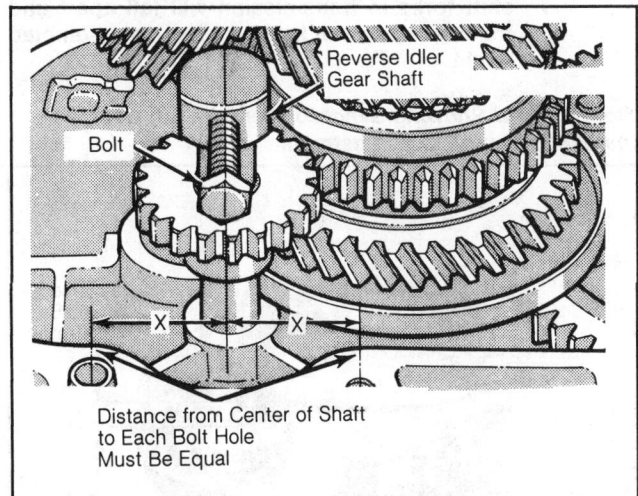

7) Remove dial indicator and separate case halves. Remove measuring sleeve and thrust washer. Install proper shim(s) just selected, into mainshaft ball bearing bore in shift housing case half.

NOTE: Closed side of bearing cage MUST be installed toward shim(s) and housing, and press tool must contact bearing outer race only.

MAINSHAFT BEARING SHIM SELECTION (4-SPEED ONLY)

End Play In. (mm)	Shim Thickness In. (mm)
0-.018 (0-.46)	None
.019-.029 (.47-.75)	.012 (.30)
.030-.041 (.76-1.04)	.024 (.60)
.042-.057 (1.05-1.45)	[1] .036 (.90)

[1] — Use .012" (.30 mm) and .024" (.60 mm) shims.

8) Install mainshaft bearing on top of shims and press into bore. Install clamping bolts and tighten to 11 ft. lbs. (15 N.m). Install plastic caps on nuts outside housing.

5-Speed

1) Install mainshaft without shims into case. Hold mainshaft in place with special tool 30-211 and adapter VW295a. Install 4th gear on pinion shaft and install circlip. Press mainshaft bearing with old shim into case. Install clamping plate and insert lower spring for selector rod into gear carrier housing.

2) Insert 1st-2nd gear shift fork into operating sleeve. Lift selector rod slightly and swing shift fork around pinion shaft, guiding 3rd-4th shift fork into synchronizer sleeve and reverse shift fork into relay lever. Push selector rod in and align shift forks.

Fig. 22: *Installing 5-Speed Shift Forks*

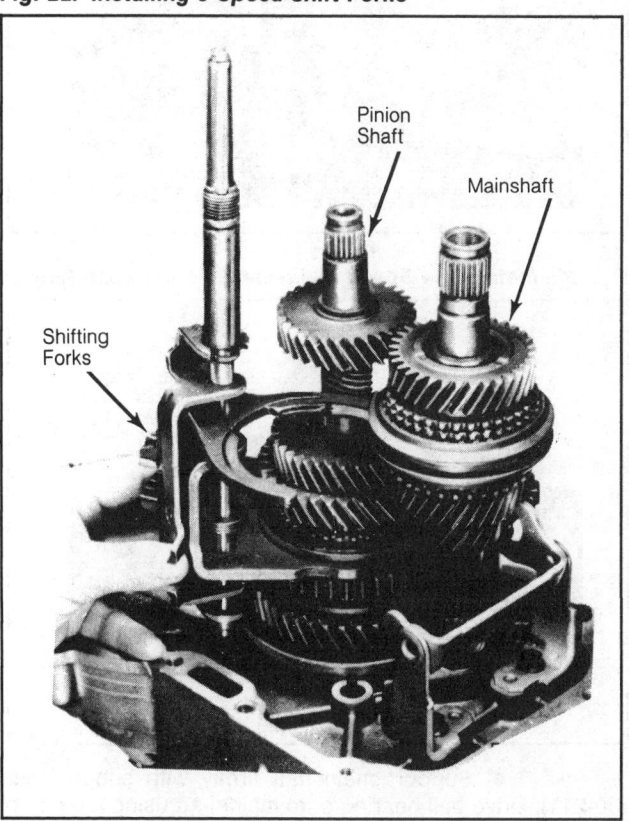

REVERSE IDLER INSTALLATION

Temporarily install reverse idler shaft retaining bolt into idler shaft, then position shaft into case bore. Center reverse idler bolt so center of shaft is equal from each bolt hole of case. Remove bolt without disturbing shaft alignment.

Manual Transmissions
VOLKSWAGEN JETTA, PICKUP, RABBIT & SCIROCCO 4 & 5-SPEED (Cont.)

SHIFT FORKS & SHIFT HOUSING INSTALLATION

4-Speed

1) Install reverse shift fork and support onto case, and engage fork with reverse idler gear. Install 1st-2nd and 3rd-4th shift forks into sleeves of synchronizer assemblies, and reverse operating fork into engagement with all 3 shift forks.

2) With all parts in correct position, press fork shaft into housing and install 2 "E" clips to secure forks. Install 4th gear onto pinion shaft and secure with snap ring.

3) Make sure reverse idler shaft is still correctly positioned and that all gears are in neutral position. Install shift housing case half onto unit, making sure mainshaft is aligned with ball bearing, and pinion shaft is aligned with its needle bearing. Dowel holes should align one half of case with other.

Fig. 23: Shift Fork Retaining Clip Locations

Secure Forks to Shaft with "E" Clips

Fig. 24: Installing 4-Speed Mainshaft Bearing Snap Ring

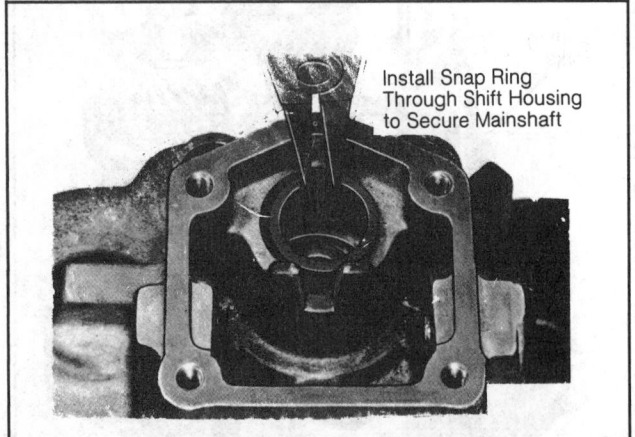

Install Snap Ring Through Shift Housing to Secure Mainshaft

4) Support mainshaft firmly with support bar (30-211). Drive ball bearing onto mainshaft using a bearing driver (30-23), applying force to inner bearing race only. Install reverse idler shaft bolt and tighten to 14 ft. lbs. (19 N.m).

5) Install case bolts and tighten in a diagonal pattern to 18 ft. lbs. (24 N.m). Working through clutch release area of shift housing, install mainshaft-to-ball bearing snap ring. See Fig. 24.

Fig. 25: Cutaway View of Case Showing Selector Shaft and Shaft Adjusting Components

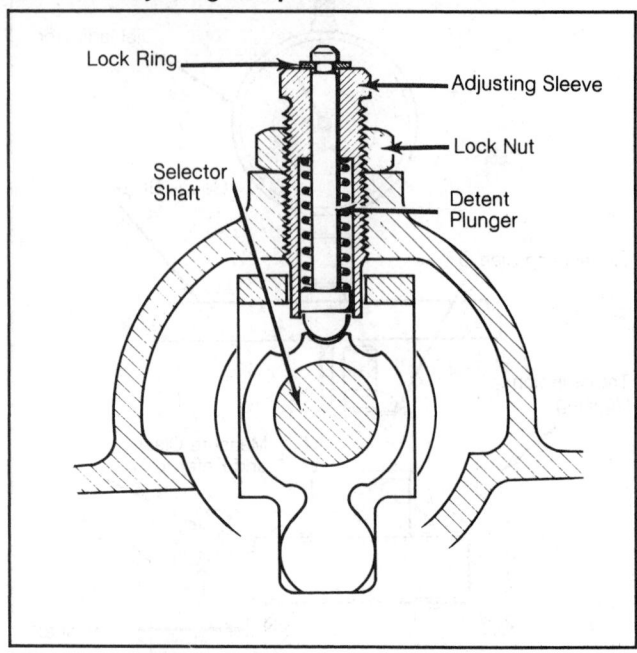

Lock Ring
Adjusting Sleeve
Lock Nut
Selector Shaft
Detent Plunger

5-Speed

1) Install special tool VW295a on mainshaft, install transmission case onto gear carrier. Install reverse gear shaft lock bolt and tighten. Install transmission case-to-gear case bolts and tighten.

2) Install backup light switch. Tighten mainshaft bearing clamping plate bolts. Install drive shaft flange, install spring washer and circlip, press circlip into place and check for proper setting.

CAUTION: Do not pull selector rod out of tube because shift forks in transmission will fall apart and transmission will have to be disassembled again.

Fig. 26: View Showing Synchronizer with 5th Gear Installation and Tube Adjustment

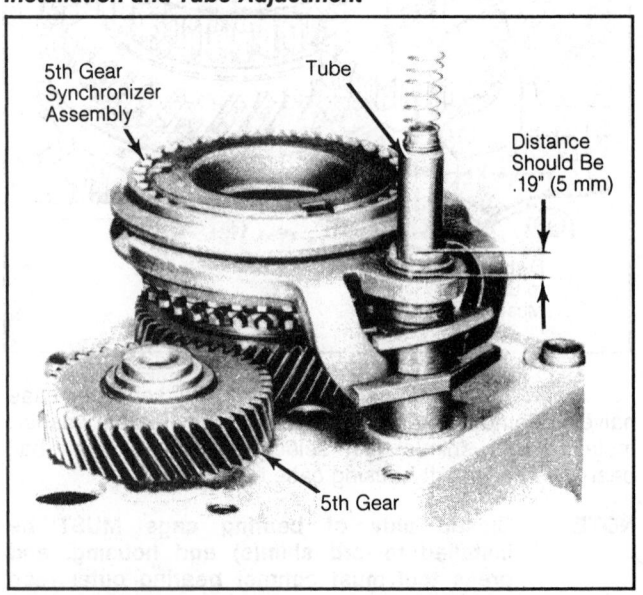

5th Gear Synchronizer Assembly
Tube
Distance Should Be .19" (5 mm)
5th Gear

VOLKSWAGEN JETTA, PICKUP, RABBIT & SCIROCCO
4 & 5-SPEED (Cont.)

3) Heat 5th gear to 212°F (100°C) and install. Install thrust washer and circlip. Install synchronizer with 5th gear onto mainshaft. Screw selector tube clockwise into shift fork, then screw tube out until it projects above shift fork by .19" (5 mm). *See Fig. 26.*

4) Coat synchronizer hub bolt with locking compound and tighten. Place transmission in neutral and install selector shaft. Install spring and cover for selector shaft. Install lock out plunger for 5th gear and detent plunger for selector shaft.

5) To adjust detent plunger, loosen lock nut and turn adjusting sleeve in until lock ring lifts off sleeve. Turn adjusting sleeve back until lock ring just contacts sleeve, tighten lock nut. Turn selector shaft slightly and check that lock ring lifts as soon as shaft is turned.

6) To adjust 5th gear lock out plunger, set transmission in neutral. Remove adjusting sleeve cap and loosen lock nut. Tighten adjusting sleeve until detent plunger just starts to move up. Loosen adjusting sleeve 1/3 turn and tighten lock nut.

7) To adjust 5th gear shift fork, shift selector lever in 5th gear position, lift 5th gear synchronizer sleeve slightly to eliminate play. Check engagement of sleeve coupling teeth on 5th gear for proper engagement. Overlap should be .039" (1 mm). Adjust by turning selector tube. *See Fig. 27.*

Fig. 27: Adjusting 5th Gear Shift Fork Position

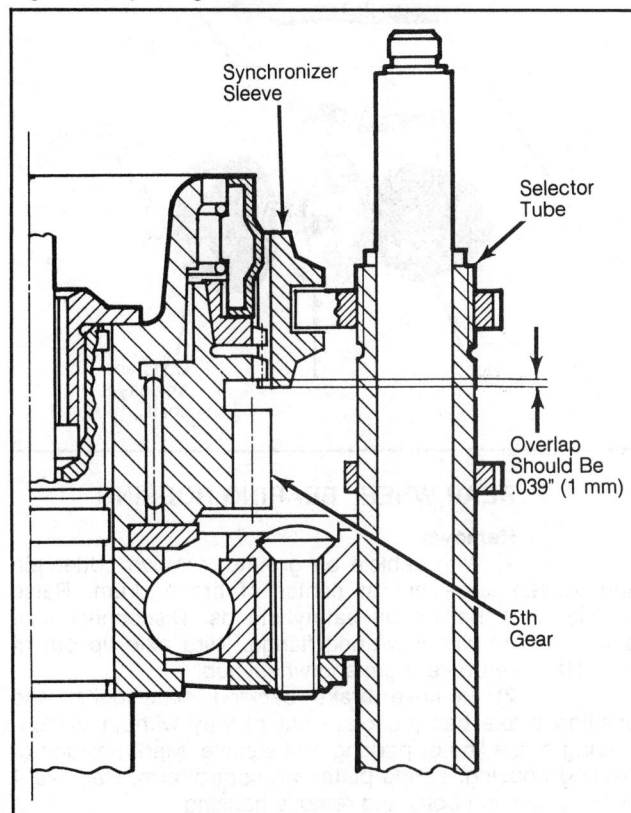

FINAL ASSEMBLY
4-Speed
1) Install speedometer drive gear assembly, being careful to mesh drive gear with teeth on drive pinion shaft. Apply grease to clutch push rod and insert into mainshaft. Install release bearing and sleeve into rear end of shift housing.

Fig. 28: Installing Clutch Release Lever Clips

Install Clips on Both Sides of Lever with a Screwdriver

2) Position clutch release lever and return spring in rear of shift housing, then install clutch operating lever through release lever and spring.

NOTE: **Bent ends of spring must contact housing, and center part of spring hooks over release lever. Install 2 snap rings to secure assembly.**

3) Apply grease to selector shaft and install into shift housing, engaging shift forks. Install 2 springs, spring seat and cover into case. Install selector shaft locking bolt into case and tighten. To adjust interlock plunger, loosen lock nut and turn adjusting sleeve in until lock ring lifts off sleeve.

4) Back off adjusting sleeve until lock ring just touches sleeve and tighten lock nut. Turn selector shaft slightly and check that lock ring lifts as soon as shaft is turned.

NOTE: **Transmission must be in neutral with linkage disconnected when adjusting selector shaft.**

5) Install rear cover with a new gasket onto shift housing. If removed, install a new seal into selector shaft bore (shift lever end).

6) Install new drive flange oil seals into housing, position drive flange onto shafts and retain with washers and snap rings. Install new plastic caps into flanges. If removed, install backup light switch, drain and fill plugs into case.

5-Speed
Install new gasket and install transmission case cover with release bearing. Lubricate clutch push rod at ends and at bearing. Select all gears in sequence and check that they engage easily without jamming.

TIGHTENING SPECIFICATIONS

Application	Ft. Lbs. (N.m)
Axle Shaft Nut	173 (235)
Transaxle-to-Engine	40 (54)
Drive Shaft-to-Flange	32 (43)
Release Bearing Cover Bolts	11 (15)
Mainshaft Bearing Retaining Nuts	14 (19)
Reverse Idler Bolt	14 (19)
Case Half Bolts	18 (24)
Selector Shaft Cover	32 (43)
Selector Shaft Lock Nut	14 (19)
Reverse Fork Support Bolts	11 (15)
Pinion Bearing Cover	29 (39)
Ring Gear Nuts	50 (68)
5th Gear Synchro Assembly	50 (68)
Reverse Shaft Bolt	22 (30)

VOLKSWAGEN VANAGON 4-SPEED

TRANSMISSION IDENTIFICATION

The Volkswagen Vanagon uses a Type 091 manual transmission. First 3 digits of transmission part number cast in right side of transmission case indicate transmission model. Transmission code letters (DK) and date of manufacture are stamped on bottom of transmission case.

DESCRIPTION

The transaxle assembly is a 2-piece unit containing both the transmission and final drive. The transmission and final drive are asembled in one section and clutch is housed in second section.

The transaxle is mounted at rear of vehicle and engine is mounted to rear of transaxle. The transmission is a 4-speed manual type. Gears are in constant mesh in all forward gears. The final drive, mounted between transmission and engine, uses a hypoid ring gear and pinion.

The rear axle unit is a double joint type, using constant velocity (CV) joints on both ends of axle drive shafts. Outer wheel bearings are mounted in a housing connected to control arm.

LUBRICATION & ADJUSTMENT

See the appropriate article in MANUAL TRANSMISSION SERVICING Section.

SERVICE (IN VEHICLE)

AXLE DRIVE SHAFTS

Removal & Installation

Remove socket head screws at each CV joint. Tilt shaft down and remove. To install, place shaft in position. Install and tighten socket head screws.

CONSTANT VELOCITY JOINTS

Disassembly

1) Carefully drive protective cap off joint with small punch and pull cap back so that boot is turned inside out on driveshaft. Remove circlip from groove in

Fig. 1: Removing Ball Hub from Ball Cage

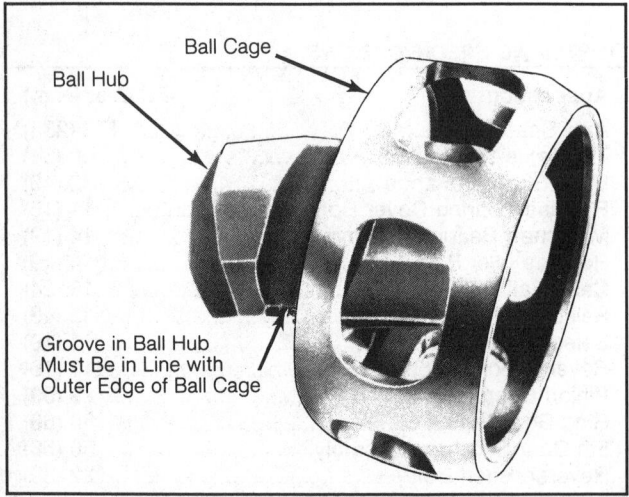

Ball Cage
Ball Hub
Groove in Ball Hub Must Be in Line with Outer Edge of Ball Cage

shaft and slide outer ring towards end of shaft. Press shaft out of center ball hub. Remove cover and boot from shaft.

2) Push ball hub and cage from outer ring. Lift the 6 steel cage balls out of cage, taking care not to damage balls or cage. Rotate center ball hub to position in cage shown in *Fig. 1*. Hub groove must be in line with outer edge of ball cage. Tip hub out of ball cage.

NOTE: **All CV joint components are machined for close tolerance fit with other components; do not intermix components of one CV joint with components of another.**

Reassembly

Clean all components and check for wear or damage. Replace as necessary. Coat all CV joint components with molybdenum grease. Reverse disassembly procedure to assemble CV joint and install on axle. Make sure chamfered end of spline in center ball hub is on same side as large diameter side of outer ring. Check joint for smooth operation throughout entire range of travel.

Fig. 2: Exploded View of Constant Velocity Joints

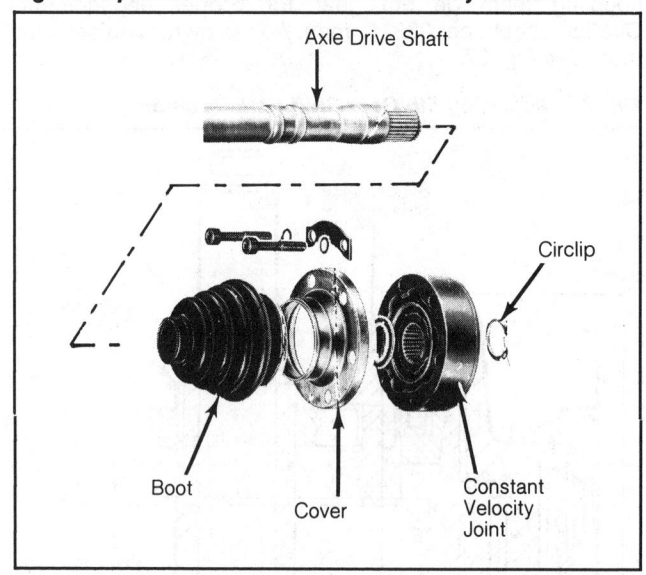

Axle Drive Shaft
Circlip
Boot
Cover
Constant Velocity Joint

REAR WHEEL BEARING HOUSING

Removal

1) With vehicle on ground, remove cotter pin and loosen large nut at center of brake drum. Raise vehicle and position on safety stands. Disconnect axle drive shaft at wheel bearing flange. Wire axle up out of way. Remove brake drum and wheel hub.

2) Remove brake backing plate bolts, and position brake backing plate out of way without disconnecting brake line or parking brake cable. Mark position of bearing housing, spring plate and control arm. Remove 4 bearing housing bolts and remove housing.

Disassembly

1) Place bearing housing in a vise and clamp against spring plate flange. Remove brake components if not previously removed. Using a puller, press axle shaft out of housing. Pry out oil seals, and remove circlip.

2) Remove inner roller bearing race and spacer sleeve. Using a punch that contacts only bearing outer race, drive ball bearing out of housing. Remove roller bearing outer race if necessary.

VOLKSWAGEN VANAGON 4-SPEED (Cont.)

Fig. 3: Exploded View of Rear Wheel Bearing Housing and Related Parts

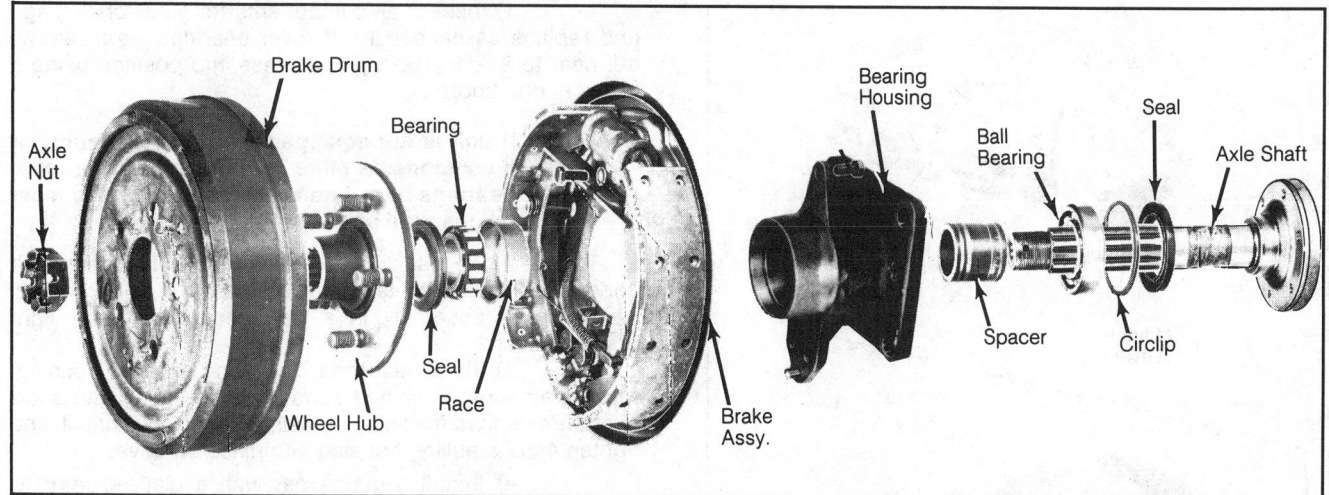

Reassembly

1) To reassemble, reverse disassembly procedure noting that if replacing spacer sleeve on one axle, the one on the opposite axle must also be replaced due to difference in diameter from original equipment.

2) Fill housing with multi-purpose grease prior to inserting spacer sleeve, then drive wheel shaft in with soft punch or pull on with two arm puller. Apply sealer to sealing edge around bearing housing and brake backing plate if installing at this time.

Installation

Install bearing housing on spring plate and control arm, carefully aligning index marks made during removal. To complete installation, reverse removal procedure. Tighten axle nut to specification with vehicle on ground and install a new cotter pin.

TRANSAXLE REMOVAL & INSTALLATION

See the appropriate article in MANUAL TRANSMISSION REMOVAL Section.

TRANSAXLE DISASSEMBLY

1) Before attempting to remove clutch housing, loosen left differential adjusting ring to relieve tension in housing. Mark position of ring before loosening for ease of assembly. Remove (10) housing nuts from studs.

2) Separate housing from transmission case. Remove circlip from input shaft. Pull reverse drive gear forward and unscrew input shaft from stud in end of mainshaft. Pry out drive flange center caps.

3) Remove circlips and wavy spacers from center of flanges. Use 2 levers to pry drive flanges off of output shafts.

4) Remove screws from adjusting ring lock plates and remove lock plates. Measure depth of adjusting ring or mark position in case. Remove adjusting rings.

5) Making sure ring gear teeth stay in mesh with pinion gear, rotate differential toward rear of transmission case and pull out through rear of case.

6) Remove attaching nuts and lift shift housing from gear carrier. Remove pinion bearing retaining ring

from bearing race on differential end of case. Remove selector link, shaft and bracket from face of gear carrier.

7) Remove (9) nuts from gear carrier mounting studs on transmission case. Apply leverage to end of pinion gear and press gear train and carrier out of case.

8) Loosen nut on reverse lever support clamp sleeve. Turn shaft far enough to remove reverse slider and shift fork. Slide shift forks off shift rods. Remove circlip from end of mainshaft.

9) Press out mainshaft and drive pinion at the same time by applying pressure to end of mainshaft. Care must be taken not to damage any gear train components.

COMPONENT DISASSEMBLY & REASSEMBLY

CLUTCH HOUSING

Disassembly

1) Pry retaining springs off spring clips and remove clutch release bearing. Remove release bearing guide sleeve. Remove circlip from end of clutch shaft. Pry off lever and remove return spring and spring collar.

2) Remove clutch shaft lock bolt. Slide shaft outward, pressing out bushing and rubber seals. Remove bushing, seals and flat washer from shaft. Pull shaft inward and out of housing to remove. Pry oil seal out of input shaft hole in housing.

Reassembly

Coat outside of new seal with a sealing compound. Position in hole with lip toward transmission side of housing and drive squarely into place. To complete clutch housing reassembly, reverse disassembly procedure.

DIFFERENTIAL

Disassembly

1) Remove ring gear bolts and drive ring gear off differential housing with a punch. Remove differential cover with a slide hammer. Remove side gears and thrust washers from housing and cover.

2) If necessary, remove roller bearing using a press and supports. Drive out pinion shaft lock pin. Drive pinion shaft out of differential housing. Remove pinion gears, spacer and thrust washer.

Manual Transmissions

VOLKSWAGEN VANAGON 4-SPEED (Cont.)

Fig. 4: Exploded View of Clutch Housing

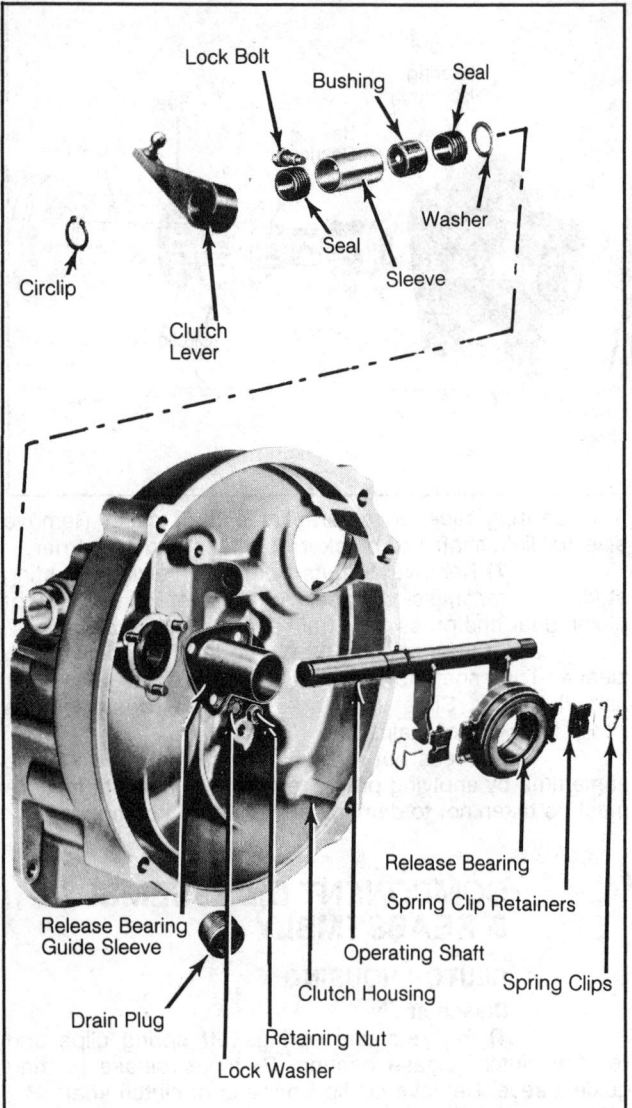

Reassembly

1) Inspect all components for wear or damage and replace as necessary. If roller bearings were removed, heat to 212°F (100°C), and press into position using a press and supports.

NOTE: If unit is not equipped with spacer sleeve, or if components other than pinion shaft or roller bearings have been replaced, axial play must be checked and adjusted.

2) To check axial play, install side gear with short shaft and both large thrust washers in differential cover. Place assembly in a vise and clamp gear tight against cover.

3) Install side gear with long shaft in housing. Place sleeve on machined surface of side gear with short shaft. Position differential housing on cover. Install and tighten 4 bolts pulling housing into place on cover.

4) Install a gauge bar with a dial indicator to end of drive gear shaft in housing. Dial indicator plunger must contact differential housing neck. Press down on side gear shaft and zero dial indicator with .080" (2 mm) preload.

Fig. 6: Measuring Differential Gear Axial Play

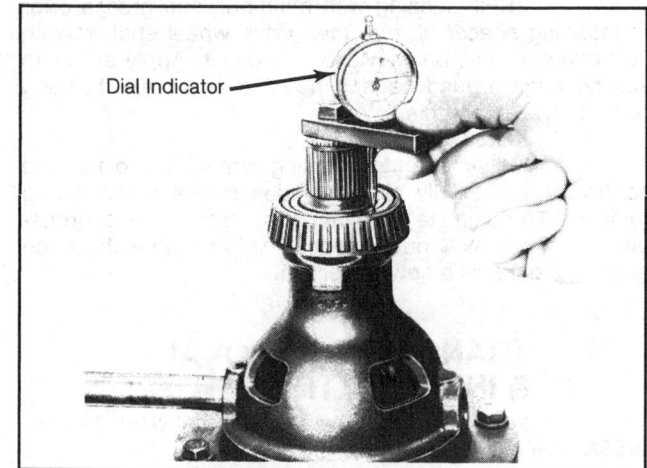

Fig. 5: Exploded View of Differential Assembly

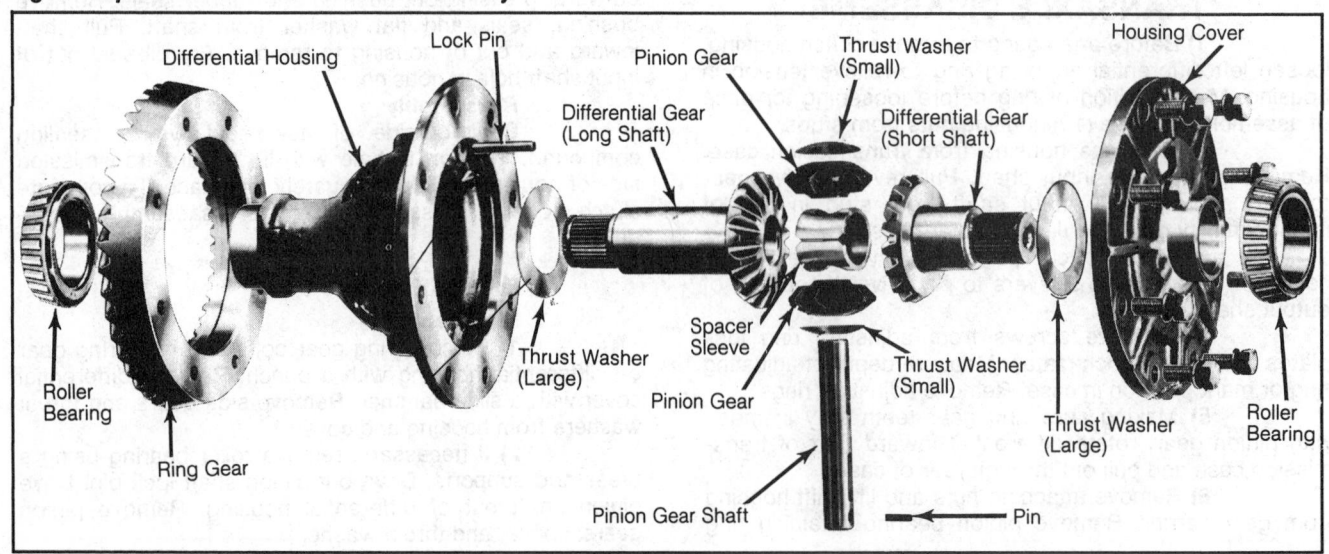

VOLKSWAGEN VANAGON 4-SPEED (Cont.)

5) Move side gear up and down to determine axial play. Play should be .001-.004" (.03-.11 mm). If not to specifications, install a spacer of correct size to obtain specified play.

6) Recheck play after installing correct spacer. Spacers are available in the following lengths: 1.253" (31.84 mm), 1.257" (31.93 mm), 1.261" (32.02 mm), 1.264" (32.11 mm), and 1.268" (32.20 mm).

MAINSHAFT
Disassembly

1) With mainshaft removed from gear carrier, remove 4th gear, needle bearing and synchro ring. Remove circlip and slide off clutch gear assembly. Remove remaining circlip and slide off 3rd gear.

Fig. 7: Exploded View of Mainshaft Assembly

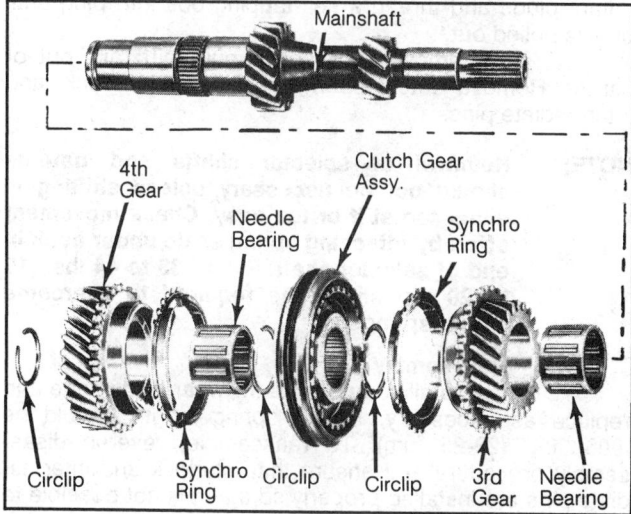

2) Open split in needle bearing cage just enough to slide over mainshaft splines and remove bearing. If necessary, remove spring rings from clutch gear assembly. Then separate synchronizer hub from sleeve.

Reassembly

1) Inspect all parts for wear or damage and replace as necessary. Press synchro ring onto gear by hand and check clearance as shown in illustration.

2) Specified clearance is .040-.075" (1.0-1.9 mm). If clearance is less than .023" (.6 mm), replace synchro ring or gear. If clutch gear assembly was disassembled, reassemble synchronizer hub to sleeve by meshing the teeth in various positions until a free sliding fit is obtained.

3) Spring ring diameter for 3rd-4th gear clutch hub is 2.91" (74 mm) while larger ring for 1st-2nd clutch

Fig. 8: Measuring Synchro Ring-to-Gear Clearance

gear should be 3.07" (78 mm). Open ends of springs on opposite sides of assembly must be installed 120° apart with angled ends over the keys.

NOTE: **Synchronizer rings must be installed in exactly the same relationships that existed before removal. The 1st gear ring can be identified by having no notches in blank area on outer edge. Synchronizers for 2nd, 3rd and 4th gears each have 3 notches (depressions) in blank area on outer edge. Replacement synchronizers for 2nd, 3rd and 4th gears have teeth completely around the outer edge with no blanked off areas.**

4) To complete reassembly of mainshaft, reverse disassembly procedure, noting the following procedures: Install clutch gear assembly so that side with .040" (1 mm) deep groove is toward 4th gear, and the side of the clutch gear hub having the wide chamfer on teeth goes toward 3rd gear.

DRIVE PINION SHAFT
Disassembly

1) Hold 4th gear down tight against spring on shaft. This will collapse spring and ease removal of circlip on end of shaft. With circlip removed, press shaft out of inner bearing race while supporting 4th gear.

2) Remove spring and next circlip. Remove 3rd gear, 2nd gear, needle bearing, synchro rings, circlip, 1st/2nd synchro assembly, 1st gear and needle bearing.

Fig. 9: Exploded View of Pinion Shaft Assembly

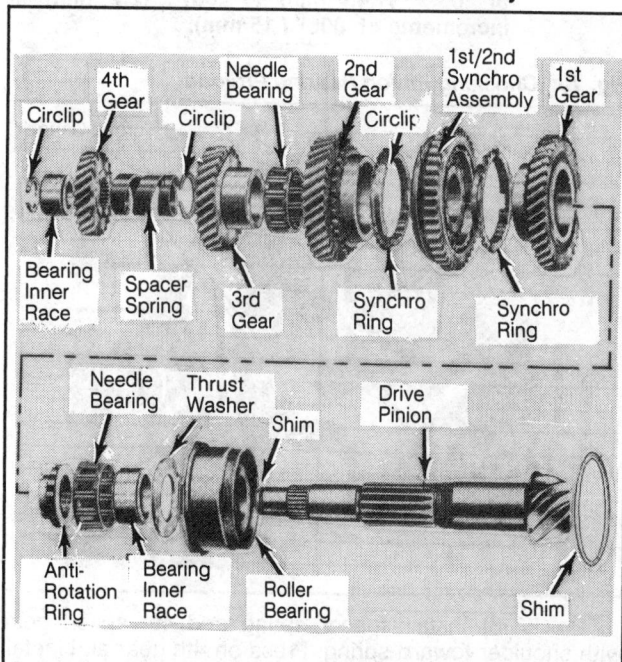

3) Note that inner needle bearing race is threaded and notched on end away from pinion. Place pinion in appliance (VW293) to hold notched race, and place splined socket over pinion shaft. Turn shaft counterclockwise to remove inner race/nut.

4) If necessary, disassemble synchro assembly hub. Press off tapered roller bearing with outer race. If required, use separating tool and press off inner race.

VOLKSWAGEN VANAGON 4-SPEED (Cont.)

Reassembly

1) Inspect all parts for wear or damage and replace as necessary. Press 1st and 2nd gear synchro rings onto gears and check clearance of 3rd and 4th gear.

2) Specified clearance for new parts is .043-.071" (1.1-1.8 mm), with a minimum clearance of .023" (.6 mm) for used parts. If 1st/2nd synchro assembly was disassembled, reassemble in the same manner as for 3rd/4th synchro assembly.

3) Heat tapered roller bearing to about 212°F (100°C) and press into position. Allow to cool to room temperature.

4) Heat inner race to about 140°F (60°C) and press on shaft by hand as far as possible. Place pinion in same appliance used for disassembly and tighten inner race to 144 ft. lbs. (195 N.m).

5) Check pinion bearing preload by installing shaft in transmission case and tightening retaining ring. Check for turning torque of 5-18 INCH lbs. (.6-.2 N.m) for new bearing and 3-6 INCH lbs. (.3-.7 N.m) for used bearing.

6) Install needle bearing, 1st gear, 1st/2nd synchro assembly with synchro rings, and install circlip. Synchro ring grooves must align with keys when pressing on. Assemble needle bearing, 2nd gear and 3rd gear on shaft, then fit circlip properly in groove.

7) Check axial play between circlip and 3rd gear. Correct play is .004-.010" (.10-.25 mm), with the lower limit preferred. Install proper circlip to obtain specified clearance.

NOTE: 3rd gear circlips are available in thicknesses of .057" (1.45 mm) to .087" (2.2 mm) in increments of .006" (.15 mm).

Fig. 10: Checking Pinion Bearing Preload

8) Install spacer spring and 4th speed gear with shoulder toward spring. Press on 4th gear and install circlip.

TRANSMISSION CASE
Disassembly

Remove reverse gear shaft circlip from inside gear case. Remove reverse drive gear, shaft and needle bearing as a unit with a plastic hammer. Remove lock rings from mainshaft needle bearing and drive bearing out.

Reassembly

Insert shaft, bearing and reverse drive gear as a unit. Drive mainshaft needle bearing in case with lettered side of bearing towards the driver. Install lock rings.

GEAR CARRIER
Disassembly

1) Remove selector link shaft and selector link. Remove 2 bolts and then remove link bracket. Remove drive pinion bearing lock bolt.

2) Using a mandrel, press out mainshaft bearing and pinion shaft bearing. Loosen clamp sleeve and remove with reverse lever support and union nut from carrier.

3) Remove (4) relay shaft bracket bolts, brackets and relay shaft. Detent plugs and shift rails should only be removed if necessary. To remove, drill out detent plugs and thread a self-tapping bolt into plug until plug is pulled out.

4) Remove circlips and pull shift rails out of carrier. Remove detent springs, balls and interlock, and intermediate pins.

NOTE: Removal of selector shafts and detents should not be necessary unless shifting is either too stiff or too easy. Check movement effort by attaching spring scale under hook in end of selector shaft. Pull of 33 to 44 lbs. (15 to 20 kg) should be required to overcome detent springs.

Reassembly

Check all components for wear or damage and replace as necessary. Detent spring length should be .906-.984" (23-25 mm). To reassemble, reverse disassembly procedure and ensure that interlock and intermediate pins are installed properly so that it is not possible to engage 2 gears at the same time.

Fig. 11: Vanagon Shift Housing Assembly

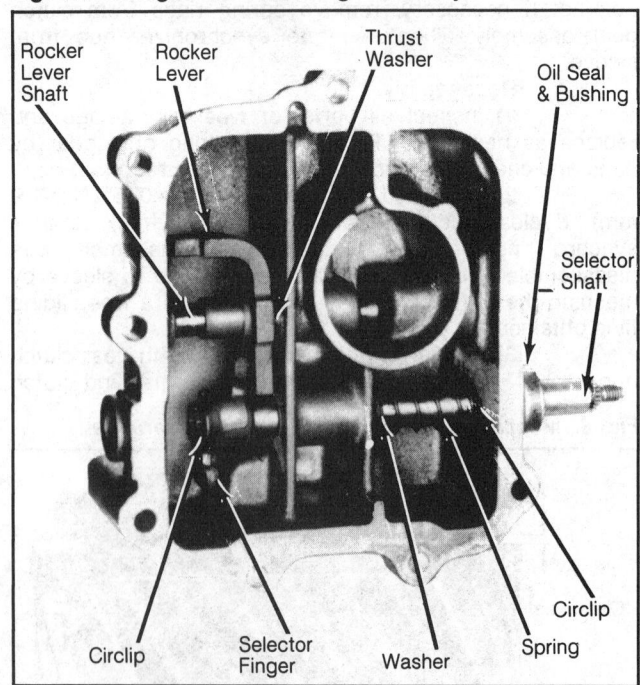

VOLKSWAGEN VANAGON 4-SPEED (Cont.)

Fig. 12: Exploded View of Gear Carrier Assembly

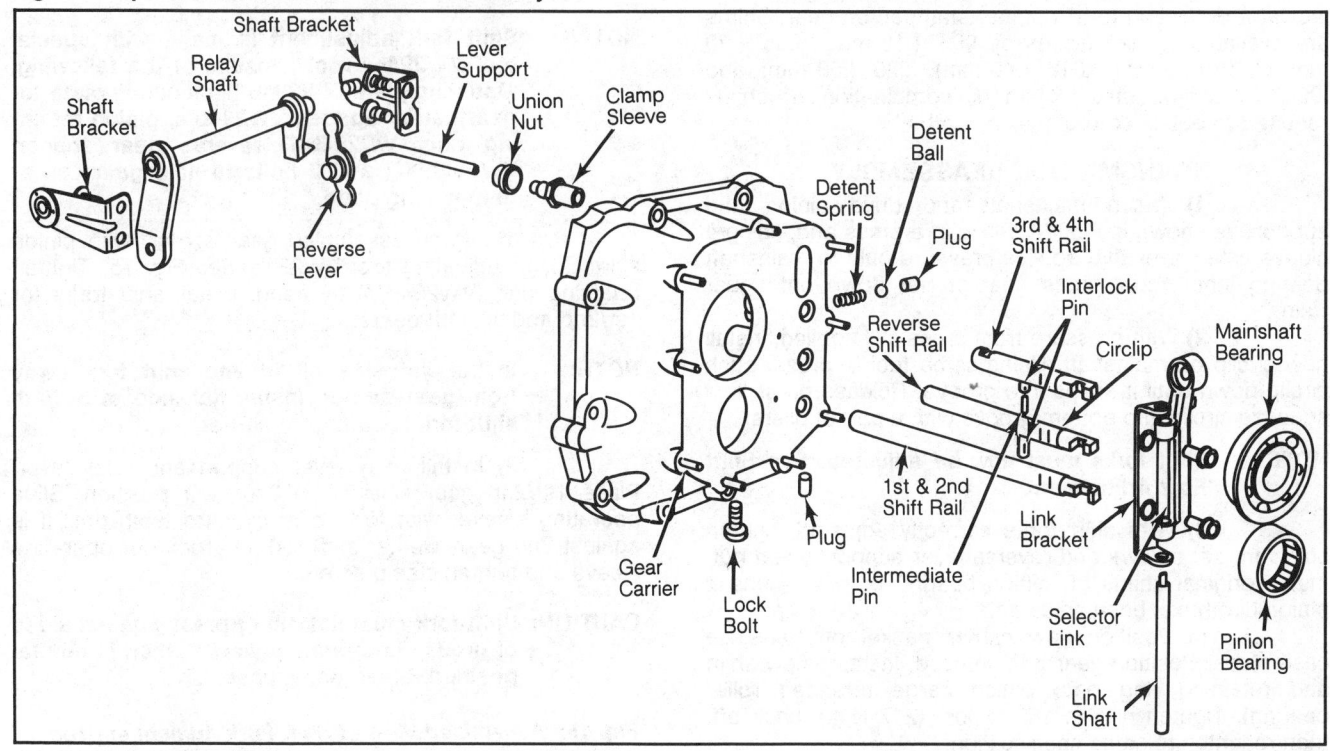

SHIFT HOUSING
Disassembly
1) Drill and tap plugs for rocker lever shaft. Remove rocker lever shaft, rocker lever and thrust washer. Remove backup light switch plug and seal. Remove selector shaft oil seal and bushing.

2) Remove circlips from selector shaft. Push selector shaft out of shift housing. As selector shaft slides out, remove selector finger, washer and spring.
Reassembly
To reassemble shift housing, reverse disassembly procedures and install new seals.

TRANSAXLE REASSEMBLY & ADJUSTMENT

PINION DEPTH

NOTE: Pinion bearing preload must be correctly adjusted before adjusting pinion depth; see Drive Pinion Shaft Reassembly

1) Pinion depth is checked using Universal Measuring Bar (VW385/1). Screw in right adjusting ring until ring outer surface is flush with transaxle case. Install magnetic measuring plate (VW385/17) on end of pinion gear.

2) Set dimension "A" (see Fig. 13) to 2.95" (75 mm) by sliding setting ring to correct distance from center of measuring bar. Slide 2 centering discs (VW385/4) onto measuring bar until they contact setting rings.

3) Attach measuring pin (VW385/14) with extension (VW385/16) to gauge pin hole in center of measuring bar. Attach a dial indicator to end of bar.

4) Position measuring bar in transaxle case. Install left adjusting ring in case until outer edge is flush with case. Loosen second setting ring and slide out with centering ring until measuring bar can just barely be turned by hand. Tighten screw in setting ring.

Fig. 13: Installation of Pinion Depth Checking Tools

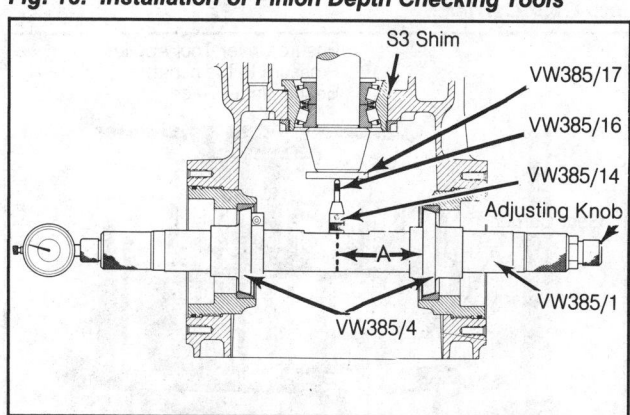

5) Using setting block (VW385/1), zero dial indicator. Turn measuring bar by hand until measuring pin extension is against measuring plate on pinion gear. Turn bar back and forth over center. Record maximum reading on dial indicator. Read deviation number stamped on ring gear.

NOTE: Although production gears are no longer marked with deviation "r" in .01 mm readings, replacement gear sets will have this number. Shims (S3) must be installed between pinion bearing shoulder and gear case to correct axial placement of pinion gear for proper meshing with ring gear teeth.

VOLKSWAGEN VANAGON 4-SPEED (Cont.)

6) To find correct shim thickness (S3), add dial indicator deflection to "r" number stamped on gear. Shims are available in thicknesses of .006" (.15 mm), .008" (.20 mm), .012" (.30 mm), .016" (.40 mm), .020" (.50 mm), and .024" (.60 mm). Install shim or combination of shims required to obtain correct pinion depth.

TRANSMISSION REASSEMBLY

1) Mesh mainshaft and drive pinion and support as shown in *Fig. 14*. Place in a press and, using a sleeve type driver that applies pressure only to mainshaft bearing inner race, press gear carrier down onto gear train.

2) With pressure from press still applied, install new circlip on mainshaft. Using same tool in press, push circlip down until it snaps into groove. Release press and squeeze circlip into bottom groove with a pair of pliers.

NOTE: **Shift forks must now be adjusted. See Shift Fork Adjustment.**

3) With shift forks correctly adjusted, tighten shift fork set screws and reverse lever support union nut. Install original shims on pinion bearing or new shims if pinion depth has been adjusted.

4) Position new carrier gasket on transaxle case studs. Position gear train in case. Install a new shim and retaining ring onto pinion (large threaded roller bearing). Tighten ring to 160 ft. lbs. (217 N.m), back off, then retighten to same specification.

5) Install and tighten gear carrier nuts in a diagonal pattern. Install selector link, bracket and link shaft. Tighten bolts. Install shift housing using new gasket. Make sure rocker lever and selector finger engages selector shafts correctly. Tighten shift housing bolts.

Fig. 14: *Pressing Mainshaft and Pinion Shaft into Gear Carrier*

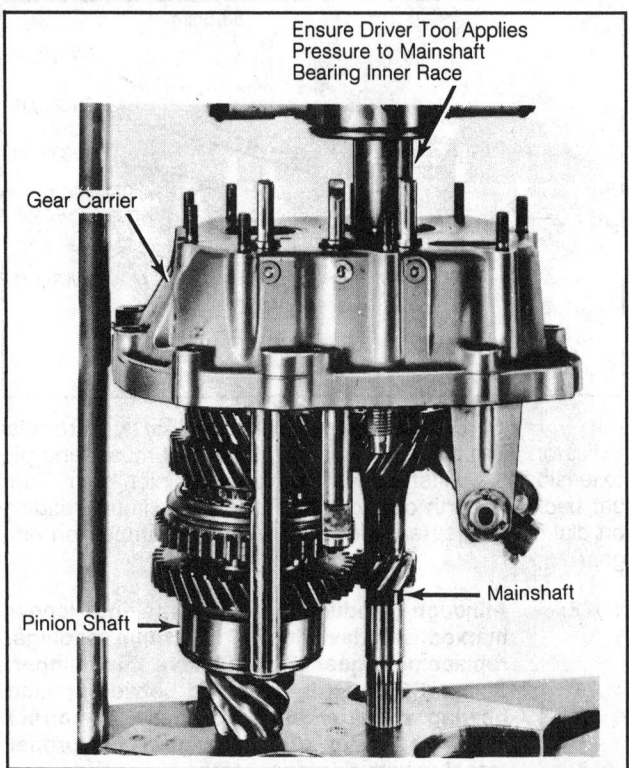

SHIFT FORK ADJUSTMENT

NOTE: **Shift fork adjustment is made with special tool VW294b. Tool consists of the following: Mounting plate, VW294b/2; mounting plate-to-gear carrier spacer, VW294b/4; pinion retaining ring, VW294b/7; reverse gear spacer, VW294b/10; and 2 bolts to hold gear carrier to mounting plate.**

1) Attach assembled gear carrier, with pinion shim S3, to adjusting tool VW294b. *See Fig. 15.* Tighten retaining ring (VW294b/7) by hand. Install shift forks for 1st/2nd and 3rd/4th gears.

NOTE: **Install flat side of 1st/2nd shift fork away from gear carrier. Install flat side of 3rd/4th shift fork toward gear carrier.**

2) Install relay lever support and relay lever. Place 1st/2nd gear selector in 2nd gear position. Slide operating sleeve, with fork, over synchro teeth until it is against 2nd gear. Center shift fork in groove of operating sleeve and tighten clamp screw.

CAUTION: **Shift fork must not rub or press against sides of groove in operating sleeve when in neutral position. Clearance must exist.**

Fig. 15: *Assembled View of Shift Fork Adjustment Tools*

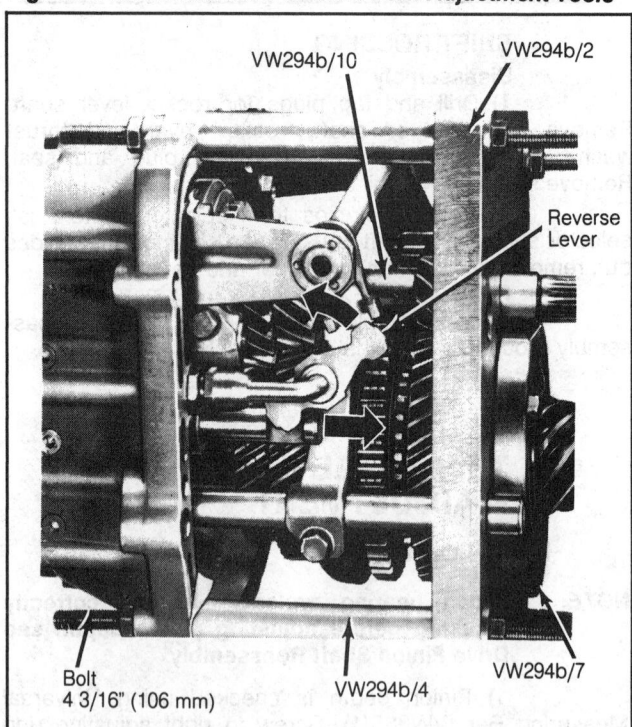

3) Select 1st and 2nd gear position several times while turning mainshaft. Check clearance of shift fork in operating sleeve in each position. If necessary, reposition shift fork until there is same amount of clearance on selector shaft in both end positions, then tighten clamp screw.

4) Place 3rd/4th gear selector shaft in 3rd gear position and adjust 3rd/4th gear shift fork in same manner as 1st/2nd.

VOLKSWAGEN VANAGON 4-SPEED (Cont.)

CAUTION: For correct adjustment of 3rd/4th gears, mainshaft bearing must be pressed fully into gear carrier housing.

5) Place reverse gear selector shaft into reverse gear position. Adjust reverse gear so that sliding gear is fully in mesh with teeth on operating sleeve for 1st/2nd gear. Tighten union nut on relay lever support.

6) Shift out of reverse gear and press sliding gear lightly toward gear carrier. Clearance between reverse gear and 2nd gear on mainshaft must be a minimum of .020" (.5 mm).

7) Engage 2nd gear and check clearance between operating sleeve and reverse sliding gear. Adjust if necessary. Check interlock mechanism. When gear is engaged, it must not be possible to engage any other gear.

SIDE BEARING PRELOAD & RING GEAR BACKLASH

1) Remove oil seals from side bearing adjusting rings. Install adjusting ring on ring gear side of case and screw in until ring is approximately .004-.008" (.1-.2 mm) below measuring surface of case.

2) Install differential in case, with ring gear on left side. Install opposite adjusting ring and tighten until differential is supported without preload.

3) Turn transaxle so that differential is at top and install spacer bridge (VW381/8) on dowel pins to prevent case spreading. Install a torque wrench on ring gear side of differential.

4) Spin differential 15-20 turns in each direction while lubricating the side bearings with hypoid oil. While turning, screw in adjusting ring on side opposite ring gear until preload measured on torque wrench is 26-30 INCH lbs. (3.0-3.4 N.m) for new bearings and 3-6 INCH lbs. (.3-.7 N.m) for used bearings.

5) Measure and record depth to which adjusting rings are screwed in. Mark position of adjusting rings in case. Remove adjusting rings and differential. Rings must be installed on the same side from which they are removed.

6) Install transmission gear train. *See Transmission Reassembly.* Install differential and adjusting rings. Turn adjusting rings until marks made during side bearing preload are aligned. Install a measuring bracket (VW381/7) on ring gear bolts.

7) Mount a spacer bar and dial indicator across ring gear end of case. Turn mainshaft until dial indicator stem contacts measuring bracket on ring gear. Continue turning mainshaft until dial indicator shows .060" (1.5 mm) preload. Lock pinion shaft with a clamping bar bolted on gear carrier.

8) Turn ring gear by hand away from dial indicator until it is stopped by locked pinion. Now zero dial indicator. Again turn ring gear by hand toward dial indicator until it is stopped by locked pinion. The reading on dial indicator is ring gear backlash.

9) Backlash should be .006-.010" (.15-.25 mm). If backlash not to specifications, screw one adjusting ring inward and the other ring outward by exactly the same amount until backlash is within specification.

10) Recheck backlash measuring procedure at three other points on ring gear, 90° apart. All measurements must be within specification and not vary more than .002" (.06 mm).

11) Install new oil seals and "O" rings in adjusting rings if not previously done. Coat outer surface of adjusting rings with an anti-rust preventative sealer. Install new adjusting ring lock plates and tighten screws evenly.

NOTE: Do not tighten left hand adjusting ring until the clutch housing has been fitted and the nuts tightened.

FINAL ASSEMBLY

Install clutch housing and tighten nuts to specification. Install thrust rings, axle drive shaft flanges and new circlips. It may be necessary to lift differential pinion gear shaft slightly to gain clearance for installation of circlips. Install new plastic caps in center of axle drive shaft flanges.

TRANSAXLE SPECIFICATIONS

Application	Measurement
Synchro Ring-to-Gear Clearance	.040-.067" (1.0-1.7 mm)
Ring and Pinion Backlash	.006-.010" (.15-.25 mm)
Pinion Bearing Preload	
New Bearings	5-18 INCH Lbs. (.6-2.0 N.m)
Used Bearings	3-6 INCH Lbs. (.3-.7 N.m)
Side Bearing Preload	
New Bearings	26-30 INCH Lbs. (3.0-3.4 N.m)
Used Bearings	3-6 INCH Lbs. (.3-.7 N.m)

TIGHTENING SPECIFICATIONS

Application	Ft. Lbs. (N.m)
Pinion Shaft Retainer Ring	160 (217)
Ring Gear Bolts	36 (49)
Gear Carrier	14 (19)
Clutch Housing	14 (19)
Reverse Shift Shaft Bracket	18 (24)
Clamp Sleeve	32 (43)
Union Nut	21 (28)
Shift Housing	14 (19)
Drive Shaft Flange Bolts	32 (43)
Wheel Hub-to-Axle Shaft Nut	253 (343)
Transaxle-to-Engine	22 (30)

Manual Transmissions

VOLVO 4-SPEED

DL, GL, GLT Turbo,
GLE, Bertone, Diesel

DESCRIPTION

Transmission is a 4-speed fully synchronized unit with all gears in constant mesh except reverse gear. Gears on mainshaft are carried by needle rollers. Input shaft and drive pinion gear are an integral shaft which is carried by needle rollers located in main pinion gear and a ball bearing located in rear cover. Depending on model application, an overdrive unit may be bolted to rear of transmission. Transmissions with overdrive are identified as M46 and without overdrive as M45.

LUBRICATION & ADJUSTMENT

See the appropriate article in MANUAL TRANS-MISSION SERVICING Section.

TROUBLE SHOOTING

HARD SHIFTING

Clutch may not release fully due to deformed clutch disc or being out of adjustment. Pilot bearing seized, damaged or dry. Selector plate damaged. Shift forks bent.

SLIPS OUT OF GEAR

Selector plate damaged or worn. Detent balls and springs worn or broken. Shift forks bent or worn. Transmission and clutch housing misaligned.

NOISY OPERATION

Insufficient or wrong type lubricant. Worn or damaged bushings and/or gears. Worn splines.

NOTE: **When checking transmission for noise, ensure that it is not coming from other parts of the drive line.**

SERVICE (IN-VEHICLE)

NOTE: **The following procedure is for "M45" transmissions (without overdrive).**

TRANSMISSION REAR OIL SEAL
Removal

Jack up rear of vehicle and place on floor stands. Drain transmission oil and disconnect propeller shaft "U" joint. Remove flange nut. Using a puller (2261), pull flange from mainshaft. With tool (5069), pull oil seal from rear cover.

Installation

Using tool (5064), drive new oil seal into rear cover with seal lip facing rear cover. Install flange onto mainshaft using tool (5149) and tighten nut to specification. Reverse removal procedure for remaining components and refill transmission with oil.

REMOVAL & INSTALLATION

See the appropriate article in MANUAL TRANS-MISSION REMOVAL Section.

TRANSMISSION DISASSEMBLY

1) Fit transmission in work stand and drain lubricant. Remove back-up light switch and overdrive switch (if equipped). Remove transmission top cover and lift out detent spring and ball. Remove selector plate assembly, return spring, gasket, glide washers and shifter lock pin.

Fig. 1: Selector Plate Assembly

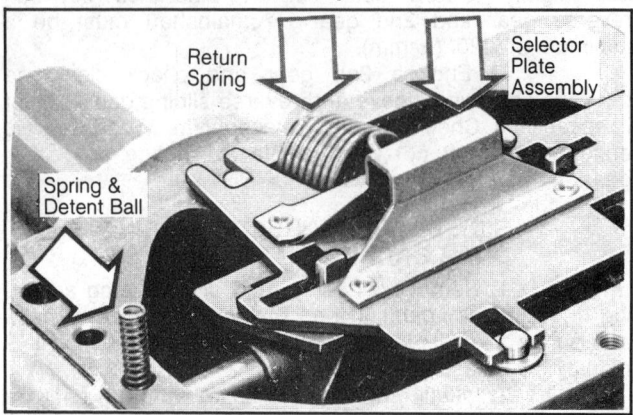

2) On M46 transmission, remove overdrive unit from intermediate flange. On all models, remove gearshift carrier assembly. On M46, remove sleeve over gearshift rod joint and knock out rear pin. Turn rod and knock out front pin, then remove rod. Unbolt intermediate housing from transmission and remove with gasket and shims.

Fig. 2: Removing Gearshift Carrier Assembly

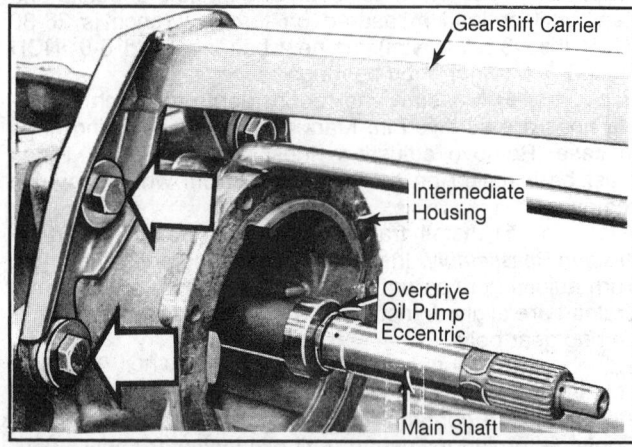

M46 Model Shown; M45 Model Similar.

3) On all models, remove selector rail, shifter and shift forks. On M45, use adapter (5149) and socket to remove flange nut, then pull off flange. Remove speedometer driven gear and take off rear cover with gasket and shims. Remove speedometer drive gear.

4) On M46, remove lock ring and pull off overdrive oil pump eccentric. Catch and retain drive key. Remove lock ring and spacer ring for main shaft bearing.

5) On all models, place adapter (2985) between input shaft and front synchronizer ring. Using puller and adapters (5058, 5147 and 5148) as required, pull off mainshaft bearing and remove thrust washer.

6) Remove clutch fork, bell housing, gasket and shims. On case iron housing models, remove intermediate shaft rear bearing race by tapping shaft back until race is free, then tap forward until front race can be

VOLVO 4-SPEED (Cont.)

Fig. 3: Removing Mainshaft Bearing

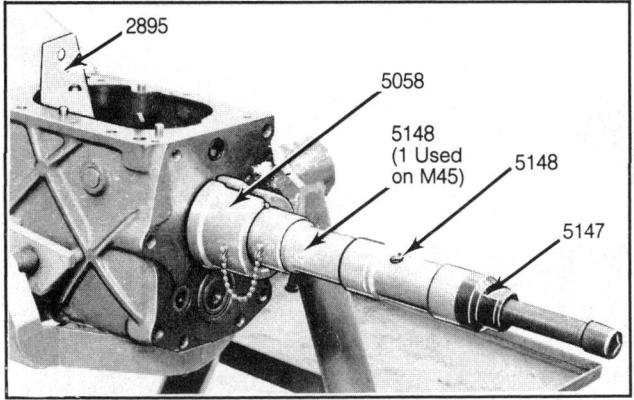

M46 Model Shown; M45 Model Similar.

removed. On aluminum housing models, tap shafts only enough to install puller (5177), and remove races.

7) On all models, pull out input shaft, then remove 4th gear synchronizer ring. Lift out mainshaft, intermediate shaft, and reverse gear and shaft. It may be necessary to tap reverse gear shaft back for removal.

8) Remove reverse gear shift fork and seal for selector rail. Using puller (5131), remove intermediate shaft bearings.

COMPONENT DISASSEMBLY & REASSEMBLY

MAINSHAFT

Disassembly

1) Remove 1st gear, needle bearings and 1st gear synchronizer ring from mainshaft. Remove synchronizer sleeves and synchronizer rings from each end of mainshaft.

2) Remove circlips retaining each synchronizer hub. Using tool (2853), press off 2nd gear and 1st-2nd synchronizer hub. Reverse shaft and press off 3rd gear and 3rd-4th synchronizer hub. Clean and inspect all parts for wear or damage, replace as necessary.

Reassembly

1) Assemble synchronizer sleeve assemblies, making sure insert springs are correctly installed. Using

Fig. 4: View of Synchro Hub

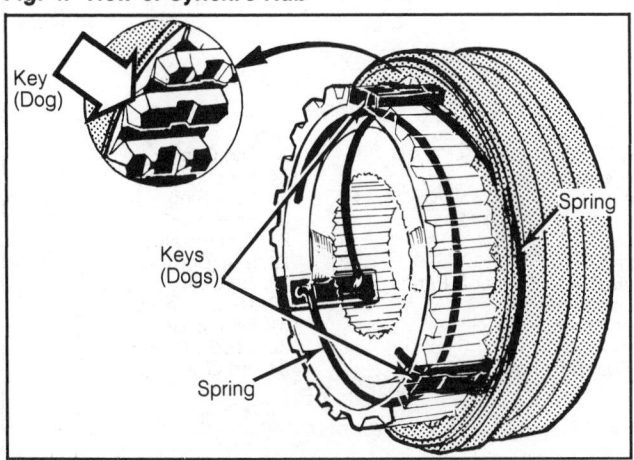

Key (Dog)

Keys (Dogs)

Spring

Spring

tool (2852), install 3rd gear and synchronizer ring, then 3rd-4th synchronizer hubs on mainshaft. Install lock ring.

2) Using same tool, install 2nd gear and synchronizer ring and 1st-2nd synchronizer hub on mainshaft, then install lock ring. Install 1st gear and synchronizer ring.

TRANSMISSION REASSEMBLY

1) Using drivers (5064, 5065, 2867 and 1801), install seals in clutch housing, rear cover (M45 only) and selector rail hole. Install intermediate shaft end bearings (if removed) noting that small end bearing is different for diesel applications.

2) On aluminum housing models, determine intermediate shaft preload. Place intermediate shaft in housing and use drift (5180) to install bearing races. Install clutch housing with gasket and tighten bolts to 25-35 ft. lbs. (34-48 N.m). Turn transmission vertically so clutch housing is down. Tap rear race in position so that clearance is eliminated and shaft turns in a slightly sluggish manner.

3) Using a depth gauge, measure distance to outer race from rear surface of housing. Add measured distance to gasket thickness of .010" (.25 mm) plus preload of .001-.003" (.03-.08 mm). Select a shim within this range and set aside for reassembly. Shims are available in the following thicknesses: .002" (.05 mm), .004" (.10 mm), .006" (.15 mm), .014" (.35 mm), .020" (.50 mm), .027" (.70 mm) and .039" (1.0 mm).

4) Remove clutch housing and gasket, then remove intermediate shaft. *See DISASSEMBLY procedures.* On all models, install reverse gear shifter and lock ring. Install reverse gear and shaft. Shaft end should be at least .002" (.05 mm) below housing face.

5) Adjust clearance between reverse gear and shift fork to give .004-.040" (.10-1.0 mm) clearance. Adjust by tapping shift fork pivot pin in or out with a punch. Place intermediate shaft in bottom of housing, then position mainshaft in housing. With positioning lock ring fitted to bearing, fit thrust washer and bearing on mainshaft.

Fig. 5: Adjusting Clearance Between Reverse Gear and Shift Fork

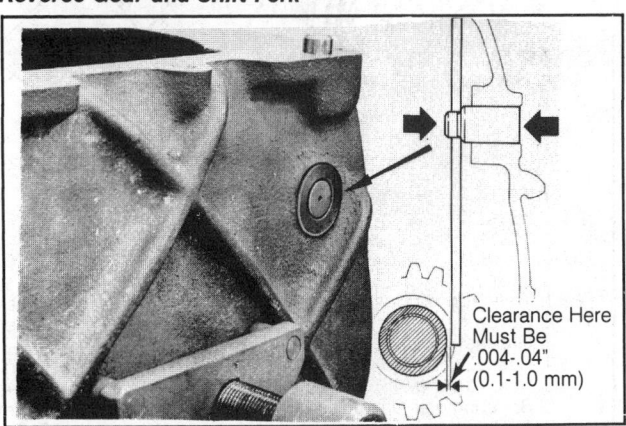

Clearance Here Must Be .004-.04" (0.1-1.0 mm)

6) Ensure that gears do not interfere with each other and use press tool (2831) to press mainshaft bearing into position. If bearing does not align correctly, use spacer between tool spindle and housing front end. Press in until positioning ring is flush with housing face.

Manual Transmissions

VOLVO 4-SPEED (Cont.)

Fig. 6: *Exploded View of Volvo M45 and M46 4-Speed Transmission Assembly*

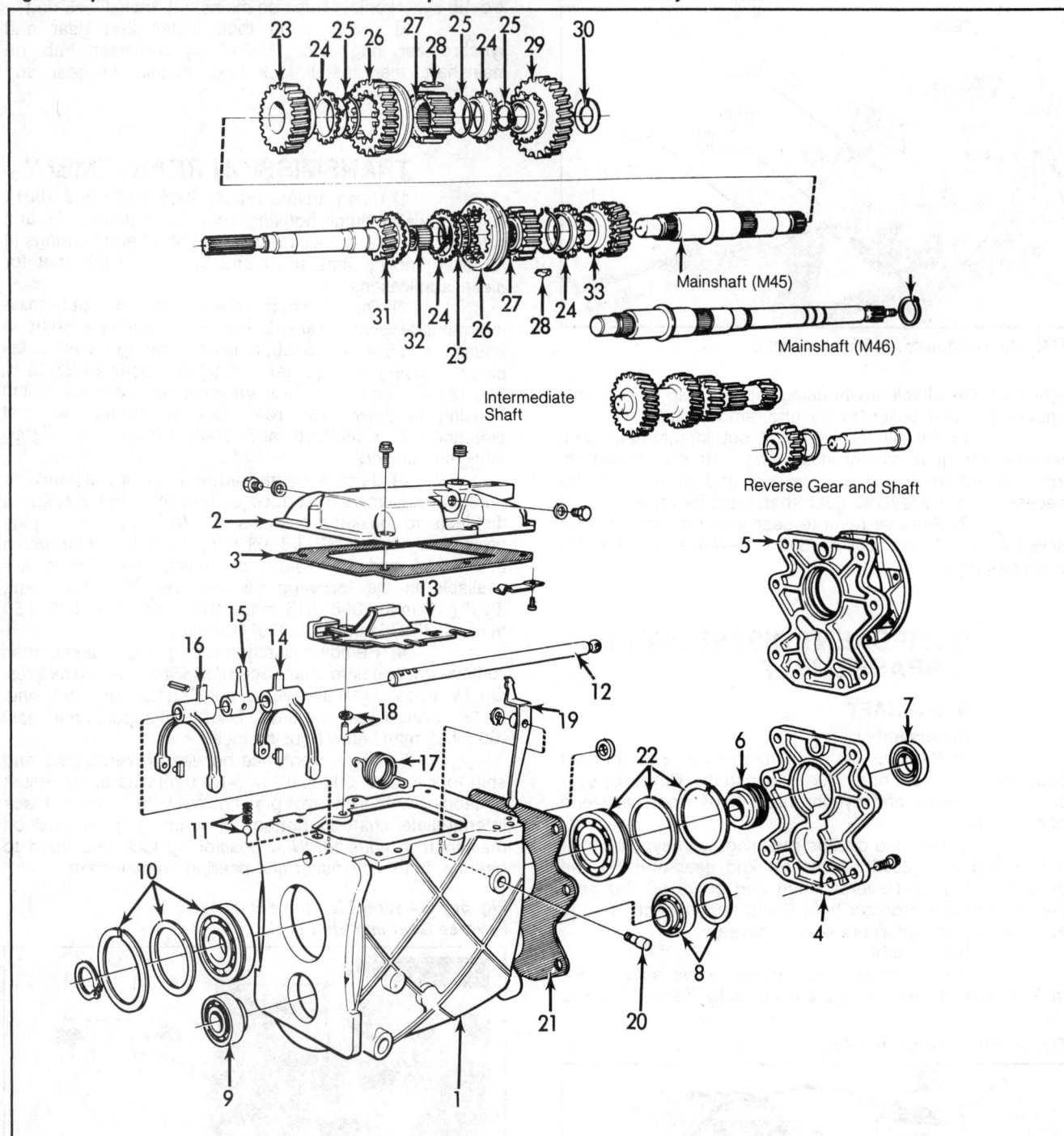

1. Transmission Case
2. Cover
3. Gasket
4. Rear Cover (M45)
5. Rear Cover (M46)
6. Speedometer Drive Gear
7. Seal (M45)
8. Intermediate Shaft Rear Bearing & Shim
9. Intermediate Shaft Front Bearing
10. Input Shaft Bearing & Shim
11. Detent Spring and Ball
12. Selector Rail
13. Selector Plate Assembly
14. 1-2 Shift Fork
15. Shifter
16. 3-4 Shift Fork
17. Return Spring
18. Selector Plate Glide Washer & Pin
19. Reverse Gear Shifter
20. Shifter Pivot Pin
21. Rear Gasket
22. Mainshaft Rear Bearing & Shims
23. 2nd Gear
24. Synchro Ring
25. Lock Ring
26. Sleeve
27. Synchro Hub
28. Key (Dog)
29. 1st Gear
30. Thrust Washer
31. Input Shaft
32. Needle Bearing
33. 3rd Gear

VOLVO 4-SPEED (Cont.)

Fig. 7: Installing Mainshaft Bearing

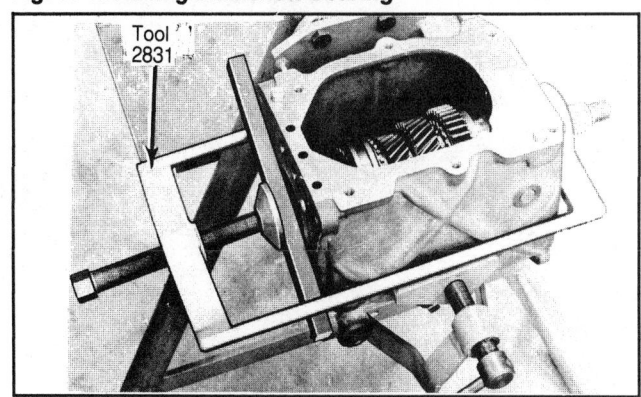

7) On M46, install lock ring on mainshaft and insert key for oil pump eccentric. Install eccentric and lock ring.

8) On all models, grease and install input shaft roller bearings, then position 4th gear synchronizer ring in synchronizer hub. Push input shaft into position on mainshaft. Lift intermediate shaft so that bearings are correctly positioned in housing.

9) Pull out input shaft so that spacer ring can be installed on bearing, then push shaft in so ring is against housing. On all housing models, install outer bearing races for intermediate shaft bearings.

10) On aluminum housing models, use depth gauge and measure distance from front of input bearing to surface of housing, then measure distance from clutch housing surface to bottom of bearing seat.

11) Add .010" (.25 mm) to clutch housing distance, then subtract distance of input bearing extension above housing. Choose shims to give .0004-.008" (.01-.20 mm) end play. Shims are available in the following thicknesses: .024" (.60 mm), .029" (.75 mm), .035" (.90 mm) and .039" (1.0 mm).

Fig. 8: Measuring Clutch Housing Surface to Bearing Seat

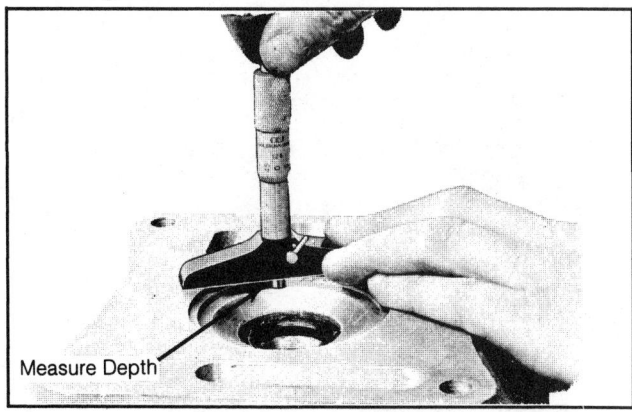

Measure Depth

12) On all models, attach clutch housing with shims, clutch fork and release bearing. Turn transmission to vertical position with housing DOWN. On aluminum housing models, tap intermediate bearing race in with drift (5180) until clearance is gone and slight drag is felt on shaft when rotated.

13) On cast iron housing models, determine shim thickness requirement for intermediate shaft to give .001" (.025 mm) to .004" (.10 mm) axial clearance. Measure distance from rear housing surface to intermediate shaft

outer race and add gasket thickness of .010" (.25 mm). Subtract axial clearance of .001" (.025 mm) to .004" (.10 mm) to determine shim thickness. Shims are available in the following thicknesses: .002" (.05 mm), .004" (.10 mm), .006" (.15 mm), .014" (.35 mm), .020" (.50 mm), .027" (.70 mm) and .039" (1.0 mm).

14) Measure distance from mainshaft bearing to housing rear surface, and distance from rear cover surface to bottom of rear bearing seat. Allow for gasket thickness of .010" (.25 mm) and select mainshaft shim thickness to give .0004-.008" (.01-.20 mm) axial clearance. Shims are available in the following thicknesses: .024" (.60 mm), .029" (.75 mm), .035" (.90 mm) and .039" (1.0 mm).

Fig. 9: Measuring Rear Housing Surface to Bearing Seat

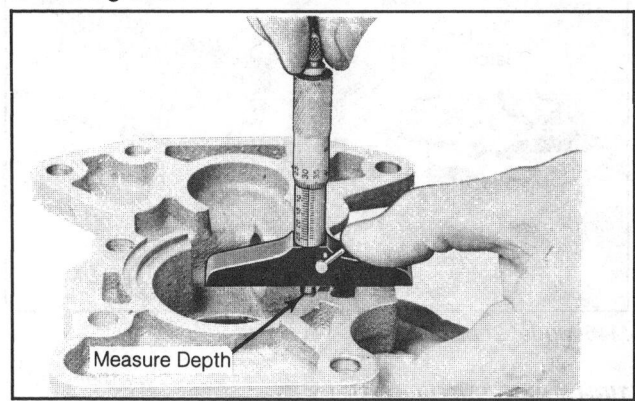

Measure Depth

15) On M45, install speedometer drive gear, gasket and previously determined shim pack. Drive gear flange must face toward bearing. Grease mainshaft rear shim and place in rear cover, then install rear cover. Tighten 2 outer (lower) bolts finger tight, then install drive flange. Install speedometer driven gear with new "O" ring.

16) On M46, install shift forks and gear selector rail. Position gasket and shim pack for intermediate shaft on transmission housing. Use grease to keep mainshaft shim pack in place and install intermediate housing. Tighten 2 outer (lower) bolts finger tight. Install gearshift rod and sleeve on joint.

Fig. 10: Installing Shift Forks and Shifter

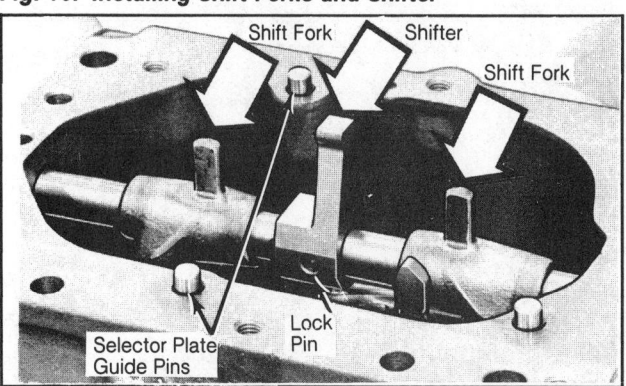

Shift Fork   Shifter   Shift Fork

Selector Plate Guide Pins   Lock Pin

17) On all models, install gearshift carrier and tighten rear cover bolts to 25-35 ft. lbs. (34-48 N.m). On M45, install shift forks and gear selector rail. Install overdrive on M46. On all models, install lock pin for shifter and glide washers for selector plate assembly. Install selector plate assembly and return spring.

Manual Transmissions
VOLVO 4-SPEED (Cont.)

18) Install gearshift lever without lock screw and lock ring to check operation. Hold selector plate down with palm of hand and check gearshift operation. Correct as necessary, then remove gearshift lever. Install detent ball and spring, then install top cover with new gasket. Install overdrive switch, back-up light switch and wires at overdrive solenoid as applicable. Fill with transmission fluid.

Fig. 11: Checking Gearshift Operation

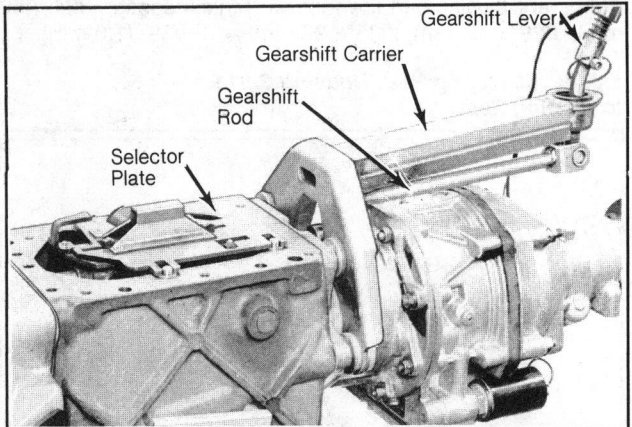

M46 Model Shown.

TIGHTENING SPECIFICATIONS

Application	Ft. Lbs. (N.m)
Clutch Housing-to-Transmission	25-35 (34-48)
Rear Cover Attaching Bolts	25-35 (34-48)
Drive Flange Nut	65-80 (88-109)
Shift Cover Bolts	11-18 (15-24)

SECTION 8

IMPORT OVERDRIVES & TRANSFER CASES

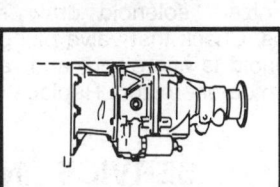

NOTE: ALSO SEE GENERAL INDEX.

Overdrives

LAYCOCK "J" TYPE

**Volvo DL, GL, GLE, GT,
Coupe & Diesel**

DESCRIPTION & OPERATION

Overdrive is a hydraulically operated unit, mounted to rear of transmission and splined directly to transmission mainshaft. Unit consists of a single planetary assembly, a sliding clutch actuated by hydraulic pressure, and an overrunning clutch. A single planetary gear train is used, consisting of a central sun gear in mesh with three planetary pinion gears, which in turn mesh with an internally toothed annulus (ring) gear. The pinion carrier is connected to transmission mainshaft through the sun gear and an overrunning clutch. The annulus gear and overdrive mainshaft are an integral one-piece assembly. Hydraulic system pressure is developed by a plunger type pump driven by a cam keyed to transmission mainshaft. Pump draws oil from sump, through oil pan filter, and delivers it through a non-return valve and pressure filter to the clutch apply pistons, solenoid valve, and relief valve assembly.

TROUBLE SHOOTING

OVERDRIVE DOES NOT ENGAGE

Low lubricant level. Solenoid is not energizing. Solenoid is energizing but not operating. Insufficient hydraulic pressure. Damaged pump or internal damage to overdrive unit.

OVERDRIVE DOES NOT RELEASE

CAUTION: Do not place vehicle in reverse or extensive damage may occur.

Electrical control circuit faulty. Solenoid valve sticking. Relief valve sticking causing high residual pressure. Control orifice blocked. Clutch sliding member sticking. Internal damage to overdrive unit.

SLIPS WHEN ENGAGED

Low lubricant level. Solenoid valve sticking. Control orifice blocked. Worn or glazed clutch linings. Defective filter, non-return valve, or relief valve causing low operating pressure.

SLOW DISENGAGEMENT AND/OR FREEWHEELS ON OVERRUN

Relief valve sticking. Control valve sticking or blocked. Control orifice blocked. Internal damage to overdrive unit.

TESTING

HYDRAULIC PRESSURE TEST

1) Lift and support vehicle so rear wheels are free to turn. Remove plug adjacent to solenoid and install pressure gauge with necessary adapter(s). With overdrive disengaged, start engine, shift into high gear and operate at 25 MPH. Hydraulic pressure should read 21 psi (1.5 kg/cm²).

2) Engage overdrive and pressure should be approximately that shown in *Hydraulic Pressure Specifica-*

tions table. Disengage overdrive and pressure should return to normal in 3 seconds or less.

HYDRAULIC PRESSURE SPECIFICATIONS

Application	psi (kg/cm²)
4-Cylinder	380-440 (27-31)
6-Cylinder	455-510 (32-36)

Fig. 1: Gauge Hook-Up for Hydraulic Pressure Test

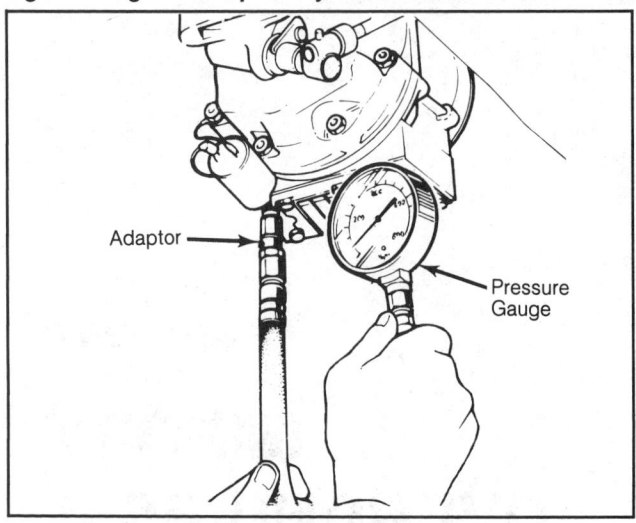

SOLENOID VALVE

Remove solenoid from overdrive unit. Test solenoid with 12 volt battery and an ammeter. When energized, solenoid draw should be approximately 2 amps. Check that valve plunger moves fully forward when solenoid is energized, and returns under spring pressure when de-energized. Replace unit if defective.

SERVICE (IN VEHICLE)

NOTE: **Upon completion of all in-vehicle service, fill transmission and overdrive unit and check operation. Recheck fluid level. DO NOT use any type of anti-friction additives.**

SOLENOID VALVE

Removal

Raise vehicle on a hoist and disconnect wires from solenoid valve. Remove valve from overdrive unit using a 25 mm open end wrench.

CAUTION: **Do not attempt to remove valve using pliers or similar tools as valve is easily damaged.**

Installation

Install new "O" ring seal on valve end of solenoid. Install solenoid into overdrive unit and tighten with a 25 mm open end wrench. Connect wires to solenoid valve.

SUMP FILTER & PRESSURE FILTER

Removal

Remove sump cover attaching bolts and sump cover. Remove gasket and pull sump filter out. Remove

LAYCOCK "J" TYPE (Cont.)

pressure filter base plug (largest plug under sump cover). Aluminum gasket and pressure filter will come out with plug.

Cleaning & Inspection

Clean pressure filter and sump filter in solvent or kerosene. Use reduced compressed air pressure to dry filters, or place on a lint-free cloth to air dry. If either filter is damaged or plugged so it cannot be cleaned, replace filter.

Installation

Install new aluminum washer on plug, then install pressure filter and plug into overdrive unit. Install sump filter, gasket and sump cover.

RELIEF VALVE ASSEMBLY

Removal

Remove sump cover, filter and gasket. Remove relief valve piston plug (bore farthest from pressure filter bore). Remove dashpot piston assembly, relief valve and spring assembly. Remove relief valve body and valve sleeve by using pliers with narrow jaws and pulling from case with firm pressure. Use wire loop to remove cylinder and washer.

Fig. 2: Disassembled View of Relief Valve Assembly

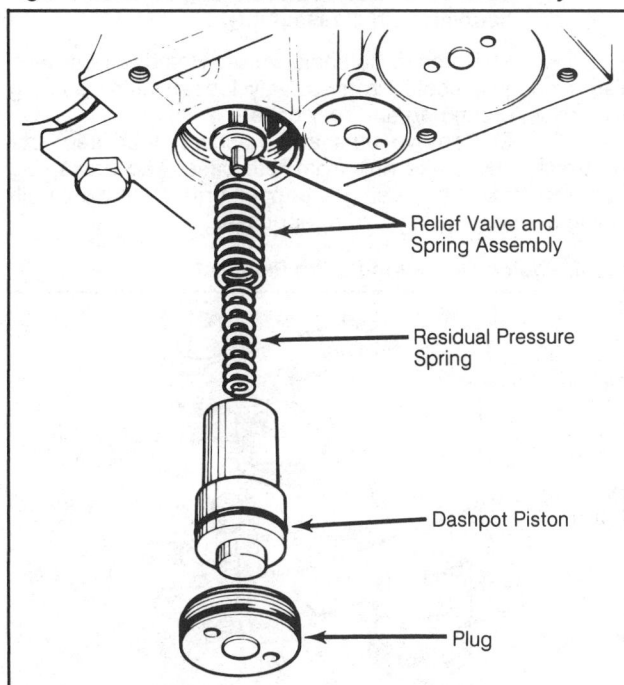

Cleaning & Inspection

Wash all parts in solvent and blow dry with filtered compressed air. Inspect piston, sleeve, and valve body for scratches, nicks, burrs, cracks, corrosion and excessive wear. Make sure piston moves freely in sleeve. Check for broken, worn or distorted springs. Discard old "O" rings.

NOTE: Do not clean orifice with wire.

Installation

1) Clean control orifice, located in relief valve bore in case, with compressed air. Install new "O" rings, lightly oil all components with transmission oil. Install relief body in bore and use relief valve outer sleeve to seat

body, making sure end of body with "O" ring is nearest to outside of case.

Fig. 3: Relief Valve Removal

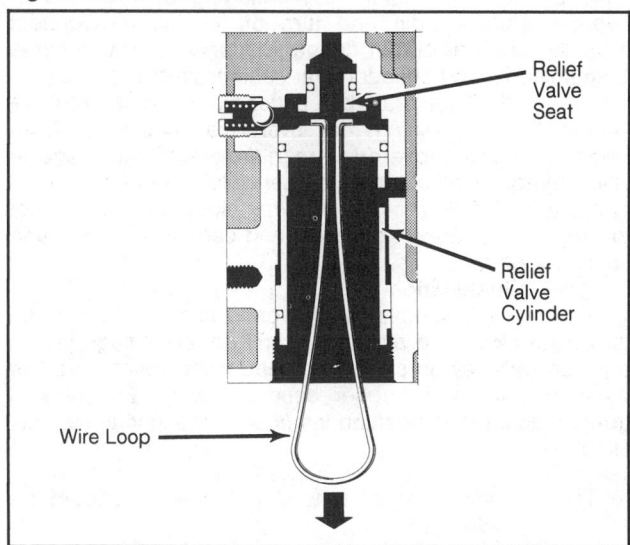

2) Position relief valve and spring assembly into dashpot cup while ensuring that both ends of residual pressure spring are correctly positioned. Position components in relief valve outer sleeve while engaging relief valve piston in housing. Install base plug and tighten until flush with casing. Install sump filter, gasket, and sump cover.

PUMP NON-RETURN VALVE

Removal

Remove sump cover, filter and gasket. Remove pump plug (center bore), then remove valve seat spring and check ball, making sure not to lose spring and ball when plug is removed. Remove non-return valve seat using a magnet or wire loop.

Cleaning & Inspection

Clean all parts in solvent and blow dry with filtered compressed air. Check valve seat and ball for pitting, corrosion, wear, nicks, burrs, and scratches. Inspect spring for distortion, loss of tension, or breakage. Discard "O" ring.

Installation

Install new "O" ring on pump plug, place spring in plug, position check ball on top of spring and valve seat on check ball. Carefully thread assembly into case and tighten until flush with casing. Install sump filter, gasket, and sump cover.

REAR OIL SEAL

Removal

Raise vehicle on hoist. Mark rear universal joint and pinion yoke for reassembly reference and remove propeller shaft. Remove drive flange nut, washer, and drive flange. Use a tool to remove rear oil seal.

Installation

Lubricate new seal with transmission oil and install in rear case, making sure seal is fully seated. Install drive flange, washer and a new self-locking nut. Install propeller shaft, aligning marks made during removal. Check and correct lubricant level in transmission and overdrive, then lower vehicle.

LAYCOCK "J" TYPE (Cont.)

ONE-WAY CLUTCH REPLACEMENT
Removal
1) With vehicle raised on hoist, unload overdrive by starting engine and engaging overdrive, then depress clutch pedal and turn off engine. Disconnect propeller shaft at output flange. Disconnect ground cable from solenoid and speedometer cable from overdrive.

2) Place drain pan under overdrive and remove nuts and bolts holding rear overdrive housing to front housing. Remove overdrive rear assembly and place in vise. Remove circlip and oil slinger holding one-way clutch in place. Carefully remove one-way clutch using care not to drop rollers. Separate rollers and cage from clutch and check for damage.

Installation
1) Assemble clutch, spring and roller cage and turn cage clockwise as far as it will go. Lock cage in this position with key on closed side and insert rollers, holding them in place with rubber band or string. Ensure that thrust washer is in position in annulus and install one-way clutch.

NOTE: **Thickness of new thrust washer should be .150" (3.8 mm).**

2) Install oil slinger and circlip. Ensure that gasket in front of brake has not been damaged. Fit new gasket to mounting face and install overdrive rear assembly. Connect ground cable, speedometer cable and drive shaft.

OVERDRIVE REMOVAL & INSTALLATION

REMOVAL

NOTE: **Before removing transmission and overdrive unit from vehicle, operate vehicle, engage overdrive, then disengage overdrive with clutch pedal depressed. This procedure will relieve torque loading on overrunning clutch and pinion carrier, thereby easing removal.**

1) Remove transmission with overdrive unit attached. *See appropriate article in MANUAL TRANSMISSION Section for transmission removal.*

2) Remove 8 nuts securing overdrive main case to adapter. Separate overdrive from transmission while leaving adaptor plate in position on transmission.

3) Slide overdrive over mainshaft and off transmission. If difficulty is encountered in separating the overdrive from transmission, proceed as follows: Remove plug adjacent to solenoid, then screw in and tighten adapter to allow oil to be pumped into unit using lubrication gun. This will pressurize unit and release spline loading on mainshaft and allow easy removal.

4) De-energize solenoid when overdrive has separated from adapter 3/4" (19.05 mm).

INSTALLATION

1) Clean gasket surfaces of overdrive case and transmission adapter. Apply a light coat of sealer to case-to-adapter gasket and position on overdrive front case, taking care not to tear gasket on studs.

2) Using a long screwdriver, rotate overrunning clutch splines (innermost set of splines) in a counterclockwise direction until splines are in line with splines in planet carrier. Ensure that pump cam and sun gear snap ring are correctly positioned on mainshaft.

3) Rotate transmission mainshaft so peak of pump cam is at bottom. Position transmission in low gear. Install overdrive to transmission while rotating output shaft of overdrive in a clockwise direction and applying slight pressure until splines are engaged.

4) Pump strap assembly should ride smoothly onto cam and overdrive should butt up to adapter plate without undue force. If overdrive unit will not come within 5/8" (15.88 mm) of adapter, then planet carrier and overrunning clutch splines are not properly aligned and overdrive must be removed and splines aligned.

5) Install and tighten 8 nuts attaching overdrive to adapter. Install transmission and overdrive into vehicle and fill with lubricant.

OVERDRIVE DISASSEMBLY

NOTE: **Extreme cleanliness must be observed at all times in working on overdrive unit. Clean outside of overdrive thoroughly before proceeding with disassembly.**

1) Remove solenoid valve. Remove operating piston bridge pieces. Progressively loosen nuts securing front case, brake ring and rear case.

2) Remove nuts and washers, then separate front case and brake ring from rear case. Tap brake ring lose from front case using a copper drift. Remove clutch sliding member springs from rear case.

Fig. 4: Clutch Operating Piston Removal

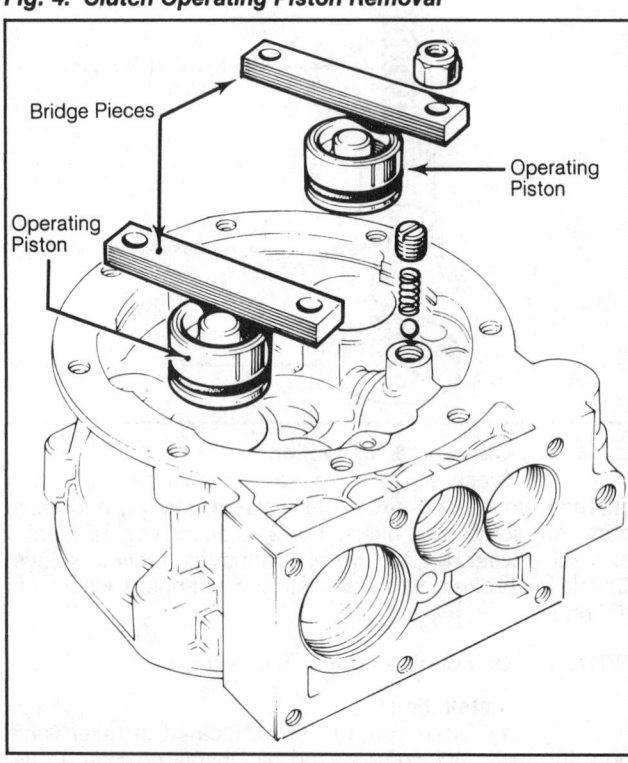

Bridge Pieces

Operating Piston

Operating Piston

3) Using a pair of pliers, carefully remove operating pistons from front case and identify them with

LAYCOCK "J" TYPE (Cont.)

their respective bores. Remove sump cover, gasket and sump filter. Remove pressure filter base plug (largest plug under sump cover), aluminum gasket and pressure filter.

4) Remove relief valve piston plug (bore farthest from pressure filter bore), dashpot piston assembly, relief valve residual pressure spring, and relief valve and spring assembly. Remove relief valve body and valve sleeve by using pliers with narrow jaws and pulling from case with firm pressure.

5) Remove pump non-return valve plug (center bore), then remove valve seat spring and check ball. Remove non-return valve seat using a magnet or wire loop with hooked end. Remove pump body and pump plunger.

Fig. 5: Exploded View of Front Case Valves and Filters

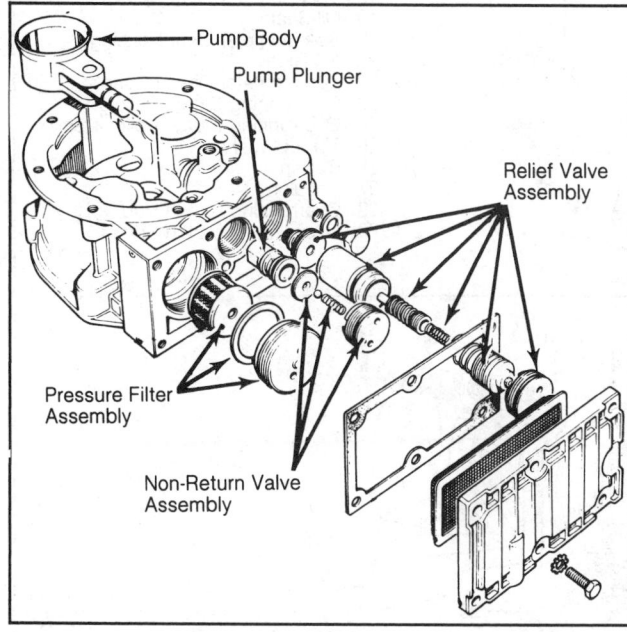

6) Remove sliding clutch, sun gear and thrust bearing cover assembly from annulus in rear case. Remove planet carrier assembly taking care not to damage oil catcher attached to underside of carrier assembly. Remove sun gear snap ring and sliding clutch snap ring, then push sun gear out of sliding clutch hub.

7) Insert a remover tool into sliding clutch hub, support thrust bearing cover, and tap on end of tool to drive clutch hub from thrust bearing. Remove thrust bearing snap ring, then press bearing from cover using an arbor press.

8) Remove snap ring and oil thrower. Insert a tool over the overrunning clutch, reach through tool with finger and pull overrunning clutch into tool, and remove tool and overrunning clutch as an assembly. Remove mainshaft thrust washer from recess in annulus.

9) Separate overrunning clutch from removal tool and disassemble. Remove speedometer driven gear attaching bolt, housing and driven gear from rear housing. Remove drive flange attaching nut and washer. Remove drive flange using a tool.

10) Drive annulus from rear case using a soft mallet and striking on end of tail shaft. Remove front bearing, speedometer drive gear and spacer from annulus. Remove oil seal from rear case and drive out rear bearing.

CLEANING & INSPECTION

CLEANING

NOTE: **Do not clean sliding clutch or solenoid valve in solvent. Wipe off with a clean lint-free cloth.**

Thoroughly wash all parts in clean solvent. After cleaning, dry all parts with dry filtered compressed air. Blow out all passages to remove any foreign material or cleaning solvent. To clean valve portion of solenoid valve, immerse valve portion (up to threads) in clean solvent, allow to soak until clean, then air dry on a clean shop cloth.

INSPECTION

Front Case

Cracks in case or in valve or piston bores. Nicks, scratches, grooves or warpage on mating surfaces or in valve or piston bores. Worn or stripped threads on plugs, studs, or in valve bores. Blocked oil passages or control orifice.

Rear Case

Cracks in case or in mainshaft bearing snap ring groove. Nick, scratches, or warpage on mating surfaces. Worn, stripped, or galled threads in stud holes. Worn or loose rear bushing.

Pump, Valves & Pistons

Scratches, nicks, burrs, excessive wear, pitting, or corrosion of any pump or valve component. Weak, broken or distorted relief valve springs. Torn, distorted or plugged sump filter or pressure filter. Cracked or warped sump cover. Nicks, scratches or wear on operating pistons. Wear, grooves, burrs and cracks in piston bores.

Brake Ring

Worn, grooved, distorted, or burned clutch surfaces. Cracks in brake ring or at stud holes.

Sliding Clutch, Thrust Bearing & Cover

Worn, burned, loose or peeling friction material. Cracks in clutch hub or friction surface. Worn, rough, galled bearings and races in thrust bearing. Weak, broken or distorted clutch return springs.

Annulus, Planet Carrier & Sun Gear

Loose or worn bushing in annulus gear bore. Chipped, worn or broken teeth in annulus gear. Worn, broken or chipped splines on sun gear and mainshaft. Bent or distorted mainshaft. Plugged lubrication holes. Worn, burned, or rough clutch surface on annulus gear. Cracks in mainshaft or sun gear. Loose or worn pins in planet carrier. Cracked, worn or chipped teeth on planet carrier gears. Rough, galled or worn bearings.

Overrunning Clutch

Cracked or worn hub and rollers. Broken or distorted spring, or cracked, bent, or broken cage. Worn thrust washer. Worn clutch race in annulus gear bore. Cracked clutch hub. Worn splines.

OVERDRIVE REASSEMBLY

NOTE: **Use new gaskets, "O" rings, lock washers and seals when reassembling. Maximum cleanliness must be maintained during all reassembly procedures.**

1) Position speedometer drive gear into rear case with plain boss facing front bearing. Press front

Overdrives

LAYCOCK "J" TYPE (Cont.)

Fig. 6: Disassembled View of Overdrive Components

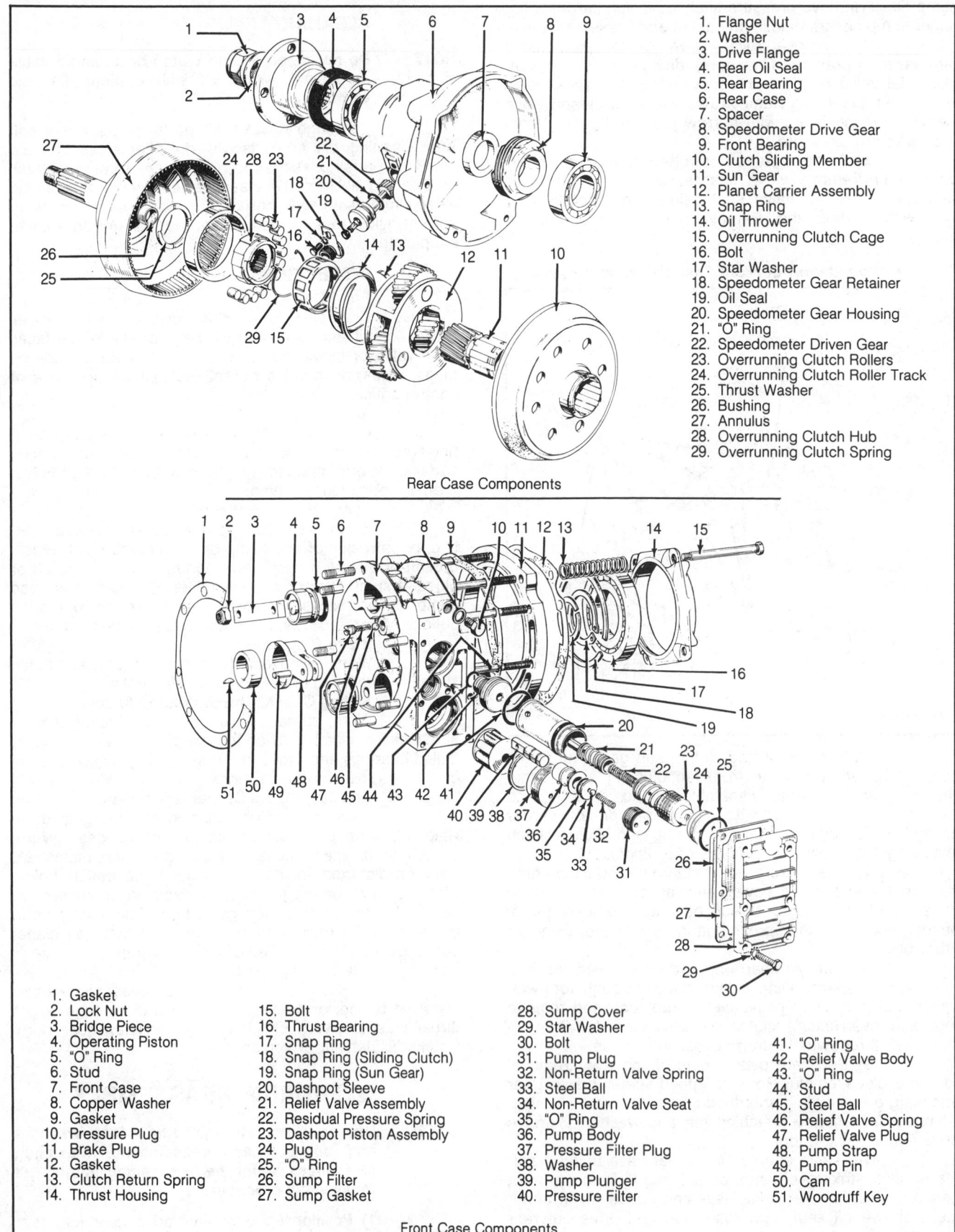

1. Flange Nut
2. Washer
3. Drive Flange
4. Rear Oil Seal
5. Rear Bearing
6. Rear Case
7. Spacer
8. Speedometer Drive Gear
9. Front Bearing
10. Clutch Sliding Member
11. Sun Gear
12. Planet Carrier Assembly
13. Snap Ring
14. Oil Thrower
15. Overrunning Clutch Cage
16. Bolt
17. Star Washer
18. Speedometer Gear Retainer
19. Oil Seal
20. Speedometer Gear Housing
21. "O" Ring
22. Speedometer Driven Gear
23. Overrunning Clutch Rollers
24. Overrunning Clutch Roller Track
25. Thrust Washer
26. Bushing
27. Annulus
28. Overrunning Clutch Hub
29. Overrunning Clutch Spring

Rear Case Components

1. Gasket
2. Lock Nut
3. Bridge Piece
4. Operating Piston
5. "O" Ring
6. Stud
7. Front Case
8. Copper Washer
9. Gasket
10. Pressure Plug
11. Brake Plug
12. Gasket
13. Clutch Return Spring
14. Thrust Housing
15. Bolt
16. Thrust Bearing
17. Snap Ring
18. Snap Ring (Sliding Clutch)
19. Snap Ring (Sun Gear)
20. Dashpot Sleeve
21. Relief Valve Assembly
22. Residual Pressure Spring
23. Dashpot Piston Assembly
24. Plug
25. "O" Ring
26. Sump Filter
27. Sump Gasket
28. Sump Cover
29. Star Washer
30. Bolt
31. Pump Plug
32. Non-Return Valve Spring
33. Steel Ball
34. Non-Return Valve Seat
35. "O" Ring
36. Pump Body
37. Pressure Filter Plug
38. Washer
39. Pump Plunger
40. Pressure Filter
41. "O" Ring
42. Relief Valve Body
43. "O" Ring
44. Stud
45. Steel Ball
46. Relief Valve Spring
47. Relief Valve Plug
48. Pump Strap
49. Pump Pin
50. Cam
51. Woodruff Key

Front Case Components

LAYCOCK "J" TYPE (Cont.)

bearing into rear case until seated against shoulder in case. Press front bearing along with rear casing and speedometer driving gear onto annulus until front bearing seats on shoulder of annulus. Install spacer onto annulus mainshaft. Press rear bearing into rear case and onto annulus mainshaft. Install new oil seal and press on drive flange. Install washer, new self-locking nut, and tighten to specifications.

Fig. 7: Speedometer Drive Gear and Front Bearing Positions in Rear Case

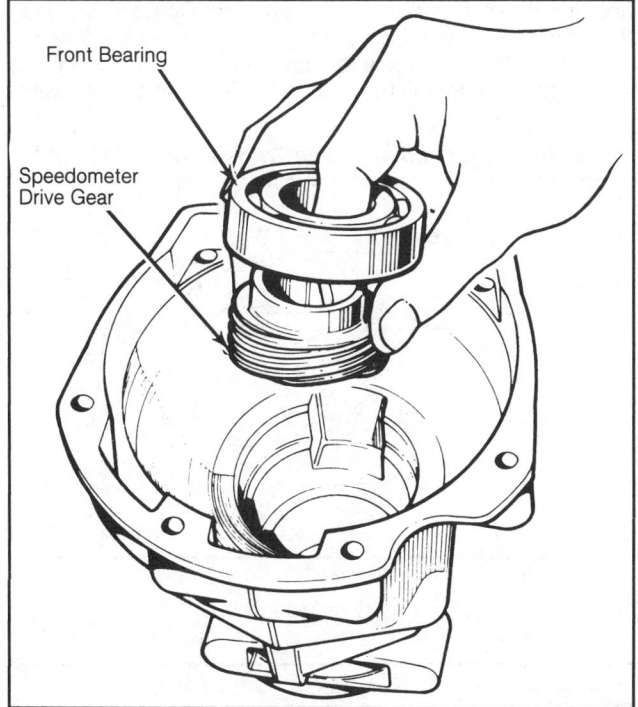

Fig. 8: Exploded View of Main Components of Laycock "J" Type Overdrive Unit

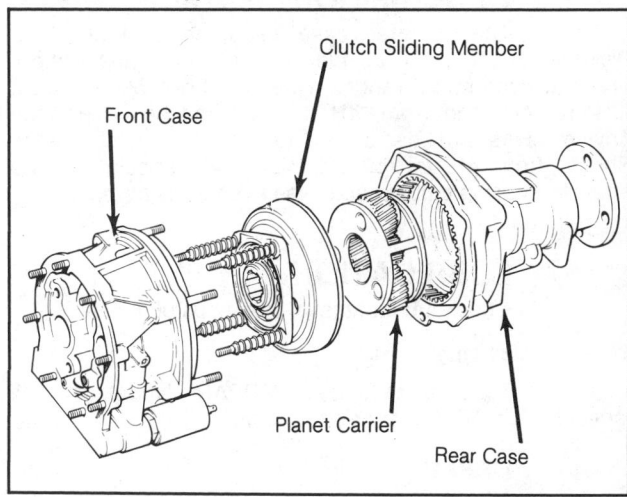

5) Install relief body in bore and use relief valve outer sleeve to seat body, making sure that end of body with "O" ring is nearest to outside of case. Position relief valve and spring assembly into dashpot cup while ensuring that both ends of residual pressure spring is correctly positioned. Position components in relief valve outer sleeve while engaging relief valve piston in housing. Install base plug and tighten. Install sump filter, gasket and sump cover.

6) Mount rear case assembly upright in a soft-jawed vise, then install planet carrier assembly. Install sliding clutch assembly including return springs onto cone of annulus. Engage sun gear with planet carrier gears. Apply light coat of sealer to new gaskets and install on both sides of brake ring. Install brake ring to rear case and align stud holes.

NOTE: **Gears can be meshed in any position.**

7) Position front case over thrust housing pins while aligning with studs in brake ring. Install and tighten nuts evenly, securing front and rear case assemblies, while making sure copper washers are installed to 2 top studs. Install 2 bridge pieces and install new self-locking nuts.

NOTE: **Clutch return spring pressure should be felt as cases draw together.**

TIGHTENING SPECIFICATIONS

Application	Ft. Lbs. (N.m)
Sump Cover	6 (8)
Pressure Filter Cover	16 (22)
Relief Valve Plug	16 (22)
Operation Piston Bridge	5-12 (7-16)
Front-to-Rear Cover	5-12 (7-16)
Drive Flange Nut	120-130 (163-176)

2) Position clutch hub and spring into cage of overrunning clutch. Position spring so cage is spring loaded in a counterclockwise direction (when viewed from front). Position assembly into assembling tool (L178 or equivalent), with open end of cage up. Rotate cage in a clockwise direction until all rollers are installed. Install thrust washer into annulus. Transfer overrunning clutch from assembly tool into its race in annulus. Install oil thrower and snap ring.

NOTE: **Check that overrunning clutch rotates in counterclockwise direction only.**

3) Press thrust bearing into housing and install snap ring. Install thrust bearing housing onto hub of clutch sliding member and install snap ring securing bearing to hub. Install sun gear into hub and install snap ring on sun gear extension.

4) Lubricate operating pistons with transmission oil, install new "O" rings, then install pistons (counterbored end out) in their respective bores. Install solenoid valve with new "O" ring, making sure not to overtighten. Install new aluminum washer on pressure filter plug, then install pressure filter and plug into front case. Install pump body and pump plunger. Install new "O" ring on pump plug, place spring in plug, position check ball on top of spring and valve seat on check ball. Carefully thread assembly into case and tighten.

Transfer Cases

CHRYSLER IMPORTS 4WD PICKUP

Dodge Ram-50
DESCRIPTION

The transfer case used on Ram-50 4WD Pickups is mounted to the side of the transmission. Transfer case has 2 ranges, High and Low. Shifting from "2H" to "4H" and from "4H" to "2H" can be done while driving; it is not necessary to depress clutch pedal. Shifting from "4H" to "4L" and "4L" to "4H" should be done after depressing clutch pedal when vehicle is stopped.

LUBRICATION

Check lubricant level every 30,000 miles.

FLUID TYPE

Transfer case uses MOPAR Hypoid gear oil (specification API GL-4) or equivalent.

CAPACITY

Fill up transfer case to slightly below oil filler plug hole.

REMOVAL & INSTALLATION

TRANSFER CASE ASSEMBLY
Removal

1) Remove transmission/transfer case assembly from vehicle. *See appropriate article in MANUAL TRANSMISSION REMOVAL Section.* Remove the back-up light switch from the lower right adapter. Take out the steel ball. Remove the plug from the right side of the transfer case. Take out select spring and select plunger.

3) Remove the bolts securing the transfer case adapter. With the change shifter tilted toward the left, remove the control finger from the shift lug groove and take out the transfer case assembly.

Installation

1) Set all the shift rails in neutral positions. With the case shifter tied to the left, install transfer case assembly. *See Fig. 2.* Manipulate change shifter to engage the control finger with shift lug groove.

2) Mount the neutral return plungers and the springs in the hole on top of the adapter. Tighten the plug until it is flush with the adapter surface. Coat the inside of the change shifter with grease.

3) Mount the select plunger and spring and install the plug. Install back-up light switch and steel ball.

Fig. 2: Removing and Installing Transfer Case Assembly

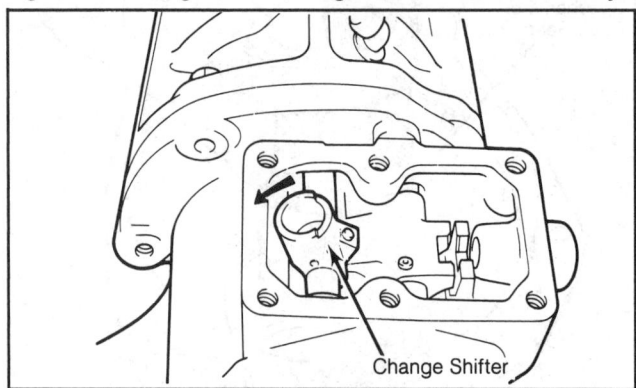

Change Shifter

Fig. 1: Exploded View of Transfer Case Assembly

Input Gear
Clutch Hub
Clutch Sleeve
Bearing
Bearing
Low Gear
Rear Cover
Clutch Hub
Lock Nut
Shift Forks
Rear Case
Front Case
Drive Sprocket
Chain
Bearing
Bearing
Oil Seal
Front Output Shaft

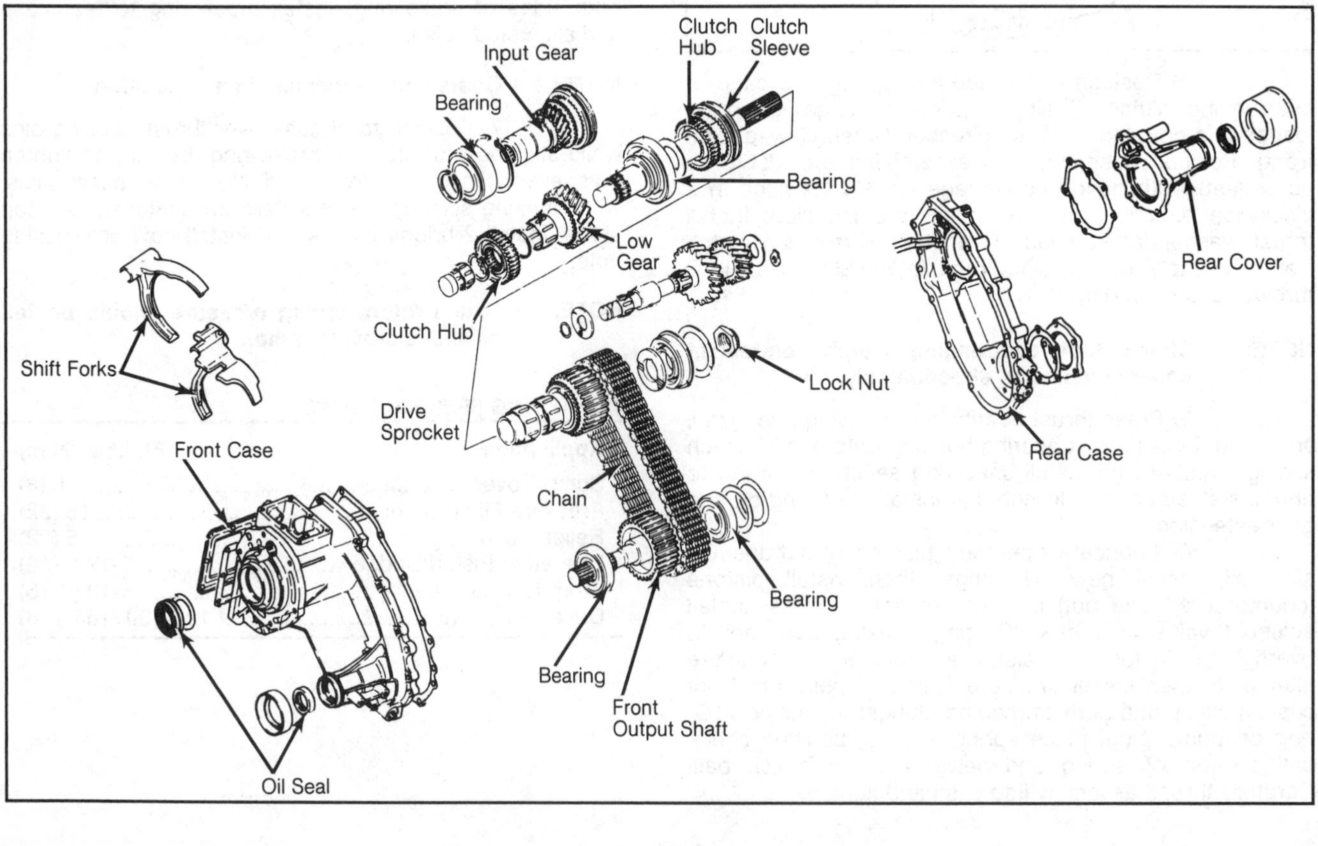

CHRYSLER IMPORTS 4WD PICKUP (Cont.)

TRANSFER CASE DISASSEMBLY

1) Remove the two 4WD lamp switches. Take out 2 steel balls. Remove the speedometer sleeve assembly. Remove the bolts securing the rear cover and remove the rear cover, gasket and wave spring. Remove cover and gasket and remove wave spring and spacer. Drive out the spring pin from the H-L shift fork with a 3/16" punch.

Fig. 3: Driving Out High-Low Shift Fork Spring Pin

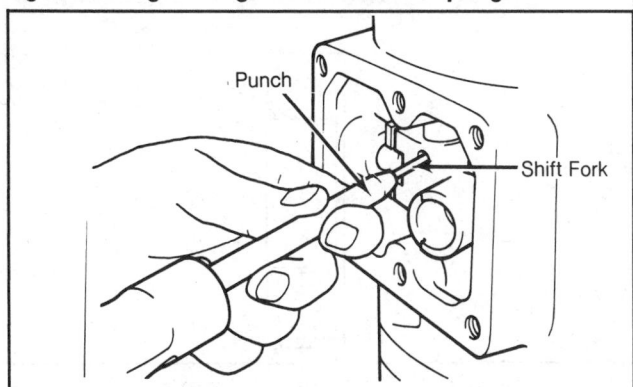

2) Remove 2 seal plugs and take out the 2 poppet springs and 2 balls. Pull out the H-L shift rail backward. Take out the interlock plunger. Remove the snap ring from the rear bearing on the output shaft. Remove the chain cover. Remove the oil guide. Remove side cover. Remove countershaft locking plate and pull out the countershaft.

3) Take out countergear and 2 thrust washers. Remove 2 needle bearings and spacer through side cover opening. Remove snap ring from 2-4WD shift rail. Remove spring retainers and spring from shift rail. Remove front output shaft, rear output shaft and chain together from transfer case.

Fig. 4: Removing Countershaft

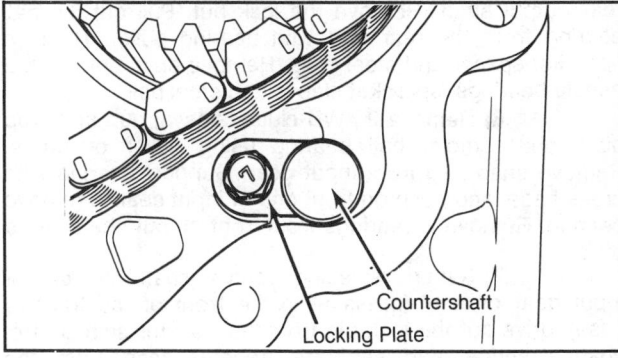

Remove locking plate and pull out countershaft.

Fig. 5: Removing Output Drive Assembly

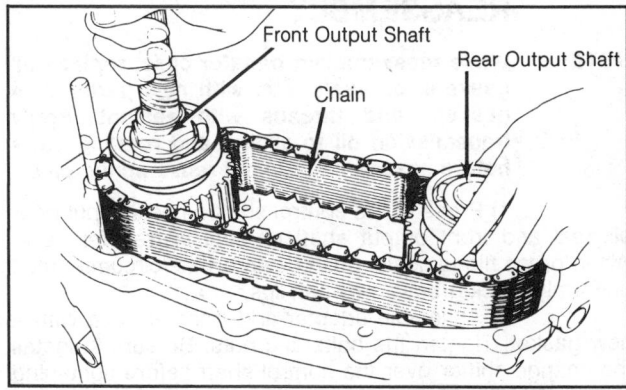

Remove shafts and chain from case together.

4) Remove 2-4WD shift rail. Remove H-L shift fork and clutch sleeve. Remove needle bearing from input gear. Remove snap ring and input gear assembly. Remove snap ring from the front of rear output shaft. Remove H-L clutch hub, low speed gear thrust washer and needle bearing.

Fig. 6: Cross Sectional View of Rear Output Shaft

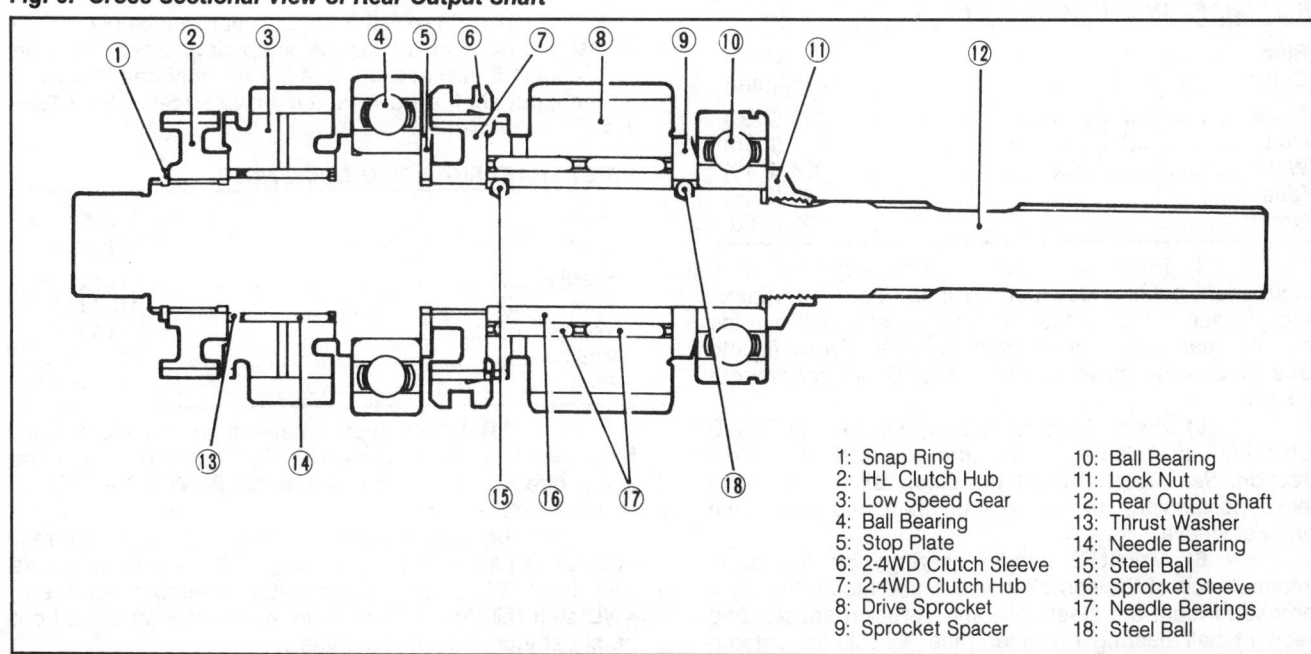

1: Snap Ring	10: Ball Bearing
2: H-L Clutch Hub	11: Lock Nut
3: Low Speed Gear	12: Rear Output Shaft
4: Ball Bearing	13: Thrust Washer
5: Stop Plate	14: Needle Bearing
6: 2-4WD Clutch Sleeve	15: Steel Ball
7: 2-4WD Clutch Hub	16: Sprocket Sleeve
8: Drive Sprocket	17: Needle Bearings
9: Sprocket Spacer	18: Steel Ball

CHRYSLER IMPORTS 4WD PICKUP (Cont.)

5) Remove the detent of the lock nut of the rear output shaft. Remove the lock nut. Pull out the ball bearing from the rear end with bearing puller. Remove sprocket spacer and steel balls. Remove drive sprocket, 2 needle bearings, sprocket sleeve and steel ball.

6) Remove 2-4WD clutch sleeve, hub and stop plate and remove ball bearing using puller or press. Remove snap ring from input gear. Support bearing with press base, and push on front end of input gear to remove bearing. Remove 2 bearings from front output shaft with a puller.

7) When replacing control shaft oil seal or input gear oil seal (press fit in the front of the transfer case), drive out the lock pin from the transmission control change shifter and separate transfer case from the adapter.

TRANSFER CASE REASSEMBLY

NOTE: **While reassembling transfer case, replace all gaskets, oil seals, etc. with new parts. Coat gaskets and threads with sealant. Apply transmission oil to sliding and rotating parts before assembling. Do not reuse spring pins.**

1) Press fit the control shaft oil seal, input gear oil seal and front output shaft oil seal in transfer case. When press fitting seals, push down on the circumference uniformly. Pack grease between lips.

2) Assemble adapter and transfer case with a new gasket. Tighten the bolts and nuts. Be sure to install the change shifter over the control shaft before tightening nuts and bolts. Make sure to remove burrs from change shifter.

3) Press fit bearing into input gear, pushing down on inner race. After fitting, check to see that bearing rotates smoothly. Fit snap ring over front end of input gear. Snap rings are available in 5 thickness; select the thickest one that will fit in groove. *See Input Shaft Snap Ring Table No. 1.*

INPUT SHAFT SNAP RING TABLE NO. 1

Ring Color	Thickness In. (mm)
None	.091 (2.30)
Red	.093 (2.35)
White	.094 (2.40)
Blue	.096 (2.45)
Green	.098 (2.50)

4) Press fit 2 ball bearings over the front output shaft, pushing down on the inner race. After fitting, check to see if they rotate smoothly. Install ball bearing over the rear output shaft from the rear. Press fit into place by pushing down on inner race. Check for smooth rotation.

5) Mount the stop plate and install the 2-4WD clutch hub and sleeve. Make sure to install in correct direction. *See Fig. 1.* Mount the steel ball (for sprocket sleeve positioning) on rear output shaft and mount the sprocket sleeve.

6) Mount 2 needle bearings on the outer circumference of the sprocket sleeve and mount the drive sprocket. Mount the steel balls and sprocket spacer, and press fit ball bearing on inner race. Check for smooth rotation.

7) Tighten the mainshaft lock nut and drive in the detent section with a punch. After the lock nut is tightened, check that drive sprocket rotates smoothly. Mount the needle bearing, thrust washer and low speed gear on the rear output shaft from the front end.

8) Mount the needle bearing, thrust washer, and low speed gear on rear output shaft from the front end. Mount the H-L clutch hub, making sure to install in correct direction. *See Fig. 7.*

Fig. 7: Direction of H-L Clutch Hub Installation

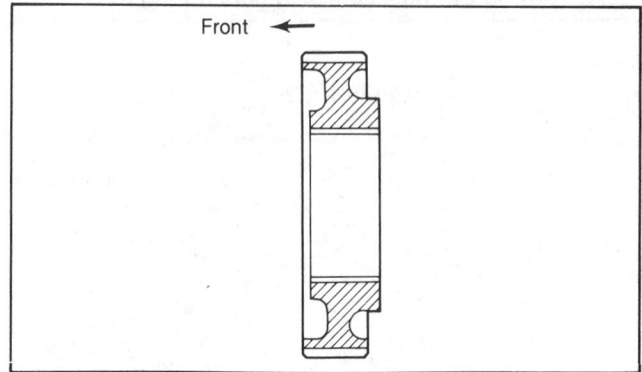

9) Mount the H-L clutch hub snap ring on the front end of the rear output shaft. Snap rings are available in 5 thicknesses. Use the thickest one that will fit in the output shaft groove. *See Output Shaft Snap Ring Table.*

OUTPUT SHAFT SNAP RING TABLE

Ring Color	Thickness In. (mm)
None	.084 (2.14)
Yellow	.087 (2.21)
White	.090 (2.28)
Blue	.093 (2.35)
Red	.095 (2.42)

10) Insert the input gear assembly in the transfer case and mount the snap ring. Snap rings are available in 5 thicknesses. Use the thickest one that will fit in the input shaft groove. *See Input Shaft Snap Ring Table No. 2.*

INPUT SHAFT SNAP RING TABLE NO. 2

Ring Color	Thickness In. (mm)
Purple	.106 (2.70)
Pink	.108 (2.75)
Yellow	.110 (2.80)
White	.112 (2.80)
Blue	.114 (2.90)

11) Insert needle bearing in the input gear. Mount the H-L clutch sleeve and shift fork, mounting in the same direction as clutch sleeve for 2-4WD. *See Fig. 7.* Install 2-4WD shift rail.

12) Securely engage chain with front and rear output shaft sprockets. Assemble the 2-4WD clutch sleeve with the 2-4WD shift fork and install assembly over the 2-4WD shift rail. At the same time, mount the rear and front output shafts and chain together.

CHRYSLER IMPORTS 4WD PICKUP (Cont.)

13) Mount the 2 spring retainers and the spring on the 2-4WD shift rail and fit snap ring. Insert the 2 needle bearings and spacer in countergear and install assembly in transfer case. Mount one thrust washer at the front of countergear and other at rear.

14) Insert side cover and gasket. Install oil guide. Install chain cover and gasket, making sure oil guide end fits in the chain cover opening. Fit snap ring in groove of rear output shaft rear bearing. Insert interlock plunger.

15) Insert H-L shift rail and pass through H-L shift fork. Unless 2-4WD shift fork is shifted to the 4WD side, H-L shift rail cannot be inserted. Mount the 2 poppet balls and 2 springs and mount the seal plug. When mounting the poppet spring, face the smaller end toward the ball.

16) With the H-L shift fork and shift rail spring holes aligned, drive in the spring pin with a punch. When installing, position the spring pin so its slit is placed on center line of shift rail.

17) Mount the wave spring on the rear end of the rear output shaft bearing and install the rear cover and the gasket. Mount wave spring on rear end of front output shaft rear bearing and install cover and gasket.

18) Check bearing rear end-to-cover clearance. If clearance exceeds .079" (2 mm), use a spacer to reduce clearance to less than .079" (2 mm). *See Fig. 8.* Insert speedometer sleeve assembly in the rear cover.

Fig. 8: Bearing-to-Cover Clearance

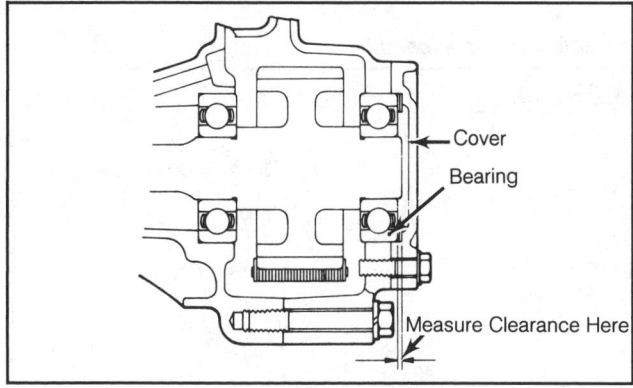

Clearance should be less than .079" (2 mm).

19) Align mating mark on the speedometer sleeve with the mark on the case according to the number of teeth on the speedometer driven gear. Mount the sleeve clamp and tighten the bolt. Install two 4WD lamp switches with steel balls.

TIGHTENING SPECIFICATIONS

Application	Ft. Lbs. (N.m)
Transfer Case Mounting Nuts & Bolts ...	22-30 (30-41)
Chain & Side Cover Bolts	22-30 (30-41)
Cover Bolts	11-15 (15-21)
Drain, Fill & Select Plugs	22-25 (30-34)
Rear Output Shaft Lock Nut	73-94 (98-127)
Speedometer Sleeve Clamp Bolt	11-15 (15-31
4WD Switch	22 (30)

Transfer Cases

DATSUN/NISSAN 4WD PICKUP

DESCRIPTION

The transfer case used on Datsun/Nissan 4WD Pickup is bolted to frame and transmission. The case is connected to rear and front axles by propeller shafts. Transfer case has 2 ranges, High and Low. Transfer case can be shifted into 4WD High range at any speed, providing locking hubs are in the lock position. Vehicle must be stopped before shifting transfer case into 4WD Low range. Transfer case is provided with an indicator switch and light. Indicator light will come on when transfer lever is in any position except 2WD High range (light is on in 4WD High, Neutral or 4WD Low).

LUBRICATION

SERVICE INTERVAL

Check fluid level every 15,000 miles or 12 months (whichever comes first). When towing trailer, change fluid every 30,000 miles or 24 months (whichever comes first).

FLUID TYPE

Use SAE 90 gear oil (API-GL-4).

CAPACITY

3.0 pts (1.4L).

REMOVAL & INSTALLATION

TRANSFER CASE ASSEMBLY

Removal

1) Disconnect negative battery cable. From inside vehicle, disconnect transfer case shift lever boot from floor pan. Raise and support vehicle. Remove transfer case protector pan.

2) Remove transfer case-to-transmission propeller shafts, front axle and rear axle. Disconnect wire connector from 4WD indicator switch. Disconnect speedometer cable and remove exhaust pipe. Support transfer case with a transmission jack.

3) Loosen transfer case insulator bolts. Make sure transfer case shift lever boot is free of floor pan and lower transfer case (with transfer case-to-transmission propeller shaft) out of vehicle. Remove insulators from transfer case.

Installation

Install transfer case in the reverse order of removal. Make sure transfer case is filled with the proper amount and type of lubricant after installation.

TRANSFER CASE DISASSEMBLY

1) Make sure transfer case is clean of dirt and grease. Drain gear oil. Place control lever in 4WD Low

---

Fig. 1: Exploded View of Datsun/Nissan 4WD Pickup Transfer Case and Shifting Assembly

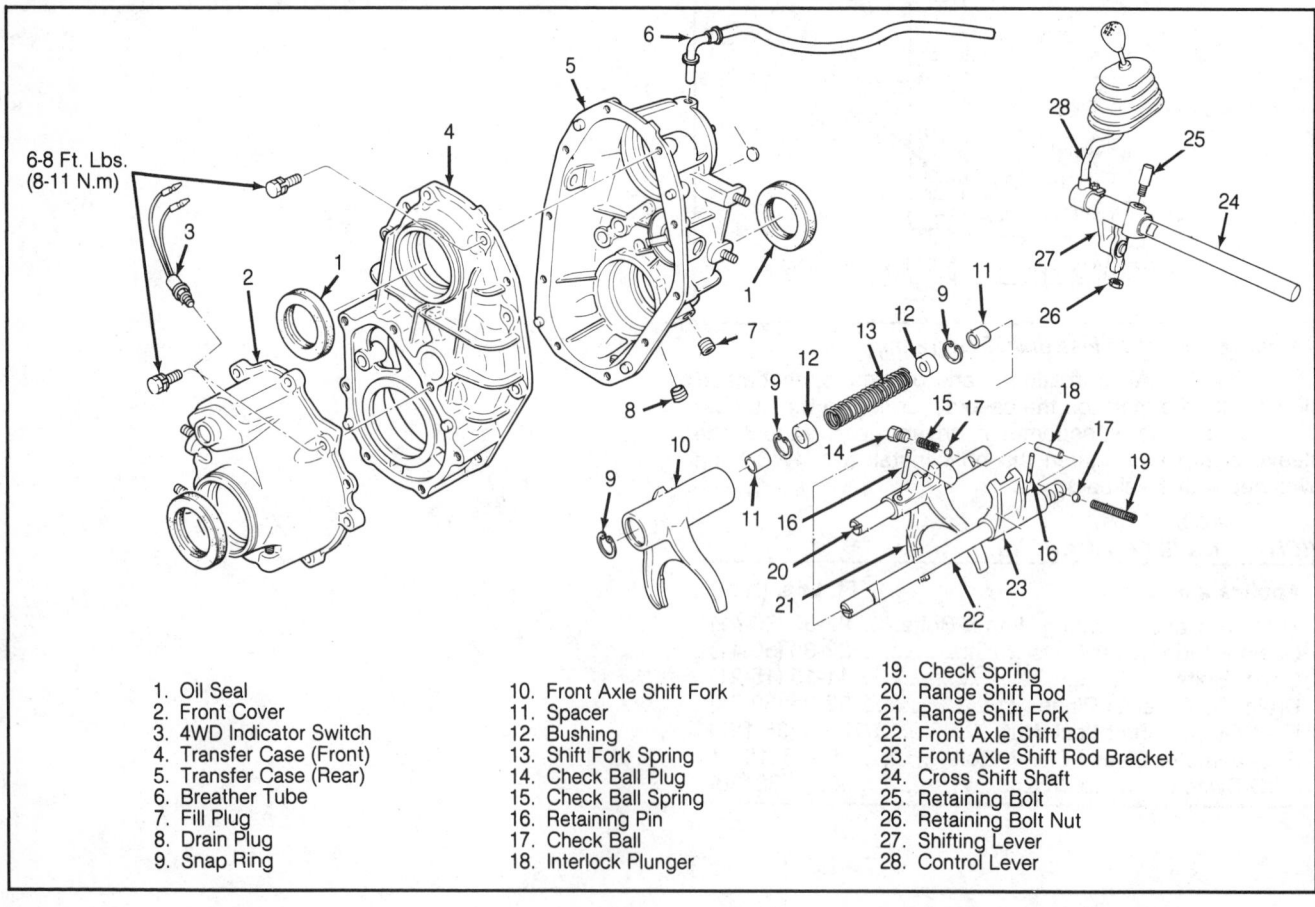

1. Oil Seal	10. Front Axle Shift Fork	19. Check Spring
2. Front Cover	11. Spacer	20. Range Shift Rod
3. 4WD Indicator Switch	12. Bushing	21. Range Shift Fork
4. Transfer Case (Front)	13. Shift Fork Spring	22. Front Axle Shift Rod
5. Transfer Case (Rear)	14. Check Ball Plug	23. Front Axle Shift Rod Bracket
6. Breather Tube	15. Check Ball Spring	24. Cross Shift Shaft
7. Fill Plug	16. Retaining Pin	25. Retaining Bolt
8. Drain Plug	17. Check Ball	26. Retaining Bolt Nut
9. Snap Ring	18. Interlock Plunger	27. Shifting Lever
		28. Control Lever

6-8 Ft. Lbs.
(8-11 N.m)

DATSUN/NISSAN 4WD PICKUP (Cont.)

range or 2WD High range to aid in removing companion flange lock nuts.

2) Place companion flange holding tool (ST31530000) on companion flange, then remove companion flanges and nuts. Remove 4WD indicator switch. Remove transfer case front cover (tapping cover with a mallet will aid in removal.)

3) Remove front axle output shaft and needle bearing. Remove snap ring retaining front axle shift fork, then remove shift fork assembly with spacer and synchro sleeve. *Refer to Fig. 1.*

4) Remove synchro hub snap ring, then remove synchro hub. Remove front transfer case bolts then front case (tapping with mallet to aid removal).

NOTE: **Do not pry the case halves apart with screwdriver.**

5) Remove retaining bolt nut then drive retaining bolt out with a punch. Remove cross shift shaft. Remove control lever retaining nut then remove control lever. Remove shifting lever with differential lever. Remove check ball plug, check spring and check ball.

6) Drive retaining pin out of range shift fork. Tap rear axle output shaft assembly with mallet and remove it with range shift fork and countergear assembly. Then remove transfer case input shaft assembly from transfer case.

NOTE: **When removing countergear assembly, be careful not to drop needle bearings.**

7) Remove transfer case front shim. Remove range fork rods, interlock plunger, steel ball and check spring. Drive roll pin out of front axle shift fork, and remove fork shaft. Insert an 8 mm bolt into front axle shift fork, install nut on bolt, and then tighten to relieve spring tension. *See Fig. 2.* Remove snap ring and then slowly remove nut from 8 mm bolt. Remove spring retainer bushings and shift fork spring. Separate components.

Fig. 2: Compressing Front Axle Shift Fork Spring with 8 mm Bolt to Remove Snap Rings

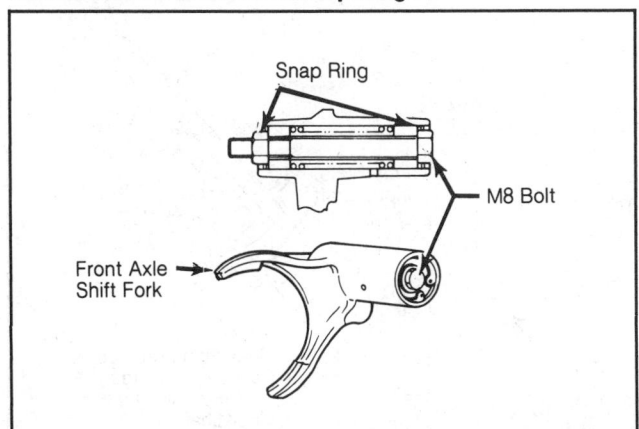

8) Press front and rear bearings off transfer case input shaft. Remove end spacers, needle bearings and center spacer from countergear. Check gear end play before disassembling rear axle output shaft. *Refer to Gear End Play chart and Fig. 3.* Press bearing off front of rear axle output shaft. Remove thrust washer and ball, then low range gear and needle bearings.

Application	In. (mm)
High Range Gear	.004-.008 (.1-.2)
Low Range Gear	.004-.008 (.1-.2)
Synchro Hub	0-.008 (0-.2)

Fig. 3: Checking Gear End Play of Rear Axle Output Shaft

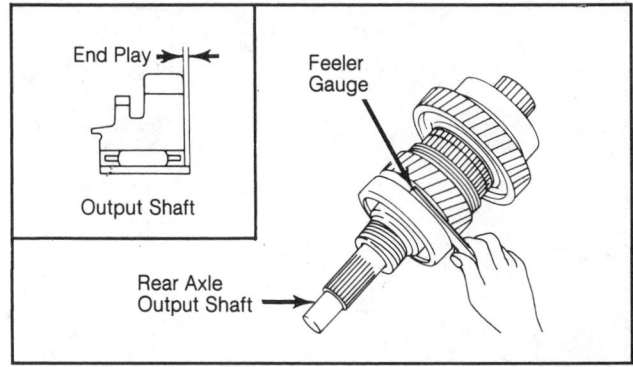

9) Press speedometer drive gear off rear of rear axle output shaft. Remove spacer and ball. Press bearing off rear axle output shaft. Remove thrust washer and steel ball, then remove high range gear, needle bearings and synchro sleeve.

10) If transfer case, bearings or oil seals are damaged in transfer case assembly, remove damaged components as follows. On front cover, pry oil seal out, remove snap ring then press bearing out. On transfer front and rear cases, pry out damaged oil seals.

TRANSFER CASE INSPECTION

1) Check transfer cases for cracks, damage or warpage. Check shift rods and forks for warpage, scoring or other damage. Inspect shift springs, check springs and interlock plunger for damage. Replace components as necessary.

2) Check all gears, input and output shafts for excessive wear, chips, cracks or other damage. Replace components as necessary.

TRANSFER CASE REASSEMBLY

NOTE: **Lubricate all bearings with gear oil, apply grease to steel balls and to thrust washers.**

1) Install needle bearings and high range gear to the rear of rear axle output shaft. Install steel ball and thrust washer against high range gear (on rear axle output shaft). Press ball bearing onto rear axle output shaft. Install spacer and steel ball with speedometer drive gear to rear axle output shaft.

2) Install needle bearings, synchro sleeve and low range gear to front of rear axle output shaft. Install steel ball and thrust washer to low range gear. Press ball bearing to front of rear axle output shaft.

3) If ball bearings, rear axle output shaft, transfer case input shaft or transfer front and rear cases are replaced, new shims need to be selected. To select shims, perform the following measuring procedures.

Transfer Cases

DATSUN/NISSAN 4WD PICKUP (Cont.)

Fig. 4: *Exploded View of Datsun/Nissan 4WD Pickup Transfer Case Gear Assembly*

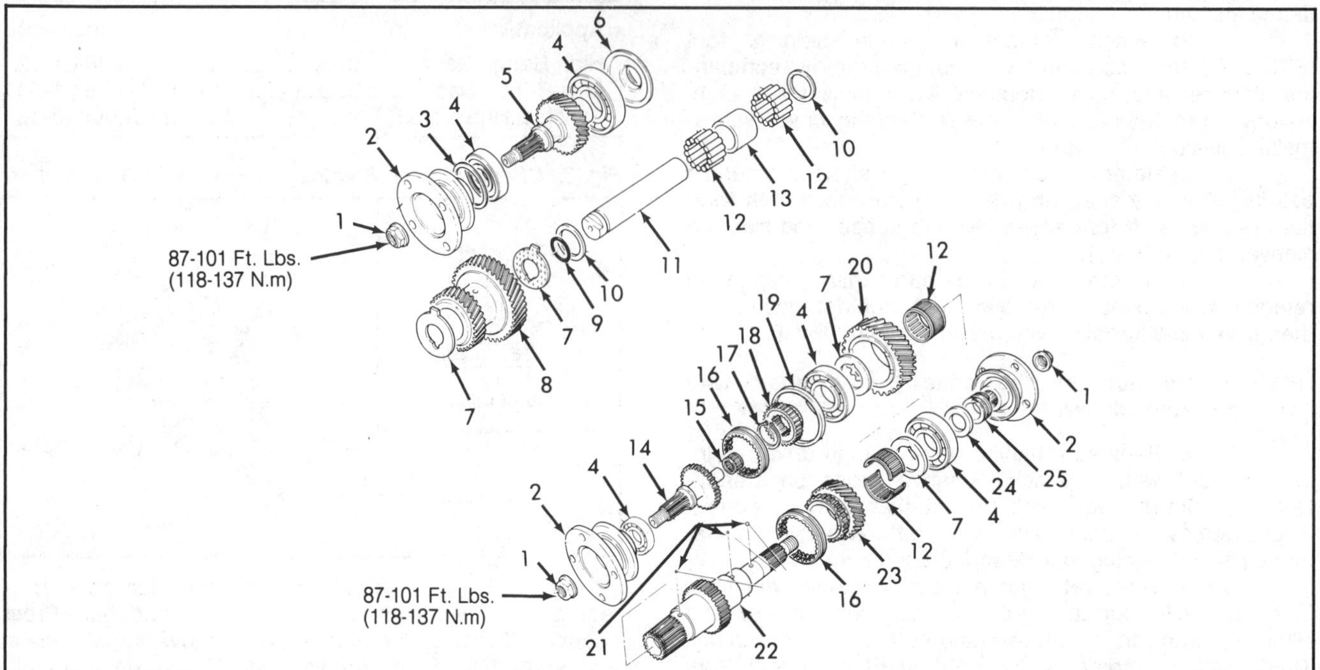

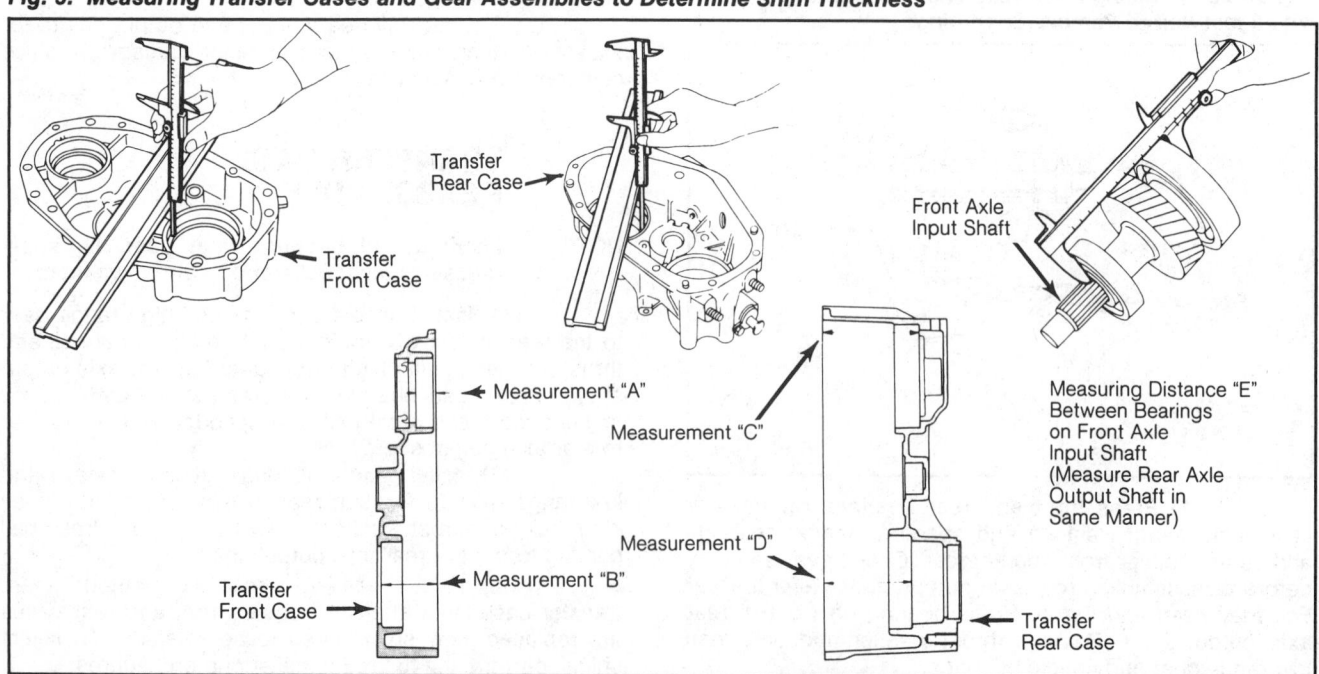

87-101 Ft. Lbs.
(118-137 N.m)

87-101 Ft. Lbs.
(118-137 N.m)

1. Companion Flange Nut
2. Companion Flange
3. Shim
4. Ball Bearing
5. Transfer Case Input Shaft
6. Breather Cover
7. Thrust Washer
8. Countergear
9. "O" Ring

10. Spacer
11. Countershaft
12. Needle Bearings
13. Spacer
14. Front Axle Output Shaft
15. Pilot Bearing
16. Synchro Sleeve
17. Snap Ring

18. Synchro Hub
19. Shim
20. Low Range Gear
21. Steel Ball
22. Rear Axle Output Shaft
23. High Range Gear
24. Spacer
25. Speedometer Drive Gear

4) Measure bearing seating depths on both transfer cases ("A", "B", "C" and "D"). *Refer to Fig. 5.* When measuring bearing seating depth "C", be sure breather cover is installed. With new ball bearings installed on transfer case input shaft, measure distance ("E") between outer edge of bearings. Then measure distance ("F") between outer edge of bearings on rear axle output shaft.

Fig. 5: *Measuring Transfer Cases and Gear Assemblies to Determine Shim Thickness*

Transfer
Rear Case

Transfer
Front Case

Front Axle
Input Shaft

Measurement "A"

Measurement "C"

Measurement "D"

Measurement "B"

Measuring Distance "E"
Between Bearings
on Front Axle
Input Shaft
(Measure Rear Axle
Output Shaft in
Same Manner)

Transfer
Front Case

Transfer
Rear Case

DATSUN/NISSAN 4WD PICKUP (Cont.)

5) To select transfer case input shaft shim, add measurement "A" to "C" then subtract distance "E". To select rear axle output shaft shim, add measurement "B" to "D" then subtract distance "F". *See Fig. 5.* Select shims so shaft end play will be .002-.006" (.06-.15 mm) on transfer case input shaft or .0-.005" (.0-.13 mm) on rear axle output shaft. Shims are available from .004" (.1 mm) to .016" (.4 mm) for transfer case input shaft or from .004" (.1 mm) to .020" (.5 mm) for rear axle output shaft.

6) If transfer case input shaft bearings are not already pressed on shaft (from shim selection), press bearings onto transfer case input shaft. Install breather cover to transfer case input shaft. Install center spacer, needle bearings and spacers to countergear.

7) Install transfer case input shaft to transfer front case. Drive front axle shift fork plug out of transfer front case (this is necessary to install front axle shift fork). Install check spring and ball into hole in transfer rear case and retain with special retaining tool (ST23620000). *See Fig. 6.*

Fig. 6: Using Retaining Tool (ST23620000) to Retain Check Ball and Spring in Transfer Front Case

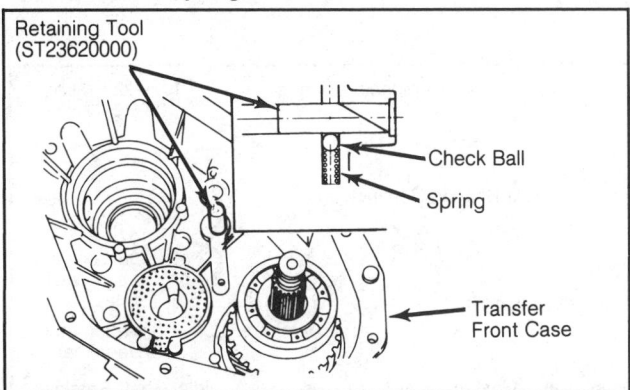

Retaining Tool (ST23620000)

Check Ball

Spring

Transfer Front Case

8) Install range shift fork to its synchro sleeve. Attach front axle shift rod bracket to front axle shift rod and secure it with a retaining pin. Install front axle shift rod to transfer rear case, pushing special tool (ST23620000) out of way. Install interlock plunger. Reassemble front axle shift fork in reverse order of disassembly (using an M8 bolt to compress spring to install snap rings).

9) Install new "O" ring (lubricated) to countershaft. Install countershaft to countergear, make sure thrust washer is already installed to countergear. Install countergear assembly to transfer rear case. Lift countergear assembly slightly and install rear axle output shaft assembly to transfer rear case. When installing rear axle output shaft gear assembly, make sure gears mesh together.

10) Install companion flange and nut to rear axle output shaft. Tighten nut finger tight. Tap on front end of rear axle output shaft to make sure it is seated properly. Install range shift rod to case and secure with retaining pin. Apply sealant to front axle shift fork plug hole, then drive plug into case. Install check ball and spring, apply sealant to plug and install plug.

11) Install synchro hub to front of rear axle output shaft. Select snap ring thickness so that synchro hub end play will be .0-.008" (.0-.2 mm). *See Fig. 7.* Snap rings are available from .051" (1.3 mm) to .067" (1.7 mm) in .004" (.1 mm) increments. Install snap rings selected.

Fig. 7: Measuring Synchro Hub to Bearing Clearance for Snap Ring Selection

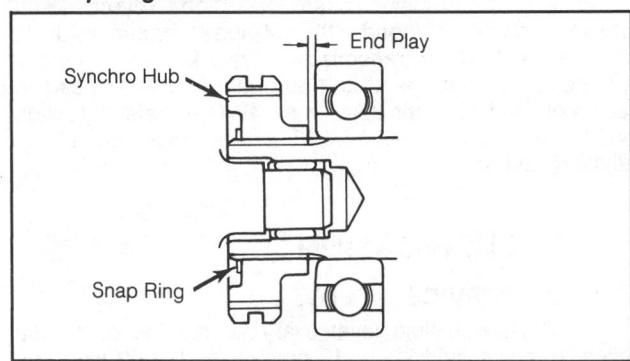

End Play

Synchro Hub

Snap Ring

12) Install shift lever with differential lever, then install cross shift shaft. Apply grease to thrust washer and shims selected in steps **4)** and **5)**, then install them in transfer front case. Clean mating surfaces of transfer cases, apply sealant to mating surfaces and install transfer front case to transfer rear case. Make sure gear assemblies, shift forks, shift rods, shims and thrust washer remain in position. Tapping case with mallet will aid in installation.

13) Install spacer, front axle shift fork assembly and spacer, then secure with snap ring. Install greased pilot bearing to rear axle output shaft, then install front axle output shaft to rear axle output shaft. Clean mating surfaces of transfer case and front cover, apply sealant to mating surfaces and install front cover. Install other 2 companion flanges.

14) Remove previously installed companion flange nut (it was tightened finger tight), then install all new companion flange nuts and tighten. Install 4WD indicator switch.

TIGHTENING SPECIFICATIONS

Application	Ft. Lbs. (N.m)
Check Ball Plug	14-18 (19-24)
Companion Flange Nuts	87-101 (118-137)
	INCH Lbs.
Case Bolts	72-96 (8-11)

Transfer Cases

TOYOTA LAND CRUISER

DESCRIPTION

The transfer case used on Toyota Land Cruiser models equipped with a 4-speed transmission is mounted on back of transmission. Transfer case provides a direct drive high speed and an underdrive low speed to rear axle and to front axle when 4WD is selected. High and low speeds as well as 4WD are selected through an auxiliary shifter.

LUBRICATION

SERVICE INTERVAL

Check fluid level every 12 months or 15,000 miles. Replace fluid every 12 months or 15,000 miles on vehicles used for pulling trailers or operated off-road.

FLUID TYPE

Use SAE-90 gear oil (API service GL-4).

CAPACITY

Fill up to just below level of filler plug hole.

REMOVAL & INSTALLATION

TRANSFER CASE ASSEMBLY

Removal

Remove PTO (if equipped) from transfer case and hang from frame with wire. Remove transmission and transfer case assembly from vehicle. *See appropriate article in MANUAL TRANSMISSIONS section.*

Installation

Reverse removal procedure and refill gear cases with lubricant.

TRANSFER CASE DISASSEMBLY

1) Remove speedometer driven gear, bolt and retainer. Remove transfer shift lever assembly. Check rear output shaft bearing preload. Preload should be 15-25 INCH lbs. (1.7-2.8 N.m) for new bearings and 6-10 INCH lbs. (.68-1.1 N.m) for used bearings. Remove detent balls and springs. Remove transmission output shaft cover and gasket.

Fig. 1: Exploded View of Toyota Land Cruiser Transfer Case

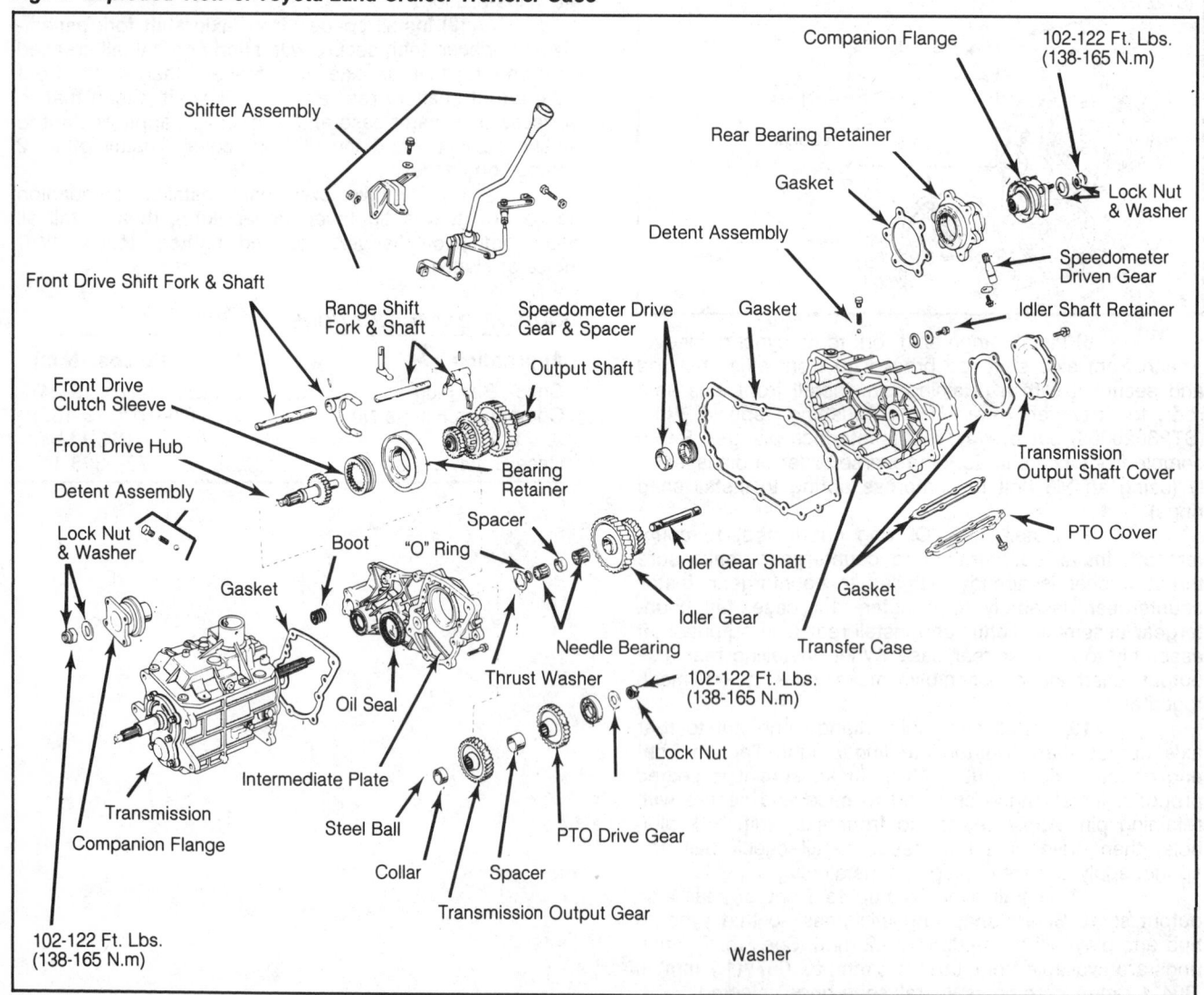

TOYOTA LAND CRUISER (Cont.)

2) Shift transfer case into 4WD Low range. Remove transmission output shaft nut and transfer case companion flange nuts. Remove both companion flanges. Remove rear output shaft bearing retainer and gasket. Remove idler gear shaft lock plate. Remove PTO cover on models not equipped with PTO.

3) Measure idler gear thrust clearance through PTO opening. Clearance should be .0108-.0246" (.274-.625 mm). If clearance exceeds specifications, idler gear thrust washer will need to be replaced at reassembly. Remove transfer case-to-intermediate plate attaching bolts.

4) Separate transfer case from intermediate plate. Remove speedometer drive gear and spacer from rear output shaft. Remove rear output shaft together with range shift fork and shift shaft. Drive roll pin out of range shift fork and separate fork from shaft.

Fig. 2: Exploded View of Transfer Case Rear Output Shaft

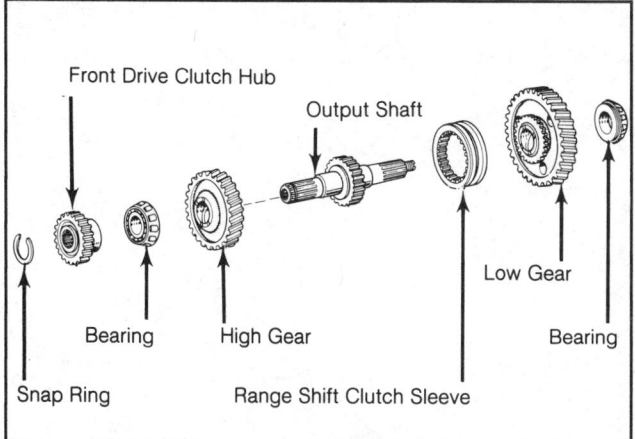

Front Drive Clutch Hub
Output Shaft
Low Gear
Bearing
Snap Ring
Bearing
High Gear
Range Shift Clutch Sleeve

5) Remove idler gear and shaft along with thrust washer, needle bearings and spacer. Using a puller, remove bearing retainer from intermediate plate. Heat retainer to 175°F (80°C) and press outer race out of bearing retainer. Remove front drive clutch sleeve, shift fork and shift shaft.

6) Drive roll pin out of front drive shift fork and separate shift shaft from fork. Remove transmission output shaft rear bearing using a puller. Remove PTO drive gear and spacer. Using a puller, remove transmission output gear. Remove intermediate plate and gasket from transmission.

Fig. 3: Output Shaft Bearing Clearance Measurement

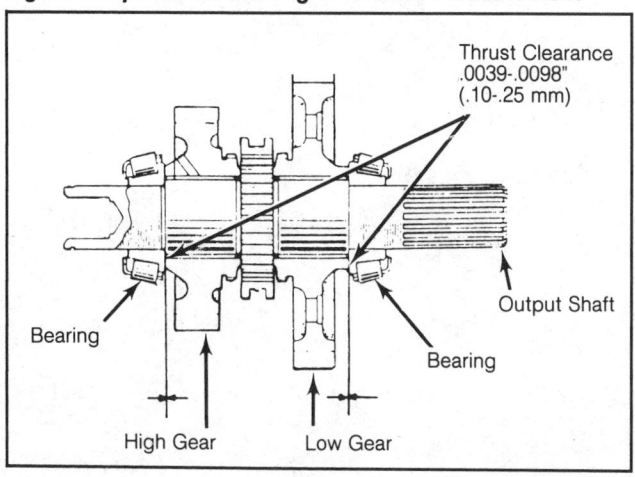

Thrust Clearance .0039-.0098" (.10-.25 mm)
Output Shaft
Bearing
Bearing
High Gear
Low Gear

7) Remove spacer and steel ball from transmission output shaft. Using a press, remove transfer case front output shaft from intermediate plate. Measure clearance between output shaft bearings and high and low gears on rear output shaft. Clearance should be .0039-.0098" (.10-.25 mm).

8) Remove snap ring from front of rear output shaft. Using a press, remove low gear and bearing from rear output shaft. Press high gear and bearing off front of rear output shaft. Remove clutch sleeve from rear output shaft.

CLEANING & INSPECTION

TRANSFER CASE & INTERMEDIATE PLATE

Inspect case, intermediate plate, PTO cover (if applicable) and bearing retainer for cracks or damage. Inspect oil seals and front output shaft bearing for wear.

OUTPUT SHAFT

Inspect front and rear output shafts for damage or wear. Check output shaft pilot bearing for rough operation and replace if necessary. Check oil clearance between gears and output shaft. Clearance should be .0014-.0032" (.035-.081 mm).

GEARS

Inspect teeth, thrust faces and inner bore diameter surfaces for excessive wear or damage.

BEARINGS

Inspect all bearings for wear, damage or rough operation. If an inner bearing race requires replacement, outer race should be replaced at the same time.

SLEEVES & SHIFT FORKS

Insert shift forks into clutch sleeves and measure clearance between fork and sleeve. Clearance should be .004-.016" (.1-.4 mm).

IDLER GEAR ASSEMBLY

Inspect idler gear for chipped teeth or excessive wear. Check idler gear shaft and bearings for wear or damage.

TRANSFER CASE REASSEMBLY

1) Install range shift clutch sleeve onto rear output shaft. Coat rear output shaft with grease and install high and low speed gears. Press rear output shaft bearing inner races onto shaft. Install front drive clutch hub onto front of rear output shaft and secure with a selective thickness snap ring.

2) Snap ring should be selected to keep axial play between .0012" (.003 mm) and .0118" (.299 mm). Apply gear oil to all moving parts on rear output shaft. Press front output shaft into intermediate plate. Install steel ball onto transmission output shaft and then slide collar over shaft and ball.

3) Coat transmission output shaft seal with grease. Install intermediate plate to transmission using sealer on all attaching bolts. Press transmission output

TOYOTA LAND CRUISER (Cont.)

gear onto shaft. Install spacer and PTO drive gear onto transmission output shaft. Press transmission output shaft rear bearing onto shaft and secure with a washer and lock nut. Install lock nut finger tight only.

4) Install front drive shift shaft into shift fork and secure with a roll pin. Place front drive shift sleeve into fork and install assembly into intermediate plate. Press rear output shaft front bearing outer race into bearing retainer. Tap bearing retainer into intermediate plate.

5) Install range shift fork onto shift shaft and secure with roll pin. Place range shift fork onto shift sleeve. Install rear output shaft and shift fork assembly into intermediate plate. Coat the idler gear thrust washer with grease and stick to intermediate plate, making sure that tab on thrust washer engages slot on plate.

6) Install front "O" ring onto idler gear shaft. Place idler gear on intermediate plate and install idler gear shaft so that 2" (50 mm) of shaft extends beyond gear. Install spacer and speedometer drive gear onto rear output shaft.

7) If idler gear thrust clearance was not to specifications at disassembly, select a thrust washer that will correct clearance. Clearance should be .0108-.0246" (.275-.625 mm). Coat idler gear thrust washer with grease and place on transfer case, making sure that tab on thrust washer engages slot in case.

8) Install transfer case onto intermediate plate, taking care to engage range selector lever tip with groove in range shift shaft. Install transfer case attaching bolts using liquid sealer.

9) Rotate idler gear shaft so that locking groove aligns with bolt hole. Install idler shaft rear "O" ring and tap shaft into place. Secure shaft with locking plate and bolt. Check operation of range shift lever to ensure smooth operation and proper engagement.

10) Recheck idler gear thrust clearance. Install rear bearing retainer, making sure that rib on case and retainer line up. Shift transfer case to 4WD Low range. Install front and rear companion flanges and secure with washers and lock nuts. Hold output shaft stationary and tighten companion flange nuts and transmission output shaft nut.

11) Disengage front drive and check rear output shaft bearing preload. Rotating torque should be 13-24 INCH lbs. (1.47-2.71 N.m) for new bearings and 6-10 INCH lbs. (.678-1.13 N.m) for used bearings.

12) If preload is not within specifications, preload shims must be changed. The preload shims are located between the rear bearing retainer and the rear output shaft bearing outer race.

13) Install PTO cover (if applicable) and transmission output shaft cover using liquid sealer on all bolts. Install shifter assembly and check for smooth operation and proper engagement of all gear ranges.

TIGHTENING SPECIFICATIONS

Application	Ft. Lbs. (N.m)
Intermediate Plate Bolts	37-57 (50-77)
Transfer Case-to-Intermediate Plate Bolts	
10 mm Bolts	26-32 (35-43)
12 mm Bolts	37-57 (50-77)
Rear Bearing Retainer	22-33 (30-45)
Companion Flange Nuts	102-122 (138-165)
Transmission Output Shaft Nut	102-122 (138-165)

TOYOTA 4-WD PICKUP

DESCRIPTION

The transfer case used on Toyota 4WD Pickup is mounted to rear of transmission by an adapter housing. Transfer case has 2 ranges, High and Low. Transfer case can be shifted into 4WD in either range (High or Low) and can be shifted into 4WD High range at any time, providing the locking hubs are in the "Lock" position. Transfer case is provided with an indicator switch to tell what position transfer selector lever is in.

LUBRICATION

SERVICE INTERVAL

Check fluid level every 12,000 miles or 15 months (whichever comes first). Drain and refill transfer case every 30,000 miles or 24 months.

FLUID TYPE

Use SAE 80W-90 gear oil (API-GL-4, GL-5).

CAPACITY

3.4 pts. (1.6 liters).

REMOVAL & INSTALLATION

TRANSFER CASE ASSEMBLY

NOTE: **Transmission and transfer case are removed together as an assembly.**

Removal

1) Disconnect battery negative cable. Using special wrench (SST09305-20011), remove transmission shift lever. Remove transfer shift lever. Raise and support vehicle.

2) Drain transfer case. Mark propeller shaft "U" joint positions on transfer case and differential flanges for reassembly reference. Remove propeller shaft. Remove clutch release cylinder and hose from transmission, but do not disconnect hydraulic line from cylinder. Disconnect all electrical connectors from transmission and transfer case. Remove starter and speedometer cable.

3) Remove engine rear mounting bolts. Support transmission case with a jack and remove crossmember. Lower jack until transmission and transfer case are low enough to be removed. Support engine with safety stand and wooden block under oil pan. Remove bolts

Fig. 1: Exploded View of Toyota 4WD Pickup Transfer Case Assembly

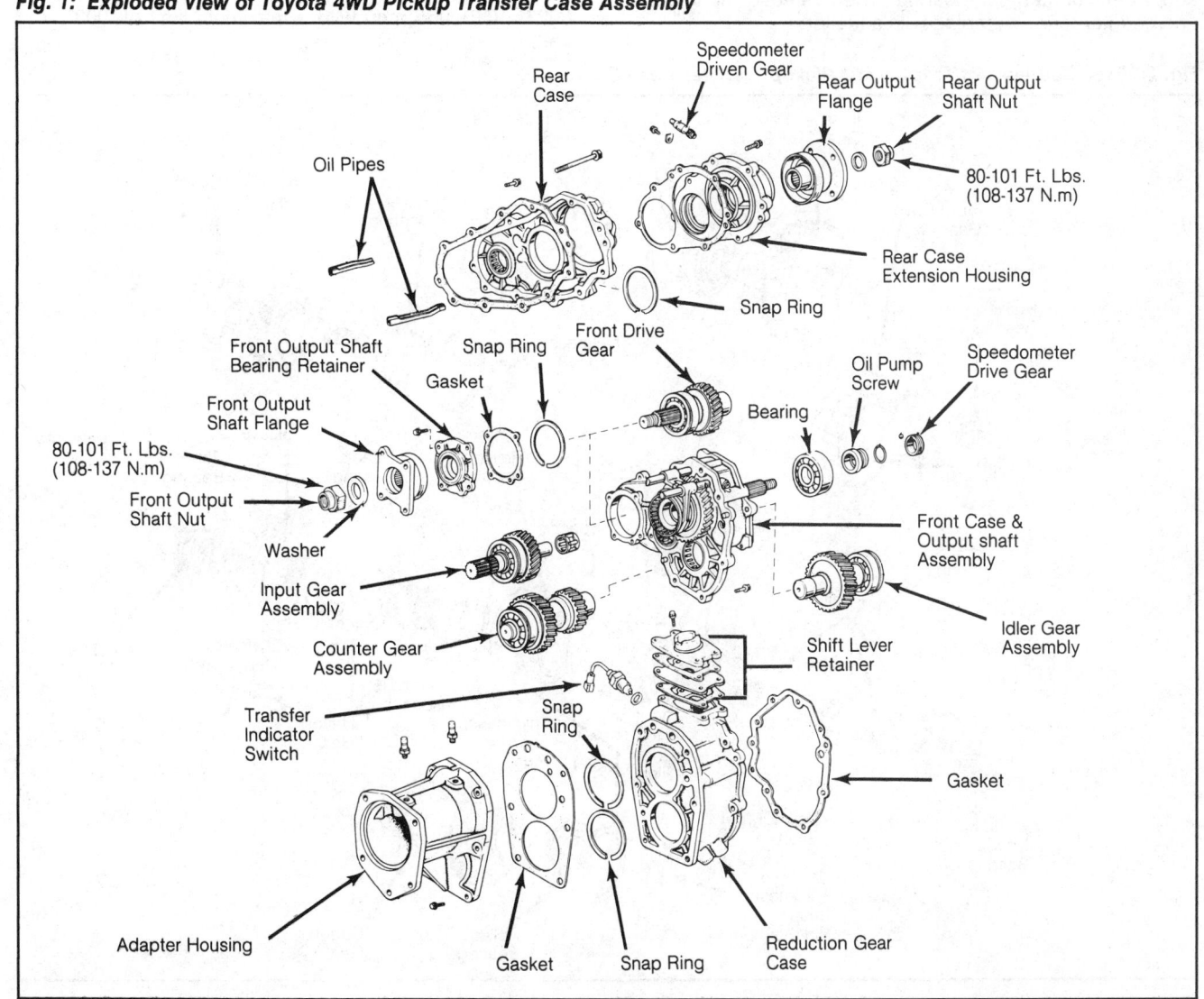

TOYOTA 4WD PICKUP (Cont.)

attaching transmission to engine and remove transmission and transfer case as an assembly.

4) Separate transfer case from transmission by removing bolts attaching adapter housing to transmission. Do not pry on transmission or adapter housing when separating.

Installation

Install transmission and transfer case in the reverse order of removal. Make sure marks on propeller shaft are aligned correctly and all electrical connectors are connected. Fill transfer case with correct type and amount of gear oil.

TRANSFER CASE DISASSEMBLY

Disassembly

1) Remove shifter assembly, speedometer driven gear and transfer indicator switch. Remove front output shaft nut. Remove flange and front drive gear bearing retainer. Remove adapter housing bolts and adapter housing. Remove reduction gear case together with input gear and countergear by tapping with a mallet.

2) Remove snap rings from input gear bearing and from countergear bearing. Then remove input gear and countergear by tapping with a mallet.

3) Remove output shaft nut, flange and bearing retainer housing. Remove speedometer drive gear, steel ball, oil pump screw and bearing. Remove case with idler gear by tapping with a mallet. Remove snap ring from idler gear bearing and remove idler gear by tapping with a mallet.

4) Hold front case upright so clutch hub and ball will not fall out. Remove snap ring from front drive gear bearing. Tap front drive gear out of front case.

NOTE: When removing front drive gear, hold front case upright or clutch hub and ball will fall out.

5) Move the shift forks to 2WD High range. Drive out spring pins from both shift forks and shift head. Remove shift forks with synchronizer sleeves. Remove synchronizer hub, transfer drive gear, needle bearings, spacer and steel ball. Remove shift head.

6) Remove detent springs, balls and plugs. Remove shift shafts and interlock pin. Remove snap ring from output shaft bearing. Place front case on wooden blocks and drive output shaft out of case with a mallet.

7) Remove snap ring on input gear shaft, then remove bearing with bearing puller. On output shaft, check oil gear clearance. Standard clearance is .0004-.0022" (.010-.055 mm) with a maximum limit of .003" (.075 mm).

Fig. 2: Exploded View of Toyota 4WD Pickup Transfer Case Gears

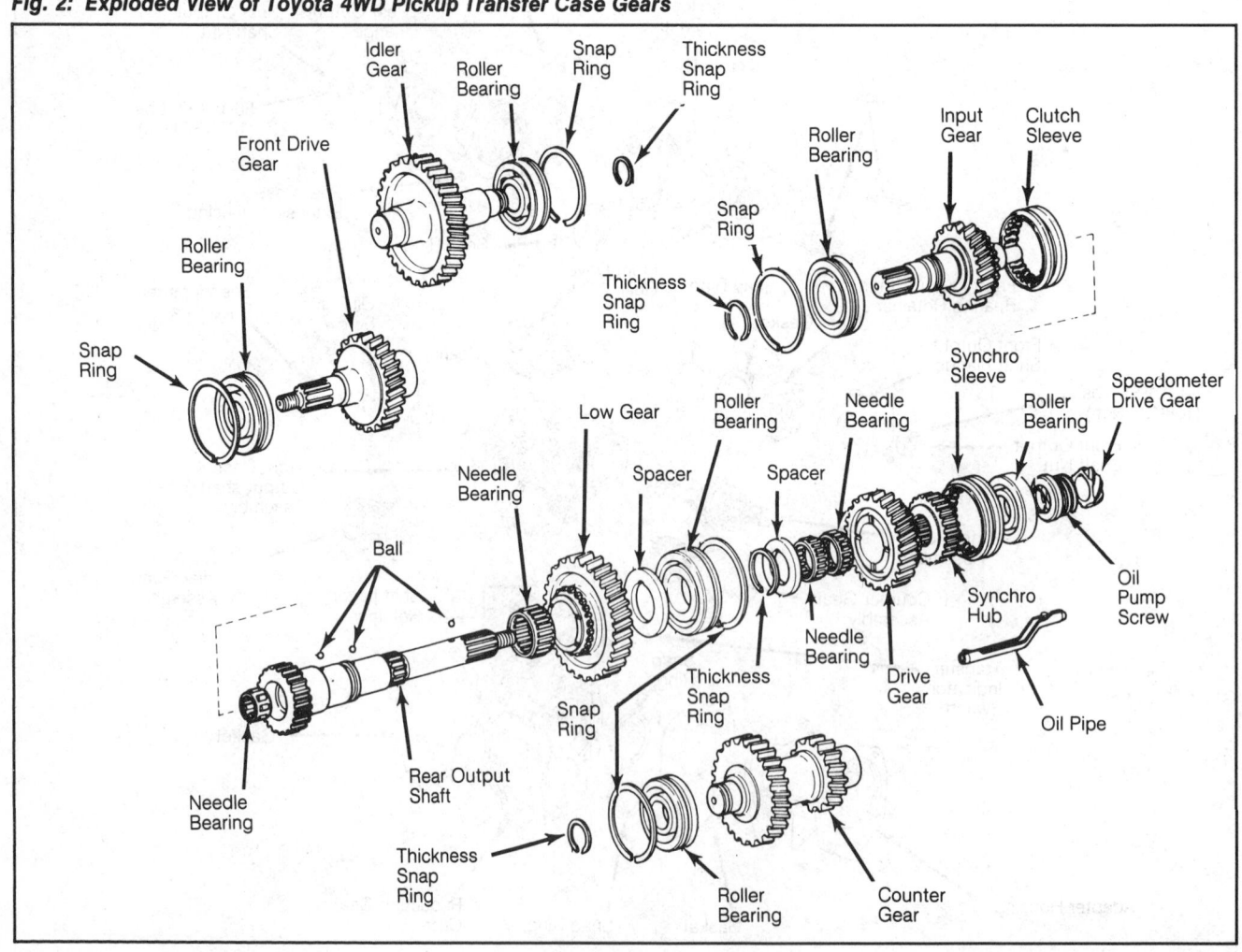

TOYOTA 4WD PICKUP (Cont.)

8) Check low gear thrust clearance by placing output shaft in a vise and attaching a dial indicator so that indicator button is against low gear. Push gear toward bearing and then pull away from bearing. Dial indicator should indicate a thrust clearance of .004-.010" (.10-.25 mm) with a maximum clearance of .012" (.30 mm).

9) If clearance is not to specifications, select thickness snap ring so that clearance will be to specifications. Remove output shaft bearing snap ring then press low gear and bearing off shaft. With gear and bearing removed from shaft, place shaft in "V" blocks and measure shaft runout. Runout should be less than .001" (.03 mm).

10) Remove snap ring on countergear, then remove bearing with puller. Remove idler gear snap ring and then remove bearing with puller. On front drive gear, press bearing off front drive gear shaft using bench press.

11) If necessary, remove bearings from transfer cases with bench press and adapter (SST09310-35010) or special bearing puller (SST09612-30012). If necessary, remove oil seals with oil seal puller (SST09308-00010).

12) Remove speedometer drive gear and ball then driven gear. Remove oil screw and ball. Remove transfer shift lever indicator.

CLEANING & INSPECTION

BEARINGS

Inspect bearings for wear and damage. Also check bearings for smooth rotation. Replace bearings as necessary.

GEARS

1) Check gear teeth, thrust faces, inside diameter surfaces, and toothed (for synchro sleeve) portion for wear or damage.

2) Check oil clearances between gears and shafts. Low gear oil clearance should be .004-.002" (.10-.25 mm) with a maximum clearance of .012" (.30 mm). Oil clearance on transfer drive gear should be .0004-.002" (.01-.05 mm) with a maximum clearance of .0028" (.071 mm).

3) Thrust clearance of low gear should be .004-.010" (.10-.25 mm) with a maximum clearance of .012" (.30 mm). Thrust clearance of transfer gear should be .004-.011" (.10-.27 mm) with a maximum clearance of .013" (.32 mm).

SYNCHRO HUBS, SLEEVES & SHIFT FORKS

Check synchro hub and sleeve for smooth sliding operation. Check synchro hub on shaft splines for smooth operation. Check clearance of shift forks to synchro sleeves. Clearance should be a maximum of .040" (1.0 mm).

SHIFT RODS

Check shift rods for wear or damage. Check plugs, springs balls and interlock pin for damage or wear. Make sure shift rods slide smoothly in transfer case.

SPEEDOMETER GEAR & OIL PUMP SCREW

Check the oil pump screw for damage, scoring or wear. Check "O" ring for damage. Check oil pipes for crimps or bending. Check speedometer gear for scoring, damage and smooth operation. Check "O" ring for damage.

TRANSFER CASE & HOUSINGS

1) Check adapter housing for cracks or damage. Check oil seal for damage, replace if necessary (when installing seal, make sure flat surface is upward).

2) Check reduction gear case for damage or cracks. Check front case for damage or cracks, and check bearings for damage, scoring and smoothness of operation. Replace bearings as necessary.

3) Check rear case for damage or cracks. Check bearing for damage, scoring and smoothness of operation. Replace as necessary.

4) Check extension housing and bearing retainer for damage or cracks. Check oil seals for damage, replace as necessary. Check flanges, shift lever and shift lever retainer for damage, scoring or wear.

5) Check transfer indicator for proper operation. Connect ohmmeter leads to switch connector. With switch plunger extended there should be no continuity (infinity reading). With switch plunger pushed in, there should be full continuity (zero reading). Replace switch if necessary.

TRANSFER CASE REASSEMBLY

NOTE: Apply gear lubricant to all gears, bearings, shafts and seals during assembly.

1) Install low gear, spacer, roller bearing and thickness snap ring to rear output shaft. Select thickness snap ring that allows minimum axial play of bearing. See Rear Output Shaft Thickness Snap Ring chart. Install rear output shaft into front case then install snap ring to roller bearing. Install bearing retainer to front case and tighten bolts.

REAR OUTPUT SHAFT SNAP RINGS

Snap Ring Mark	Thickness In. (mm)
0	.094-.096 (2.40-2.45)
1	.096-.098 (2.45-2.50)
2	.098-.100 (2.50-2.55)
3	.100-.102 (2.55-2.60)
4	.102-.104 (2.60-2.65)
5	.104-.106 (2.65-2.70)

2) Install range shift rod and interlock pin in front case. Install 4WD shift rod in front case. Install clip on rod. Move range shift rod to the high 2WD position, then install detent ball and spring (to both rods). Apply sealant to plugs and install.

3) Install shift head. Install synchronizer sleeve and shift fork to range shift rod. Install spring pin through range fork and into rod. Install steel ball and spacer to output shaft. Install 2 sets of needle bearings and transfer drive gear to output shaft.

4) Install synchro hub to output shaft. Install synchro sleeve and shift fork (together) to output shaft. Install spring pin through shift fork into shift rod.

TOYOTA 4WD PICKUP (Cont.)

5) Place front case (with output shaft installed) into upright position. Install front drive gear (with roller bearing installed) to front case. Install snap ring onto bearing. Apply grease to oil seal in bearing retainer and install bearing retainer to front case.

NOTE: **Bearing retainer has an oil groove. Make sure this groove is aligned to oil hole in front case.**

6) Install oil pipes to front case with cut out sides of oil pipes towards top of front case (as case would be installed in vehicle).

7) Install bearing on idler gear. Select proper thickness snap ring that allows minimum axial play and install. *See Idler Gear Snap Ring chart for snap ring sizes available.* Install idler gear into rear case. Install snap ring on bearing. Install rear case, with idler gear, onto front case. Install six 1.9" (47 mm) bolts to rear case as shown in *Fig. 3.*

Fig. 3: Installation Bolts Needed when Installing Rear Case to Front Case

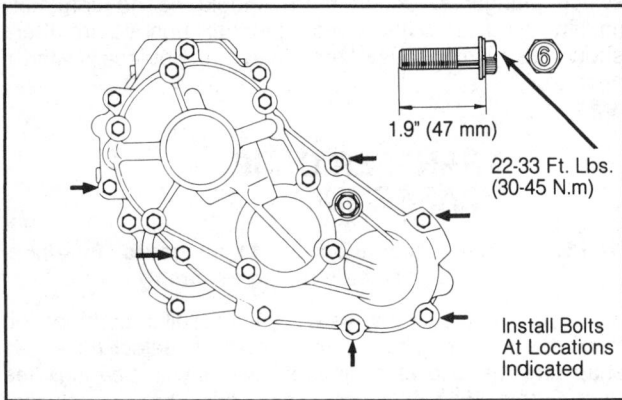

1.9" (47 mm)

22-33 Ft. Lbs. (30-45 N.m)

Install Bolts At Locations Indicated

IDLER GEAR SNAP RINGS

Snap Ring Mark	Thickness In. (mm)
A	.059-.061 (1.50-1.55)
B	.063-.065 (1.60-1.65)

8) Install roller bearing and oil pump screw to output shaft. Install steel ball and speedometer drive gear to output shaft. Apply grease to oil seal of front case extension housing. Install extension housing using seven 1.5" (37 mm) bolts as shown in *Fig. 4.*

Fig. 4: Installation Bolts Needed when Installing Extension Housing to Rear Case

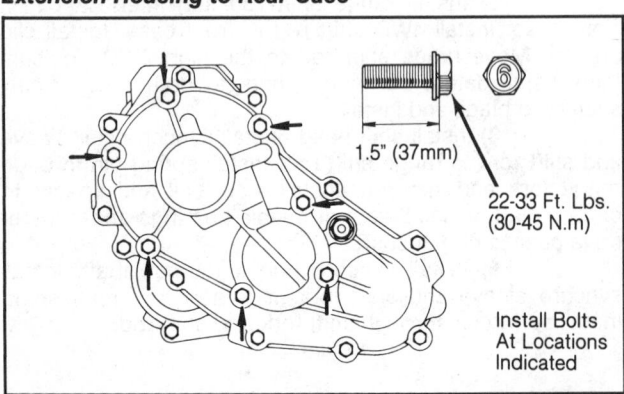

1.5" (37mm)

22-33 Ft. Lbs. (30-45 N.m)

Install Bolts At Locations Indicated

9) Install output flange then output shaft nut. After tightening nut, stake nut to output shaft. Install needle bearing to front of output shaft (inside end of shaft).

10) Install roller bearing and proper thickness snap ring to input gear. *See Input Gear Snap Ring chart for snap ring sizes available.* Install roller bearing and proper thickness snap ring to countergear. *See Countergear Snap Ring chart for snap ring sizes available.* Install input gear to reduction gear case, then install snap ring on roller bearing.

INPUT GEAR SNAP RINGS

Snap Ring Mark	Thickness In. (mm)
1	.081-.083 (2.05-2.10)
3	.085-.087 (2.15-2.20)
5	.089-.091 (2.25-2.30)

COUNTERGEAR SNAP RINGS

Snap Ring Mark	Thickness In. (mm)
1	.083-.085 (2.10-2.15)
3	.087-.089 (2.20-2.25)

11) Install reduction gear case to front case. Install four 4.4" (112 mm) bolts and two 1.9" (47 mm) bolts to case as shown in *Fig. 5.* Apply grease to adapter housing oil seal and install housing to reduction gear case using six 1.5" (37 mm) bolts as shown in *Fig. 6.*

Fig. 5: Installation Bolts Needed when Installing Reduction Gear Case to Front Case

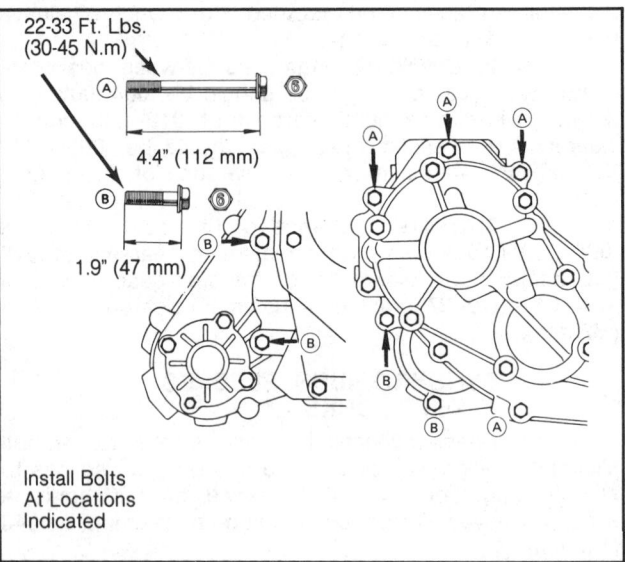

22-33 Ft. Lbs. (30-45 N.m)

4.4" (112 mm)

1.9" (47 mm)

Install Bolts At Locations Indicated

12) Install flange to front output shaft, and install front output shaft nut. After tightening, stake nut to shaft. Install transfer indicator switch. Connect ohmmeter leads to switch and move shift forks to make sure switch operates. Place forks in 4WD High range.

13) Install shift lever retainer and speedometer driven gear and sleeve. Attach transfer case to transmission. Apply sealant to bolts. Install transmission shift lever retainer to adapter housing. Attach engine rear mount to transfer case.

TOYOTA 4WD PICKUP (Cont.)

Fig. 6: Installation Bolts Needed when Installing Adapter Housing to Reduction Gear Case

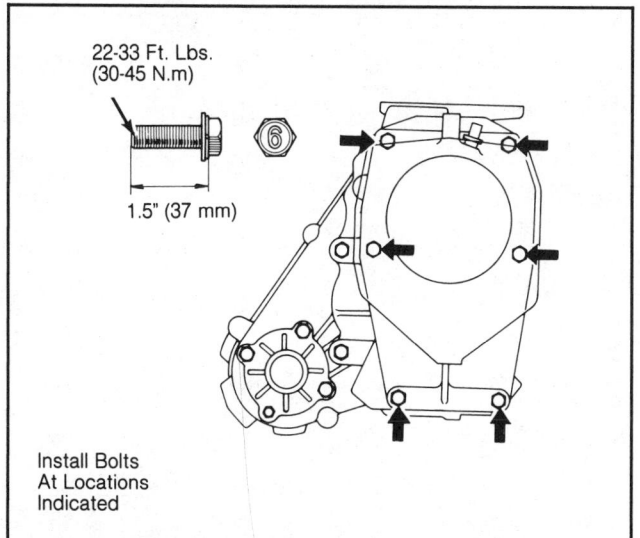

22-33 Ft. Lbs.
(30-45 N.m)

1.5" (37 mm)

Install Bolts
At Locations
Indicated

TIGHTENING SPECIFICATIONS

Application	Ft. Lbs. (N.m)
Adapter Housing Bolts	22-33 (30-45)
Bearing Retainer Bolts	
Front Output Shaft	12-16 (16-22)
Rear Output Shaft	7-12 (9-16)
Crossmember-to-Frame	54-76 (73-103)
Crossmember-to-Transfer Case	7-12 (9-16)
Front Output Shaft Nut	80-101 (108-137)
Propeller Shaft-to-Flange	29-43 (39-58)
Rear Case-to-Front Case	22-33 (30-45)
Rear Case-to-Extension Hsg.	22-33 (30-45)
Rear-Output Shaft Nut	80-101 (108-137)
Reduction Gear Housing Bolts	22-33 (30-45)
Shift Lever Retainer	7-12 (9-16)
Speedometer Driven Gear Retainer	7-12 (9-16)
Transfer Indicator Switch	22-36 (30-40)
Transmission-to-Engine Bolts	36-58 (49-79)

Notes

Notes

Notes

Notes

Notes

Notes

Notes

Notes

Notes

TRANSMISSION SERVICING

FIAT

[1]   1979-81 FIAT STRADA WITH MANUAL TRANSAXLE: SHIFT LINKAGE VIBRATION — Some 1979-81 Strada vehicles may develop a vibration in the shift linkage. This condition may be caused by the plastic sleeve sliding off the arm of the shift linkage anti-vibration bracket.

    Install a 5/16" interior diameter push nut on the end of the anti-vibration bracket swing arm.

Fiat Strada Push Nut Installation on Swing Arm Bracket End

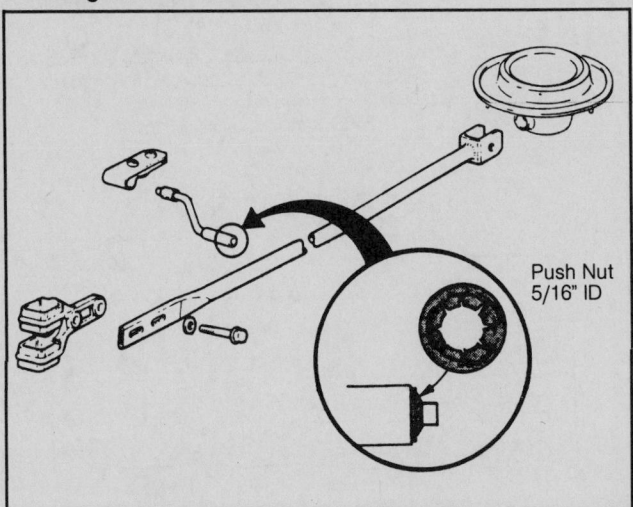

Push Nut 5/16" ID

HONDA

[2]   1981-82 HONDA ACCORD, CIVIC AND PRELUDE WITH AUTOMATIC TRANSAXLE: ROUGH SHIFTING AND/OR CLUTCH CHATTER — Some 1981-82 Accord, Civic and Prelude models with automatic transaxle may exhibit rough shifting and/or clutch chatter. This condition may be caused by improper type automatic transmission fluid usage.

    If improper type automatic transmission fluid usage is suspected, drain transaxle and replace fluid with that of a recommended type. Recommended types of automatic transmission fluid are: Dexron or Dexron II®.

VOLKSWAGEN

[3]   1980-82 VOLKSWAGEN JETTA, RABBIT, RABBIT PICKUP AND SCIROCCO WITH 5-SPEED MANUAL TRANSAXLE: JAMMING SHIFT LINKAGE — Some 1980-82 Volkswagen Jetta, Rabbit, Rabbit Pickup and Scirocco models with 5-speed manual transaxles may develop a "spongy" or "jamming" shift linkage condition. A revised shift rod adjustment procedure has been released to correct this condition.

    1) Adjust shift rod end so that distance "A" is 9/16" (15 mm) as shown. *See Shift Rod Adjusting Illustration.*

    2) Tighten shift rod clamp to 14 ft. lbs. (20 N.m). Shift through all gears and check that they engage easily and without "jamming".

    3) If shift linkage is still "spongy" or "jamming" after adjustment, adjust "A" to 1/2" (13 mm) and recheck operation.

Shift Rod Adjusting Illustration

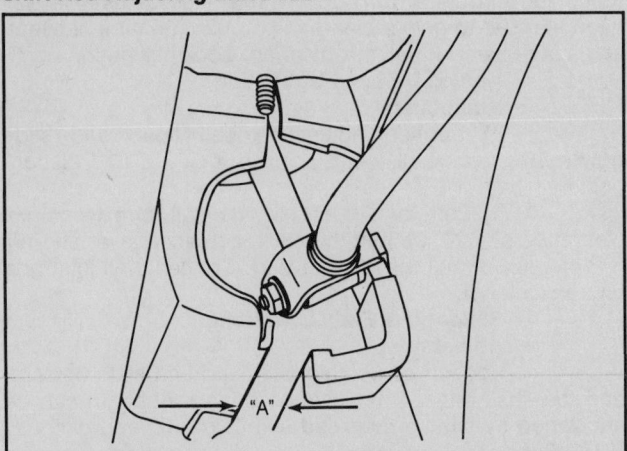

"A"

AUTOMATIC TRANSMISSIONS

AUDI

[1]   1980 AUDI 5000 MODELS WITH 087 AUTOMATIC TRANSMISSIONS: STRAINER DELETED — Beginning with transmission number 21040, the strainer in the pressure channel has been deleted from production. During repairs to transmissions built prior to number 21040, do not reinstall the strainer.

CHRYSLER CORP. IMPORTS

[2]   1981 DODGE CHALLENGER & PLYMOUTH SAPPORO WITH AUTOMATIC TRANSMISSIONS: DRIVELINE SHUDDER DURING ACCELERATION — On these vehicles, a shudder noise may be heard during medium or heavy acceleration up to 15-20 MPH. This may be caused by excessive drive line angle at the center universal joint. To correct this problem, replace the center bearing with the new, redesigned, center bearing (MB154086). This new bearing raises the propeller shaft slightly to provide an improved universal joint angle.

MERCEDES-BENZ

[3]   1980 MERCEDES-BENZ DIESEL ENGINE MODELS EXCEPT TURBOCHARGED ENGINES: ADJUSTMENT OF VACUUM MODULATING VALVE — Since December 1979, a modified vacuum modulating valve was installed on the transmission. Shifting complaints such as hard, delayed or light slipping, and premature up-shifting at partial load can be corrected by adjusting vacuum modulating valve individually. Vehicles which do not have the modified valve and have the complaints listed, must have the valve installed in conjunction with a push rod and plastic connector. The modified vacuum valve has a full throttle stop and an idle stop. This stop prevents the deviation of the predetermined tensioned spring in modulating valve, due to overexertion of actuating lever against spring. Adjustment is as follows:

Latest Changes & Corrections
FOR 1982 & EARLIER MODELS (Cont.)

1) Basic adjustment requires that the rod be adjusted to a length of 4-13/16" (122 mm). Compensating adjustment is made with ball head at regulating lever.

2) Apply full throttle, causing actuating lever to touch full throttle stop. Loosen and slide adjustable ball head in order to gain a clearance of .020" (.5 mm) between actuating lever and full throttle stop. Lock ball head.

Hard & Delayed Upshifting Adjustment

1) Loosen adjustable ball head and slide downward. Lock ball head. Loosen lock nut and disconnect ball joint.

2) Lengthen push rod via ball joint to gain a clearance of .020" (.5 mm) between actuating lever and full throttle stop in full throttle position. Connect ball joint and tighten lock nut.

Slippage & Early Upshifting Adjustment

Loosen adjustable ball head and slide upward, and lock ball head. If necessary, push rod length can be shortened by cutting threaded end of rod by approximatly 3/16" (5 mm).

NOTE: After adjustments of vacuum modulating valve, the EGR vacuum control must be tested and corrected if required.

4) MERCEDES-BENZ 240D AND 300 SERIES MODELS WITH AUTOMATIC TRANSMISSION: MODIFICATION OF SHIFT VALVE HOUSING FOR MODIFIED PARTIAL LOAD SHIFT POINTS — Since June, 1980, the large intermediate steel plate with a larger restricting bore of .1181" (3 mm) was installed in transmissions on these vehicles. In addition, a modified control pressure increase valve with corresponding spring, as well as modified springs on 1st and 2nd gear shift control valve and control pressure regulating valve were installed. These changes will prevent rapid successive upshifts and spread partial load downshifts to high side.

If complaints of this nature exist on earlier production vehicles, the restricting bore of large intermediate plate can be enlarged using the following procedure:

1) Remove valve body from transmission. Disassemble valve body.

2) Enlarge restricting bore in large intermediate plate to diameter of .1181" (3 mm).

NOTE: 240D models use a different intermediate plate than 300 series models. Be sure that proper hole is enlarged on correct plate.

3) Remove any burrs from enlarged hole. Loosen fastening screws on end plate and remove all except one.

4) Swing out end plate far enough to allow for removal of plug, control pressure regulating valve and both springs.

5) Replace heavier spring with new spring (123 993 41 01). Reinsert lighter spring, regulating valve and plug. Tighten end plate screws.

6) Loosen fastening screws on opposite side of end plate and remove all screws except one. Swing out end plate far enough to allow removal of control pressure increase valve and 1-2 shift valve with piston and spring.

7) Replace increase valve and spring with new valve (123 993 40 01). Insert 1-2 shift valve with piston and

spring in valve body. Tighten screws and assemble valve body and install in transmission.

8) Check and, if necessary, refill fluid level.

Mercedes-Benz Intermediate Plate Resticting Bores

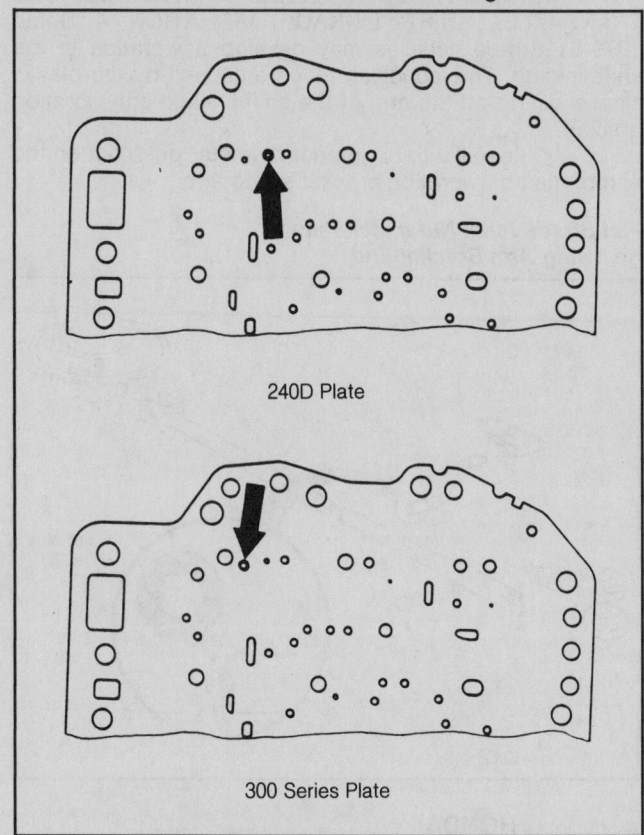

240D Plate

300 Series Plate

RENAULT

5) 1981 RENAULT 18i WITH AUTOMATIC TRANSMISSION: GOVERNOR COMPUTOR — The governor computor on the 1981 Renault 18i may have to be insulated from heat to ensure proper operation. To install the new heat shield (7701 263 923), perform the following:

1) Raise vehicle on hoist. Loosen 2 differential-to-transmission bolts on left side of transmission. Position shield so that shield clip faces side-member. Shield will be 180° away from installed position at this point.

2) Move shield upward and turn it counterclockwise to align seat notches in shield with bolts loosened in step **1)**. Insert governor computor plastic cable into shield clip. Tighten differential-to-transmission bolts to 15 ft. lbs. (20 mm).

6) 1981 RENAULT 18i WITH AUTOMATIC TRANSMISSION: NO START IN PARK — The 1981 Renault 18i may develop a problem in that the engine will not start with the transmission gear selector in the park position. This problem is corrected by installing a gasket (7703 061 013) between the multi-function switch and the transmission housing. Also, adjust transmission shift linkage if necessary.

FOR 1982 & EARLIER MODELS (Cont.)

SAAB

⑦ SAAB VEHICLES WITH TYPE 35 AUTOMATIC TRANSMISSIONS: NEW PINION SEAL SHAFT OIL SEAL — An improved pinion shaft seal (9346602) is available for use on Saab 99 and 900 models with type 35 automatic transmission. The seal is a "V" ring design and replaces one of two seals previously used.

A new distance spacer (8791022) must be used with installing tool (8790164) to properly position seal (8707176) so new seal will seat against it properly. The following procedure should be used to install the seal:

1) Press seal (8707176) into pinion housing installing tool and distance spacer. Be sure seal lip faces toward transmission.

2) Place seal protector (8791006) on pinion shaft. Lubricate new seal and slide onto pinion shaft with thick portion against pinion bearing.

3) Reassemble pinion shaft, housing and governor following standard reassembling procedures.

TOYOTA

⑧ 1978-82 TOYOTA CELICA, COROLLA, CORONA, CRESSIDA & SUPRA WITH A40D AUTOMATIC OVERDRIVE TRANSMISSION: COASTING DOWNSHIFT SHOCK OR CLUNK — Some 1978-82 Toyota vehicles with A40D automatic overdrive transmission may develop a clunk when coasting to a stop in "D" range. This transmission is designed to shift from 3rd to 1st gear when coasting, but may shift from 3rd to 2nd, and then to 1st gear if excessive throttle pressure exists. The shock, or clunk, occurs as B-1 brake engages at 3rd to 2nd gear downshift and may also be caused by an improperly adjusted transmission throttle cable.

1) Inspect and, if necessary, adjust throttle cable. Raise vehicle on hoist. Drain transmission fluid. Remove oil pan, taking care not to damage oil filler tube and "O" ring.

2) Remove detent plate. Install up to 3 "E" rings (90523-06023) between throttle valve and secondary spring. Each "E" ring reduces throttle pressure approximately 3 psi.

3) Install detent plate and oil pan. Fill transmission with 2.4 qts. of type F automatic transmission fluid. Check line pressure. Road test vehicle. Recheck fluid level after engine is at normal operating temperature.

Sectional View of Toyota A40D Detent Plate

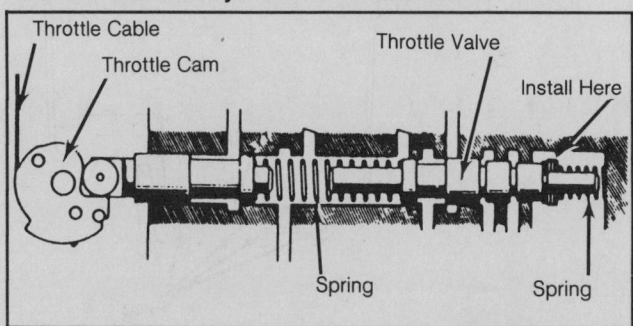

VOLVO

⑨ 1976-81 VOLVO 240 AND 260 WITH BW55 AUTOMATIC TRANSMISSION: TRANSMISSION AUXILIARY OIL COOLER KIT — Some 1976-81 Volvo 240 and 260 models with BW55 automatic transmissions may experience premature transmission failure when operated under extreme conditions such as towing a trailer or camper or driving fast for long periods at high ambient temperatures. An auxiliary transmission oil cooler kit (1188253-7) is available for use when operating under these conditions.

1) Remove grille. Remove air guide, if equipped.

2) On models with air conditioning, remove washer reservoir. Remove bolts holding cover plate, but do not disconnect the hood lock cable from its attachment. Swivel cover plate 1/4 of a turn toward left front inner fender panel.

3) Remove 4 screws retaining the condenser. Pull condenser as far forward as possible and push radiator as far to the rear as possible.

4) Using the template provided in kit, mark radiator right side plate on the engine compartment side. Drill two .82" (21 mm) holes where indicated, taking care not to drill into the condenser or damage the freon pipes and hoses.

5) On models without air conditioning, push radiator as far to the rear as possible. Using the template provided in kit, mark exterior radiator right side plate. Drill two .82" (21 mm) holes where indicated.

6) On all models, assemble the oil cooler. Connect hoses to oil cooler. Place opposite ends of the hoses together. Align hoses with cooler and tighten connections.

7) Fit oil cooler bracket (2 bolts) to oil cooler. Feed cooler hoses through the holes previously drilled and install rubber grommets. Mark holes for the oil cooler mounting bracket.

8) Drill .27" (7 mm) hole closest to the radiator right side plate first. Using the oil cooler mounting bracket as a template, drill the .27" (7 mm) oil cooler left hand mounting hole.

9) Refit air guide, if equipped. Mount oil cooler. Install the thermostat, if equipped, to the upper radiator transmission cooler pipe connection. Carefully reshape the oil pipe from the transmission and connect to the thermostat.

10) On models with V6 engines, fit the thermostat to the lower radiator tramsmission cooler pipe connection. Ensure thermostat does not turn when connecting the pipe.

11) On all models, attach angled connectors. Using a counterhold on the thermostat connectors to prevent deformation of the walls inside the thermostat, connect the hoses from the oil cooler.

12) Start engine and warm to normal operating temperature. Check transmission fluid and add as necessary. Check for leaks. Reinstall parts previously removed for access purposes. Road test vehicle and recheck for leaks.

⑩ VOLVO MODELS WITH BORG-WARNER 55 TRANSMISSIONS: PUMP OIL SEAL — The green pump oil seal for BW55 transmissions can, in extreme cases,

Latest Changes & Corrections

FOR 1982 & EARLIER MODELS (Cont.)

cause an oil leakage. This will only occur when towing a heavy trailer, driving in mountainous terrain or after prolonged high speed driving in hot temperatures. This can be corrected by replacing the green seal with a red Koyo seal with same part number. Red seal has been put into production in transmissions after the following numbers; 014-24256, 019-5155, 020-3549 and 023-7027.

MANUAL TRANSMISSIONS

AUDI

1 ⟩ 1981 AUDI 400 WITH MANUAL TRANSMISSION: MODIFIED TRANSMISSION MOUNTING — During the 1981 model production year the transmission mount was modified. As a result, mounting bolt torques are now as follows: Subframe-to-Body is 51 ft. lbs. (69 N.m); Rubber Mount-to-Body is 80 ft. lbs. (108 N.m); Rubber Mount-to-Support is 18 ft. lbs. (24 N.m)

2 ⟩ 1981 AUDI 4000 WITH MANUAL TRANSMISSION: RELOCATED TRANSMISSION BREATHER — On 1981 Audi 4000 models, the transmission breather has been relocated from the shift housing to the top of the final drive housing. The new breather should be installed with a drift punch. The new breather is correctly installed when distance from top of breather to final drive case is 27/32" (21 mm). When the new breather is installed, be sure to plug old breather hole in shift housing with a 1/8" (3 mm) pop rivet.

3 ⟩ 1980 AUDI 4000 MODELS WITH 014 4-SPEED TRANSMISSIONS: TRANSMISSION BREATHER MODIFIED — The breather on these transmissions has been relocated onto the final drive housing. When installing a new housing on 014 transmissions, drive the breather into the housing to a depth of 27/32" (21 mm). When re-using gear shift housings, the old breather hole must be plugged with a 1/8" (3 mm) pop rivet. Gear shift housings with and without breather holes are available as spare parts, however, only install housings with breather hole in transmissions up to number 21 01 0.

CHRYSLER CORP. IMPORTS

4 ⟩ 1982 CHRYSLER CORP. CHAMP AND COLT WITH KM 160 AND KM 165 MANUAL TRANSAXLES: INTERMEDIATE SHAFT AND OUTPUT SHAFT ADJUSTMENT PROCEDURE — The rear cover was eliminated during production for 1982 models. New procedures are required for intermediate and output shaft adjustments. These adjustments can be performed as follows:

1) With transmission assembled to the point where it is ready to go into the transmission case, put soft solid core wire solder "fuses" on the outer race inserting portion of the case and press in the outer race. Place the fuses at diametrically opposed positions as shown in the illustration.

2) Install the transmission case gasket. Do not apply sealant to gasket. Install the fuse and outer race attached case and tighten all bolts.

3) Remove transmission case. Remove outer race. Remove the fuses and measure their thickness with a micrometer.

4) Based on the measurements, select the appropriate spacers to assure the specified end play and preload. Spacers are the same as conventional ones.

INTERMEDIATE & OUTPUT SHAFT SPECIFICATIONS

Application	Specification
Intermediate Shaft	0-.05" Loose
Output Shaft	.15-.20" Tight

Chrysler Corp. Imports Intermediate & Output Shaft End Play Checking

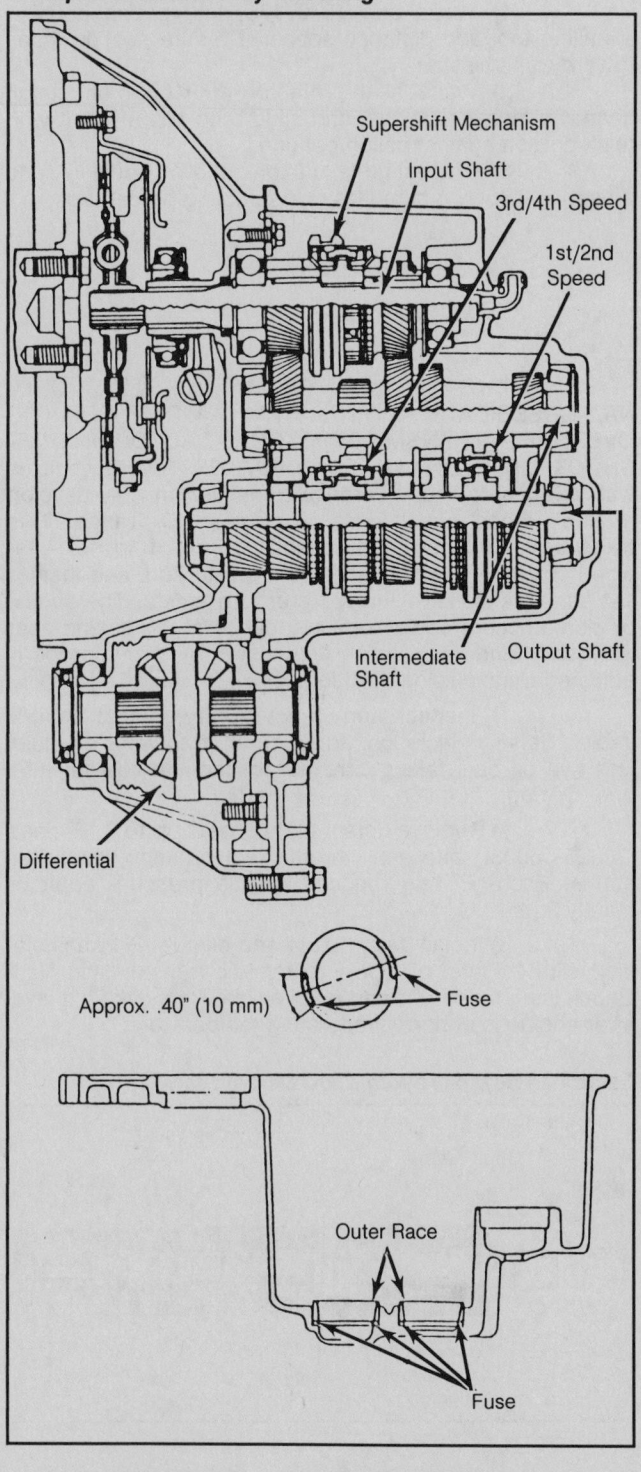

FOR 1982 AND EARLIER MODELS (Cont.)

⑤ 1981 DODGE RAM-50 PICKUP & PLYMOUTH ARROW PICKUP WITH 2.6L ENGINE & 5-SPEED MANUAL TRANSMISSION: CLUTCH CHATTER — These models may develop a clutch chatter when clutch is first being engaged, especially when starting from a complete stop. To correct this problem, a new clutch friction disc is now available (MD802132). This disc uses new friction material that should eliminate the chatter condition under normal use.

HONDA

⑥ 1980-81 HONDA CIVIC WITH MANUAL TRANSAXLE: STIFF SHIFTING — Some 1980-81 Civic models may exhibit stiff gearshift lever action. This condition may be caused by the collar/bushing set in the transaxle linkage being too tight. There is now a redesigned collar/bushing set (106877) available to replace the old style collar/bushing set, as shown in the illustration.

Exploded View Of Honda Shifting Lever Linkage

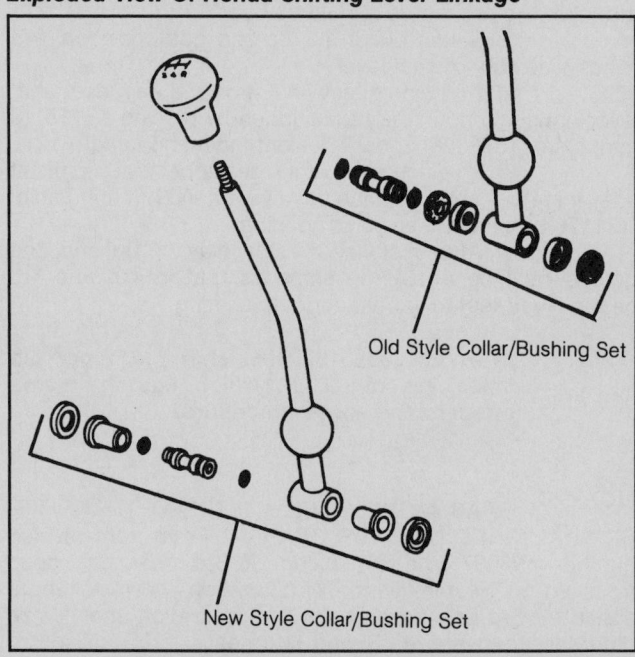

Old Style Collar/Bushing Set

New Style Collar/Bushing Set

1) Using an impact driver, remove holder plate attaching screws. Slide interlock bar from assembly.

2) Pull shift arm shaft out and catch detent ball and spring when they drop from shift arm. Lift shift arm, spring seats and springs from holder.

3) Install new collar/bushing set, then position shift arm, spring seats and springs into holder.

4) Invert assembly and install detent ball and spring into bore in shift arm. Hold ball and spring in place and insert shift shaft through arm, seats, and springs.

5) Install interlock bar. Install holder plate and tighten attaching screws, then stake screws in place with a center punch.

⑦ 1979-81 HONDA ACCORD AND PRELUDE WITH 5-SPEED MANUAL TRANSAXLE: TRANSAXLE SLIPS OUT OF GEAR — Some 1979-81 Accord and Prelude models with 5-speed transaxle may slip out of gear.

This condition may be corrected by replacing the detent spring of the gear transaxle is slipping out of. When removing detent spring from transaxle use care not to lose check ball which may fall out when removing detent spring. These springs can be easily replaced from the underside of the transaxle as shown in the illustration.

Exploded View of Honda Transaxle

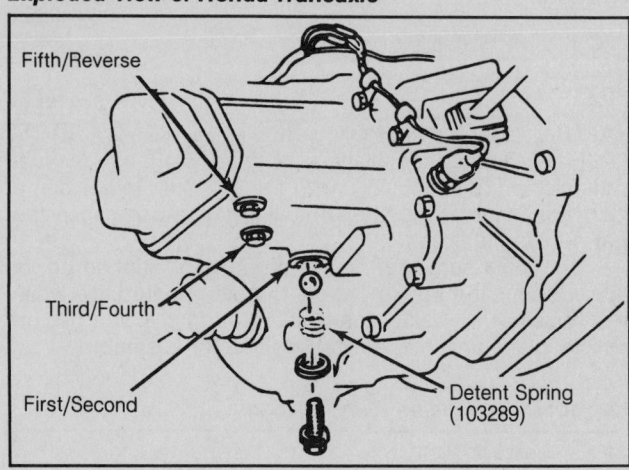

Fifth/Reverse

Third/Fourth

First/Second

Detent Spring (103289)

⑧ 1979 HONDA ACCORD AND PRELUDE: HARD TO SHIFT 5-SPEED — Some 1979 Accord and Prelude models may experience a condition in which it is hard to shift into one or more forward gears. This can be repaired as follows:

1) Check clutch adjustment for 1/8" (3.2 mm) free play between the clutch arm and the slave cylinder push rod. Check transaxle oil level and add if necessary. Test drive vehicle to confirm that condition still exists.

2) Remove the shift lever console and pull the shift boot up. Check the screws for both shift lever stops. If a screw has fallen out, the stop may have dropped into the mount where it can interfere with shift lever travel.

3) Remove both shift lever stops and replace them if they are damaged. Reinstall the shift lever stops, using lock washers and Loctite on the screws.

4) If the transaxle is still hard to shift, remove the transaxle from the vehicle. Remove the shift guide shaft and the shift guide from the transaxle.

5) Inspect the guide for wear. If the guide bore is out-of-round or tapered, replace the shift guide shaft (H/C 72749) and the shift guide (H/C 72762).

6) Inspect the large hole in the shift arm holder for wear. If the large hole is worn, replace the shift arm holder (H/C 76935) and the shift guide shaft.

7) Replace the 1-2 synchronizer sleeve (H/C 72717) and springs (H/C 72727). Replace the 3-4 synchronizer sleeve (H/C 72720). Reinstall the transaxle in the vehicle and road test to verify that the problem has been corrected.

MERCEDES-BENZ

⑨ MERCEDES-BENZ VEHICLES WITH 716.005/006 TRANSMISSIONS: MODIFIED COUNTERSHAFT — Since August, 1979, this transmission is equipped with a countershaft on which constant-mesh and third gear are assembled by shrink fitting. In case of

Latest Changes & Corrections

FOR 1982 & EARLIER MODELS (Cont.)

repair, the complete countershaft must be replaced. On modified countershaft, constant-mesh, third and reverse gears were secured with one circlip each. Previously these gears were secured with one hex nut. In addition, on modified countershafts, no spacer shim will be fitted between ball bearing and constant-mesh gear. Replacement countershaft assemblies (115 260 3024) are now available.

PEUGEOT

10> PEUGEOT 505 AND 604 WITH 5-SPEED MANUAL TRANSMISSION: REAR HOUSING BREAKAGE — During installation of the 5-speed manual transmission rear housing, with transmission in vehicle, a mispositioning of ring shown in illustration can cause the rear housing to break.

Be sure that ring is properly positioned on its flats. Use multi-purpose grease to hold ring in place while the housing is being installed. If transmission is off vehicle, place unit in a vertical position for assembly.

Peugeot Rear Housing Ring Position

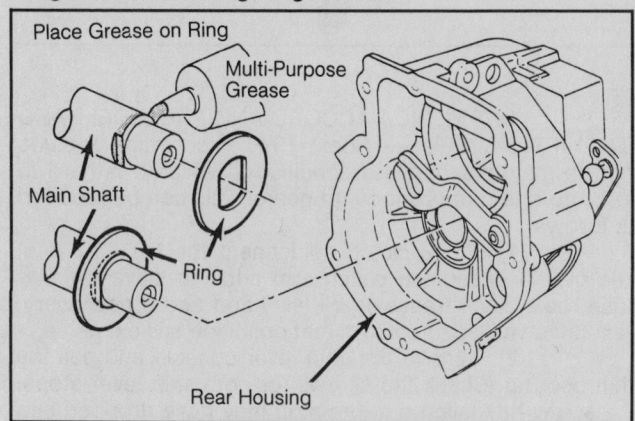

Place Grease on Ring
Multi-Purpose Grease
Main Shaft
Ring
Rear Housing

SAAB

11> SAAB MODELS WITH 4-SPEED MANUAL TRANSMISSION: JUMPING OUT OF THIRD GEAR UNDER LOAD — The problem of third gear jump out began appearing with the introduction of synchro hub (8712283). Although the hub is correctly designed, machining tolerances could create a condition that prevents operating sleeve from accomplishing a complete engagement of 3rd gear. New parts have been corrected, and to eliminate this condition, synchro hubs should be replaced with parts from the new inventory.

12> SAAB MODELS WITH MANUAL TRANSMISSION: HARD SHIFTING AND/OR IGNITION KEY WILL NOT RELEASE — If complaints of hard shifting and ignition keys not being released from switch are encountered, check the rubber dampner bushing in the shift rod to the transmission. The rubber dampner forms a moulded joint in the rod to eliminate vibration transfer to the shift lever. Should the joint begin to pull apart, the first sign is a loss of adjustment, preventing locking in reverse and the inability to remove ignition key. Hard shift lever movement will be noticed next. In most cases the joint can be pushed

together, drilled and pinned to eliminate the problem. If complete separation occurs, however, the rod will have to be replaced.

13> SAAB MODELS WITH MANUAL TRANSMISSION: BRASS PARTCLES IN CASE — When rebuilding manual transmissions which have a damaged synchro ring, it is very important that all brass particles be removed from the case. Places often neglected during such cleaning are the front primary gear cover oil collector and differential side cover oil dam. Both areas can fill with brass particles. If not removed, these particles will be circulated and coat the new synchro ring, which results in a synchro ring failure in a very short time.

14> SAAB MODELS WITH 5-SPEED TRANSMISSIONS: DIFFICULT ENGAGEMENT OF FIRST AND SECOND GEARS — Whenever difficult engagement of 1st and 2nd gear is noticed, the gear shift lever should be adjusted according to procedures in *Transmission Servicing Section*. If this fails to correct the difficult engagement, the following procedure should be used:

1) Select either 1st or 2nd gear position and check side play of shift lever.

2) If no side play with 1st or 2nd engaged, shift lever housing should be repositioned by placing a .118" (3 mm) shim (7061328) under left front mounting flange.

3) If selection of other gears becomes difficult after installing shim, replace shim with a .039" (1 mm) shim (7311764) to reduce angle of housing.

4) After installation, side play in 1st and 2nd gear should be about the same as that in 3rd and 4th gears. Road test to verify adequate shifting.

NOTE: After VIN 90801020095, shift rod taper pin holes are offset 3°, which has the same effect as the above procedure.

15> SAAB MODELS WITH 5-SPEED TRANSMISSION: ALTERED CLUSTER GEAR — From transmission number 408097, the dimension of 3rd gear has been modified on cluster gears. The alteration allows for more space for 3rd gear guide ring. The illustration shows size difference between early and late gears. It is advised to update 5-speed transmissions when rebuilding to prevent damage to 3rd gear guide ring.

Saab 5-Speed Transmission Dimension Change

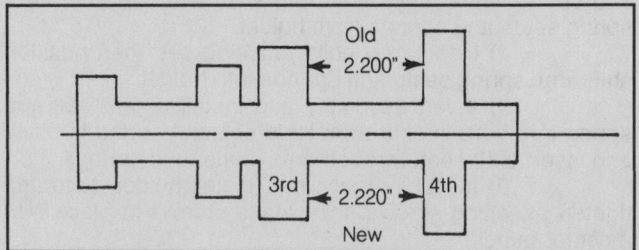

Old 2.200"
3rd 2.220" 4th
New

FOR 1982 & EARLIER MODELS (Cont.)

TOYOTA

▷16 1981 TOYOTA CELICA & CORONA WITH W55 5-SPEED TRANSMISSION: SHIFT LEVER VIBRATION NOISE — To reduce the shift lever vibration noise during acceleration, a Teflon bushing has been added to the shift lever housing. The Teflon bushing was installed in vehicles beginning with those manufactured in Febuary of 1981. The shift lever housing with the Teflon bushing (33502-22180) is now available as a replacement part for earlier models.

VOLVO

▷17 VOLVO MODELS WITH M45 AND M46 MANUAL TRANSMISSIONS: REPLACING PULL ROD INTERLOCK SLEEVE — Replacement of the pull rod for reverse lockout does not require replacement of the complete gearshift lever. Only pull rod requires replacement. Rod can be replaced by disconnecting and removing upper section of shift lever. When replacing pull rod, early type interlock sleeve should also be replaced with a new type sleeve (1232687-2). New sleeve has a locating notch which prevents it from rotating on shift lever, and a groove in which pull rod is fitted. This prevents pull rod from wearing against interlock plate.

When fitting older type gear lever with new interlock sleeve, place a .078" (2 mm) by 1/2" (13 mm) O.D. washer to act as a spacer on knob before pressing it onto lever. This is necessary since new interlock sleeve is .078" (2 mm) longer and it must be replaced at same time with a new, harder type screw (1232688-0)

▷18 VOLVO MODELS WITH MANUAL TRANSMISSIONS: PRESSURE PLATES AND RELEASE BEARINGS — Two different designs of pressure plates and release bearings are used on Volvo 240 and 260 models. The two designs are easily reconizable by the fingers of the pressure plate. Plates for 260 models have fingers that are raised approximately 9/32" (7 mm) at the center. Plate fingers on 240 model plates are straight. Because of the finger difference, there are two different release bearings for these models. Release bearings for 260 models are approximately 1-7/16" (36.5 mm) long. Release bearings for 240 models are approximately 1-11/16" (43 mm) long. Pressure plates and release bearings must be used in the correct combination and should never be mixed.

OVERDRIVES & TRANSFER CASES

CHRYSLER CORP. IMPORTS

▷1 1982 CHRYSLER CORP. IMPORT RAM-50 PICKUP WITH FOUR WHEEL DRIVE: REVISED TRANSFER CASE REMOVAL PROCEDURES — The following procedures should be used to remove the transfer case on 1982 Ram-50 pickups.

1) Remove the back-up light switch from the lower right of the transfer case adapter and take out the

steel ball. Remove the select plunger plug from right side of case and remove select spring and plunger.

2) Remove 6 bolts securing control housing to transfer case and remove transfer control lever assembly and control lever together with housing and gasket.

3) Remove plug from top of transfer case adapter and take out resistance spring and steel ball. Remove plugs from top of transfer case adapter and take out neutral return springs and plungers.

4) With change shifter tilted to left, drive out lock pin from transmission control shaft change shifter.

NOTE: If the lock pin does not fully come out, drive out the lock pin using a punch after grinding down the beveled end of the pin.

5) Remove bolts securing transfer case and adapter. Remove transfer case from adapter and take out change shifter from transfer case. Remove bolts securing adapter and transmission and remove adapter from transmission.

Removing Lock Pin from Transfer Case

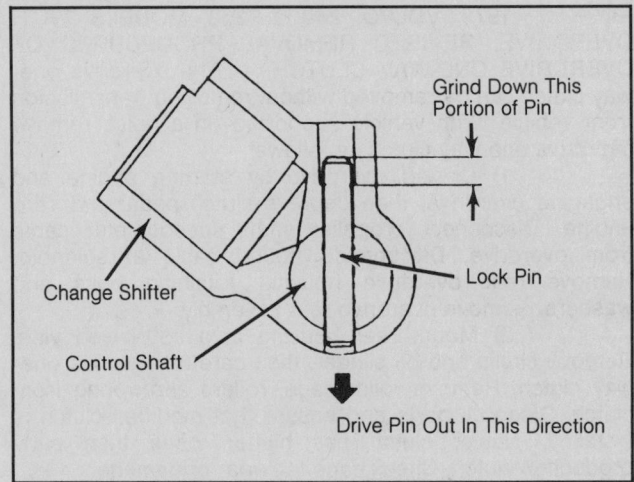

VOLVO

▷2 1972-80 VOLVO MODELS WITH OVERDRIVE: OVERDRIVE CLUTCH REPLACEMENT — The overdrive one-way clutch on 1972-80 Volvo models can be replaced without having to remove the gearbox from the vehicle, as follows:

1) Raise vehicle on hoist. Start engine. Engage overdrive. Depress clutch pedal. Turn engine off.

2) Disconnect drive shaft from the overdrive output flange and the speedometer cable from the overdrive. Disconnect ground cable from the solenoid.

3) Place a pan underneath the overdrive. Remove nuts holding the rear overdrive housing. Remove the spring washers. Remove the sealing washers from the 2 top bolts.

4) Remove the overdrive rear assembly. Taking care not to damage housing, clamp the overdrive rear housing in a vise. Remove circlip and oil slinger.

5) Carefully remove one-way clutch since rollers are loose. Separate and clean parts of the one-way clutch. Replace the existing clutch with new, higher lobe design type clutch.

6) Check that roller cage is not damaged or cracked. If so, replace it. Assemble clutch, spring and roller cage of one-way clutch.

7) Rotate roller cage clockwise as far as possible and lock in position with key. Insert rollers and hold in position with a rubberband.

8) Check that thrust washer is in position. Remove rubberband holding rollers and install one-way clutch. Install oil slinger and circlip.

9) Clean mounting face and install new gasket. Check that gasket in front of the brake has not been damaged when removing the cone-clutch and housing.

10) Install overdrive rear assembly. Install sealing washers on the 2 upper bolts. Install spring washers and nuts.

11) Connect ground cable to the solenoid. Connect speedometer cable to the overdrive. Connect the drive shaft to the overdrive.

12) Fill gearbox with ATF. Start engine and run it with overdrive engaged. Stop engine. Check oil level. Lower vehicle.

3 1979 VOLVO 240 & 260 MODELS WITH OVERDRIVE: REVISED REMOVAL PROCEDURES OF OVERDRIVE ONE-WAY CLUTCH — The overdrive one-way clutch can be removed without removing transmission from vehicle. With vehicle supported on a hoist, remove overdrive one-way clutch as follows:

1) Unload overdrive by starting engine and engaging overdrive, then depress clutch pedal and stop engine. Disconnect propeller shaft speedometer cable from overdrive. Disconnect ground cable at solenoid. Remove rear overdrive housing retaining bolts and washers. Remove overdrive rear assembly.

2) Mount rear housing in a soft-jawed vise. Remove circlip and oil slinger, then carefully remove one-way clutch. Remove roller cage, rollers and spring from clutch. Clean all parts and ensure that modified clutch is installed. Newer clutch has higher lobes than early production clutch. Check cage for wear or damage.

3) Install spring and roller cage. Rotate cage clockwise, and lock in farthest position of rotation. Insert rollers and hold in place using a rubber band or string. Ensure correct thrust washer is installed in overdrive output shaft. Install one-way clutch and remove rubber band or string used to secure rollers.

4) Install oil slinger and circlip. Check all gaskets and replace those which show damage. Reverse removal procedure and install overdrive rear assembly. Fill transmission with ATF, start engine and engage overdrive. Stop engine and check fluid level.

WE NEED YOUR ADVICE!

As part of our continuing labor time evaluation program, we would appreciate your comments or suggestions regarding the labor times in the Mitchell Parts/Labor Estimating Guides.

NOTE: This form must be filled out completely to be considered.

Mitchell Manual (Title, Volume & Number) _____

Section _____ Page _____ Operation _____

Vehicle (Make, Model & Year) _____ Engine _____ Transmission _____

Mitchell Time _____ Recommended Time _____ Reason _____

We appreciate receiving this information. Do you have any other comments on this guide?

_____

Name _____ Company _____

Address _____ City _____ State _____ Zip _____

Phone ( ) _____ Date _____

THANK YOU

- -

WE NEED YOUR ADVICE!

As part of our continuing labor time evaluation program, we would appreciate your comments or suggestions regarding the labor times in the Mitchell Parts/Labor Estimating Guides.

NOTE: This form must be filled out completely to be considered.

Mitchell Manual (Title, Volume & Number) _____

Section _____ Page _____ Operation _____

Vehicle (Make, Model & Year) _____ Engine _____ Transmission _____

Mitchell Time _____ Recommended Time _____ Reason _____

We appreciate receiving this information. Do you have any other comments on this guide?

_____

Name _____ Company _____

Address _____ City _____ State _____ Zip _____

Phone ( ) _____ Date _____

THANK YOU

- -

WE NEED YOUR ADVICE!

As part of our continuing labor time evaluation program, we would appreciate your comments or suggestions regarding the labor times in the Mitchell Parts/Labor Estimating Guides.

NOTE: This form must be filled out completely to be considered.

Mitchell Manual (Title, Volume & Number) _____

Section _____ Page _____ Operation _____

Vehicle (Make, Model & Year) _____ Engine _____ Transmission _____

Mitchell Time _____ Recommended Time _____ Reason _____

We appreciate receiving this information. Do you have any other comments on this guide?

_____

Name _____ Company _____

Address _____ City _____ State _____ Zip _____

Phone ( ) _____ Date _____

THANK YOU

Name _____

Address _____

City _____ State _____ Zip _____

BUSINESS REPLY MAIL

FIRST CLASS   PERMIT NO. 3701   SAN DIEGO, CA

POSTAGE WILL BE PAID BY ADDRESSEE

MITCHELL MANUALS, INC.

P.O. BOX 26260
San Diego, California 92126

NO POSTAGE
NECESSARY
IF MAILED
IN THE
UNITED STATES

Name _____

Address _____

City _____ State _____ Zip _____

BUSINESS REPLY MAIL

FIRST CLASS   PERMIT NO. 3701   SAN DIEGO, CA

POSTAGE WILL BE PAID BY ADDRESSEE

MITCHELL MANUALS, INC.

P.O. BOX 26260
San Diego, California 92126

NO POSTAGE
NECESSARY
IF MAILED
IN, THE
UNITED STATES

Name _____

Address _____

City _____ State _____ Zip _____

BUSINESS REPLY MAIL

FIRST CLASS   PERMIT NO. 3701   SAN DIEGO, CA

POSTAGE WILL BE PAID BY ADDRESSEE

MITCHELL MANUALS, INC.

P.O. BOX 26260
San Diego, California 92126

NO POSTAGE
NECESSARY
IF MAILED
IN THE
UNITED STATES

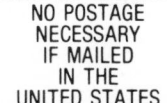

NO POSTAGE
NECESSARY
IF MAILED
IN THE
UNITED STATES

BUSINESS REPLY CARD

FIRST CLASS   PERMIT NO. 3701   SAN DIEGO, CA

POSTAGE WILL BE PAID BY ADDRESSEE

MITCHELL MANUALS, INC.

P.O. BOX 26260
San Diego, California 92126

DOMESTIC CAR: Through 1983

Air Conditioning & Heating Service Manual

The manual that's used and respected by the people who KNOW the air conditioning industry. Now service any air conditioning or heating system profitable! You get everything you need to make system servicing quick and easy: in-depth trouble shooting and diagnosis ... servicing, repair and overhaul data ... thousands of illustrations ... hundreds of spec tables and charts ... factory bulletins ... labor estimating section ... and more! Coverage for all U.S. factory-installed systems since 1974. Big two-volume set! **Price: only $75.00**

Air Conditioning Older Models

Covers vehicles from 1966-73. **Price: only $35.00**

Emission Control Service Manual

Tough new pollution laws mean big profits for you in emission control servicing! Cash in on it with Mitchell! You get the most complete and current data available ... anywhere! Description, operation, trouble shooting, maintenance, repair and overhaul info for all domestic car emission systems produced since 1975! PLUS — you get a complete fuel system section, engine I.D., all system wiring and vacuum diagrams. Application charts. **Price only: $58.00**

1966-74 emission info also available. **Price: only $30.00**

IMPORTED CAR & LIGHT TRUCK:

Air Conditioning & Heating Manual

Brand New! Only book of its kind! Comprehensive coverage on factory-installed air conditioning and heating systems in the leading imports: Toyota, Datsun, Volkswagen, Honda, Chrysler Imports, Mercedes-Benz, Audi, BMW, Fiat and Volvo. Actually a total of 62 models! Big, easy-to-use manual covers servicing, repair, overhaul and trouble shooting. Now, with this money-maker, you can increase the list of services you offer! **Price: only $60.00**

Emission Control Service Manual

Imported cars need pollution control servicing too ... and that means more profit opportunities for your shop! Cash in on it with this fantastic coverage — over 30 foreign manufacturers are covered, in complete detail, since 1975. Description, operation, trouble shooting, maintenance, repair, and overhaul — you get it all with Mitchell. PLUS ... you get a complete carburetion and fuel injection section, emission system wiring and vacuum diagrams and more! Over 3,800 pages — it's the most in-depth, money-making repair tool you'll find. Start enjoying big emission profits today! **Price: only $58.00**

1968-74 emission info also available. **Price: only $30.00**

YES!

I want to save time and increase my shop profits — at no risk to me at all for 30 days. Please send me the manuals I have checked off below. I understand that if I am not completely satisfied, I can return the books within 30 days of delivery for a full refund.

☐ Air Conditioning & Heating 1966-73.............$35.00
☐ Air Conditioning & Heating 1974-78.............$30.00
☐ Air Conditioning & Heating 1979-83.............$55.00
☐ Air Conditioning & Heating 1974-83.............$75.00
☐ Imported A/C & Heating 1976-82.............$60.00
☐ Domestic Emission Control 1975-83.............$58.00
☐ Domestic Older Model Emission.............$30.00
☐ Imported Emission Control 1975-83.............$58.00
☐ Imported Older Model Emission.............$30.00
☐ Computerized Engine Controls Manual, '8
☐ Computerized Engine Controls Manual, '8
☐ Electronic Fuel Injection Manual
☐ Emission Control Training Manual.............
☐ Electrical Component Locator, '83 Edition
☐ Electrical Component Locator, Older Mod
☐ Electronic Ignition Service Manual.............$10.00
☐ Domestic Car Tune-Up Manual.............$92.00
☐ Domestic Car Mechanical Manual
☐ Imported Car & Truck Tune-Up
☐ Imported Car & Truck Mechanical
☐ Light Truck Tune-Up.............
☐ Light Truck Mechanical.............

Please check one:
☐ Check or money order enclosed
☐ Send my order C.O.D.
☐ Charge to Master Charge/Visa

☐ Please send me more information
☐ Please send a sales representative to see me

Account # _____ Expiration Date _____

Issuing Bank _____

Company
Address
Phone ( )
Zip

*NOTE: Your appropriate state sales tax must be included to process your order.

State Sa
Shipping &
If C.O.D. a
FINA

n as a business tax deduction.
n CA call collect, 619-578-8770) Ask for Eve Shaw.
to change without notice.   ATDI 83

LS, INC.

MORRIS AUTOMATED INFORMATION NETWORK
0 1022 0088400 9

629.287
Tra
Q
Transmission service & repair

Copy 2

1983 ed.

DATE DUE

R22011 36254
ON-LINE

The Joint Free Public Library
of
Morristown and Morris Township
1 Miller Road
Morristown, New Jersey 07960

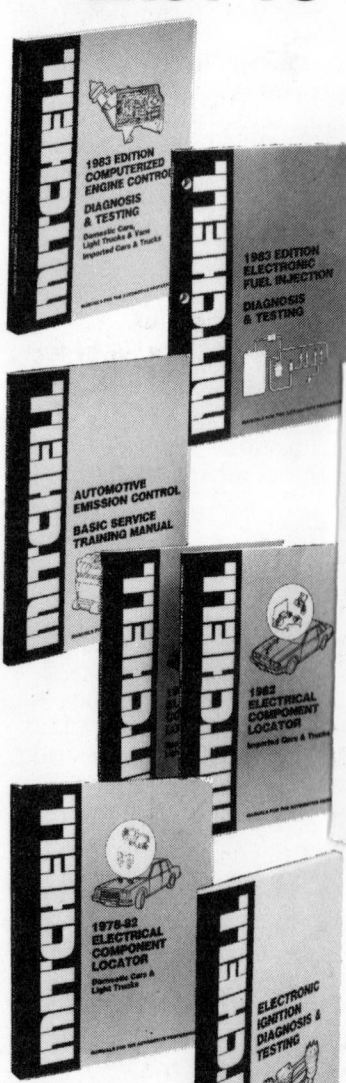

EASY-TO-U...   ...CH MANUALS

...ANUAL

...ow about the seventeen computer
...us the seven popular 1982 imports,
...ter systems on the 1984 Bronco II,
...ting procedures, diagnostic charts.

...2 Domestics. **$10.00**

...L

...1975 through 1983 domestic fuel
...2 imports as well. Outlines different
...specialized component, gives full
...hooting tables and shows steps for
...s included. **Price: only $10.00**

...L

...nual, but even the old timers will
...emission systems, regardless of
...entilation to computerized engine
...government standards, and how
...pful illustrations. 156 pages. **Price:**

...1983 EDITION (Two Books)

...Quickly locates those hidden and
...the illustrations identify both the
...for group of look-alike components
...mestic cars and light trucks plus all
...ce: only $40.00 for both books**

ELECTRICAL COMPONENT LOCATOR, OLDER MODELS

Same helpful information as Locator above, but covers Domestic models only for the years 1978 through 1982. Perfect companion book to 1983 Edition above. Includes Domestic Light Trucks as well as cars. **Price: only $60.00**

ELECTRONIC IGNITION SERVICE MANUAL

Easy-to-follow step-by-step coverage of each electronic ignition system, including description, operation, and test procedures specs. You get: basic wiring diagrams, voltmeter & ohmmeter hook-up locations for testing and easy to understand instructions. Also includes cautions to help prevent errors and a history of ignition development. Covers '71-'82 Domestics and '77-'81 Imports. **Price: only $10.00**